HOWELL'S TEXTBOOK OF
PHYSIOLOGY

Edited by
JOHN F. FULTON, M.D.

Sterling Professor of Physiology,
Yale University School of Medicine

With the collaboration of

DONALD H. BARRON
JOHN R. BROBECK
ROBERT W. CLARKE
GEORGE R. COWGILL
WILLIAM U. GARDNER

DAVID I. HITCHCOCK
HAROLD LAMPORT
DAVID P. C. LLOYD
LESLIE F. NIMS
THEODORE C. RUCH

Fifteenth Edition, Illustrated

W. B. SAUNDERS COMPANY

PHILADELPHIA AND LONDON

1946

CONTRIBUTORS

DONALD HENRY BARRON, Ph.D.

Associate Professor of Physiology, Yale University School of Medicine

JOHN RAYMOND BROBECK, M.D.

Assistant Professor in Physiology, Yale University School of Medicine

ROBERT WATKINS CLARKE, Ph.D.

Assistant Professor of Physiology, Yale University School of Medicine

GEORGE RAYMOND COWGILL, Ph.D.

Professor of Nutrition, Yale University School of Medicine

JOSEPH RUSSELL ELKINTON, M.D.

Assistant Professor of Medicine, Yale University School of Medicine

JOHN HOWARD FERGUSON, M.D.

Professor of Physiology, University of North Carolina School of Medicine

JOHN FARQUHAR FULTON, M.D.

Sterling Professor of Physiology, Yale University School of Medicine

WILLIAM ULLMAN GARDNER, Ph.D.

Professor of Anatomy, Yale University School of Medicine

ROBERT GORDON GRENELL, Ph.D.

Instructor in Neuro-Anatomy, Yale University School of Medicine

WILLIAM FERGUSON HAMILTON, Ph.D.

Professor of Physiology and Pharmacology, University of Georgia School of Medicine

DAVID INGERSOLL HITCHCOCK, Ph.D.

Associate Professor of Physiology, Yale University School of Medicine

HEBBEL EDWARD HOFF, M.D.

Professor of Physiology, McGill University

EBBE CURTIS HOFF, M.B. Lond.

Lieutenant Commander, MC-V(S)USNR, Bureau of Medicine and Surgery, Navy Department

CHARLES WRIGHT HOOKER, Ph.D.

Assistant Professor of Anatomy, Yale University School of Medicine

HAROLD LAMPORT, M.D.

Research Associate in Physiology, Yale University School of Medicine

WALTER LANDAUER, Ph.D.

Professor of Genetics, Storrs Agricultural Experiment Station, University of Connecticut

DAVID PIERCE CARADOC LLOYD, D.Phil.

Associate Member, The Rockefeller Institute for Medical Research

LESLIE FREDERICK NIMS, Ph.D.

Associate Professor of Physiology, Yale University School of Medicine

ROBERT FRANKLIN PITTS, Ph.D., M.D.

Associate Professor of Physiology, Cornell University Medical College

ERIC PONDER, M.D.

Research Investigator and Attending Physician, The Nassau Hospital

HARRY DICKSON PATTON, Ph.D.

Research Assistant in Physiology, Yale University School of Medicine

THEODORE CEDRIC RUCH, Ph.D.

Assistant Professor of Physiology, Yale University School of Medicine

FRANK WALTER WEYMOUTH, Ph.D.

Professor of Physiology, Stanford University

ALFRED ELLIS WILHELMI, D.Phil.

Assistant Professor of Physiological Chemistry, Yale University School of Medicine

PREFACE TO THE FIFTEENTH EDITION

In revising Howell's *Textbook of physiology* it proved essential to prepare many new chapters and to rewrite others in their entirety. It was felt that the text would gain in clarity if the newer developments in physiology were presented de novo rather than worked into the older text.

Editors were appointed for each of the ten sections (nine originally), and they were authorized to obtain such help as they needed for the revision of individual chapters. Dr. Lloyd's section on muscle and nerve has been rewritten completely, and the chapters on the central nervous system have been largely recast save for the passages on the labyrinth and the cranial nerves. Dr. Ruch has presented sensory physiology in clinical language, and has attempted to coordinate the large clinical literature on sensory problems in terms that will be understood by both the clinician and the physiologist. Dr. Hitchcock has brought his broad knowledge of physical and protein chemistry to bear in revising the section on the formed elements of the blood and the blood plasma proteins. The section on the cardiovascular system, which has been jointly edited by Drs. Barron, Lamport and myself, has been presented on somewhat novel lines, and we have been fortunate in securing the contributions of Dr. H. E. Hoff who interprets the problem of excitability and conductivity of cardiac muscle in the light of modern electrophysiology—making it, incidentally, quite clear that the membrane theory as applied to muscle and nerve is directly applicable to the problem of the interpretation of the electrocardiogram.

In the section on respiration, the newer concepts of high altitude physiology which have emanated from the war have been incorporated, and Dr. Nims has included much else that is new in the broad field of aviation medicine. Drs. Clarke and Elkinton have entirely rewritten the section on water metabolism and the kidney, and have brought it into line with current teachings concerning renal clearance. The section on gastro-intestinal physiology follows the outline of previous editions, but Dr. Cowgill has incorporated new work in the field. Dr. Brobeck has reorganized the section on basal metabolism, adding recent disclosures on the part played by the endocrines and the central nervous system in the integration of metabolic processes. The physiology of sex has become a precise science since Dr. Howell's last revision, and Dr. Gardner has rewritten the entire section, summarizing the present status of this rapidly unfolding branch of experimental medicine.

In preparing the revision we have attempted to keep the text within reasonable limits and at the same time preserve its general character, realizing, however, that the fluent prose style of the original will be difficult to equal. Early in his career Dr. Howell had taken a leaf from Sir Michael Foster, and it is doubtful whether any American writer on physiology other than he has approached Foster's eloquent use of language. So we offer the new edition with misgivings, but also with a sense of pride that a work of such importance has been committed to our hands.

The Editors wish to express their gratitude to the large number of authors and publishers who have generously permitted reproduction of figures and the use of certain quoted passages from monographs and journal articles. Full acknowledgment is given in the legends and text, and written authorization has been obtained in each case. Thanks are also due Mr. Carl P. Rollins, Printer to Yale University, for advice concerning typographical design. To the W. B. Saunders Company we are grateful for unfailing courtesy and cooperation. Mr. Bertram G. Bruestle is responsible for the majority of the new line drawings. We thank him, and also Miss Mary P. Wheeler, who has not only prepared all copy for press but has been responsible for conducting correspondence and for reading both galley and page proof.

J. F. FULTON

YALE UNIVERSITY

PREFACE

In the preparation of this book the author has endeavored to keep in mind two guiding principles: first, the importance of simplicity and lucidity in the presentation of facts and theories; and, second, the need of a judicious limitation of the material selected. In regard to the second point every specialist is aware of the bewildering number of researches that have been and are being published in physiology and the closely related sciences, and the difficulty of justly estimating the value of conflicting results. He who seeks for the truth in any matter under discussion is oftentimes forced to be satisfied with a suspension of judgment, and the writer who attempts to formulate our present knowledge upon almost any part of the subject is in many instances obliged to present the literature as it exists and let the reader make his own deductions. This latter method is doubtless the most satisfactory and the most suitable for large treatises prepared for the use of the specialist or advanced student, but for beginners it is absolutely necessary to follow a different plan. The amount of material and the discussion of details of controversies must be brought within reasonable limits. The author must assume the responsibility of sifting the evidence and emphasizing those conclusions that seem to be most justified by experiment and observation. As far as material is concerned, it is evident that the selection of what to give and what to omit is a matter of judgment and experience upon the part of the writer, but the present author is convinced that the necessary reduction in material should be made by a process of elimination rather than by condensation. The latter method is suitable for the specialist with his background of knowledge and experience, but it is entirely unfitted for the elementary student. For the latter, brief comprehensive statements are oftentimes misleading, or fail at least to make a clear impression. Those subjects that are presented to him must be given with a certain degree of fullness if he is expected to obtain a serviceable conception of the facts, and it follows that a treatment of the wide subject of physiology is possible, when undertaken with this intention, only by the adoption of a system of selection and elimination.

The fundamental facts of physiology, its principles and modes of reasoning, are not difficult to understand. The obstacle that is most frequently encountered by the student lies in the complexity of the subject—the large number of more or less disconnected facts and theories which must be considered in a discussion of the structure, physics, and chemistry of such an intricate organism as the human body. But once a selection has been made of those facts and principles which it is most desirable that the student should know, there is no intrinsic difficulty to prevent them from being stated so clearly that they may be comprehended by anyone who possesses an elementary knowledge of anatomy, physics, and chemistry. It is doubtless the art of presentation that makes a textbook successful or unsuccessful. It must be admitted, however, that certain parts of physiology, at this particular period in its development, offer peculiar difficulties to the writers of textbooks. During recent years chemical work in the fields of digestion and nutrition has been very full, and as a result theories hitherto generally accepted have been subjected to criticism and alteration, particularly as the important advances in theoretical chemistry and physics have greatly modified the attitude and point of view of the investigators in physiology. Some former views have been unsettled and much information has been collected which at present it is difficult to formulate and apply to the explanation of the normal processes of the animal body. It would seem that in some of the fundamental problems of metabolism physiological investigation has pushed its experimental results to a point at which, for further progress, a deeper knowledge of the chemistry of the body is especially needed. Certainly the amount of work of a chemical character that bears directly or indirectly on the problems of physiology has shown a remarkable increase within the last decade. Amid the conflicting results of this literature it is difficult or impossible to follow always the true trend of development. The best that the textbook can hope to accomplish in such cases is to give as clear a picture as possible of the tendencies of the time.

Some critics have contended that only those facts or conclusions about which there is no difference of opinion should be presented to medical students. Those who are acquainted with the subject, however, understand that books written from this standpoint contain much that represents the uncertain compromises of past generations, and that the need of revision is felt as frequently for such books as for those constructed on more liberal principles. There does not seem to be any sound reason why a textbook for medical students should aim to present only those conclusions that have crystallized out of the controversies of other times, and ignore entirely the live issues of the day which are of so much interest and importance not only to physiology, but to all branches of medicine. With this idea in mind the author has endeavored to make the student realize that physiology is a growing subject, continually widening its knowledge and readjusting its theories. It is important that the student should grasp this conception, because, in the first place, it is true; and, in the second place, it may save him later from disappointment and distrust in science if he recognizes that many of our conclusions are not the final truth, but provisional only, representing the best that can be done with the knowledge at our command. To emphasize this fact as well as to add somewhat to the interest of the reader short historical *résumés* have been introduced from time to time, although the question of space alone has prevented any extensive use of such material. It is a feature, however, that a teacher might develop with profit. Some knowledge of the gradual evolution of our present beliefs is useful in demonstrating the enduring value of experimental work as compared with mere theorizing, and also in engendering a certain appreciation and respect for knowledge that has been gained so slowly by the exertions of successive generations of able investigators.

A word may be said regarding the references to literature inserted in the book. It is perfectly obvious that a complete or approximately complete bibliography is neither appropriate nor useful, however agreeable it may be to give every worker full recognition of the results of his labors. But for the sake of those who may for any reason wish to follow any particular subject more in detail some references have been given, and these have been selected usually with the idea of citing those works which themselves contain a more or less extensive discussion and literature. Occasionally also references have been made to works of historical importance or to separate papers that contain the experimental evidence for some special view.

W. H. HOWELL

CONTENTS

Historical Backgrounds of American Physiology 1
    BY J. F. FULTON

I. PRINCIPLES OF NERVOUS AND MUSCULAR ACTIVITY
BY DAVID P. C. LLOYD

1. Electrical Properties of Nerve and Muscle 7
    BY DAVID P. C. LLOYD
Introduction. 7
Electrical phenomena at rest and in action 8
    Demarkation potential 9
    The recording of monophasic and diphasic spike potentials 11
    Distribution of electric currents in volume conductors 14
Electrotonus 17
    Core conductor theory 17
Electrical excitation 19
    Stimulation by brief shocks 19
    Stimulation by constant currents 21
    The strength-duration curve 23
    Excitability changes at the anode 25
Conduction at a nerve block 26
    The extrinsic potential 26
Concept of the nerve impulse 27
    Local circuit theory 28
    Energy relations 30
    Refractory period 30

2. Functional Activity of Muscle 32
    BY DAVID P. C. LLOYD
Elementary features of muscle contraction 33
    Latent period 33
    Course of isometric contraction 34
    Types of skeletal muscle 34
    Response of muscle to two stimuli 35
    Response of muscle to repetitive stimulation 37
    Relation between length and tension 38
    Contracture 39
    Natural contraction and the motor unit 39
    Innervation ratios 40
    Average motor unit tension 40
    Discharge rates of motor units 40
    Voluntary contraction 42
    Action of muscles in the body 42
    Advantage of two joint muscles 45
Smooth muscle 46
    Multi-unit smooth muscles 46
    Visceral smooth muscles 48
    Mechanical properties of smooth muscle 49

Cardiac muscle   51
    Electrical and mechanical events.   51
    Mechanical properties of heart muscle   51
All-or-nothing relation   52

3. Energy Transformations in Muscle   56
    BY ALFRED E. WILHELMI
Some general characteristics of muscle   56
  Introduction   56
    Structure.   57
    Chemical composition   59
    Phosphate bond energy   60
Energy production in muscle.   61
  Anaerobic energy production in muscle   62
    Enzymatic breakdown of glycogen to lactic acid 64
    Formation of phosphotriose from glycogen   65
    Conversion of phosphotriose to lactic acid 67
  Oxidative energy production in muscle   70
  Respiratory systems of muscle   71
    Muscle hemoglobin   71
    The aerobic enzyme systems   71
    Carbohydrate oxidation   72
    Oxidation and phosphate bond energy   74
    Oxidation quotient   76
    Summary.   77
Energy liberation in muscle   78
    Phases of heat production in muscle   79
    Heat production and chemical change   80
    Factors governing energy liberation during contraction 83
    Energy liberation during contraction 85
    Heat of shortening   87
    Rate of extra energy liberation during shortening 88
    Work   88
    Force and speed of shortening   89
    Maintenance heat   90
  Conclusion   96

4. Functional Properties of Neurons   96
    BY DAVID P. C. LLOYD
    Compound spike potential of nerve   96
    A proof of independent conduction   98
Types of nerve fibers   98
  The properties of A fibers.   100
    Relation between fiber size and conduction velocity 100
    Relation between conduction velocity and spike amplitude 101
    Relation between conduction velocity and threshold 102
    Synthesis of the compound spike potential 102
    After-potentials   104
    Recovery of excitability   104
  Comparison of B and C fibers with A fibers   105
Fiber constitution of various nerves   107
    Somatic motor fibers.   107
    Afferent fibers   109
Fiber constitution of spinal tracts.   109
    Propriospinal fibers   110

Conduction in immature and regenerating fibers 112
    Conduction velocity during growth 112
    Conduction and regeneration 112
Conduction in the neuron soma. 113
Interaction between nerve cells 114
Heat production, after-potentials and metabolism 116
    Resting heat of nerve 116
    Heat production during and following activity 117
    Correlation of heat production with potential signs of activity and chemical changes in nerve 118

5. Intercellular Transmission 121
    BY DAVID P. C. LLOYD
Neuromuscular transmission 121
    Neuromuscular delay 121
    End-plate potential 121
    Relation of end-plate potential to propagated impulse 123
    Summation of end-plate potentials and neuromuscular facilitation. 125
    Interpretations 125
    Electrical hypothesis 125
    Chemical hypothesis 125
Synaptic transmission in ganglia 126
    Functional consequences of convergence 126
    Occlusion 127
    Facilitation 128
    Potential signs of ganglionic activity 128
    Degrees of synaptic excitation. 129
    Two periods of facilitation in ganglia 130
    After-discharge 130
    Hypotheses relating to the synaptic transmitter in ganglia. 131
    Electrical hypothesis 131
    Chemical hypothesis 131
    Acetylcholine and cholinesterase. 132
    Liberation of acetylcholine 132
    Action of acetylcholine. 133
    Action of eserine 133
    The function of cholinesterase. 133
Synaptic transmission in the central nervous system 134
    Synaptic stimulation as a local process 138
    Summation at the synapse 140
    The problem of synaptic delay 140
    Interpretation of synaptic delay 141
    The relation between subliminal fringe and discharge zone 142
    Prolonged excitation in the nervous system and "central excitatory state" 143

6. Principles of Spinal Reflex Activity 146
    BY DAVID P. C. LLOYD
Structure of the reflex mechanism 146
The stretch reflex 149
    The knee jerk. 152
    Genesis of clonus 153
    Distribution of stretch reflexes 154
    Functional significance of stretch reflexes 155
Flexor reflexes 156

Transmission of stretch and flexor reflexes 158
  Two-neuron arcs and stretch reflexes 160
  Multineuron arcs and flexor reflexes 160
  Functional significance of reflex connections 161
Reflex coordination 162
  Crossed extensor reflexes 162
  Reciprocal innervation 162
  Double reciprocal innervation 162
  Pseudantagonists and co-contraction 163
  Genesis of stepping movements 163
Inhibition 165
  Inhibition may have brief latency 165
  Inhibition may have long duration 166
  Inhibition can be graded in intensity 166
  Inhibition and excitation exist in parallel 167
  Inhibitory convergence 167
 Nature of central inhibition 167
  Indirect inhibition 167
  Subnormality and reciprocal innervation 169
  Direct inhibition 170
Long spinal reflexes 171
Extrinsic control of spinal reflex mechanisms 173
  Bulbospinal mechanisms 173
  Control by the pyramidal system 176
  Dissociation of cortical control 176

II. THE CENTRAL NERVOUS SYSTEM: MOTOR FUNCTIONS

BY JOHN F. FULTON

7. The Human Spinal Cord: Spinal Injuries 178
 BY JOHN F. FULTON
Complete spinal transection 178
 Spinal shock 178
  Hyporeflexia 178
  The mass reflex 179
  Extension reflexes 179
  Autonomic reflexes 179
  Bladder reflexes 180
  Reflexes of the rectum 180
  Level of transection 181
 Physiology of spinal compression 182
Spinal injuries: incomplete transections 183
 Brown-Séquard's syndrome 183
 Quadrant lesions 183
  Dorsal quadrant 183
  Ventral quadrant 184
 Chordotomy 184

8. Decerebrate and Decorticate Rigidity: The Postural Reflexes 187
 BY JOHN F. FULTON
Decerebrate rigidity 188
 Decorticate rigidity and decerebrate rigidity in man 191
Postural reflexes (static reactions) 192
 The spinal animal 192

The decerebrate animal 193
   Local static reactions 193
   Segmental static reactions 194
   General static reactions (decerebrate preparation) 194
      Tonic neck reflexes 194
      Tonic labyrinthine reflexes 194
The midbrain preparation ("thalamus" animal) 195
   Righting reflexes 195
      Labyrinthine righting reflexes 196
      Body righting reflexes 197
      Neck righting reflexes 197
      Body righting reflexes acting on the body 197
      Optical righting reflexes 197
      Grasp reflex 197
Postural reflexes depending upon cerebral cortex 198
   Placing reactions 198
   Hopping reactions 200
      Functional localization of placing and hopping 200

9. Labyrinthine Acceleratory Reflexes: The Medulla Oblongata and Cranial Nerves 202
   BY JOHN F. FULTON

Position and structure of labyrinth 202
Function of the semicircular canals 205
   Acceleratory reflexes 205
      Linear acceleration 205
      Angular acceleration and nystagmus 206
      Mechanism of stimulation of the canals 206
   Caloric reactions 209
   Temporary and permanent effects of labyrinthectomy 210
The saccule and utricle 211
The medulla oblongata 212
   Nuclei of origin and functions of the cranial nerves 212
      Third cranial nerve (n. oculomotorius) 212
      Fourth cranial nerve (n. trochlearis) 215
      Fifth cranial nerve (n. trigeminus) 215
      Sixth cranial nerve (n. abducens) 215
      Seventh cranial nerve (n. facialis) 216
      Ninth cranial nerve (n. glossopharyngeus) 216
      Tenth cranial nerve (n. vagus or pneumogastricus) 216
      Eleventh cranial nerve (n. accessorius) 216
      Twelfth cranial nerve (n. hypoglossus) 216

10. Autonomic Nervous System: Peripheral Division 218
   BY ROBERT GORDON GRENELL
Thoracolumbar division (sympathetic) 222
Craniosacral division (parasympathetic) 225
   Hypothalamic outflow 225
   Tectal outflow 225
   Bulbar outflow 225
   Sacral outflow 225
Outline of autonomic innervation of individual viscera 226
   Visceral afferents 227
Nature of autonomic activity 228
   Autonomic regulation: general principles 228

General actions of the autonomic system   230
Substances associated with autonomic stimulation   233
Effects of sympathectomy   235
    Sensitization of denervated structures to autonomic neurohormones.   236

11. Autonomic Nervous System: Central Division   241
    BY JOHN F. FULTON
Levels of autonomic function   241
    Spinal level   241
    Medullary level   241
    Pontine level   242
    Hypothalamic level   242
Functions of the hypothalamus   242
    Anatomical organization   243
    Diabetes insipidus and water metabolism   245
    Heat regulation   246
        Mechanisms of heat loss   247
        Mechanisms of heat production and heat conservation   248
    Obesity   249
    Sexual functions   249
    Hypothalamus and emotional expression   249
Cerebral regulation of autonomic function   250
    Experimental evidence   251
        Cardiovascular system   251
        Gastro-intestinal tract   251
        Other autonomic effects   252
    The autonomic motor area   252

12. Cerebral Cortex: Cytoarchitecture and Projections   255
    BY JOHN F. FULTON
Laminar organization of the cerebral cortex   256
    The medulla of the cerebrum   258
    Physiological deductions from the histology of the cortex   260
Cytoarchitectural maps of the cortex   263
    Maps of subhuman primate compared with man   266
Motor projections from the cerebral cortex   269
    Corticospinal projections (pyramidal tract)   269
    Extrapyramidal projections from the cortex   270

13. Cerebral Cortex: Motor Functions   273
    BY JOHN F. FULTON
Excitability   274
    Factors affecting excitability   274
        H-ion concentration   274
        Facilitation and inhibition   276
        Direct inhibition   276
    Extent of the excitable cortex   277
        Area 8 (frontal eye fields)   277
        Area 6 (premotor area)   278
        Areas 17, 18 and 19   278
        Areas 3–1, 5 and 7   279
    Interaction between cortical areas   279
        Suppressor strips   279
        Interaction of other areas   280

Regional ablation of cortical areas 281
  Precentral convolution 281
  Area 4 (primary motor area) 281
    Movement 281
    Flaccidity 282
    Reflex changes 282
    Behavior disturbances 283
    Autonomic disturbances 283
  Area 6 (premotor area) 283
    Reflex changes 283
  Area 8 (frontal eye fields) 284
  Area 13 (cortical respiratory center) 285
  Areas 17–19 (occipital eye fields) 286
  Areas 3–1–3, 5 and 7 286
  Ipsilateral control and interaction between cerebral hemispheres . . . 286
    Corpus callosum 286
    Cerebral dominance 286

14. Cerebrum and Basal Ganglia 288
  BY JOHN F. FULTON
Anatomical considerations 288
Excitability 289
  Inhibitory effects 289
  Activation of basal ganglia by cerebral cortex 290
Experimental lesions 291
  Striopallidum alone 291
  Combined lesions of striopallidum and cerebral cortex 291
Clinical physiology 292
  Athetosis 292
  Tremor 292

15. Cerebrum and Cerebellum 294
  BY JOHN F. FULTON
Anatomical organization 294
  Primary divisions 294
  Anatomical structure and relations of the cerebellum 295
Functional analysis 299
  Complete ablation 299
  Regional ablation 300
    Flocculonodular lobe 300
    Posterior lobe 300
    Anterior lobe 301
  Cerebral and cerebellar interrelations 302

III. THE NERVOUS SYSTEM: SENSORY FUNCTIONS
BY THEODORE C. RUCH

16. Somatic Sensation 305
  BY THEODORE C. RUCH
  Introductory concepts 305
  Classification of the senses 306
  Adequate stimulus and "specific nerve energies" 308
Sense organ discharge 309
  Differential sensitivity and nonspecific discharge 309
  Intensity 310

Adaptation 312
   Rate of adaptation in different sense organs. 313
Weber-Fechner law 313
Temperature senses 314
Pain 317
   Neurohistological basis of pain 318
   Measurement of pain sensibility 320
Touch-pressure 321
Deep sensibility 322
Vibratory sensibility 325
Localization or topognosis 326
Projection of sensations 328
Two-point sensibility. 329
   Neural basis of localization and two-point discrimination 330
Size, shape, figure writing, etc. 331
   Stereognosis 332

17. Neural Basis of Somatic Sensation 334
   BY THEODORE C. RUCH
Peripheral nerve and spinal roots 334
Dissociation and overlap 334
Dermatomes 338
Conduction of sensory nerve impulses 341
   Double pain response 344
   Tabes dorsalis and peripheral neuropathy. 344
   Dysesthesia 344
Sensory tracts of spinal cord 345
Spinothalamic tract 346
   Functional anatomical details. Origin and decussation 347
   Lamination. 349
   Chordotomy 349
Posterior columns 350
   Sensory functions 350
   Control of movement 351
Sensory systems of the brain stem 352
Trigeminal nerve 352
Trigeminal neuralgia. 353
Spinothalamic tract and medial lemniscus 353
Thalamus and cerebral cortex 354
Thalamus 354
Functional organization of thalamocortical projections 357
Topographical organization 357
   Ipsilateral character of the projections 358
   Density and extent of cortical projections. 358
Cortical localization of sensory functions 359
   Electrical stimulation 360
   Strychnine stimulation 360
   Electrical activity of the sensory cortex 360
   Ablation experiments 362
Cortical function in man 365
Thalamus and sensation 366

18. Taste 371
   BY HARRY D. PATTON AND THEODORE C. RUCH
Distribution of receptors 371
Thresholds for taste 373

Neural pathways for taste 374
  End-organs 374
  Peripheral pathways 376
  Bulbar nucleus 376
  Bulbothalamic pathways 378
    Thalamic nucleus 379
  Cortical representation 379
  Summary of taste pathways 381
  Clinical examination of taste 382
Biological value of taste 383

19. Visceral Sensation and Referred Pain 385
  BY THEODORE C. RUCH
  Reflex afferents 385
  Organic sensations 386
  Hunger 386
    Appetite 387
    Hunger as a physiological state or drive 388
    Thirst 389
  Visceral pain 390
  Types of visceral pain 393
    1. Unreferred parietal pain 393
    2. Referred parietal pain 395
    3. Referred visceral pain 396
    4. Unreferred visceral pain (splanchnic pain) 396
  Deep pain and referred pain 397
  Mechanism of referred pain 397
    Convergence-projection theory 398
  Central pathways of visceral sensation 400

20. Olfaction and Olfactory Pathways 402
  BY HARRY D. PATTON
    End-organs 402
    Olfactory stimuli and olfactory threshold 402
    Olfactory bulb 405
    Central olfactory pathways 405

21. Audition and the Auditory Pathways 408
  BY THEODORE C. RUCH
  External ear 409
  Middle ear 409
    Ear bones 409
    Mode of action of the ear bones 411
    Muscles of the middle ear 411
    The eustachian tube 412
  Inner ear 413
    Sensory epithelium of the cochlea 415
  Physical and psychological dimensions of sound 416
  Pitch 417
  Loudness and intensity 417
    Audibility curve 418
    Audiometry 419
    The decibel 420
  Quality or timbre 421
  Mechanism of the cochlea 423

Electrical activity of cochlea   425
Action potentials of auditory nerves   426
Total localization in the cochlea   429
Routes of conduction   431
Types of deafness   433
Auditory pathway   434
    Thalamocortical auditory radiations   436
    Bilaterality of the auditory pathway   437
    Topographical organization   438

22. The Eye as an Optical Instrument   440
    BY FRANK W. WEYMOUTH
    Formation of an image by a convex lens   440
    Formation of an image by the eye   443
    Retinal image and spatial perception   444
    Size of the retinal image   445
    Accommodation of the eye for objects at different distances   446
    Limit of the power of accommodation—near point of distinct vision .   448
    Far point of distinct vision   449
    Refractive power of the eye and amplitude of accommodation   450
    Optical defects of the emmetropic eye   450
    Abnormalities in the refraction of the eye: ametropia   451
    Astigmia or astigmatism   453
    Iris and pupil   455
        Light reflex   456
    Intra-ocular pressure and the nutrition of the eye   457
        Intra-ocular pressure   457
        Nutrition of the lens and cornea   457

23. Vision   463
    BY THEODORE C. RUCH
    Visual stimulus   463
    Intensity functions   465
Photochemical basis of vision   466
    Visual purple—rhodopsin   466
    Rhodopsin and the visibility curve   468
    Dark adaptation   468
    Factors influencing dark adaptation   469
        Avoidance of light   469
        Pre-adaptation illumination   470
        Hemeralopia   470
        Vitamin A deficiency   470
        Anoxia and metabolic factors   471
    Curve of light adaptation   471
    Mechanism of rod stimulation and dark adaptation   471
    Photochemical cycle of the retina   472
Neural basis of retinal function   473
    Functional anatomy of the retina   473
        Neural basis of a real interaction   476
        Regional variations of the retina   476
    Electrical activity of the retina   477
        Electroretinogram   477
    Optic nerve potentials and retinal interaction   478
Visual acuity and detail vision   480
    Factors determining detail vision. Dioptric factors   481

Stimulus factors. 481
Retinal grain 482
    Retinal region 485
    Functional grain and contour vision 488
    Clinical tests of visual acuity 488
Color vision. 489
Achromatic and chromatic series 489
    Color saturation 490
Laws of color vision 490
    Color mixture. 490
    Primary colors 491
    Complementary colors 491
    After-images 491
    Color contrasts 492
Theories of color vision 492
    Young-Helmholtz theory 492
Site of color mixture. 494
Specific color receptors. 495
Color blindness 496
Classification of color blindness 496
    Luminosity of the spectrum in color blindness. 497
    Color confusions 498
    Subjective phenomena 499
Tests of color blindness 500

24. Binocular Vision and Central Visual Pathways 503
    BY THEODORE C. RUCH
Eye movements 503
Movements of the eye 503
Coordination of the eye muscles—muscular insufficiency—strabismus. 505
Visual fields and binocular vision 506
Visual fields—perimetry 506
    Visual fields for color 507
Binocular vision. 507
    Corresponding points 508
    Suppression of visual images 509
    Binocular rivalry 510
    Judgments of solidity and depth. 510
Central visual pathways 511
Retina, optic nerve and chiasm 511
Lateral geniculate bodies and striate cortex 513
Topographical organization of the visual area 515
    Functional significance of topographical organization 517
Macular sparing. 518
Visual function of the striate area 521
    Pattern vision. 522
    Interconnection of visual areas 522
    Higher levels of visual sensation in man 523

25. Association Areas and the Cerebral Cortex in General 525
    BY THEODORE C. RUCH
Electrical activity of cerebral cortex 525
Electroencephalogram 525
Learning 529
    Conditioned responses 529

1

Establishment of conditioned reflexes 531
Reinforcement and extinction 531
Neurophysiological basis of conditioning 532
Limits of conditioning 534
Experimental neurosis 534
Association areas 535
Prefrontal area 535
Hyperactivity 535
Delayed response 538
Experimental neurosis and prefrontal lobotomy 540
Frontal lobe function in man 541
Intelligence and intellectual functions 541
Emotional behavior and personality 541
Temporal lobes 542
Agnosia, apraxia, aphasia 542
Agnosia 542
Apraxia 543
Aphasia 543
Motor or expressive aphasia 543
Sensory or receptive aphasia 545
Aphasia as an intellectual defect 545

IV. PROPERTIES AND CONSTITUENTS OF THE BLOOD

BY DAVID I. HITCHCOCK

26. General Properties of Blood: The Formed Elements 548
BY JOHN H. FERGUSON
General properties of blood 548
Functions of the blood 548
Cells, plasma and serum 549
Viscosity of blood 550
Specific gravity and sedimentation 550
Relative volumes of cells and plasma 551
Total blood volume 552
The formed elements 553
Hemocytometry 553
Morphology of the formed elements 553
Erythrocytes 555
Life history of the erythrocyte 555
Normal mechanisms of red blood cell destruction 557
Abnormal mechanisms of red blood cell destruction 558
Osmotic fragility test 559
Toxic hemolysis 560
Serological agglutination and hemolysis 560
Chemical alteration of hemoglobin 561
Red blood cells in relation to spleen 562
Leukocytes 562
Ameboid motility and chemotaxis 562
Functions of leukocytes 563
Phagocytosis 563
Fate of the leukocytes 563
Blood platelets 564

27. Chemical Aspects of the Physiology of Blood   566

BY DAVID I. HITCHCOCK

Chemical composition of blood.   567
   Distribution of substances between cells and plasma   567
Osmotic equilibrium   568
   Total osmotic pressure of blood   568
   Colloid osmotic pressure of plasma   569
Membrane equilibrium   570
   Distribution of ions across a membrane   570
   Colloid osmotic pressure and Donnan equilibrium   571
   Distribution of ions between cells and plasma   572
Acid-base equilibrium.   573
   Hydrogen ion concentration and buffer action.   573
   Buffers in blood.   575
   Physiological buffer action of carbon dioxide   576
   Kidney action and neutrality of blood   578
   Experimental shifts in the acid-base balance.   579
Proteins of the blood   581
   Properties of hemoglobin.   581
   Plasma proteins   583
      Specific gravity and protein concentration   584

28. Coagulation of Blood; Transfusion Problems in Hemorrhage and Shock .   586

BY JOHN H. FERGUSON

Coagulation of blood   586
   Scope of the coagulation problem   588
   Individual factors in the coagulation mechanism.   589
     Fibrinogen   589
      Physiological significance of fibrinogen   590
     Prothrombin   590
      Physiological significance of prothrombin.   591
      Dicumarol   591
     Thrombin   591
      Hemostatic uses of thrombin   592
     Calcium and blood clotting.   592
      Blood calcium and bleeding conditions   593
     Thromboplastic substances   593
     Proteolytic enzymes   594
      Hemophilia.   594
      Clot retraction   596
     Surface factors   596
   Clot modifying mechanisms.   597
     Heparin   598
      Clinical uses of heparin   598
      Fate of thrombin in serum   599
   Interpretations of the data on blood clotting   599
     The Howell theory   599
     Eagle's view   600
     Nolf's views   600
     Ferguson's views   600
Transfusion problems in hemorrhage and shock   601

V. PHYSIOLOGY OF THE ORGANS OF CIRCULATION OF THE BLOOD AND LYMPH

BY DONALD H. BARRON, HAROLD LAMPORT AND JOHN F. FULTON

29. The Capillaries and the Lymphatics 607
  BY ERIC PONDER
  Circulation through the capillaries 607
    The capillary wall 608
    Capillary reactions 610
      Vascular reactions in the skin (the "triple response"). 611
    Capillary permeability 612
      Capillary pressure 614
      Gradient of capillary permeability 616
      Variations in capillary permeability 616
      Capillary poisons 619
      Lymphagogues 620
      Atypical capillaries 620
  The lymphatics 620
    Arrangement and structure of the lymphatics 620
    Formation of lymph 622
      Composition of lymph 623
      Flow of lymph 623
      Rate of lymph flow 626
    Cell content of lymph 626
    Lymphoid tissue 627

  Addendum: clinical applications—pressure bandages and the closed plaster treatment of burns, frostbite and flesh wounds 628

30. Hemodynamics 630
  BY HAROLD LAMPORT
  Physical principles of liquid flow 630
    Steady flow of a homogeneous viscous fluid in rigid tubules 631
      Turbulence 631
      Wetting 632
      Energy of fluid 632
        Pressure measurement 633
      Measurement of flow 634
      Resistance to flow—Poiseuille's law 635
        Length of tube 635
        Caliber of tube 636
        Pressure and flow 636
        Viscosity 636
        Fluidity 637
        Resistance 637
    Steady flow of colloidal fluids: viscous flow 639
    Steady flow of suspensions: plastic flow 640
      Resistance to the flow of suspensions: hindrance 642
    Nonrigid tubes and steady flow 643
    Pulsatile pressure 643
      Rigid tubes 643
      Elastic tubes 644
  Hemodynamics: application of physical principles of flow to the circulation . 644
    Blood 644
      Turbulence 644

Forces maintaining the circulation   645
Relation of pressure to flow: peripheral resistance or hindrance   646
  Aorta   646
  Dimensions of vessels   649
  Arterioles   650
  Capillaries   651
  Venules and veins   651
  Serum and plasma: their lack of plasticity   652
    Elasticity of vessels   652
  Blood: its plasticity   652
    In vivo properties   653
Peripheral resistance and hindrance: vasomotor tone   657
    Peripheral resistance   657
    Vasomotor tone   658
    Hindrance   658

31. The Velocity and Pressure of Blood Flow   660
  BY ERIC PONDER
    The circulation as seen under the microscope   660
    Velocity and volume of the blood flow   660
    Mean velocity of blood flow in arteries, veins and capillaries   664
      Explanation of differences in velocity of flow   665
    Circulation time   666
    Volume of blood flowing through an organ   667
    Pressure in the vascular system   667
      Methods of recording blood pressure   668
      Systolic, diastolic and mean arterial pressure   670
      Data as to the mean pressure in arteries, veins and capillaries . . .   671
      Blood pressure in the large arteries of man   672
      Normal arterial blood pressure   674
      Essential hypertension: hyperpiesia   675
      Gravitational effects   676
      Measurement of venous pressure   678
      Accessory factors aiding the circulation   679

32. The Pulse   682
  BY WILLIAM F. HAMILTON
    Velocity of the pulse wave   683
    Sphygmographs   684
    Manometers   685
    Form of the pulse   686
    Reflected waves   687
    Characteristics of the pulse in health and disease   689
    Venous pulse   689

33. Vasomotor Regulation   692
  BY DONALD H. BARRON
Methods used to determine vasomotor action   692
Nervous regulation of the arterioles   694
    General distribution and course of the vasoconstrictor nerves   694
    General course and distribution of the vasodilator fibers   696
      Via the parasympathetic outflow   697
      Via the sympathetic system   697
      Via the somatic nervous system   697

Vasomotor centers 698
    Spinal vasomotor center 698
    Medullary vasomotor center 698
    Nervous control of the vasomotor centers 701
        Depressor afferents 701
        Pressor afferents. 703
        Control by higher centers. 705
    Chemical regulation of the arterioles 705
        Via the carotid and aortic bodies 705
        Direct action on the vasomotor centers. 706
        By direct action on the arterioles 707
        Metabolites. 708
        Hormones 708

34. Regulation of Arterial Pressure. 710
    BY WILLIAM F. HAMILTON

35. Events of the Cardiac Cycle 717
    BY HEBBEL E. HOFF

Origin of the heart beat. 717
    Structure of the pacemaker in mammalian hearts 718
    Experimental localization of the pacemaker. 719
    Refractory period and rhythmic discharge 721
    Pacemaker potentials 723
    The supernormal period 724
Distribution of the cardiac impulse 725
    Intra-auricular conduction 725
    Auriculoventricular conduction 726
    Intraventricular conduction. 727
Mechanical events of the cardiac cycle 729
    Auricular systole 729
    Ventricular systole. 731
Heart sounds 732
    First heart sound 732
    Second heart sound 734
    Third heart sound 735
    Abnormalities. 736
        Splitting of heart sounds 736
        Opening snap of mitral valves. 738
        Gallop rhythms 738
        Murmurs. 738
The electrocardiogram 741
    Conventions 741
    Auricular and ventricular components 747
    Electrical activity of cardiac muscle 748
        Membrane and dipole hypotheses 748
        Interference theory 749
    Geographical representation 750
        Significance of leads 750
        Dextro- and levocardiograms 758
    Calculation of the electrical axis 762
        Conduction disturbances 765
    Ectopic beats 769
        Bigeminy. 773
    Auricular fibrillation. 775
    Ventricular fibrillation 776

36. Cardiac Output: Regulation and Estimation 781
BY HEBBEL E. HOFF

The heart rate and its regulation 781
   Normal standards and physiological variations 781
   Pathological variations 784
   Parasympathetic control: the vagus 785
   Reflex regulation of the vagus. 787
   Sympathetic control: adrenaline 789
   Influence of heart rate upon cardiac output 790
Regulation of stroke volume 792
   Starling's law of the heart 792
   Cardiac reserve and heart failure 794
Estimation of cardiac output 795
Physiological and pathological variations in cardiac output 801

37. The Nutrition of the Heart 803
BY HEBBEL E. HOFF

Cardiac circulation 803
   Arterial supply 803
   Cardiac veins and the thebesian vessels 804
   Nervous control of the coronary vessels 806
   Chemical control: autonomic hormones 808
   Oxygen, carbon dioxide, and other metabolites 809
   Mechanical regulation of coronary blood flow 810
      Aortic pressure 810
      Heart rate 811
   Mechanical interference with blood flow during systole 812
Oxygen metabolism 812
   Oxygen requirement 812
      Cardiac efficiency 812
   General anoxemia 814
   Localized anoxemia 816
Inorganic ions and the heart 819
   Ringer's solution 819
   Sodium 819
   Potassium 821
   Calcium 821
   Magnesium 823
   Acid-base equilibrium 824
Carbohydrate metabolism 825
   Lactic acid 825
   Glycogen and glucose 826

38. Circulation through Special Regions 828
BY WILLIAM F. HAMILTON

Regulation of blood flow to the several organs 828
Blood flow to the skin 829
   Chemical mechanisms 829
   Nervous mechanisms 830
   Hormonal mechanisms 831
Blood flow through the kidney 833
Blood flow to the viscera 834
   Chemical control 834
   Nervous control 834
   Hormonal control 834

Blood flow through the liver   834
Blood supply to the skeletal muscles   836
Blood flow through the uterus   837
Blood flow through the lungs.   840
Blood stores: circulation through the spleen   844
Vascular reaction to injury   846
Venous return   847

Circulation through the brain   848
   BY ROBERT G. GRENELL AND EBBE C. HOFF
     Angioarchitecture   848
     End-arteries of the brain   849
     The hemato-encephalic barrier   850
Regulation of cerebral circulation   851
     Extrinsic control   851
     Intrinsic control   852
     Summary   854

VI. RESPIRATION
BY LESLIE F. NIMS

39. Anatomy and Physics of Respiration   858
   BY LESLIE F. NIMS
Mechanics of external respiration   859
     Breathing movements   859
   Inspiration   860
     Contraction of the diaphragm   861
     Elevation of the ribs   862
     Expiration   863
     Accessory respiratory movements   864
     Breathing movements of the lungs   864
Pressure changes   864
     Intrapulmonic pressure   865
     Intrathoracic pressure   865
     Pneumothorax   867
Lung volume   867
     Vital capacity   868
Pulmonary ventilation   869
     Physiological anatomy   869
     Alveolar ventilation   870
     Pulmonary ventilation   871
     Artificial respiration   871
Properties of gases and liquids   873
     Partial pressures   874
     Vapor pressures   874
     Solubility and partial pressures of gases in liquids   874

40. Gas Exchange and Transportation   877
   BY LESLIE F. NIMS
     Physiological significance of N_2   878
     Respiration and temperature control   878
     Partial pressure and gas exchange   878
Gas exchange in the lungs   879
     Alveolar function   879
     Alveolar air   881
     Diffusion of gases through body tissues   882

Transport of O_2 and CO_2 882
　O_2 dissociation curve. 883
　Effect of CO_2 and *p*H on the O_2 dissociation curve 884
　Condition of CO_2 in the blood 884
　$HHbCO_2$. 885
　Velocity of the reactions 886
Gas exchange in the tissues 886
　Supply of O_2 to the tissues 888
　Respiration and acid-base balance 888
　Combination of CO with HHb 889
Anoxia 889
　Stagnant anoxia 889
　Anoxic anoxia 890
　Histotoxic anoxia 890
　Anemic anoxia 891
　Effects of O_2 lack 891
　Fulminating anoxia 891
　Acute anoxia 891
　Chronic anoxia 892
　Acclimatization 892
　Cyanosis 892
　Hyperpnea 893
　Therapeutic use of oxygen 893
　O_2 toxicity 894

41. Organization of the Neural Mechanisms Responsible for Rhythmic Respiration 896
　BY ROBERT F. PITTS
Medullary respiratory center 896
　Localization 896
　Organization of the respiratory center 898
　Respiratory motor pathways 899
　Properties of the respiratory center 899
　Nature of respiratory motor nerve discharge 900
　Pattern of respiratory motor impulses 900
　Mechanism of grading the depth of breathing 901
　Mechanism of repetitive discharge of impulses 901
Hering-Breuer vagal reflexes 903
　Respiratory reflexes stimulated by inflation of the lungs 903
　Respiratory reflexes stimulated by deflation of the lungs 904
　Sensitization of the Hering-Breuer reflexes in diseases affecting the
　　lungs 905
　Effects of vagotomy on breathing 905
　Effects of stimulation of the vagus nerves on breathing 906
Pneumotaxic center and the rhythm of breathing 906
　Location and function of the pneumotaxic center 906
　Properties of the isolated respiratory center 908
　Relative contribution of the two inhibitory mechanisms to the
　　rhythm of breathing 909
Functional organization of the respiratory complex 909
　Respiratory center-motoneuron mechanism 909
　Vagal inhibitory mechanism 910
　Pneumotaxic inhibitory mechanism 911

42. Regulation of Respiration 913
  BY ROBERT F. PITTS
  Chemical control of respiration 913
    Chemical control of the respiratory center by CO_2 913
      Relation between pulmonary ventilation and alveolar pressure of
        CO_2 914
      Periodic breathing in disease 916
      Variations in the sensitivity of the respiratory center to CO_2 . . . 916
      Mode of action of CO_2 on the respiratory center 918
    Control of the respiratory center by changes in rate of flow, tempera-
      ture, and O_2 pressure of the arterial blood 919
      Significance of the several factors which affect the activity of the re-
        spiratory neurons 920
    Reflex chemical control of the respiratory center. 921
      Morphology of the carotid and aortic receptors 922
      Chemoreceptor reflexes from the carotid and aortic glomi 922
        Role of chemoreceptor reflexes in respiratory regulation 923
      Effects of a reduction in oxygen pressure on the respiration of man . 925
      Effects of O_2 administration at high altitudes 926
  Nervous control of respiration 927
    Voluntary control of respiration. 927
    Reflex control of respiration 928
      Pressoreceptor respiratory reflexes 928
      Protective reflexes 929
      Reflexes from muscle and joint receptors and from receptors in the
        right heart 929
    Stimulation of respiration in exercise. 930

VII. BODY FLUIDS AND KIDNEY

BY ROBERT W. CLARKE

43. Physiology of Body Fluids 935
  BY J. RUSSELL ELKINTON
  Functional divisions 935
    Extracellular and intracellular phases 935
    Blood plasma and interstitial fluid 936
    Individual tissue fluids 936
  Internal exchanges 937
    Fluid exchanges between blood plasma and interstitial fluid 937
      Volume of blood and plasma 938
      Blood and lymph 939
    Fluid exchanges between cells and extracellular fluid 939
      Identity and volume of extracellular fluid 939
      Volume of the total and intracellular fluid 942
      Transfers of water 943
      Transfers of electrolytes 944
  External exchanges 944
    Regulation of acid-base equilibrium 944
    Fluid exchanges through lungs and skin 947
      Insensible perspiration 947
      Sensible perspiration (sweating) 947
    Fluid exchanges in the gastro-intestinal tract 948
    Fluid exchange in the kidney 950
      Water and urea 950

Water and electrolytes 951
Water and glucose. 951
Renal regulation of acid-base balance 952
Endocrine control of renal fluid exchanges 952
The circulation and renal exchanges 953
Water balance. 953
Water requirements 953
Measurement of water balance 954
Pathological physiology of body fluids. 956
Diminished plasma volume 958
Depletion of water in excess of salt 959
Water deprivation 959
Depletion of salt in excess of water 959
Depletion of salt in proportion to water 960
Retention of water in excess of salt 961
Retention of salt in excess of water 961
Retention of salt in proportion to water 961

44. The Kidney 964
   BY ROBERT W. CLARKE
Structure of the kidney 964
Form and structure of the nephron 964
Blood vascular system 965
Juxtaglomerular apparatus 965
Renal lymphatic system 966
Amount and composition of urine. 966
Quantitative methods in renal physiology 966
Renal clearance 967
Glomerular function 968
Glomerular function in man 968
Tubular functions 970
Renal excretion of typical solutes 971
Limits of tubular activity 974
Renal circulation 976
Measurements of blood flow 976
Dynamics of glomerular function 977
Regulation of renal activity 978
Hormonal control 978
Acid-base balance of the urine 979
Renal hypertension. 980

VIII. PHYSIOLOGY OF DIGESTION AND SECRETION OF THE ALIMENTARY TRACT

BY GEORGE R. COWGILL

45. General Functions of the Alimentary Tract 982
   BY GEORGE R. COWGILL
Movements of the alimentary canal. 982
Mastication. 982
Deglutition 985
Cardiac sphincter 988
Anatomy of the stomach 989
Musculature of the stomach 990
Movements of the stomach 991

Innervation and movements of the stomach 993
Effects of stomach movements on food 993
Hunger contractions 994
Emptying of the stomach 997
Movements of the small intestine 999
    Rhythmical movements 999
    Peristalsis 1001
Movements of the intestinal villi 1003
Nervous control of the intestinal movements 1003
Factors effecting intestinal movements 1004
Movements of the large intestine 1005
Defecation—the laxation problem 1007
Vomiting 1009
    Nervous mechanism of vomiting 1010

46. General Considerations upon the Composition of Food and the Action of Enzymes 1014
    BY GEORGE R. COWGILL
Food and foodstuffs 1014
Accessory articles of diet 1019
Chemical changes of the foodstuffs during digestion 1019
Enzymes and their action 1019
Reversible reactions 1020
Specificity of enzymes 1021
Definition and classification of enzymes 1022
General properties of enzymes 1024
    Solubility 1024
    Temperature 1024
    Precipitation, adsorption 1024
    Incompleteness of their action 1024
    Active and inactive form 1024
    Co-enzymes or coferments 1025
Chemical composition of enzymes 1026

47. The Salivary Glands and Their Digestive Action 1028
    BY GEORGE R. COWGILL
Salivary glands 1028
Histological structure 1029
Composition of the secretion 1030
The secretory nerves 1031
    Relation of the composition of the secretion to the strength of stimulation 1032
Theory of trophic and secretory nerve fibers 1032
Histological changes during activity 1034
Action of atropine, pilocarpine, and nicotine upon the secretory nerves. 1036
Paralytic secretion 1037
Normal mechanism of salivary secretion 1037
Electrical changes in the gland during activity 1038
Digestive action of saliva—ptyalin 1038
Conditions influencing the action of ptyalin 1040
    Temperature 1040
    Effect of reaction 1040
    Condition of the starch 1040
Functions of the saliva 1040

48. Digestion and Absorption in the Stomach 1042
    BY GEORGE R. COWGILL
    Gastric glands 1042
    Histological changes in the gastric glands during secretion 1042
    Means of obtaining the gastric secretion and its normal composition . 1043
    Acid of gastric juice 1046
    Origin of the HCl 1047
    Secretory nerves of the gastric glands 1049
    Normal mechanism of the secretion of the gastric juice 1050
    Nature and properties of pepsin 1053
    Artificial gastric juice 1054
    Pepsin hydrochloric acid digestion of proteins 1054
    The rennin enzyme (rennet, chymosin, or chymase) 1055
    Digestive changes undergone by the food in the stomach 1056
    Absorption in the stomach 1057
        Water 1057
        Salts 1058
        Sugars and peptones 1058
        Fats 1058

49. Digestion and Absorption in the Intestines 1061
    BY GEORGE R. COWGILL
    Pancreas 1061
        Composition of the secretion 1061
        Secretory nerve fibers to the pancreas 1062
        Curves of secretion 1064
        Normal mechanism of the pancreatic secretion—secretin 1064
        Activation of the trypsin—enterokinase 1066
        Digestive action of pancreatic juice 1066
            Action of the proteolytic enzymes 1066
            Significance of protein digestion 1069
            Action of the diastatic enzyme (amylase) of the pancreatic secretion. 1070
            Action of the lipolytic enzyme (lipase) 1070
    Intestinal secretion (succus entericus) 1072
    Small intestine 1073
        Absorption 1073
        Absorption of the carbohydrates 1074
        Absorption of fats 1075
        Absorption of proteins 1076
        Reaction of the intestinal contents 1078
    Large intestine 1078
        Digestion and absorption 1078
    Bacterial action 1079
        Small intestine 1079
        Large intestine 1079
        Is the putrefactive process of physiological importance? 1080
        Composition of the feces 1081

IX. METABOLISM AND NUTRITION

BY JOHN R. BROBECK

50. Introduction to Quantitative Metabolism 1084
    BY JOHN R. BROBECK
    Food 1084
    Heat 1084

Work 1085
Storage 1086
Basal metabolism 1087
Direct calorimetry 1087
Indirect calorimetry 1088
Carbon dioxide production 1089
Oxygen consumption 1089
Calorific value of oxygen. Respiratory quotient 1091
Physiological conservation of energy 1094
Factors which affect basal metabolism 1094
Body size 1094
Growth 1096
Miscellaneous factors 1097
Total metabolism 1098
Effect of food 1098
Muscular exercise 1099
Environmental temperature 1099
Thyroid gland 1100
Fever 1101

51. Intermediary Metabolism 1102
BY JOHN R. BROBECK
Enzymatic catalysis 1104
Carbohydrate metabolism 1104
Carbohydrates of biological importance 1104
Carbohydrate supply of the body 1104
Blood glucose as a dynamic equilibrium 1104
Liver glycogen and carbohydrate storage 1107
Gluconeogenesis 1109
Peripheral utilization of carbohydrate 1109
In skeletal muscle 1109
Significance of blood lactic and pyruvic acids 1110
Utilization in other organs 1110
Diversion of carbohydrate into pathways of protein or lipid metabolism 1111
Protein metabolism 1111
Amino acids as protein constituents 1111
Sources of amino acids 1111
Products of digestion 1111
From tissue proteins 1112
Parenteral administration 1112
Amino acid utilization 1112
Protein synthesis 1112
Deamination 1116
Conversion to glucose or glycogen 1116
Conversion to fat 1118
Synthesis and excretion of urea 1118
Nitrogen equilibrium 1119
Other protein derivatives 1121
Lipid metabolism 1121
Nutritive value of lipids 1121
Plasma lipids 1121
Lipid utilization 1122
Fat storage 1122
Pathways of oxidation 1123
Role of the liver in lipid metabolism 1126
Conversion of carbohydrate to fat 1128

52. Nutrition 1130
   BY JOHN R. BROBECK
  Food as a source of energy 1130
    Caloric requirements. 1130
    Distribution of calories. 1134
      Carbohydrate and fat used almost interchangeably. 1135
      Irreplaceabil ty of amino nitrogen 1135
    "Essential" amino acids 1137
    "Essential" fatty acids 1138
  Vitamins 1138
    Thiamine. 1139
      Symptoms of deficiency 1140
      Human requirements 1140
      Dietary sources 1140
    Riboflavin 1141
      Sources and requirements 1141
    Niacin (nicotinic acid) 1142
      Symptoms of deficiency 1142
      Sources and requirements 1142
    Pyridoxine—B_6 1143
    Choline 1143
    Ascorbic acid. 1144
      Requirements and sources 1144
    Vitamin A 1145
      Evidences of deficiency. 1145
      Sources and requirements 1146
    Vitamin D 1146
      Vitamin D deficiency 1147
      Sources and requirements 1147
    Vitamin K 1148
      Deficiency in infants 1148
  Inorganic components of the diet 1149
  Nutrition in public health 1153

53. Regulation of Energy Exchange 1156
   BY JOHN R. BROBECK
  Regulation of food intake 1156
    Desire for food 1156
    Objective study of food intake 1157
  Regulation of motor output 1159
    Measurement of locomotor activity 1159
      Normal activity rhythms 1160
      Regulatory deficits. 1162
  Regulation of heat loss 1163
    Nature of thermal equilibrium 1163
    Heat production 1166
    Heat loss. 1167
      Physical processes 1167
      Physiological mechanisms 1168
    Role of the central nervous system in temperature regulation 1171
      Effects of hypothalamic lesions 1171
      Temperature-sensitive receptors 1172
      Fever 1174
  Regulation of energy storage 1175
    Nature of energy reserves. 1175

Carbohydrate reserves 1176
Protein reserves 1178
Lipid reserves 1179

X. PHYSIOLOGY OF REPRODUCTION

BY WILLIAM U. GARDNER

54. Reproduction in the Female 1184
   BY WILLIAM U. GARDNER
The ovary and its hormones 1184
The menstrual cycle 1187
   Relation between the ovaries and the menstrual cycle 1189
   Endocrine factors in the menstrual cycle 1189
   Evidence of hormone production during the menstrual cycle 1191
   Comparison of the menstrual and estrous cycles 1192
   Time of ovulation 1193
   Regulation of ovarian function during the menstrual cycle 1193
Life cycle of the ovary 1196
   Puberty 1197
   Menopause 1197
Pregnancy—the reproductive cycle 1198
   Physiology of the placenta 1200
   Influence of maternal hormones upon the embryo and fetus 1201
   Mechanism of parturition 1201
Mechanism of sperm transport 1202
   Some additional actions of female sex hormones 1203
     Carcinogenesis 1203
     Calcium and lipid metabolism 1203
     Pelvis 1203
Ovulation 1203
Physiology of the myometrium 1205
Physiology of the vagina 1206
Inactivation of hormones 1206
Development and function of the mammary glands 1207
   Normal development 1207
   Experimental studies on mammary development 1208
     Lactation 1209
     Mechanisms regulating the onset of lactation 1209

55. Reproduction in the Male 1213
   BY CHARLES W. HOOKER
   Effects of castration—transplantation of testes 1213
   Androgens—chemistry and metabolism 1214
   Actions and functions of androgen 1217
     Genital system 1217
     Hair 1218
     Sebaceous glands 1219
     Color of skin 1219
     Subcutaneous fat 1219
     Voice 1219
     Skeleton 1219
     Muscle 1220
     Vascular system 1220
     Metabolism 1220

Androgen in different periods of life 1220
   Puberty 1221
   Sexual maturity 1222
   Old age 1222
Site of production of testicular androgen 1223
Regulation of production of androgen 1223
Extratesticular androgen 1224
Spermatogenesis and spermatozoa 1224
Functions of genital organs 1226
Erection 1227
Ejaculation 1229

56. Genetic Aspects of Physiology 1232
   BY WALTER LANDAUER
Determination of sex 1232
Genetic factors and physiological functions 1235
Form and function 1235
Heredity and environment 1236
Sensory reactions, temperament, mentality 1240
Developmental correlations 1242
Some practical applications 1245

Index 1249

HISTORICAL BACKGROUNDS OF AMERICAN PHYSIOLOGY

BY J. F. FULTON

From sturdy beginnings dating back to the early Philadelphia and New York schools at the end of the eighteenth century, American physiology has progressed, slowly at first but lately with great rapidity, and it has now come to occupy a position of prominence and dignity among the other medical sciences. Students entering upon the subject for the first time should be familiar with the backgrounds of physiology, and since Howell's *Textbook* has influenced the development of the subject in this country more perhaps than any other work, it has seemed proper in undertaking a revision to introduce the new text by a brief historical résumé. This will serve not only to orient the student with regard to his subject, but it will also afford welcome opportunity to tell something of Dr. Howell himself.*

In his *History of the American Physiological Society* (8) Howell writes:

"From Galen to Lavoisier Physiology won its chief victories by the use of the experimental method, but it did not become established as a separate experimental science, after the pattern of physics and chemistry, until well into the nineteenth century. Its foundations were laid, roughly speaking, in the second quarter of the century, largely by the work and influence of Johannes Müller in Germany and Magendie and Bernard in France. Other European countries followed this lead in due course of time. In the United States there were individual workers who soon felt the influence of the new movement, but the full recognition of physiology as an independent science, with laboratories and techniques of its own and facilities for the training of specialists in the subject, did not occur until the latter part of the seventies, when nearly simultaneously three such laboratories were organized, one at the Harvard Medical School under Bowditch, one in the Graduate School of the Johns Hopkins University under Newell Martin, and one a little later in biochemistry, or physiological chemistry as it was then called, in the chemical department of Yale University under Chittenden."

Howell also mentions that there was an early laboratory at Michigan, where in 1876 Victor Vaughan gave practical laboratory exercises in physiological chemistry, and where, a few years later, Henry Sewall, fresh from Johns Hopkins, founded a flourishing physiological laboratory. Howell was identified with all three of these primary centers of American physiology—Michigan, Harvard and Johns Hopkins; after being graduated from Johns Hopkins in 1881, he received his Ph.D. there in 1884, and, after five years with H. Newell Martin, proceeded in 1889 at the age of twenty-nine to the Chair of Physiology at Michigan. Although he remained only three years in Ann Arbor, he gave to the school great impetus in physiology—an impetus which has continued and extended itself quickly to many other state univer-

---

* William Henry Howell (1860–1945) died suddenly of a coronary seizure on February 6, 1945, a few days before his eighty-fifth birthday. The day before his death he had been in his laboratory in Baltimore and had performed an experiment—one of a series he had been making on his hemophilic laboratory assistant. Dr. Howell had been following the progress of this revision with lively interest, and had read and emended the historical introduction.

sities. In 1892 he accepted an Associate Professorship at the Harvard Medical School where he served for a year under Bowditch. In 1893 he returned to Johns Hopkins to accept the newly created Chair of Physiology which was now attached to the Medical School.

Howell thus brought to the subject the two mainstreams of influence which had shaped the development of American physiology. From Bowditch he acquired the traditions of the German school, as Bowditch had learned them while under Carl Ludwig; and from his years with Newell Martin he absorbed the best traditions of Michael Foster and the English school. Newell Martin (1848–1896), one of Foster's first pupils, went from University College, London, to Trinity College, Cambridge, on a scholarship, and there acted as Demonstrator to Foster who had been called to Trinity as Praelector in Physiology (16). At the age of twenty-eight (i.e., in 1876), he was called to the Chair of Biology in the newly established Johns Hopkins University at Baltimore. In this department, as a part of the Philosophical Faculty, he and his graduate students published numerous experimental investigations in physiology. In 1883, in the preliminary steps taken to organize a Medical Faculty, Martin was designated also as Professor of Physiology in that faculty, but failing health caused him to resign and return to England before the Medical School of the University was actually founded in 1893. In tribute to Newell Martin, Howell republished in 1895 a collected volume of Martin's physiological papers and addresses (10). The most original of his contributions was a method of isolating the mammalian heart and keeping it alive by means of an artificial respiration. In recognition of this work one of his papers was made the Croonian Lecture, Royal Society, for 1883. Newell Martin left something intangible with his many pupils—a point of view and an approach to the subject which all who came in contact with him seemed immediately to feel. One of the most eloquent tributes to Martin is that of Sewall (16). He introduces his subject with the comment: "It is, I think, worthwhile enquiring how a young man entering at the age of twenty-eight, without the foundation of experience, upon an academic position whose ideals from the outset departed radically from any that had been hitherto aimed at the pedagogic history of America, had, as I believe, come to deserve the foremost niche in the temple of American physiology, which, I venture to hold, is the fountain head of American medicine."

In February 1941 a group of Howell's pupils and friends foregathered at the Welch Medical Library in Baltimore to pay tribute to the sixtieth anniversary of his graduation from Johns Hopkins (15). No mention was made of his years, but much was said of his influence upon younger men and of the widespread admiration which all felt for the man who had for so long carried on with teaching and research, maintaining it on a plane of undiminished quality and vigor. It was also pointed out that Howell was the first American to write a comprehensive textbook on the subject in the post-laboratory period, and that by so doing he influenced more men in American medicine than any other physiologist of our time. In once more presenting Howell's great text to students in this country as well as abroad, we do so with full knowledge of the place that it has occupied in the history of the subject.

It has already been indicated that physiological teaching in the United States, as we now understand it, began in 1871 in Boston soon after Henry Pickering Bowditch (1840–1911) returned from two years of postgraduate study in England and Germany.* Charles Eliot, the new president of Harvard, was especially eager that the more recent chemical approaches to medicine should find expression in the Medical School, and had urged Bowditch to reorganize the course of teaching in this regard. Bowditch in his first meager laboratory on North Grove Street began to insist, on the basis of his German experience, that physiology cannot be taught satisfactorily without laboratory experimentation (1); and it thus transpired that each medical student at Harvard soon was obliged to perform a series of carefully planned experiments to demonstrate basic physiological principles, such as the transmission of the nerve impulse to muscle, the development of fatigue in muscle, the "staircase" phenomenon, the all-or-nothing principle and certain of the reflexes underlying the regulation of blood pressure—these and many others.

One of Bowditch's pupils was Harvey Cushing (1869–1939) who in 1891–92 attended the course in physiology at Harvard, and he has left a detailed record of the laboratory work and the lectures of that academic year. It affords an excellent cross-section of physiology as taught at Harvard in those days, and it no doubt reflects what might have been learned in certain other American schools in the early nineties. There was much emphasis on the body "proteids"; frogs and turtles were dissected, and much time was devoted to nerve muscle physiology. The factors involved in digestion, as well as in urinary excretion, were studied at first hand. The lectures on the functions of the central nervous system likewise were discussed in great detail, and Dr. Cushing's notes, and subsequent annotations in his lecture notebook, indicate that these lectures served for him as a special stimulus, and they no doubt turned his interest to the field which he subsequently made his life's work.

Another student of Bowditch was Walter Bradford Cannon (b. 1871), who as a medical student in the spring of 1896 had been stirred by the discovery of Conrad Roentgen, announced in December 1895, of a new kind of ray that enabled one to photograph bones and metal objects through the soft tissues (15). Cannon undertook to study the movements of the gastro-intestinal tract of animals after ingestion of barium. All this quickly led to further practical experiments of great value to medicine; and it also led to Walter Cannon's becoming first Instructor, then Assistant Professor, and finally Higginson Professor of Physiology at Harvard. With his retirement in 1943 American physiology has lost from its active academic ranks one of its most original contributors and staunchest advocates.

Prior to the time of Bowditch various medical schools had offered lectures in physiology, or the "Institutes," but without exception there was no opportunity for laboratory experimentation (6). The earliest professorship was established at Philadelphia. In 1789 the College of Philadelphia, which later merged with the University of Pennsylvania in 1791, founded a Chair of the Institutes of Medicine. It stands as the first devoted to physiology and at this writing has had 156 years of continued existence. The name was changed to Physiology in 1878 and it was put on a full-time basis in 1886. The present incumbent, Professor H. Cuthbert Bazett, who took over in 1921, has brought to it a vital renewal of the best English traditions of physiology. Other chairs appeared elsewhere during the nineteenth century. In 1843 the Cleveland Medical School (after 1881 the Western Reserve) established a professorship of Anatomy and Physiology which in 1892 became a full-time physiological chair occupied successively by G. Gad, 1893–94, G. N. Stewart, 1894–1903, J. J. R. MacLeod, 1904–1918, and C. J. Wiggers, 1918–   . Boston University established a Professorship of Physiology in 1873, while Buffalo as early as 1846 had created a Chair of Physiology and Medical Jurisprudence occupied from 1851 to 1855 by John C. Dalton.

It would be unjust to imply that Michigan, Harvard and Johns Hopkins

---

* It is interesting to recall that the rival candidate at the time of Bowditch's appointment at Harvard was the obstetrician, William Thompson Lusk, the father of Graham Lusk. The authorities at Harvard had been under some uncertainty concerning which of the two candidates to select and Lusk, being impatient, moved to New York and declined to become a candidate in 1871 when he was formally approached (9).

alone gave birth to American physiology. They were the first to establish teaching laboratories for training specialists in the subject, and, as in Chittenden's laboratory of physiological chemistry at Yale, they were the first to insist upon practical laboratory experimentation as part of the student's training. Other schools such as those at Philadelphia and New York had gained distinction in physiological research long before Harvard, Yale, Johns Hopkins or the University of Michigan. Thus in Philadelphia between 1789 and 1810 a generation of men were trained in the experimental method by Benjamin Rush (1745–1813), who had derived his inspiration largely from the Edinburgh school (Meek, 11). Later, through the resourcefulness and imagination of the young Silas Weir Mitchell (1825–1914), the son of a prominent Pennsylvania physician, physiology as an experimental science again flourished in Philadelphia. Mitchell went to Paris in 1850 where he attended the lectures of Claude Bernard, who then was conducting his epic experiments on vasomotor nerves and on carbohydrate metabolism.* Mitchell returned to this country burning with enthusiasm for the new science which Magendie and Bernard were introducing in France. In collaboration with the elder Samuel Gross, a new journal was established, entitled *North American Medico-Chirurgical Review*, and in the second volume, issued in 1858, Mitchell published an important paper on the history of experimental physiology in the United States (12). This well documented review stands as the first history of the subject by an American author. Mitchell continued for several years to publish résumés of recent advances in physiology, but his efforts in this direction were interrupted by the Civil War. He plunged into the War with characteristic energy and found time for a close physiological analysis of many of the more interesting cases of injury to the nervous system. With G. R. Morehouse and W. W. Keen, he published a short treatise through the Surgeon General's Office entitled *Reflex paralysis* (13) in which he discussed traumatic shock in a thoroughly modern manner, with full application of Claude Bernard's latest disclosures concerning the vasomotor system. With Keen and Morehouse he also issued a book on gunshot wounds (14) in which, among other things, the syndrome of causalgia was described. The monograph itself ranks in importance with William Beaumont's earlier *Experiments and observation on the gastric juices and physiology of digestion* (1833). Mitchell, through his war experience, was drawn away from pure physiology into clinical neurology, and it is probable that he did more than any other individual to put American clinical neurology on a solid footing.

Mention must also be made of the important New York schools where individual physiologists flourished throughout the nineteenth century, even though they did not establish teaching laboratories in the modern sense. The most influential of the New York physiologists during this time was undoubtedly John Call Dalton (1825–1889), who, like Mitchell, served as an army surgeon from 1861 to 1864. After taking his M.D. at Harvard he studied under Claude Bernard in 1850 along with Mitchell. He returned to this country as Professor of Physiology and Morbid Anatomy at Buffalo in 1854, but within a year he was called to the Chair of Physiology and Microscopic Anatomy at the College of Physicians and Surgeons in New York. He stands

---

* Weir Mitchell's student notebook, kept while in Paris, is now in the possession of Dr. Clements C. Fry of the Yale School of Medicine.

as the first American to give himself exclusively to physiology as a profession. He studied the corpus luteum in relation to menstruation and pregnancy, sugar formation in the liver, and the production of anesthesia through cerebral compression. Dalton was also historically minded, and did much to arouse an interest in the historical approach of physiology to medicine. His most notable work in this field lay in his authoritative volume entitled *Doctrines of the circulation—A history of physiological opinion and discovery, in regard to the circulation of the blood* (1884). Dr. Howell has said appropriately (8), "Dalton was an important influence in spreading a knowledge of modern physiology and of scientific methods in medicine, and in preparing the way for a fuller development of the subject in the next generation."

It would be impossible to trace the development of physiology in all modern schools. Western Reserve, Minnesota, Wisconsin, Chicago, New Orleans, California, have all sponsored the subject, and nearly all Class A medical schools of the country now have flourishing departments. At Yale physiology as such developed relatively late, but the first teaching laboratory in the sister science of physiological chemistry had been established there in 1875 by the late Russell Chittenden (1856–1943). At his instigation Graham Lusk was called to Yale in 1893 to become head of a newly constituted Department of Physiology. He was at that time twenty-six years of age, and his annual stipend was three hundred dollars. He was succeeded in 1900 by the young Irish biochemist, Benjamin Moore (1867–1922), who, in turn, was followed in 1905 by the late Yandell Henderson (1874–1944).

The future of American physiology cannot easily be predicted. For a time following the last war, there was a tendency to prepare bedside texts of physiology, and, while such textbooks have in large measure always been intended for those engaged in clinical medicine, the fact remains that physiology is an academic discipline in its own right, and its future will undoubtedly be determined by the extent to which it remains a pure, rather than an applied, science. In times of war it is a universal wish that everyone associated with medical science should pursue applications with the utmost vigor, even to the exclusion of basic research. When peace comes again every physiologist who has the future of his subject at heart will hope to pursue the science for its own sake, even as Howell pursued it during sixty-five years of unremitting endeavor—an endeavor dedicated in the first instance to physiology pure and unapplied.

REFERENCES

1. BOWDITCH, H. P. and PORTER, W.T. The department of physiology, pp. 87–95 in: *The Harvard Medical School 1782–1906.* 1906.

2. CANNON, W. B. The movements of the stomach studied by means of Röntgen rays. *Amer. J. Physiol.*, 1898, *1*:359–382.

3. CANNON, W. B. Biographical memoir Henry Pickering Bowditch 1840–1911. *Mem. nat. Acad. Sci.*, 1924, *17*:183. See also: The history of the physiology department of the Harvard Medical School. *Harv. med. Alumni Bull.*, 1927, *1*:12–19.

4. CUSHING, H. *Life of Sir William Osler.* Oxford, 1925. 2 v.

5. DALTON, J. C. *Doctrines of the circulation. A history of physiological opinion and discovery, in regard to the circulation of the blood.* Philadelphia, 1884.

6. ELLIS, F. W. Henry Pickering Bowditch and the development of the Harvard Laboratory of Physiology. *New Engl. J. Med.*, 1938, *219*:919–928.

7. FULTON, J. F. *Physiology.* Clio medica series. New York, 1930.

8. HOWELL, W. H. The American Physiological Society during its first twenty-five years, pp. 1–89 in: *History of the American Physiological Society Semicentennial 1887–1937.* Baltimore, 1938.

9. LUSK, G. ed. Physiology at the Harvard Medical School, 1870–1871, given by William Thompson Lusk. *Boston med. surg. J.*, 1912, *167*:921–922.

10. MARTIN, H. N. *Physiological papers.* Baltimore, 1895.

11. MEEK, W. J. The beginnings of Ameri-

can physiology. *Ann. med. Hist.*, 1928, *10*:111–125.

12. MITCHELL, S. W. American progress of medical science. Report on the progress of physiology and anatomy. *North American Medico-Chirurgical Review*, 1858, *2*:105–131.

13. MITCHELL, S. W., MOREHOUSE, G. R. and KEEN, W. W. *Reflex paralysis.* Circular, No. 6, Surgeon General's Office, Washington, March 10, 1864.

14. MITCHELL, S. W., MOREHOUSE, G. R. and KEEN, W. W. *Gunshot wounds and other injuries of nerves.* Philadelphia, 1864.

15. ROENTGEN, W. C. Ueber eine neue Art von Strahlen. *S. B. phys.-med. Ges. Würzburg,* 1895, 132–141.

16. SEWALL, H. Henry Newell Martin. Professor of Biology in Johns Hopkins University, 1876–1898. *Johns Hopk. Hosp. Bull.*, 1911, *22*:327–333.

SECTION I

PRINCIPLES OF NERVOUS AND MUSCULAR ACTIVITY

BY DAVID P. C. LLOYD

CHAPTER 1

ELECTRICAL PROPERTIES OF NERVE AND MUSCLE

INTRODUCTION

If one's hand by accident touches some hot object, such as a lighted stove, it is instantly withdrawn. The movement is reflex; it involves a sequence of reactions beginning with excitation by the external agent of sensory end-organs. The excitation is conducted to the central nervous system by impulses in afferent neurons and transmitted therein to other neurons lying wholly within the nervous system. These are known as internuncial neurons, or, for brevity, interneurons. From interneurons the excitation is transmitted to efferent neurons, or motoneurons as they are called, by which the excitation is conducted away from the central nervous system to the muscles. The ensuant muscle contraction causes the withdrawal of the hand. It may be seen, therefore, that the operation of the reflex sequence depends upon three fundamental properties, *excitation, conduction* and *contraction*. Other, and infinitely more complex, series of events in the nervous system are mediated in a like manner.

The structures through which the reflex sequence is mediated are presented diagrammatically in Figure 1, which represents a cross section of the spinal cord. They are (i) the afferent neuron, (ii) the interneuron, (iii) the motoneuron, and (iv) the muscle cell. The junction between nerve cells is called the "synaptic" region, while that between motoneuron and muscle cell is called the neuromuscular junction. During the course of the reflex sequence excitation of the afferent neuron occurs at point A. Conduction of impulses occurs in the nerve fibers labeled B. The elongated conducting processes of neurons are frequently referred to as nerve fibers. Synaptic transmission, i.e., the excitation of one nerve cell by another, takes place at the points C. Neuromuscular transmission, the excitation of a muscle cell by its nerve fiber, occurs at D. The muscle response, i.e., contraction, follows at E. In this and the following chapters the fundamental properties that form the basis of activity in the nervous and muscular systems will be considered.

Nerve cells and muscle cells are highly specialized—the former to conduct impulses, the latter to contract—but the fact of specialization does not mean that properties other than that most highly developed in a given cell are not present. Excitability and conduction, as well as contraction, are exhibited by muscle cells. It is frequently convenient to consider the properties of excitation and conduction in relation to nerve, where they are most highly developed and where other factors add the least complication, but

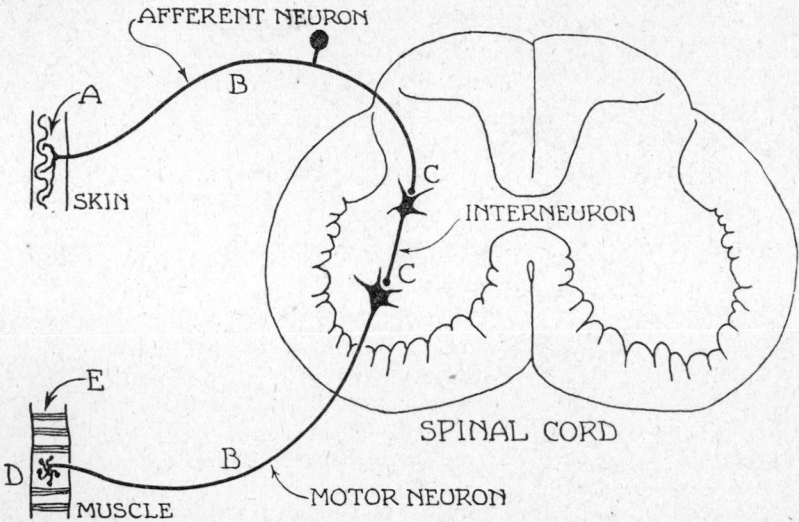

Fig. 1.—Diagram to illustrate the structures through which are mediated simple reflex acts. *Excitation* of afferent neurons occurs at point A. *Conduction* of impulses takes place in the nerve fibers, B, toward the central nervous system in the afferent fibers, away from the central nervous system in motoneurons. *Synaptic transmission* between neurons occurs at C. *Neuromuscular transmission* occurs at D. *Contraction* occurs in the muscle fiber E.

there is no reason to believe that there is any qualitative difference between nerve and muscle with respect to these properties; indeed, our knowledge of conduction and excitation is derived from experiment not only on nerve, but also on muscle, on large plant cells, and other living tissues.

ELECTRICAL PHENOMENA AT REST AND IN ACTION

The prime function of neurons is the conduction of impulses. The nerve impulse is always associated with an electrical change of characteristic time course, the action potential. Conversely, an action potential is never encountered in resting neurons. There are other changes, chemical and thermal, that occur in active neurons, but these appear to play a supporting role in contrast to that of the electrical change.

Fortunately it is possible to measure the electrical events in excitable tissues with the greatest accuracy by means of the cathode ray oscillograph introduced into physiology by Gasser and Erlanger in 1922. In principle the use of the cathode ray oscillograph in nerve physiology is quite simple. A beam of electrons is focused on a fluorescent screen to yield a luminous spot that can be photographed. The beam can be deflected by a system of charged parallel plates, the electrons being repulsed by a negatively charged plate and attracted by a positively charged plate. By varying the charges on plates set parallel to one another, the "spot" can be made to "sweep" in a horizontal plane across the fluorescent screen face of the cathode ray tube (cf.

Fig. 2). The electrical changes occurring in a nerve are feeble and must be amplified by means of radio tubes. To accomplish this the electrical charges are led off to an amplifier by a pair of electrodes suitably placed on the nerve. As the spot sweeps across the screen in a horizontal plane, the amplified nerve "signals" are impressed upon another pair of parallel plates so placed as to deflect the beam in a vertical plane. The resulting movement of the spot, deflected by the two sets of plates, traces out the nerve activity as a function of time. Thus in many of the illustrations which follow, action potentials are recorded, the vertical components of the records indicating the potential difference between two points on the nerve, the horizontal components the course of time.

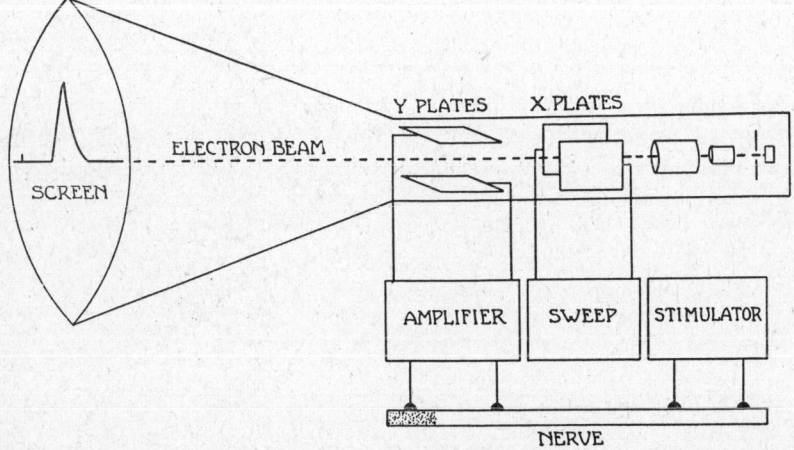

Fig. 2.—Block diagram of apparatus for studying, by means of electrical changes, the activity of nerves, muscles and of the central nervous system. The recording instrument is a cathode ray oscillograph. Permanent records are obtained by photographing the screen as the spot, formed by the electron beam striking the fluorescent material on the screen, traces out the electrical changes impressed upon the deflecting plates X and Y. The nerve is stimulated by thyratron controlled condenser discharges led to the nerve by "stimulating" electrodes. Potential changes in the nerve, consequent upon activity, are led to a vacuum tube amplifier by means of "recording" electrodes and thence to the Y deflecting plates of the cathode ray oscillograph to cause vertical displacements of the spot. The sweep, operating through the X plates, yields in the horizontal axis "sawtooth" deflections so that the nerve activity is traced as a function of time as indicated on the screen of the diagram. (Modified from Erlanger and Gasser, *Electrical signs of nervous activity*, University of Pennsylvania Press, 1937.)

Demarkation potential. The study of electrical properties of tissues had its origins in the observations of Galvani on "animal electricity" published in 1791, and the controversy with Volta that ensued. However, it was only after the development of the first galvanometers that it became possible to measure electrical currents in animal tissues. This was done first by Matteuci (1838) and Du Bois-Reymond (1843) who discovered that current flowed through a galvanometer connected by electrodes to the longitudinal surface or side of a muscle, and to a cut end. The longitudinal surface is electropositive, the cut end electronegative, and the flow of current in the external circuit is from longitudinal surface to the cut end.

Du Bois-Reymond considered that the difference in electrical potential that gives rise to the current flow exists normally in muscle at rest, although masked by an opposing potential in the tendinous ends. It was later shown by Hermann that this view is incorrect; that the perfectly normal uninjured muscle or nerve has the same electrical potential throughout and will therefore exhibit no flow of current when any two points are connected through a galvanometer. Moreover, the completely dead muscle or nerve shows no current flow. Hermann established the fact that the difference of potential found in excised muscle or nerve is due to the injury at the cut ends. The potential difference between intact longitudinal surface and injured end is known as the demarkation (or injury) potential, the resulting flow of current as the demarkation (or injury) current.

The problem presented in understanding the demarkation current is essentially that of locating the electromotive force. It is generally agreed that the seat of the electromotive force is at the uninjured surface, the injured region serving only to provide an electrical connection from the outside to the inside of the muscle or nerve fiber. This is the concept embodied in the membrane theory of Bernstein.

Even before Hermann had clarified the nature of the demarkation current, Du Bois-Reymond had noted that the flow of current diminished when the muscle or nerve was stimulated into activity. This fact indicated that the potential difference between intact longitudinal surface and cut end was diminished; that is to say, the active surface became negative with respect to the resting surface. The effect was accordingly spoken of as the "negative variation." With the apparatus available at the time, it was impossible to tell whether or not the negative variation, like the demarkation potential, was a steady state. The next step was made by Bernstein who proved in 1871 that the negative variation takes the form of a wave, and that the wave is propagated along a nerve at a finite velocity. The negative variation now came definitely to be associated with the nerve impulse, for its conduction velocity proved to be similar to that of the nerve impulse as determined in 1852 by Helmholtz.

The determination of the velocity of the nerve impulse was first made by Helmholtz upon the motor nerves of frogs. His experiment consisted in stimulating the sciatic nerve, first, near its ending in the muscle, and second, near its origin from the cord, and measuring the time that elapsed in each case between the moment of stimulation and the moment of the muscular response. It was found that when the nerve was stimulated at its far end this time interval was longer, and since all other conditions remained the same, this difference in time could only be due to the interval required for the nerve impulse to travel the longer stretch of nerve.

It is interesting to recall that only six years before Helmholtz's first publication Johannes Müller had stated that we should never find a means of determining the velocity of the nerve impulse, since it would be impossible to compare points at great distances apart, as in the case of the movement of light. "The time," said he, "required for the transmission of a sensation from the periphery to the brain and the return reflex movements of the muscles is infinitely small and unmeasurable." The mode of reasoning by which Helmholtz was led to doubt the validity of this assertion is interesting. He says (Müller's Archiv, 1852, p. 330): "As long as physiologists thought it necessary to refer nerve actions to the movement of an imponderable or psychical principle, it must have appeared incredible that the velocity of this movement could be measured within the short distances of the animal body. At present we know from the researches of Du Bois-Reymond upon the electromotive properties of nerves that those activities by means of which the conduction of an excitation is accomplished are in reality actually conditioned by, or at least closely connected with, an altered arrangement of their material particles. Therefore conduction in nerves must belong to the series of self-propagating reactions of ponderable bodies, such, for example, as the conduction of sound in the air or elastic structures, or the combustions in a tube filled with an explosive mixture."

The "potential wave" described by Bernstein is now designated the "spike potential." The original designation was "current of action" or "action potential," terms that found general use until it was shown that the action potential contains several elements, including not only the event under discussion, but a succession of after-potentials. The introduction of the term "spike potential" serves to differentiate in a precise manner the wave described by Bernstein from the after-potentials which follow in point of time. The several components of the action potential are described in Chapter 4.

The recording of monophasic and diphasic spike potentials. Once it was proved that the spike potential (negative variation) is not, like the demarka-

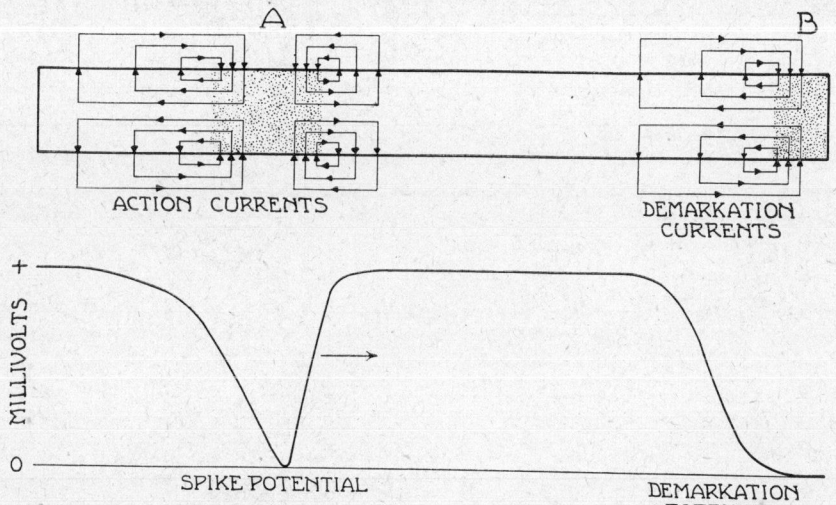

Fig. 3.—Diagram of the electrical condition of a single nerve or muscle fiber to illustrate the potential changes and current flow during activity (A) and about an injured region (B). In the upper part of the diagram the depolarized zones are represented by the shaded portions of the nerve fiber, and the current flow about these zones is indicated by the flow lines. The direction of current flow is given by the arrows on the flow lines. Current *in the external medium* flows from the polarized regions to the depolarized zone. In the lower part of the diagram is represented the potential difference in millivolts (1 millivolt = 0.001 volt) between the outside and inside of the nerve or muscle fiber membrane. In the resting cell the outside is positive relative to the inside of the membrane. The potential difference is abolished at the killed end, and in a wavelike manner it disappears and reappears during the passage of an impulse. The arrows indicates the direction of conduction.

tion potential, a steady state but rather a wave propagated along a nerve or muscle at finite velocity, the concept of local self-propagating electrical change gained general acceptance. Only a small region* of a long nerve fiber is active at any one time as a single nerve impulse passes along the fiber. Maintained activity of a nerve fiber takes the form of a series or train of impulses, the effect being more like the succession of machine gun bullets than the steady stream of a water pistol.

In order to form a clear picture of electrical events during activity, let us consider first the electrical condition of a nerve fiber at one instant during the act of propagating an impulse. At one end the nerve is killed so that a

* About 6 cm. in the case of the largest mammalian nerve fibers down to a few mm. for the smallest. The length of nerve occupied by the monophasic spike potential is sometimes called the wave length of the impulse.

demarkation potential exists there. At a region along the fiber an impulse is being propagated in the direction of the killed end. The shaded areas of the fiber shown in diagram (Fig. 3) represent the regions in which the polarized membrane is "broken down" by activity (A) and by local death of the fiber (B). These regions are spoken of as *depolarized zones*. The arrows indicate the flow of current about the active zone A and the killed zone B. The graph below shows the potential along the external surface of the fiber relative to the killed end. The wavelike change in potential at A is the *spike potential*.

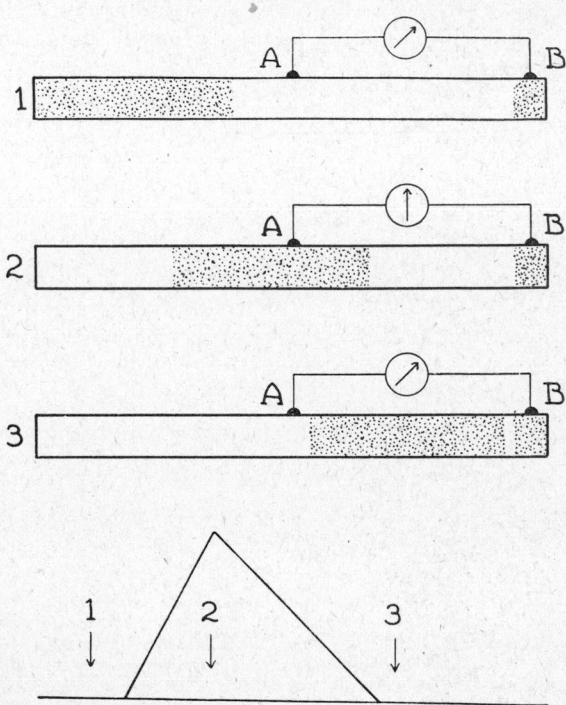

Fig. 4.—To illustrate the recording of a monophasic spike potential in nerve, electrode A is placed on the normal surface, electrode B at the killed end. The flow of current is indicated by the galvanometer connecting electrodes A and B. 1, 2, 3, show successive stages of the passage of the impulse from left to right along the fiber. Below, a diagram of the recorded spike potential. The numbered arrows 1, 2, 3, indicate the times during the passage of the impulse represented by the corresponding stages above. Note that the spike potential is recorded upright in the physiological convention rather than downward, although the spike is *negative* deflection; also that the time reads from left to right.

As the nerve impulse progresses along the nerve fiber, the electrical changes plotted in space (along the fibers) in Figure 3 will take place in time at any given point of the nerve. The duration of the change will be the time taken for the whole event to pass that given point at the characteristic rate of propagation. Figures 4 and 5 illustrate the recording of spike potentials. In Figure 4 recording electrodes to an oscillograph are represented as placed one at a point on the intact longitudinal surface, the other at the killed end. A difference of potential (the demarkation potential) is recorded. As an impulse reaches the electrode A, the potential difference between A and the killed end B is abolished. Then, as the impulse passes beyond A, the potential difference is restored. The impulse does not reach the second electrode B for it cannot progress beyond the demarkation line between living and dead tissue. The potential wave recorded in this fashion is known as the *mono-phasic spike potential.*

In practice the demarkation potential is balanced out by introducing an opposing potential in the recording circuit or else it is blocked by introducing a condenser into the input of the amplifier (a condenser forms a barrier to the flow of direct current but allows alternating current to pass). Consequently only the spike is recorded. It has become generally accepted practice to record a negative direction of the electrode on active tissue as an upward deflection; thus the spike potential appears usually as an upward deflection as in Figure 4.

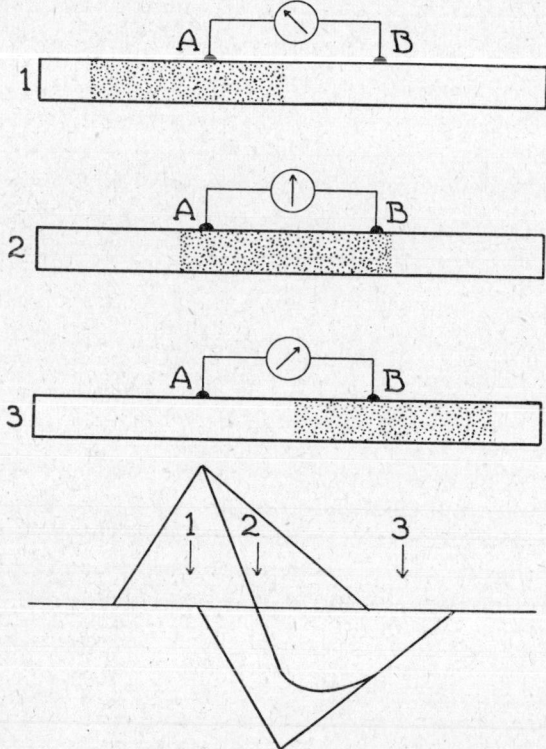

Fig. 5.—To illustrate the recording of a diphasic spike potential in nerve. Note that electrodes A and B are both placed on the normal surface of the fiber; otherwise arrangements are similar to those in Figure 4. Arrows 1, 2, 3 represent three stages in the passage of the impulse from left to right past the electrodes A and B. In the diagram below it will be seen that the spike potential is recorded *twice* as each electrode is affected in turn. Since the difference in potential between the two electrodes and the direction of current flow is all that can be measured, the effect of the impulse at electrode B is the same as its effect at electrode A but *in the opposite sense and shifted in time by the amount required for conduction from electrode A to electrode B.* The diphasic spike potential is the algebraic sum of the two interfering recordings of the single spike potential process.

Arrangements leading to the recording of the *diphasic spike potential* differ in one important respect from those yielding a monophasic spike potential. Both electrodes are placed on living tissue. The fundamental processes involved are identical, only the disposition of electrodes being changed. As a consequence of the fact that the surface of intact nerve or muscle fibers is everywhere equipotential, the oscillograph connected through both electrodes to the normal surface records nothing. As an impulse reaches the first electrode A, in Figure 5, the region at A will become electronegative to B, and so to all other parts of the surface at rest. When the propagated impulse reaches B, the situation with respect to the electrodes is exactly reversed, B becoming electronegative relative to A. Thus a single spike potential, by virtue of traveling along the nerve fiber to pass both electrodes, is recorded twice and in opposite directions. The recording in opposite directions follows from the fact that an electrometer measures only the difference in potential between two electrodes, relative negativity of one being equivalent to relative positivity of the other. The second phase of the diphasic spike potential disappears if the impulse in the nerve fiber is blocked between the two electrodes, and so is prevented from reaching the second electrode.

Distribution of electric currents in volume conductors (13). Up to this point nerve and muscle have been considered as linear conductors surrounded by a dielectric medium. For many reasons the isolation of tissues in air or other suitable dielectric medium is a most useful procedure for experimental analyses of fundamental electrical properties; but frequently this cannot be done, the study of the human heart by electrocardiography (cf. Chap. 35) being an obvious case in point. Within the living organism the natural environment of excitable tissues—nerves, muscles, heart, brain and spinal cord—is an extensive watery medium containing dissociated electrolytes. Such a medium conducts electricity and is spoken of as a volume conductor. Consequently, to appreciate the electrical activity of tissues in situ, it is necessary to gain at least an elementary understanding of the distribution of electrical currents in volume conductors. For instance, an interpretation of the electrocardiogram, except for the empirical correlation of wave pattern with demonstrated pathology, depends upon this understanding, for the laws governing distribution of currents in volume conductors determine the distribution throughout the body of the currents produced by the beating heart. The principles of volume conduction may be presented by a study of the external field of an impulse traveling in a straight length of nerve situated in a volume conductor. The results of such a study are directly applicable to the problems of conduction in the central nervous system (Chap. 4) and of transmission at synapses (Chap. 5), for such conduction and transmission occur in regions that are in effect volume conductors. In fact, a nerve in a conducting medium forms an excellent model of a spinal tract.

It is helpful before considering the external field of a nerve impulse to examine the relatively more simple situation existing when leads from the two poles of a battery are placed in an electrolytic medium (Fig. 6). Current will flow through the medium from one pole to the other in the manner indicated by the solid lines. If the conducting medium is sufficiently extensive, only a negligible current will flow through a point distant from the two poles. By employing a suitable electrometer, isopotential contours may be plotted for the conducting medium. They are indicated by the hatched lines. The lines of current flow and the isopotential lines intersect one another at right angles. An exploring electrode pitted against another electrode placed at a distance from the two poles will record a positive potential when located near the source of current flow and a negative potential when located near the sink of current flow. The magnitude of the potential difference depends upon the proximity of the exploring electrode to either source or sink of current flow.

In principle the situation with active nerve in a volume conductor is similar to that just presented. The external field is determined by the spatial arrangement of the sources and sinks of current. Reference to Figure 3 shows that, during the course of the spike potential, current first flows out through the membrane, then in through the membrane, and finally out through the membrane; that is to say, there are two reversals of membrane current during the monophasic spike potential. There is therefore a sequence of source-sink-source. For purposes of comparison with Figure 6 one may think of the conducted disturbance in nerve as representing a double dipole arranged in opposition along the active length of nerve. The field throughout the conducting medium at a selected instant during the passage of an im-

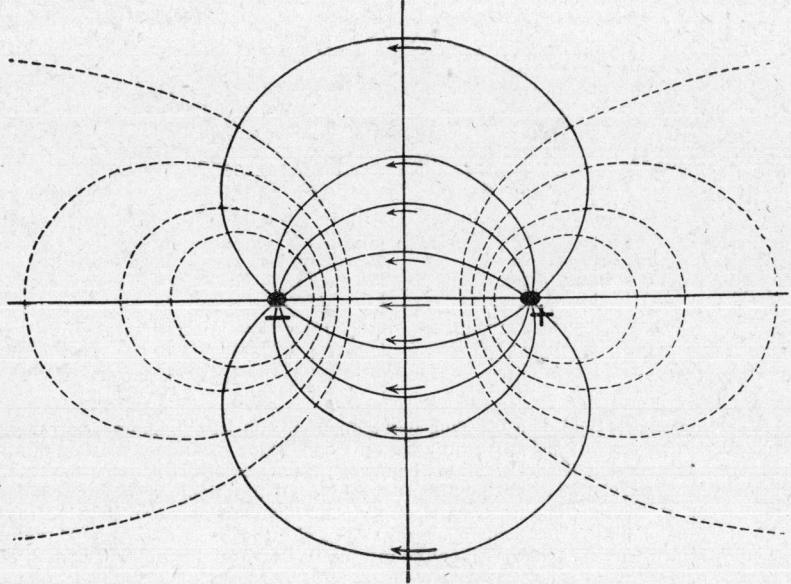

Fig. 6.—Diagram of the potential field and current flow about a dipole set in a conducting medium. Hatched lines = isopotential contours. Solid lines = current flow, the direction being indicated by arrows.

pulse along a nerve is illustrated in Figure 7. The essential details of the experiment are given in the legend below the figure.

As the impulse is propagated along the nerve fibers, certain potential sequences may be recorded at points along the nerve. It is important fully to realize one essential difference between the recording of potential changes in nerve when the nerve is surrounded by a dielectric medium and when immersed in a conducting medium. In the former instance an oscillograph will record nothing until the traveling spike potential reaches the point of electrode contact. In a conducting medium, however, a fluctuating field of current flow exists throughout the medium during the whole time that an impulse exists in any part of the nerve in the conducting medium. Now consider a nerve lying in a conducting medium and conducting an impulse from one end to the other. The passage of the impulse is recorded by four electrodes each pitted against an electrode located at some distance from the nerve. Electrode 1 is placed at the point where the nerve enters the conducting medium (0 on the longitudinal scale in Fig. 7). Electrodes 2 and 3 are

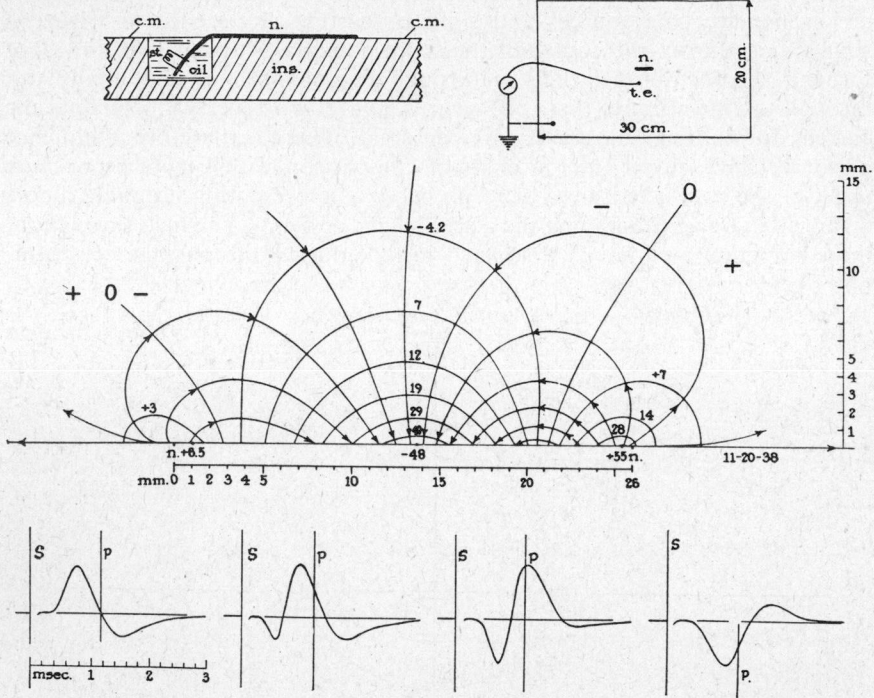

Fig. 7.—The electrical field of a traveling nerve impulse. Top left: diagram of arrangement of stimulating electrodes (St) and nerve (n) lying on a conducting medium consisting of a large blotting paper soaked with Ringer solution. Top right: technique of determining the field of a traveling nerve impulse, viewed from above. The nerve (n) lies in the middle of the large conducting medium (30 cm. × 20 cm.). The traveling electrode, t.e., is moved about so that records may be taken at various points of the field. When the testing electrode is 25 mm. beyond the nerve, the flow of current is so small that it cannot be measured. Therefore the potentials at all points more than 25 mm. beyond the nerve may be regarded as being constant and since the conducting medium is grounded, the potential at relatively great distances from the nerve may be taken as zero. In the middle of the figure are shown the equipotential contours and lines of current flow about the traveling impulse as recorded and plotted. The potential contours are labeled according to the value of the potential in arbitrary units; the lines of current flow have been provided with arrows to indicate the direction of current flow. The nerve stretches from n to n a distance of 26 mm. The reversal points of membrane current fall at the intersection with the nerve of the contours marked. Between the two reversal points (the sink), the potential contours have negative values which are given for each contour. Beyond the two reversal points are sources with the potential values, now positive, labeling each contour. The maximal and minimal values of the potential are given below the horizontal line that represents the nerve. The impulse is traveling toward the right. Below are shown four records taken with the traveling electrode at 0, 7, 15 and 26 mm. along the nerve and slightly to one side. The vertical lines marked S denote the time of stimulation; those marked P, by their intersections with the recorded potentials, give the instantaneous potential values for the negative points at the time of the plot above. Hundreds of such records are required to construct the field about a traveling impulse. Note the characteristic changes in the form of the wave recorded at different points in the medium. (From an unpublished figure provided by the kindness of Dr. Rafael Lorente de Nó.)

placed at two points (7 and 15) along the length of the submerged nerve. Electrode 4 is placed at the other end of the nerve (26 on the longitudinal scale). Each of the electrodes will detect the existence of currents as long a$_s$

the impulse occupies any part of the nerve within the conducting medium. The form of the recorded potential will be different at each electrode position. Electrode 1, being at the point of origin of the impulse, will record a diphasic wave, first negative, then positive (cf. the first record at the bottom of Fig. 7). At electrodes 2 and 3, the recorded potential will be triphasic (positive, negative, positive), indicating that the nerve at electrodes 2 and 3 acts in succession as a source, a sink and a source, as may be seen in the second and third recording at the bottom of Figure 7. The relative size and duration of the three phases of the triphasic potential recorded along the nerve will vary according to electrode position. At electrode 2 the first positive phase will be brief, for that region will rapidly become a sink as the impulse travels. At electrode 3 the first phase will be relatively long, for it will take a longer time before the impulse reaches that point. At electrode 4 the recorded potential as shown by the fourth record at the bottom of Figure 7 is diphasic, positive while that point acts as a source and negative when the impulse reaches electrode 4. Since the end of the nerve is at electrode 4, the impulse can go no further. Therefore a sink exists at electrode 4 until the spike process is over. To sum up: as an impulse approaches a point, that point acts as a source; as the impulse reaches that point, it acts as a sink; as the impulse recedes from that point, it again acts as a source.

In the foregoing discussions the term "impulse" has frequently been encountered, but it has not yet been defined. The implications of the term will be grasped more easily after consideration has been accorded to the effect on nerve or muscle of the passage of an applied electrical current (electrotonus and excitation) and to the concept of threshold. For the time being it may be stated that the impulse begins at the first reversal point of membrane current and exists during a part at least of the sink of current flow.

ELECTROTONUS

An electrical current flowing longitudinally from one to another of two electrodes in contact with a stretch of nerve is distributed in the manner illustrated in Figure 8. Part of the current flows along the outside of the nerve fiber sheaths or membranes; part flows across the membranes and through the cytoplasm inside the membrane. The current that flows across the membrane in both inward and outward directions does so not only at the points of electrode contact, but also along an area extending into the intrapolar stretch of nerve (lying between the points of electrode contact) and laterally into the extrapolar regions. An electromotive change has taken place in the nerve membranes and this change is commonly referred to as *electrotonus*. The spread of current is caused by polarization of the membranes, and is referable to the condenser-like properties of the membrane.

Core conductor theory. It is helpful to consider the nerve (or muscle) fiber membrane as a core conductor in a manner originally proposed by Hermann. By core conductor one implies a cylindrical cable-like tube having a conducting inside (or core) separated from a conducting outside by a resistive and capacitative sheath or membrane. In the equivalent electrical circuit (Fig. 9), resistances are arranged in such a way as to represent the conducting pathways for longitudinal flow of current outside and inside the fiber membrane. The membrane itself is represented by an infinite series of elements, each containing a resistor and condenser in parallel, to represent the conductivity across the membrane and the capacity of the membrane, and a battery with positive plate outwardly directed to represent the source of membrane electromotive force.

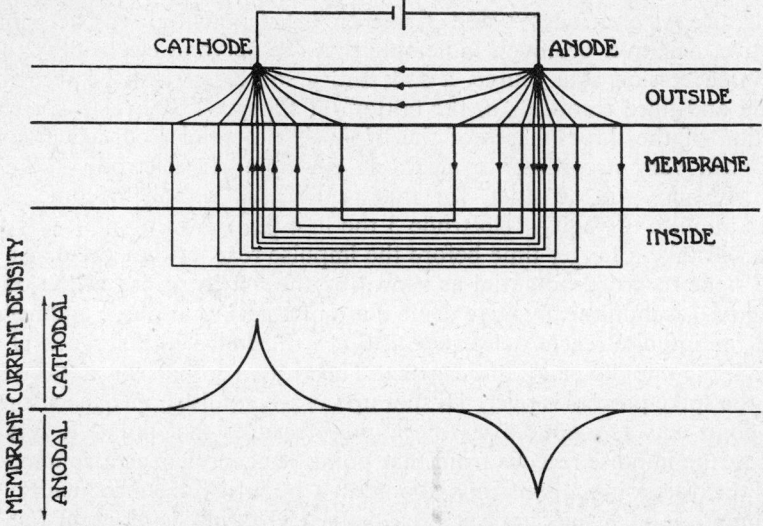

Fig. 8.—Diagram of current distribution in nerve during passage of a constant current. Only a segment of the nerve membrane is represented. Above, the current lines represent the spatial spread and direction of the flow of current outside, through, and inside the membrane. Note that the current spreads laterally into the *extrapolar* regions. The lateral spread of the penetrating current lines is illustrated below by plotting density of the penetrating current (membrane current) against length of nerve. Current density falls off in an approximately exponential manner with distance from the electrode. If the electrodes are brought closer together, cathodal and anodal effects interfere in the *interpolar* region.

Let us consider that an external electromotive force is applied through electrodes A and C of Figure 9, which are the anode and cathode respectively. Current will flow with ease through condenser C_6, the internal resistance, and

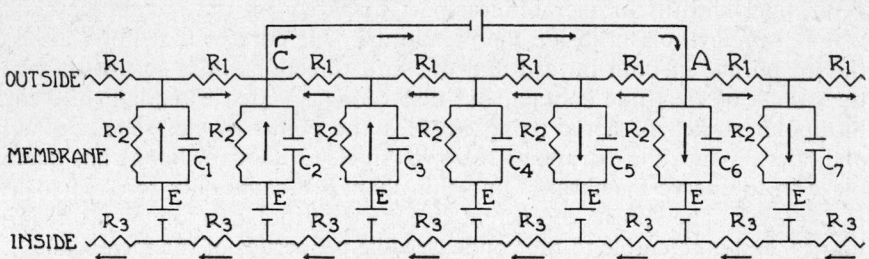

Fig. 9.—Diagram of an electrical circuit equivalent of the nerve membrane in which the membrane is represented as a leaky condenser. R_1 = external conducting path. R_2 = transverse resistance of the membrane. R_3 = internal conducting path. $C_1 - C_6$ = series of condensers to represent the membrane capacity. The arrows give the flow of current through the membrane model when a current is passed through electrodes A (anode) and C (cathode). Compare this representation of the membrane with Figure 8.

condenser C_2 and to some slight extent through the adjacent condensers C_5 and C_7 near the anode and C_1 and C_3 near the cathode. As condensers C_6 and C_2 are charged, they interpose a counter electromotive force, blocking current flow through C_6 and C_2, thus forcing current to flow increasingly through the adjacent condensers which in turn charges them, and so on.

The spatial and temporal characteristics of electrotonus in nerve and muscle are predicted by the core conductor theory and proved by experiment. Spatially, the electrotonic potential extends beyond the point of electrode contact with a decrement that follows an exponential relation law, as indicated in the lower part of Figure 8. Temporally, the electrotonic potential spreads as a pseudowave. The development of the electrotonic potential begins at all points along the nerve at the instant current begins to flow, but the steepness of the rise in electrotonic potential decreases with increase in distance from the electrode.

Interruption of the externally applied current leaves the condensers charged, and the system returns to normal only after the condensers have discharged through the shunting resistances. The discharge of the condensers follows a characteristic curve defined by the resistance-capacity constant of the membrane; that is to say, the electrotonus decays along an exponential relation curve having a time constant characteristic for the tissue under consideration.

The intensity of the electrotonic potential depends upon the strength of the externally applied current. As the impressed current is increased, electrotonus increases until a point is reached at which stimulation of the nerve takes place at the cathode of the electrode pair and a spike potential is produced. The *threshold* of the nerve has been reached.

ELECTRICAL EXCITATION

A brief electrical (cathodal) shock is the method of choice for stimulating excitable tissues, one very important advantage being that it can be graded accurately in strength. A shock may be subliminal, in which case the conducted spike potential response is not elicited, but once the strength is liminal (that is, of threshold strength), further increase does not increase the response. The actual threshold strength for a given fiber will vary up or down, depending upon the condition or "excitability" of the membrane. Hence the exact strength of a shock necessary to reach threshold forms a measure of the excitability of the membrane.

The preceding statement applies only when a single unit (nerve or muscle fiber) is considered. A nerve or muscle contains hundreds or thousands of such units having, for one reason or another to be discussed later, different thresholds. When a whole nerve trunk is stimulated, further grades of stimulation are recognized. There is first the subliminal stimulus which does not reach threshold for any of the constituent fibers. Next there is the liminal or threshold stimulus for the nerve, at which strength the most excitable fiber in the nerve discharges an impulse. As the strength is progressively increased (submaximal stimuli), more and more fibers are brought to threshold and discharge impulses until all the fibers have responded. The stimulus is then maximal. The stimulus, thereafter called supramaximal, may be still further increased without evoking a greater response.

Stimulation by brief shocks. A brief subliminal electrical shock applied to a nerve results in a change in excitability that extends in space beyond the region of electrode (cathode) contact and that lasts in time beyond the duration of the applied shock. The course of this excitability change can be plotted by applying a second subliminal shock at several time intervals after the first, and finding by trial the exact strength required of the second

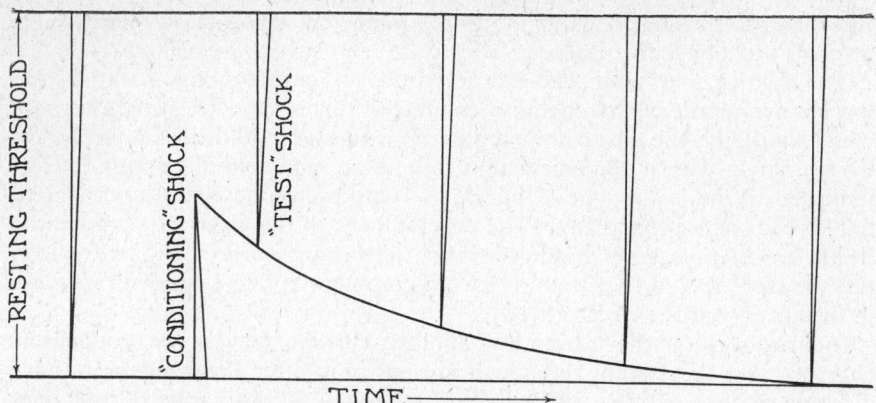

Fig. 10.—Diagram to illustrate the transient increased excitability existing in the neighborhood of the cathode as the result of a brief "conditioning" shock of intensity less than that of the "threshold" shock at the extreme left. The required size of "test" shock to bring excitation to threshold level after the subthreshold conditioning shock is shown at four different time intervals. Excitability stands in inverse proportion to the strength of test shock required to excite. The curve plots increase in excitability upwards against time. (After Katz, *Electric excitation of nerve*, Oxford University Press, 1939.)

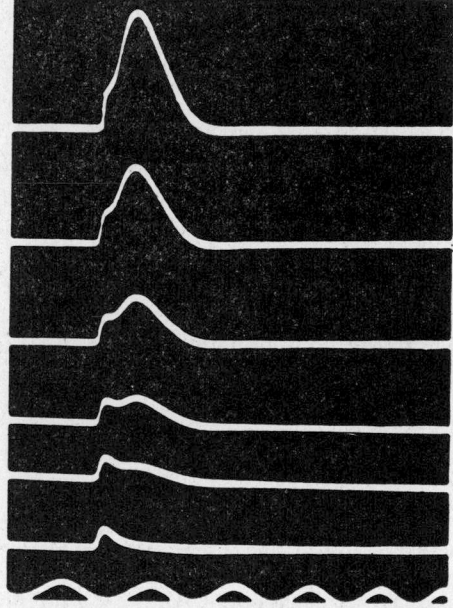

Fig. 11.—Electrotonic potentials and spike potentials recorded with the lead at the cathode of the stimulating circuit. The stimulus is a brief shock applied to a spinal root of the bullfrog. The lowermost record is below threshold and only the electrotonic potential is seen. In the next record above, the electrotonic potential is increased by stronger stimulation and a small spike potential is added. As the shock is further increased both potentials increase, the progressive increase in the spike potential being due to the response in increasing numbers of nerve fibers of higher threshold. This is characteristic of a nerve containing many fibers. The spike potential of a single nerve fiber, by way of contrast, appears when the electrotonic potential reaches threshold and it does not change with further increase in the shock; it is said to be *all-or-nothing* in nature (cf. Chap. 2). Gradation of the spike potential response of a nerve depends on a change in the number of responding fibers, not the size of the response in each constituent fiber. Time in milliseconds (0.001 sec.). (From Erlanger and Gasser, *Electrical signs of nervous activity*, University of Pennsylvania Press, 1937.)

shock just to reach threshold. The method and result are illustrated by diagram in Figure 10. The method is used over and over again in physiology, being, in fact, the basic maneuver in all studies on excitability and excitation. One stimulus is usually called the "conditioning" shock; it has an effect on the stimulated tissue and that effect may be gauged as to temporal, spatial and intensity characteristic by the action of a suitably chosen second stimulus, the "test" shock. The local disturbance of excitability instituted by such a conditioning shock, or *local excitatory state* as it is frequently called (Lucas), subsides along an exponential course at a rate characteristic of the tissue and comparable to that of the electrotonic potential. By stimulating with two pairs of electrodes, one for conditioning, the other for testing, and by separating the cathodes of the two pairs of electrodes, it is found that the local excitatory state extends a short distance along the nerve with an exponential decrement. The excitability change evoked by a brief shock corresponds, in space and time, to the electrotonic potential

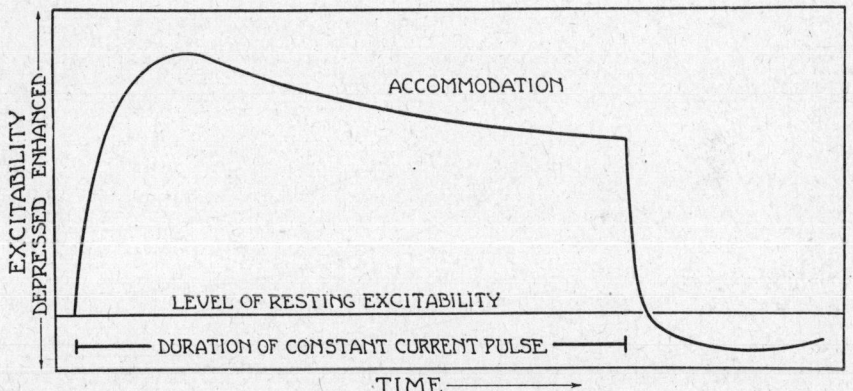

Fig. 12.—Diagram of excitability change at the cathode during and after the passage of a brief subthreshold constant current pulse to illustrate the two opposing factors *excitation* and *accommodation*. The membrane reacts by opposing the influence of current flow. After the current flow stops, excitability drops below the resting level for a short interval (postcathodal depression). (After Erlanger and Blair, *Amer. J. Physiol.*, 1931, 99:129–155.)

similarly produced. As conditioning shocks of progressively increasing size are applied to a nerve, both electrotonic potential and local excitatory state increase until the critical threshold strength is reached, at which time a propagated impulse is initiated (Fig. 11).

Stimulation by constant currents. Changes in excitability during the passage of a constant current are studied by the same technique of testing outlined above. In place of the conditioning shock a constant current of subthreshold strength is substituted, and a brief shock is again employed for test stimulation. Figure 12 illustrates in a diagram, based on the experiments of Erlanger and Blair, the changes in excitability occurring at or near the cathode of an electrode pair when a subthreshold constant current of finite duration is passed through a nerve. Excitability increases for a short period of time and then tends to fall off again while the current is still flowing. After the current ceases to flow, excitability falls below the resting level before returning finally to normal. Considerable interest attaches to the fact that excitability initially increases only to decrease again while the current continues to flow unchanged. This secondary fall in excitability is known as *accommodation*, by which is meant that the nerve reacts to the flow of current in such a way as to oppose, by an active process, the tendency of the current to excite. The decrease in excitability below the resting level after current ceases to flow is called *postcathodal depression*.

Consideration should now be accorded to the course of events when constant currents of various strengths are imposed upon a nerve. Let R, in Figure 13, represent the resting excitability and T the threshold. Constant currents of increasing strength are caused to flow through the nerve. By means of test shocks the excitability is plotted as in Figure 11. The curves *a, b, c* are obtained by allowing successively greater but still subliminal

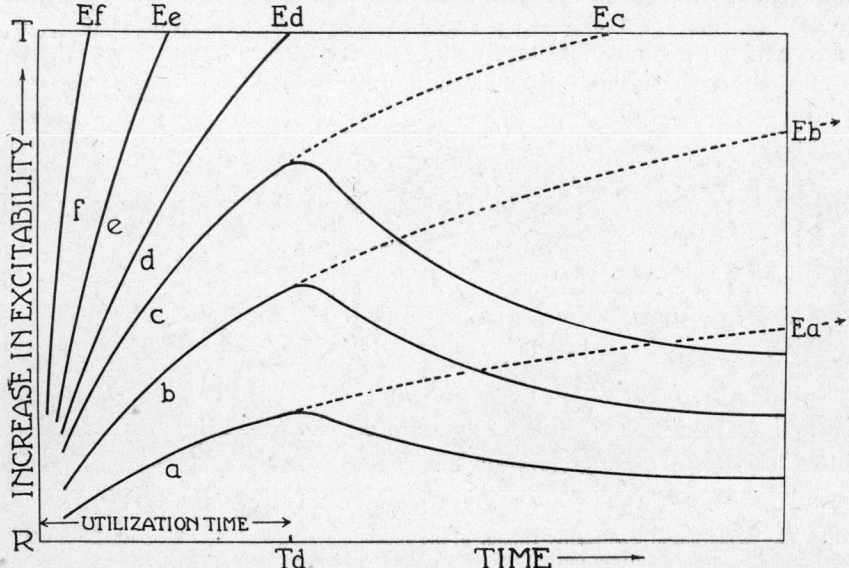

Fig. 13.—Effect measured by the same technique outlined in Figure 10 of constant currents of various intensities on the excitability of a nerve fiber. R = resting excitability. T = threshold. Curves a–f result from the application of successively greater currents. Curves a, b, c are subliminal and show the course of excitation and accommodation. Such currents never reach threshold because accommodation intervenes. In the absence of accommodation the curves would continue as extrapolated by dotted lines to Ea, Eb and Ec when excitation would occur. The current strength giving curve d is just sufficient to excite (it is *rheobasic*) and it does so after a time delay known as *utilization time* (Td). Curves e and f show that excitation occurs earlier with stronger currents.

currents to flow. Curve *d* is obtained by the use of a current that is just sufficient to excite by itself. The curves *e* and *f* are obtained by the use of currents of supraliminal strength, *f* being stronger than *e*. Inspection of this family of curves illustrates a number of facts concerning excitation. If a response is not evoked within a certain time, there will be no response regardless of the duration of current flow. For instance, if the excitability continued to increase in a manner represented by the hatched lines of curves *a, b* and *c*, threshold would eventually be reached at *Ea, Eb* and *Ec* respectively, but accommodation supervenes before threshold is reached and excitability decreases. When a current of strength *d* flows through the nerve, as shown by curve *d*, excitability just reaches threshold and a response occurs at *Ed*. The current which is just able to excite when flowing for a long time is called *rheobasic*. The time during which the rheobasic current must flow in order to excite (*Td* on the diagram) is known as the *utilization time*. When the current is further strengthened (*e* and *f*), excitation occurs earlier, at *Ee* and *Ef* respectively; i.e., the stronger the current the shorter the time during which it need flow in order to excite. This relationship forms the basis of strength-duration curve, a description of which follows.

The strength-duration curve. Since the work of Hoorweg (1892) and Weiss (1901) it has been known that, within certain limits, the longer the duration of current flow the weaker may be the current required to excite. As a consequence of the fact that threshold excitation by the constant current itself forms the "end-point" of measurement, the excitability changes

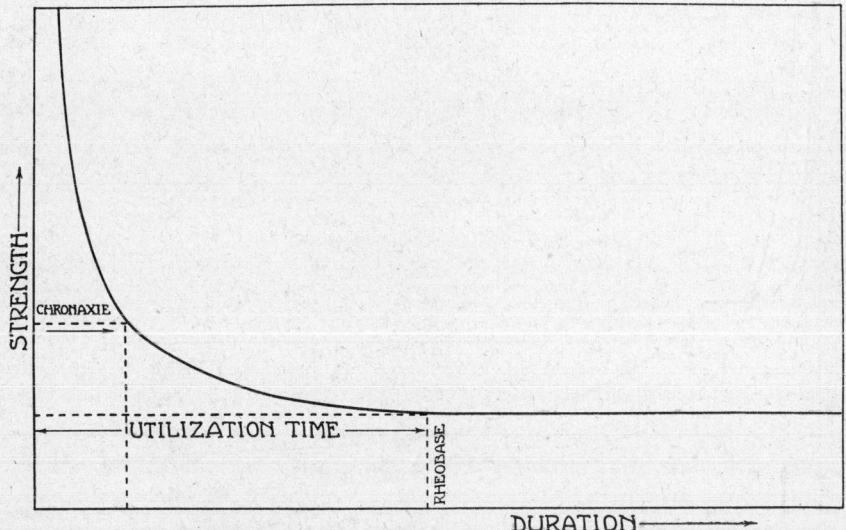

Fig. 14.—The strength-duration curve. This curve expresses the relation between the least strength of a constant current and the least time during which it must flow in order to reach threshold. The curve shows that there is a minimum current density below which excitation does not take place, but unlike Figure 13 gives no expression to subliminal events. Since utilization time is difficult to measure accurately, Lucas, Lapique and others have taken the time during which a current of 2× rheobase must flow to excite as a measure of the excitability. This time interval is called *chronaxie* or *excitation time*.

evoked by subliminal currents find no expression in the resulting curves relating strength and duration. Again it will be seen from the strength-duration relation plotted in Figure 14 that there is a finite strength of current below which excitation will not occur, however long the current may flow. This critical strength of current is called by Lapique the *rheobase*. The minimum time during which a rheobasic current must flow in order to excite is again the utilization time. Lapique and others have found it useful, for the purpose of comparing tissues, to stimulate with a current twice the rheobasic strength and to find the minimum duration of flow required to excite. This duration of time has been called *excitation time* (Lucas) or *chronaxie* (Lapique). Some tissues are slow in action, others fast; in fact, a graded series of excitabilities may be found with smooth muscles at one extreme and the largest nerve fibers at the other. In between lie heart muscle and striated muscles in ascending order of excitability. Lapique has found that the strength-duration curves of all these tissues will coincide if suitably scaled. The values of chronaxie or excitation time for the several tissues give a measure of the relative scales required for coincidence of the curves, and so form a basis for comparing in a general way the excitability of one tissue with another.

On studying a muscle by means of the strength-duration relation, it is frequently found that the resulting curve does not present a simple form like that in Figure 14. The type of curve that may be obtained is illustrated in Figure 15. According to the analysis of Lucas, and later Rushton, the compound curve indicates two distinct excitabilities, alpha and

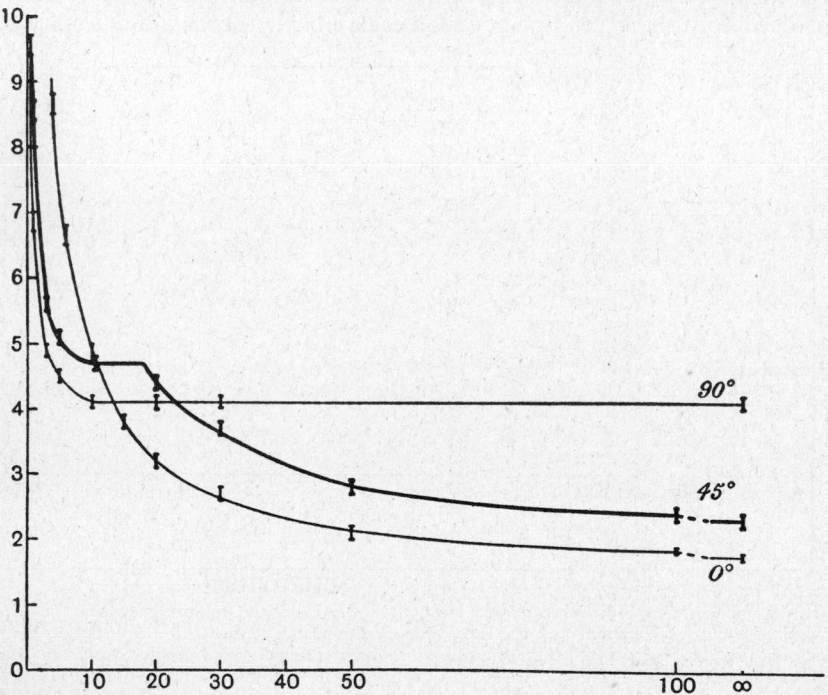

Fig. 15.—Strength-duration curves obtained from an isolated sternocutaneous muscle of the frog. The three curves were obtained with the muscle variously orientated in a uniform electrical field, the labeling of each curve, in degrees, denoting the angle between the lines of current flow and the muscle fibers. With current flow and muscle fibers parallel, the *alpha* curve is obtained, indicating direct stimulation of the muscle fibers. At 90° angle the *gamma* curve results, indicating indirect stimulation of the muscle through its nerve supply. At 45°, a compound curve is obtained, showing indirect stimulation at short durations and direct stimulation at long durations of current flow. (From Rushton, *J. Physiol.*, 1930, *70*:317–337.)

gamma, the former having slower characteristics than the latter. A number of experiments indicate that the gamma curve results from indirect stimulation of muscle through excitation of the intramuscular nerve fibers while the alpha curve results from direct excitation of the muscle fibers themselves. Nerve fibers respond to currents of much shorter duration than do muscle fibers. If a muscle is stimulated at a region free of nerve fibers (for instance, the nerve-free pelvic end of sartorius), the alpha curve is obtained in simple form, but stimulation of the muscle elsewhere yields the compound curve. Subsequent application of curare, a poison that blocks neuromuscular transmission (cf. Chap. 5), abolishes the gamma excitability, leaving a simple alpha curve. Still another type of experiment performed by Rushton depends upon (i) the fact that the efficacy of a current for stimulation is proportional to the component resolved parallel to the nerve or muscle fibers, and (ii) the anatomical relation between nerve fibers and muscle fibers in a muscle such as the sterno-cutaneous of the frog, they being for the most part at right angles to one another. With the current field parallel to the muscle fibers, Rushton obtained a simple alpha curve. With the field at 90 degrees to the muscle fibers, and hence largely parallel to the nerve fibers, a simple gamma curve resulted. At 45 degrees, however, the compound curve comprising both alpha and gamma excitabilities appeared. The reason for appearance of compound curves lies apparently in the two facts (i) that nerve fibers respond to currents of shorter duration than the minimum required for muscle fiber excitation, hence at short durations the gamma curve is followed, and (ii) that once a current fails to excite nerve fibers by reason of their accommodation it may, by continuing to flow, excite the more sluggishly reacting muscle fibers, hence at long durations the alpha curve is followed.

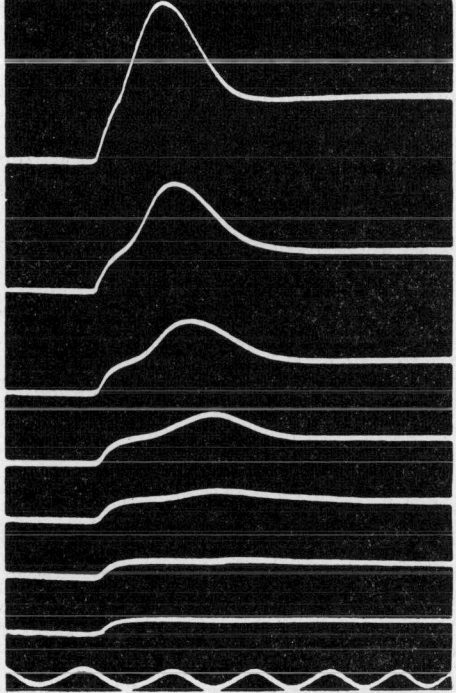

Fig. 16.—Stimulation of nerve by constant currents of increasing strength. Electrotonic potentials and spike potentials recorded with the lead at the cathode of the stimulating circuit. The lowest record was obtained with a current of subthreshold strength. In the records above, successively stronger currents were employed. Note (i) the increase in electrotonic potential with concomitant (ii) increase in the spike potential due to increase in the number of responding fibers and (iii) progressively earlier appearance of the spike response with increasing strength of current as predicted in Figure 13. These records were obtained from the same preparation employed for Figure 11 with which they may be compared. Time in milliseconds. (From Erlanger and Gasser, *Electrical signs of nervous activity*, University of Pennsylvania Press, 1937.)

Initiation of the spike response in nerve by the flow of constant current is particularly well illustrated in Figure 16 for which records were obtained at the cathode of the electrode pair carrying the constant current. As the nerve contains many fibers of different thresholds, the spike potential increases progressively from threshold to maximum. The latency of the spike potential likewise decreases as progressively stronger currents are applied to the nerve, as predicted from the family of curves presented in Figure 13.

Excitability changes at the anode. All of the remarks so far made have been concerned with changes in excitability at the cathode. These are of particular importance, for it is the excitability change at the cathode that has the direction leading to excitation and response of the tissue; it is current flowing through the membrane in an outward direction that leads to stimulation. At the anode current flows inwardly through the membrane, and similar electrotonic and excitability changes to those at the cathode occur, but in the opposite direction. Accordingly one frequently encounters the terms *catelectrotonus* and *anelectrotonus* or simply cathodal and anodal polarization. Accompanying these opposed electrical states are the excitability changes which may be called cathodal enhancement and anodal depression respectively.

CONDUCTION AT A NERVE BLOCK

An elementary knowledge of the events that occur at a block to conduction in nerve is useful for an appreciation of the nature of the conduction process itself, and also of events at the junctions between cells, i.e., the synapse and neuromuscular junction. Indeed, Wedensky in 1903 compared the properties of a block with those of the neuromuscular junction and Lorente de Nó in 1939 drew extensive parallels between events at a nerve block and at synapses in the central nervous system. There are a number of ways to induce blockade, cocaine, heat, cold and pressure being the more usual agents.

A partial block may transmit impulses at low frequencies, but fails to transmit at higher frequencies. This phenomenon was described by Wedensky, and has come to be known as *Wedensky inhibition.* A complete block fails to transmit impulses, but, as the impulses are stopped at the upper margin of a block, the threshold of the nerve below the block, to electrical stimulation, is lowered. This fact, also observed by Wedensky, may be called *Wedensky facilitation** or facilitation across a block. Recently Hodgkin and Lorente de Nó have studied Wedensky facilitation beyond a complete block in nerve and also the potential signs (the extrinsic potential) associated with the threshold change.

The extrinsic potential. It has been found by Hodgkin that a potential can be recorded beyond a block in nerve as a traveling spike potential reaches the upper margin of the block, although no impulses are transmitted through the block (cf. Col. 1 of Fig. 17). The "extrinsic potential," as this electrical charge beyond a complete block is called, is easily distinguished from a spike potential by the fact that it decrements exponentially along the stretch of nerve beyond the block, whereas a spike potential is conducted with uniform amplitude. The electrotonic nature of the spread of Hodgkin's extrinsic potential is confirmed by the fact that it has the same spatial distribution as an applied catelectrotonic potential of similar dimensions (Fig. 17). Further comparisons have been made between the extrinsic potential, the electrotonic potential and the excitability changes, both in time and space, that are associated with those potentials, leading to the conclusion that electrotonic spread of blocked impulses beyond the block is responsible for facilitation across the block. Furthermore, if the electrotonic potential beyond the block is greater than a certain fraction (possibly 10 per cent)

---

* The term "facilitation" is frequently encountered in neurophysiology. It is derived by translation from the German word "Bahnung" and means, in a general way, that because of some antecedent or concomitant event "the job is more easily done" or "a bigger job can be done."

of the propagated spike potential, the impulses "jump the block" and are propagated in the region of the nerve below the block. The length of a blocked segment is an important factor in determining whether or not impulses will jump across the unresponsive gap.

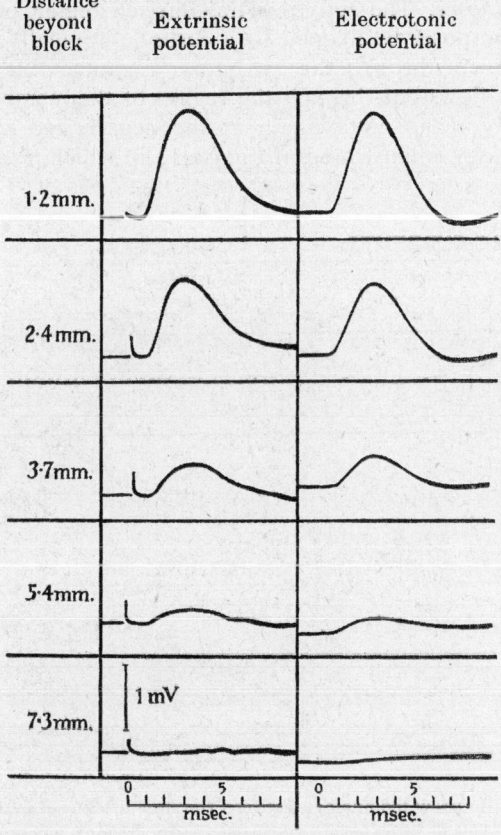

Fig. 17.—Demonstration of the potential change (called the "extrinsic" potential) beyond a complete block in nerve as a single volley of impulses reaches and dies out at the block (column 1). A wavelike lowering of threshold is associated with the extrinsic potential. In column 2 are shown records of the electrotonic potential caused by a subthreshold current pulse arranged to imitate in time course the spike potential and recorded at the same electrode positions used to record the extrinsic potential. Note: The extrinsic potential and electrotonic potential have the same spatial decrement. (From Hodgkin, *J. Physiol.*, 1937, *90*:183–232.)

CONCEPT OF THE NERVE IMPULSE

Having now considered electrical events in nerve (and muscle) and the physiological effect of current flow in terms of excitability changes, it is possible to form some idea of the mechanism of propagation. As we have seen, an applied current builds up a potential difference across the membrane in proportion to its strength. At the anodal region the added charge of the membrane has the same sign as the charge that exists in the resting state. At the cathodal region it has the opposite sign to the resting charge. The membrane is thus *discharged* at the cathode; that is, the membrane electromotive force is reduced. When the membrane is discharged to a critical level (i.e., threshold) at the cathode, the membrane at that point continues, of itself, to lose its remaining electromotive force. The applied current plays no further role once the critical discharge level is reached. The nature of the sudden change by which the membrane "collapses" without further external intervention is not known.

Local circuit theory. The active or depolarized region of the nerve fiber may for some purposes be likened to a cathode applied to the nerve. Just as current flows out through the extrapolar region of the membrane to a cathode, current flows out through the region of the membrane adjacent to the depolarized zone to enter again at the depolarized zone (see Figs. 3 and 7). The analogy is illustrated in Figure 18 in which it will be seen again

ELECTROTONIC CURRENTS   CATHODE

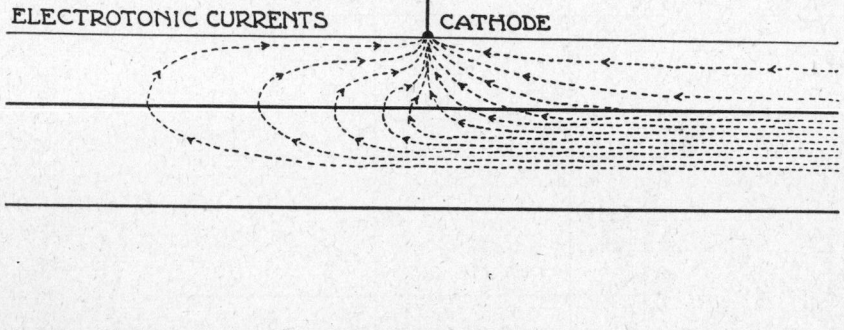

LOCAL CIRCUITS AT BOUNDARY OF IMPULSE

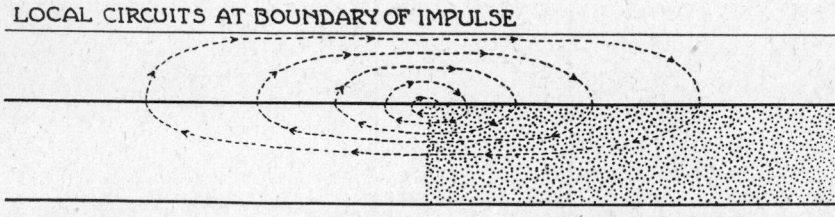

DEPOLARIZED ZONE

Fig. 18.—Diagram to show the analogy between the flow of current in the extrapolar region near the cathode of a pair of stimulating electrodes and the flow of current ahead of the impulse. (Modified from Hodgkin, *J. Physiol.*, 1937, *90*:183–232.)

how the depolarized zone and adjacent region form a "local" closed electrical circuit. The flow of current out through the membrane progressively depolarizes the region adjacent to the active zone and, since the flow of current in the local circuit is several times the critical strength required to bring the resting membrane to threshold, the membrane in that region in turn "collapses." In terms of the analogy, the collapse of the membrane and movement of the depolarized zone to a new position are equivalent to moving the cathode along the nerve. A new fresh segment of the nerve is subjected to the flow of current. The wave front is pushed a little further along the nerve and the whole process is repeated. The impulse, then, is propagated by a process of electrotonic extension into the resting membrane.

Although the nature of the change that occurs at threshold is not yet understood, attempts have been made to describe the change in terms of core-conductor theory by supposing an alteration in one or more of the equivalent electrical components of the membrane. A local increase in the capacity of the membrane has been suggested by Schmitt. As a result of this, the charge on neighboring condensers (in the core-conductor model—Fig. 9) would be drained. Recovery would take place as the local capacity returns to its original size and is recharged by the source of electromotive force. Cole and Curtis (1) regard a drop in membrane resistance as the

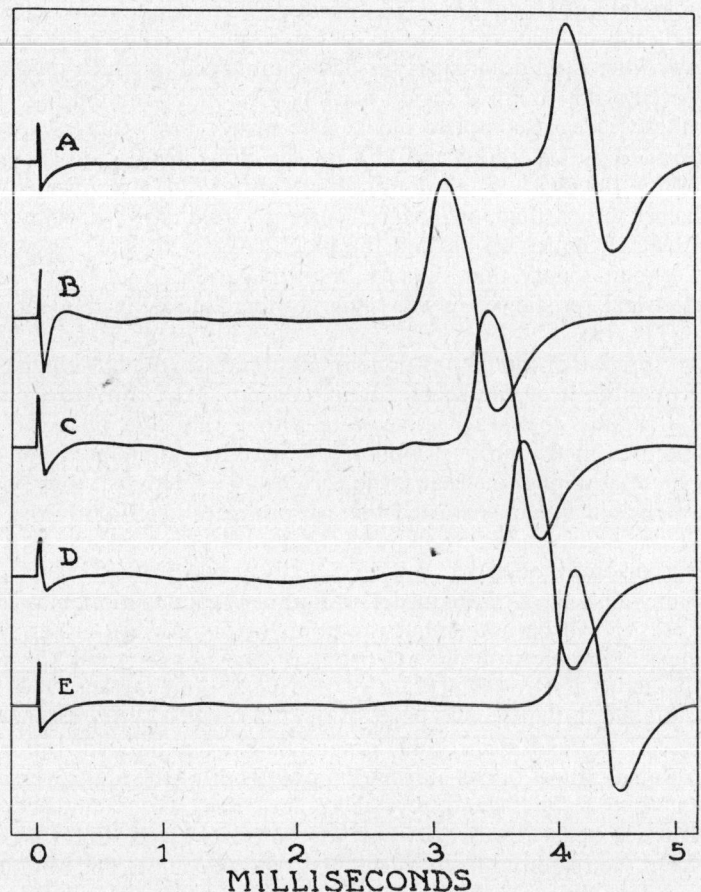

Fig. 19.—Records obtained from a single nerve fiber preparation to show the influence on conduction velocity of alteration in the external resistance. The fiber is placed partly in oil (to restrict the external medium and so increase the external resistance), and partly in isotonic electrolyte (to decrease the external resistance). The electrolyte is sea water which is normal for the crab nerve fiber. The conduction time (between stimulus artefact and beginning of the spike potential) varies inversely as the conduction rate. A and E = fiber completely immersed in oil. B = 95 per cent of conduction stretch immersed in sea water. C = 67 per cent in sea water. D = 33 per cent in sea water. An increase of 30 to 40 per cent in conduction velocity may be appreciated by transferring from oil to sea water. Note that the spike potentials are diphasic. (From Hodgkin, *J. Physiol.*, 1939, *94*:560–570.)

major feature, since, in their studies on the isolated single giant nerve fiber of the squid, they found an increase in transverse conductance during activity. Rushton (16) assumes that the battery disappears in the active region without any other change. The resulting loss of electromotive force at the active region would start the characteristic current flow. One should emphasize that these formal representations are nothing but ways of thinking about the actual event in living nerve, and are as artificial as the model upon which they are founded. It is difficult, for instance, to conceive of membrane electromotive force and resistance as being unassociated properties.

It should be noted that the local circuit theory is an integral part of all schemata of conduction. It is the part that rests on the most secure experimental foundation. Hodgkin's work on nerve blockade, already cited, is an outstanding recent piece of evidence. Other support is derived from a number of experiments on different types of excitable cell in which a conducting bridge placed across a killed region permits the spike potential to pass what would otherwise be a complete block. The prototype of these experiments was performed by Osterhout and Hill on the elongated excitable plant cell, *Nitella*. With the strict time relations that obtain, it is inconceivable that any influence other than an electric current could flow through the salt bridge to excite the region beyond the block. Again, it is a consequence of the local circuit theory that velocity of propagation should vary inversely as the electrical resistance outside a nerve fiber. Hodgkin has shown that this is so (Fig. 19).

Lillie's "iron wire" model has done much to convince physiologists of the physical possibility of the local circuit concept. An iron wire placed in nitric acid rapidly enters a passive state with a thin film of oxide formed and maintained at the surface. Now if the wire be "stimulated" at a point by any one of a number of means, the wire becomes active at that point and the electrochemical change started there propagates itself along the wire in a manner not unlike the nerve impulse. Many features of nerve activity can be imitated on this model.

Remaining details of the concept of impulse propagation may now be summarized. It will be noted that the point of division (in either space or time) between the electrotonic extension of the impulse and the impulse itself falls at the first reversal point of the membrane current. The foot of the spike potential, that part in front of the first reversal point of membrane current, therefore, is an electrotonic potential. The depolarized zone between the two reversal points draws current from in front of the first reversal point and from behind the second reversal point. The nerve impulse may be regarded as coextensive with that part of the depolarized zone that accepts current from the region in front of the first reversal point. The remainder of the current flow, from the region behind the second reversal point, is part of the recovery process.

Energy relations. All of the currently accepted views represent the membrane as a leaky condenser system that is only maintained in the charged state by the constant performance of metabolic work, as evidenced by heat production, oxygen consumption and carbon dioxide production of a nerve at rest. The immediate energy for propagation of the impulse is supplied by the charged membrane in front of the impulse. Behind the impulse the membrane charge must be reconstituted. Presumably the energy source for recharging the membrane is the same as that for maintaining the charge in the resting state. The conduction of impulses involves an increase in heat production and respiration. For further details of these, as yet insufficiently understood, aspects of conduction see Chapter 4.

Refractory period.   The region of nerve occupied by an impulse cannot be stimulated by the most drastic means. It is said to be refractory. In a manner of speaking, the membrane of the region not being polarized cannot be depolarized. There is not yet general agreement as to the duration of the refractory period relative to that of the spike potential, nor is it possible to say at this time whether some fixed relation holds between them. Theoretically, it would seem that as a minimum the stretch of nerve between the two reversal points would be refractory, but how much more would also be refractory is an open question. Before normal excitability returns, the nerve passes through a period of relative refractoriness, during which time it can be excited by stimuli of greater than normal, resting, threshold strength. The transition from absolutely refractory state to normal resting state is smoothly progressive.

REFERENCES

1. COLE, K. S. and CURTIS, H. J. Electric impedance of the squid giant axon during activity. *J. gen. Physiol.*, 1939, 22:649–670.

2. CREMER, M. Die allgemeine Physiologie der Nerven. *Handb. Physiol. Mensch.*, 1909, 4:793–992.

3. CREMER, M. Erregungsgesetze des Nerven. *Handb. norm. path. Physiol.*, 1929, 9:244–284; 1932, 18:241–246.

4. DAVIS, H. and FORBES, A. Chronaxie. *Physiol. Rev.*, 1936, 16:407–441.

5. EBBECKE, U. Zur Lehre vom Elektrotonus. *Ergebn. Physiol.*, 1933, 35:756–826.

6. ERLANGER, J. and BLAIR, E. A. The irritability changes in nerve in response to subthreshold constant currents, and related phenomena *Amer. J. Physiol.*, 1931, 99:129–155.

7. ERLANGER, J. and GASSER, H. S. *Electrical signs of nervous activity.* Philadelphia, University of Pennsylvania Press, 1937, 221 pp. (See Chaps. 3 and 4).

8. HERMANN, L. Allgemeine Muskelphysik. *Handb. Physiol.*, 1879, 1:3–260.

9. HODGKIN, A. L. Evidence for electrical transmission in nerve, Part I. *J. Physiol.*, 1937, 90:183–210.

10. HODGKIN, A. L. Evidence for electrical transmission in nerve, Part II. *J. Physiol.*, 1937, 90:211–232.

11. HODGKIN, A. L. The relation between conduction velocity and the electrical resistance outside a nerve fibre. *J. Physiol.*, 1939, 94:560–570.

12. KATZ, B. *Electric excitation of nerve.* London, Oxford University Press, 1939, 151 pp.

13. LORENTE DE NÓ, R. Transmission of impulses through cranial motor nuclei. *J. Neurophysiol.*, 1939, 2:402-464.

14. OSTERHOUT, W. J. V. and HILL, S. E. Salt bridges and negative variations. *J. gen. Physiol.*, 1930, 13:547–552.

15. RUSHTON, W. A. H. Excitable substances in the nerve-muscle complex. *J. Physiol.*, 1930, 70:317–337.

16. RUSHTON, W. A. H. Initiation of the propagated disturbance. *Proc. roy. Soc.*, 1937, B124:201–243.

17. SCHAEFER, H. *Allgemeine Elektrophysiologie.* Vienna, Deuticke, 1940, 522 pp.

18. WEDENSKY, N. E. Die Erregung, Hemmung und Narcose. *Pflüg. Arch. ges. Physiol.*, 1903, 100:1–144.

19. WILSON, F. N., MACLEOD, A. G. and BARKER, P. S. *The distribution of the currents of action and of injury displayed by heart muscle and other excitable tissues.* Ann Arbor, University of Michigan Press, 1933, 57 pp.

CHAPTER 2

FUNCTIONAL ACTIVITY OF MUSCLE

A skeletal muscle consists of thousands of individual muscle fibers arranged side by side attached at one end, the origin, either directly or indirectly through tendinous bands, and at the other end through tendon to a bony insertion. The characteristic feature of muscular tissue is its ability to exert tension between its points of attachment, the origin and insertion respectively. Skeletal muscles utilize tension by acting on and setting into motion a system of levers made up of bones articulated at joints. By way of contrast, smooth muscles and cardiac muscle, to be considered later, utilize tension for the most part by exerting pressure on the fluid contents of the hollow viscera, the walls of which are in part made up of layers of muscle.

Although the essential action of muscle is the production of tension, external work is done only when the muscle fibers shorten. The work done by a muscle is measured by the product of muscle tension and distance through which the muscle shortens; that is, Work = Load × Lift. Obviously if either the load or the lift is zero, no external work is done. Conversely, work is done upon a muscle when it is stretched, as by the action of opposing muscles. The work done upon a muscle in such circumstances is degraded by the muscle into heat and so dissipated. If the two ends of a muscle remain fixed relative to one another during contraction, that is, if no shortening occurs, the contraction is called *isometric*. The contractile effort appears as tension and no external work is done. If a muscle is free to shorten under constant load, there is no change in tension and the contraction therefore is referred to as *isotonic*. This classification of contractions introduced by Fick in the last century has been most useful for the analysis of muscle contraction, one important reason being the fact that the isometric method allowed the results of experiments to be expressed with reasonable validity in the single term, "tension." Since the time of Fick, the isometric method has been used almost to the exclusion of any other to measure the *intensity* of muscle response. However useful the method may be for quantitative measure of muscle response, it does have limitations. For example, Fenn has pointed to the fact that a muscle in the course of natural performance in the body must produce tension under all possible conditions of relative movement of the two attachments of that muscle, i.e., while the muscle is shortening, while it is lengthening, and while no change in length is taking place. Since the goal is an understanding of muscle performance in natural rather than artificial conditions, the simple classification into isometric and isotonic contractions is not adequate. One will realize immediately that the greatest deficiency lies in the failure to consider muscles contracting while undergoing stretch. In order to provide a better framework for study of muscle, Fenn has proposed the following classification of muscle contractions into three different categories:

1	2	3
Tension during shortening	Isometric tension	Tension during lengthening
Accelerates or raises load	Fixation	Decelerates or lowers load
Positive work	No work	Negative work
Positive excess energy	No excess energy	Negative excess energy

An amplification of this abbreviated schema will appear in this and the succeeding chapter, particularly in consideration of the action of muscles in the body, the utilization of energy by muscle and of such relations as that which holds between the tension developed and the speed of shortening.

ELEMENTARY FEATURES OF MUSCLE CONTRACTION

Many aspects of muscle physiology may be considered in terms of the tension developed by isometric contraction. To this end a description of events in a muscle following maximal synchronous stimulation forms a suitable point of departure.

The first event following excitation of a muscle is the appearance of a spike potential, which is propagated along the muscle fibers at a finite velocity. In general outline the features of the propagated electrical response have been treated in Chapter 1. In addition to the spike potential proper, there are electrical changes that follow the spike potential in time and last through or beyond the contraction period—so-called after-potentials. They are presumably associated with the chemical changes that occur during contraction.

Latent period. Between onset of electrical response and onset of mechanical change within the muscle there is a brief interval that has been called the *latent period.** Some measurements have been made according to this definition; others have taken the interval between direct stimulation and the onset of contraction as a measure of latency. Much discussion has surrounded not only the duration of contraction latency but the question of whether there is any such latency at all. At the present time there appears to be little doubt that the electrical response of muscle does, in fact, antecede the onset of mechanical response by a brief but very definite interval. In mammalian muscle this interval, or latent period of contraction, is 1 msec. (msec. $= 0.001$ sec.) or somewhat less.

Just as the electrical response of muscle is conducted, so contraction progresses in a wavelike manner along a muscle fiber from the point of stimulation. If a muscle be stimulated directly at one end, a wave of contraction passes to the other end. However, the junction between nerve fibers and muscle fibers lies near the midregion of a muscle with the result that indirect stimulation through the motor nerve causes spike potentials and contraction waves to pass along the fiber in both directions from the junctional region (Fig. 20). The electrical and mechanical responses are conducted at the same rate, the electrical event preceding the mechanical event by a brief interval

---

* Speaking in a general sense, latent period is a term applied to the interval of time between events in a causal sequence. For example, the elapsed time between stimulation of the sciatic nerve and the onset of contraction in the gastrocnemius muscle may be called a latent period, the elapsed time representing the sum of conduction time in the nerve, neuromuscular delay, and time lag between electrical and mechanical responses. The latent period for the contractile response to direct stimulation of the muscle has quite another and shorter value, encompassing only a utilization period. Hence it is that the term latent period must be defined carefully each time that is used.

and standing in causal relation to it. The conduction rate of activity varies between 3 and 7 meters per sec. for mammalian muscles.

Course of isometric contraction. The course of a muscle contraction is most suitably determined by firmly fixing the bony origins of the muscle in question and attaching the tendon to a satisfactory isometric myograph. When this is done and the muscle is excited by a single nerve volley, it is found (Fig. 21) that increase in tension begins abruptly after the electrical response, showing a brief period of upward concavity followed by an upward convexity. The relaxation from the curved summit progresses with upward concavity to follow an exponential relation curve until resting tension is again reached. This typical mechanical response to a single stimulus is frequently called a *twitch contraction.*

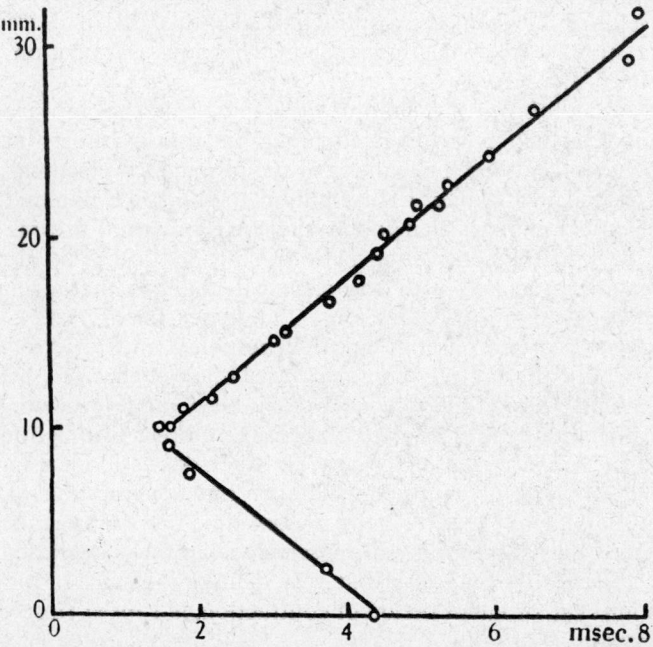

Fig. 20.—Conduction in mammalian muscle following stimulation of motor nerve by a single shock. The muscle impulses begin at the junctional region about one third the distance along the muscle and are conducted in both directions at a linear velocity of 3.2 meters per sec. The plot was obtained by measuring the time interval after the stimulus at which the impulses reached successive electrode positions along the muscle; hence time of arrival in msec. is plotted against distance along the muscle in mm. (From Eccles and O'Connor, *J. Physiol.,* 1939, *97:*44–102.)

Types of skeletal muscle. The form of the contraction curve is similar for all skeletal muscles, but the total duration of the twitch contraction is very different for different types of muscles, and these differences serve as one basis for the classification of skeletal muscles, the two major categories being the so-called pale (or rapid) and red (or slow) muscles. Color, be it noted in passing, is not an infallible guide to the speed of action of a given muscle. It is important to have a convenient and reliable expression for comparison of various types of muscle. Such an expression is *contraction time,* a term introduced by Cooper and Eccles in 1930. *Contraction time is defined as the interval between the onset of the action potential and the peak of tension under isometric conditions.* Figure 22, based on data obtained by Cooper and Eccles, illustrates the relative speed of action of three types of skeletal muscles. The extra-ocular muscles, which provide for movement of the eyeball, are extremely rapid in their action. Cooper and Eccles found that the contraction time of internal rectus was no more than 7.5 msec. The contraction time of pale muscles such as gastrocnemius, extensor digitorum

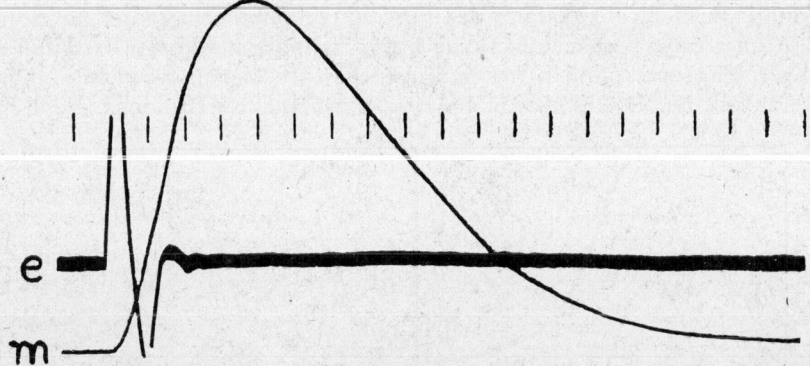

Fig. 21.—Maximal isometric twitch of tibialis anterior muscle elicited by single stimulus to the motor nerve. Electrical (e) and mechanical (m) records were made simultaneously. Note that the mechanical response follows by a brief interval and far outlasts the conducted spike potential. Time is recorded in 10 msec. intervals by the vertical strokes. (From Creed, Denny-Brown, Eccles, Liddell and Sherrington, *Reflex activity of the spinal cord*, Oxford, Clarendon Press, 1932.)

longus, and sartorius lay between 23 and 40 msec. At the slow extreme soleus, a red muscle, was found to have a contraction time of 94 to 120 msec. The speed of action of the several types of muscles, as measured by contraction time, is directly related to functions which those muscles subserve. It is an obvious advantage to have extremely rapidly acting muscles to effect the movements of the eyeball. Again at the other extreme, the slow

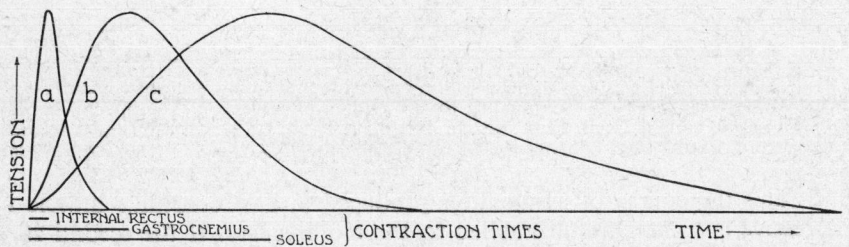

Fig. 22.—Comparison of the twitch contractions of different types of skeletal muscle, a = internal rectus, b = gastrocnemius, c = soleus. The horizontal lines below indicate by their length the contraction times of the several muscles. The actual values for the contraction times may be found in the text.

contraction of the red muscles is eminently fitted for the role these muscles play in postural contraction.

Response of muscle to two stimuli. In a single twitch contraction, a muscle does not exert the maximum tension of which it is capable; it will produce greater total tension on double stimulation. Even in the most rapid muscles the mechanical effect far outlasts the propagated excitation. Since the refractory period of muscle is associated with the propagated excitation, and approximately equals in duration the muscle spike potential, it follows that a second excitation may take place while the mechanical effect still lasts. Here, then, is the basis for summation of contractions, for a muscle can be re-excited as soon as it recovers from refractoriness, and hence long before it recovers its resting mechanical state.

Summation of contractions occurs with the use of maximal successive stimuli, which fact eliminates the possibility that the increased tension is due to a greater number of muscle fibers responding when two stimuli are delivered in succession. In the circumstance each fiber must yield a greater tension on double stimulation than when stimulated but once. Figure 23

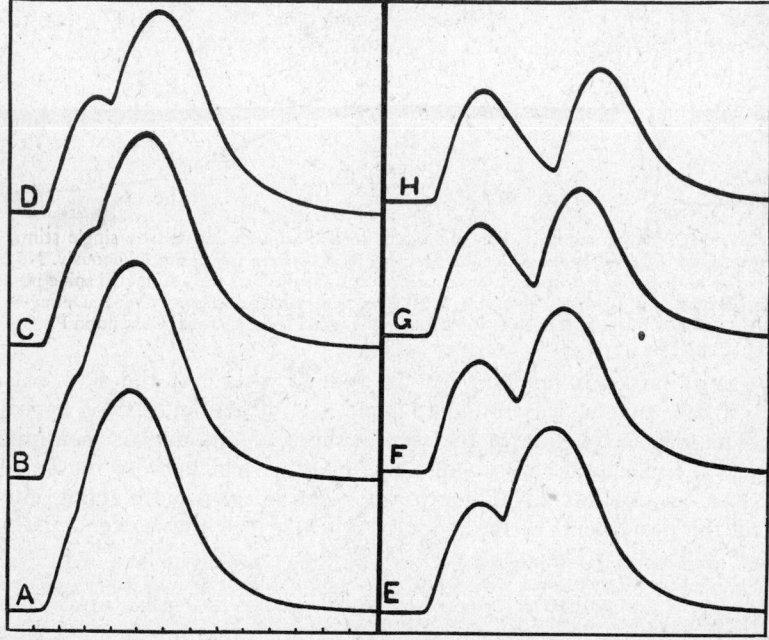

Fig. 23.—Summation of muscular contraction by double stimulation. Isometric records of the median head of gastrocnemius responding to two stimuli in succession. The interval between stimuli in msec. are: A, 24; B, 32; C, 40; D, 48; E, 57; F, 69; G, 77; H, 88. Time is recorded below record A in 20 msec. intervals. (After Cooper and Eccles, *J. Physiol.*, 1930, *69*:377–385.)

illustrates the course of summation produced in gastrocnemius muscle by successive maximal stimuli applied to the motor nerve. If the second stimulus falls within the refractory period, of course no increment of tension results. Likewise if the stimuli are widely spaced, each produces a simple twitch.* In between these two extremes summation occurs with a greater or lesser degree of mechanical fusion, depending upon the stimulus interval; that is, the shorter the interval the more complete the mechanical fusion.

* When a resting muscle is stimulated repetitively at a rate sufficiently slow that no mechanical fusion takes place, it may still be that an increase in tension occurs on each successive response for a few responses. This effect is known as the staircase phenomenon or treppe. It was first demonstrated in heart muscle by Bowditch. It represents a transition from one steady state (rest) to another (some constant level of activity). The changed conditions within the muscle influence the absolute height of tension which the muscle exerts in the absence of summation. Similar changes are seen when a single twitch follows by a short interval an intensive bout of activity.

The tension of the summated contraction is greatest when the two stimuli are close together, and at this maximum the summated contraction may produce two to three times the tension of a single twitch.

Response of Muscle to Repetitive Stimulation. When a series of stimuli are delivered through its nerve supply to a skeletal muscle, a prolonged contraction results (Fig. 24). At slow rates of stimulation successive twitches have no effect on one another, there is no summation, and, as a result, the maximum tension developed at any time during the series is equal to the twitch tension. With increasing rates of stimulation the tension progressively mounts until an undulatory plateau is reached. Further increases in the stimulus rate produce progressively more complete fusion and higher tension until all mechanical evidence of the repetitive nature of the response disappears. At this time the tension attained by a muscle may be four times that of a single twitch, as one may see by comparing the first two columns

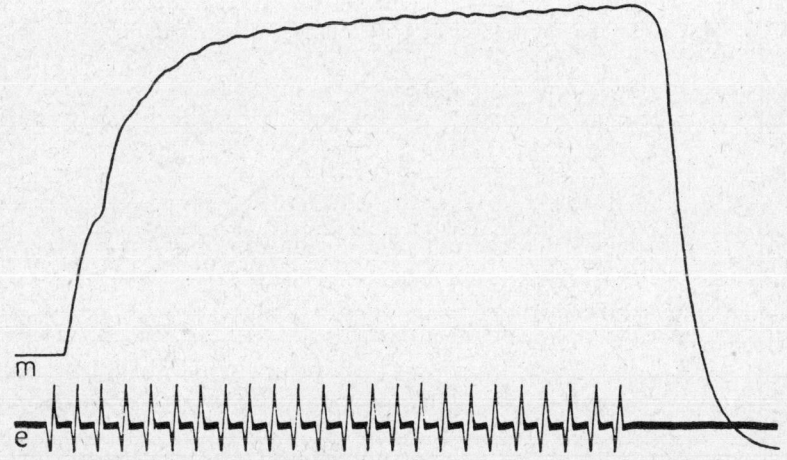

Fig. 24.—Electrical (e) and mechanical (m) recordings of a nearly completely fused tetanic contraction of extensor digitorum longus. Rate of stimulation, 67 shocks per sec. Note that the spike potentials are quite discrete although the contractions are almost perfectly fused. (From Creed, Denny-Brown, Eccles, Liddell and Sherrington, *Reflex activity of the spinal cord*, Oxford, Clarendon Press, 1932.)

of Table 1, in which the twitch tension and tetanus tension of representative muscles are presented. Beyond the critical fusion rate practically no further increase in tension is obtained by increasing the rate of stimulation; the muscle may be said to be maximally active. The conditions of partial fusion and complete fusion are sometimes referred to as *incomplete tetanus* and *complete tetanus* respectively, while the stimulations evoking these responses are known as subtetanic and tetanic stimuli respectively.

The spike potentials of a muscle remain discrete, one for each stimulus of a series, even when the mechanical response is complete or nearly complete tetanus (cf. Fig. 24). The frequency of stimulation necessary to promote full mechanical fusion of the contraction response is related inversely to the duration of the twitch contraction, and is therefore different for different muscles. The internal rectus with its short contraction time requires approximately 350 stimuli per sec. to achieve a smooth complete tetanus. The gastrocnemius, extensor digitorum longus and other pale muscles require a rate of about 100 per sec. for fused contraction. The red soleus muscle, on the other hand, because of its prolonged twitch response, needs no more than 30 stimuli per sec. to achieve a fused tetanus.

Relation between length and tension (23, 24). A muscle or a muscle fiber has elastic properties as may easily be seen by the return to original length after release from stretch. Until recently it has been thought that the elastic tension exhibited by resting muscle was a property of the muscle substance, but it now appears that this is not true, for Ramsey and Street find that all of the tension of resting muscle may be ascribed to the sarcolemma. The muscle substance itself behaves in a purely plastic fashion. As we have already seen, an active muscle produces "active" tension. This active tension, moreover, is a function of the initial length of the muscle fiber. We have then

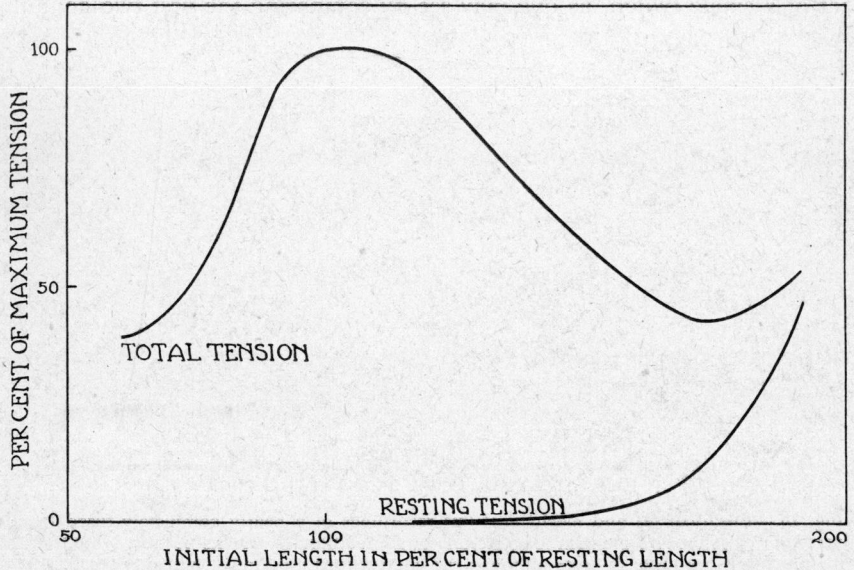

Fig. 25.—Length-total tension and length-resting tension relations of an isolated muscle fiber. The difference between the two curves gives the actively developed tension at various initial lengths. Note that the greatest tension is developed at or near rest length. Compare this with Figure 35 in which similar relations for heart muscle may be found. (Adapted from Ramsey and Street, *J. cell. comp. Physiol.*, 1940, *15*:11–34.)

two relations to consider, that between length and resting tension and that between length and total tension, with active tension being the difference between the resting and total tension. Figure 25 based on data obtained by Ramsey and Street illustrates these relations in graphic form. The maximal isometric tension is developed by a muscle fiber at resting length, the amount of tension achieved falling off rapidly as the muscle fiber is stretched to greater initial lengths or allowed to shorten to lengths less than that at rest. The range of lengths through which normal reversible contraction occurs lies between 70 per cent and 200 per cent of the normal resting length. If stretched more than twice its normal length the fiber can produce no active tension. If allowed to shorten below two-thirds of its normal length a striking change in the properties of the muscle fiber occurs: it no longer relaxes but retains the length to which it was allowed to shorten. This condition of muscle that has shortened excessively is called by Ramsey and Street the "delta" state, and is of considerable interest for the partial resemblance it bears to the type of muscle shortening known as contracture.

Contracture (18). Skeletal muscle may enter into a reversible shortened state in which some of the signs of contraction, discussed above, are absent. Commonly, the mechanical change is not propagated and is not associated with a propagated spike potential. Fractional involvement of the muscle in the mechanical change may be a feature. There may be still greater deficiencies. Such mechanical shortenings of muscle are known as *contractures;* they are entirely distinct from tetanic contractions. On the other hand, contractures are all too often confused with muscle tone which is of reflex origin and employs the normal mode of contraction, and with pathological shortenings of other types, e.g., fibrosis. Emphasis is placed on the reversibility of contractures; when irreversible changes set in, the muscle has passed into *rigor*.

Contractures may be brought on by a number of agents, thermal, electrical, mechanical, or chemical. It seems probable that some, if not all, of these agents achieve their effect by acting upon the contractile mechanism directly. At least this supposition would help to explain the nonpropagated and local nature of certain contractures when only one end of a muscle is subjected to the agent. In many instances contracture appears to be the result of faulty relaxation. Relaxation is now generally recognized to be an active process since it is not necessary to have an extending force in order for a contracting muscle fiber to return to rest length. As a result of this newer concept of relaxation (older ideas held that relaxation occurred passively as a result of the action of extending forces), it seems likely that the whole problem of contracture must be reopened and that a better understanding will result. Presumably, if agents produce contracture by interfering with the process of active relaxation, they do so by direct action on that process. This mode of action would accord with that of substances, such as veratrin, that produce contracture following a twitch. Indeed the resemblance between the prolonged veratrin twitch and the prolonged twitch of a muscle fiber in the delta state (Ramsey and Street) is remarkable. The form of the latter is apparently due to the loss of the power of active relaxation; that of the former is very likely of similar origin.

One should not leave the subject of contractures without a word of warning to the effect that many of the foregoing possibilities are just that, and require much experimental verification yet to be advanced.

Natural Contraction and the Motor Unit. One of the basic concepts in the physiology of muscle response to natural events is that of the motor unit, which is, by way of brief definition, an individual motoneuron together with the muscle fibers it innervates. The term was first introduced in 1925 by Liddell and Sherrington. Although a muscle consists of thousands of individual muscle fibers, each muscle fiber is not supplied by an individual nerve fiber. Instead, the single axon of each motoneuron branches many times just before and after entering the body of a muscle to innervate on an average more than one hundred muscle fibers. Since the minimum possible or "quantum" reaction in natural movement is a single discharge of an impulse by a single motoneuron, the group of a hundred or more muscle fibers having common innervation must act together as a unit. Skeletal muscle then is organized on the basis of motor units.

Innervation ratios. By the term "innervation ratio" is meant the relation between the number of motor nerve fibers supplying a muscle and the number of muscle fibers constituting that muscle. The ratio thus expresses the number of muscle fibers in the average motor unit. Probably the most accurate estimates of innervation ratios are those of Clark (6) who counted the motor nerve fibers to soleus (slow) and extensor digitorum longus (rapid) as well as the total number of muscle fibers in those muscles. Clark found that the innervation ratio for soleus was 1:120 while that for extensor digitorum longus was 1:165. This means that a single ventral horn cell (motoneuron) controls on the average 120 muscle fibers in the slow muscle and 165 muscle fibers in the rapid muscle. Although no accurate counts are available, there is some indication that the extremely rapid extrinsic muscles of the eye, such as the internal rectus, have a much lower innervation ratio than do the grosser muscles. In general it would seem that delicacy of action varies inversely with innervation ratio.

Table 1.—*Contraction Tension of Representative Muscles and of Average Single Motor Units.* (After Eccles and Sherrington, *Proc. roy. Soc.*, 1930, *B106*, 326–357.)

MUSCLE	TOTAL CONTRACTION TENSION IN GRAMS		NO. MOTOR FIBERS (I.E., MOTOR UNITS)	AVERAGE MOTOR UNIT TENSION IN GRAMS	
	TWITCH	TETANUS		TWITCH	TETANUS
Gastrocnemius medialis	2500	9080	393	6.4	23.1
Soleus	580	2230	233	2.48	9.57
Semitendinosus	1020	3310	549	1.8	6.02
Extensor digitorum longus	710	2010	247	2.8	8.1
Crureus	690	2600	256	2.7	10.2

Average motor unit tension. From what has been said above, it follows that the tension yielded by a whole muscle under maximal stimulation of its nerve when divided by the number of motor fibers in the nerve will give the average tension of the individual motor units. In order to find the tension developed by the average motor unit, Eccles and Sherrington (13) determined the total tension developed by representative muscles in motor twitches and tetani after removing the dorsal root ganglia and allowing the afferent fibers of those muscles to degenerate. Subsequently, and in the absence of afferent fibers in the motor nerves to the several muscles, it was possible to enumerate the motor fibers to the tested muscle and to make calculations of the average motor unit tension. Table 1 presents representative results obtained from several muscles, tension being expressed in grams.

Discharge rates of motor units (3). The volleys of nerve impulses delivered to a muscle as the result of nerve stimulation are synchronous, whereas the impulses usually distributed to muscle during the course of natural motor performance are highly asynchronous. Because of this very fact of asynchronous motor unit discharge, one cannot approach the study of discharge rates during natural activity by studying the whole muscle or its motor nerve. It is necessary to isolate by one means or another a single unit. This can be done by inserting into a muscle belly a minute electrode with which it is possible, on mild activity, to record the action potentials of a single or at most of a few units. With suitable placing of the electrode, only a single active unit need be in a location to effect the recording electrode. Figure 26 shows a record obtained by Denny-Brown utilizing this method. It illustrates the rhythmic discharge at slightly different frequencies of two motor units under the influence of an even, slight reflex drive. Some of the discharges are labeled (a) and (b) to aid identification. Another technique introduced by Adrian and Bronk is to cut down the motor nerve until only one or two fibers retain continuity with the central nervous system. Records of spike potentials are then obtained from the nerve distal to the section.

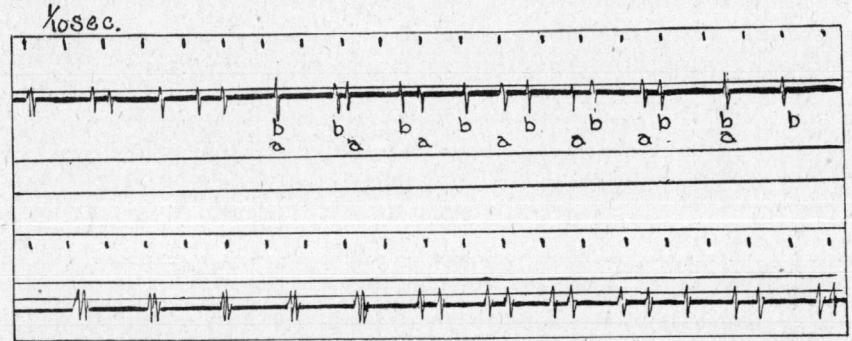

Fig. 26.—Discharge of two motor units at characteristic but different frequencies under the influence of a steady reflex drive. The spike potentials representing the discharges were recorded from the soleus muscle. In part of the upper record the spike potentials are labeled (a) and (b) to aid in recognizing the two rhythmic series. Note that the unit (a) drops out of the response near the end of the upper record. (After Denny-Brown, *Proc. roy. Soc.*, 1929, *B104*:252–301.)

In many studies by the experimental methods just outlined it has been found that motor unit discharge rates increase as the intensity of activity increases, but they do not exceed 80 to 90 per sec. during the most profound activity. When the slower acting red muscles are observed, the maximum rates of discharge for motor units are somewhat lower. One means by which muscle activity is graded, therefore, is by changes in the rate of motor unit discharge.

Another means by which muscle activity is graded is by the *recruitment* of motor units, that is, by the bringing of more motor units into activity. When several, or indeed many, units are active together, their individual rates of discharge vary one from another. The result is an asynchronous response of the group taken as a whole. This is a very important fact because it means that a muscle is able to exert smooth tension when the discharge rates of individual motor units are well below the critical fusion frequencies. As was pointed out on page 37, the critical fusion frequencies for pale and red muscles stimulated by artificial means were about 100 per sec. and 30 per sec. respectively. But artificial stimulation yields synchronized volleys of impulses, and in the resulting contraction all the motor units are in phase. In most contractions of natural, i.e., reflex or volitional, origin, the motor units are discharging asynchronously and their individual contraction efforts are out of phase. As a result much lower discharge rates are required for mechanical fusion.

Voluntary contraction (3, 19). Voluntary movement has been studied in the human by the method of inserting fine needle electrodes through the skin into the bellies of selected muscles. Piper in 1907 was the first to attempt electrical recording of human muscle activity. Later Adrian and Bronk found motor unit discharge rates of 5 to 50 per sec., depending upon the degree of voluntary effort. At the same time they demonstrated recruitment of motor units on increased voluntary effort. There is then no question but that voluntary activity of human muscle is controlled and graded according to the means just described, that is, by variation in the number of active units and in the frequency of discharge in the individual units. One center of contention has been the question whether or not voluntary activity could be sufficiently brief to involve but a single discharge of a motor unit, and the

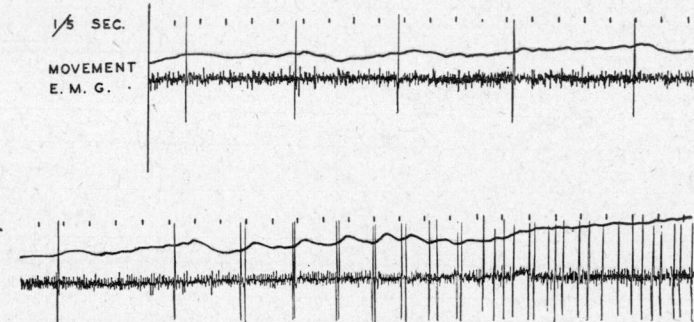

Fig. 27.—Record of a single motor unit discharge during volitional activity in the human. At the beginning of the record very slight movements were made, resulting in single discharges of the recorded motor unit. Toward the end of the record a sustained movement was made, resulting in a continuous series of discharges. (From Gilson and Mills, *Proc. Soc. exp. Biol.*, *N. Y.*, 1940, 45:650–652.)

usual conclusion was in the negative. However, Gilson and Mills have demonstrated recently that single discharges of a motor unit in brachialis could be obtained by slight flexion movements of the forearm. Slightly greater flexion movements caused the appearance of double discharges and finally, when sustained effort was made, the usual rhythmic discharge was recorded. It is improbable that many usual voluntary acts are of such a brief nature; nevertheless, great interest attaches to the fact that the electrical record of a willed movement need not exceed a single discharge. A record from one of Gilson's and Mills' experiments is presented in Figure 27.

Action of Muscles in the Body (14, 15). It was stated at the beginning of this chapter that skeletal muscles act in the body by producing rotation of bony levers at the joint articulations. The lever system of the body is acted upon by many forces, including gravity, acceleration, deceleration and external forces applied to one or another part of the body—for instance, wind resistance in running. To meet these forces, muscles must exert opposing forces in order to prevent movement and so maintain position. Furthermore, muscles must be able to accelerate and decelerate movement, this being done by contributing energy to the lever systems, or by removing energy, by dissipation into heat, from the lever systems.

In general muscles are arranged in antagonistic pairs about a joint, an arrangement which permits rotation of the levers in both directions through the utilization of muscle tension. Energy is supplied to a lever system when a muscle shortens, during which process chemical energy is converted into work, measured by the product of muscle tension and the distance through which it is shortened. This was called *positive work* by Fenn. Energy is removed from a lever system by stretching a muscle; the lever system stretching the muscle does work on it and the energy involved is degraded by the muscle into heat to be dissipated. This has been called *negative work*. Thus the fundamental pattern of muscle action involves stretching of the muscle as it slows movement in one direction (deceleration), followed by shortening as it accelerates movement in the opposite direction.

The effectiveness of a muscle in producing rotation about a joint depends upon the force (tension) exerted by the muscle and the length of lever through

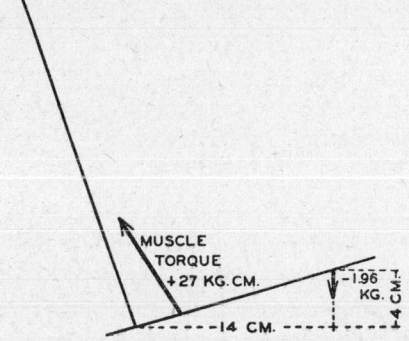

Fig. 28.—Forces involved in the measurement of the torque exerted by muscles about the elbow joint when the arm is held stationary against the force of gravity. This simple example is to illustrate the method by which the energy expenditure of the muscles is calculated for various conditions: at rest, running, and walking. (From Elftman, *Biol. Symp.*, 1941, *3*:191–209.)

which it works, that is, the distance from the center of rotation within the joint to the insertion of the muscle in question. The product of tension and length of the lever arm (from the muscle insertion to the center of rotation) is the moment of force or *torque* of the muscle. The method of finding the torques exerted by muscles can be illustrated by a simple case in which the arm is held stationary at the completion of its forward swing in running (cf. Fig. 28). With the whole body motionless, the only force tending to move the forearm would be gravity. This would constitute a vertical force of -1.96 kilograms acting at the center of gravity of the forearm. The lever arm of this force would be the distance from elbow joint to the center of gravity of the forearm, say 14 cm. The torque of gravity then would be $-1.96 \times 14 = -27$ kilogram-centimeters. The flexor muscles of the elbow would need to provide a torque of $+27$ kilogram-centimeters in the opposite direction in order to prevent movement of the forearm. Now, since the torque is known, the tension exerted by the forearm flexors can be obtained by dividing the torque by the length of the lever arm through which the flexors act. If this lever arm is 3.3 cm., the flexor would have to exert a tension of 27/3.3 = 8.2 kilos in order to prevent movement by the force of gravity. By similar calculation it can be shown that the flexors of the elbow

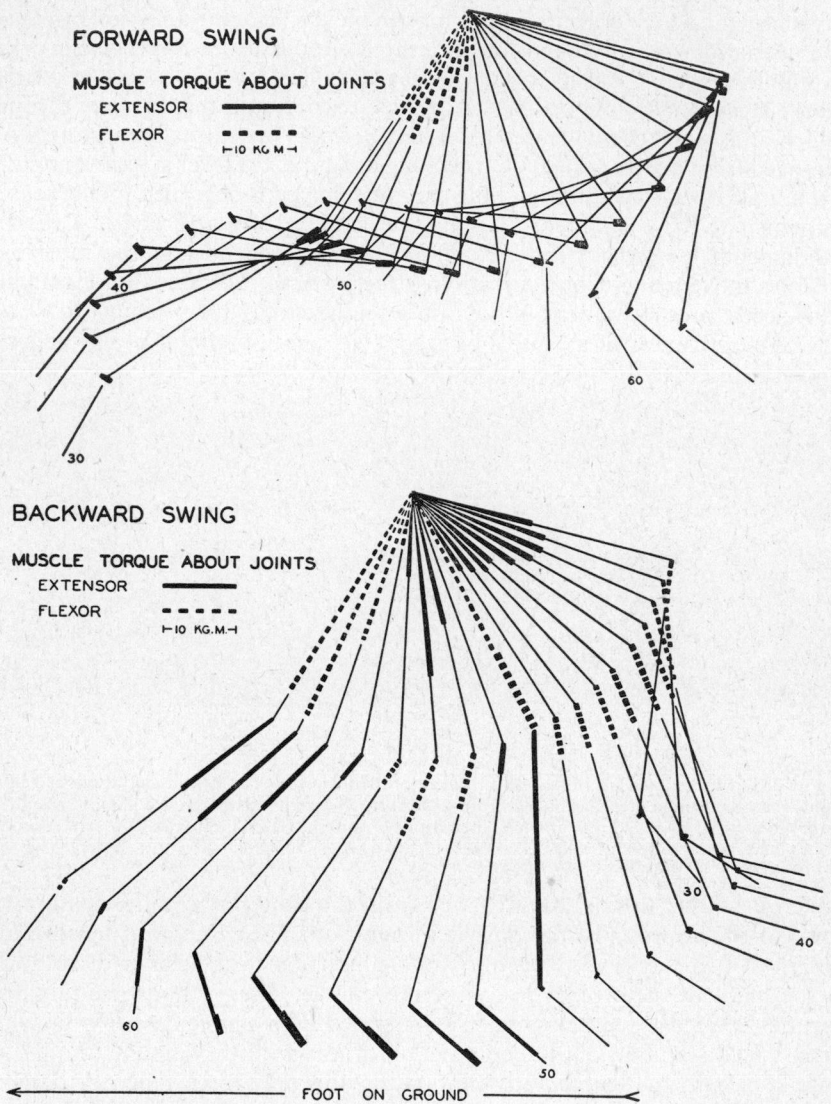

Fig. 29.—Torques developed about the leg joints in running. The thin lines represent the position of the legs at each stage in the running step. The torques are represented by heavy lines proceeding distally from the joints about which they act, being therefore superimposed on the thin lines representing the positions of the thigh, shank and foot. (From Elftman, *Biol. Symp.*, 1941, *3*:191–209.)

of each arm may exert a force of a half ton during the simple act of chinning the bar.

The torques exerted about joints by muscles during walking or running can be found by taking into consideration in addition to gravity the other forces that come into play, viz., acceleration, deceleration, movements of the body, wind resistance, and the ground reaction. The successive torques exerted by the muscles of the leg in the course of a running step are shown in Figure 29, taken from Elftman's recent study (15). The successive positions of the thigh, shank and foot are shown by the thin lines for intervals of 1/75 sec. and are numbered successively from 30 to 64. The heavy lines superimposed on the thin lines, solid lines for extensor, dotted for flexor, indicate the torques involved at each stage in the running cycle. Torques about the hip are plotted along the thigh, those about the knee along the shank, and those about the ankle along the foot. The foot, in the backward swing of the leg, is in contact with the ground during the interval indicated by the arrow. A study of Figure 29 shows that the extensors of the hip become active at stage 60 just before the end of the forward swing to retard the forward movement of the leg, and continue in activity until stage 46 of the backward swing, serving now to accelerate movement in the new direction. Like-

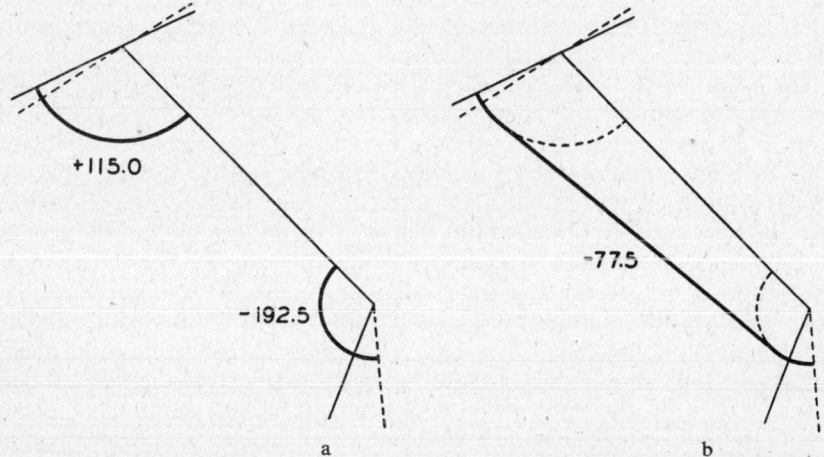

a   b

Fig. 30.—Comparison of the work done by one joint muscles (left) and an equivalent two joint muscle (right); figures represent the rate of work in kilogram-meters per sec. Solid lines give position 32; dotted lines position 36 in the backward swing of the leg seen in Figure 29. (From Elftman, *Amer. J. Physiol.*, 1940, *129*:672–684.)

wise the flexors of the hip become active in the last stages of the backward swing (58 to 64) and continue in activity as the leg reverses direction (30 to 56 in the forward swing). Sudden and brief changes take place at the instant the foot touches the ground in the backward swing (stage 48).

Advantage of Two Joint Muscles. At certain stages of leg swing the muscles of one joint are shortening while those of the next joint are being stretched. An example of this situation may be found in stages 32 to 36 of the back swing in Figure 29. During these stages the torque at the hip is extensor, that at the knee is flexor. The hip extensors are shortening, producing acceleration, and so doing positive work. The knee flexors are being stretched to decelerate the knee extension, they are accepting energy from the lever system and dissipating it to heat; they are doing negative work. Figure 30 shows that the hip muscle is doing work at the rate of +115.0 kilogram-meters per sec., while the knee muscle is doing negative work at the rate of −192.5 kilogram-meters per sec. The combined work of the two muscles, therefore, is $(+115.0) + (-192.5) = -77.5$ kilogram-meters per sec. The duplication of work is 115.0 kilogram-meters per sec. and this work can be saved by a two joint muscle, for the rate at which a two joint muscle works is the algebraic summation of the rates of work of the one joint muscles which it replaces. Now, for the example that has been selected (simultaneous extensor torque at the hip and flexor torque at the knee), the hamstring muscles, being extensors of the hip and flexors of the knee, fulfill the requirements. Figure 30b shows how the hamstring muscles save the duplication of work necessitated by equivalent one joint muscles. Elftman (1940) found that the available two joint muscles would reduce the average work rate of running by 1.36 horsepower. The actual work rate for the limb muscles during running was 2.61 horsepower. The saving in work by two joint muscles is therefore an important factor in body architecture.*

SMOOTH MUSCLE

Smooth muscles are to be found in a variety of situations in the body, usually forming in part the walls of blood vessels, alimentary canal, genito-urinary passages and bronchi. Other smooth muscles are not so arranged, as, for example, the pilo-erector muscles of the hair follicles, the intrinsic muscles of the eye, and in some animals the nictitating membrane. Smooth muscles are differentiated from striated muscles histologically by the absence of cross-striation and physiologically by their relative slowness of action.

Smooth muscles may be classified into two groups which differ from each other in a number of fundamental features. In one group are the smooth muscles which are organized in motor units and which have a true motor innervation in somewhat the same way as do the skeletal muscles. This group includes the muscles of the blood vessels, the pilo-erectors and the nictitating membrane. The other group, of which the intestinal and uterine muscles are typical examples, are automatically active as is the striated heart muscle. Indeed, Bozler (5) draws very close analogies between the two groups of smooth muscles on one hand and striated and cardiac muscle on the other hand, according to the following schema:

$$
\text{striated muscle}
\begin{cases}
\text{skeletal} \begin{cases} \text{many units} \\ \text{motor nerves} \end{cases} \text{multi-unit} \\
\text{cardiac} \begin{cases} \text{syncytial} \\ \text{automatic} \end{cases} \text{visceral}
\end{cases}
\text{smooth muscle}
$$

Multi-unit smooth muscles. Study of the multi-unit smooth muscles is complicated by the small size of the units. In consequence, the fundamental processes in such muscles are not as well established as they are for skeletal muscle. Analysis is further complicated by the apparent duality of the action of single motor volleys which usually give rise to a tetanic response rather than a truly single response, or twitch, to a single motor volley.

The retrolingual membrane of the frog is a useful object for the study of the responses of smooth muscle of blood vessels. Fulton and Lutz (17) discovered, on stimulating small nerves lying in the membrane, that the smooth muscle reaction was sharply limited to a very small area of the

* This brief account devoted to but a few principles of body mechanics cannot do justice to this important subject that now is enjoying a rebirth of interest largely through the efforts of Elftman. His papers should be consulted for further details and for references to the older literature.

vascular bed of the membrane. Figure 31, taken from a motion picture sequence, shows constriction confined to a precapillary (B) on stimulation of the fine nerve (E). Because of the highly restricted nature of the response

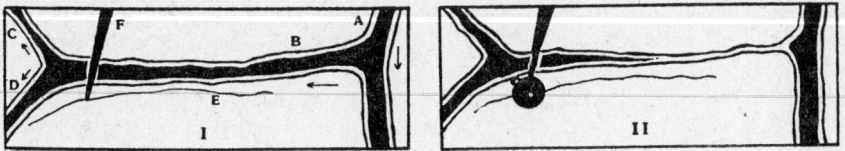

Fig. 31.—Localized contraction of vascular smooth muscle on stimulation of a small nerve twig. I = condition before stimulation: A, arteriole; B, precapillary; C, capillary; D, capillary; E, nerve twig; F, stimulating micro-electrode. The arrows indicate the direction of blood flow. II = condition following stimulation; constriction (i.e., smooth muscle contraction) is confined to the precapillary. (From Fulton and Lutz, *Amer. J. Physiol.*, 1942, *135*:531–534.)

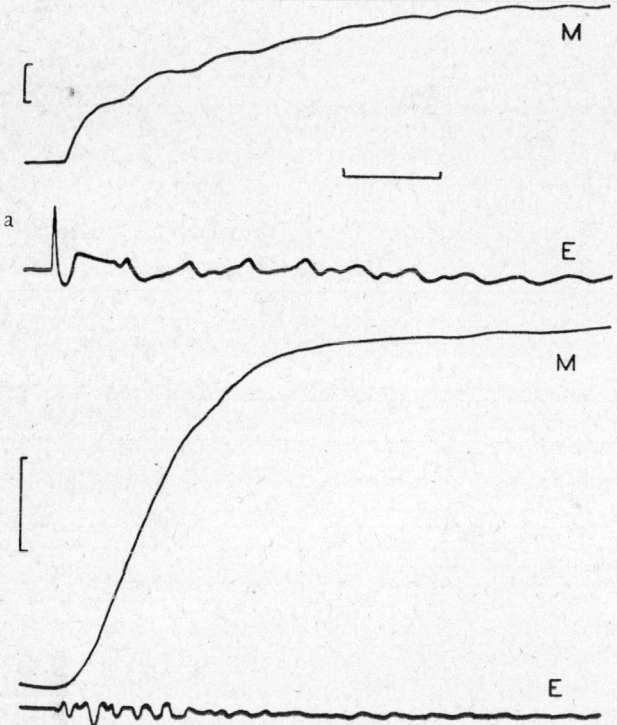

Fig. 32.—Electrical (E) and mechanical (M) responses of the nictitating membrane to a single maximal stimulation of the motor nerve (upper records) and to the intravenous injection of adrenaline (lower records). The vertical scales in each case indicate 1 gram in the tension records. The horizontal scale is 2 sec. In the upper records the first electrical wave results from the direct action of the nerve volley; the later waves from liberated chemical mediator. Each electrical response is followed by an increment in tension. Note general similarity to an incomplete tetanus in skeletal muscle. The response to injected adrenalin is qualitatively similar but less synchronous. (Rearranged from Eccles and Magladery, *J. Physiol.*, 1937, *90*:31–99.)

it follows that the smooth muscle of the vascular bed is functionally discontinuous, which in turn suggests the existence of smooth muscle motor units.

A more detailed study of multi-unit smooth muscle has been carried out by Eccles and Magladery (10, 11), utilizing the nictitating membrane of the cat as a test object and studying not only mechanical events but also the electrical responses of the muscle. When stimulated by a single motor nerve volley (cervical sympathetic), the nictitating membrane begins to contract after a total latency of about 150 msec. Contraction is preceded by an electrical response, just as it is in skeletal muscle. When contraction is uncomplicated by repetitive action, as it sometimes is, the contraction evoked by a single motor nerve volley resembles in shape the twitch of a striated muscle, the time course being about ten times slower than that of a slow striated muscle such as soleus. When the more usual rhythmic response occurs (Fig. 32a), repetitive electrical discharge at a frequency of 1 to 2 per sec. is seen as the result of a single nerve volley. Corresponding to each wave in the electrical response there is an increment of tension in the myographic record. The whole response rather resembles that of an incomplete tetanus of skeletal muscle. Each successive response of the smooth muscle units appears to have associated with it a refractory period. These experiments of Eccles and Magladery indicate a dual mechanism of transmission from sympathetic postganglionic fibers to the nictitating membrane. In addition to the direct action of the nerve volley, the liberation of an adrenaline-like substance takes place. It is believed that the onset of the smooth muscle response is the result of the direct action of the nerve fibers, the smooth muscle fibers subsequently responding in a rhythmic repetitive manner to the liberated chemical mediator.

The response of the nictitating membrane to injected adrenaline is very much like that during the rhythmic response to a single nerve volley (cf. Fig. 32b).

One curious result of the dual nature of transmission to the nictitating membrane is that summation of contraction results when two stimuli are delivered at no greater interval than the refractory period of the nerve (about 2 msec.) although the refractory period of the smooth muscle fibers is some 50 msec. in duration. Although the second nerve volley fails to exert any direct effect on the smooth muscle, due to its refractoriness, another quantum of adrenaline-like substance is liberated by the motor nerve fibers, which intensifies the rhythmic activity with resulting summation of contractions.

Visceral smooth muscles (5). The study of visceral smooth muscle is less fraught with uncertainty than that of multi-unit smooth muscle, and the experimental results are correspondingly more clear-cut. The most useful experiments are those of Bozler, utilizing strips of uterine muscle which has a syncytial character. When such a muscle strip is stimulated by a single electrical shock, a contraction wave is conducted along the entire muscle. The conduction depends only upon the muscle tissue itself, for ganglion cells and other nerve elements that might account for conduction are absent. The preparations of uterine muscle showed a definite strength-duration curve, a refractory period, and adherence to the all-or-nothing principle (cf. p. 52). In short, the smooth muscle strip, although consisting of innumerable small cells, behaves as a single large muscle fiber.

Spontaneous contraction which characterizes the activity of visceral smooth muscle is always accompanied by conducted impulses identified by the recording of conducted spike potentials (Fig. 33). The fact that nerve-free segments of smooth muscle show spontaneous contraction seems conclusive evidence for the myogenic origin of such contractions. It has long been known that contractions of visceral muscles may remain localized, or, having conducted for some distance, die out. This might seem at first sight to vitiate the view that conduction occurs by an all-or-nothing process, but this is not the case, for, with a small safety factor, variations in excitability would be a sufficient explanation for blocking of impulse conduction. It seems very likely that the extremely fine protoplasmic bridges between smooth muscle cells with their abrupt transitions in size would be difficult structures at best for the conducted excitation to negotiate, and block could easily occur at such points.

Spontaneous contractions differ widely in strength and duration (cf. Fig. 33) and the strength of the individual impulses is often greater in powerful than in feeble contractions. This fact can be explained logically on the basis of incomplete and variable activation of the syncytium due to fluctuations in excitability. A particularly interesting example of alteration in excitability is that of the anestrus uterus following injection of theelin (Bozler). During the anestrus phase of the sexual cycle (cf. Chap. 54) uterine muscle has a very low electrical excitability and such responses as are obtained remain

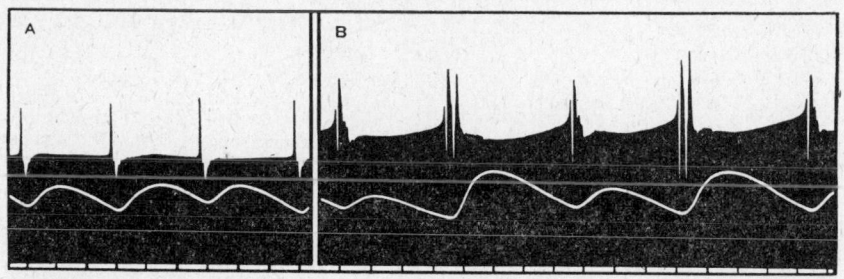

Fig. 33.—Spontaneous electrical and mechanical activity of visceral smooth muscle. Pendular movements of guinea pig intestine. Note the conducted spike potentials above that are simple in record (A) but more complex in record (B) as the activity becomes stronger. (From an unpublished figure presented through the kindness of Dr. Emil Bozler.)

local and unpropagated. The administration of theelin rapidly alters this condition; the electrical excitability is enhanced, the responses are propagated, and spontaneous activity in the form of strong rhythmic contractions pervades the whole musculature.

"Tone" of smooth muscle, by which is meant a protracted moderate degree of activity, results from persistent weak contraction, frequently irregular, with uncoordinated contractions occurring in all parts of the muscle. Sometimes tonic activity is accompanied by a regular discharge of impulses at low frequency. Smooth muscles exhibit tone when removed from the influence of the central nervous system, for which reason it is said to be a property of the muscle itself. In this way smooth muscle is very different from skeletal muscle, in which tone is of reflex origin (cf. Chap. 6). Skeletal muscles become quite atonic on severing connection with the central nervous system.

Mechanical properties of smooth muscle (4). One of the important features of smooth muscle activity lies in its ability to assume considerable change in length without accompanying change in tension, that is to say, its plasticity. Bozler has studied this property by recording the changes in length when a constant load is applied to a smooth muscle and conversely by observing the tension changes when the muscle is stretched to a constant length. Figure 34 summarizes the results of such experiments. When a load is applied to a relaxed smooth muscle, a sudden increase in length takes place after which the muscle continues to lengthen slowly (Fig. 34A). When the load is removed, the muscle does not return to its original length, which can only be restored by evoking a contraction. Conversely, when a smooth muscle is subjected to sudden stretch, elastic tension is produced. As soon as the stretch is maintained at a constant degree, the tension begins to fall along

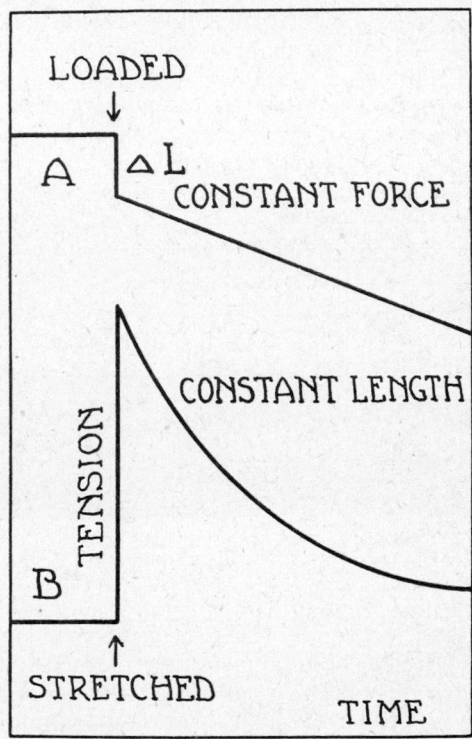

Fig. 34.—Schematic representation of the mechanical properties of smooth muscle. A = extension-time curve, to show the lengthening in two phases after applying a load which is then maintained constant. B = tension change produced by sudden stretch. Note the immediate rise and secondary fall of tension as the length is maintained constant in the stretched position. (After Bozler, *Cold Spr. Harb. Symposia*, 1936, *4*:260–266.)

an exponential curve and disappears (Fig. 34B). Under conditions of equilibrium, there is no measurable tension within the physiological range of lengths. This disappearance of tension in smooth muscle is called "release of tension" to distinguish it from relaxation of contraction.

Although these mechanical properties are quite different from those of skeletal muscle, it must not be concluded that the nature of the contractile substance or mechanism is entirely different in the two types of muscle. In striated muscle, as seems now to be generally accepted, the length and tension of the resting muscle fiber are due to the sarcolemma, the muscle substance itself behaving in a purely plastic fashion. In consequence, there is now more than ever before less reason for considering the muscle substances of striated and smooth muscle as wholly distinct entities.

CARDIAC MUSCLE

The muscle tissue of the heart is comparable in some ways with the visceral smooth muscles. It has a syncytial structure and any given preparation of heart muscle behaves electrically and mechanically as a unit. Furthermore, heart muscle has the power of spontaneous activity which, with the exception of certain invertebrate hearts, is myogenic. There is no true motor nerve supply to heart muscle in the sense that striated muscle or multi-unit smooth muscle has a motor supply, but it does receive a regulatory nerve supply through the vagus nerve and sympathetic system (cf. Chap. 10).

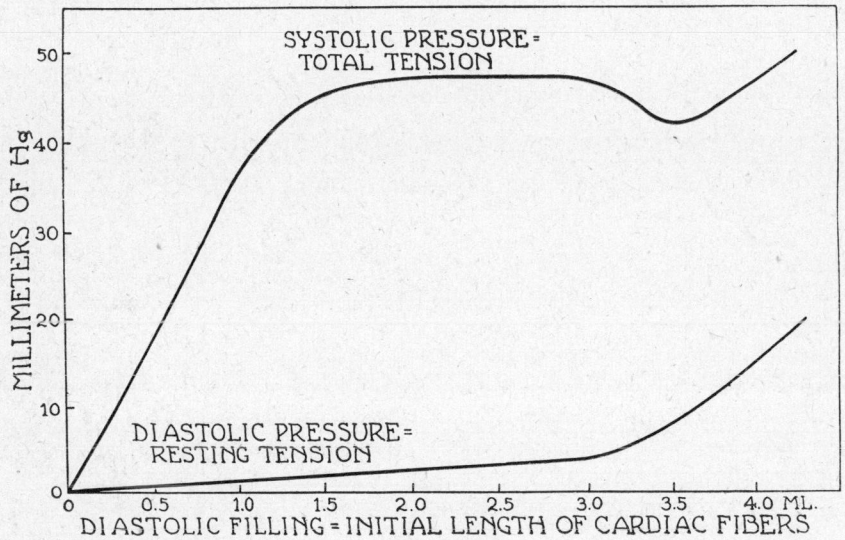

Fig. 35.—Length-total tension and length-resting tension relations of cardiac muscle. The difference between the two curves gives the active tension developed by the heart beat for various degrees of filling. Note the general similarity between these curves and those of a single skeletal muscle fiber presented in Figure 25. The relation between length and developed tension in heart muscle is known as Starling's Law of the Heart. (Constructed from data on p. 237 of Kozawa, *J. Physiol.*, 1915, *49*:233–245.)

Electrical and mechanical events. The prolongation of the spike potential and associated refractory period to the point at which they outlast the contraction time is the salient feature of cardiac muscle activity. This relationship between electrical action and refractoriness on one hand and contraction on the other stands in sharp contradistinction to that obtaining in skeletal muscle and most, though not all, smooth muscle. The consequence is that heart muscle, unlike striated muscle, cannot be restimulated during its contraction phase, or systole, as it is called in the nomenclature of cardiac physiology, and cannot therefore yield fused contraction.

Excitation and contraction are propagated in cardiac muscle as in other types of striated muscle, the rate of conduction being probably about 2 to 3 meters per sec. in mammalian ventricular muscle.

Mechanical properties of heart muscle (20). The length tension relations of cardiac muscle resemble rather more those of striated muscle than of smooth muscle. An isometric length-total tension diagram for the heart can be obtained on the basis that fiber length varies with the filling of the ventricular cardiac chamber. The ventricle is connected to a pressure manometer and a reservoir from which increments of fluid can be admitted to the ventricular cavity. The ventricle can be isolated from the reservoir during observation, being then only connected to the isometric manometer. Figure 35 shows in a diagram the results of such an experiment performed in Starling's laboratory. It is of interest to compare this behavior of cardiac muscle with that of skeletal muscle, the length-total tension relations of which are presented in Figure 25, for such a comparison illustrates the fundamental mechanical similarity of the two tissues. It is seen in Figure 35 that there is only a slight initial tension increase as diastolic filling increased from 0 to 3 ml. Further increase in diastolic filling causes a considerable rise in initial tension to 20 mm. Hg. On the contrary, the maximum contraction tension as measured by systolic pressure is developed before the sharp increase in initial tension occurs, after which the tension developed by contraction diminishes. There is therefore a characteristic relation between length of the muscle fibers and energy of contraction that reveals the existence of an optimum length, divergence from which in either direction results in a decrease in contraction. The statement, "The energy of contraction is a function of the *length* of the muscle fibers," when applied to the particular case of heart muscle, is commonly known as *Starling's Law of the Heart*. One will recall from the discussion of length-tension relations in skeletal muscle that the maximum active tension was developed at resting length. It is perhaps futile to speculate on what the resting length of the cardiac muscle fibers may be, from the experimental evidence that has been presented. It would, however, seem reasonable on analogy with the skeletal muscle to suggest that the resting length of cardiac muscle likewise is the length at which the maximum contraction tension is produced.

ALL-OR-NOTHING RELATION (1, 2, 21, 22)

There have been isolated references in the preceding discussions to the all-or-nothing relation, but it has seemed better to defer until this point discussion of the relation itself. The all-or-nothing relation was first enunciated by Bowditch in 1871, in the following sentence, which reads in Bayliss' translation, "An induction shock produces a contraction or fails to do so according to its strength: if it does so at all it produces the greatest contraction that can be produced by any strength of stimulus in the condition of the muscle at the time." Bowditch employed the nerve-free apex of the frog ventricle, and for many years it was thought that this property of cardiac muscle was unique, since obviously the contraction of a striated muscle could be graded. Bowditch was quite aware of the fact that the extent of a contraction in cardiac muscle was not always the same, as his demonstration of the staircase "phenomenon" bears testimony.

It was not until 1905 that the all-or-nothing relation was definitely understood to have wider applicability. At that time Keith Lucas, working with a frog muscle containing but a few fibers, discovered that the strength of contraction increased in discontinuous steps when the stimulus applied directly to the muscle was progressively increased, and that the number of steps never exceeded the number of muscle fibers. Since the contraction of a fiber would not increase in steps, Lucas concluded that each fiber must contract fully if it contracts at all. In 1938, Bozler showed clearly for the first time the adherence of visceral smooth muscle to the all-or-nothing relation. As early as 1902, Gotch suggested that the increase in response of a nerve with increasing stimulation was the result of an increase in the number of responding fibers, not in the size of response in the individual fibers. These earlier observations on muscle and nerve led to the view that the all-or-nothing relation was a property of a unit, a single muscle or nerve fiber; the heart, by virtue of its syncytial structure, being a unit. The final confirmation, however, did not come until Pratt and Eisenberger in 1919 obtained records from single muscle fibers; and Adrian and Zotterman in 1926 recorded the response of single nerve fibers.

As long as one considers the criterion of excitation to be the response occurring with threshold or greater than threshold stimuli, there is no real difficulty with the statement as advanced by Bowditch, but as attention is directed to the subliminal responses of tissues, it becomes clear that a restatement is in order. It is Adrian who brings most clearly to mind the fact that the all-or-nothing relation is concerned with the *conducted* response in regions away from the direct effects of the stimulus. Adrian's general statement is, "In nerve fiber, skeletal muscle fiber and in the heart the intensity of the propagated disturbance at any point is determined solely by the local conditions at that point." On the basis of Bozler's observations, visceral muscle should be included in this definition.

The concept of local conditions determining the response at a point stems largely from Adrian's own observation that a nerve volley emerged from a narcotized zone with the same characteristics it had before entering the zone. Although the phenomenon of the refractory period is in itself not a full proof of an all-or-nothing relation, still it seems almost inevitable from the fact that a propagated disturbance produces a refractory period that the fiber could do no more until recovery has taken place.

The more recent investigations on the all-or-nothing relation with respect to striated muscle have been largely conditioned by the use of stimulating electrodes of highly restricted dimension (so-called pore electrodes) by means of which a single fiber in a sheet of muscle could be stimulated. Pratt and Eisenberger, using this technique, recorded the contraction of single muscle fiber and found that the contraction was uniform so long as one fiber alone responded. As a second or third fiber responded, abrupt increases in contraction resulted (cf. Fig. 36). Shortly thereafter Adrian, utilizing Pratt's method of stimulation, showed that the action potential response of single muscle fibers follows the same relation, which led him to suggest that the all-or-nothing relation "intervenes at an early stage in the chain of processes which lead up to contraction."

In 1929 Gelfan, also using a pore electrode, discovered graded contractions of a single muscle fiber. Shortly afterward Gelfan and Gerard noted that the graded contractions were localized and occupied a progressively greater length of fiber on increasing the stimulus until the conducted response occurred. Likewise Gelfan and Bishop found that the graded responses were not associated with an electrical response. The essential difference between the experiments of Gelfan and those of Pratt appeared to be the smaller pore electrode employed by Gelfan, and the results suggested that the smaller pore electrode initially stimulated the contractile mechanism directly, and only secondarily by spread of current on increasing the stimulus stimulated a sufficient length of fiber to activate the conducting mechanism.

The suggestion made by Adrian in 1922 (1), that the all-or-nothing relation appears at an early stage in the events leading to contraction, now became a definite probability; and with this concept in mind, Brown and Sichel in 1939 devised the method of stimulation by massive electrodes of single muscle fibers. The electrodes extended the whole length of the muscle fiber so that the whole fiber was excited simultaneously. The factor of conduction was eliminated. It was soon found that the mechanical shortening evoked by stimulation with the fiber-length electrodes was graded, and in 1940 Sichel and Prosser showed that the graded shortenings instituted by stimulation with fiber-length electrodes were characterized by the absence of a refractory period.

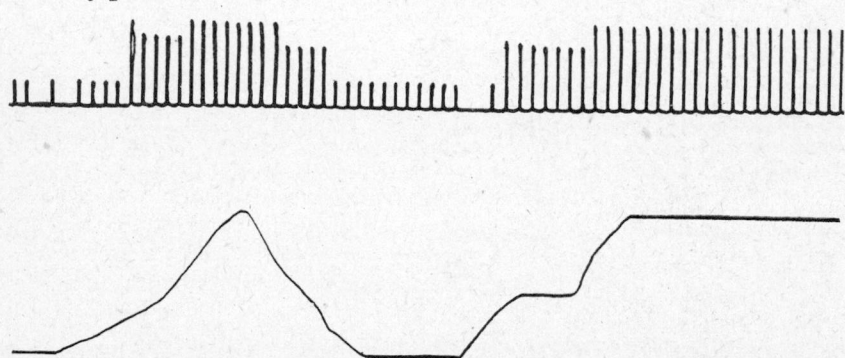

Fig. 36.—To illustrate the all-or-nothing relation as it applies to skeletal muscle. Upper record, extent of contraction (i.e., as measured by photographing the excursions of a droplet of mercury on the muscle surface). Lower record, variation in strength of stimulus (increase upwards) delivered to a very restricted number of fibers by means of a "pore" electrode. Note that the contractions increase and decrease by sharp steps as one, two, three or no fibers contract although the stimulus is varied up and down in a fairly even continuous manner. Thus, in response to single shocks, a muscle fiber either contracts fully or not at all. (After Pratt and Eisenberger, *Amer. J. Physiol.*, 1919, *49*:1–54.)

As a result of these various investigations, it appears certain today that the contractile process of muscle is not an all-or-nothing mechanism; it is capable of full gradation in response and does not exhibit a refractory period. The conducting mechanism that normally transfers excitation to the contractile mechanism, on the other hand, is an all-or-nothing mechanism just as is the conducting mechanism in nerve. In the normal course of events, then, it is a necessary consequence that the contraction follows an all-or-nothing relation, for the stimulus transferred to it from the conducting (and excitable) mechanism is of necessity a constant stimulus. The transfer of excitation from the conductile mechanism of muscle to the contractile mechanism is little understood, but it would seem that the flow of current in the local circuit of the impulse is a sufficient cause for activation of the contractile mechanism in a direct manner. Such a view would find support in the experiments of Gelfan and of Brown and Sichel which suggest that the contractile mechanism can be stimulated directly by electrical current flow.

REFERENCES

1. ADRIAN, E. D. The relation between the stimulus and the electric response in a single muscle fiber. *Arch. neerl. Physiol.*, 1922, 7:330–332.

2. ADRIAN, E. D. The all-or-nothing reaction. *Ergebn. Physiol.*, 1933, 35:744–755.

3. ADRIAN, E. D. and BRONK, D. W. The discharge of impulses in motor nerve fibres. II. The frequency of discharge in reflex and voluntary contractions. *J. Physiol.*, 1929, 67:119–151.

4. BOZLER, E. An analysis of the properties of smooth muscle. *Cold Spr. Harb. Symposia*, 1936, 4:260–266.

5. BOZLER, E. Action potentials and conduction of excitation in muscle. *Biol. Symp.*, 1941, 3:95–109.

6. CLARK, D. A. Muscle counts of motor units.—A study in innervation ratios. *Amer. J. Physiol.*, 1931, 96:296–304.

7. COOPER, S. and ECCLES, J. C. The isometric responses of mammalian muscles. *J. Physiol.*, 1930, 69:377–385.

8. DENNY-BROWN, D. E. On the nature of postural reflexes. *Proc. roy. Soc.*, 1929, B104:252–301.

9. DENNY-BROWN, D. E. The histological features of striped muscle in relation to its functional activity. *Proc. roy. Soc.*, 1929, B104:371–411.

10. ECCLES, J. C. and MAGLADERY, J. W. The excitation and response of smooth muscle. *J. Physiol.*, 1937, 90:31–67.

11. ECCLES, J. C. and MAGLADERY, J. W. Rhythmic responses of smooth muscle. *J. Physiol.*, 1937, 90:68–99.

12. ECCLES, J. C. and O'CONNOR, W. J. Responses which nerve impulses evoke in mammalian striated muscles. *J. Physiol.*, 1939, 97:44–102.

13. ECCLES, J. C. and SHERRINGTON, C. S. Numbers and contraction values of individual motor-units examined in some muscles of the limb. *Proc. roy. Soc.*, 1930, B106:326–357.

14. ELFTMAN, H. The work done by muscles in running. *Amer. J. Physiol.*, 1940, 129:672–684.

15. ELFTMAN, H. The action of muscles in the body. *Biol. Symp.*, 1941, 3:191–209.

16. FENN, W. O. Isotonic contractions of muscle. *Cold Spr. Harb. Symposia*, 1936, 4:233–241.

17. FULTON, G. P. and LUTZ, B. R. Smooth muscle motor-units in small blood vessels. *Amer. J. Physiol.*, 1942, 135:531–534.

18. GASSER, H. S. Contractures of skeletal muscle. *Physiol. Rev.*, 1930, 10:35–109.

19. GILSON, A. S. and MILLS, W. B. Single responses of motor units in consequence of volitional effort. *Proc. Soc. exp. Biol., N. Y.*, 1940, 45:650–652.

20. KOZAWA, S. The mechanical regulation of the heart beat in the tortoise. *J. Physiol.*, 1915, 49:233–245.

21. PRATT, F. H. Muscle and the heart's motto. *Biol. Symp.*, 1941, 3:35–50.

22. PRATT, F. H. and EISENBERGER, J. P. The quantal phenomena in muscle: methods with further evidence of the all-or-none principle for the skeletal fiber. *Amer. J. Physiol.*, 1919, 49:1–54.

23. RAMSEY, R. W. and STREET, S. F. The isometric length-tension diagram of isolated skeletal muscle fibers of the frog. *J. cell. comp. Physiol.*, 1940, 15:11–34.

24. RAMSEY, R. W. and STREET, S. F. Muscle function as studied in single fibers. *Biol. Symp.*, 1941, 3:9–34.

25. SNYDER, C. D. The latencies of mechanical and electrical responses in skeletal muscle. *Amer. J. Physiol.*, 1936, 115:441–454.

CHAPTER 3

ENERGY TRANSFORMATIONS IN MUSCLE

BY ALFRED E. WILHELMI

SOME GENERAL CHARACTERISTICS OF MUSCLE

Introduction. Muscle is an excitable organ that transforms chemical energy into mechanical energy. Since a muscle may be stimulated at will, it can be made to work under a wide variety of controlled conditions, and its mechanical behavior may be accurately measured and correlated with chemical, thermal, or other physical changes taking place during contraction. Muscle therefore lends itself particularly well to the study of problems of energy transformations in living tissue, and it has always aroused the attention of physiologists, whose chief interest is in how living things work. An excellent impression of the vigor and continuity of this interest may be gained from Fulton's account of the history of muscle physiology (9).

The general problems of energy transformation in muscle fall into three large groups: (i) The properties and organization of the structures responsible for the contractile behavior of the tissue; (ii) the nature of the chemical systems producing energy, and the form in which the energy is made available; (iii) the manner in which energy is utilized—the rules governing the relations between the contractile system and the chemical systems, which must ultimately determine the mechanical behavior of the tissue.

The experimental material most often used in attacking these problems is frog skeletal muscle, primarily because of its convenient properties. It can be isolated from the animal, and with exercise of due care it will remain excitable for many hours. It may be studied at rest or during sustained measurable activity, unlike cardiac muscle which is continuously active, or smooth muscle which often tends to accommodate itself rather than the investigator in the course of an experiment. A frog sartorius or gastrocnemius muscle is not too large for accurate measurements of heat production under conditions in which adequate oxygen must diffuse to all parts of the isolated organ, and not too small to permit accurate measurements of its chemical constituents or its respiratory exchange during rest or activity. The comparative physiology of muscle is not as well known as it should be, but it appears that the different kinds of muscle employ the same principles in their contractile systems and in their methods of energy production, differing mainly in the relations between these two dynamic components.

Muscle, as a living system, requires a continuing energy supply for normal excitability and mechanical behavior. Any factor exhausting or interrupting the energy supply—stimulation to fatigue, lack of oxygen, exposure to heat or extreme cold, and numerous poisons—will induce a condition known as *rigor*. The muscle, normally flexible and translucent, becomes moderately stiff, opaque, and inexcitable. The onset of rigor during a series of contractions is distinguished by progressive failure of the muscle to relax completely in the period before excitability is lost. The rigor of fatigue or anoxia is reversible;* long rest in oxygen permits restoration of normal activity. Rigor from heat or poisons is irreversible; the muscle is killed.

Structure (1, 3–5, 7, 8, 14, 15). The individual unit of a skeletal muscle is a long, slender, polynucleated cell, the muscle fiber. The fibers have an elastic connective tissue covering, the sarcolemma, which has slender extensions joining the fiber with the tendons. The muscle fibers contain a number of *fibrils*, running the length of the fiber, embedded in the cytoplasm—the sarcoplasm—and separated from one another by intervals of about 5μ. An outstanding histological feature of voluntary muscle, muscle fibers, and fibrils is the regular striations at right angles to the long axis of the fibers. These give the fibers the appearance, in transmitted light, of being composed of alternate light and dark discs. During contraction it can be seen that shortening takes place chiefly in the dark regions, while the light portions shorten only a little or may even be slightly stretched.

The dark portions of the fiber (Q or A regions) are optically inhomogeneous (anisotropic) or doubly refracting. Plane-polarized light is elliptically polarized in passing through the A regions. Hence, if a muscle is viewed between crossed Nicol prisms the A regions appear light, while the intermediate isotropic (J or I) regions are dark, since the light passing through them is extinguished by the second prism.

Optical anisotropy, or birefringence, is invariably a property of contractile tissues. It may be due (i) to submicroscopic elements (e.g., rods or plates) uniformly arranged in a medium of different refractive index (form birefringence), (ii) to a regular arrangement of similar elements which are themselves birefringent (intrinsic birefringence), or (iii) to deformation under strain of isotropic substances with a regular fine structure (strain birefringence). Muscle fibers have both form and intrinsic birefringence. Hence the fibrils must have a regular structure based on organized aggregates of molecules (micelles) arranged in a regular pattern and the micelles must be anisotropic, in consequence of the orderly arrangement of the molecules making up the micellar units. Von Muralt and Edsall in 1930 first showed that solutions of the muscle protein, myosin, exhibit birefringence when the solution is agitated. Long, slender aggregates of myosin molecules, seeking the line of least resistance, arrange themselves regularly in the lines of flow of the moving solution. The similar alignment of many anisotropic particles makes it possible to perceive and measure their birefringence in plane-polarized light.

From the relation between the volume of the fibrils and the amount of myosin in the muscle it can be calculated that the principal structural element of the fibrils must be myosin. The micellar units of the fibrils therefore may be largely composed of submicroscopic fibers of myosin in which the individual molecules are regularly disposed in the direction of the long axis of the fiber. Myosin is the principal, but not the only, chemical constituent of the fibrils. Other constituents may be of fundamental importance in determining the contractile behavior of the protein fiber. Although myosin is present in the I regions of the fibrils, the absence (or very low order) of bire-

* The term "rigor" is, in this instance, used rather loosely. A reversible state of this kind might better be termed "contracture," in the sense of Gasser's distinction (Chap. 2, p. 39).

fringence indicates that the micellar and molecular organization is quite different from that of the A regions. The nature of this difference is not yet clear.

The importance of protein fibers as the fundamental structures of a contractile tissue lies in their property of changing length under certain conditions. The molecules of fiber-forming proteins like myosin are asymmetrical—thin bundles of long polypeptide chains—and the fibers may be regarded as chains made up of these protein chains. Changes in fiber length may occur (a) if the polypeptide chains slide over and between one another, (b) if the chains, originally oriented with their long axes in the long axis of the fiber, are partly or completely disoriented, or (c) if the degree of folding of the polypeptide chains is altered. From the studies of Astbury and others on the x-ray diffraction patterns of protein films and fibers and of muscle, it appears that changes in the degree of folding of the polypeptide chains may be chiefly responsible for changes in length of the protein fibers (i.e., for muscular contraction). Polypeptide chains are composed of many amino acid units joined in series—

$$NH_2.CH.CO-NH.CH.CO-NH.CH.CO-\ldots\ldots\ldots NH.CH.COOH,$$
$$\quad R \qquad\quad R \qquad\quad R \qquad\qquad\qquad R$$

(where R represents the characteristic side groups of the individual amino acids). The flexibility of these structures is attributed to a limited amount of movement taking place at the CO-NH linkages. The degree of folding is also limited by the size and nature of the R groups, and by temporary or permanent bonds (S-S linkages, for instance) between the adjacent polypeptide chains, which tend to make the whole structure more rigid. The temporary formation of such bonds may be responsible for the increased rigidity of muscle during contraction. Knowledge of the exact nature of the folding of the long protein molecules of muscle during contraction is as yet incomplete. Improvements in the technique of obtaining x-ray diffraction patterns, and new information obtained with the electron microscope and by other new physical methods, may make possible a more accurate visualization of changes in the molecular structure of muscle during contraction. The principal value of the observations so far has been to indicate that muscular contraction is an affair of *intramolecular* changes in aggregates of protein molecules arranged in an orderly three-dimensional array. The application of chemical energy in contraction must therefore be concerned with bringing about conditions (changes in *p*H, in the ionization of polar groups in the molecules, or in the energy distribution within the molecules or between the molecules and the surrounding medium) in which such intramolecular rearrangement not only can, but must, forcibly take place.

Since a muscle returns spontaneously to the relaxed, resting state after the end of a stimulus, the changes leading to contraction must be reversed and terminated by the contractile units themselves. The chemical reactions yielding energy to bring about these changes, or to reverse them, must be controlled by the contractile system. It cannot be said that the nature of this control is well understood, but striking evidence of the intimate relationship between the contractile and the chemical systems has been obtained. Engelhardt and Ljubimova (6) have observed that the muscle protein, myosin, is intimately associated with an enzyme, adenylpyrophosphatase, which hydrolyzes the terminal phosphate bond of adenosine triphosphate, a compound responsible for the distribution of chemical energy in the muscle cell (p. 69). The association of myosin with the catalysis of a primary energy-liberating reaction in muscle is very exciting, but the meaning of this relationship is not yet clear. It must be fitted into the larger context of the relation between the contractile units and their surrounding medium, and in this respect information is still very incomplete.

Chemical composition. (3) Muscle contains about 75 per cent of water. Proteins make up about four-fifths of the solids; the remainder is carbohydrate, lipid, inorganic salts, and a heterogeneous group of organic crystalloids—the "extractives" of muscle. The proteins are roughly classified in four types: myosin, globulin X, myogen, and stromaprotein. Myosin is evidently the contractile substance of muscle. The other types comprise numerous individual proteins. Some may be structural elements in the muscle cell, but most of them are functional components—the biological catalysts called enzymes.

A detailed account of the composition of muscle can be found in any textbook of physiological chemistry. Only these points need be stressed here: (i) the composition of muscle differs widely in different species and in different muscles in the same animal; (ii) there are many differences in composition between voluntary, cardiac, and smooth muscle; (iii) the study of these differences in relation to structure, function, and activity—the comparative biochemistry of muscle—is not yet well enough advanced for us to understand their significance; (iv) a number of constituents, present in appreciable amounts, have not yet been assigned a place in the metabolism of muscle. These points counsel restraint in accepting without reservation the current hypotheses of muscle physiology.

The study of chemical composition—the "morphological" chemistry of muscle—has two useful functions. It is a check upon hypotheses, which ought to account adequately for all the known constituents, and it is the basis for the study of muscle metabolism. In the last forty years growing knowledge of the place of enzymes, hormones, and vitamins in biological processes has shown that many substances present in traces, or only fleetingly present in the course of a coordinated series of chemical reactions, may be essential to normal cell function. The *physiological* chemistry of muscle is concerned with such trace substances and evanescent intermediate reactions, since it is in their interplay that one may discover the principles by which energy is realized and put to work. Only a few of the major participants in these events need a prior introduction.

Glycogen (13). Skeletal muscle contains from 0.5 to 1 per cent of the polysaccharide glycogen. It is the chief carbohydrate of muscle (which contains very little free glucose) and is its store of readily available foodstuff. Glycogen is composed of numerous glucose units bound together by loss of water; its empirical formula is $(C_6H_{10}O_5)n.H_2O$. Glycogen is prepared by the method of Pflüger, which involves the digestion of the tissue with KOH in a boiling water bath, and the subsequent precipitation of the glycogen with alcohol. Lazarow (11) has prepared another form of glycogen from liver by a gentler method. His "particulate" glycogen has a vastly greater molecular weight than "Pflüger" glycogen, is more homogeneous, and appears to depend for its organization upon a small amount of associated protein and lipid. In muscle, glycogen is doubtless also highly organized, in a special relation to the contractile mechanism and to the enzyme systems that are thrown into action when the muscle contracts.

Phosphocreatine (2). The base, creatine—methylguanidino-acetic acid—is present in muscle in amounts up to 400 mg. per cent. It was discovered by Chevreul in 1832. Almost 100 years later the Eggletons, and Fiske and Subbarow independently discovered that most of the creatine in muscle is in labile combination with phosphoric acid:

$$
\begin{array}{c}
\quad\quad\;\;\text{H}\\
\text{O}\;\;\;\text{H}\;\;\;\text{N}\;\;\;\text{CH}_3\\
\;\parallel\;\;\;\mid\;\;\;\parallel\;\;\;\mid\\
\text{HO--P}\sim\text{N--C--N--CH}_2\text{COOH}\\
\;\mid\\
\text{OH}
\end{array}
$$

Phosphocreatine

Phosphocreatine is easily hydrolyzed to creatine and inorganic phosphate. The hydrolysis is strongly exothermic: about 10,000 small cal. of heat are produced per mol of phosphate set free. The concentration of phosphocreatine is highest in skeletal muscle, next highest in cardiac muscle, and least in smooth muscle. Small amounts are present in nerve and in mature spermatozoa. In invertebrate muscle the amino acid, arginine, takes the place of creatine.

Adenosine triphosphate. Another labile organic phosphate was found in muscle extract by Lohmann in 1928. This compound is adenylpyrophosphoric acid, or adenosine triphosphate:

Adenine   Ribose   Phosphate   Pyrophosphate

Adenosine

Adenylic acid
(Adenosine monophosphate)

The nature of the phosphate linkages is important. One (i) is a stable ester bond with ribose but (ii) and (iii) are acid anhydride bonds, much less stable (or more energetic). The hydrolysis of these bonds is accompanied by the evolution of about 10,000 cal. of heat per mol of phosphate set free. In resting muscle only adenosine triphosphate (ATP) is found, but ATP can transfer its phosphate to other compounds, forming successively adenosine diphosphate (ADP) and adenosine monophosphate (AMP). The two latter compounds can act as phosphate acceptors. ATP, ADP, and AMP, known collectively as the *adenylic acid system*, act as middlemen in the cycles of phosphate transfer in the cells.

Phosphate bond energy. In the hydrolysis of phosphocreatine and of ATP a large amount of energy is set free, appearing in these instances as heat. These organic compounds of phosphate may be regarded as forms in which chemical energy is stored. Since their energetic characteristics are associated with the phosphate linkages, Lipmann (12) has aptly described their potential chemical energy as "phosphate bond energy," and has introduced the convenient notation, "$\sim$ph," for an "energy-rich" phosphate bond representing about 10,000 cal. per mol of phosphate. The concept of energy associated with a chemical group, transferable without loss, and *capable of being used to do work* in the cell, is a new and important idea in physiology. Phosphocreatine and ATP represent such energy reserves in the muscle. The magnitude of these reserves in different muscles may be seen in Table 2.

Table 2.—*Concentration of Phosphocreatine and Adenylpyrophosphate Phosphorus* (~*ph*) *in Different Muscles*

	PHOSPHOCREATINE PER 100 GRAMS		ADENYLPYROPHOSPHATE PER 100 GRAMS	
	Mg. P	cal.*	Mg. P	cal.
Skeletal muscle, frog	54	17.4	24	7.7
" " rabbit, white	....	....	32	10.3
" " " red	....	....	21	6.8
" " cat	60	19.4	..	....
Muscle, crab	61†	19.7	32	10.3
" amphioxus	37	11.9	..	....
Heart muscle, rat	4.7	1.5	..	....
" " rabbit	....	....	9	2.9
Uterus, rabbit	1.4	0.4	8	2.6

* Based on 10,000 cal. per mol of energy-rich P.
† Phosphoarginine.
    [Adapted from Lipmann (12), Tables V and VII]

It is now known that many of the energy-yielding cellular reactions are associated with the transformation of inorganic phosphate or of phosphate esters to energy-rich phosphate. The energy, instead of being liberated as heat, is conserved by the intermediate formation of organic acid anhydrides —$R- COO \sim PO_3H_2$—or enol-phosphates—$R—CH = C(O \sim PO_3H_2)—COOH$ — which can transfer $\sim$ph to the adenylic acid system for redistribution and use elsewhere. The energy is liberated when $\sim$ph is degraded to inorganic or ester phosphate in the course of doing chemical or other work.

ENERGY PRODUCTION IN MUSCLE

Near the close of the nineteenth century the general view of the chemistry of muscular contraction was expressed in the "inogen" theory of Hermann and Pflüger. The energy for contraction was thought to arise from the explosive decomposition of an unstable complex of oxygen and some oxidizable substance—the so-called "inogen" molecule—yielding carbon dioxide and lactic acid. Contraction was independent of the oxygen supply, since oxygen was stored in the inogen complex, rebuilt during the recovery period. The experimental basis of the theory was (i) that carbon dioxide production during contraction was the same in oxygen and in nitrogen, and (ii) that if the inogen was "fixed" by scalding the muscle, no lactic acid and no carbon dioxide was produced during the time required to kill the muscle.

An experimental examination of this hypothesis was begun by Fletcher in 1898, and continued, for the next 15 years, in collaboration with Brown, and with Hopkins. Their results may be stated briefly: (i) carbon dioxide production by resting or working muscle keeps pace with acid production,

and can be accounted for by the displacement of carbon dioxide from carbonates; (ii) the rate of carbon dioxide production by resting muscle is about
three times as great in oxygen as it is in nitrogen, and stimulation of the
muscle in oxygen is followed by a large output of carbon dioxide; (iii) muscles
killed by scalding produce little lactic acid but a great amount of carbon
dioxide (due, as we now know, to its displacement from loose combination
with the muscle proteins).

These observations demolished the inogen hypothesis. Fletcher and
Hopkins (19) proposed another hypothesis arising from their work on
lactic acid production in muscle. By methods based upon the appreciation
of muscle as an irritable organ capable of sudden swift chemical change,
they established the following facts: (i) resting muscle contains about 0.02
per cent of lactic acid; (ii) in nitrogen, at rest, lactic acid is slowly produced
to a maximum of about 0.4 per cent at death of the muscle in rigor (the
same maximum is found when rigor is brought on rapidly by heat, injury,
or chloroform); (iii) if muscle is stimulated to fatigue, rapid acid production
(to about 0.25 per cent) occurs; (iv) the fatigued muscle, placed in oxygen,
recovers its irritability, and lactic acid disappears; cycles of stimulation
followed by recovery can be repeated many times, yet if the muscle is then
killed, the usual lactic acid maximum of rigor is attained; (v) muscles resting
in oxygen retain their irritability for long periods, and no lactic acid
accumulates.

Fletcher and Hopkins concluded that lactic acid production (probably
from glycogen) was the fundamental chemical reaction producing energy
for muscular contraction. The reaction does not require oxygen; muscular
contraction is essentially an anaerobic process. The oxidative removal of
lactic acid is necessary, since its accumulation in the muscle leads to loss
of irritability. This process may involve some resynthesis of glycogen, since
the appearance of the full rigor maximum in death after repeated stimulation to fatigue and recovery in oxygen (involving the production and removal of lactic acid in excess of the amount of any reasonable precursor) is
otherwise difficult to explain. Finally, they suggested that lactic acid itself,
acting upon the colloidal protein contractile substance, might be responsible
for initiating the contraction.

This work marks the beginning of modern muscle physiology. The facts
have been confirmed and amply extended; the theory has not endured, but
the volume of work inspired by it proves its usefulness. These points may
be emphasized: (i) muscle can produce large amounts of energy for a limited
time in the absence of oxygen; (ii) one source of this energy is the partial
decomposition of glycogen to lactic acid. Such energy-yielding reactions of
partial decomposition, not requiring oxygen, are called *fermentations*.
Muscle, then, obtains energy independently of its immediate oxygen supply
by the rapid fermentation of glycogen to lactic acid, in the same way as
brewer's yeast derives energy by the fermentation of sugars to alcohol;
(iii) *ultimately*, muscle requires oxygen for the maintenance of normal irritability, for oxidative energy production, and for the restoration of its anaerobic energy-yielding systems.

Anaerobic Energy Production in Muscle (12, 24, 30). The formation of
lactic acid from glycogen (glycolysis) is accompanied by a large change in
free energy:

$$C_6H_{10}O_5 \text{ (glycogen)} + H_2O \longrightarrow 2\ C_3H_6O_3;\ \Delta F = -58{,}000 \text{ cal.}^*$$

This means that for each mol of lactic acid formed, about 29,000 cal. are made available for doing work. In familiar terms, the free energy released by the formation of 90 gm. of lactic acid, perfectly realized and applied, could do 89,523 foot-pounds of work. Or, in 100 gm. of muscle stimulated to fatigue, the formation of 250 mg. of lactic acid could yield about 248 foot-pounds. Muscle is not perfectly efficient, and not all of this energy appears as work; nevertheless, the net yields of chemical energy are quite high, and even the working efficiency, about 40 per cent (43), is respectable compared with other engines.

The free energy of *oxidation* of a glucose unit of glycogen to carbon dioxide and water is $-699{,}000$ cal., or about 12 times the free energy of glycolysis.

Table 3.—Effect of Oxygen on Glycolysis

ORGANISM OR TISSUE	Q_{O_2}*	$Q^{O_2}_F$†	$Q^{N_2}_F$†	SUBSTRATE CONSUMPTION		CALORIC YIELD	
				RATE‡	ANAEROBIC / AEROBIC	RATE§	ANAEROBIC / AEROBIC
Torula							
anaerobic	......	..	260	1.04		0.31	
aerobic	—180	18	...	0.31	3.4	0.94	0.33
Embryonic heart							
anaerobic	......	..	28	0.11		0.034	
aerobic	—13.6	0	...	0.018	6.0	0.071	0.48
Pigeon brain							
anaerobic	......	..	28	0.11		0.034	
aerobic	—16	0	...	0.022	5.0	0.083	0.41
Fish retina (30° C.)							
anaerobic	......	..	29	0.12		0.035	
aerobic	—9.6	1	...	0.017	7.0	0.050	0.70

* Oxidation: cu. mm. O_2 per mg. dry wt. per hr.
† Fermentation: cu. mm. CO per mg. dry wt. per hr. in oxygen and nitrogen respectively.
‡ mg. glucose per mg. dry weight per hour.
§ calories per mg. dry weight per hour.

If oxidative and anaerobic energy are used equally well, then the oxidation of one hexose unit can satisfy the same energy requirement as the glycolysis of 12 units (and the system is not embarrassed by the accumulation of 24 mols of lactic acid). Thus, *from the point of view of economy of substrate*, fermentation is much *less* efficient than oxidation (Table 3). However, the costs of glycolysis in this respect are modest when weighed

* In thermodynamics it is customary to assign a negative value to the heat or free energy in reactions in which a decrease in free energy takes place (i.e., in which work may be done). The heat change in a reaction (ΔH) is not an accurate measure of the free energy change (ΔF). Their relation is given by the expression, $\Delta F = \Delta H - T\Delta S$, in which the entropy factor, $T\Delta S$, may be very large. Entropy can be described as a quantitative measure of probability: are the atoms involved in a reaction more likely to be arranged in the configuration of the starting material or in that of the products? If the products represent a more probable state, there is an increase in entropy, and in suitable circumstances the reaction will run spontaneously.

against the survival value of the ability to make powerful exertions in the absence of oxygen for a limited period.

Enzymatic breakdown of glycogen to lactic acid (10, 12, 17, 20, 24, 30). Intact muscle yields little insight into the course of lactic acid formation; the only intermediate substance accumulating during contraction is hexose-monophosphate (a broad, but merely tantalizing hint). The present view of the course of glycolysis is based on the study of muscle extracts. This work was immeasurably aided at the outset by Meyerhof's discovery that almost the whole of the enzyme system effecting glycogen breakdown to lactic acid is easily extractable by fairly simple salt solutions.* This is an ideal situation for the chemist, and it has been ably exploited by Meyerhof, Embden, Neuberg, the Coris, Warburg, von Euler, and a host of their brilliant collaborators during the past 25 years.

The general methods used in the analysis of muscle extracts involve (i) dialysis, to separate essential diffusible components from nondiffusible (protein) components; (ii) partial inactivations, by aging, controlled changes of temperature, and poisons (arsenate, bisulfite, fluoride, iodo-acetate, phloridzin) which bring about the accumulation of intermediate substances otherwise difficult to isolate and identify; (iii) the study of reactions involving these intermediates; (iv) chemical fractionations, leading to the isolation of the enzymes catalyzing the single reaction steps; (v) the reconstitution of parts of the system, using the purified enzymes. An excellent review by Parnas (30) gives a lively account of the rationale of these methods.

Co-enzyme of fermentation (32). Harden and Young, in 1906, found that the fermentation system of yeast could be separated into a nondialyzable, heat-labile part (containing mainly the protein enzymes) and a diffusible, heat-stable component, a *coferment*, which von Euler later named cozymase. The co-enzyme has since been found to be almost universally distributed in living tissues, and to be essential for respiration as well as fermentation. The work of von Euler's school, and later that of Warburg and Christian (who isolated nicotinic acid amide from a related co-enzyme from red blood cells and showed that the vitamin was responsible for the peculiar function of the co-enzyme), finally established the constitution of cozymase:

Adenine   Ribose   2 Phosphate   Ribose   Nicotinic acid amide

Warburg's co-enzyme (phosphocozymase) has one more molecule of phosphoric acid than cozymase.† Both are hydrogen acceptors, each acting with a different group of specific protein enzymes in reactions of the type:

$$A-H_2 + CoZ \rightleftharpoons A + CoZ-H_2$$

dehydrogenase
or
hydrogenpherase

Nicotinic acid amide is the vitamin necessary to prevent pellagra in human beings (Section IX). In cozymase, the physiologist, the enzyme chemist, and the student of nutrition find an unexpected convergence of interest.

* An intimation of this happy event was provided by Buchner's (1897) demonstration of fermentation in a cell-free preparation from yeast.

† Nomenclature in enzymology is partly historical, partly rational, and wholly confusing. Cozymase has the following aliases: co-enzyme I; diphosphopyridine nucleotide; nicotinamide nucleotide; pyridine-adenine nucleotide. It is not to be confused with co-enzyme II: triphosphopyridine nucleotide—phosphocozymase.

The essential reactions of glycolysis can be described quite simply (Fig. 37). A hexose unit of glycogen is esterified with phosphate and split into two triosephosphate molecules. Phosphotriose is oxidized, and then dehydrated. Energy realized in each of these reactions is conserved by the formation of labile organic phosphate compounds ($\sim$ph), and is transferred to members of the adenylic acid system. Cozymase, reduced in the triosephosphate oxidation, is reoxidized, and pyruvic acid (acting as hydrogen acceptor) is reduced to lactic acid. So long as lactate can accumulate, the co-enzyme can be reoxidized and can in turn help to oxidize more phosphotriose. The reactions stop when more lactic acid is formed than can be neutralized by the buffers of the system.

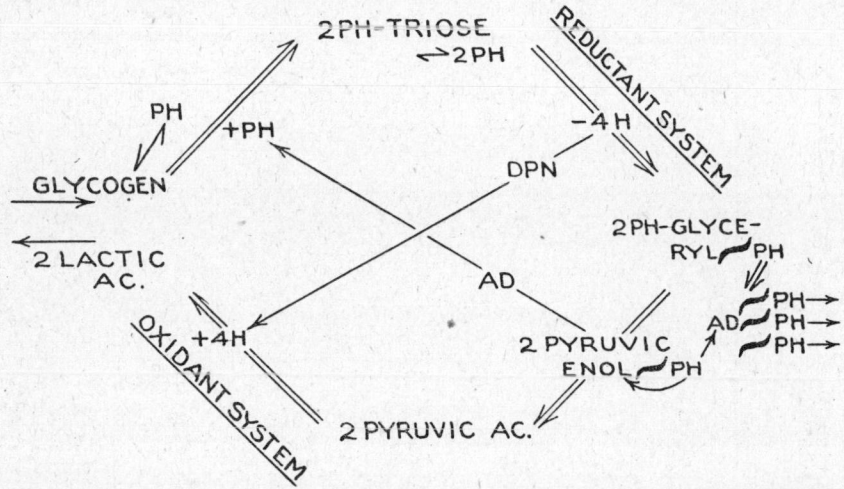

Fig. 37.—Simplified scheme of glycolysis. PH = inorganic phosphate; $\sim$PH = energy-rich phosphate; DPN = cozymase; AD = adenylic acid. (After Lipmann, *Advances in Enzymology*, 1941, *1*:99–162.)

These reactions are worth considering in some detail, since they illustrate general principles of great importance in the metabolism of living tissues.

Formation of phosphotriose from glycogen. The enzymatic breakdown of glycogen to triosephosphate is outlined in Figure 38. Inorganic phosphate is directly introduced into a glucose unit of glycogen by the enzyme, *phosphorylase*. This reaction, discovered by the Coris and their coworkers (17), is one of a newly recognized class of enzymatic reactions of general biological importance. Enzymatic hydrolysis is a familiar process in digestion:

$$\text{Sucrose} + \text{HOH} \xrightarrow{\hspace{2cm}} \text{Glucose} + \text{Fructose}$$
$$\text{Invertase}$$

If the elements of phosphoric acid instead of those of water took part in this reaction, we should expect to find:

$$\text{Sucrose} + \text{HO—PO}_3\text{H}_2 \xrightleftharpoons{\hspace{2cm}} \text{Glucose-1-phosphate} + \text{fructose}$$
$$\text{Phosphorylase}$$

and, in fact, Doudoroff and his colleagues (18) have prepared from the bacterium, *Pseudomonas saccharophila* Doudoroff, a sucrose phosphorylase which does just that. By analogy with hydrolysis, this process was called *phosphorolysis* by Parnas. The phosphorolysis of glycogen differs critically from its enzymatic hydrolysis by amylase—*it is easily reversible under physiological conditions;* glycogen synthesis as well as glycogen breakdown is catalyzed by phosphorylase.

It follows from the phosphorolysis of glycogen and the subsequent changes in the hexosephosphate molecule that *glucose* must be phosphorylated before it can be utilized. For this, the phosphate bond energy of ATP is put to work. The high potential energy of ATP ($\sim$ph: 10,000 cal. per mol) is the

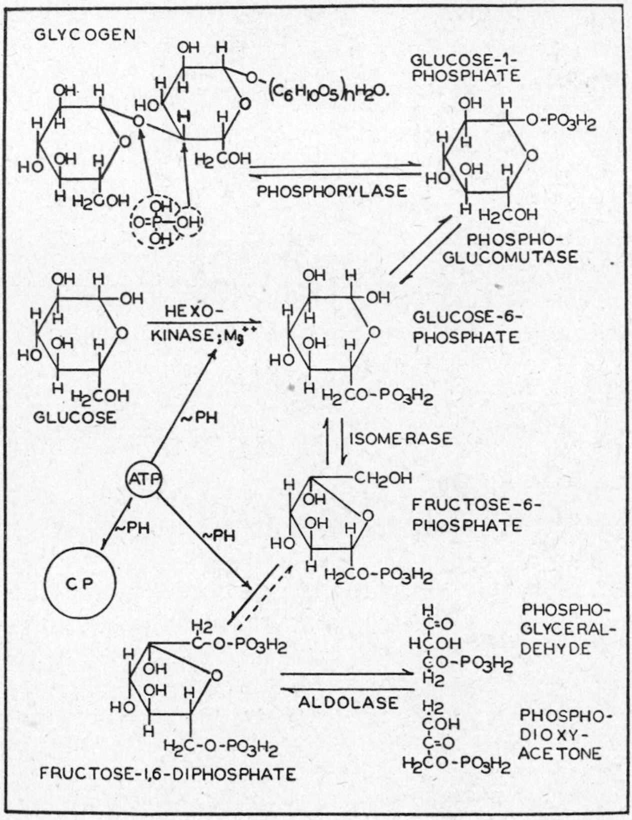

Fig. 38.—Enzymatic breakdown of glycogen to phosphotriose. Two terminal glucose units of a glycogen molecule are represented. ATP, adenosine triphosphate; CP, phosphocreatine. Magnesium ions are essential in every step in which exchange of phosphate between the adenylic acid system and its donors or acceptors takes place.

driving force for synthesis of the hexosephosphate ester bond of much lower energy (1000-3000 cal. per mol). This done, the hexosephosphate stands in freely reversible equilibrium with the adjacent members of the series. Colowick and Sutherland (16), using ATP, the purified enzymes hexokinase, phosphoglucomutase, and phosphorylase, and barium ions (to remove inorganic phosphate), have synthesized glycogen from glucose in vitro.

ATP is also required in the synthesis of fructose diphosphate. The dashed arrow in Figure 38 indicates that this reaction is not directly reversible. The 1-phosphate bond is hydrolyzed by a phosphatase. It may be significant that in working muscle not hexose diphosphate but the monophosphate accumulates; there is normally some restraint upon the formation of the di-ester (and a consequent saving of energy expenditure).

The splitting of fructose diphosphate is a reversal of an aldol condensation —one half the molecule is oxidized to an aldehyde, the other (keto) half reduced to a primary alcohol. The two phosphotrioses are interconvertible enzymatically, but ordinarily equilibrium (greatly favoring dihydroxyacetone phosphate) is not attained, since phosphoglyceraldehyde is rapidly removed in succeeding reactions.

Up to this point no energy has been realized; indeed, it is expended, to form hexosediphosphate and (starting with glucose) hexosemonophosphate. Glycolysis must be primed, and the chemical energy of ATP is the primer. The limited amount of ATP is replenished from the reservoir of $\sim$ph in phosphocreatine:

$$\text{AMP} + \text{Phosphocreatine} \rightleftharpoons \text{ADP} + \text{Creatine}$$

$$\text{ADP} + \text{Phosphocreatine} \rightleftharpoons \text{ATP} + \text{Creatine}$$

The discovery of these reactions by Parnas and his coworkers made clear the relation between phosphocreatine and the adenylic acid system. Their

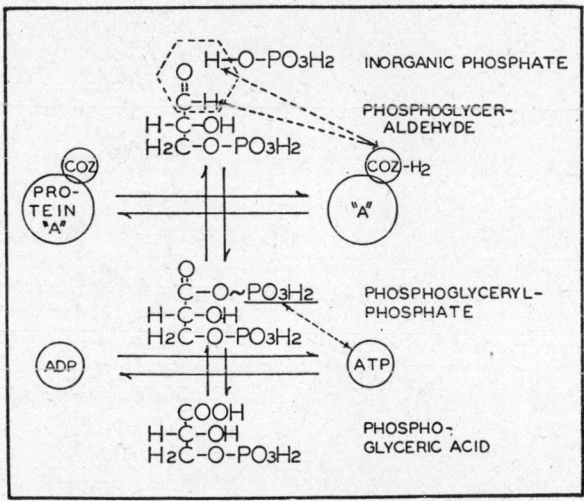

Fig. 39.—The oxidative phosphorylation of phosphoglyceraldehyde to phosphoglyceryl-phosphate. COZ = cozymase. Both inorganic phosphate and an acceptor of $\sim$ph (ADP) are essential. This reaction is typical of many coupled oxidative phosphorylations.

function is like that of the battery and distributor in an ignition system, providing energy to start an engine. When energy is available from the running engine, the battery may be recharged.

Conversion of phosphotriose to lactic acid. The first energy-yielding step of glycolysis is the oxidation of phosphoglyceraldehyde to phosphoglyceric acid (Fig. 39). According to Meyerhof (26, 32), for each molecule of phosphoglyceraldehyde oxidized, (i) a molecule of inorganic phosphate is taken up from the medium, (ii) a molecule of ATP is formed from ADP, (iii) a molecule of cozymase is reduced. The reaction is easily reversible, which means that the energy of the oxidation is absorbed in raising inorganic phosphate to the energy level of ATP, and the reaction is therefore nearly isothermal. This is a *strictly coupled oxidative phosphorylation;* the oxidation fails in the absence of inorganic phosphate. The mechanism of the reaction was further clarified by Warburg and his colleagues (28, 31), who prepared the specific dehydrogenase (protein "A") and isolated the intermediate acid anhydride, phosphoglyceryl-phosphate, which can *donate* $\sim$ph to ADP. In this reaction phosphoglyceraldehyde plays two parts: it is the substrate oxidized—the source of the energy—and by coupling with inorganic phosphate it acts as a *transformer* upon which the chemical energy of the acid anhydride bond is generated. This is one of the fundamental methods by which the energy of biological oxidations is made available.

The phosphate group of 3-phosphoglyceric acid is next shifted to the 2-position:

$$
\begin{array}{c}
\text{COOH} \\
| \\
\text{HCOH} \\
| \\
\text{H}_2\text{CO—PO}_3\text{H}_2
\end{array}
\quad
\underset{\text{mutase}}{\overset{\text{phosphotriose}}{\rightleftharpoons}}
\quad
\begin{array}{c}
\text{COOH} \\
| \\
\text{HCO—PO}_3\text{H}_2 \\
| \\
\text{H}_2\text{COH}
\end{array}
$$

This is followed by the second energy-yielding reaction, the dehydration of 2-phosphoglyceric acid to phospho-enol-pyruvic acid:

$$
\begin{array}{c}
\text{COOH} \\
| \\
\text{HCO—PO}_3\text{H}_2 \\
| \\
\text{H}_2\text{COH}
\end{array}
\quad
\underset{\text{enolase}}{\overset{\text{mg}^{++}}{\rightleftharpoons}}
\quad
\begin{array}{c}
\text{COOH} \\
| \\
\text{C—O}\sim\text{PO}_3\text{H}_2 + \text{H}_2\text{O} \\
|| \\
\text{CH}_2
\end{array}
$$

Energy is conserved by the generation of $\sim$ph from the ester phosphate. The phosphate may be transferred either to adenylic acid or to adenosine diphosphate:

$$\text{Pyruvate} \sim\text{ph} + \text{AMP} \longrightarrow \text{Pyruvate} + \text{ADP}$$
$$\text{Pyruvate} \sim\text{ph} + \text{ADP} \longrightarrow \text{Pyruvate} + \text{ATP}$$

This reaction has recently been shown (54) to be reversible. The resynthesis of carbohydrate from lactate or allied substances by reversal of the steps of glycolysis is therefore possible.

The available energy of glycolysis has been realized and transferred; one essential step of the fermentation remains: the reoxidation of cozymase:

$$
\begin{array}{c}
\text{COOH} \\
| \\
\text{C=O} + \text{CoZ—H}_2 \\
| \\
\text{CH}_3 \\
\text{pyruvic acid}
\end{array}
\quad
\rightleftharpoons
\quad
\begin{array}{c}
\text{COOH} \\
| \\
\text{HCOH} + \text{CoZ} \\
| \\
\text{CH}_3 \\
\text{lactic acid}
\end{array}
$$

Lactic acid formation in glycolysis serves only to maintain cozymase in the oxidized state essential for carrying out the oxidation of phosphoglyceraldehyde. The hydrogen of this oxidation is shunted into lactic acid until the main line of its further oxidation to H_2O is reopened by the admission of oxygen to the system. When the main line is open, cozymase may also be more directly reoxidized, *and lactic acid need not be formed at all.* Each atom of oxygen reduced to H_2O can "spare" one molecule of lactic acid. This is, however, merely a *logistic* relation, disregarding the difference in the energy yields of oxidation and glycolysis and the effect of this difference on the utilization rates of carbohydrate in oxygen and in anaerobiosis (Table 3).

The reactions of glycolysis may be summarized in a new equation:

glucose (from glycogen) $+ \sim$ph (ATP) $+ 3$ H$_3$PO$_4$ $= 2$ lactic acid $+ 4 \sim$ph (40,000 cal.)

The *gross* yield of phosphate bond energy is about 70 per cent of the total free energy change of $-58,000$ cal. The *net* yield (from glycogen) is $3 \sim$ph, or about 50 per cent. The system realizes energy with high efficiency, and this energy may be used efficiently, too. Lundsgaard found that nearly two mols of phosphocreatine were resynthesized per mol of lactic acid formed in frog muscle immediately after a brief tetanus. The energy stored is almost equivalent to the gross energy yield per mol of lactate formed.

The role of the adenylic acid system in the distribution of phosphate bond energy (21) is summarized in Figure 40. The supply of energy to the con-

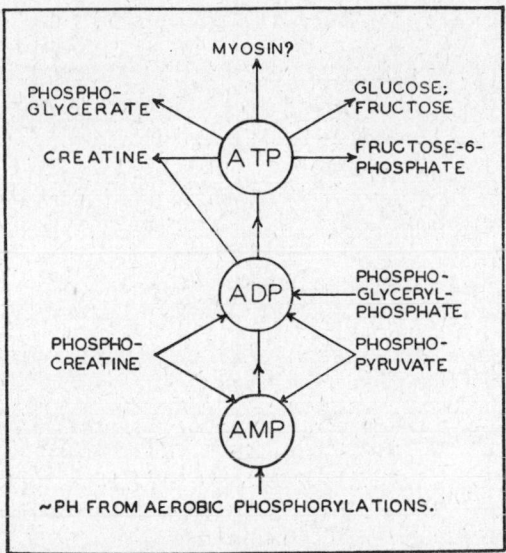

Fig. 40.—The relations of the adenylic acid system as donor, acceptor, and distributor of phosphate bond energy.

tractile mechanism is thought to take place through ATP. An enzyme splitting ATP (adenylpyrophosphatase) is found in many tissues; in muscle, this enzyme is (or is closely associated with) *myosin*, the principal contractile element of muscle. Thus ATP may connect the energy-producing systems of glycolysis and respiration and the energy-liberating system of the muscle. The energy stored in ATP and phosphocreatine is at the *immediate* service of this system during the time when the rate of glycolysis or oxidation is accelerating to meet the increased requirement of activity. Thus the *initial* energy-yielding reactions in contraction are anaerobic whether oxygen is present or not. As energy is used, $\sim$ph is degraded to inorganic phosphate, which facilitates glycogen breakdown and increases the rate of oxidative phosphorylation. The primary reactions in which the muscle uses energy also activate the energy-yielding systems.

Oxidative Energy Production in Muscle (10, 12, 17, 20, 25, 29, 32). A 70 kg. man in good training might have a resting oxygen consumption of 300 ml. per minute. About one third of this is used by his muscles, roughly, 50 per cent of his body weight: 100 ml. O_2 per minute for 35 kg. of muscle. He can exercise at moderate rates for many minutes, and his oxygen uptake may rise to 2 liters per minute (Fig. 41). The increase over the resting rate (1700 ml. per minute) is due largely to the active muscles; their rate of oxidation (or energy production) is about 17 times the resting rate. This is not a maximum rate (the O_2 uptake may reach 4 liters per minute) but it is a rate that can be maintained for relatively long periods. *In these circumstances the*

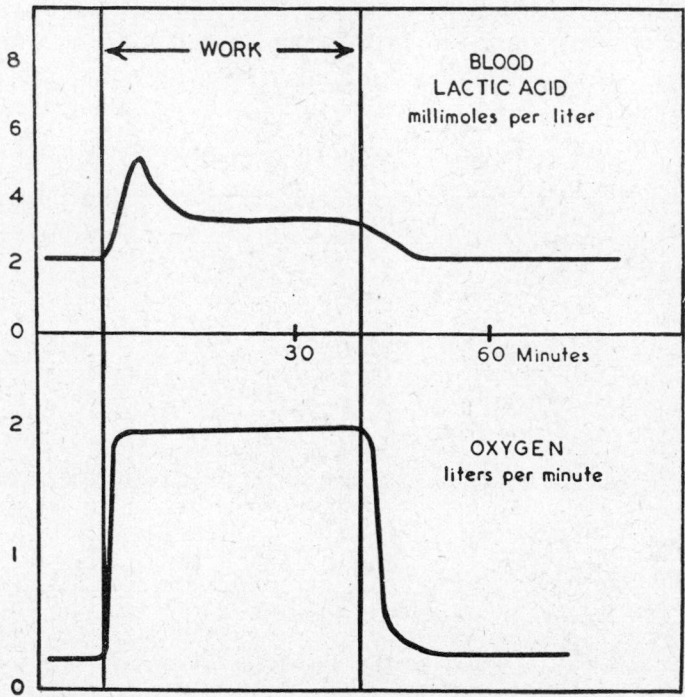

Fig. 41.—Oxygen consumption and blood lactic acid during moderate exercise in man. The slight initial rise in lactate output coincides with the period of adaptation, before the oxygen supply rises to meet the oxygen requirement. (After O. Bang from Lipmann, *A symposium on respiratory enzymes*, University of Wisconsin Press, 1942.)

energy requirements of the muscles are being met by contemporary oxidations. At the outset of exercise, time is required for adjustment of the circulation and respiration to meet the increased oxygen demand. During this period of relative oxygen insufficiency, the blood lactic acid rises, indicating that the muscles are deriving energy from glycolysis. Later, in the steady state of adequate oxygen supply, the blood lactate may be unchanged or may *fall*. One may reasonably conclude that no lactic acid is formed after the oxygen supply to the muscles becomes adequate to meet their energy requirements. After exercise, the oxygen consumption does not at once return to the resting level; there is oxidative recovery, associated with the removal of lactate and the refilling of the energy stores (resynthesis of phosphocreatine; formation of glycogen from blood sugar and lactate). The amount of oxidative recovery after exercise is related to the severity of the exertion (Fig. 42). In severe exercise, requiring rates of energy expenditure vastly in excess of any possible rate of oxygen supply, practically all of the oxygen is used in the recovery period. The ability of muscle to accumulate, in A. V. Hill's phrase, an "oxygen debt," is very useful, but emphasis upon this property of muscle ought not to obscure an equally important point: that most of the energy requirement of moderate, rhythmic muscular activity is met by *concurrent oxidative* energy production.

Respiratory Systems of Muscle. (i) *Muscle hemoglobin* (27). Muscles engaging in slow, repeated, powerful movements (hearts of large mammals, leg and back muscles) may contain from 0.1 to over 1 per cent of a hemoglobin similar to that of blood (Chap. 27). Muscle hemoglobin combines more rapidly with oxygen, so that the curve relating oxygen saturation to

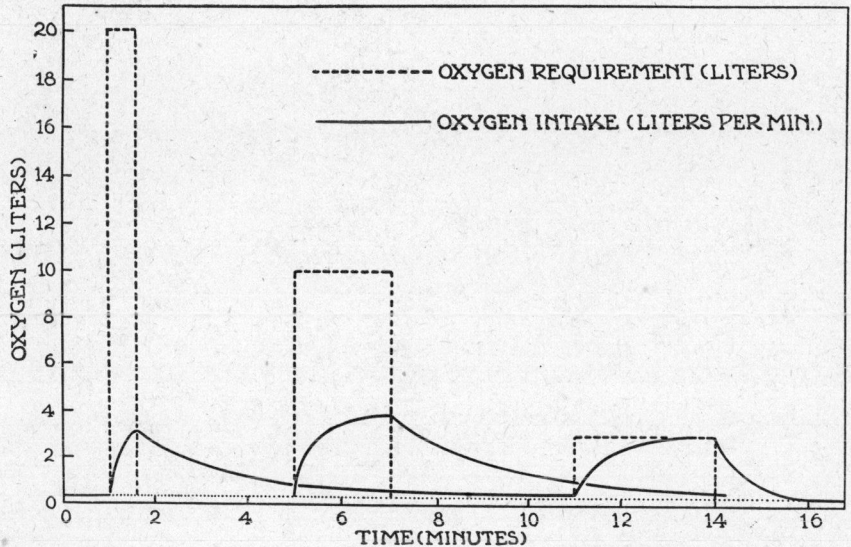

Fig. 42.—The oxygen requirement and the oxygen intake during three periods of exercise of different severity in man. The area of an oxygen requirement rectangle is the same as that of the complete oxygen intake curve, each measured from the level of the resting oxygen intake (shown dotted). (After Furusawa, Hill, Long and Lupton, *Proc. roy. Soc.*, 1924, *B97*:155–176.)

oxygen pressure is a rectangular hyperbola rather than the inflected curve of blood hemoglobin. This means that it is almost saturated at the oxygen pressure of venous blood (40 mm. of mercury) and is unloaded at the low pressures (5 mm.) in cells most remote from the capillaries. Muscle hemoglobin provides a local store of oxygen that may cover the oxygen supply in slow, sustained contractions, when blood flow through the tensed muscle is interrupted. In muscles of rapid movement (hearts of small mammals; breast muscles of birds) rapid oxygen utilization is assured by an increased concentration of the enzymes concerned with the activation of molecular oxygen (cytochrome oxidase system).

(ii) *The aerobic enzyme systems* (20, 22, 32).* In tissues with an adequate

---

* It is regretted that so brief a summary of the principles of biological oxidation is all that can be mentioned here. This work, to which Battelli and Stern, Thunberg, Wieland, Warburg, Keilin, Szent-Györgyi, and many others have made distinguished contributions, is in itself a long and fascinating chapter in physiology.

oxygen supply, the hydrogen of reduced cozymase, instead of being shunted into lactic acid, may be completely oxidized to water. This occurs in several steps. First, cozymase is reoxidized by a member of the class of enzymes called *Flavoproteins*:*

$$CoZ—H_2 + (Flavoprotein) \longrightarrow CoZ + (Flavoprotein) - H_2.$$

The reduced flavoprotein is oxidized by a member of the *cytochrome system*. The cytochromes are proteins with iron-porphyrin prosthetic groups similar to the heme of hemoglobin. The iron alternates between the ferrous and the ferric state; that is, the cytochromes are *electron donors and acceptors:*

i $(Flavoprotein)—H_2 \longrightarrow (Flavoprotein) + 2H^+ + 2 e,$

ii $2 e + 2Cyt—Fe^{+++} \longrightarrow 2Cyt—Fe^{++},$

i+ii $(Flavoprotein)—H_2 + 2Cyt—Fe^{+++} \longrightarrow (Flavoprotein) + 2Cyt—Fe^{++} + 2H^+.$

Hydrogen yields electrons to cytochrome and becomes hydrogen ion. The electrons are transferred to the *cytochrome oxidase system*, which is responsible for the activation of molecular oxygen. The principal member of this system also appears to be an iron-porphyrin protein:

$$2Cyt - Fe^{++} + 2CytOx—Fe^{+++} \xrightarrow{(2 e)} 2Cyt—Fe^{+++} + 2CytOx—Fe^{++};$$

$$2CytOx—Fe^{++} + \tfrac{1}{2} O_2 \xrightarrow{(2 e)} 2CytOx—Fe^{+++} + (O)^=.$$

Finally (the steps are not known, and are certainly not this simple) the "activated" oxygen is combined with hydrogen ions to form water:

$$(O)^= + 2H^+ \to H_2O.$$

These relationships are summarized in Figure 43. This is a gross simplification of the complex oxidation systems of living cells. It is intended only to illustrate the principles of these operations. Fundamentally, energy is obtained by the oxidation of the hydrogen of the metabolites to water. Two complementary principles are employed: the activation of substrate hydrogen by the dehydrogenases, and the activation of molecular oxygen by the heavy-metal proteins. Note that in this system *electrons* are brought to oxygen *after* most of the energy of the "oxidation" has been realized. Oxygen seems to be carefully excluded from direct combination with the metabolites; in cellular oxidations it is a scavenger of electrons and hydrogen ions. For this reason it has been suggested that this process of electron transfer through several energy levels be called "energesis" rather than oxidation.

The *direct* oxidation of a mol of hydrogen to water yields about 60,000 cal. of energy as *heat*. In the cell, the oxidation is conducted indirectly, in a series of piecemeal oxidations. This elaborate indirection reduces loss of energy as heat, which the cell cannot use. Energy is transformed into units of convenient size by the generation of phosphate bond energy, as in the oxidation of phosphoglyceraldehyde (Fig. 39). Some of the subsequent oxidation steps are also coupled with phosphorylations, but the details of these reactions are still a matter for speculation (20).

Carbohydrate oxidation (17, 20, 23). If glucose (or hexosemonophos-

* The prosthetic group of these enzymes, the flavin nucleotides, are derivatives of vitamin B_2. Their constitution is discussed in Section IX.

phate) is oxidized directly in muscle (which has not been proved) it is probable that the product at the three-carbon stage will be an intermediate of glycolysis so that the two routes of carbohydrate breakdown lead in either case to pyruvic acid. Since lactate is also first oxidized to pyruvate during recovery, the problem of carbohydrate oxidation in muscle concerns mainly the fate of pyruvic acid. Krebs and others (23) have found, in pigeon breast muscle, an oxidation system for removing pyruvate which they have called the "citric (or tricarboxylic) acid cycle" (Fig. 44). The principal reactions are: (i) the condensation of oxaloacetic and pyruvic acids; (ii) three oxidative decar-

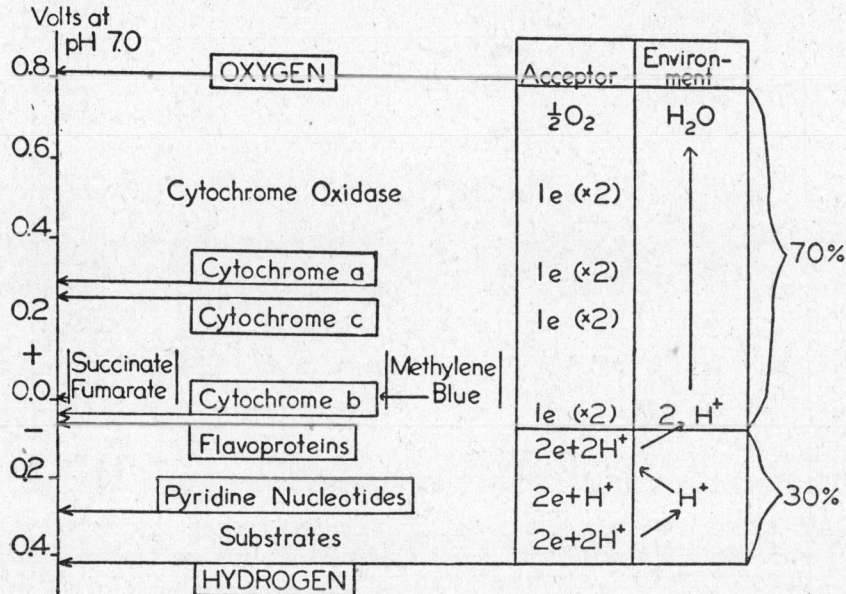

Fig. 43.—Oxidation-reduction systems concerned in biological oxidations, in relation to their oxidation-reduction potentials. (Each system can be reoxidized by the next more positive system.) (From E. G. Ball, *A symposium on respiratory enzymes*, University of Wisconsin Press, 1942.)

boxylations, accounting for the pyruvate carbon as CO_2; (iii) the oxidation of succinic to oxaloacetic acid. The net result:

$$CH_3COCOOH + 2.5\ O_2 \longrightarrow 3\ CO_2 + 2\ H_2O.$$

The oxidation cycle neatly solves the problem of oxidizing a small molecule to carbon dioxide and water, and at the same time, of developing and conserving the energy of that oxidation. The intermediate members of the cycle furnish possible *transformers* upon which the energy of each primary oxidation step can be realized by coupled oxidative phosphorylations analogous to that occurring in glycolysis (Fig. 39). No phosphorylated intermediates of the cycles have been isolated, but their discovery can be confidently anticipated.*

* Carbohydrate is, of course, not the sole source of energy in muscle. The impression that it is might easily be gained, however, because so much more is known about carbohydrate metabolism than about that of fat and protein. There is ample evidence that muscle not only uses ketone bodies formed from fat by the liver, but also uses fat directly, to cover a large part of its energy requirement. The details of these processes are, however, still undetermined.

Oxidation and phosphate bond energy (10, 12, 17, 20, 21, 29, |32). How many ~ph are produced per atom of oxygen used? Kalckar in 1937 showed that oxidative phosphorylations take place readily in tissue extracts, but the quantitative relationship between oxygen used and ~ph generated is disturbed by adenylpyrophosphatase, which splits off phosphate from ATP. This can be prevented only in part by fluoride ions (which also inhibit glycolysis, preventing the formation of phosphopyruvic from phosphoglyceric acid). An ingenious solution of the problem is provided by Severo Ochoa (29). If (a) aerobic phosphorylation and (b) the anaerobic phosphorylation of phosphoglyceraldehyde (Fig. 39) are measured in parallel samples of a heart

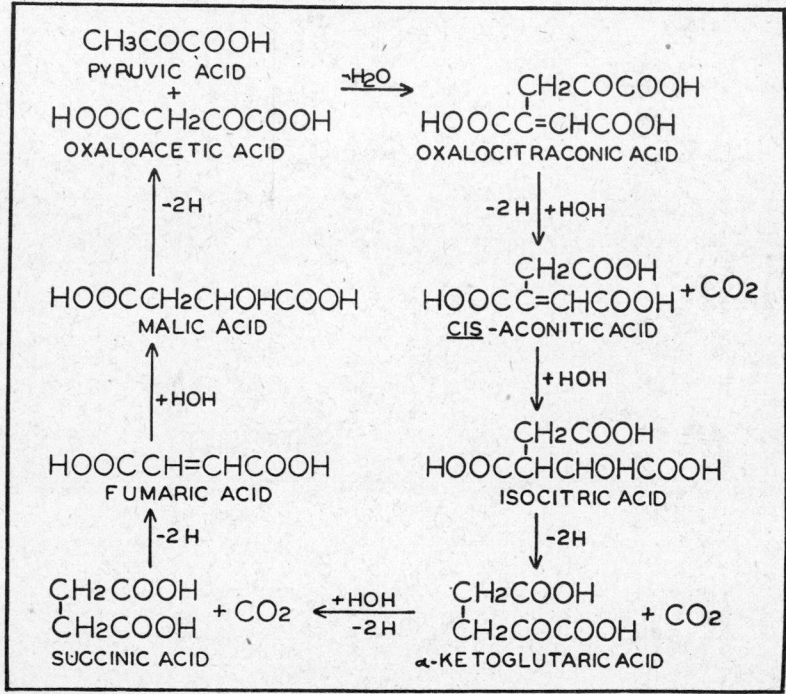

Fig. 44.—The oxidation of pyruvic acid through the tricarboxylic acid cycle. The reaction steps are probably reversible, but the scheme is presented to emphasize the cyclic operation. Each step is catalyzed by a specific enzyme; the oxidation steps probably require cozymase or phosphocozymase, and hydrogen and electron transport follow the pathways outlined in Fig. 43. (Adapted from Krebs, *Advances in Enzymology*, 1943, *3*:191–252.)

muscle extract poisoned with fluoride, each system is subject to the same proportionate loss of ~ph through adenylpyrophosphatase action. If, then, the ratio of ~ph generated to oxygen used is determined for each system,* the *ratio* of these ratios gives the best estimate of the *net* yield of ~ph per atom of oxygen used. The results of these experiments are presented in Table 4. For each atom of oxygen used, the mean net yield is three ~ph, or about 50 per cent of the free energy of oxidation of 2 H to H_2O. Thus the oxidation of a hexose unit of glycogen might provide energy for the resynthesis of 36 mols of phosphocreatine, whereas by glycolysis only 3 mols

* For the anaerobic phosphorylation, 1 ~ph = 2H = $\frac{1}{2}O_2$. P esterified/equivalent oxygen reduced = 1 (theoretically).

Table 4.—Efficiency of Aerobic Phosphorylation in Heart Muscle Extracts

All samples contained 1.0 cc. of dialyzed phosphate extract, 0.005 M MgCl₂, 0.001 M adenosine triphosphate (0.1 mg. of acid-labile P), 0.025 M NaF, and either 0.037 M glucose or 0.042 M creatine. In addition, the aerobic samples contained 0.036 M pyruvate, and 0.001 M succinate; the anaerobic samples contained 0.0007 M cozymase, 0.036 M pyruvate, 0.009 M hexose diphosphate (0.8 to 1.0 mg. of P), and 0.001 M NaHCO₃. Temperature 37°. Gas phase, aerobic 100 per cent oxygen; anaerobic, 95 per cent nitrogen and 5 per cent carbon dioxide.

Experiment No.	Phosphate Acceptor	Aerobic Reaction				Anaerobic Reaction							P Esterified per 1 Equivalent Oxygen Atom Reduced (P : O)		Esterification Ratio, Aerobic/Anaerobic (a)/(b)
		Incubation Time	R.Q.	Equivalent Oxygen Reduced*	Phosphate Esterified	Incubation Time	Equivalent Oxygen Reduced				Phosphate Esterified		Aerobic (a)	Anaerobic (b)	
							Pyruvate Removed	Lactate Formed	Phosphoglycerate Formed	Mean					
		min.		micro-atoms	micro-atoms P	min.	micro-moles	micro-moles	micro-moles	micro-moles	micro-atoms P		atoms	atoms	
1	Glucose	25	1.31	19.6	48.5	20	26.0	22.5		24.2	15.2		2.5	0.63	4.0
2	"	25	1.41	15.4	37.4	20	18.2	17.4		17.8	12.6		2.4	0.71	3.4
3	"	26	1.11	37.8	55.5	20	33.3			33.3	19.7		1.5	0.59	2.5
4	"	35	1.16	13.2	24.0	30	27.0	24.4		27.0	17.1		1.8	0.63	2.9
5	"	31	1.17	16.4	37.4	26	22.3			23.3	15.0		2.3	0.64	3.6
6	"	20	1.11	25.4	24.5	15	17.4			17.4	7.1		0.96	0.41	2.3
7	Creatine	26	1.17	18.8	28.7	20	20.0	21.5	19.0	20.2	10.3		1.5	0.51	2.9
8	"	35	1.21	11.6	26.8	10		12.9	12.0	12.5	11.3		2.3	0.94	2.4
9	"	18	1.10	21.4	43.5	12	18.2	18.2	18.4	18.3	11.0		2.0	0.60	3.3
10	"	20	1.14	29.2	48.0	10	14.6	13.5	11.6	13.2	7.4		1.6	0.56	2.9
Averages			1.19										1.9	0.62	3.1

* Oxygen uptake.

Overall anaerobic reaction:
2 phosphoglyceraldehyde + 2 pyruvic acid + 2H₃PO₄ + 1 glucose (or 2 creatine) = 2 3-phosphoglyceric acid + 2 lactic acid + 1 fructose diphosphate (or 2 phosphocreatine).

Overall aerobic reaction:
1 pyruvic acid + 2.5 O₂ + 2x H₃PO₄ + x glucose (or 2x creatine) = 3 CO₂ + 2 H₂O + x fructose diphosphate (or 2x phosphocreatine).

could be resynthesized. The observed ratio, three $\sim$ph per atom of oxygen used, is approached even in intact muscle. With isolated frog muscle at 0° C., during oxidative recovery from a series of 30 to 40 tetani at 4 second intervals, Meyerhof and Nachmansohn (24) found that 30 to 35 cu.mm. of extra oxygen were used, and 0.4 to 0.75 mg. of inorganic phosphate were esterified to phosphocreatine, per gm. of muscle. This amounts to 1.6 to 2.9 $\sim$ph per atom of oxygen used; in some instances the whole of the available oxidative energy was used for phosphocreatine resynthesis.

Oxidation quotient (24, 25, 32). Lactic acid disappears during oxidative recovery, and as Fletcher and Hopkins suspected, more lactate disappears than can be accounted for by the extra oxygen used. In balance experiments on frog muscle, Meyerhof (24) showed that (i) during activity in nitrogen, glycogen is used and a roughly equivalent amount of lactate appears; (ii) during recovery in oxygen, lactate is removed and a somewhat smaller amount of glycogen is formed; (iii) the *extra* oxygen used (above the basal level) can account for only one-third to one-sixth of the total lactate disappearing. The "oxidation quotient":

$$\frac{\text{Mols lactate removed}}{\text{Mols lactate oxidized (by the recovery oxygen)}} = 3 \text{ to } 6,$$

indicates what proportion of the lactate disappearing is not accounted for by the extra oxygen uptake during recovery. Meyerhof's method is best appreciated from a typical protocol of his balance experiment (24, pp. 45–46).*

Exp. 1. Anaerobic conversion of carbohydrate to lactic acid. Two pairs of hind legs. One leg of each pair (10.9 gm. of muscle) worked up at once, the other legs (10.2 gm.) stimulated indirectly with the metronome for 30 minutes (60 stimuli per minute; 1 accumulator; inductorium 18 to 5 cm.).

	Before	After	Difference
	Mg. carbohydrate per gm. muscle		
Glycogen	10.3	7.2	−3.1
Other carbohydrate	2.35	2.85	+0.50
sum	12.65	10.05	−2.6
Corrected value			−2.75
Lactic acid	(0.20)	3.35	+3.15

Exp. 2. Carbohydrate synthesis and lactate disappearance, during recovery. Three hind leg pairs, stimulated indirectly with the metronome for 15 minutes (60 stimuli per minute), then allowed to recover for 23 hours at 14° C. From each pair, one gastrocnemius taken for measurement of oxygen uptake. The remaining muscles yielded the following balance in mg. per gm. of muscle:

	Before recovery	After recovery	Difference
Glycogen (as glucose)	3.37	4.75	+1.38
Other carbohydrate	2.01	1.66	−0.35
Together:	5.38	6.41	+1.03
Lactic acid:	2.56	0.44	−2.12

Exp. 3. Oxygen uptake. Three gastrocnemii, weighing 0.65, 0.5, and 0.45 gm. used respectively 372, 249, 238 mm.³ of recovery oxygen up to complete recovery: together 859 mm.³ O_2 for 1.6 gm. Therefore for 1 gm.: *0.766* mg. O_2. In addition there was an hourly resting uptake of 10.2, 8.3, 7.2 mm.³ O_2, or in all three muscles, 16.5 mm.³ per gm.; in 23

* Author's translation.

hours, *0.54* mg. O_2. In the respiration expts., 2.45 mg. of lactic acid disappeared and 0.766 mg. of extra oxygen were used per gm. of muscle. But in Expt. 2, 0.44 mg. of lactate, instead of 0.1 mg., remained at the end. Therefore, for a lactate disappearance of 2.12 mg. only *0.66* mg. of recovery oxygen are required. In addition there were *0.54* mg. of basal O_2 used, so that altogether *1.20* mg. of oxygen were used, which could oxidize *1.12* mg. of lactic acid or glucose. Of the *2.12* mg. of lactic acid, the remainder, about *1.0* mg., has therefore disappeared by nonoxidative reactions. This is accounted for by the new formation of carbohydrate: 1.03 + 0.06 (correction) = 1.1 mg. *Deducting the basal oxygen, 0.66 mg. of recovery oxygen are used, whereby 2.12 mg. of lactic acid have disappeared, which yields an oxidation quotient of 3.4.**

The oxidation quotient is often interpreted to mean that for each mol of lactate oxidized during recovery, 3 to 6 mols are *resynthesized to carbohydrate*. This is not the case, as the protocol clearly shows. The total lactate disappearing comprises (i) 0.50 mg. probably oxidized in supporting the basal respiration; (ii) 0.62 mg. oxidized by the extra oxygen used in recovery; (iii) 1.0 mg. converted to glycogen. Only about one half of the lactate is actually accounted for as glycogen. Later interpreters of these experiments usually neglect the part very likely played by the basal oxygen uptake in the removal of lactic acid during recovery. These considerations apply to similar experiments on recovery from muscular exercise in man (A. V. Hill and others) and to those of A. V. Hill (39) on the relation of recovery heat in oxygen to initial heat, in isolated frog muscle, from which the oxidation quotient is calculated. It must be remembered that a large part of the energy of oxidative recovery is used for phosphocreatine resynthesis. The energy for carbohydrate synthesis from lactate is therefore limited by this prior requirement.

The energetics of another form of the Meyerhof experiment are interesting. One of a pair of muscles is kept for several hours in nitrogen, the other in oxygen. Lactic acid production (in nitrogen) and oxygen consumption are measured and compared. It may be found, for example, that 6 mols of lactate are formed by the muscle in nitrogen, while the other muscle uses oxygen equivalent to 0.5 mol of glucose. The oxidation quotient is 6, in agreement with the logistic relation between the alternate means of reoxidizing cozymase (p. 68). But, taking the net energy yields of glycolysis and oxidation, 6 mols lactate = 9 ~ph; 0.5 mol glucose (3 O_2) = 18 ~ph. Either the rate of energy production in oxygen is twice that in nitrogen, or 9 mols of phosphocreatine must also have broken down in nitrogen. The oxidation quotient does not bring out the points of this experiment: (a) that in meeting the *same* energy requirement, oxidation is about 12 times as economical of substrate as glycolysis, and (b) that the "oxygen debt" after anaerobic activity (p. 71) must be concerned not merely with the removal of lactate, but also with meeting any additional energy deficit *not* covered by glycolysis.

Summary. Glycolysis and oxidation in muscle are directed mainly toward the production of phosphate bond energy. Potential chemical energy in this form is available to the contractile system, in order of immediacy, through ATP and phosphocreatine. The relations of the chemical systems, and the relative energy reserves, for frog muscle, are summarized in Figure 45 (adapted from an earlier scheme of Lohmann). In activity, the *initial* energy requirements are met by ATP and phosphocreatine, but glycolysis and oxidation accelerate rapidly to meet the continuing energy requirements of

* Author's italics.

activity. Great speed and mobility are made possible by rapid glycolysis in muscle, but ultimately oxidative energy production is essential for maintenance of normal function.

The principles of metabolism that have been so largely derived from the study of muscle apply in many respects to other tissues. Muscle physiology, in fact, is a good introduction to the physiology of living tissues as a whole.

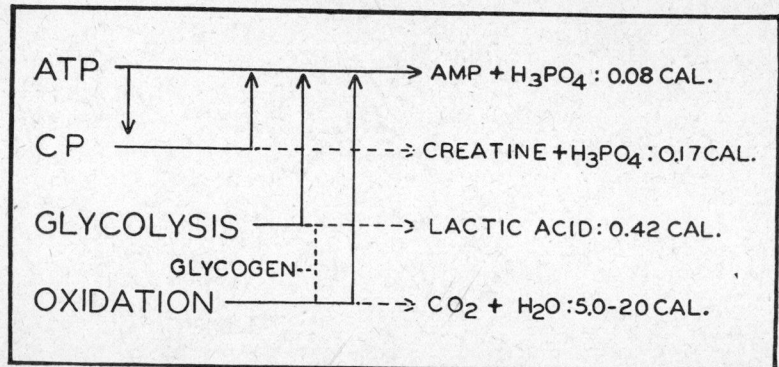

Fig. 45.—The energy reserves present in one gram of fresh frog muscle. Caloric values calculated on the basis of 10,000 cal. per mol of energy-rich P. Values for adenosine triphosphate (ATP) and phosphocreatine (CP) derived from Table 2. Values for glycolysis based on the production of 0.25 per cent of lactic acid (fatigue level), with a *net* yield of 3 ~ph per mol of glucose used. Values for oxidation based on oxidation of 0.25 to 1.0 per cent of glycogen, with a net yield of 3 ~ph per atom of oxygen required. Part of the oxidative energy may also be used in the resynthesis of glycogen from lactic acid. (After Lohmann, revised from Meyerhof, *Biol. Symp.*, 1941, 3:239–258.)

It appears that most cells employ similar energy-producing systems; the uses to which that energy is put are determined by (or may help to determine) the characteristics by which one type of cell is differentiated from another.

ENERGY LIBERATION IN MUSCLE

In active muscle, chemical and physical changes are the *resultant* effects of several energy-yielding and energy-using processes—chemical breakdown and resynthesis; contraction and relaxation—connected in series. If any chemical change is not reversed during activity and recovery it will bear a constant relation to the energy liberated during activity (expressed as gm.-cm. of total force exerted or cal. of heat liberated). In muscle under anaerobic conditions lactic acid accumulates in such an end-process, and that is mainly why the formation of lactic acid came to be regarded as essential for muscular contraction. In 1930, Lundsgaard (49) showed that the muscles of frogs poisoned with iodo-acetic acid could contract vigorously for a time before going into rigor without producing any lactic acid. Iodo-acetate inhibits the oxidation of phosphoglyceraldehyde, and no lactic acid can be formed. In these circumstances, phosphocreatine breakdown is the principal unreversed energy-yielding reaction, and this process now bears a constant relation to the energy liberated by the muscle during activity. Since phosphocreatine serves as a reservoir of ~ph for the resynthesis of ATP, the latter must break down first when the muscle contracts. The nature of this primary reaction, and the stages through which the chemical energy of ATP passes in the course of transformation into mechanical energy in the contractile elements, are still unknown. Beyond this point, for the moment, the energy exchanges of muscle must be studied by other than chemical methods.

A muscle may be fixed at both ends, so that it contracts without shortening: *isometric* contraction. Tension is developed but no work is done, and the energy liberated by the muscle all appears as heat. If the muscle is fixed at one end only, it shortens under constant load when stimulated: *isotonic* contraction. In lifting a load the muscle does work; during relaxation, an equal amount of work is done upon the muscle by the falling load, and this is dissipated as heat. Thus the chemical and mechanical energy liberated by the muscle during activity appears as an increase of heat production over the resting level. In addition, during the recovery period after activity, there is continued extra heat production which represents the *excess* expenditure of chemical energy over that required to restore the energy liberated during activity. The study of heat production—the resultant effect of chemical change and mechanical response—therefore permits continuous observation of the energy exchanges of muscle under a wide variety of conditions·

Measurement of heat production in muscle (19, 40). Attempts to measure heat production in muscle were often made in the last century, beginning with the observations of Helmholtz in 1847 (9). These experiments were only partly successful; they did help to define the problem and to encourage others in applying physical and chemical principles in the study of biological phenomena. A new method was introduced by A. V. Hill in 1913, later improved in collaboration with W. Hartree and others, and brought to an advanced state of elegance and accuracy by Hill in 1937. Fundamentally, the problem is this: to measure without distortion and with little time lag the course of heat production in an isolated muscle during a single twitch, lasting, for a frog sartorius at 20° C., about 100 msec. and accompanied by a rise in temperature of about 0.003° C. Hill employed the principle of the thermocouple: in a circuit containing two or more junctions of two different metals, a difference in temperature between the junctions results in a flow of current roughly proportional to the temperature difference. In practice a number of thermocouples are combined to make a thermopile. Short lengths of fine constantin and iron (or manganin) wire are soldered together and mounted upon a thin mica rectangle so that one set of junctions lies along the center of the frame, the others along its sides. A pair of muscles is mounted, one on each face of the thermopile, lying closely upon the "hot" junctions in the center. The "cold" junctions (at the sides) are carefully insulated so that they are only slowly affected by temperature changes at the hot junctions. Suitable arrangements are made to stimulate the muscles and to record their mechanical response. The temperature of the system is rigorously controlled. The thermopile is connected to a galvanometer system designed for adequate sensitivity, great stability, and prompt response to the changes in current flow set up in the thermopile by the successive phases of heat production in the muscles during activity. The galvanometer deflections are recorded photographically, and the records may be analyzed to give the heat rate and the total heat in absolute units (cal. or gm.-cm.).

This brief description cannot convey the technical skills, perseverance, and attention to detail exercised in the development and successful use of the myothermic method. The reader is urged to consult the original papers for a classical lesson in the necessity of these virtues in experimental science.

Phases of heat production in muscle (19, 44–47, 50). For myothermic experiments the muscle used must be small and of uniform cross section, so that heat is uniformly distributed in it; it must be thin, so that the oxygen supply can be met by simple diffusion; the fibers should be parallel, so that all of their force is exerted in the direction of shortening; and the muscle should be able to function at low temperatures (0° C.), because the difficulty of accurate temperature control is greatly eased if the system can be equili-

4

brated in crushed ice, and because physical and chemical changes are sufficiently slow to permit separation in time of the successive phases of activity. These qualifications are best filled by the sartorius muscles of small frogs, and they have been most widely used in myothermic work. Their behavior in some respects may be characteristic only of the isolated frog sartorius, but it is reasonable to assume (until experiment proves otherwise) that their general behavior is truly representative of all voluntary muscle.

Six phases of heat production have been observed in active muscle. The first three accompany the mechanical events and are called, together, the *initial* heat. (i) The *shortening* (or contraction) heat accompanies the development of isometric tension or the shortening of the muscle as it lifts a load in an isotonic contraction.* (ii) The *maintenance* heat is liberated steadily while tension is sustained during a tetanus. (iii) The *relaxation* heat arises from energy of strain degraded during relaxation after an isometric contraction, or from heat dissipated by the muscle when work is done upon it by the falling load after an isotonic contraction. These phases of the initial heat may be discerned in Figure 51, page 87. The remaining three phases of heat production, known collectively as the *delayed* heat, appear after the mechanical events are over. (iv) The anaerobic *negative* delayed heat was first observed by Hartree (1932) in frog muscle in nitrogen at 0° C. In 2 to 4 seconds after a brief tetanus, absorption of heat occurs, lasting from 15 to 50 seconds and amounting to 1 to 8 per cent of the initial heat. It is seen in unfatigued muscle when the chemical events are slowed, at 0° C. (v) The anaerobic *positive* delayed heat, firmly established by Hartree in 1929, was at first rather difficult to understand. At the time, lactic acid formation was thought to be coincident with (and the cause of) contraction. There was no room in the current theory for glycolysis to continue after relaxation. This small heat (3 to 20 per cent of the initial heat, lasting many minutes) was a harbinger of the revolution of 1930, when Lundsgaard showed that muscles could contract without lactic acid formation. It was then admitted and proved that, as Gustav Embden had insisted, a large part of the lactic acid formed during anaerobic activity appears in the recovery period. Since glycolysis is coupled with phosphocreatine synthesis, most of the energy is absorbed in this process and the resultant heat excess is small. (vi) The *oxidative* delayed heat was first observed by A. V. Hill in 1913. He noticed that after activity of a muscle in oxygen, but not in nitrogen, the galvanometer deflection persisted for many minutes: there is a continued slow heat production during oxidative recovery. The various phases of the delayed heat are illustrated in Figures 46 and 47.

Heat production and chemical change (24, 39, 44–47, 50). The course and quantity of the initial heat are identical for equal activity of muscles contracting isometrically in nitrogen, in oxygen, or after treatment with iodoacetate. This means that the fundamental processes of contraction and relaxation are anaerobic and are *also* independent of glycolysis. The immediate energy exchanges must therefore take place through ATP and phosphocreatine; glycolysis and oxidation are slower recovery processes. Lundsgaard has shown that phosphocreatine continues to break down after relaxation,

---

* There is some shortening even in an isometric contraction. The muscle shortens against its own elastic components and its connections to the recording lever. During relaxation these stretched elements return to their initial length. The energy degraded in this process appears as part of the relaxation heat.

so that this, too, is a recovery process. At present there is not quite enough evidence to make certain whether the breakdown of ATP is also a recovery process. If so, there must first be a change in the contractile system, accompanied by the liberation of energy, which is *reversed* by the chemical energy of ATP: energy is required for relaxation, and liberated in the subsequent contraction. Some points may be cited in favor of this view. (i) At the onset of rigor from fatigue or poisons there is progressive failure of the muscle to *relax* completely. (ii) In the period during the development of rigor in iodo-acetate-poisoned muscles contracting isometrically the energy liberated (expressed as gm.-cm. of total tension per gm. of H_3PO_4 set free) is much higher than it is during the earliest contractions, and greater than one would anticipate from the final breakdown of the residual phosphocreatine and ATP. This extra energy liberation is associated with the irreversible shortening of rigor. (iii) Ramsey and Street (52) have shown that a single frog muscle

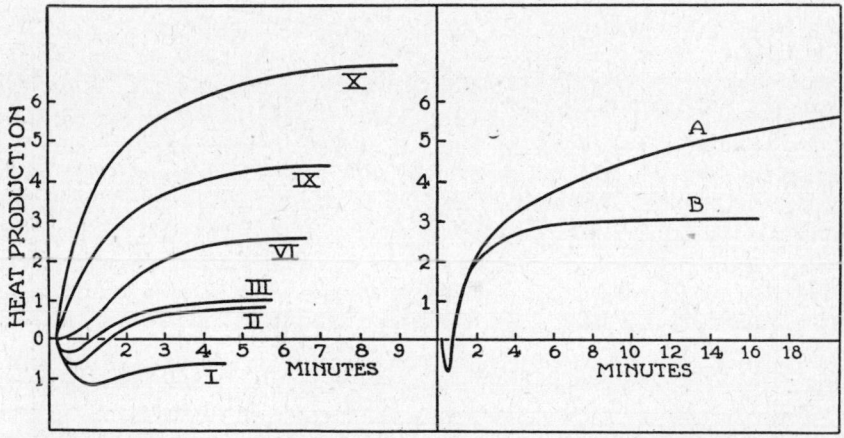

Fig. 46.—Anaerobic delayed heat in frog sartorius at 0° C. Curves I–X: series at *p*H 6 (alactacid), successive stimulations of the same pair of muscles. The delayed heat is wholly negative only when the muscles are fresh. Curve A: anaerobic delayed heat at *p*H 7.2; Curve B: a member of a series under alactacid conditions (*p*H 6.0) for comparison. Note the slow, small delayed heat of postcontractile lactic acid formation. Heat expressed as a percentage of initial heat. Duration of tetanus, 12 sec. (Adapted from D. K. Hill, *J. Physiol.*, 1940, *98*:460–466.)

fiber floating in Ringer's solution returns spontaneously to its resting length after stimulation, provided that it is not allowed to shorten more than one-third of its rest length. This relaxation is active; it is more rapid than can be accounted for by any external force acting upon the fiber. This is suggestive but not conclusive evidence that the chemical changes so far known in muscle may all be recovery processes. It is a useful reminder that knowledge of the final steps of conversion of chemical to mechanical energy in muscle is still quite incomplete.

In unfatigued muscle at 0° C. and *p*H 6.0 (lactic acid formation inhibited) the anaerobic delayed heat after a 12 second tetanus may be entirely negative. The initial course of the anaerobic delayed heat may also be the same whether glycolysis is permitted or not (Fig. 46). D. K. Hill attributes the anaerobic negative delayed heat to the resynthesis of ATP from phosphocreatine, a process requiring a small heat absorption. Other evidence is consistent with this point of view. Measurement of the pH changes in muscle during and after activity show that the alkaline shift due to liberation of the relatively strong base, creatine, has its maximum just after relaxation (47, 50). It persists if glycolysis is inhibited, but in normal muscle it is rapidly reversed as lactic acid accumulates and phosphocreatine is resynthesized. These observations help to establish the order of the chemical events during activity. The experimental conditions are chosen to separate them as widely as possible, and it should be appreciated that changes in temperature, degree of fatigue, pH, and duration of stimulus will alter the relative rates and magnitudes of the chemical changes and the associated heat production during recovery.

Oxygen is required for complete recovery of the muscle after contraction. Three important questions are raised, therefore, by a consideration of the oxidative delayed heat. (i) Do the delayed heat production and the oxygen

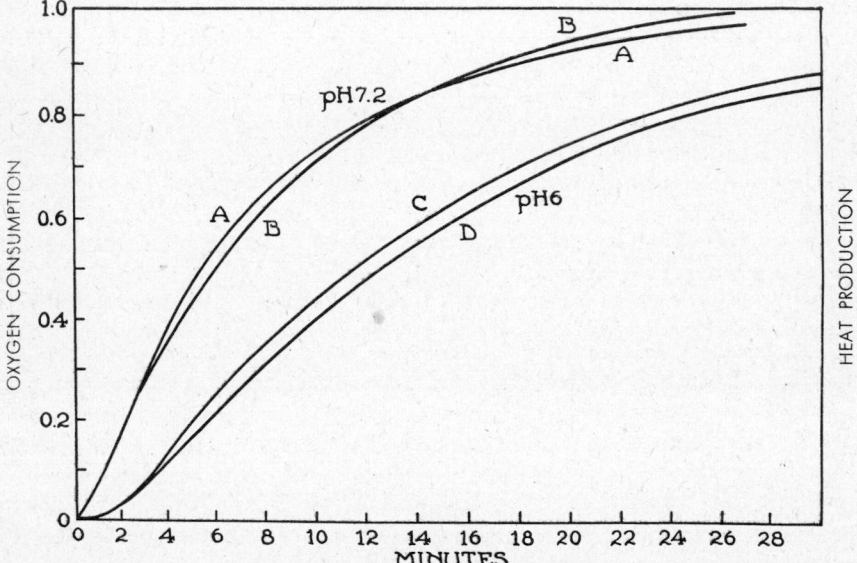

Fig. 47.—Comparison of the time courses of recovery oxygen consumption and heat production. At pH 7.2: A, oxygen; B, heat. At pH 6.0 (lactic acid production inhibited): C, heat; D, oxygen. (After D. K. Hill, *J. Physiol.*, 1940, *98*:207–227.)

consumption really run parallel? D. K. Hill (45) finds that they do, in normal muscle (Fig. 47); when lactic acid formation is inhibited; after poisoning with caffeine, which progressively inhibits both the resting and the activity oxygen consumption; and after treatment with sodium azide, which inhibits only the extra oxygen uptake due to activity. (ii) What is the cost of oxidative recovery? It has often been observed that the oxidative delayed heat is about equal to the initial heat. A. V. Hill (41) has re-determined this relation, using his improved apparatus, for the frog sartorius at 0° C. in a wide range of activity from a single twitch to a series of tetani (1.2 sec. every 4 min. for 40–60 min.) with maximum work. The ratio of total energy (initial energy + recovery heat) to initial energy (initial heat + work) is consistently about 2. During recovery, the energy liberated in activity is restored, and an equal amount of energy is lost as heat: the efficiency of oxidative recovery is therefore 50 per cent. This may be compared with Ochoa's data on the efficiency of aerobic phosphorylation (Table 4). The two series of observations suggest that nearly all of the energy realized (as $\sim$ph) in oxidative recovery is effectively absorbed. Hill (43) has also found that the maximum mechanical efficiency of frog muscle (work/initial heat + work) is about 40 per cent. The overall efficiency including recovery is therefore about 20 per cent. (iii) Is the oxidative delayed heat really due to oxidative recovery or is it due, as has been suggested, to an increased basal metabolism, that is, to the inertia of chemical changes set in motion during activity? The correspondence of oxygen uptake with heat production and the consistent relation of total energy to initial energy in the most diverse circumstances argue against the delayed heat being due merely to an accelerated basal metabolism. In a muscle in steady rhythmic contraction, where recovery occurs in the intervals between contractions, the *rate* of the oxidative heat may be six to twelve times the resting heat rate. It seems reasonable to ascribe so large an increase to a process of recovery from activity rather than to the inertia of chemical change. The notion of inertia was put forward by Sachs (53), who observed that the phosphocreatine level in a cat soleus muscle (in situ, with circulation intact) did not diminish with increasing activity of the muscle. He concluded that in oxygen a more direct oxidative process supersedes the chemical events described earlier in this chapter. This conclusion is taken without regard for the dynamics of a steady state. Water may enter and leave a bath at the rate of 10 gallons or 100 gallons per minute. The level of water in the bath may be 6 inches or 6 feet; it remains unchanged so long as the rates of inflow and outflow are equal. Similarly, the amount of any intermediate in a series of coupled reactions gives no indication of the rate of the overall process in which it is taking part.

Factors governing energy liberation during contraction (33–43, 50). Initial heat represents the energy liberated during the mechanical activity of a muscle. The study of the course, rate, and magnitude of initial heat production in relation to load, amount of shortening, speed of shortening, duration of stimulus, and temperature, may therefore contribute to an understanding of some of the rules governing the relationship between the contractile system and the systems providing energy for contraction.

The most obvious point about this relationship is that it is sharply altered when the muscle is stimulated. The resting muscle is flexible and elastic, with a low heat production. After a single stimulus the muscle becomes moderately rigid and inextensible, and its heat production rises sharply, well before any signs of activity appear in the mechanical record. This early fundamental change in a muscle after stimulation was first demonstrated by Gasser and Hill in 1924; they showed that if a muscle is given a small quick stretch shortly after a single stimulus, much greater tension is developed more rapidly than in an ordinary isometric twitch. This effect of the quick stretch is most marked during the first eighth of the contraction period. It declines rapidly thereafter, so that if a stretch is imparted at the time of maximum tension it has no further effect on the mechanical response of the muscle. Gasser and Hill concluded that the muscle is fully active (tending to contract) almost immediately after stimulation, but that the mechanical evidence of this activity is not perceptible until the elastic components of the muscle (its tendons and the connections to the recording lever) are fully stretched.

The quick stretch, by taking up the slack due to the elastic components, reveals that the contractile elements are active.

Independent evidence of the early appearance of an active state in a stimulated muscle has been obtained by Brown (33), who showed that the abrupt application of very high pressure to a muscle at or just after the time of stimulation leads to more rapid development of greater tension than in an ordinary twitch. Again, the pressure is progressively less effective if it is applied at increasing intervals after stimulation (Fig. 48). A similar effect on the mechanical response of a muscle to a single stimulus is observed if a second shock is administered shortly after the first. The three methods agree fairly well in indicating the time course of the active state in the muscle

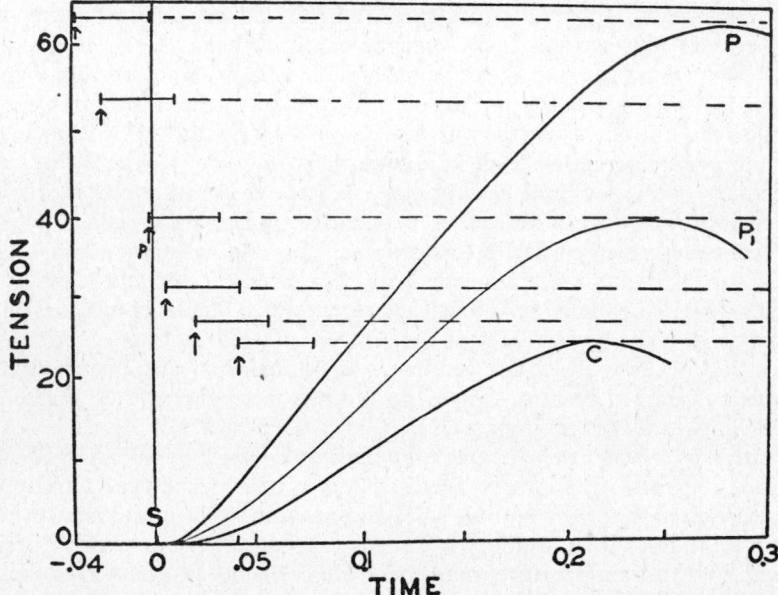

Fig. 48.—Curve C: Isometric myogram recorded at atmospheric pressure. Curve P: Myogram recorded at 272 atmospheres, the pressure being applied 15 sec. before stimulation at S. Curve P_1: Myogram recorded following an abrupt compression applied at the moment of stimulus. Total tension attained is indicated by the dotted line. Moment of compression is indicated by the arrows, one of which is marked p. Total pressure is attained within the interval indicated by the bracketed solid lines that follow the arrows. Remaining solid lines: total tensions attained after compressions at times indicated by the arrows. Note that compression beginning 0.04 sec. after stimulation does not affect the developed tension. (From Brown, *Biol. Symp.*, 1941, *3*:161–190.)

after stimulation. The shaded area in Figure 49 indicates the time during which a quick stretch, abrupt compression, and a second shock from massive electrodes are effective in augmenting the normal mechanical response of a muscle in a single isometric twitch.

These experiments suggest that stimulation of the muscle initiates a new state in which a vigorous exchange of energy may take place between the contractile elements and the chemical system. The contractile elements respond mechanically, exhibiting increased rigidity and a tendency to shorten. Perhaps in consequence of this response, other chemical processes are set in motion which tend to restore the resting condition, and the activated state of the muscle is rapidly dissipated.

The fully active state of a muscle can be maintained with repeated moderately rapid stimulation—by a tetanus. In these circumstances, the conditions of maximal energy exchange in the muscle can be maintained at will, and the phases of contraction, maintenance of tension, and relaxation can be separated and studied more effectively.

Energy liberation during contraction. It has long been known that the tension attained in an isometric tetanus is a function of the length of the muscle. It is greatest at about 90 per cent of rest-length (the length of the muscle in its natural site) and it diminishes at greater or smaller lengths (Chap. 2, Fig. 25, p. 38). This relation determines how far a muscle can shorten (or lengthen) with a given load. With no load the muscle can shorten

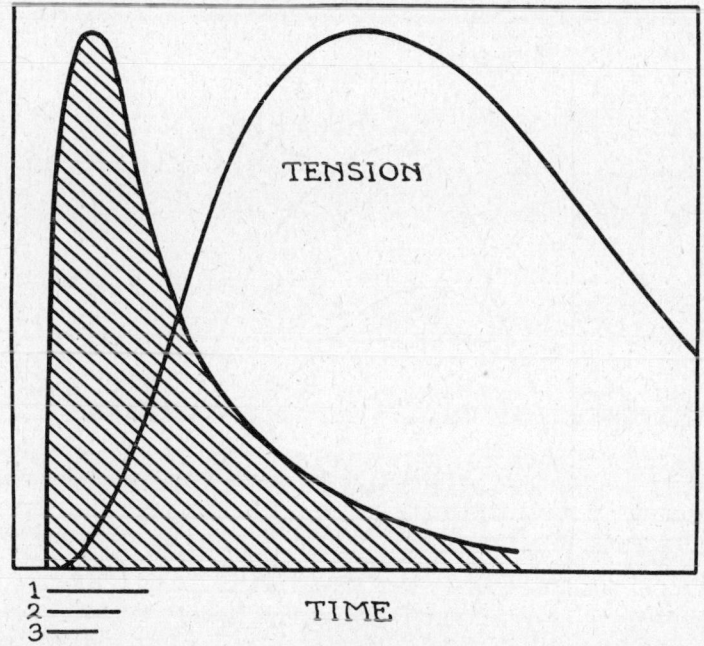

Fig. 49.—Time course of the alpha process (shaded area) relative to that of tension during an isometric twitch. Horizontal bars indicate the time to the maximum of the alpha process as determined by the method of (1) quick stretch, (2) abrupt compression, and (3) excitation by massive electrodes. (After Brown, *Biol. Symp.*, 1941, *3*:161–190.)

to about two-thirds rest-length, at which point the supporting structures (sarcolemma, etc.) interfere with further shortening. A single muscle fiber can shorten much further, but if it is permitted to do so, it may lose permanently its ability to return spontaneously to rest-length during relaxation (51). This altered state of the muscle fiber is called the *delta state* by Ramsey. It may be defined as a condition induced by excessive shortening, in which the processes of energy liberation in the muscle are no longer adequate to bring about relaxation. Another factor influencing the tension attained in a contraction is temperature. With increasing temperature, the rate of the chemical reactions that liberate energy for contraction is increased, and the speed and force of the contraction are also increased.

The first studies of heat production in muscle by Hill and his colleagues were made on muscles contracting isometrically at rest-length, both because errors arising from movements of the muscles on the thermopile could thereby be avoided, and because maximum energy liberation was expected to occur with the development and maintenance of maximal isometric tension. A good account of this work may be found in Hill's Herter lectures (39). In brief, energy liberation in isometric contractions was associated with the development and maintenance of tension. Since the observations were made at constant (resting) length of the muscles, heat production during contraction was determined by the tension maintained and the time during which it was maintained. If this relation held at all lengths of the muscle (i.e., for any amount of tension) then the muscle could be considered as an engine for developing mechanical potential energy at the expense of chemical

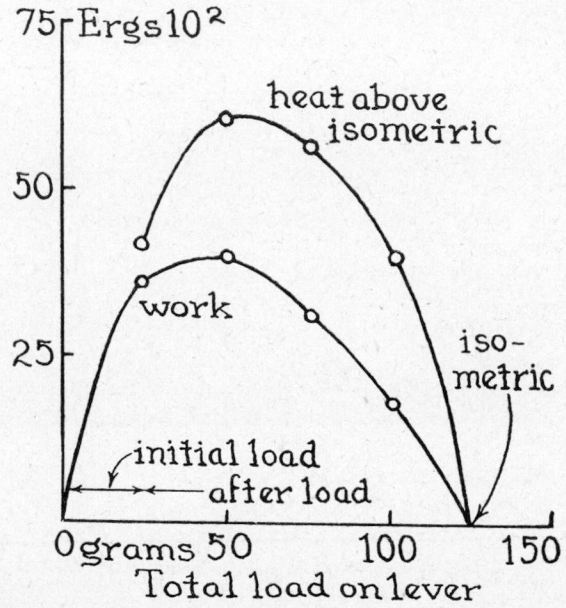

Fig. 50.—Variations of work and heat in isotonic contractions against increasing loads. The heat represents only the heat *in excess* of the isometric heat, which is made to coincide arbitrarily with the line of zero work. (After Fenn, *J. Physiol.*, 1924, *58*:175–203.)

energy. This potential energy could be used to do work if the muscle were permitted to shorten with a load. The proportion of energy realized as work would depend, however, on the mechanical arrangements of the lever system and on the amount of energy required to overcome resistance of the muscle to change in shape.

In 1924 Fenn (34, 35) showed that this was too simple a view. He observed that whenever muscles were allowed to shorten under constant tension *extra* heat in addition to the isometric heat was produced (Fig. 50). For the same shortening with increasing loads, the extra heat was proportional to the load. For increasing shortening with constant load, the extra heat was proportional to the shortening. Since wt. × distance equals work, the extra heat liberated in each instance was roughly proportional to the work done. In these experiments the muscle lowered the load in relaxing, and the energy of the load appeared in the muscle as heat. If, however, the weight was held up so that the muscles relaxed unloaded, this heat did not appear. Nevertheless, some extra heat was still liberated during the contraction, and in addition, of course, work was done in lifting the load. Consequently, in shortening with a load, extra *heat* is liberated by the muscle in shortening and extra *energy* is liberated in doing work, in excess of the isometric heat. The muscle is therefore not *merely* an engine for developing and maintaining tension. The isometric heat may represent energy used for maintaining the conditions for doing work, but when the muscle shortens and lifts a load, extra energy above the isometric heat is liberated in an amount determined by the amount of shortening and the load.

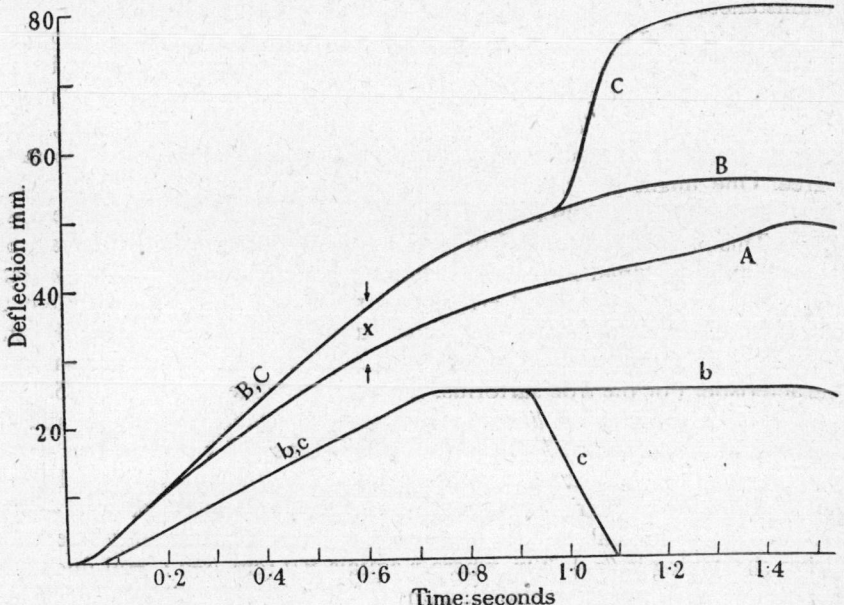

Fig. 51.—Galvanometer records of initial heat in isometric and isotonic contractions (frog sartorius, 0.6 sec. tetanus at 0° C.). Curve A: isometric. Curve B: isotonic, 38.6 gm. after-load, held up. Curve C: isotonic, same load, lowered by muscle during relaxation. The energy of the load appears as heat, and C rises sharply above B during relaxation by an amount equal to the work. Both B and C rise faster than A, owing to the shortening heat. Curves b and c: mechanical records of the isotonic contractions. End of stimulus at x. The rate of heat production at any instant is given by the slope of the galvanometer record. (From A. V. Hill, *Proc. roy. Soc.*, 1938, *B126*:136–195.)

Heat of shortening. A. V. Hill (42) has extended this analysis of energy liberation during contraction in muscle, using a greatly improved myothermic apparatus. He finds that the total energy liberated by a muscle in a contraction is the sum of (a) heat liberated in shortening, (b) work done, and (c) a large remainder, which Hill calls the *maintenance heat*. In agreement with Fenn, Hill finds that extra heat (over the isometric heat) is liberated whenever a muscle shortens (Fig. 51). This *shortening heat* is proportional to the amount of shortening, independent of the work done, and independent of the speed of shortening, which diminishes with increasing loads. In general terms, a muscle in shortening x cm. liberates ax gm.-cm. of heat in excess of the isometric heat, where a is the shortening heat per cm.

Since ax has the dimensions of work, a is expressed as a force, in gm., and the shortening heat is thus regarded as energy used to overcome some resistance in the muscle. It may, however, be expressed in cal., as a heat of reaction —potential energy lost by the contractile elements in taking up a shorter configuration. The latter view may be more nearly correct. If the shortening heat is energy degraded in overcoming, say, viscosity in the muscle, then extra heat would also be produced in overcoming the same force when the stimulated muscle *lengthens* under a load greater than the maximum isometric tension. This is not the case. Although Hill could not prove experimentally that heat equal to the shortening heat was *absorbed* when a stimulated muscle was stretched, there was certainly no increase in heat production in these circumstances.

If the shortening heat, a, is regarded as potential energy lost in shortening, then it must be related to the maximum potential energy developed by the muscle, and the best estimate of this quantity is the maximum isometric tension at rest-length, T_0. Factors affecting T_0 (cross-sectional area, temperature, number of fibers contracting) are likely to affect a to the same degree. One might therefore expect that the ratio, a/T_0, would be fairly constant for different muscles and for the same muscle at different temperatures. This is what Hill finds. For a series of frog sartorius muscles, capable of developing maximal isometric tension, T_0, the relation a/T_0 is constant (within limits of experimental error ± 10 per cent), and is independent of temperature, speed of shortening, work done, and (Brown, 33) pH and pressure. For different *kinds* of muscle, a/T_0 is of course different and characteristic. For the frog sartorius, the average value of a/T_0 is 0.25.

Rate of extra energy liberation during shortening. When a muscle shortens, lifting a load of T gm. through a distance of x cm., it does work, Tx gm.-cm., and liberates shortening heat, ax gm.-cm. The total extra energy above the isometric heat liberated during shortening must be $(a + T)x$ gm.-cm., and if this takes place in t sec., the *rate* of extra energy liberation during shortening is $(a + T)v$, where v equals x/t (cm./sec.). Hill finds that the rate of extra energy liberation is a linear function of the difference between the maximal isometric tension, T_0, and the load, T:

$$(a + T)v = b(T_0 - T),$$

where b is a velocity constant related to the absolute rate at which the muscle can liberate energy. Since it defines the chemical activity of the muscle, b is dependent on the temperature and upon other factors (pH, fatigue, etc.) affecting the rates of chemical reactions in the muscle. In muscles of uniform cross section the number of contractile elements increases with length, and the velocity of shortening with a given load must increase in the same proportion. The value of b (regarded as a velocity, in cm./sec.) must also increase with the length, l, of the muscle, but the ratio, b/l, should be fairly constant in a series of muscles at the same temperature. For the frog sartorius at $0°$ C., b is found to be $0.33 \times$ length per sec., with an average variation of ± 9 per cent for the series of observations made.

Work. The foregoing equation may be rearranged to give the rate of doing work during shortening under constant load:

$$Tv = bT\left[\frac{T_0 + a}{T + a} - 1\right].$$

At zero load, the rate of doing work is of course zero. When $T = To$, the work done is also zero, since no shortening can take place. At some intermediate load the rate of doing work will be a maximum. From the equation Hill has calculated (using $a/T_o = 0.25$ and $b = 0.33$ length/sec.) that the load for maximum rate of doing work in isotonic contractions should be about three-tenths of the maximum isometric tension. The rate of doing work varies with the amount and speed of shortening, both of which are controlled by the load, which thus determines the rate of extra energy liberation. A point of great importance is that no extra *heat* (other than the shortening heat) is liberated when work is done during shortening. The extra energy for work seems to be applied in an isothermal process, and equivalent extra heat does not appear unless the muscle lowers the load in relaxing (Fig. 51). This does not mean that work is done by an independent process

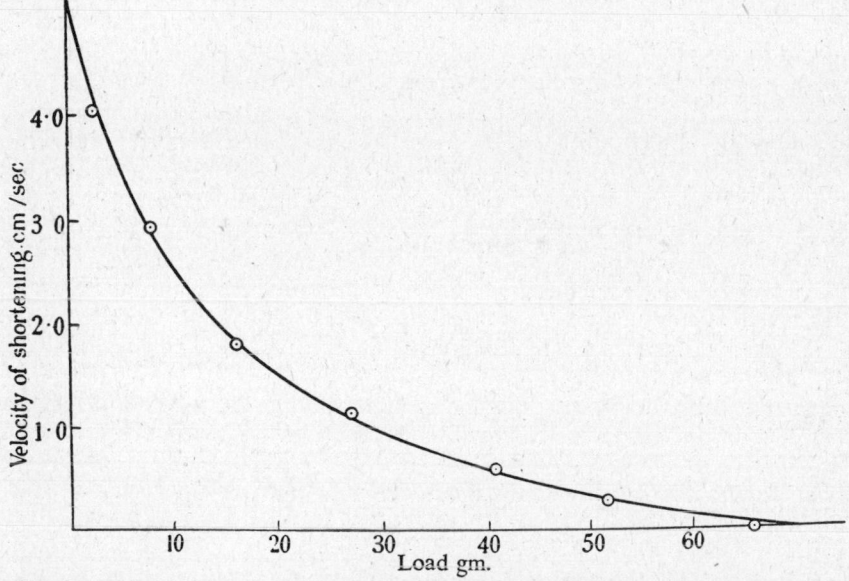

Fig. 52.—Relation between load (gm. wt.) and speed of shortening (cm./sec.) in isotonic contractions at 0° C. The curve is calculated from the equation $(T + 14.35)(v + 1.03) = 87.6$. Hence $a = 14.35$ gm. wt.; $b = 1.03$ cm./sec.; $a/T_o = 0.22$; $b = 0.27$ length/sec. (From A. V. Hill, *Proc. roy. Soc.*, 1938, *B126*:136–195.)

operating with 100 per cent efficiency. All of the energy liberated by the muscle may be required in some way for doing work (34, 43). Further investigation of the problem of how work is done may require consideration of the rate of total energy liberation during shortening. More insight may be gained by the analysis of the relation between energy liberation and load in single twitches, which may one day be practicable with improved myothermic apparatus.

Force and speed of shortening. Hill's equation may be written in the form:

$$(T + a)(v + b) = (T_o + a)b = \text{constant},$$

which Hill calls the "characteristic equation" of muscle. It describes the relation between velocity of shortening and force exerted, or load, as a rectangular hyperbola with asymptotes at $T = -a$ and $v = -b$, and it fits the experimental observations quite well (Fig. 52). Hill's observations are in substantial agreement with those of Fenn and Marsh (38), who carefully determined the relation between velocity of shortening and load in isotonic contractions of frog sartorius muscles. Under constant load the elastic component of muscle does not change in length during shortening, and the form of the curve obtained must be due to the characteristics of the contractile element. In explanation of the curvilinear relation between force and speed of shortening, Levin and Wyman (1927) had proposed that muscle contained two elements in series, one freely elastic (undamped), the other also elastic, but viscous, so that its rate of movement was diminished (damped) by a large internal resistance. The *interaction* of the two elements in series could account for the curvilinear force-velocity relationship found experimentally in muscle. Fenn and Marsh prevented this interaction in their experiments, and nevertheless obtained curves of the same form as those obtained by Levin and Wyman, and earlier by Gasser and Hill. The contractile element of muscle therefore does not behave like an elastic body which, whether damped or not, should exhibit a linear relation between velocity of shortening and load. Fenn and Marsh argued from this, and from the evidence that extra energy is liberated whenever a muscle shortens and does work, that the form of the force-velocity curve is determined by the mode of energy liberation during shortening. The apparent viscosity of stimulated muscle is not a factor modifying its dynamic behavior, but is rather a consequence of the processes of energy liberation in muscle. With this view Hill now agrees in principle. Muscle does contain an undamped elastic element (principally the tendons), but the contractile element cannot any longer be regarded as a viscous-elastic body. Its behavior in shortening is determined by the processes of energy liberation as defined by the characteristic equation.

If the rates of shortening with different loads are determined experimentally, then the constants a and b may be calculated from the characteristic equation independently of the thermal method. The constants derived by the two methods are, in general, in fairly good agreement. In the mechanical method, however, the observations deviate from the expected relation at small loads and at loads near the maximal isometric tension. The speeds of *lengthening* with loads greater than T_o are also much less than the predicted speeds, and the temperature coefficient of lengthening is only about 1.5, while that of shortening is about 2.0 (48). This suggests that the characteristic equation yields a good approximate definition of the mode of extra energy liberation during contraction, but that it does not hold finally and for all conditions. It is remarkable that in addition to defining the force-velocity relation, the characteristic equation (with a few additional assumptions) may also be used to predict the form of the mechanical response in a tetanus, the optimum speed for doing work in isotonic contractions, and the optimum speed for doing work against the inertia of a mass, when the load is always just equal to the force that the muscle can exert.

Maintenance heat. Shortening heat and work comprise only two parts of the total energy liberated in a contraction. There is always a third large component, called the maintenance heat. The maintenance heat in a contraction may be calculated by subtracting from the total initial heat (i) the shortening heat, (ii) the work,* and (iii) the relaxation heat (energy of the elastic elements stretched in the isometric phase of the contraction, which is dissipated as heat during relaxation). In an isometric contraction the muscle shortens against its elastic elements, doing work in stretching them which is degraded into heat during relaxation. The amount of shortening and the work done cannot be exactly measured but they can be estimated with reasonable accuracy (42).

An analysis of the principal components of the initial energy for a series of contractions with equal duration of stimulus, in which increasing amounts of shortening were permitted to take place, is plotted in Figure 53. The initial heat is practically constant and is not affected by the work or the

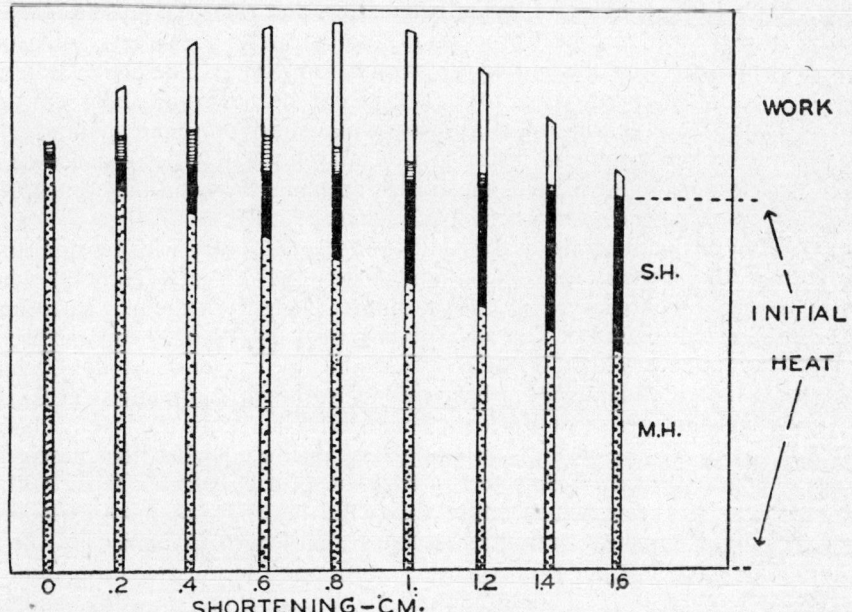

Fig. 53.—Components of the initial energy in a series of contractions with varying work and increased shortening up to the maximum. Frog sartorius at 0° C., tetanus, 0.5 sec. Load removed at end of shortening, and work calculated from the mechanical record. Note that only the work appears as excess energy above the init al heat, and that the shortening heat (S.H.) and maintenance heat (M.H.) exhibit an inverse relationship. (After observations of A. V. Hill, from Brown, *Biol. Symp.*, 1941, 3:161–190.)

amount of shortening. The maintenance heat decreases with increasing shortening by about the same amount as the shortening heat increases. Since the initial heat is the same whether work is done or not, it follows that the maintenance heat is independent of the work and the speed of shortening, but depends on the amount of shortening and the duration of the tetanus (the length of the isometric phase of the contraction). Extra energy (work plus shortening heat) above the isometric heat is liberated during shortening. In the complete cycle of contraction and relaxation only the work appears as extra heat. An amount of energy equal to the shortening heat must there-

* Work done does not appear as heat unless the load is lowered in relaxing. Usually the muscle carries a light load (3 to 5 gm.) to insure its return to rest-length. The heat produced in the muscle as this load is lowered must be subtracted from the initial heat.

fore be absorbed in lengthening during relaxation. The inverse relation between the shortening and maintenance heats suggests that some of the maintenance energy may be used to replace the energy lost as heat during shortening. Perhaps evidence of this is seen in the fall in heat rate occurring at the end of the stimulation period (Fig. 51). Sometimes it is so marked that, according to Hill (42), there is an "angle" in the heat record due to the abrupt change in slope. The rate of energy production does not necessarily change suddenly at the end of the stimulation period. The rate of its dissipation as *heat* may, however, be diminished as the energy is diverted to other purposes. This point illustrates one of the difficulties of analysis of heat production in muscle. The frog sartorius at 0° C. continues to shorten and do work for about 0.3 sec. *after* the end of the stimulation period. Steady tension is maintained for a few tenths of a second thereafter, and then the muscle relaxes (Fig. 51). Maintenance heat production is only one of the events going on during the time after the end of the stimulation period. The active state is being dissipated; energy equal to the shortening heat is being absorbed; the muscle may be preparing to relax even while shortening and maintaining tension. The heat produced in this period may not safely be regarded as a full measure of the intensity of the energy exchange between the contractile elements and the chemical systems of the muscle.

The rate of maintenance heat production seems to vary with tension and length of the muscle. Both Fenn and Latchford (37) and Hill (42) who measured the maintenance heat rate at different lengths of the frog sartorius, found that it increased at first with decreasing length, and then decreased, in correspondence with the isometric tension at each length. Hill (43) has observed that the maintenance heat rate in isometric contractions at 0° C. is fairly constant per second of contraction time, and that the rate is about equal to $a \times b$, i.e., to the shortening heat produced when the muscle is contracting at velocity b. Since a is a function of the isometric tension, the maintenance heat rate will therefore vary with the length of the muscle and the maximum isometric tension attainable at that length. One may say, then, that in the isometric phase of a tetanus, although the muscle is apparently still, the muscle fibers are intermittently contracting and relaxing, and in this process energy is degraded into heat at a rate equal to the rate of extra heat production when the muscle is shortening at velocity b. In this view, energy is used to maintain tension because the process resulting in the development of tension is being constantly opposed by a process tending to diminish tension. The relative rates of these processes determines whether the muscle shortens, maintains steady tension, or relaxes. An alternative view is that no energy is required to maintain tension (since no work is done in this process) and that the maintenance heat represents energy being "spilled" as heat until the muscle lengthens, when this energy is used in part to replace energy lost by the contractile elements as shortening heat. An interesting discussion of this point of view has been presented by Ramsey (51). It may be well to regard the term "maintenance heat" as a term of convenience without emphasizing the implications of "maintenance."

Conclusion. It is not practicable to summarize current knowledge of energy transformations in muscle in a theory of muscular contraction, since it is clear that not enough facts are available to permit decisions on a number of vital points. In considering the nature of muscular contraction there are grounds for differing opinions at the very outset. Two interdependent dynamic systems are present in muscle, the contractile system, and the chemical system producing energy. One can speak of (a) energy of the contractile element, and (b) chemical energy, stored or produced. The undecided question is this: does the contractile element become active because it is *energized* at the expense of the chemical stores, or is potential energy, already stored in the contractile element, liberated and used in contraction, and is chemical energy drawn upon for relaxation, for restoring the lost potential energy? Are these alternatives in every respect mutually exclusive? The answer to these questions must influence one's view of the significance of the active state, of the primary components of the initial heat, and of the relation of the contractile system to the chemical system. The explanation of the nature of the process responsible for doing work, and of the appearance of heat in the muscle equal to the work done when a muscle lowers a load during relaxation, will also depend on this decision. At the moment there is ample raw material for a number of working hypotheses; judgment on these points must be suspended until more evidence is available.

A sense of regret that we do not really know how a muscle works should not diminish appreciation of the very real progress of muscle physiology in the past forty years. The general principles of operation of the energy-yielding processes in the muscle cell are fairly well outlined, and these principles are found to apply very widely in other cells and tissues. One form (the high-energy phosphate bond) in which the energy of oxidations and fermentation is realized is now known. The concept of bond energy not only broadens understanding of the cell as a chemical engine but also focuses attention on the kind of chemical reactions that must be primarily concerned in the transformation of chemical energy into other forms.

The myothermic studies have evolved from the stage of considering energy liberation principally in physical terms—tension, viscosity, elasticity—to a more fruitful stage in which the nature, order, and relative rates of chemical and physiochemical processes concerned with energy utilization in muscle are shown to be the principal determinants of its physical properties and mechanical behavior during contraction. In this advance the view that muscle, as a biological system, can be understood best in terms of its physiological processes has played an important part. Finally it is realized that the contractile elements are responsible not only for shortening and doing work or developing tension but also for activating the chemical processes yielding energy. One need only consider the 1/1 relation between initial energy and recovery energy in muscle to realize how intimately the contractile and chemical systems must be related.

The studies of the fine structure of muscle and of myosin and other protein fibers are a modest beginning of the analysis of the contractile element. As a contractile substance with possible catalytic activity, myosin has attracted much speculative attention. One must remember, however, that myosin is only one component of the contractile element. It is present in an organized intracellular environment, and perhaps alterations in this environment, in response to a stimulus, will prove to be as important in determining the contractile behavior of myosin as its associated property of hydrolyzing adenosine triphosphate. A full understanding of the organization of the contractile element may wait upon a clearer solution of the related problems of protein structure and of the kinds of forces capable of bringing about active changes in the inter- and intra-molecular arrangement of protein fibers.

REFERENCES

A. *Some General Characteristics of Muscle*

1. ASTBURY, W. T. and DICKINSON, S. X-ray studies of the molecular structure of myosin. *Proc. roy. Soc.*, 1940, *B129:*307–331.

2. BALDWIN, E. The phosphagens. *Biol. Rev.*, 1933, *8:*74–105.

3. BAILEY, K. The proteins of skeletal muscle. *Advances in Protein Chemistry*, 1944, *1:*289–317.

4. BERNAL, J. D. A speculation on muscle. pp. 45–65 in: *Perspectives in biochemistry*, ed. by J. Needham and D. E. Green. Cambridge, University Press, 1937.

5. COWDRY, E. V. *A textbook of histology*, 3d ed. Philadelphia, Lea and Febiger, 1944, 426 pp.

6. ENGELHARDT, W. A. Enzymatic and mechanical properties of muscle proteins. *Yale J. Biol. Med.*, 1942–43, *15:*21–38.

7. FISCHER, E. The submicroscopical structure of muscle and its changes during contraction and stretch. *Cold Spr. Harb. Symp. Quant. Biol.*, 1936, *4:*214–223.

8. FISCHER, E. Changes during muscle contraction as related to the crystal pattern. *Biol. Symp.*, 1941, *3:*211–238.

9. FULTON, J. F. *Muscular contraction and the reflex control of movement.* Baltimore, Williams & Wilkins Company, 1926, 644 pp.

10. KALCKAR, H. M. The function of phosphate in cellular assimilations. *Biol. Rev.*, 1942, *17:*28–45.

11. LAZAROW, A. Particulate glycogen: a submicroscopic component of the guinea pig liver cell; its significance in glycogen storage and the regulation of the blood sugar. *Anat. Rec.*, 1942, *84:*31–50.

12. LIPMANN, F. Metabolic generation and utilization of phosphate bond energy. *Advances in Enzymology*, 1941, *1:*99–162.

13. MEYER, K. H. The chemistry of glycogen. *Advances in Enzymology*, 1943, *3:*109–136.

14. MEYER, K. H. and PICKEN, L. E. R. The thermoelastic properties of muscle and their molecular interpretation. *Proc. roy. Soc.*, 1937–38, *B124:*29–56.

15. SCHMITT, F. O. Structural proteins of cells and tissues. *Advances in Protein Chemistry*, 1944, *1:*25–68.

B. *Energy Production in Muscle*

16. COLOWICK, S. P. and SUTHERLAND, E. S. Polysaccharide synthesis from glucose by means of purified enzymes. *J. biol. Chem.*, 1942, *144:*423–437.

17. CORI, C. F. Phosphorylation of glycogen and glucose. *Biol. Symp.*, 1941, *5:*131–140.

18. DOUDOROFF, M., KAPLAN, N. and HASSID, W. Z. Phosphorolysis and synthesis of sucrose with a bacterial preparation. *J. biol. Chem.*, 1943, *148:*67–75.

19. FLETCHER, W. M. and HOPKINS, F. G. The respiratory process in muscle and the nature of muscular action. *Proc. roy. Soc.*, 1916–17, *B89:*444–467.

20. FRUTON, J. S., BALL, E. G., BERGMANN, M., KALCKAR, H. M., MEYERHOF, O. and SMYTHE, C. V. Energy relationships in enzyme reactions. *Ann. N. Y. Acad. Sci.*, 1944, *45:*357–436.

21. GREEN, A. A. and COLOWICK, S. P. Chemistry and metabolism of compounds of phosphorus. *Ann. Rev. Biochem.*, 1944, *13:*155–186.

22. HOGNESS, T. R. Oxidation catalysts. *Biol. Symp.*, 1941, *5:*119–130.

23. KREBS, H. A. The intermediary stages in the biological oxidation of carbohydrate. *Advances in Enzymology*, 1943, *3:*191–252.

24. MEYERHOF, O. *Die chemische Vorgänge im Muskel.* Berlin, Julius Springer, 1930, 350 pp.

25. MEYERHOF, O. The significance of oxygen for muscular contraction. *Biol. Symp.*, 1941, *3:*239–258.

26. MEYERHOF, O. Oxidoreductions in carbohydrate breakdown. *Biol. Symp.*, 1941, *5:*141–156.

27. MILLIKAN, G. A. Muscle hemoglobin. *Physiol. Rev.*, 1939, *19:*503–523.

28. NEGELEIN, E. and BRÖMEL, S. Isolierung eines reversiblen Zwischenprodukts der Gärung. *Biochem. Z.*, 1939, *301:*135–136.

29. OCHOA, S. Efficiency of aerobic phosphorylation in cell-free heart extracts. *J. biol. Chem.*, 1943, *151:*493–505.

30. PARNAS, J. K. Der Mechanismus der Glykogenolyse im Muskel. *Ergebn. Enzymforsch.*, 1937, *6:*57–110.

31. WARBURG, O. and CHRISTIAN, W. Isolierung und Kristallization des Proteins des oxydierendes Gärungsferments. *Biochem. Z.*, 1939–40, *303:*40–68.

32. *A symposium on respiratory enzymes.* Madison, University of Wisconsin Press, 1942, 281 pp.

C. *Energy Liberation in Muscle*

33. BROWN, D. E. S. The regulation of energy exchange in contracting muscle. *Biol. Symp.*, 1941, *3:*161–190.

34. FENN, W. O. A quantitative comparison between the energy liberated and the work performed by the isolated sartorius muscle of the frog. *J. Physiol.*, 1924, *58:*175–203.

35. FENN, W. O. The relation between the work performed and the energy liberated in muscular contraction. *J. Physiol.*, 1924, *58:*373–395.

36. FENN, W. O. Isotonic contractions in muscle. *Cold Spr. Harb. Symp. Quant. Biol.*, 1936, *4:*233–241.

37. FENN, W. O. and LATCHFORD, W. B. The effect of muscle length on the energy for

maintenance of tension. *J. Physiol.*, 1933–34, *80*:213–220.

38. FENN, W. O. and MARSH, B. S. Muscular force at different speeds of shortening. *J. Physiol.*, 1935, *85*:277–297.

39. HILL, A. V. *Muscular activity*. Baltimore, Williams & Wilkins Company, 1926, 115 pp.

40. HILL, A. V. Methods of analysing the heat production of muscle. *Proc. roy. Soc.*, 1937–38, *B124*:115–136.

41. HILL, A. V. Recovery heat in muscle. *Proc. roy. Soc.*, 1939, *B127*:297–306.

42. HILL, A. V. The heat of shortening and the dynamic constants of muscle. *Proc. roy. Soc.*, 1938, *B126*:136–195.

43. HILL, A. V. The mechanical efficiency of frog's muscle. *Proc. roy. Soc.*, 1939, *B127*:434–451.

44. HILL, D. K. The time course of the oxygen consumption of stimulated frog's muscle. *J. Physiol.*, 1940, *98*:207–227.

45. HILL, D. K. The time course of evolution of oxidative recovery heat of frog's muscle. *J. Physiol.*, 1940, *98*:454–459.

46. HILL, D. K. The anaerobic recovery heat production of frog's muscle at 0° C. *J. Physiol.*, 1940, *98*:460–466.

47. HILL, D. K. Hydrogen-ion concentration changes in frog's muscle following activity. *J. Physiol.*, 1940, *98*:467–479.

48. KATZ, B. The relation between force and speed in muscular contraction. *J. Physiol.*, 1939, *96*:45–64.

49. LUNDSGAARD, E. Untersuchungen über Muskelkontraktionen ohne Milchsäurebildung. *Biochem. Z.*, 1930, *217*:162–177.

50. VON MURALT, A. Zusammenhänge zwischen physikalischen und chemischen Vorgänge bei der Muskelkontraktion. *Ergebn. Physiol.*, 1935, *37*:406–491.

51. RAMSEY, R. W. Muscle: physics. pp. 784–798 in: *Medical physics*, ed. by Otto Glaser. Chicago, Year Book Publishers, 1944.

52. RAMSEY, R. W. and STREET, S. F. Muscle function as studied in single muscle fibers. *Biol. Symp.*, 1941, *3*:9–34.

53. SACHS, J. Recovery from muscular activity and its bearing on the chemistry of contraction. *Amer. J. Physiol.*, 1938, *122*:215–223.

54. LARDY, H. A. and ZIEGLER, J. A. The enzmatic synthesis of phosphopyruvate from pyruvate. *J. biol. Chem.*, 1945, *159*:343–352.

CHAPTER 4

FUNCTIONAL PROPERTIES OF NEURONS

Neurons form the conducting elements of the entire nervous system. They exist in a wealth of shapes and sizes, yet they all have many features in common. About the nucleus there is an accumulation of cytoplasm which may be called the *perikaryon*. From the perikaryon processes of two types are given off: *dendrites* and *axon*. It is often convenient from the functional standpoint to consider the perikaryon and dendrites together under the name of *soma*. In this way we come to divide the neuron into soma and axon. The soma receives impulses brought to it by other neurons, and normal conduction in a neuron takes place in the direction from soma to axon.

Compound Spike Potential of Nerve (4). Our modern knowledge concerning the properties of the individual fibers that together constitute a nerve trunk begins with the discovery by Gasser and Erlanger of the compound nature of the spike potential. The fibers of a nerve conduct impulses at various velocities; hence if a nerve be stimulated by a single shock, all the impulses will start out together, but, as they travel along the nerve, the fast impulses will outstrip the slow.

The required experimental procedure for studying the spike potential as it progresses along a nerve is to place recording electrodes at one end of the nerve and then to locate several pairs of stimulating electrodes on the nerve at known distances from the recording electrodes. The nerve is then stimulated by single shocks through each pair of stimulating electrodes in turn, with the result that successive recordings show the spike potential after different distances of conduction. When this is done and the records are arranged in order of increasing conduction distance, it is found that the spike potential of the whole nerve forms a simple elevation at or near its point of origin, but that it increases in duration and breaks up progressively until, at the far end of the nerve, a series of more or less distinct elevations is formed (Fig. 54). Several features of the nerve response are immediately discernible. In the first place, inspection of Figure 54 reveals that the change in form of the spike potential as it travels along the nerve is the result of the conduction of two elevations at different *linear* velocities. Secondly, not only do distinct components separate from one another as a result of conduction, but, in addition, each component tends to broaden and become lower progressively with increasing conduction distance. Finally, measurement of the area enclosed by the recorded elevations and the base line (the so-called area of the spike potential) would show that it remains constant despite the change in configuration with conduction distance. Therefore, each elevation is formed by the sum of a number of smaller elevations traveling at a range of velocities, the unit response, which does not change in amplitude nor in duration by virtue of conduction, being that of a single nerve fiber. The fact that a series of elevations is encountered after conduction clearly indicates that the individual fibers constituting a nerve are not distributed evenly with respect to conduction velocities; otherwise the spike potential would always have a simple contour, becoming progressively broader and lower with conduction distance but showing no tendency to subdivision. The fibers are in fact gathered about several modes, each mode corresponding to one of the distinct elevations in the spike potential record.

The elevations in the compound spike potential of a nerve appear in succession as the strength of stimulus is progressively increased; the most rapidly

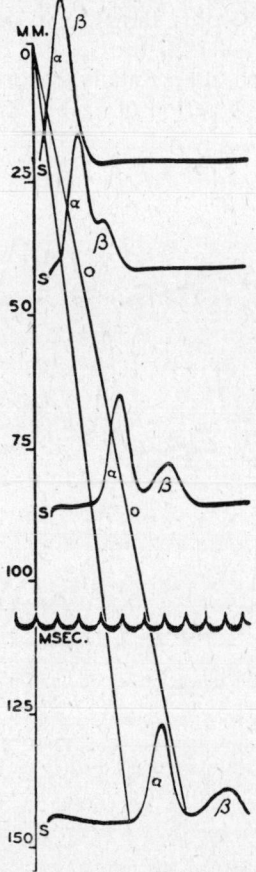

Fig. 54.—Demonstration of the linear conduction, at different velocities, of the *alpha* and *beta* elevations of the compound spike potential (frog sciatic nerve). Elevations designated by the Greek letters, α, β, are subdivisions of the A spike potential. At the left is a scale representing in mm. the conduction distance along the nerve. The several records are placed on the scale according to the conduction distance employed between stimulating and recording electrodes in each instance. (From Erlanger and Gasser, *Electrical signs of nervous activity*, University of Pennsylvania Press, 1937.)

conducting first, the others in descending order of conduction velocity; thus, as may be seen in the experiment illustrated in Figure 55, a single shock stimulus (labeled S_1 in Fig. 55A) results in the appearance of but the first elevation (a_1) of the compound spike potential. Another stronger shock stimulus (S_2 in record B) yields the first and second elevations, a_2 and β_2. This finding shows that a relationship exists between conduction velocity and threshold of the individual axons constituting the nerve.

A proof of independent conduction. The fact that one can obtain from a nerve stimulated at one shock strength, the first elevation alone, and at another greater shock strength, the first and second elevations, makes possible a further proof of the independent conduction of the successive elevations. This proof, illustrated in Figure 55, is based on the refractory period (Chap. 1). To perform the experiment, the stimuli S_1 and S_2, which singly yield the spike potentials recorded in Figure 55 A and B respectively, in records C to H are delivered in succession with S_2 falling at progressively shorter intervals after S_1. Study of these records shows that the second alpha response (a_2) becomes smaller and smaller as the second stimulus (S_2) moves into the relatively refractory period of a_1. Finally (record H), a_2 disappears as S_2 falls in the absolutely refractory period of a_1, but β_2 persists unchanged, with the

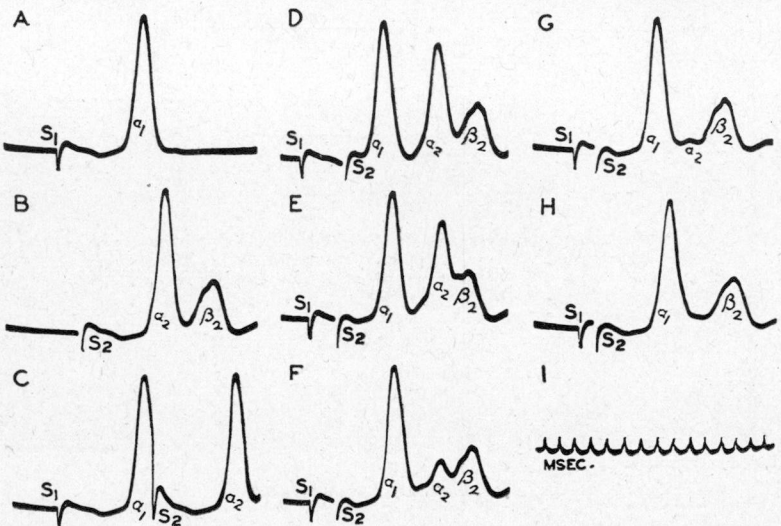

Fig. 55.—Demonstration of the independent conduction of the elevations of the compound spike potential. A = stimulation by a single shock (S_1) at strength just maximal for the alpha elevation (a_1). B = stimulation by a stronger shock (S_2) that produces an alpha elevation (a_2) and a just maximal *beta* elevation (β_2). In records C–H, S_2 follows S, at progressively shorter intervals with the result that a_2 falls increasingly early in the relatively refractory period following a_1 until, in record H, a_2 is obliterated by absolute refractoriness. Note that β_2, the beta response to the second stimulus, is not altered in any way by the removal of a_2. (From Erlanger and Gasser, *Electrical signs of nervous activity*, University of Pennsylvania Press, 1937.)

result that the recorded potential consists of a_1, and β_2. Now since a_2 can be blocked completely without altering β_2 in any way, it follows that the *alpha* and *beta* elevations are conducted in a completely independent fashion, one from the other. The only conceivable explanation for this fact is that the two elevations are contributed by different sets of axons having different conduction velocities. Although Figure 55 illustrates the principle of independent conduction only for the first two elevations of the complete spike potential, the same method can be applied to show that all of the elevations are mediated by separate and individual groups of axons.

TYPES OF NERVE FIBERS (7)

Systematic study of a number of different nerves has revealed the fact that there are three major groups of nerve fibers as judged by significant discontinuities in properties. These groups are known by the alphabetical designations "A" "B" and "C."

The A group includes all of the myelinated axons of the somatic nerves, these varying in diameter from 20 μ to 1 μ. The B fibers are myelinated fibers of 3 μ diameter or less, found in the autonomic nerves but not in somatic nerves. The C fibers are unmyelinated. For a number of reasons most of the general properties of nerve fibers have been delineated by experiments on A fibers. It is advisable, therefore, to consider those properties as they appear in A fibers, leaving until later a discussion of the differences between the major fiber groups.

But first let us consider the appearance of the complete spike potential of a nerve with all its constituents brought into their proper magnitude and time

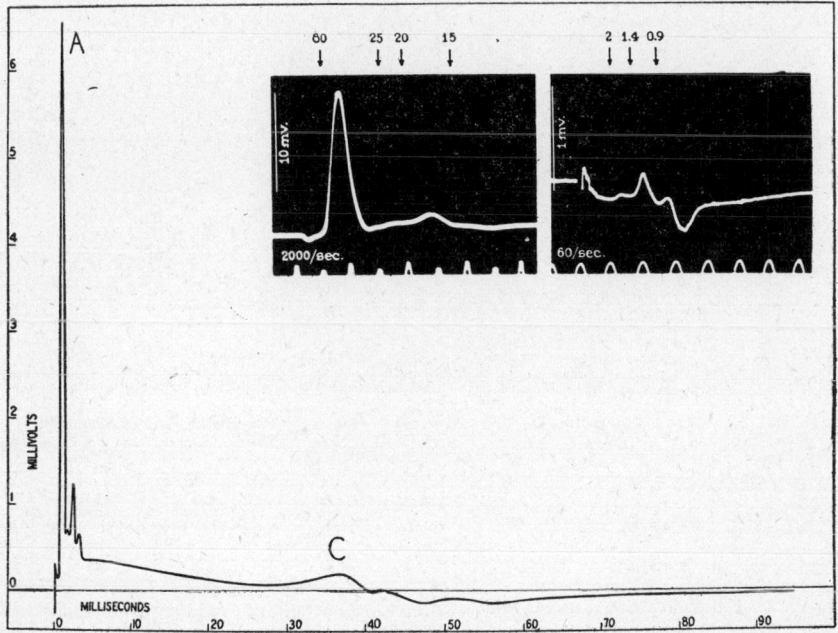

Fig. 56.—Complete spike potential of a mammalian saphenous nerve showing the various elevations drawn in their correct time and amplitude relations. The inset shows in actual recordings on the left the several components of the A elevation and on the right the response of C fibers. The figures above the arrows give, in meters per sec., the characteristic maximal conduction velocity of each component. (Combined from Gasser, *J. appl. Phys.*, 1938, *9*:88–96, and *Ohio J. Sci.*, 1941, *41*:145–159.)

relations. The saphenous nerve, which has been most intensively studied, will serve the purpose. Because of the tremendous variation in speed of conduction and amplitude of the several components of the complete spike potential it is not feasible to record the whole event on a single sweep of the oscillograph, but the data from several records may be synthesized to form a complete picture of the spike potential after conduction. Figure 56 presents such a picture. Inasmuch as the saphenous nerve is afferent from the skin, the largest fibers are not present, for they are distributed exclusively to muscle and so are confined to the mixed nerves and their purely muscle branches. Likewise there are no B fibers present. The fastest component in the saphenous nerve has a velocity of about 80 meters per sec. There follow other elevations with maximum velocities of 25, 20 and 15 meters per sec. These elevations, which may be seen in the inset to the left in Figure 56 represent the components of the A fiber group in the saphenous nerve. After an interval, a second major elevation appears, made of components having velocities of 2 to 0.9 meters per sec. This elevation, seen in the inset to the right of Figure 56, represents the C or unmyelinated fibers. It is immediately evident from Figure 56 that the A fibers contribute vastly greater potential to the record of saphenous nerve than do the C fibers.

The Properties of "A" Fibers (8, 9, 14). When a volley of impulses travels along the A fibers of a nerve such as the sciatic, which contains mixed cutaneous and muscular innervation, the spike potential gradually spreads out in

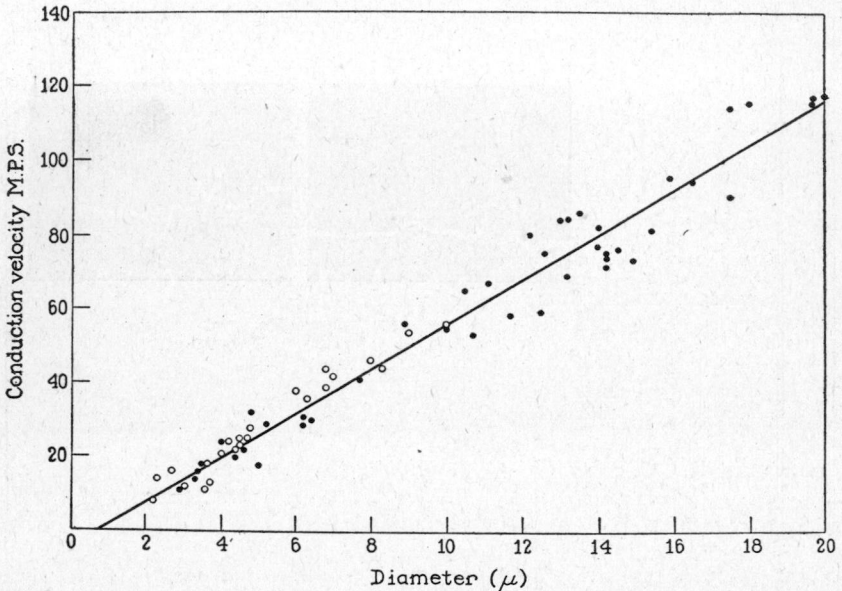

Fig. 57.—Linear relation between diameter and conduction velocity of mammalian nerve fibers. Each point represents a determination of the maximum conduction velocity in meters per sec. and of the diameter in micra of the largest fiber of an individual nerve. Dots = adult nerves. Circles = immature nerves. (After Hursh from Gasser, *Ohio J. Sci.*, 1941, *41*:145–159.)

time until four daughter elevations are discernible. These elevations are frequently referred to as the *alpha, beta, gamma,* and *delta* elevations respectively. The alpha and beta elevations of a frog sciatic nerve were seen in Figures 54 and 55. The gamma elevation is usually small but delta again is prominent. Actually a continuous gradation of properties is found among the fibers of the A group, the presence of distinct elevations in the conducted A spike potential merely signifying the disparity in numbers of fibers at several places on the A fiber "spectrum." Although the division into sub-groups corresponding to the several elevations is useful for some purposes, when discussing the general properties of A fibers it is quite unnecessary.

Relation between fiber size and conduction velocity. This relation is fairly simple. The A fibers vary from 20 μ to approximately 1 μ in diameter and in conduction rate from 120 meters per sec. to approximately 6 meters per sec.

A wealth of experimental effort has shown that the fibers of large size are those of high conduction velocity and that those of small size conduct at low velocities. One of the more recent experimental techniques, employed by Hursh (17), for demonstrating the relation of diameter to velocity is that of correlating the maximal conduction velocity of a given nerve with the size of the largest fiber found on histological examination of the nerve in cross section. In his experiments, Hursh selected nerves to yield a wide range of maximal fiber diameters and the results that were obtained by such correlations, illustrated in Figure 57, show that the relation between diameter and velocity of conduction is approximately linear, with diameter in micra multiplied by six yielding the approximate conduction rate in meters per sec. Gasser and Grundfest (9), employing the more precise method of reconstructions discussed below, have found that a closer approximation to exact linearity is attained if the diameter of the axon within the myelin sheath rather than the overall fiber diameter is related to conduction velocity.

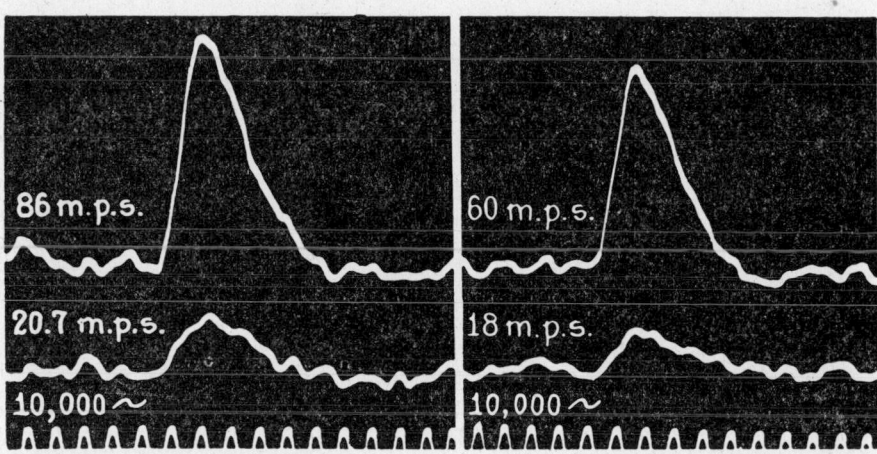

Fig. 58.—Records of the spike potentials of single mammalian nerve fibers of various conduction velocities, indicated for each record in meters per sec. (m.p.s.). Note the general relation between conduction velocity and spike amplitude. (From Gasser, *Ohio J. Sci.*, 1941, *41*:145–159.)

Relation between conduction velocity and spike amplitude. A number of investigators, working with various nerve preparations, have studied the relation between the amplitude of a single fiber spike and the conduction velocity of the fiber yielding the spike, and have come to the conclusion that the relation between the two is linear, the high velocity fibers yielding large spikes, the low velocity fibers small spikes. Figure 58 shows, at equal amplification, the spike potentials of single nerve fibers possessed of varied conduction velocities. On comparing the amplitudes and velocities of the two single spikes from each nerve preparation illustrated in Figure 58 it is found that amplitude$_1$/amplitude$_2$ = velocity$_1$/velocity$_2$ within a narrow margin of error.

Now, since both spike amplitude and fiber diameter stand in direct linear relation to conduction velocity, it follows that spike amplitude varies directly as the diameter. Thus we find that the largest A fibers have the highest conduction velocity and contribute the greatest potentials to the spike potential of a nerve, whereas the smallest A fibers have the lowest conduction velocities and contribute the smallest potentials.

Relation between conduction velocity and threshold. Mention has already been made of the fact that high velocity fibers have a lower threshold to electrical stimulation than have low velocity fibers (Fig. 55). Examining the relation in more detail with brief shock stimuli, Blair and Erlanger (4) found that threshold increases with decrease in conduction velocity along a smooth curve of the hyperbolic type. In a general way this relation means that Δ threshold/Δ velocity increases as stimulation progresses from a strength adequate for the largest fibers to one adequate for the smallest fibers in the scale of diameters.

Synthesis of the compound spike potential. It is possible to reconstruct the spike potential of a nerve from a well prepared histological section, given the relations between fiber diameter conduction velocity, spike amplitude and spike duration. When finished the reconstructed spike potential can be com-

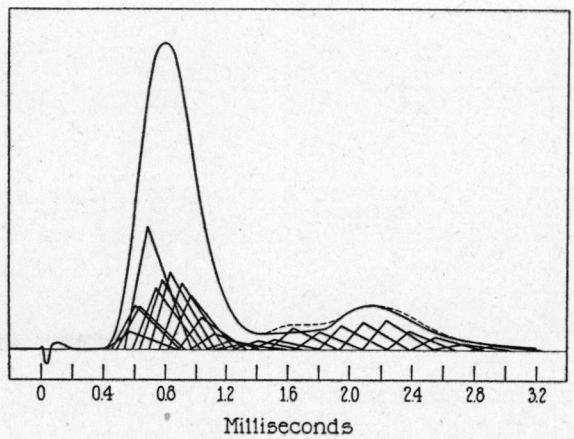

Fig. 59.—Reconstruction of the A spike potential of a mammalian saphenous nerve. The dotted lines represent the reconstructed potential where it does not coincide exactly with the recorded potential. The method employed in reconstruction is detailed in the text. (From Gasser and Grundfest, *Amer. J. Physiol.*, 1939, *127*:393–414.)

pared with that actually recorded from the nerve before fixation and sectioning. The degree of fit obtained between reconstructed and recorded potentials forms a critical measure of the correctness of the proposed relations between fiber diameter and the other properties.

To make a reconstruction, such as that to be found in Figure 59, the fibers are enumerated and classified in groups according to diameter. Triangles are then drawn (having the shape of an axon spike) for each mean diameter, the height of the triangles being the product of the mean diameter of the group and the number of fibers in the group. In this way the diameter-spike amplitude relation is accommodated and the potential contributed by each size group is found in arbitrary units; for example, 50 fibers of 10 μ diameter would give a triangle of 500 arbitrary units in height, and for the fibers of 2 μ, 50 fibers would give a triangle of but 100 arbitrary units or one fifth the amplitude. Next the triangles are located on an abscissa relative to one another by means of the diameter-velocity relationship. It is an easy matter to locate the first triangle on the abscissa, for the conduction time of the fastest fiber (and hence the largest fiber) is the latency for the first elevation of the previously recorded spike potential. In the example presented in Figure 59, that latency (conduction time) was 0.4 msec. and the conduction distance was 4 cm. Hence the fastest fiber in the nerve conducted at 100 meters per sec. From the section of the nerve it is known that the largest fiber is 14 μ in diameter. Now since a fiber of 14 μ conducted impulses at 100 meters per sec., it follows that the factor for converting diameter to conduction velocity (for the conditions in which the spike potential was recorded and assuming a linear relation) is 100/14 or 7.14. By means of this factor, conduction velocities are assigned to each of the size groups. The 10 μ fibers would have a velocity of 71.4 meters per sec. and 5 μ fibers a velocity of 35.7 meters per sec.

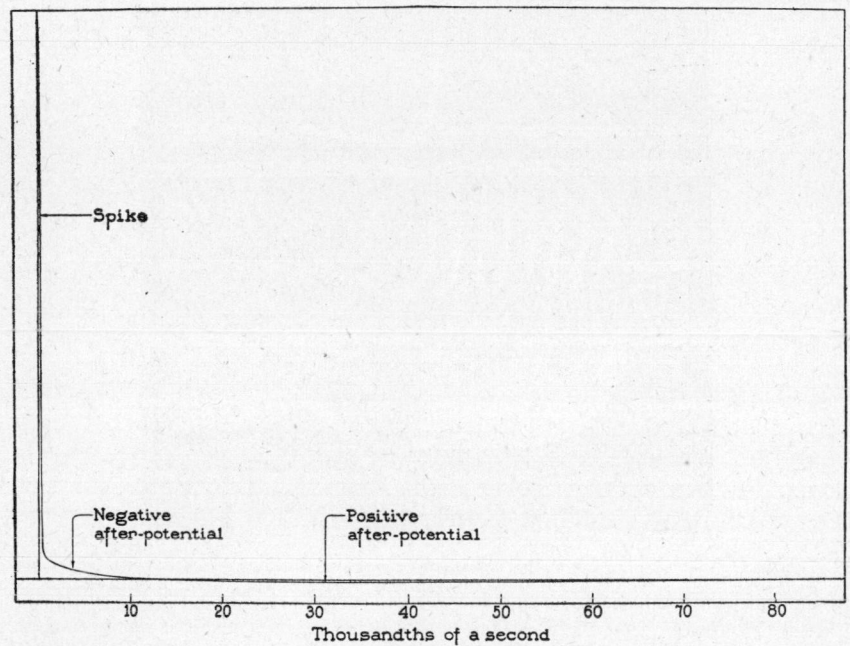

Fig. 60.—Diagram of the complete action potential of mammalian A fibers drawn so that the spike potential and after-potentials appear in their correct size and time relations. (From Gasser, *J. appl. Phys.*, 1938, *9*:88–96.)

Having arrived at the conduction velocity for each size group, the conduction time required for 4 cm. conduction distance is calculated. Thus, just as the 100 meter per sec. fibers required 0.4 msec. conduction time, so the 71.4 meter per sec. (or 10 μ) fibers would require 0.56 msec. and the 35.7 meter per sec. (or 5 μ) fibers would require 1.12 msec. Having now calculated the conduction time for each size group at 4 cm. conduction, the triangles representing the spike potentials of the size groups may be placed on the time abscissa in proper relation to the triangle of the fastest fibers, which was located by reference to the recorded spike potential. The succession of triangles so placed may be seen in Figure 59. All that now remains is to draw the complete spike potential by algebraic summation of the individual triangles and to compare it with the recorded potential. In Figure 59 such a comparison is made, the hatched line showing the reconstructed potential at the two points where it did not coincide exactly with the recorded potential.

After-potentials (4, 11, 12). The electrical record of nerve activity does not end abruptly with the completion of the spike potentials; it is rather continued into a potential sequence, initially negative, then positive, indicative of a series of processes following upon the completion of the spike. The potentials following the spike are known as *after-potentials*, negative and positive respectively; they appear in their simplest form following a single stimulation. Figure 60 illustrates, in their proper potential and time relations the spike potential and after-potentials of A fibers. In size the after-potentials are but a few per cent of the spike potential. The negative after-potential lasts up to 15 msec., and then gives way to positive after-potential lasting about 80 msec.

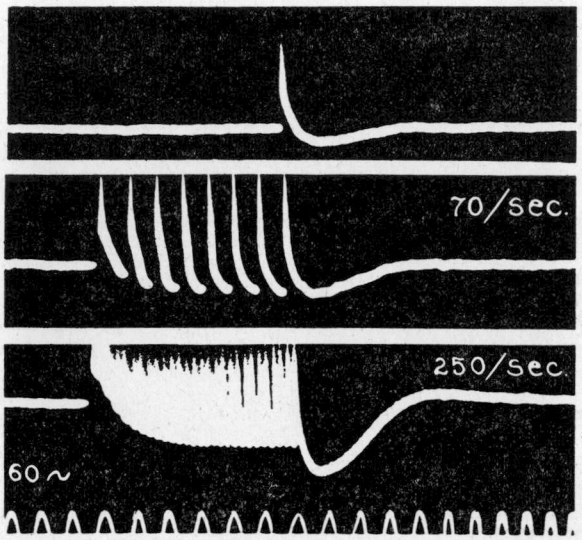

Fig. 61.—Changes produced in the after-potentials of a phrenic nerve (A fibers) by short tetanic stimulations. The spike potentials are not visible so the records begin with the negative after-potential and continue into positive after-potential. The top record shows the after-potential response evoked by a single stimulus, for comparison with the curves below at the designated frequencies of stimulation. Time line = 60 cycles. (From Gasser, *J. appl. Phys.*, 1938, *9*:88–96.)

In contrast with the spike potential, the after-potentials are highly labile, changing form with slight changes in activity or environment of the nerve. Repetitive stimulation, for instance, produces important changes in configuration of the after-potentials. As the frequency of repetitive stimulation is increased the negative after-potential is progressively curtailed while the positive after-potential is progressively increased. These effects may be seen in Figure 61, in which, at the top, is the after-potential response following a single stimulus, and then in succession the changed after-potentials following tetanic stimulation of two degrees of severity.

Recovery of excitability. When an impulse traverses an A fiber, no stimulus, however strong, can re-excite the fiber until the spike is nearly completed (the absolutely refractory period). Shortly thereafter excitability returns to normal, the interval required for this return being the relatively refractory period. Excitability changes after a single response do not, however, cease at the close of the classical refractory period. The refractory periods are succeeded by deviations of threshold from normal that last throughout the period of the after-potentials. Following refractoriness, there is a period of supernormal excitability lasting 15 msec. and a period of subnormal excitability lasting 80 msec. These changes may be seen in the plotted recovery curve at the top of Figure 62. The refractory period, supernormal period and subnormal period are related to the spike, negative after-potential and positive after-potential respectively.

After-potentials and excitability changes go hand in hand with the relation between them rigidly maintained although parallel alterations of major proportions take place. For example, repetitive stimulation, while curtailing after-negativity and increasing after-positivity, at the same time and in

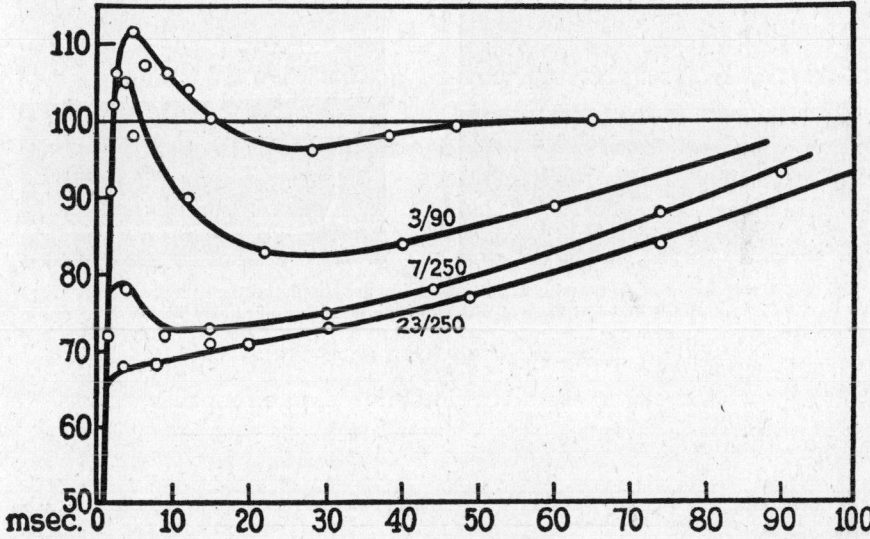

Fig. 62.—Recovery cycle of mammalian A fibers (saphenous nerve). Ordinates = excitability in terms of resting threshold. Abscissae = time interval between conditioning and testing stimuli. The upper curve shows recovery after a single stimulus. Note that the nerve is first supernormal, and then subnormal in correspondence with the negative and positive after-potentials. The other curves result from tetanic stimulations as indicated, e.g., 3/90 means 3 stimuli at 90 per sec. Note summation of subnormality and finally recovery (23/250) through a course of subnormality giving no sign of supernormal process. (From Gasser and Grundfest, *Amer. J. Physiol.*, 1936, *117*:113–133.)

parallel, suppresses supernormality and enhances subnormality (Fig. 62). This increase in subnormality contingent upon repetitive stimulation is called *summation of subnormality;* a high degree of unresponsiveness having an extended time course may be attained by this process.

Comparison of B and C Fibers with A Fibers (7, 13, 14, 15). An idea of the distinctions between A, B and C fibers can best be attained by a study of Figures 63 and 64, in which the spikes of single fibers, the after-potentials and the recovery cycles are contrasted. Conduction velocity of B fibers varies between 15 and 3 meters per sec., in consequence of which they overlap to some extent the lower range of A fibers which conduct at velocities as low as 5 meters per sec. There is likewise an overlap in threshold. In other properties, however, there is a sharp break between A and B fibers. The duration

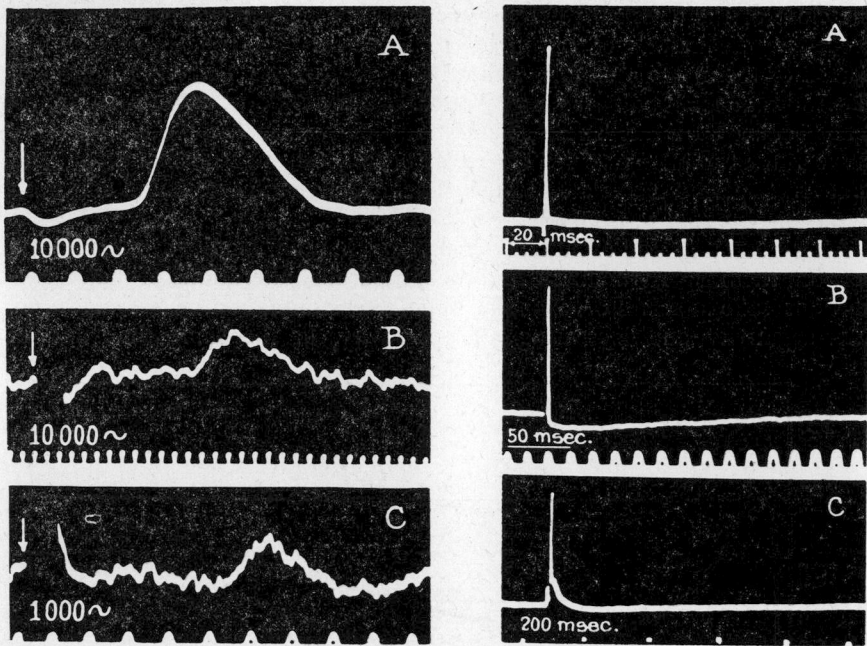

Fig. 63.—Comparison of A, B and C fibers. At the left are compared the spikes of single axons. The uneven line of the B and C spikes results from the need for extremely high amplification. At the right are compared the after-potentials of the three types of fiber. Further details may be found in Table 5. (From Gasser, *Ohio J. Sci.*, 1941, *41*:145–159.)

Recovery of excitability after a single response

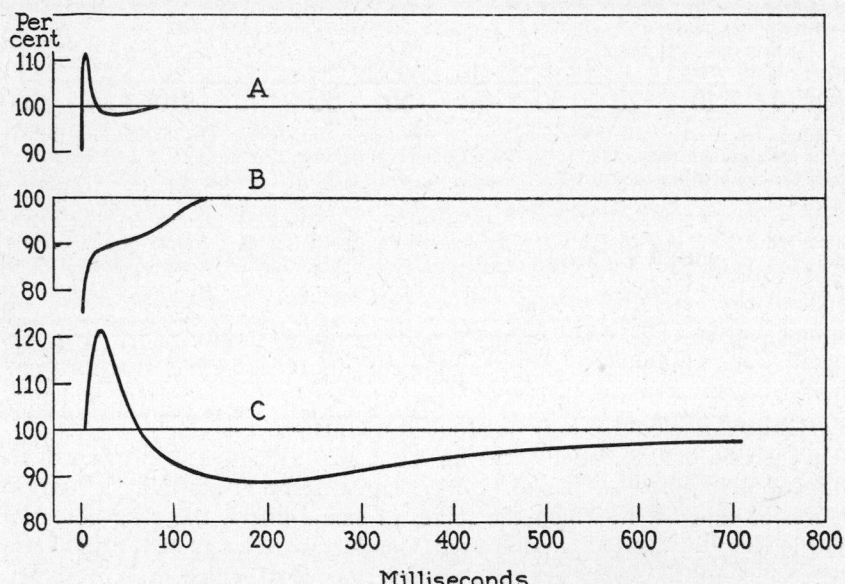

Fig. 64.—Comparison of A, B and C fibers. The recovery curves obtained following single responses of fibers belonging to the three major fiber groups and plotted on similar coordinates. Ordinates = excitability in terms of resting threshold. Abscissae = time interval between conditioning and testing stimuli. (From Gasser, *Ohio J. Sci.*, 1941, *41*:145–159.)

of the B fiber spike is about 1.2 msec., being approximately twice that of an A spike duration. In the after-potential and recovery cycles there is considerable disparity as between A fibers and B fibers. Whereas the A fibers exhibit a negative after-potential and supernormality following a single action, there are no visible counterparts in the B fibers. The B spike ends precipitously in positive after-potential and recovery progresses through a continuously subnormal course. In distribution B fibers appear to be confined to the autonomic nervous system in which they serve almost exclusively as preganglionic fibers. A probable exception is that the postganglionic fibers of the ciliary ganglion belong to the B group.

Between B fibers and C fibers, which conduct impulses at velocities between 2 and 0.6 meters per sec., another sharp discontinuity in properties occurs. The duration of a single axon spike is 2 msec. or approximately four times that of the single fiber A spike. The absolutely refractory period is correspondingly long. There is a negative after-potential of some 80 msec. duration followed by a positive after-potential that may be detectable for more than a second. The C fibers embrace the whole group of unmyelinated fibers. In Table 5 may be found a summary of the principal properties of the three groups of mammalian nerve fibers.

Table 5.—*Properties of Mammalian Nerve Fibers*
(Slightly modified from Grundfest, 14)

Group	A	B	C
Fiber diameter in micra	20–1	<3	unmyelinated
Conduction velocity in meters per sec.	120–5	15–3	2–0.6
Spike duration, msec.	0.4–0.5	1.2	2.0
Absolutely refractory period, msec.	0.4–1.0	1.2	2.0
Negative after potential			
Amount (per cent of spike)	3–5	none	3–5
Duration, msec.	12–20	. . . .	50–80
Positive after potential			
Amount (per cent of spike)	0.2	1.5–4.0	1.5
Duration, msec.	40–60	100–300	300–1000
Period of latent addition, msec.	0.2	0.2	2.5
Order of susceptibility to asphyxia	2	1	3

FIBER CONSTITUTION OF VARIOUS NERVES (2, 3)

All of the velocities in the A fiber band are not equally present in all somatic nerves. The constitution of ventral roots is different from that of dorsal roots, cutaneous nerves differ from muscle nerves, and the afferent fibers from muscle are characteristically different in size distribution from those arising in the skin. The major characteristics of nerve constitution can be illustrated by fiber distribution plots of a ventral root to show motor fiber types, of a cutaneous nerve to show cutaneous afferent types and of a "demotored" muscle nerve (that is, a muscle nerve from which the motor fibers have been removed by degeneration following ventral root section) to show muscle afferent fiber types.

Somatic motor fibers. Figure 65 (upper left) illustrates the fact that the fiber distribution plot of a ventral root, which contains motor fibers, has two prominent peaks. These occur in the ranges from 20 μ to 12 μ and from 8 μ

to 2 μ. There are very few fibers in the range between 12 μ and 8 μ. Certain differences are to be found in the fiber constitution of individual ventral roots, the most marked difference being that between ventral roots of segments which contribute to the sympathetic chain (that is, the thoracic and upper lumbar roots) and those that do not. The former are characterized by a much higher peak in the region of the fiber distribution plot below 3 μ (Häggqvist). The fibers so represented are B fibers. The ventral root fibers between 20 μ and 12 μ in diameter are the motor fibers to skeletal muscles.

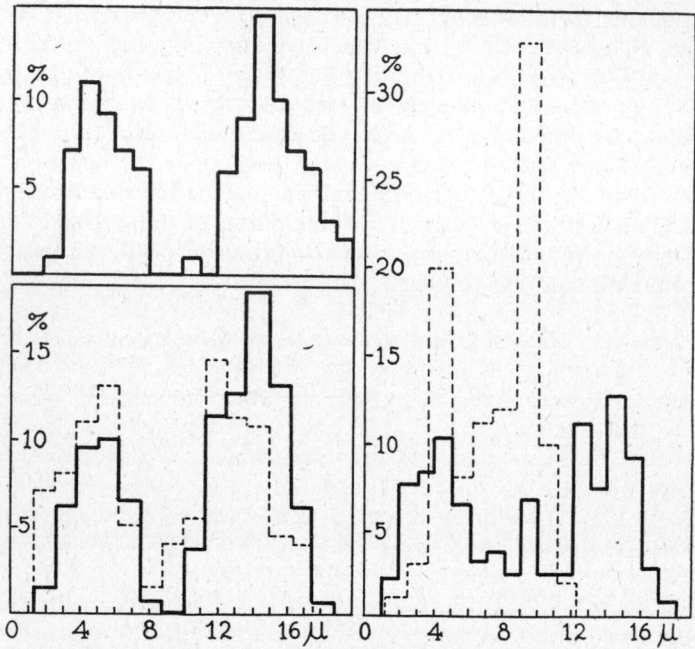

Fig. 65.—Fiber distribution plots according to diameter in characteristic spinal roots and nerves. *Upper left*—sacral ventral root, showing two peaks, one between 20 μ and 12 μ, the other between 8 μ and 2 μ. *Lower left*—Deafferented nerve of gastrocnemius medialis. Solid line = sectioned at 50 mm. from muscle; hatched line = 8 mm. from muscle. Note that the distribution of fiber sizes is similar to that in ventral root; also, slight shift in fiber sizes due to branching of fibers at some distance from the muscle. *Right*—Solid lines = fiber size distribution among afferent fibers arising in muscle; counts made on nerve of gastrocnemius medialis muscle after degeneration (by ventral root section) of all motor fibers. Hatched line = size distribution of fibers in a cutaneous afferent nerve (dorsal digital). Note that the largest afferent fibers are distributed exclusively to muscle, also that there are very few muscle afferent fibers in the band occupied by the first peak in the cutaneous fiber distribution (12 μ–6 μ). (After Eccles and Sherrington, *Proc. roy. Soc.*, 1930, *B106*:326–357.)

There is no agreement on, and very little understanding of, the function of the pile of fibers between 8 μ and 2 μ. These fibers are present in the muscle nerves as well as in the ventral roots and they clearly supply muscle. They may form the motor nerve supply for the intrafusal muscle fibers of the muscle spindles (see Chap. 8).

As the motor fibers leave the ventral roots and pass into the nerves, a certain amount of axon branching takes place, the daughter fibers being of smaller diameter than the parent fibers. This results in an increase in the total number of fibers and a slight but significant shift in the fiber size plot of a muscle nerve (Fig. 65—lower left). Erlanger, during the course of action potential studies, has found evidence that a single axon may branch into as many as three daughter fibers, the daughter fibers conducting impulses at different velocities.

Afferent fibers. In the dorsal roots all fiber sizes from 20 μ to 1 μ are to be found. These fibers are afferent in function, that is to say, they normally conduct impulses from the periphery to the central nervous system. Before the afferent fibers reach the dorsal roots they are to be found both in muscle nerves and in skin nerves, the distribution, in terms of fiber size, not being equal in the two cases (Fig. 65—right). All of the afferent fibers in the size range from 20 μ to about 13 μ reach the dorsal roots from the muscle nerves. In the next group ranging in size from 12 μ to 8 μ, a few have their origin in muscle nerves, but the overwhelming majority are to be found in the skin nerves. The small fibers, below 8 μ in diameter, again are to be found both in muscle and skin nerves.

For a number of years interest has centered on the significance of the wide range of fiber sizes (and so of conduction velocities), particularly in the afferent nerves. Certain relations between afferent fiber size and reflex effect are known. These are discussed in Chapter 6. Early work on the compound spike potential, by showing that the afferent fibers were distributed about a number of modes, suggested that there might be a relationship between the elevations of the compound spike potential and the modalities of sensation. Such a simple relation failed to materialize when investigated. The relation of fiber sizes to the modalities of sensation is discussed in Section III.

Unmyelinated or C fibers form an impressive percentage of the total bulk of the afferent fibers, but not all of the C fibers in a skin nerve are afferent fibers. Depending upon the nerve examined, the ratio of unmyelinated to myelinated fibers varies from one to four. Of these some 10 to 20 per cent have been shown to be contributed by the sympathetic system.

Sympathetic nerves differ from one another principally in the ratio of B fibers to C fibers. Most nerves in the sympathetic system contain both preganglionic and postganglionic fibers by reason of the fact that a number of ganglia appear along the course of the sympathetic pathways from the spinal cord to the innervated organs. Although the evidence (Langley) is quite clear that only one cell station occurs in each peripheral pathway of the sympathetic, some cell stations are in the sympathetic chain, others at the collateral ganglia. With respect to any particular ganglion, the ratio of C fibers to B fibers is greater in nerves leaving the ganglion than in nerves entering the ganglion. Some sympathetic nerves consist almost entirely of C fibers; the colonic nerves leaving the inferior mesenteric ganglia to supply the large bowel, for instance, exhibit nothing but a C elevation on oscillographic study, and on histological study may be seen to contain but two or three fine myelinated fibers or perhaps none at all. There are some fine myelinated postganglionic fibers leaving the superior cervical ganglion and ciliary ganglion, situations that show a particular relation to the structures of the eye.

FIBER CONSTITUTION OF SPINAL TRACTS (20)

The white columns of the spinal cord consist for the most part of fibers extending longitudinally for variable distances up and down the spinal cord. All sizes of myelinated fibers are represented, as are unmyelinated fibers. As yet only scattered information is available on the fiber constitution and conduction properties of spinal tracts based on histological and oscillographic studies, but several important generalizations can be made from what information there is.

Propriospinal fibers. The spinal cord contains vast numbers of fibers that arise and terminate wholly within the spinal cord. These are known by several names, the most usual being propriospinal fibers or intrinsic spinal fibers. Tower, Bodian and Howe (25) have studied the propriospinal fibers after all other (extrinsic) fibers have been removed by sectioning the cord above and below a selected region and all the dorsal roots to that region. When sufficient time was left for degeneration of all extrinsic fibers only those propriospinal fibers of the region itself remained. Upon examination of histological prepara-

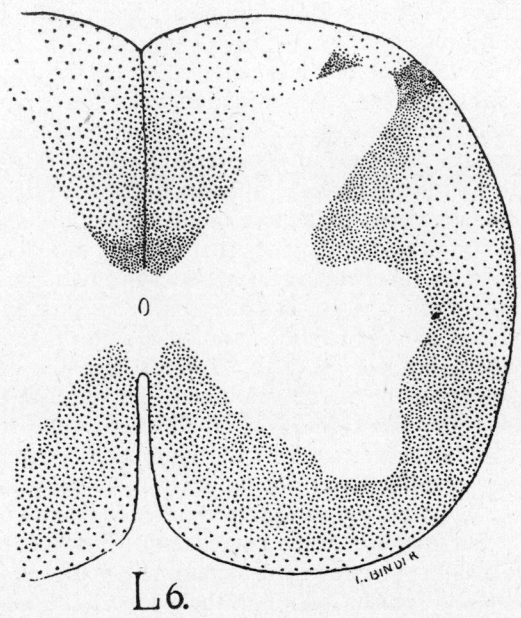

Fig. 66.—Distribution of propriospinal fibers throughout the white columns of the spinal cord. The density of fibers is greatest close to the gray substance, particularly at the tip of the dorsal horn and at the depth of the posterior columns, but note that there is at no place a region free from propriospinal fibers. (From Tower, Bodian and Howe, *J. Neurophysiol.*, 1941, *4*:388–397.)

tions after this procedure one finds that the number of fibers remaining in the cord is so great that it is difficult to appreciate the loss of fibers. The propriospinal fibers exist everywhere throughout the white matter although they are not evenly distributed (cf. Fig. 66). In the dorsal columns most of the fibers are small (about 1 μ), but there is a scattering of larger fibers. By way of contrast, the ventrolateral columns contain fibers of all sizes, a considerable number beging as large as any to be found in the normal spinal cord. These large propriospinal fibers are the only ones that have been studied by oscillographic methods; they are known to conduct impulses at velocities characteristic of *alpha* fibers (up to 120 meters per sec.).

Ascending fibers in the spinal cord arise from neurons within the cord itself, or, in the case of the dorsal columns, from neurons in the dorsal root ganglia.

All sizes of fiber are represented, but again, as in the afferent nerves, significant segregations of fiber sizes occur. The spinocerebellar tracts contain fibers of large size, and impulses in these tracts are conducted at velocities even exceeding 120 meters per sec. The dorsal columns, containing for the most part the intraspinal projection of dorsal root fibers, are of medium size and are characterized by a maximum conduction velocity usually not exceeding 70 meters per sec. The spinothalamic fibers are small and at present there is no evidence available on conduction velocities of these fibers. Some idea of the fiber constitution of these several tracts can be gained from Figure 67, but one must remember that the fiber counts were made on the *area* of spinal cord containing the tract in question, with the result that fibers of other origin (chiefly propriospinal) are represented as well as those belonging specifically to the named tracts.

Descending fibers of the spinal cord include all the fibers that enter the spinal cord from more rostral regions of the central nervous system. Prom-

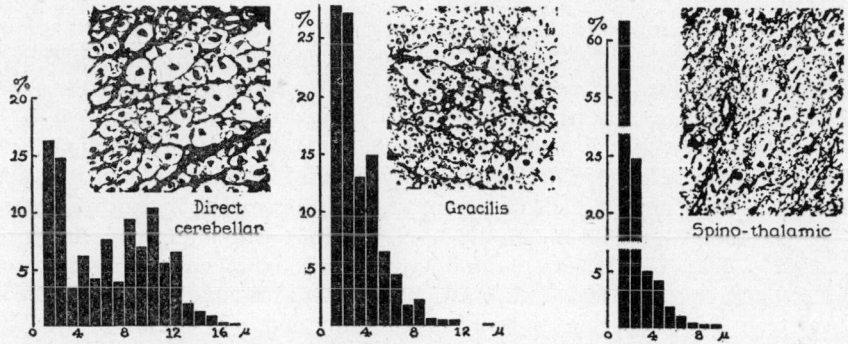

Distribution of fiber sizes in the tracts of the spinal cord

Fig. 67.—Fiber distribution plots and typical sections of areas of the white columns containing in order (*1*) the direct cerebellar tract (Flechsig); (*2*) the fasciculus gracilis; and (*3*) the spinothalamic tract. The selected areas contain, in addition to the tracts named, numerous propriospinal fibers. Note the large fibers present in the cerebellar tract and for contrast the fact that over 60 per cent of fibers in the spinothalamic tract are 1–2 μ in diameter. Fasciculus gracilis is intermediate in character. (After Häggqvist, *Z. micr.-anat. Forsch.*, 1936, *39*:1–34.)

inent among these are the fibers of the vestibular and reticular systems and of the pyramidal tract. The former are of fairly uniform large size and have conduction velocities comparable to those of peripheral alpha fibers. The latter are spread throughout a wide band of fiber sizes, the largest having a conduction velocity of about 65 meters per sec. (cat). Larger fibers are present in the pyramidal tracts of the higher apes and man. Presumably the presence of large pyramidal fibers in apes and man is to be correlated with the performance of fine individual movements.

Despite the lack of systematic observations such as we have on peripheral fibers, it may be said in general conclusion that nerve fibers in the central nervous system have the same properties of conduction as do peripheral nerve fibers. Scattered data on the refractory period, diameter-velocity relation, velocity-threshold relation and velocity-spike amplitude relation of fibers in the central nervous system indicate that the properties of these fibers are not seriously at variance with those of peripheral nerve fibers.

5

CONDUCTION IN IMMATURE AND REGENERATING FIBERS (1, 18, 26)

Conduction velocity during growth. The conduction velocity of nerve fibers at birth is very low. As growth takes place it increases progressively until the velocities characteristic of adult nerves are attained. Hursh used the length of the leg from the head of the femur to the tip of the toes as a measure of growth and found that a linear relation holds between the length of the leg and the conduction velocity of fibers in a leg nerve such as saphenous. The diameter of nerve fiber likewise increases during growth, and it has been found that the increase in conduction velocity stands in linear relation to the increase in diameter. These relations are such that the time involved in conduction of impulses, say from a toe to the spinal cord, and presumably therein, is the same when the animal is newborn and when fully grown, a fact that may be of considerable importance in learning and maintaining well coordinated reactions. Although conduction velocity increases during growth, other features appear not to change. For example, after-potentials depend more upon fiber type than upon fiber size.

Conduction and regeneration. Regeneration of nerve fibers takes place in two steps which may be termed "rate of advance of the axon tips" and "maturation of the new nerve trunks" (26). The rate of advance of the axon tips varies with conditions and may be as great as 3.5 to 4.5 mm. per day. Maturation, by which is meant increase in diameter and myelination, is a slower process. Much of the evidence suggests that maturation is progressive along a regenerating stretch of nerve, that is, the proximal region is more advanced than the distal region at any given time. One might expect this to result in progressive slowing of conduction along the regenerating stretch of nerve, but some recent observations have shown that conduction velocity is linear over a considerable length of regenerating nerve (5 cm.).

Conduction velocity in regenerating nerve increases as the regeneration time is lengthened, and, in fact, forms a measure of the process of maturation. If nerves are cut and resutured, it may be that the normal conduction velocity is never regained; for example, Berry, Grundfest and Hinsey (1) found after 450 days of regeneration that the highest velocity of fiber in a sciatic nerve was but 80–85 meters per sec., compared with a normal velocity of approximately 120 meters per sec. Likewise, on histological examination the largest fibers were 16 μ as compared with the normal of 20 μ. This failure is presumably due to the extensive branching (branching results in daughter fibers of smaller size and lower conduction velocity than the parent fiber) that takes place at the suture line, for Guttman and Sanders find complete recovery of axon diameter on regeneration, if the nerve is merely crushed and the fibers are free to grow in their normal sheaths. As fiber diameter increases during the course of regeneration, as in normal growth, the relation between conduction velocity and fiber diameter is linear.

In a recent note (*Nature*, 1945, *155*:237–238) Sanders and Young present experiments to show that the re-establishment of connection between nerve fibers and end-organs has a profound effect on the size attained by the regenerating fibers. Following a crush, many new fibers grow down the Schwann tubes, and if one connects with an end-organ, it hypertrophies at the expense of others in the same tube. If no connection is made, the fibers begin to myelinate, but none enlarges to approach normal diameter.

CONDUCTION IN THE NEURON SOMA (19, 21, 24)

For some years a controversy has centered about the question of whether or not impulses are conducted over the soma of a neuron as they are over the axon. The problem was intensified by the introduction of antidromic* stimulation as a means for analyzing the activity of neurons. One view held that the conducted impulse traversed the whole neuron, conduction in soma

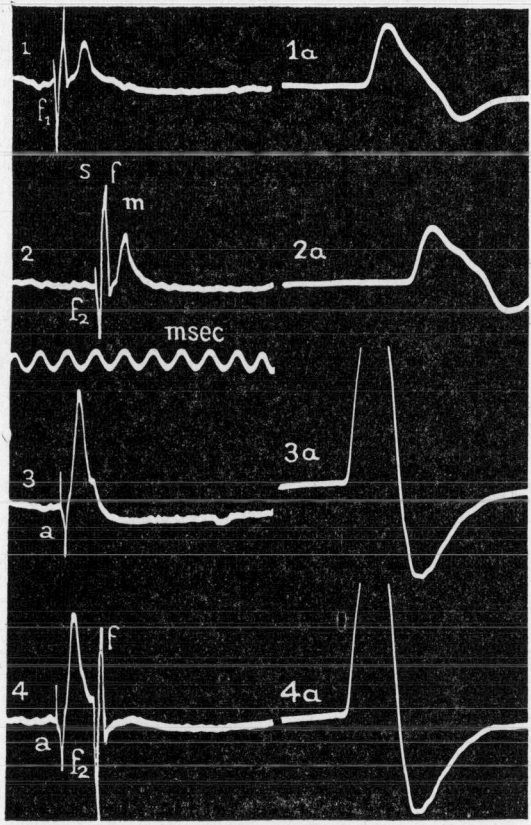

Fig. 68.—Spike potentials of motoneuron somata recorded by means of a micro-electrode situated in the oculomotor nucleus (1–4) and response of internal rectus muscle (1a–4a). 1 and 2, Response to stimulation of dorsal longitudinal bundle. S = stimulus; f = presynaptic impulses entering nucleus; m = response of motoneurons; 1a and 2a = resulting action of muscle. 3, Response of motoneurons to maximal antidromic stimulation. 4, A synaptic stimulus (f_2) follows an antidromic stimulus (a) by a brief interval. One can see the response of the motoneurons to the antidromic stimulation. Before this is completed the spike potential of the entering presynaptic volley f appears, but there is practically no motoneuron response because of refractoriness. (From Lorente de Nó, *J. Neurophysiol.*, 1939, *2*:402–464.)

and axon being qualitatively, if not quantitatively, similar. The other view held that the activity of the soma was quite different, only the axon participating in conduction proper. With regard to antidromic volleys, one group

---

* Although a nerve trunk will conduct impulses in either direction, normal activity occurs in but one direction which is from dendrite to axon. Stimulation of axons in such a way as to "backfire" impulses into the neuron somata, that is, against the direction of normal conduction, is commonly called "antidromic stimulation" and the volley of impulses backfired into the neuron somata is an "antidromic volley."

held that they passed from the axon to the soma, the other that they stopped at the axon hillock.

Lorente de Nó (21) was the first to record, by means of a minute electrode inserted into the oculomotor nucleus, the potential changes of the soma following antidromic stimulation and normal synaptic stimulation.* These potential changes may be seen in Figure 68. Records 1 and 2 of Figure 68 illustrate the response of the oculomotor nucleus to normal synaptic stimulation. The initial triphasic spike potential (f) records the presynaptic impulses entering the oculomotor nucleus. Then follows the response of the motoneurons (m). Record 3 shows the response of the motoneurons to antidromic stimulation. The initial positive deflection denotes the impulses entering the nucleus (i.e., approaching the micro-electrode), then follows the negative and final positive phases as the impulses sweep over the motoneuron somata. To obtain record 4 a synaptic stimulation follows an antidromic stimulation by a brief interval. The motoneuron somata do not respond to the synaptic stimulation; they are refractory, which is to say that the electrical response of the soma is associated with a refractory period. This fact alone is presumptive evidence in favor of the view that conduction in the soma is qualitatively similar to conduction in axons, and this is the view most generally accepted today.

INTERACTION BETWEEN NERVE CELLS (10, 22, 23)

The fact that one tissue can stimulate another has been known since Galvani's classical experiment on "contraction without metals" published in 1794. Couched in present day terms, Galvani found that the demarkation currents and action currents of a muscle would stimulate another muscle indirectly if the nerve of the second muscle was placed so that it touched the normal surface and cut end of the first muscle. Cross stimulation of nerve fibers by other nerve fibers appears first to have been noted by Hering nearly a hundred years later. The classical Hering experiment consists of stimulating one of the two branches of the sciatic nerve centrally after sectioning the main trunk where the fibers of both branches are intermingled. The muscles innervated by the other sciatic branch contract as the result of cross stimulation near the cut ends of the intermingled fibers pertaining to the two branches. The essential factor in such experiments seems to be the lowered threshold of the intermingled fibers resulting from the flow of demarkation current near the cut end. For many years serious doubt existed that the activity of some nerve fibers would affect neighboring fibers in the absence of injury or some other artificially induced conditions, and indeed this doubt was substantiated by negative experiments.

It is, of course, true that nerve fibers in the absence of injury exhibit independent conduction, impulses traveling along certain stimulated fibers, but not laterally to excite and travel along neighboring fibers. However, recent experiments have shown that subtle threshold changes occur in resting fibers when impulses pass by in adjacent fibers. These threshold effects are small and so do not imperil the basic principle of isolated conduction in the individual nerve fibers.

* A nucleus such as the oculomotor consists of a group of nerve cells situated in the central nervous system. The mass of the central nervous system acts as a volume conductor, and the records obtained by the use of micro-electrodes accordingly must be interpreted in the light of the laws governing distribution of currents in conducting media, for which cf. Chapter 1.

To gain an understanding of the nature of interaction between adjacent nerve fibers, one must call to mind the facts of conduction in volume conductors (Chap. 1) and realize that each nerve fiber in a nerve forms part of the external conductor of other adjacent nerve fibers. For simplicity consider as in the lower part of Figure 69 just two adjacent fibers C, in which an impulse is being conducted, and T, the excitability of which is to be tested during the passage of the impulse in C. During the monophasic spike potential in fiber

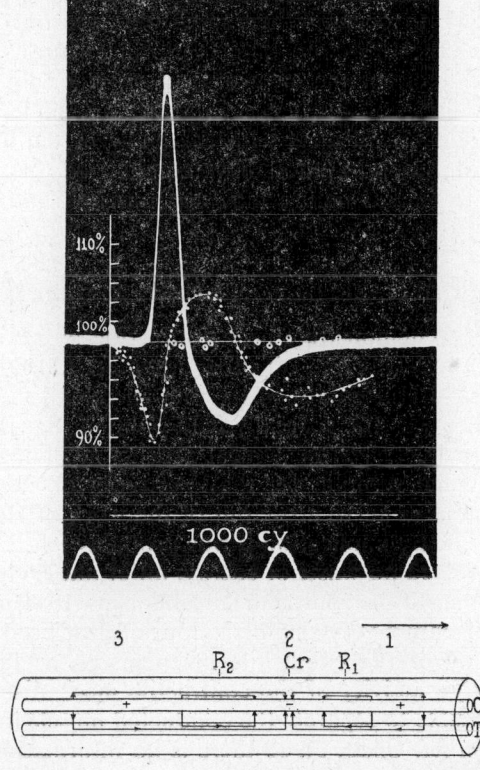

Fig. 69.—Interaction of nerve fibers. The effect of an impulse traveling in some fibers upon the threshold of neighboring fibers to electrical stimulation. *Below*—diagram of the conditions about an active fiber to illustrate how a neighboring fiber would be affected. 1, 2, 3 = the three phases of the current flow about an impulse. R_1, R_2 = the first and second reversal points of current flow. Cr = crest of the spike potential. The impulse is supposed to be traveling in the direction of the arrow in fiber C. The excitability of fiber T is tested. *Above*—curve of threshold of fiber T superimposed upon a record of the *longitudinal* flow of current of the conditioning fibers. Note the three phases of threshold variation in the tested fibers: depression, enhancement, depression, in that order. (After Marrazzi and Lorente de Nó, *J. Neurophysiol.*, 1944, 7:83–101.)

C, current successively flows outwards, inwards and outwards; that is, the membrane current of fiber C reverses twice. Now a fraction of this current will flow through fiber T, and in so doing will produce changes in excitability of fiber T. The effect of the current flow about C will be a succession of anodal, cathodal, and anodal flow of current through the membrane of fiber T. The excitability of fiber T, therefore, should pass through the successive phases: depression, enhancement, and depression. Figure 69 shows that this expectation is realized.

The temporal relations of the excitability curves of fiber T do not fit exactly the changes in membrane current of C. The excitability change begins earlier, the reversal points do not coincide exactly with the reversals of membrane current in C, and the final depression phase far outlasts the detectable flow of membrane current in C. These discrepancies are due to two major factors: (i) the spread through the conducting volume of the conditioning stimulus, and (ii) the course of electrotonus in the axons. They do not invalidate the fundamental relation. For a full discussion of interaction, one should refer to the paper of Marrazzi and Lorente de Nó (21) which, in addition, gives other important references.

Interaction between one nerve cell and another in the central nervous system has been shown to occur. When some motoneurons are activated by antidromic volleys, the threshold of neighboring neurons may be altered either in the direction of enhancement of depression, or not at all, depending upon the anatomical relationship between the active and affected neurons (23). The interaction commonly begins with the entry of the antidromic volley into the spinal cord. Several authors have emphasized the view that depressant actions of this general nature may account for central inhibition (cf. Chap. 6).

HEAT PRODUCTION, AFTER-POTENTIALS AND METABOLISM (5)

The first attempt to demonstrate heat production by nerve was published in 1848 by Helmholtz. This and all other attempts failed until 1926 when Downing, Gerard and Hill published the first successful measurements, and blasted what till then was the generally held opinion that the nerve impulse consisted of a reversible physicochemical process involving no expenditure of energy. The original stimulus for the long series of attempts to demonstrate heat production in nerve arose out of the work of Helmholtz on heat production in muscle. By implication it was probably felt that conduction in muscle likewise involved no waste of energy, all of muscle heat being related in one way or another to the contractile mechanisms. It seems just as evident today that some, if only a very small fraction, of heat production in muscle results from activity of the conductile mechanism, the larger fraction of course resulting from activity of the contractile mechanism. Unfortunately it has not been possible to separate the conducted muscle impulse from subsequent contraction (cf. Chap. 3), so there is no information on the heat of conduction in muscle. In practice it is neglected. The difficulty attending studies on heat production in nerve derives from the fact that it is about 10,000 times smaller in nerve than in muscle. Most of the available information on heat production stems from experiments on frog or crab nerve; however, incomplete studies on mammalian nerve suggest that in broad outline the heat response is the same as in frog nerve.

Resting heat of nerve. The resting heat production rate of frog nerve in oxygen at 20° C. is 4.14×10^{-3} cal. per gm. per min. (Beresina). When oxygen is replaced by nitrogen, the resting heat production falls slowly over a period of several hours to some 25 per cent of its level in oxygen, or approximately 10^{-3} cal. per gm. per min. On readmission of oxygen, the rate of heat production rises rapidly and overshoots the original level before returning to that level (Fig. 70). Since nerve produces carbon dioxide under anaerobic conditions, the slow fall from the aerobic heat production level to the anaerobic level after transferring the nerve to nitrogen is attributed to the utilization of an oxygen reserve to carry on oxidative processes in the absence of external oxygen supply, and to the consequent slow depletion of this reserve. The final steady level of heat production in nitrogen is probably the result of chemical breakdown; it can be accounted for on the basis of lactic acid formation. On readmission of oxygen, extra oxygen is used to replenish the reserve, and possibly for the oxidation of some of the lactic acid accumulated during the anaerobic period (Feng). The extra heat is presumably related to these processes. A comparison of the extra heat and extra oxygen shows that they amount to about 15 per cent of the heat missed and from 10 to 25 per cent of the oxygen missed (Fenn) during the anaerobic period.

Heat production during and following activity. When nerve is stimulated to activity it produces additional heat over and above the resting level. The additional heat of activity far outlasts the period of stimulation. When stimulation begins there is an abrupt rise in the rate of heat production followed by

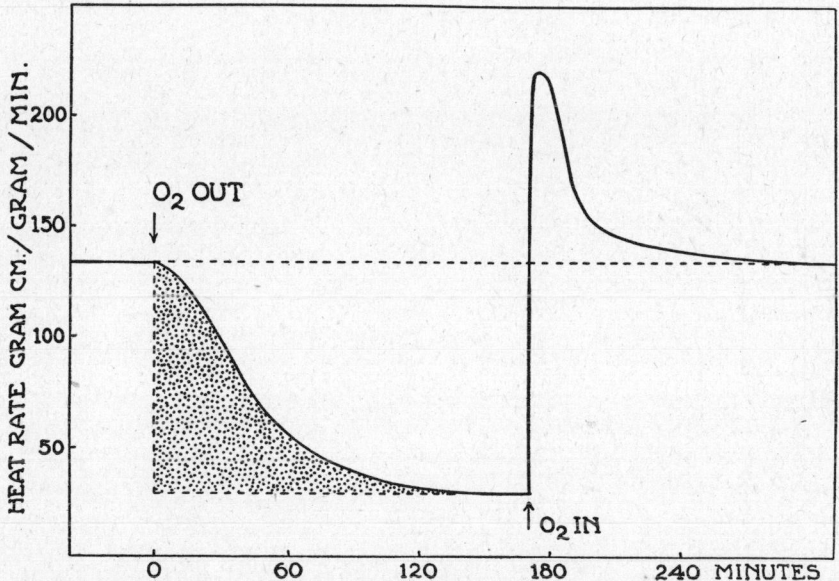

Fig. 70.—Resting heat production of nerve (frog). At the first arrow the nerve is placed in nitrogen, with resulting slow fall in heat rate. At the second arrow the nerve is replaced in oxygen. (After Beresina, modified from Feng, *Ergebn. Physiol.*, 1936, *38*:73–132.)

a slower rise that is co-extensive with the period of stimulation. At the close of stimulation there is an abrupt fall which is equal to the abrupt rise at the onset of stimulation. Following this there is a fall in the rate of heat production which presents two components. Each component follows an exponential course; the first is rapid, reaching half completion in 3 to 4 sec., the second is slow and requires some 4 minutes for half completion. The only plausible explanation of the abrupt rise and fall in rate of heat production coincident with the beginning and end of stimulation is that there is a distinct phase of heat production which is coincidental with the stimulation period. This phase of heat production is called *the initial heat*. The two components of heat production following the cessation of stimulation may be called *early delayed heat* and *late delayed heat*. Figure 71, based on A. V. Hill's analyses of heat production, serves to illustrate the components of heat production during and following stimulation. It will be noted that the secondary slow rise in heat production during stimulation is related to recovery heat which underlies the "area" referable to initial heat. The ratio of initial to recovery heat is approximately one to thirty.

In the absence of oxygen, the total heat produced by a bout of activity is less than that produced with the nerve in oxygen, all other considerations being equal. Of particular interest, however, is the fact that initial and recovery heat are not dissociable by oxygen deprivation, the course of heat production being similar under aerobic and anaerobic conditions. This suggests that the underlying reactions are the same in nitrogen as in oxygen, which again points to the existence of an oxidizing reserve. One may note in passing how different this behavior of nerve is from that of muscle (Chap. 3).

Correlation of heat production with potential signs of activity and chemical changes in nerve. At the present state of knowledge one cannot attempt to effect a satisfactory correlation between the various manifestations of nerve

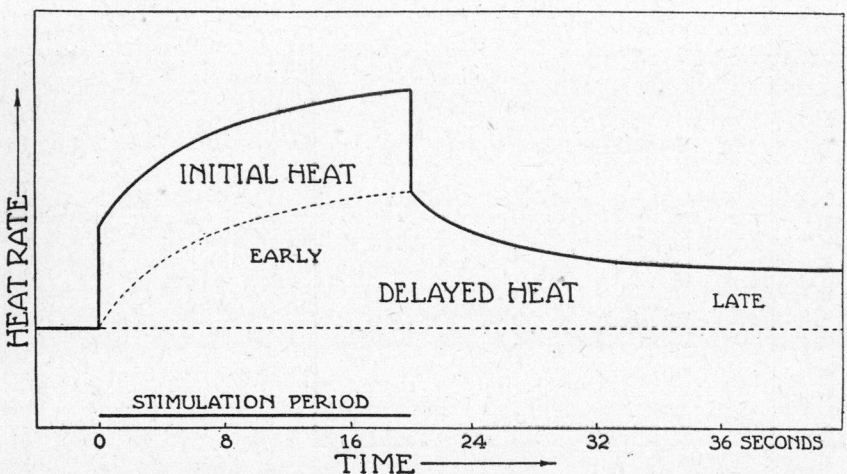

Fig. 71.—The phases of heat production by nerve during and after a bout of activity. According to Hill's analysis, heat is divided into initial heat, early delayed heat and late delayed heat, as indicated. (After Hill, modified from Feng, *Ergebn. Physiol.*, 1936, *38*:73–132.)

activity. One thing is certain: except for a very few per cent at most, the heat of nerve activity is produced after spike potential production has ceased. Furthermore, it is quite impossible to decide, with present techniques, whether that few per cent of total heat is produced during the spike potential or as much as 200 msec. after the spike potential (Feng). There is more reason to believe that there is an association between heat production and afterpotential.

One plausible point of reference for relating after-potential, heat production, respiration and chemical reaction may be found in the action of veratrine. In 1931, Graham and Gasser noted that the negative after-potential of nerve is greatly increased and greatly prolonged under the influence of veratrine, although the spike potential is not appreciably altered. Later, Schmitt and Gasser found a greater than normal oxygen consumption (about 15 per cent) in resting veratrinized nerves, and, whereas a slow tetanus did not produce a measurable increase in oxygen consumption in normal nerve, it did produce a marked increase in veratrinized nerve. These conclusions lead to the association of negative after-potential with a process involving oxidative metabolism. Turning to heat production of nerve, Hill has found that veratrine causes an increase of some 1000 times to the point where the heat of a single impulse is measurable. Finally Gerard in 1934 found that creatine phosphate breakdown, which occurs during activity in normal nerve, was markedly increased by veratrine. Now the breakdown of creatine phosphate is a strongly exothermic reaction and would probably account in great part for the large increase in heat production but it is not an oxidative reaction and so cannot of itself account for increased oxygen consumption. However, Schmitt, Graham and Schmitt calculated that the increased oxygen consumption of veratrinized nerve would represent something less than 10 to 20 per cent of the increased heat production. It is logical, therefore, that creatine phosphate breakdown, itself not oxidative, coupled with an oxidative reaction would together account for increased oxygen consumption and heat.

Phosphate compounds other than creatine phosphate have been found in nerve, notably adenyl pyrophosphate. This substance may, on oxidation, account for the ammonia production of nerve. Recent work suggests that the maintenance of the polarized structure in nerve may depend in part on phosphorylations supported by the oxidation of pyruvic acid. Furthermore, there is some reason to suppose that the reversible breakdown of acetylcholine to choline and acetate, under the action of choline esterase may form part of the metabolic cycle of nerve fibers (cf. also Chap. 5).

In a general sense it would seem correct to say, by way of summary, that the polarized structure of nerve is constantly maintained by metabolism, which in the long run depends upon oxidation. A nerve is brought to a higher metabolic level by activity and the large share, if not all, of the metabolic excess is concerned with restoration of the resting state. The existence of these activities and something of their nature may be inferred from various electrical, thermal, and respiratory manifestations of activity. Some of the chemical compounds present in nerve have been identified, and some of their reactions have been outlined. Taken altogether, however, knowledge of nerve metabolism represents not an orderly structure but rather a collection of fragments.

REFERENCES

1. BERRY, C. M., GRUNDFEST, H. and HINSEY, J. C. The electrical activity of regenerating nerves in the cat. *J. Neurophysiol.*, 1944, *7*:103–115.

2. ECCLES, J. C. and SHERRINGTON, C. S. Numbers and contraction-values of individual motor-units examined in some muscles of the limb. *Proc. roy. Soc.*, 1930, *B106*:326–357.

3. ERLANGER, J. The interpretation of the action potential in cutaneous and muscle nerves. *Amer. J. Physiol.*, 1927, *82*:644–655.

4. ERLANGER, J. and GASSER, H. S. *Electrical signs of nervous activity.* Philadelphia. University of Pennsylvania Press, 1937, 221 pp.

5. FENG, T. P. The heat production of nerve. *Ergebn. Physiol.*, 1936, *38*:73–132.

6. GASSER, H. S. Electric signs of biological activity. *J. appl. Phys.*, 1938, *9*:88–96.

7. GASSER, H. S. The classification of nerve fibers. *Ohio J. Sci.*, 1941, *41*:145–159.

8. GASSER, H. C. and GRUNDFEST, H. Action and excitability in mammalian A fibers. *Amer. J. Physiol.*, 1936, *117*:113–133.

9. GASSER, H. S. and GRUNDFEST, H. Axon diameters in relation to the spike dimensions and the conduction velocity in mammalian A fibers. *Amer. J. Physiol.*, 1939, *127*:393–414.

10. GERARD, R. W. The interaction of neurones. *Ohio J. Sci.*, 1941, *41*:160–172.

11. GRAHAM, H. T. Supernormality, a modification of the recovery process in nerve. *Amer. J. Physiol.*, 1934, *110*:225–242.

12. GRAHAM, H. T. The subnormal period of nerve response. *Amer. J. Physiol.*, 1935, *111*:452–465.

13. GRUNDFEST, H. The properties of mammalian B fibers. *Amer. J. Physiol.*, 1939, *127*:252–262.

14. GRUNDFEST, H. Bioelectric potentials. *Ann. Rev. Physiol.*, 1940, *2*:213–242.

15. GRUNDFEST, H. and GASSER, H. S. Properties of mammalian nerve fibers of slowest conduction. *Amer. J. Physiol.*, 1938, *123*:307–318.

16. HÄGGQVIST, G. Analyse der Faserverteilung in einem Rückenmarkquerschnitt (TH III). *Z. mikr.-anat. Forsch.*, 1936, *39*:1–34.

17. HURSH, J. B. Conduction velocity and diameter of nerve fibers. *Amer. J. Physiol.*, 1939, *127*:131–139.

18. HURSH, J. B. The properties of growing nerve fibers. *Amer. J. Physiol.*, 1939, *127*:140–153.

19. LLOYD, D. P. C. The interaction of antidromic and orthodromic volleys in a segmental spinal motor nucleus. *J. Neurophysiol.*, 1943, *6*:143–151.

20. LLOYD, D. P. C. Functional organization of the spinal cord. *Physiol. Rev.*, 1944, *24*:1–17.

21. LORENTE DE NÓ, R. Transmission of impulses through cranial motor nuclei. *J. Neurophysiol.*, 1939, *2*:402–464.

22. MARRAZZI, A. S. and LORENTE DE NÓ, R. Interaction of neighboring fibers in myelinated nerve. *J. Neurophysiol.*, 1944, *7*:83–101.

23. RENSHAW, B. Influence of discharge of motoneurons upon excitation of neighboring motoneurons. *J. Neurophysiol.*, 1941, *4*:167–183.

24. RENSHAW, B. Effects of presynaptic volleys on spread of impulses over the soma of the motoneuron. *J. Neurophysiol.*, 1942, *5*:235–243.

25. TOWER, S. S., BODIAN, D. and HOWE, H. Isolation of intrinsic and motor mechanism of the monkey's spinal cord. *J. Neurophysiol.*, 1941, *4*:388–397.

26. YOUNG, J. Z. The functional repair of nervous tissue. *Physiol. Rev.*, 1942, *22*:318–374.

CHAPTER 5

INTERCELLULAR TRANSMISSION

To accomplish the motor performances of the body, transmission of excitation from one cell to another must take place. Transmission from nerve cell to muscle cell is termed neuromuscular transmission; that from one nerve cell to another, synaptic transmission. Neuromuscular and synaptic transmission have many qualitative features in common, the major distinctions, indeed, resulting from the variable anatomical complexity of interrelation between the cellular elements involved. From a quantitative standpoint, differences are due in the main to the speed of reaction of the several elements taking part in transmission; for example, muscle is slow in its action compared with the nerve that supplies it (cf. Chap. 1 and Fig. 15).

NEUROMUSCULAR TRANSMISSION

Histological study has shown that the motor nerve fiber loses its myelin sheath before penetrating the sarcolemma with which the neurolemma fuses. The naked axon then terminates at a specialized region of the muscle fiber known as the end-plate, where numbers of muscle cell nuclei are packed together in a granular cytoplasm. It is at this region that excitation is transmitted from nerve fiber to muscle fiber. From a functional viewpoint, this region has been called the neuromuscular or neuromyal junction. The weight of evidence is against the possibility of protoplasmic continuity between nerve fiber and muscle fiber, but extensive contact between the two fibers occurs.

A single impulse in a motor nerve fiber evokes, at the motor end-plate of each of the muscle fibers with which it is connected, a single muscle fiber impulse which is propagated as an all-or-nothing response along the full length of each of those muscle fibers. As Adrian emphasized a number of years ago, the conducted impulse is the primary response of muscle; the mechanical response ensues. Neuromuscular transmission is thus essentially the process by which action currents are evoked in a muscle fiber by the action currents of a nerve fiber, the ultimate question being (and this is where recourse to hypothesis is made) whether the process is simple and direct or whether an intermediate step in the form of the release and action of a chemical *compound* intervenes.

Neuromuscular delay. Between the arrival of a nerve impulse at the muscle and the onset of the muscle fiber impulse there is a slight delay, according to the most accurate measurements that have yet been made. This is neuromuscular (or end-plate) delay; it has a duration of about 0.55 msec. in mammalian striate muscle. The significance of functional delays in general can be discussed to better advantage later in this chapter (p. 140).

End-Plate Potential(9). As is the case of studies on nerve, considerable information on the mechanism of neuromuscular transmission derives from studies utilizing blockade, which can be produced at the junctional region of muscle by the action of curare, the South American Indian arrow poison. Pelouze and Claude Bernard are usually credited with the observation in 1850 that curare acts in such a way that transmission from nerve to muscle is lost although both nerve and muscle severally retain their excitability. An electrical record obtained from the junctional region of a muscle following full curarization reveals that the spike potential of the muscle is absent, and in its place there is a prolonged negative potential called the "end-plate" or junctional potential. In the fully curarized muscle the end-plate potential is at best about 5 per cent of the maximal muscle spike recorded in the uncurarized muscle. Figure 72 illustrates semidiagrammatically the appearance of the conducted spike potential of muscle, and of the end-plate potential that is found after complete curarization. To obtain such records, both recording electrodes are placed on the normal muscle, one at the junctional region, the other at some distance. Hence the spike potential, conducted away from the junctional

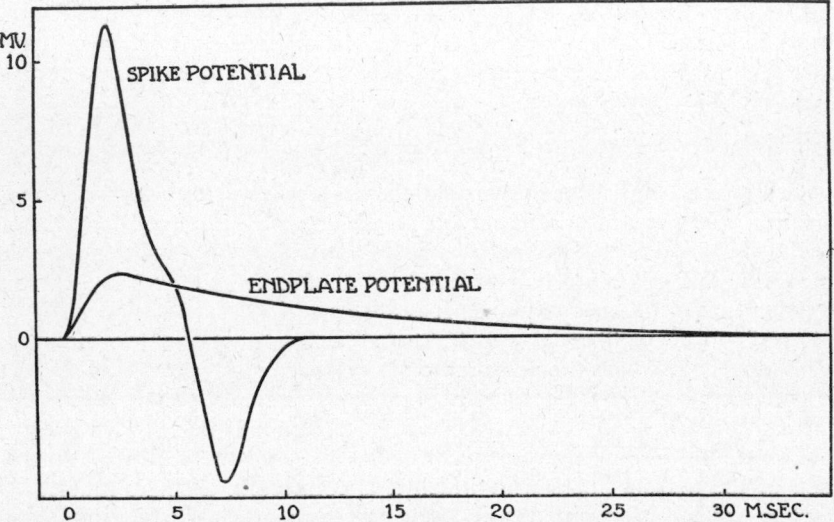

Fig. 72.—Comparison between the spike potential of muscle and the end-plate potential recorded after complete curarization. Semidiagrammatic. Note (i) similar latency; (ii) spike potential is diphasic, indicating conduction away from end-plate region; (iii) end-plate potential is not conducted—it is an electrotonic potential. (Constructed from data in Eccles, Katz and Kuffler, *J. Neurophysiol.*, 1941, *4*:362–387.)

region, appears as a diphasic change. End-plate potentials are not propagated like the spike potential; they are of a local nature. If the electrode at the junctional region is moved away a millimeter at a time, it is found that the end-plate potential decrements rapidly to disappear within a few millimeters (cf. Fig. 73). The spatial decrement of the end-plate potential follows an exponential relation and its time course of decay at any given point likewise follows an exponential relation. In Chapter 1, these spatial and temporal relations were shown to be characteristic of electrotonus, which suggests that the end-plate potential is electrotonic in nature. However, before one would accept this suggestion it must be shown that the end-plate potential and electrotonus in muscle have the same space constant and time constant. A comparison of end-plate potential and catelectrotonus in muscle does in fact reveal close identity of the two processes (31). Both of these potential processes, one the result of nerve activity, the other of passage of a subliminal current, have similar rates of decay along an exponential curve. Summation is a feature of electrotonic potentials. Therefore it is significant that an end-plate potential will sum with the extrinsic or electrotonic phase of an approaching muscle spike potential, but not with the active phase of the spike potential or impulse proper. To demonstrate this fact one stimulates a curarized muscle directly; then, as the conducting spike potential traverses the end-plate region, the nerve is stimulated to evoke an end-plate potential. Recordings are made from the end-plate region. The result is precisely what one would expect of an electrotonic potential. Another point of agreement between end-plate potential and electrotonic potential is the fact that they both are associated with changes of threshold which resemble one another and which follow the time-intensity course of the potentials themselves. The homology between end-plate potential and the classical electrotonus appears to be complete.

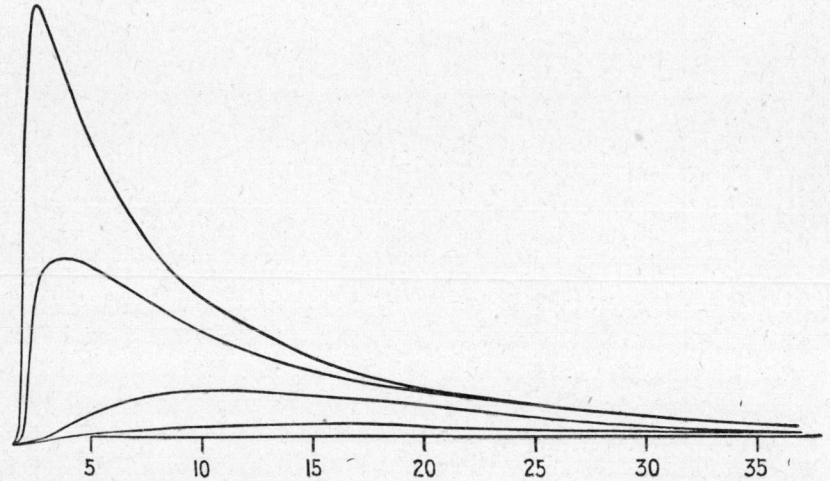

Fig. 73.—Spatial decrement of end-plate potential evoked by a single motor nerve volley following complete curarization. Top curve recorded at end-plates. The succeeding curves were recorded at distances of 1, 2 and 3 mm. from the end-plates. The intensity of the end-plate potential falls off rapidly with distance to disappear within a few mm. (From Eccles, Katz and Kuffler, J. Neurophysiol., 1941, 4:362–387.)

Relation of end-plate potential to propagated impulse. It appears likely that the initial event taking place in a muscle fiber following motor nerve stimulation is the same, whether or not neuromuscular block is achieved by the use of curare. This event is electrotonic depolarization of the excitable membranes of the muscle fibers.*

The latency for onset of the end-plate potential and the muscle spike is identical when comparison is made between the responses of fully curarized muscle and of normal muscle. A most instructive experiment consists, however, of following the intermediate course of events as curarization progresses from the normal state to the fully curarized state. Some of these intermediate

* At this point one should recall that the initial phase of the action potential (the extrinsic phase), which lasts up to the time of the first reversal point of the membrane current, is an electrotonic extension of the impulse proper. That is to say, the region in front of the first reversal point of membrane current is acting as a source of current flow to the sink immediately behind, and therefore is being depolarized (cf. Chap. 1).

stages may be seen in Figure 74. As the degree of curarization increases, the spike response falls progressively later with respect to the end-plate potential which can be seen to decrease progressively in intensity. As the spike response falls later, it decreases in size, and by the time that the end-plate potential is reduced to about 30 per cent of the total potential in the normal muscle, the spike response fails altogether. Compare now this series of events with those occurring in a nerve that is stimulated by constant currents of progressively decreasing intensity (Chap. 1, Fig. 16). The two experiments are exactly comparable. The relationship between end-plate potential and propagated

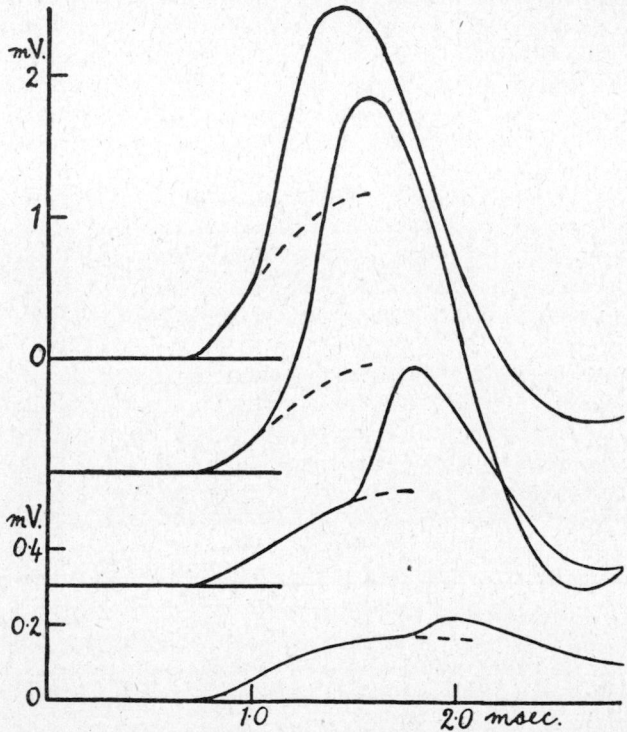

Fig. 74.—Changes in the potential recorded at the end-plate region of a muscle as it becomes progressively curarized. Three things happen: (i) the spike potential decreases in amplitude, (ii) it begins later in time, (iii) the end-plate potential decreases in amplitude; its supposed course is indicated by the hatched line extrapolating the first phase of the recorded potential. Compare these records with those in Figure 16, Chapter 1, in which a nerve is stimulated by constant currents of several intensities, but note that these muscle records are diphasic, whereas in Figure 16 the records are monophasic. The upper two records made with amplification approximately $\frac{2}{5}$ that of the lower two records. (From Eccles and Kuffler, *J. Neurophysiol.*, 1941, *4*:402–417.)

spike response is that between electrotonic polarization potential (local excitatory state) and spike response in nerve. In the normal nerve-muscle preparation the electrotonic potential rises rapidly to threshold and the active phase of the spike potential supervenes. There can be no distinction between end-plate potential and extrinsic phase of the spike potential under such conditions, for in fact they are one and the same process. As the neuromuscular junction is blocked by the application of curare, the electrotonic potential of the muscle fibers does not reach threshold and is not interrupted by the active phase of the spike process. It therefore continues along a course determined by the condenser-like properties of the muscle membranes, the time constant of which is indicated by the exponential decay of the electrotonic potential, or end-plate potential.

Summation of end-plate potentials and neuromuscular facilitation (9). If two stimuli are applied in succession to the motor nerve of a curarized muscle, the end-plate potentials evoked by the two nerve volleys sum, and, if the summated end-plate potential reaches a critical intensity, a conducted spike potential will appear and contraction follow. The effect fully resembles facilitation across a block in nerve (cf. Chap. 1) and has accordingly been called Wedensky facilitation at the neuromuscular junction.

Interpretations. Up to this point in the discussion of neuromuscular transmission consideration has been given to the question of what happens in muscle following the arrival of a motor nerve volley. Briefly, electrotonic currents flow through the muscle fiber membrane, and, if these are sufficiently intense, threshold is reached and a conducted impulse traverses the muscle fibers.

A great deal of effort has been directed toward solving the problem of how the nerve impulse exerts its effect upon the muscle fiber. The results of this endeavor have led to the promulgation of two hypotheses of the intercellular mediator. These hypotheses are commonly denoted by the adjectives "electrical" and "chemical." Stripped to their bare essentials, the former hypothesis states that the muscle fiber is stimulated by the outward flow of current from the muscle fiber to the nerve fiber as the nerve impulse reaches into the nerve fiber terminations and the muscle fiber forms the source of current flow; the latter that a specific substance, in this case acetylcholine, is liberated at the nerve terminations, that this substance stimulates the muscle fiber, and is then destroyed within the span of the refractory period by an enzyme, cholinesterase.

Electrical hypothesis. The electrical hypothesis of neuromuscular transmission forms a part of the almost universally accepted theory of impulse conduction. It has the great advantage of simplicity; furthermore, it states with clarity and unequivocally the precise role played by the supposed mediator. The view that the current flow about the nerve endings would form an adequate stimulus for the muscle fibers stems from Hermann (1879).

With the accumulation of information on excitation and conduction since that time (cf. Chap. 1), the hypothesis has gained in stature. Particular emphasis must be placed on the modern work on the properties of conduction at a nerve block (cf. Chap. 1), for the events at a nerve block form a very complete and detailed analogy for the events at a neuromuscular or synaptic junction.

Whatever the nature of the mediator, its action must fit, in time, the known course of the events in the structures forming the junction. This, the most exacting requirement of any hypothetical transmitter, is satisfactorily met by the electrical hypothesis.

Chemical hypothesis (4). The chemical hypothesis of neuromuscular transmission is a recent outgrowth of the earlier work that went to show that chemical substances (acetylcholine and sympathin, the latter being an adrenaline-like substance) mediate the action of nerve stimulation on autonomic effectors: smooth muscle, some glands, etc. (cf. Sect. II). The crux of the hypothesis lies in the function of cholinesterase, the enzyme that hydrolyzes acetylcholine. Cholinesterase is present in all tissues including blood. For this reason eserine, which prevents the hydrolysis of acetylcholine by cholinesterase, is routinely employed in experiments designed to demonstrate the liberation of acetylcholine by nerve stimulation.

Dale and Feldberg (5) first demonstrated the presence of acetylcholine in an eserinized fluid perfusing muscle following stimulation of the motor nerve supply. Shortly thereafter Brown, Dale and Feldberg (2) showed that the injection of a small amount of acetylcholine into the artery of a given muscle evoked a short asynchronous tetanic contraction of the muscle. The hypothesis states that the acetylcholine liberated by motor nerve activity stimulates the muscle fibers in the normal course of events, and is in fact the transmitter of the effect of nerve stimulation.

Since a single motor nerve volley evokes a single twitch contraction of a muscle, it follows, as Dale has said (4), that a chemical mediator would have to disappear within the period of refractoriness, else a second response would occur. No better proof of this requirement exists than the fact that repetitive action of a muscle results from a single motor nerve volley after the administration of eserine. This fact is interpreted to mean that eserine, by preventing the action of cholinesterase, has prevented the destruction of liberated acetylcholine which is then free to continue stimulating the muscle. Now it is known that cholinesterase is more concentrated in the end-plate regions of the muscle than elsewhere (14), and Marnay and Nachmansohn (28), by calculations, came to the conclusion that cholinesterase is concentrated sufficiently in the end-plate region to hydrolyze within the refractory period the calculated amount of acetylcholine liberated by a single nerve volley.

The two hypotheses relating to neuromuscular transmission appear again in relation to synaptic transmission in autonomic ganglia. For this reason further consideration will be deferred until the activity of ganglia has been treated, after which a more general discussion will be possible.

SYNAPTIC TRANSMISSION IN GANGLIA

The anatomical substrate of synaptic transmission in sympathetic ganglia is more complex than that of neuromuscular transmission. A preganglionic fiber divides many times to supply a number of ganglion cells, just as a motor fiber divides to supply many muscle fibers, but, in addition, each ganglion cell is supplied by a number of preganglionic fibers. The synaptic innervation of a number of cells by one fiber is known as the *principle of divergence*. The overlapping synaptic innervation of one cell by a number of fibers is known as the *principle of convergence*. In ganglia of the autonomic nervous system the fibers that enter the ganglion innervate the ganglion cells directly, that is, the preganglionic fiber terminations are applied directly to the postganglionic neurons; there are no interneurons. The conditions of synaptic transmission in ganglia are therefore simple compared with the immensely complex conditions attributable to the presence of interneurons in the central nervous system.

Functional Consequences of Convergence (32). The fact of convergence in ganglia, and in the central nervous system as well, introduces into the general picture of intercellular transmission some new features that are not properties of neuromuscular transmission. These new features, *occlusion* and *facilitation*, were first described in relation to the reflex activity of the spinal cord (Sherrington), and only later, by the experiments of Eccles (6), were they recognized as playing a role in transmission through ganglia.

Within a group of ganglion cells supplied by two preganglionic nerves, some of the cells are activated by one of the preganglionic nerves, some by the other, while still other cells are shared by the two preganglionic nerves. Each of those nerves, when stimulated by a single shock, causes the group of ganglion cells supplied by it to discharge synchronously, and the resulting volley of impulses may be recorded from the postganglionic nerve trunk. The amplitude of the recorded spike potential is a measure of the number of responding cells. When both preganglionic nerves are stimulated synchronously, the total, or summated response as it is called, may not be equal to the sum of the responses evoked by stimulation of the two preganglionic

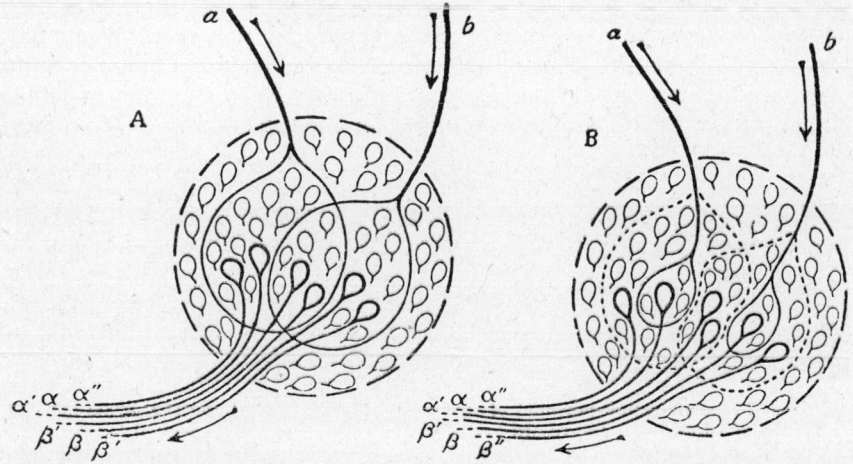

Fig. 75.—Diagrams to illustrate *occlusion* (A) and *facilitation* (B). A, The hatched line encloses a pool of neurons some of which are discharged by presynaptic fiber *a*, some by fiber *b*. The fields overlap so that when *a* and *b* are stimulated together, the discharge is less (4 neurons in the diagram) than the sum of the discharged evoked by *a* and *b* severally (6 neurons in the diagram). B, The hatched line encloses a pool of neurons, some of which are discharged by presynaptic fiber *a*, some by fiber *b*. The subliminal fields of fiber *a* and fiber *b* are enclosed by dotted lines. These subliminal fields overlap. According to the diagram (B) stimulation of *a* or *b* would cause the discharge of 1 neuron each; the sum, 2 neurons; but, stimulated together, *a* and *b* cause 4 neurons to discharge because of summation in the subliminal fringe. Two neurons are represented as remaining in the subliminal fringe on combined stimulation of *a* and *b*. (From Sherrington, *Proc. roy. Soc.*, 1929, *B105*:332–362.)

nerves in isolation. Whether the summated response is greater or smaller than the simple sum of the two separate responses is in part dependent upon the size of the incoming or preganglionic volleys of impulses.

Occlusion. If the two preganglionic volleys are powerful, the summated response may be less than the sum of the several responses. This is *occlusion*. The concept of occlusion is most easily grasped by reference to Sherrington's diagram reproduced in Figure 75 *A*. The cells of the whole group (in this case the ganglion) are enclosed within a circle. The fractions of the cell group excited by preganglionic volleys in the nerves *a* and *b* are shown in the smaller areas. For simplicity only six neurons are supposed to be concerned, four of these being within the field of nerve *a* and four in the field of nerve *b*, so that two neurons are common to both fields. Separate stimulation of either nerve will evoke the response of four neurons, but simultaneous combined stimulation of both nerves will yield only the response of six neurons, a deficit of two from the theoretical addition.

Facilitation. If the two preganglionic volleys are small, each may result in the discharge of impulses by a certain number of neurons while exciting others to a degree short of that required to procure the discharge of impulses; in other words, subliminally. Under such circumstances, the field occupied by neurons excited to discharge is called the *discharge zone*, while the field of neurons receiving subliminal excitation is the *subliminal fringe*. When the two preganglionic nerves are stimulated together, the resulting discharge may be greater than the sum of the discharges taken severally. This is *facilitation*. Again, the concept of facilitation may be illustrated by Sherrington's diagram in Figure 75 *B*. Let us suppose that the discharge zone of each preganglionic nerve contains one neuron; the subliminal fringe, three neurons. Summation may occur at the neurons common to the subliminal fringes of nerve *a* and nerve *b* with the result that threshold is reached. Concurrent stimulation of nerves *a* and *b* would place four neurons in the discharge zone, whereas simple addition of the several responses would give the discharge of but two neurons.

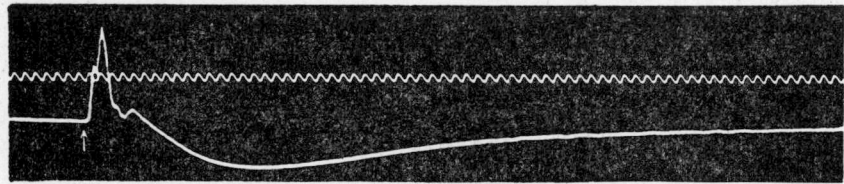

Fig. 76.—Complete action potential of the superior cervical ganglion. The arrow indicates the moment of stimulation. The record begins with a compound spike potential indicating the discharge of several groups of ganglion cells having different time constants. Then follow the negative and positive after-potentials. Note the great amplitude of the after-potential relative to the spike potential; for comparison with nerve fibers cf. Figure 63, Chapter 4. Time = 100 cycles. (From Eccles, *J. Physiol.*, 1935, 85:179–206.)

Potential Signs of Ganglionic Activity (6, 18). Following single shock stimulation of a preganglionic nerve, a single volley of impulses is discharged by the ganglion cells. Several major groups of ganglion cells may be distinguished in the superior cervical ganglion by reason of differences in conduction velocities and synaptic delays, whereas many other ganglia appear to be more homogeneous. The most rapidly acting group, prominent in the superior cervical ganglia, are large cells that appear to be supplied by preganglionic fibers of the "A delta" group (cf. Chap. 4), and when discharging after preganglionic stimulation do so with a synaptic delay of about two msec. The second group of cells supplied by "B" type preganglionic fibers, is made up of medium-size cells which respond after a synaptic delay of about 5 msec. There are still other groups consisting of small cells. These groups are quite distinct, convergence occurring within each group but not between groups. The faster acting ganglion cells are distributed to structures in the orbit; the slower acting ganglion cells are prominently vasomotor and pilomotor in function.

Following the spike potentials of a ganglion, there are, in order, a negative after-potential and a positive after-potential (Fig. 76). These after-potentials are much larger in the ganglion, inhabited by ganglion cells, than in the postganglionic trunk where after-potentials are contributed by the postganglionic fibers alone. As in nerve (Chap. 4), the after-potentials are associated with threshold changes, the ganglion cells being in a state of supernormal excitability during the negative after-potential and in a state of subnormal excitability during the positive after-potential.

Degrees of synaptic excitation (17). Supernormality and subnormality are changes in threshold; they modify the ease with which the tissue exhibiting them may be stimulated, but they do not determine whether stimulation can or cannot occur. Thus it is a common practice in demonstrating these changes in nerve to select a test stimulus somewhere between threshold and maximum for the whole nerve. In this way all grades of excitation by the test stimulus are represented among the fibers of the nerve. Some, which are just subliminally excited, will come to threshold by virtue of being in the supernormal state and the response of the nerve as a whole to such a test stimulation will be increased. Later, during the subnormal phase, some fibers which are

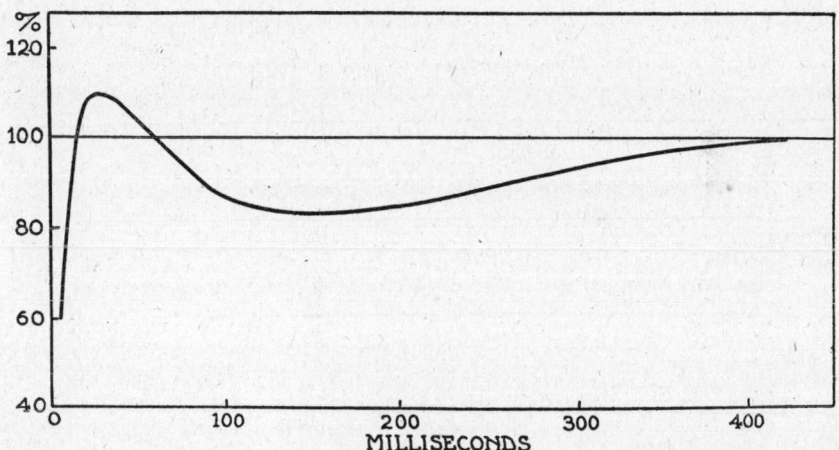

Fig. 77.—Recovery curve of a sympathetic ganglion following a single preganglionic volley. Recovery progresses through absolute and relative refractory periods, supernormality and subnormality. Supernormality may result in facilitation of the ganglionic response; subnormality in inhibition of the response. Note the correspondence between after-potentials (Fig. 76) and recovery. (Based on data in Lloyd, *J. Physiol.*, 1939, *95*:464–475.)

brought to threshold by the test stimulus applied alone to the resting nerve will fail to reach threshold because of the subnormality, and the response of the nerve as a whole will be decreased. It follows that a nerve tested by a threshold stimulus can reveal only an increase in response, and one tested by a maximal stimulus only a decrease in response. Similarly, a nerve tested by a stimulus considerably in excess of maximal would reveal no tangible evidence of excitability changes other than the refractory period. The situation is somewhat comparable when experiments are designed to demonstrate supernormality and subnormality of the somata of ganglion cells, because the stimulus delivered to the ganglion cells by the preganglionic terminations is a quantity fixed, to a remarkable degree, by anatomical factors. In one or another ganglion evidence may be found for the conclusion that the synaptic relations between preganglionic fibers and ganglion cells are such that some fibers when stimulated have a subliminal action on ganglion cells, and hence

Summation is necessary to secure their discharge; others have a liminal action, while still others excite cells with a strength well above threshold. Thus, although ganglion cells clearly recover from activity along a course that includes, as seen in Figure 77, first a refractory period, then, in succession, a supernormal period and a subnormal period, there may be no sign of an increase in response to a test volley during the supernormal period (facilitation) nor a decrease in response during the subnormal period (inhibition) for the simple reason that the synaptic stimulus may be well in excess of maximal. Indeed, the synaptic connections in some ganglia are so powerful in action that convergence of preganglionic fibers at the ganglion cells would, in such situations, appear to be an incidental factor in securing transmission.

Two periods of facilitation in ganglia. It follows from the foregoing discussion that there are two distinct periods of facilitation in ganglia. The initial facilitation is brief (being about 2 msec. in duration at ganglionic synapses) and results from summation of subliminal excitatory effects of convergent impulses at the ganglion cell. The convergent impulses must arrive at the ganglion cells synchronously or very nearly so in order that the effects at

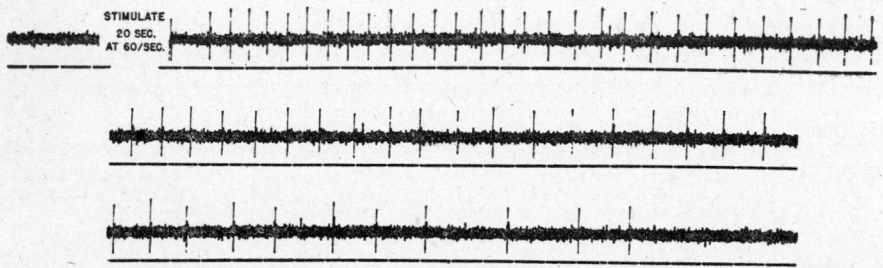

Fig. 78.—After-discharge in a sympathetic ganglion. The postganglionic nerve is subdivided so that the response of a single nerve is recorded as a series of regular spikes. At the break in the record the preganglionic nerve is stimulated at a frequency of 60 per sec. for 20 sec., following which there is a slight pause as the ganglion passes through its subnormal phase. Then the recorded neuron discharges impulses for a period of 27 sec. in the absence of further stimulation. (After Larrabee and Bronk from Bronk, *J. Neurophysiol.*, 1939, *2*:380–401.)

the several synapses may sum. This is *spatial summation.* The brief excitatory action has frequently been called *detonator action,* a term introduced by Eccles (7). The second period of facilitation is long lasting (up to 120 msec.), and results from the period of supernormality. Since the supernormal period succeeds the refractory period, it is possible for the effects of two successive impulses in the same presynaptic fiber to summate. This is *temporal summation.*

After-discharge. After-discharge is a term frequently used, but difficult to define in terms of mechanism, a fact that is due as much to changing concepts over the last decade as to anything else. The best definition available today would regard after-discharge as a discharge of impulses by nerve cells as the result of the arrival of presynaptic impulses, but not immediately dependent upon the continued arrival of such impulses. Such a discharge, therefore, would not be the result of detonator actions. It is, curiously enough, only in sympathetic ganglia that there is available an unequivocal example of after-discharge as so defined. Figure 78 presents an experiment of Larrabee and Bronk (16). In this experiment a preganglionic nerve was stimulated for a period of 20 sec. following which a ganglion cell was found to discharge at a rhythmic but decelerating rate for 27 sec. after the termination of the stimulation. There is no doubt that this "after-discharge" resulted from the stimulation, and likewise, since there are no interneurons, there is no doubt that presynaptic impulses ceased impinging upon the ganglion cells at the end of the stimulation period. After-discharge in a sympathetic ganglion cannot be considered a normal event, for it only appears after inordinately high rates of stimulation.

In the older view, after-discharge is simply a discharge which continues after withdrawal of an external stimulus. It is this definition of after-discharge that must be employed in relation to the analysis of activity by myographic technique. In the central nervous system this would include some, at least, of the discharge resulting from the activity of interneuron chains (see p. 136) which are arranged to continue the arrival of impulses over a finite period of time. In addition, there may be an after-discharge following the cessation of internuncial activity, but such has not yet been found. One will appreciate the fact that a myograph, recording only the end product of the nervous action, namely muscle contraction, could not distinguish between two possible central mechanisms for securing the end result. Hence the older definition.

Hypotheses Relating to the Synaptic Transmitter in Ganglia. Just as the means by which the excitatory effect of a nerve impulse is transmitted to a muscle fiber falls into the realm of dispute, so are there two hypotheses on the nature of mediation of the effect of presynaptic impulses on ganglion cells. The principles underlying the hypotheses as they relate to ganglia are the same as those considered in neuromuscular transmission. Again the labels "electrical" and "chemical" are applied to the respective hypotheses.

Electrical hypothesis. Qualitatively speaking, all of the features of neuromuscular transmission are reproduced in transmission through ganglia. The nerve block again forms a significant model for synaptic transmission. Electrotonic potentials—now called synaptic potentials, Eccles (8)—have been recorded after block of a ganglion by curare. The quantitative differences, such as those between the characteristic delays involved at the neuromuscular junction and at the synaptic junctions of the several ganglion cell groups, are of the kind to be expected of tissues having different characteristic time constants of activity.

The electrical hypothesis as applied to ganglia is a part of the theory of conduction. It makes no assumptions other than the reasonable one that the flow of current that must exist about the presynaptic fiber terminations has the effect upon the ganglion cells that such a flow of current would be expected to have.

Chemical hypothesis. The chemical hypothesis holds that liberation of acetylcholine at the presynaptic terminations results in stimulation of ganglion cells by the liberated acetylcholine. Kibjakow (15) was the first to detect the presence of acetylcholine in ganglia and suggest its role as a synaptic transmitter. Later Feldberg and Gaddum (12) demonstrated the release of acetylcholine in eserinized ganglia following stimulation of a preganglionic nerve, and Feldberg and Vartiainen (13) showed that perfused acetylcholine has a stimulating effect on a ganglion. The argument concerning the necessity for removal of acetylcholine within the refractory period, discussed in connection with neuromuscular activity (4), holds, for it is known that a single preganglionic volley yields a single discharge of the ganglion cells. Cholinesterase is present in ganglia and presumably acts for rapid removal of acetylcholine.

Acetylcholine and Cholinesterase. In the decade that has passed since the hypothesis of chemical mediation at synapses was first promulgated, experimental evidence and particularly the interpretations of experimental evidence have followed so many paths that it is no longer practical to discuss the functions of acetylcholine and cholinesterase in terms of a specific hypothesis. It is only possible to deal with various aspects of their supposed functions under appropriate headings.

Liberation of acetylcholine. At first it was thought that acetylcholine was liberated specifically at presynaptic endings, and indeed this finding was used in formulating the hypothesis of chemical mediation at cell junctions. More recent work, however, has shown that such is not the case. Lorente de Nó (24) has demonstrated release of acetylcholine by the ganglia of the vagus nerve,

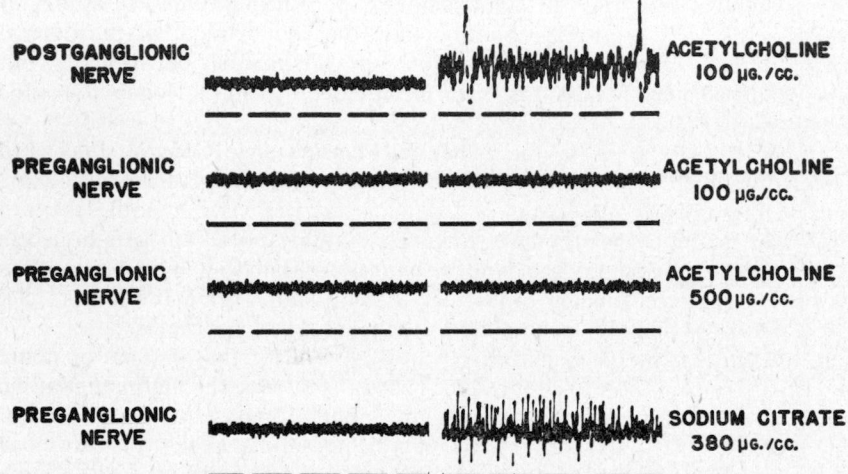

Fig. 79.—Preganglionic and postganglionic responses of perfused sympathetic ganglion to acetylcholine and sodium citrate. Controls with Ringer's fluid in left hand column. Acetylcholine perfusing through the ganglion causes a postganglionic discharge, but not a preganglionic discharge. Sodium citrate does cause a preganglionic discharge, proving the preganglionic fibers viable and subject to the perfusion. Thus acetylcholine is inert with respect to the preganglionic fibers. (From Bronk, *J. Neurophysiol.*, 1939, *2*:380–401.)

which contain the somata of monopolar neurons but no synapses. A number of workers have found acetylcholine in many nerve trunks, where, under appropriate conditions, it is liberated following activity.

Estimation of the amount of acetylcholine liberated during activity has proved a difficult problem and the results controversial. Large amounts of the substance were found in the earlier experiments, but Lorente de Nó (24) has shown that the amount of acetylcholine liberated by preganglionic stimulation is very small in ganglia maintained in good condition, and that it increases as deterioration progresses until finally liberation occurs in the absence of stimulation.

A most important consideration concerning the significance of acetylcholine liberation is the time, relative to the spike potential, at which it occurs. On this point there is no information. Because of the currently inescapable crudity of the experimental methods applicable to the study of acetylcholine liberation, it is possible that acetylcholine appears at any time up to many seconds after transmission has occurred, whereas the chemical hypothesis of synaptic transmission demands that acetylcholine be liberated no later than the time of spike transmission. It would be difficult to over-emphasize the fact that the impulse, as defined in Chapter 1, is the only event, having the power of stimulating, that is known to occur at the appropriate time to account for transmission at synapses or conduction in nerve.

Action of acetylcholine. Nerve cells and the end-plate region of muscle fibers are sensitive to the action of acetylcholine. This action in a ganglion is particularly well illustrated by Figure 79 in which it will be noted that the ganglion cells respond to acetylcholine added to a fluid perfusing a ganglion. The preganglionic fibers, the intraganglionic parts of which are likewise subjected to the perfused acetylcholine, do not show any trace of activity. Lorente de Nó (26) has recently shown that acetylcholine is virtually inert with respect to nerve fibers. Thus, although the presence and liberation of acetylcholine may be very widespread in nervous tissue, its power of irritating nervous tissue is more sharply delimited.

Action of eserine. The principal action of eserine in calculated small doses is to prevent the action of cholinesterase. In addition, eserine causes a rise in excitability by some action other than that of protecting acetylcholine from cholinesterase. The evidence that eserine prolongs the action of a nerve volley on muscle or ganglion cells is good. This prolongation leads to repeti-tive response after single stimulation and consequent summation of muscular action. There is a suggestion that the end-plate potential set up in muscle by a single nerve volley is prolonged, but, according to Eccles, the synaptic potential of ganglia similarly evoked is unaffected by eserine.

When ganglia are stimulated with inordinately high frequencies of stimu-lation, a prolonged synaptic potential may be recorded from a blocked ganglion (8) and after-discharge is seen in the normal ganglion (1) (cf. Fig. 78). These actions are increased by the use of eserine. Experimental results of the sort just related are of no assistance in designating the intercellular mediator, for their interpretation is equivocal. It seems likely that the pro-longed actions, including after-discharge, provoked by high frequency stimu-lation, or the use of eserine, are due to stimulation by liberated acetylcholine, but the evidence does not permit one to say whether this effect results from a prolongation of the transmitter action or whether it is added to the trans-mitter action.

The function of cholinesterase. Cholinesterase hydrolyzes acetylcholine, but the role that it plays in so doing is a matter for conjecture. One assumption, already presented, holds that cholinesterase destroys acetylcholine immedi-ately after transmission has occurred and within the refractory period of the muscle or ganglion cells. Another view (13) suggests that the function of cholinesterase may be to prevent diffusion of acetylcholine away from the synapse, rather than to remove it at the synapse by hydrolysis. This is the so-called "barrier" function of cholinesterase. An additional assumption, that acetylcholine is removed normally by some other means such as resyn-thesis to an inactive precursor, is needed to account for the normal absence of after-discharge.

Still another view of cholinesterase and acetylcholine now appears slowly to be emerging on the basis of continuing experimental effort. Although the view has not yet been fully stated in a formal sense, the growth of information points in this direction, and suggestions of the view can be found in the literature. In its initial form, first proposed by von Muralt (29), the release of acetylcholine with subsequent synthesis was envisaged as an important event in the conduction of impulses in nerves. This proposal has been espoused and extended by Nachmansohn (30). Against the proposal is the demonstration by Feldberg (11) that the power to synthesize acetylcholine is lost by the nerve before the ability to conduct impulses. It seems, then, more likely that the synthesis and breakdown of acetylcholine follow the conduction of an impulse and are part of the metabolic cycle underlying the maintenance and recovery of nerves. Cholinesterase would play an important role in the choline metabolism of nerve. The conduction of impulses and synaptic transmission would take place by electrotonic invasion according to the theory of conduction (Chap. 1). This characteristic activity would be supported by a complex metabolism involving many reactions among which would be those of a choline cycle. Acetylcholine would only appear at strategic points to irritate nerve cells or muscle cells when, by artificially induced hyperactivity, the cholinesterase is saturated, or when, by the use of eserine, the cholinesterase is inactivated. Presumably it is possible that the excess acetylcholine acting on nerve cells might perform a useful function in an "overworked" ganglion. Likewise from the realm of therapeutics it is known that the administration of prostigmine, an eserine-like drug, temporarily restores muscular action to something resembling normal in all but the most advanced cases of myasthenia gravis.

Bronk (1), in his survey of synaptic mechanisms in sympathetic ganglia, the most recent general account of ganglionic transmission, points out that many influences affect the environment of ganglion cells and that the sum total of these influences determines the degree of excitation. Just as there are many influences affecting excitability, there are many relatively distinct chemical hypotheses, rather than one. This fact reflects the fundamental deficiencies of information on the function of such compounds as acetylcholine and cholinesterase.

SYNAPTIC TRANSMISSION IN THE CENTRAL NERVOUS SYSTEM (19, 20, 21, 22, 23, 25)

The examples of junctional transmission so far considered, neuromuscular and ganglionic, take place at regions of relatively simple anatomy. In the central nervous system the structural pattern underlying transmission assumes almost indescribable complexity. A working concept of the structural conditions of synaptic transmission in the central nervous system may be gained by a careful study of Figure 80 *A*, in which is shown an example of the interlacing termination of ten presynaptic fibers to form what is known as the *synaptic scale* of a single neuron such as that illustrated in Figure 80 *B*.

We have seen how the principle of divergence is exemplified by the relation between motor nerve fiber and muscle fibers. In ganglia the principle of convergence comes into operation, making for an increased flexibility of action. In the central nervous system the divergent and convergent mechanisms are present and operate with vastly increased flexibility because of the interneurons arranged in characteristic fashion. Another important consequence of the arrangement of interneurons is known as the *principle of reciprocity*.

All of the neurons of the central nervous system are reciprocally connected by many pathways of a greater or lesser degree of complexity. It has been possible, largely through the work of Lorente de Nó, to reduce the actual structural complexity of connection, for purposes of argument, to a systematic repetition of two fundamental types of circuit, the multiple chain (M in Fig.

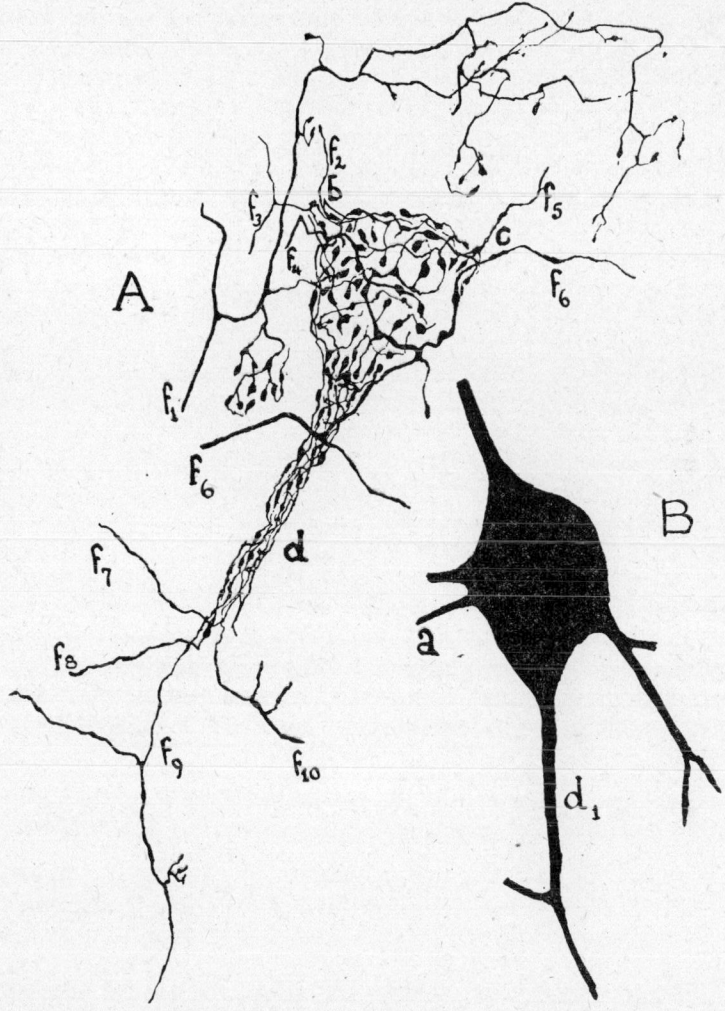

Fig. 80.—Structure of the synaptic scale of an interneuron. A, Ten fibers (f_1 to f_{10}) enter into synaptic junction with the perikaryon and dendrite (d) of a cell similar to that seen in B. Note the thickenings called synaptic knobs. Fibers f_1 to f_6 have junctions with the perikaryon. Fibers f_7 to f_{10} join the dendrite (d), investing it and forming contact by knobs, then reach the perikaryon to form further knobs there. a = axon; b, c, d, d_1 = dendrites. (From Lorente de Nó, *J. Neurophysiol.*, 1938, *1*:195–206.)

81) and the closed chain (C in Fig. 81) of neurons. The closed chain, by which a given neuron can be re-excited as impulses complete the circuit, represents the principle of reciprocity of connections. One important feature of central nervous activity which receives its explanation in the convergence of these chains of neurons is that a single presynaptic volley may give rise not to a

single postsynaptic volley as in ganglia, but rather to a diffuse prolonged discharge. In effect the multiple and reciprocal connections of the interneurons provide for a continuing arrival of impulses at the motoneurons which in turn respond with a continuing discharge of impulses.

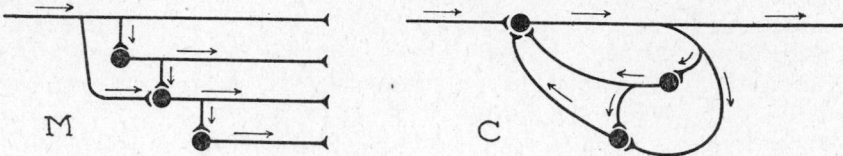

Fig. 81.—Plans of the two fundamental types of neuron circuits. M = The multiple chain. C = The closed chain. (After Lorente de Nó, *J. Neurophysiol.*, 1938, *1*:207–244.)

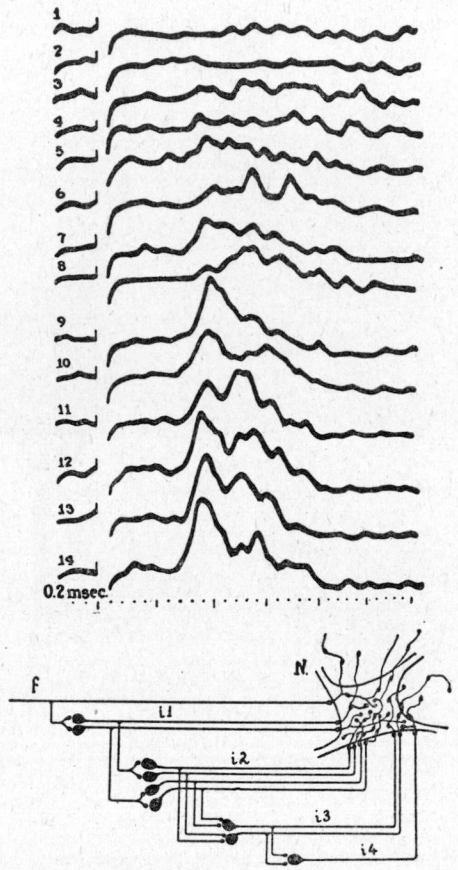

Fig. 82.—1 to 14: Motoneuron responses to presynaptic volleys of increasing size. Below is a diagram to indicate the circuits through which impulses are distributed to the motoneuron (N) after a single stimulation of fiber (f); *i*1, *i*2, *i*3, *i*4: internuncial paths. (From Lorente de Nó, *J. Neurophysiol.*, 1938, *1*:207–244.)

The continued discharge of motoneurons under the influence of "internuncial barrage," that is, the continued delivery by the interneuron chains of impulses to the motoneurons, may be seen to advantage in Figure 82 illustrating an experiment by Lorente de Nó. Motoneuron activity was recorded by means of electrodes placed on the fourth cranial nerve. Stimulation was effected by means of electrodes in the dorsal longitudinal bundle at a point that would correspond to f in the diagram that appears below the oscillograph records in Figure 82. To obtain records *1* to *14* the strength of the shock was progressively increased.

For records *1* and *2* the stimulus was barely at threshold, and there is an indication of response only in record *1;* in records *3* and *4* a definite response to stimulation is present. The response increased when the shock was strengthened (records *5, 6, 7, 8*), with the largest potential waves appearing in the middle part of the response. Further strengthening of the stimulus (records *9, 10, 11*) to maximal (record *12*) and supermaximal strength (record *13, 14*) causes additional increase of the response. However, the increase of the early potential waves is not accompanied by increase of the late ones; on the contrary, the late waves disappear and the total response becomes shorter in duration (contrast records *13* and *14* with *6, 7* and *8*).

The type of response shown in records *1* to *8* of Figure 82 is one that might be expected. The stimulating shock creates a volley of impulses delivered partly to the motoneurons and partly to interneurons; some motoneurons respond to the volley and their impulses reach the recording electrodes. Some interneurons also fire and cause other motoneurons and interneurons to respond. Likewise, this second volley of internuncial impulses stimulates other motoneurons and interneurons to discharge impulses into their axons, etc. The process is completed when the internuncial volleys fail to reach threshold value for the next neurons. Since the average synaptic delay at interneurons is about 0.7 msec., it is fair to assume that responses such as those shown in records *7* and *8* involve passage of the impulses through four or five internuncial relays.

Particular interest attaches to the fact that strengthening of the shock, i.e., increase of the size of the f volley, causes the response to lose the late waves. This has only one explanation, namely, that the motoneurons, which in weak responses fire upon arrival of late internuncial volleys, in response to strong shocks fire when stimulated either by the impulses of the initial (f) volley or by the early internuncial volleys, and they cannot fire again for the remainder of the response. The late internuncial volleys are ineffective because they are delivered to refractory neurons.

This result is expressed in graphic form in the diagram at the bottom of Figure 82. The fiber marked f belongs to the dorsal longitudinal bundle and is supposed to reach a motoneuron eventually engaged in the response to the f shocks. $i1, i2, i3,$ and $i4$ are those internuncial pathways which are passed by the impulses on their way to the motoneurons. It will be seen from the diagram that if the motoneuron (N) does not respond to the f impulses, it may respond to the internuncial impulses after a latency equal to one, or to the sum of several synaptic delays; but if it is fired by the f impulses it will not reappear in the response as long as the i impulses find it in a refractory state.

Since even the strongest responses (*12* to *14*) contained only a small fraction of the total cell population of the motor nucleus, the diagram also illustrates the fact that the internuncial volleys are delivered repeatedly to a small number of neurons; or in other words, that despite the many possible channels for conduction the impulses remain confined within a few selected channels, so

that the majority of the neurons of the motor pool receive only subthreshold
stimuli. It may be said that during activity the internuncial and motor pools
become *fractionated* into active and inactive groups, part of the latter group
constituting a *subliminal fringe*, the activation of which demands stimulation
by another set of pathways.

Synaptic Stimulation as a Local Process (22). Transmission of excitation in
the central nervous system is a much less stereotyped process than it is in
neuromuscular junctions and in ganglia. At the normal neuromuscular junction transmission is obligatory. This is true also for most of the synapses in
sympathetic ganglia in spite of the rudimentary integrative mechanism to be
found there. In the central nervous system, however, it may be said that
synaptic transmission is optional for any neuron. In order to predict whether
activity in a given pathway will result in transmission it is necessary to have
intimate knowledge of the synaptic relations involved. Knowledge of these
relations began with the celebrated researches of Cajal, while many of the
recent significant data stem from the studies of Lorente de Nó.

Figure 83 illustrates the structure of the synaptic junctions on motoneurons
and interneurons. Numbers of presynaptic fibers converge on these neurons
to form the synaptic scale, which is very incompletely stained in these preparations. This is an advantage at the moment for it allows an accurate picture
of the distribution of terminations (synaptic knobs) of individual fibers.
A, B, C, D and E are bodies of motoneurons; I is the body of a similar large
neuron of the internuncial system. Numerals *1* to *16* indicate presynaptic
fibers forming synapses on the cell bodies and also on dendrites as indicated
by the letter (d). Fibers *17* and *18* form synapses only on dendrites. A careful
study of the distribution of synaptic knobs will reveal (i) that none of the
fibers *1* to *16* has on any neuron more than a small number of knobs, which
cover only a small part of the cell surface; and (ii) that the knobs of any one
fiber are not close together, but separated by large spaces that would be filled
in by knobs from still other fibers if these had been stained in the preparation.
It follows from this structure that activation of the whole synaptic scale of a
neuron would demand that a tremendous number of presynaptic fibers be
active, but that total activation of a discrete zone such as zone (S) on cell I
would be achieved by a relatively small number of presynaptic fibers (*12,
14, 15, 16*).

Now it is known that threshold stimulation of a neuron does not require
total activation of the synaptic scale because (i) a neuron can be discharged
by different intensities of stimulation (and hence by varying fractions of the
synaptic scale) under different conditions; and (ii) a neuron can be discharged
from different sources, that is, by a part of the presynaptic fibers converging
at the neuron. Secondly, threshold stimulation requires convergence of several presynaptic impulses, but under appropriate selection a very large presynaptic volley may be ineffective, and yet if that large volley is reduced in
size and combined with other subliminal impulses from another source,
discharge results.

Applying the known facts of electrotonic invasion as developed in Chapter
1 and applied earlier in this chapter, we reach the following interpretation:
an impulse in a synaptic knob sets up on the cell surface, by electrotonic
spread, a state of excitation analogous to the local excitatory state in nerve.
The state has a sharp spatial decrement, but being subliminal is capable o$_f$

summation with similar events set up by other synaptic knobs in the immediate neighborhood, but not by those scattered on other parts of the cell surface. Threshold excitation would occur when all, or at least a majority, of the knobs at a discrete zone such as (S) in Figure 83 are activated simultaneously or

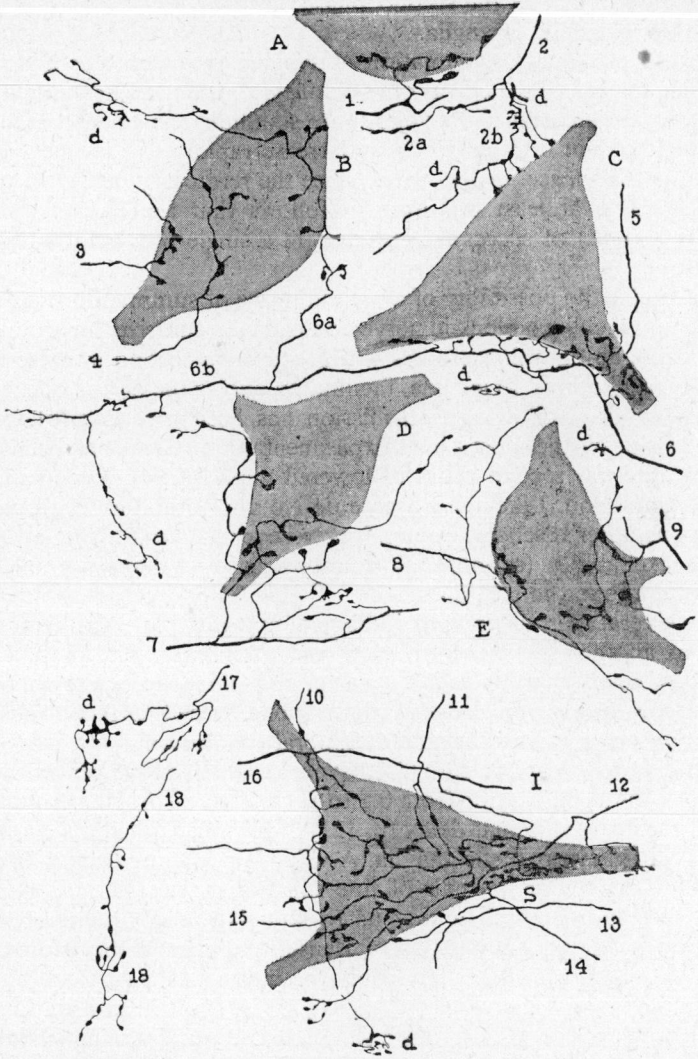

Fig. 83.—Synapses on motoneurons (A–E) and on a large interneuron (I) of the spinal cord. 1 to 18: presynaptic fibrils carrying synaptic knobs to the several cells. d = synaptic knobs in contact with dendrites. Note (i) how fiber 6 supplies both cell B and cell C and in addition some dendrites: *divergence;* (ii) that many fibers supply each cell: *convergence;* (iii) that the knobs of any given fiber are widely scattered on the cell surfaces; (iv) that fibers 12 ,14, 15, 16 together form the complete synaptic scale in the zone labeled S of cell I. (From Lorente de Nó, *J. Neurophysiol.,* 1938, *1:*195–206.)

within a very short period of time. Simultaneous activation of scattered synaptic knobs would produce only a lowering of threshold at corresponding loci on the surface. If impulses from another source activated the remaining knobs at one of these loci, discharge would result.

Summation at the synapse. The essential spatial conditions for summation in the central nervous system have now been discussed, but the temporal conditions remain to be considered. Two questions are involved; the first concerns the duration of the excitatory event at a single synapse, the second concerns the problem of the second phase of summation such as has been described in sympathetic ganglia.

The period of effective summation at synapses is brief. The chances for effective summation of the effects of two volleys of impulses arriving at different synapses are greatest if the volleys are simultaneous or separated by an interval of less than 0.15 msec. They decrease rapidly to disappear at time separations of 0.5 msec. or less. Now since the refractory period of the presynaptic fibers is at least this long, it follows that the immediate effects (detonator actions) of successive impulses in a single presynaptic fiber may not sum.

There remains the possibility of a second phase of summation. It is known that impulses reaching a block in nerve or a partially curarized neuromuscular junction cause an enduring process which enables a second impulse to pass (Wedensky facilitation). In ganglia, facilitation during the period of the supernormal excitability following transmission has been recorded (cf. p. 130). Lorente de Nó, by the most direct experimental approach, has been unable to demonstrate any second phase of lowered threshold following subliminal synaptic stimulation. Likewise Lorente de Nó and Graham (27) found that motoneurons, after discharging impulses, recover through a single phase of depressed excitability (subnormality) unbroken by a supernormal period such as Eccles found in ganglia.

For the several reasons presented above, it appears that transmission from one cell to another in the central nervous system depends upon the synchronous or nearly synchronous arrival of convergent impulses at synaptic knobs occupying a discrete zone of the responding cell surface. The fundamental process is spatial rather than temporal facilitation.

The problem of synaptic delay (21). Synaptic delay in the central nervous system has a duration varying from 0.5 to 1.0 msec. This figure is comparable to that of the neuromuscular delay (p. 121) but is much smaller than that for synaptic delay in sympathetic ganglia. A value for synaptic delay is obtained in the following manner: a pair of fine stimulating electrodes is placed in the gray substance in such a way as to stimulate both interneurons and motoneurons with properly adjusted densities of the stimulating current (Fig. 84). A weak shock stimulates only the interneurons (2, 3, 4, 5 of Fig. 84), but as the shock is increased (records 6, 7, 8, 9) motoneurons, at a greater distance from the electrodes, also are stimulated. With recording leads placed on the motor nerve that contains the axons of the stimulated motoneurons, two spike potentials (m and s) may be recorded, separated by a brief interval of time. The first results from direct stimulation of the motoneurons, the second from synaptic stimulation by the excited interneurons; the interval between the two spike potentials gives an estimate of the synaptic delay.

The limits of variation in the duration of synaptic delay may be found by raising or lowering the excitability of the motoneurons. If the motoneurons have just conducted an impulse and are still in the period of relative refractoriness, it takes more time for a synaptic volley to bring them to threshold. Under these circumstances synaptic delay amounts to 0.9–1.0 msec. If, on the other hand, the motoneurons are receiving impulses from other sources with which the synaptic volley can summate, the fact that their excitability is already very great permits the rapid arrival at threshold and synaptic delay is reduced to 0.5–0.6 msec.

Interpretation of synaptic delay. It seems certain that two factors must be considered in the interpretation of synaptic delay. The interval between

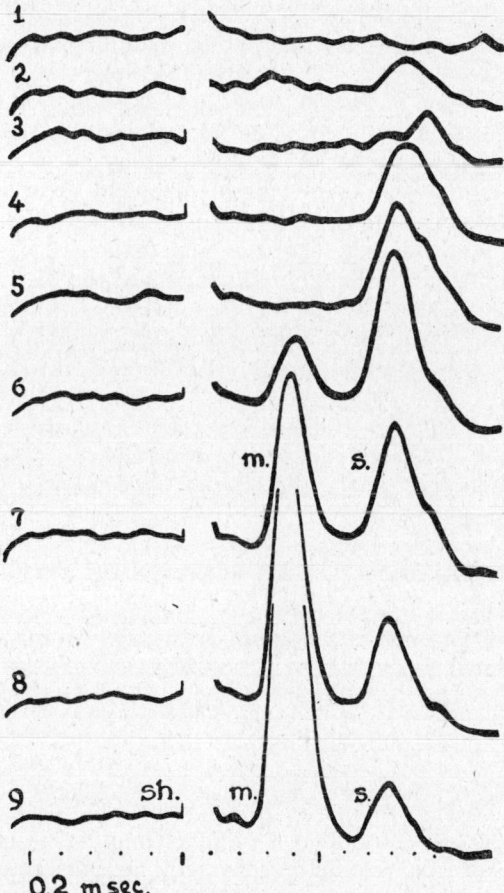

Fig. 84.—Synaptic delay of motoneurons. Stimulating electrodes arranged to stimulate inter-neurons and motoneurons. Responses recorded from motor nerve. Records 1 to 9 obtained with increasing strength of stimulus. Sh = time of stimulus; m = responses of motoneurons to direct stimulation; s = responses of motoneurons to indirect stimulation through synapses of the interneurons. The interval between m and s forms a measure of synaptic delay. (From Lorente d ɛNó, *J. Neurophysiol.*, 1939, *2*:402–464.)

minimum and maximum synaptic delay represents an utilization period (cf. Chap. 1 and Fig. 13) with excitability of the neurons beginning to rise at the close of a minimal synaptic delay and with the end of synaptic delay falling whenever the increasing excitability of the cells reaches threshold. The fixed duration of the minimum synaptic delay presents another problem. One factor of undoubted importance is conduction time in the fine terminal fibers of the presynaptic axons. The estimation of synaptic delay includes the assumption that conduction is uniform in the presynaptic fibers right up to the synaptic knobs and again in the whole postsynaptic element, soma as well as axon. Now the presynaptic fibers branch profusely and follow tortuous courses in the terminal regions. Hence (i) the actual conduction length is not known, but is certainly greater than the straight line distance, and (ii) conduction is certainly slower in the terminal region than in the parent fiber. Both these factors consume time that is included in the minimum synaptic delay as measured. It now seems probable, when a valid estimate of the time lost by the operation of these factors is available, that the minimum synaptic delay in the strictest sense will prove vanishingly small (20).

The relation between subliminal fringe and discharge zone (19). When a volley of impulses impinges upon a pool of quiescent neurons, some of those neurons are excited to discharge impulses; others receive only subliminal grades of excitation; still others remain quiescent. The subliminal fringe forms the liaison between the discharge zone and the quiescent members of the neuron pool (Sherrington). That is to say, if the volley is increased, neurons are recruited from the subliminal fringe into the discharge zone, while others from the quiescent pool enter the subliminal fringe; if the volley is decreased, neurons from the discharge zone are shed into the subliminal fringe and other neurons from the subliminal fringe retire into the quiescent pool.

Recently it has become possible to observe quantitatively the growth of a discharge zone from the subliminal fringe by study of a simple reflex system consisting of but two elements, the afferent and efferent neurons (called a two-neuron arc reflex).

The technique for obtaining the subliminal fringe-discharge zone relation is as follows. The dorsal root and ventral root of a single segment of the spinal cord are equipped with recording leads; the dorsal root with stimulating electrodes in addition. To measure subliminal fringe a test reflex volley of standard size is employed and the facilitatory action of a measured variable dorsal root volley on the test reflex volley is found. A measure of discharge zone is obtained directly by the motoneuron discharge evoked by measured dorsal root volleys and recorded on the ventral root. Since in these experiments the size of the subliminal fringe and the size of the discharge zone are both related to the same independent variable (the size of the dorsal root volley), they may be related to one another directly by eliminating the common variable. This has been done in Figure 85.

A study of Figure 85 shows that a volley of impulses in presynaptic fibers must attain considerable size before any motoneurons enter from the subliminal fringe into the discharge zone. Once a discharge zone is formed it increases rapidly and progressively with increase in the subliminal fringe until a linear relation between the two is established. This relation is exactly that which would be predicted from the histological observations illustrated in Figure 83. With the synaptic knobs of any one presynaptic fiber widely spread as they are over the soma, the statistical chances of a cluster of knobs in any one region being active as the result of weak stimulation of the presynaptic pathway are very small indeed, and the cells in consequence remain in the subliminal fringe. On the contrary, as more and more presynaptic fibers are activated by increasing the stimulation, the statistical chances would increase until the situation is such that the recruitment of each presynaptic fiber into the stimulated volley is virtually certain to complete the activation of localized regions of the synaptic scale. From then on, as stimulation is further increased, the chances are that the discharge zone would increase in linear relation to the subliminal fringe, as indicated by Figure 85, until the presynaptic pathway is maximally active.

Prolonged Excitation in the Nervous System and "Central Excitatory State" (3, 23). We have seen already that there is no known mechanism for temporal summation at the synapses within the central nervous system, and yet prolonged "states of excitation" exist. The fact that spatial summation of brief detonator actions is the only significant means for effecting junctional transmission at central synapses re-emphasizes the important role of interneurons in securing prolonged excitation.

Now there are two ways in which pools of neurons may respond to the arrival of a volley of impulses. They may discharge a volley as synchronous

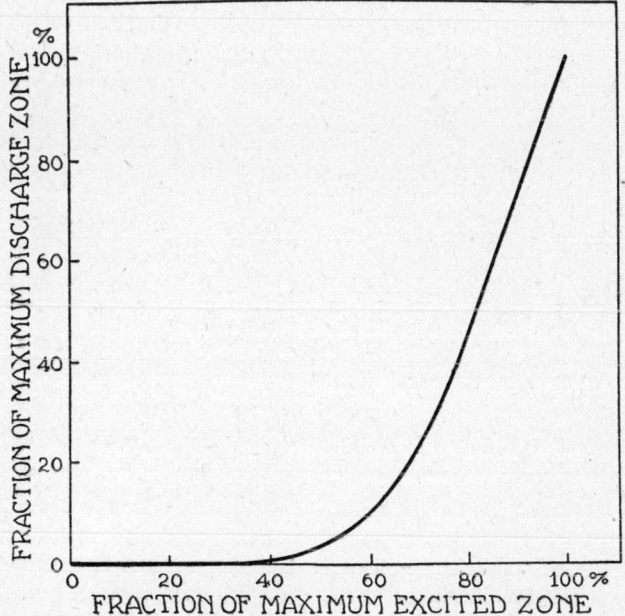

Fig. 85.—Relation between the size of a motoneuron pool excited by a presynaptic volley and the size of the discharge zone within the excited pool. Note that quite a large subliminally active pool develops (as presynaptic stimulation is increased) before any discharge of impulses from the pool occurs. The discharge zone then develops rapidly until a linear relation exists.

as that they received or, by virtue of reciprocal connections on the patterns illustrated in Figure 81, they may discharge a barrage of impulses that waxes and wanes over a considerable interval of time. Accordingly, another pool of neurons, "down stream" from the first pool, in its turn would receive in the first instance a synchronous volley of impulses and in the second instance an asynchronous barrage of impulses that increases slowly in intensity. Carrying in mind the fact that impulses must arrive at different synaptic knobs in practically synchronous fashion to secure summation at the soma, one will realize that an asynchronous barrage of impulses will have to grow in intensity until the *instantaneous* value of the barrage equals the threshold of some of the recipient neurons, which then fire impulses in turn. This may require a time interval many times that of the synaptic delay lost when a pool of neurons responds synchronously to the arrival of a synchronous volley. The time required for an asynchronous barrage of presynaptic impulses entering a pool of neurons to secure the first discharge of postsynaptic impulses by those neurons is known as *nuclear delay*.* Since most of the actions of the nervous system are performed by means of such barrages rather than by synchronous volleys, the total time taken for passage of activity through the central nervous system is the sum of conduction time (along fiber tracts) and nuclear delays (at the nuclei or relay stations interrupting the fiber tracts). The time occupied in this fashion is known as *central latency* and with special reference to studies on reflexes is commonly called *central reflex time*.

"*Central excitatory state*" was the descriptive term introduced by Sherrington to denote without prejudice as to mechanism the relatively prolonged waxing and waning excitation of motoneurons characteristic of most reactions mediated through the central nervous system. It seems relatively certain today, and the view is almost universally held, that the characteristic activity of interneurons playing upon the motoneurons forms a necessary and sufficient explanation of the properties of central excitatory state.

REFERENCES

1. BRONK, D. W. Synaptic mechanisms in sympathetic ganglia. *J. Neurophysiol.*, 1939, *2*:380–401.

2. BROWN, G. L., DALE, H. H. and FELDBERG, W. Reactions of the normal mammalian muscle to acetylcholine and eserine. *J. Physiol.*, 1936, *87*:394–424.

3. CREED, R. S., DENNY-BROWN, D., ECCLES, J. C., LIDDELL, E. G. T. and SHERRINGTON, C. S. *Reflex activity of the spinal cord.* Oxford, Clarendon Press, 1932, 183 pp.

4. DALE, H. H. Transmission of nervous effects by acetylcholine. *Harvey Lect.*, 1937, pp. 229–245.

5. DALE, H. H. and FELDBERG, W. Chemical transmission at motor nerve endings in voluntary muscle. *J. Physiol.*, 1934, *81*:39P.

6. ECCLES, J. C. The action potential of the superior cervical ganglion. *J. Physiol.*, 1935, *85*:179–206.

7. ECCLES, J. C. Synaptic and neuromuscular transmission. *Ergebn. Physiol.*, 1936, *38*:339–444.

8. ECCLES, J. C. Synaptic potentials and transmission in sympathetic ganglion. *J. Physiol.*, 1943, *101*:465–483.

9. ECCLES, J. C., KATZ, B. and KUFFLER, S. W. Nature of the "endplate potential" in curarized muscle. *J. Neurophysiol.*, 1941, *4*:362–387.

10. ERLANGER, J. The initiation of impulses in axons (synapse symposium). *J. Neurophysiol.*, 1939, *2*:370–379.

11. FELDBERG, W. Synthesis of acetylcholine in sympathetic ganglia and cholinergic nerves. *J. Physiol.*, 1943, *101*:432–445.

12. FELDBERG, W. and GADDUM, J. H. The chemical transmitter at synapses in a sympathetic ganglion. *J. Physiol.*, 1934, *81*:305–319.

13. FELDBERG, W. and VARTIAINEN, A. Further observations on the physiology and pharmacology of a sympathetic ganglion. *J. Physiol.*, 1935, *83*:103–128.

14. FENG, T. P. and TING, Y. Studies on the neuromuscular junction. XI. A note on the local concentration of cholinesterase at motor nerve endings. *Chin. J. Physiol.*, 1938, *13*:141–144.

15. KIBJAKOW, A. W. Über humorale Übertragung der Erregung von einem Neuron auf das andere. *Pflüg. Arch. ges. Physiol.*, 1933, *232*:432–443.

16. LARRABEE, M. G. and BRONK, D. W. Persistent discharge from sympathetic ganglion cells following preganglionic stimulation. *Proc. Soc. exp. Biol.*, *N. Y.*, 1938, *38*:921–922.

17. LLOYD, D. P. C. The excitability states of inferior mesenteric ganglion cells following preganglionic activation. *J. Physiol.*, 1939, *95*:464–475.

18. LLOYD, D. P. C. The origin and nature of ganglion after-potentials. *J. Physiol.*, 1939, *96*:118–129.

19. LLOYD, D. P. C. Reflex action in relation to the pattern and peripheral source of afferent stimulation. *J. Neurophysiol.*, 1943, *6*:111–119.

20. LLOYD, D. P. C. Functional organization of the spinal cord. *Physiol. Rev.*, 1944, *24*:1–17.

21. LORENTE DE NÓ, R. Limits of variation of the synaptic delay of motoneurons. *J. Neurophysiol.*, 1938, *1*:187–194.

22. LORENTE DE NÓ, R. Synaptic stimulation as a local process. *J. Neurophysiol.*, 1938, *1*:195–206.

* For a discussion of the terms "synaptic delay" and "nuclear delay" and their implications cf. (20).

23. LORENTE DE Nó, R. Analysis of the activity of the chains of internuncial neurons. *J. Physiol.*, 1938, *1*:207–244.

24. LORENTE DE Nó, R. Liberation of acetylcholine by the superior cervical sympathetic ganglion and the nodosum ganglion of the vagus. *Amer. J. Physiol.*, 1938, *121*:331–349.

25. LORENTE DE Nó, R. Transmission of impulses through cranial motor nuclei. *J. Neurophysiol.*, 1939, *2*:402–464.

26. LORENTE DE Nó, R. Effects of choline and acetylcholine chloride upon peripheral nerve fibers. *J. cell. comp. Physiol.*, 1944, *24*:85–97.

27. LORENTE DE Nó, R. and GRAHAM, H. T. Recovery cycle of motoneurons. *Amer. J. Physiol.*, 1938, *121*:388–399.

28. MARNAY, A. and NACHMANSOHN, D. Choline esterase in voluntary muscle. *J. Physiol.*, 1938, *92*:37–47.

29. VON MURALT, A. Observations on chemical wave transmission in excited nerve. *Proc. roy. Soc.*, 1937, *B123*:399–403.

30. NACHMANSOHN, D. On the rôle of acetylcholine in the mechanism of nerve activity. *Vitamins and Hormones*, 1945, *3*:134.

31. SCHAEFER, H. and HAASS, P. Über einem lokalen Erregungstrom an der motorischen Endplatte. *Pflüg. Arch. ges. Physiol.*, 1939, *242*:364–381

32. SHERRINGTON, C. S. Some functional problems attaching to convergence. Ferrier Lecture. *Proc. roy. Soc.* 1929, *B105*:332—362.

CHAPTER 6

PRINCIPLES OF SPINAL REFLEX ACTIVITY

The preceding chapters have dealt with the activity of the several elements that participate in the working of the reflex mechanism. The aims of the present chapter are to describe largely in terms of mechanism the coordinated functioning of these various elements in the performance of simple reflex acts, and how some of the simple reflexes are welded together to provide for smoothly integrated action to subserve the needs of posture and performance of movement.

STRUCTURE OF THE REFLEX MECHANISM (2, 3)

The gray substance of the spinal cord contains the somata of motoneurons lying in the ventral horn, and interneurons set in a tight lacework of collateral axons penetrating from the surrounding white columns to reach the somata and form synaptic knobs thereon. The dorsal white columns are made up very largely of the central continuation of primary afferent neurons reaching the spinal cord through the dorsal roots. The motoneurons send their axons through the ventral white columns to form the emergent ventral roots, but otherwise the ventral and lateral white columns contain the axons of interneurons coursing up and down the spinal cord. These features are illustrated in Figure 86 in which may be seen at the top primary afferent fibers entering the cord and branching to form the dorsal column with its fibers running (horizontally in the picture) in both directions up and down the cord. At points along the course of these column fibers collaterals descend into the gray substance. In the lower part of the figure are five neurons contributing axons to the formation of the ventral column, while the axons of other neurons send collaterals from the column into the gray substance of the ventral horn. It is important to keep in mind the fact that the interneurons linking together segments of the spinal cord send their axons out to the surrounding white substance and then back in again to the gray substance to form synaptic connections with other interneurons. Conduction over any appreciable distance does not take place in the gray substance.

With attention focused on the reflex function of the spinal cord it is of interest to consider, in relation to Figure 87, the distribution of dorsal root (i.e., afferent) collaterals throughout the gray substance. These may be considered as forming two groups: those that articulate principally in the dorsal horn with interneurons, which in turn send their axons up through the great afferent tracts to superior parts of the nervous system for the mediation of sensation; and those that articulate (i) directly with motoneurons and (ii) with interneurons which in turn supply motoneurons for the mediation of spinal reflex action. Figure 87 shows a number of the afferent fiber collaterals and their characteristic distribution. Those marked *C* and *c* are directed to the *nucleus proprius* of the dorsal horn and the *substantia gelatinosa*, being concerned probably with the relay of impulses to the ascending tracts. The long collaterals, *a*, descend through the gray substance to the ventral horn, B, where they supply motoneurons directly, giving off a few collaterals, *b*, to the intermediate nucleus. On the other side a dense supply of collaterals (A) is shown terminating in the intermediate nucleus.

It is to Cajal, whose preparations are seen in Figures 86 and 87, that we owe the fundamental simplification of the anatomical complexities of the reflex system into two types illustrated in Figure 88. On the left of Figure 88 is

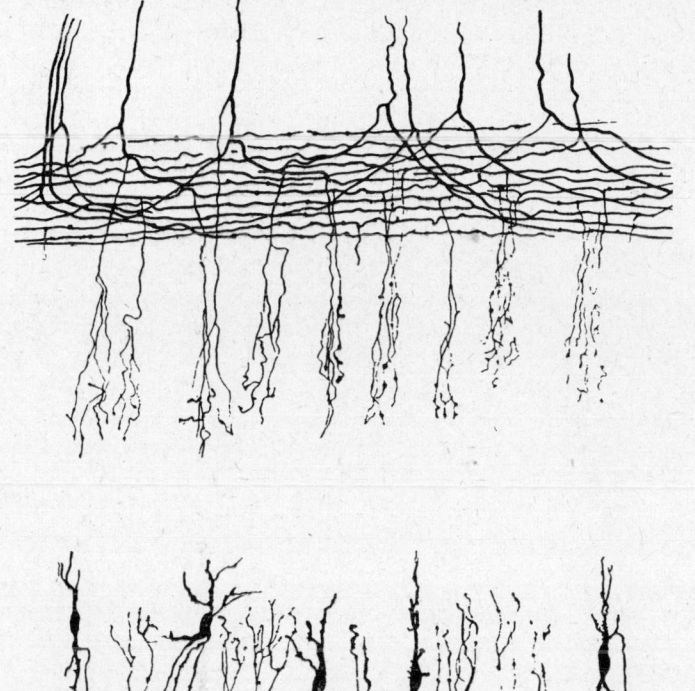

Fig. 86.—Longitudinal section of the spinal cord to one side of the midline. The dorsum is at the top of the figure. Dorsal root fibers enter the dorsal column, divide and send collaterals into the gray substance. Below, the ventral column. Five cells of the ventral horn contribute axons to the ventral column. Other axons of the ventral columns send collaterals into the ventral horn. (After Cajal, *Histologie du système nerveux*, Paris, Maloine, 1909.)

shown the "circumscribed" reflex mechanism, in which afferent collaterals articulate directly with motoneurons in a restricted region to form what is often called a *two-neuron arc*. On the right of Figure 88 there is the "diffuse" reflex mechanism in which interneurons intercalated between afferent fibers and motoneurons serve to diffuse activity over a wider field up and down the spinal cord. The pathways so formed are called *multineuron arcs*, the simplest such, given in the illustration, being a *three-neuron arc*. Although Cajal's fundamental concept was lost sight of for a number of years, it is now known that it is just these structural patterns that are responsible for many of the functional properties of and distinctions between the reflexes mediated through them.

A functional picture of Cajal's restricted and diffuse reflex mechanisms may be obtained by stimulating with a single shock a dorsal root while recording from the ventral root of the same segment. The *segmental reflex discharge*

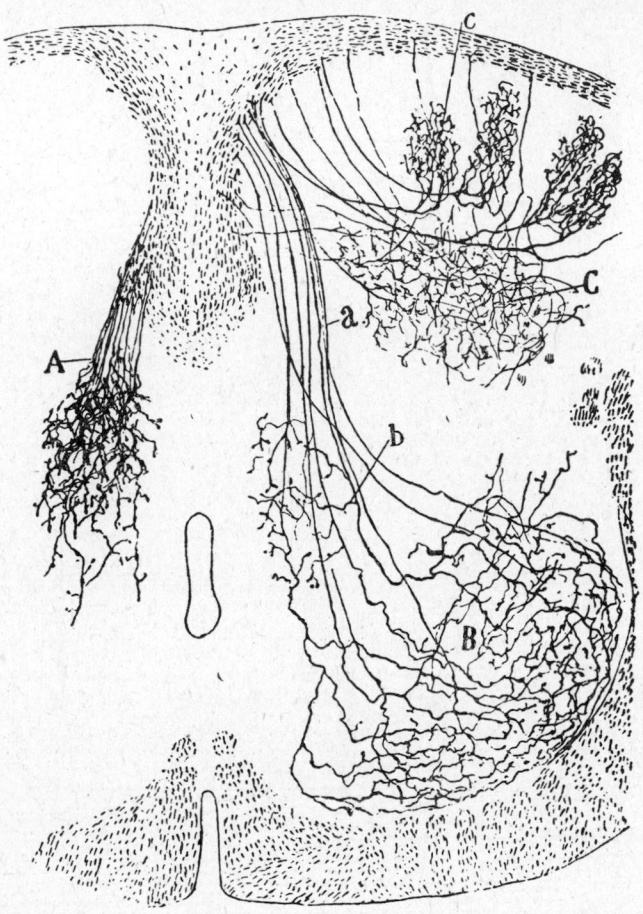

Fig. 87.—Cross section of the spinal cord. Distribution of the primary afferent collaterals is shown. On the right, collaterals *C* and *c* are distributed to the dorsal horn and substantia gelatinosa Rolandi. *a* = reflexomotor collaterals extending to the ventral horn (*B*). *b* = collaterals to the intermediate nucleus of Cajal. On the left, dense collaterals (*A*) to the intermediate nucleus. (After Cajal, *Histologie du système nerveux*, Paris, Maloine, 1909.)

obtained by this means may be seen in Figure 89. The first spike potential of the reflex discharge so obtained stands more or less in isolation and results from conduction through reflex arcs of two neurons. The later discharges form an irregular discharge elevation, the result of conduction through multi-neuron arcs of varying complexity. In accordance with Cajal's diagrams, the two-neuron arc response is highly restricted to the immediate region of the stimulated dorsal root, but the multineuron arc discharges leave the cord over a number of ventral roots up and down the cord. The significance of these facts will become apparent after we have considered some of the typical reflexes elicitable in a reflex preparation. The first of these reflexes to be described is known as the *stretch* or *myotatic reflex*.

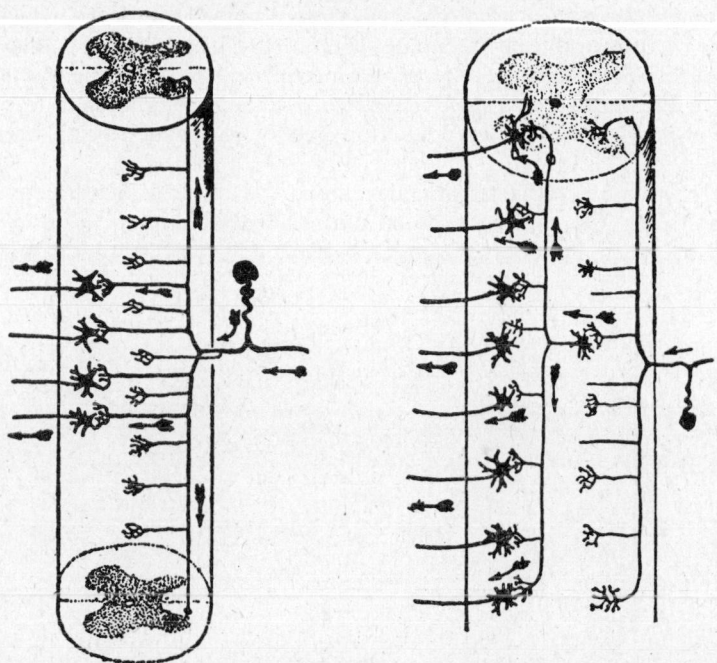

Fig. 88.—Diagrammatic representation of the circumscribed reflex mechanism of Cajal (left showing direct connection between afferent collaterals and motoneurons and the diffuse reflex mechanism of Cajal (right) in which an interneuron is intercalated between afferent fibers and motoneurons. (Slightly modified from Cajal, *Histologie du système nerveux*, Paris, Maloine, 1909.)

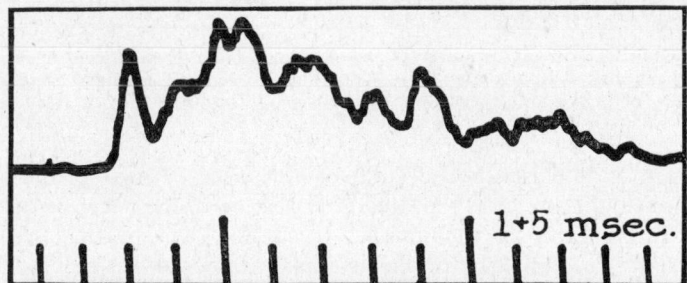

Fig. 89.—Segmental reflex discharge evoked by stimulation of a dorsal root (S₁) and recorded from the ventral root of the same segment. The first deflection is conducted through arcs of two neurons (circumscribed reflex of Cajal). The remainder of the reflex discharge is conducted through multineuron arcs (represented by the diffuse reflex diagram of Cajal). The minimum multineuron arc pathway is one of three neurons (one interneuron).

THE STRETCH REFLEX (8, 9, 19, 20, 38)

If a pull is exerted upon the tendon of a muscle by the contraction of an opposing muscle, as the result of gravity acting upon the organism, or by any number of artificial means, the muscle resists actively the extending force. The active resistance of the muscle is a reflex contraction, the *stretch reflex*.

The afferent neurons for this reflex arise within the muscle itself, being stimulated into activity by *tension receptors*. The stretch reflex is thus a *proprioceptive reflex.**

The nature of the stretch reflex was first shown in 1925 by Liddell and Sherrington (19). They employed the decerebrated animal in which exaggeration of "postural tone" facilitates elicitation of the response.† The tendon of quadriceps was attached to an isometric myograph while the femoral origin of the muscle was firmly fixed to a table, underneath but separate from the myograph, that could be lowered or raised to stretch or slacken the muscle.

Figure 90 records the tension developed (M) by the quadriceps muscle when a stretch of 8 mm. is imposed upon it within a period of one second. Part of this tension of course is merely passive tension, resulting from stretch-

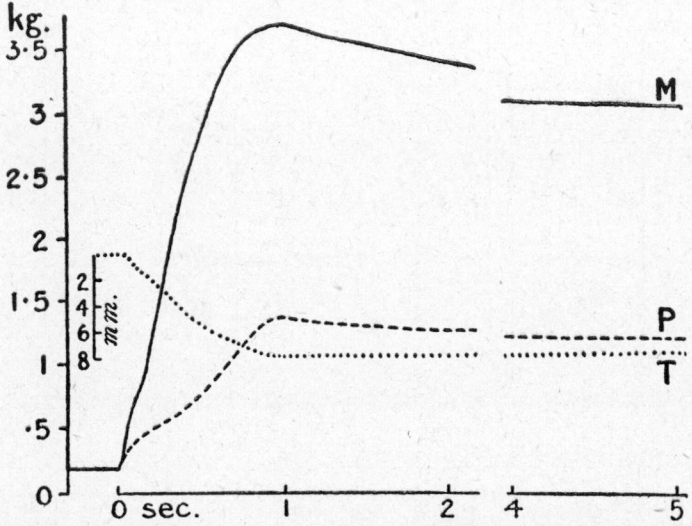

Fig. 90.—Stretch, or myotatic, reflex. *M* = reflex contraction of quadriceps in response to 8 mm. stretch indicated by dotted line (*T*). *P* = purely elastic tension developed by similar stretch after paralysis of muscle by denervation. The tension difference (*M–T*) represents the active reflex tension. (From Liddell and Sherrington, *Proc. roy. Soc.*, 1924, *B96*:212–242.)

ing the muscle, an elastic body. To determine what fraction of the total tension is passive, the stretch is repeated after section of the nerve to quadriceps, resulting in paralysis of the muscle. It cannot then participate in reflex activity; it can develop only the elastic tension imposed by stretch. The curve P measures this elastic tension. The reflex tension, therefore, is given by the difference between curves M and P. If afferent impulses from the muscle are interrupted by severance of the dorsal roots (deafferentation) the tension developed on stretch is merely elastic tension entirely comparable to that seen with the paralyzed muscle.

* Proprioceptors occur in muscles, tendons and the labyrinth and yield reflex actions and information concerning movements and position of body parts in contrast to exteroceptors in the surface membranes sensitive to pain, cold, heat, touch, etc., and interoceptors, located in and transmitting impulses from the viscera. Further discussion of this classification of sensory receptors will be found in Chapter 16.

† A description of the decerebrate state and a consideration of the integrated activity known as "posture" follow in Chapter 8.

Further proof of the reflex nature of the response to stretch derives from experiments on reflex inhibition. The stretch-evoked activity of the moto-neuron pool of quadriceps is prevented by stimulation of any afferent nerve that promotes flexion of the limb. An example of this effect is found in Figure 91. As before, the curve M gives the full tension of the stretched muscle, and curve P the elastic tension of the paralyzed muscle. To obtain curve I the muscle was reflexly inhibited during the early part of the stretch reaction by stimulation of an ipsilateral afferent nerve beginning just before the onset of stretch and ending at i'. When so inhibited the tension curve of the muscle follows exactly the course given by the paralyzed muscle only to revert to the tension level normally developed when the inhibitory stimulation is ended. If the inhibitory nerve is stimulated late in the stretch reaction (during the plateau), tension falls abruptly to the paralyzed level, or, if the inhibitory

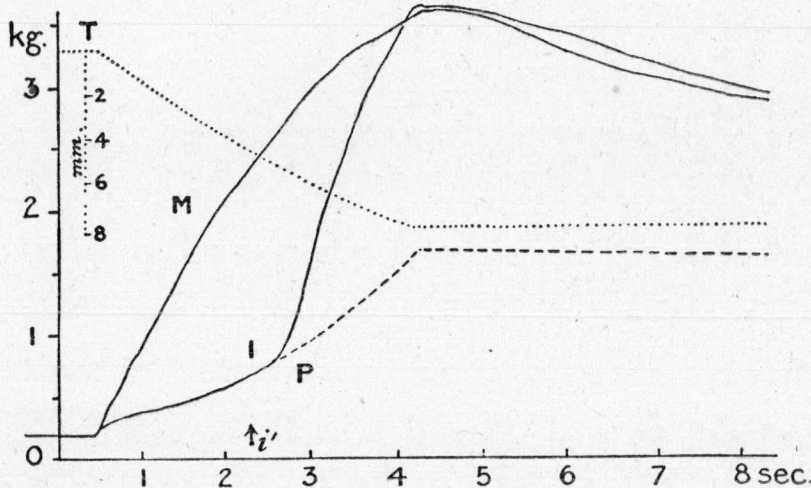

Fig. 91.—Stretch reflex of vastocrureus. M = response of normal muscle to stretch of 8 mm. indicated by dotted line (T). Solid line (I) = muscle response to similar stretch when inhibited by stimulation of ipsilateral nerve during earlier half of response. Broken line (P) = response of paralyzed muscle. Note inhibition causes muscle to behave as if paralyzed; also, on relief of inhibition, muscle rapidly develops tension comparable to that of curve M. Stimulation of inhibitory afferent nerve begun before onset of stretch and discontinued at i'. (From Liddell and Sherrington, *Proc. roy. Soc.*, 1924, *B96:*212–242.)

stimulation is maintained throughout, the curve is indistinguishable from that of the paralyzed muscle.

Stretch reflexes contain an inhibitory component. This is best revealed by recording the effect exerted on an extensor muscle by stretch of flexor muscles such as biceps femoris. In the experiment illustrated in Figure 92, quadriceps was first stretched to produce the characteristic reflex contraction of that muscle. At B stretch of biceps resulted in the virtually complete inhibition of the response in quadriceps. It is evident that afferent impulses from biceps prevent the response of quadriceps motoneurons to afferent impulses from quadriceps itself.

The peak of the reflex tension in a stretch reflex response occurs at the time of completion of the stretch-movement, following which there is a plateau usually of slightly declining tension that is maintained during the period of static stretch or stretch-posture. The degree of contraction tension during the plateau is regulated with extreme delicacy by the degree of static stretch imposed on the muscle. When the stretch is relieved, the contraction tension falls instantly, there being no trace whatever of after-action, as may be seen at t′ of Figure 100. It is customary to think of the stretch response as consisting of a stretch-movement or phasic reflex and a stretch-posture or static reflex. When the stretch is very brief only the phasic component is realized; the classical example of phasic stretch reflex is the *knee jerk*, isometric recordings of which are to be found in Figure 101.

The stretch reflex is a spinal reaction (9), both phasic and static reactions being elicitable from leg muscles after the lumbar spinal cord has been isolated from higher centers by transection. The static reaction is more seriously affected than the phasic reaction by such lesions of the neuraxis.

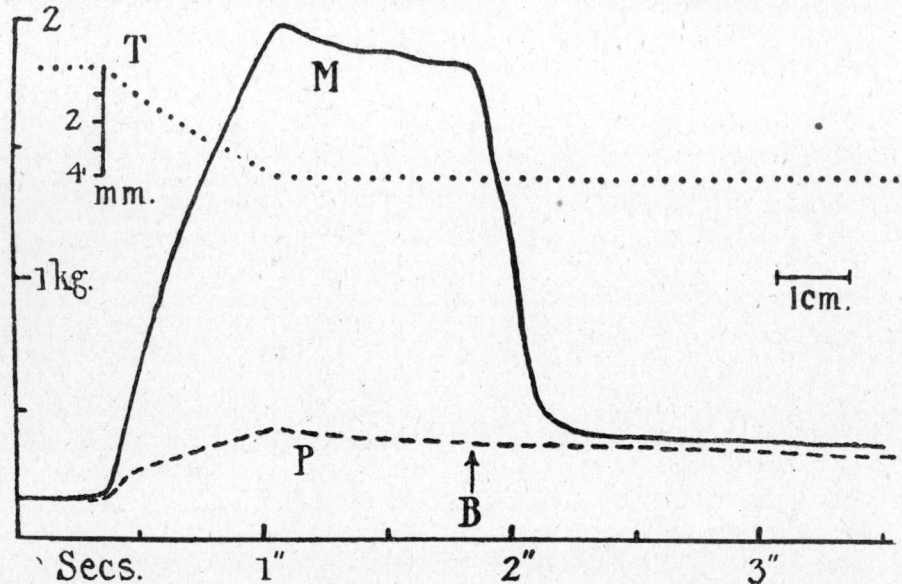

Fig. 92.—Inhibition of stretch reflex in extensor muscle by stretch of flexor muscle. *M* = response of quadriceps to stretch of 4 mm. indicated by dotted line (*T*). At the arrow (*B*) a similar stretch was applied to biceps (antagonist), inhibiting quadriceps so that tension falls to that given by the paralyzed muscle (*P*). (From Liddell and Sherrington, *Proc. roy. Soc.*, 1925, B97:267–283.)

The knee jerk. This response is usually the first to return after isolation of the spinal cord by injury or experimental lesion. It is elicited by tapping the tendon of quadriceps at a point where it is unsupported by bone, thus imparting a brief and slight stretch to the muscle. Other tendon jerks, for instance the ankle jerk, are identical in nature. The essential difference between a full static stretch reflex and its fractional manifestation, the tendon jerk, results from the nature of the afferent activity reaching the spinal cord from the stretched muscle. In the former instance, afferent activity takes the form of a steady, completely asynchronous discharge of impulses into the reflex center. The afferent activity of the tendon jerk, by way of contrast, is a synchronous or nearly synchronous volley of impulses. A number of features of these reflexes become almost self-evident when considered in the light of this essential distinction. When subjected to the steady asynchronous impulse barrage of maintained stretch, the motoneurons respond with a low frequency of discharge but so asynchronously that smooth tension is maintained. Each motoneuron on firing passes through its cycle of recovery, and the rate of firing depends largely upon the intensity of the asynchronous barrage impinging upon the motoneurons and the recovery through subnormality of the motoneurons. It is precisely this maintained, low grade, asynchronous, stretch-evoked reflex activity, an instance of which may be seen in Figure 26, that forms the mechanism of what is called *tone* in striated muscle. Cut the tendon of a muscle away from its insertion, allowing it to slacken, and tone disappears. Sever the dorsal root supply of a given muscle and tone disappears in that muscle. Diminish the background of impulses impinging upon the motoneurons from higher centers by severing the spinal cord and tone disappears from the muscles innervated from below the section, although in this case tone later returns and may become exaggerated (hypertonus), making the limbs quite stiff and unyielding to passive manipulation.

The tendon jerk operating through the same stretch reflex mechanism appears quite different. A sharp tap delivered to the tendon activates a number of stretch receptors in synchrony and a synchronized afferent volley results. The motoneurons respond in a synchronized fashion and a brief contraction ensues. Since a large number of motoneurons respond together, their recovery cycles likewise will be synchronized. These motoneurons, instead of being subnormally excitable in rotation, as in asynchronous activity, will all be subnormal at the same time. Further afferent activity entering the motoneuron pool is confronted for a period of time with a high motoneuron threshold that prevents response. The motoneurons are "silent." The period is known as the *silent period*. But this is not all. As the muscle contracts, some of the strain is taken off the tension receptors (cf. Chap. 8) so that they cease responding. If the muscle has been under a slight stretch, thus giving rise to a steady afferent inflow, then, following the tendon tap and during the jerk contraction, there is actually a deficiency in afferent impulses from the previous level (29). This, with subnormality of the motoneurons, is an important factor in production of the silent period.

Silent periods occur in other associated muscles at the same time as in the muscle jerked. Since these associated muscles have not been subjected to mechanical change and since their motoneurons have not fired, change in afferent influx and subnormality are not the cause. These motoneurons are inhibited (7). Recent work has proved that afferent fibers of the largest diameter arising from one muscle are inhibitory to the motoneurons of neighboring associated muscles (28).

Genesis of clonus (8). Elicitation of clonus, particularly of the ankle extensors, is an important maneuver in the clinic. Clonus occurs when the asynchronous character of motoneuron discharge in a stretch reflex is lost. The contraction tension is no longer smooth but shows a series of waves at regular intervals (Fig. 93). The mechanism of clonus is simple. If a rapid stretch is forced upon a muscle, exaggerated tone being a predisposing influence, it may happen that so many motoneurons are discharged in fairly synchronous manner during the stretch-movement that a significant fraction of the motoneuron pool of the muscle enters into the subnormal period with its members in step. Even though the extending force still operates, the muscle tension falls and, as it does so, the strain on the tension receptors that was materially lessened when the muscle contracted in response to the initial stretch movement is re-exerted. An outburst of afferent activity results. This reaches the motoneurons as recovery from subnormality is complete, so a large number of motoneurons respond again in step with each other. The cycle repeats itself and the clonic response is established.

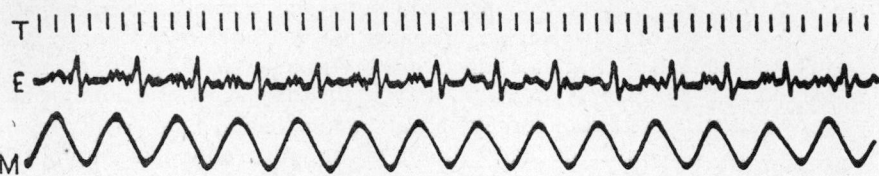

Fig. 93.—Clonic response of quadriceps muscle at 13 per sec. E = electrical response of muscle showing synchronized discharges. M = myogram. Time = 20 msec. (From Creed, Denny-Brown, Eccles, Liddell and Sherrington, *Reflex activity of the spinal cord*, Oxford, Clarendon Press, 1932.)

Figure 94 illustrates particularly well the precipitation of clonus. Before the beginning of the record a slight stretch was applied to the quadriceps to provide the background of exaggerated tone. A tendon jerk is then elicited after which there follows a well-defined clonus. .

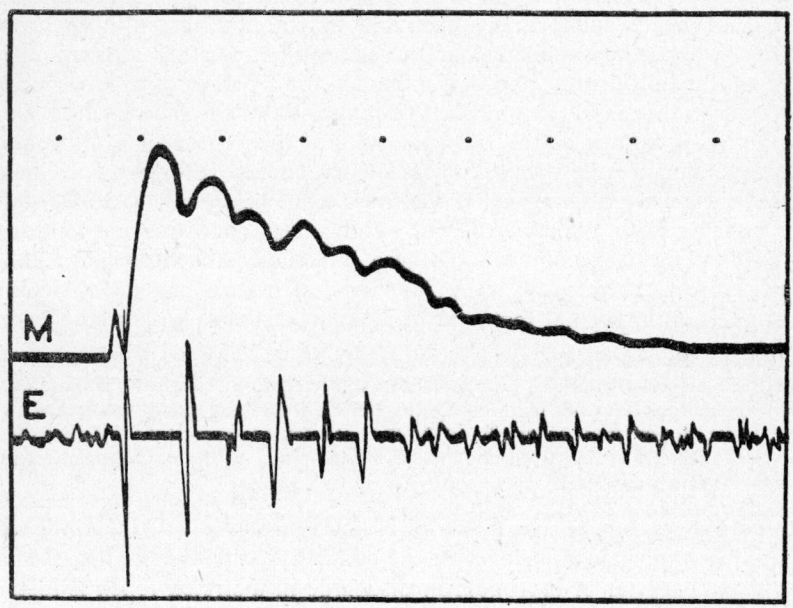

Fig. 94.—Genesis of clonus. Electrical (E) and mechanical (M) records of quadriceps. A slight stretch, previously applied, produces a high degree of tone. A tendon jerk is then elicited, indicated by the first sharp deflection in the mechanical record; thereafter follows a well-defined clonic discharge, marked in both electrical and mechanical records. Time, indicated by the dots, in 100 msec. intervals. (After Denny-Brown, *Proc. roy. Soc.*, 1929, *B104*:252–301.)

Distribution of stretch reflexes. All muscles that have been examined have been found to respond in some degree to the stimulus of stretch, but wide variations are found in the readiness of a muscle to respond thus. The stretch reflex is most fully developed in the muscles of physiological extension:

muscles that counteract the force of gravity, and so permit the organism to maintain a posture in the face of gravitational attraction. Included in this group with the extensor muscles of the limb joints are the elevators of the lower jaw. As a general rule, the extensor muscles contain two components that may be two muscles in the anatomical sense inserted into a common point (an example would be soleus and gastrocnemius), or may be anatomical heads of a single muscle (e.g., the deep and superficial heads of supraspinatus). One component is deep and slow acting, the other superficial and rapid in its action (cf. Chap. 2). Differences in color of muscles can be made out by simple inspection, the deep, slow contracting muscles commonly being relatively red, the superficial rapid muscles being "pale," although exceptions occur. Flexor muscles as a rule are rapidly contracting muscles. Dual mechanism of muscular contraction has long been postulated, slow muscles for sustained tonic contraction and rapid muscle for phasic contractions; and Denny-Brown has shown the measure of truth in this hypothesis, for indeed the slow muscles are those in which the stretch reflex is most easily provoked and is best maintained as a static reaction. After spinal transection the slow muscles recover and respond to stretch more readily than do the rapid muscles.

Pale muscles in general respond well to stretch movement, yielding tendon jerk reflexes, but fail to exhibit well-maintained stretch posture or static reflexes. This is particularly the case with flexor muscles, although flexor tendon jerk reflexes (the "pluck" reflex) may be elicited. The inhibitory action on extensors of traction on a flexor tendon, described by Liddell and Sherrington (cf. Fig. 92), is seemingly more prominent than the excitatory effect on the flexor muscle itself.

One important feature of the stretch reflex, no matter in what muscle it may be elicited, is its intensely restricted field of action. A stretch reflex response appears only in a muscle subjected to stretch, other muscles being unaffected or inhibited. The "unit" of the stretch reflex, however, is smaller than the anatomical muscle, but how much smaller is not yet known. Certainly traction on one head of a muscle provokes a reflex only in that head of the muscle, the others remaining quiescent. As we shall see below, this characteristic restricted distribution of a stretch response is of the greatest functional importance and incidentally is of considerable aid in unraveling the central pathways involved in transmission of stretch reflexes.

Functional significance of stretch reflexes (38). The weight of the body in most animals tends to flex the joints, and by so doing acts as a stretching force on the extensor tendons bridging these joints. The resulting reflex contraction of the extensors serves, then, to counteract gravity and assist in the maintenance of a standing posture. Sherrington has shown how the extreme localization of stretch reflex response allows great latitude in detail. Thus with slight shifts in position, the influence of gravity is shifted and the distribution of stretch is changed. By the consequent change in distribution of the reflex, the altered incidence of gravity is compensated. The body by reflex adjustment retains the standing position.

In stepping or running the stretch reflex plays an important role. We have already seen (Chap. 2) that the movement of progression consists of two phases, a flexion phase, carrying the foot forward clear of the ground, and an extension phase, straightening the leg, bringing the foot in contact with the ground, and pushing the body forward. In the flexion phase the bending of the knee stretches the extensor muscle of the knee, but the reflex is inhibited after the manner illustrated in Figure 92, the purpose being presumably to prevent a stretch reflex from impeding active flexion. At the conclusion of the flexion phase, the stretch reflex is freed from inhibition to provide the main drive for the ensuing extension phase. As the knee straightens, the reflex is self-limited by the relief of stretch.

The contribution of the stretch reflex to the extension phase occurs in another way. Some extensor muscles bridge across two joints; part of the knee extensors (rectus femoris), for example, bridges the flexor aspect of the hip as well as the extensor aspect of the knee. Now in the early part of the extension phase of the step, extension at the hip must necessarily stretch the muscle part lying over the hip and this, at the knee, must reinforce the extensor movement already under way.

Finally stretch reflexes play an important role in securing smooth execution of movement. This action is well illustrated in experiments involving reflex

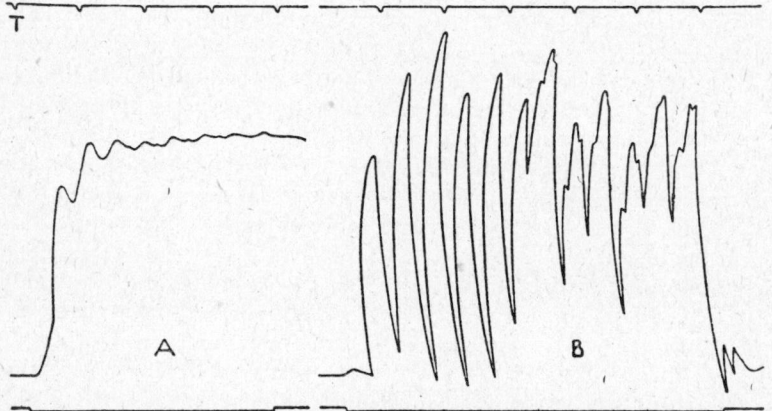

Fig. 95.—Reflex of crossed extension in quadriceps muscle elicited by stimuli at 8 per sec. (low frequency). A = response of normal muscle. B = response of deafferented muscle (dorsal roots cut 82 days previously). Note ataxia of deafferented muscle. (From Creed, Denny-Brown, Eccles, Liddell and Sherrington, *Reflex activity of the spinal cord*, Oxford, Clarendon Press, 1932.)

production by stimulation of afferent nerves, for the afferent drive so engendered is necessarily in the form of synchronized volleys favoring unsteady muscle response or *tremor*. The stimulation tremor may be well-smothered in the contraction of normal muscle only to appear in exaggerated form after deafferentation of the muscle (Fig. 95). The muscle becomes *ataxic* through loss of the proprioceptive reaction arising within itself. Loss or impairment of the knee jerk in *tabes dorsalis* points clearly to loss or impairment of the stretch reflex as the dominant factor in production of the ataxy characteristic of that disease. The observation illustrated in Figure 95 forms the experimental clarification of the nature of the deficiency wrought by the disease.

FLEXOR REFLEXES (13)

Flexor reflexes would seem to play two conspicuous roles in body reactions. One type of response is the abrupt withdrawal of an injured part from the source of hurt. This was called by Sherrington a *nociceptive* reaction. Secondly, reflex flexion takes part in the rhythmic stepping movements just considered. In almost every detail flexor reflexes differ from the stretch reflexes. In operation the flexor reflex shows considerable "after action," that is to say, motoneuron discharge into the muscle continues after the cessation of the specific afferent activity provoking the response. This stands in contrast to the "dead beat" conclusion of a stretch reflex.

The flexor reflex is an ipsilateral reaction, flexor contraction occurring in the limb that is injured. Experimentally, reflex flexion is promoted by stimulation of almost any nerve within the limb.* If one considers the response of a given flexor muscle, for example tibialis anterior, the flexor of the ankle, it is found that many afferent nerves when stimulated provoke the reflex, as may be seen in Table 6. Several facts emerge from experiments such as that summarized. Only a fraction of the motoneurons take part in the reflex response elicited from any one afferent nerve since the motor nerve tetanus tension exceeds the reflex tension. Thus the motoneuron pool of the muscle

Table 6.—*Reflex Fractionation of a Flexor Motoneuron Pool.* (*From Creed, Denny-Brown, Eccles, Liddell and Sherrington, Reflex activity of the spinal cord, Oxford, Clarendon Press.*)

M. TIBIALIS ANTERIOR	MAXIMUM MOTOR TENSION 2160 GRAMS	
AFFERENT NERVE STIMULATED	TENSION OF MAXIMAL REFLEX TETANUS IN GRAMS	REFLEX TENSION EXPRESSED AS PERCENTAGE OF MAXIMAL MOTOR TETANUS
Internal saphenous	800	32
Superficial obturator	165	6.7
Deep obturator	400	16
N. to quadriceps and sartorius	1190	44
Branch of peroneal	1700	69
External plantar	1240	50
Internal plantar	1330	54
Small sciatic	680	28
Hamstring	565	23
Nerve to sural triceps	300	12
Total	8370	

is said to be *fractionated* by a reflex. The sum of the reflex tensions yielded by stimulation of individual afferent nerves (8370 grams) far exceeds the maximal motor tetanus tension. This can only mean that motoneurons of the pool are excited from more than one afferent nerve (the principle of convergence discussed in Chap. 5). The extensive convergence characteristic of the flexor reflex pathways brings with it ample opportunity for occlusion and facilitation, the former prominent if the convergent reflexes are strong, the latter if they are weak (cf. Chap. 5, Fig. 75).

If attention is directed not to a single flexor muscle but to a wider field embracing all the flexor muscles of a limb, it will be seen that all of them on stimulation of an afferent nerve respond to a greater or less degree (Sherrington). There is characteristically a variation in the fractions of various flexor muscles involved in the response to maximal stimulation of a given afferent nerve, yielding a pattern of response. The pattern differs for each individual

* In the forelimb stimulation of nerves, particularly of the digital branches of the median nerve, promotes ipsilateral extension (10).

afferent nerve in a manner illustrated in Table 7, in which the tensions of the reflex responses for each afferent nerve are expressed as percentages of the strongest reflex contraction.

By the use of synthetic reasoning based on the data in Table 7 one can readily appreciate that the limb will take up different final positions depending upon the nerve stimulated to elicit the limb flexion. For example, hip flexion evoked by saphenous nerve is greater than that by popliteal nerve. Reflex

Table 7.—*Variation in Pattern of Reflex Flexion Involving Several Joints Depending upon the Nerve Stimulated. (After Creed and Sherrington, from Creed, Denny-Brown, Eccles, Liddell and Sherrington, Reflex activity of the spinal cord, Oxford, Clarendon Press, 1932.)*

AFFERENT NERVE	HIP FLEXOR (TENS. FASCIAE FEM.)	KNEE FLEXOR SEMITENDINOSUS	ANKLE FLEXOR TIBIALIS ANT.
Internal saphenous	100	56	87
Popliteal (Tibial)	3 or less	42	100
Peroneal (distal to Tib. Ant. N.)	14	100	69

actions thus exhibit *local sign.* The classical demonstration of local sign in reflex performance features the scratch reflex, which is compounded of two elements, one a smoothly maintained positional reflex carrying the limb to the appropriate site, the other a pendular scratching movement of obvious purpose superimposed upon the positional reflex. The scratching movement is the same wherever the locus of adequate stimulation, but the degree of positional contraction varies with the site of stimulation, and therefore with the afferent nerve fibers mediating the reflex.

TRANSMISSION OF STRETCH AND FLEXOR REFLEXES (25, 26, 27, 28)

The problem of analysis of the pathways and central connections mediating the stretch and flexor reflexes is essentially that of dissecting the segmental reflex discharge, seen in Figure 89, into its functional components. The first step in this process is to determine the reflex effect (as recorded from a ventral root) of stimulating not a dorsal root as was done to obtain Figure 89, but a muscle nerve and a skin nerve severally. Figure 96 illustrates the fiber constitution of a muscle nerve after degeneration of the motor fibers, and of a skin nerve; a comparison of the afferent fibers contained in each will give an idea of the character of an afferent volley in each instance. The largest fibers are found only among the muscle afferent fibers, whereas the first peak in the skin nerve distribution is well below that in the muscle nerve in point of fiber size. These fibers, centered about a mean diameter of 9–10 μ, are numerous in the skin nerves but are relatively few in number in the muscle nerves. Fibers below 6 μ form a peak in the distribution of fibers in both nerves. It is instructive to carry in mind these characteristic differences between the fiber constitutions of muscle and skin afferent nerves when observing the type of reflex discharge obtained by stimulating each in isolation. A maximal afferent volley in a muscle nerve yields a powerful reflex discharge through arcs of two neurons, but little through the multineuron arcs (Fig. 97 A). On the contrary, maximal stimulation of skin nerves does not evoke any reflex response through two-neuron arcs although the multineuron reflex fraction is ample (Fig. 97 B).

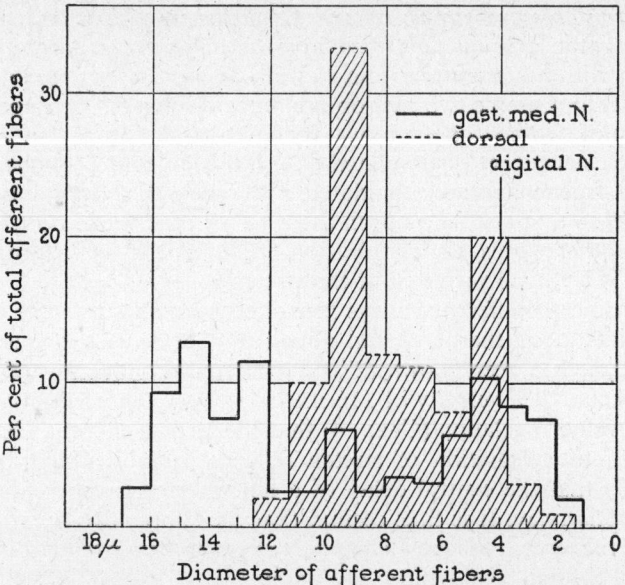

Fig. 96.—Distribution of afferent fibers in a muscle nerve (nerve to gastrocnemius medialis) and in a cutaneous nerve (dorsal digital). Note: The largest afferent fibers are found only in the muscle nerve; these fibers mediate stretch reflexes. Compare these fiber distribution plots with the reflex effects of stimulating a muscle nerve and a cutaneous nerve respectively (Fig. 97). (Modified from Eccles and Sherrington, *Proc. roy. Soc.*, 1930, *B106*:326–357.)

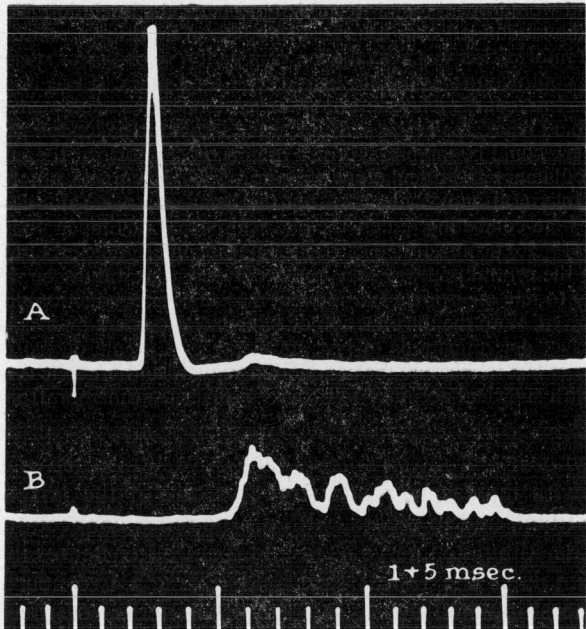

Fig. 97.—Reflex discharges recorded from a ventral root. A = response to afferent stimulation of a muscle nerve. B = response to stimulation of a cutaneous nerve. Note the two-neuron arc discharge (the first spike potential) in A, and its absence in B; also, ample multineuron arc discharge (in B) as response to afferent stimulation of cutaneous nerve. (From Lloyd, *J. Neurophysiol.*, 1943, *6*:111–119.)

Two-neuron arcs and stretch reflexes (27). Recent experiments have shown that it is only the large afferent fibers in muscle nerves that form direct synaptic relation with motoneurons, and that an afferent volley confined to these fibers results in a simple two-neuron arc reflex discharge. Examination of the distribution of two-neuron arc reflex discharges reveals that they appear only in the muscle nerve that is stimulated (26). If the large afferent fibers from one head of gastrocnemius are stimulated, the reflex discharge appears in the motor fibers to that head but not in those to the other head nor to any other muscle. In other words, the distribution of stimulated two-neuron arc reflex discharges is identical with that of the stretch reflex.

By recording the afferent volleys provoked by brief stretch of a muscle at several points along the nerve and dorsal root between the muscle and the spinal cord, it has been shown (27) that afferent conduction of the stretch response occurs at a velocity of 116 meters per sec. which proves according to the size velocity relation (Chap. 4) that the largest afferent fibers are concerned with the mediation of stretch reflexes. Finally it has been shown directly (27) that the central delay of a tendon jerk is only sufficient for a single synaptic relay. It is thus certain that the simple two-neuron arc pathways serve the stretch reflexes. The pluck reflex or flexor tendon jerk likewise is mediated through two-neuron arc pathways.

The development of thought on the subject of tendon jerks forms a fascinating story. About the turn of the century it was stoutly held by many that the tendon jerk was due not to a reflex act but to direct mechanical stimulation of the muscle. It was known that the reflex connections of the muscle must be intact to obtain a jerk response, but adherents of the mechanical stimulation concept countered with the suggestion that an atonic muscle was less irritable and would not respond to sudden mechanical stimulation. They claimed that the latency of the tendon jerk was too short to admit of its being a reflex, although at the time no critical information was available on conduction velocities or synaptic delays. The duration of the contraction was held to be too brief for a reflex. It was largely through the work of Sherrington that the reflex nature of the tendon jerk was accepted. He showed that another undoubted reflex, the *extensor thrust*, was as brief as the tendon jerk. His evidence that a tendon jerk could be inhibited formed important support for the reflex view. Many measurements of latency and calculations of central delay were made, notable among which were those of Jolly (18) and Snyder (41), but the techniques were not adequate, and the interpretations were conflicting. Later, the classical papers of Liddell and Sherrington on stretch reflexes (19, 20) demonstrated clearly the nature and significance of these responses, but concerning the central pathway they could only say that it must be short. As long as it was necessary to rely on estimates or indirect measures of conduction time, the problem could not be solved. With the introduction of direct measurement by means of electronics, and with the exact determinations of synaptic delay by Lorente de Nó (cf. Chap. 5), it became possible at last to measure the conduction velocity and synaptic time of the tendon jerk response with sufficient accuracy to prove its direct transmission from afferent fibers to motoneurons.

Multineuron arcs and flexor reflexes (26). A very instructive experiment is to stimulate with increasing shock strengths one of the mixed nerves of a limb, say the tibial, and to record, with all the reflex connections of the limb intact, from the stimulated nerve itself and from other nerves in the limb. As the shock stimulates the lowest threshold fibers, a two-neuron arc reflex appears in the stimulated nerve, but the other nerves of the limb are not active. With increase in the shock to the strength at which the first skin afferent fibers in the mixed nerve are stimulated, multineuron arc reflex discharges appear for the first time, and they are found in the nerves to flexor muscles. On further increase in the shock to include the smallest fibers in the stimulated volley, prolongation of the reflex discharges into the flexor muscle nerves takes place. These discharges into the flexor nerves represent the flexor reflex. The minimum pathway for the mediation of flexor reflexes contains an interneuron and is therefore a three-neuron arc.*

Two distinct groups of afferent fibers, those centered about the 10 μ peak and the 4 μ peak give rise on stimulation to flexor reflexes of characteristically different latencies (Fig. 98). The flexor reflexes of brief latency are easily elicited by stimulation of skin nerves but not of muscle nerves. On the other hand, the flexor reflexes of longer latency, so-called "delta" flexor reflexes, of skin and muscle origin are equally prominent. Although the fact that two groups of afferent fibers exist for the mediation of flexor reflexes is presumably of functional importance, there is as yet no clear indication of its significance.

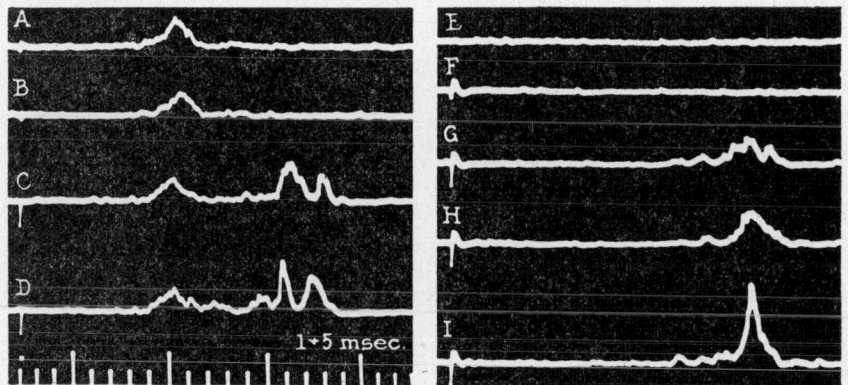

Fig. 98.—Motoneuron discharges of flexor reflexes; A, B, C, D = on stimulation of cutaneous nerve (sural), F, G, H, I = on stimulation of muscle nerve (gastrocnemius). A, B = reflex discharge in response to stimulation of cutaneous afferent fibers in group centered about 10 μ diameter (Fig. 96). C, D = strength of stimulation increased so that delta fibers are stimulated. The initial discharge is not altered by the increased stimulation, but another later discharge is added. E = blank sweep of oscillograph spot. F = stimulation of muscle afferent fibers at strength comparable to that employed for A and B: no reflex discharge. G, H, I = stimulation of muscle afferent fibers at increased strength so that delta fibers are stimulated. Note absence of reflex discharge with short latency, but appearance of late flexor reflex discharge, comparable to late discharge in C and D. To interpret these reflex discharges note distribution (Fig. 96) of afferent fibers smaller than 12 μ in cutaneous and muscle nerves. (From Lloyd, *J. Neurophysiol.*, 1943, *6*:293–315.)

Functional significance of reflex connections. Once it is understood that the direct (two-neuron arc) reflex connections subserve stretch reflexes and that the indirect (multineuron arc) reflex connections subserve flexor reflexes within the limb, the functional significance of the "circumscribed" and "diffuse" reflex mechanisms of Cajal, illustrated in Figure 88, becomes quite clear. The direct and restricted two-neuron arc pathway serves to limit the reflex field of action of the afferent influx from tension receptors. In contrast, the interneurons intercalated in the flexor reflex pathway with their axons spreading up and down the spinal cord provide the structural mechanism for insuring the diffusion of the flexor reflex to many or all of the flexor muscles of the limb.

* Until recently it has been supposed that direct connections between afferent fibers and motoneurons serve flexor reflexes as well as stretch reflexes, but it is now known that the evidence upon which the supposition was based was faulty.

REFLEX COORDINATION

Crossed extensor reflexes. The crossed extensor reflex may be regarded as the contralateral accompaniment of the flexor reflex. Stimulation of an afferent nerve of a limb leads to generalized flexion of that limb and generalized extension of the opposite limb. Features of the crossed extensor reflex are its long and variable latency, its slow development of tension, and prolonged after-discharge. Interneurons lie between afferent fibers and motoneurons in all of the pathways mediating the reflex. Stretch reflexes are inextricably grafted onto every crossed extensor reflex unless the reacting muscles be deafferented. When this is done the crossed extensor reflex tends toward a more precipitate onset and ending; hence the autogenous control of the muscle over itself is in large measure responsible for the "recruiting" or slow onset of the crossed reflex and the prolonged after-action. In Figure 95 was seen an example of the blending of crossed reflex and stretch reflex and the loss of taxis when the latter was obliterated by deafferentation.

Reciprocal innervation (35, 36, 39). Since stimulation of an afferent nerve as a rule promotes ipsilateral flexion and contralateral extension, one can understand that reflexes will come into conflict in the spinal reflex centers if symmetrical afferent nerves on the two sides of the body be stimulated concurrently, for each afferent nerve will act in the sense of exciting flexors on its own side and extensors of the opposite side. The key to the result of such concurrent stimulation is to be found in the fact that stimulation of an afferent nerve, while provoking ipsilateral contraction of flexor muscles, causes the extensor muscles of the same side to relax by the process known as inhibition, that is to say, each reflex has an inhibitory field as well as an excitatory field. An excellent example illustrating this fact was seen in Figure 92. Stretch of a flexor muscle in that instance was found to have an inhibitory effect on the opposing extensor muscle, this action being the inhibitory component of the stretch reflex in the flexor muscle itself. The inhibitory field of a reflex commonly embraces the motoneurons of muscles whose action is directly antagonistic to that of the excited muscles. This is the principle of *reciprocal innervation*. It is important, however, to recognize that the distribution and occurrence of reciprocal innervation extend beyond the simple case of antagonistic muscles at a joint. Thus stimulation of a limb nerve (peroneal) promotes contraction of a contralateral extensor and inhibition of the ipsilateral counterpart. The reflex influence over such paired symmetrical muscles therefore is reciprocal, although the muscles are not antagonistic in any ordinary sense; they do not belong to the same limb, much less to the same joint. They are, however, muscles that commonly operate in reciprocal relation for walking and running.

The coordination of paired symmetrical muscles is less rigidly according to the principle of reciprocal innervation than is that of antagonistic muscles about a single joint. In some circumstances, and with selected afferent nerves, afferent stimulation sets paired symmetrical muscles into concurrent contraction; the muscles are coordinated by *identical innervation* rather than reciprocal innervation, in likeness to their performance in galloping and sitting.

Double reciprocal innervation (33, 35). The projection into the spinal cord of the influences of two symmetrical afferent nerves places the motoneurons of flexors and extensors of both sides alike under combined excitatory and inhibitory drive. If the influences from the two sides are markedly unequal, the stronger rules and the muscles fall into reciprocal response. The result is different if the influences are approximately equal. With the flexors the excitatory effect of each afferent is stronger than the inhibitory effect and on both sides they enter into concurrent contraction. Inhibition gains the upper hand with the extensors and they relax together. Thus with both flexors and extensors the ipsilateral effect is the stronger: excitatory for flexors, inhibitory for extensors. These observations show that "double reciprocal innervation" can change reciprocal innervation of *symmetrical* muscles into identical innervation. Opposition of excitation and inhibition is quantitative and the end result is an algebraic summation of these actions.

Pseudantagonists and co-contraction. A distinction must be made between true antagonists, such as tibialis anterior and gastrocnemius at the ankle joint, which stand in reciprocal relation to one another, and *pseudantagonists*. Gastrocnemius is a two-joint muscle, extensor at the ankle, but, crossing the flexor surface of the knee joint, it opposes quadriceps, the knee extensor. In action, quadriceps and gastrocnemius together fix the knee joint so that

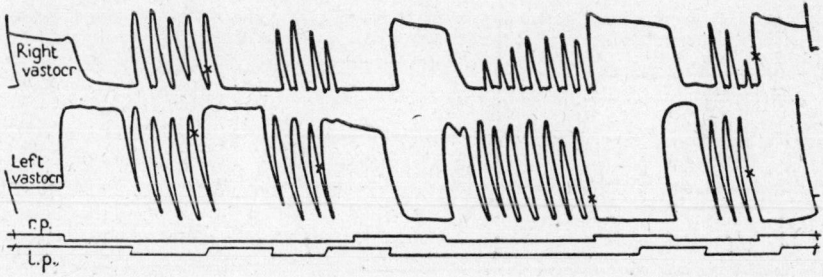

Fig. 99.—Production of rhythmic reflexes (stepping movements) by double reciprocal innervation. Mechanical records of right and left vastocrurei (extensors of the knee). r.p. = downward deflection indicates stimulation of right peroneal nerve (afferent). Right vastocrureus (ipsilateral) relaxes, left (contralateral) contracts: reciprocal innervation. l.p. = downward deflection indicates stimulation of left peroneal nerve (afferent). Left vastocrureus relaxes, right contracts. Whenever the two afferent nerves are stimulated concurrently, contraction and relaxation of each muscle alternates; contraction of one coincides with relaxation of the other. The crosses mark simultaneous points on the two graphs. (After Sherrington, 1913, from Creed, Denny-Brown, Eccles, Liddell and Sherrington, *Reflex activity of the spinal cord*, Oxford, Clarendon Press, 1932.)

extension of the ankle by gastrocnemius is enhanced. Pseudantagonists in this sense are really synergists and are coordinated by identical innervation (co-contraction) rather than by reciprocal innervation.

Genesis of stepping movements (36). The result of combined simultaneous stimulation of symmetrical afferent nerves within the limbs is frequently not co-contraction of symmetrical muscle pairs, but rhythmic alternation. Thus, in Figure 99 may be seen the results of an experiment in which the contraction and relaxation of both vastocrureus muscles were recorded during stimulation of one or the other, or both peroneal nerves. If either afferent nerve alone were stimulated, the ipsilateral muscle relaxed, the contralateral contracted, and the position was maintained. With the advent of concurrent stimulation the muscles entered into alternating reciprocal innervation. The mechanism responsible for the rhythmic action lies within the spinal cord, for a perfectly steady drive serves to institute alternation, and furthermore, complete deafferentation of the muscles blocking rhythmic stimuli from the muscles themselves modifies but does not prevent rhythmic response.

One may be sure that an understanding of rhythmic alternation in reflexes will not exceed that of the central inhibitory process, the importance of which is paramount in reflex coordination. It is time now to devote further attention to the manifestations, mechanisms and significance of central inhibition. As an introduction to the problem of inhibition and a summary of the reflex responses that have been considered, nothing serves better than a study of one of Liddell and Sherrington's experiments illustrated in Figure 100. The contraction of vastocrureus, a part of quadriceps, was recorded myographically. At *c* stimulation of the contralateral sciatic nerve was commenced, evoking a crossed extensor reflex contraction in the muscle. At *t* a slight stretch was applied to the muscle with the result that a stretch reflex was superimposed on the contralateral reflex. At *i* stimulation of an ipsilateral

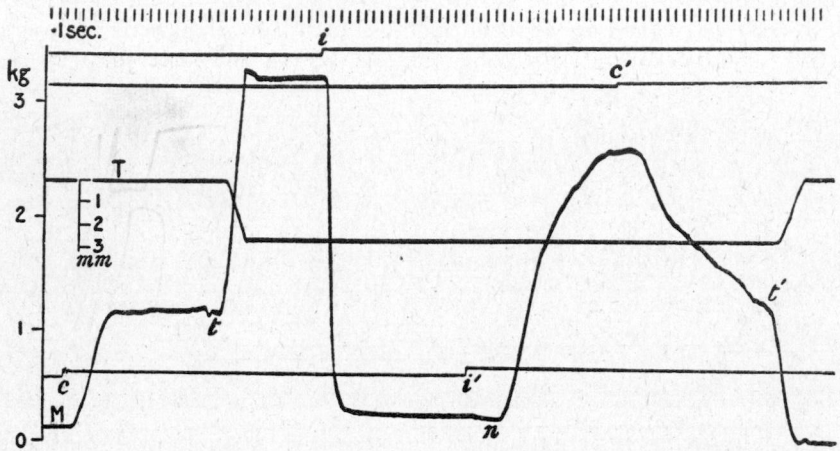

Fig. 100.—Interaction of several reflexes at the final common path as expressed by an extensor muscle, vastocrureus. From *c* to *c'*, stimulation of the contralateral sciatic nerve evokes a crossed extensor reflex. At *t* a 2.5 mm. stretch is imposed upon the muscle; this is relieved at *t'*, ending the residual stretched-posture. From *i* to *i'*, an ipsilateral afferent nerve is stimulated (to cause a flexor reflex in the limb); the extensor muscle documents this stimulation by inhibition of both stretch and crossed extensor components of the contraction. Recovery from inhibition shows two parts, indicating more rapid return of stretch component; slower return of crossed extensor component. Note slow ending of crossed reflex and abrupt ending of stretch reflex. Time 0.1 sec. (From Liddell and Sherrington, *Proc. roy. Soc.*, 1925, *B96*:212–242.)

nerve evoked a flexor reflex, which is of course not recorded, but prompt inhibition of the extensor is recorded, the inhibitory component of the flexor reflex making no distinction between the stretch evoked fraction and the crossed extensor fraction of the contractile effort. At *i'* cessation of the ipsilateral (inhibitory) stimulation allowed the muscle to commence regaining contractile effort. At *c'* the contralateral stimulation was stopped with the result that the muscle began slowly a partial relaxation, while at *t'* relief of the imposed stretch brought on the abrupt end of contractile response. The slow return to resting state in the crossed extensor response, and in the flexor reflex after the cessation of stimulation, is related in no small degree to the presence of interneurons in their central pathways. By the same token, the absence of interneurons in the stretch reflex pathway accounts for the abrupt termination on relief of stretch.

INHIBITION (5, 14, 15, 28)

The meaning of the term inhibition is nowhere better expressed than in the words of Gasser, "Inhibition is a term of convenience used without exact definition in connection with a group of phenomena having certain qualities in common. The essential condition is the stoppage or prevention of action through the temporary operation of a process which does not harm the tissue. It is usually implied that the process results from nervous activity, or imitates the results of nervous activity."*

The problem of inhibition was brought to attention when the brothers Weber, in 1845, arrested the heart beat by stimulating the vagus nerve. In the course of time intensive searches were made for inhibitory nerves to skeletal muscles. Inhibitory nerves indeed were found quite widely in the autonomic nervous system (e.g., the splanchnic nerve in its effect on gut movements) and to the claw muscles of crayfish, but uniform failure attended all efforts to demonstrate peripheral inhibition of vertebrate skeletal muscle. Thus one speaks of *central inhibition.*

Knowledge of central inhibitory mechanism, in contrast to conjecture, is so meager that for the most part it is only possible to consider seriatim some

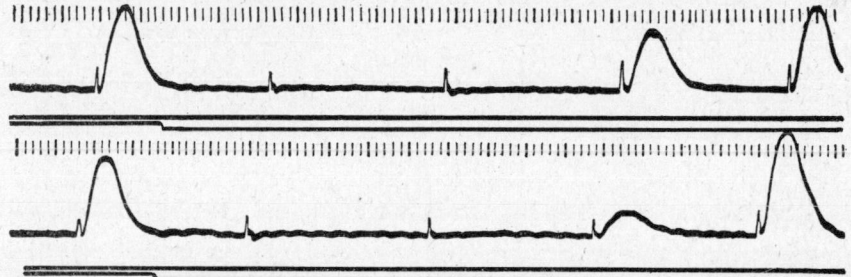

Fig. 101.—Knee jerks of spinal preparation delivered at 3 per sec. The sharp upward deflexions record the tendon taps, after which follow the jerk contractions. The signal at the bottom of each record indicates the time of a single stimulus of an ipsilateral afferent nerve. As a result, the knee jerks are inhibited for a second. (From Ballif, Fulton and Liddell, *Proc. roy. Soc.*, 1925, *B98*:589–607.)

of the qualities of central inhibition with suitable examples. It cannot be said that there is a general theory of inhibition, the multiplicity and diversity of hypotheses, mostly discredited, forming a measure of the obscurity which has surrounded the subject. At the present time it does seem that more than one mechanism is concerned in the phenomena collectively known as central inhibition.

Inhibition may have brief latency (1, 22). In fact, the central latency of reflex inhibition is as variable as the central latency of reflex discharge. Ballif, Fulton and Liddell in 1925 showed that a stimulus delivered to an ipsilateral nerve coincidentally with a tendon tap would inhibit the ensuing jerk response. More recently it has been shown that an "inhibitory" volley and an excitatory volley in two-neuron arc reflex systems delivered in synchrony will result in inhibition of the reflex response (22). The most careful measurement reveals that the inhibitory process can exert a tangible effect if it begins to act, at the motoneuron, at the same time as the excitatory process. The excitatory process

* From H. S. Gasser, The control of excitation in the nervous system, *Harvey Lectures*, 1936–37, p. 185.

at the synapse, once instituted, cannot be checked by the subsequent arrival of "inhibitory" impulses. Thus the minimal latency for inhibition is similar to the minimal latency for excitation. Longer latencies in both instances would appear to have a common explanation, namely, complexity of executant pathways.

Inhibition may have long duration. Inhibition of knee jerks by a single shock stimulus to an ipsilateral nerve may last for two seconds (Fig. 101). In other examples of reflex inhibition, the depression of response may last only 100 msec. The duration of inhibition is thus variable. Presumably, as in excitation, long and variable duration depends upon the repetition of inhibitory actions by virtue of internuncial chains. Unfortunately there is no information on

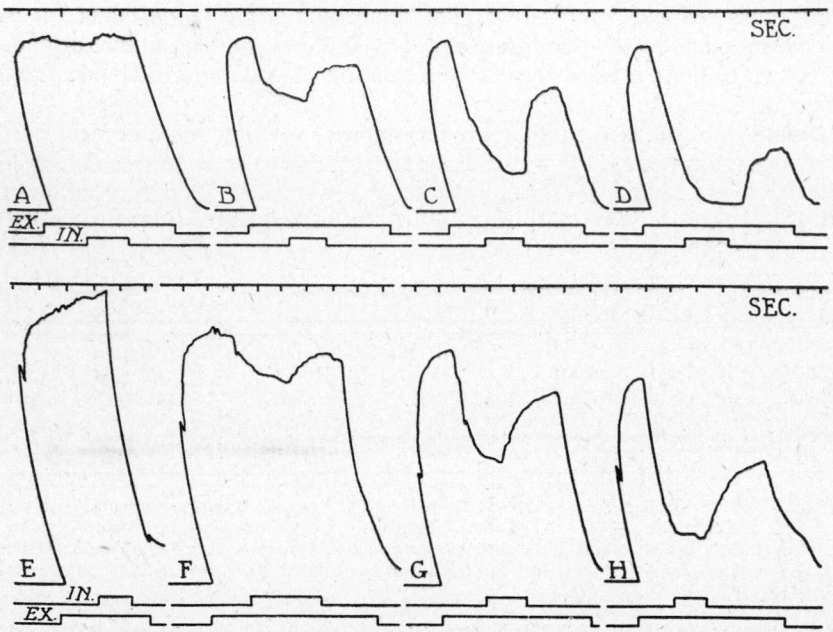

Fig. 102.—Reflex con ractions of semitendinosus evoked by stimulation of ipsilateral peronea nerve; indicated in eachtobservation by the signal marked *EX*. Inhibition secured by stimulation of contralateral tibial nerve (signal marked *IN*). A, B, C, D = excitatory stimulation constant; inhibitory stimulation progressively increased. E, F, G, H = inhibitory stimulation constant; excitatory stimulation progressively decreased. Time in sec. (After Sherrington, *Proc. roy. Soc.*, 1909, *B81*:249–268.)

the duration of the single inhibitory event which presumably is relatively fixed as is the single excitatory event (cf. p. 140).

Inhibition can be graded in intensity (33). The classical examples of grading of inhibition are to be found in Sherrington's experiments on inhibition of the knee flexor, semitendinosus, by stimulation of a contralateral nerve (Fig. 102). Two variations of the experiment may be related. In the first, a reflex of constant strength was evoked, and with each successive observation the strength of an intercurrent inhibitory stimulation was increased with the result that the inhibitory "notch" cut into the heart of the reflex increases in depth with each successive increment (Fig. 102 A). For the other variation the excitatory reflex is increased while the intercurrent inhibitory stimulation is maintained constant. The stronger the reflex contraction the less is the effect of the constant inhibitory stimulation until it fails altogether to affect the reflex (Fig. 102 B).

Inhibition and excitation exist in parallel. From a number of examples of central inhibition already presented it will be clear that stimulation of a given leg nerve yields excitation and inhibition in parallel, each action having its characteristic distribution. As a general rule: on the same side, flexor muscles are excited and extensor muscles inhibited; on the opposite side, extensor muscles are excited and flexor muscles inhibited. If we refer to the excited muscles as prime movers or agonists, we find that the inhibited muscles are the antagonists.

Inhibitory convergence. Inhibitory influences from two separate afferent sources can sum to increase the total inhibitory action on a testing reflex. It often happens that the inhibitory effect of the combined influences is less than the sum of the inhibitions acting severally on the test reflex. Thus reflex inhibition exhibits *occlusion*.

Nature of Central Inhibition. One can see from the foregoing that central inhibition is possessed of the same general properties as central excitation, the only outstanding difference between the two, indeed, being the direction of their influence. Attempts to penetrate deeper into the nature of central inhibition have met with some success. At least two phenomena occur with inhibitory result in the central nervous system. Both may be included under the heading of central inhibition, broadly defined. In the first order there are those effects that receive their explanation on the basis of the subnormal period following response. This includes the silent period of tendon jerks and the qualitatively similar inhibition of the second of two successive single shock flexor reflexes. In the second order are those effects that cannot be so explained. For convenience we may refer to these phenomena as "indirect" and "direct" inhibition respectively.

Indirect inhibition. The simplest example of indirect inhibition may be found in the silent period of the knee jerk, since only afferent neurons and motoneurons are involved in transmission. We have already seen that subnormality following activity is a property general to nervous tissue, the motoneurons proving no exception. Thus, inasmuch as the tendon jerk involves relatively synchronous discharge of a large number of motoneurons, a good fraction of the muscle pool of motoneurons will be in a state of raised threshold at one time, with the result that the pool is inaccessible to otherwise adequate stimulation; it is inhibited. This result is entirely comparable to the inhibition encountered in sympathetic ganglia (p. 129).

In 1931 Eccles and Sherrington (13) demonstrated that the flexor reflex to the second of two single shock stimuli in successive combination may be depressed unless the second shock succeeds the first by an interval greater than 120 msec. Now we know that the flexor reflex in all its pathways involves transmission through interneurons, so the situation becomes more complex than that of the tendon jerk. Hughes and Gasser (17) discovered that the interneurons necessary for transmission of flexor reflex effect enter a subnormal period following the first of two successive afferent volleys resulting in diminution of the internuncial response to the second. The deficit wrought in the internuncial response to the second stimulus results in a smaller motoneuron discharge. In their experiments attention was focused on the role of interneurons, for inhibition of the second response occurred when the first stimulus, although activating interneurons, was subliminal for the moto-neurons, for which reason the motoneurons could not have been subnormal.

One will appreciate the fact that an experiment such as this one of Hughes and Gasser would, on myographic recording alone, suggest that beyond the afferent volley itself no central activity had taken place in the flexor reflex pathway to the observed muscle on the occasion of the first stimulus. On this supposition, depression of the response to the second stimulus would logically result from an hypothetical prolonged inhibitory action. By the method of direct recording of internuncial activity introduced by Gasser and Graham(16), Hughes and Gasser could prove the interneurons active and subsequently subnormal in circumstances that would reveal nothing of activity to a myo-

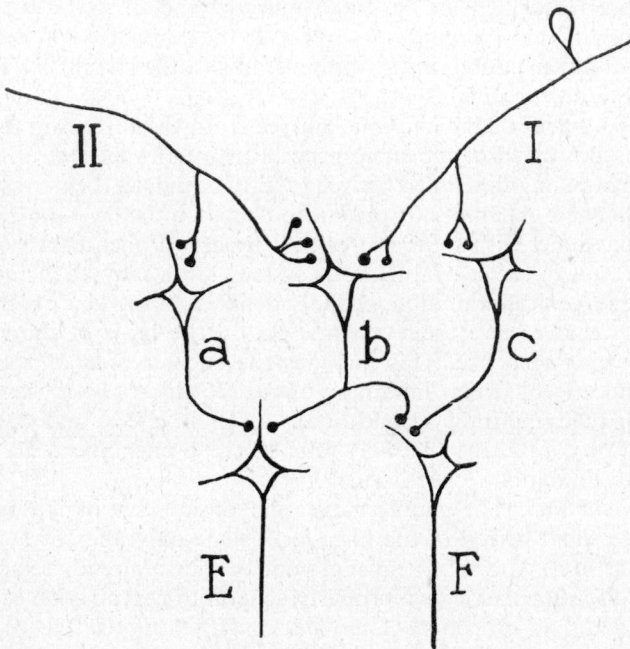

Fig. 103.—Diagram to account for reciprocal innervation on basis of subnormal process. (From Gasser, *Harvey Lect.*, 1937, *32*:169–193.)

graph. Subnormality of the interneurons becomes a sufficient explanation for this inhibition of the flexor reflex.*

Convergence of flexor reflex afferent pathways occurs at the internuncial level as well as at the motoneuron level. Therefore subnormality of inter-neurons common to two converging flexor reflexes could result in the one inhibiting the other. The two situations are not essentially different. An important consideration for the occurrence of inhibition by the intervention of subnormality lies in the necessity for other than synchronous convergence of interacting volleys, which event would lead to summation.†

* These experiments illustrate well the advantage of direct observation of central activity over the older necessity of inferring central events from peripheral events in the causal sequence.

† This consideration is more important to the theoretical concept of inhibition than it is to the specific experiments that have been related, for nonsynchronous convergence is a condition of the experiments.

Subnormality and reciprocal innervation (14, 15). Gasser has shown by means of a simplified diagram, illustrated in Figure 103, how the principle of inhibition by subnormality may be used to account for reciprocal innervation. Such a diagram of course must be considered as an aid to thought rather than a specific representation of neuronal interrelationships. In the diagram the several neurons are provided with a number of synaptic knobs and, in accordance with the fact that transmission requires that a certain minimal number of knobs be active at once, let us suppose that this minimal number be two. Then, if a neuron is subnormal, it will require stimulation by a greater number of knobs to secure transmission; suppose this number to be three. It must be borne in mind that the period of summation at the synapse is so brief as to be shorter than the refractory period of a synaptic delay (Chap. 5); hence impulses separated by a synapse time will not sum.

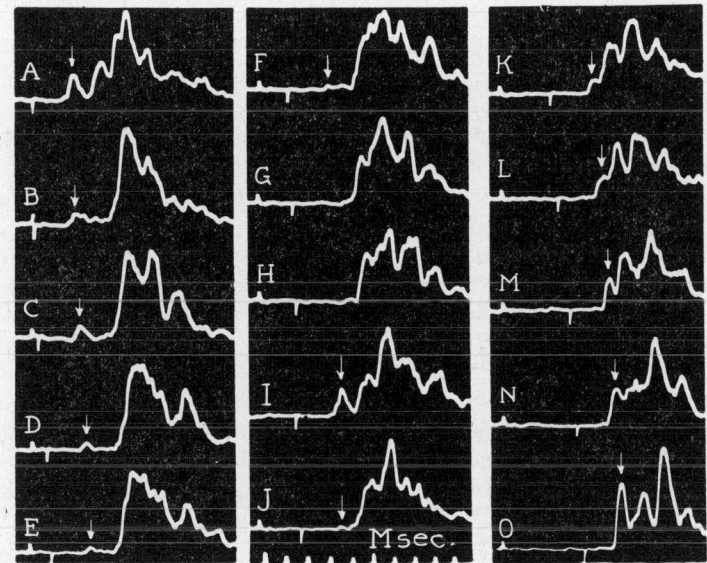

Fig. 104.—Demonstration of inhibition of two-neuron arc reflex (marked by arrows) by direct action of impulses in afferent fibers. Conditioning shock delivered to L₄ dorsal root. S₁ motoneurons tested by S₁ dorsal root shock. Following the brief inhibitory period the motoneurons are facilitated. (From Lloyd, *J. Neurophysiol.*, 1941, *4*:184–190.)

Now, in the diagram (Fig. 103), E and F are motoneurons innervating antagonistic muscles, extensor and flexor; *a*, *b* and *c* are interneurons. A train of impulses arriving over I, an afferent fiber, would excite *b* and *c* simultaneously and repetitively. The two synaptic knobs on F would be active synchronously and F would respond to each impulse in the afferent train. If now an opposing reflex comes into operation by impulses in axon II, impulses would arrive at *a* and *b*. With three synaptic knobs at their disposal, impulses in II could excite *b* in the interval between its responses to I and therefore when it is subnormal. Accordingly *b* will begin to respond in synchrony with *a* and together having two knobs on E, E will respond. Meanwhile I, having but two knobs on *b*, cannot be effective when *b* is dominated by II. Hence, as long as I and II are even slightly out of phase, impulses in *b* and *c* will be out of phase and F would become inactive. Thus on the supposition that some interneurons may be capable of functioning in the service of either flexor or extensor reflexes, but not both at the same time, it is possible on the basis of subnormality to account for inhibition in reciprocal reflex action as well as in allied reflex action.

Direct inhibition (22, 28). There are certain examples of central inhibition that, by recent documentation, cannot be explained on the basis of the subnormal period. The essential experimental conditions for an unequivocal demonstration of direct inhibition are: (i) a two-neuron arc reflex system, to avoid the complexities introduced by intercalated interneurons, and (ii) synchronous or near synchronous convergence at the motoneuron of "inhibitory" and "excitatory" afferent volleys. These conditions are met in experiments of which Figure 104 presents an example. To obtain the records of direct inhibition, a segmental test reflex was evoked in the first sacral ventral root by a single volley in the first sacral dorsal root (records A and I). This reflex was conditioned by a volley in the sixth lumbar dorsal root of the same side. If the two afferent volleys were synchronous, or if the test volley followed the conditioning volley by a brief interval, the reflex discharge through two-neuron arcs was inhibited. Other experiments have shown, in this instance, that direct inhibition is mediated by the large low-threshold afferent fibers of muscle origin. In distribution it has been shown that the large afferent fibers that yield reflex excitation of the muscle from which they arose serve for inhibition of neighboring muscles.*

The fact that inhibition of two-neuron arc pathways occurs when conditioning and testing volleys are synchronous is in itself strong evidence for the existence of some form of direct inhibitory action, but still further evidence may be found in the fact that this inhibition occurs with threshold conditioning volleys, which are well below the size requisite to produce motoneuron discharges (cf. Fig. 85, Chap. 5). If near threshold conditioning dorsal root volleys are utilized the period of depression of a two-neuron arc test reflex volley may last for 7 or 8 msec.(28), whereas with larger conditioning volleys internuncial pools are powerfully activated and inhibition is truncated by the advent of facilitation. When a more physiological selection of motoneurons is made by utilizing an extensor muscle nerve rather than ventral roots for recording, an inhibitory period of more than 100 msec. may be realized which suggests the participation of interneurons in the inhibitory conditioning activity.

In spite of the proven fact of direct inhibition, nothing that is yet known serves to indicate the mechanism entailed. There is no reason to suppose that distinct inhibitory fibers exist in the mammalian spinal cord, nor is there any evidence for or against the existence of specific inhibitory collaterals or synaptic knobs. At one time or another, a number of proposals have been advanced to account for inhibition, but they all involve assumptions for which there is little support, and none has secured wide acceptance. One view holds that synaptic knobs achieve different end-results, not by any differences in their action, but by reason of their location on the soma or dendrites. According to this hypothesis there is a constant flow of current between dendrites

---

* The significance of this distribution of excitation and inhibition has not been fully grasped. It is possibly important as an adjuvant factor in restricting the field of stretch reflex effect. Be that as it may, the experiments show that direct inhibitory action of stretch-excited afferent fibers accounts for the silent period shown by Denny-Brown (7) to occur in the gastrocnemius muscle as a reflex accompaniment of the knee jerk in quadriceps.

and axon, which serves as a constant source of excitation to the axon, the conducted impulses being initiated at the axon. Depending upon their position, the flow of current about active synaptic knobs would add to and so increase the current from dendrites to axon, leading to greater excitation, or would subtract from that current and lead to lesser excitation, or inhibition.

Another view proposes specific differences between synaptic knobs, possibly of a chemical nature. This, one of the older hypotheses, flourished as a result of the stimulus provided by Loewi's original experiments on humeral action of the vagus nerve on the heart. Yet another hypothesis, of considerable stature at the present time, looks to a process essentially analogous to anodal polarization as the means of suppressing response. This last view has the advantage of resting on the firm experimental basis that actions of the postulated sort are known to occur in the spinal cord. Most of the views concerning the mechanisms of inhibition can neither be accepted nor rejected in the present state of knowledge. Few of the many experiments that concern inhibition have a bearing on the mechanisms involved; one can only wait for future endeavor to provide the basis for a better understanding.

LONG SPINAL REFLEXES (24)

Reflex responses that have, up to now, received attention are those occupying only a limited region of the spinal cord, as may easily be proved by their presence after isolation of a short segment of the cord from the remainder

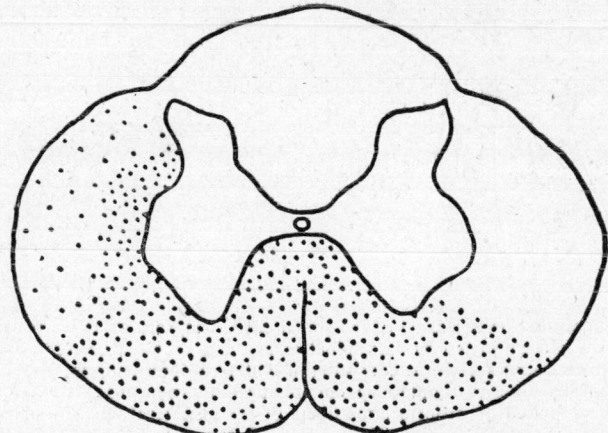

Fig. 105.—Distribution of propriospinal neurons mediating unilateral long spinal reflexes. Note that both ventral columns are involved, but only the ipsilateral lateral column. Hence lateral columns serve strictly unilateral conduction, ventral columns bilateral conduction. (From Lloyd, *J. Neurophysiol.*, 1942, *5*:435–458.)

of the nervous system. There are other reflexes that are mediated through long stretches of the spinal cord interposed between afferent and efferent paths. The scratch reflex and hand-foot reactions are examples of this group which Sherrington called *long spinal reflexes*. In 1903, the classical paper of Sherrington and Laslett (40) showed that the aborally directed propriospinal neurons could, with justice, be classified as "short" and "long." Short fibers are those that do not pass beyond a region (i.e., cervical, lumbar). The long fibers run from one region to another, thus serving to weld together into one

organ the otherwise rather isolated regions. In passing the whole length of
the spinal cord, the long fibers nowhere cross from the columns of one half
of the cord to the other half. However, at the two enlargements, cervical and
lumbar, the halves of the cord are strongly yoked together by commissural
neurons.

Some long spinal reflexes maintain strict unilaterality of conduction. For
example, stimulation of the skin within a saddle-shaped area of the back, in
a spinal dog or cat, elicits a scratch reflex, in which the ipsilateral limb alone
is involved. Shifting the stimulus but slightly across the mid-dorsal line causes
the one leg to stop, the opposite to start the scratching movements. The
scratch reflex is prevented by ipsilateral hemisection; is unaffected by contra-

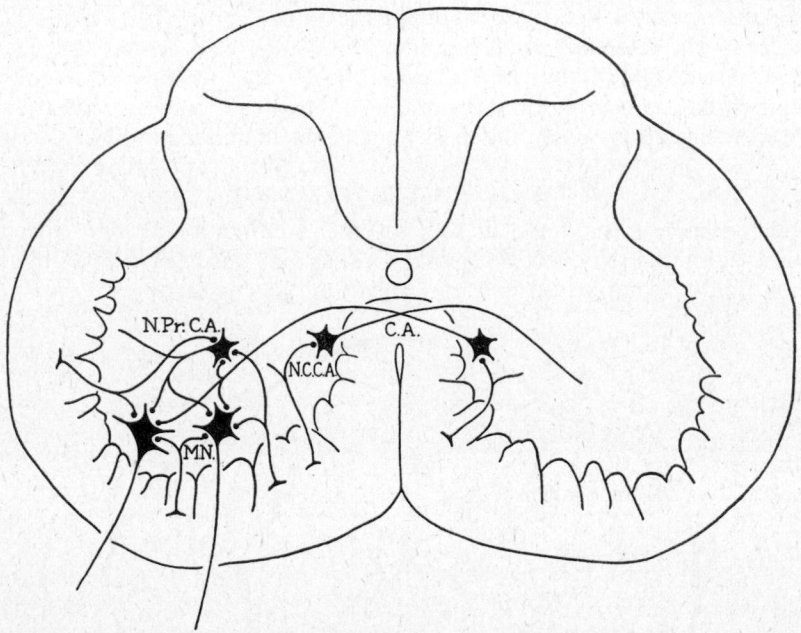

Fig. 106.—Functional organization of the spinal cord. Diagram of active neuron pools when
spinal mechanism is fractionated by long spinal reflex. C.A. = anterior commissure; N.Pr.C.A.
= nucleus proprius cornu anterioris, consisting of unilateral interneurons; N.C.C.A. = nucleus
cornu commissuralis anterior, containing commissural interneurons; M.N. = motoneurons.
The neurons are supplied by propriospinal fibers of the ipsilateral lateral and ventral columns
and the contralateral ventral column. (From Lloyd, *J. Neurophysiol.*, 1942, 5:435–458.)

lateral hemisection. Other long spinal reflexes, hand-foot reactions, elicited
by stimulation of foreleg nerves on one side, employ both sides of the spinal
cord for aboral conduction. This is true whether the end effect is ipsilateral
with respect to the stimulation, or contralateral. Thus a contralateral hemisection severely interferes with ipsilateral responses, showing that part of the
functional pathway crosses and recrosses the cord. Contralateral lesions of
the lateral column alone have no effect on ipsilateral responses. These observations may be brought together by consideration of Figure 105, in which
the shaded area represents the part of the cord containing fibers for the transmission of ipsilateral long spinal reflexes. The dorsal columns appear not to
be involved, nor is the contralateral lateral column, whereas the ipsilateral

lateral and both ventral columns are. The lateral columns, therefore, are concerned with strictly unilateral conduction. The ventral columns serve bilateral conduction.

In recent years it has been possible, by the use of extremely fine electrodes inserted into the spinal cord, to record directly the activity of interneurons during the stimulation of selected reflex or tract systems, and so to determine which pools of interneurons are active in any given set of circumstances. The results of such explorations are summarized in Figures 106, 107 and 108. Studies by this method are not limited to descriptions in three dimensions as are those based on anatomical methods, for it is possible to determine when events occur relative to each other in the active neuron pools. Another advantage lies in the possibility of tracing activity through complex series of neurons from the site of origin to the final common path.

Studies on localization in the gray substance of activity provoked in the course of long spinal reflex transmission tend to show that the ventral horn alone is concerned (Fig. 106). Collaterals from the lateral and ventral columns enter into the ventral horn to supply interneurons that together may be designated the *nucleus proprius* of the ventral horn (*N.Pr.C.A.*). Other collaterals, from the ventral column alone, reach the nucleus of the anterior commissure (N.C.C.A.). The interneurons of the nucleus proprius of one side, and of the commissural nucleus of the other side, converge upon the motoneurons constituting the final common path.

EXTRINSIC CONTROL OF SPINAL REFLEX MECHANISMS (21, 23)

All the reactions that have been discussed so far are purely spinal and can be elicited with all of the central nervous system other than the spinal cord itself removed. The fundamental patterns of spinal activity and the functional organization that underlies them operate just as surely in the decerebrate, decorticate or intact animals as in the spinal preparation, but this is not to say that the end result is identical in each, for influences brought to bear upon the spinal mechanism by the several supraspinal mechanisms tend to upset the spinal balance in one direction or another. If the neuraxis is severed just above the vestibular nuclei rather than at the junction of brain and spinal cord, the reactions have the same fatality of pattern, but new reactions are added and others, present and elicitable but feeble in the spinal state, are exaggerated to dominate the reflex performance. The intact animal has the power of volition that to a greater or less degree does away with fatality of reaction and imparts to the spinal cord a flexibility that is not of itself in isolation.

Bulbospinal mechanisms. The bulbospinal (or decerebrate) preparation exists in a state of decerebrate rigidity, characterized by exaggerated extensor posture. Decerebrate rigidity disappears if the brain stem is transected below the vestibular nuclei, or if isolated destruction of the nuclei is carried out. There is no doubt that the bulbospinal system (Fig. 107), dominated by the vestibule, is the most important implement of the habitus and reactions of the decerebrate preparation, as they differ from those of the spinal preparation.

The bulbospinal system consists of large fibers of vestibular and reticular origin that course largely through the dorsal longitudinal bundle and ventral columns of the spinal cord. These fibers propagate impulses at high and relatively uniform velocity. When activated in isolation, they have little direct

action upon the spinal motoneurons, but do exert a powerful driving force
upon the short propriospinal neurons of the ventral horn. The short propriospinal neurons in turn play powerfully upon the motoneurons. Backing up

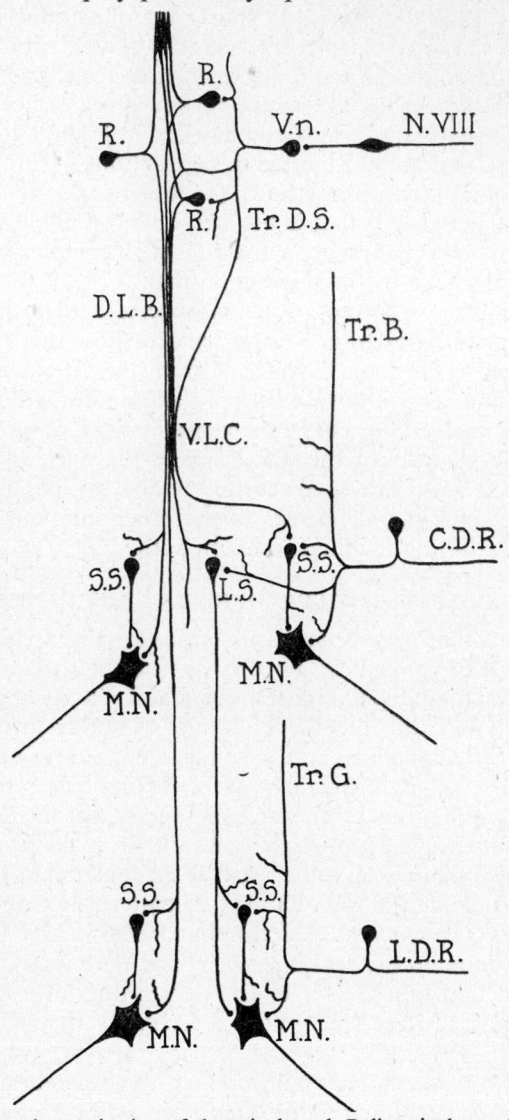

Fig. 107.—Functional organization of the spinal cord. Bulbospinal correlation system. Connections from dorsal roots are shown at the right. C.D.R. = cervical dorsal roots; D.L.B. =
dorsal longitudinal bundle; L.D.R. = lumbar dorsal roots; L.S. = long propriospinal neurons;
M.N. = motoneurons; N.VIII = vestibular nerve; R. = neurons of the reticular formation;
S.S. = short propriospinal neurons; Tr.B. = fasciculus cuneatus of dorsal column; Tr.D.S.
= vestibulospinal tract; Tr.G. = fasciculus gracilis of dorsal column; V.L.C. = ventrolateral
column; V.n. = primary vestibular nuclei. The spinal neurons of the bulbospinal correlation
system lie in the ventral horn. (Slightly modified from Lloyd, *J. Neurophysiol.*, 1941, *4*:115–134.)

this powerful three-neuron pathway is a wealth of asynchronous internuncial
discharge within the ventral horn. It is an interesting observation that the
short propriospinal neurons in the bulbospinal sequence retain control of

motoneuron discharge just as long as the interneuron pools of the ventral horn alone are active, even if their activity is very intense. If, on the other hand, the interneurons situated more dorsally in the spinal gray substance become active, as by stimulating local reflex arcs, control of motoneuron discharge advances from the short propriospinal neurons to the bulbospinal

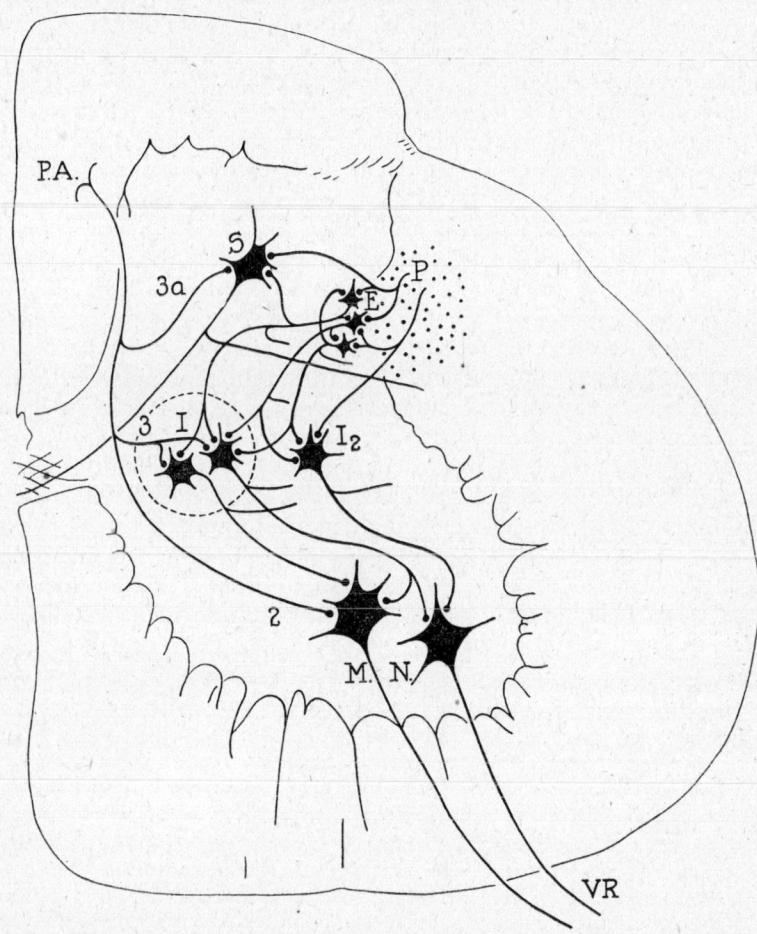

Fig. 108.—Functional organization of the spinal cord. Neurons active when spinal cord is fractionated by the pyramidal system. Connections from the pyramidal tract and primary afferent collaterals are represented. The interneurons activated by the pyramidal system lie in the dorsal half of the cord. E. = small cells of the external basilar region of the dorsal horn; I. = intermediate nucleus of Cajal; I_2. = other interneurons of intermediate region; M.N. = motoneurons; P. = pyramidal tract and fibers; P.A. = primary afferent (dorsal root) fibers; S. = large interneurons of dorsal horn; V.R. = ventral root; 2, 3, 3a = collaterals of dorsal root fibers. (From Lloyd, *J. Neurophysiol.*, 1941, *4*:525–546.)

tract fibers, and the direct functional pathway from the tract fibers to the motoneurons supersedes the indirect pathway through the short propriospinal neurons. The most likely explanation for this mode of behavior may be found in the way in which synaptic knobs from different sources are distributed on neuron somata (Chap. 5 and Fig. 83). Thus if the knobs of the bulbospinal fibers and of dorsal interneurons were close to one another but distant from synaptic knobs of the ventral interneurons, then the dorsal, but not the ventral, interneurons would provide the appropriate background to permit the individually weaker bulbospinal volleys to take control of the motoneurons away from the more powerful propriospinal volleys that immediately follow.

Control by the pyramidal system. Stimulation of the pyramidal tract in strict isolation from other systems has shown that pyramidal influences are mediated to the motoneurons through a complex series of interneurons located in the dorsal half of the cord (Fig. 108). Convergence of pyramidal activity and flexor reflex activity takes place in the internuncial nuclei, for the most part presumably in the intermediate nucleus. Most of the evidence, histological and functional, is against the possibility that pyramidal fibers terminate on motoneurons in significant numbers or exert any direct effect upon the motoneurons.

Dissociation of cortical control. Activity transmitted into the spinal cord directly through the pyramidal tract forms only a part of the cortical influence on the spinal reflex mechanism, a fact that has been demonstrated by observing the results of cortical stimulation following section of the pyramids just before the tract enters the spinal cord (42). Under these circumstances the pyramidal collaterals into the reticular formation are preserved and (by stimulation of the cortex) the reticular elements of the bulbospinal system are activated (cf. Fig. 106), and these in turn project activity into the *ventral* horn of the spinal cord. It follows, then, that cortical control of the dorsal and ventral halves of the local spinal mechanism is dissociated at a prespinal level, impulses to the dorsal half being conducted directly by the pyramidal fibers themselves, those to the ventral half being relayed by reticular elements. There are indications today that fractionation of the spinal mechanism into dorsal and ventral systems is of very general significance in the management of reflex and higher control.

REFERENCES

1. BALLIF, L., FULTON, J. F. and LIDDELL, E. G. T. Observations on spinal and decerebrate knee-jerks, with special reference to their inhibition by single break-shocks. *Proc. roy. Soc.*, 1925, *B98*:589–607.

2. CAJAL, S. R. *Les nouvelles idées sur la structure du système nerveux chez l'homme et chez les vertébrés.* Paris, C. Reinwald et Cie., 1894, 200 pp.

3. CAJAL, S. R. *Histologie du système nerveux de l'homme et des vertébrés.* Vol. 1. Paris, Maloine, 1909, 986 pp.

4. COOPER, S., DENNY-BROWN, D. E. and SHERRINGTON, C. S. Interaction between ipsilateral spinal reflexes acting on the flexor muscles of the hind-limb. *Proc. roy. Soc.*, 1927, *B101*:262–303.

5. CREED, R. S., DENNY-BROWN, D., ECCLES, J. C., LIDDELL, E. G. T. and SHERRINGTON, C. S. *Reflex activity of the spinal cord.* Oxford, Clarendon Press, 1932, 183 pp.

6. CREED, R. S. and SHERRINGTON, C. S. Observations on concurrent contraction of flexor muscles in the flexion reflex. *Proc. roy. Soc.*, 1926, *B100*:258–267.

7. DENNY-BROWN, D. On inhibition as a reflex accompaniment of the tendon-jerk and of other forms of active muscular response. *Proc. roy. Soc.*, 1928, *B103*:321–336.

8. DENNY-BROWN, D. On the nature of postural reflexes. *Proc. roy. Soc.*, 1929, *B104*:252–301.

9. DENNY-BROWN, D. E. and LIDDELL, E. G. T. The stretch reflex as a spinal process. *J. Physiol.*, 1927, *63*:144–150.

10. DENNY-BROWN, D. E. and LIDDELL, E. G. T. Extensor reflexes in the fore-limb. *J. Physiol.*, 1928, *65*:305–325.

11. ECCLES, J. C. Synaptic and neuromuscular transmission. *Ergebn. Physiol.*, 1936, *38*:339–444.

12. ECCLES, J. C. and SHERRINGTON, C. S. Numbers and contraction-values of individual motor-units examined in some muscles of the limb. *Proc. roy. Soc.*, 1930, *B106*:326–357.

13. ECCLES, J. C. and SHERRINGTON, C. S. Studies on the flexor reflex I–VI. *Proc. roy. Soc.*, 1931, *B107*:511–605; *B109*:91–113.

14. GASSER, H. S. The control of excitation in the nervous system. *Harvey Lect.*, 1937, *32*:169–193.

15. GASSER, H. S. *Reciprocal innervation. Volume jubilaire publié en l'honneur du Prof. J. Demoor.* Liège, G. Thone, 1937, pp. 212–218.

16. GASSER, H. S. and GRAHAM, H. T. Potentials produced in the spinal cord by stimulation of dorsal roots. *Amer. J. Physiol.*, 1933, *103*:303–320.

17. HUGHES, J. and GASSER, H. S. The response of the spinal cord to two afferent volleys. *Amer. J. Physiol.*, 1934, *108*:307–321.

18. JOLLY, W. A. On the time relations of the knee-jerk and simple reflexes. *Quart. J. exp. Physiol.*, 1911, *4*:68–87.

19. LIDDELL, E. G. T. and SHERRINGTON, C. S. Reflexes in response to stretch (Myotatic reflexes). *Proc. roy. Soc.*, 1925, *B96*:212–242.

20. LIDDELL, E. G. T. and SHERRINGTON, C. S. Further observations on myotatic reflexes. *Proc. roy. Soc.*, 1925, *B97*:267–283.

21. LLOYD, D. P. C. Activity in neurons of the bulbospinal correlation system. *J. Neurophysiol.*, 1941, *4*:115–134.

22. LLOYD, D. P. C. A direct central inhibitory action of dromically conducted impulses. *J. Neurophysiol.*, 1941, *4*:184–190.

23. LLOYD, D. P. C. The spinal mechanism of the pyramidal system in cats. *J. Neurophysiol.*, 1941, *4*:525–546.

24. LLOYD, D. P. C. Mediation of descending long spinal reflex activity. *J. Neurophysiol.*, 1942, *5*:435–458.

25. LLOYD, D. P. C. Reflex action in relation to the pattern and peripheral source of afferent stimulation. *J. Neurophvsiol.*, 1943, *6*:111–119.

26. LLOYD, D. P. C. Neuron patterns controlling transmission of ipsilateral hind limb reflexes in cat. *J. Neurophysiol.*, 1943, *6*:293–315.

27. LLOYD, D. P. C. Conduction and synaptic transmission of reflex response to stretch in spinal cats. *J. Neurophysiol.*, 1943, *6*:316–326.

28. LLOYD, D. P. C. Functional organization of the spinal cord. *Phvsiol. Rev.*, 1944, *24*:1–17.

29. MATTHEWS, B. H. C. Nerve endings in mammalian muscle. *J. Physiol.*, 1933, *78*:1–53.

30. SCHÄFER, E. A. Experiments on the paths taken by volitional impulses passing from the cerebral cortex to the cord: The pyramids and the ventro-lateral descending tracts. *Quart. J. exp. Physiol.*, 1910, *3*:355–373.

31. SHERRINGTON, C. S. The spinal cord. Vol. 2, pp. 783–883 in: SCHÄFER, E. A. *Textbook of physiology*, 1900.

32. SHERRINGTON, C. S. *The integrative action of the nervous system*. New York, Scribner's, 1906, 412 pp.

33. SHERRINGTON, C. S. Reciprocal innervation of antagonistic muscles. Fourteenth note. On double reciprocal innervation. *Proc. roy. Soc.*, 1909, *B81*:249–268.

34. SHERRINGTON, C. S. Flexion-reflex of the limb, crossed extension-reflex, and reflex stepping and standing. *J. Physiol.*, 1910, *40*:28–121.

35. SHERRINGTON, C. S. Reciprocal innervation and symmetrical muscles. *Proc. rov. Soc.*, 1913, *B86*:219–232.

36. SHERRINGTON, C. S. Nervous rhythm arising from rivalry of antagonistic reflexes: reflex stepping as outcome of double reciprocal innervation. *Proc. roy. Soc.*, 1913, *B86*:233–261.

37. SHERRINGTON, C. S. Postural activity of muscle and nerve. *Brain*, 1915, *38*:191–234.

38. SHERRINGTON, C. S. Problems of muscular receptivity. *Nature*, 1924, *113*:732; 892–894; 924–932.

39. SHERRINGTON, C. S. *Selected writings of Sir Charles Sherrington*, ed. D. Denny-Brown, New York, Paul B. Hoeber, 1939, 531 pp.

40. SHERRINGTON, C. S. and LASLETT, E. E. Observations on some spinal reflexes and the interconnection of spinal segments. *J. Physiol.*, 1903, *29*:58–96.

41. SNYDER, C. D. The latency of knee-jerk response in man as measured by the thread galvanometer. *Amer. J. Physiol.*, 1910, *26*:474–482.

42. TOWER, S. S. Extrapyramidal action from the cat's cerebral cortex: motor and inhibitory. *Brain*, 1936, *59*:408–444.

SECTION II

THE CENTRAL NERVOUS SYSTEM: MOTOR FUNCTIONS

BY JOHN F. FULTON

CHAPTER 7

THE HUMAN SPINAL CORD: SPINAL INJURIES

The broad principles of reflex action outlined in the previous chapters find immediate practical application in dealing with cases of spinal cord injury in man. Injuries of the entire cerebrospinal axis are common both in peacetime and in war, but spinal injuries are especially prone to occur during military operations. Since the phenomena associated with such injuries are of immediate physiological interest, we shall preface our study of the suprasegmental levels of the nervous system by a discussion of the human spinal cord and its reactions to injury.

COMPLETE SPINAL TRANSECTION

The spinal cord may be transected at any level from coccyx to atlas, but the manifestations resulting from such an injury may vary considerably with the level of transection; the phenomenon of "spinal shock," however, occurs irrespective of the level of injury.

Spinal shock

When the spinal cord is severed in the midthoracic region, all body segments below the level of transection become paralyzed and completely anesthetic, i.e., all sensation appears to be abolished save in rare instances in which crude unlocalized pain perception may persist, evidently conveyed by sensory fibers entering the spinal cord above the level of transection through the various peripheral ramifications of the sympathetic nervous system (Foerster, 6). In monkeys, following a lumbar spinal transection, reflex withdrawal accompanied by signs of discomfort has occasionally been evoked by intense pressure or by vigorous electrical stimulation of the lower extremities, but the reaction is capricious and unpredictable (unpublished observations). Sensory fibers are found in all parts of the sympathetic chain (see Chap. 10) and they are no doubt responsible for conveying the impulses underlying these reactions into the spinal cord from levels below that of the transection.

Hyporeflexia. The most conspicuous symptom of spinal shock is the suppression of all forms of reflex response, the suppression being usually complete during the first week or two following transection (11). The intensity and duration of the reflex depression varies widely from case to case, and tends to

178

be more severe and enduring in the older age groups. Prior to the First World War, it was widely believed that reflexes were completely and permanently abolished after spinal transection. This belief no doubt arose from the fact that the problems of nursing care prior to the advent of chemotherapy were so formidable that cases sustaining such injury usually succumbed to bladder and other infections before reflexes had returned.

In a normal young male adult who has been carefully nursed following spinal transection, it is generally impossible to evoke either deep reflexes or flexion withdrawal responses for at least 18 days after the injury. Then the flexion reflex begins slowly to emerge in response to intense stimulation of the plantar surface. In the course of the third and fourth weeks following the injury, withdrawal responses become more vigorous, and the reflexogenous zone tends gradually to spread up the inner side of the leg toward and beyond the ankle. As the withdrawal reflex becomes more brisk, the toes, especially the great toe, tend to become extended upward during the response (the sign of Babinski). The withdrawal response is brought about by strong contraction of the hamstring muscles of the thigh. The upgoing of the toe, which is a specific sign of pyramidal tract injury in the otherwise uninjured nervous system, is thus a part of a more generalized withdrawal response (7). *Babinski's sign is never present in pure form without some degree of concurrent contraction of the hamstrings.*

The mass reflex. Several months after spinal transection, withdrawal reflexes tend to become exaggerated and to spread to the visceral and autonomic outflow. Thus, if the plantar surface is vigorously scratched, both extremities may withdraw violently, the skin sweats profusely, and concurrent contraction may occur of both the bladder and the rectum. This mass discharge of the spinal human being is usually referred to as the "mass reflex" (11). From the standpoint of nursing care this reflex has a certain usefulness since, once the reflexes of bladder and rectum have become re-established, it can be used by the nurses to initiate evacuation of urine and feces; but its usefulness is often less than the inconvenience, since mass reflexes are often evoked unintentionally and at times they may appear to develop spontaneously without obvious stimulation.

Extension reflexes. A spinal human being shows conspicuous flaccidity during the first weeks following spinal transection, i.e., the extremities are limp and can be moved about without encountering resistance of any sort. When withdrawal reflexes have returned, the extremities are as a rule still flaccid except in the presence of a nocuous stimulus, when they go into flexor spasm—paraplegia in flexion. Many months after spinal transection, a slight degree of resting extensor posture may develop, but the extremities never become strongly spastic or exhibit rigidity of the type seen following a hemiplegia. The presence of spasticity, therefore, after a spinal injury indicates that the spinal cord is not completely severed and that some degree of functional recovery can be anticipated. A few cases of complete cervical transection have been recorded in which the lower extremities became moderately spastic, but extreme resistance to passive movement never develops in spinal man, and there is some doubt whether the cord was completely severed in certain cases of high cervical transection in which spasticity has been recorded.

Autonomic reflexes. Autonomic reflexes are even more completely suppressed in spinal shock than are somatic reactions. During the first month or two the skin is completely dry, sweating being wholly abolished, and the skin tends to be warm and pink owing to the widespread vasodilatation stemming from paralysis of the vasomotor reflexes. In monkeys sweating and vasomotor reactions tend to return during the fifth and sixth weeks (22). In man reflex sweating generally does not appear until the third month, but the actual time interval probably varies in different climates, and the nutritional status of the individual no doubt has a bearing upon the rate of recovery of autonomic reactions.

Bladder reflexes. The reactions of the urinary bladder involve both he somatic and the autonomic divisions of the nervous system, and their suppression in spinal shock presents formidable nursing problems. The expression "cord bladder" or "spinal cord bladder," often used in neurological literature, has reference to a state of partial restoration of normal bladder reflexes in which a bladder contraction can be induced by certain forms of stimulation, e.g., as in the mass reflex, but in which, between bouts of contraction, the sphincters tend to be incompetent, permitting periodic dribbling of urine. Immediately after the cord has been severed, however, the bladder reflexes are abolished and the sphincters tend to contract forcibly, particularly in the male, with the result that urine may be indefinitely retained unless the bladder is catheterized. Once bladder reflexes become restored (usually during the third week), retention passes off and incontinence tends to develop. A second difficulty with the cord bladder is that it never expels its urine completely. This residual urine therefore tends to act as a culture medium favorable to infection. Consequently, the bladder content must be watched with the utmost care for infection at all stages after a spinal injury. Some authorities recommend manual expression of residual urine to lessen the possibility of infection, but now that the sulfa drugs and penicillin are available, less concern is felt about cystitis.

Reflexes of the rectum. Reflex evacuation of the rectum presents a problem similar to that of the bladder. The normal reflexes of evacuation are abolished or greatly diminished in spinal shock, but they tend to return as do those of the bladder during the third and fourth weeks. Reflex evacuation thus becomes possible, but during the stages of extreme shock evacuation can be induced only by use of enemas. More details concerning the reflexes of defecation are reported in the important paper of Denny-Brown and Graeme Robertson (5) who find that reflex contraction of the colon and the attendant relaxation of the anal sphincter is made possible by local nerve plexuses since the reaction still occurs after destruction of the sacral segments of the spinal cord; the reaction, however, is depressed in spinal shock.

Nature of spinal shock. The phenomena underlying spinal shock are not clearly understood. In the presence of higher centers, sensory impulses received at the spinal level tend to pass to suprasegmental levels for higher integration. As the central nervous system has evolved, the cerebral cortex has tended more and more to suppress lower centers and to take over their functions. This evolutionary process is generally referred to as "encephalization." The older pathways pass directly across the spinal cord (and intersegmental pathways within the cord), but they have been largely suppressed by the growing dominance of the cerebral hemispheres with the result that when the influence of the higher centers is abruptly withdrawn, as after a spinal transection, a considerable time must elapse before these older reflex paths within the spinal cord can be re-established. It is significant that spinal shock is more profound in man and chimpanzee than in monkey, and in monkey much more profound than in dog, cat or rabbit. Some lower animals, instead of passing into shock, exhibit varying degrees of hyperactivity in segments normally suppressed by the forebrain. Thus, if a crawling earthworm is divided quickly in two, the forward segment crawls on without apparent concern and the hindmost segment squirms in a state of great agitation. Much the same reaction is also seen in snakes, and it is generally referred to as a "release phenomenon." Spinal shock is also a release phenomenon in the strict sense of the term, but a release characterized by temporary suppression of activity.

Those who have analyzed spinal shock point to one conspicuous characteristic, namely, as far as the extension muscles are concerned, there is an increased susceptibility to reflex inhibition. Thus in the spinal cat a single ipsilateral break shock stimulus will completely abolish knee jerks for a period of several seconds (see Chap. 6, Fig. 101), whereas the same cat in the decerebrate state would have its knee jerks inhibited for only a tenth of a second by a comparable shock. However central inhibition is brought about, it is clear that in spinal shock inhibitory reactions are more readily obtained than when the higher centers are intact.

Two additional points bearing on the nature of spinal shock must be mentioned. McCouch (16) pointed out that if the lower spinal centers of a monkey are *gradually* released from forebrain centers by destroying descending tracts seriatim the degree of shock is never as profound as when all descending pathways are cut off abruptly by complete spinal transection. Thus, if a monkey's motor cortex is removed a moderate reflex suppression develops in the paretic extremity (Chap. 13). The reflexes, however, recover; if then the spinal cord is transected the previously paretic extremities develop only moderate signs of shock, whereas the previously normal extremities are profoundly affected (10).

The second point has to do with the reverse release of function demonstrable in the reflexes of the upper extremities when the lower extremities are separated by midthoracic spinal transection. Known as the Schiff-Sherrington phenomenon (19, 21), it is best demonstrated in the decerebrate preparation of cat or dog. When the spinal cord of such an animal is severed above the lumbar region the stretch reflexes and other postural reactions of the upper extremities become notably exaggerated. Similar reflex exaggeration can be demonstrated in the hind extremities when the sacral cord is divided. This indicates that intersegmental spinal projections exert influence in both directions and that in a quadruped coordination is brought about through mutual interaction between successive spinal segments.

Pharmacological agents affecting spinal shock. If spinal shock is due to release from higher control with consequent augmentation of inhibitory reflexes, it should be possible through the use of appropriate pharmacological agents to diminish the degree of shock. This has in fact proved feasible. Drugs such as ephedrine, adrenaline, and probably also benzedrine, which have a strong central action, serve conspicuously to diminish spinal shock in monkeys (12). Bladder reflexes are restored under the influence of ephedrine, and problems of nursing care can be greatly minimized through the use of these agents. It is probable also that acetylcholine and its various derivatives likewise have a beneficial action in spinal shock since they tend to restore reflexes in much the same way as does ephedrine even though the peripheral effects of these two drugs are opposite in character (23, 24). Further clinical evidence bearing on these points is needed, and it will no doubt become available during the war period.

Level of transection. It has been mentioned above that the manifestations of spinal injuries vary to some extent with the level of transection. In general, cervical transections are associated with less spinal shock in the lower extremities than is encountered in cases of low thoracic or lumbar transection. Reflexes tend to return earlier after cervical transections and the lower extremities may ultimately develop a slight degree of spasticity. In the adult male a state of persistent satyriasis is prone to develop following cervical transections, but not with those of the lower cord. In this connection it should be mentioned that the state of priapism often observed in hanged criminals no doubt results from cervical transection of the cord.

Cervical transections resulting from dislocation of the cord vary in severity with the actual cervical level. Transections above the fourth cervical segment are followed by prompt paralysis of breathing movements, and for this reason sudden death is the usual result unless artificial respiration is immediately instituted. Dislocations of the cervical vertebra at C3 or C4 occur commonly on the football field, and since in these cases the cord may not actually be transected, prompt reduction of dislocation may be lifesaving. Section of the cord at C4 leaves diaphragmatic breathing unaffected (as Galen originally showed), but a state of quadriplegia develops in which all four extremities become paralyzed and pass into spinal shock. Transections at C5, C6 and C7 give a partial paralysis of the upper extremities, the actual level being determinable from the level of anesthesia and analysis of the particular muscle groups paralyzed. Transections at C8 or D1 and D2 leave the upper extremities unimpaired, but owing to the sympathetic outflow emerging from these levels, Horner's syndrome develops, which is characterized by pupillary contraction, enophthalmos, flushing of the skin, and absence of sweating over the face and neck. Unilateral injuries of the cord at this level can often be recognized by the presence of these unilateral ocular symptoms.

Physiology of spinal compression

Of considerable practical interest to those who care both for wartime and civilian injuries of the cord is the problem of functional suppression resulting from mechanical compression, and its relation to the therapeutic handling of such injuries. A high-velocity missile may cause symptoms of complete cord transection without having touched the cord in its trajectory. Such cases were described in the last war as "spinal concussion" (Mussen,17).* Although the syndrome was recognized, the basis of it has not been clearly elucidated. The energy transmitted to tissues by a high-velocity missile is imparted radially to the trajectory of the missile, and the actual energy varies with the square of the velocity. A bullet traveling at 1000 feet per sec. may traverse the spinal canal, and if it does not touch the cord it may fail to do it injury. A missile of the same size traveling at 4000 feet per sec. along exactly the same trajectory might cause a functional transection without involving anatomical discontinuity (3). This is due to the fact that the pressure wave set up by the more rapidly traveling missile distorts surrounding structures with greater violence than the slower missile. It behooves a surgeon, therefore, in the presence of such an injury to ascertain by direct examination whether or not the cord has suffered direct injury. Exploration of the cord actually serves a dual purpose in such instances, since, if the cord has not actually been hit by the missile, it may have been contused by the pressure wave and the resulting

*Livingston and his associates (15) point out that much the same phenomenon occurs in peripheral nerve when an extremity is injured by a high-velocity missile. The cavitation which develops in soft tissues as a result of impact with a fast-moving fragment may so stretch adjacent nerve trunks (without actually touching them) that function is completely suppressed for weeks or even months. Soldiers experiencing such trauma are at first convinced that the injured extremity has been blown off since all sensory transmission is abolished. On exploring the wound, however, the nerves may be wholly intact and essentially normal in appearance. In such instances spontaneous recovery can generally be anticipated, either from restoration of function in overstretched but viable fibers; or through regeneration in those fibers which have actually degenerated as the result of the traumatic insult. A highly illuminating histological study of the effects of abrupt concussion of peripheral nerve has just been published by Denny-Brown and Brenner (*J. Neurol., Neurosurg., Psychiat.*, 1944, 7:76–95). They find that percussion of a moderate degree may cause complete and often permanent blocking of motor impulses with subsequent degeneration of motor fiber, while axis cylinders of the smaller sensory fibers remain intact and quickly recover function. They also note that recovery from a local percussion is facilitated by local "decompression," i.e., relief of edema through rupture of the perineurium.

edema in these circumstances might of itself have interrupted the conduction pathways. The exposure of the cord with opening of the dura serves to "decompress" it and in that way facilitate functional recovery.

As already mentioned, dislocations of the cervical cord are notoriously common in football, and also in automobile and airplane crashes. It should be remembered that cervical dislocations seldom transect the cord, but rather compress it to greater or less degree. Hence the need for prompt reduction of any cervical fracture, and if the fracture for any reason cannot be reduced, immediate laminectomy is indicated in order to relieve pressure and restore function. The spinal canal of the average adult varies from 20 to 22 mm. in diameter, and dislocations of the cervical vertebra of less than 10 to 12 mm. are of favorable prognosis if promptly reduced. Such compression is usually sufficient to interrupt function, but it does not immediately destroy pathways. A cord compressed in this manner for a period of weeks is sometimes capable of recovery if dislocation is reduced or pressure relieved through laminectomy.

SPINAL INJURIES: INCOMPLETE TRANSECTIONS

Complete transections of the spinal cord fortunately are rare. Much more common are partial injuries, and it is important to be able to distinguish an incomplete from a total transection. Broadly speaking, incomplete transections are associated with spasticity and great reflex hyperactivity. A case of cervical dislocation which appears completely paralyzed below the level of dislocation but which nevertheless is spastic has an incompletely divided cord, and it presents good possibility of functional recovery if the dislocation can be reduced. Some cases of incomplete transection may show flaccidity and areflexia shortly after the injury, and later develop spasticity and active reflexes. This is particularly true of gunshot wounds and wounds from high-velocity bomb fragments. *It must never be assumed that a spinal cord is comletely transected until proved by direct surgical examination.*

Brown-Séquard's Syndrome (1). In 1855 the French-American neurologist Brown-Séquard observed that when the spinal cord of an animal is subjected to a lateral semisection (Fig. 109A), motor power is lost on the side of the lesion and sensation is impaired on the side opposite. This dissociation between sensory and motor functions stems from the fact that incoming sensory fibers cross within one or two segments of their point of entry, whereas descending motor fibers, having already crossed in the medulla or midbrain, pass directly to the ventral horn cells of the same side. There is one qualification, however, namely, that there are two general modalities of sensation: (i) pain and thermal sensibility which pass in ventrolateral columns via the spinothalamic tracts and cross soon after entering the cord; and (ii) proprioceptive sensibility, on the other hand, which is mediated by fibers of the posterior columns which do not cross until they reach the brain stem. Hence position and proprioceptive sensibility are lost along with motor power on the side of the lesion, whereas only cutaneous sensibility is lost on the opposite side.

The Brown-Séquard syndrome is frequently encountered in spinal injuries, and proof of its presence is of important diagnostic significance in establishing both the level and the extent of the lesion.

Quadrant Lesions. *Dorsal quadrant.* Except in cases of stab wounds with a sharp instrument, clear-cut lateral semisection of the cord rarely occurs.

Usually injuries are incomplete and involve to a greater or less extent one or more quadrants of the cord. The reflex changes which ensue vary with the part of the cord severed. Broadly speaking, interruption of the dorsal quadrant causes disturbance of proprioceptive sensibility and volitional power through interruption of the posterior columns and the descending corticospinal tracts. Such lesions tend also to result in spasticity and a great increase in the deep reflexes (Fig. 109B).

Cairns and Fulton (2) succeeded in producing extensive lesions of the dorsal quadrants in cats through implantation of seeds containing radium emanation. It was possible by accurately adjusting the dose to destroy the dorsal two-thirds of the spinal cord on one side. In the case of a cat in which such a lesion was made, the hind extremity became completely paralyzed as far as volitional movement was concerned, and passed into an enduring state of extreme hyperextension that continued long after any possible irritating effect of the radium emanation. Similar results were obtained by Liddell and associates (8, 14) following large dorsal quadrant lesions made mechanically.

Ventral quadrant. Injury to the ventral quadrant of the spinal cord causes impairment of cutaneous sensation on the opposite side of the body and a tendency toward flaccid paresis on the same side. Interruption of the vesti-

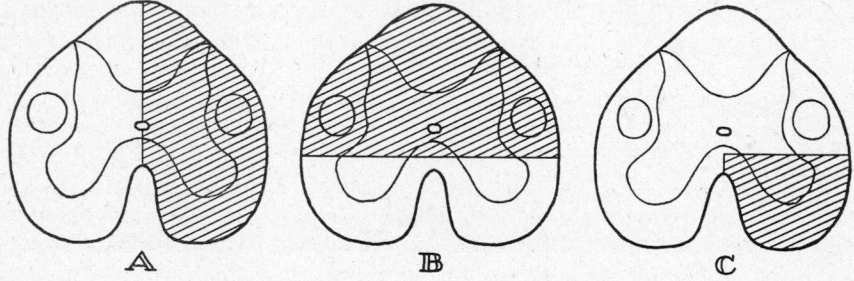

Fig. 109.—Diagram of three illustrative spinal lesions: A. Right lateral semisection of thoracic cord—the basis of the Brown-Séquard syndrome. B. Bilateral lesion of the dorsal quadrants; this would cause the loss of position sense and motor paralysis (pyramidal tracts). C. Lesion of ventral quadrant; this would cause (i) flaccid weakness and loss of vestibular reactions on the side affected; (ii) disturbance of cutaneous sensibility on the opposite side.

bulospinal pathways in a decerebrate animal leads to prompt disappearance of the exaggerated posture on the side of the lesion (9). The vestibulospinal pathways may be interrupted at their source through the destruction of the vestibular nuclei, or by severing the ventral quadrant of the spinal cord (Fig. 109C) through which they pass (14). It thus becomes possible through analysis of the postural and sensory changes in a given spinal lesion to localize not only the level of the lesion but also the part of the spinal cord involved. Such analysis in the case of incomplete lesions, particularly those from compression, gives one some indication as to prognosis. Spinal injuries are poorly understood, and those who have occasion to study them in peacetime or in war should make it a point to record their observations in full.

Chordotomy (6). Lesions of the spinal cord have been made intentionally by neurosurgeons with the end in view of relieving pain or correcting abnormal motor postures. The operation was originally proposed by the late W. G. Spiller of Philadelphia, and was first carried out by his colleague, C. H. Frazier, and later by the German neurosurgeon, Otfrid Foerster of Breslau.

The spinal column fibers carrying pain pass upward in the lateral part of the ventral quadrant. If a patient is suffering from intractable pain caused, for example, by a malignant growth of the hip joint, it is possible to give relief by sectioning the lateral part of the ventral quadrant of the cord at any level above the hip innervation. The operations are usually carried out under local anesthesia, and it is possible by making sensory examinations during the procedure to demonstrate that the fibers lying most lateral in the cord are those from the lowest sacral segments, while those from the lumbar segments lie medially; indeed, a precise topographical lamination is found. Failures to relieve localized pain are usually the result of making the section of the cord too superficial and thus failing to interrupt the more medial projection.

The use of chordotomy for the relief of abnormal postures has been less successful than for the relief of pain. Putnam (18) has attempted to sever the anterolateral columns of the cord of patients suffering from involuntary torsion spasm and also from choreo-athetosis. Favorable results have been obtained in certain instances, but most neurosurgeons believe that such conditions can be more readily ameliorated through regional ablation of appropriate areas in the cerebral cortex (see Chap. 13).

REFERENCES

1. BROWN-SÉQUARD, C. E. Recherches expérimentales sur la transmission croisée des impression sensitives dans la moelle épiniere. *Gaz. hebd. Med. Chirurg.*, 1855, 9.

2. CAIRNS, H. and FULTON, J. F. Experimental observations on the action of radon on the spinal cord. *Lancet*, 1930, 2:16–18.

3. CALLENDER, G. R. Wound ballistics: mechanism of production of wounds by small arms bullets and shell fragments. *War Med.*, 1943, 3:337–350.

4. DENNY-BROWN, D. and ROBERTSON, E. GRAEME. On the physiology of micturition. *Brain*, 1933, 56:149–190.

5. DENNY-BROWN, D. and ROBERTSON, E. GRAEME. An investigation of the nervous control of defaecation. *Brain*, 1935, 58:256–310.

6. FOERSTER, O. *Die Leitungsbahnen des Schmerzgefühls und die chirurgische Behandlung der Schmerzstände.* Berlin, Urban & Schwarzenberg, 1927, viii, 360 pp.

7. FULTON, J. F. and KELLER, A. D. *The sign of Babinski. A study of the evolution of cortical dominance.* Springfield, Ill., C. C Thomas, 1932, xv, 165 pp.

8. FULTON, J. F., LIDDELL, E. G. T. and RIOCH, D. McK. The influence of experimental lesions of the spinal cord upon the knee-jerk. I. Acute lesions. *Brain*, 1930, 53:311–326.

9. FULTON, J. F., LIDDELL, E. G. T. and RIOCH, D. McK. The influence of unilateral destruction of the vestibular nuclei upon posture and the knee-jerk. *Brain*, 1930, 53:327–343.

10. FULTON, J. F. and McCOUCH, G. P. The relation of the motor area of primates to the hyporeflexia ('spinal shock') of spinal transection. *J. nerv. ment. Dis.*, 1937, 86:125–146.

11. HEAD, H. and RIDDOCH, G. The automatic bladder, excessive sweating and some other reflex conditions, in gross injuries of the spinal cord. *Brain*, 1917, 40:188–263. Reprinted: HEAD, H., *Studies in neurology*, 1920, 2:467–530.

12. JACOBSEN, C. F. and KENNARD, M. A. The influence of ephedrine sulphate on the reflexes of spinal monkeys. *J. Pharmacol.*, 1933, 49:362–374.

13. LIDDELL, E. G. T. Spinal shock and some features in isolation-alteration of the spinal cord in cats. *Brain*, 1934, 57:386–400.

14. LIDDELL, E. G. T. The influence of experimental lesions of the spinal cord upon the knee-jerk. II. Chronic lesions. With an appendix "a note on the 'spinal' and 'decerebrate' type of knee-jerk in the cat." *Brain*, 1936, 59:160–174.

15. LIVINGSTON, W. K., DAVIS, E. W. and LIVINGSTON, K. E. "Delayed recovery" in peripheral nerve lesions caused by high velocity projectile wounding. *J. Neurosurg.*, 1945, 2:170–179.

16. McCOUCH, G. P. The relation of the pyramidal tract to spinal shock. *Amer. J. Physiol.*, 1924, 71:137–152.

17. MUSSEN, A. The finer histological changes in the traumatic degenerations of the spinal cord, following bullet wounds of the cord substance, or shock to the vertebral column. *Rev. Neurol. Psychiat.*, 1916, 14:417–446.

18. PUTNAM, T. J. Treatment of athetosis and dystonia by section of extrapyramidal motor tracts. *Arch. Neurol. Psychiat., Chicago*, 1933, 29:504–521.

19. RUCH, T. C. Evidences of the non-segmental character of spinal reflexes from an analysis of the cephalad effects of spinal transection (Schiff-Sherrington phenomenon). *Amer. J. Physiol.*, 1936, 114:457–467.

20. Ruch, T. C. The spinal cord and reflex action. *Ann. Rev. Physiol.*, 1942, *4*:359–374.

21. Ruch, T. C. and Watts, J. W. Reciprocal changes in reflex activity of the fore limbs induced by post-brachial "cold-block" of the spinal cord. *Amer. J. Physiol.*, 1934, *110*:362–375.

22. Sahs, A. L. and Fulton, J. F. Somatic and autonomic reflexes in spinal monkeys. *J. Neurophysiol.*, 1940, *3*:258–268.

23. Ward, A. A., Jr. and Kennard, M. A. Effect of cholinergic drugs on recovery of function following lesions of the central nervous system in monkeys. *Yale J. Biol. Med.*, 1942, *15*:189–228.

24. Wolf, A. A method of shortening the duration of lower motor neurone paralysis by cholinergic facilitation. *J. nerv. ment. Dis.*, 1940, *92*:614–622.

CHAPTER 8

DECEREBRATE AND DECORTICATE RIGIDITY: THE POSTURAL REFLEXES

In Chapters 5 and 6 the principles of reflex action have been described in some detail, and mention was made of the concept of functional levels. The spinal animal is capable of integrating certain elementary movement patterns, including the flexion reflex which is a primitive defense reaction evoked by a nocuous stimulus applied to the surface of the skin (Chap. 6); the spinal animal also exhibits extension responses such as the knee and ankle jerks. Close examination of these extension responses indicates that they are normally evoked by stretching the muscle in question, and that physiologically the extensor muscles are so disposed as to be stretched by the action of gravity. The stretch reflexes are mediated by nerve fibers of high conduction rates;

Fig. 110.—A cat in decerebrate rigidity. Note the hyperextended posture of the neck, the arching of the back (opisthotonos), and extension of tail. Sherrington has designated the total pattern as "an exaggerated caricature of reflex standing." (From Pollock and Davis, *J. comp. Neurol.*, 1930, *50*:384.)

the reflex arcs subserving these "myotatic" reactions are made up of but two neurons (see Chap. 6), namely, the stretch receptor and the motor horn cell in the spinal cord which it directly activates. *Although stretch reflexes can readily be demonstrated in spinal animals including man, they tend, in the absence of the higher centers, to be poorly maintained and are seldom of sufficient intensity to support the full weight of the animal against the force of gravity.* For this higher centers of integration are essential, particularly those in the medulla oblongata.

Historical note. The phenomenon of decerebrate rigidity had undoubtedly been observed by many early experimenters, but the significance of the exaggerated posture was not understood until Sherrington's classical paper on the decerebrate state (17) was published in 1898. When the brain stem of an animal is transected at the level of the corpora quadrigemina (i.e., just rostral to the cerebellum), the animal, shortly after the section, develops

187

an exaggerated extensor posture affecting all four extremities as well as the neck and tail (Fig. 110). This might be due to irritation caused by the lesion, but this possibility was ruled out when it was disclosed that the rigid posture persisted indefinitely and was not further increased by secondary transection (and irritation) of the brain stem a few millimeters more posteriorly. The reaction obviously falls into the category of a "release" phenomenon; i.e., centers normally dominated by more rostral levels within the basal ganglia and the cerebral cortex are released from this control, giving positive signs of exaggerated activity. Sherrington sought to analyze the phenomenon, finding first that on decerebration similar rigidity developed in all warm blooded laboratory animals, and he then looked into the functional anatomy, i.e., what nuclei and sensory motor pathways are essential for its continuance.

Sherrington was quick to recognize that decerebrate rigidity is an affair primarily of the antigravity muscles, i.e., the muscles most affected are the extensors and the retractors of the neck and tail (Fig. 110). A decerebrate animal, if propped up on its feet, may stand as if on tiptoe for an indefinite period. It was concluded from this that decerebrate rigidity is, in fact, reflex standing in an exaggerated form—an accentuation of a normal posture.

DECEREBRATE RIGIDITY

Sherrington (17) attempted first to ascertain what forebrain centers must be removed in order for decerebrate rigidity to develop. As far as cat and dog were concerned, it could not very well be the centers from which the pyramidal tracts arise, since these can be removed without causing conspicuous rigidity. Furthermore, when the forebrain was excluded unilaterally by semisection at the level of the corpora quadrigemina, the rigidity developed on the homolateral side, whereas the pyramidal pathways control the opposite extremities (see Chap. 13). Sherrington concluded that the phenomenon must result from interruption of *extrapyramidal* motor projections from some part of the forebrain. In more recent years it has been ascertained that a great many descending systems are actually concerned, including projections (extrapyramidal) from the cerebral cortex, the basal ganglia, and the cerebellum (see Chaps. 13–15). In man the rigidity which develops following cerebral hemorrhage is due primarily to interruption of extrapyramidal projections from the cerebral cortex. The rigidity is akin in most respects to decerebrate rigidity, being responsive to the same postural reactions (see below) as those observed in a decorticate monkey or chimpanzee. The rigidity, however, is less intense owing to the fact that the release is less complete than a true decerebration (see below).

There has been much discussion concerning the nuclei in the brain stem whose integrity is essential for *maintaining* decerebrate rigidity. At one time the red nuclei were implicated (Rademaker), but it was later found that the red nuclei could be destroyed in a decerebrate preparation and the rigidity would yet persist (7). By carrying the brain stem section more and more posteriorly, it has been disclosed that the level of the vestibular nuclei appears essential for the phenomenon; furthermore, isolated destruction of the vestibular nuclei in a decerebrate preparation causes rigidity to vanish on the side of the lesion (5). Similarly, section of the ventral quadrant of the spinal cord in which the vestibulospinal projections pass causes disappearance of rigidity on the side of the lesion (Chap. 7), while section of the dorsal quadrants is without effect on posture.

All reflex reactions result from sensory stimulation. Sherrington therefore asked himself what sense organs were responsible for maintaining continuously the stimulus responsible for the sustained response. He destroyed the labyrinth, and while this caused abolition of certain reactions (such as occur when the body is moved rapidly through space), the rigidity still persisted. Turning to the extremity itself, he found that the skin nerves could be completely severed without affecting the rigidity; indeed, the whole extremity could be deprived of its skin without materially influencing the reaction. If, however, the dorsal nerve roots supplying the extremity were severed, the rigidity then vanished. The extremity thus deafferented was still responsive to

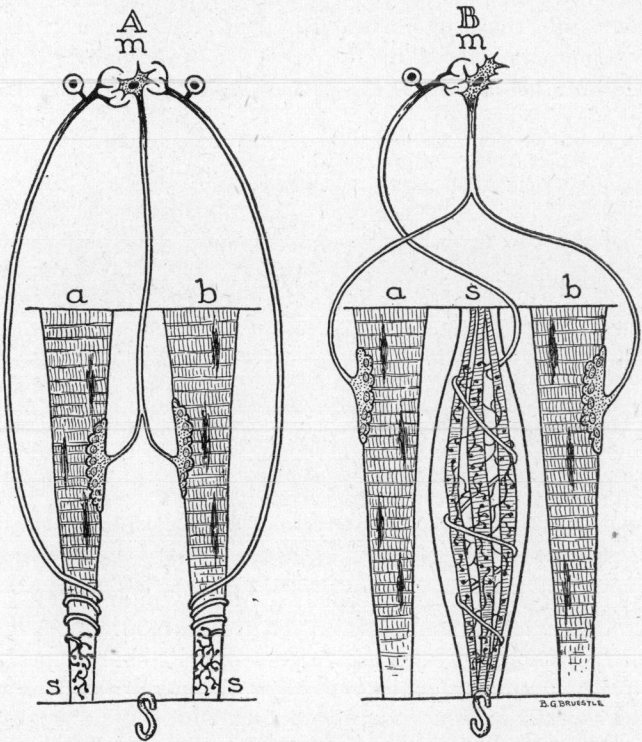

Fig. 111.—The muscle spindle contrasted with the receptor end-organs in the tendon. Note that the muscle spindle lies in parallel with the contracting fibers, and that when these fibers contract stretch on the spindle will be taken up and the stretch stimulus will cease to be effective; in the tendon organ any tensile force, whether active or passive, will affect the end-organs indiscriminately. The tendon organs are thus regarded as tension recorders. *a* and *b*, muscle fiber; *m*, motoneuron; *s*, spindle muscle. (After Fulton and Pi-Suñer, *Amer. J. Physiol.*, 1928, *83*:554.)

reflex stimulation, e.g., the crossed extensor reflex, but the posture of exaggerated reflex standing had been abolished. Along with it the knee jerk had also disappeared. Sherrington concluded that decerebrate rigidity results from impulses arising within the muscle itself; or to use his language, it is a "proprioceptive" reflex.

Some years earlier Sherrington had studied the sensory nerve endings in muscle, finding that at least 40 per cent of the nerve fibers innervating a given muscle subserved the sensory rather than motor end-organs (16). The types of sensory ending found in muscle have been described in the previous chapter. He did not commit himself as to which type of ending was responsible for decerebrate rigidity. More recently reasons have been adduced for regarding the *muscle spindle* as the stretch afferent. In the first place, muscle spindles are absent from striated muscles not subject to gravitational stretch, i.e., muscles of the tongue, larynx and also the extra-ocular muscles (Sherrington, 16); in the second place, muscle spindles, unlike the tendon endings, lie in parallel with the muscle fibers (Fig. 111), and if stretch is applied the spindle at first stretched would no longer be under tensile stress when the muscle fibers immediately surrounding it contracted. We have seen that the stretch reflex is usually intensely local in that only the muscle or the part of the muscle actually stretched responds. It is probable, therefore, that a given muscle spindle serves only those fibers which immediately surround it. *Taken together, the spindle and this cluster of muscle fibers form the ultimate reflex unit of the postural mechanism.*

Close study of the histology of muscle indicates that it is made up of fasciculi—in the larger extensor muscles bundles of one to two hundred fibers grouped together, possibly as a single functional unit. At all events, these fasciculi sometimes have but a single muscle spindle within them, and it is no doubt significant that in diseases such as poliomyelitis in which ventral horn cells are first irritated and then die, one of the prodromal symptoms is an involuntary "fasciculation" of the muscle. The muscle fascicles discharge as groups during the stage of irritation. Histologically, muscles of patients who have been victims of poliomyelitis at times show atrophy of whole muscle fasciculi with complete sparing of adjacent fasciculi (22). This can only mean that the muscle fascicle in such instances is in fact the motor unit, i.e., the cluster of fibers innervated by a single ventral horn cell. Occasionally half a muscle fascicle is completely degenerated and the remaining fibers appear normal. In such an instance no doubt two or more ventral horn cells have innervated the fasciculus. It must be recalled that there are large and small motor units even as there are large and small ventral horn cells, and it is therefore possible that some fasciculi may have multiple innervation, but it would seem impossible to account for the phenomenon of fasciculation or for a complete fasciculus disappearing as is often the case in poliomyelitis muscle, without one's assuming that such fascicles receive unitary innervation from a given ventral horn cell.

Decerebrate rigidity can be abolished in one additional way, namely, by the dissection of extensor muscle from its normal anatomical insertion. If quadriceps, for example, is detached at the patella tendon and thus freed from all stretch imposed by the normal anatomical attachments, rigidity vanishes entirely, but returns promptly (along with muscle action currents) when the muscle is elongated even slightly. We may conclude, therefore, that decerebrate rigidity results from the slight stretch of normal anatomical attachments, that it is accentuated by gravitational stretch, and that the threshold of this response is under the direct influence of the vestibular nuclei and the vestibulospinal pathways.

Further study of muscles in the decerebrate state indicate that their proprioceptive nerve endings are responsive, not only to slight stretch, but also to severe stretch. When tensions develop that threaten injury to the muscle, reflex relaxation develops through operation of nociceptive sensory endings. This is generally referred to as "autogenous inhibition," and is responsible for the so-called "lengthening reaction" of decerebrate muscle. If one attempts forcefully to flex the extended knee joint of a decerebrate preparation, at first vigorous resistance is felt, and then, with persistence of the forced flexion maneuver, the resistance melts and the muscle relaxes (19). It is probable that this reaction results from stimulation of the Golgi tendon organs which register the existence of excessive tensions irrespective of whether the tension is active (from contraction) or passive (from imposed stretch)—tensions which, if they persisted, might disrupt the tendon. The lengthening reaction is thus a protective reflex.

The "shortening reaction" which was described before the stretch reflex was discovered, has reference to the fact that decerebrate muscle tends to remain at any length at which it is passively placed, i.e., when the relaxed extension muscle is stretched ever so slightly from any resting length it immediately responds by contraction (stretch reflex).

The posture assumed in the decerebrate state differs widely in different animals, even as normal postures differ from animal to animal. The three-toed sloth, which normally defies gravity with its flexor muscles, assumes an attitude of exaggerated flexion when decerebrated (15). Dog and cat develop exaggerated extensor reactions in both the upper and lower extremities, and also

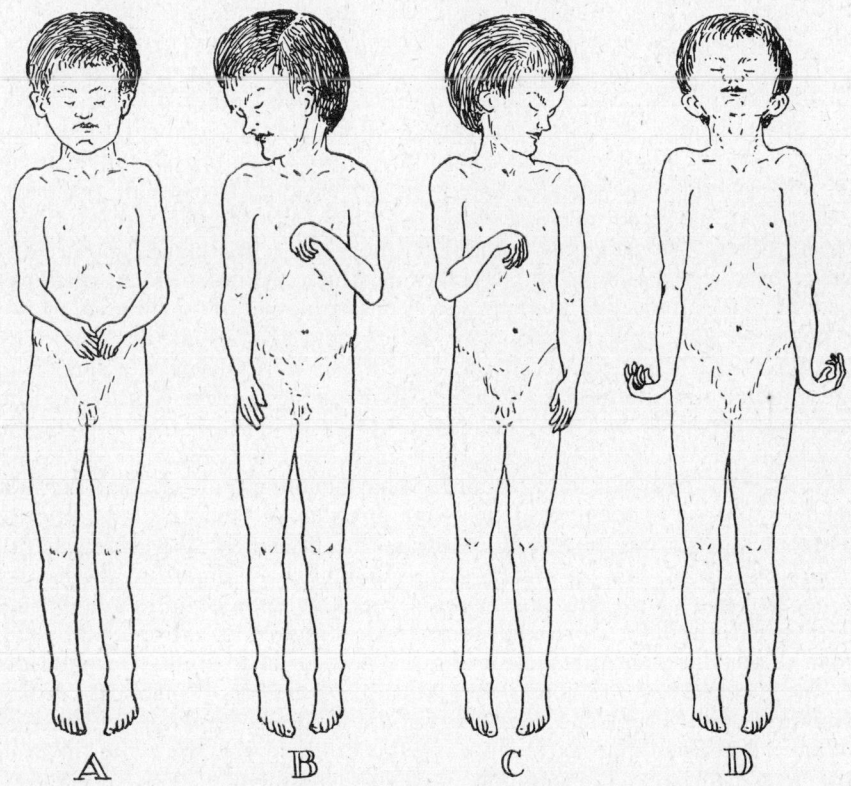

Fig. 112.—A diagram illustrating the differences in man between decorticate rigidity and true decerebrate rigidity. A—Lying prone with head unturned; note that both forelimbs are flexed. B and C—Note changes of position with head-turning. D—True decerebrate rigidity in man with arms rigidly extended and pronated.

in the neck muscles. In man, following hemiplegia, the exaggerated posture is one of extension in the lower extremities and flexion in the upper, again reflecting an exaggeration of an habitual attitude.

Decorticate Rigidity and Decerebrate Rigidity in Man (Fig. 112). It was pointed out above that rigidity of the decerebrate state is an additive affair, the intensity of which depends upon the number of descending pathways interrupted. In cat and dog there is very great exaggeration of the rigidity if, subsequent to section of the brain stem, the cerebellum is removed, and the same obtains in man and monkey except that in primates, when the cerebellum is removed in addition to the extrapyramidal projections in the forebrain, the upper extremities become extended as well as the lower extremities. The state generally referred to as decerebrate rigidity in man is actually a decorticate rigidity, the posture being similar to that seen in a thalamic monkey (3). A true decerebrate rigidity in the primate is associated with intense spastic rigidity of all four extremities, the upper extremities being thrust backward in rigid extension with pronation (see Fig. 112D); the back is arched, the neck retracted, the postural status designated opisthotonos.

POSTURAL REFLEXES (STATIC REACTIONS)

Postural reactions, sometimes designated the "attitudinal" reflexes (Magnus, 9, 10), are of three categories, (i) local static reactions, (ii) segmental static reactions, and (iii) general static reactions which include the tonic neck and labyrinthine reflexes. All are proprioceptive in nature, the local static reactions stemming primarily from gravitational stimuli, segmental reactions arising from the effects of movement of one extremity on the opposite extremity, and general static reactions, i.e., tonic neck and labyrinthine reactions, arising from the actual position of the head in space. Acceleratory reactions, e.g., postrotatory nystagmus, come from the semicircular canals and are distinct from the tonic labyrinthine reactions which are independent of movement or acceleration. The afferent sources of stimulation of the three categories of postural reflexes are as follows: (i) static reactions originate in the muscles themselves; (ii) segmental reactions develop as a result of afferents from one muscle acting upon fellow muscles of the same segment on the opposite side; and (iii) neck and labyrinthine reactions stem from receptors in the membranous labyrinth (the otolith) and in the neck muscles.

We owe to the late Rudolf Magnus, pharmacologist of Utrecht, the first clear-cut analysis of the three-dimensional problem of the attitudinal reflexes. His book, which appeared in 1924 under the brief title *Körperstellung* (9), meaning literally "body posture," stands as a great landmark in the history of modern neurology. The investigation which culminated in this book had its origin in the laboratory of Professor Sherrington in Liverpool in 1908, when it was disclosed that on turning the head of a decerebrate animal the rigidity increased on the side toward which the head was turned and became diminished on the opposite side. This had originally been noted by Sherrington, and it appears that he turned it over to Professor Magnus with the brief comment that the phenomenon deserved further study.

The spinal animal

The basic pattern of the local and segmental static reflexes is to be found in the spinal animal. The stretch reflex is the most prominent of the *local static reactions*, and the crossed extensor reflex may also be obtained, again in accordance with a definite pattern, indicating that *segmental static reactions* are also laid down at the spinal level. *General static reactions* are also seen, for when a crossed extensor reflex is obtained in the spinal preparation, the ipsilateral forelimb also extends, this being a reaction pattern which tends to keep the animal from toppling over, and it is also a part of the quadrupedal pattern of movement involved in forward locomotion. Tonic neck reflexes (see later) are also said to be present in a high spinal animal.

The decerebrate animal

All three static reactions are well developed in the decerebrate animal.

Local Static Reactions. Local static reactions are most conspicuously developed in the extremities, and they have to do primarily with stance—the fixed standing posture that prevents collapse of the extremity under force of gravity. As Sir Thomas Browne once pointed out, "For station is properly no rest, but one kinde of motion, relating unto that which Physitians (from Galen) doe name extensive or tonicall, that is an extension of the muscles and organs of motion maintaining the body at length or in its proper figures, wherein although it seem to be immoved is neverthelesse [not] without all motion, for in this position the muscles are sensibly extended, and labour to support the body, which permitted unto its proper gravity would suddenly subside and fall unto the earth, as it happeneth in sleep, diseases and death; from which occult action and invisible motion of the muscles in station (as Galen declareth) proceed more offensive lassitudes then from ambulation."*

Magnus put the problem of the local static reaction as follows (10): "A movable limb is at times used as an *instrument* for very different purposes (such as scraping, scratching, fighting, etc.), and moves freely in all joints, whereas at other times it is transformed into a stiff and strong *pillar*, which gives the impression of being one solid column, able to carry the weight of the body. Experiments have shown that this is accomplished by a series of local static reflexes." In becoming pillar-like, joints must become fixed; this involves simultaneous contraction of opposing muscle groups. The stretch reflex, which is at the basis of the antigravity response, is not of itself sufficient to fix a given joint; opposing muscles must contract simultaneously to insure the joint fixation, but must relax reciprocally when position of the extremity is changed even in slight degree.

The basis of this coordinated response involving the entire musculature of an extremity was discovered by Magnus in a decerebellated dog. Here the stretch reflexes as judged by the knee jerk were exaggerated, but even more exaggerated was an extension response which followed when the pads of the feet were lightly touched. The extremity in these circumstances followed one's finger as if one's finger were a magnet. Although now designated the "positive supporting reaction," when it was first described it was referred to as the "magnet reaction." On close analysis it was found that the reaction started from a touch stimulus to the skin of the toe pad, i.e., *exteroceptive* stimulus; this, however, is followed by a *proprioceptive* stimulus, i.e., stretch of the interosseus muscles by separation of the toe pads. When the skin of the foot was anesthetized, the exteroceptive phase was abolished, but immediately the toe pads became separated, the proprioceptive stimulus promptly initiated the response. Once the extremities encountered active resistance, other muscles were stretched, and they in turn reinforced the reaction initiated from the skin and small muscles of the toe pads. The reaction itself transforms the extremity from a flexible toneless extremity into a supporting member having the stiffness of a rigid pillar. The reaction is present in normal animals and also in man, but is less readily demonstrated than in a decerebrate preparation in which all of the static reactions are released and exaggerated. Once the stretch stimulus of the small muscles of the foot are removed, the extremity

*Enquiries into vulgar and common errors, 1646, Book 3, Chap. I. Of the Elephant, p. 105.

again loses its rigid attitude and the various muscle groups become inactive. This process is sometimes referred to as the negative supporting reaction.

Segmental Static Reactions. The segmental static reaction has already been mentioned in connection with the spinal preparation. The crossed extension reflex is one of the classical reactions of the decerebrate animals. One must also recognize intersegmental static reactions. For example, when a hindlimb is caused to extend either through the positive supporting reaction or from a crossed extension reflex, the opposite forelimb also extends, thus demonstrating the influence of the lumbar segments upon the cervical. The same pattern also occurs in reverse, namely, the extension of one forelimb is accompanied automatically by the extension of the opposite hindlimb, all of which is a pattern essential for quadrupedal standing as well as for locomotion.

General Static Reactions (Decerebrate Preparation). Once an animal succeeds in standing, various modifications of stance can develop in accordance with the needs of a given situation. If, for example, a cat lifts its head to look on a shelf, the forelimbs become automatically extended on both sides. If it in turn tries to look under a sofa, both forelimbs become flexed. The general static reactions are due in part to the influence of one muscle group upon muscle groups in other segments, but they are also modified by the tonic neck and labyrinthine reflexes which we will now discuss.

Tonic neck reflexes. In order to differentiate neck from labyrinthine reflexes, both labyrinths must be destroyed and sources of stimulation for the static reactions removed, so that on turning the neck the influence of the neck muscles alone will be observed. As already mentioned, rotation of the jaw to the right in such a preparation causes prompt increase in the extensor posture of both limbs to the right side, and relaxation of the limbs on the other side. Dorsal flexion of the head of non-hopping animals causes extension of both forelimbs and relaxation of the hindlimbs (cat looking up on shelf); ventral flexion of the head causes relaxation of both forelimbs and extension of the hindlimbs (cat looking under sofa).

These reactions are obviously purposeful; thus, if a cat walking forward in a straight line hears a mouse to the right of it, mere turning of the head to the right causes the extremities on that side to become extended and the animal is automatically prepared for a quick takeoff with its left foot—it has only to decide whether to go for the mouse. The neck reflexes arrange the rest. Clear-cut purpose is also seen in extension and flexion of the forelimbs when the gaze is directed upward and downward respectively. Section of the dorsal nerve roots in the anterior cervical region abolish these reactions, indicating that they are mediated through the three uppermost cervical roots. These reactions are prominent in decerebrate cats, and they have also been clearly demonstrated in labyrinthectomized monkeys following bilateral removal of the motor and premotor areas (see Chap. 15).

Tonic labyrinthine reflexes. Separation of the tonic neck from the labyrinthine reactions can be brought about through the use of animals in which the upper four cervical sensory roots have been severed bilaterally. It must be recalled that the labyrinth itself has two distinct mechanisms, one the otolith and the other the semicircular canals. The static labyrinthine reactions are probably mediated by the otolith, whereas the reactions to angular acceleration appear to stem primarily from the semicircular canals, but clear-cut separation between the two end-organs has never been achieved. The static labyrinthine reactions manifest themselves through changes in resting posture brought about by alterations of the animal's position in space. When placed on its back, i.e., in a horizontal supine position, the extremities are maximally extended. In this position the snout lies at an angle of approximately forty-five degrees above the horizontal plane. The extensor pattern seen in these circumstances is referred to as the maximal labyrinthine position; the minimal is that seen in the prone position with the snout tilted forty-five degrees to the horizontal plane. In intermediate positions between maximal and minimal, the intermediate degrees of extensor tone are encountered. It should be mentioned again that these are purely static reactions, having nothing to do with acceleration of the animal in space. Their source from the otolith was believed established in guinea pigs through centrifugalization. If centrifuged at a high rate of speed, the otolith organ is destroyed without harming the semicircular canals. When destroyed, the static labyrinthine reactions are impaired.

The tonic neck and the static labyrinthine reactions operate in the same direction, and they consequently tend to support one another.

Magnus and de Kleijn (11) had at first believed that the functions of the otoliths and the semicircular canals were distinct and separable, the semicircular canals mediating reactions to angular acceleration and the otolith organ the tonic labyrinthine reflexes and reactions to vertical acceleration. De Kleijn and Versteegh (8) were later forced to modify this position since tonic labyrinthine reflexes were demonstrated after the otolith membranes had been entirely destroyed. Tait and McNally (21) state that normal righting reflexes are present after the nerves of the two utricular maculae have been destroyed. In the frog, furthermore, the semicircular canals appear not to be stimulated by linear acceleration but rather by the position of the head in space. These discrepancies have led some to conclude that the labyrinth probably functions as a whole, and that the semicircular canals and the otolith organs each play a part in evoking acceleratory as well as tonic static reactions.

Motion sickness. It is now well established that the phenomenon of motion sickness, both in animals and man, is due primarily to the effects of repeated acceleration of the body in space, and that the otolith organs are chiefly responsible for the general reaction. Recent studies on animals and man indicate that repeated vertical accelerations are more effective in causing motion sickness than are horizontal or rotational accelerations, and it is perhaps significant that monkeys, which are more accustomed to three dimensional accelerations by virtue of their normal habits, are much less susceptible to motion sickness than are non-climbing animals such as dog, cat and man. Quite recently Bard has found that ablation of the flocculonodular lobe of the cerebellum (see Chap. 16) makes animals immune to motion sickness.

The midbrain preparation ("thalamus" animal)

Righting Reflexes. The second category of general static reaction analyzed by Magnus and his collaborators has to do with the so-called righting reflexes. The decerebrate preparation exhibits no tendency to regain the upright position once it topples over. When the centers of the midbrain remain intact (the so-called "thalamus" animal of Magnus), decerebrate rigidity is not present (cats and dogs), but the animal, when placed on its side, tends first to right its head, then its body, and through a series of such maneuvers it may achieve an upright position, standing essentially normally on all four extremities. The midbrain primate shows a similar tendency, but it is unable actually to stand even though the righting reflexes to be described below are conspicuously present. The adult primate differs from the dog or the cat in greater encephalization of motor function in the cerebral hemispheres.

The classical righting reflex can readily be demonstrated in the intact animal by merely dropping it blindfolded with legs pointed upward. A cat in these

circumstances turns with almost incredible speed, and lights deftly on all
fours. It was pointed out by the French physiologist Marey (12) that the turn
is brought about by the animal's first arching its back muscles as indicated
in Figure 113, i.e., retracting its head toward its tail, then arching the trunk
laterally, and in that way executing a half turn which is quickly followed by
contraction of the belly muscles which rotates the trunk another ninety degrees and brings the animal to an upright position. In the language of the
orthopedic surgeon, the animal first develops a lordosis and scoliosis, then a
scoliosis and a kyphosis, and finally it straightens itself out in the normal upright posture (14). When the labyrinths are destroyed, a blindfolded cat fails
entirely to turn if dropped in this manner, and plummets to the floor on its

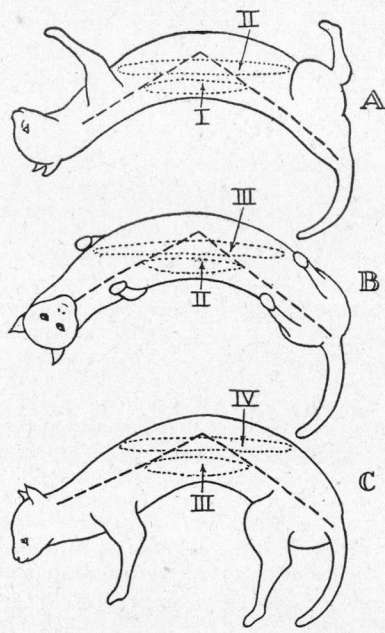

Fig. 113.—Diagram showing series of maneuvers which a cat executes in order to turn itself
in the air. I, back muscles; II, muscles of the right side; III, muscles of the abdominal wall;
IV, muscles of the left side. (After Rademacher and Ter Braak, *Acta oto-laryng.*, *Stockh.*, 1935,
23:313.)

back. It is not yet clear which part of the labyrinth is responsible for the reaction, but most investigators believe that the utricle is the primary receptor.

The reflexes responsible for the righting tendency have been separated into
five principal groups. The reactions are of a sequential nature, like those involved in the act of swallowing. Movements of the head initiate the responses;
these are followed by reactions of the head and neck, etc.

Labyrinthine righting reflexes. If the sensory channels contributing to the
righting reflex are systematically obliterated, the animal lies on its side, disoriented, and makes no attempt to bring its head or its body into the horizontal position. This state of disorientation has been designated the "zero
condition." If both labyrinths are destroyed, with animal blindfolded, the upper
cervical sensory nerve roots cut, and a weight equal and opposite to the force
of gravity is applied to the upper surface of the animal's body, its righting

cues are completely abolished. If, however, any one of these sensory fields remains intact, the contribution of the particular field, e.g., the labyrinth, can be analyzed. With an animal blindfolded but labyrinth still intact, the head tends to assume the horizontal position irrespective of the position in space of the remainder of the body, i.e., the head is given orientation in space. This reaction, like that of a tonic labyrinthine response, disappears if the otoliths are destroyed. The reaction is thus static, having nothing to do with the acceleratory responses of the semicircular canals. For this reason the labyrinthine righting reactions are undoubtedly primary, and take the lead, as it were, in bringing the body as a whole into the upright position.

Body righting reflexes. If a labyrinthectomized animal, blindfolded, is held in the lateral position without compressing the body wall from above, the head also tends to assume a horizontal posture. The reaction can be inhibited by placing a weighted board on the animal's upper surface. The reaction thus is due to asymmetrical stimulation of receptors within the body surface. These reactions are seen quite as prominently in a thalamic primate as they are in a cat and dog.

Neck righting reflexes. Once the neck has been turned in response to the labyrinthine and body righting reflexes, the neck muscle proprioceptors become stimulated and the body itself then tends to be brought into the horizontal position so as to follow the head. This likewise is seen in the primate, and is accompanied by a grasping reflex presently to be described.

Body righting reflexes acting on the body. Magnus distinguished a fourth category of righting response, probably less significant than the first three, which can be demonstrated in a blindfolded labyrinthectomized animal. If the head and shoulders are held in the lateral position, the hind quarters tend, despite this circumstance, to assume the horizontal position independently of the forward segments. This reaction can be inhibited by the board test, i.e., by applying weight to the upper surface.

Optical righting reflexes. The eyes in the normal animal contribute to the righting reactions, but since the occipital lobes are absent in the thalamic preparation, visual data play no part in midbrain righting. If, however, the labyrinths and neck muscles are denervated in the normal animal and it is dropped with its eyes open, righting still occurs, but this fails if such a preparation is blindfolded. The optic cues are particularly important in the primates, for in monkeys whose motor and premotor areas have been completely removed bilaterally (Chap. 13), optical righting tends still to be demonstrated.

Grasp reflex. The thalamic primate has an abnormal postural distribution (unlike cat and dog) such that when the animal is in the lateral position the lowermost extremities are vigorously extended and the uppermost extremities flexed (Fig. 114). The uppermost extremities, furthermore, exhibit an involuntary grasp reflex which no doubt facilitates the animal in achieving the upright posture. When the animal is turned to the opposite side, the thalamic reflex pattern is reversed; the extremities previously extended now become flexed and also show a grasp reflex which previously has not been present. Careful analysis of the grasp reflex shows that it obviously belongs to the general static reactions, and probably to the righting reactions, since it is affected by the labyrinthine, neck, and body righting reactions, but is unaffected by complete sensory denervation of the skin (3). The grasp reflex is well known to clinical neurologists in a slightly modified form known as "forced grasping," and is seen following isolated cortical lesions of the premotor area of the cerebral cortex (Chap. 15). The term "forced" implies its involuntary character; the intensity of the reaction, however, varies with the state of the cerebral cortex and can be influenced by visual and other sensory stimuli. It is a sign of localizing value, but it is mediated subcortically, being a part of the thalamic grasp reflex, since it is subject, as is the grasp reflex, to influence from the neck and labyrinthine receptors.

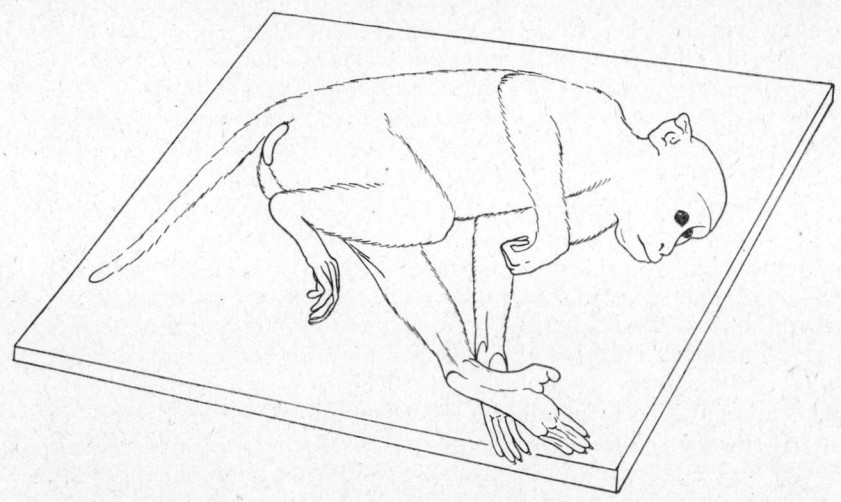

Fig. 114.—The thalamic reflex posture as seen in a decorticate monkey. Note that the lowermost extremities are extended and the uppermost flexed. When the animal is turned over, the condition reverses itself. (From Bieber and Fulton, *Arch. Neurol. Psychiat.*, *Chicago*, 1938, *39*:435–454.)

Postural reflexes depending upon cerebral cortex

There are two groups of reactions important to the postural mechanism which depend, as Bard has clearly shown, upon the integrity of the cerebral cortex. These are the placing and hopping reactions.

Placing Reactions. The placing reactions ensure that the foot shall be in a position suitable for normal standing and normal locomotion. Placing reactions are of two types, visual and nonvisual. When an animal is lowered toward a visible supporting surface, the forelimbs are put down in such a way that without further adjustment the limb is in a position to support the weight of the body. When blindfolded, a similar reaction occurs as a result of a combination of exteroceptive and proprioceptive stimuli. Five nonvisual placing reactions have been described. To quote Bard (1),

1. *Visual and vestibular placing.* When the animal is moved toward a supporting surface, visual stimuli cause the feet to be put down in such a way that without further adjustment they can support the body in standing. If the movement of the body is downward and sufficiently rapid, vestibular stimuli will bring about a similar response. The remaining placing reactions can be elicited in pure form only when visual placing is excluded by blindfolding or by removal of the occipital lobes.

2. *Contact placing.* If the animal is held in the air with legs free and independent, the slightest contact of any portion of the hand or foot with the edge of a table results in either an immediate and accurate placing of the palm or sole on the table or by a grasping of its edge by fingers or toes. This response is usually followed immediately by placing of the unstimulated opposite hand or foot (cross-placing).

3. *Chin placing*. If with arms free, the chin, lips, sides of the jaw, or merely the hairs of the face are brought into light contact with some supporting surface both hands are instantly raised and placed on the source of the stimulus. Occasionally the feet are also placed. When the arms are held such stimulation causes the feet to be brought up and placed.

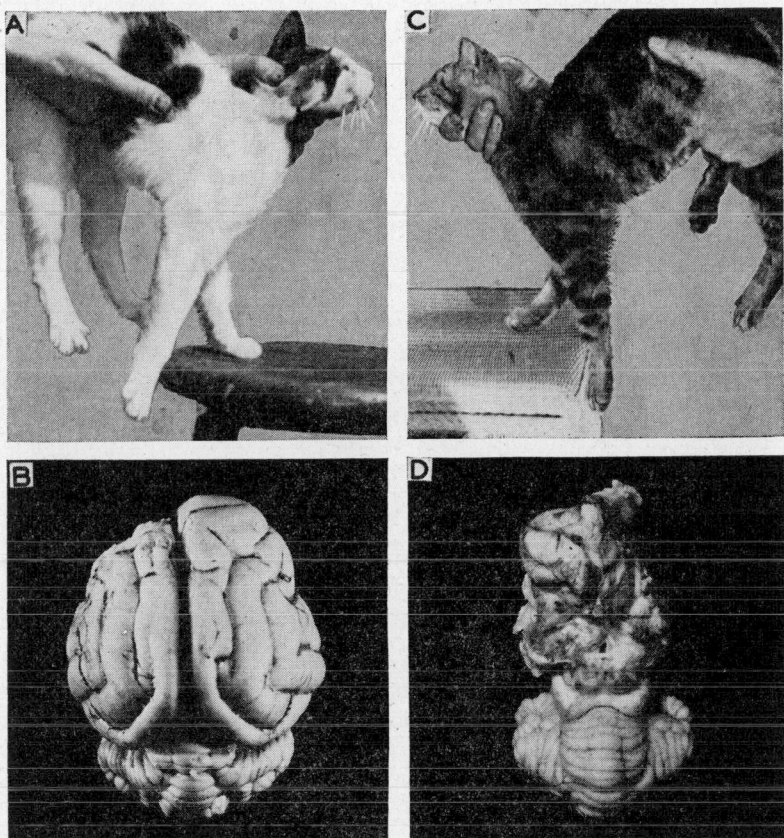

Fig. 115.—Bard's figure illustrating the influence of the cerebral cortex on the placing reactions. Photographs which indicate the nature and the localized cortical control of the placing reactions of the cat. A is a picture of an animal whose brain is shown below in B. Removal of a small area of cortex at the frontal pole of the left hemisphere has permanently abolished the placing reaction of the right foreleg which occurs when the dorsum of the foot is lightly touched to the edge of a supporting surface (top of stool). As can be seen in A, the ablation has not affected the response of the ipsilateral foreleg. The defect is as great as that shown by animals from which the entire cortex of one side has been removed. C shows a cat which had been subjected to removal (in two stages) of all cortex except the frontal area which was ablated in the other animal. Its brain is shown in D. Note that the cat has placed the right foot. This and other tests show that the small remnant of the left cortex was capable of managing in normal fashion the nonvisual placing reactions and the hopping reactions of the opposite (right) foreleg. (From Bard, *Macleod's Physiology*, 9th ed., 1941, p. 141.)

4. *Positional placing*. When the arms or legs are thrust over the edge of a table on which the animal is standing, lying or sitting they are immediately lifted so that their original position on the table is regained.

5. *Proprioceptive placing*. A proprioceptive placing reaction of the limb may be evoked in animals in which reaction 2 has been differentially abolished by appropriate surgical procedures, e.g., parietal lobectomy. In such preparations contact of the apical portions of the limb with a table edge does not of course evoke placing. When, however, forward

displacement of the body has induced a considerable degree of retroflexion at shoulder or hip, the hand or foot is lifted, carried forward and placed far inside the table edge. This is a reaction which Rademaker termed a proprioceptive correcting movement of the limb.

Hopping Reactions. Hopping reactions are evoked when the body is displaced in a horizontal direction, and the reaction is obviously designed to maintain the animal in a normal standing posture. If an animal is held so that it stands on one leg and the body moved sideways, the leg hops in the direction of the displacement so that the foot is maintained more or less vertical to the horizontal axis of the body. When the leg is vertical to the axis, the positive supporting reaction (described above) is at a maximum, i.e., the leg is acting as a rigid pillar. With lateral deviation, the intensity of the supporting reaction diminishes, the foot becomes raised and carried quickly in the direction of the displacement. Rademaker has pointed out that the reaction is due to stretching of the adductor muscles and probably is little affected by exteroceptive stimuli.

Functional localization of placing and hopping. Through the studies of Philip Bard (2), it is now clear that the placing reactions have a precise functional localization. They disappear completely and permanently in a given extremity when the opposite cerebral hemisphere is removed. Both in cats and monkeys the placing reactions also disappear when the motor area is removed, and in the monkey Bard finds that several other parts of the cerebral hemisphere can be removed without affecting the placing reactions, so long as area 4 remains intact (Fig. 115). The hopping reactions are transiently depressed by certain cortical ablations; thus removal of the postcentral convolution appears to abolish the contact placing reaction and cross placing, but such lesions have little if any effect upon proprioceptive placing.

REFERENCES

1. BARD, P. Studies on the cortical representation of somatic sensibility. *Harvey Lect.*, 1937-38, *33*:143–169.

2. BARD, P. The autonomic nervous system, or the efferent pathway to visceral effectors, pp. 165–186 in: MACLEOD's *Physiology in modern medicine*, 9th ed., 1941.

3. BIEBER, I., and FULTON, J. F. The relation of the cerebral cortex to the grasp reflex and to the postural and righting reflexes. *Arch. Neurol. Psychiat., Chicago*, 1938, *39*:435–454.

4. DENNY-BROWN, D., and PENNYBACKER, J. B. Fibrillation and fasciculation in voluntary muscle. *Brain*, 1938, *61*:311–343.

5. FULTON, J. F., LIDDELL, E. G. T., and RIOCH, D. McK. The influence of unilateral destruction of the vestibular nuclei upon posture and knee-jerk. *Brain*, 1930, *53*:327–343.

6. FULTON, J. F., and PI-SUÑER, J. A note concerning the probable function of various afferent end-organs in skeletal muscle. *Amer. J. Physiol.*, 1928, *83*:554–562.

7. INGRAM, W. R., and RANSON, S. W. Effects of lesions in the red nuclei in cats. *Arch. Neurol. Psychiat., Chicago*, 1932, *28*:483–512; and, The place of the red nucleus in the postural complex, *Amer. J. Physiol.*, 1932, *102*:466–475.

8. DE KLEIJN, A., and VERSTEEGH, C.

Näheres über die Auslösungsstelle der Labyrinthreflexe im peripheren Labyrinth. *Acta oto-laryng., Stockh.*, 1935, *22*:327–337.

9. MAGNUS, R. *Körperstellung.* Berlin, J. Springer, 1924, xiii, 740 pp. [Full bibliography].

10. MAGNUS, R. Some results of studies in the physiology of posture. (Cameron Prize Lectures.) *Lancet*, 1926, *2*:531–536; 585–588.

11. MAGNUS, R., and DE KLEIJN, A. Die Abhangigkeit des Tonus der Extremitatenmuskeln von der Kopfstellung. *Pflüg. Arch. ges. Physiol.*, 1912, *145*:455–548.

12. MAREY, E. J. Mécanique animale.—Des mouvements que certains animaux exécutent pour retomber sur leurs pieds, lorsqu'ils sont précipités d'un lieu élevé. *C. R. Acad. Sci., Paris*, 1894, *119*:714–717.

13. POLLOCK, L. F., and DAVIS, L. E. The reflex activities of a decerebrate animal. *J. comp. Neurol.*, 1930, *50*:377–411.

14. RADEMAKER, G. G. J., and TER BRAAK, J. W. G. Das Umdrehen der fallendèn Katze in der Luft. *Acta oto-laryng., Stockh.*, 1935–36, *23*:313–343.

15. RICHTER, C. P., and BARTEMEIER, L. H. Decerebrate rigidity of the sloth. *Brain*, 1926, *49*:207–225.

16. SHERRINGTON, C. S. On the anatomical constitution of nerves of skeletal muscles; with remarks on recurrent fibres in the ventral

spinal nerve-root. *J. Physiol.*, 1894, *17*:211–258.

17. SHERRINGTON, C. S. Decerebrate rigidity, and reflex coordination of movements. *J. Physiol.*, 1898, *22*:319–332.

18. SHERRINGTON, C. S. On the proprioceptive system, especially in its reflex aspect. *Brain*, 1907, *29*:467–482.

19. SHERRINGTON, C. S. Postural activity of muscle and nerve. *Brain*, 1915, *38*:191–234.

20. SHERRINGTON, C. S. Problems of muscular receptivity. *Nature*, 1924, *113*:732; 892–894; 924–932.

21. TAIT, J., and McNALLY, W. J. Some features of the action of the utricular maculae (and of the associated action of the semicircular canals) of the frog. *Proc. roy. Soc.*, 1934, *224*:241–286.

22. WOHLFART, G. Über das Vorkommen verschiedener Arten von Muskelfasern in der Skelettmuskulatur des Menschen und einiger Säugetiere. *Acta Psychiat.*, *Kbh.*, 1937 (Suppl. 12) 1–119.

23. WOHLFART, G., and SWANK, R. L. Pathology of amyotrophic lateral sclerosis. Fiber analysis of the ventral roots and pyramidal tracts of the spinal cord. *Arch. Neurol. Psychiat.*, Chicago, 1941, *46*:783–799.

CHAPTER 9

LABYRINTHINE ACCELERATORY REFLEXES: THE MEDULLA OBLONGATA AND CRANIAL NERVES

Reflexes associated with the labyrinth, although an organ of special sense, are so closely linked with the postural reflexes that it is essential to describe them here. The labyrinth, often referred to as the vestibular organ, is made up of two principal parts: the semicircular canals and the otolith organs (saccule and utricle).

POSITION AND STRUCTURE OF LABYRINTH

The membranous semicircular canals lie within the bony semicircular canals, the space between being filled with perilymph which communicates freely with that in the rest of the labyrinth. Within the membranous canals is the endolymph, which communicates through the five openings with the endolymph in the utricle. The canals lie in three planes that are, approximately at least, at right angles to one another (Fig. 116). The horizontal or external

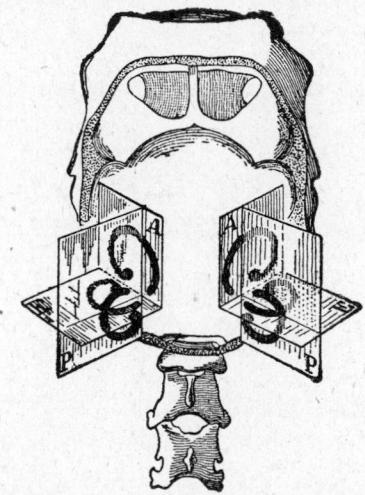

Fig. 116.—Diagram to show the position of the semicircular canals in the head of the bird. On each side it will be seen that the three canals lie in planes at right angles to one another. The external or horizontal canals (E) of the two sides lie in the same plane. The anterior canal of one side (A) lies in a plane parallel to that of the posterior canal (P) of the other side. (Ewald.)

canals lie in a horizontal plane at right angles to the mesial or sagittal plane of the body, and the vertical canals on each side make an angle of about 45 degrees with this mesial plane. The plane of each of the anterior canals is parallel to that of the posterior or inferior vertical canal of the opposite side, as represented in the figure. At one end of each canal, near its junction with the utricle, is the swelling known as the ampulla, and within the ampulla lies the crista acustica, containing the hair cells with which the nerve fibers communicate, and which therefore are considered as the sense cells of the organ. Sitting astride the hair cells and crista for purposes of stimulation is a gelatinous partition known as the "cupula," which rises like a swinging door to the roof of the ampulla, filling the whole cross-section of this structure. It thus responds to hydrostatic forces acting upon it through the endolymph—indeed, it may be regarded as a highly damped jelly pendulum with a natural vibration period of about 20 sec. (Steinhausen, 14). The hair cells are cylindrical and each gives off a long hair, consisting of a bundle of finer hairs, which projects into the interior of the cupula for a distance of at least 28 μ (Fig. 117). The nerve fibers distributed to these hair cells are given off by the vestibular branch of the eighth nerve, or more properly the vestibular nerve, one branch of which (ramus utriculo-ampullaris) supplies the utricle and the ampulla of the superior and horizontal canals, while the other (ramus sacculo-ampullaris) furnishes fibers to the saccule and the posterior ampulla.

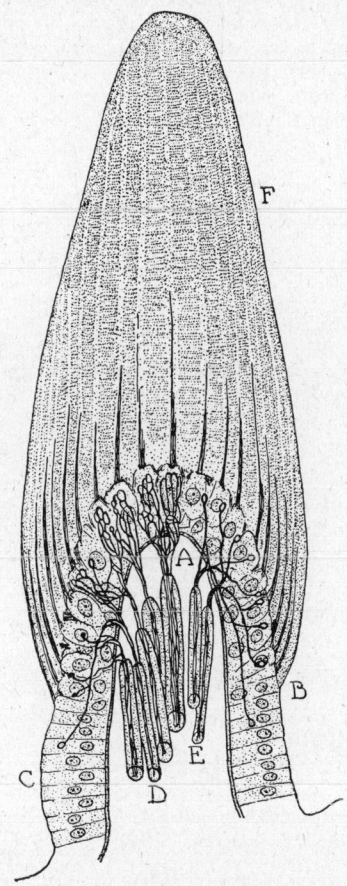

Fig. 117.—A diagrammatic sketch of the cupula and crista after Kolmer (from Camis,2). Note that the hair cells A protrude into the gelatinous substance of the cupula F; B supporting cells; C undifferentiated epithelial cells at the base of the crista; D large nerve fibers, the endings of which are connected with an intracellular network at the base of the hairs; E the fibers of smaller diameter innervating the lateral parts of the crista having free intercellular endings. The cupula is a constant structure in the ampulla of the semicircular canals of all animals from fish to man. In the living state it is larger relatively than here shown, extending through the full diameter of the ampulla.

Historical note. Modern experiments and theories concerning the functions of the semicircular canal date from the classical researches of Flourens (5). This investigator laid bare the canals in birds and mammals and studied the effects of sectioning one or more of them. The experiments have since been repeated by numerous observers, and the results obtained have been described in great detail, for an account of which reference must be made to original sources.* In general, it may be said that injuries to the canals are followed by cer-

* The literature of the semicircular canals and the vestibule is very extensive. The principal bibliography may be obtained from the following sources: *Die Lehren von den Funktionen der einzelnen Theile des Ohrlabyrinths*, by von Stein, 1894; Richet's *Dictionnaire de physiologie*,

tain more or less definite movements of the head, eyes, and body, and by a disturbance in the power of the animal to coordinate normally the muscles used in standing, locomotion, or flying. The character and extent of these results vary with the number of canals injured and, indeed, show a more or less definite relationship to the separate canals. When the horizontal canal is cut on one side in pigeons the animal makes movements of the head in the plane of that canal, and if the similar canal on the other side is also sectioned these movements are more pronounced. The animal may also in moving show an inability to walk normally and a tendency, especially when excited, to make abnormal forced movements of rotation of the whole body. After such an operation the pigeon will not fly voluntarily and if thrown into the air is not able to guide its flight with accuracy and soon descends. Similar operations on the anterior or the posterior canals cause movements of the head in the corresponding planes and a tendency in walking or flying to make forced move-

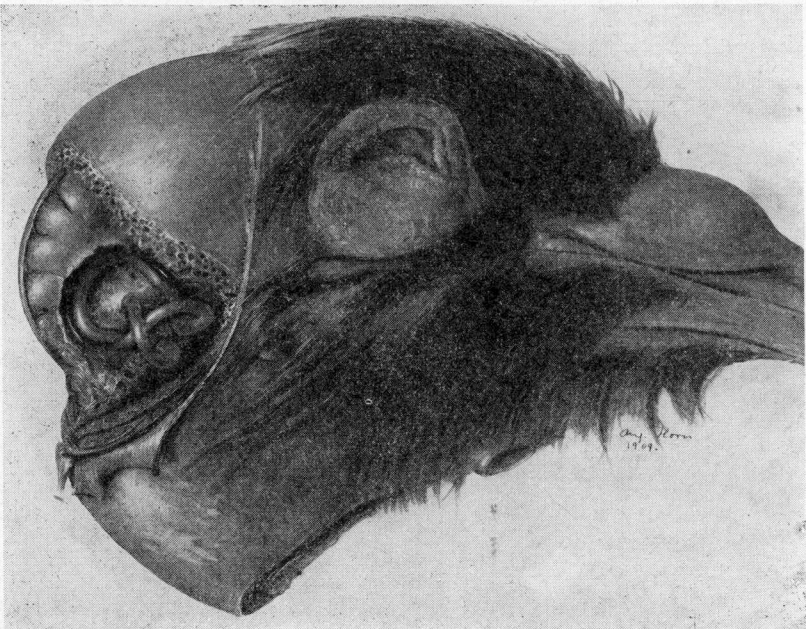

Fig. 118A.—Dissection to show the position of the three semicircular canals in the pigeon and the relations of their ampullary ends (from preparation made by Dr. Esther Rosencrantz.)

ments—somersaults—forward or backward. When all three canals are cut on one or both sides the animal shows a distressing inability to maintain a normal position. The head is twisted, it is not able to stand unless supported, and any attempt at walking or flying results in violent forced and incoordinated movements. The animal makes continual somersaults at each attempt to stand or walk and the head is kept in spasmodic, forceful movements, which may produce injury or death. To preserve the animal from injury after such an extensive operation it is necessary to keep it wrapped in bandages. It should be added that results of this character are obtained only when the membranous canals are injured. If the bony canal alone is cut and even if the perilymph is removed by suction no such effects are obtained. At most, slight and relatively transient movements of the head are observed. If the exposed membranous canal is pricked with a needle more violent movements result, and if sectioned these movements are maintained for a longer period and are accompanied by the other reactions described. Similar effects have been obtained from operations on mammals and other animals, but the results are more pronounced in some animals than in others, varying apparently with the delicacy of the coordination necessary for the movements (Ewald). Thus, the movements of walking or flying in the pigeon may be assumed to

article by Cyon, on "Espace," 1900; Ewald, *Physiolog. Untersuchungen u. d. Endorgan des Nervus Octavus*, 1892; Camis, *The physiology of the vestibular apparatus*, trans. by R. S. Creed, Oxford, 1930; also McNally and Stuart (10).

require a nicer adjustment of the muscles used than is necessary in the swimming movements of the fish, and in correspondence with this idea it is found that operations on the canals of fishes are not followed by conspicuous effects upon the movements of the animals.

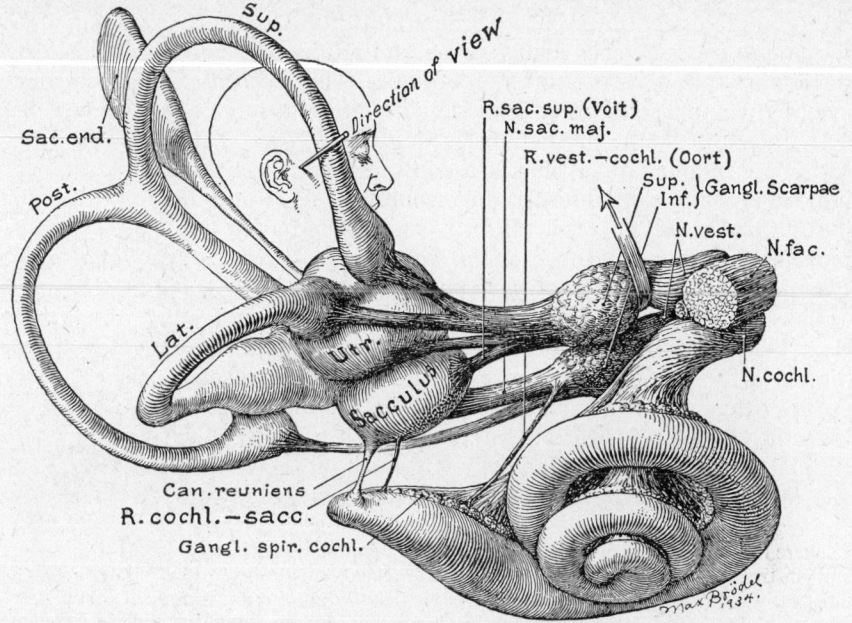

Fig. 118B.—A semidiagrammatic drawing showing the structural relations of innervation of the human labyrinth, by Max Brödel. The orientation of the three nerves supplying the macula sacculi is clearly brought out—also Cort's nerve, passing through the cochlea. (From Hardy, *Anat. Rec.*, 1934, *59*:402.)

FUNCTION OF THE SEMICIRCULAR CANALS

The work of Flourens and other investigators who followed him in the nineteenth century made it evident that a primary function of the semicircular canals is to register movement of the body in space; expressed more precisely, the vestibular organ responds to any *change in the rate of movement*, i.e., to acceleration or to deceleration. In fast flying aircraft, for example, acceleratory forces of great intensity may develop, particularly in the "pull-out" from a dive or in a close turn such as fighter pilots use in evasive maneuvers. In these circumstances the semicircular canals may be so profoundly stimulated as to cause complete disorientation of the pilot in space, especially if the pilot should inadvertently turn his head during the high acceleration. Acceleratory reflexes may be described under two heads: (i) linear acceleration and (ii) angular acceleration.

Acceleratory Reflexes. *Linear acceleration.* One of the best known responses to acceleration can readily be demonstrated in an intact cat. With the animal blindfolded and head down, if the animal is suddenly lowered through the air, the forelegs become extended and the toes spread (vestibular placing reaction). This is the normal response to linear acceleration, and is similar to the visual placing reaction. The obvious purpose of the reaction is to facilitate landing when jumping from a high place. Such acceleratory reactions can be demonstrated in completely deafferented muscle, and therefore do not depend upon proprioceptive afferents from the muscles themselves.

Angular acceleration and nystagmus. Following rapid rotation around the vertical axis of the body, a series of reactions occur that affect the muscles of the eyes, neck, limbs and trunk. As the head turns, the eyes turn slowly in the opposite direction in order to maintain the gaze at a fixed point; but as the body turns, the eyes finally swing and fix upon a new point which they once more follow as the turning continues. This alternate movement of the eyes, a quick phase followed by a slow deviation, is referred to as *nystagmus.* The direction of the nystagmus is designated by its quick phase. When rotation continues for a time at a constant rate, the nystagmus disappears, indicating that the stimulus for the response is one of acceleration rather than motion per se. If the acceleration is suddenly stopped, the involuntary eye movements commence once again, *but in postrotatory nystagmus the quick phase is the opposite of that which occurred during the acceleration.*

The semicircular canals are arranged in three planes of space, and it is now clear that since nystagmus may be either horizontal, vertical or rotatory in direction, the particular response depends upon which semicircular canals or groups of canals are stimulated, i.e., upon the direction of the acceleration. If the head is bent forward at an angle of thirty degrees the horizontal semicircular canals are in the plane of rotation about the vertical axis of the body and they become responsible for the nystagmus caused by rotation.

There is a large literature on the relation of individual semicircular canals to nystagmus and on the interaction between corresponding canals on the two sides of the body. The most satisfactory experiments from a physiological standpoint are those of Lorente de Nó, whose papers should be consulted for further details (7, 8, 9). From the clinical standpoint, the most illuminating analysis is that of Dohlman whose papers have appeared over a period of twenty years in the *Acta Oto-laryngologica,* his early work having been summarized in 1935 (3, 4). In human cases in which the membranous labyrinth has been opened so as to expose the horizontal canal to mechanical stimulation, he finds that sudden pressure applied to the canal causes a horizontal nystagmus lasting about twenty seconds. He infers that this gives an index of the time required for return of the cupula from an initial quick displacement. The direction of nystagmus is similar to that of a postrotatory nystagmus.

Mechanism of stimulation of the canals. The membranous canals or their ampullary enlargements have been stimulated by many observers and by many different methods—electrical, chemical, and mechanical. The results of electrical stimulation are not constant nor striking, but chemical and especially mechanical stimulation in the hands of many observers has called forth definite movements of head or eyes similar in a general way to those caused by section of the canal, but lasting, of course, for a short time only. In experiments made upon dog-fish Lee found that when the animal is rotated in the planes of the several canals there are definite movements of the eyes and fins for each plane of rotation. Moreover, since mechanical stimulation of an ampulla causes movements of the eyes and fins identical with those resulting from rotation of the animal in the plane of that canal, it follows as a probable conclusion that the sense cells in each ampulla are actually stimulated by movements in the plane of its canal.

Important work of Steinhausen (14) and of Dohlman (3) has shed new light upon the mode of action of the semicircular canals. Steinhausen has devised an ingenious method of visualizing the semicircular canals in the living animal. Through the use of dyes structures within the ampulla of fish can be directly visualized, and Dohlman has succeeded in introducing a drop of oil into the canal and in that way been able to follow the movement of the endolymph during angular acceleration. Steinhausen has disclosed that the *cupula* (which some histological texts still regard as an artifact of fixation appended to the hair cells of the crista) is actually a large gelatinous structure which occupies the greater part of the lumen of the ampulla. It sits astride the crista and its hair cells, as shown in the histological texts (Fig. 117), but it extends beyond the crista to the roof of the ampulla (Fig. 119). When the endolymph moves into the ampulla, the cupula bends over toward the utricle, and after the acceleration it slowly returns to its resting position.

These relations are clearly shown in the excellent figures published by Dohlman (Fig. 120). The relations of the canal to the ampullar nerve, the crista, and the cupula are particularly well shown in Figure 120. In Figure 120*A* one sees a semicircular canal at rest, with a drop of oil in the lumen of

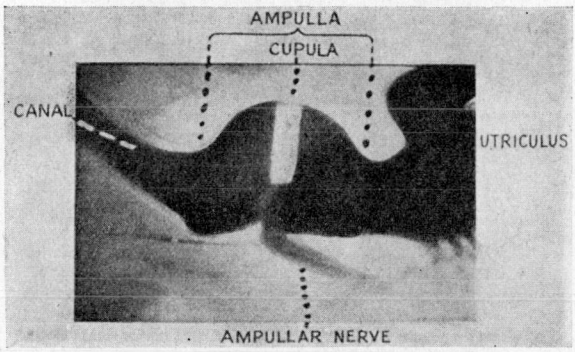

Fig. 119.—A photograph taken through binoculars of the ampulla of a living fish (pike obtained by Steinhausen. Note the ampullar nerve of the crista and the cupula (white) mounted on the dark surface of the crista; note also that the cupula traverses the entire lumen of the ampulla (Dohlman, *Proc. R. Soc. Med.*, 1935, *28*:1371.)

the canal; in Figure 120*B* the same canal is shown during angular accelera-tion. The oil droplet has moved forward, and the cupula is bent over through an angle of some thirty degrees. Dohlman points out that when the rates of displacement and return of the cupula are actually determined, they coincide precisely with the duration of nystagmus during the acceleration and with that of the postrotatory nystagmus which follows. To quote (3),

"The cupula deviates during, perhaps, the first, or possibly also the second, revolution as long as the rotation is accelerated. On reaching a constant speed the rotation no longer affects the fluid or the cupula in any way. The deviation of the cupula is now, however, gradually diminished by its elasticity; and after about half a minute it has returned to the original position. It is to be expected that the nystagmus *during rotation* should cease when the cupula resumes its normal position, and it does, as Buys showed by nystagmographic registration several years ago.

"When rotation stops we again have, as a result of the effect of retardation on the endo-lymph, a deviation of the cupula, this time in the opposite direction. A post-rotational nystagmus occurs, and lasts as long as the cupula needs to return once more, through its elasticity, to its starting position. This explains why a post-rotatory nystagmus does not occur until after a longer continued rotation. And it explains why we must have a rotational time of about twenty seconds to obtain the longest nystagmus for any rotational speed. For the cupula has by that time regained its initial position by its elasticity, so that it might be ready for the maximal displacement in the opposite direction through the inertia of the endolymph when the rotation ceases. So the nystagmus *during* rotation, like the *post-rotational* nystagmus, is a consequence of the deviation of the cupula; and its duration depends on the time the cupula requires to reassume its normal position."

To date no one has succeeded in visualizing the semicircular canal within the bony labyrinth of any of the higher animals, but since the cupula is also seen histologically, albeit in a shrunken state in all the higher animals, it is logical to believe, as Dohlman points out, that the mechanisms found in fish also obtain in higher forms.

A

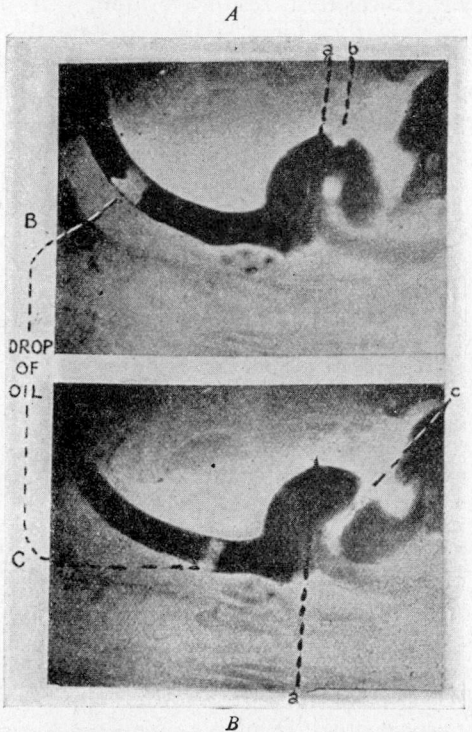

B

Fig. 120.—Dohlman's figure showing the ampulla and semicircular canal in the living state before and during an angular acceleration. Point B in the canal is a droplet of oil which moves toward the ampulla during acceleration. Note that the cupula, at first nearly vertical, bends forward toward the utricle at an angle of nearly sixty degrees as a result of the flow of endolymph into the ampulla. *a* Initial position of cupula in both figures. *b* Top of cupula before acceleration. Point C is an oil droplet during acceleration. *c* Top of cupula during acceleration (Dohlman).

Löwenstein and Sand (6) have confirmed Steinhausen's observations, and they point out that the cupula and the hair cells are mechanically a single unit; the mechanical properties governing the displacement of the cupula must also determine the deformation of the sense hairs from which arises the excitation of the end-organ. These investigators succeeded in preparing a single nerve fiber preparation from the horizontal ampulla of the isolated labyrinth of a ray (*Raja*). They find at rest a spontaneous rhythmic discharge on the single nerve fiber and that the rate of discharge is increased by ipsilateral rotation and decreased by contralateral. During uniform angular acceleration the frequency increases or decreases in a linear manner, and the rate of increase is proportional to the degree of acceleration measured in "g's" ($1g = 33$ ft. per sec. per sec.). During prolonged rotation at constant speed, the frequency of discharge returns to the resting value twenty or thirty seconds after the initial acceleration. They point out further that the spontaneous discharge at rest and its augmentation and diminution by ipsilateral and contralateral rotation provide an explanation, not only of resting labyrinthine tone, but of the fact that reflex responses can be obtained following rotation in any direction in animals from which the labyrinth has been unilaterally extirpated. They believe that the physical properties of the cupula account for the time relations of optic and postrotatory nystagmus. Löwenstein and Sand have examined the influence of individual semicircular canals upon eye movements. They find that the horizontal canals respond to rotation about the vertical axis but are unaffected by rotation about the two horizontal axes. The anterior and posterior canals, on the other hand, respond to rotation about all three axes.

Caloric Reactions. In 1908 the Swedish neurologist, Robert Bárány (1), found on irrigating the external auditory meatus with water having a temperature lower than that of the body that nystagmus tended to occur after an interval of about one minute and that the characteristics of the nystagmus varied with the position of the head in space. There had been various theories proposed concerning the mechanism of caloric nystagmus, and that suggested by Dohlman would appear to be the most satisfactory. He points out that after nystagmus has been obtained (when the horizontal canal is in the vertical position) and has subsided, raising of the head causes nystagmus to recommence and to continue for a further period of thirty to forty seconds, or approximately as long as the postrotatory nystagmus in the same subject. During caloric stimulation, he argued, the endolymph within the canal is gradually cooled at the point in the canal nearest to the auditory meatus. This focal chilling causes the endolymph to flow, thus leading to a deviation of the cupula through the convection currents. The difference between the two forms of stimulation—rotational and caloric—lies in this. By rotation both labyrinths are stimulated suddenly while the caloric test stimulates only one labyrinth and the stimulus is gradual. When the position of the head is changed the previously deviated cupula returns once more to its position of rest so that the secondary nystagmus caused by change of position of the head may be likened to a postrotatory nystagmus. For this reason he designates the secondary reaction "a post-caloric nystagmus."

The caloric reactions have been used extensively in clinical neurology for testing both labyrinthine function and the integrity of the vestibular nerve. In the presence of a lesion involving the labyrinth itself or the eighth nerve, caloric stimulation fails to evoke a response.

McNally (10a) gives the following illuminating rules for interpreting labyrinthine reactions:

"When a spontaneous nystagmus is present before doing labyrinthine tests, careful search should be made for some point at which the eyes are steady. The test should be done with gaze directed at this point; any resulting nystagmus is thus due to the test and can be more easily assessed.

"Rule 1. Flouren's law—Stimulation of a semicircular canal elicits nystagmus in the plane of that canal.

"Rule 2. Ewald's first law—A horizontal semicircular canal is maximally stimulated by a movement of the endolymph in the canal towards its ampulla. A vertical semicircular canal is maximally stimulated by a movement of the endolymph in the canal away from the ampulla.

"Rule 3. Ewald's second law—When a semicircular canal, either horizontal or vertical, is maximally stimulated it elicits a nystagmus to its own side (quick phase). Minimal stimulation causes a nystagmus to the opposite side.

"I have worked out the following rule and found it of practical value because it simplifies the interpretation of all turning tests irrespective of the head position. It is based upon the fact that the quick phase of nystagmus is anti-compensatory and is therefore always in the direction of the turning at the beginning of rotation and in the opposite direction after a sudden stop. It is as follows:

"Rule 4. After-nystagmus (quick phase) is always in the opposite direction to the rotation.

"In attempting to assess the results of the turning tests it is necessary to remember that it is after-reaction that is being considered and that the sudden stop has reversed the direction of the endolymphatic flow in the canals. Also it must be remembered that changing the position of the head may alter the relation of the canals, both to gravity, and to the axis of rotation.

"Arellano made an exhaustive study of canal reactions during rotation in different planes, and about different axes, and he derived the following very important rule:

"Rule 5. Nystagmus due to rotation is always in a plane at right angles to the axis of rotation, irrespective of the position of the head.

"If the axis of rotation is vertical and the head is tilted to one side 45 degrees the resulting nystagmus will be in the horizontal plane, but in relation to the mid-line of the head it will be a diagonal nystagmus.

"Rule 6. Following labyrinthine stimulation, vertigo is directed to the same side as the nystagmus, whereas, the past-pointing and falling and head turning are in the opposite direction to the nystagmus.

"The following is an example of how these rules may be applied to interpret the results of a caloric test; if the head is erect and the right ear is irrigated with ice water, there is a cooling of the endolymph in the labyrinth and convection currents are started in a downward direction. Dohlman, during operation, has actually measured the temperature change on the wall of the external canal while syringing the external meatus with cold water and has been able to register a fall in the temperature of the surface of the bony external semicircular canal wall. With the head erect the vertical canals are in a vertical position so there results a downward flow of endolymph in the anterior and posterior vertical canals. Since the canals stimulated are two vertical canals of the same side the nystagmus is (Flouren's law) in a plane which is the resultant of the diagonal planes of these two canals, that is, a rotary nystagmus in the sagittal plane. The flow is downward towards the ampullae and since the canals are vertical, the stimulation will be minimal (Ewald's first law). Because it is a minimal stimulation the nystagmus will be to the opposite side (Ewald's second law). Thus the effect of syringing a normal right ear, head erect, with cold water is a rotary eye nystagmus to the left. The past-pointing, head turning and falling are to the right side."

States of abnormal stimulation of the semicircular canals or of the nerves which innervate them are also known, the classical syndrome being that described in the nineteenth century by the French neurologist, Ménière. Characteristically the patient afflicted with the condition experiences buzzing in the ear, and concomitantly a sensation of dizziness can develop which may assume such extreme severity as to prevent not only standing, but when reclining, the patient may, during the height of an attack, have forced rolling movements. The condition is sometimes associated with advancing arteriosclerosis. While it can sometimes be alleviated through diet and sedation, the only known cure lies in surgical severance of the vestibular branch of the eighth cranial nerve.

Little is known concerning the pathways of the labyrinthine projections of the brainstem to the thalamus and cerebral cortex. Spiegel (12,13), through local application of strychnine to the temporal lobe, believed that he was able to demonstrate excessive responsiveness to caloric stimulation. He believed that labyrinthine representation in the cortex lies close to that of auditory representation (see Chap. 21). Rotatory accelerations also cause movements of the head and body. The neck muscles may develop a nystagmoid movement entirely similar to that executed by the eye muscles. This reaction is commonly designated "head nystagmus." The body as a whole may continue to turn in the direction of the previously experienced movement with the result that the body may fall to one side.

Temporary and Permanent Effects of Labyrinthectomy. The general effects of operations on the semicircular canals, so far as disturbances of equilibrium and occurrence of forced movements are concerned, resemble those resulting from operations upon the cerebellum, and, as in the case of the last mentioned organ, it is found by most observers that if the animal is properly cared for the severity of the first effects passes off to a greater or less extent. All are agreed that the acceleratory reflexes (linear and angular) are abolished when the labyrinths are destroyed, but recent studies indicate that the mode of operation of the semicircular canals and otolith organs is not simple.

Flourens states that his pigeons, with two or more canals cut, continued to show the effects of the operation almost with the same intensity for nearly a year. Some unpublished experiments made in Dr. Howell's laboratory have given different results. Pigeons with only one canal cut recover practically completely within ten or more days. Those with two canals cut recover nearly completely within a month, so far as walking is concerned, although they exhibit an unwillingness to fly. Those with three or more canals cut never recover completely, but their final condition is very different from that exhibited shortly after the operation. Even when all six canals have been cut, the animal, if well cared for in the beginning, is able finally to stand and walk and feed itself. It is not able, however, to fly, and in walking its progress is uncertain; there is a tendency to walk zigzag or in circles, first to one side, then to the other. If hurried or excited some return of the violent movements of the head and incoordination of the movements of locomotion may be seen. If, instead of cutting the canals, the ampullae are destroyed, the initial effects of the operation seem to be less violent, owing possibly to the fact that in the former case the irritative effects of the lesion still have the end-organs in the ampullae to act upon. Pigeons with all six ampullae destroyed eventually may make an excellent recovery. Within a few months they walk and perch with little difficulty when not frightened. In the matter of flying they do not recover their former skill, but this may be due to lack of practice, since in the experiments quoted (Rosencrantz) no provision was made for exercise in flying. The very marked degree of recovery noted, even after loss of all six ampullae, seems to be due to the fact that the animal learns to use his other sensory data in coordinating his muscles. If after a nearly complete degree of recovery has taken place a new operation is performed in which the canals are cut, the resulting disturbance to motion is relatively small and soon passes off. That there is any effect at all from the second operation may be due to the emptying of the endolymph and the consequent effect upon the remaining ampullae, or, if these had all been previously destroyed, to the effect upon the sense organs of the vestibular sacs.

THE SACCULE AND UTRICLE

McNally (10) has recently given a detailed critical summary of the vast and conflicting literature concerning the discrete functions of the various parts of the labyrinth. He draws attention to the work of Ross (11) who succeeded in recording action currents from individual fibers of the vestibular nerve, finding that the labyrinthine receptors can be divided into three groups, the first responding to slow mechanical vibration but not to tilting or to acceleration; the second and third groups of impulses owe their origin respectively to tilting movements (linear acceleration), and to rotatory movements. It is quite clear from evidence recounted above that the semicircular canals are stimulated by rotatory movements and probably not by gravity per se, since the cupula projecting from the floor of the ampulla would not respond to an increased gravitational force. The otolith organ in the utricle does respond both to linear acceleration and tilting, and McNally concludes that the utricle must be assigned this function since in frogs whose utricles have been destroyed without encroaching upon the semicircular canals the normal response to linear acceleration and tilting was abolished.

Evidence concerning the function of the *saccule* is also conflicting, but the consensus at the present time is that the saccule is not an essential part of the vestibular mechanism but rather an organ associated with the cochlea and designed for the reception of slow vibrational stimuli.

McNally concludes his review of vestibular function with a brief consideration of seasickness. Some individuals are susceptible primarily to linear acceleration, others to rotational acceleration. He draws the inference that the utricle is responsible for seasickness in individuals sensitive to linear acceleration (horizontal or vertical), and that the semicircular canals would be responsible for seasickness in those individuals susceptible to rotational acceleration.

THE MEDULLA OBLONGATA

In the medulla oblongata we must recognize a region of special physiological importance in that it is the seat of certain centers which control the activity of the circulatory and respiratory organs. If the medulla is severed from the portion of the brain lying anterior to it the animal continues to live for a considerable period. The respiratory movements are performed rhythmically, and the blood vessels retain their tone so as to maintain an approximately normal blood pressure. On the contrary, destruction of the medulla, or severance of its connections with the underlying parts, is followed by a cessation of respiration and a loss of tone in the arteries, either of which results in the rapid death of the organism as a whole. The portions of the medulla which exercise these important functions are designated, respectively, as the respiratory and the vasomotor or vasoconstrictor centers. Their location and to some extent their connections have been determined by physiological experiments, the most important being the recent studies of Pitts (Chap. 41). The position and physiological properties of these centers are described in the sections on respiration and circulation. These centers are of especial importance because of their wide connections with the body, their essentially independent activity in reference to the higher parts of the brain, and the absolutely necessary character of the regulations they effect. In the development of the brain the functions originally mediated by the lower parts have been transferred more and more to the higher parts, especially in regard to conscious sensation and motion, and the so-called higher psychical activities. But the unconscious and involuntary regulation of the organs of circulation and respiration and to a certain extent of the other visceral organs has been centralized, as it were, in the medulla. In addition to the control of the respiration and circulation other important reflex activities are effected through the medulla by means of the vagus nerve, which has its nucleus of origin in this part of the brain. Such, for instance, are the reflex control of the heart through the cardio-inhibitory center and the motions and secretions of the alimentary canal.

Nuclei of Origin and Functions of the Cranial Nerves. The origin, course, anatomical and physiological relations of the first or olfactory, second or optic, and eighth or auditory nerves are referred to elsewhere. For the sake of completeness the origin and functions of the other cranial nerves may be summarized briefly in this connection.

Third cranial nerve (n. oculomotorius). This nerve arises from the base of the brain on the median side of the corresponding pedunculus cerebri. It is, so far as is known, only a motor nerve, supplying fibers to four of the extrinsic muscles of the eyeballs—namely, the internal rectus, the superior rectus, the inferior rectus, and the inferior oblique—and to the levator palpebrae. It innervates also two important intrinsic muscles of the eyeball, the ciliary muscle used in accommodating the eye in near vision, and the sphincter of the iris, which controls in part the size of the pupil. These two latter muscles belong to the type of plain muscle, and the fibers of the third nerve which innervates them terminate in the ciliary ganglion, whence the path is con-

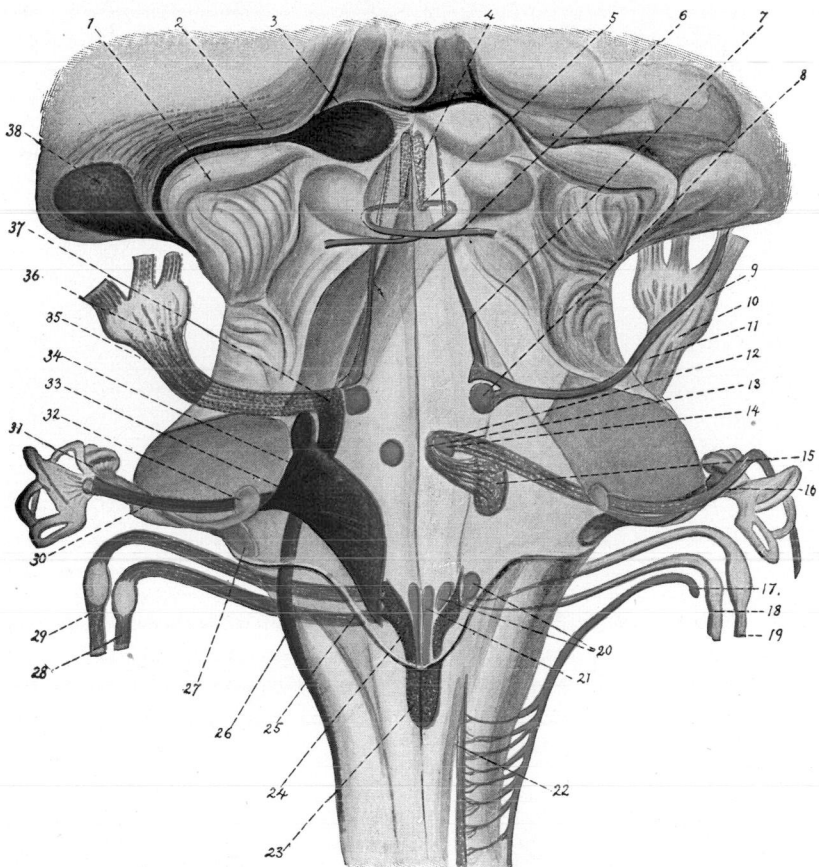

Fig. 121.—Nuclei of origin of cerebral nerves (*Held*): Schematically represented in a supposedly transparent brain stem viewed from behind. (Nuclei and roots of motor nerves in light red, of sensory nerves in purple. Cochlear nerve in yellow.) 4, nucleus of the third nerve (n. oculomotorii); 5, nucleus of the fourth nerve (n. trochlearis); 6, the fourth nerve; 7, the descending (motor) root of the fifth nerve; 8, the principal motor nucleus of the fifth nerve; 9, the semilunar ganglion (g. Gasseri); 26, the ascending (sensory) root of the fifth nerve; 14, nucleus of the sixth cranial nerve; 15, nucleus of the facial (seventh) nerve; 16, the facial nerve; 33, 34, nucleus of the vestibular branch of the eighth cranial nerve; 32, ventral nucleus of the cochlear branch of the eighth nerve; 27, dorsal nucleus of the cochlear branch of the eighth nerve; 19, 29, the glossopharyngeal nerve; 18, 28, the vagus nerve; 20, motor nuclei of vagus and glossopharyngeal (nucleus ambiguus and nuclear dorsalis); 23, 24, nucleus of the alae cinereae, the solitary bundle and its nucleus; 17, the eleventh or spinal accessory nerve; 22, nucleus of the spinal accessory; 21, nucleus of the hypoglossal nerve. (From Spalteholz, *Human anatomy*.)

tinued by autonomic nerve fibers (postganglionic fibers) to the muscles. In the interior of the brain the fibers of the third nerve arise from a conspicuous nucleus or collection of nuclei situated in the central gray matter of the midbrain at the level of the superior colliculus. The fibers for the ciliary muscle and sphincter pupillae arise more anteriorly than those for the extrinsic muscles. Histologically three parts at least may be distinguished, as shown in Figure 122, i. e. the lateral (or principal) nucleus, which gives origin chiefly to the fibers innervating the extrinsic muscles; the median nucleus; and the

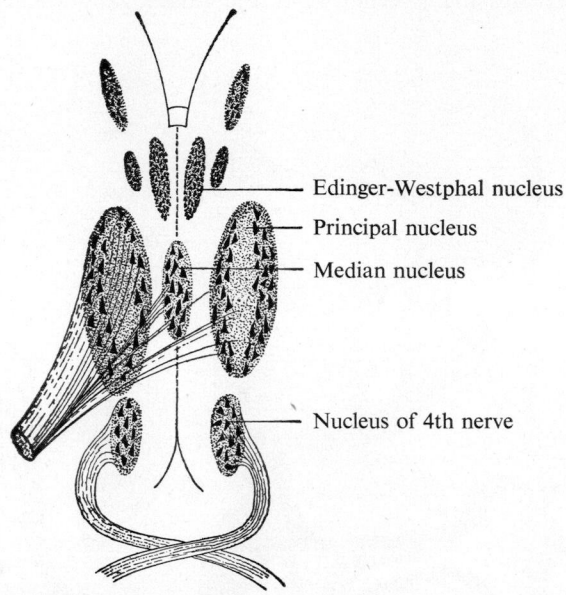

Edinger-Westphal nucleus

Principal nucleus

Median nucleus

Nucleus of 4th nerve

Fig. 122.—Nuclei of origin of the third and fourth nerves. (From Poirier and Charpy.)

nucleus of Edinger-Westphal. The large median nucleus gives rise to the fibers that innervate the ciliary muscles, while the Edinger-Westphal nuclei (accessory nuclei) control the movements of the sphincter muscle of the iris. Some

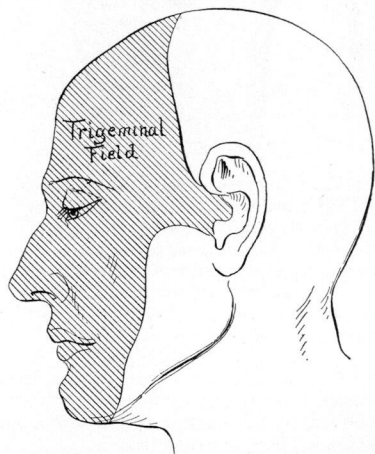

Fig. 123.—Diagram showing the average area of distribution of the sensory fibers of the trigemina nerve. (After Cushing.)

of the fibers, particularly those from the lateral nucleus to the inferior rectus, the internal rectus, and the inferior oblique, cross the midline and emerge in the nerve of the opposite side.

Fourth cranial nerve (n. trochlearis). This nerve emerges from the brain in the anterior medullary velum (valve of Vieussens) just posterior to the inferior colliculus. It curves around the pedunculus cerebri to reach the base of the brain. It is a motor nerve, and supplies fibers to the superior oblique muscle of the eyeball. In the interior of the brain the fibers arise from a nucleus in the central gray matter just posterior to that of the third nerve (Fig. 122). The fibers pass dorsalward toward the velum and make a complete decussation before emerging.

Fifth cranial nerve (n. trigeminus). This nerve arises from the side of the pons by two roots, a small motor root, portio minor, and a large sensory root, portio major. It is, therefore, a mixed motor and sensory nerve, supplying motor fibers to the muscles of mastication and sensory fibers of pressure, pain, and temperature to the face, the forepart of the scalp, the eye, nose, portions of the ear, mouth, and tongue, and to the dura mater (Fig. 123). In the interior

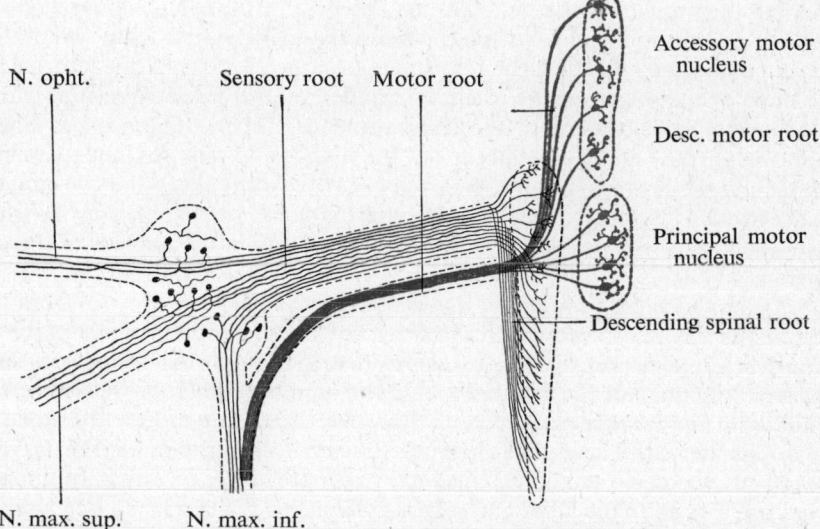

Fig. 124.—Nuclei of origin of the fifth cranial nerve. (From Poirier and Charpy, after Van Gehuchten.)

of the brain the motor portion, portio minor, arises partly from a small nucleus in the pons and partly from a long column of cells extending along the lower margin of the central gray matter throughout the midbrain. This column and the fibers arising from it constitute the descending motor root of the fifth nerve (see Fig. 124). The sensory fibers originate from the nerve cells in the Gasserian ganglion (g. semilunare). The branch that enters the brain ends partly in a collection of cells in the pons, the so-called sensory nucleus, and partly in a column of cells extending posteriorly throughout the length of the medulla. These cells and the fibers ending in them constitute the descending spinal root of the fifth nerve (see Fig. 124).

Sixth cranial nerve (n. abducens). This nerve arises from the base of the brain at the posterior edge of the pons. It is a motor nerve, and supplies fibers to the external rectus muscle of the eyeball. In the interior of the brain its fibers originate in a small spherical nucleus lying beneath the floor of the fourth ventricle. Connections have been traced between this nucleus and the pyramidal tract of the opposite side (Fig. 121).

Seventh cranial nerve (n. facialis). This nerve appears on the base of the brain at the inferior margin of the pons, lateral and somewhat posterior to the emergence of the sixth nerve. It is mainly a motor nerve, but carries some sensory fibers (fibers of taste and general sensibility) received through the n. intermedius of Wrisberg. The motor fibers of the nerve supply the muscles of the face, part of the scalp, and the ear, including its intrinsic muscles, and in addition secretory fibers are supplied to the submaxillary and sublingual glands. Within the brain these fibers arise from a conspicuous nucleus in the tegmental region of the pons lying ventral to the nucleus of the sixth, beneath the middle of the fourth ventricle (Fig. 121). The sensory fibers of the nerve of Wrisberg originate in the nerve cells of the geniculate ganglion.

Ninth cranial nerve (n. glossopharyngeus). This nerve arises from the side of the medulla—the restiform body. It is a mixed nerve, supplying motor fibers to the muscles of the pharynx and the base of the tongue and secretory fibers to the parotid gland. Within the brain these fibers arise from two motor nuclei common to this and the tenth nerve, namely, a dorsal nucleus below the floor of the fourth ventricle and a smaller ventral nucleus, n. ambiguus, in the reticular substance of the tegmentum (Fig. 121). The sensory fibers supply in part the mucous membrane of the tongue and pharynx, the tympanic cavity, and the Eustachian tube. These fibers arise from cells in the two ganglia on the trunk of the nerve, the ganglion superius and g. petrosum. The branches from these cells that pass into the medulla terminate in the nucleus of the ala cinerea.

Tenth cranial nerve (n. vagus or pneumogastricus). This nerve arises from the side of the medulla posterior to the origin of the glossopharyngeal nerve. It is also a mixed nerve, with an extensive distribution to the respiratory and digestive organs and the heart. Its efferent or motor fibers arise within the brain from the same masses of cells that give rise to the motor fibers of the glossopharyngeal. These fibers supply the intrinsic muscles of the larynx, esophagus, stomach, small intestine, and part of the large intestine. Inhibitory fibers are carried to the heart and secretory fibers to the gastric and pancreatic glands. Its sensory or afferent fibers are distributed to the mucous membrane of the larynx, trachea, and lungs, and to the mucous membrane of the esophagus, stomach, intestines, and gallbladder and ducts. These fibers arise from cells in the ganglia on the trunk of the nerve, the ganglion jugulare and g. nodosum. The branches from these cells that pass into the medulla terminate in the gray matter of the ala cinerea.

Eleventh cranial nerve (n. accessorius). This nerve is usually described as arising by upper roots from the medulla, and by a series of lower roots from the spinal cord as low as the fifth to the seventh cervical segment. It is a motor nerve, supplying fibers to the sternomastoid and trapezius muscles. The medullary branches arise from the posterior portion of the dorsal motor nucleus which gives origin to the vagus, while the spinal branches originate from cells in the anterior horn of the gray matter of the cord (Fig. 121).

Twelfth cranial nerve (n. hypoglossus). This nerve arises from the medulla in the furrow between the anterior pyramid and the olivary body. It is a motor nerve, supplying the muscles of the tongue and the extrinsic muscles of the larynx and hyoid bone. Within the brain these fibers originate from a distinct nucleus lying in the floor of the fourth ventricle near the midline (Fig. 121).

REFERENCES

1. BÁRÁNY, R. Die modernen Untersuchungsmethoden des Vestibularapparates und ihre praktische Bedeutung. *Med. Klinik*, 1908, *4:*1903–1905.

2. CAMIS, M. *The physiology of the vestibular apparatus*, trans. R. S. Creed, London, Oxford University Press, 1930, xiv, 310 pp.

3. DOHLMAN, G. Some practical and theoretical points in labyrinthology. *Proc. R. Soc. Med.*, 1935, *28:*1371–1380.

4. DOHLMAN, G. Towards a method for quantitative measurement of the functional capacity of the vestibular apparatus. *Acta otolaryng., Stockh.*, 1935–36, *23:*50–62.

5. FLOURENS, P. *Recherches expérimentales sur les propriétés et les fonctions du système nerveux dans les animaux vertébrés.* Paris, Crevot, 1824, xxvi, 332 pp.

6. LÖWENSTEIN, O., and SAND, A. The mechanism of the semicircular canal. A study of the responses of single-fibre preparations to angular accelerations and to rotation at constant speed. *Proc. roy. Soc.*, 1940, *129B:*256–275.

7. LORENTE DE NÓ, R. Researches on labyrinth reflexes. *Trans. Amer. otol. Soc.*, 1932, *22:*287–303.

8. LORENTE DE NÓ, R. Vestibulo-ocular reflex arc. *Arch. Neurol. Psychiat., Chicago*, 1933, *30:*245–291.

9. LORENTE DE NÓ, R. Observations on nystagmus. *Acta oto-laryng.*, 1933, *18:*187–189.

10. McNALLY, W. J., and STUART, E. A. Physiology of the labyrinth reviewed in relation to seasickness and other forms of motion sickness. *War Medicine*, 1942, *2:*683–771.

10a. McNALLY, W. J. Physiology of the ear and its clinical interpretation. In: McNALLY, W. J., and ANDREWS, A. H., Jr. *Physiology of the ear—nose—throat.* [St. Louis], American Academy of Ophthalmology and Otolaryngology, 1944. 39 pp.

11. ROSS, D. A. Electrical studies on the frog's labyrinth. *J. Physiol.*, 1936, *86:*117–146.

12. SPIEGEL, E. The cortical centers of the labyrinth. *J. nerv. ment. Dis.*, 1932, *75:*504–512.

13. SPIEGEL, E. A. Labyrinth and cortex. The electroencephalogram of the cortex in the stimulation of the labyrinth. *Arch. Neurol. Psychiat., Chicago*, 1934, *31:*469–482.

14. STEINHAUSEN, W. Ueber den experimentellen Nachweis der Ablenkung der Cupula terminalis in der intakten Bogengangsampulle des Labyrinths bei der thermischen und adäquaten rotatorischen Reizung. *Z. Hals-Nas.-u. Ohrenheilk.*, 1931, *29:*211–216.

CHAPTER 10

AUTONOMIC NERVOUS SYSTEM: PERIPHERAL DIVISION

by Robert Gordon Grenell

The nervous system has two primary divisions of motor outflow: (i) the somatic which presides over reflex and volitional activities of skeletal muscle, and (ii) the autonomic which innervates smooth or involuntary muscle and glands. Both divisions are governed by the central nervous system and both have widespread peripheral ramifications. The present chapter will be concerned with the *peripheral* autonomic division which emerges from the brain and spinal cord via a system of *"preganglionic"* fibers which, unlike the emergent neurons of the somatic division, establish connection with postganglionic fibers lying outside the spinal cord. The next chapter will deal with the *central* organization of the autonomic system.

Historical note (41). The first definitive description of the sympathetic ganglion chain and its connections with the spinal cord was that of Willis (1664). Since these connections were found "near the roots of the ribs," he named the chain the "intercostal" nerve. He also described cardiac branches and the celiac plexus, noting that the latter sent out its nerve fibers like sun rays, a simile which has given rise to the name "solar plexus." Willis noted the separate course of the vagus nerve and sympathetic chain, but subscribed to the intracranial origin of the latter. This question of the origin of the sympathetic trunks was finally settled in 1727 by Pourfour du Petit who cut the so-called "intercostal" nerve in the neck and observed the resultant disturbances in the ipsilateral eye and face; he was the first to describe pupillary paralysis and ptosis following cervical sympathectomy—a syndrome now associated with the name of J. F. Horner. The Danish anatomist, Winslow, supported (1732) Petit's conclusions, and proposed changing the name "intercostal" to "great sympathetic" nerve.

Work on the autonomic nervous system was vigorously pursued during the nineteenth century. Xavier Bichat, French anatomist and physiologist (1771–1802), discussed nervous regulation of "la vie organique" and "la vie animale"—the earliest recognition of the distinction between visceral and somatic function. Unfortunately he was unaware of the significance of the rami communicantes and hence allotted to the sympathetic ganglia much greater independence of the spinal cord than actually exists. Several anatomical observations made at this period had far-reaching results. Ehrenberg (1833) described cell bodies in the sympathetic ganglia; Remak (1854) noted the existence of unmyelinated fibers; and Beck (1846) made distinction between the white and gray rami. The disclosure of Johannes Müller (1840) that skeletal muscle differed structurally from the visceral "smooth" muscle, and the findings of von Kölliker (1849) and Henle (1868), who noted respectively the muscular media of the arteries and its innervation by a periarterial sympathetic plexus, cleared the way for the discovery of the vasomotor nerves by Claude Bernard (1851) and Brown-Séquard (1852). Bernard's investigations led him to formulate several historic concepts: the "milieu intérieur" with its hypothesis of nervous regulation of internal conditions of the animal organism; the suggestion that vasomotor fibers arise in the thoracic levels of the spinal cord; and overthrow of the theory of independence of the sympathetic system originated by Bichat.

With the investigations of the Webers (1845—disclosing vagal inhibition), of Ludwig (1851—on salivary secretion from stimulation of the chorda tympani), and of Budge and Waller (1851—innervation of the eye), the ground was laid for the classical studies of Gaskell and Langley. Their researches form the basis of the present-day concept of the autonomic nervous system. By means of the osmic acid technique, Gaskell investigated the

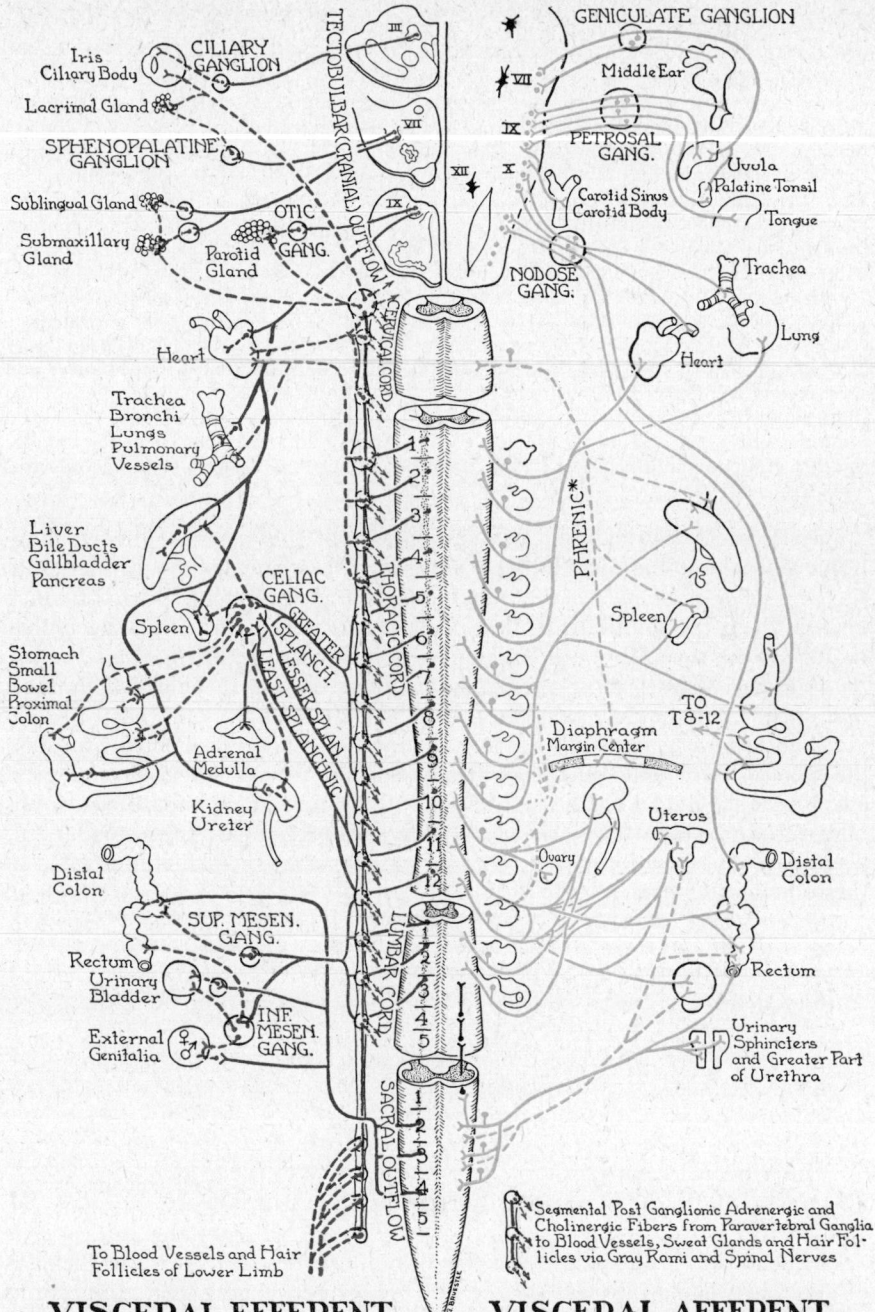

VISCERAL EFFERENT   VISCERAL AFFERENT

Fig. 125.—The visceral nervous system. Blue = cholinergic; red = adrenergic; green = visceral afferent; ———— = preganglionic (efferent); - - - - = postganglionic (efferent). The asterisk on the plate indicates that although some afferent fibers from the viscera are present in the phrenic nerve, it is a mixed nerve, not usually included as part of the autonomic system. Afferent fibers from the borders of the diaphragm have been drawn in broken lines, since the diaphragm is a somatic structure although it lies in the visceral cavity.

peripheral autonomic plexuses and described the bulbar, thoracolumbar and sacral out-flows. These observations suggested to him the term "involuntary nervous system" (1916) which he defined as a "system of motor nerve cells to involuntary structures." Langley's final formulation of his concept of the two divisions of the autonomic nervous system was the result of two prior discoveries—those of Hirschmann and of Oliver and Schäfer. Hirschmann (1863) demonstrated that moderate doses of nicotine abolished the pupillary reaction to stimulation of the cervical sympathetic nerve. Langley and Dickinson extended this investigation, finding that they could induce pupillary dilatation after nicotinization when they stimulated the sympathetic trunk above the superior cervical ganglion, thus disclosing that nicotine paralyzes cells in the sympathetic ganglia; from this they proceeded through local application of nicotine to map out the position of the cell stations and dis-tribution of autonomic neurons, which, in 1893, Langley designated "preganglionic" and "postganglionic." In 1898 he formulated the term "autonomic nervous system" which included the cranial, thoracolumbar and sacral divisions. The second part of Langley's concept followed the discovery of adrenaline by Oliver and Schäfer in 1894. The similarity of its action to that of sympathetic stimulation was recognized almost immediately; and soon thereafter Langley observed that its effects were confined to areas innervated by the thoracolumbar outflow. The effects produced by stimulation of the cranial and sacral outflows were simulated by drugs such as pilocarpine, and with this in mind, Langley in 1905 grouped the craniosacral fibers together as the "parasympathetic nervous sys-tem" (25, 26, 41, 42).

Physiological and anatomical investigations of the origin of the pregang-lionic fibers thus indicate that the autonomic system may be divided into (i) the *cranial autonomic* (*parasympathetic*), the preganglionic fibers of which emerge from the midbrain in the third cranial nerve, and from the bulbar region in the seventh, ninth and tenth nerves; (ii) the *thoracolumbar auto-nomic* (*sympathetic*), whose preganglionic fibers emerge through the thoracic and upper lumbar spinal ganglia of the sympathetic chain; and (iii) the *sacral autonomic* (*parasympathetic*), the preganglionic fibers of which emerge through the second, third and fourth sacral nerves (Fig. 125). In their physiological and pharmacological reactions, the sympathetic and parasympathetic groups offer certain contrasts. For this and other reasons Langley suggested a com-prehensive classification based on anatomical grounds which is illustrated in the following schema:

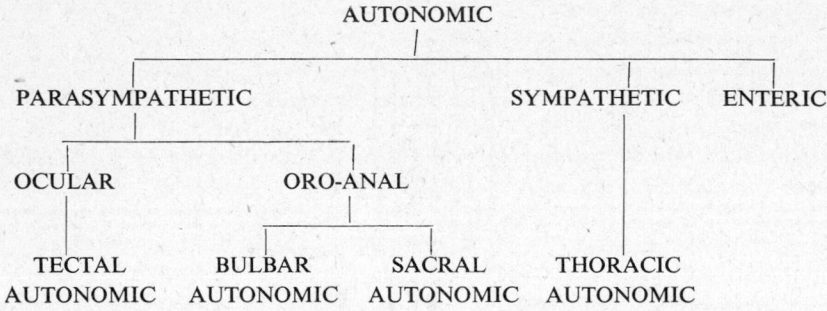

The "enteric" group comprised the system forming the extensive plexuses of Auerbach and Meissner; lack of knowledge concerning their connections caused Langley to set them aside as a separate group. His classification, how-ever, can be further simplified. The essential organization of the autonomic system is set down in Table 8 in a way which emphasizes its basic relation-ship to the central nervous structures.

Table 8.—Autonomic Nervous System

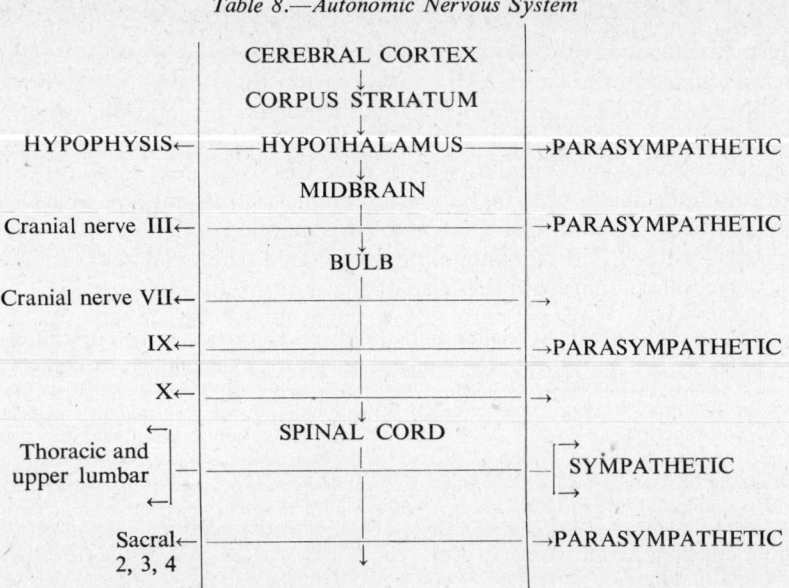

Certain aspects of the embryology of the autonomic system are essential to an understanding of its function (5,9). The anlage of the sympathetic nerves and ganglia appear early in embryonic life as cell masses migrating from the neural tube. These cell masses have been followed through the ventral roots to the sympathetic trunks and from the trunks into the developing networks of abdominal visceral plexuses. A similar cell migration is responsible for the development of the adrenal medulla, i.e., chromaffin tissue is made up of modified postganglionic neurons. The autonomic system is thus derived in its entirety from the cells of the central nervous system; the embryonic migrating cells divide and form the visceral plexuses, and there is, therefore, no basic difference between autonomic and cerebrospinal neurons.

Both the sympathetic and parasympathetic peripheral pathways are characterized by two major points of difference from the somatic: (i) *by having synaptic connections situated in peripherally located ganglia which lie outside the central nervous system,* and (ii) *by the formation of peripheral plexuses— networks absent in the somatic system.* Each pathway contains one synapse, connecting pre- and postganglionic neurons. In the sympathetic division, each preganglionic fiber bifurcates in such a way that synaptic relationship is established with many postganglionic neurons. This diffuse contact forms the anatomical basis for widespread, massive sympathetic responses of the body. The parasympathetic fibers form synapses in ganglia located in greater proximity to the organ to be innervated, as well as in the walls of the organs themselves, and thus establish synaptic relationship with a much smaller number of postganglionic neurons. This permits highly localized, discrete responses of single organs. Ranson and Billingsley determined the ratio of preganglionic to postganglionic neurons in the superior cervical ganglion (sympathetic) of the cat as 1:32; Wolf later found it to be 1:15. He also reported the ratio in the ciliary ganglion (parasympathetic) as about 1:2.

Thoracolumbar division (sympathetic)

The sympathetic division of the autonomic nervous system takes origin in neurons situated in the lateral cell column of the spinal cord in the thoracic and upper two or three lumbar segments. The fibers in question, which are "preganglionic," pass via the ventral nerve roots and spinal nerves to group themselves into discrete bundles which leave the spinal nerves as the white "rami communicantes." Through the white rami the preganglionic fibers enter the sympathetic ganglion chain to establish synaptic connection with "post-ganglionic"* fibers. The sympathetic ganglionated trunk runs on either side of the vertebral column from the base of the skull to the coccyx.

The sympathetic chains lie in relation to the transverse processes in the cervical region, to the heads of the ribs in the thorax, and to the surfaces of the lumbar vertebrae. Each spinal nerve has a corresponding ganglion. The three ganglia in the cervical region (probably formed by fusion of eight original ganglia) are named the *superior, middle and inferior cervical.* The superior ganglion is the largest—a fusiform structure lying near the second and third cervical vertebrae, which gives rise to the sympathetic supply to the head. The sheath of the internal carotid artery, internal jugular vein, and vagus nerve lies in front of it. It is connected inferiorly by the cervical sympathetic trunk with the middle cervical ganglion. The middle cervical ganglion may or may not be present. The inferior cervical ganglion, usually placed at the level of the eighth cervical vertebra (or between the last cervical and first thoracic vertebrae), is connected with the middle ganglion in two ways: by the sympathetic trunk and by filaments passing to the ansa subclavia. It (the inferior ganglion) is often fused with the first thoracic ganglion into a dumb-bell shaped structure called the *stellate ganglion.* The remaining thoracic, lumbar and sacral ganglia are small, variable and segmentally arranged.

In addition to the chain ganglia described above, there are two other groups of sympathetic ganglia, the *prevertebral* or *collateral,* and the *terminal* or *peripheral* ganglia. The prevertebral ganglia form several masses lying in the mesenteric plexuses around the visceral aortic branches, namely, the celiac, superior mesenteric, aorticorenal and inferior mesenteric ganglia. The celiac ganglia are situated on either side of the celiac artery and are connected by several delicate strands.

According to Sheehan (43), the level of preganglionic outflow differs in different animals (Table 9).

Table 9.—*Usual Arrangement of Thoracolumbar and Sacral Outflows in Man and Common Laboratory Animals (Sheehan, 1941)*

	THOROCOLUMBAR OUTFLOW	SACRAL OUTFLOW
Man	T1 − L2	S3 + S4
Monkey	T1 or T2 − L3 or L4	S1 + S2 + S3
Dog	T1 or T2 − L4	S1 + S2 + S3
Cat	T1 or T2 − L4	S1 + S2 + S3
Rabbit	T1 − L5	S2 + S3 + S4

The preganglionic fibers which have traveled out along ventral roots leave the *spinal nerve* (and not the ventral root) at a point just distal to the junction of the gray ramus with the spinal nerve. The preganglionic fibers may terminate (i.e., form synapses) in the corresponding ganglion, or may run through this ganglion to establish synapses in ganglia elsewhere in the chain, or in one of the prevertebral ganglia. The white rami are specifically termed "white" because of the myelinization of the fibers in contrast to the darker, for the most part unmyelinated, *postganglionic* fibers.

* In only one instance does a preganglionic fiber go directly to the organ it supplies; that is in the case of the adrenal medulla which is innervated by preganglionic and not postganglionic fibers. There may be a few preganglionics which run directly into the plexuses of Auerbach and Meissner in the wall of the intestine.

The cells of the vertebral and prevertebral sympathetic ganglia give rise to the postganglionic fibers which run to smooth muscle, cardiac muscle, or glands, in spinal or cranial nerves or along blood vessels as a perivascular network. On leaving the sympathetic chain they unite into bundles that connect the ganglia with the corresponding segmental nerves. The fibers, being

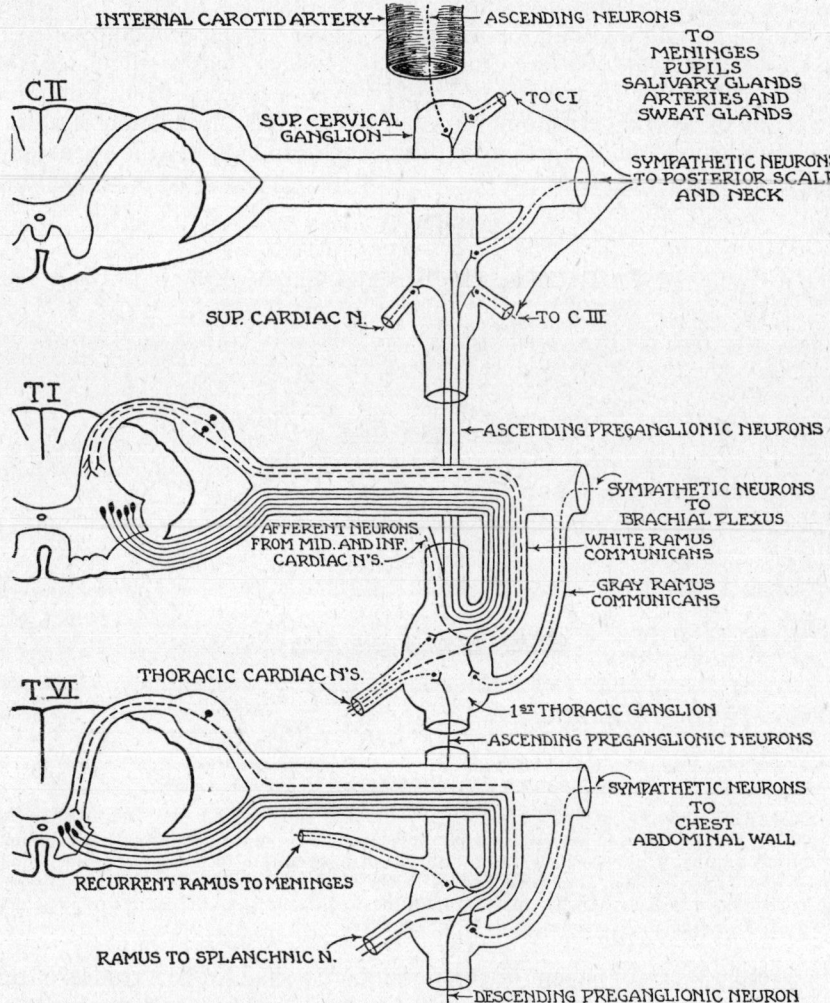

Fig. 126.—The visceral reflex arc. ——— = preganglionic; - - - - = postganglionic; - - - - = visceral afferent. (Redrawn from White and Smithwick, *The autonomic nervous system*, 2nd ed. The Macmillan Company, 1941, p. 36.)

dark and largely unmyelinated, form the gray rami communicantes. Four general types of rami communicantes are recognized: one filled with myelinated fibers of all sizes termed the white ramus; two other types, representing variations of the gray ramus, composed of unmyelinated fibers with varying amounts of myelinated fibers; the fourth type mixed, with areas of "gray" and "white" in the same bundle. *Gray rami pass to every spinal nerve, while the white rami (of which there are 14 or 15) are restricted to the segments of the thoracolumbar outflow* (Figs. 125 and 126; also Fig. 133 below).

In a discussion of the connections to spinal nerves one must consider the sympathetic system in relation to the segmentation of the body. The spinal nerves have a primarily segmental distribution corresponding to their segmental origin from the cord. The segmental cutaneous area of distribution of any one nerve is always overlapped by areas of innervation of the nerves arising from the cord just above or below it. These segmental cutaneous areas are known as *dermatomes* (see Chap. 17). If a white ramus is stimulated, the resultant pilomotor responses can be seen over a comparatively wide area comprised of several dermatomes. As opposed to this, stimulation of a gray ramus results in pilomotor activity in the area corresponding to the dermatome innervated by that nerve.

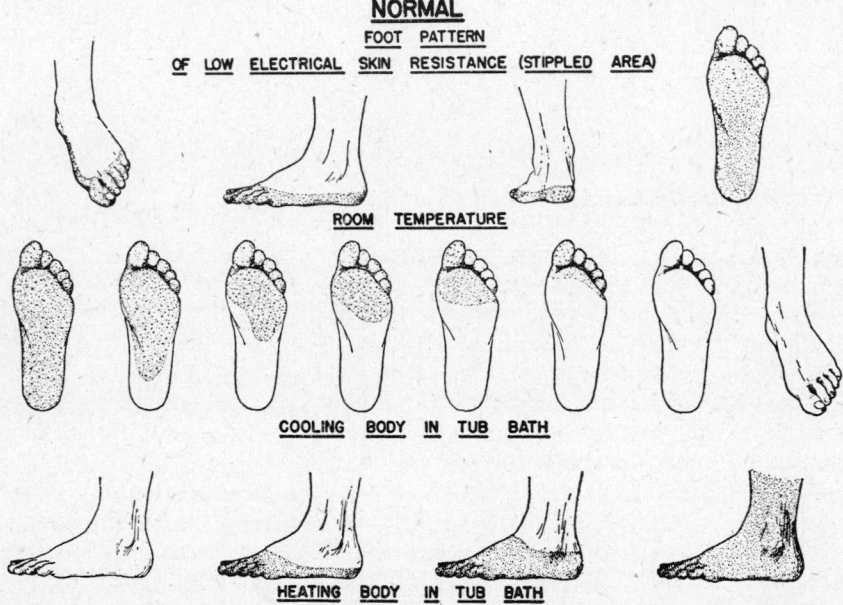

Fig. 127.—Foot patterns of low electrical skin resistance: at room temperature; during cooling; and during heating. The normal distribution at room temperature includes the entire plantar surface, and a narrow band, about one inch in width, which runs around the foot laterally and up over the dorsal surface to include part or all of the dorsal surface of the toes. (From Richter, Woodruff and Eaton, *J. Neurophysiol.*, 1943, 6:420.)

In a recent series of papers, Richter and his associates report studies of the patterns of electrical skin resistance of the body (37,38,39) that show that sympathectomized areas on any part of the body can be sharply defined by this method. These areas do not sweat and have a higher resistance than the surrounding normal areas. In sympathectomized patients these patterns of high skin resistance agree closely with the distribution of the sensory dermatomes and are clearly demonstrated after the entire body has been heated; the temperature used is that which, in the normal person, causes a general decrease in skin resistance to a low level, with the disappearance of all patterns.

At room temperature, most normal individuals show well-defined areas of low resistance on the face, hands, feet, axillae and antecubital fossae. Cooling and sleep cause marked constriction of the face area to a small region which finally includes only the lips. The patterns of the areas of low skin resistance coincide closely with the patterns of areas of remaining sensitivity found on the faces of patients with syringobulbia, and, like them, vary concentrically around the mouth. Under normal conditions (room, temperature etc.), the hands and feet have sharply defined areas of low electrical skin resistance. On the hands, these patterns include the entire palmar surface up to the line which divides the dorsal and ventral parts of the hand. On the feet, the areas of low electrical skin resistance usually include the entire plantar surface, and a small band along the side of the foot and over the toes. On both hands and feet there is close correspondence between the most common patterns of low skin resistance and the porous areas of the skin—the areas having a rich supply of sweat glands. There appears to be little relation between the resistance patterns and the distribution of the blood vessels. However, a distinct similarity exists between these skin patterns and patterns of hair distribution.

Observations on some fifty cases having upper thoracic or lumbar sympathectomies failed to disclose an instance of low resistance in either hands or feet. This indicates at least partial dependence of these areas on sympathetic innervation of the extremities. This conclusion is further substantiated by the fact that the hand and foot patterns are enlarged during sympathetic activation (emotional excitement, etc.), and become constricted consequent to sympathetic inhibition. *These skin patterns do not coincide with the distribution of any of the segmental nerves, but may correspond more nearly with the distribution of sympathetic nerve patterns from cerebral cortical or subcortical areas.*

Craniosacral division (parasympathetic)

The arrangement of fiber connections of the craniosacral outflow differs from that of the thoracolumbar. The somata of the preganglionic fibers do not form a single continuous column such as exists in the sympathetic division but occur in groups at various levels of the neuraxis. Further, the synaptic connections between the pre- and postganglionic fibers lie close to or within the walls of the structures to be innervated. The four levels of outflow are as follows.

Hypothalamic outflow. From the hypothalamic level, preganglionic fibers emerge via the pituitary stalk to innervate the posterior lobe of the pituitary gland. These fibers arise in the hypothalamus from the paraventricular, supraoptic and other nuclear areas concerned with autonomic integrations (Chap. 11).

Tectal outflow. The Edinger-Westphal nucleus lies close to the midline beneath the aqueduct of Sylvius. Its neurons are intimately concerned with pupillary constrictor activity. The fibers join the oculomotor nerve to make synaptic connections in the ciliary ganglion.

Bulbar outflow. Lying in the floor of the fourth ventricle are the salivatory nucleus, the dorsal motor nucleus of the vagus, and the facial visceral motor nucleus (see Chap. 9, Fig. 121). Fibers from these cell groups innervate thoracic and abdominal viscera, salivary and lacrimal glands. In close proximity to these nuclei are two important reflex centers, the vasomotor and the respiratory.

Sacral outflow. The sacral preganglionic fibers arise from the third and fourth, and in many cases, the second and fifth sacral segments of the spinal cord. Their initial course is similar to that of the previously described preganglionics. After leaving the spinal nerves the fibers form the *nervi erigentes**

* The term *nervi erigentes* derives from the observation that stimulation of the pelvic nerve in the male causes active dilation of the vessels of the corpora cavernosa, with consequent erection of the penis. Ejaculation, for which erection is not prerequisite, results from stimulation of sympathetic fibers (coursing through the hypogastric plexus) which brings about contraction of the muscular walls of the seminal vesicles and ejaculatory ducts.

or pelvic nerves, which scatter to pass through the pelvic plexuses to terminal ganglia in the walls of the pelvic viscera. From these ganglia postganglionic fibers course directly to the prostate gland, the seminal vesicles, the external genitalia, the bladder, the descending colon and rectum. In the female these fibers extend to the uterus and vagina, oviduct and ovary. In both male and female this postganglionic supply also innervates the blood vessels of the pelvic organs (including the generative organs—in the male, stimulation of the pelvic nerves produces erection of the penis; in the female, these vasodilator fibers supply the clitoris and labia minora).

OUTLINE OF AUTONOMIC INNERVATION OF INDIVIDUAL VISCERA

Lacrimal Glands

Parasympathetic. *Preganglionic neurons:* Leave the brain in the facial nerve, but from the geniculate ganglion on travel as part of the great superficial petrosal and Vidian nerves to the sphenopalatine ganglion. *Postganglionic neurons:* Fibers arising in the sphenopalatine ganglion run in a branch of the maxillary division of the trigeminal nerve to the lacrimal gland. Some fibers also run to the gland in the ophthalmic division of V.
Function: Vasodilatation and stimulation of secretion.
Sympathetic. *Preganglionic neurons:* From intermediolateral cell column of the spinal cord ascend the sympathetic chain to the superior cervical ganglion. *Postganglionic neurons:* Fibers arising in the superior cervical ganglion ascend through the carotid plexus and run the terminal part of their path with the parasympathetic fibers in the deep petrosal and Vidian nerves.
Function: Vasoconstriction.

Salivary Glands

Parasympathetic. *Preganglionic neurons:* Cells of origin in the superior salivatory and inferior salivatory nuclei. Fibers from the superior nucleus run in the nervus intermedius of VII → main trunk of the facial nerve (VII) → chorda tympani → lingual nerve → submaxillary and sublingual ganglia. Fibers from the inferior nucleus run in the glossopharyngeal nerve (IX) → tympanic branch (of Jacobson) → lesser superficial petrosal nerve → otic ganglion. *Postganglionic neurons:* Run to the submaxillary and sublingual glands, and by way of the auriculotemporal nerve (V) to the parotid gland.
Function: Vasodilation and salivary secretion.
Sympathetic. *Preganglionic neurons:* Same as for the lacrimal gland. *Postganglionic neurons:* Fibers from the superior cervical ganglion ascend along plexuses on the external carotid and maxillary arteries to the glands.
Function: Vasoconstrictor and secretory.

Heart

Parasympathetic. *Preganglionic neurons:* Arise in the dorsal motor nucleus of the vagus (X) nerve and terminate in ganglia of the cardiac plexus or in the auricular walls. *Postganglionic neurons:* Run along the coronary arteries from the intrinsic ganglia to auricular muscle, to the sino-auricular node (chiefly right ventricle) and to the auriculoventricular bundle (chiefly left ventricle). (Some afferent fibers from the cardiac ganglia run in the depressor part of the vagus nerve.)
Function: Cardiac inhibition and *probable coronary artery constriction.*
Sympathetic. *Preganglionic neurons:* Fibers arise from the intermediolateral cell column of the spinal cord and form two groups, one terminating in upper thoracic chain ganglia, the other ascending to synapse in the cervical ganglia. *Postganglionic neurons:* One group arises in the thoracic ganglia; a second group in the cervical ganglia. Both run as superior, middle, inferior and thoracic cardiac nerves, to form the superficial and deep cardiac plexuses. Afferent, sensory fibers (cell bodies in the upper thoracic dorsal root ganglia) run in the middle, inferior and thoracic cardiac nerves. Their cardiac terminations are found in the pericardium, heart wall, and walls of the aorta and coronary vessels. The afferent fibers of the ventricles are primarily concerned with cardiac and vascular reflexes.
Function: Cardiac acceleration, *coronary artery dilation,* and conduction of cardiac pain.

Lungs

Parasympathetic. *Preganglionic neurons:* From the vagi and run to the hilus of the lung. *Postganglionic neurons:* In the anterior and posterior pulmonary plexuses.

Sympathetic. *Preganglionic neurons:* From the intermediolateral cell column of the spinal cord—upper 3 or 4 thoracic segments to thoracic and inferior cervical chain ganglia. *Postganglionic neurons:* From thoracic ganglia and inferior cervical ganglion to the pulmonary plexuses.

Function: Stimulation of the thoracic sympathetic chain produces bronchodilatation as does section of the vagi, which demonstrates the parasympathetic tonic constrictor action on the bronchi. This constriction may be brought on by vagal stimulation or reflexly from irritation of the mucous membrane of the upper respiratory tract.

Esophagus

Parasympathetic. Supplied by the vagus nerves.
Function: Stimulation of contraction of the muscular wall.

Sympathetic. Supplied with motor and sensory nerves by thoracic fibers primarily from the fifth and sixth segments. The lower portion and the cardiac sphincter of the stomach are supplied by branches from the aortic plexus and the splanchnic nerves, which run through the celiac plexus and along the arterial branches.

Function: Stimulation of cardiac sphincter. Conduction of pain in sudden distension (44).

Abdominal Viscera

Parasympathetic. Fibers of the vagus nerves course through the preaortic plexuses *without synaptic connections*, to terminate in the intrinsic visceral plexuses, i.e., phrenic, adrenal, renal, spermatic or ovarian, gastric, hepatic, splenic and superior mesenteric. In the intestinal wall they end around ganglion cells in the plexuses of Auerbach and Meissner. From the splenic flexure to the rectum the wall is supplied by the sacral parasympathetics.

Function: Stimulation of peristalsis, secretion and vasodilatation of the digestive glands. The vagi also carry afferent fibers. (According to White and Smithwick no pain sensation is carried in these sensory nerves.)

Sympathetic. Fibers from the lower 7 or 8 and upper lumbar segments pass through the chain ganglia and along the splanchnic nerves to terminate in cells of the preaortic ganglia. Postganglionic fibers from these ganglia accompany the blood vessels to the various viscera. In the case of the adrenal glands, the preganglionic axons terminate directly around the medullary cells. Afferent fibers follow courses similar to the above. Their cell bodies are in the lower 6 thoracic dorsal root ganglia.

Function: Inhibition of peristalsis, secretion, and vasoconstriction. The afferent fibers transmit reflex stimuli, sensation of nausea and pain of distension.

Pelvic Viscera

Fibers reach the viscera from the inferior mesenteric ganglia (fibers to the sigmoid colon and rectum) via the plexus; via the hypogastric plexuses; and via the pelvic splanchnics or nervi erigentes. These nerves all contain sensory fibers.

The ovary is said to have only sympathetic nerve supply but the uterus, tubes and testes are said to have parasympathetic innervation from the nervi erigentes. The functional significance of the parasympathetic innervation of the uterus is not clear. All erectile tissue, including clitoris and corpora spongiosa penis, has extensive innervation—as do the goblet cells responsible for the lubricant secretions of the genital tract.

Visceral afferents

Following Langley, it has been the tradition to regard the autonomic system as purely efferent, since he was of the opinion that the afferent neurons from the viscera were in essence the same as those of the somatic system. However, any part of the integrated nervous system of the body has the reflex arc as its functional basis. The reflex arc cannot exist without an afferent neuron. The visceral reflex arc therefore must have its sensory side; since the existence of these fibers is no longer doubted, the controversy from this point becomes essentially one of terminology or classification. The visceral afferent fibers are concerned with the conduction of impulses from the viscera to the brain and spinal cord. Many of these fibers are found in sympathetic and parasympathetic nerves. Anatomically, however, the visceral afferent neurons differ in no way from the homologous neurons of the somatic system. Their cell bodies lie in the dorsal root ganglia or in similar cranial ganglia such as the ganglion nodosum of the vagus nerve. They have no synapses in either sympathetic or spinal ganglia; nicotinization of the sympathetic ganglia is without influence on conduction of visceral afferent impulses. The central processes of these neurons establish connections with cells of the dorsal horn of the spinal cord; the peripheral processes run via the dorsal roots and autonomic nerves to the visceral tissues.

Some of the visceral afferent fibers mediate the sensation of pain; others take part in aortic, carotid sinus, vasomotor, visceromotor, viscerovisceral, viscerosomatic, viscerosensory (referred pain) and somatovisceral reflexes. They regulate interrelated visceral activities, and serve to protect the viscera from injury. These neurons are thus of prime importance, and to quote White and Smithwick (44),"A thorough understanding of the visceral sensory pathways is of the greatest practical importance to the neurosurgeon interested in the control of pain." Figure 125 diagrammatically presents some of the afferent connections.

NATURE OF AUTONOMIC ACTIVITY

Autonomic Regulation: General Principles. That the autonomic nervous system has also been designated as "visceral," "involuntary," etc., indicates that it subserves functions different from those mediated by somatic nerves. The autonomic nerves innervate smooth muscle throughout the body, cardiac muscle and glands; they are the regulators concerned with emergency mechanisms, with repair, and with preservation of constancy of the internal environment. The somatic nerves, on the other hand, control striated muscle and relate the organism to its external environment. When somatic nerves are severed, the muscles they innervate degenerate. Such degeneration does not usually occur following autonomic nerve section; the organs, deprived of autonomic innervation, remain morphologically and physiologically intact, but develop increased sensitivity to the neuro-endocrine secretions, adrenaline and acetylcholine. There are also metabolic differences between the somatic and autonomic systems, demonstrated to some degree by the much more marked susceptibility of the somatic system to anoxia and interruption of the blood supply.

Schwartz (40), by applying pressure on a completely deafferented limb, caused a decrease in skin resistance. He suggested a nervous pathway for this reflex, as follows: afferent fibers from the blood vessels course through a gray ramus to the stellate ganglion, and efferent sympathetic fibers leave the ganglion to supply peripheral structures. This pathway presupposes the existence of sympathetic sensory neurons with their cell bodies in autonomic ganglia as originally suggested by Dogiel (Kuntz). Following supposedly complete separation of the celiac ganglion from the central nervous system, stimulation of mesenteric nerves faradically or by iliac and colonic distention resulted in a reduction in the flow of bile (24). Conduction of impulses through the enteron was prevented by duodenal transection. The reaction could not be obtained after application of nicotine to the celiac ganglion. It appeared to be a definite autonomic reflex. Freund and Sheehan (14) also studied the problem, and concluded that the intestino-intestinal inhibitory reflex can be obtained after bilateral vagotomy, bilateral splanchnicotomy or bilateral abdominal sympathectomy, but is completely abolished by complete sympathectomy—"removal of both sympathetic chains from above the stellate ganglion down to the level of the brim of the pelvis." They did adduce evidence supporting the postulated reflexes through the decentralized celiac ganglia. More recently, however, Kuntz and Saccomanno (23) have re-examined the question and conclude: "Distention of the distal segment of the transected colon or direct faradic stimulation of its nerves has resulted in inhibition of motility in the proximal segment both before and after degeneration of the interrupted nerve fibers following decentralization of the inferior mesenteric ganglia. Distention of the ileum or direct faradic stimulation of mesenteric nerves, likewise, has resulted in inhibition of motility in a more proximal segment of the small intestine following decentralization of the celiac ganglia by removal of the spinal cord from the lower cervical region caudalward and section of the vagi. Demonstration of the intestino-intestinal inhibitory reflex in the large intestine following degeneration of the visceral afferent fibers which reach the colon via the inferior mesenteric plexus and the preganglionic fibers of spinal origin to the inferior mesenteric ganglia supports the assumption that true reflex connections are effected in the prevertebral ganglia."

Despite the evidence in favor of a true autonomic reflex, the name "autonomic" suggests, as Langley stated, "a much greater degree of independence of the central nervous system than in fact exists." Recent investigations have demonstrated representation of autonomic activity in somatic areas of the central nervous system and vice versa (18). These interrelationships have been discussed by Sheehan who concluded: "One is left with a concept of a single nervous system physiologically speaking, where visceral and somatic activities are closely integrated, and where each is probably under a certain control of the other" (see Chap. 11).

The autonomic system, then, may act independently of the somatic system, or may act in association with the somatic (Chap. 11). It can also supplement somatic function in such a way that the two become interdependent. The organism constantly reacts to changes in its external environment. Autonomic adjustments take place through cardiac, visceral and vascular response to probably every somatic activity no matter how slight, although this response is more marked, and thus more readily evoked during situations of stress or emergency.

Claude Bernard pointed out that the blood and lymph which bathe the cells of organisms constitute the "milieu interne" or internal environment. This internal environment, a product of the organism and controlled by it, has been termed the *fluid-matrix* by Cannon, who expressed the belief that the organism's freedom from disturbance "in spite of extensive changes in the outer world, has been brought about by mechanisms, which maintain uniformity of the fluid-matrix." This concept of the steady states maintained in the internal environment or fluid-matrix, and of the importance of constancy of the matrix for continuous efficient action of the organism, ultimately became known as Cannon's doctrine of *homeostasis* (5).

Many examples of homeostasis might be cited. In some animals stabilizing mechanisms are absent. The frog, which has no temperature regulating mechanism, must live in the depths of its pond during the winter months in order to survive the cold. Its lack of a "water balance" mechanism will cause it to desiccate completely if left in the air for a day or two. Other animals escape these events by means of mechanisms arranged to regulate body temperature and preserve water content. In man, muscular exercise causes increased venous return to the heart which is accommodated by reflex cardiac acceleration and peripheral vasoconstriction. The subsequent rise in blood pressure is counteracted by increased activity of the aortic and carotid sinus reflexes. The autonomic nerves are responsible for quick, sudden adjustments of this type. Slower adjustments are possible through hormone and chemical activity with or without associated autonomic function. As the events of sudden stress pile up on one side of the scales, the autonomic system throws its weight to the other side and restores the normal equilibrium.

In many situations the organism is called upon to cope with a sudden emergency—some sudden change in its environment such as severe temperature changes, severe hemorrhage, combat, attack, etc.—to meet which a massive autonomic response is necessary. This massive response, without which the body cannot be rapidly and completely mobilized, is achieved by the sympathetic division with the resultant secretion of great quantities of adrenaline. That sympathetic stimulation can produce a massive, widespread reaction—a reaction which parasympathetic stimulation is unable to produce—is of vital significance. Because of this dramatic sympathico-adrenal activity, the blood vessels of the skin and viscera constrict, while the vessels of organs essential in overcoming the immediate crisis, such as skeletal muscles, the heart, etc., dilate and allow greatly increased blood flow (and thus increased supply of oxygen, etc.) through them. An animal under these conditions demonstrates what are regarded as typical signs of fright: cardiac acceleration, sweating, marked pilomotor activity, deep respiration and gastro-intestinal inhibition. All or any of these symptoms may be seen to varying degrees under different conditions. Sympathetic activity must not be regarded as occurring only in moments of extreme emergency but also during normal activity of the organism. In the latter case the activity will be less in degree, and the tissues reacting will be those under the greatest sympathetic control. The so-called "fight, flight or fright reaction" is a product of *maximal* generalized sympathetic activity.

The parasympathetic division, on the other hand, is primarily concerned with the protection, conservation and restoration of the bodily resources. For example, the cardiac inhibitory action of the vagus nerve prevents overexertion of the heart. The essential processes of digestion and absorption, i.e., salivation, secretion of gastric and pancreatic juices, peristalsis, etc., are mediated by the parasympathetic. The massive response discussed above is not seen here. Reactions to parasympathetic stimulation are highly localized. Another problem remains to be discussed, namely, the functional relationship of the sympathetic and parasympathetic divisions to one another.*

General Actions of the Autonomic System. As indicated in the outline on pages 226–227, the sympathetic and parasympathetic tend to have antagonistic actions on most individual viscera; thus the sympathetic accelerates and the parasympathetic slows the heart. On the gut the action of the two systems is reversed, for the vagus augments gut movement and the sympathetic inhibits. Kuntz (22) has compared these antagonistic effects to the reciprocal innervation of flexor and extensor muscles acting at a single joint. With certain organs, however, interaction between the two divisions of the autonomic is less simple and cannot be set down as exemplifying pure antagonism (27). The sympathetic and parasympathetic systems may act either independently (in a sense) or synergically. This is especially true of the bladder and iris.

* For details of innervation of each organ, the student is referred to the texts of Kuntz (22), Müller (36), Miller (35), Livingston (31), and White and Smithwick (44).

Innervation of the bladder. In the case of vesical innervation, section of the sympathetic fibers has no significant effect, but section of the parasympathetics paralyzes the bladder completely. After section of the preganglionic parasympathetic fibers, bladder activity depends upon sympathetic nerve supply, upon intrinsic contractility in smooth muscle fibers, and upon the influence of peripheral postganglionic parasympathetic neurons present in the organ. As a result, during vesical filling small waves of contraction are present, apparently dependent, according to Langworthy (27), on asynchronous contraction of different portions of the muscle in the bladder wall. At the height of each such contraction fluid is apt to escape. When the normal nerve supply exists, it is possible to suppress the waves of contraction voluntarily through parasympathetic mediation. These findings lead to the conclusion that parasympathetic influence controls vesical tone and action during filling without the participation of the sympathetic. The sympathetic system functions primarily in relation to vasomotor and sexual activity.

Innervation of the eye. Sympathetic nerves have been described as supplying a dilator pupillae, and parasympathetics the constrictors; the size of the pupil at any time is the result of a balance between impulses received from these two sets of fibers. Parasympathetic fibers from the tectal outflow reach the eye via the oculomotor nerve and the ciliary ganglion. The preganglionic fibers originate in the region of the oculomotor nucleus. The postganglionic neurons arise in the ciliary ganglion and reach the constrictor muscle of the iris and the ciliary muscle by way of the short ciliary nerves, forming the efferent limbs of the light and accommodation reflex pathways. Preganglionic sympathetic fibers take origin in the intermediolateral cell column of the spinal cord, run through the upper two thoracic white rami, and ascend in the cervical sympathetic chain to the superior cervical ganglion. Here originate the postganglionic neurons which travel in the carotid plexus to innervate the eyeball through the nasociliary branch of the ophthalmic nerve. They innervate the blood vessels of the eyeball, the "dilator pupillae" and smooth muscles in the upper eyelid. (In lower animals they also innervate the nictitating membrane and Müller's orbital muscle.)

Stimulation of the cervical sympathetics results in a generalized orbital vasoconstriction, dilatation of the pupil and elevation of the eyelid. This last produces a widening of the palpebral fissure simulating exophthalmos, but recent measurements have shown that no actual exophthalmos or enophthalmos are induced in man by stimulation or paralysis of the sympathetic nerves. These symptoms are definite in lower animals, but human exophthalmos is due solely to overgrowth of retrobulbar structures.

Paralysis of the cervical sympathetic trunk induced experimentally or seen clinically as a result of disease produces a tetrad of symptoms known as *Horner's syndrome.* It is to be expected that the observed symptoms would be the reverse of those occurring following sympathetic stimulation. There is pupillary constriction, accompanied by drooping of the upper eyelid (ptosis) as well as elevation of the lower (producing a narrowing of the palpebral fissure). There may also be dilatation of the orbital blood vessels with resultant redness of the conjunctiva, together with warm, flushed skin of the face, and finally an apparent enophthalmos due to narrowing of the palpebral fissure. A subsidiary symptom is a marked loss of iridial pigment. Parasympathetic stimulation of the eye via the oculomotor nerve and ciliary ganglion are considered by many investigators to be exactly antagonistic to the sympathetic effects—the sympathetic causing dilatation, parasympathetic causing constriction of the pupil.

Stimulation of the oculomotor nerve causes constriction of the pupil, and section causes maximal pupillary dilatation. Stimulation of the sympathetics causes dilation of the pupil; section of the sympathetics, however, produces a constriction of the pupil which is by no means maximal. Langworthy states, "Recent physiologic studies have shown that reflex responses of the iris producing changes in the diameter of the pupil are mediated largely, if not entirely, through the parasympathetic pathway. Pain may possibly produce reflex dilatation of the pupil through the sympathetic pathway, but even this dilatation may be largely a response to epinephrine."

Coordinated sympathetic and parasympathetic activity has also been demonstrated in the regulation of ciliary muscle control. *Accommodation* for far vision consists of two phases: (i) relaxation of the circular fibers of the ciliary muscle (supplied by the oculomotor nerve), and (ii) simultaneous active contraction of the radial fibers of the ciliary muscle (mediated by sympathetic nerves). Contraction of the radial fibers is said to increase the tension on the fibers of the suspensory ligament, with consequent flattening of the lens. Stimulation of the cervical sympathetics (in dogs, cats and rabbits) increases flattening of the lens (and thus "far" vision) even after section of the oculomotor nerve or inhibition of the parasympathetics with atropine. The opposite effect (increased "near" vision) results from section of the cervical sympathetic and stimulation of the parasympathetic nerves. Experimentally, then, it appears that visual accommodation is accomplished through the simultaneous, coordinated activity of the two divisions of the autonomic system.

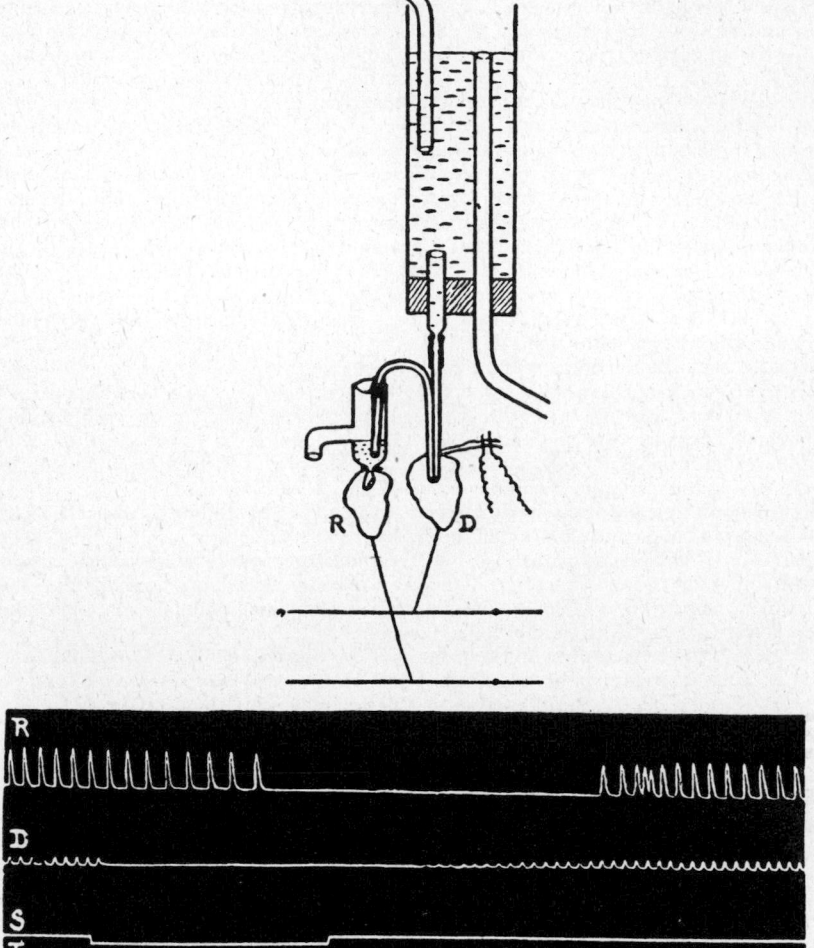

Fig. 128.—Bain's modification of Loewi's technique for demonstrating the release of the "vagus substance" upon stimulation of the cardiac nerve to the frog's heart. The donor heart (D) with nerves intact is perfused at constant pressure with a balanced salt solution. The perfusion fluid then passes to the isolated recipient heart (R). Cardiac contractions are recorded by means of writing levers; time (T) in 5 sec. intervals. The vagus fibers to the donor heart are stimulated (S) for 40 sec., and the donor heart is arrested. Slowing of the recipient heart is apparent within 15 sec. after arrest of the donor heart and asystole occurs shortly thereafter. (After Bain, from Goodman and Gilman, *The pharmacological basis of therapeutics*, 1941, p. 325.)

Pilomotor and sudomotor activity. Fibers controlling the contraction of the smooth muscle of the hair follicles are solely of sympathetic origin. The erection of the hair is of much greater importance in lower animals than in man, but disappearance of pilomotor activity indicates sympathetic paralysis. These pilomotor fibers are adrenergic. The postganglionic sympathetic fibers innervating the sweat glands in man are cholinergic (in contrast to the usual situation, such as the pilomotor fibers, in which they are adrenergic). These glands are unaffected by adrenaline. This makes it apparent that, although sweating may accompany peripheral vasodilatation, it is independent of vasomotor activity. The most recent investigations of the sudomotor mechanisms are those of List and his associates (16, 30). Several types of sweating have been described, namely, thermoregulatory (in response to heat), emotional, sweating induced by drugs such as pilocarpine, and reflex gustatory sweating of the face (from chewing spicy foods). This last appears primarily around the lips and tip of the nose, and may be greatly increased following degeneration of the postganglionic sympathetic sudomotor fibers because of increased sensitivity of the sweat glands to acetylcholine.

Substances Associated with Autonomic Stimulation. In 1904, Elliott observed that following section of sympathetic nerves, the structures they had innervated characteristically responded to adrenaline. This suggested to him that

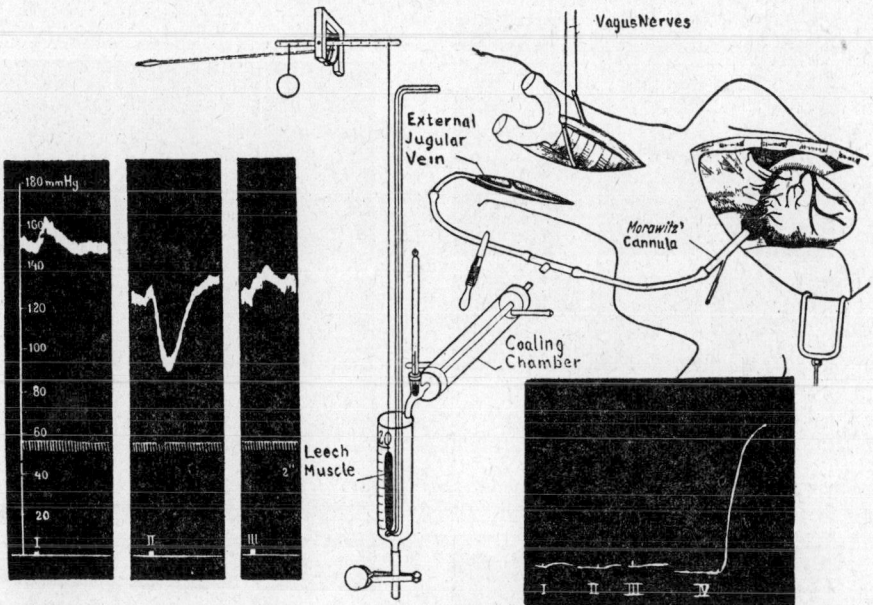

Fig. 129.—The release of acetylcholine in the mammalian heart. Schematic representation of exposed dog's heart, vagus nerves and external jugular vein. A Morawitz cannula is inserted into the coronary sinus, from which blood can be diverted at will into a cooling chamber preparatory to testing it on the sensitized leech muscle for its content of acetylcholine. The lower right hand tracings represent responses of the leech muscle to coronary blood obtained under the following circumstances: I, control; II, during vagus stimulation; III, control after eserinization of the dog; IV, during vagal stimulation after eserinization. The carotid blood pressure tracing on the left is that of a cat injected with samples of the dog's coronary blood taken as follows: I, control after eserinization of the dog; II, during vagal stimulation after eserinization. The cat was then atropinized, and at III is shown the absence of the vasodepressor response to the same sample of blood used at II. Note that only when the chemical mediator of the vagal impulses is protected by eserine from enzymatic destruction is it possible to demonstrate its presence by the use of appropriate test objects. (After Feldberg and Krayer, from Goodman and Gilman, *The pharmacological basis of therapeutics*, 1941, p. 326.)

adrenaline might normally be liberated when the impulse reached the periphery. The parasympathetic parallel of this situation was discovered by Dale (10), i.e., that acetylcholine was able to simulate the effects of parasympathetic excitation. This in turn was followed by Loewi's experiments (35) which demonstrated the existence of a cardio-inhibitory substance in a perfusate following vagus stimulation (Fig. 128). Stimulation of sympathetic fibers to increase the heart rate produced a cardio-accelerator substance—a

9

substance that was sympathomimetic. Loewi's work was confirmed and amplified by many studies (8). In brief, acetylcholine is liberated at parasympathetic postganglionic neuro-effector junctions. It is broken down readily by cholinesterase, but this breakdown is delayed considerably by serine or prostigmine (Fig. 129). This rapid evanescence of acetylcholine is sometimes overcome therapeutically by the administration of a more stable form of the drug—acetyl-beta-methylcholine hydrochloride (mecholyl). Injection of such substances produces increase in muscle tone of the gastro-intestinal tract, and intense activity of glands throughout the body, viz., sweat, salivary, mucous and other glands. The secretion of these glands is inhibited by the administration of atropine, which paralyzes the parasympathetic nerves. The puzzling

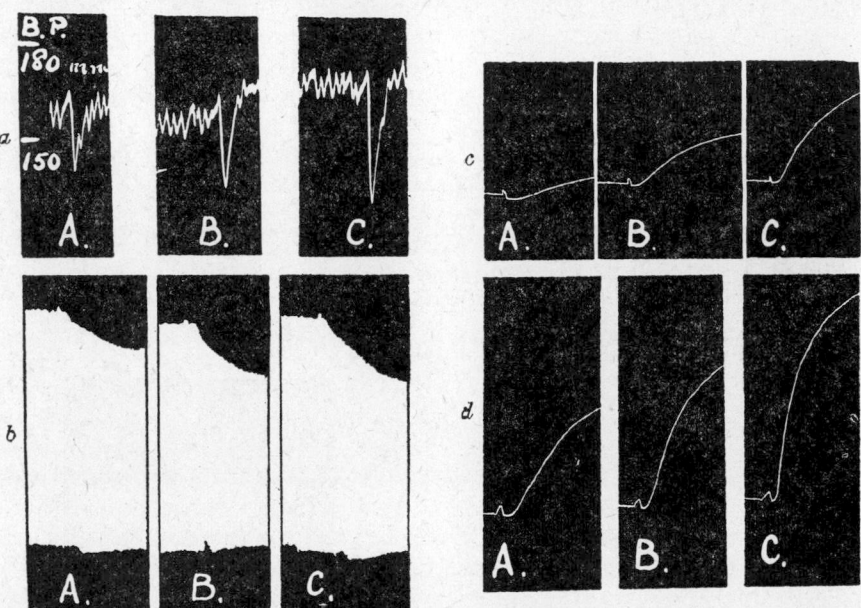

Fig. 130.—Tests of a perfusate of eserinized Locke's solution passing through the vessels of the stomach of a dog during vagal stimulation. The perfusate before stimulation was virtually inactive. Record a = effects on the blood pressure of an eserinized cat under chloralose; b = isolated frog heart (Straub method); c = eserinized rectus abdominus of the frog; d = eserinized leech muscle. In each series, B shows the effect of the concentrated perfusate, tested in a constant ratio to two strengths of acetylcholine, at A and C. That at C was double that at A. All four tests yield quantitatively consistent results. (After Dale and Feldberg, from Cannon and Rosenblueth, *Autonomic neuro-effector systems*, 1937, p. 39.)

phenomenon that atropine also inhibited secretion of the sweat glands (innervated by sympathetic nerves) was solved when it was shown that the sympathetic nerves in question were cholinergic. Vagal effects are also mediated by acetylcholine in the stomach as elsewhere (see Fig. 130) despite the fact that atropine does not completely block vagal impulses to the stomach although the mimetic influence of acetylcholine is abolished. According to Dale (10), acetylcholine activity at synaptic junctions resembles the action of nicotine, as distinct from its action at parasympathetic effectors where it resembles muscarine. Atropine blocks the latter effects without disturbing the former. Cannon and Rosenblueth further point out that some of the peculiar experimental results have been due to the fact that the nicotine-like action of acetylcholine is excitatory after comparatively small doses, but paralyzes at high concentrations.

Dale classified the autonomic neuro-effector mechanisms into adrenergic and cholinergic divisions. In other words, sympathetic effects are associated with an adrenaline-like mediator, and parasympathetic effects with acetyl-choline. This clear-cut division can only be carried to a certain point, since it has been demonstrated that in some cases sympathetic excitation causes the liberation of acetylcholine. As yet no adrenergic parasympathetic fibers have been adequately demonstrated, although there is some evidence that the vagi contain adrenergic cardio-accelerator fibers.

Following the discovery of the existence of cholinergic fibers in the sympathetic system, Dale pointed out that the substance liberated on sympathetic stimulation might not be adrenaline itself, but some substance closely related to it. According to Cannon and Rosenblueth, consequent to parasympathetic or sympathetic stimulation, a substance is liberated into the blood stream and is carried elsewhere in the organism, where it may have effects similar to parasympathetic or sympathetic impulses. The substance produced by sympathetic stimulation was designated *sympathin*. Sympathin was said to come from all smooth muscle and to exist in two forms: *Sympathin E* is the excitor form, liberated from smooth muscle, contracting as a result of sympathetic stimulation; *Sympathin I* is the inhibitor form (is liberated in intestine which is inhibited by sympathetic excitation). Sympathin differs from adrenaline in several respects (8). Cannon and Rosenblueth briefly summarize the role played by the two substances as follows: "When the sympathetic system goes into vigorous action . . . it liberates sympathin at perhaps all its myriads of endings—sympathin in such excess that it overflows and enters the circulation; and it liberates, also into the circulation, adrenine. These two substances . . . have additive effects. To what degree sympathin may be important in the presence of a normal discharge of adrenine has not been determined, but it is clear that locally produced sympathin, circulating sympathin, and circulating adrenine all work together to unify and synchronize the operation of the sympathetic system." It has also been shown that both substances are liberated consequent to stimulation of the hypothalamus (33).

Effects of Sympathectomy. Understanding of sympathetic and parasympathetic activity and of the effects of autonomic stimulation has been materially aided, in many respects, by observations of the consequences of total sympathectomy in animals and partial sympathectomy in animals and man. Cannon (4) succeeded in removing the entire sympathetic chain in cats, and found that the animals lived in apparent good health if kept under protected conditions. Body temperature and blood pressure are maintained within normal limits, basal metabolism is slightly reduced, and their hair fails to show erection in anger. Visceral and glandular functions proceed normally, but they cannot adjust to the stress of emergency, such as acute change in temperature, anoxia, hemorrhage, etc. These results indicate that the sympathetic system is not essential to life, but functions to adapt the body to changes in environment. However, it does not mean that this system remains inactive unless the organism is subjected to stress. It does imply that the body has additional mechanisms which can be called upon up to a certain point, when necessary. A major consequence of sympathetic excision is the increased response of the denervated structures to neurohormones and other substances in the blood.

Sensitization of denervated structures to autonomic neurohormones. Living-ston has aptly stated that the ideal sympathectomy is one which selectively and permanently interrupts the impulses of sympathetic origin supplied to a particular part of the body. One of the reasons why this "ideal" is rarely accomplished by the surgeon is that when the sympathetic supply is removed the tissues become remarkably sensitive to circulating adrenaline or sym-pathin. The sensitization appears following section of either stimulatory or inhibitory adrenergic fibers. This condition is at its height after destruction of the postganglionic neurons—a fact of utmost importance to the surgeon. *The sympathetic pathway must be interrupted at the preganglionic neuron if minimal sensitization and maximal reduction in tone are to result.* Care must also be taken to guard against regeneration. Hampel (17) denervated the nictitating membrane and traced the course of its increasing sensitivity. He found that preganglionic denervation produces approximately half the sensitization that appears following postganglionic section (see Fig. 131).

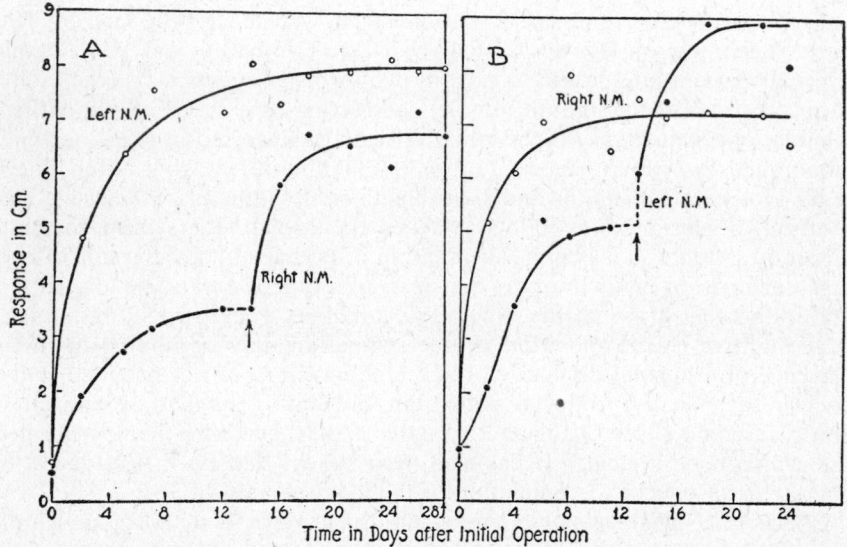

Fig. 131.—A, Isotonic responses of the nictitating membranes to 1 cc. of adrenaline, 1:100,000, after removal of the left superior cervical ganglion and section of the right cervical sympathetic nerve. The right superior cervical ganglion was removed 14 days after section of the right nerve, as indicated by the arrow. B, Isotonic responses of the nictitating membranes to 1 cc. of adren-aline, 1:100,000, after removal of the right superior cervical ganglion and section of the left cervical sympathetic nerve. The left superior cervical ganglion was removed 13 days after section of the left nerve, as indicated by the arrow. (From Hampel, *Amer. J. Physiol.*, 1935, *111*:615.)

These surgical points are of particular importance in cases of peripheral vascular disease, such as *Raynaud's disease*. This condition has been defined by the peripheral vascular clinic of the Massachusetts General Hospital as a form of peripheral vascular disturbance caused by tonic contraction of the smaller arteries in the extremities. During the early uncompli-cated stages of the disease there are no obvious pathological changes in the walls of the arteries. The disease commonly involves symmetrical areas in the hands and feet, causing circulatory stasis with periods of cyanosis or pallid asphyxia. The severe cases go on to dry gangrene of the phalanges. The spasm is intermittent and occurs on exposure to cold or emotional stimuli; it involves only the terminal arteries, while the main vessels continue their normal pulsations. Frequently these patients complain of excessive perspiration, which is also limited to the extremities. The disease most commonly occurs in young individuals with hyperirritable nervous constitutions. The preoperative vasospasm is considered by the majority of investigators to be the result of abnormal activity of the vasoconstrictor nerves; any postoperative vasospasm is explained on the basis of increased sensitivity of the arteriolar muscle to circulating adrenaline. The common treatment for this condition is denervation of the extremities. The leg may be sympathetically denervated by excision of the second and third, or first, second and third lumbar ganglia; the arm, by dividing the rami of the second and third thoracic ganglia and cutting the sympathetic chain below the third ganglion. Much discussion has concerned itself with the question of the transmission of sympathetic fibers to the arm in the first thoracic nerve, but surgical evidence as well as experimental do not support such a distribution (44).

It also follows that *the denervation of any structure must be complete* if it is to be of value. If partial innervation is left intact, diffusion of neurohormones occurs from the normally supplied cells to those whose sensitivity has markedly increased. Responses similar to those following adrenergic denervation

Fig. 132.—Sensitization of the sphincter of the iris to acetylcholine by section of the parasympathetic nerve supply. A, Cat with its left ciliary ganglion excised two weeks previously. B, Thirty-five minutes after A, when the right ciliary ganglion and both superior cervical ganglia had been removed. Now two drops of eserine (1 per cent) were instilled into both of the conjunctival sacs. C, Five minutes after the eserine instillation; no change in size of pupils. D, Five minutes later; two drops of acetylcholine (0.01 per cent) instilled into each conjunctival sac. E–L, Successive stages of pupillary change. (After Chen and Cannon, from Cannon and Rosenblueth, *Autonomic neuro-effector systems*, 1937, p. 192.)

have also been observed consequent to cholinergic nerve section. Increased sensitivity of the pupillary sphincter to acetylcholine has been observed as a result of excision of the ciliary ganglion (see Fig. 132). Denervated sweat glands and skeletal muscle also demonstrate this phenomenon. On the basis of the regularity of appearance of these reactions throughout the body, Cannon (7) suggested a law of denervation, stated as follows: "When in a series of efferent neurones a unit is destroyed, an increased irritability to chemical agents develops in the isolated structure or structures, the effect being maximal in the part directly denervated."

Full discussion of the vasomotor system will be found in a following chapter. The vasomotor center is one of the central autonomic areas found in the floor of the fourth ventricle. Its control is exerted over the widespread network of vasoconstrictor and vasodilator fibers which run throughout the body in the sympathetic and parasympathetic nerves.

Detailed knowledge of the vasoconstrictor outflow has become increasingly important during the last few years, as a result of the attempts to cope with

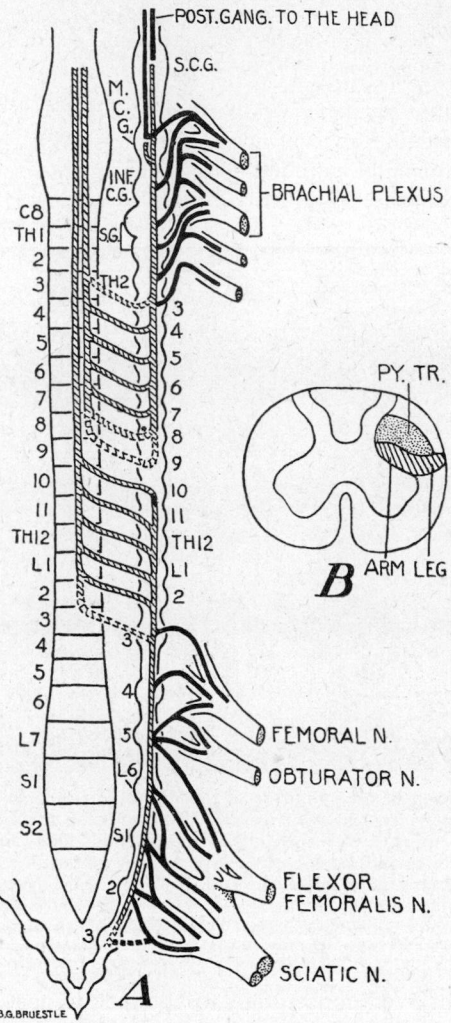

Fig. 133.—A, Diagram of outflow from spinal cord of preganglionic fibers (hatched) and post-ganglionic fibers (heavy black) for vasomotor supply of upper and lower extremities of macaque. Broken lines indicate inconstant fibers. SCG, superior cervical ganglion; MCG, middle cervical ganglion; Inf. CG, inferior cervical ganglion; SG, stellate ganglion; Th2, second thoracic ganglion; L1, first lumbar ganglion; S1, first sacral ganglion. B, Diagram showing position of vasomotor pathways in spinal cord. (From Ascroft, *Brit. J. Surg.*, 1937, *24*:792.)

abnormal vasospasm by section of the vasoconstrictor fibers. Electrical records have demonstrated that in the monkey (Fig. 133) the fourth to the eighth thoracic segments contribute sympathetic fibers to the arm. White and Smithwick (44) have reported results of postoperative tests in man. When the sympathetic chain is cut below the third thoracic ganglion, vasoconstriction and sweating persist in the head and upper extremity. If, in addition to this, the second and third intercostal nerves are divided proximal to their rami communicantes, these functions are abolished.

REFERENCES

1. ASK-UPMARK, E. The carotid sinus and the cerebral circulation. An anatomical, experimental, and clinical investigation. *Acta psychiat., Kbh.*, 1935, Suppl. 6, 374 pp.

2. BAYLISS, W. M. On the origin from the spinal cord of the vasodilator fibres of the hind-limb and on the nature of these fibres. *J. Physiol.*, 1901, *26*:173–209.

3. BURN, J. H. On vasodilator fibres in the sympathetic and on the effect of circulating adrenaline in augmenting the vascular response to sympathetic stimulation. *J. Physiol.*, 1932, *75*:144–160. (See also: Sympathetic vasodilator fibres. *Physiol. Rev.*, 1938, *18*:137–153.)

4. CANNON, W. B., NEWTON, H. F., BRIGHT, E. M., MENKIN, V. and MOORE, R. M. Some aspects of the physiology of animals surviving complete exclusion of sympathetic nerve impulses. *Amer. J. Physiol.* 1929, *89*:84–107.

5. CANNON, W. B. *The wisdom of the body.* New York, W. W. Norton, 1932, 312 pp.

6. CANNON, W. B. The argument for chemical mediation of nerve impulses. *Science*, 1939, *90*:521–527.

7. CANNON, W. B. A law of denervation. *Amer. J. med. Sci.*, 1939, *198*:737–750.

8. CANNON, W. B. and ROSENBLUETH, A. *Autonomic neuro-effector systems.* New York, The Macmillan Co., 1937, xiv, 230 pp.

9. COWGILL, E. J. and WINDLE, W. F. Development of the cranial sympathetic ganglia in the cat. *J. comp. Neurol.*, 1942, *77*:619–630.

10. DALE, H. H. The occurrence in ergot and action of acetylcholine. *J. Physiol.*, 1914, *48*:iii–iv.

11. FOERSTER, O. Über die Vasodilatoren in den peripheren Nerven und Lintern Rückenmarkswurzehn beim Menschen. *Dtsch. Z. Nervenheilk.*, 1928, *107*:41–56. (See also: The dermatomes in man. *Brain*, 1933, *56*:1–39.)

12. FRANKLIN, K. J. *A monograph on veins.* Springfield, Ill., Charles C Thomas, 1937, xii, 410 pp.

13. FULTON, J. F. *Physiology of the nervous system*, 2d ed. New York, Oxford University Press, 1943, ix, 614 pp.

14. FREUND, S. and SHEEHAN, D. Experimental investigation of visceral afferent synapses in coeliac ganglia. *J. Neurophysiol.*, 1943, *6*:263–268.

15. GELLHORN, E. *Autonomic regulations, their significance for physiology, psychology and neuropsychiatry.* New York, Interscience Publishers, Inc., 1943, xii, 373 pp. [Excellent bibliography.]

16. GUTTMANN, L. and LIST, C. F. Zur Topik und Pathophysiologie der Schweissekretion. *Z. ges. Neurol. Psychiat.*, 1928, *116*:504–536.

17. HAMPEL, C. W. The effect of denervation on the sensitivity to adrenine of the smooth muscle in the nictitating membrane of the cat. *Amer. J. Physiol.*, 1935, *111*:611–621.

18. HINSEY, J. C. The hypothalamus and somatic responses. *Res. Publ. Ass. nerv. ment. Dis.*, 1940, *20*:657–685.

19. HINSEY, J. C. and GASSER, H. S. The Sherrington phenomenon. I. The nerve fibers involved in the sensitization of the muscle. II. The nerve fibers which produce the contraction. III. Antagonism by adrenalin. *Amer. J. Physiol.*, 1928, *87*:368–380.

20. HODES, R. and MAGOUN, H. W. Autonomic responses to electrical stimulation of the forebrain and midbrain with special reference to the pupil. *J. comp. Neurol.*, 1942, *76*:461–473.

21. KENNARD, M. A. Vasomotor disturbances resulting from cortical lesions. *Arch. Neurol. Psychiat., Chicago*, 1935, *33*:537–545.

22. KUNTZ, A. *The autonomic nervous system*, 2d ed. Philadelphia, Lea and Febiger, 1934, 697 pp.

23. KUNTZ, A. and SACCOMANNO, G. Reflex inhibition of intestinal motility mediated through decentralized prevertebral ganglia. *J. Neurophysiol.*, 1944, *7*:163–170.

24. KUNTZ, A. and VAN BUSKIRK, C. Reflex inhibition of bile flow and intestinal motility mediated through decentralized celiac plexus. *Proc. Soc. exp. Biol., N. Y.*, 1941, *46*:519–523.

25. LANGLEY, J. N. Sketch of the progress of discovery in the eighteenth century as regards the autonomic nervous system. *J. Physiol.*, 1916, *50*:225–258.

26. LANGLEY, J. N. *The autonomic nervous system. I.* Cambridge, W. Heffer and Sons, Ltd., 1921, 80 pp.

27. LANGWORTHY, O. R. General principles of autonomic innervation. *Arch. Neurol. Psychiat., Chicago*, 1943, *50*:590–602.

28. LANGWORTHY, O. R., KOLB, L. C. and LEWIS, L. G. *Physiology of micturition.* Baltimore, Williams & Wilkins Company, 1940, vii, 232 pp.

29. LEWIS, T. *The blood vessels of the human skin and their responses.* London, Shaw & Sons, Ltd., 1927, xvi, 322 pp.

30. LIST, C. F. and PEET, M. M. Sweat secretion in man. I. Sweating responses in normal persons. *Arch. Neurol. Psychiat., Chicago*, 1938, *39*:1228–1237; II. Anatomical distribution of disturbances in sweating associated with lesions of the sympathetic nervous system. *Ibid.*, *40*:27–43; III. Clinical observations on sweating produced by pilocarpine and mecholyl. *Ibid.*, 269–290; IV. Sweat secretion of the face and its disturbances. *Ibid.*, 443–470; V. Disturbances of sweat secretion with lesions

of the pons, medulla and cervical portion of the cord. *Ibid.*, 1939, *42*:1098–1127.

31. LIVINGSTON, W. K. *The clinical aspects of visceral neurology with special reference to the surgery of the sympathetic nervous system.* Springfield, Ill., Charles C Thomas, 1935, xiii, 254 pp.

32. LOEWI, O. Über humorale übertragbarkeit der Herznervenwirkung. *Pflüg. ges. Physiol.*, 1921, *189*:239–242.

33. MAGOUN, H. W., RANSON, S. W. and HETHERINGTON, A. The liberation of adrenin and sympathin induced by stimulation of the hypothalamus. *Amer. J. Physiol.*, 1937, *119*: 615–622.

34. McDOWALL, R. J. S. *The control of the circulation of the blood.* New York, Longmans, Green and Co., 1938, xv, 619 pp.

35. MILLER, H. R. *Central autonomic regulations in health and disease with special reference to the hypothalamus.* New York, Grune and Stratton, 1942, xx, 430 pp.

36. MÜLLER, L. R. *Lebensnerven und Lebenstriebe. Dritte wesentlich erweiterte Auflage des vegetativen Nervenssystems.* Berlin, J. Springer, 1931, xii, 992 pp.

37. RICHTER, C. P. and WOODRUFF, B. G. Changes produced by sympathectomy in the electrical resistance of the skin. *Surgery*, 1941, *10*:957–970.

38. RICHTER, C. P. and WOODRUFF, B. G. Facial patterns of electrical skin resistance— Their relation to sleep, external temperature, hair distribution, sensory dermatomes and skin disease. *Johns Hopk. Hosp. Bull.*, 1942, *70*:442–459.

39. RICHTER, C. P., WOODRUFF, B. G. and EATON, B. C. Hand and foot patterns of low electrical skin resistance: their anatomical and neurological significance. *J. Neurophysiol.*, 1943, *6*:417–424.

40. SCHWARTZ, H. G. Reflex activity within the sympathetic nervous system. *Amer. J. Physiol.*, 1934, *109*:593–604.

41. SHEEHAN, D. Discovery of the autonomic nervous system. *Arch. Neurol. Psychiat.*, Chicago, 1936, *35*:1081–1115.

42. SHEEHAN, D. The autonomic nervous system prior to Gaskell. *New Engl. J. Med.*, 1941, *224*:457–460.

43. SHEEHAN, D. Spinal autonomic outflows in man and monkey. *J. comp. Neurol.*, 1941, *75*:341–370.

44. WHITE, J. C. and SMITHWICK, R. H. *The autonomic nervous system*, 2nd ed. New York, The Macmillan Company, 1941, 469 pp.

CHAPTER 11

AUTONOMIC NERVOUS SYSTEM: CENTRAL DIVISION

Acceptance of Langley's definition of the autonomic nervous system made it customary in the past to regard this system as a purely peripheral motor outflow without central ramification in the brain and spinal cord. This limited concept has done much to retard progress and to conceal the true nature and significance of the autonomic system. Actually, the autonomic division has representation at all levels of the cerebrospinal axis, and it receives impulses through afferent channels, some of which, e.g., those from the carotid sinus, are specifically set aside for the mediation of autonomic reflexes. Other sensory channels appear to be used in common with the somatic division; for this reason it seems unwise to attempt a hard-and-fast classification of afferent nerve fibers based on affiliation with one or other of the two systems—somatic or autonomic. One can therefore accept the autonomic as a motor system, and it is proposed in this chapter to describe its central organization.

LEVELS OF AUTONOMIC FUNCTION

Spinal level. Well developed autonomic reflexes are present in spinal animals, including dogs, cats, monkeys and man. Immediately after spinal transsection, all reflexes, somatic and autonomic alike, become depressed ("spinal shock"); indeed, in man they may be completely abolished for periods ranging from two to four weeks. Thereafter noxious stimuli applied to the skin may cause profuse reflex sweating in parts of the body below the transection; the blood pressure may fluctuate as a result of such stimulation; and reflex emptying of the hollow viscera such as bladder, rectum and seminal vesicles may be induced by suitable stimulation.

A pattern of response peculiar to man and all quadrupeds is the vasomotor response to heat and cold. When one extremity is plunged into ice water, the other three extremities show prompt reflex vasoconstriction (31); or, conversely, when an extremity is abruptly heated, the other three extremities exhibit vasodilatation—the responses in question being part of a primitive spinal heat-regulating mechanism. Although present in spinal animals, the reactions tend, even after full recovery from spinal shock, to be sluggish as compared with the exquisite delicacy of reaction seen when the higher centers remain intact; but the fact that the pattern is laid down in the spinal cord is obviously significant, and it indicates that, as with the somatic reflexes, the basic reaction patterns are spinal in origin. Other basic patterns are those of defecation and sex. A spinal dog, on emptying its rectum, assumes the familiar position of an intact canine performing the same function. A male spinal cat, when its perineum is stimulated, assumes the position of copulation and develops priapism (10). Sherrington, who had also noted these reaction patterns in spinal animals, succeeded in having a spinal bitch impregnated; at term, it brought forth a litter of healthy puppies.

Medullary level. When the brain stem is severed above the medulla oblongata decerebrate rigidity ensues and, associated with this highly organized somatic reaction pattern, one finds more highly organized autonomic integrations. In the spinal animal the level of the blood pressure fluctuates, whereas with medullary centers present the blood pressure is maintained at a normal level and is responsive to such reflex mechanisms as those controlled by the carotid sinus (see Chap. 41). The systolic pressure responds appropriately to diminished oxygen partial pressures, and the vasomotor responses to heat and cold are less sluggish than in the spinal preparation, but despite this the animal has only a limited capacity for heat regulation (20, 21).

The medullary preparation has other complex reaction patterns that involve simultaneous or sequential discharge of the somatic and autonomic divisions; it can sneeze, cough, vomit and swallow. The most potent stimulus to the swallow is a solution of 20 to 30 per cent alcohol. If a few drops of the alcoholic beverage are dropped on the back of the tongue, the animal promptly salivates (an autonomic reaction) and then swallows two or three times in sequence—a primitive reaction pattern developed in the early stages of the nervous system's evolution.

Pontine level. If the brain stem is severed so as to leave nuclei of the midbrain intact, ocular responses are retained. The pupil responds to light by constriction, and certain other reflexes, including the consensual reaction of the pupils to light, are also retained.

Hypothalamic level. More elaborate reaction patterns find functional localization in the part of the diencephalon known as the hypothalamus. Indeed, the recent disclosures concerning the hypothalamus make it quite clear that it is the principal focus of integration of the entire autonomic system; in the forepart one finds primary parasympathetic representation, and in the posterior part, sympathetic. Through interaction between the two areas, highly organized integrations are carried out, such as that essential for heat regulation as well as the regulation of water metabolism and probably other phases of general metabolism. It will be the purpose of this chapter to describe in greater detail the function of the hypothalamic area and the extent to which it is regulated by the cerebral cortex.

FUNCTIONS OF THE HYPOTHALAMUS

The importance of the hypothalamus as a center for integration of visceral function has come to be appreciated only in recent years. The history of the development of knowledge of the hypothalamus is of some interest, and may be recounted briefly.

*Historical note.** Early in the nineteenth century the Viennese pathologist, Rokitansky, noted that infections at the base of the brain are usually accompanied by lesions of the stomach, often with perforation—an observation long forgotten, but now one of high relevance in relation to the hypothalamus and gastric function. At the beginning of this century the French neurologist, Babinski, and a Viennese pathologist, Fröhlich, observed that individuals having pituitary tumors developed regression of secondary sexual characteristics along with marked adiposity. Both Babinski and Fröhlich believed the symptoms to be due to the destruction of the pituitary itself. Later Cushing produced the Fröhlich syndrome experimentally in hypophysectomized dogs, he too believing that the syndrome resulted from damage to the pituitary. Camus and Roussy, however, produced the syndrome in dogs through lesions restricted to the hypothalamus without injury to the pituitary. This was confirmed in 1921 by Bailey and Bremer.

* References cited in this historical note will be found in the bibliography on the hypothalamus appended to the special volume on the hypothalamus issued in March 1940 by the Association for Research in Nervous and Mental Disease (New York).

Meanwhile Karplus and Kreidl by electrical stimulation of the hypothalamic area caused acceleration of the heart, rise in blood pressure, sweating, pupillary dilatation, and inhibition of gastric intestinal peristalsis. They proved that the reactions were due to stimulation of nerve centers in the area and could not be due to activation of fibers of passage since the responses still persisted three weeks after all the rest of the forebrain had been removed, at which time its motor projection fibers would have degenerated. They established, furthermore, that the descending pathways from the hypothalamus conveying the effects on the heart traverse the brain stem around the aqueduct of Sylvius and descend in the medial part of the medulla oblongata to the anterolateral tracts of the spinal cord to the lateral columns, thence synapsing in the lateral columns, and emerging via the nerve roots at the first through the fifth thoracic levels; they pass from there directly to the sympathetic ganglion chain. In 1928 Philip Bard (3) established that the phenomenon of sham rage in cats depends upon integrity of the posterior hypothalamic area, and Beattie, Brow and Long (5) shortly thereafter reported that the extrasystoles which occur during sham rage depend upon pathways identical with those worked out by Karplus and Kreidl. In short, the posterior hypothalamic area is the center in which reactions of the sympathetic division of the autonomic system may originate, and this region appears to be in direct connection with the postganglionic outflow to the heart in the upper thoracic levels.

Anatomical Organization (Fig. 139). The hypothalamic area is made up of a constellation of nuclei which may be divided anatomically into six groups (30): the preoptic, periventricular, lateral, supra-optic, middle, and mammillary. Omitting the preoptic nuclei (Fig. 134, _1_ and _2_) about which little is known, only four groups at present need be recognized: (i) anterior, including the supra-optic and paraventricular nuclei (Fig. 134, _6_ and _3_), (ii) middle, including the tuber nuclei (Fig. 134, _4_ and _7_), (iii) the lateral nuclear masses (Fig. 134, _15_), and (iv) the posterior nuclei, including the posterior hypothalamic nuclei and the mammillary bodies (Fig. 134, _9, 10_ and _11_).

Connections. The _afferent_ connections of the hypothalamus are numerous, and include projections from the cerebral cortex (e.g., the medial forebrain bundle) and from the thalamus and corpus striatum. The _efferent_ connections include the path of Vicq d'Azyr from the mammillary bodies to the anterior thalamic nuclei, the descending pathways of Karplus and Kreidl from the posterior hypothalamus to the thoracic levels of the spinal cord, and, finally, the large supra-opticohypophysial system which in man contains more than 100,000 fibers.

Blood supply of the hypothalamus. The hypothalamus has the richest blood supply of any part of the brain (11,37). The principal supply comes directly from the circle of Willis but the anterior cerebral artery supplies the pituitary stalk; the supra-optic and paraventricular nuclei have a blood supply six times richer than the motor cortex, each neuron being liberally bathed in capillary blood. No doubt associated with this rich blood supply is the fact that the neurons which constitute these nuclei are pear-shaped and largely without dendritic projections, the assumption being that the neurons in question are activated by changes in the blood, chemical and thermal, rather than by other neuron elements.

Supra-opticohypophysial system. Studies of Rasmussen (28) indicate that the supra-optic and paraventricular nuclei give rise to the greater proportion of the fibers in the pituitary stalk. This has been established through painstaking cell counts of the nuclei in normal animals and in animals with the pituitary stalk severed some weeks previously. Each supra-optic nucleus of a rat has an average of 7,000 cells, the dog and monkey, 38,000 cells, and man, 60,000 cells. Following section of the pituitary stalk in these forms the cell counts drop by 80 to 85 per cent. Thus in one animal with a normal cell count of 38,000, only 6,000 cells remained after low stalk section; if the stalk is severed closer to the base a larger proportion of cells in the supra-optic nuclei degenerate, indicating that some fibers terminate in cells of the pars tuberalis which surround the stalk. Total fiber counts in the stalk itself disclose the following: rat, 10,000 fibers, dog and monkey, 60,000, man, 100,000.

A human case of stalk section has been described by Rasmussen and Gardner (29)—a 47 year old male who died of a stroke five months after the pituitary stalk had been severed for the relief of malignant hypertension. The right supra-optic nucleus displayed 9,200 cells, the left 8,720, while in a normal human subject there are 61,000 cells. There was also cell

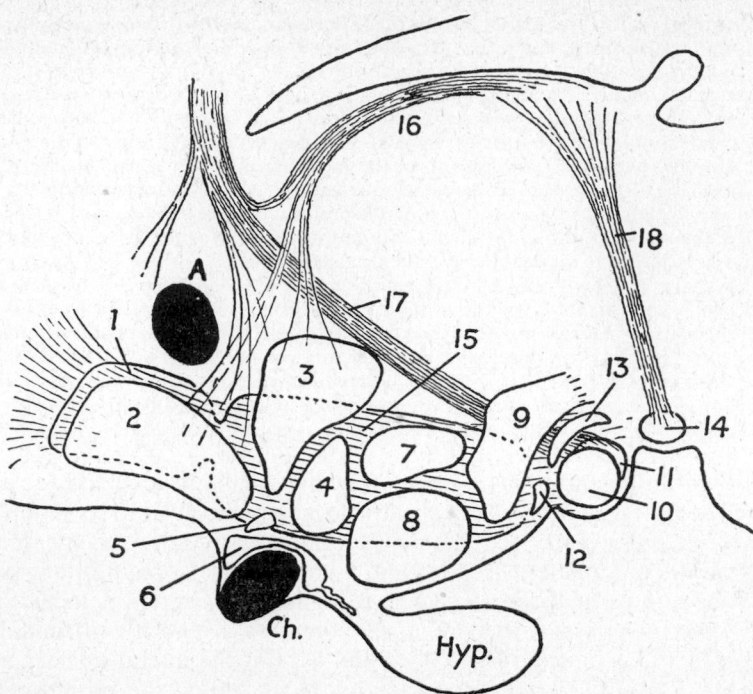

Fig. 134.—Diagram showing the relative positions in a sagittal plane of the hypothalamic nuclei in a typical mammalian brain, and their relation to the fornix, stria habenularis, and fasciculus retroflexus. A, Anterior commissure. Ch, Optic chiasma. Hyp, Hypophysis. 1. Lateral preoptic nucleus (permeated by the medial forebrain bundle). 2. Medial preoptic nucleus. 3. Paraventricular nucleus. 4. Anterior hypothalamic area. 5. Suprachiasmatic nucleus. 6. Supra-optic nucleus. 7. Dorsomedial hypothalamic nucleus. 8. Ventromedial hypothalamic nucleus. 9. Posterior hypothalamic nucleus. 10. Medial mammillary nucleus. 11. Lateral mammillary nucleus. 12. Premammillary nucleus. 13. Supramammillary nucleus. 14. Interpeduncular nucleus (a mesencephalic element in which the fasciculus retroflexus terminates). 15. Lateral hypothalamic nucleus (permeated by the medial forebrain bundle). 16. Stria habenularis. 17. Fornix. 18. Fasciculus retroflexus of Meynert (habenulo-peduncular tract). (From Clark, W. E. Le Gros, Beattie, J., Riddoch, G., and Dott, N. M. *The hypothalamus*, London, Oliver and Boyd, 1938.

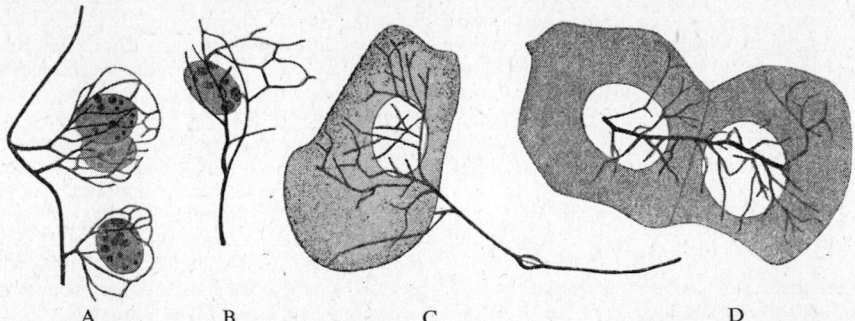

Fig. 135.—Innervation of the secretory cells of the pituitary from unpublished studies by Dr. I. Gersh and kindly supplied by him for the present revision. The cells lettered A and B are characteristic posterior lobe cells from a camera lucida drawing by Mr. Didusch (cytoplasm unstained). Note basket network about individual cells. Figs. C and D show innervation of cells in the anterior lobe. (See Brooks, C. M. C., and Gersh, I. *Endocrinology*, 1941, *28*:1.)

loss in the paraventricular nuclei. The 15 per cent normal cells remaining correspond with similar findings in monkeys—and they proved sufficient to prevent the onset of diabetes insipidus (see below).

Posterior lobe innervation. The secretory cells of the posterior lobe are modified neurons, hence the term *neurohypophysis*. As is well known, the cells of the neurohypophysis take origin in embryological development from cells in the hypothalamus. It is scarcely surprising, therefore, to learn from the studies of Fisher, Ingram and Ranson (12) that the parenchymatous cells of the posterior lobe degenerate when their "preganglionic" fibers arising in the supra-optic nuclei are destroyed. So intimately dependent are these secretory elements upon their innervation that, unlike many other glandular cells, they disappear once their innervation is withdrawn. Brooks and Gersh (8) have devoted attention to the morphology of the nerves ending the neurohypophysis, finding that they surround cells in an elaborate basket network, establishing contact at many points of the surface of the cell (Fig. 135A and B). The innervation of anterior lobe cells is distinctive and quite different from that of the posterior lobe (Fig. 135C and D).

Innervation of other endocrines. Rasmussen (29) and Vazquez-Lopez (37) discuss the innervation of the pituitary gland in detail. Hypothalamic regulation of the anterior lobe is not fully established. Evidence of this control was first suggested by Uotila's (36) investigation of thyroid activity during exposure to cold. Under the conditions of his experiments thyrotropic hormone caused an increase in thyroid secretion, which failed to occur following section of the infundibular stalk, thus suggesting stimulation of the thyroid mechanism by impulses traversing this stalk. That the anterior pituitary receives sympathetic fibers from the carotid plexus via the blood vessels is now generally accepted. Truscott (35) describes three sources of supply of the anterior lobe: (i) the infundibular tract, by way of the capsular sheath; (ii) the hypophysial fasciculi, by way of the pars intermedia; and (iii) the small nerves supplying the hypophysial blood vessels. He stresses the interconnections between the pars anterior and the other lobes. The fibers reaching the gland from the carotid plexus have synaptic connections in the superior cervical ganglion, and probably receive parasympathetic components from the Vidian ganglion. It has also been reported that action potentials may be recorded from the anterior lobe during stimulation of the cervical sympathetic trunk.

Nonidez (26a) carefully investigated *thyroid* innervation and concluded that there is no true secretory nervous supply. Regulation of hormonal secretion may be partially controlled by the vasomotor nerves. The principal stimulus for secretion may be thyrotropic hormone resulting from primary stimulation of the pituitary.

Nervous control of the *islands of Langerhans* in the pancreas is still under discussion. Parasympathetic excitation stimulates release of insulin—that is, a vago-insulin system lowers blood sugar in contrast to the sympathico-adrenal system which depletes stored glycogen and raises the blood sugar level.

Diabetes Insipidus and Water Metabolism. Bailey and Bremer (1) found that prolonged diabetes insipidus may follow when small lesions were placed in the hypothalamic region near the pituitary stalk. The augmented thirst and pronounced polyuria which characterize the condition can be ameliorated through administration of crude posterior lobe extract or through the more purified antidiuretic principle. This has proved true in animals and in human beings suffering from diabetes insipidus. One would anticipate, therefore, that removal of the pituitary itself or of the posterior lobe alone would precipitate the syndrome. Actually this is seldom the case. This confusing finding had been a source of bafflement until Gersh disclosed that the secretory posterior lobe cells are found surrounding the pituitary stalk well above the diaphragm of the sella turcica and extending for various distances along the base of the infundibulum. When the pituitary is removed, Gersh (16) reported that the remaining cells of the posterior lobe family become enormously hypertrophied, and no doubt contributed sufficient antidiuretic hormone to prevent polyuria. Gersh, furthermore, deprived normal animals of water which then exhibited hypertrophy of secretory cells throughout the entire posterior lobe, this, no doubt, being the body's mechanism for preserving water. It is estimated that 12 to 15 per cent of the Gersh cells are sufficient to prevent the onset of diabetes insipidus.

Finally, Fisher, Ingram and Ranson, following isolated destruction of the supra-optic nuclei, precipitated severe diabetes insipidus in animals; following such a lesion all secretory cells of the posterior lobe, wherever situated, degenerate. This means that the kidney tubules which normally absorb water in varying amounts (depending upon the amount of antidiuretic hormone being secreted in the posterior lobe), are as immediately under the control of the central nervous system as though they had direct innervation. Hence, we must conclude that the central nervous system through the posterior lobe is directly responsible for the regulation of water elimination by the kidneys.

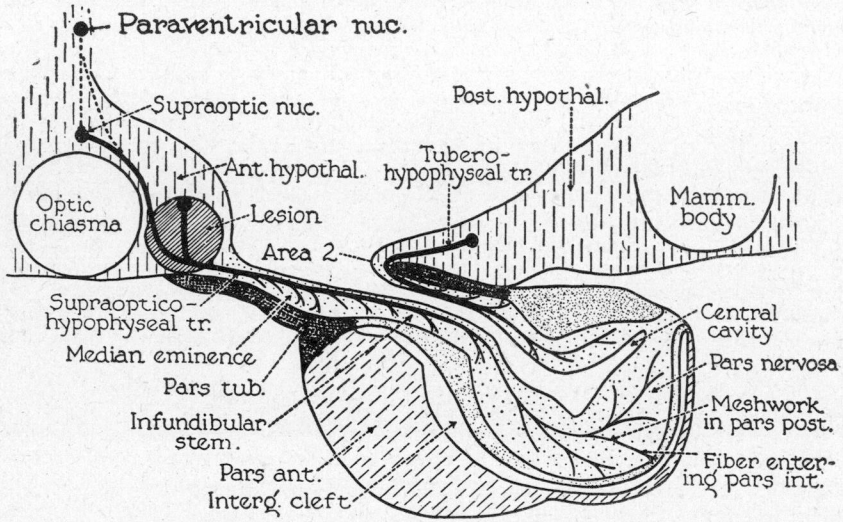

Fig. 136.—Longitudinal section of cat's hypothalamus, showing tractus supra-opticohypophysis, whose interruption causes diabetes insipidus. (From the monograph [12] on diabetes insipidus by Fisher and his collaborators, 1938.)

Heat Regulation. The fact that electrical stimulation of the hypothalamus causes sweating and changes of heart rate and blood pressure reveals little concerning the actual function of the area in the intact animal. It was noted that the spinal animal had a primitive pattern of response, evidently linked with heat regulation, for when one extremity of a spinal dog is chilled the other three tend to conserve heat through reflex vasoconstriction; but a spinal animal cannot maintain the temperature of its body constant. A decerebrate animal may shiver when exposed suddenly to extreme cold, but again the reaction is of insufficient intensity to maintain body temperature (20). Similarly a decerebrate preparation, if placed in a heated room, becomes overheated without panting or sweating, and for this reason it may succumb rapidly to "hyperthermia." An animal with its hypothalamus completely intact, shivers in cold, pants and sweats in heat, and is able through coordinated action of these mechanisms to maintain a relatively constant body temperature in the face of a rapidly changing thermal environment. This is what is meant by functional integration.

Historical note. In 1912 the late Henry Barbour (2) suggested that the thalamus was implicated in heat regulation for, on perfusing warmed blood into the basal areas of the brain, an animal would show signs of panting and sweating, evidently initiated by the local thermal change in the cerebral substance. The hypothalamus at that time had not been recognized as a functional entity; consequently it was scarcely surprising that Barbour ascribed the function of heat regulation to the thalamus rather than to the hypothalamus. He had used a sound experimental approach which has more recently been employed to great advantage by Ranson and his colleagues. Basing the inference upon the disclosures which Karplus and Kreidl had just made concerning responsiveness of hypothalamus to stimulation, the Viennese pharmacologists Isenschmidt and Schnitzler suggested in 1914 that the hypothalamus was essential for temperature control; but the war came and this important early suggestion was forgotten. The first to establish experimentally that the hypothalamus is essential to heat regulation was Allen Keller of Baylor University, who found while at Yale in 1929–30 that animals with the posterior hypothalamus intact could regulate against cold, but that the anterior hypothalamus must remain intact to enable them to regulate against heat (21). Meanwhile, the work of Ranson and his colleagues had amply corroborated and extended Keller's original disclosure.

Mechanisms of heat loss. Although Keller had established that the anterior hypothalamus is essential for regulation against heat, Magoun et al. (24), on locally heating a small area of the anterior hypothalamus (by placing an animal's head in an electrical field after previously placing a small iron grill on the hypothalamus), produced profound activation of the heat-loss mechanisms, with profuse sweating, vasodilatation, and panting. The heart slowed, and within a few minutes rectal temperatures might drop as low as 93° or 94°. In the course of a brain operation White (36) had opportunity to stimulate the same area in a conscious human subject which likewise induced sweating, slowing of the heart, and, interestingly enough, loss of consciousness. The primary heat-loss mechanisms, then, are: sweating, vasodilatation, and panting. It is probable also that there is active inhibition of metabolic processes which would be in keeping with the slowing of the heart.

The autonomic responses which occur when heat-loss mechanisms are activated are mediated primarily through the parasympathetic system, i.e., the effectors involved are cholinergic; but somatic mechanisms are also involved in bringing about the panting reflex. In the heat-loss mechanisms, therefore, one finds an example of a vast functional integration involving simultaneous discharge of both the somatic and autonomic divisions, with evidence of active inhibition of the sympathetic division.

Intraventricular injections. Cushing was the first to suggest the existence of a parasympathetic center in the hypothalamic area (1930). He based his deduction upon reactions to intraventricular injection of small amounts of pituitrin and certain other drugs. If pituitrin is injected into the cerebrospinal fluid of the third ventricle, profuse sweating develops over the entire body and there is generalized vasodilatation of the skin, along with marked slowing of the heart and conspicuous increase in gastro-intestinal peristalsis. The reaction is confined to skin areas having a normal innervation. Many of Cushing's cases had had recent cerebral operations with resultant denervation of the skin of the forehead and scalp on one side, the denervated skin failing to sweat or to show vascular change. In one instance the activation of heat-loss mechanisms reduced the rectal temperature of the patient to 92° Fahrenheit within forty minutes of the injection. The effect could be prevented by intraventricular injection of small amounts of atropine, and Cushing was of the opinion that the atropine probably acted centrally, but convincing proof of this deduction was not forthcoming. Cushing's studies did not give clear-cut localization; however, the centers of response were evidently at the base, for in cases in which the hypothalamus had been destroyed by a pituitary tumor, injection of pituitrin was without central effect. Clinical cases of paroxysmal discharge of the autonomic system, referred to by Penfield as "autonomic epilepsy," run a course closely similar to that resulting from intraventricular pituitrin.

With autonomic epilepsy in man, however, there tends to be a simultaneous parasympathetic and sympathetic discharge, whereas with pituitrin the parasympathetic response dominates.

Mechanisms of heat production and heat conservation. When an animal with posterior hypothalamus intact is placed in the cold, a characteristic pattern of response ensues, characterized by widespread vasoconstriction in the skin, elevation of the hair (pilo-erection), shivering, mobilization of carbohydrate reserves (an elevation of blood sugar), and a rise of the basal metabolic rate. These reactions are calculated either to increase heat production or to conserve heat already available (vasoconstriction and pilo-erection). The pattern of response is made possible through widespread discharge of the sympathetic nervous system, but as in the case of the heat-loss mechanisms, there is simultaneous activation of the somatic outflow involved in the response of shivering.

These disclosures concerning the central organization for heat regulation account for a large number of phenomena observed in clinical cases. Experimentally it has been found that small isolated lesions of the posterior hypothalamus cause an animal to become poikilothermic, i.e., as the environmental temperature was lowered the animal's body assumes a temperature only a degree or two higher than the environment—like a frog or a turtle. Similarly, human beings whose posterior hypothalamus has been destroyed by tumor or infection are rendered completely incapable of maintaining the body temperature—they too become poikilothermic.

Lesions of the anterior hypothalamus, on the other hand, are prone to cause hyperthermia. There are many clinical cases on record of human beings who have had temperatures ranging from 103° to 106° F. and maintained the elevation over a period of months or even years. A male patient with such a history succumbed not long ago in the New Haven Hospital, and on autopsy a small benign fatty tumor was found precisely in the middle of the hypothalamic area less than a millimeter from the pituitary stalk. Surgical operations at the base of the brain are notoriously prone to be followed by bouts of hyperthermia. It would seem that when mechanically disturbed the anterior hypothalamus becomes disorganized and "releases" the more posterior nuclei of the sympathetic division, permitting the heat producing mechanisms to become abnormally active. Following operations for pituitary cysts in children, abrupt thermal elevations have been encountered with temperatures as high as 108° to 109° F., developing within a few minutes of the surgical interference at the base. Such reactions, because of their explosive abruptness, are both dangerous and difficult to handle, since the sympathetic system cannot easily be paralyzed in its peripheral ramifications, and it is also difficult to subdue it from the vantage point of the hypothalamus itself. However, the anesthetics of the barbiturate series act specifically to suppress the hypothalamic nuclei, and the only certain way of dealing with hyperthermia in man or animals is through the use of large anesthetic doses of drugs of the barbituric acid group, i.e., nembutal, amytal, dial, etc. The antipyretic drugs in general owe their action to their specific affinity for the hypothalamic nuclei. Dial, for example, can be detected in tissues by a modified Prussian blue reaction, and brains of "dialized" animals invariably exhibit larger concentrations of the drug in the hypothalamic area than other parts of the central nervous system.

It is interesting in this connection that reflexes known to involve centers in the pons and diencephalon are abolished by subanesthetic doses of any one of the barbiturates. Thus the corneal reflex which the ether anesthetists have used since October 16, 1846, as an index of the depth of anesthesia, may be completely abolished while a patient is still more or less conscious. An anesthetist accustomed to the volatile anesthetics is prone to become alarmed, for, with the corneal reflex gone, he is accustomed to conclude that his patient is profoundly narcotized, when, in fact, the barbiturate may have given only a mild degree of sedation. In recovering from a barbiturate anesthesia, one of the first reflexes to emerge is that of shivering, for under the barbiturates the body temperature invariably falls.

Obesity. In his original description of his syndrome, Fröhlich drew attention to the abnormal adiposity of his patient; it was not only abnormal in amount but also in distribution. Many investigators have found that certain brain lesions cause profound adiposity in animals. It was thought at first that animals developed an abnormal capacity for converting a normal quantity of food ingested into fat, but the recent pair-feeding experiments of Brobeck, Tepperman and Long (7) indicate that hypothalamic rats laid on fat no more rapidly than the controls if both groups have exactly the same caloric intake; but that, when unlimited access to food is permitted, the hypothalamic rats put on weight with abnormal rapidity. They have thus come to the conclusion that hypothalamic obesity stems from hypothalamic *hyperphagia*, i.e., for some reason, as yet ill understood, animals having the particular lesion developed abnormal hunger. This may be due to the fact that gastric peristalsis is augmented as a result of hypothalamic disturbance; there is some evidence to bear this out since gastro-intestinal disturbances are highly prone to occur both in man and in animals following lesions of the base, especially of the anterior or middle nuclei. An acute perforation of the gut has frequently been reported following operations at the base, and in monkeys gastric hemorrhages are not uncommon (19).

The disturbances in carbohydrate metabolism have been described following hypothalamic lesions, but the early work on this topic has not been confirmed and further experimental studies are needed. The basal metabolic rate may certainly be altered as a result of hypothalamic disturbance, and lesions to the posterior nuclei have led to depression of the basal metabolism rate and there is some evidence that anteriorly situated lesions cause an elevation of the basal metabolism rate. Here again, well controlled studies are lacking, and further data required.

Sexual Functions. The extensive literature which now exists concerning the part played by the nervous system in regulating sexual functions will be dealt with below in the section on reproduction. It may be mentioned here that Bard (4), who finds that animals during their estrus cycle have a highly organized pattern of sexual behavior, reported that precisely the same pattern obtains in a decorticate cat when estrus is precipitated by hormone injection. The thalamus, basal ganglia and anterior hypothalamus can be removed without impairing the sexual behavior pattern, but the posterior hypothalamus and lower mesencephalon appear to be essential for the response.

Certain animals such as the ferret ovulate only after copulation. Section of the pituitary stalk or injury to the tuber nuclei in the ferret prevents postcopulatory ovulation, suggesting that the hypothalamic nuclei regulate the secretions of gonadotropic hormone of the anterior lobe.

Hypothalamus and Emotional Expression. Many years ago Goltz noted that dogs from which the cerebral hemisphere had been removed may snarl and show signs of rage. In 1928 Bard (3) proved conclusively that the capacity to display anger depends upon central mechanisms which lie below the cortical level; for continuance of the "sham" rage reaction he found the presence of the hypothalamus essential. The reaction consists of periodic agitation with biting, struggling, clawing, lashing of the tail, accompanied by signs of widespread activation of the sympathetic nervous system (erection of hair, a rise in blood pressure, sweating, protrusion of the eyes, dilatation of the pupil, and cardiac acceleration). Following upon Bard's work, Ranson and his pupils found that stimulation of the lateral hypothalamic area in normal unanesthetized animals (electrodes put in place previously under deep anesthesia) caused rage reactions of a most conspicuous character. Even more striking was the unrecorded experience of the late Professor Dusser de Barenne who inadvertently injected a small amount of strychnine into a cat's hypothalamus (intending it for the thalamus). The cat recovered from its ether anesthesia and within a few seconds a frightening seizure of unleashed fury developed in which the cat dashed madly from one end of the room to the other, from the floor to the ceiling, savagely attacking anything in its path.

Cases of acute belligerence and fury have been recorded in human beings following surgical operations involving this area of the brain, and the reactions have also been seen following head injury in man. It had been known that bilateral lesions of the prechiasmal region tended to cause savage behavior in cats, but not until the recent important study of Wheatley (38) had it been clearly demonstrated that isolated destruction of the ventromedial hypothalamic nuclei (Fig. 134, 8) transformed the normal "favorable response to friendly treatment and handling" into a conspicuous reaction of "malevolence and savageness." Other bilateral lesions consistently failed to cause the reaction. Efforts to modify the belligerent behavior pattern by subsequent lesions or ablations of higher regions of the brain were also entirely unsuccessful.

There is no doubt that mental disorders, especially the manic-depressive neuroses, are in some way associated with disturbed hypothalamic activity. In these circumstances brain stem nuclei fail to receive their normal inhibitory control, e.g., from the ventromedial nuclei; it is no doubt significant that the anesthetics of the barbiturate acid series which have a profound affinity for the hypothalamic nuclei appear to be effective therapeutically in promoting recovery of human beings from agitated anxiety states, such as those induced by the stresses of war. It is thus possible that the organic background of anxiety states in man lies in a disturbance of hypothalamic interrelations.

CEREBRAL REGULATION OF AUTONOMIC FUNCTION

It has long been recognized that mental experience, particularly experience with strong emotional content, may have profound effects upon the circulatory and gastro-intestinal systems. William Beaumont noted that the gastric mucosa of Alexis St. Martin's stomach showed pallor when Alexis was angry, but that there was increased vascularity on sight or smell of good food. Similarly, in the human face the pallor of fear, the blushing of embarrassment, may be accompanied by changes of blood pressure, heart rate and by sweating. Through training and strengthening of the "will" it becomes possible to "control" the autonomic manifestations of emotion, and certain individuals have gained volitional control over one or more specific autonomic functions such as the sphincter of the pupil, pilo-erection and the rate of the heart (23). There can be no doubt, therefore, from these *a priori* considerations that the autonomic system is under domination from the cortical level. Clinical and experimental evidence bearing on this subject are available in recent reviews (13,14,23,26,33) and can be briefly summarized.

Experimental Evidence. *Cardiovascular system.* Stimulation of certain foci on the gyrus proreus and the sigmoid gyri of cats or the premotor area of monkeys may evoke acceleration of the heart and rise of blood pressure; from other points in the adjacent eye fields retraction of the nictitating membrane and the dilatation of the pupils can be obtained. In animals from which the stellate ganglion and the adrenal glands have been removed stimulation of these areas causes marked slowing of the heart and fall in blood pressure. That the reactions are the direct result of the stimulation of nerve elements within the cortex was established by four lines of evidence (18): (i) pressor and depressor points were geographically separate from one another, (ii) local anesthesia of the cortex to a depth of 3 mm. abolished the response, (iii) undercutting of a responsive area eliminated the reaction, and (iv) after anesthetizing the responsive area with procaine the reactions could again be evoked by plunging the electrodes through the cortex into the white matter. The reactions are independent of concomitant movement since they could still be evoked after curarization.

In other experiments (17) in which limb and renal volumes were recorded simultaneously during cortical stimulation, the limb volume increased while the kidney volume fell. It was established furthermore that the rise in limb volume took place largely as a result of an increased blood supply to the muscles themselves since, after the extremity in question had been skinned, a similar reaction could be obtained. "Since dilatation of the limbs occurs with a fall of blood pressure and constriction with a rise; since these alterations of limb volume are abolished by denervation of the limbs, and since they can be produced in noncurarized animals with stimuli too weak to cause muscular activity, it is concluded that alterations of blood flow in the extremities occurring as a result of excitation of the cortex are active phenomena mediated through nervous channels and not the product of epileptic seizure nor passive changes due to alteration in blood pressure" (17). It is thus evident that the local circulation in muscles is to some extent controlled at the cortical level; this affords an excellent illustration of the way in which the autonomic and somatic divisions of the nervous system cooperate in carrying out complex integrations. Muscular effort requires an increased blood supply and the impulses responsible for augmenting the local circulation in muscle presumably originate simultaneously in the same area of the cortex that integrates the somatic movement pattern. This no doubt accounts for the overlapping distribution of autonomic and somatic motor foci in the cerebral cortex (Chap. 13).

Gastro-intestinal tract. There have been many reports of gastro-intestinal disturbances following cerebral injuries both in man and in animals (9). Acute ulceration of the gastric mucosa may develop within a few hours of a cerebral injury, especially one affecting both cerebral hemispheres (19,34). In the cat following removal of both motor areas a greater persistency and constancy of strength of gastric peristalsis is noted with a considerable increase in resting contraction (23). Others have reported changes in gastric motility on stimulation of area 6 and it now appears that the region most responsible is on the orbital surface of the frontal lobe and known as area 13 (Chap. 13). Stimulation of this area in both cats and monkeys causes widespread vagal effects including a prompt inhibition of gastro-intestinal peristalsis.

Other autonomic effects. Chimpanzees with bilateral premotor ablation develop marked and persistent pilo-erection; in a human being capable of voluntary pilo-erection it has been reported that marked electroencephalographic changes could be detected from the skull over the premotor regions. Pupillary changes have already been mentioned; shivering has been noted in an exaggerated form after bilateral removal of the motor areas in monkeys.

The Autonomic Motor Area. Study of the distribution of autonomic foci in the cerebral cortex leads to the conclusion that an autonomic motor area

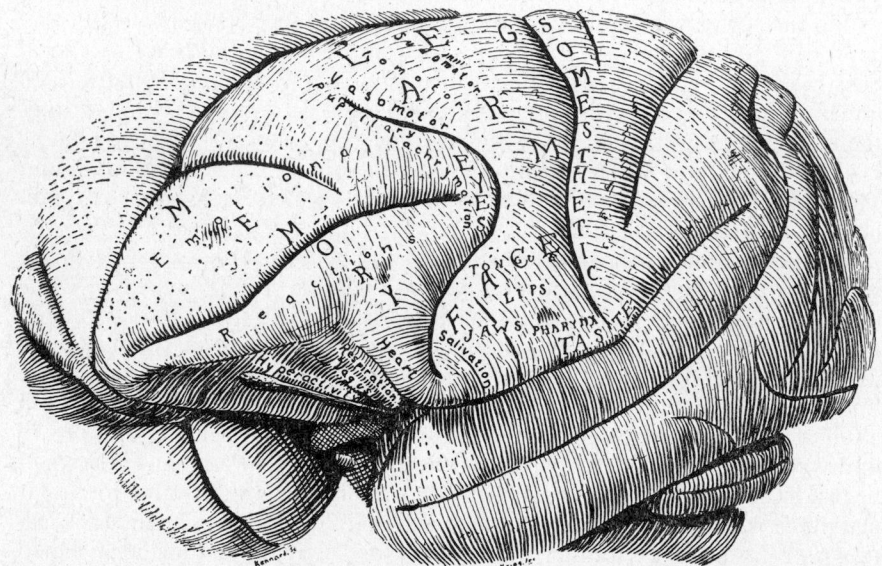

Fig. 137.—Diagram of a macaque brain showing the relation of the autonomic representation to that of the somatic motor (Chap. 13). (Prepared for Dr. Kennard by Dr. Wendell J. S. Krieg and reproduced by permission of the University of Illinois Press; from Bucy, *The precentral motor cortex,* 1944.

exists which is almost as well defined as the somatic motor area. "The accumulation of evidence on cortical autonomic function points to a focal representation on the cortical surface which is very similar to that of the somatic representation and which exists to some degree in the cat, dog, monkey, and man. Admittedly the cortical foci are less definite in the autonomic than in the somatic sphere but so also is the autonomic activity more diffuse in nature than is somatic. As is shown in Fig. 137 cortico-autonomic representation lies mainly in a band extending along the rostral border of the motor area lying between these and the frontal areas which are known to relate to such affective functions as behavior, personality and the more complex emotional reactions. Within this band cortico-autonomic activity is closely integrated with the somatic." Thus pseudomotor, pilomotor and vasomotor representation which primarily affect the extremities overlap with the part of the cortex in which somatic movement patterns are integrated. Similarly lacrimation may be evoked just rostral to the eyefield and foci causing salivation just rostral to the face area.

REFERENCES

1. BAILEY, P., and BREMER, F. Experimental diabetes insipidus. *Arch. intern. Med.*, 1921, *28*:773–803.

2. BARBOUR, H. G. Die Wirkung unmittelbarer Erwärmung und Abkühlung der Wärmezentra auf die Körpertemperatur. *Arch. exp. Path. Pharmak.*, 1912, *70*:1–26.

3. BARD, P. A diencephalic mechanism for the expression of rage with special reference to the sympathetic nervous system. *Amer. J. Physiol.*, 1928, *84*:490–515.

4. BARD, P. Oestrual behavior in surviving decorticate cats. *Amer. J. Physiol.*, 1936, *116*:4–5.

5. BEATTIE, J., BROW, G. R., and LONG, C. N. H. The hypothalamus and the sympathetic nervous system. I. The dependence of the extrasystolic arrhythmia of the heart produced by chloroform, upon the integrity of the sympathetic nervous system; and the use of this arrhythmia as an indicator of sympathetic activity. *Res. Publ. Ass. nerv. ment. Dis.*, 1930, *9*:249–294; II. The higher connections of the sympathetic nervous system as studied by experimental lesions of the hypothalamus, 295–316; Physiological and anatomical evidence for the existence of nerve tracts connecting the hypothalamus with spinal sympathetic centres. *Proc. roy. Soc.*, 1930, *106B:* 253–275.

6. BECHTEREW, W. VON. *Die Funktionen der Nervencentra.* Jena, G. Fischer, 1908–11, 3 vols.

7. BROBECK, J. R., TEPPERMAN, J., and LONG, C. N. H. Experimental hypothalamic hyperphagia in the albino rat. *Yale J. Biol. Med.*, 1943, *15*:831–853.

8. BROOKS, C. McC., and GERSH, I. Innervation of the hypophysis of the rabbit and rat. *Endocrinology*, 1941, *28*:1–5.

9. CUSHING, H. *Papers relating to the pituitary body, hypothalamus and parasympathetic nervous system.* Springfield, Ill., C. C Thomas, 1932. vii, 234 pp.

10. DUSSER DE BARENNE, J. G., and KOSKOFF, Y. D. Flexor rigidity of the hind legs and priapism in the "secondary" spinal preparation of the male cat. *Amer. J. Physiol.*, 1932, *102*:75–86.

11. FINLEY, K. H. Angio-architecture of the hypothalamus and its peculiarities. *Res. Publ. Ass. nerv. ment. Dis.*, 1940, *20*:286–309.

12. FISHER, C., INGRAM, W. R., and RANSON, S. W. *Diabetes insipidus and the neurohormonal control of water balance: A contribution to the structure and function of the hypothalamico-hypophyseal system.* Ann Arbor, Edwards Brothers, 1938. x, 212 pp.

13. FULTON, J. F. The interrelation of cerebrum and cerebellum in the regulation of somatic and autonomic functions. (Harvey Lect.) *Medicine, Baltimore,* 1936, *15*:247–306.

14. FULTON, J. F. *Physiology of the nervous system,* 2nd ed. New York, Oxford University Press, 1943. x, 614 pp.

15. FULTON, J. F., and KELLER, A. D. *The sign of Babinski. A study of the evolution of cortical dominance.* Springfield, Ill. C. C Thomas, 1932, xv, 165 pp.

16. GERSH, I. The structure and function of the parenchymatous glandular cells in the neurohypophysis of the rat. *Amer. J. Anat.*, 1939, *64*:407–429.

17. GREEN, H. D., and HOFF, E. C. Effects of faradic stimulation of the cerebral cortex on limb and renal volumes in the cat and monkey. *Amer. J. Physiol.*, 1937, *118*:641–658.

18. HOFF, E. C., and GREEN, H. D. Cardiovascular reactions induced by electrical stimulation of the cerebral cortex. *Amer. J. Physiol.*, 1936, *117*:411–422.

19. HOFF, E. C., and SHEEHAN, D. Experimental gastric erosions following hypothalamic lesions in monkeys. *Amer. J. Path.*, 1935, *11*:789–802.

20. KELLER, A. D. Observations on the localization in the brain stem of mechanisms controlling body temperature. *Amer. J. med. Sci.*, 1933, *185*:746–748.

21. KELLER, A. D. Separation in the brain stem of the mechanisms of heat loss from those of heat production. *J. Neurophysiol.*, 1938, *1*:543–557.

22. KENNARD, M. A. Vasomotor disturbances resulting from cortical lesions. *Arch. Neurol. Psychiat., Chicago,* 1935, *33*:537–545.

23. KENNARD, M. A. Autonomic functions, Chap. XI in: BUCY, P. C., ed., *The precentral motor cortex,* Urbana, Illinois, 1944.

24. MAGOUN, H. W., HARRISON, F., BROBECK, J. R., and RANSON, S. W. Activation of heat loss mechanisms by local heating of the brain. *J. Neurophysiol.*, 1938, *1*:101–114.

25. MILLER, F. R., and SHERRINGTON, C. S. Some observations on the buccopharyngeal stage of reflex deglutition in the cat. *Quart. J. exp. Physiol.*, 1916, *9*:147–186.

26. MILLER, H. R. *Central autonomic regulations in health and disease with special reference to the hypothalamus.* Introduction by J. F. Fulton. New York, Grune and Stratton, 1942. xx, 430 pp.

26a. NONIDEZ, J. F. Innervation of the thyroid gland. III. Distribution and termination of the nerve fibers in the dog. *Amer. J. Anat.*, 1935, *57*:135–169.

27. RASMUSSEN, A. T. Innervation of the hypophysis. *Endocrinology*, 1938, *23*:263–278.

28. RASMUSSEN, A. T. Effects of hypophysectomy and hypophysial stalk resection on the hypothalamic nuclei of animals and man. *Res. Publ. Ass. nerv. ment. Dis.*, 1940, *20*:245–269.

29. RASMUSSEN, A. T., and GARDNER, W. J. Effects of hypophysial stalk resection on the

hypophysis and hypothalamus of man. *Endocrinology*, 1940, *27*:219–226.

30. RIOCH, D. McK., WISLOCKI, G. B., and O'LEARY, J. L. A précis of preoptic, hypothalamic, and hypophysial terminology, with atlas. *Res. Publ. Ass. nerv. ment. Dis.*, 1940, *20*:3–30.

31. SAHS, A. L., and FULTON, J. F. Somatic and autonomic reflexes in spinal monkeys. *J. Neurophysiol.*, 1940, *3*:258–268.

32. SHERRINGTON, C. S. The spinal cord. Vol. 2, pp. 782–883 in: SCHÄFER, E. A. *Textbook of physiology*, 1900.

33. SPIEGEL, E. A., and HUNSICKER, W. C., JR. The conduction of cortical impulses to the autonomic system. *J. nerv. ment. Dis.*, 1936, *83*:252–274.

34. TEDESCHI, C. S. Gastric mucosal lesions in rats submitted to head trauma. *Proc. Soc. exp. Biol.*, *N. Y.*, 1944, *57*:268–270.

35. TRUSCOTT, L. B. The nerve supply of the pituitary of the rat. *J. comp. Neurol.*, 1944, *80*:235–255.

36. UOTILA, U. U. On the role of the pituitary stalk in the regulation of the anterior pituitary, with special reference to the thyrotropic hormone. *Endocrinology*, 1939, *25*:605–614.

37. VAZQUEZ-LOPEZ, E. Structure of the neurohypophysis with special reference to nerve endings. *Brain*, 1942, *65*:1–33.

38. WHEATLEY, M. D. The hypothalamus and affective behavior in cats. A study of the effects of experimental lesions, with anatomical correlations. *Arch. Neurol. Psychiat.*, 1944. *52*:298–316.

CHAPTER 12

CEREBRAL CORTEX: CYTOARCHITECTURE AND PROJECTIONS

Since ancient times the cerebral hemispheres have been looked upon as the organ of intelligence and conscious sensation. Consequently the structure of this region of the brain has long aroused curiosity. Ancient writers, and even those of the Renaissance, speculated widely about the localization of consciousness; some placed the "psyche" in the cerebral ventricles, others drew diagrams suggesting precise localization of various mental faculties in different regions of the forebrain. Neurologists of the seventeenth century such as Willis and Vieussens carried out experiments which indicated that the brain substance and not the ventricles was the seat of consciousness. Willis, moreover, proclaimed the cerebrum the seat of volitional movements and the cerebellum the source of involuntary movements; he also described the gross structure and blood supply of the brain accurately and in considerable detail.

Modern work indicates that the seat of consciousness lies in the forebrain and possibly in the cerebral hemispheres themselves. It is still an open question, however, whether consciousness depends upon other parts of the nervous system, i.e., upon the cerebral hemispheres acting in cooperation with lower levels of nervous function; but there is no doubt that the highest development of psychical activity in man is associated with the cortical matter of the cerebrum. In the young infant the dawn of its mental powers is correlated with the development of its normal cortical structure, while in extreme age the failure in the mental faculties goes hand-in-hand with an atrophy of discrete elements of the cortex. If these cortical elements were removed, most, if not all, intelligence, sensation, and thought—the qualities that characterize the highest psychical life of man—would be destroyed; indeed, abnormalities in the structure or properties of this cortical material are accepted as the probable causal factor of those perversions in reasoning and in character which are exhibited by the insane. The cortical gray matter, therefore, is the chief organ of the psychical life, the tissues through whose activity the objective changes in the external world, so far as they affect our sense organs, are converted into the subjective changes of consciousness. The nature of this relation constitutes the most difficult problem of physiology and psychology, a problem which perhaps is beyond the possibility of a satisfactory scientific explanation. There is a physicochemical mechanism in the brain matter which is capable of giving us a reaction in consciousness. The methods of physiology are adapted to the investigation of the nature of this mechanism, but the reaction in consciousness deals with a something which, so far as we know, is not matter or energy, and, therefore, is not at present within the scope of physiological or, indeed, scientific explanation (9). The psychical response, however, whatever may be its nature, has certain relations with the structure, arrangement, and properties of the underlying nervous mechanism which may be studied by physiological methods.

Historical note (6). The microscope came late in the analysis of the structural organization of the nervous system. The story actually begins in the eighteenth century with an Italian medical student, Francesco Gennari, who in February 1776 observed, on dissecting the occipital lobes of the brain, a well defined white line which indicated special structural organization of this region of the cerebral mantle. This line is now recognized as a primary landmark within the so-called visual cortex. Its importance was promptly recognized by other continental neurologists, but a closer analysis and comparison with other regions of the cortex did not come until 1840.

In that year the French psychiatrist, J.-P. Baillarger, using his own unaided eye and resourceful intellect, found on placing thin sections of human cerebral cortex between two plates of glass that six discrete layers could be identified in all areas of the cortex but that the relative width of individual layers varied widely from one region to another. He republished the plates of Gennari, and established that Gennari's white line of the occipital cortex extended into other cortical areas and corresponded with Baillarger's external band. Baillarger himself sought to discover how the brains of the insane differed in structure from those of normal human beings, but his method of examination, ingenious though it was, failed to disclose significant differences except in microcephalics and congenital monsters. Little did he realize that one hundred years of uninterrupted study of the minute structure of the cerebral cortex, with far more refined methods than he could command in 1840, has similarly failed—except in cases of senile degeneration—to disclose consistent structural changes in the brains of the mentally ill.

Baillarger's observations aroused wide interest, but not until methods for staining tissues became current was a more detailed histological differentiation possible. In 1867 another alienist, Meynert of Vienna, subdivided the cerebral mantle into a primitive olfactory brain, the so-called "rhinencephalon," and the newer brain, the "pallium," subdivisions now generally referred to as "allocortex" and "isocortex" (Vogt). The outer lamina of the primitive allocortex is white, whereas that of the isocortex is gray, but both, as Baillarger and Meynert originally pointed out, are made up of six layers.

Modern study of the cellular architecture of the cortex is associated with the names of Golgi, Ramón y Cajal, Hammarberg, Campbell, Brodmann, and the Vogts. Cajal studied the ramification of different types of cortical neurons by silver impregnation. Hammarberg and Campbell studied cell types by means of stains that did not disclose dendritic structure. The Vogts concentrated on fiber systems in various parts of the cortex, using myelin stains. Hammarberg, Campbell and Brodmann thus founded the cytoarchitectural analysis, Cajal and the Vogts myeloarchitecture, and Vogt and his followers have attempted to combine cytoarchitectural maps of the cortex with the myeloarchitectonic equivalents.

LAMINAR ORGANIZATION OF THE CEREBRAL CORTEX

Through such microscopic analysis Cajal, Campbell, et al. have subdivided the isocortex into areas of specific structure in the belief that structural differences bespeak differences of function. Within each area two primary divisions are recognized: (i) the external lamina with its four layers, and (ii) the internal lamina with two. The stratification is based on the presence of specific types of cell peculiar to each layer as indicated in Table 10.

Table 10.—Stratification of Parieto-temporo-occipital Isocortex*

External lamina	I (1). Plexiform layer, II (2). Small pyramids, III (3). Medium sized pyramids, IVa (4). Star pyramids, IVb (5). Star cells,
Internal lamina	V (6). Large deep pyramids, VI (7). Spindles.

* Arabic numerals were used by Cajal and Campbell (Fig. 138), who differentiated a layer, their layer 4 of external large pyramids, which in this report is called a layer of star pyramids and must be incorporated into Bevan Lewis' diagram (1). However, since the latter has come into general use, the additional layer is designated IVa. It must be emphasized that the boundaries between layers, with the exception of the boundary between IVb and V, are never sharp, and that

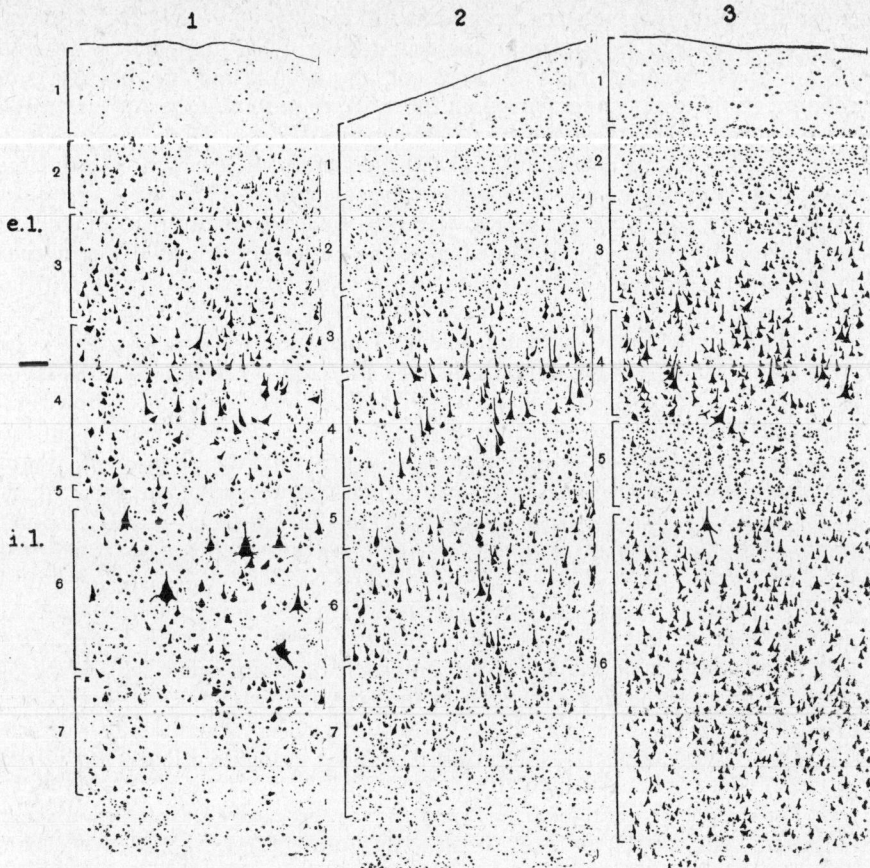

Fig. 138.—Cytoarchitectonic pictures of representative areas of human brain. Only cell bodies are stained. (Campbell, 1905.)

1. *Motor cortex* (area 4 of Brodmann). Stratification (arabic numerals at left) suggested by Campbell does not agree with later established facts and is probably incorrect. Limit between external (e.1.) and internal (i.1.) laminae lies approximately at upper fourth of layer 4. This area is often called gigantopyramidalis from the presence of Betz cells. Its architectonic limits are, therefore, easily determined.

2. *Postcentral cortex*, near to wall of central sulcus (area 3 of Brodmann). Comparison of 1 and 2 reveals that without knowledge of structure of cortex, existence of two different areas can be ascertained. In fact, division was made despite a wrong concept of the structure of the pre-central cortex.

3. *Temporal transverse cortex* (auditosensory of Campbell, probably 41 or 42 of Brodmann). There are striking similarities and differences between postcentral and temporal transverse areas; e.g., while stratification appears to be the same in both cases, thickness of layers, their densities, sizes and forms of cells, etc., are very different. No difficulty is experienced in distinguishing architectonic areas as different as these two. It is to be noted that Campbell did not distinguish between layers 6 and 7. (From Fulton, *Physiology of the nervous system*, 2nd ed. Oxford University Press, New York, 1943.)

---

if they are ascertained with the help of only the architectonic picture are entirely hypothetical. Figure 143 shows several drawings of the architectonic picture of representative areas of the human brain taken from Campbell's book. Although not as perfect as the photographs published by the German school, they clearly demonstrate the differences in cell size, density of the layers, layer thickness, etc., upon which the architectonic subdivision of the brain has been based. (From Lorente de Nó in Fulton, *Physiology of the nervous system*, 2nd ed. New York, Oxford University Press, 1943.)

The six layers may be characterized as follows:

I. The superficial, plexiform, or molecular layer, lying immediately beneath the pia mater, and having a thickness of about 0.25 mm. In this layer, in addition to the supporting neuroglia, there are found a number of very small nerve cells of several types lying with their processes parallel to the surface of the brain. The axons and dendrites of these small cells terminate within the layer, so that they take no direct part in the formation of the white matter of the brain, but have, probably, a distributive or associative function. In this layer, also, end many of the dendrites of the larger nerve cells of the deeper layers and the terminal arborization of entering nerve fibers (axons) from other regions.

II. The layer of small pyramidal cells. This layer is characterized by the presence of numerous pyramidal cells (see Fig. 138, 1), which in general increase in size in passing from the upper to the lower strata. The apices of these cells are directed toward the external surface. The dendrites from the apical process terminate in the molecular layer, while the axon arising from the basal side of the cell passes inwardly to constitute one of the nerve fibers of the medullary portion of the cerebrum. This thick lamina of cells is sometimes subdivided into three layers of small, medium, and large pyramidal cells.

III. A layer of larger pyramidal cells which are sometimes difficult to distinguish from layer II.

IV. The granular or stellate layer composed of many small cells, some of which are pyramidal and some stellate in form, with short branching axons. These latter belong to Golgi's second type of nerve cell. The thin layer of star cells (layer 5 in Campbell's diagram, Fig. 138) is designated layer IVb in the more modern texts (see Table 10).

V. The deep pyramidal layer or layers of large (see area 4) or medium sized pyramidal cells, similar in form to those in layer II, and the axons of which pass into the medulla or white matter of the cerebrum as nerve fibers.

VI. The layer of fusiform or spindle-shaped nerve cells. A layer of cells whose form is more irregular than that of the pyramidal cells, but whose axons also pass into the medullary portion of the cerebrum, while their dendrites stretch externally into the layers of pyramidal cells. In this layer are found also some cells belonging to the second type of Golgi (Martinotti cells).

The medulla of the cerebrum. The white matter of the cerebrum begins immediately below the last-named layer, and consists (i) of nerve fibers which originate from the pyramidal and polymorphic cells immediately exterior to it, and which carry outgoing impulses from that part of the cortex, and (ii) of fibers arising elsewhere in the cortex or in the lower portions of the brain, which terminate in the cortex and carry the incoming impulses—impulses which are afferent as regards that part of the cortex. The fibers in this white matter may be classified under three heads: First, the *projection system* (*A, B, C, D,* and *E* of Fig. 139), comprising those fibers, afferent and efferent, which connect the cortex with underlying parts of the central nervous system—the spinal cord, medulla, pons, midbrain, or thalamus. This great projection system emerges, for the most part, through the internal capsule and the peduncles of the cerebrum. Second, the *association system.* Certain parts of the cortex are seemingly lacking in a projection system; the fibers arising from these parts do not enter the capsule to make connection with the motor and sensory paths below, but pass to other parts of the cortex, forming a part of the system of association fibers. This system may be defined as comprising

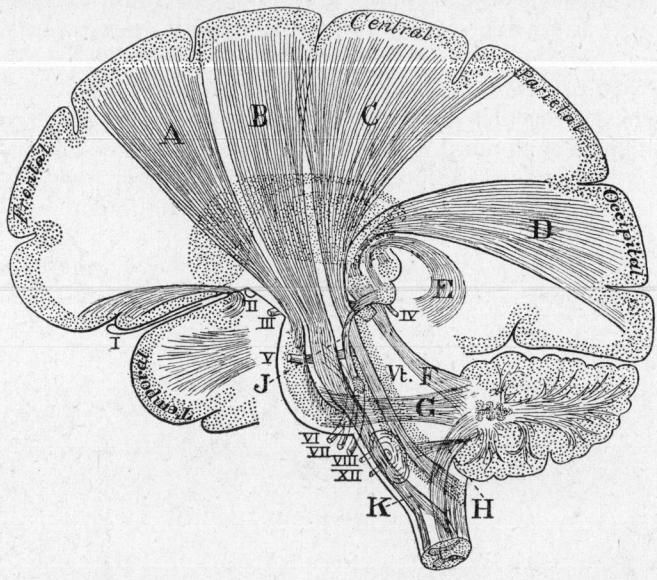

Fig. 139.—Simplified schema of the projection fibers of the cerebrum and of the peduncles of the cerebellum; lateral view of the internal capsule: A, Tract from the frontal gyri to the pons nuclei, and so to the cerebellum (frontal cerebro-cortico-pontal tract); B, the motor (pyramidal) tract; C, the sensory (lemniscus) tract; D, the visual tract; E, the auditory tract; F, the fibers of the superior peduncle of the cerebellum; G, fibers of the middle peduncle uniting with A in the pons; H, fibers of the inferior peduncle of the cerebellum; J, fibers between the auditory nucleus and the inferior colliculus; K, motor (pyramidal) decussation in the bulb; Vt, fourth ventricle. The numerals refer to the cranial nerves. (Modified from Starr.)

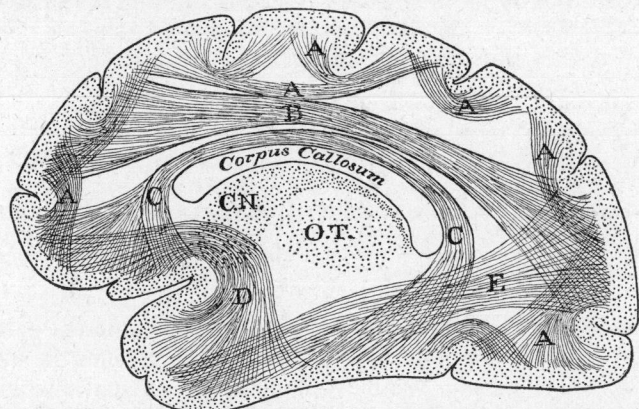

Fig. 140.—Lateral view of a human hemisphere, showing bundles of association fibers (Starr): A, A, between adjacent gyri; B, between frontal and occipital areas; C, between frontal and temporal areas, cingulum; D, between frontal and temporal areas, fasciculus uncinatus; E, between occipital and temporal areas, fasciculus longitudinalis inferior; C.N., caudate nucleus; O.T., thalamus.

those fibers which connect one part of the cortex with another (Fig. 140). Association fibers are found in the regions giving rise to projection fibers as well as in the areas lacking in a projection system. There are short association tracts (*A*, *A*) connecting neighboring convolutions and long tracts passing from one lobe to another. Third, the *commissural system*, consisting of association fibers that cross the midline and connect portions of one cerebral hemisphere with the cortex of the other. These fibers make up the commissural bands, known in gross anatomy as the corpus callosum, anterior white commissure, fornix, etc.

Physiological Deductions from the Histology of the Cortex. Cajal (8) lays stress upon some anatomical features which seem to justify certain generalizations of a physiological nature. In the first place, every part of the cortex receives incoming impulses and gives rise to outgoing impulses. Every part

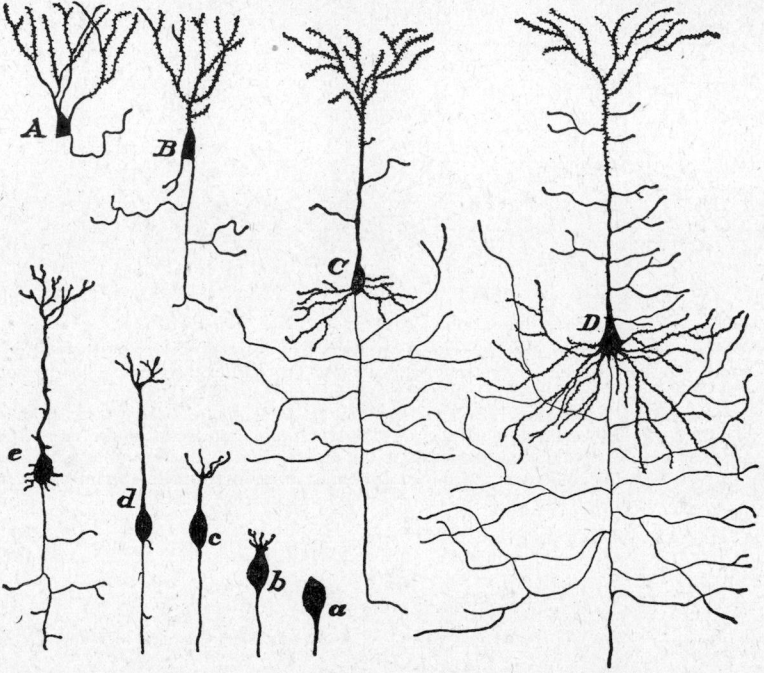

Fig. 141.—*A–D*, showing the phylogenetic development of mature nerve cells in a series of vertebrates: *a–e*, the ontogenetic development of growing cells in a typical mammal (in both cases only pyramidal cells from the cerebrum are shown): *A*, frog; *B*, lizard; *C*, rat; *D*, man; *a*, neuroblast without dendrites; *b*, commencing dendrites; *c*, dendrites further developed; *d*, first appearance of collateral branches; *e*, further development of collaterals and dendrites. (From Ramón y Cajal.)

of the cortex is, therefore, both a termination of some afferent path and the beginning of some efferent path; it is, in other words, a reflex arc of a greater or less degree of complexity. We may suppose that efferent discharges from any part of the cortex are aroused by afferent impulses reaching that point from some other part of the nervous system. Whether or not there is such a thing as absolutely spontaneous mental activity cannot be determined by physiology, but on the anatomical side at least all the structures exhibit connections that fit them for reflex stimulation, and many of our apparently spontaneous acts must be of this character. Secondly, all parts of the isocortex exhibit an essentially similar basic structure. Modern physiology has taught that different parts of the cerebrum have different functions. Definite differences in the thickness of the layers, in the size or shape of the cells, or in the character of the fibrillation, have been pointed out, but one might, perhaps, have expected greater differences in structure, considering the widely varying character of the reactions in different cortical areas. Numerous special studies made upon the lamination of different parts of the human cortex, and comparative observations upon the cerebral cortex in different vertebrates have served to give an anatomical foundation for certain speculations which subsequent work may or may not confirm. It is pointed out that if we omit the outer or molecular layer the other cells of the cortex fall into three groups, namely, the *granular layer*, 3 in Figure 138, the *supragranular layer*, 2, comprising the pyramidal cells external to the granular layer, and the *infragran-*

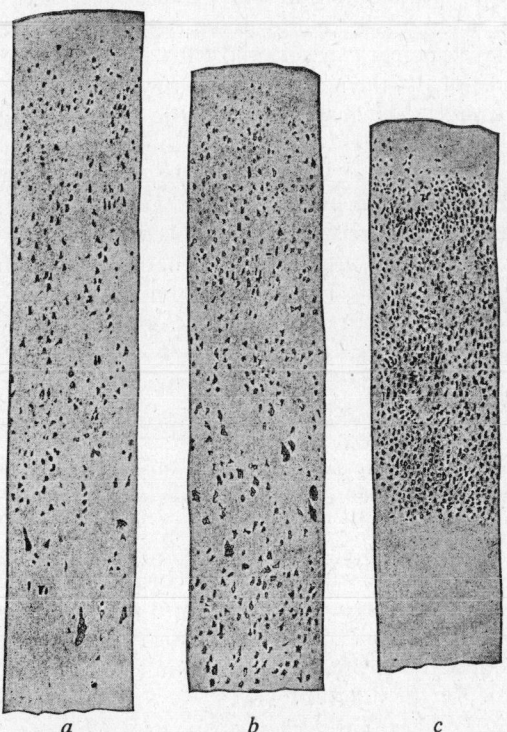

a b c

Fig. 142.—Sections through corresponding parts of the cortex in: *a*, man; *b*, dog; and *c*, mole, to show the greater separation of the nerve cells in the higher animals. (Bethe, after Nissl.)

ular layer, 4 and 5, comprising the pyramidal and fusiform cells internal to the granular layer. Comparison of the cerebral cortex in the brains of the different vertebrates indicates that the supragranular cells have appeared relatively late in the phylogeny of the vertebrates, and have reached their greatest development in the human brain. The suggestion occurs, therefore, that these cells may have a different functional significance from those in the infragranular layer. It has been supposed that the supragranular cells mediate the so-called higher psychical processes, which characterize man and the related mammalia as compared with the lower vertebrates. The infragranular cells, on the other hand, constitute a primitive layer which has obvious connections, through projection fibers, with the underlying parts of the brain and of the body at large. These cells form, therefore, a mechanism through which the brain is connected directly with the rest of the body, and through which the older instinctive reactions are controlled. In the matter of lamination and variations in the character of the strata of cells and fibers the human cortex shows more differentiation than is found in the lower animals. It is especially characterized by a large development of what are known as associational areas, particularly in the frontal lobe. In the third place, the central nervous system throughout the vertebrates is constructed upon the same lines, a mechanism of interconnecting neurons. There is a vast difference in the mental activity of a bird and a man, but the cortex of the cerebrum shows a fundamental similarity in structure in the two cases. In addition to the variations in stratification or lamination referred to above, one general distinction that comparative anatomy is able to make is that in the higher animals the greater mental development is associated with a greater complexity and richness in the connections of the neurons. As shown in Figures 141 and 142, the number of processes, particularly the dendritic processes, is much greater in the cortical cells of the higher animals; or, to put this fact in another way, the number of cells in the cortex of the higher animals is much less for an area of the same size than in lower animals. The amount of inbetween substance or the richness of the network of processes is increased. This anatomical fact would indicate that the greater mental activity in the higher animals is dependent, in part, upon the richer interconnection of the nerve cells, or, expressed physiologically, our mental processes are characterized by their more numerous and complex associations.

The cortex is thus made up of four main types of cell:

1. Cells with descending axons often reaching the white substance, to be continued by a fiber of projection or of association.
2. Cells with short axons ramified in the proximity of the cell body, often within a homogeneous zone of the dendritic plexus.
3. Cells with ascending axons ramified in one or several cortical layers.
4. Cells with horizontal axons.

Study of the cellular organization of the cerebral cortex leads to the conclusion that the cortical neuron chains "are in no way different from chains of internuncial neurons in any part of the central nervous system" (7). A diagram of an intracortical neuron chain is given in Figure 143. Lorente de Nó (7) who is responsible for the diagram writes:

"When the chains of neurons in Figure 143 are examined closely it will be observed that they are of two types. Some of the chains include short links with cells of a single layer, as for example links 25-8' in layer V, and links 24-5' in layer IV. Other links are long and include cells of different layers, as, for instance, links 18-2, 15-4, 8'-2', etc. The long links vary but little in different mammals, but the short links increase progressively in number from the mouse to man. Thus, in the cortex of the mouse, cells with ascending axons are relatively numerous, while those with short axons are relatively rare. In the human cortex there is an increase in the number of cells with ascending axons, but the increase in the cells having short axons is much more pronounced, so much so that in some cortical regions they outnumber the cells with descending axons. Furthermore, the increase in the short axon cells is not restricted to any one layer, but takes place in all of them, although in different cortical regions the increase is more pronounced in certain layers, for example, in the area striata in layer IV and the motor area in layer V. *Cajal assumed that the large number of cells with short axons was the anatomical expression of the delicacy of function of the brain of man.* At present that assumption is almost a statement of fact, for it is known that synaptic transmission demands the summation of impulses under strict conditions, and it is evident that the more heterogeneous is the origin of the synapses on the cells with descending axons, the more rigid become the conditions for threshold stimulation, and the more accurate the selection of the paths through which the impulses may be conducted. The reduction of the number of cells with short axons, without essential modification of the long links in the chains of cortical neurons, makes the cortex of the mouse the "skeleton" for the human cortex, and no objection can be raised against the use of the diagrams given in Figure 143 as a first approximation for interpretation of experimental results obtained in the higher mammals. These diagrams reproduce the elementary cortical pattern."

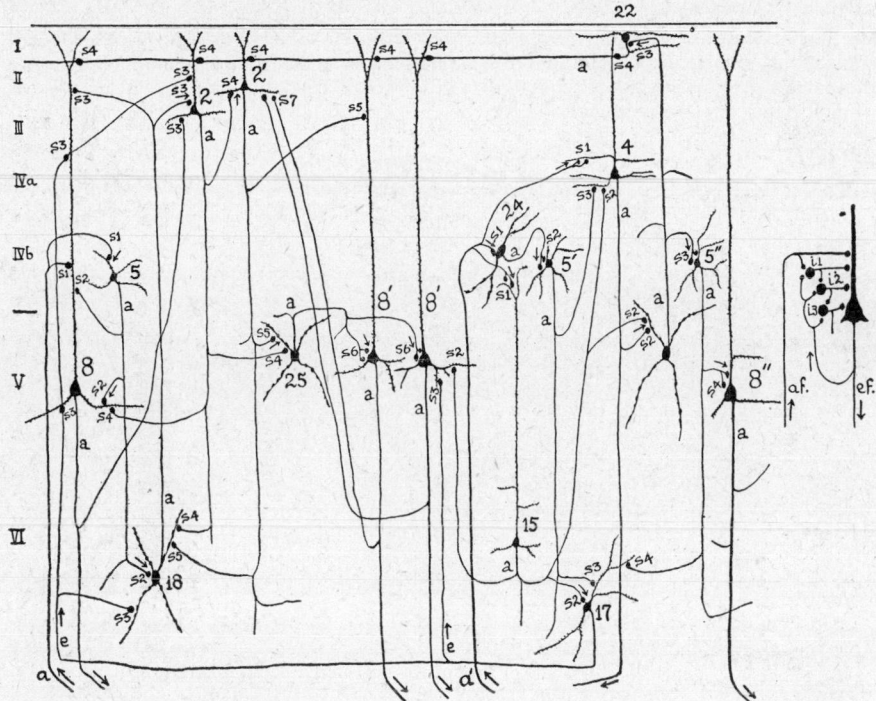

Fig. 143.—Diagram of some of intracortical chains of neurons. Axons of cortical cells are marked with *a*. Note that only a few dendrites and axonal branches have been included in diagram. Synaptic junctions are indicated by letter *s* (*s1*, *s2*, etc.) and by thickening of axon. It is assumed that synapses marked with an arrow are traversed by impulses.

Small diagram at right is a simplification of diagram at left. Afferent fiber *af.* activates large pyramid which is the origin of efferent fiber *ef.* and also a system of cortical internuncial cells (*i1, i2, i3*); recurrent collateral of *ef.*, delivers impulses again to internuncial system. This diagram exemplifies the broad plan upon which the central nervous system is organized. Roman numerals at the left indicate cortical layers. (From Fulton, *Physiology of the nervous system*, 2nd ed., 1943.)

CYTOARCHITECTURAL MAPS OF THE CORTEX

The cytoarchitectural map of the cerebral cortex most commonly used is that of the Vogts (Fig. 144) based on Campbell (4), and it becomes necessary to ascertain whether the areas of discrete structure are, in fact, areas of specific function. Several methods of approaching the problem have been used, stimulation, regional ablation, and more recently the late Professor Dusser de Barenne introduced the method of laminar thermocoagulation by means of which the functions of individual layers in a given cortical area could be analyzed. To Dusser de Barenne we also owe a modified method of stimulation and recording which made it possible to uncover the fact that activity of one cortical area may influence all other cortical areas, both in the same and in the opposite hemisphere. Details concerning the specific area will be described below and in Chapter 13.

Stimulation. Electrical stimulation of any part of the nervous system, peripheral or central, has limitations, since the stimulus is essentially unnatural and since it tends to call into simultaneous activity units which generally discharge in definite temporal sequence. Stimulation could never have disclosed that in the intact animal the hypothalamus is responsible for integrating the heat regulatory mechanisms. Similarly, in the focal irritation of the cerebral cortex one can evoke motor movements of an isolated purposeless character, but one cannot cause an integrated movement with a purposeful objective. In a conscious human subject it is possible, by stimulation, to separate sensory areas from regions yielding motor movements. Excitation of the occipital cortex gives gross visual sensations—stars and flashes of light but no well-formed visual image.

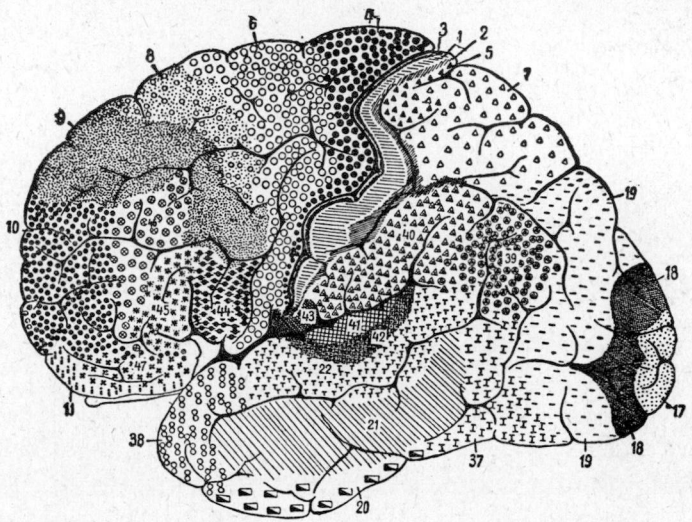

Fig. 144.—The detailed subdivisions of the cortical regions as determined by Brodmann, seen from the left side. Each area or field which is here designated by a number and conventional symbols has a distinctive lamination of its cells and fibers (Herrick).

Regional ablation. Excision of specific cortical areas has proved a useful research tool, but it, too, has limitations. The area removed must be taken out with the greatest delicacy so as not to impinge upon adjacent areas; it must be removed in its entirety lest remaining cells of similar function take over and obscure the result. By means of regional ablation, however, clear-cut functional meaning has been given to the cytoarchitectural maps of Campbell, Brodmann and the Vogts, and we are now able to say with some degree of assurance that the functions of area 4—the motor area—can be distinguished from those of area 6, the premotor, and from the sensory areas lying rostral to the central sulcus.

Broadly speaking, the cerebral hemispheres are made up of two primary divisions; those lying in front of the central sulcus are primarily motor in function, while the posterior half of the hemisphere is primarily sensory. But from studies of the sensory projections from the thalamus and the motor projections from the cortex itself, we know that there is an admixture in nearly all parts of the cortex of sensory and motor function. The motor cortex receives proprioceptive sensory projections from the thalamus and the parietal or sensory cortex contributes motor fibers that pass into the pyramidal pathways. It is no doubt through this overlapping of sensory and motor projections that ultimate coordination is achieved between incoming and outgoing impulses. There are also large association areas within which the complex motor, sensory and behavior patterns are integrated. These, too, have specific cytoarchitectural structure—large numbers of internuncial neurons and purely sensory motor projections. The largest association areas are those in the anterior part of the frontal lobes and in the temporal lobe.

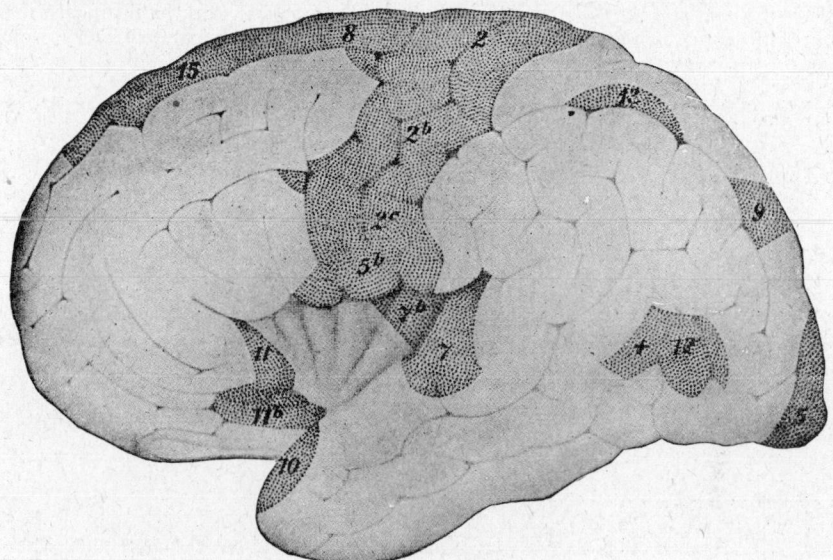

Fig. 145.—Lateral surface of the brain, showing the primordial areas, both sensory and automatic, in dotted zones (Flechsig).

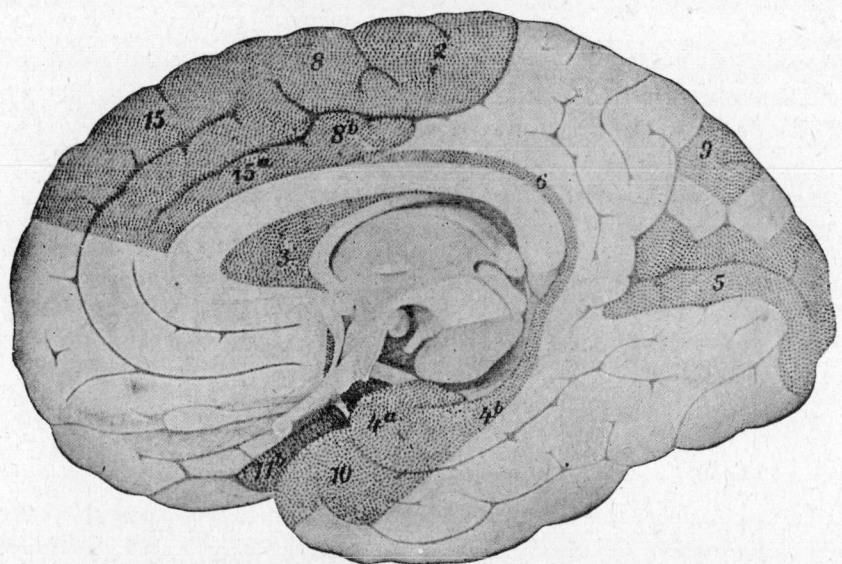

Fig. 146.—Same zones on the mesial surface of the brain (Flechsig).

Development of the projection areas. Flechsig (5) has published the results of an extensive study of the time of myelinization of the fibers in the cerebrum of man from the fourth month of intra-uterine to the fourth month of extra-uterine life. The first areas to develop in the cortex are the primary sense centers (smell, cutaneous and muscle sense, sight, hearing, and touch), and later, in connection with these centers, systems of motor fibers appear. There are thus formed seven primary zones, sensory and motor, to which he gives the name of *projection areas*. The location of these areas is shown in part in Figures 145 and 146, 2 (2b, 2c), 5, 6, 7 (7b), 8, 15. Later there is developed around these primary zones areas that Flechsig calls marginal or border zones, which are connected by short association fibers with one or more of the primary projection zones. Later still the great association areas acquire their myelinated fibers. As the result of his histological work he distinguished 36 areas in the cortex in which the myelinization of the fibers occurs separately, and in which, therefore, by inference different physiological activities are mediated.

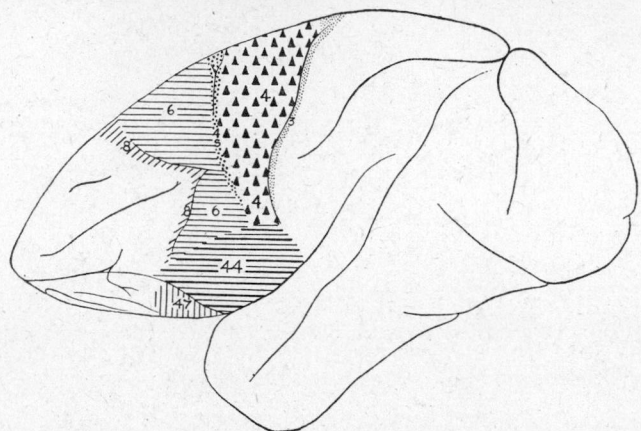

Fig. 147.—The precentral motor cortex of the macaque. The principal areas are indicated in accordance with Brodmann's numerical scheme. The stippled strip between areas 4 and 6 is the suppressor band, area 4s. (After von Bonin in Bucy, *The precentral motor cortex*, University of Illinois Press, Urbana, 1944.)

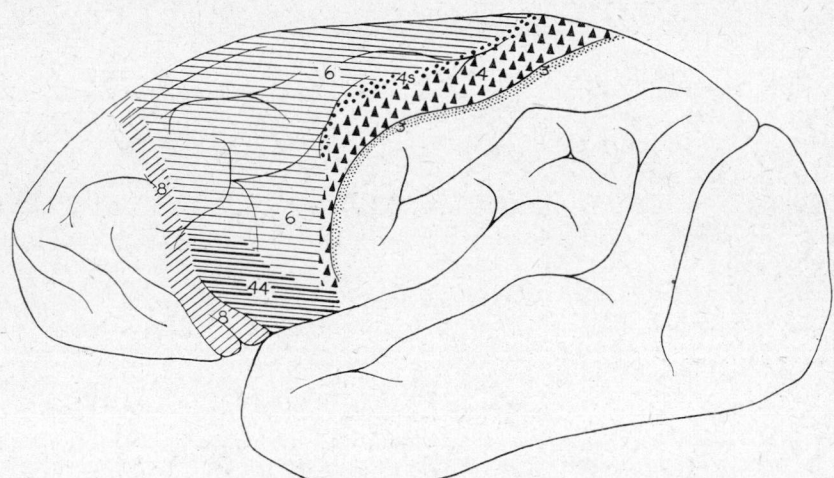

Fig. 148.—The precentral motor cortex of the chimpanzee with areas homologous with those in the macaque (Figs. 151, 152) indicated by corresponding symbols. (After von Bonin in Bucy, *The precentral motor cortex*, University of Illinois Press, Urbana, 1944.)

Maps of Subhuman Primate Compared with Man. The recent studies of Gerhardt von Bonin (2) have thrown fresh light upon the structural organization of the cerebral hemispheres of subhuman primates, and the homologies between functionally discrete areas in man and his near of kin in the primate tree now become more apparent, particularly with regard to the precentral motor regions (Figs. 147–149). Von Bonin recognizes five primary regions in the precentral cortex, namely, areas 4, 4a, 4s, 6 and 44.

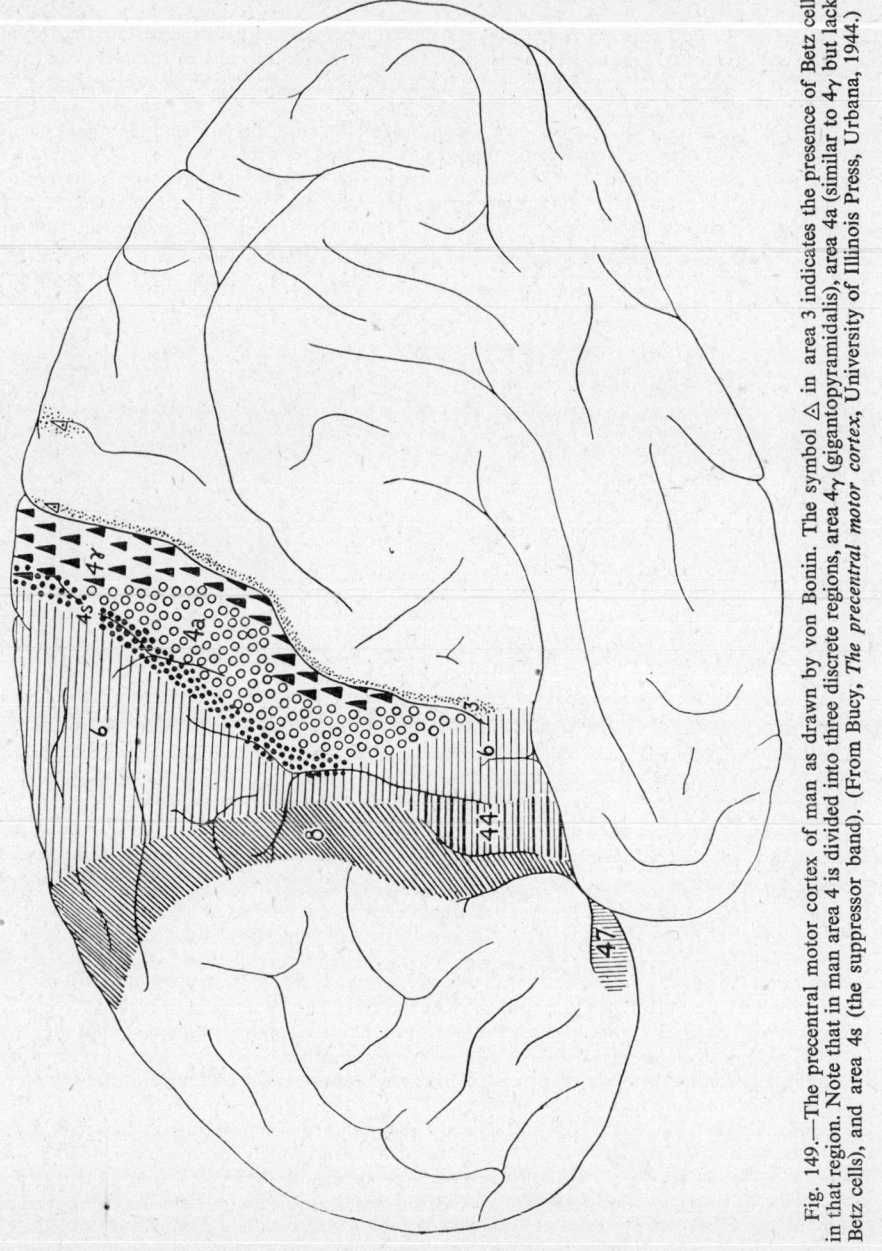

Fig. 149.—The precentral motor cortex of man as drawn by von Bonin. The symbol △ in area 3 indicates the presence of Betz cells in that region. Note that in man area 4 is divided into three discrete regions, area 4γ (gigantopyramidalis), area 4a (similar to 4γ but lacks Betz cells), and area 4s (the suppressor band). (From Bucy, *The precentral motor cortex*, University of Illinois Press, Urbana, 1944.)

Area 4. *Area 4γ.* This, the area gigantopyramidalis, giving rise to the larger fibers in the pyramidal tract, is characterized by the presence of large motor cells in the fifth cortical layer. They are seen in the galago, the monkey (Fig. 147), the chimpanzee (Fig. 148) and man (Fig. 149). In man area 4 has become further differentiated in that the area gigantopyramidalis (area 4γ) lies principally within the central sulcus and the functionally discrete region on the surface of the precentral convolution, which is peculiar to the human cortex. This has been designated area 4a.

Area 4a. As indicated in Figure 149, area 4a lies between area 4γ and area 4s. Area 4a is agranular, has no giant cells of Betz, but otherwise the structure is identical with area 4γ and similar to area 6.

Area 4s. The strip region has, as with all the suppressor bands in the cerebral cortex, a characteristic feature—the presence of moderately large motor cells in the *fourth* cortical layer. Otherwise its structure resembles that of area 6 and area 4a. There are no Betz cells in the fifth layer.

Area 6. This is agranular but shows a columnar pattern. Cells are slightly smaller, and the second layer is better demarcated from the third than in area 4.

Area 44. This lies just rostral to the face area, and is the region known in the earlier Brodmann maps as area 6b. Its homology in monkeys with area 44 of the human cortex has now been clearly established by von Bonin, so that we are justified in looking upon it

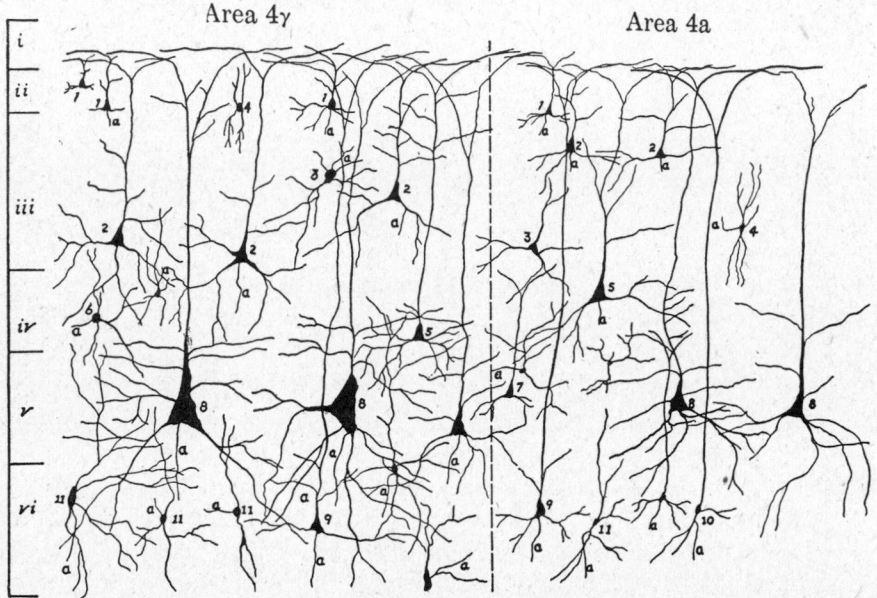

Fig. 150.—Cell types in area 4γ and 4a respectively as seen in Golgi preparations. Stratificated on left margin. Note absence of large pyramidal cells in the fifth layer of area 4a. (From von Bonin in Bucy, *The precentral motor cortex,* University of Illinois Press, Urbana, 1944.)

as an homologous region present in all the higher primates. It is composed of small cells intermingled with much larger ones in the fourth layer. The upper part of layer IV contains numerous very large pyramidal cells. Both layers III and V can be subdivided, and layers II and III are particularly well demarcated one from the other.

Areas 4 and 6. In the early maps of the primate brain, areas 4 and 6 were thought to be identical with one another except for the absence of Betz cells from area 6. Many authors (e.g., 10) have expressed doubt concerning the justifiability of separating the two regions on morphological grounds, since the size of motor cells varies widely, even among the so-called Betz cells. Occasionally a stray motor cell as large as a small Betz cell is found far forward in area 6. The discreteness of the two areas, however, became evident when they were studied functionally. The consequences of removal of area 4 differ widely from those of primary removal of area 6. They differ from one another also on stimulation; on recognition of the suppressor band as a functionally discrete region, interest was centered anew upon the structural organization of these areas, and to von Bonin (2) we owe the disclosure that area 4s in all primates studied has a highly discrete structure which had not been previously recognized. The existence of the separate region lying between areas 4 and 6 gives further evidence that area 4γ and probably area 4a are to be regarded as areas of discrete function wholly separate from area 6.

The cell types found in areas 4γ and 4a respectively are indicated in Figure 150 taken from von Bonin. The cell types encountered in area 44 are indicated in Figure 151.

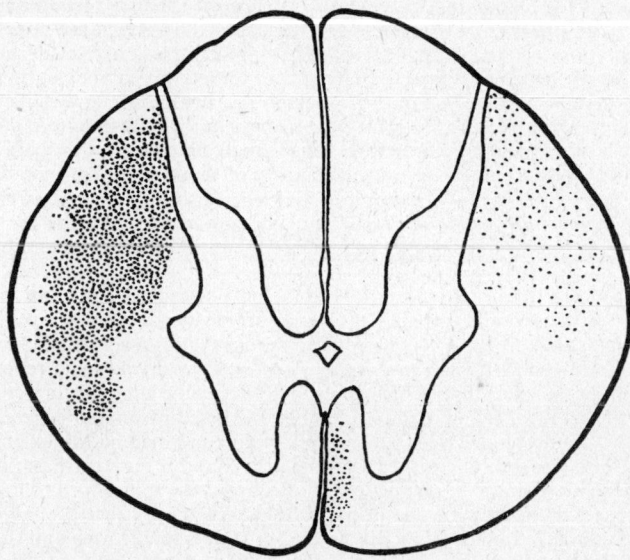

Fig. 151.—Cross section of the spinal cord of a chimpanzee, showing Marchi degeneration following an isolated lesion of the right foot area. Note that the degeneration is heaviest in the anterolateral column on the side opposite to the lesion, but that there is also degeneration in the ipsilateral anterolateral column and in the ventral funiculus on the same side. (After Fulton and Sheehan, *J. Anat., Lond.*, 1935, *69*:181–187.)

MOTOR PROJECTIONS FROM THE CEREBRAL CORTEX

The motor pathways from the cerebral cortex fall into two separate groups: (i) the corticospinal projections (pyramidal tract) arising from the precentral, postcentral and possibly also from the temporal convolutions; and (ii) the extrapyramidal motor systems arising from all parts of the frontal, parietal, and temporal lobes and also from certain parts of the occipital area. Knowledge of these cortical projections is essential to an understanding of motor activities originating within the cerebral cortex in respect of both phasic movement and postural adjustment.

Corticospinal Projections (Pyramidal Tract). In most mammals* a large motor pathway passes from the cerebral cortex via the internal capsule and medullary pyramids directly into the spinal cord. In man the important studies of Lassek (15) show approximately one million separate fibers in each medullary pyramid, 61 per cent of which are myelinated (15). Of these less than 2 per cent range from 11 to 20 μ in diameter, 9 per cent from 5 to 10 μ, while nearly 90 per cent are in the 1 to 4 μ range. The remaining 39 per cent of unmyelinated fibers in the pyramids have received little attention, and their function, as well as their origin, is unknown. It has been established that the human motor area has approximately 34,000 Betz cells in each hemi-

* It was first pointed out by Spitzka (*J. comp. Med. Surg.*, 1886, *7*:1–61) that the pyramidal tracts are best developed in animals having opposable digits, and that there are virtually no corticospinal projections in ungulates (hoofed animals) and cetaceans (whales). The comparative anatomy of the pyramidal tract in mammalian forms deserves further study.

sphere (15), which would account for the 2 per cent of fibers which range from 11 to 20 μ in diameter (15). The remaining motor fibers in the pyramids arise from motor neurons other than the cells of Betz.

The early work of Holmes and Page May (13) suggested that the pyramidal tract took origin solely from the Betz cells in area 4. They based this premature conclusion upon series of observations on the cerebral cortex following spinal lesions. Retrograde degeneration in these circumstances appeared to be restricted to Betz cells alone. At that ime, however, the total number of the fibers in the pyramids was not known, and as just stated it is now clear that approximately 98 per cent of the fibers in the human pyramidal tract arise from motor cells other than those of Betz. Being of small diameter, it is probably impossible to trace by the Marchi technique the great majority of those which degenerate (i.e., those smaller than 5μ); for this reason, *many statements in the literature concerning the site of origin of the pyramidal projections are fallacious* (21), *save as they relate to the fibers of the largest diameter* (5 to 20 μ or about 10 per cent of the myelinated fibers and 6 per cent of the total).

A few large fibers from areas 5 and 3-1-2 in the postcentral convolution have been traced into the spinal cord, and there is also indisputable evidence of small myelin fibered degeneration from area 6 (probably much more numerous than can actually be demonstrated by the Marchi technique). This was first emphasized by Kennard (14) who reported a light Marchi degeneration passing to the cord—presumably only the larger fibers were detected—and by E. C. Hoff (12) who found a considerable uncrossed pyramidal degeneration from area 6 by the bouton technique. His studies have been confirmed by Minckler (18,19) and more recently by Minckler, Klemme and Minckler (20) who report a large and discrete ipsilateral degeneration in the human ventral funiculus of the spinal cord following lesions restricted to area 6. It seems probable in the light of recent work that a small fibered projection passes into the pyramids from a large area of the cerebral cortex and that only area 4 contributes the large fibered group (17).

The myelinated corticospinal projection on reaching the cord distributes itself into three discrete regions (Fig. 151): (i) *an uncrossed ventral tract*, present in man and chimpanzee and generally referred to as the tract of Türck. Recent studies indicate that many of these uncrossed ventral fibers originate in area 6 (20); (ii) *an uncrossed lateral tract* passing in the lateral columns of all primates thus far examined, and in the chimpanzee constituting about one-tenth of the total corticospinal projection; (iii) *a crossed lateral tract* common to all mammals, but passing to the lower segments of the spinal cord only in the higher mammalian forms, particularly the primates (11). The crossed tract constitutes 70 to 85 per cent of the total corticospinal projection both of man and chimpanzee. A fair proportion of the lateral and ventral uncrossed fibers terminate on ipsilateral motor cells of the spinal cord. These have been variously estimated as 10 to 15 per cent and they undoubtedly are responsible for ipsilateral effects obtainable on stimulation of the posterior premotor area of the cerebral cortex (Chap. 13). The site of termination has been established by E. C. Hoff and others through the use of the bouton technique (12,18). The degenerating terminals of the descending tracts such as are represented by the projections of the corticospinal system can be detected in the early stages of their degeneration and the site of their termination thus established (12,18,19).

Extrapyramidal Projections from the Cortex (16,22). Probably more numerous even than the corticospinal projections are those of extrapyramidal projections which pass to various suprasegmental nuclei lying between cortex and spinal cord. They can be summarized as follows.

Corticostriatal projections. The existence of a corticostriatal system has long been suspected, but until recently it had proved impossible to dei..onstrate it with certainty by any of the usual degeneration techniques. Dusser de Barenne and his colleagues provided physiological evidence (Chap. 13) that fiber systems from the suppressor bands of the cortex, i.e., areas 2s, 4s and 8s, must impinge directly upon the caudate. In 1944 Glees (11a) demonstrated unequivocally in the cat that an extensive unmyelinated degeneration passes from the suppressor areas to the cells of the caudate. More recently Dr. Glees reports (personal communication) that a similar unmyelinated network from area 4s to caudate can be demonstrated in the macaque. The work of Glees emphasizes that older methods of analyzing anatomical interconnections of various parts of the brain are inadequate, and deductions based upon them should be accepted with reserve.

Corticothalamic tracts. The entire cerebral mantle, except for a small region in the temporal lobe, sends and receives fibers from the thalamus. The significance of these projections will be discussed later in the chapters on sensation.

Corticopontine tracts. There are four major projections from the cerebral cortex to the pons in the primate form, namely, the frontopontine, parietopontine, occipitopontine and temporopontine, the frontopontine being much the largest. It arises equally from areas 4 and 6 and forms the anatomical bases for the corticopontocerebellar system which has come to occupy a most prominent position in the organization of the primate brain.

Other extrapyramidal projections. Levin (16) gives an up-to-date summary of all the other projections from the cerebral cortex. Mention should be made of the corticonigral tract which with the corticostriate projection stands on equal footing with the corticopontocerebellar; the corticostrionigral systems are concerned primarily with postural adjustments, whereas the corticopontocerebellar preside over phasic movement. The hypothalamus also receives projections both directly and indirectly from the frontal area; this system of fibers is the basis of the control exercised by the cerebral cortex on the autonomic system (Chap. 11).

REFERENCES

I. Cytoarchitecture

1. BEVAN LEWIS, W. On the comparative structure of the cortex cerebri. *Brain*, 1878, *1*:79–86.

2. BONIN, G. VON. Architecture of the precentral motor cortex and some adjacent areas, Chap. II in: BUCY, P. C., ed., *The precentral motor cortex*, Urbana, Ill., 1944.

3. BRODMANN, K. *Vergleichende Lokalisationslehre der Grosshirnrinde in ihren Prinzipien dargestellt auf Grund des Zellenbaues.* Leipzig, J. A. Barth, 1909; reprinted, 1925, xii, 324 pp.

4. CAMPBELL, A. W. *Histological studies on the localisation of cerebral function.* Cambridge, University Press, 1905, xx, 360 pp.

5. FLECHSIG, P. Einige Bermerkungen über die Untersuchungsmethoden der Grosshirnrinde, insbesondere des Menschen. *Ber. sächs. Ges. (Akad.) Wiss.*, 1904, *56*:50–104.

6. FULTON, J. F. A note on Francesco Gennari and the early history of cytoarchitectural studies of the cerebral cortex. *Bull. Hist. Med.*, 1937, *5*:895–913.

7. LORENTE DE NÓ, R. Cerebral cortex: Architecture, intracortical cortical connections, motor projections, pp. 274–301 in: FULTON, J. F., *Physiology of the nervous system*, 2d ed., 1943.

8. RAMON Y CAJAL, S. La fine structure des centres nerveux. (The Croonian Lecture.) *Proc. roy. Soc.*, 1894, *55*:444–468.

9. SHERRINGTON, C. S. *The brain and its mechanism.* Cambridge, University Press, 1933, 35 pp.

10. WALSHE, F. M. R. The giant cells of Betz, the motor cortex and the pyramidal tract: A critical review. *Brain*, 1942, *65*:409–461.

II. Projections

11. FULTON, J. F., and SHEEHAN, D. The uncrossed lateral pyramidal tract in higher primates. *J. Anat., Lond.*, 1935, *69*:181–187.

11a. GLEES, P. The anatomical basis of cortico-striate connexions. *J. Anat., Lond.*, 1944, *78*:47–51.

12. HOFF, E. C. Corticospinal fibers arising in the premotor area of the monkey: Distribution of bouton terminations. *Arch. Neurol. Psychiat., Chicago*, 1935, *33*:687–697.

13. HOLMES, G., and MAY, W. PAGE. On the exact origin of the pyramidal tracts in man and other mammals. *Brain*, 1901, *32*:1–43.

14. KENNARD, MARGARET A. Corticospinal fibers arising in the premotor area of the monkey as demonstrated by the Marchi method. *Arch. Neurol. Psychiat., Chicago*, 1935, *33*:698–711.

15. LASSEK, A. M. The human pyramidal tract. I. A fiber and numerical analysis (with G. L. Rasmussen). *Arch. Neurol. Psychiat. Chicago*, 1939, *44*:872–876; II. A numerical investigation of the Betz cells of the motor area. *Ibid.*, 1940, *44*:718–724; III. Magnitude of the large cells of the motor area (area 4). *Ibid.*, 1941, *45*:964–972; IV. A study of the mature, myelinated fibers of the pyramid. *J. comp. Neurol.*, 1942, *76*:217–225; V. Postnatal changes in the axons of the pyramids. *Arch. Neurol. Psychiat., Chicago*, 1942, *47*:422–427; VI. An evaluation of the pyramidal syndrome. *J. S. C. med. Ass.*, 1942, *38*:243–245.

16. LEVIN, P. M. Efferent fibers, Chap. V in: BUCY, P. C., ed., *The precentral motor cortex*, Urbana, Ill., 1944.

17. METTLER, F. A. On the origin of the fibers in the pyramid of the primate brain.

Proc. Soc. exp. Biol., N. Y., 1944, *57*:111–113.

18. MINCKLER, J. Distribution of nerve terminals (*boutons*) in the human spinal cord. Quantitative studies. *Arch. Neurol. Psychiat., Chicago*, 1941, *45*:44–55.

19. MINCKLER, J. Pathologic alterations in surface relationships and morphology of the human synapse. *Amer. J. Path.*, 1942, *18*:1061–1103.

20. MINCKLER, J., KLEMME, R. M., and MINCKLER, D. The course of efferent fibers from the human premotor cortex. *J. comp Neurol.*, 1944, *81*:259–277.

21. TOWER, S. S. The pyramidal tract, Chap. VI in: BUCY, P. C., ed., *The precentral motor cortex*, Urbana, Ill., 1944.

22. VERHAART, W. J. C., and KENNARD, M. A. Corticofugal degeneration following thermocoagulation of areas 4, 6 and 4-s in *Macaca mulatta. J. Anat., Lond.*, 1940, *74*:239–254.

CHAPTER 13

CEREBRAL CORTEX: MOTOR FUNCTIONS

As indicated in the last chapter the cerebral mantle conveys its integrations to motoneurons of the brain stem and spinal cord through projection systems of two categories: (i) by the direct pyramidal projection which passes from the cerebral cortex without interruption to the final column pathway in the spinal cord, i.e., to the ventral horn cells and their associated internuncial neurons; and (ii) extrapyramidal motor projections which pass from the cerebral cortex to various suprasegmental levels of integration, i.e., corpus striatum, thalamus, hypothalamus, red nucleus, substantia nigra, etc. It has gradually been recognized that the motor deficits resulting in primates from severing the direct pyramidal projections differ conspicuously from those stemming from interruption of extrapyramidal pathways, since pyramidal interruption of itself causes a flail or "flaccid" paralysis in which fine volitional movements are lost and in which the affected extremity offers little or no resistance to passive movement. Extrapyramidal interruption, on the other hand, may cause varying degrees of paralysis of volitional movement, but *it is associated with augmented resistance to passive movements*, i.e., the paresis is said to be "spastic" in character. With these basic differences in mind between the two projection systems, we may proceed to analyze the motor functions of the cerebral cortex in greater detail.

Historical note. Neurologists of the early nineteenth century looked upon the brain as something that functioned as a homogeneous unit, and for several decades many were unwilling to admit the existence of functional localization. When the sensory pathways were studied, however, it became clear that visual function was associated with the occipital cortex and hearing with the temporal, which suggested that other functions may also have precise localization. It had been known since the time of Hippocrates that cerebral hemorrhage causes motor paralysis, but not until Wepfer's studies on apoplexy in the seventeenth century was it clearly recognized that the paralysis following cerebral hemorrhage occurs on the side of the body opposite to the hemorrhage. Robert Boyle in 1691 (2) described the case of a young man who, following a depressed fracture of his skull, suffered a "dead palsy" of his right arm and leg. The extremities were sensitive to pinprick, but had lost their sense of position and also the power of movement. After the removal of a spicule of bone which had pressed on the surface of the brain, the paralysis both of movement and sensation promptly cleared. Here, then, was the first suggestion of the existence of a motor (and a sensory) area, but nearly two hundred years elapsed before the motor area was demonstrated experimentally through electrical stimulation of the brains of animals. Fritsch and Hitzig, two German investigators, announced in 1870 (8) that electrical stimulation of the brain just rostral to the central sulcus caused well defined movements of the opposite extremities, and that a mosaic of foci existed from which discrete individualized movements could be evoked. Thus, from one focus the thumb was caused to move, from another closely adjacent the fingers, etc. Foci were located for movements at all the main joints both of the arm and of the leg, and for the face, tongue and eyes. At the same time Hughlings Jackson (13), the British neurologist, independently of Fritsch and Hitzig, postulated the existence of a motor area on the basis of a study of focal epileptic seizures which he had observed in clinical cases. In a given case a seizure might start in the thumb and spread to the fingers and later to the upper arm. Jackson argued that such attacks must be due to irritation of areas in the brain having specific motor function. His reasoning was vindicated more promptly than he could have anticipated by the discovery of Fritsch and Hitzig and by the later disclosure of another Englishman, David Ferrier, who found in monkeys that if an area which on stimulation causes movements of the arm is removed, the arm becomes paralyzed (7). If a spicule of bone impinges upon this area, the arm would become similarly paralyzed as in the case reported by Robert Boyle.

EXCITABILITY

In the seventy-five years which have elapsed since the discovery of the motor area, attention has been concentrated primarily upon analysis of the excitable properties of this and other adjacent regions of the brain. The excitable foci first disclosed in 1870 have been found in a great variety of warm blooded animals including the anthropoids and man. Distribution of excitable foci is similar in all forms, the representation of the sacral and lumbar segments being on the medial surface of the cortex, representation of the upper extremities more laterally, and the head and eyes more laterally still, as indicated in Figure 152. In animals having a prehensile tail, the tail area lies medially to the leg representation (10). It should be emphasized that although the mosaic of foci is arranged by segmental levels, the responses evoked from stimulation of the cortex present patterns of movement rather than isolated responses of individual muscles. For example, one can cause flexion or extension of the digits, each being a movement pattern involving reciprocal action of antagonistic muscle groups. One cannot excite a single muscle through cortical stimulation without affecting other—usually antagonistic—muscle groups. The cerebral cortex "thinks," so to speak, in terms of movement rather than of muscles (Sherrington).

Factors Affecting Excitability. The neurons of the cerebral cortex are subject to changes in excitability thresholds, analogous to those in any other neuron. Once discharged, a refractory period ensues, followed by periods of supernormal and a period of depressed excitability similar to the subnormal period in a peripheral neuron. The cerebral cortex differs from peripheral neurons only in respect of the actual time sequence, for all reactions at the cortical level appear much more prolonged than in peripheral neurons.

"*Extinction*." The excitable properties of the motor area have been studied in some detail by Dusser de Barenne and McCulloch (5), who observed in animals under dial anesthesia that a given focus may become refractory to further stimulation for a period of some fifteen to twenty seconds after having been activated. In order to avoid identification of this period of depressed excitability with similar periods of depression in the peripheral nerve, they designated the phenomenon "extinction." The period of extinction coincided with electrical changes similar to those occurring during the subnormal period of peripheral nerve, and it is now generally believed that the phenomenon of extinction represents a fluctuation in excitability identical with the period of subnormality in peripheral nerve.

H-ion concentration. In peripheral nerve, a shift in H-ion concentration toward the alkaline side causes increased excitability, whereas an acid shift diminishes excitability. Precisely the same relation holds in the cerebral cortex, for, if the blood bathing the brain is made more alkaline through hyperventilation, the excitability of the motor area is increased, as is the spontaneous electrical activity ("brain waves") which normally can be detected in an intact and healthy brain. If a shift occurs to the acid side and lactic or other acids accumulate in the blood stream, the excitability is impaired. We owe to Leslie Nims (6) the perfection of a device which has permitted correlation of local pH shifts in groups of neurons with their electrical activity (Fig. 153). When a neuron discharges, a transient alkaline shift occurs at its cell surface; this is followed by a slower shift to the acid side, and the curve of the *p*H change coincides closely in any given neuron or center with the

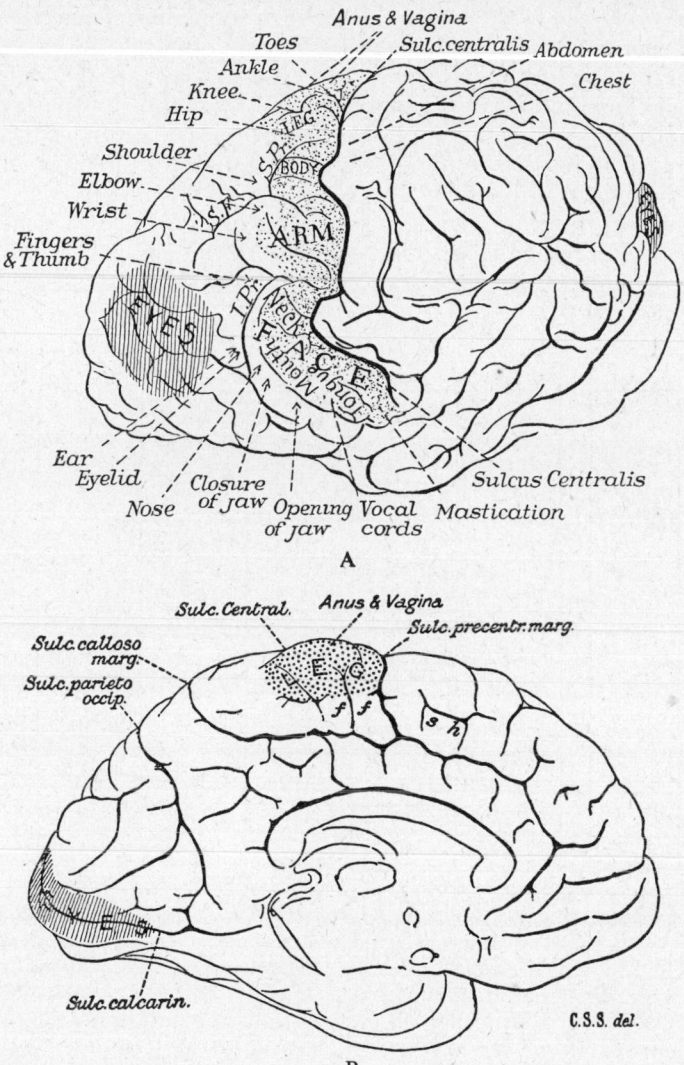

Fig. 152.—A, Location of motor areas in brain of chimpanzee as originally reported by Grün-baum and Sherrington. The extent of the excitable areas is indicated by stippling; they lie entirely in front of the fissure of Rolando (sulcus centralis). Much of the motor area is hidden in the sulci. The regions marked EYES indicate the areas whose stimulation gives conjugate movements of the eyeballs. B, Extension of motor areas on to the mesial surface, chimpanzee brain. Mesial surface of left hemisphere: Stippled region marked LEG gives the motor area for lower limb; *f, s,* and *h* indicate regions from which movements were obtained occasionally with strong stimuli; *f,* foot and leg; *s,* shoulder and chest; *h,* thumb and fingers. The shaded area marked EYES indicates a part of occipital region stimulation of which gives conjugate movements of the eyes. (From Grünbaum and Sherrington.)

curve of depressed excitability. While the acid shift is on, excitability is depressed, etc.

Facilitation and inhibition (see Chap. 5). A demonstrable increase in the resting excitability of a given neuron or center is referred to as "facilitation"; consideration must therefore be given to factors which influence facilitation. (i) One neuron may facilitate another through subliminal stimulation. Stimulation of neurons in area 6, although they may not of themselves cause neurons in area 4 to discharge, may so lower the threshold as to make them susceptible to discharge by a subthreshold electrical stimulus. (ii) The presence of facilitation can be detected by the occurrence of negative voltage drifts which are similar in all respects to negative after-potentials. (iii) Finally, an alkaline shift in the milieu surrounding a nerve cell causes facilitation.

Inhibition in the central nervous system may be regarded as identical with the period of unresponsiveness in peripheral nerve. The phenomenon of ex-

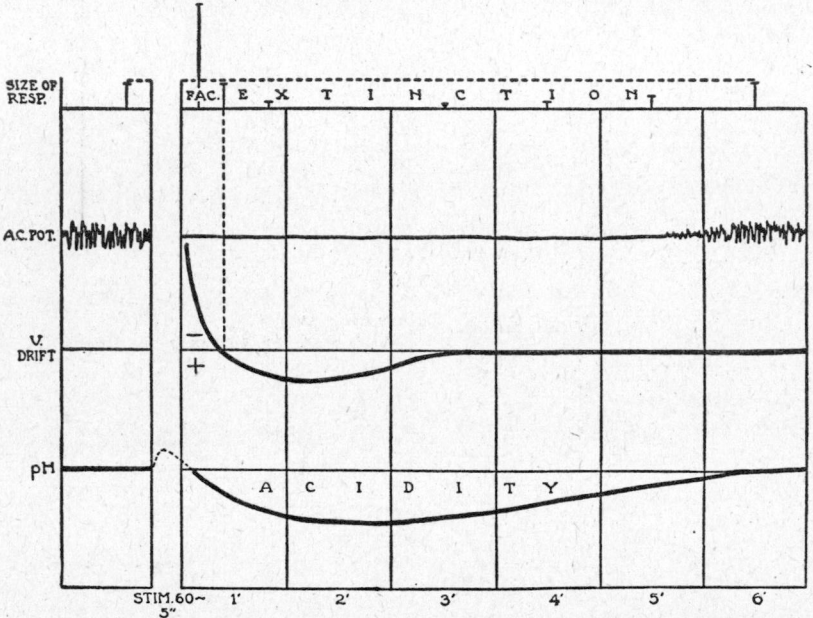

Fig. 153.—Diagram correlating facilitation and extinction (subnormal excitability) with changes in electrical potentials and *p*H at the site of stimulation of the macaque motor area. (From Dusser de Barenne and McCulloch, *J. Neurophysiol.*, 1939, *2*:319–355.)

tinction just referred to is an example of localized inhibition which normally follows activity. In the cerebral cortex one neuron or group of neurons may suppress the activity of another group of neurons. Although generally referred to as "suppression" rather than inhibition, there is ample reason to believe that active suppression of nerve cell activity is brought about by identical mechanisms whenever it occurs. When a group of neurons are in a state of suppression (or inhibition), positive voltage drifts develop (positive after-potentials), accompanied by an acid shift in *p*H of the neuron.

Direct inhibition. The only unexplained phase of central inhibition is that of "direct" inhibition described by Lloyd (19). As pointed out in Chapter 5, reflexes involving the two-neuron arcs can be suppressed by impulses impinging directly on the ventral horn cell without discharging it. In the cerebral cortex, activity of one focus in the motor area tends to suppress other adjacent foci without causing them to discharge, and there is every reason to believe that whatever the mechanism may be of Lloyd's direct inhibition, it occurs in the cortex as well as in the spinal cord. Wyss (25) believes that impulses impinging on a neuron at the axon hillock depolarize the soma without evoking an impulse in the axon.

Extent of the Excitable Cortex. With appropriate electrical stimulation, or through the use of locally applied strychnine as a source of excitation, motor effects can be obtained, not only from area 4, the primary motor area, but from practically the whole extent of the pre- and postcentral convolution, including areas 8 and 6 of the precentral convolution and areas 3, 1, 5 and 7 of the postcentral and parietal lobes. The responses vary with the regions stimulated and some depend for their continuance upon the integrity of area 4 and its projections. Certain motor effects from area 6 persist after removal

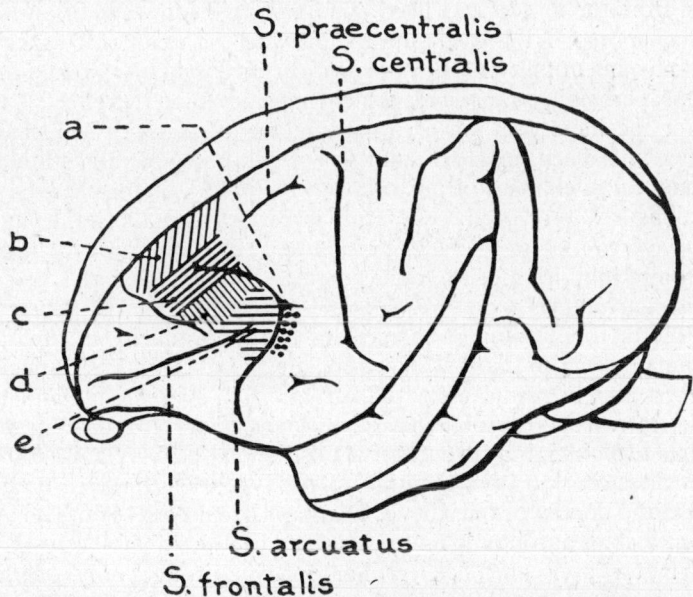

Fig. 154.—Indicated subdivisions of the frontal eye field and the area yielding closure of the eyes in the monkey (*Macaca mulatta*) according to W. K. Smith (1936). Designations: a, closure of eyes; b, pupillary dilation; c, "awakening"; d, conjugate deviation to opposite side; e, nystagmus to opposite side. (From Smith, in Bucy, *The precentral motor cortex*, 1944.)

of area 4 or after interruption of the pyramidal tracts in the region of the medulla oblongata, indicating that they are mediated by extrapyramidal motor projections originating in area 6. The characteristics of responses from individual areas may be briefly summarized (see Figs. 147–149; also 155).

Area 8 (Frontal eye fields). Stimulation of area 8 (25), both in man and animals, causes motor responses affecting the extra-ocular muscles of the pupils and the eyelid musculature. From the superior part of the area pupillary dilatation may regularly be obtained (Fig. 154b); points more lateral give lid opening "awakening" response, (Fig. 154c), while conjugate deviation of the eyes to opposite side may be evoked from the region indicated in Figure 154d. Lid closure is generally obtained from more lateral points; lacrimation is also encountered but is not precisely localized. It is no doubt significant that autonomic motor responses (lacrimation and pupillary dilatation) are obtainable from foci closely adjacent to, and sometimes overlapping with, foci giving rise to somatic motor effects on the eye musculature. Foerster also describes turning of the head (adversive movement) as a result of strong stimulation of the frontal eye fields. Similar reactions are evoked from the occipital eye fields (areas 17, 18 and 19).

Area 6 (Premotor area). From area 6 a variety of somatic and autonomic effects may be obtained with a distribution of foci corresponding roughly to those of area 4, i.e., responses in the leg and perineal regions come from medial points, arm movements and vasomotor effects on the arm from more lateral points and complex patterns of response affecting the lips, tongue and vocal cords from the most lateral parts of area 6 (grunting, vocalization, etc.). Speaking broadly, the reactions evoked from the premotor region are in the nature of complex movement patterns and lack the discreteness of reaction obtained from the motor area itself. The threshold for stimulation is considerably higher than for area 4; the majority of the reactions, especially the complex movement patterns, disappear if the cerebral cortex between areas 6 and 4 is superficially transected, which indicates that the effects are transmitted for the most part via area 4 by means of transcortical projections. After area 4 has been removed and its projections degenerate, stimulation of area 6 may cause changes of posture, but the predominant response in such preparations is one of inhibition. Thus in certain stages of ether anesthesia when the extremities are held in rigid extension stimulation of area 6 will cause prompt inhibition of the rigid posture.

Autonomic reactions from area 6 coincide closely with the distribution of somatic motor foci. Vasomotor reactions can be obtained in arms and legs from points on the premotor area opposite the arm and leg areas respectively. These may be associated with fluctuations in the systolic blood pressure and heart rate. Vasopressor points are usually discrete and separable from vasodepressor points, but their relative position varies from animal to animal and they are notoriously susceptible to the type of anesthesia used and to changes in the depths of anesthetic. Margaret Kennard (16) draws attention to the fact that an autonomic motor area can be plotted similar to that of the somatic motor area and has emphasized that it not only overlaps the somatic motor area, but that from the distribution of somatic motor foci one can predict the position of autonomic foci (Chap. XI).

Areas 17, 18 and 19. Excitation of the occipital visual cortex (areas 17 and 18) in man causes visual sensation of great intensity, consisting of flashes of light (area 17) and occasional well formed visual impressions recalling some vivid happening in past experience (areas 18 and 19). Epileptiform manifestations from scars or tumors in area 19 may begin with realistic visual hallucinations referred to the opposite homonymous field. An American admiral, a patient of the late Harvey Cushing, had as a presenting symptom of a tumor in this region a recurring hallucination in which he visualized his battleship on which Mr. Theodore Roosevelt was seen shaking hands with a Japanese dignitary who had come on board the admiral's ship to meet the American president. The scene in question had actually occurred. When the tumor was removed from area 19 the hallucinations immediately ceased, and the normal fields of vision were gradually restored. Stimulation of area 19 in monkeys causes dilatation of the pupil and stimulation of areas 17 and 18 causes conjugate deviation of the eyes to the opposite side. Responses from the occipital eye fields are more fickle and less intense than those of area 8, as far as extra-ocular movements are concerned.

Areas 3–1, 5 and 7. All authorities are agreed that the postcentral areas are far less excitable than those of the precentral convolution. It is generally impossible even with very strong stimulation to obtain primary movements from areas 3–1 or 5, but facilitation of responses from area 4 is readily demonstrated. This was first emphasized by Graham Brown and confirmed by the Vogts and by Dusser de Barenne and his colleagues. The extent and character of the responses in the chimpanzee brain are clearly illustrated in Figure 155. Note that area 7 (and 19—see Fig. 152) give reactions restricted to the eye.

Interaction between Cortical Areas. We have seen that both the premotor and the postcentral areas may facilitate responses in area 4, which brings us to the larger consideration of the motor organization of the cortex as a whole,

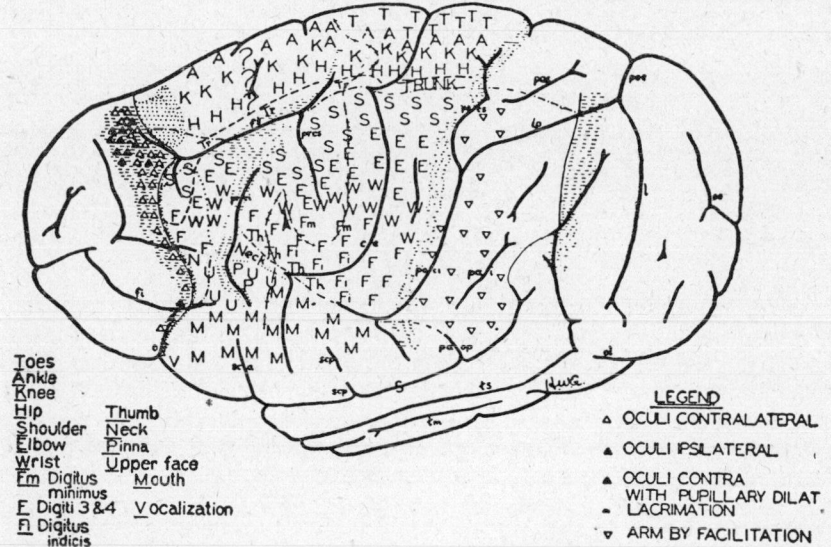

Toes
Ankle
Knee
Hip   Thumb
Shoulder   Neck
Elbow   Pinna
Wrist   Upper face
Fm Digitus Mouth
   minimus
F Digiti 3 &4 Vocalization
Fi Digitus
   indicis

LEGEND
△ OCULI CONTRALATERAL
▲ OCULI IPSILATERAL
▲ OCULI CONTRA
   WITH PUPILLARY DILAT.
- LACRIMATION
▽ ARM BY FACILITATION

Fig. 155.—The motor cortex of a chimpanzee. The primary motor area lies rostral to the central fissure, but widespread areas of facilitation as well as of suppression (see hatched bands) are clearly evident. (After Dusser de Barenne, Garol and McCulloch, *J. Neurophysiol.*, 1941, *4*:324–330.)

and to study the widespread interaction between cortical areas which has been disclosed and elucidated to great advantage during the past fifteen years by Dusser de Barenne and his colleagues.

Suppressor strips. In 1936 Marion Hines (12) discovered that a small strip of precentral tissue lying between areas 4 and 6 (and designated area 4s) on electrical stimulation evoked inhibition of any existing contraction in skeletal muscles on the opposite side of the body. In keeping with this, Dusser de Barenne, Garol and McCulloch (4) found that excitation of the strip region (by strychnine or faradization) causes a marked rise in the threshold of area 4 associated with suppression of spontaneous electrical activity. It was further disclosed that the reaction was not mediated transcortically, but through a complex circuit involving the caudate nucleus, thalamus and the thalamocortical projections to area 4 (to be discussed further in Chapter 14 on the basal ganglia).

Using the strychnine technique (to avoid escape of current and complication in electrical recording) Dusser de Barenne et al. later found three other suppressor areas, namely, 8s, 2s and 19s which for the chimpanzee cortex are shown in Figure 156. Each suppressor area acts via a specific projection

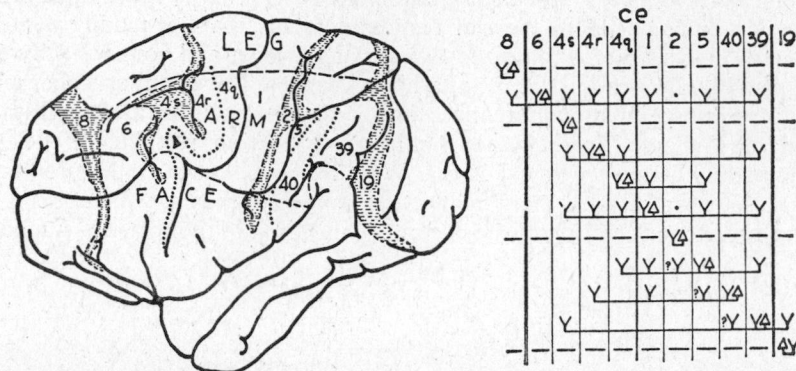

Fig. 156.—Diagram showing primary cytoarchitectural areas of chimpanzee sensorimotor cortex with indication of the four suppressor bands, i.e., areas 8s, 4s, 2s and 19s, as elucidated by the strychnine method. Area 6, 4, 3, 1, 5 and 7 constitute the sensorimotor cortex with area 4 as the primary motor area. At the right is the "firing" diagram: Y, activation; —, suppression; Δ area strychninized. Areas 8s and 19s are immediately adjacent to areas of thalamocortical projection and are not, strictly speaking, to be regarded as sensory cortex. (From McCulloch, in Bucy, *The precentral motor cortex*, Urbana, 1944, by kind permission.)

(probably unmyelinated, Glees, 11), which passes from the suppressor band in question to the caudate nucleus. The discovery of the suppressor areas and of their physiological connections with the basal ganglia will no doubt serve to explain the close association existing between the cerebral cortex and the basal ganglia.

Table 11.—Showing Homolateral Areal Interrelations of Chimpanzee Cerebral Cortex as Elucidated by the Strychnine Method (From McCulloch in Bucy, 1944)

AREA STRYCH.	32	24	47	8	6	4s	4r	4q	1	2	5	40	39	19	18	17
32	A	0	0	0	0	0	0	0	0	0	0	0	0	0	0	0
24	+	L	−	−	−	−	−	−	−	−	−	−	−	−	−	−
8	+	−	−	L	−	−	−	−	−	−	−	−	−	−	+	−
6	0	0	?	0	A	+	+	+	+	?	+	0	+	0	0	0
4s	+	−	−	−	−	L	−	−	−	−	−	−	−	−	−	−
4r	0	0	0	0	0	+	R	+	0	0	0	0	+	0	0	0
4q	0	0	0	0	0	0	0	R	+	0	+	0	0	0	0	0
1	0	0	0	0	0	+	+	+	F	?	+	0	+	0	0	0
2	+	−	−	−	−	−	−	−	−	−	−	−	−	−	−	−
5	0	0	0	0	0	0	0	+	+	?	F	+	0	0	0	0
40	0	0	0	0	0	0	+	0	+	0	?	F	0	0	0	0
39	0	0	0	0	0	+	0	0	0	0	0	?	0	+	0	0
19	+	−	−	−	−	+	−	−	−	−	−	−	−	R	−	−
18	0	0	0	0	0	0	0	0	0	0	0	0	0	0	+	A	+
17	0	0	0	0	0	0	0	0	0	0	0	0	0	0	0	+	L

The + sign indicates well established firing; 0, well established lack of firing; L, strictly local firing; R, firing restricted to a large part of the same area; F, firing of whole area; A, same area; −, suppression.

Interaction of other areas. Through the use of charts and tables McCulloch has developed an ingenious method for indicating the action of one cytoarchitectural area upon another. Thus in the chart in Figure 156, showing the suppressor strips, one finds that activation of area 6 by strychnine leads to activation ("firing") of areas 8, 4, 1, 5 and 39, whereas activation of 4s leads to active suppression of all areas charted. Other interrelations for the homolateral hemisphere are indicated in Table 11.

Certain areas cause activation of the opposite cerebral cortex; a given area on one side generally activates the corresponding area on the opposite side; but area 8, significantly enough, also activates area 18, which establishes both an ipsilateral and a homolateral connection of each frontal eye field with the two occipital eye fields. For further detail concerning the integration of the various cortical areas one should consult Bucy's monograph entitled *The precentral motor cortex*, 1944.

REGIONAL ABLATION OF CORTICAL AREAS

Further information concerning functional localization within the cerebral cortex has come from study in the higher primate forms of the effects of regional ablation.

Precentral Convolution. Bilateral removal of areas 4 and 6 in their entirety from an adult macaque or chimpanzee reduces the animal's motor status virtually to that of a completely decorticate animal. He is unable to stand or feed himself and lies helplessly on his side exhibiting the thalamic reflex posture shown in Figure 114. If the operation is carried out in infancy the animal is at first little affected by the procedure, but serious motor deficits begin to appear as the animal matures and while it may never become as gravely affected as when the areas are removed from an adult animal, it is profoundly incapacitated, exhibiting scissors gait, extreme spasticity, a clinical picture indistinguishable from the spastic birth paralyses first described by Little, the British orthopedic surgeon (and sometimes still referred to as Little's Disease). The specific reflex changes which develop in such a bilateral motor-premotor preparation can best be elucidated through an analysis of individual regional ablations.

Area 4 (Primary Motor Area). Symptoms following isolated ablation of area 4 increase in severity as one ascends the scale of animals, particularly among the primates. The lemurs, including forms such as marmosets, pottos and galagos as well as ordinary lemurs, exhibit minor degrees of paresis following motor area ablation and tend quickly to recover motor power. The lower monkeys such as the cercopithiques exhibit more conspicuous motor deficit, whereas monkeys such as macaques, mangabeys and spiders, with more highly encephalized motor function, develop more enduring paralysis. Finally, chimpanzees and man develop profound disturbances after isolated lesions of this region. The specific effects of ablation in chimpanzees and man fall into five categories: (i) movement, (ii) posture, (iii) reflexes, (iv) behavior patterns, and (v) autonomic functions. For purposes of exposition the effects of ablating the foot area of a chimpanzee will be described.

Movement. Immediately following the ablation a profound flaccid paralysis develops affecting muscles of the entire lower extremity. The animal, usually somewhat mystified at first by its inability to move the affected member, looks at it as though it didn't belong to him. It may be readily ascertained, however, that despite the profound paralysis the extremity is sentient, for on pinching the plantar surface the animal evinces signs of pain, but often as not it appears unable accurately to localize the pain; and from evidence derived from human beings who have suffered similar lesions (usually less well circumscribed) there is loss of position sense immediately after the ablation, but this tends quickly to return as does the capacity to localize painful stimuli. The power of movement does not begin to return for four or five days, and then hip flexion appears followed a few days later by knee flexion, and finally some degree of control at the ankle. The digits tend to remain permanently paralyzed. Finer movements of the fingers such as hallux-toe approximation (or corresponding movements of the thumb and index after an arm area ablation) have failed to appear even after two years. It is therefore highly significant that movements such as those of the digits having the largest representation in the cortex are the most profoundly affected by an area of lesion.

Flaccidity. The flaccid character of the paralysis following an area 4 lesion deserves emphasis since it is generally believed in neurological circles that an upper motor neuron lesion gives rise to spastic paralysis. This is definitely not the case if the lesion is sharply restricted to the pyramidal projection. When removing area 4 some extrapyramidal projections are always removed at the same time, and this may account for the fact that four to five weeks after an area 4 lesion the animal may develop a transient spastic resistance, especially of its digits (Denny-Brown). When, however, the pyramids are sectioned in the medulla, the paralysis which follows is highly flaccid in character and remains so in both monkeys and chimpanzees for an indefinite period of time (Tower).

If the second leg area is removed at an interval after the ablation on the first side, the leg originally paralyzed suffers a further increase in flaccidity and motor deficit, suggesting that such recovery as had occurred was due in some measure to *ipsilateral* representation. Ipsilateral pyramidal projections constitute about 15 per cent of the total projections in chimpanzees and macaques; evidence of ipsilateral control is also evident from stimulation experiments (3).

Reflex changes. All reflexes are profoundly depressed for several days following area 4 lesions. The knee jerk may return on the second day and weak reflex withdrawals can generally be evoked about the same time in response to strong plantar stimulation. In man reflex depression endures for about the same period, and the sequence of return is similar to that in a chimpanzee. The depression of reflexes is similar to that seen following transection of the spinal cord. The spinal chimpanzee begins to have reflexes return within eight to ten days of cord transection, whereas man without pharmacological stimulants usually fails to show reflex recovery for eighteen to twenty days following spinal transection.

There is one group of reflex changes pathognomonic of pyramidal injury, i.e., *the sign of Babinski*, a group of similar reactions used by clinical neurologists as variants of the Babinski reflex (9, 18). In man and in the chimpanzee (but not in the monkey) plantar stimulation causes flexion of the toes in the normal adult individual. In human infants prior to the eighth or ninth month, plantar stimulation causes *extension*, especially of the great toe. This is known as the sign of Babinski, and it is consistently found in adults after pyramidal tract interruption. Babinski also described fanning of the outer toes in certain types of neurological cases. In the chimpanzee fanning occurs only when area

6 has been encroached upon, and thus gives evidence of extrapyramidal injury at the cortical level.

Behavior disturbances. Observations on animals which had previously been trained to perform complex manipulations involving the use both of the hands and the feet (undoing latches, turning cranks, pulling strings, etc., in order to open a box for food) show, when their motor areas are removed, that the paralysis is in fact purely motor in character, for the animal, following the operation, gives every indication that it has not forgotten how to carry out the manipulation, i.e., maneuvers previously carried out with its paretic extremities are quickly performed either with its teeth or with the extremities on the unparalyzed side (Jacobsen). The animal thus exhibits no trace of mental confusion or amnesia; its behavior indicates that it "knows" what to do. In sharp contrast with this, animals having lesions of the premotor areas and the frontal association areas, especially when bilateral, exhibit confusion of a type which the clinician would in man designate as "apraxia." With motor area lesions, even when bilateral, there is no trace of mental confusion of this type.

Autonomic disturbances. These are minimal with lesions restricted to area 4; there may be moderate vasomotor disturbance in the affected extremity and Schwartz (22) finds that the change in the psychogalvanic reflex is likewise minimal in contrast to the conspicuous changes in psychogalvanic reactions which develop following lesions of area 6. Bilateral lesions of area 4 are, however, followed by abnormal shivering, and the slightest drop in environmental temperature tends to evoke a shivering reflex that will increase the body temperature somewhat above normal levels (1). It is thus evident that the cerebral cortex plays some part in the heat regulatory mechanism.

Area 6 (Premotor Area). Lesions of the upper part of area 6 (arm and leg) cause changes both of movement and of reflexes wholly different from those seen with lesions of area 4. When unilateral, a soft plastic rigidity develops, characterized by the presence of lengthening and shortening reactions and the presence of a strong involuntary grasp reflex, identical in its general characteristic with forced grasping in human subjects. It consists of a slow flexion of the digits in response to contact with the palmar or plantar surfaces. The response itself is of varied intensity depending upon the position of the animal in space and upon secondary stimuli, visual, auditory, etc., which may cause it to fluctuate.

The forced grasping reaction tends after two to three weeks to disappear, but it returns in an augmented form in both extremities if the premotor is removed from the second hemisphere. The animal becomes seriously incapacitated when the second premotor area is ablated, and if trained in maneuvers requiring manual dexterity, it not only exhibits awkwardness when attempting to carry out the maneuver but a considerable degree of amnesia and confusion. During the first week after the second lesion the animal is so incapacitated it cannot be tested, but little by little forced grasping diminishes in intensity and finally after three weeks to a month disappears altogether. It has been concluded from these studies that the premotor region presides, on the one hand, over postural adjustments, and that it also is the region in which complex movement patterns are learned and organized.

Reflex changes. In addition to forced grasping and movement disturbances, lesions of the premotor area tend to cause augmentation of the deep reflexes especially when area 4s is included in the ablation, and specific tendon reflexes of the digits such as are involved in Rossolimo's sign (flicking the end of one digit causes the other four to flex involuntarily). Babinski's sign does not develop, but lateral deviation of the toes, the so-called *fanning sign of Babinski*, develops after premotor lesion. When area 6 is removed *secondarily* to a lesion of area 4, all of the reflex changes just described are seen in greatly exaggerated form, and a well developed spastic hemiplegia ensues associated with conspicuous signs of Rossolimo (foot) and Hoffmann (a reaction similar to that of Rossolimo but in the hand). Tabulation of the various reflex changes which follow isolated lesions of area 4 and of 6 and of a combination of the two is given in Table 12 (9).†

One is thus brought to the conclusion that the symptoms commonly observed following an apoplectic "stroke" (in which projection systems of the internal capsule are affected by the hemorrhage) are due to simultaneous interruption of fibers from the motor and premotor areas. It is seldom that an isolated lesion of area 4 would occur in man, but several have been de-

Table 12.—*Showing Reflex Changes Following Unilateral Upper Motor Neuron Lesions (Cortical)*

	MOTOR (PYRAMIDAL)	PREMOTOR (EXTRA-PYRAMIDAL)	COMBINED MOTOR AND PREMOTOR
Babinski	+	0	++
Chaddock	+	0	+
Gonda	+	?	+
Spasticity	0	++	+++
Toe fanning	0	+	+
Rossolimo	0	+	++
Mendel-Bechterew	0	+	++
Forced grasping	0	+	+
Hoffmann	0	+	++
Tendon	+*	++	+++
Abdominal	0	?	0
Vasomotor disturbance	0	++	++

* Depressed or absent in early stages following a motor area lesion.

scribed involving hemorrhage of the vessels within the central sulcus. In these circumstances flaccid hemiplegias have developed (usually with some attendant sensory disturbance), and similar flaccid pareses have been encountered by neurological surgeons following extirpation of tumors or of cortical scars affecting area 4.

Area 8 (Frontal Eye Fields). Lesions restricted to the eye fields have little or no effect on the reflex status of the extremities; a conspicuous syndrome, however, follows unilateral ablation of area 8 characterized by turning of the head to the side of the lesion, transient paralysis of conjugate lateral eye movements to the opposite side, and in addition the animal, in moving about, circles involuntarily toward the side of the lesion (15). The latter phenomenon has been referred to as "forced circling," and it continues for many weeks after the paralysis of eye movements has disappeared. In addition to dis-

† In April, 1945, Wartenberg published a brief monograph entitled *The examination of reflexes — a simplification* (Year Book Publishers, Inc., Chicago) in which all of the reflexes described in Table 12 are discussed in detail and their physiological and clinical significance elucidated. He stresses the fact that the eponymic plantar reflexes such as that of Babinski, Chaddock, Gonda and Hoffmann are variations of the same basic reaction pattern. The monograph is also useful because of its full list of references to the original descriptions of the reflexes in question.

turbed eye movements and circling, the animal exhibits a curious form of hemianopic visual disturbance characterized by retention of light perception, but disorganization of the ability to recognize objects brought to the hemianopic field on the side opposite to the lesion. It quickly recognizes and grabs a banana brought into the field on the side of the lesion, but recognition of the banana fails on the side opposite, and, indeed, until it actually reaches its central visual axis. This interesting visual disturbance is no doubt due to disorganization of proprioception—a failure of correlation between impulses from the retina integrated in the visual association areas (areas 18 and 19) and extraocular proprioceptive impulses which find integration in area 8. When areas 8 are removed simultaneously from both hemispheres, the animal has complete object-vision blindness for several weeks, and develops an expressionless facies akin to that seen in advanced Parkinsonism (17).

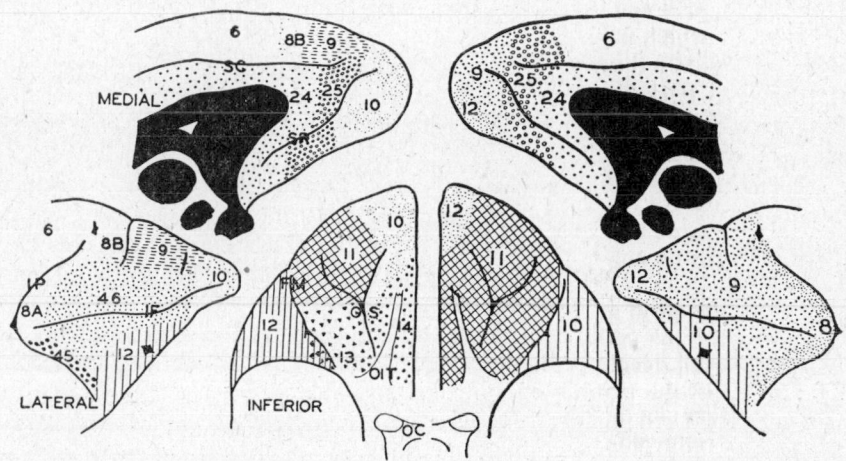

Fig. 157.—A. E. Walker's cytoarchitectural map of the prefrontal lobe of *the Macaca mulatta* monkey (left) side by side with Brodmann's map for the *Cercopithecus* monkey (right). The numerical designations in Walker's map are derived from Brodmann's designations of comparable areas in the human cerebral cortex and hence do not in most cases agree with Brodmann's and Vogt's designations for the monkey. (From Ruch and Shenkin, *J. Neurophysiol.*, 1943, *6*:349–360.)

Area 13 (Cortical Respiratory Center). It has recently been disclosed that area 13 (area 47 in Brodmann's map of the human brain) on the orbital surface of the frontal lobe is closely associated with activities of the vagus nerve as well as with respiratory movements (24). Stimulation of the central end of the vagus causes sharply circumscribed electrical discharge in area 13 and in no other part of the cerebral cortex (Fig. 157). Stimulation of area 13, on the other hand, causes inhibition of peristaltic movements of the gut as well as prompt arrest of respiratory movements. On bilateral ablation of this area in monkeys the animals become abnormally restless almost to the point of a maniacal behavior (21). The spontaneous hypermotility associated with frontal lobe lesions in animals no doubt depends in intensity upon the extent to which area 13 has been encroached upon in the ablation. It is possible that simultaneous injury to the head of the caudate nuclei, should this occur with frontal ablation, may increase the hypermotility, but to date there is no adequate experimental evidence to support this inference.

Areas 17–19 (Occipital Eye Fields). Ablation of area 17 is probably without primary motor effects, but light perception as well as object vision is completely abolished in the opposite hemianopic field (Chap. 18). When areas 18 and 19 are included in the lesion, motor effects of a somewhat transient character develop; especially when the lesions are bilateral there tends to be hippus, i.e., alternate constriction and dilatation of the pupils. Unilateral lesions cause transient paresis of conjugate deviation of the eyes to the opposite sides, but the effects are much less conspicuous than with lesions of area 8.

Areas 3–1–2, 5 and 7. Lesions of the parietal lobe cause primary sensory disturbances which will be discussed in the following section. The motor difficulties are partly those resulting from sensory impairments (loss of position sense), but a part of the awkwardness which follows upon lesions of the parietal lobes are no doubt due to interruption of motor projections originating in these areas. It has, however, been impossible clearly to distinguish the purely sensory from the purely motor effects. Parietal lobe lesions tend of themselves to give a flaccid paresis, but when added to a previous lesion of the precentral convolution, any existing spasticity from the precentral lesion tends to be augmented by a parietal lesion for reasons not yet clearly understood.

Ipsilateral Control and Interaction between Cerebral Hemispheres. Regional stimulation of the cerebral cortex and regional ablation give confirmatory evidence of well developed ipsilateral control of the body musculature. Thus from points in the posterior part of the premotor area, well developed primary responses can often be obtained in the ipsilateral hind leg; and when the foot area is removed, first from one hemisphere and then from the second, there is always an increase in motor deficit in the limb ipsilateral to the second ablation. This overlapping of control is no doubt responsible for facilitating recovery from what might otherwise be a completely incapacitating hemiplegia. A patient of Dr. Gardner, the Cincinnati neurosurgeon, who survived complete removal of the right cerebral hemisphere for a malignant tumor, was able after six months to walk without the support of a crutch.

Corpus callosum. The large projection passing from one hemisphere to another via the corpus callosum fulfills some function as yet not clearly understood. In man the corpus callosum has been divided to afford a surgical approach to the third ventricle without causing a recognizable motor or psychological disturbance. From the studies of Curtis in Baltimore and McCulloch et al. it is apparent that activation of a specific area in one hemisphere causes electrical discharge in the corresponding area of the opposite hemisphere, and that such discharge is abolished by section of the corpus callosum, but what function is achieved through this interaction has not yet been ascertained.

Cerebral dominance. The left hemisphere in right-handed individuals is said to be dominant over the right hemisphere in so far as the faculty of articulate speech is concerned. Small lesions restricted to area 46 (the motor speech area lying just rostral to the motor face area) cause motor speech disturbances generally referred to as motor aphasia, and to the speech disturbance there is added inevitably some degree of mental confusion. A corresponding lesion in the right hemisphere of a right-handed individual has no such effect on speech. It is said that left-handed children, if they are forced to be dextromanual, tend to develop speech difficulties, believed due to interhemispheric rivalry.

REFERENCES

1. ARING, C. D. Clinical symptomatology, Chap. XVI in BUCY, P. C. ed., *The precentral motor cortex*, 1944.

2. BOYLE, R. *Experimenta et observationes physicae*, London, J. Taylor, 1691. 26, 158, 32 pp.

3. BUCY, P. C. Effects of extirpation in man, Chap. XIV in his: *The precentral motor cortex*, 1944.

4. DUSSER DE BARENNE, J. G., GAROL, H. W., and McCULLOCH, W. S. Functional organization of sensory and adjacent cortex of the monkey. *J. Neurophysiol.*, 1941, *4*:324–330.

5. DUSSER DE BARENNE, J. G., and McCULLOCH, W. S. Factors for facilitation and extinction in the central nervous system. *J. Neurophysiol.*, 1939, *2*:319–355.

6. DUSSER DE BARENNE, J. G., MARSHALL, C. S., McCULLOCH, W. S., and NIMS, L. S. Observations on the pH of the arterial blood, the pH and the electrical activity of the cerebral cortex. *Amer. J. Physiol.*, 1938, *124*:631–636.

7. FERRIER, D. Experimental researches in cerebral physiology and pathology. *West Riding Lunatic Asylum med. Rep.*, 1873, *3*:1–50.

8. FRITSCH, G., and HITZIG, E. Ueber die elektrische Erregbarkeit des Grosshirns. *Arch. Anat. Physiol. wiss. Med.*, 1870, *37*:300–332.

9. FULTON, J. F. *Physiology of the nervous system*, 2nd ed. New York, Oxford University Press, 1943. x, 614 pp.

10. FULTON, J. F., and DUSSER DE BARENNE, J. G. The representation of the tail in the motor cortex of primates, with special reference to spider monkeys. *J. cell. comp. Physiol.*, 1933, *2*:399–426.

11. GLEES, P. The anatomical basis of cortico-striate connexions. *J. Anat., Lond.*, 1944, *78*:47–51.

12. HINES, M. The anterior border of the monkey's (*Macaca mulatta*) motor cortex and the production of spasticity. *Amer. J. Physiol.*, 1936, *116*:76.

13. JACKSON, J. HUGHLINGS. A study of convulsions. *Trans. St. Andrews Med. Grad. Ass.*, 1870, *3*:162–207. (Repr. *Selected writings*, London, 1931, v. 1, 8–36.)

14. KENNARD, M. A. Reorganization of motor function in the cerebral cortex of monkeys deprived of motor areas in infancy. *J. Neurophysiol.*, 1938, *1*:477–496.

15. KENNARD, M. A. Somatic functions, Chap. IX in: BUCY, P. C., ed., *The precentral motor cortex*, 1944.

16. KENNARD, M. A. Autonomic functions, Chap. XI in BUCY, P. C., ed. *The precentral motor cortex*, 1944.

17. KENNARD, M. A., and ECTORS, L. Forced circling in monkeys following lesions of the frontal lobes. *J. Neurophysiol.*, 1938, *1*:45–56.

18. LASSEK, A. M. The human pyramidal tract. X. The Babinski sign and destruction of the pyramidal tract. *Arch. Neurol. Psychiat., Chicago*, 1944, *52*:484–494.

19. LLOYD, D. P. C. A direct central inhibitory action of dromically conducted impulses. *J. Neurophysiol.*, 1941, *4*:184–190.

20. McCULLOCH, W. S. Cortico-cortical connections, Chap. VIII in: BUCY, P. C., ed., *The precentral motor cortex*, 1944.

21. RUCH, T. C., and SHENKIN, H. A. The relation of area 13 on orbital surface of frontal lobes to hyperactivity and hyperphagia in monkeys. *J. Neurophysiol.*, 1943, *6*:349–360.

22. SCHWARTZ, H. G. Effect of experimental lesions of the cortex on the "psychogalvanic reflex" in the cat. *Arch. Neurol. Psychiat., Chicago*, 1937, *38*:308–320.

23. SMITH, W. K. The frontal eye fields, Chap. XII in: BUCY, P. C., ed., *The precentral motor cortex*, 1944.

24. WALKER, A. E. A cyto-architectural study of the prefrontal area of the macaque monkey. *J. comp. Neurol.*, 1940, *73*:59–86.

25. WYSS, O. A. M. Personal comunication.

CHAPTER 14

CEREBRUM AND BASAL GANGLIA

It was pointed out in the previous two chapters that the motor activities of the cerebral cortex are facilitated through the operation of two widely ramifying projections to subcortical systems: (i) the cortico-strio-nigral which is largely concerned with postural adjustments, and (ii) the cortico-ponto-cerebellar which is primarily associated with the control of phasic movements. The first involves the so-called basal ganglia and their interrelations with the cerebral cortex, which will be the subject of this chapter, and the second a consideration of the cerebellum, which will be taken up in the following chapter.

ANATOMICAL CONSIDERATIONS (12, 13, 14)

By basal ganglia we refer to all subcortical motor nuclei of the forebrain, including the caudate nucleus, putamen, globus pallidus, and several brain stem nuclei, i.e., corpus luysii and substantia nigra, to which the basal ganglia discharge. The caudate nucleus and the putamen are known collectively as the "corpus striatum" while the putamen and globus pallidus are known as the "lenticular" nuclei. Lying deep to the cerebral mantle and forming a lateral boundary of the cerebral ventricles, the basal ganglia have long remained obscure from a functional standpoint and until recently their anatomical connections have been almost as unsettled as their functional activity. It has now been established, however, that the caudate nucleus receives a large projection of unmyelinated fibers from areas 8s, 4s and 2s of the cerebral cortex (5). The putamen receives a cortical projection from areas 4 and 6, and it is probable that the globus pallidus also receives projections from the premotor region. Both the caudate and the putamen discharge through the globus pallidus which, in turn, sends a motor projection to the thalamus and, via the ansa lenticularis, to the substantia nigra and corpus luysii. These anatomical relations are diagrammatically indicated in Figure 158.

Historical note. Speculation concerning the functions of the basal ganglia has been based in the past largely upon clinical evidence. Hyperkinetic syndromes such as chorea and athetosis have been attributed to primary lesions of the basal ganglia; paralysis agitans (Parkinsonism) has likewise been attributed to basal ganglia disturbance, since evidence of irritation or destruction of basal ganglia nuclei has generally been found in patients who have succumbed to the disease. In all these clinical conditions the pathological alterations in the brain are generally widespread, and there have been few instances in which lesions have been sufficiently restricted to a given area to warrant conclusions concerning function. The interrelations of the basal ganglia with the cortex have been little stressed in the clinical literature, and there has been a tendency to regard the extrapyramidal system as something quite separate and independent of the cerebral cortex and its projections. From the physiological standpoint, this is highly misleading, since it has now become clear that the basal ganglia and the cerebral cortex actually function as a single closely integrated functional unit; the evidence leading to this conclusion can best be summarized under the following headings: (i) excitability, (ii) experimental lesions, and (iii) combined lesions of cerebral cortex and basal ganglia.

EXCITABILITY

Early attempts to stimulate the basal ganglia brought conflicting results, largely because phasic movements were looked for rather than changes of posture. The British neurologist, Kinnier Wilson (18), who used the Horsley-Clarke technique of stimulation, declared the putamen and globus pallidus of monkeys completely inexcitable, and it is now clear that others who had reported phasic movements had not adequately controlled their experiments for spread of current to the internal capsule. Rioch and Brenner (15) who stimulated the basal ganglia of experimental animals three weeks after removing the cerebral hemispheres failed to obtain motor responses in the extremities, but noted chop licking, swallowing, salivation, sniffing, etc., which they attributed, no doubt correctly, to the adjacent olfactory system rather than to the striopallidum.

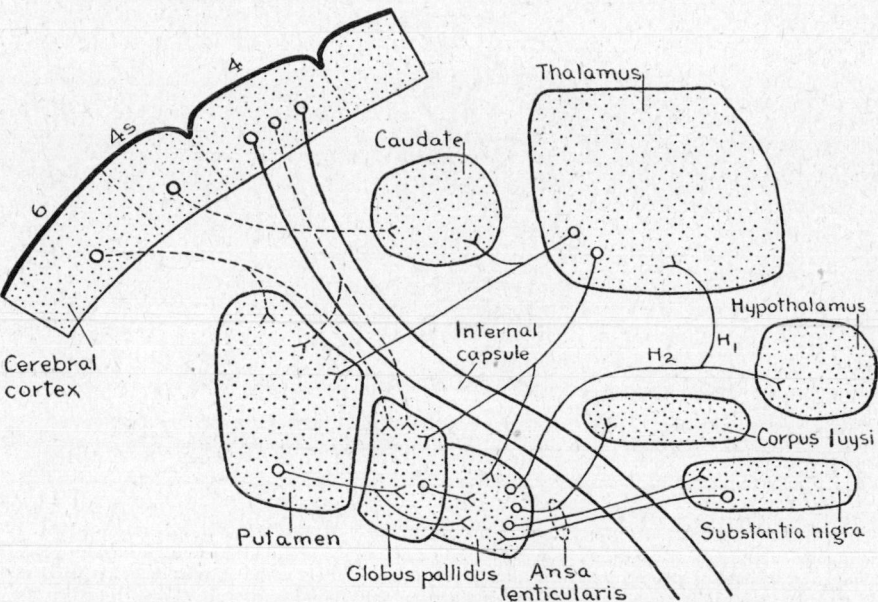

Fig. 158.—Diagram of interconnections between basal ganglia and cerebral cortex. Projections from areas 4, 4s and 6 have been established by physiological techniques of Dusser de Barenne and his colleagues and are indicated by dotted lines. Note that area 4s projects only to caudate, whereas areas 4 and 6 have connection with putamen and globus pallidus. (Kennard, *J. Neurophysiol.*, 1944, 7:142.)

Inhibitory effects. If the responsiveness of the basal ganglia is examined against a background either of posture or of concurrently induced movements from the cerebral cortex, it has been found that the striatum and also the globus pallidus cause vigorous inhibitory responses. Primary motor movements are never obtained, but somatic motor reactions initiated by the cerebral cortex can be dramatically inhibited even by weak stimulation of the striopallidum (16, 9). It has been disclosed further that the reactions in question are unobtainable if the caudate nucleus had been previously destroyed. These results accordingly point to a predominantly inhibitory role exercised by the basal ganglia upon cortically induced movements and postures. When the cerebral cortex has been removed, the basal ganglia have no background through which to operate, since the primary inhibitory effects are exerted through the cerebral cortex itself.

Activation of basal ganglia by cerebral cortex. Dusser de Barenne and McCulloch (4) find that stimulation of certain regions of the cerebral cortex mentioned in the last chapter, namely, areas 8s, 4s, 2s and probably 19s, cause a specific activation of the caudate nucleus which can be readily detected by recording electrically from the caudate. A well organized topographical projection exists from these areas, for 8s activates only the head of the caudate, 4s the middle region, and 2s the tail—these relations having been established both for monkeys and for chimpanzees (Fig. 159). Stimulation of area 6 and of area 4, on the other hand, causes activation of the putamen and the globus pallidus, but never the caudate. At the time these studies were made, no anatomical projections had been established between the cortex and the caudate

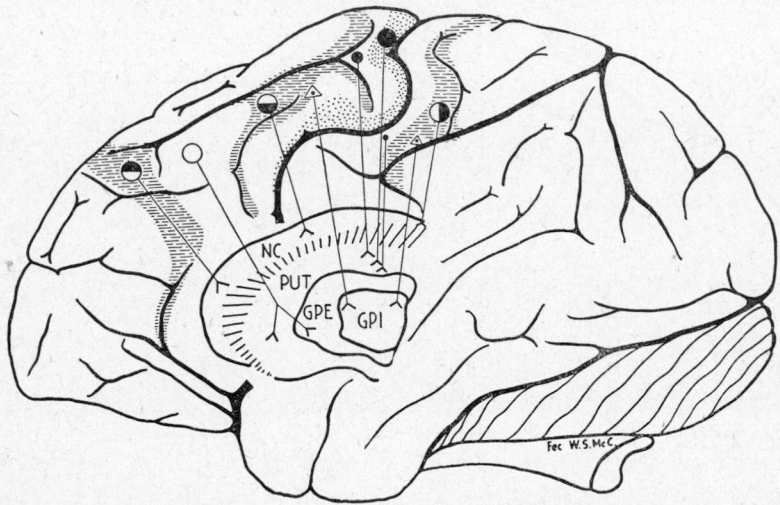

Fig. 159.—Corticostriate connections in the chimpanzee. Half filled circles denote projections from the suppressor areas 8s, 4s and 2s; note that these all pass to the caudate nucleus (NC). Open circle denotes projection from area 6 to putamen (PUT) and globus pallidus externus (GPE). Triangles indicate border areas projecting to globus pallidus internus (GPI). Filled circles, points on area 4 projecting to posterior putamen. (From Garol and McCulloch, *J. Neurophysiol.*, 1944, 7:202.)

nucleus, but Dusser de Barenne and his colleagues insisted that they must exist, and it is gratifying to learn that they have now been disclosed through the use of improved silver impregnation methods introduced by Glees (5). When activated, the caudate discharges to the globus pallidus, which in turn activates the thalamus, which discharges to area 4 via its thalamocortical projection. By this complex circuit the suppressor areas of the cerebral cortex govern and restrain the activity of the motor area.

Other evidence pointing to a close functional interrelationship between cortex and basal ganglia lies in the fact that spontaneous electrical rhythms in the basal ganglia are of small amplitude, but once all connection with the cerebral cortex is severed, spontaneous bursts of high voltage activity appear both in the caudate and the putamen. A small remnant of anatomical connection between cortex and basal ganglia may serve completely to suppress these high voltage bursts (8).

EXPERIMENTAL LESIONS

Striopallidum alone. Isolated lesions of any one of the basal ganglia in the absence of injury to the cerebral cortex give little in the way of positive symptomatology. Larger lesions, especially those involving the globus pallidus, may give rise to moderate increase in rigidity of the skeletal musculature, but little else in the way of motor deficit or reflex change. Kennard (7) reports that large lesions in any one of the basal ganglia of monkeys and chimpanzees, especially when present bilaterally, cause some degree of resting tremor, but she was unable to detect changes of resting posture except with lesions of

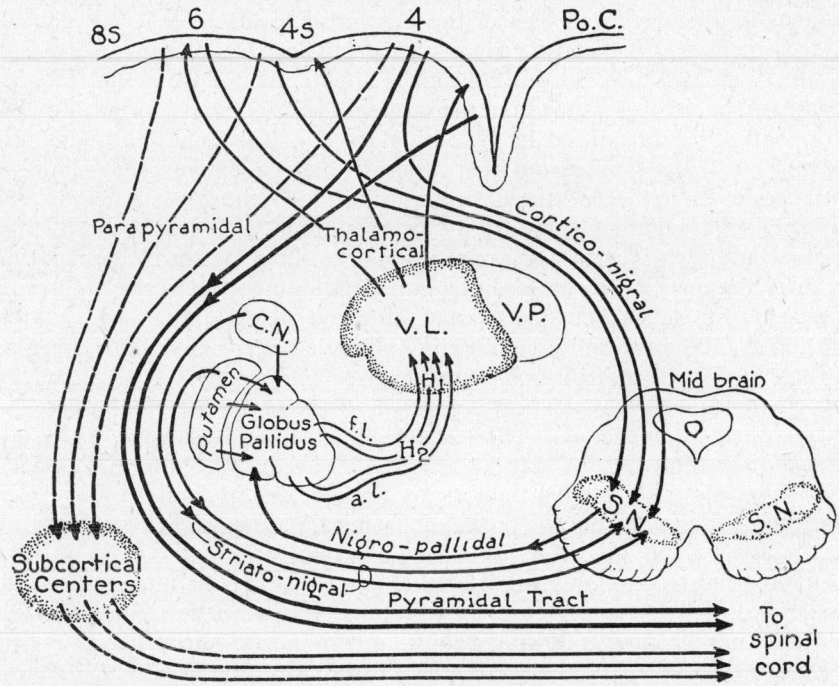

Fig. 160.—Probable neural mechanism of parkinsonian tremor. The inhibitory impulses arise from the precentral cortex, pass through the cortico-nigral fibers to the *substantia nigra* (*S.N.*) thence to the globus pallidus, through the nigropallidal fibers recently demonstrated by Ranson, then to the ventrolateral nucleus of the thalamus (*V.L.*), and back to the precentral cortex. When this system is interrupted the abolition of its suppressor impulses allows tremor at rest (parkinsonian) to be produced primarily by impulses passing by way of the pyramidal tract. (From Bucy, *The precentral motor cortex*, 1944.)

the pallidum. Following a lesion restricted to the caudate in two chimpanzees, a marked choreo-athetosis developed, quite similar to that seen clinically.

Combined lesions of striopallidum and cerebral cortex. When lesions of area 6 coexisted with lesions of the basal ganglia, tremor and choreo-athetosis, especially in chimpanzees, became prominent. There is likewise a marked increase in rigidity following combined lesions of the striatum and the premotor cortex. The rigidity had a quality entirely similar to that seen in clinical cases of basal ganglia disease, and was more conspicuous and more enduring than that following lesions of area 6 alone. It would appear from Kennard's analysis (7) that the clinical symptoms associated with disease entities such as paralysis agitans and chorea must be attributed to an overall disturbance involving both the cerebral cortex and the nuclei of the striopallidum.

CLINICAL PHYSIOLOGY

Athetosis. Kinnier Wilson (18), in discussing basal ganglia mechanisms, insisted that the hyperkinetic states, i.e., tremor, chorea and athetosis, probably resulted from activity of the cerebral cortex unsupported by the basal ganglia, and for this reason he predicted that severe choreo-athetosis, and probably also tremor, could be relieved if the site of origin of the movements in the cortex could be removed. It was on the basis of this concept that Sir Victor Horsley in 1909 removed part of the precentral cortex to relieve a man of severe athetosis (16). The procedure turned out to be moderately successful in this particular case, but his colleagues apparently felt that the resulting motor incapacity was worse than the original disease, and the procedure was dropped until reintroduced in 1932 by Bucy and Buchanan (3). Bucy more recently (1, 2) has pointed out that athetosis may be encountered clinically with lesions in either of these situations, i.e., (i) those restricted to the striatum, (ii) the globus pallidus; and other authors have described athetosis in association with (iii) a lesion of the thalamus. Bucy points to the fact that all three stations causing athetosis lie in the circuit involved in the suppressor reactions from area 4s, i.e., the striopallidum and the thalamus, and the interruption of the suppressor circuit at any point releases the motor area from its normal inhibitory control; involuntary movements result in consequence of this circumstance. Bucy advocates removal of the premotor area in cases of severe athetosis, and he has reported a number of highly satisfactory results of such procedure.

Tremor. The basal ganglia tremors are thought due to similar interruption of suppressor circuits, but the precise anatomical pathways involved have not been fully worked out; the globus pallidus and substantia nigra are the structures most commonly implicated (Fig. 160). Cortical interruption has been advocated for severe cases of paralysis agitans, since tremor has disappeared in such cases following a capsular hemiplegia. There is some reason to believe that whereas ablation of area 6 is the operation of choice to relieve severe choreo-athetosis, ablation of area 4 is the operation of choice for the relief of Parkinson tremor. Further clinical evidence is needed before a final decision can be made concerning either the rationale or the justifiability of recommending such intervention. The same is true of the operation of pyramidal tract section at the spinal cord recommended by Putnam (11).

REFERENCES

1. BUCY, P. C. Effects of extirpation in man, Chap. XIV in his: *The precentral motor cortex,* 1944.

2. BUCY, P. C. Relation to abnormal involuntary movements, Chap. XV in his: *The precentral motor cortex,* 1944.

3. BUCY, P. C., and BUCHANAN, D. N. Athetosis. *Brain,* 1932, *55:*479–492.

4. DUSSER DE BARENNE, J. G., and McCULLOCH, W. S. Suppression of motor response obtained from area 4 by stimulation of area 4s. *J. Neurophysiol.,* 1941, *3:*311–323.

5. GLEES, P. The anatomical basis of cortico-striate connexions. *J. Anat., Lond.,* 1944, *78:*47–51.

6. HORSLEY, V. The Linacre Lecture on the function of the so-called motor area of the brain. *Brit. med. J.,* 1909, *2:*125–132.

7. KENNARD, M. A. Experimental analysis of the functions of the basal ganglia in monkeys and chimpanzees. *J. Neurophysiol.,* 1944, *7:*127–148.

8. KENNARD, M. A., and NIMS, L. F. Effect on electroencephalogram of lesions of cerebral cortex and basal ganglia in *Macaca mulatta. J. Neurophysiol.,* 1942, *5:*335–348.

9. METTLER, F. A., ADES, H. W., LIPMAN, E., and CULLER, E. A. The extrapyramidal system. An experimental demonstration of function. *Arch. Neurol. Psychiat., Chicago*, 1939, *41*:984–995.

10. METTLER, F. A., and METTLER, C. C. The effects of striatal injury. *Brain*, 1942, *65*:242–255.

11. PUTNAM, T. J. Treatment of unilateral paralysis agitans by section of the lateral pyramidal tract. *Arch. Neurol. Psychiat., Chicago*, 1940, *44*:950–976.

12. RANSON, S. W., and RANSON, M. Pallidofugal fibers in the monkey. *Arch. Neurol. Psychiat., Chicago*, 1939, *42*:1059–1067.

13. RANSON, S. W., and RANSON, S. W., JR. Efferent fibers of the corpus striatum. *Res. Publ. Ass. nerv. ment. Dis.*, 1942, *21*:69–76.

14. RANSON, S. W., RANSON, S. W., JR., and RANSON, M. Corpus striatum and thalamus of a partially decorticate monkey. *Arch. Neurol. Psychiat., Chicago*, 1941, *46*:402–415.

15. RIOCH, D. McK., and BRENNER, C. Experiments on the striatum and rhinencephalon. *J. comp. Neurol.*, 1938, *68*:491–507.

16. TOWER, S. S. The dissociation of cortical excitation from cortical inhibition by pyramid section, and the syndrome of that lesion in the cat. *Brain*, 1935, *58*:238–255.

17. WELCH, W. K., and KENNARD, M. A. Relation of cerebral cortex to spasticity and flaccidity. *J. Neurophysiol.*, 1944, *7*: 255–268.

18. WILSON, S. A. KINNIER. An experimental research into the anatomy and physiology of the corpus striatum. *Brain*, 1914, *36*:427–492.

CHAPTER 15

CEREBRUM AND CEREBELLUM

The cerebellum, like the basal ganglia, has until recently largely defied functional analysis. The early investigators such as Rolando, Flourens and Luciani, succeeded in removing the cerebellum in whole or in part, and they describe in clear language the nature of the motor deficit which resulted. All investigators during the nineteenth century had agreed that ablation of the cerebellum is without effect on conscious sensation and entirely without influence upon the general intelligence of the animal; but volitional movements are gravely affected by decerebellation and Flourens insisted that as more and more of the cerebellum was removed, the gait of the animal became more and more like that of a human being suffering from alcoholic intoxication. He suggested, in fact, that the primary locus of action of alcohol must be the cerebellum—and there is little in recent work which could be held as contrary to this suggestion, provided one recognizes that alcohol also affects the higher intellectual faculties.

Actually the syndrome of cerebellar deficit is made up of a number of discrete and separable components, namely, disturbances of volitional movements, disturbances of posture, and impairment of equilibration. The anatomical subdivisions of the cerebellum give the basis for this tripartite symptom complex.

ANATOMICAL ORGANIZATION

Phylogenetically and embryologically, the cerebellum is an outgrowth from the vestibular complex of nuclei in the medulla oblongata. First appearing in primitive fish, the cerebellum comes to have greater prominence in the amphibia where it begins to receive ascending fibers from the spinal cord and trigeminal nuclei, as well as from the vestibular nuclei. In warm blooded animals the cerebellum receives a third important projection from the cerebral cortex via the pontine nuclei. This triple origin no doubt gives rise to the three fundamental subdivisions found in the cerebellum of all higher animals.

Primary Divisions. The fundamental landmark of cerebellar morphology is the posterolateral fissure which is shown in Figure 161, and which separates the flocculonodular lobe from the corpus cerebelli. The corpus cerebelli is itself made up of two primary divisions, i.e., the anterior and posterior lobes.

Flocculonodular lobe. This lobe, a direct outgrowth of the vestibular margin of the rhombic lip of the medulla oblongata, is the most constant structure in the cerebellum throughout the vertebrate series. From the studies of Larsell and of Dow (17, 9, 11), it is known that the flocculus and nodulus are the only parts of the cerebellum that receive and send fibers exclusively to the vestibular nuclei (Fig. 162).

Corpus cerebelli. In amphibia, reptiles and birds, the corpus cerebelli is a simple cellular mass, forming an arch over the medulla oblongata. In the reptiles, however, a sulcus develops, the *fissura prima* of Elliot Smith, which divides the corpus cerebelli into an anterior and a posterior lobe. A secondary fold, the so-called *fissura prepyramidalis*, develops in the posterior lobe. The part of the *posterior lobe* lying between fissura prima and prepyramidalis becomes enormously developed in mammals in association with the differentiation of the skeletal musculature and the growth of the cerebral hemispheres. In the primates, this division of the cerebellum becomes so greatly elaborated that it literally overshadows all the rest of the cerebellum. Because of its recent phylogenetic history, this part of the posterior lobe is known as the *neocerebellum* and is characterized by a new connection with the brain stem, namely, the pontocerebellar tract, from the pontine nuclei which are in direct connection with the cerebral cortex.

The anterior lobe, made up of lingula, centralis and culmen (Figs. 161, 162), and the posterior part of the posterior lobe, made up of pyramis, uvula and paraflocculus, being phylogenetically old, are often referred to as the *paleocerebellum*. This general term may also include the flocculonodular lobe.

The flocculonodular lobe thus has primary connections, afferent and efferent, with the vestibular nuclei; the posterior lobe which comprises all of the

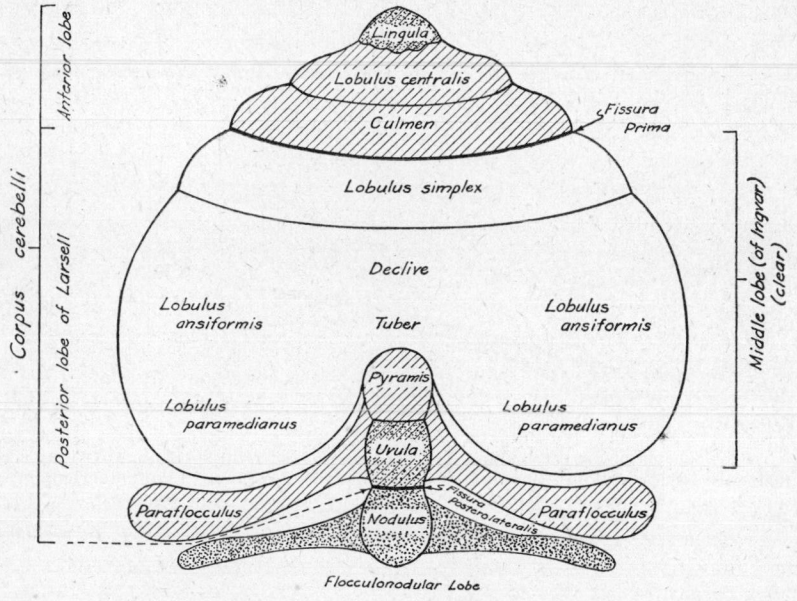

Fig. 161.—Diagram of primate cerebellar cortex to show principal divisions and afferent fiber connections (after Larsell). The fissura posterolateralis separates the two primary divisions, flocculonodular lobe and corpus cerebelli (see text). (From Dow, *J. Neurophysiol.*, 1942, *5*: 121–136.)

cerebellar hemispheres (neocerebellum) has primary associations, again both afferent and efferent, with the thalamus and the motor regions of the cerebral cortex on the afferent side, and with the cerebral cortex via the pontine nuclei on the efferent; the anterior lobe is connected with spinal reflex mechanisms on the afferent side and its efferent projections are to brain stem nuclei. Before attempting to give a summary of the functions of the cerebellum, it will be helpful to recall briefly some points in its structure which have a direct bearing upon its physiological relations and activities.

Anatomical Structure and Relations of the Cerebellum. The finer histology of the cerebellar cortex is represented in Figure 163. Three layers may be distinguished. The external molecular layer (*A*), the middle granular layer (*B*),

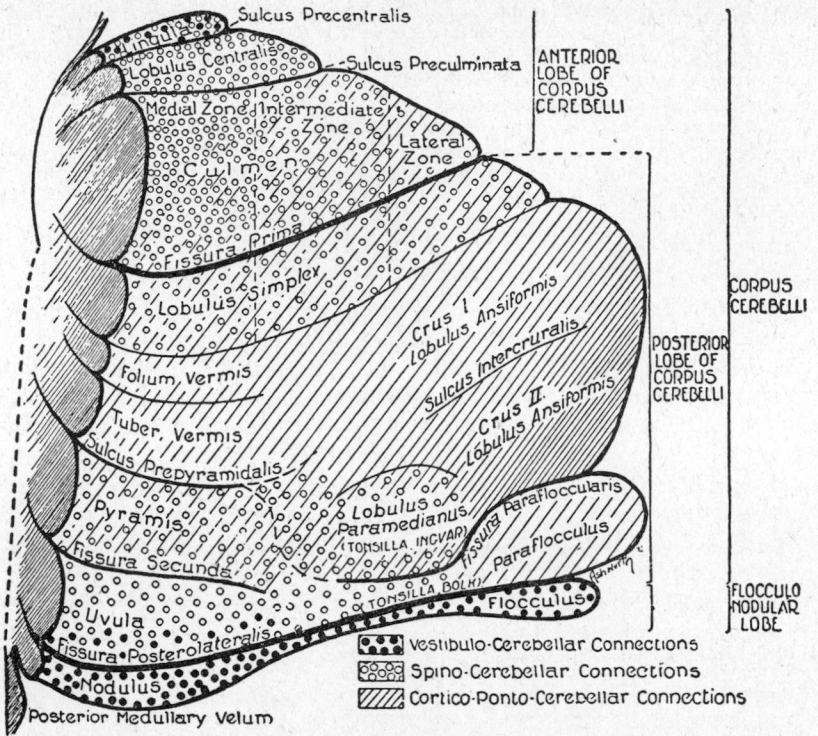

Fig. 162.—Schema of the cerebellum. The brackets on the right show the divisions according to Larsell's classification. Afferent fiber connections as determined by oscillographic studies are indicated by the different types of shading. (From Dow, *Biol. Rev.*, 1942, *17*:179–220.)

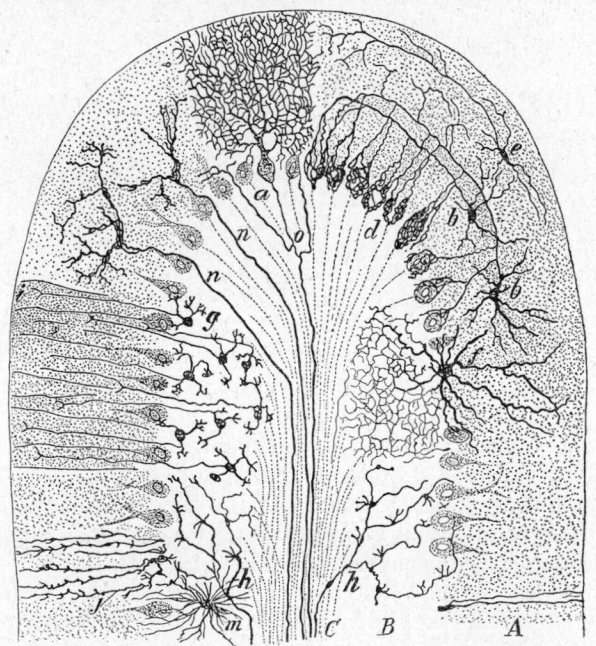

Fig. 163.—Histology of the cerebellum. (From Obersteiner.)

and the internal medullary layer consisting of the white matter or medullated nerve fibers, afferent and efferent (*C*). Between the molecular and granular layers lie the large and characteristic Purkinje cells (*a*). The dendrites of these cells branch profusely in the molecular layer; their axons pass into the medullary layer. From the standpoint of the neuron doctrine these cells, so far as the cerebellum is concerned, are efferent. They form, indeed, the sole efferent system of the cerebellar cortex. The afferent fibers of the cerebellum end in both the granular and the molecular layers. Those that terminate in the granular layer—designated by Cajal as moss fibers—have at their terminations and points of branching curious clumps of small processes; they probably connect with the dendrites of the nerve cells in this layer. Those that pass deeper into the molecular layer come into connection with the dendrites of the Purkinje cells, around which, indeed, they seem to twine, so that Cajal designated them as climbing fibers. The granular layer (*B*) contains numerous granules (*g*) or small nerve cells. These cells are spherical, and have a relatively large nucleus and a small amount of cytoplasm. Their dendrites are few and short; their axons run into the molecular layer, divide in T, and the two branches then run parallel to the surface and doubtless make connections with the dendrites of the Purkinje cells as well as with the cells of the molecular layer. A few larger nerve cells of Golgi's second type (*f*) are found in the granular layer. In the molecular layer are found two types of cells: the larger basket cells (*b*) whose axons terminate in a group of small branches that inclose the body of the Purkinje cells, and a number of smaller cells (*e*) situated more superficially, whose axons pass longitudinally in the molecular layer and terminate in arborizations or baskets that doubtless make connections with the dendrites of the Purkinje cells.

A consideration of this peculiar and intricate structure enables us to comprehend that the cerebellar cortex presents a reflex arc of a very considerable degree of complexity. Speaking in general terms we may emphasize the fact that the only efferent or discharging cells of the cortex are the Purkinje cells. None of the cells of the molecular and granular layers send axons into the white matter; they belong rather to the second type of Golgi cells whose axons break up into branches within the gray matter. Afferent fibers coming up in the white matter make connections with these small cells of the molecular and granular layer, and thus the incoming impulses at any point are distributed through intervening neurons and finally affect the cells of Purkinje. In addition to the cortex, the cerebellum contains several masses of gray matter in its interior: the large dentate nucleus in the center of each hemisphere and the group of nuclei lying in or near the middle of the medullary substance of the uvula and pyramis (nucleus fastigii, n. globosi, and the n. emboliformis). The axons of the Purkinje cells of the cortex terminate in these subcortical nuclei, and the efferent path from the cerebellum is then continued by new neurons. Thus, the fibers of the superior peduncles (branchium conjunctivum) of the cerebellum arise chiefly from the dentate nuclei, and only indirectly from the cortex. The anatomical connections, afferent and efferent, between the cerebellum and other parts of the nervous system are very complex and not yet entirely known. Without attempting to recall all of these connections, which will be found described in works upon anatomy or neurology, emphasis may be laid upon those which are at present helpful in discussing the physiology of the organ, as illustrated schematically in Figure 164.

1. *Connections with afferent paths of spinal cord.* Through the inferior peduncles (restiform bodies) the cerebellum receives afferent fibers from the spinal cord and the medulla (Fig. 164, tracts 1 and 2). The spinocerebellar fasciculus (tract of Flechsig) undoubtedly terminates in the cerebellum, entering the organ through the inferior peduncle or restiform body. Another afferent tract of the cord, that of Gowers (fasciculus anterolateralis superficialis), ends in the cerebellum, in large part at least, forming in fact a part of the spinocerebellar system. According to Ingvar (16), this system of fibers does not make connections with the cortex of the cerebellar hemispheres, but rather with the median lobes, lobus anterior, and lobus posterior. The nature of the afferent impulses conveyed in this way to the cerebellum is not entirely understood, but it seems certain that in good part the peripheral nerve fibers concerned arise in the muscles and their ligaments, and in the ligaments around the joints. This tract and the similar tract of Flechsig give a path through which afferent impulses arising in the muscles of the body reach the cerebellar cortex. This connection throws much light upon the functions of the cerebellum.

2. *Efferent paths from the cerebellum.* The axons arising from the Purkinje cells enter the white matter and make their first termination in the gray matter of the dentate nucleus (Fig. 164, tract 5), and the other nuclei in the medullary substance. Thence the path is con-

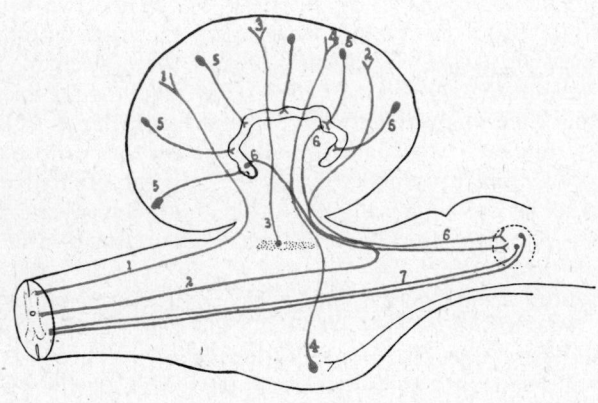

Fig. 164.—Some of the afferent and efferent connections of the cerebellum. Afferent or incoming paths are indicated in blue; efferent or outgoing paths in red: 1, fibers from the tract of Flechsig; 2, fibers from the tract of Gowers; 3, fibers from Deiters' nucleus; 4, fibers of the corticopontocerebellar tract; 5, fibers arising from the Purkinje cells and ending in the dentate nucleus; 6, fibers from the dentate nucleus ending in the red nucleus; 7, fibers of the rubrospinal tract.

tinued by new neurons whose axons pass out in the superior peduncle, brachium conjunctivum, tract 6, to end in the red nucleus of the midbrain. The red nucleus, in turn, is connected through the rubrospinal tract (7) with the motor cells of the anterior horn of the gray matter of the spinal cord. There is thus formed a reflex arc or circle between the muscles and the cerebellum, the afferent paths being in tracts 1 and 2 and the efferent paths in tracts 5, 6, and 7.

3. *Path between cerebellum and cerebrum.* The cerebellar cortex is connected with the cerebral cortex by the large system known as the corticopontocerebellar tract (see Fig. 144A and Fig. 164, tract 4). The fibers of this tract arise in the motor area of the cerebrum or in the frontal cortex anterior to the motor area, descend in the internal capsule and cerebral peduncle, and end in the gray matter of the pons. Some of this group of fibers are said to arise from the temporal lobe, so that there is a temporo-pontine as well as a fronto-pontine path. From the nuclei of the pons new axons continue the path across the midline by way of the middle peduncle (brachium pontis) to end in the cortex of the cerebellum, particularly the cortex of the hemispheres. The tract would seem to convey efferent impulses

from the cerebral cortex (motor region) of one side to the cerebellar cortex of the opposite side, and it forms a possible anatomical basis for the associated activity of the cerebrum and cerebellum in the execution of the voluntary movements.

4. *Connection with labyrinth of ear.* As will be seen later on there are physiological reasons for assuming that afferent impulses from the labyrinth of the ear reach the cerebellum. On the anatomical side this connection is not so well established, although comparative anatomy shows that in the vertebrates the cerebellum develops in intimate relationship with the vestibular nerves (Ingvar). The afferent fibers from the labyrinth pass to the medulla in the vestibular branch of the eighth nerve. Some of these fibers pass on directly to end in the cortex and basal ganglia of the vermiform lobe (lobus anterior and lobus posterior), and some end in the large nuclei of Deiters and Bechterew which lie in the floor of the fourth ventricle. Through these nuclei secondary connections are probably made with the cerebellum.

FUNCTIONAL ANALYSIS

Analysis of cerebellar function has been made through total and regional ablation, also by stimulation, and finally by the newer techniques of recording intrinsic electrical activity in response to stimulation of other areas of the brain.

Complete Ablation. Complete removal of the cerebellum in dog, cat or monkey is followed by essentially the same symptom complex: the animal becomes at once completely incapacitated as far as volitional movements are concerned; it is unable to stand; and it exhibits periodic bouts of extensor spasm in which the legs, neck and tail all become rigidly extended, even more so than an animal in extreme decerebrate rigidity. As time goes on, the bouts of hyperextension diminish in intensity, the animal recovers some degree of equilibration, and volitional movements of an awkward and ataxic sort ultimately return in a dog after four to six weeks. The animal is able to get about on all fours, but only by dint of great voluntary effort and with extreme ataxic unsteadiness. Monkeys go through much the same phases of extreme initial incapacitation, followed by a gradual but highly ataxic restoration of progression movements. In the original analysis by the Italian physiologist, Luciani, a special terminology was introduced to describe cerebellar symptoms, but these more recently have been dropped since some, at least, of Luciani's symptoms were due to his having encroached on structures such as the vestibular nuclei. Several of Luciani's terms, however, are so firmly ingrained in the literature that they will be used in the account which follows.

Ataxia refers to the gross discontinuities of movement characteristic of large lesions of the cerebellum. It is a comprehensive term which includes all the more specific deficits of the cerebellar syndrome.

Dysmetria has reference to any disturbance in the range of a volitional movement.

Hypermetria indicates excessive range, i.e., overshooting; *hypometria*, deficient range, stopping before the object is reached.

Tremor is of two types, static tremor, an oscillating movement seen when a posture is being maintained; kinetic tremor, regularly recurring discontinuities of movement taking place during volitional act.

Regional Ablation. It may thus be seen that the syndrome of complete cerebellar ablation involves at least three components, phasic, postural, and equilibratory, and one wishes to know whether there may be a morphological basis for triad.

Flocculonodular lobe. Dow (9) has shown that an isolated ablation in monkeys of the flocculonodular lobe causes conspicuous disturbances of equilibrium without postural changes or difficulties in volitional movements. A monkey following such a lesion can feed itself manually without the slightest difficulty, but the animal is unable to stand in a cage without swaying on a broad base, and for this reason it generally sits propped up in a corner, supported by the two sides of the cage. It is an interesting fact that certain cerebellar tumors of childhood, namely, the medulloblastomas, take origin through growth of embryonic "rests" in the flocculonodular lobe and the first presenting symptom in such cases is unsteadiness of gait, usually accompanied by progression on a broad base. Knowledge of this phase of functional localization of the cerebellum is therefore of the utmost importance in the diagnosis of this relatively common tumor.

Posterior lobe. Extirpations limited to the cerebellar hemispheres, i.e., the posterior lobe, cause specific disturbances in volitional movements of the extremities characterized by errors in the rate, range, force and direction of a volitional movement. In the neurologist's terms, there tends to be dysmetria, which includes both hypermetria and hypometria, and when these errors are taken together, the end result is an oscillating tremor which tends to become exaggerated as the objective of a particular movement is reached. Thus, when a cerebellar patient feeds himself, his hand may come half way to his mouth, at which time tremor becomes conspicuous and it may then become so coarse as to prevent the hand from actually reaching the mouth. This is known as terminal tremor, and it differs from tremors of basal ganglia disease which tend in general to occur during rest, i.e., one maintaining a posture. A more or less profound degree of hypotonia is associated with the volitional tremor and errors of movement, especially in the higher primates and man. This is not seen to any great extent in cats and dogs but is marked in the monkey and highly conspicuous in chimpanzees and man. The symptom is peculiar to lesions of the posterior lobe, for with anterior lobe lesions marked hypertonia rather than hypotonia develops.

In man the manifestations of neocerebellar lesions coincide precisely with those seen in the higher primates. Owing to the hypertonia, the knee jerk is pendular in character, and the tendency to overshoot the mark in volitional movements and the phenomenon of inability to arrest a limb when suddenly released is no doubt also due to the flaccid state of the musculature. The classical clinical signs of cerebellar disease such as adiadokokinesia (awkwardness in attempting rapidly to supinate and pronate the forelimbs) is probably explicable in terms of the areas of rate, range and force into which Gordon Holmes (15) has analyzed the specific motor disabilities of cerebellar origin.

Anterior lobe. The anterior lobe of the cerebellum responds to local faradic stimulation by causing inhibition of resting posture in the homolateral extremities. In this respect it behaves much as does the corpus striatum, but the effect is mediated, not through the cerebral cortex, but via brain stem nuclei situated at the level of the red nucleus. If tested in a decerebrate preparation in which strong extensor rigidity exists, the inhibition is particularly marked. There is evidence of somatotopic localization in that the right half of the anterior lobe inhibits the musculature on the same side of the body. There is also an anteroposterior localization, i.e., the hindlimbs are inhibited from the lobulus centralis, the forelimbs from the culmen, whereas stimulation of the lobulus simplex gives rise to inhibition of the neck muscles (23) and also to movements of the jaws and orbicularis muscles (24).

Ablation of the entire anterior lobe in dogs and monkeys whose nervous systems are otherwise intact gives rise to a profound postural disturbance characterized by release of extensor centers, i.e., marked extensor hypertonia (7, 8). In the dog this manifests itself by an augmented positive supporting reaction ("Magnet" reaction) and a conspicuous increase in the tendon

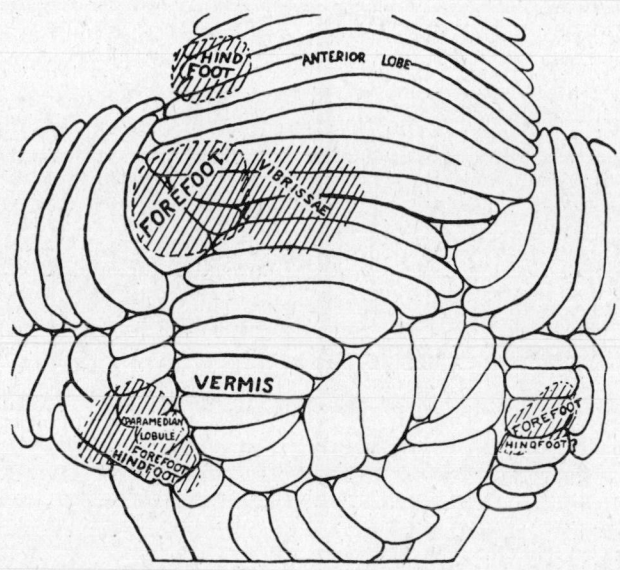

Fig. 165.—Drawing of dorsal surface of cat's cerebellum showing tactile areas as determined by distribution of electrical responses evoked by stimulation of receptors in feet and upper lip of left side. Note overlap of forefoot and hindfoot areas of paramedian lobules and their complete topographical separation in anterior lobe. This drawing is derived from results obtained in entire series of experiments on tactile representation. (From Snider and Stowell, *J. Neurophysiol.*, 1944, 7:331–358.)

reflexes. If the anterior lobe is ablated in a decerebrate preparation, the decerebrate rigidity becomes strongly augmented in all four extremities. *Regional ablation* of the anterior lobe gives rise to localized deficits, the details of which are being studied by Gervase Connor (7) and by Woolsey (24) and his associates. Connor at first believed that hindlimb representation lay caudal to that for the forelimbs. More recent studies with smaller lesions indicate that while overlapping between fore- and hindlimb areas exists, the hindlimb area is predominantly in the centralis and the forelimb in the culmen (Fig. 166) as one would anticipate for stimulation. The most rostral segment of the ananterior lobe is the lingula. This, as with the flocculonodular lobe, receives a certain number of vestibular projections. Connor finds, in keeping with this, that an isolated lesion of the lingula causes an augmentation of labyrinthine reflexes. This reaction is absent after a primary labyrinthectomy. These localized deficits are evidently an expression of a well organized topographical organization within the anterior lobe.

In 1942 Snider and Stowell (21) at Johns Hopkins found that tactile stimulation of an extremity in cat or monkey gave rise to sharply localized electrical responses at foci within the anterior lobe and also in the paramedian lobule. The localization thus disclosed is shown in Figure 165. The sensory projections to the anterior lobe are thus organized in a fashion topographically similar to those for the motor outflow, i.e., the face sensory projections pass to the simplex, those from the forelimbs to the culmen, and from the hind

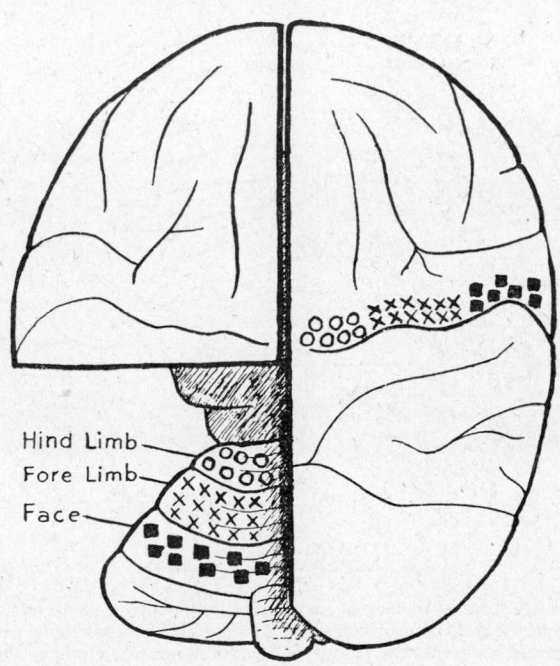

Hind Limb
Fore Limb
Face

Fig. 166.—Subdivisions of pontocerebellar receiving area in the monkey, showing their connection with different parts of the motor cortex. (From Adrian, Afferent areas in the cerebellum connected with the limbs. *Brain*, 1943, 66:301.)

extremities to the centralis (21a). Some localization in the rat was disclosed independently in 1942 by Dow and Anderson (12) and in 1943 by Adrian for the monkey. Adrian also correlated the sites of impingement of the spinocerebellar and the pontocerebellar projections (Fig. 166). Snider and Stowell (21) in addition located an auditory area in the vermis just behind the primary fissure. These newer approaches to the cerebellum inaugurated by Dow and by the group at Johns Hopkins are leading to a rapid advance, and, to quote Adrian, "It is difficult to foresee how far it may not go."

Cerebral and Cerebellar Interrelations. The simultaneous phylogenetic development of the cerebral cortex and the neocerebellum (posterior lobe) has long been recognized. Luciani (18) gave experimental proof of the interrelation by showing that removal of the motor area following decerebellation led to return of motor incapacity. Actually, the tremors characteristic of volitional movement vanish, since volitional movement as such becomes impossible after bilateral removal of the motor and premotor regions.

The newer techniques of electrical recording used by Dow, Snider and others have made possible further study of the interrelations of the cerebellum with other parts of the nervous system. Rossi (20) had disclosed that stimulation of the posterior lobe of the cerebellum enhances the excitability of the motor area, and Walker (22) observed that such stimulation alters the spontaneous action current waves from area 4. André-Thomas (3) is of the opinion that some degree of functional localization exists in the cerebellar hemispheres, the anterior region being concerned with the forelimb, the posterior region with the hind, but as far as the motor area is concerned, there has been little electrical evidence to support this contention. Dow (10) found on stimulating the arm area that a diffuse discharge occurred throughout the whole posterior lobe. Weak stimulation of the foot area, however, did tend to affect the rostral part of the anterior lobe more than the caudal. Similarly, weak stimulation of the arm area tended to activate the more caudal parts of the posterior lobe to the exclusion of the rostral areas. Adrian (1, 2), however, has recently obtained more positive evidence of localization by recording the electrical reactions of the cerebellum to stimuli applied to the motor area (Fig. 166).

REFERENCES

1. ADRIAN, E. D. Afferent areas in the cerebellum connected with the limbs. *Brain*, 1943, *66*:289–315.

2. ADRIAN, E. D. Localization in cerebrum and cerebellum. *Brit. med. J.*, 1944, *2*:137–140.

3. ANDRÉ-THOMAS. *La fonction cérébelleuse*. Paris, Doin et fils, 1911, xii, 326 pp.

4. BAILEY, P. *Intracranial tumors*. Springfield, Ill., C. C Thomas, 1933, xxii, 475 pp.

5. BOTTERELL, E. H., and FULTON, J. F. Functional localization in the cerebellum of primates. I. Unilateral section of the peduncles. *J. comp Neurol.*, 1938, *69*:31–46. II. Lesions of midline structures (vermis and deep nuclei). *Ibid.*, 47–62. III. Lesions of the hemispheres (neo-cerebellum). *Ibid.*, 63–87.

6. BOTTERELL, E. H., and FULTON, J. F. Functional localization in the cerebellum of primates. IV. 'Hypotonia' and 'ataxia' following lesions of the cerebellum in the chimpanzee (to appear).

7. CONNOR, G. J. Anterior cerebellar function. *Trans. Coll. Phys. Philad.*, 1945 (to appear).

8. CONNOR, G. J., and GERMAN, W. J. Functional localization within the anterior cerebellar lobe. *Trans. Amer. neurol. Ass.*, 1941, *67*:181–186.

9. DOW, R. S. Effects of lesions in the vestibular part of the cerebellum in primates. *Arch. Neurol. Psychiat.*, Chicago, 1938, *40*:500–520.

10. DOW, R. S. Cerebellar action potentials in response to stimulation of the cerebral cortex in monkeys and cats. *J. Neurophysiol.*, 1942, *5*:121–136.

11. DOW, R. S. The evolution and anatomy of the cerebellum. *Biol. Rev.*, 1942, *17*:179–220.

12. DOW, R. S., and ANDERSON, R. Cerebellar action potentials in response to stimulation of proprioceptors and exteroceptors in the rat. *J. Neurophysiol.*, 1942, *5*:363–371.

13. FLOURENS, P. *Recherches expérimentales sur les propriétés et les fonctions du système nerveux dans les animaux vertébrés*. Paris, Crevot, 1824, xxvi, 332 pp.

14. FULTON, J. F., and DOW, R. S. The cerebellum: A summary of functional localization. *Yale J. Biol. Med.*, 1937, *10*:89–119.

15. HOLMES, G. The Croonian Lectures on the clinical symptoms of cerebellar disease and their interpretation. *Lancet*, 1922, *1*:1177–1182; 1231–1237; *2*:59–65; 111–115.

16. INGVAR, S. Studies in neurology. I. The phylogenetic continuity of the central nervous system. *Bull. Johns Hopk. Hosp.*, 1928, *43*:315–337. II. On cerebellar function. *Ibid.*, 338–362.

17. LARSELL, O. The cerebellum. A review and interpretation. *Arch. Neurol. Psychiat.*, Chicago, 1937, *38*:580–607.

18. LUCIANI, L. *Il cervelleto. Nuovi studi di fisiologia normale e patologica*. Florence, Monnier, 1891, ix, 320 pp.

19. ROLANDO, L. *Saggio sopra la vera struttura del cervello dell'uomo degl'animali e sopra le funzioni del sistema nervoso.* Sassari, Stamperia Privilegiata, 1809, xiv, 98 pp., 3 pl.

20. ROSSI, G. Sui rapporti funzionali del cervelletto con la zona motrice della corteccia cerebrale. *Arch. Fisiol.,* 1913, *11*:258–264.

21. SNIDER, R. S., and STOWELL, A. Evidence of a representation of tactile sensibility in the cerebellum of the cat. *Fed. Proc. Amer. Soc. exp. Biol.,* 1942, *1*:82–83; 84. See also: *Anat. Rec.,* 1942, *82*:99; 1944, *88*:457.

21a. SNIDER, R. S., and STOWELL, A. Receiv-

ing areas of the tactile, auditory, and visual systems in the cerebellum. *J. Neurophysiol.,* 1944, *7*:331–357.

22. WALKER, A. E. An oscillographic study of the cerebello-cerebral relationships. *J. Neurophysiol.,* 1938, *1*:16–23.

23. WOOLSEY, C. N., HAMPSON, J. L., and HARRISON, C. R. Somatotopic localization in anterior lobe and lobulus simplex of cerebellum in cat and dog. *Fed. Proc. Amer. Soc. exp. Biol.,* 1945, *4*:31.

24. WOOLSEY, C. N. [Personal communication.] See *Fed. Proc. Amer. Soc. exp. Biol.,* 1945, *4*.

SECTION III

THE NERVOUS SYSTEM: SENSORY FUNCTIONS

BY THEODORE C. RUCH

CHAPTER 16

SOMATIC SENSATION

Introductory Concepts. The number of senses, and just what constitutes a separate sense, are by no means fixed; in fact, some of the senses are of recent discovery. By a "sense" or a modality of sensation is usually meant a *kind* of response to stimulation, the nature and distinctive features of which are recognized subjectively. Conscious sensations are therefore said to differ in quality or modality, i.e., in kind as opposed to intensity. The classical five senses, seeing, hearing, smelling, tasting and feeling, were presumably demarcated on the basis of subjective experience with relatively little knowledge of their anatomical and physiological characteristics. The belief has grown that differences in quality on a conscious level are associated with a distinctness in one or more of the following: the sense organ and the sensory nerve fiber which conducts to the central nervous system, the pathway through the central nervous system, and certainly the ultimate or terminal neurons of the cerebral cortex underlying the conscious experience.

Within the limits of any sensation of a given quality or modality, we distinguish certain subqualities. In vision we have many different qualities which we designate by special names, the primary colors, for example. In sound sensations we distinguish different tones and different qualities of tones. In addition to the subqualities of a sense there are sensory processes of a higher order than sensation which for convenience of expression may be grouped under the general category of perceptions. Perceptions, which are elaborations of sensations, may involve the fusion of information from more than one sensory channel. It is said, for example, that the perception of heat is a fusion of warmth and pain sensations and that "wetness" is a fusion of cold and pressure. Other forms of perception have a spatial element—the awareness of the location of a stimulus, of its size, shape, etc. These are often carelessly termed sensations, especially in clinical literature, but the distinction between sensation and perception should be preserved, although this difference is sometimes difficult to define.

It is customary to divide the sensations into two different groups—the *special* and the *common* senses, the former including the so-called five senses, namely, sight, hearing, taste, smell and *touch* or *pressure;* while under the latter were grouped pain and sensations from muscles and viscera and all other sensations of indistinct quality. The number of senses has been increased over the original five, and it is now believed that cutaneous pain is in all essential respects as "special" and characteristic as touch or pressure which traditionally is a special sense. The original distinction between special and common sensation is no longer useful, and the words have been gradually appropriated to designate a more useful dichotomy. Thus the "special senses" are coming to mean those of sight, hearing, taste, smell and equilibrium, which are special because they are situated in the head and have elaborately evolved sense organs, and because they serve to orient the body to the distant environment. The term "common sensation" often means touch and the other forms of sensibility common to the whole surface of the body. Another reason for redefinition is that in the neurological examination the special senses, being served by cranial nerves, are examined along with the other cranial nerves, while "common sensation," or simply "sensation" in neurological parlance, is examined along with movements and reflexes of the limbs and trunk.

Touch was, until nearly the turn of the last century, treated as though it were a single, unitary sense which appreciated many characteristics of the stimulus object. Thus warmth or coldness, and pressure, etc., were thought of as subqualities of the single sense of feeling or touch. About 1890 it was independently discovered in Europe and in this country that the skin was not everywhere uniformly sensitive to all aspects of the stimulating object. If the stimulating object is made very small, and the skin marked off in millimeter squares and systematically explored first with a small blunt object (pressure), then with a sharp object (pain), and then with a warm and finally with a cold object, it is found that some spots give rise to sensations of warmth but not of cold or pain, while others respond only to a cold stimulus and with a sensation of coldness, and still other areas respond only with sensations of pressure or pain. Cutaneous sensibility is therefore punctiform or "pointlike" in its distribution. This was one of the fundamental experiments in the physiology of sensation. On the basis of such experiments touch was easily divided into several separate senses—pressure or touch, warmth, and cold.

The establishment of pain as a separate modality of sensation was more difficult because pain sensations can be aroused from virtually every spot stimulated. Indeed, there are today those who argue that pain is not a separate sense but is the result of overstimulation of sense organs which to less intense stimulation yield other sensations. The detailed arguments for the distinctness of pain as a form of sensation are presented later, but the fact that this controversy exists emphasizes the fact that the experience resulting from stimulation of a sense organ has two aspects. One has already been discussed—the quality of the sensation or that which distinguishes it from other kinds of sensation; the other is known in psychological terms as the *affect*, or *feeling tone*, which is the feeling of pleasantness or unpleasantness evoked by a stimulus. Certain modalities of sensation are strongly pleasant or unpleasant, e.g., pain, while others are relatively neutral, e.g., muscle sense. The possibility that quality and affect depend upon different cerebral mechanisms is one of the interesting questions in neurophysiology.

Classification of the Senses. The senses and sense receptors are classified in several ways, all of which are useful for they are not contradictory systems but merely utilize a different basis for classification. Since parts of each system are in common use, it is well to become familiar with all.

In the preceding paragraphs we have traced the manner in which the original five senses have been expanded to eleven or more. Before discussing the several classifications, the various modalities of sensation may be listed as follows under what are perhaps their most common names: (i) vision, (ii) audition, (iii) olfaction, (iv) gustation, (v) labyrinthine or vestibular sensation, (vi) touch-pressure, (vii) warmth, (viii) cold, (ix) pain, (x) muscle, tendon and joint sense, or kinesthesia, (xi) organic or visceral sensation. From this list it can be seen that several bases of classification have contributed the most commonly used name for each sense. The following are the more important classifications of sensation.

Sherrington's classification. Sherrington (18) introduced a classification which is much used in physiological literature. It is based on the source of the stimulus, the location of the receptor, the projection of the sensation (see below), and the main biological function of the particular type of receptor. The *proprioceptors* give information concerning the movements and position of the body in space and these include the muscle spindles, the sense organs of the tendons, and the labyrinthine receptors. The *exteroceptors*, the sense organs of the skin, give information of changes in the immediate external environment. The *interoceptors* transmit impulses from the visceral organs. The *teleceptors* or *distance receptors*, which give information concerning changes in the more remote environment, are the sense organs of the eyes, ears, and nose. The term "proprioceptive" has gradually come to apply only to receptors in, and sensations or reflexes arising from, muscles and tendons, i.e., labyrinthine receptors are not usually included in this group.

Clinical classification of sensation. The clinical classification of sensation is strongly influenced by morphological considerations. The following list shows how the modalities of sensation are grouped by clinicians; in the right-hand column is given a sample term to illustrate clinical terminology of sensation and its disturbances.

I. *Special senses* served by the cranial nerves
   1. Vision.. Hemianopia
   2. Audition.. None
   3. Taste... Ageusia
   4. Olfaction .... Anosmia
   5. Vestibular.. None

II. *Superficial or cutaneous sensations* served by the cutaneous branches of spinal and certain cranial nerves
   1. Touch-pressure....................................... Hypesthesia
   2. Warmth..⎫
   3. Cold...⎬ Hypothermesthesia
   4. Pain .... Hyperalgesia

III. *Deep sensations* served by muscular branches of spinal nerves and certain cranial nerves
   1. Muscle, tendon and joint sensibility, or position sense........Bathesthesia
   2. (Deep pain)
   3. (Deep pressure)

IV. *Visceral sensations* served by fibers conducted with the autonomic nervous system
   1. Organic sensation
   2. Visceral pain

As a comprehensive classification this is perhaps the most generally useful, though the position of pain in the scheme is anomalous. Thus the phrase "deep sensation" as ordinarily used does not include muscular pain, and sometimes does not include deep pressure.

Other classifications. Sensory receptors are sometimes designated by their adequate stimulus. Olfactory and gustatory sense organs are collectively termed the *chemoreceptors* because they are sensitive to the chemical nature of substances. *Mechanoreceptors* are stimulated by the physical aspects of objects. The term *nociceptors* was applied to pain receptors by Sherrington because they respond to a variety of stimuli which have in common the property of being noxious or damaging to the tissues. Finally, a useful dichotomy applicable to both motor and sensory phenomena is *somatic* and *visceral* for sensations arising in structures derived from the somatopleura and visceropleura respectively. Somatic sensation (or *somesthesia*) is a convenient name for superficial and deep sensation together.

Adequate Stimulus and "Specific Nerve Energies." The principle or law of the adequate stimulus is that for each type of sense receptor there is one (in some cases more than one) form of energy to which the receptor is especially sensitive. The adequate stimulus for vision is the radiant energy of the visible spectrum; for hearing, sound waves; etc. Other forms of energy, if strong enough, can excite the sense receptors and hence are stimuli for them but are not considered to be *adequate* stimuli, e.g., pressure on the eyeball can excite the retina. The biological function of the elaborate sense organ is, as Sherrington (18) pointed out, to lower the threshold of the nerve fiber to some *one form* of energy. The histological diversity of sensory receptors presumably reflects the evolution of selectively sensitive receptors from undifferentiated sense organs responsive to a much wider range of energies. A quantitative illustration of the adequate stimulus is the fact that the warmth end-organs are nearly two thousand times as sensitive to radiant heat as are the intermingled pain end-organs, which are bare axon ramifications. Another quantitative illustration of the degree to which sensitivity to the adequate stimulus has evolved is found in the eye, in which the theoretical maximum sensitivity—the ability to respond to one quantum of energy—is closely approximated by the receptor cells of that organ. Recent calculations (Hecht) place the minimum effective energy for the human eye at five quanta.

What is the biological significance of the adequate stimulus? The sense organs collectively act not unlike a series of light filters. Collectively they analyze the complex energy pattern of the external world—just as color filters do in color photography—and translate the complex impression into an intricate pattern of action currents which are recombined in the cerebral cortex—just as in color printing the various colors are recombined—to give a picture of the external world.

Closely related to the principle of the adequate stimulus is another law enunciated by Johannes Müller (16), which is known as the *doctrine of specific nerve energies*. Although a sense organ can be stimulated by other than the adequate stimulus, the subjective response is always the same and hence is not influenced by the *kind* of stimulus. Thus the excitation of the visual system by pressure on the eye, by electrical stimulation, or by irritation from a pathological process, gives rise to *visual* sensation only. From the vantage point gained by knowledge of the all-or-nothing law, this seems obvious. However, prior to Johannes Müller it was naively assumed that "copies" or corpuscles from objects traversed nerve fibers to the brain. His principle amounts to saying that the quality of sensation resulting from a given type of stimulus depends upon *what* nerve fibers are stimulated and not *how* the nerve fibers are stimulated.

The phrase "specific nerve energy" is in some respects unfortunate because it suggests that the action current in the axons from a given kind of receptor are specific and different from those in other types of sensory fibers, a suggestion which has been directly disproved. It would be anachronistic to ascribe to Müller's word "energy" its meaning in present day physics. Müller probably meant nerve action rather than nerve energy—that each sensory system or chain of fibers within a system at some point acts in a specific fashion to produce its own specific quality or kind of sensation. Whether this specificity in the reaction of each sensory nerve is due to some peculiarity in the nerve itself or in its peripheral end-organ, or to a peculiarity of the part of the brain in which the nerve terminates, Müller left an open question, although he called attention to the fact that the central ending is capable of giving its specific effect in consciousness independently of the conducting nerve fibers. Dramatic evidence of this is the production of visual sensation by stimulation of the cortical visual area and of somatic sensation by stimulation of the cortical somatosensory area, in conscious human patients. Most physiologists adopt the view that the specific reaction in consciousness depends upon the central ending—that, in other words, the different sensory parts of the cortex give different kinds of qualities of consciousness, while the sensory nerve fibers are simply conductors of nerve impulses which, however much they may differ in rate or amplitude, are qualitatively the same in all nerve fibers. According to this view, as du Bois-Reymond expressed it, if the auditory nerve fibers were attached to the visual cortex and the optic fibers to the auditory cortex, we would see thunder and hear lightning. The fact, therefore, that light waves can stimulate the rods and cones of the retina, but are probably an inadequate stimulus to the hair cells of the cochlea or the taste buds of the tongue, is due to a peculiarity in structure of the rods and cones; but the fact that the impulses conducted by the optic fibers arouse a peculiar quality of sensation is not due to any peculiarity in structure in these fibers or in the rods and cones, but to a characteristic structure of the optic centers.

While something is known of the point at which specificity is introduced, *how* one central neuron gives rise to visual sensation and another to auditory sensation is a problem which physiology has not yet dared to attack. Specificity of action implies a localization of function in specific fibers, a degree of localization unacceptable to many neurophysiologists who are influenced by Gestalt psychology and field theories derived from theoretical physics.

SENSE ORGAN DISCHARGE

The most direct knowledge of the sense organ function is that gained when the spike potentials of the axon leading from sense organs were first adequately recorded by Adrian and Zotterman. This procedure was analytical in two ways: the response of sense organs to stimulation was studied without recourse to conscious experience and without the complications introduced by impulses traversing the spinal nerves, spinal cord, and brain tracts; secondly, *single* sensory nerve fibers were recorded, thus greatly simplifying the complexity encountered when many units are active.

Adrian, who first recorded action potentials of single units, employed vacuum tube amplification and a capillary electrometer. With electrodes applied to the sciatic nerve of a frog, traction on the Achilles tendon resulted in a succession of irregularly shaped and spaced potentials. Too many fibers were simultaneously active. Adrian and Zotterman turned to a tiny skin muscle from the frog's thorax (sternocutaneous muscle), whose nerve contains from 15 to 25 fibers, of which only a few are sensory. Traction on this muscle resulted in a simpler but still too complex record. By cutting off strips of muscle and thereby eliminating the muscle spindles, one by one, the record became progressively less complex, and finally was reduced to a regularly repeated sequence of spike potentials of uniform amplitude and duration. A single unit preparation had been achieved. With this preparation it was immediately apparent that the frequency of discharge was lessened when the weight stretching the muscle was decreased, and that the rate of discharge was initially high and then decreased (adaptation) despite continuance of stretch. Thus in the first experiments the main facts of sense organ discharge were broadly outlined.

The contribution of the sense organ to the total sensory process has naturally been learned largely from electrical studies and can now be summarized systematically. These are the characteristics imposed by the sense organ upon sensation; other characteristics are contributed by the central pathways.

Differential Sensitivity and Nonspecific Discharge. In many instances the recording of sensory impulses affords final proof of the specificity of end-organs and of what constitutes the adequate stimuli for individual receptors. Such studies have strengthened the belief that the impulses arising from different types of sense organs are approximately identical and that the difference in the sensations they produce is to be sought in their central connections (doctrine of specific nerve energies). No pronounced differences in wave form have been discovered. There are differences in the amplitude and rate of conduction in sensory nerve fibers correlated with differences in fiber size and myelinization, but there is no reason to believe that these differences, rather than the mode of termination, determine the kind of sensation resulting.

Intensity (1, 5, 15). Adrian's initial experiments on the single unit showed that the sensory end-organ and axon obey the all-or-nothing law. Stronger stimulation does not result in larger action potentials. How then does the end-organ "signal" to the brain the elementary aspect of the stimulus, its intensity? All sense organs so far examined signal intensity of stimulus by

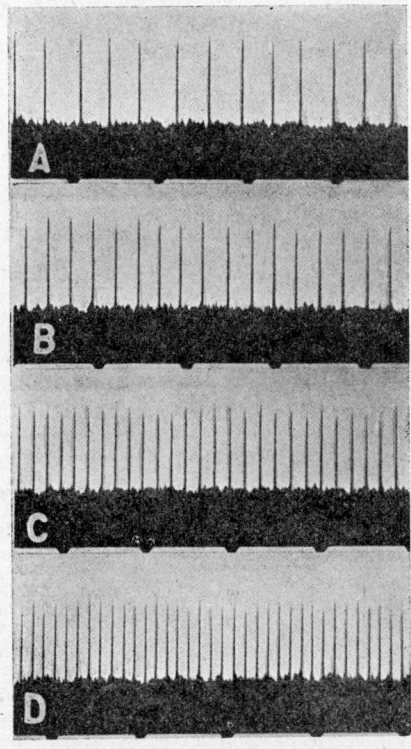

Fig. 167.—Oscillographic records showing the relationship of frequency of discharge to intensity of stimulation. A single end-organ in the carotid sinus was stimulated by four different pressures within the sinus: in A, 40 mm. Hg; in B, 80 mm. Hg; in C, 140 mm. Hg; and in D, 200 mm. Hg. Time is 0.2 sec. intervals. (From Bronk and Stella, *Amer. J. Physiol.*, 1935, *110*:708–714.)

changes in the rate of discharge. Weak stimulation causes a discharge at a slow rate and a stronger stimulation causes a discharge at a more rapid rate. This is most clearly shown in Figure 167, which represents the discharge of sensory receptors in the walls of the carotid artery to four different degrees of internal pressure, the natural mode of stimulation.

The second way in which intensity of the stimulus affects the discharge is in the number of sense organs active. With a sternocutaneous preparation containing several units under observation, a light weight attached to its tendon may cause only one unit to discharge. With increasing tension on the muscle a point is reached at which a second unit commences discharge, which usually can be identified by a slightly different amplitude of the potential due to a less or more favorable position of the fiber with respect to the leading electrodes, and by the fact that the two discharges work in and out of phase due to slightly different rates of discharge. Further tension brings in additional receptors, each at different frequencies until the record becomes totally irregular. This process is picturesquely known as *recruitment of end-organs*. The neural correlates of stimulus intensity are therefore two: number of end-organs discharging and the frequency of discharge in each. By spatial and temporal summation, the rapid, multifiber discharge to intense stimulation presumably becomes translated into a greater activation of spinal tract fibers and ultimately of cells in the cerebral cortex.

A possible mechanism by which intensity of stimulus determines rate of discharge, based upon the phenomenon of the relative refractory period, has been suggested by Adrian (1). The stimulus produces a steadily maintained

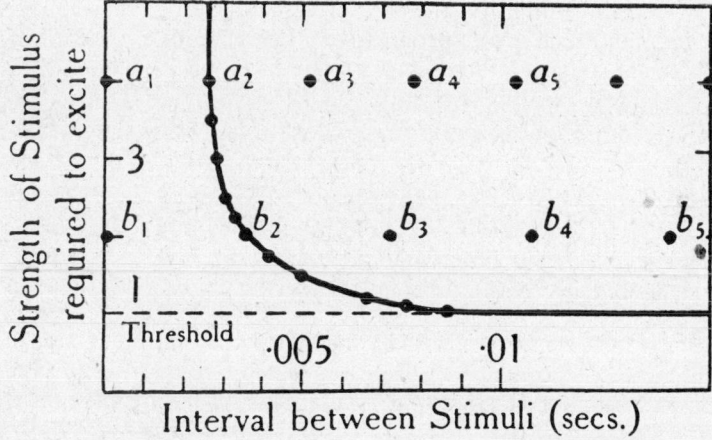

Fig. 168.—A hypothetical mechanism whereby stimulus intensity determines rate of discharge of a sense organ. The curve represents the return of excitability of the frog's sciatic nerve stimulated at zero time (absolute and relative refractory periods) as obtained by electrical stimulation. Superimposed on this curve is a series of dots (a_1–a_5 and b_1–b_5), representing the times at which the sense organ will discharge (if refractory period is the governing factor) in response to continuous stimulation equal in intensity to 2 and 4 units of electrical stimulation. (From Adrian, *The basis of sensation*, 1928.)

change to which the neural elements of the receptor respond only periodically because of the refractory state following each response. The stronger the stimulus the earlier in the relatively refractory period will the sense organ respond. The absolute refractory period therefore fixes the upper limit of discharge frequency; by definition, discharge must await the recovery of some excitability. Only a very strong stimulus will fire the sense organ early in the relatively refractory period, resulting in a short interval between discharges, and hence a high frequency of discharge to strong stimulation. The weak stimulus, near threshold, must wait until the neural elements have largely passed through their relatively refractory period and virtually returned to resting excitability before such a stimulus can discharge the axon. This is illustrated in Figure 168, using the recovery curve of the frog's sciatic nerve as determined by the conditioning-testing shock technique. A stimulus of a-strength will discharge the sense organ at zero time (a_1), at 2.5 msec. (a_2), again at 5 msec. (a_3), at 7.5 msec. (a_4), etc., which would result in a rate of 400 per sec. But a shock of b-strength will cause a discharge at zero time, at 3.5 msec., again at 7 msec., and again at 10.5 msec., giving a rate of 300 per sec. This explanation encounters one grave difficulty. Sense organs, except under abnormal conditions, do not fire nearly as rapidly as the absolute refractory period would predict, the upper limit usually lying between 100 and 200 per sec. And they do maintain rhythm at rates far slower than the rate predicted from the length of the absolute and relative refractory period, but that may mean only that the terminal fibrils of the sense organ, because they are of smaller diameter and unmyelinated, or for other reasons, have a slower recovery cycle. On the other hand, the actual basis of the rhythm may be an entirely different process, connected with the non-neural parts of the receptor.

Adaptation. The number of impulses which a sense organ discharges per sec. depends not alone upon the intensity of the stimulus, but also on the length of time which the stimulus has been acting (1, 5, 15). To a maintained stretch of constant intensity, the rate of discharge from muscle receptors is initially high and then grows progressively slower until a plateau rate of discharge is struck and maintained many minutes or hours. The end-organ has partially adapted. An oscillographic record showing adaptation is given in

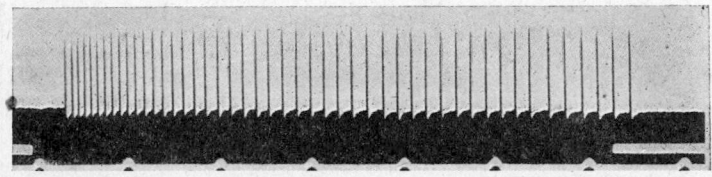

Fig. 169.—Record showing adaptation of a sense organ (photoreceptor). The stimulus was maintained at constant strength throughout but the interval between discharges steadily diminished. Signal indicates the duration of stimulus application and time is in 0.2 sec. intervals. (Record of Hartline cited from Bronk, *Res. Publ. Ass. nerv. ment. Dis.*, 1934, *15*:60–82.)

Figure 169. Probably similar in cause is the fact that a rapidly applied stretch is more effective (produces a higher rate of discharge) than a slowly applied stretch of the same degree. The end-organ adapts to the slowly applied stretch during its application. One is accustomed to designating any decrement in response which comes as a result of activity as "fatigue." In the case of a slowly applied stimulus, fatigue is distinguishable from adaptation because such a stimulus produces fewer discharges and therefore less opportunity for fatigue than the more rapidly applied stimulus; the lesser response to slow stretch is therefore not due to activity (fatigue). In fact, with the touch receptor, adaptation can occur to a slowly applied contact without a single discharge having occurred. Bronk (5) lists three additional reasons for classifying the response decrement as adaptation rather than fatigue. (i) It is manifest at the very beginning of activity or soon thereafter and disappears within a few seconds after cessation of stimulation, whereas fatigue typically develops more slowly and recovery from it is a slower process. (ii) Initial rapid decline in frequency is little affected by the presence or absence of oxygen; development of fatigue is dependent upon oxygen. (iii) Adaptation is strongly influenced by ionic composition of the fluid bathing the end-organ; no such relation to fatigue is known. Thus sense organs are subject to two types of activity decrement: fatigue and adaptation. Axons are also subject to both

types of phenomena, and Adrian draws a parallel between sense organ and
nerve, adaptation (for nerve called accommodation) being much more rapid
in nerve so that one or at most two or three discharges occur at the onset of
a strong constant current.

Rate of adaptation in different sense organs. Adaptation is not equally
characteristic of all sense organs (Fig. 170). Certain types of end-organs
adapt very little after the initial few seconds of response, but are able to
maintain discharge for minutes and hours. In the class of slowly adapting
end-organs come the muscle spindle, tension receptors at the root of the
lung, pressure receptors of the carotid sinus and the arteries in general, and
the pain receptors of the cornea. Pressure receptors adapt somewhat more
rapidly but not so rapidly as touch receptors, especially those associated with

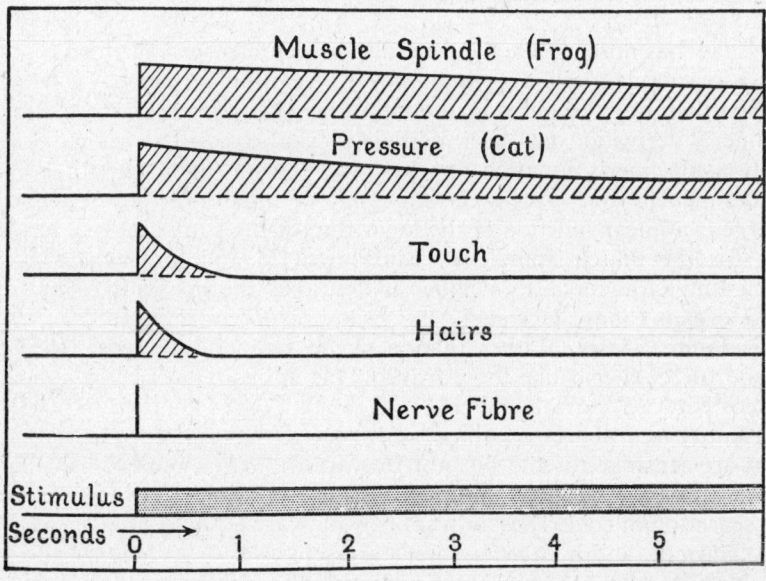

Fig. 170.—Summary diagram showing rapidity of adaptation of various sense organs and of
the nerve fiber to continuous constant stimulation. The height of the curves indicates the rate of
discharge at various times after application of the stimulus. Except for the nerve fiber, the manner
of stimulation was that adequate for the particular sense organ. (From Adrian, *The basis of
sensation,* 1928.)

hairs. The latter give rise to a burst of impulses largely ended within a fifth
of a second. Adaptation to this degree would obviously unfit an end-organ
for serving long sustained postural reflexes or for recording the pressure of
blood within the carotid sinus. Similarly, if pain end-organs were to cease
generating pain impulses before the noxious stimulating agent is removed,
pain would lose much of its protective function. On the other hand, the rapid
adaptation may be an advantage to an exploratory sense such as touch.
Contacts are perceived, then the slate is wiped clean by adaptation and made
ready to receive a new impression.

Weber-Fechner Law. Another problem to be decided by electrical methods
is whether the Weber-Fechner law, where it applies, is a characteristic of the
sense organ or of the central phases of the total sensory process. Weber
made the important discovery that the smallest difference between two weights

which can be discriminated (just noticeable difference, j.n.d.) is a constant fraction of the weights themselves, the so-called Weber fraction. For weights this was approximately 1/30, meaning that 31 gm. is discriminated from 30, 62 gm. from 60, and so on. This is usually stated as

$$\frac{\Delta I}{I} = C,$$

in which delta I means a just discriminable increment of intensity. Fechner's name is linked to Weber's because he sought by mathematical manipulation to derive the relationship between stimulus and sensation. By assuming that discriminable increments are equal units of sensation he derived the following formula:

$$Sensation = k \log I + C.$$

Weber's law has nothing like the generality which has been ascribed to it; for most sensory modalities it only applies over a very limited range of intensities, and often then only because small continuous changes of j.n.d. are ignored.

Fechner's derivation has been endlessly criticized. Whatever its original derivation, Fechner's equation appears to express a fundamental feature of sense organ behavior. Over a certain range of intensities, the frequency of discharge is a linear function of the logarithm of the stimulus. This has been shown for the muscle spindle by Matthews (15) and for *Limulus* eye by Hartline and Graham (12). Whether it describes the behavior of all forms of sense organs cannot be stated.

Temperature Senses. Rather than a single temperature sense, there are two, one for cold and one for warmth. This is based on a clear subjective difference between warmth and cold and the fact that temperature sensibility is distributed in a punctate fashion and some areas (the central zone of the cornea) are sensitive to cold but not to warmth. When the skin is explored systematically, millimeter by millimeter, spots are found which respond only with a sensation of cold. The warm spots, which are fewer in number, respond only to warmth, and intervening areas are sensitive to neither. On the forearm cold spots average about 13–15 per mm.^{2} and warm spots only 1 or 2 per mm.^{2} Cold spots may be stimulated with a warm stimulus (above 45° C.) but the resulting sensation, in agreement with the law of specific nerve energies, is not one of warmth but so-called *paradoxical cold*. These facts suggest that beneath each spot is a distinctive type of end-organ specifically sensitive to one or the other thermal stimuli. However, it has not proved possible to get direct proof of this by mapping spots and identifying histologically the underlying sense organ; in fact, the existence of restricted sensitive spots has been called into question (Jenkins).

The Krause end-bulb (Fig. 171) is believed to be the receptor for cold, largely on the basis of von Frey's (1895) observation that the margin of the cornea is sensitive only to pain and cold and contains only free nerve endings and the Krause end-bulbs. This observation was made more precise by Strughold and Karbe (19) who stained the conjunctivum in vivo with methylene blue which has a selective affinity for nervous tissue. The end-bulbs so revealed could not be stimulated because of the depressant effects of the dye but in distribution they coincided satisfactorily with subsequent mappings of the cold spots. The Krause end-bulbs are certainly cold receptors but histological experiments on other parts of the body have not proved that all cold spots overlie Krause end-bulbs (7), but intravital staining was not used, hence encapsulated end-organs might have been present though not revealed by the methods used.

The receptor assigned to warmth is a large, loose ramification of nerve fibers, first described by Ruffini, lying deep (300 μ) in the skin or even in the subcutaneous tissue. Bazett et al. (2) have estimated the depth of the thermal receptors by measuring with thermocouples the rate of penetration of heat through double folds of skin obtained by the Spartan procedure of stretching the prepuce out into a flat sheet by means of fish hooks. Rate of

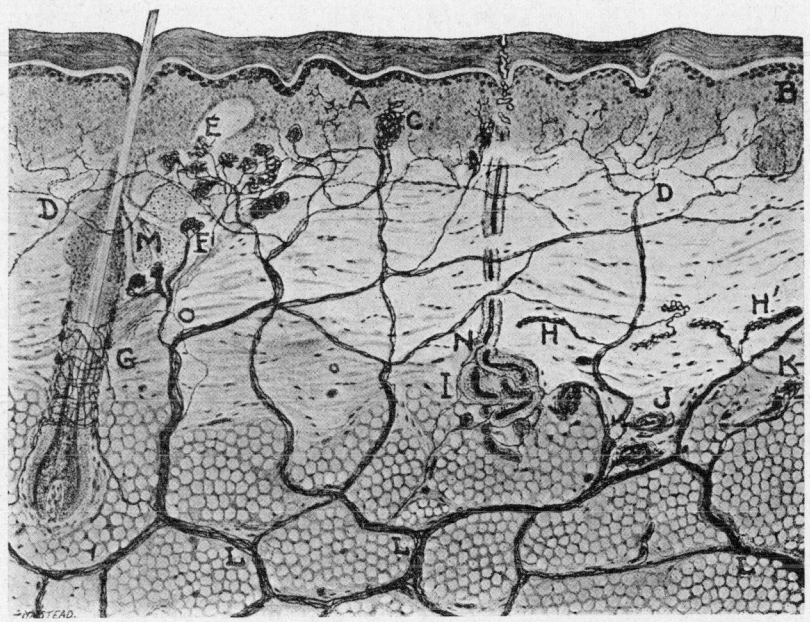

Fig. 171.—Composite diagram showing the innervation of the human skin. A, Merkel's discs, subserving touch. B, Free endings, subserving pain. C, Meissner's corpuscles, subserving touch. D, Nerve fibers, subserving pain. E, Krause's end-bulbs, subserving cold. F, Nerve endings, subserving warmth (sometimes called Ruffini's endings). G, Nerve fibers and endings on hair follicle, subserving touch. H, Ruffini's endings, subserving pressure. I, Sympathetic nerve fibers innervating a sweat gland. J, Pacinian corpuscles, subserving pressure. K, Golgi-Mazzoni endings, subserving pressure. L, Nerve trunks containing thick and thin fibers. M, Sebaceous gland. N, Sweat gland. O, Sympathetic nerve fibers supplying erector pili muscle. Drawing composed from methylene blue and silver preparations. (From Woollard, Weddell and Harpman, *J. Anat., Lond.*, 1940, *74:*413–440.)

penetration correlated with latency of sensation yielded an estimated depth for the cold and warmth receptor which agreed well with the measured depth of the Krause and Ruffini types of end-organ respectively. In view of the fact that sensations of warmth can be elicited by vascular changes (blushing), it is perhaps significant that the warmth receptor should lie close to the inner plexus of blood vessels.

The notion of one spot-one sense organ is probably an oversimplification. Repeated mapping reveals considerable instability of cold and warm spots. A number of sources of error make for a false appearance of instability. Dallenbach (7) by meticulous exclusion of disturbing factors was able to obtain virtually complete stability as is shown in Figure 172. Jenkins (13) has put forth maps of temperature sensibility which indicate not islands or spots of sensitivity but "hills and valleys" as also shown in Figure 172. This type of map was obtained when the subject was allowed to report grades of sensation and the results for repeated examinations were totalled to give a quantitative indication of thermal sensitivity at each point. The explanation is apparently not as simple as conduction of heat to a sense organ situated at the center of each "hill." To Jenkins this distribution suggests groups of sensory endings rather than single endings, an effect which would be given by multiple branching sensory fibers of the free nerve ending type usually exclusively associated

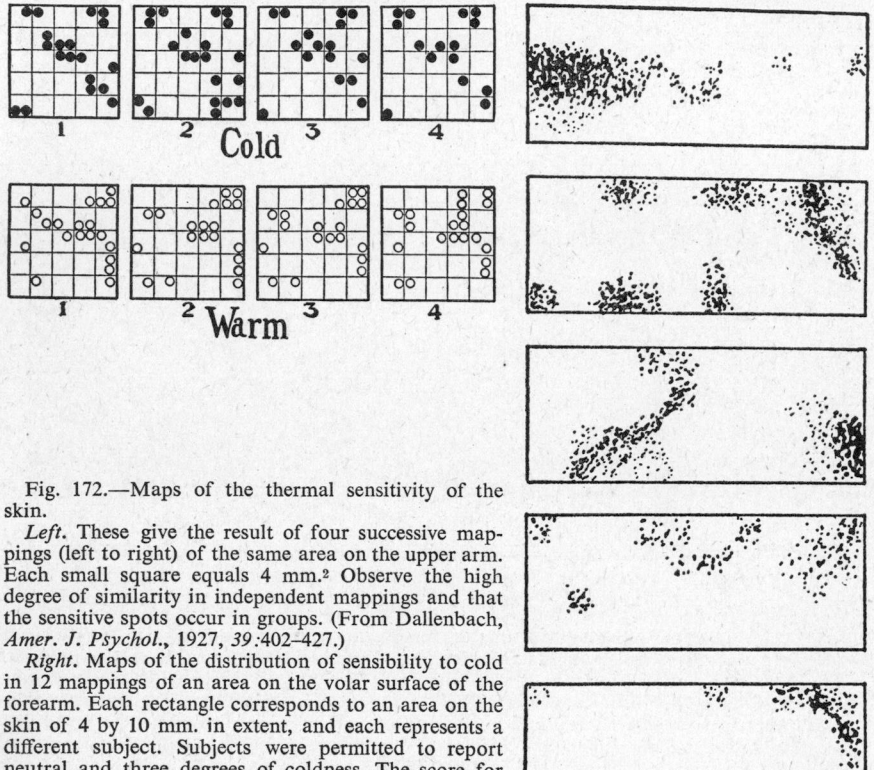

Fig. 172.—Maps of the thermal sensitivity of the skin.

Left. These give the result of four successive mappings (left to right) of the same area on the upper arm. Each small square equals 4 mm.² Observe the high degree of similarity in independent mappings and that the sensitive spots occur in groups. (From Dallenbach, *Amer. J. Psychol.*, 1927, *39*:402–427.)

Right. Maps of the distribution of sensibility to cold in 12 mappings of an area on the volar surface of the forearm. Each rectangle corresponds to an area on the skin of 4 by 10 mm. in extent, and each represents a different subject. Subjects were permitted to report neutral and three degrees of coldness. The score for each square is crudely given by depth of shading. (From Jenkins, *J. exp. Psychol.*, 1939, *25*:373–388.)

with pain. However, recent histological studies (22) find Krause end-organs occurring in groups. It must be remembered that it is the anatomical specificity of the sense organ, not the functional specificity that has been questioned. The latter is well demonstrated by the minimum effective energy to elicit the sensation of warmth which according to Hardy and Oppel (10) is 0.00015 gm. cal./cm.²/sec. acting for 3 secs.; that for pain is 0.218. Thus, the functional specialization of the warmth receptor lowers its threshold to approximately 1/1900 of the heat threshold for pain.

The adequate stimulus for both warmth and cold is heat. Though one speaks of *cold* stimulating the *cold* receptor, cold is not a positive quantity and hence cannot stimulate. The stimulus for a cold receptor is not cold but simply a degree of heat less than that adequate for the warmth receptors. The thermal sense organs record not the temperature of objects but the temperature of the skin at the depth at which they are situated. Hence they are subject to stimulation by internal heat as well as the heat of the environment. The patient with Raynaud's disease experiencing a vasospasm in the fingers complains bitterly of the cold even in a warm room. A metal object and a wooden object of the same temperature do not seem equally cold to the touch because the metal object conducts heat from the skin readily and thereby lowers its temperature more rapidly.

So many factors influence the effectiveness of temperature stimuli that it is difficult to learn the exact nature of the temperature stimulus. The threshold stimulus for cold receptors is a fall in temperature at the rate of 0.004° C. /sec. and warmth receptors is a rise of 0.001° C. /sec., both continuing for 3 secs. Increasing the area of stimulation greatly lowers the threshold for stimulation and the relationship has been quantitatively determined for warmth by Hardy and Oppel (10) (log Intensity $+$ 0.78 log Area $= -$ 2.09). The mechanism is presumably the same as that underlying similar areal summation in the retina. A most important factor is the temperature of the skin. Objects having a temperature close to the physiological zero, i.e., the temperature of the skin, elicit neither warmth nor cold sensations. On the other hand, even warm air falling on the warm skin during fever arouses distressing sensations of cold. Rate of change in temperature is an important factor, but temperature sensations occur during prolonged immersion of a hand in warm water long after the temperature of the skin has ceased changing. Adaptation to temperature stimuli is marked.

The explanation which best fits the facts (Bazett, 2) is that the cold receptors are superficial to the most superficial arterial net and respond to the gradient of temperature between the surface and the vascular layers of the skin, the gradient being maintained by heat brought to the skin by the blood stream. A quick change to a lower temperature steepens the gradient between the temperature of the skin surface and the blood temperature. With continuance of cooling the gradient flattens but persists. The temperature end-organ lies along this gradient and is subject to a temperature deformation comparable to the mechanical deformation essential for contact stimulation with a resulting discharge presumably proportional to the steepness of the gradient. For the explanation of stimulation of warm receptors the original literature (2) should be consulted.

Pain. The sensory mechanism for pain is in many ways unique. The sensory end-organs for pain are spread through virtually all of the tissues of the body, so that three kinds of pain are recognized and designated: (i) superficial or cutaneous pain, (ii) deep pain from muscles, tendons, joints and fascia, and (iii) visceral pain. The first two together form somatic pain. The pain endings are unique in exhibiting only to a limited degree the phenomenon of the adequate stimulus. Several kinds of stimulus energy are adequate to elicit pain, namely, electrical, mechanical, extremes of heat and cold, and chemical stimuli of a wide variety. The pain ending is therefore not specialized to react to a single form of energy but reacts to extreme degrees of several kinds of stimulation. Sherrington (18) pointed out that the property common to the various stimuli adequate to excite pain endings is that such stimuli threaten damage to the tissues. Thus, increasing degrees of heat first stimulate warmth endings and at 52° C. commence to stimulate pain endings. At about this temperature histological damage to the skin can be demonstrated. In Sherrington's classification of the senses, pain was termed *nociceptive*, meaning sensitive to noxious agents. The function of the pain sense is protective, whereas the other modalities of sensation are primarily informative or gnostic. Other differences are that pain possesses to a high degree the quality of being unpleasant, or in other words, possesses a considerable *affect;* that pain leads to more precipitate action; and, finally, that certain types of pain tend to radiate and to be poorly localized.

Because pain is so unlike other forms of sensation, it was long considered not to be a separate form of sensation with its own sense organs and nerve fibers but rather a form of common sensation elicited by intense stimulation of other forms of sensory end-organs. Though not generally accepted, this overstimulation or intensive theory is still supported by several present day investigators. But there is considerable evidence that a pure pain receptor must exist. Von Frey is credited with establishing the existence of a specific pain receptor by finding in the mosaic of sensory spots minute areas of skin sensitive to pain and no other sensation. Certain regions of the body—the teeth, the tympanic membrane, and the central zone of the cornea—give rise only to pain sensations. Section of a cutaneous nerve produces a bordering zone which is sensitive only to pain. Asphyxia of a nerve by pressure leaves pain persisting after all other types of sensation have disappeared. That overstimulation of touch and pressure organs does not cause pain is proved by the well-known experiment of Cattell and Hoagland (6). The result of intense stimulation of an end-organ is to increase the frequency with which it discharges nerve impulses. By stimulation of the skin of a frog with a jet of air interrupted by a toothed wheel high rates of discharge (300 per sec.) were produced and their existence proved by recording action currents. When such stimuli are applied to an unanesthetized frog, none of the signs of pain is exhibited. Stimulating the skin electrically without mechanical contact (Bishop, 3) results in sensations of touch and pricking-pain which are elicited from different points on the skin and have many points of dissimilarity.

Encapsulated end-organs such as Meissner's touch corpuscle (Fig. 173) frequently receive in addition to the large medullated fiber a small unmyelinated one. This fiber intertwines extensively with the varicose termination of the larger fiber but does not form a protoplasmic junction with it. This "accessory" fiber is said not to be derived from the sympathetic nervous system, and is morphologically similar to a pain fiber. It is situated in relation to end-organs of touch, pressure, cold and proprioception. Though direct evidence that the accessory fibers serve pain is lacking, their situation suggests the possibility that weaker stimulation may discharge the large, low threshold fibers while intense stimulation discharges the small, high threshold fibers to produce pain. Such an arrangement is compatible with the doctrine of specific nerve energies, whereas the intensive theory is not.

Neurohistological basis of pain. Consistent with the wide range of stimuli which arouse pain is the fact that the sensory end-organ for pain is not specialized but consists of unencapsulated or "free nerve endings." This allocation was originally made by von Frey (1895), who found that the center of the cornea gave painlike sensation rather than a sensation of touch to the weakest perceptible stimuli, and contained free nerve endings only. Such terminations are the only type distributed widely enough to account for the pain sensitivity of skin, muscle and viscera. The skin at the border of a denervated area possesses only pain sensibility. Woollard, Weddell and Harpman (25) examined this border region histologically and found in it only free nerve endings.

Such endings are formed by an axis cylinder dichotomizing repeatedly, losing its medullary sheath and ultimately the neurilemma as well. The fine naked branches of the axis cylinders ramify among the cells of the deeper layers of the epidermis, and, according to some writers, actually penetrate cells; some free nerve endings also end subepidermally. Knowledge of these terminations has been greatly enlarged by recent anatomical studies using the methylene blue staining technique. The free nerve endings are not disposed in the skin like trees in the forest with trunks widely separated and branches touching. Rather the arrangement is plexiform, with considerable intermingling of the branches of separate neurons. A deep and a superficial plexus can be identified. One plexus lies in the deeper layers of the dermis and consists of thick and thin medullated and nonmedullated fibers (subepidermal plexus). This plexus gives rise to a more superficial plexus consisting of thinner medullated as well as nonmedullated fibers, forming a delicate network (intra-epidermal plexus). Nerve fibers from this plexus branch repeatedly

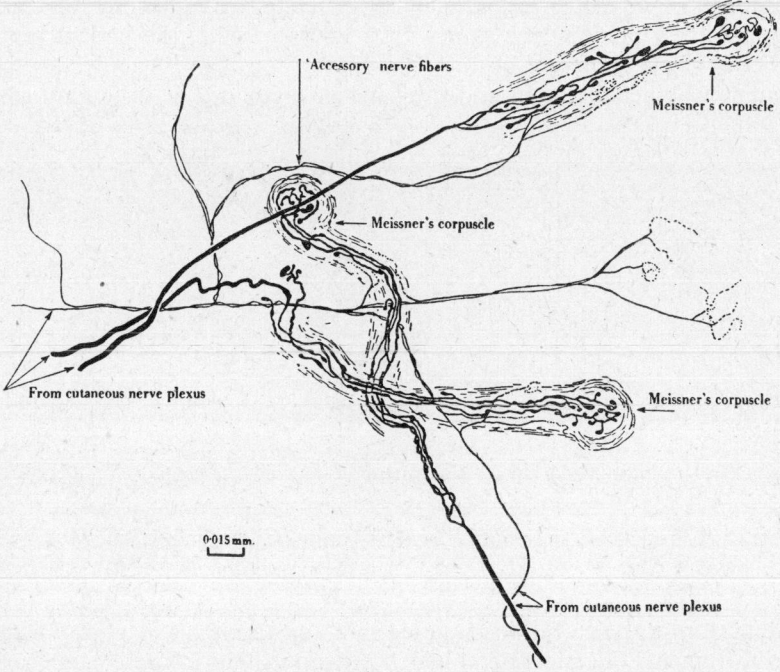

Fig. 173.—Meissner's corpuscles (touch) and unmyelinated accessory fibers. Note that three end-organs, each borne upon separate nerve fibers, were found within an area approximately 0.15 mm. wide. (From Weddell, *J. Anat., Lond.*, 1941, 75:441–446.)

over a wide area and end in "fine, naked, beaded terminals disposed below and among the cells of the deeper layers of the epidermis." The free nerve endings are thus found in the dermis as well as the epidermis. In the margins of a denervated area are found the fibers of the superficial plexus and a few fine fibers from the deep plexus. The finer fibers and free nerve endings are thus associated with pain. Though pain endings are arranged in a plexiform fashion, the resulting network does not form a syncitium, i.e., they are closely interlocked but there is no protoplasmic connection between them.

The contribution to this plexus, made by a single sensory fiber, i.e., the fiber and all its branches, was termed the "sensory unit" by Tower (20, 21), who investigated it with respect to size and to its topographical relation with other sensory units. For this purpose Tower chose the pure pain zone of the cornea. Action currents were led from a fine filament of the long ciliary nerves or a nerve cut down to a few fibers so that the responses of single fibers could be identified. A single fiber was caused to discharge by stimuli applied over an area forming roughly a quadrant of the cornea together with adjacent portions of the sclera and conjunctiva. In size the unit areas varied between 50 and 200 or more square millimeters. Within this field there were, of course, areas that were silent and sometimes stimulation of these would cause a different sensory fiber to discharge. Since the number of pain fibers passing to the cornea is large, and since each fiber is distributed over such a wide area, it follows that the branches of a large number of fibers must interdigitate and that each point on the cornea must be innervated by a large number of fibers.

Measurement of pain sensibility. Pain is elicited for purposes of clinical examination by pricking the skin with a pin or needle; the patient reports whether it "feels" different on the two sides of the body. Another test is to determine whether the point and the head of a pin can be distinguished. In

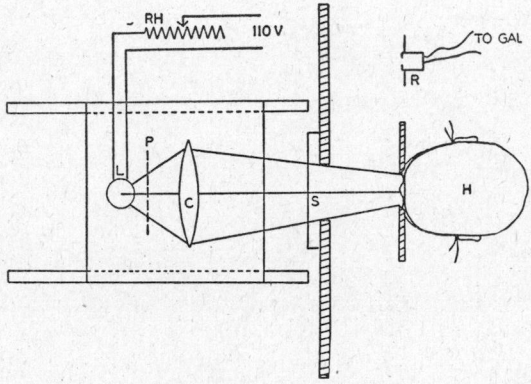

Fig. 174.—Radiant energy apparatus for measuring warmth and pain sensibility. For description and key to symbols see text. (From Hardy, Wolff and Goodell, *J. clin. Invest.*, 1940, *19*:649–657.)

the laboratory a spine of a thistle glued to a von Frey hair is used. For deep pain, instruments (algesiometers) which measure the pressure of application necessary to elicit pain have been devised.

All of these instruments suffer from the defect that touch and pressure receptors are stimulated along with the pain receptors. Recently this drawback has been circumvented in two ways. Bishop (3) employs an ingenious apparatus by which a spark jumps to the skin from an electrode held just above the surface of the epidermis. Hardy, Wolff and Goodell (11) have introduced an apparatus employing radiant energy (Fig. 174). The light from a 1000 watt lamp, L, is focused by a condensing lens, C, through a fixed aperture of 3.5 cm.² on the forehead of the subject which is blacked by India ink. The intensity of the radiation is controlled by means of a rheostat, RH, and the duration by a shutter, P, which automatically limits the exposure to 3 secs. The shutter S is hand operated. A sensation of heat is of course experienced, but is easily distinguished from the quick, sharp, stinging sensations of pain. By repeated responses to increasing intensities of light, a threshold for pain is obtained and a radiometer is placed in front of the

aperture and the intensity of the radiation measured in gm. cal./sec./cm.²
If precautions are taken to avoid sweating, drafts, and variations in room
temperature, thresholds of a single individual are remarkably invariable
(S.D. = 2.0 per cent). Threshold is independent of size of area stimulated.
Spatial summation between fibers supplying a given area, or between the
branches of a single fiber, apparently does not occur. Visceral pain, deep
pain and special forms of pain are discussed in Chapter 19.

Touch-Pressure. Pressure is one of the four fundamental cutaneous sense
modalities. Whether pressure forms a single sense modality like warmth or
cold or whether there are subqualities, served by distinct neural mechanisms,
is uncertain.

The existence of two end-organs of quite different properties is conclusively proved by
Adrian and Zotterman's records of sensory discharges (1). Touch or light pressure applied
to the cushion of a cat's toe produces an outburst of impulses in the medial plantar nerve
at the moment of contact which lasts for only one-fifth of a second despite continuance
of the stimulus. Stimulation with von Frey hairs or with the Bishop apparatus produces
a sensation described as a "minute pat" or tap. Increase of the stimulus intensifies the tap
but does not cause it to persist. Therefore a submodality of light touch or light pressure,
with a quick adapting end-organ, may be established. A second receptor was isolated by
Adrian and Zotterman from the toe pad of the cat which responded after the first had
adapted. Its discharge decreased rapidly to a plateau rate (see Fig. 170) which was maintained for seconds, and the frequency graded with the intensity of pressure. The word
"pressure" can be used to mean a persisting sensation produced by heavier and broader
applications of mechanical force to the skin, such as is supplied by a relatively light pressure of a blunt object applied to the skin. "Deep pressure" is best reserved for the sensations from massive pressure on muscles and tendons. Head identified the nonadapting
pressure sensations with deep pressure, which is probably incorrect. Unfortunately there
is neither precise knowledge nor a precise terminology of pressure sensibility, and this is
probably a factor in the ambiguity which exists with respect to the spinal pathway of
pressure impulses (Chap. 17).

It suffices at the moment that objects brought into contact with the skin
give rise to a feeling of touch or pressure. To some degree that name is misleading because the actual stimulus appears not to be pressure acting equally
in all directions on the sense organs but the deformation of the tissue and
the contained end-organ. A pressure gradient with resulting deformation
or bending of the membranes of the sense organ is the effective aspect of
contact. The classic illustration of this (Meissner) is gained by thrusting the
finger into a vessel of mercury. The sense of pressure comes not all over the
submerged portions of the finger but only at the surface between air and
mercury; below the mercury level the receptors are compressed; at the phase
boundary they are deformed. Light traction on the skin by means of a hair
glued to the skin is an effective stimulus to the pressure end-organs though
it produces deformation without pressure.

That pressure sensibility is distributed in a densely punctiform fashion
was demonstrated by von Frey who explored the skin with hairs mounted
on a wooden handle, a device which has become standard for this purpose.
A threshold of punctate pressures is obtained by stimulating the skin with
von Frey hairs of different lengths and diameters calibrated for bending
strength by means of a chemical balance. The hair, by bending, determines
the pressure exerted and neutralizes the effect of variation in rate and force
with which the hair is applied. Various laboratory devices are used to produce
graded *areal* pressure stimuli requisite for obtaining a threshold. Clinically,

light contact is conveniently assayed by the cotton wool test of Head in which the skin is lightly stroked with a few loose strands of a wad of absorbent cotton (not the wad itself). A heavier stimulus is given by contact with a small camel-hair brush. Pressure is also tested by the discrimination of weights placed in the supported hand which is not moved, else muscle sense is involved. Pressure sensibility is sometimes expressed in gm./mm., not gm./mm.[2], since tension and not pressure is the real stimulus.

At least three sense organs are generally believed to give rise to pressure sensations. Over hairy regions touch-sensitive "spots" are largely found in juxtaposition to the hairs, especially on the "windward" side of the sloping hair. Masses of bare nerve endings can be identified histologically about the roots of hairs. By leverage the force of a light contact with hair is greatly magnified and shaving greatly reduces the sensitivity of the skin to cotton wool. Over hairless areas, so-called Meissner corpuscles located in the papillae of the corium are held to be "touch corpuscles" (Figs. 171, 173); but other encapsulated end-organs are undoubtedly concerned (Merkel's discs and Golgi-Mazzoni corpuscles).

The third type of end-organ, the giant Pacinian corpuscle, is found in the subcutaneous tissues, and in still deeper structures. From time to time doubt is expressed whether, in addition to the encapsulated type of receptor, free nerve endings may not also be concerned with pressure. The evidence is not sufficiently decisive one way or the other to warrant presentation, but it has not been indisputably proved that the Meissner corpuscle is, or that the free nerve ending is not, concerned with pressure sensibility.

Touch sensibility is distributed in a punctiform fashion over the skin surface. At first glance it might seem that the touch spot signified the existence beneath it of a sense organ from which a single axon leads to the central nervous system. Recent studies suggest that this is not the case and that the touch spot should be thought of merely as a point of heightened sensibility. The touch-sensitive spot appears to result not from a single end-organ and a single fiber but from a group of end-organs innervated by several fibers (Fig. 173). Weddell (23) stained with methylene blue the skin of a finger about to be amputated and found the Meissner corpuscles to occur in groups of two or three but never singly, and approximately ten such groups were found in 1 sq. mm. Each corpuscle is supplied by its own myelinated fiber which can be traced for considerable distance through the cutaneous nerve plexus of the skin. The fibers are often seen to approach the cluster from several different directions, all of which suggests that the touch spot contains more than one sense organ and is innervated by more than one dorsal root fiber. A physiological consequence of this is that each touch spot can grade activity by recruitment of sense organs as well as by increased frequency of discharge. The innervation of the hairs is even more diffuse. The distribution of endings to the hair of a rabbit is such that one fiber may innervate as many as 300 hairs probably spread over several square centimeters of area, and a hair receives fibers from more than one axon. The functional unit of touch subserved by hairs is therefore a system of multiple innervation by interlocking or interdigitating fibers.

Deep Sensibility. Though it is a matter of common knowledge that a person with eyes closed knows the direction of a movement, active or passive, and is aware of the position of his arms or legs, muscle sense was not included in the early tabulations of the senses. Some ascribed such knowledge of movement and position to "feelings of innervation," a sort of centrally aroused sensory process; others believed the cutaneous receptors to be involved. Charles Bell (1844) clearly and explicitly described the sixth sense—"muscle sense." For example, he said, "Between the brain and the muscles, there is a circle of nerves; one nerve conveys the influence from the brain to the muscle; the other gives the sense of the condition of the muscle to the brain." Conclusive proof of this was the demonstration by Sherrington very much later (1894) that muscular branches of nerves contain a high percentage (40 per cent) of afferent fibers. The principal sensory end-organ of muscles was not fully described until 1892 by Ruffini and by Sherrington. The types of sense organ found in muscle are (i) the muscle spindle, (ii) the Golgi tendon organ, (iii) the Pacinian corpuscle, and (iv) free nerve endings.

The muscle spindle or "stretch afferent" is situated mainly in the fleshy parts of all skeletal muscles with the exception of the ocular and facial muscles. It consists of a spindle-shaped connective tissue envelope a few millimeters in length, enclosing several modified muscle fibers (intrafusal fibers). Passing through the envelope and the layer of tissue fluid surrounding the intrafusal fibers are (i) their motor fibers, small myelinated fibers which derive from the anterior roots; (ii) *flower spray endings*, highly branched, delicate, finger-like terminations which are applied closely to the sarcolemma; (iii) *annulospiral endings*, large fibers which lose their myelin and neurolemmal sheaths and branch to form wide ribbon-like terminals wrapped around and around the intrafusal fiber; and (iv) an unmyelinated fiber resembling the "accessory fiber" of encapsulated end-organs. A second type of ending is found in the tendons, close to their muscular origins, and consists of a group of tendon fascicles surrounded by a connective tissue sheath containing tissue fluid. An afferent myelinated fiber of medium size branches profusely and ramifies as unmyelinated terminals among the tendon fibrils. This is called the Golgi tendon organ. Pacinian corpuscles are found in the fascia of muscles, and especially beneath the tendinous insertions of muscles at joints. In this position they are pressed upon when muscles are contracted or stretched. Fine, unmyelinated nerve endings are found, distributed widely through muscle, tendons, joints, fascia and ligaments.

Analysis of what constitutes the stimulus to muscle receptors depends upon recording the nerve impulses set up in single sense organs when the muscle is stretched or caused to contract by stimulation of its motor nerve fibers (15). One of the sensory endings penetrating the spindle responds to active contraction of the intrafusal fiber by initiating or accelerating its discharge, and the resulting impulses must, from their rate of conduction, travel in fibers of large diameter. The characteristics are those of the annulospiral ending which has a large fiber, and, because of its position, would be deformed by an increase in the diameter of the intrafusal fiber; this ending is also stimulated by passive elongation of the muscle. A second type of ending responds to passive stretch even more actively than the first type. Furthermore, the discharge is *interrupted*, not accelerated, during active contraction. This ending is believed to be the flower spray type. Both endings respond to stretching of the muscle and both cease firing if only the ordinary muscle fibers are made to contract by a stimulus too weak to excite the slender motor axon of the intrafusal fiber. Thus the muscle spindle as a unit is "in parallel" with the ordinary muscle fibers surrounding it (Fulton). When the latter contract, the intrafusal fiber is slackened and both types of endings are protected from stimulation by stretch. A third type of ending responds to tension, whether produced by passive stretch or by active contraction. The tendon organ, being surrounded by tendon fibrils which do not change shape, is presumably sensitive only to tension. This analysis suggests, therefore, that muscle receptors taken as a whole record three aspects of the states of a muscle, active contraction, passive stretch (length of fiber), and tension, whether produced by passive stretch or active contraction.

The forms of deep sensibility exclusive of pain and deep pressure are known by several synonyms, all of which are in common use, namely, muscle sense, or more completely muscle, tendon and joint sensibility, kinesthesis (Bastian), proprioception (Sherrington), position sense (Head). Classified on the usual basis of quality, deep sensibility seems to consist of the following subqualities: (i) active and passive movement, (ii) active and passive position, (iii) tension, (iv) pain and (v) pressure. Separate sense organs, however, cannot be ascribed to these with certainty and some may depend on more than one sense organ. Although these may not be unique functions or subqualities, they serve to classify the various tests of deep sensibility.

Deep pressure and deep pain are elicited by firm, massive pressure over muscles or tendons, especially the latter. That muscles and tendons possess an exquisite pain sensibility is shown by the pain of muscle cramps, sprains, etc. Muscles give rise to pain when exercised in the absence of adequate blood supply (ischemic pain).

The appreciation of passive movement of a single joint is commonly tested in the neurological examination. If the finger or a toe is grasped by the side (to minimize cues from pressure) and moved up or down, a patient with normal sensibility is able to state the direction of quite small angular displacements. A rough quantitative idea of the threshold can be attained, especially when this is elevated. Elaborate studies (14) using mechanical devices have shown that the threshold expressed in terms of angular deviation varies between 0.2 and 0.7 degrees for different joints. The threshold tends to be lower for proximal than for distal joints. For the perception of active movement there is no convenient classical test. Laboratory experiments show that it is slightly more acute than the perception of passive movement. Sense organs which record active movement are of paramount importance in the regulation of movement.

The sense of position is tested in a variety of ways. A limb is placed in an unusual position and the subject asked to duplicate the posture with his other limb. Another maneuver—the finger-to-finger test—consists of passively moving the arm to be tested and bringing it to rest with finger extended and asking the patient to touch the extended forefinger with the forefinger of the other hand. By interposing a screen between the two fingers and marking positions of the two fingers, a quantitative estimate of the error can be obtained. In animals something akin to the sense of position is tested by determining whether a false or abnormal position, not sufficiently extreme to be painful, is corrected, a test which is valid only when motor ability is normal. A similar procedure applicable to animals is the "proprioceptive placing" reaction (Chap. 8). The front of the paw of the blindfolded animal is brought strongly into contact with the edge of the table so that the joints are passively moved through several degrees. The foot is lifted and the paw is placed upon the table top. If the side of the paw is touched, the leg is moved towards that side. In the intact animal cutaneous sensation is also involved and has a lower threshold so that touch rather than proprioceptive impulses control the movement. Another maneuver which may involve both cutaneous and deep sensibility is the hopping reaction of Rademaker. The animal is blindfolded and held so that only one leg is in contact with the table and bearing the weight of the animal. The animal is then translocated in any desired direction and the leg executes a series of short, brisk hops which serve to keep the leg under the body and support its weight. If the animal is moved forward the leg hops forward; the opposite tensions produced by moving the animal backwards cause backward hopping. Thus in both the placing reaction and the hopping reaction there is an element of local sign or a spatial organization of the response, perhaps related to a sense of position and the appreciation of passive movement as tested clinically.

The appreciation of resistance or tension is studied by determining the ability to detect difference in weight of objects by lifting them. Two weights are usually presented and the subject asked to state which is the heavier. This is a classical laboratory procedure which has proved useful in studying neurological patients and has been adapted to monkeys and chimpanzees in the study of cortical localization of sensory functions. The large number of ways for conducting these experiments (psychophysical method) and for expressing the thresholds statistically (psychophysical process) fall outside the scope of this book. A method applicable to both man and animals consists in presenting the subject with two weights (ointment jars filled with cotton wool and lead shot wrapped in adhesive tape) and having him indicate which is the heavier. The difference in weights is initially very large and easily discriminable but is progressively reduced until the heavier weight cannot be designated with more than chance success. This value is the relative threshold and the weight difference is known as a j.n.d. (just noticeable difference). The difference for 75 or 80 per cent success is sometimes taken as the threshold because many trials are necessary to determine the 50 per cent threshold. A monkey or chimpanzee, instead of indicating the selected weight verbally, makes the choice after hefting the weights by placing the chosen one into a certain aperture in a discrimination apparatus and receives food if correct. The fact that the method is applicable both to animals and to man emphasizes that it is objective in addition to being quantitative. Discrimination ability rather than subjective sensation need be the only concern of the physiologist, whether the subject be man or animal.

Vibratory Sensibility (9). The appreciation of vibration, or *pallesthesia*, is tested crudely by placing the base of a vibrating tuning fork upon the skin. A thrill or feeling of vibration is experienced if sensibility is intact while only a sense of continuous contact is felt after certain neurological lesions. Within recent years stimulating devices activated by vacuum tube oscillators have been introduced. With them a threshold is obtained in terms of the amplitude of the vibration which is just perceptible. Whether vibratory sensibility is mediated by a separate set of end-organs and pathways and hence is a separate sense modality or whether it is simply a special way of exciting sense organs for touch-pressure and proprioception has been much discussed. Because application of the fork over bone intensifies the stimulus in a purely mechanical fashion vibratory sensation has been erroneously called "osseous sensation." The sense organs are not related to the bones and the experience of vibration can be elicited from fleshy parts remote from bone. That vibratory sensibility is a form of pressure sense—more explicitly a temporal pattern of pressure sensation—and not a separate, unique modality is suggested by several considerations. Geldard (9) identified on the skin a series of spots having low thresholds for pressure and another series of high thresholds. The sensitivity of the spots to vibration was lower for the low threshold group. Vibration applied through a liquid in which the finger is immersed is felt, as is pressure, only at the border between liquid and air, showing that distortion due to a pressure gradient is essential for both forms of stimulation (Békésy). Local anesthetization of the skin reduces or abolishes the appreciation of a stigmatic vibrating stimulus *pari passu* with the effects on light pressure (Weitz, 24). While the superficial end-organs of the touch-pressure variety can give rise to a perception of vibration, it is less clear whether sense organs for deep sensibility do likewise. Anesthetization of the skin or blocking of cutaneous nerves does not yield a clear-cut answer to this question. Weitz (24) by direct observation showed that vibration waves will extend beyond an anesthetized area unless it is many centimeters in extent; cocainization by changing the physical properties of the skin and the use of large vibrating stimulation favor spread to normal skin areas. However, in the face, section of the sensory root of the fifth cranial nerve leaves only deep sensory fibers to the facial musculature and some appreciation of vibration is retained (Pollack).

Vibratory sensibility is certainly not a separate sense and it is certainly not bone sensibility, nor does it seem to be associated exclusively with either deep or superficial pressure fibers. Vibratory sensibility is a perception of a *temporal* pattern of pressures, somewhat like the flicker phenomenon in vision (Chap. 23). As such, at some rate of pulsation, all forms of somatic sensation must yield a sensation of "vibration." As a perception it falls into the general group with the perceptions depending on the spatial aspects of sensation. This interpretation is supported by the behavior of vibratory sensibility in various clinical neurological conditions (8)

In peripheral nerve disorders the sense of position may be preserved in spite of severe impairment of vibratory sensibility. On the other hand, vibratory sensibility is never significantly affected when both touch and kinesthetic sense are undisturbed, as might happen were separate receptors and fibers involved. Chordotomy leaves vibratory sensibility unimpaired. In cases of spinal cord damage, if position sense is affected, vibratory appreciation is always affected. However, vibratory sensibility may be severely disturbed while position sense is little affected. The reverse appears to hold for lesions of the cerebral cortex which rarely affect vibratory sensibility, unless they penetrate deeply, in which case damage to the thalamus may be responsible (Fig. 175). Though not subject to any simple explanation this difference in vulnerability of vibratory sensitivity at the spinal and the cerebral level makes vibratory sensibility helpful in clinical diagnosis. Laidlaw and Hamilton have published norms for various regions of the body based upon the study of 60 normal individuals in which a pallesthesiometer was used.

Localization or Topognosis (4). Every somatic sensation has in addition to its quality and its intensity a localization upon the body surface. A stimulus can be localized by means of cues of unknown nature which are for convenience called "local signs," though it is probable that localization like quality is a matter of central termination rather than any peculiarity of the nerve impulses or of pattern of impulses which identifies them as having come from a given point on the skin. Although little is known of the mechanism of localization the accuracy of localization has been extensively investigated both in normal individuals and in neurological cases. Weber (1852) touched the skin with a pointer dipped in powdered charcoal to mark a spot on the skin; the subject, with eyes closed throughout, tried to touch the same spot with another pointer. The measured discrepancy between the two gives the error of localization when repeated a sufficient number of times to provide a reliable average. The error of localization varies markedly in different regions of the body surface.

Testing of the accuracy of localization can be conducted in a variety of ways, each calling forth a somewhat different psychological process. Thus when vision is excluded, the spot touched is located with reference to the region as kinesthetically conceived or as seen in visual imagery. Muscle sense may be simultaneously involved in both the part touched and the hand used for pointing to the spot. Groping for the spot touched increases accuracy by giving a comparison of two touches. The point stimulated is an important factor because of the regional variations which are usually controlled by side-to-side comparisons; and the kind of stimulus is another factor. With so many factors involved, the localization test in clinical neurology needs careful standardization.

It is often stated that pain is poorly localized. Although this is true of certain types of visceral pain, cutaneous pain is accurately localized. Zigler, Moore and Wilson (26) found that the average error of localization of touches on the back of the hand with von Frey hairs was 4.49 mm. as opposed to 3.81

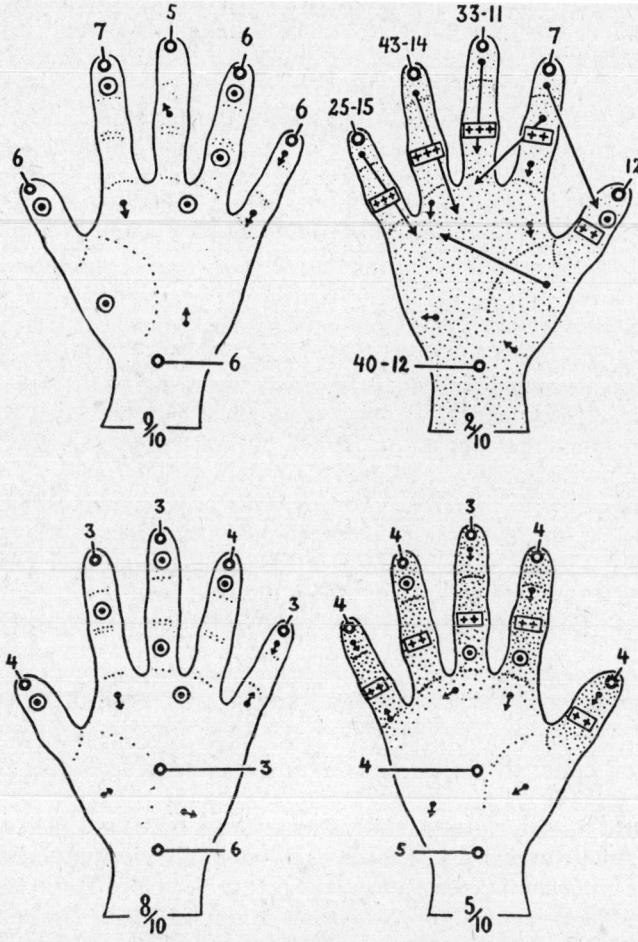

Fig. 175.—An example of Fox's chart used for recording the sensory examination of neurological patients. The lower two hands are from a case in which only the cerebral cortex appeared to be affected; the upper two, those of a patient with a deeply infiltrating cerebral tumor. The degree of loss of position sense in the phalangeal joint is indicated by $+$, $++$ and $+++$; accurate localization of a point touched is designated by a circle and dot, and the amount and direction of displacement of an erroneous localization by an arrow. Areas of hypesthesia are indicated by dots. The fraction at the wrist is a measure of stereognosis, and shows the number successfully identified in a series of 10 objects presenting increasing difficulty. The numbers connected by a line with a heavy circle give in arbitrary units the threshold of vibration at the point indicated; a large number signifies a large amplitude of vibration. (From Fox and Klemperer, *Arch. Neurol. Psychiat.*, Chicago, 1942, *48*:622–645.)

mm. for pricks with a thistle (pain) which according to the observer's report gave rise to a sensation only of pain; when the thistle gave a sensation of pressure as well as pain, the contact was still more accurately localized. Localization is, however, quite defective in the border of an anesthetic area produced by section of a peripheral nerve where only pain sensations can be elicited, but such a region possesses less than the normal density of innervation (Chap. 17). Localization is usually tested only for light pressure and it is sometimes forgotten that every modality of sensation is localizable with the result that the study of the localization of warmth, cold, and pain in clinical cases has been almost entirely neglected. Blake Pritchard (17) measured the localization error for heat without contact and found it to be two to three times greater than the error for touch. All sensations can be localized, though not with the same degree of accuracy as touch. The only difference appears to be that the systems of fibers serving touch possess a topographical and physiological organization which makes possible a high degree of accuracy in localization. Despite certain convenient but misleading expressions current in neurological usage, there are no sense organs or tracts which serve localization as an entity distinct from sensation. Localization without a sensation to be localized is inconceivable. However, localization may be severely impaired by damage to the central pathway when mere awareness of the stimulation is preserved, because the former depends on a large number of spatially organized sensory fibers whereas the latter may be carried out by a relatively few remaining fibers (Fig. 177 and Chap. 17).

Projection of Sensations. This is a phenomenon closely related to localization.* We may assume that all of our sensations are aroused directly in the brain, but in no case are we conscious of this. On the contrary, our sensations are projected either to the exterior of the body or to some peripheral organ in the body, i.e., to the place where experience has taught us that the acting stimulus arises. The exteroceptive sensations are therefore projected exterior to our body. Sound seems to come from the bell, light from the lamp, etc. Interoceptive sensations are projected to the interior of the body. Among the internally projected senses must be included pain, muscle sense, labyrinthine sensations, hunger, thirst, sexual sense, fatigue, and in addition perhaps other less definite sensations from the visceral organs. The temperature senses are, so to speak, on the borderline between the two groups; we may project this sensation either to the exterior or to the interior according to circumstances.

An important aspect of sensation which deserves to be called the *law of projection* is that stimulation of a sensory system at any point central to the sense organ gives rise to a sensation which is projected to the periphery and not to the point of stimulation. Numerous examples of this law can be cited. After amputations impulses set up in the nerve stump may give rise to projected sensations so elaborate that they amount to a feeling that the limb is still present and executing movements, often painful—the phenomenon of "phantom limb." Irritation of a dorsal spinal root by a ruptured intervertebral disc of the fifth lumbar segment often gives rise to a sensation of pain over the knee, which is the region innervated by the affected root. Dusser de Barenne applied strychnine to the root-entry zone of the spinal cord, which stimulates the nerve cell bodies of the second order sensory fibers; the cats turned and inspected or bit the area of skin supplied by the treated root, indicating that the sensation seemed to be coming from the skin. Stimulation of the cerebral cortex in conscious human patients at the time of intracranial operation gives rise to sensations which appear to come not from the head

---

* The distinction between projection and localization is that the former has more to do with the envelope or layer, external or internal, from which a sensation appears to come. Localization has more to do with where on these envelopes the sensation is localized.

but from the skin of some part of the body. In all these cases the cerebral cortex interprets the nerve impulses as though they had come from the sense organ. For further example of projection see the section on referred pain (Chap. 18).

Two-Point Sensibility. If the blunt points of a compass-like instrument called an esthesiometer are applied simultaneously to the skin with a sufficient distance between them, they are perceived as two separate points of contact. If the points are brought progressively closer together in successive applications, they eventually give rise to a sensation of a single point applied to the skin. The smallest distance between points at which the points are still perceived as two separate contacts is the *two-point threshold*. Just as all forms

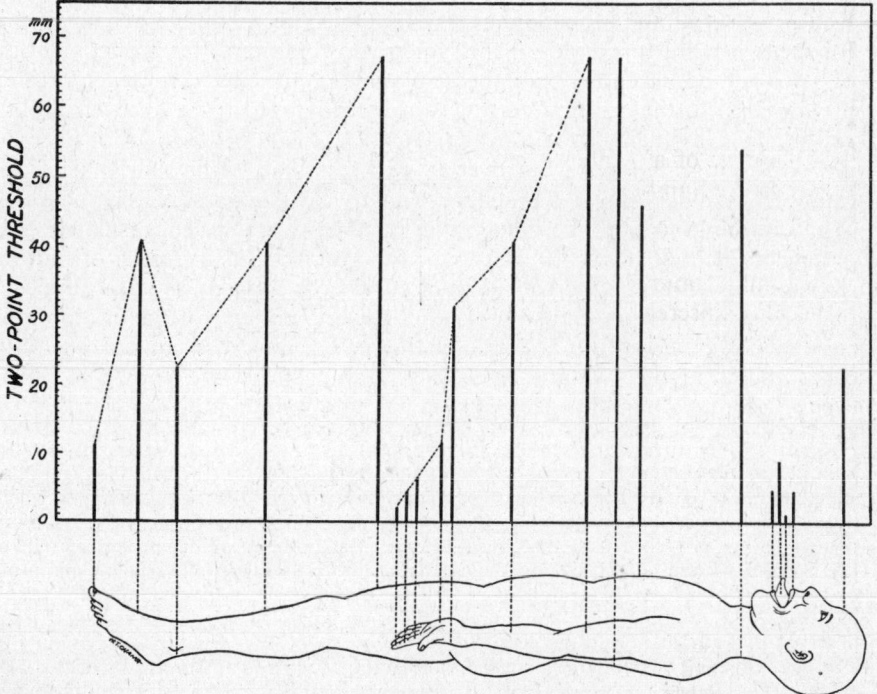

Fig. 176.—Regional variation in the two-point threshold for touch. The length of the vertical lines is approximately equal to the magnitude of the two-point threshold. (Data from Weber cited by Sherrington in Cutaneous sensations, pp. 920–1001 in Schäfer, *Text-book of physiology,* 1900.)

of sensation can be localized, a two-point threshold can be determined for all forms of sensation, though for reasons of convenience only light pressure and occasionally pain (prick) are tested clinically. The two-point threshold is a smaller distance for touches than for warmth or cold stimuli. But the ability of the skin to resolve two points is only one three-thousandths of that of the eye. Regional differences are pronounced (Fig. 176) and broadly parallel the accuracy of localization. They can usually be controlled in the neurological examination by testing corresponding areas on the two sides of the body. Regional variations of the two-point threshold do not run parallel with regional variations in the intensity threshold. The forehead will perceive a pressure of 2 mg., while the skin of the fingers needs a pressure of 5 to 15 mg. to arouse a perceptible sensation. However, when tested by the ability to discriminate two points, the tips of the fingers are far more sensitive than the skin of the forehead.

Neural basis of localization and two-point discrimination. Weber assumed that the two-point threshold for a given region was fixed by the size of the skin area to which terminals of a single nerve fiber are distributed (so-called Weber's sensory circles). As long as one unexcited sensory unit remained between the two on which the compass rested the points were, according to Weber, appreciated as two. The size of the sensory unit's distribution is to some degree correlated with the size of the two-point threshold. For example, Weddell (22) has found the area on the back of the human hand covered by the terminals of a single sensory fiber to approximate 7.5 mm. in diameter while on the thumb of the monkey it is 1.5 mm. These values agree fairly well for the two-point thresholds of the same regions in man. But Weber's notion of two excited receptors and the intervening unexcited one, each with a private path to the cerebral cortex, is now recognized to be an oversimplification. The ramifications within the skin of a single posterior root fiber do not occupy discrete areas but overlap and interlock. Each hair follicle, for example, is innervated by branches from two to seven different neurons. What amounts to multiple innervation of a skin area by encapsulated end-organs of the Meissner type results from their occurrence in clusters of endings representing several different neurons. Weber's conception also supposes that the three neurons making up the sensory pathway from receptor to sensory cortex constitute a simple chain having no cross connections with other chains at the synaptic levels. Such connections are known to occur even in the most highly organized system—the visual pathways.

Figure 177 shows how two closely adjacent points can be perceived as two, despite the multiple factors making for merging of the streams of impulses arising from the two points stimulated. "a" consists of a regularly disposed sheet of cutaneous sense organs which through two synapses connect with a uniformly disposed sheet of cells in the sensory cortex. This is in accord with anatomical evidence of "point to point" projection (Chap. 17). Stimuli s and s′, representing the points of the esthesiometer, stimulate receptors on both sides of the core neurons n and n′, due to the spread of the gradient of deformation and because of multiple innervation of each point on the skin surface. Tower (20, 21) has observed that stimulation in the periphery of the area served by a sensory unit results in a lower frequency of discharge than the same stimulus applied to the center of the skin as shown by the spike potentials b and b′. Frequency of discharge for each unit in Figure 177 could be diagrammed as a triangle. Summation of such triangles set close together to represent interlocking of sensory units results in a peak of excitation at the central neuron. Cross connections at the synaptic levels termed "partially shifted overlap" (Lorente de Nó) and "reciprocal overlap" (Marshall and Talbot) provide avenues for further lateral spread of impulses which tend to involve a wide extent of the cortical field. The height of curves d and d′ represent frequency of impulses at each point on the cortex, and it will be recalled that frequency of discharge is the neural correlate of intensity of a sensation. The justification for drawing peaks is that the receptors of the core neurons are more strongly stimulated, and while the stimulation of adjacent and interdigitating fibers tends to spread the excitation, collaterals at the synaptic layer tend to concentrate it by facilitating the core neurons as indicated by the dotted arrows. Therefore, lateral connections channel as well as spread the stream of impulses. The existence of such peaks of excitation upon the cerebral cortex has been directly proved by Marshall, Woolsey and Bard (Chap. 17). So long as there is an intervening region between the peaks in which the summed (solid line) excitations are less than that of the two peaks by an amount making possible an intensity discrimination between peak and valley, then an experience of two points will result. On analysis the discrimination of two points reduces to an intensity discrimination. The fact that a cylinder with a wide, flat, conical end can be discriminated by the method of successive applications when the areas stimulated overlap greatly demands some such explanation, for such stimulating objects when applied close together must produce the peak and valley pattern of cortical activity. It may be concluded that point stimulation of the skin gives rise to patterns of cortical activity consisting of *modal excitation fields** rather than of points. This principle appears to apply to the cochlea and the retina as well as the skin.

Size, Shape, Figure Writing, Etc. The ability of the cutaneous and proprioceptive sensory systems to appreciate the spatial aspect of objects is

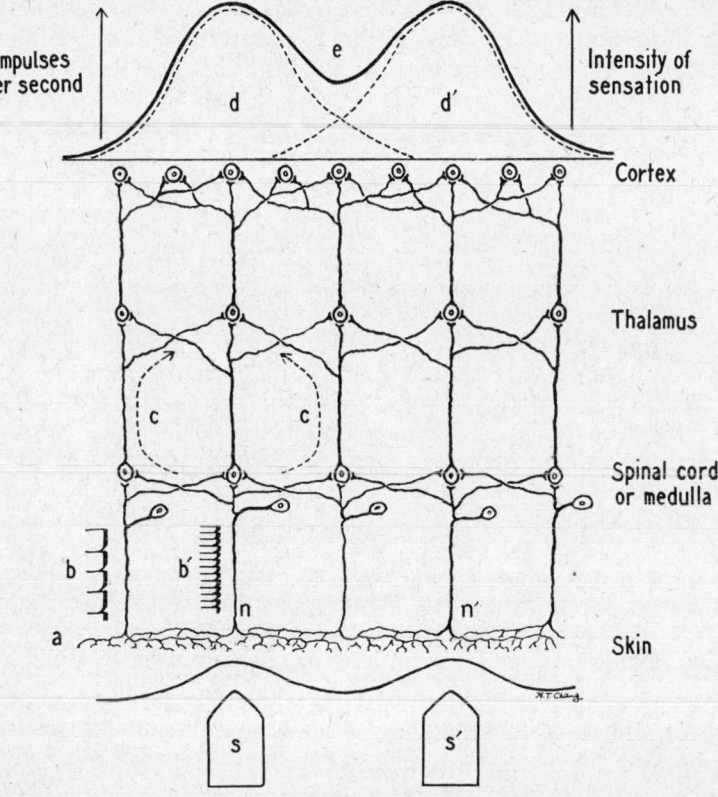

Fig. 177.—Schematic diagram illustrating some of the neural factors involved in localization and in the discrimination of two points; s and s' are the points of the esthesiometer or compass used in the determination of the two-point threshold; a is a plexus of interlocking terminals of the pain variety; b and b' show the rate of discharge from a sensory neuron stimulated at the periphery of the terminal brush and a second neuron stimulated at the center of its peripheral distribution. Arrows c illustrate that the tendency of the excitation to spread in the first synaptic layer results in intensification by facilitation of the core neuron in the next synaptic layer; d and d' represent graphically the frequency of corticopetal impulses arriving upon, and hence the activity of, each cortical cell when due to s and s' respectively; e represents the summed activity pattern. In the text d, d' and e are termed "modal excitation fields." In the diagram an attempt has been made to combine the views of Weber, Bernstein, Lorente de Nó, Tower, and Marshall and Talbot.

demonstrable by a variety of simple maneuvers. Spheres or coins of graded size placed successively in the hand are discriminated by proprioceptive awareness of the position or the posture of the fingers. The direction and

* In a frequency curve in which classes are arranged along the abscissae from small to large and the number falling within each class is graphed, the mode is that class which contains the argest number of frequencies or members.

length of a line drawn upon the skin are recognized. Touch and pressure are mainly responsible for such discrimination. Recognition of geometrical patterns of warmth produced without contact (radiation) are virtually unrecognizable (Stone). Perhaps the most convenient and thorough test of the spatial aspect of skin sensibility is the "figure writing" test introduced by Otfried Foerster. While the observer's eyes are closed numerals between 0 and 9 are written on the palm or other smooth surface of the body with a blunt, pointed object using a slow, even movement. Although mistakes are rarely made by a normal person after the first few trials, certain neurological patients do little better than chance, which is approximately one correct response.* The manner of recording the observations is:

As written	1	2	7	4	8	6	9	5	3	0
As reported	1	2	6	3–2	6	6	1	7	7	0

Figure writing, left hand. J. P., a white youth aged 18. Tests were conducted subsequent to a right occipital craniotomy which disclosed an aneurysm of the posterior cerebral artery, with a hemorrhagic cyst in the anterior portion of the occipital lobe. The resection included the midportion of the posterior parietal lobe.

Stereognosis. The appreciation of the form of three dimensional objects by palpation without the aid of vision is termed *stereognosis* or the knowledge of (geometrical) solids. A key, a coin, a pencil may serve as a test object, in which case the "recognition of common objects" is being tested. For exact testing a series of standardized objects or geometrical forms of graded difficulty as employed by Fox (8) is desirable because it allows a rough quantitative statement of ability. Stereognosis is not a "sense" despite the common clinical usage. It is a complex perception or concept based upon the synthesis of several somatic sensations. Touch and kinesthesis perhaps yield the most information but all senses may be involved. For example, the roundness of a cylinder is recognized by the even pressure on the pulp of the fingers when it is rolled, kinesthetic sense giving information on the diameter and weight of the object. It is soon appreciated that the object rolls in one direction but not in the other. As the finger slides along the smooth surface an end is discovered which proves to be a flat smooth surface, the circular border of which confirms the original impression. And when the identical impression is gained from the opposite end, the data are synthesized into the conclusion that the object is a cylinder. Additional data with regard to smoothness and temperature complete the recognition as a metal cylinder. It is not difficult to understand how stereognosis becomes defective when either tactual or kinesthetic sense is blunted, though one in a measure can substitute for the other. But in certain instances, especially after lesions of the posterior parietal lobe, stereognosis seems to be affected out of proportion to the deficit in the basic sensations—so-called pure astereognosis. At some point difficult to define, disturbances of the higher levels of sensation merge into agnosia and aphasia (see Chap. 25).

* The relative difficulty of different numbers and the influence of size, degree of pressure and other factors have not been determined. Nor have regional variations been studied. Therefore no quantitative statement of the deficiency is possible. The affected side is, however, easily compared with the normal side.

REFERENCES

1. ADRIAN, E. D. *The basis of sensation.* London, Christophers, 1928, 122 pp.

2. BAZETT, H. C. Temperature sense in man, pp. 489–501 in: *Temperature: its measurement and control in science and industry.* New York, Reinhold Publishing Corporation, 1941, xiii, 1362 pp.

3. BISHOP, G. H. Responses to electrical stimulation of single sensory units of skin. *J. Neurophysiol.*, 1943, *6*:361–382; The peripheral unit for pain. *Ibid.*, 1944, *7*:71–80; The structural identity of the pain spot in human skin. *Ibid.*, 1944, *7*:185–198.

4. BORING, E. G. *Sensation and perception in the history of experimental psychology.* New York, D. Appleton-Century Co., 1942, xv, 644 pp.

5. BRONK, D. W. The mechanism of sensory end organs. *Res. Publ. Ass. nerv. ment. Dis.*, 1935, *15*:60–82.

6. CATTELL, McK. and HOAGLAND, H. Response of tactile receptors to intermittent stimulation. *J. Physiol.*, 1931, *72*:392–404.

7. DALLENBACH, K. M. The temperature spots and end-organs. *Amer. J. Psychol.*, 1927, *39*:402–427.

8. FOX, J. C., JR. and KLEMPERER, W. W. Vibratory sensibility: a quantitative study of its thresholds in nervous disorders. *Arch. Neurol. Psychiat., Chicago*, 1942, *48*:622–645.

9. GELDARD, F. A. The perception of mechanical vibration. Parts I–IV. *J. gen. Psychol.*, 1940, *22*:243–308.

10. HARDY, J. D. and OPPEL, T. W. Studies in temperature sensation. III. The sensitivity of the body to heat and the spatial summation of the end organ responses. *J. clin. Invest.*, 1937, *16*:533–540.

11. HARDY, J. D., WOLFF, H. G. and GOODELL, H. Studies on pain. A new method for measuring pain threshold: observations on spatial summation of pain. *J. clin. Invest.*, 1940, *19*:649–657.

12. HARTLINE, H. K. and GRAHAM, C. H. Nerve impulses from single receptors in the eye. *J. cell. comp. Physiol.*, 1932, *1*:277–295.

13. JENKINS, W. L. Studies in thermal sensitivity: 12. Part-whole relations in seriatim cold-mapping. *J. exp. Psychol.*, 1939, *25*:373–388.

14. LAIDLAW, R. W. and HAMILTON, M. A. The quantitative measurement of apperception of passive movement. *Bull. neurol. Inst. N. Y.*, 1937, *6*:145–153; A study of thresholds in apperception of passive movement among normal control subjects. *Ibid.*, 1937, *6*:268–273; Thresholds of vibratory sensibility as determined by the pallesthesiometer. A study of sixty normal subjects. *Ibid.*, 1937, *6*:494–503.

15. MATTHEWS, B. H. C. The response of a single end organ. *J. Physiol.*, 1931, *71*:64–110; The response of a muscle spindle during active contraction of a muscle. *Ibid.*, 1931, *72*:153–174; Nerve endings in mammalian muscle. *Ibid.*, 1933, *78*:1–53.

16. MÜLLER, J. *Handbuch der Physiologie des Menschen für Vorlesungen.* Coblenz; J. Holscher, 1834–40, 2 vols. Translated selections in: RAND, B. *The classical psychologists.* Boston, Houghton Mifflin Company, 1912, xxi, 726 pp.

17. PRITCHARD, E. A. B. Cutaneous tactile localization. *Brain*, 1931, *54*:350–371.

18. SHERRINGTON, C. S. *The integrative action of the nervous system.* New Haven, Yale University Press, 1926, xvi, 411 pp.

19. STRUGHOLD, H. and KARBE, M. Vitale Färbung des Auges und experimentelle Untersuchung der gefärbten Nervenelemente. *Z. Biol.*, 1925, *83*:297–308.

20. TOWER, S. S. Unit for sensory reception in cornea, with notes on nerve impulses from sclera, iris and lens. *J. Neurophysiol.*, 1940, *3*:486–500.

21. TOWER, S. S. Pain: definition and properties of the unit for sensory reception. *Res. Publ. Ass. nerv. ment. Dis.*, 1943, *23*:16–43.

22. WEDDELL, G. The pattern of cutaneous innervation in relation to cutaneous sensibility. *J. Anat., Lond.*, 1941, *75*:346–367.

23. WEDDELL, G. The multiple innervation of sensory spots in the skin. *J. Anat., Lond.*, 1941, *75*:441–446.

24. WEITZ, J. Vibratory sensitivity as affected by local anesthesia. *J. exp. Psychol.*, 1939, *25*:48–64.

25. WOOLLARD, H. H., WEDDELL, G. and HARPMAN, J. A. Observations on the neurohistological basis of cutaneous pain. *J. Anat., Lond.*, 1940, *74*:413–440.

26. ZIGLER, M. J., MOORE, E. M. and WILSON, M. T. Comparative accuracy in the localization of cutaneous pressure and pain. *Amer. J. Psychol.*, 1934, *46*:47–58.

CHAPTER 17

NEURAL BASIS OF SOMATIC SENSATION

In the previous chapter the stimuli, the sense organs and the peripheral nerve plexuses for somatic sensation were described; in this the sensory pathways are taken up in functional sequence, beginning with peripheral nerve trunk and ending with thalamus and cortex. At each level pathological or experimental lesions produce characteristic dissociations of sensation. These are of three types: (i) *topographical dissociations*, in which certain regions show abnormal sensitivity whereas others remain normal; (ii) *modality dissociation*, in which one or more kinds of sensation are lost or impaired while others are preserved; and (iii) *dissociations of levels of sensation*, in which the more complex sensory functions are lost and the simpler ones retained.

PERIPHERAL NERVE AND SPINAL ROOTS

Dissociation and Overlap (31). A peripheral nerve field is the area of skin innervated by a given cutaneous nerve. Charts showing the distribution of the major cutaneous nerves are commonly used by neurologists to record the distribution of sensory disturbances in order to determine whether this coincides with a peripheral nerve field. Such charts are somewhat misleading since the fields are shown as contiguous areas, whereas there is usually some overlap between fields, i.e., border areas receive sensory fibers from two adjacent nerves. Interruption of a small cutaneous branch may thus produce little or no area of complete anesthesia. Weddell, Guttmann and Gutmann (32) term the area central to the zone of overlap which is supplied by only one nerve the "autonomous zone." Peripheral nerve section leaves a central or autonomous zone of total anesthesia about which is an intermediate zone of hypesthesia and apparent dissociation. The zone immediately adjacent to the anesthetic zone is sensitive to painful stimuli (18, 33) or possibly to pain and pressure (14, 26), but not to temperature stimuli, to stroking with cotton wool, or to light von Frey hairs. Woollard, Weddell and Harpman (33) novocainized separately two nerve branches supplying contiguous fields on the forearm (medial and lateral cutaneous nerves) and found that the resulting areas of touch anesthesia have a common border, indicating the absence of overlap of touch fibers. On the forearm the margin for pain sensibility extends approximately 1 cm. farther into the anesthetic field beyond that for touch, but on the fingers the margins coincide.

Trotter and Davies (26, 27) state that the boundaries of anesthesia for touch and pain, and for warmth and cold, are virtually identical. The lack of agreement among various investigators probably lies in difference in stimulus intensities used. Certainly in an area in which sensory endings are thinning out, the border obtained will depend on the intensity of the stimulus insofar as the threshold depends on the number of sense organs stimulated. And if stimuli for two modalities are not truly maximal or equivalent, *false dissociations* will result. Thus cotton wool may not be appreciated out to the margins for pain, not because touch fibers stop short but because cotton wool, a weak stimulus, requires a certain density of touch endings to be effective.

In addition to the dissociations, the intermediate zone is characterized by hypesthesia. Examination with graded light pressure stimuli to determine the threshold of sensibility shows not an abrupt but a gradual transition from anesthesia to normal threshold. Perceptual tests, two-point threshold and localization, show a similar gradation in the intermediate zone.

Recovery of sensibility occurs by a circumferential shrinkage of the anesthetic area by progressive extension of the hypesthetic zone into it. The early phase of this shrinkage occurs before regenerating fibers could possibly reach the cutaneous surface; in fact, Weddell, Guttmann and Gutmann (32) demonstrated this shrinkage in the first few days after operation. Pollock (18) believed that this narrowing of the insensible area is due to an ingrowth of fibers from the adjacent peripheral nerve fields and recorded that the recovery is not lost by a second section of the regenerating nerve. Weddell, Guttmann and Gutmann (32) have demonstrated by intravital staining that unmyelinated fibers do grow out from the intermediate zone and that the extent of their penetration as determined histologically coincides with the new sensory boundary. Shortly after nerve section, pain and to some degree touch sensibility are qualitatively altered in the intermediate zone. Although, as mentioned above, it is more difficult to arouse a sensation of pain within the border zone, once the threshold is exceeded the pain has a peculiarly strong and unpleasant quality. This phase passes off, but about the time that sensation returns to the anesthetic area as a consequence of regeneration of the divided nerve, the tendency to abnormal pain responses is again manifest.

Head (11), from the study of sensation in the intermediate zone and during nerve regeneration, propounded the provocative theory of *epicritic* and *protopathic sensibility*. In brief, he believed that certain of the sense modalities were served by two distinct systems of nerve fibers, one for protopathic and one for epicritic sensibility, and that the former alone was to be found in the intermediate zone and was first to regenerate. Critics of the theory of dual innervation hold that density of receptors in the intermediate zone and during regeneration is adequate to explain the status of sensation, and that altered sensitivity of receptors while regenerating may account for the sensory overresponse. This quantitative theory has received much support from anatomical studies of the pattern of cutaneous innervation using the methylene blue technique.

Epicritic and protopathic sensibility (2, 31). Despite almost universal criticism of both the factual basis and the interpretations, the theory of dual innervation put forth by Head has a wide currency in secondary sources. Head's theory is based upon a study of (i) the zones bordering on an area of cutaneous anesthesia consequent to section of a cutaneous nerve; (ii) the return of sensation within the central zone in the course of nerve regeneration; and (iii) regions of special sensitivity, notably the glans penis. Head divided sensation into deep sensibility, served by muscular branches of nerves, and cutaneous sensibility, served by skin nerves. The latter system was divided into two parts, each supposedly subserved by a different system of end-organs and nerve fibers: *protopathic* sensibility, viewed as a primitive system capable of crude sensory responses likely to be unusually pleasant or unpleasant; and the *epicritic* system, more recently and more highly evolved, capable of fine discrimination of intensity and spatial relations. The following tabular summary of the hypothesis is modified from Boring (2).

Tabular Summary of Head's Protopathic-epicritic Hypothesis

	PROTOPATHIC	EPICRITIC
Evolutionary aspect	Phylogenetically old	Phylogenetically recent
Distribution	(i) Intermediate zone following nerve section; (ii) Central zone during regeneration; (iii) Glans penis	Normally innervated skin except glans penis
Rate of regeneration	Early	Late
Touch and pressure	Tingling or formication from stimulation of hairs	Recognition of light touch over hairless skin or shaved skin
Pain	Purely protopathic; excessively painful	Pain not represented
Heat and cold	Above 45° C. and below 20° C. and no adaptation	Discrimination within 40° C.–25° C. range and marked thermal adaptation
Localization	Poor; sensations radiate, are diffuse or remotely referred	Localization accurate; partially inhibits protopathic system, prevents irradiation
Two-point threshold	Poor or nonexistent	Low threshold
Intensity threshold	High but response is overly intense once threshold is exceeded	Low threshold
Intensity discrimination	Coarse gradations only	Fine gradations discernible
Affect	Disagreeable	Relatively neutral; inhibits affective overresponse
Punctiform	Punctiform	Not punctiform
Central connections	Thalamic	Cortical

Others repeating Head's experiments on nerve overlap (2, 14, 18, 26, 27) have confirmed many, though not all, of his observations; but few investigators accept the interpretation in terms of two distinct sets of nerve fibers. One of the main obstacles is that the sharp boundaries between a "protopathic" zone and normal skin described by Head are not found. Rather the intermediate zone is one of graded hypesthesia, and the alternative interpretation is that the supposed protopathic characteristics are simply the response of a relatively thinned-out mosaic of receptors—the quantitative theory. For temperature the thinning-out results in broadening of the neutral zone because the number of fibers stimulated is one factor in determining the threshold (area effects, Chap. 16). Contrary to Head's contention that the appreciation of extremes of temperature is unaffected, discrimination of graded thermal stimuli in the range above and below the neutral zone is much coarser than in normally innervated skin, and again the number of fibers active is believed to be one factor which determines the threshold for intensity discrimination. Absence of light touch in the intermediate zone is confirmed when cotton wool is used for testing; but other investigations (14, 26, 27), using graded and somewhat stronger stimuli, have demonstrated a graded sensitivity to light pressure in this zone. Increase of the two-point threshold and decreased accuracy of localization can also be explained on the basis of a zone of reduced concentration of receptors (see p. 330).

Hyperpathia, a subjective overresponse to painful stimuli, combined with an elevated threshold, occurs from stimulation in the intermediate zone. The cause of this phenomenon is not known. Head ascribed such "hyperpathia" to the activities of the protopathic system of pain, freed from inhibition by the epicritic forms of sensation. However, the phenomenon first appears ten days after nerve section, and persists for about six weeks; moreover, it does not occur at all if the cutaneous nerve is blocked by novocaine. Fibers of the adjoining cutaneous branches probably have an altered sensitivity if they are growing into the anesthetic zone (32) and vasomotor changes may alter the condition of the receptors. But since the change is not a lowering of threshold but a change in the quality of subjective response, the notion that pain sensations and other cutaneous sensory impulses interact centrally is not improbable.

Approximately three months after nerve section, or longer, return of sensation throughout the anesthetic field is first manifest. The subsequent period is characterized by progressive return of sensitivity, which at first is of abnormal quality, but becomes more normal as sensory acuity returns. Pain stimuli produce an especially unpleasant sensation which tends to persist, to radiate and to be poorly localized. Other forms of stimulation may also give rise to abnormally vivid sensations (*intensification*, 27). To Head this meant that his hypothetical protopathic fibers regenerate most quickly, permitting "protopathic" features of sensation to be seen unmasked or uncontrolled by epicritic impulses. The alternative explanation is the same for this phenomenon as for the hyperpathia in the intermediate zone—increased excitability of regenerating neurons, preponderance of un-myelinated fibers, or altered pattern of stimulation. Other protopathic characteristics are accounted for by the low density of innervation. Finally, C fibers regenerate more rapidly than A fibers, and while fibers of the former category cannot be identified with the proto-pathic system, skin innervated by pain fibers alone does give rise to abnormal sensory responses.

In favor of Head's hypothesis of epicritic and protopathic sensation, it may be said that pain as opposed to all other modalities has some, though not all, of the characteristics which Head identifies as protopathic; however, these must not be overemphasized. It may

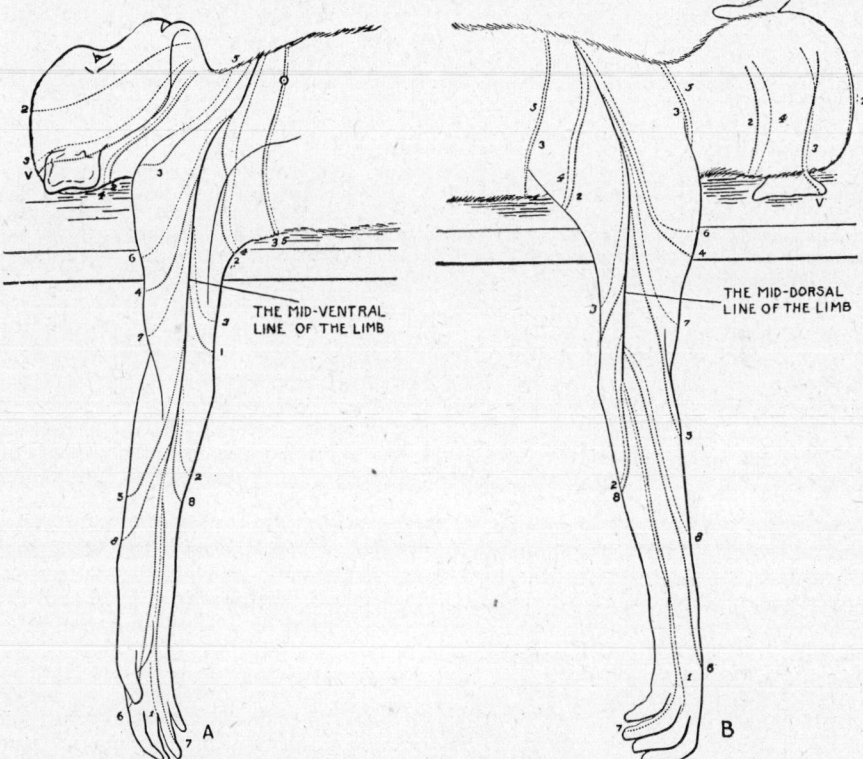

Fig. 178.—The cervical and upper thoracic dermatomes of the macaque monkey determined by the method of "remaining sensibility." V is the trigeminal field; the upper (fine dots) and lower (coarse dots) borders of 8 cervical and 5 thoracic dermatomes are numbered. Note that arm dermatomes overlap extensively with the trigeminal field as they do also with each other. (From Sherrington, *Philos. Trans.*, 1898, *B190*:45–186.)

be argued that the pain mechanism continues to accomplish its biological role by remaining at a low evolutionary level in the following respects: (i) the high threshold for pain serves to signal not minimal contact as does the touch end-organs but contacts sufficiently severe to threaten damage to the skin; (ii) responsiveness to a wide range of stimuli, together with the ubiquitous undifferentiated endings, serves for the protection of skin surface, while specialized end-organs, responsive to only one form of energy and capable of minute gradations of response, serve to give knowledge (gnosis) of the environment; (iii) the feelings of unpleasantness and the protective reflexes resulting from pain stimulation are adaptive in bringing about a prompt withdrawal from and future avoidance of the noxious object, but would be nonadaptive in a modality of sensation serving a gnostic function. However, pain does not have all of the characteristics termed protopathic; in cutaneous surfaces pain is well localized.

Dermatomes. The area of skin supplied with afferent fibers by a single posterior root is a *dermatome*, and because of their importance to clinical neurology the dermatomes of the whole body have been repeatedly mapped. Such charts, which are used in recording the results of a sensory examination, show the dermatomes as contiguous fields. Actually the dermatomes of

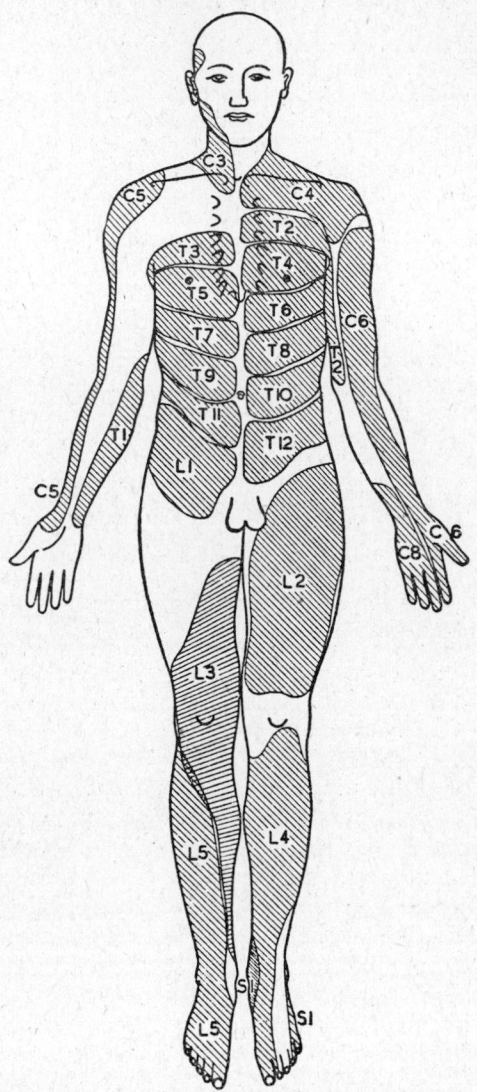

Fig. 179.—The dermatomes of man determined by the method of "remaining sensibility." Half the dermatomes are shown on the left and the remainder on the right in order to display the overlap. (Data of Foerster, *Brain*, 1933, *56*:1–39, redrawn by Lewis, *Pain*, New York, 1942.)

adjacent roots overlap greatly, so that always two and sometimes three roots may supply a single point on the skin. The dermatomes are therefore considerably larger than those shown on most clinical charts (cf. Figs. 178 and 179). The size though not the shape of a dermatome is slightly different for touch, temperature and pain, as tested by the usual procedures, being somewhat smaller for pain than for temperature and smaller for temperature than for touch, which is just the reverse of the dissociation in the border surrounding a peripheral nerve injury. Dermatomes, or *sensory root fields*, must not be confused with peripheral nerve fields. The two are quite different in shape, and often the fibers of one dermatome are conducted to the spinal cord in two different peripheral nerves. Only over the trunk where the primitive segmentation has survived are they the same.

In demarcating the dermatomes it is obviously impossible to section a posterior root and map the resulting area of anesthesia, since, due to overlap, none may be found. Several methods have been employed for mapping dermatomes. (i) The method of *remaining sensibility* was introduced by Sherrington, who sectioned three roots above and three below the intact root to be studied, thus producing an island of sensitivity in a sea of anesthesia; this method has recently been applied by Foerster (6) to clinical patients on whom posterior root sections were performed for the relief of pain. (ii) Herpes zoster ("shingles"), a virus infection of posterior root ganglia which causes an eruption that in classical cases is dermatomal in distribution, was used by Head as one of the first methods of plotting the dermatomes in man. (iii) Strychninization of the root entry zone of the cat causes sensations which are projected to the dermatome of that root (Dusser de Barenne). (iv) Vasodilatation of skin vessels by posterior root stimulation in man automatically maps a dermatome which resembles that of pain (6). (v) Hyperesthesia of skin surface induced by injection of 5 per cent saline solution into the interspinous ligaments is a recently introduced (15) method of dermatomal mapping. (vi) Sympathetic dermatomes have been demarcated by electrical determination of skin resistance following section of ventral nerve roots; there is little overlapping in sympathetic dermatomes and Richter believes that they can be established more accurately than sensory dermatomes as determined by the method of remaining sensibility (see Chap. 10).

The question which the dermatome map answers for skin sensation has been answered for proprioceptive fibers of muscle by Sherrington, who mapped out the roots which supply proprioceptive fibers to each muscle of the limb; deep pain fibers have not been studied in detail. Visceratomes have been studied relatively little in view of their extreme importance, and the pleuratomes and peritoneatomes of the body wall have not yet been mapped, but these presumably resemble the overlying dermatomes.

The dermatomes represent the distorted remnants of what was originally an orderly metameric arrangement that has survived with clarity only in the trunk. There the dermatomes consist of a series of 12 narrow (overlapping) bands running from the vertebral column to the midventral line. The band slopes downwards as it passes around the body to the ventral surface due to the fact that man's front has blossomed while his back has regressed as the result of his upright posture. In the limbs the segmental organization is less clear because a number of metameres have been combined to form the limb. The apparent complexity of the dermatomes is reduced if man is placed in the posture of his forebears as in Figure 180.

The whole of the face and head in front of the line passing through the ear is innervated by the fifth cranial nerve, which bears many resemblances to a spinal nerve. The first spinal segment usually possesses no posterior root; the dermatomes of the remaining seven cervical roots consist of successive bands which pass around the back of the head and neck and give way to more or less triangular shaped dermatomes progressing from the thumb, across the fingers, and up the back of the arm, where the band-like dermatomes of the trunk begin again. The dermatomes of the arms as viewed from the side are "rays" which take origin from a mid-dorsal line, as brought out in Figure 178. Actually the dermatomes, as the name suggests, are not bands but cuts or slices of the arm. This is obvious in the neck and trunk. In the arm a dermatome consists of the skin of a wedge which passes through the arm in the same plane as, but diverging from, the plane established by the mid-dorsal and midventral line of the limb from which the dermatomes take

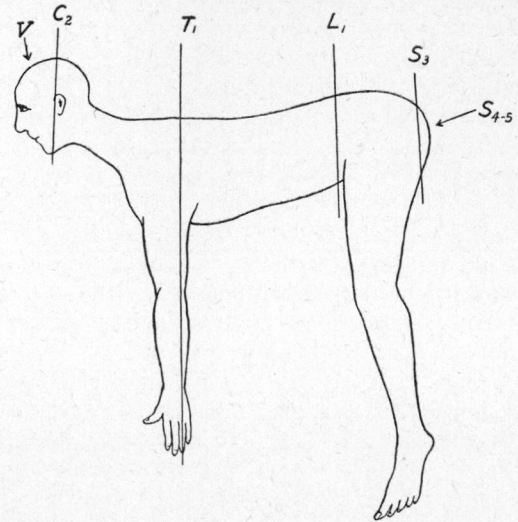

Fig. 180.—Key dermatomal boundaries as they appear on a man in the quadrupedal position The first spinal dermatome is shown as C₂ because the first cervical segment lacks a posterior root. (After Monrad-Krohn, *The clinical examination of the nervous system*, 3rd ed., 1926.)

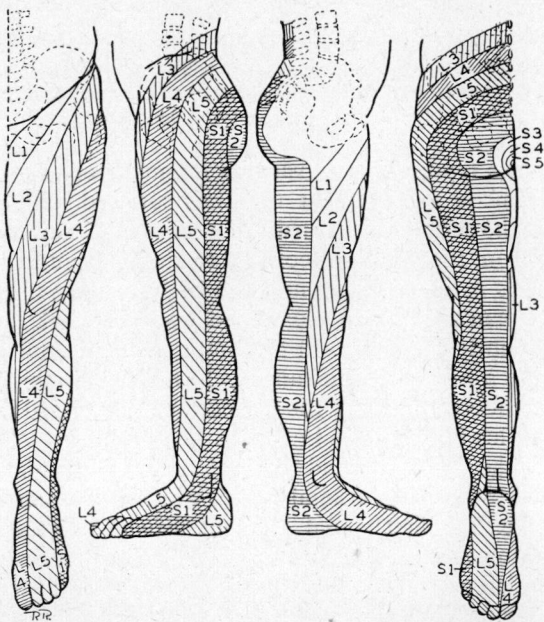

Fig. 181.—Dermatome chart of the lower extremity determined by hypalgesia from single nerve root loss. (From Keegan, *Arch. Neurol. Psychiat.*, Chicago, 1943, *50*:67–83.)

origin. Ignoring overlap, the same dermatome includes the back and the front of the middle finger. Dermatomes anterior to the mid-dorsal and the midventral plane are *pre-axial*, those posterior are *postaxial*.

Figure 180 brings out the fact that the perianal region, which was once ornamented by a tail, and not the foot is innervated by the lowermost (sacral 4–5) posterior roots. Our erect posture should not cause us to forget that this region rather than the foot is the most caudal point of the body. The rationale of the dermatomes is not so clear for the leg as for the trunk and arms, nor are the dermatomes so well worked out. In fact, a revised map of the leg dermatomes has only recently been published (Fig. 181). The dermatomes of the legs resemble those of the arm insofar as the lower sacral segments are slices through the body parallel to the line labeled S_3 in Figure 180. So, too, the upper lumbar dermatomes appear to be slices through the anterior half of the limb which, in accord with the rotation of the lower limb, pursue a somewhat spiral course. However, the intervening dermatomes are shown as stripes appearing on only one surface of the limb. No explanation of these departures from plan has been advanced, and it is possible that the true map of the dermatomes has not yet been made.

The dermatomal pattern is significant in several ways both to clinical medicine and to physiology, namely: (i) in distinguishing peripheral nerve injury from root injury; (ii) in the localization of the level of a spinal cord injury; (iii) in determining the levels for root sections or chordotomy for relief of pain; (iv) in herpes zoster which is often distributed on the skin according to dermatomes; (v) in recognizing the origin of visceral pain which is often referred to a dermatome; and (vi) in the lamination of spinal tracts and in the projection of the body surface upon the cerebral cortex (see below). The dermatome is therefore a part of the fundamental organization of the nervous system, which, despite the complexity of that system, has been retained and becomes a part of the neural organization for the appreciation of spatial relation.

Conduction of Sensory Nerve Impulses (9, 15). A spatial dissociation of sensation results from a pathological interference with the spinal nerves. A temporal dissociation of sensory impulses occurs as a normal physiological phenomenon by virtue of different conduction rates in the fibers making up the nerves. To what degree can conduction rate be associated with the modality of somatic sensation? Fundamental to the consideration of conduction rates is the analysis of sensory nerves with respect to distribution of fiber size or the so-called "fiber spectrum" of the nerve, as described in Chapter 4.

The first great step in disentangling the functional anatomy of the sensory nerve fibers was Sherrington's discovery that the muscle branches contribute to the nerve trunks large numbers of sensory fibers originating in muscles, tendons and joints. The second great step was Ranson's studies (19, 20) which showed that nerves contain large numbers of extremely small unmyelinated fibers.

Ranson's attention was directed to the unmyelinated fibers because his counts of cell bodies in the spinal ganglia were always much greater than the count of nerve fibers in the corresponding posterior roots. He correctly reasoned that the missing fibers must be unmyelinated fibers (first seen by Cajal and Dogiel) which did not appear in the fiber count of the roots stained for myelin sheaths, whereas the cell bodies of these fibers were counted in the silver-stained sections of ganglia. Application of the pyradine silver stain which stains the axis cylinders revealed the picture shown in Figure 182, in which a posterior root in cross section and stained for axons (b) is shown side by side with one stained for sheaths (a). In the former are seen a few very large fibers and more numerous medium to small fibers which can also be identified in the sheath-stained root. But lying in the spaces between large fibers are clusters of extremely fine axis cylinders for which no corresponding myelin rings can be found in the other section. These are the unmyelinated fibers. When they are included in the fiber count, the ratio of cell bodies to fibers comes close to 1:1. Ranson and his coworkers came to the conclusion, largely from histological studies, that fine unmyelinated fibers subserve some form of pain. Their evidence was as follows: (i) unmyelinated fibers are more numerous in cutaneous than in muscular branches, which correlates with greater pain sensitivity of skin than of muscle; (ii) unmyelinated fibers traverse the lateral divisions of the posterior root, ascend and descend 1 to 3 segments in the tract of Lissauer and terminate in relation to the cell bodies forming the substantia gelatinosa Rolandi, thus following the course known from functional studies to be that taken by pain impulses; (iii) Ranson and Billingsley state that section of the fiber of the lateral division at the root entry zone in a cat abolishes struggling and other signs of pain upon stimulation of the posterior root without interfering with other forms of sensation.

Recent studies (20) suggest that the finest of the fibers possessing myelin sheath may be classed with the unmyelinated. The former seem to have increased at the expense of the latter in cranial nerves as opposed to spinal nerves, and in higher as opposed to lower animals. For this reason the whole fiber spectrum in relation to sensation must be considered.

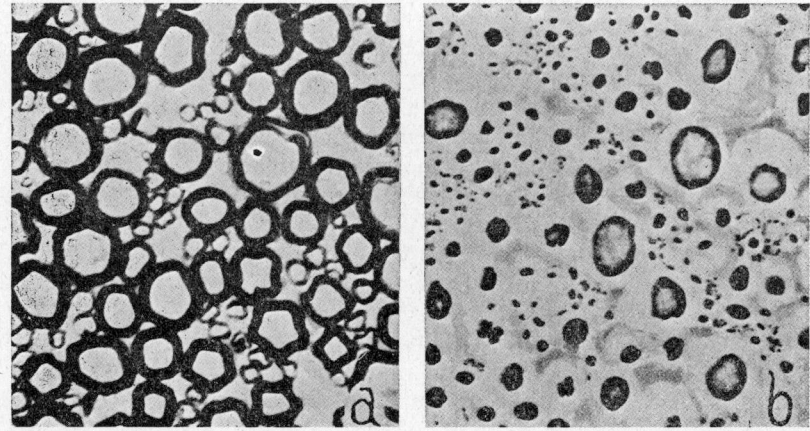

Fig. 182.—A cross section of a posterior spinal root. a, the third sacral root of a dog stained with osmic acid so that the myelin sheaths appear as black rings (×1000); b, the same root prepared with a silver stain (×1400) to show axis cylinders of both myelinated and unmyelinated fibers. (From Davenport and Ranson, *Amer. J. Anat.*, 1931, *49*:193–207.)

It will be recalled from Chapter 4 that the spike potential of a mixed nerve recorded at sufficient distance from the stimulating electrodes separates into a series of elevations corresponding to fiber groups of different conduction velocity. Only fibers belonging to the A and the C groups are concerned with somatic sensation, B consisting of sympathetic preganglionic fibers. The C wave is contributed by fine unmyelinated fibers which are approximately 1μ in diameter and conduct at the rate of 0.5 to 2.0 meters per sec. The A group in turn has been resolved into four principal fiber populations, with progressively slower conduction rate and smaller fiber diameter. The largest A fibers (20–13 μ in diameter) are found only in the muscular branches (Lloyd), so that conduction of cutaneous sensory impulses is carried out by A fibers ranging from 13 μ in diameter down to the smallest A fibers, together with C fibers. The maximal conduction velocity of cutaneous sensory impulses is thus about 80 meters per sec.

The existence of fiber groups with different conducting velocities raised the possibility of direct proof of Ranson's inference that the unmyelinated fibers are concerned with pain. The first step was to demonstrate by the technique described in Chapter 4 that such fibers contributed the C wave of the compound action potential. The slowest fibers of the next most slowly conducting group, δ fibers (B fibers in earlier literature), conduct impulses at 30 to 6 meters per sec. and are clearly separated from C fibers conducting at a rate of 2.0 to 0.5 meters per sec. Evidence that pain reflexes, and therefore presumably pain, are elicited by C impulses was provided by the experiments of Clark, Hughes and Gasser (3). Irregularities of rhythm in pneumographic records of breathing were taken as an index of pain. The saphenous nerve

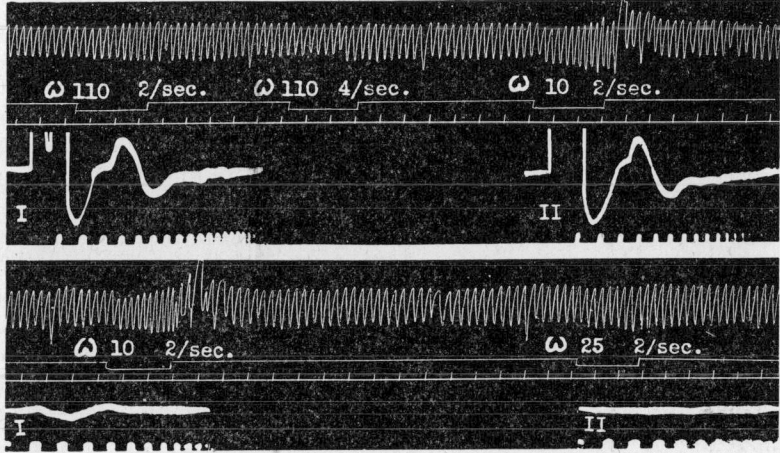

Fig. 183.—Pneumographic tracings of breathing movements and electroneurograms of the cat's saphenous nerve during stimulation ("δ-strength" and "C-strength"). Beginning at the top the tracings are (i) the pneumograph, (ii) duration of stimulation at rate of 2 or 4 per sec., (iii) time for pneumograph tracing in 6 sec. intervals, (iv) superimposed electroneurogram, and (v) its time scale in 1 msec. intervals.

Upper record. I. The electroneurogram of δ-strength (100 ohms in the primary of an induction coil) showing successively the shock artifact, the truncated initial phases of the A-elevation, and the full δ-elevation. II. The same but with less resistance (10 ohms) in the primary. The pneumographic record indicates that fibers affecting breathing rhythm are now excited though no substantial change in the δ-wave is to be noticed.

Lower record. Made later in the same experiment, with a slower time interval (16.6 msec.) to bring out the C-elevation. I. With 10 ohms in the primary circuit definite disturbance of breathing rhythm occurred and a C-elevation appears in the electroneurogram. II. With a weaker stimulus (25 ohms), C-elevation and breathing changes disappear together. (From Clark, Hughes and Gasser, *Amer. J. Physiol.*, 1935, *114*:69–76.)

of the cat, which is purely sensory, apart from sympathetic postganglionic fibers, was stimulated with graded stimuli and the resulting nerve impulses were recorded with a cathode ray oscillograph. Three main experiments were: (i) upon increasing the strength of current in successive stimulation, attainment of C strength was accompanied by a considerable increase in rate and depth of breathing; (ii) by passing the nerve through a small chamber where it was subjected to pressure the fibers of the A group were blocked and only C fibers continued to conduct; stimulation continued to produce blood pressure and respiratory change when C wave only was detectable in the electroneurogram; (iii) the duration of asphyxiation necessary to block all forms of sensation in the human arm except delayed sensation of warmth and sensation of burning pain coincides with duration necessary to block all but C fibers in the cat's saphenous nerve. Similar types of experiments on man and animals by Heinbecker, Bishop and O'Leary suggest that pain is conducted by A-delta fibers (once called B fibers) as well, especially in man. Pain, then, is conducted in unmyelinated fibers and in small myelinated ones.

Double pain response (9, 15). Evidence for the existence of a dual system of pain fibers, a fast and a slow system, comes from several sources: (i) *Psychological*. Several investigators have described under the name of double pain, delayed pain, echo pain, or first and second pain the fact that the sensation of pain from a brief stimulus is often experienced as two pulses or peaks of pain. The existence of a double pain response is easily demonstrated by a transitory (0.3 sec.) contact of the hand or foot with an incandescent light bulb or other hot (60°–65° C.) object. (ii) *Latency studies*. If this phenomenon is due to the existence of a fast and a slow set of pain fibers, it follows that the discontinuity between the two pulses of pain should be greater for stimuli applied to the distal ends of extremities than to the proximal end, because the longer the conduction pathway the greater the lead attained by the fast impulses; such has been found experimentally (Lewis and Pochin, 15). The delays are compatible with the difference between C and delta rates of conduction. (iii) *Cocaine and asphyxial block*. While both kinds of block affect the components of the A wave in the same order (9), C fibers are last to be blocked by asphyxia and first to be blocked by cocaine. Pain is the last sensation to be blocked by asphyxia and the type of pain which is last to disappear is of the delayed type. Cocaine, on the other hand, blocks the slow pain component first. Asphyxial block is produced by a tourniquet or an inflated blood pressure cuff about the arm. Ischemia rather than pressure is the agent which blocks transmission of nerve impulses, and asphyxia is the result of ischemia.

Tabes dorsalis and peripheral neuropathy. It has long been remarked that damage to the posterior roots in neurosyphilis of the spinal cord may result in loss of certain types of sensation with preservation of pain. Such pain is characteristically experienced after a delay of one or two seconds, and is often of a disagreeable character, or hyperpathic. Pochin (17) found that the latencies of the pain response in most tabetic patients and of second pain from normal individuals are approximately the same. Further, the delay in the pain response in the tabetic was about one second for stimulation of the knee but nearly two seconds for stimulation of the toes. This rules out the possibility that delay is due to slowed conduction through the affected stretches of the posterior root fibers since impulses from both sources would be equally slowed. The more probable explanation is that the delta and other fibers of the A group are damaged to a greater extent than are the C fibers. That light touch, position sense and vibratory sensibility are affected early in tabes dorsalis and nutritional neuropathy is explicable on the same grounds —that these impulses travel in fast conducting fibers of the A group.

Dysesthesia. Dissociations of sensation in which pain sensibility is selectively preserved are often associated with a qualitative change in pain, by which its disagreeable character is heightened—the phenomenon of dysesthesia or hyperpathia. Such pain, even more than is normally the case, has the characteristics which Head termed protopathic—diffuseness, inaccuracy of localization, etc. From time to time it is suggested that the unmyelinated C fibers serve protopathic sensibility, or at least a kind of pain different from the more rapid one. However, most observers agree, and one can easily verify this himself, that the quality of the two flashes of pain as elicited from normally innervated skin is similar if not identical, though the second form tends to be more prolonged. Lewis and Pochin (15) state that the two types of pain are equally well localized. Though subtle differences may exist, second pain is certainly not identical with dysesthesia. It is therefore not possible to look to the unmyelinated fibers for an explanation of hyperpathia or dysesthesia, however attractive such a theory may be because it accords with the law of specific nerve energies. Nor is it possible for the unmyelinated fibers to be identified with Head's hypothetical protopathic sensibility. However, some hint of the mechanism of dysesthesia can be found.

An explanation applicable to several of the situations in which hyperalgesia or hyperpathia occurs is that pain responses become especially disagreeable when pain sensibility persists while the other modalities of sensation are blocked or interfered with. This is the dysesthesia of modality dissociation. Head, as noted earlier, called attention to such an instance in the intermediate zone surrounding an anesthetic peripheral nerve field and postulated a central inhibitory interaction between pain and the other modalities of sensation. Lewis and Pochin (15) and Stein, Wortis and Jolliffe (25) have called attention to the dysesthesia following asphyxial or pressure blocks. Both the first and second pain are altered in the direction of increased disagreeableness and the alteration seems to set in exactly at the time when other sensory functions begin to disappear. The latter writers advance the theory that dysesthesia occurs in peripheral neuropathy (i) because of the earlier and more severe disturbance of large fibers carrying touch and temperature impulses (presumably due to their greater metabolic needs), and (ii) because the central response to delta and C fiber impulses is normally "inhibited" centrally by the more rapidly conducted tactual impulses. When the later are blocked the pain responses are no longer inhibited. A possible basis for such central inhibition will be discussed in connection with the thalamus.

The more common explanation of dysesthesia—that it is due to "irritation"—is attractive because it is easy to visualize changes in the peripheral nerves during regeneration, asphyxia, or disease of the nerves which might alter their excitability or cause spontaneous discharge. Such changes unquestionably contribute to *hyperalgesia* and produce spontaneous pain. However, dysesthesia or hyperpathia is a qualitative and subjective, rather than a quantitative, change, and the doctrine of specific nerve energies makes quality dependent on the central apparatus and not on the peripheral fiber or sense organ. Head's inhibitory theory, though without direct proof, has the virtue of making the site of interaction the central terminal portions of the sensory systems.

SENSORY TRACTS OF SPINAL CORD

The conduction pathways of the spinal cord for various kinds of sensory impulses was, and in some respects still is, a rather puzzling affair. Early investigators had to disentangle the fact that there is a posterior and an anterolateral* sensory path, and that one is crossed and the other remains uncrossed until the medulla is reached; they were also handicapped by not appreciating the difference between the gray and the white matter of the cord; and finally, most of their observations were made on animals, and that is a grave handicap in investigating sensory functions. In this field of neurology, as in many others, cases of gunshot wounds in the first World War advanced knowledge greatly. Furthermore, the fact that the anterolateral sensory tract of the spinal cord is often sectioned surgically has provided material for study, but it is a sad commentary on the unscientific state of

* The anterolateral region of the spinal cord (sometimes loosely called the anterolateral columns) contains three tracts, the spinothalamic, spinotectal and spinobulbar.

neurology that in this country not one such case has been studied adequately from the point of view of sensory physiology.

Of the various somatic and visceral modalities of sensation, some are exclusively dependent on the posterior columns, another group is dependent on anterolateral columns, and still others utilize both pathways.

Spinothalamic Tract (7, 29, 30). Impulses conducted in the lateral and ventral spinothalamic tracts subserve the following kinds of sensation:

Partially spinothalamic:

    1. Pressure and touch

Exclusively spinothalamic:

    1. Pain from skin, muscles, tendons, joints and viscera

    2. Warmth

    3. Cold

    4. Sexual and bladder sensations

    5. Tickle, itch, feelings of muscular fatigue.

Head pointed out that there is a regrouping of sensory fibers at the spinal level somewhat different from that at the peripheral nerve level, so that the fibers for cutaneous and deep sensibility are no longer separate. Sensory fibers serving the *same quality* of sensation are sorted out and grouped together. Thus, pain fibers from cutaneous, muscular and visceral nerves are collected together in the anterolateral tract and the muscle sense impulses from the deep branches pass into the posterior columns. Both temperature senses go together. This grouping according to modality may be carried even further. It is usually stated that the ventral tract is concerned with pressure while the lateral tract is concerned with pain and temperature. Foerster (7) believes that pain and the temperature senses are further "sorted out" so that the order from posterior to anterior is temperature, pain, touch-pressure. However, most writers believe this functional organization is far from complete.

Examination of this list shows that all forms of sensation which to a marked degree are either pleasant or unpleasant are found in this list. Pain requires no comment. Warmth and cold tend to be either pleasant or unpleasant. Sensations of the sexual orgasm and the sensory impulses from the genital organs which arouse the libido are spinothalamic. After section of the anterolateral columns, the tip of a vibrating object placed on the skin is felt as a "buzz" but quite without the tickle or itch it ordinarily elicits; the experience is a cold sensory one, devoid of the unpleasant effect. According to Zotterman, "tickle," like pain, is tied up with unmyelinated and small myelinated fibers in the δ and C fibers of the peripheral nerves. This correlation continues to hold in the spinal pathways. Häggqvist states that the spinothalamic tract contains no fibers greater than 10 μ and only 2.3 per cent are larger than 6 μ, whereas in the two portions of the posterior columns 16.7 per cent and 10.5 per cent are larger than 6 μ and some are as large as 15 μ. The fibers of the spinocerebellar tracts are even larger, with almost half of the fibers larger than 6 μ (Fig. 183A).

Another characteristic of spinothalamic sensory impulses is that they signal the state of the tissues, or threats of injury to the skin. For pain this is obvious. Warmth and cold impulses give information about both the environment and the temperature of the skin. It is tempting to call these functions "primitive," but "vital" is probably a better term. By contrast, impulses conducted in the posterior columns give information about the external world and produce relatively neutral sensations, being neither pleasant nor unpleasant.

The degree to which the anterolateral pathways are concerned with pressure and tactile sensibility is not fully known. Also the interesting question whether there is a *qualitative* difference between the touch-pressure sensations served by the anterolateral and by the posterior columns is not fully answered as yet. The older teaching was that the posterior columns and the anterolateral pathways are two equipotent tracts and that loss of either singly produces no tactual defect. Recent observations on human patients in which the anterior columns have been sectioned for the relief of pain minimize the role of the spinothalamic tract in contact sensibility. According to Foerster (7), bilateral section of the anterolateral columns gives rise to no interference with touch and pressure sensibility detectable by ordinary clinical methods. But by the use of exact, quantitative methods, a reduction in the number of touch spots, elevation of the threshold of single touch spots, and a lengthening of the chronaxie can be demonstrated. However, the delicate cotton wool test of touch is not affected. Since the posterior columns are indisputably an important tract for touch and pressure, marked sensory loss from anterolateral lesions would not be expected. Only after interruption of the posterior pathway can the maximum functional capacity of the anterior tract be seen. Such analysis proves that the discriminative and spatial aspects of spinothalamic sensation are poorly developed (see p. 351).

Functional anatomical details. Origin and decussation (23). Each posterior root breaks up into a fan of rootlets which, with other roots, enter the spinal

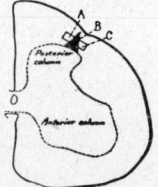

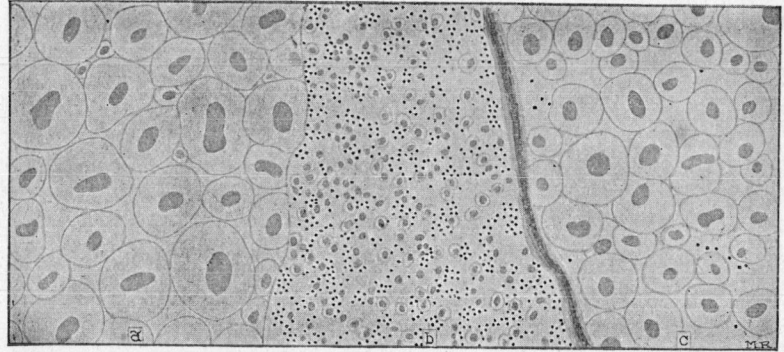

Fig. 183A.—Silver stained cross section through the white matter at the tip of the dorsal horn of the spinal cord (cat), as shown in the insert at the top. *a*, large fibers of the medial division of the dorsal root after entering the fasciculus cuneatus; *b*, unmyelinated and fine myelinated fibers of the lateral division after entering the fasciculus dorsolateralis (Lissauer); *c*, second order fibers of the dorsal spinocerebellar tract. The unmyelinated fibers appear as black dots. (From Ranson, *The anatomy of the nervous system*, 1943.)

cord along the dorsolateral sulcus to form a continuous line of rootlets extending from the sacral to the cervical region. At the point of entry the fibers sort out according to size to form a *medial division* containing the large myelinated fibers which, instead of entering the posterior horn, swing across the tip to enter the posterior columns (Fig. 184). The unmyelinated and small myelinated fibers are grouped into a *lateral division* which swings laterally, and bifurcating, forms the tract of Lissauer (*dorsolateral fasciculus*) at the tip of the posterior horn. This is not a tract in the usual sense of the word, since the fibers ascend only one to three segments before terminating in the substantia gelatinosa Rolandi, a cell column capping the posterior horn which is named for its discoverer and for its homogeneous, finely "granular" or "molecular" appearance under low power magnification. Its appearance is due to the smallness of the cells and the absence of large myelinated fibers traversing it. The difference in diameter of fibers derived from the medial and from the lateral division is dramatically shown in Figure 183A.

According to conventional neuro-anatomy, fibers of the medial division, immediately or after ascending several segments, terminate upon large pericornual cells of the posterior gray horn. The axons of these cells decussate in the ventral gray commissure to ascend in the ventral portion of the antero-lateral column (ventral spinothalamic tract). The lateral division conducts impulses to the substantia gelatinosa Rolandi and second order fibers conduct impulses across the spinal cord and to the thalamus in the lateral spino-thalamic tract. The scheme is probably too rigid; both divisions of the posterior root probably contribute to the lateral and ventral spinothalamic tracts.

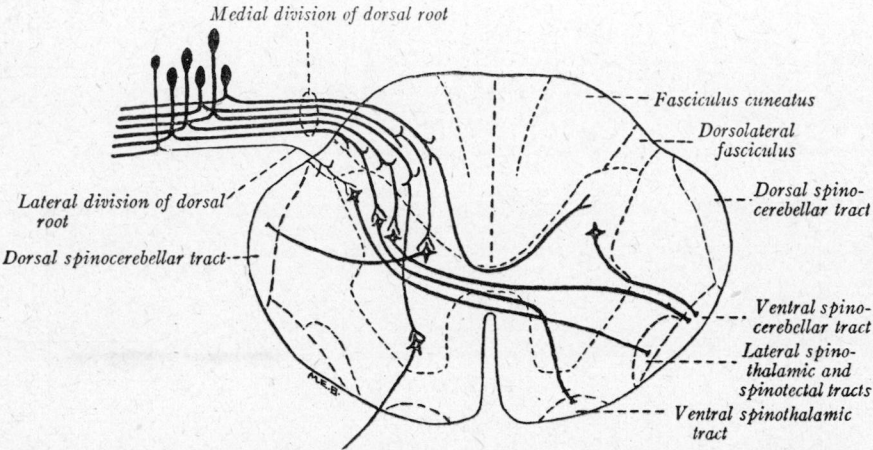

Fig. 184.—Diagram of the cross section of the spinal cord showing the destination of the fibers composing the medial and lateral divisions of the dorsal root and the position of ascending tracts. (From Ranson, *The Anatomy of the nervous system*, 1943.)

The proximity of the anterior gray commissure to the central canal makes the decussating fibers liable to interruption by a widening of the central canal (syringomyelia), producing a clinical syndrome characterized by loss of pain, warmth, and cold sensations on *both* sides of the body at the level of the segments affected. Touch, pressure and deep sensibility are not affected. There is some evidence, though not conclusive, that the fibers for pain cross within the segment of entry, while fibers for warmth and cold cross in three to five segments and those for touch and pressure filter across the cord all the way up to the medulla oblongata. Such an arrangement would result in a lower border for temperature than pain sensibility, which is often found after interruption of the spinothalamic tract. Foerster believes that crossing for all fibers occurs in one or two segments. Possibly some fibers fail to decussate and thus pass up the ipsilateral spinothalamic tract. Foerster and Gagel (7) report that section of the anterolateral column produces retrograde degeneration in large cells of the posterior horn on the ipsilateral side, but since several other tracts are found in the anterolateral columns, this evidence is not crucial for the long sensory tracts. On the other hand, there is evidence of ipsilateral representation of the cutaneous surface in the cerebral cortex.

Lamination. The ascending tracts of the anterolateral region (spinobulbar, spinotectal and spinothalamic) are laminated. This means that the contributions of successive dermatomes form adjacent, more or less distinct, layers or laminae of fibers, and a tract so arranged is said to be "topographically organized." The lamination is in the form of imperfect annular rings with the fibers of most caudal origin lying superficially because the long fibers from sacral segments are pushed outwards by the accretion of fibers at each successive root. Some other influence, perhaps the increasing size of the ventral pyramidal tract which lies near the midline in the ventral column, pushes the longer sacral fibers laterally and dorsally away from the margin of the ventral horn where they originally lay. This results in the arrangement seen in Figure 185.

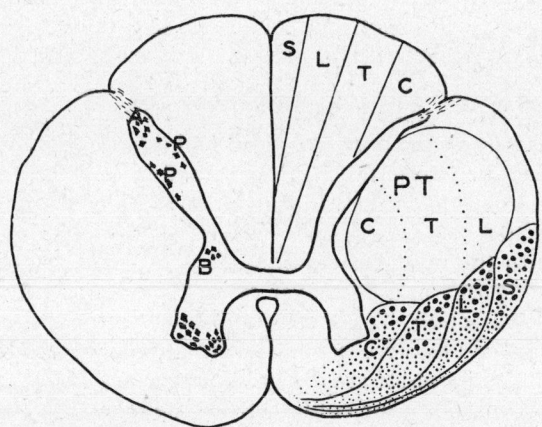

Fig. 185.—Semischematic cross section of the spinal cord in the lower cervical region, showing one conception of the lamination of spinothalamic and other tracts. In the anterolateral column, heavy dots represent fibers concerned with temperature; medium-sized dots, fibers mediating pain; and fine dots, fibers carrying touch and pressure impulses. The abbreviations are: C, cervical; T, thoracic; L, lumbar; S, sacral; PT, pyramidal tract. A, P and B are apical, pericornual and basal groups of large cells of the posterior horn. (From Walker, *Arch. Neurol. Psychiat.*, Chicago, 1940, *43*:284–298.)

The physiological significance of such lamination is that a topographical organization of fibers is preserved, whereby the dermatomes of the body surface may ultimately be projected onto the cortical sensory areas. Clinically, this arrangement explains certain features of the symptomatology produced by spinal cord tumors. Extramedullary tumors, those originating outside of the spinal cord, tend to cause hypalgesia in the caudal segments first, and as the cord is further pressed upon, the sensory border creeps up. On the other hand, intramedullary tumors or a chordotomy which spares the posterior portion of the spinothalamic tracts may leave a characteristic region of intact sensibility in the anogenital region (corresponding to the lowest sacral roots).

Chordotomy. The separation of sensory impulses to travel in the lateral and posterior columns of the spinal cord allows surgical interruption of the pain pathway without producing a disabling anesthesia and ataxia. Such anterolateral chordotomies are often performed for relief of unbearable pain not tractable to medical control. The operation is effective for superficial,

13

deep, and visceral pain, though for the latter, bilateral operations are required. The operation was first carried out in 1911 at the suggestion of Spiller who had earlier (1905) observed complete loss of pain and temperature as a result of a tuberculous lesion restricted to the anterolateral region. The laminae of two or three vertebrae are removed, the dura opened, the spinal cord rotated, and a small knife inserted into the spinal cord just below the dentate ligament and drawn downwards through the anterolateral columns. Despite the fact that the ventral spinocerebellar and various descending motor tracts —vestibulospinal, tectospinal and ventral corticospinal tracts, etc.—are partially sectioned, little motor disturbance is apparent. Bilateral chordotomy rarely interferes permanently with bladder function or with sensations of bladder fullness. These impulses entering the sacral roots may traverse the most posterior portion of the spinothalamic tract (Fig. 185) and hence escape section, or they may travel by way of the posterior columns (White). However, sensations of the sexual orgasm are usually lost.

Posterior Columns. The posterior columns, like the spinothalamic tract, are topographically organized. Two sectors are distinguished. The one lying nearest the midline (column of Goll or fasciculus gracilis) carries fibers from the lumbar and sacral regions which end in the nucleus gracilis of the medulla, while the sector nearest the posterior horn (column of Burdach or fasciculus cuneatus) carries fibers from the arm which end in the cuneate nucleus (Fig. 188). Even finer than this regional localization is a dermatomal localization. By sectioning different posterior roots in a series of animals and tracing the degeneration into the posterior columns, it is found that the fibers from a given root are disposed in a thin layer or an elongated wedge arranged in a postero-anterior direction. The most caudal dermatomes are found closest to the midline, and the more cephalic dermatomes are found in order in passing towards the posterior gray horn. The reason for this is that posterior root fibers enter the posterior column from the side (Fig. 184) so that the fiber contributions from the brachial region push those from the sacral region to the midline. These facts can be summarized as follows:

Midline

Leg ⟶ Lumbosacral posterior roots ⟶ Column of Goll ⟶ N. gracilis
Arm ⟶ Cervical posterior roots ⟶ Column of Burdach ⟶ N. cuneatus
Posterior gray horn

Sensory functions. The sensory impulses conducted in the posterior columns serve the sensory functions listed below. In this tabulation appear not only simple sensations but also processes of a perceptual nature, some of the latter involving more than one modality of posterior column sensibility. A test of each sensory or perceptual function is also given.

   A. Muscle, tendon and joint sensibility (proprioception, kinesthesia)
      1. Passive movement—threshold angular movement for appreciation of movement
      2. Threshold of tension—discrimination of lifted weights
      3. Position of limb in space—finger-to-finger test
   B. Touch and pressure
      1. Light touch—cotton wool
      2. Light pressure—von Frey hairs
      3. Massive pressure—weight discrimination with supported hand

C. Perceptual functions
   1. Topognosis or localization—spot finding test
   2. Two-point discrimination—compass test
   3. Spatial functions—figure writing, length and direction of a line
   4. Appreciation of vibration—tuning fork test or pallesthesiometer
   5. Stereognosis—recognition of common objects by palpation

Characteristic of the sensations served by the posterior columns is that they are gnostic, discriminative, epicritic and spatial. This sensory system gives knowledge of the position of members of the body in space and knowledge of the external world, especially of the objects making up the external world. It does this by making fine discriminations of intensity of pressures, and of the size and texture of objects with which the skin comes into contact. However, intensity, spatial and temporal discriminations are not exclusively the attributes of posterior column sensibility; neither are there fibers serving localization and others for intensity discrimination. These are functions common to all forms of sensation. But the sensory systems of the posterior column are sufficiently elaborate and topographically organized so that they exhibit such functions as localization, resolution of two stimuli, or discrimination of intensity to a very high degree.

Although the spinothalamic tract appears also to conduct some pressure and touch impulses, the role of the spinothalamic tract is relatively insignificant in this respect. Surgical section of it produces no obvious interference with touch and pressure sensibility. On the other hand, what pressure and touch sensibility remains after damage to the posterior columns must be of a very low order since the perceptual functions listed above, with possible exception of localization, are severely impaired by interference with the posterior columns (7), even though the spinothalamic tract is uninterrupted. That the posterior and anterior pathways are of equal significance for touch and pressure, as is often stated, is certainly incorrect. It is not impossible that the anterolateral touch-pressure pathway is to some degree a scientific myth; on the other hand, the following view has considerable support. The spinothalamic tract is phylogenetically old, having developed from the so-called Edinger fibers, a primitive system of fibers found in *Amphioxus*. On the other hand, the posterior column system is absent in *Amphioxus*, fish and amphibia, and appears first in reptiles. Since the forms below the reptiles certainly appreciate contacts, it follows that these functions were originally served by the Edinger fiber system. With the emancipation of the vertebrated animals from the relatively homogeneous fluid environment came the development of a more elaborate sensory system, represented by the posterior columns, capable of fine intensity and spatial discrimination. The degree to which the spinothalamic tract of the primates has retained touch and pressure function is not clear. It is certain that the posterior columns have increased in size progressively throughout the lower vertebrate and primate series, in this respect paralleling the development of the cerebral cortex. Later it will be shown that posterior column sensibility, especially the perceptual functions, are most easily disturbed by damage to the cortex, while certain of the anterolateral forms of sensibility are relatively little affected.

Control of movement. Injury of the posterior columns gives rise to extreme ataxia or inability to regulate the direction, rate, force and extent of voluntary movements. This is to be expected since the posterior columns are an extension of the posterior roots and conduct impulses from muscles destined for both the cerebellum and the sensory areas of the cerebral cortex. Lesions of the cerebellum, or, to a lesser degree, lesions of the parietal lobe, produce ataxia. If the posterior columns are damaged in the *cervical* region, the ataxia (and perhaps certain sensory disturbances) is greater in the arm than the leg. The reason is that many posterior column fibers from the leg have left the posterior columns and after synapse in the Clarke-Stilling or other gray column have entered one of the spinocerebellar tracts and so escape section. For the arm, the fibers destined for the cerebellum as well would be interrupted by a cervical lesion and the degree of ataxia is correspondingly greater.

SENSORY SYSTEMS OF THE BRAIN STEM

At the upper border of the medulla oblongata impulses derived from the fifth and other mixed cranial nerves are added to the ascending sensory systems, and the ascending systems here undergo some rearrangement.

Trigeminal nerve. Pain, temperature and touch-pressure sensibility of the face and buccal cavity, except for a few minor areas, is served by trigeminal neurons. Their cell bodies are located in the semilunar ganglion (Gasserian), and their central processes enter the ventral surface of the pons and make connections with the *main sensory nucleus* located in the pons and with the elongated *spinal nucleus,* which is a continuation of the main nucleus through the medulla, to become continuous with the substantia gelatinosa Rolandi at the second cervical segment of the spinal cord. Second order neurons with cell bodies in the above nuclei decussate and ascend to the thalamus as the ventral secondary afferent tract of the trigeminal nerve; these will be discussed in greater detail in Chapter 18. The spinal nucleus is primarily concerned with pain and temperature and the main nucleus with touch and pressure sensation.

Approximately half of the first order fibers, mostly of large diameter, bifurcate on entering the pons, giving a branch to the main nucleus and a descending branch to the spinal nucleus; but some large fibers ascend to the main nucleus without bifurcation. A few of the fine fibers bifurcate, but the majority turn downward to the spinal nucleus. Pain and temperature impulses pass exclusively by way of the spinal nucleus so that complete thermal anesthesia and analgesia are produced by lesions which destroy the spinal nucleus without damaging the main nucleus. It follows that all fibers ascending to the main nucleus are devoted to touch and pressure. Some of the fibers descending to the spinal nucleus appear to be concerned with touch and pressure (otherwise it is difficult to interpret dichotomizing fibers). Tactual disturbances from lesions of the spinal nucleus are not obvious upon gross examination but can be demonstrated by careful determination of the threshold with graded stimuli (von Frey hairs).

Harrison and Corbin (10) recorded tactual impulses from the spinal tract of the trigeminal nerve, set up by stroking the skin and hair of the face with a camel-hair brush, thus establishing the fact that some tactual impulses are relayed through the spinal nucleus. The rate of conduction (50 M./sec.) was about that of the more rapid fibers in cutaneous spinal nerves. They also confirmed various anatomical studies showing that the topographical order of the three divisions of the trigeminal nerve is "reversed," i.e., the ophthalmic division is inferior and the mandibular components superior in the tract; a cephalocaudal lamination ("onion skin"), often postulated, was not demonstrated. It may be concluded that the trigeminal and spinal sensory systems present the following parallel: that a small and functionally unimportant component of the touch-pressure system pursues the same course as the impulses for pain and temperature. With respect to touch, the pathways traversing the main sensory nucleus are homologous with those traversing the posterior columns to the cuneate and gracilis nucleus.

The homology of the central connections of the trigeminal and spinal nerve is shown in tabular summary (p. 353), which includes the facial, glossopharyngeal and vagus nerves.

The proprioceptive innervation of the striate muscles of the face and the orbit has long been a neurological puzzle. Recent studies suggest that the mesencephalic extension of the trigeminal nucleus contains the cells of origin of afferent fibers passing to the muscles of mastication (which also receive motor fibers from the trigeminal nerve). If so, this is the one known instance

Sensory Connections of Spinal and Cranial Nerves

SPINAL NERVE	TRIGEMINAL NERVE	FACIAL, GLOSSOPHARYNGEAL AND VAGUS NERVES
Lateral division		
Tract of Lissauer	Descending fibers	Tractus solitarius
Substantia gelatinosa Rolandi	Spinal nucleus	Nucleus of tractus solitarius
Spinothalamic tract	Ventral secondary tract	Unknown
Medial division		
Posterior columns	Ascending fibers	
N. gracilis and cuneatus	Main sensory nucleus	
Medial lemniscus	Dorsal secondary tract	

in which cell bodies of afferent neurons are found *within* the substance of the central nervous system. Though proprioceptive end-organs have been demonstrated in eye muscles, the location of cells of origin of the fibers supplying them is unknown.

Trigeminal neuralgia. This consists of paroxysmal attacks of pain projected to the area innervated by one or more divisions of the trigeminal nerve. Vasomotor and secretory disturbances may accompany the pain, and the facial musculature undergoes clonic contractions—hence the common name *tic douloureux.* The area of the skin affected is often hyperesthetic and hyperalgesic, but measurements of threshold indicate a decreased sensitivity, suggesting a central overresponse rather than true hyperesthesia. In instances of severe trigeminal neuralgia the trigeminal neurons may be sectioned surgically, usually central to the ganglion (retrogasserian neurectomy) to avoid regeneration. Though effective, this operation sacrifices touch sensitivity with resulting unpleasant feeling of numbness over the face and keratitic changes in the cornea due to loss of protective pain reflexes. Preservation of touch while abolishing pain is accomplished by section of the spinal tract of the trigeminal root, an operation recently introduced under the name *trigeminal tractotomy* (Sjöqvist).

Spinothalamic tract and medial lemniscus (30). The spinothalamic tract, on entering the medulla, lies just anterior to the nucleus and spinal root of the trigeminal nerve. It is superficially situated throughout the medulla and again, after traversing the pons, is superficially situated in the midbrain. Surgical section for the relief of pain has been carried out at both sites (mesencephalon by Dogliotti and medulla by Schartz and O'Leary). The tract is topographically organized (Walker, 30); in the mesencephalon the lamination is dorsoventral, fibers from the caudal segment lying more dorsal, a tendency noticed in the spinal cord (Fig. 185).

All first order fibers making up the posterior column are synaptically interrupted in the nucleus gracilis and nucleus cuneatus situated in the posterior aspect of the medulla oblongata (at the head of the posterior columns). Second order fibers originating in these nuclei form a compact tract known as the medial lemniscus or fillet. The fibers swing ventrally from the nucleus, encircle the central gray (internal arcuate fibers), decussate, and turn rostrally. The decussation is apparently complete. In their upward course the fibers at first form a band extending dorsoventrally on either side of the midline, and the lamination noticed in the posterior columns is continued. Fibers from the cuneate nucleus (arm) at the level of the upper medulla occupy the most dorsal portion of the medial lemniscus; and in the midbrain, where the lemniscus occupies a more horizontal position, these fibers are the most medial.

All fibers of the medial lemniscus are interrupted by a synapse in the thalamus and continue as third order fibers to the cerebral cortex.

THALAMUS AND CEREBRAL CORTEX

Thalamus (4, 8, 28). All sensory tracts except the olfactory are interrupted by a synapse in the optic thalamus of the diencephalon before continuing to the cerebral cortex. The original belief of Galen that the thalamus is connected exclusively with the optic nerve (hence the name *optic* thalamus) has proved inapt; it is a relay station for somatic and visceral sensory impulses as well as for visual and auditory ones. In fact, the tendency is now to drop the modifier and use the word "thalamus" loosely to mean the nuclei other than those concerned with vision and audition. Knowledge of the thalamus is largely owed to anatomical studies, which have been greatly advanced in recent years, especially with respect to the thalamocortical projections. This

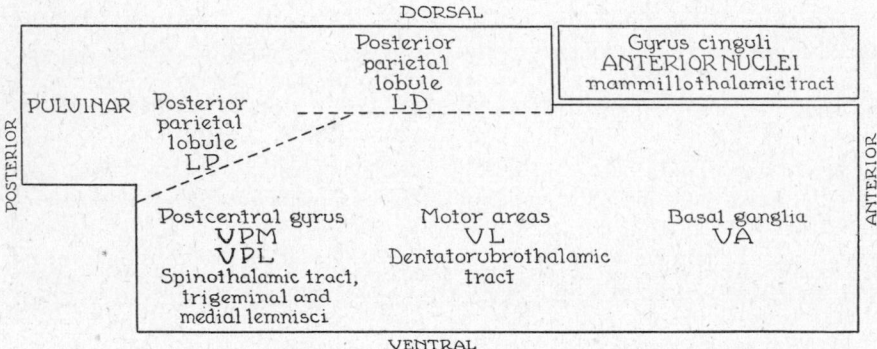

Fig. 186.—The lateral nuclear mass of the macaque thalamus in schematic parasagittal section. Abbreviations of nuclei as in Figure 187. Above the abbreviation is given the cortical projection of the nucleus; below, the afferent connection. (Data from Walker, *The primate thalamus*, 1938, and after Ranson, *The anatomy of the nervous system*, 1943.)

relation of thalamus to cortex is, of course, the central problem, and modern tendency is to consider thalamus and cortex as a single functional unit.

In 1932 Polyak published a monograph on the thalamocortical projection systems which was definitive insofar as Marchi studies are concerned. In a series of monkeys, lesions were made in the radiations to the cerebral cortex close to where they issue from the thalamus in order to cause the axons of thalamocortical fibers to degenerate. The destination in the cerebral cortex of the degenerating axons was then studied by the Marchi method which stains the fat droplets of the disintegrating myelin sheaths. Polyak suggested to A. E. Walker a reinvestigation of the projections by an entirely different procedure, one which has been applied to the same problem with great success by Le Gros Clark (4) in England. Section of axons in certain, though not all, situations in the nervous system causes changes in the cell body—chromatolysis, eccentric placement of the nucleus, and blurring of the cell outline—first stained and described by Nissl. Whereas this process is reversible in most situations and hence is a retrograde degenerative reaction, in the thalamocortical neurons it goes on to degeneration, disappearance and gliosis. By making lesions in the cerebral cortex of the monkey in accordance with cytoarchitectural areas and determining in which nuclei retrograde degenerative changes occur as a result of truncating their cortically directed axons, one link in the sensory chain is supplied. Tracing the great ascending sensory systems into the thalamus by the Marchi method completes the knowledge of the pathway. Finally, this method has led to a parcellation and naming of the nuclear masses of the thalamus differing somewhat from the conventional one, which is purely cytological and takes no account of connections.

The thalamus is a large oval mass lying along the wall of the third ventricle and the floor of the lateral ventricle. Internally the thalamus is divided into three parts by a vertical sheath of white matter known as the internal medullary lamina, a lateral and a medial nuclear mass, and an anterior mass enclosed by a bifurcation of the lamina. The lateral mass is for purposes of nomenclature divided into a lateral and a ventral portion (see Figs. 186 and 187). The following grouping of thalamic nuclei respects morphological, cytological and functional considerations; only the more important nuclei are mentioned.

I. *Anterior nuclei.* Enclosed by internal medullary lamina, they receive fibers from the mammillothalamic tract and project to the gyrus cinguli.
II. *Nuclei of the midline.* These are clusters of cells lying along the walls of the third ventricle which have hypothalamic connections.
III. *Medial nuclei.* They lie within or medial to the internal medullary lamina.
    i. Medialis dorsalis is a large nucleus which projects to the hypothalamus and the prefrontal lobe.
    ii. Centrum medianum (centre médian of Luys) has no cortical connections.
    iii. Intralaminar nuclei.
IV. *Lateral nuclear mass.*
    i. N. ventralis anterior, the anterior portion of the ventral mass, is connected with the basal ganglia.
    ii. N. ventralis lateralis, somewhat misnamed since it consists of the anterior half of the lateral mass exclusive of the preceding nucleus, is an important nucleus which receives fibers from superior cerebellar peduncle and projects to the motor areas.
    iii. N. lateralis dorsalis et posterior, of which the lateral posterior is the larger, occupy the superior portion of the posterior part of the lateral mass. They project to the posterior parietal lobule.
    iv. N. ventralis posterior (the posteroventral nucleus) lies inferior to the preceding nuclei and occupies the ventral part of the posterior half of the lateral mass. This nucleus is further divided into the medial portion (arcuate) and a lateral portion, N. ventralis posterolateralis. They project to the postcentral gyrus.
V. *Posterior nuclei.* These lie posterior to the ventral and lateral nuclei and medial to the internal medullary lamina.
    i. Nucleus pulvinaris, a large posterior outgrowth of N. lateralis posterior, projects to the parietal association area.
    ii. Corpus geniculatum laterale, a prominent laminated nucleus which receives the fibers of the optic tract and projects to the visual area of the occipital lobe.
    iii. Corpus geniculatum medialis lies inferior and medial, and projects to the auditory area of the temporal lobe.

Physiologically the above nuclei can be classified on the basis of their connections as follows:

Nuclei with subcortical connections are the nuclei which do not project to any portion of the cerebral cortex. Thus, if a monkey is subjected to hemidecortication, these nuclei alone remain undegenerated and to them must be accredited such sensory functions that exist after complete decortication. In view of the extensive ability for independent function often ascribed to the thalamus, the purely subcortical nuclei seem surprisingly small. They consist chiefly of (i) the nuclei of the midline or paleothalamus which appear to have hypothalamic and tegmental connections; (ii) intralaminar nuclei which are small and the centre médian, a long nucleus which has developed in the phylogenetic series and perhaps serves an intrathalamic association function; and (iii) the anterior ventral nucleus, which appears to receive fibers from the globus pallidus.

Cortical relay nuclei are those which possess a definite afferent input and project to the cerebral cortex in or close to a known sensory area. The lateral and medial geniculate bodies are classic examples of relay nuclei, as is the posteroventral nucleus. The latter receives fibers from the trigeminal and medial lemnisci and the spinothalamic tract and projects to the postcentral gyrus, especially the portion forming the posterior wall of the central fissure. It is highly organized topographically and is the most direct pathway to the cortex because it is interrupted by only one thalamic synapse.

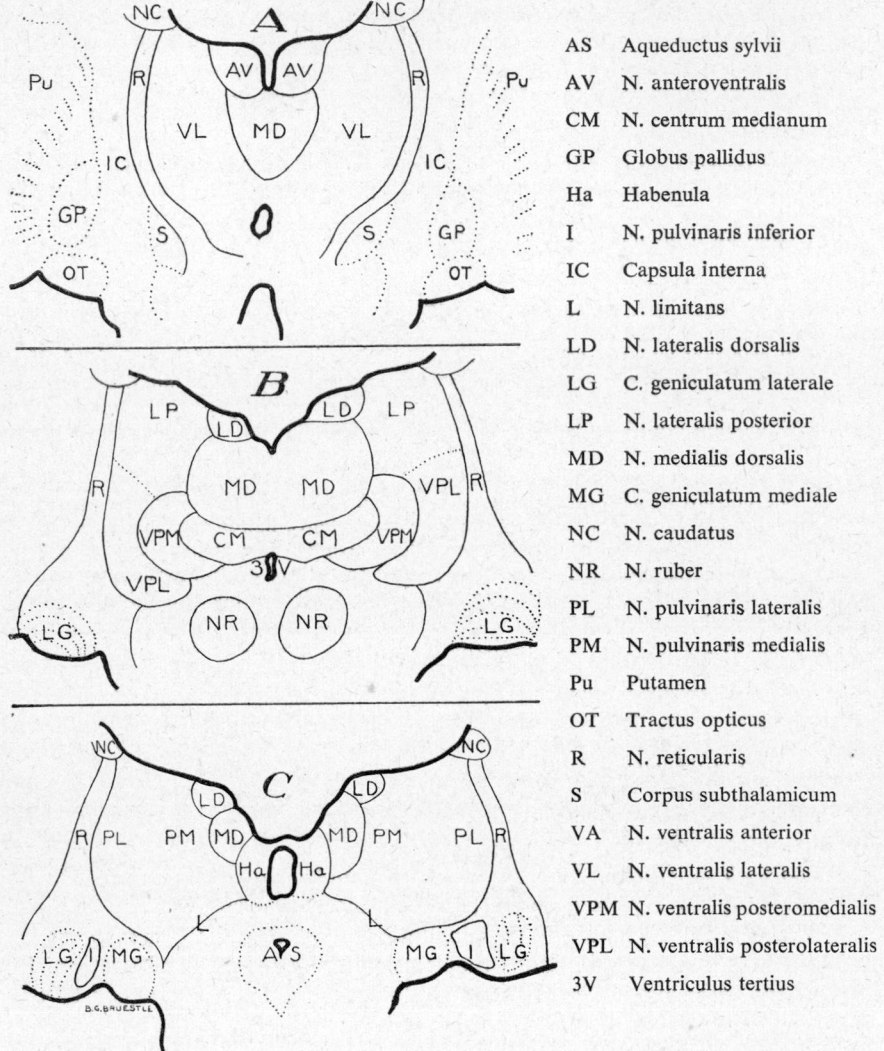

AS	Aqueductus sylvii
AV	N. anteroventralis
CM	N. centrum medianum
GP	Globus pallidus
Ha	Habenula
I	N. pulvinaris inferior
IC	Capsula interna
L	N. limitans
LD	N. lateralis dorsalis
LG	C. geniculatum laterale
LP	N. lateralis posterior
MD	N. medialis dorsalis
MG	C. geniculatum mediale
NC	N. caudatus
NR	N. ruber
PL	N. pulvinaris lateralis
PM	N. pulvinaris medialis
Pu	Putamen
OT	Tractus opticus
R	N. reticularis
S	Corpus subthalamicum
VA	N. ventralis anterior
VL	N. ventralis lateralis
VPM	N. ventralis posteromedialis
VPL	N. ventralis posterolateralis
3V	Ventriculus tertius

Fig. 187.—Cross section of chimpanzee thalamus at three levels. *A*, anterior thalamus. *B*, mid-thalamus. *C*, posterior thalamus. (From Fulton, *Physiology of the nervous system*, 1943.)

The lateroventral nucleus relays to the motor areas (4 and 6) impulses which are derived from the dentate nucleus via the superior cerebellar peduncle. In view of the well developed sensory input to the cerebellum represented by the spinocerebellar tracts, the projections of the lateroventral system place the motor areas in potential communication with proprioceptive sense organs of the body. Finally, the anterior group are relay nuclei since they receive a definite bundle of fibers from the mammillary bodies and project to the cingular gyrus and paracentral lobule.

Association nuclei receive no considerable number of impulses directly from the ascending sensory systems but only indirectly via the relay nuclei. They project to the so-called association areas, notably those of the prefrontal lobe (dorsomedial), the posterior parietal lobe (dorsolateral and posterolateral), and to the common ground between the sensory areas of the parietal, occipital and temporal lobes (pulvinar) though not to the temporal lobe proper, which has no known thalamic projection apart from that to the auditory area. Like the areas to which they project, these nuclei have steadily increased in size throughout the primate series.

Functional Organization of Thalamocortical Projections. The main function of the thalamus is clearly to relay impulses to the cerebral cortex. On the other hand, the association nuclei, superimposed, as it were, on the relay nuclei, have no raison d'être unless in some manner they integrate impulses before relaying them to the cortex. But the final expression of the activity of the association nuclei comes through the cerebral cortex, and they degenerate like relay nuclei after cortical lesions. Therefore the role of the thalamus in sensation cannot be gauged from observations on decorticate animals. Lastly, the two levels are connected by an elaborate system of corticothalamic fibers. The rule appears to be that the thalamic nucleus which projects to a given cortical area receives corticothalamic projection fibers from that same, or at least an adjacent, cortical area. Thus there is formed a potential circuit between thalamus and cortex with the potentialities of interplay between them (5). Cortical and thalamic functions are therefore inseparable and the ability of the thalamus to function independently after destruction of the cerebral cortex is subordinate to the question of the thalamocortical sensory function.

Somatic sensory impulses from the body traverse the brain stem, grouped into two tracts bearing different modalities, as in the spinal cord. But the spinothalamic tract and the medial lemniscus terminate in the thalamus in such a way that this grouping by modality is largely obliterated. Both tracts partially interdigitate and terminate in the posteroventral nucleus. Within this nucleus there is at most only a slight localization, with the spinothalamic tract ending somewhat more posteriorly. Therefore the dissociations of modalities so conspicuous in lesions of the spinal cord cannot be expected, and do not occur from lesions at the level of the thalamus.

Topographical Organization. Quite otherwise is the fate of the topographical organization of the ascending sensory systems manifested at the spinal and brain stem level by a dermatomal lamination. This organization is preserved. The ventral secondary trigeminal tract carrying impulses from the cutaneous and mucous surfaces of the head terminates in the most *medial* portion of the posteroventral nucleus (arcuate nucleus); the medial lemniscus and the spinothalamic tract carrying impulses from the trunk and limbs give no fibers to this portion of the posteroventral nucleus. The latter two tracts terminate in the *lateral* portion of the posteroventral nucleus. An even finer topographical organization has been demonstrated. Marchi degeneration in the fibers of the medial lemniscus following destruction of the nucleus gracilis, which receives fibers from the leg, can be traced to the extreme lateral portion of the posteroventral nucleus bordering on the internal capsule, while fibers from the nucleus cuneatus (arm) lie intermediate between this region and the arcuate nucleus. The reason for the termination of the leg fibers more laterally is evident if one recalls that the medial lemniscus decussates, and thereby reverses the side-to-side relationship (Fig. 188). To maintain the medial to lateral relationship unchanged, it would be necessary for the arm and leg fibers to decussate with each other.

The topographical organization manifested in the termination of sensory systems in the thalamus is preserved in the thalamocortical projections (Fig. 189). Fibers from the medially situated arcuate nucleus terminate in the inferior or lateral end of the postcentral gyrus, while those from the lateral end (leg) of the nucleus ventralis posterior terminate near the midline; those for the arm are intermediate in both thalamus and cortex. It will be noted that the side-to-side relationship is opposite in the thalamus and cortex. However, the order of projection of somatosensory impulses is the same as the order of representation of the musculature in the precentral gyrus. Thus, insofar as anatomy can discover, the body surface is projected upon the

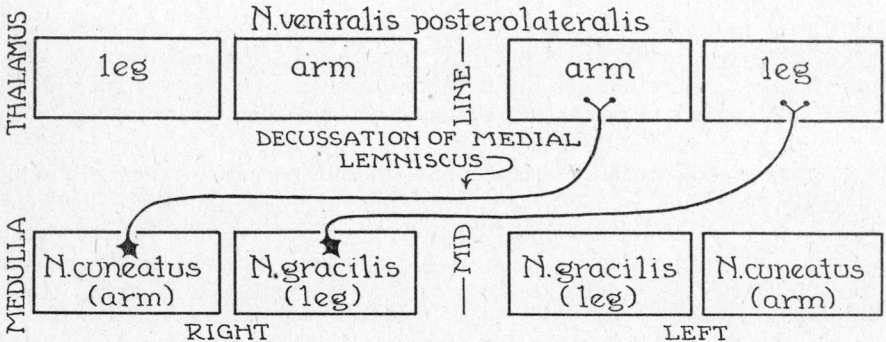

Fig. 188.—Diagram illustrating the topographical relationship of fibers from the right nucleus cuneatus (arm) and gracilis (leg) as affected by the decussation of the medial lemniscus. Note that in crossing the neural axis the side-to-side relationship of the fibers from arm and leg within each half of the lemniscus is reversed. Fibers passing from the left half of the medulla to the right thalamus are not shown.

postcentral gyrus, with spatial relations preserved, much as a lantern slide is projected upon a screen. This point-to-point relationship is unquestionably of significance in the localization of stimuli, in distinguishing two points from one, and in other functions having a strong spatial element. The degree to which the thalamocortical projection systems to areas 4 and 6 and to areas 5 and 7 are spatially organized is not certain and is not easy to discover.

Ipsilateral character of the projections. All anatomical information agrees that the whole of the cortical projection from one half of the thalamus passes to the ipsilateral cerebral cortex; none of it crosses in the corpus callosum to the opposite cortex. The retrograde degeneration produced by cortical lesions is confined to the thalamus of the same side as the lesion. Any representation of one lateral half of the body surface in the ipsilateral cortex must then come about by virtue of failure of some fibers to decussate at levels below the thalamus or by a double decussation, at a spinal and brain stem level, which is not improbable in a system of fibers made up of chains of neurons.

Density and extent of cortical projections. The extent of the cerebral cortex involved in somatosensory function has never been settled. A *potential somatosensory area*, as delineated anatomically, may be defined as that region which receives projection fibers from the thalamus exclusive of the geniculate bodies. It includes the whole of the prefrontal lobes, the motor areas, and the whole of the parietal lobe. Some of these projections originate in relay nuclei, others in association nuclei, and some in nuclei connected with the cerebellum, so that the areas are certainly not equivalent, but they all are potentially sensory in function in the broadest sense. The projections to various cortical regions are likewise not equivalent in density, as shown in Figure 190. The floor and posterior wall of the central fissure is a region of great density of projection which thins out markedly in passing posteriorly; but in view of the area represented by the posterior parietal lobule, the total

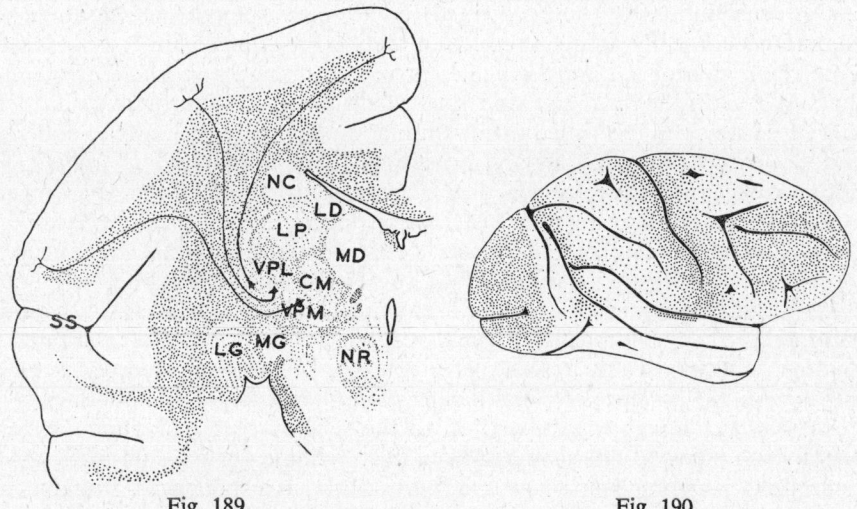

Fig. 189.   Fig. 190.

Fig. 189.—Schematic frontal section through the thalamus and the postcentral gyrus of the cerebral cortex to show the topographical arrangement of the projection fibers from the postero-ventral nuclei. Nucleus ventralis posteromedialis (VPM) projects to the inferior end of the post-central gyrus near the sylvian fissure (SS), whereas nucleus ventralis posterolateralis (VPL) projects to the middle and superior thirds of the postcentral gyrus. For other abbreviations see Figure 187. (From Walker, *The primate thalamus*, 1938.)

Fig. 190.—The cerebral cortex of the macaque, showing the extent and relative density of the thalamocortical projections. (From Walker, *The primate thalamus*, 1938.)

number of fibers to this region is considerable. Certainly the nuclear masses projecting to this region are of considerable size. The anterior wall of the central fissure is likewise a region of great density of projection, rivaling that of the posterior wall. The concentration of fibers thins out rapidly in passing towards the anterior border of area 6. The prefrontal area, including its orbital surface, receives quite a dense projection, and the dorsomedial nucleus which furnishes these fibers is prominent throughout nearly the whole length of the thalamus.

Cortical Localization of Sensory Functions. At the cortical level, as at lower levels, localization of function has two aspects—first, whether and how the body surface is represented in the cortex, and second, whether different modalities of sensation or levels of sensation are separately localized. Related to the first is the question of the extent of the sensory cortex. The same experiment usually yields some information on both scores.

Electrical stimulation. It is paradoxical that the first experimental studies of the cortical localization of somatic sensations to yield concrete results were on man and involved electrical stimulation of the cerebral cortex in a conscious patient through a wound in the skull. This was first done in 1874 by Bartholow, just three years after Fritsch and Hitzig discovered the electric excitability of the motor cortex. The technique of the osteoplastic bone flap performed under local anesthesia presented to the neurosurgeon a wide expanse of cortex for stimulation, and such observations have been made by Cushing (1909), and recently by Foerster and by Penfield and Boldrey. Stimulation of the postcentral gyrus near the midline gives rise to sensations which seem to come from the foot, while stimulation near the sylvian fissure causes sensations which are projected to the face. Though the sensation is elaborated cortically at the site of stimulation, it is interpreted as coming from the region of the body which is projected upon that cortical area (see the *law of projection*). The second fact which emerges from these studies is that sensations can be elicited from stimulation of the motor areas (4 and 6), and, according to some, they are indistinguishable in quality and frequency of occurrence from the responses of the classic sensory area of the postcentral gyrus. The map showing the distribution of responses forms a striking parallel with the map of the density of thalamocortical projection fibers, though the sensory excitable area falls somewhat short both anteriorly and posteriorly. Sensations of the spinothalamic category—pain, warmth and cold—were rarely reported, the usual response being a sense of numbness, tingling, and especially a sense of movement unaccompanied by actual movement. No evidence of zonal localization of modalities was obtained.

Strychnine stimulation. Application to the sensory cortex of a monkey or cat of small pieces of filter paper soaked in strychnine produces unmistakable signs that a spontaneous sensation (paresthesia) is experienced and that a portion of the body surface is made abnormally sensitive to touches (hyperesthesia) and painful stimulation (hyperalgesia). The animal actively licks, bites, or scratches some portion of his body, indicating that the centrally aroused sensation is projected to the body surface. By correlating the points on skin and cortex in successive experiments, a map such as shown in Figure 191 results.

The following features are notable: (i) the responsive area corresponds accurately with that receiving projection fibers apart from the prefrontal lobe; (ii) no difference in symptomatology was observed from strychninization of pre- and postcentral areas; (iii) there was an evident regional (leg, arm, head) localization but not a dermatomal one; (iv) the boundary lines between zones were sharp to within a few millimeters; (v) hyperexcitability upon cutaneous stimulation was evident from both sides of the body, but upon deep stimulation it was manifested only on the side contralateral to the cortex stimulated; (vi) stimulation of a single point within the representation of one limb causes electrical activity throughout nearly the whole of the cortical area for that limb and of the thalamus as well, but not in other cortical subareas. Because the thalamus is also involved, strychnine experiments must not be closely interpreted, especially with respect to the kind of sensations resulting. As Dusser de Barenne pointed out, "Strychnine, in bringing about the maximum of sensory functions, blurs finer functional differentiation."

Electrical activity of the sensory cortex (1, 34). The anatomical and physiological methods of mapping the projection of the body surface upon the postcentral gyrus so far described yields maps only in terms of regions—head, arm, leg. Recording of action currents (Woolsey, Marshall and Bard, 34) from the cerebral cortex in response to cutaneous stimulation reveals a detailed *dermatomal* projection. Intermittent tactual stimulations were applied to the skin by means of a small camel-hair brush or a stiff hair mounted on a vibrating lever. The head of the monkey was mounted in a Horsley-Clarke apparatus bearing a wick electrode, which was moved systematically over the cortex, generally in steps of one millimeter through successive bands of cortex. For each cortical point a large number of cutaneous spots were examined and the depths of fissures were exposed when necessary by removal of the opposite wall of the fissure. Maximal potentials in response to stimulation were recorded only from those areas known to receive projection fibers from the posteroventral nucleus, namely, cytoarchitectural areas 3-1-2. Only small potentials without clear topographical localization were recorded from areas 5 and 7 or from areas 4 and 6. This is in accord with the extrasynapses traversed by sensory impulses passing to these regions as opposed

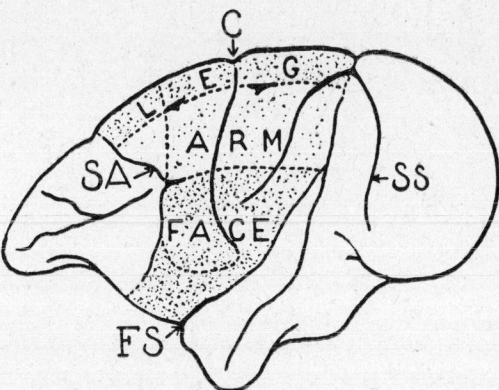

Fig. 191.—Map of the somatosensory cortex in the macaque as outlined by the method of strychnine stimulation. The abbreviations used are: C., central fissure; FS., sylvian fissure; SA., arcuate sulcus; and SS., simian sulcus (external parieto-occipital sulcus). (After Dusser de Barenne, *Proc. roy. Soc.*, 1924, *B96*:272–291.)

to the more direct path to the postcentral gyrus. Electrical responses were confined to the contralateral cortex except for stimulation of the face, which gave rise to ipsilateral cortical responses as well.

The main conclusion reached from these experiments was that "the parts of contralateral body surface are represented in an orderly sequence. In the case of the lower extremity this sequence clearly reflects the metameric origin of the dermatomes; the arrangement is in the order of spinal innervation, not in the order—hip, thigh, knee, leg, ankle, foot, toes." Thus the order may be termed dermatomal or metameric as opposed to regional, the term segmental being ambiguous. For the leg the order of representation ascends the postaxial surface of the leg, across the toes from small toe to hallux and up to the preaxial surface of the leg to the trunk. The dermatomes are represented by overlapping bands of various widths which parallel one another and are arranged roughly at right angles to the central fissure. The serial order of these dermatomes is shown by a reconstruction diagram in Figure 192. For Th_1 to Caudal 4 the order is the same in cerebral cortex as in spinal cord. However, the cervical dermatomes appear to be reversed *en bloc* so that the cortical field for the upper cervical nerve which supplies the occiput and neck is contiguous with the cortical fields for the postaxial surface of the arm (Th_1 and Th_2). The cause of this reversal is unknown but the fact of the reversal probably explains the sharpness of lines separating face, arm and leg area in strychnine experiments. Another fact apparent in this diagram is that the extent of cortical area devoted to a given region parallels the tactual acuity and innervation density of the areas. Thus a wider strip is devoted to the distal than to the proximal portion of limbs or to the trunk dermatomes. Th_{1-12}, representing an extensive skin area, are compressed into a strip of

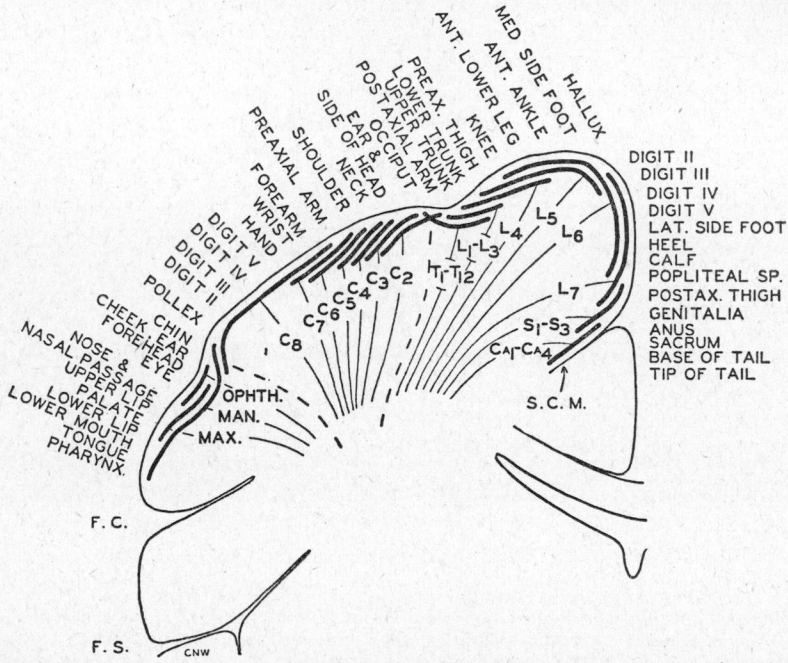

Fig. 192.—Schematic section through the postcentral gyrus, showing the projection of dermatomes as reconstructed from correlating point of stimulation on body surface with point of maximum electrical activity on cerebral cortex. Abbreviations used are: F.S., sylvian fissure; F.C., central fissure; S.C.M., callosomarginal sulcus; MAX., maxillary division of the trigeminal nerve; MAN., mandibular; OPHTH., ophthalmic; C., cervical; T., thoracic; L., lumbar; S., sacral; Ca., caudal. (From Woolsey, Marshall and Bard, *Johns Hopk. Hosp. Bull.*, 1942, 70:399–441.)

cortex only 2.5 mm. wide. On the other hand, the dermatome for C_8, which in the monkey centers on the thumb and forefinger, is extremely large. In the large number of sense organs and cortical neurons devoted to the relatively small skin areas of thumb and fingers lies the explanation for the low two-point threshold and the small error of localization for stimuli in those regions. And in general the orderly dermatomal and presumably point-to-point representation of the body surface on the cortex constitutes the neural substrate on which the spatial aspects of sensation are built.

Ablation experiments (1, 16, 22). Such experiments have not the same value in investigating sensations, which are subjective and not directly observable, as in the study of cortical motor representation. However, in special instances the sensory status can be safely inferred from overt behavior. Two such methods applied successfully in recent years to the primates are the hopping and placing reactions (Rademaker-Bard reactions) and the discrimination techniques (Chap. 16). The former tests the spatial aspects of sensation, for in the placing reaction the direction the limb moves depends on which aspect of the foot is brought into contact with a solid surface. In the hopping reactions the direction of the hopping depends on just which muscle groups are subjected to tension in translocating the animal in different directions. The discrimination technique, as applied to the study of the primate cortex, has employed weights and roughness. The discrimination of weight is an intensity discrimination with no spatial element.

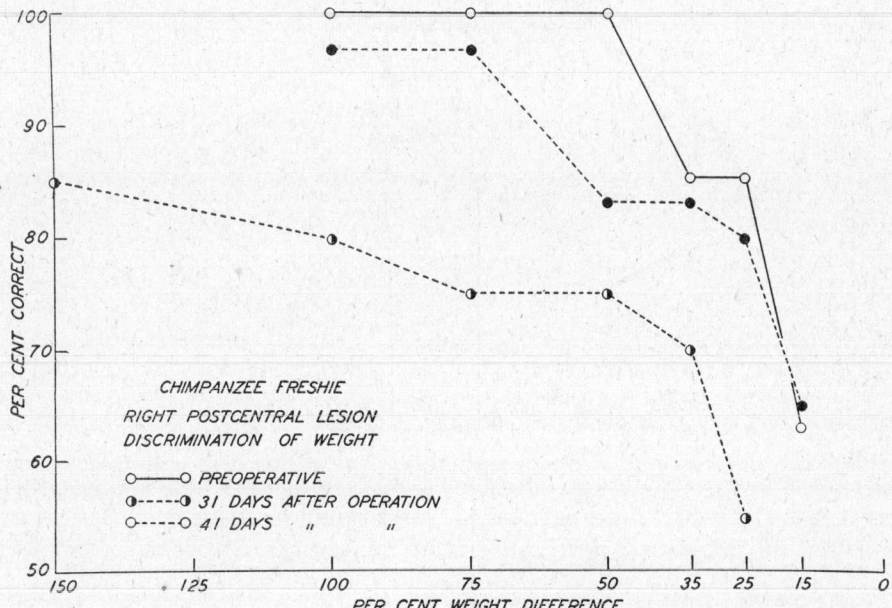

Fig. 193.—Threshold curves for the discrimination of lifted weights by a chimpanzee before and after ablation of the postcentral gyrus. Discrimination with 50 per cent accuracy is a chance performance and represents the absence of discriminatory ability. The abscissae are weight ratios, with the difference in weight expressed as a per cent of the standard 100 gram weight. The discrimination ability was severely affected a month after operation but with practice approached preoperative ability. (From Ruch, Kasdon and Fulton, unpublished.)

The degree to which hopping and placing reactions are focally localized in the cerebral cortex is not entirely settled, perhaps because different investigations use different strengths of contact in eliciting the reflex—thereby stimulating touch receptors alone, or touch, pressure and proprioceptive sense organs in combination. According to Bard (1), contact placing is focally localized in the postcentral gyrus, whereas others believe that some ability returns unless the posterior parietal lobe is removed as well. Parietal lobectomy has a less permanent effect on the hopping than on the placing reactions, and Bard believes the former is represented precentrally. With respect to the placing reaction, it has been suggested that "spatial elements may make the reactions dependent on a relatively few, specific neurons of a topographically organized projection such as the postcentral gyrus possesses."

Discrimination of weight, roughness and geometrical forms after various cortical lesions has been studied in a phylogenetic series embracing monkey, chimpanzee and man (22). Ablation of the postcentral gyrus reduces weight discriminatory ability in the chimpanzee (Fig. 193) and to a lesser degree in the monkey. In all forms it has been found that lesions confined to the posterior parietal lobe (areas 5 and 7) produce a degree of sensory impairment not greatly different from that consequent to lesions of the postcentral gyrus (areas 3-1-2). Secondly, a parietal lobectomy produces a far greater interference with the ability to discriminate weight and roughness than does ablation of the postcentral gyrus alone. This means that the posterior parietal lobule has the ability to function independently from the postcentral gyrus

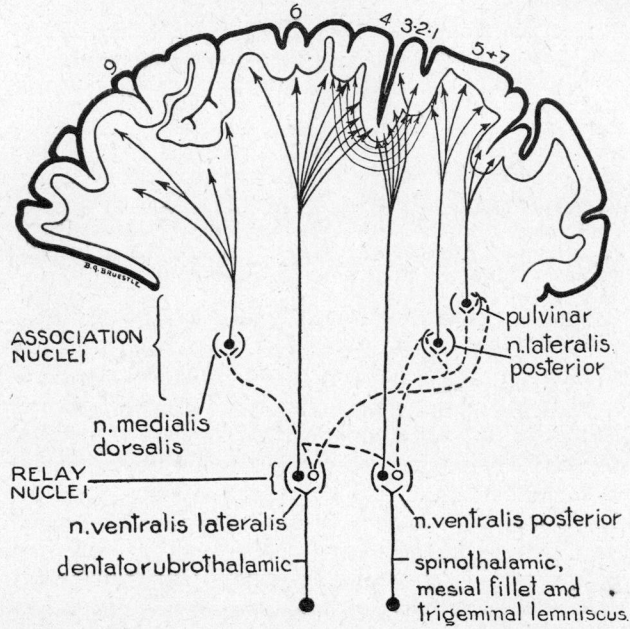

Fig. 194.—Diagram of the connections and projections of the main thalamic nuclei. The geniculate bodies and nuclei with purely subcortical connection are not shown. The details of the connections indicated by the dotted lines are not known. The numbers along the cerebral cortex designate Brodmann areas. (Based upon the work of Walker and of Le Gros Clark. From Ruch, Kasdon and Walker, unpublished.)

and is not dependent solely upon sensory impulses relayed through the short association fibers from the postcentral gyrus. This result became intelligible when the extent of the projection to the posterior parietal lobule became known. Besides the direct pathway between relay nuclei and areas 3-1-2 (Fig. 194), there is a "by-pass" whereby impulses from the great ascending sensory systems pass from relay nuclei to association nuclei to areas 5 and 7. Whether this system is capable of spatial and temporal discriminations as well as intensity discriminations has not been discovered. It may be concluded from much recent anatomical and physiological information that the classic pathway of impulses from thalamus to primary sensory area to posterior lying association area is not the only course open to sensory impulses.

Ablation of the parietal lobe does not entirely end the ability of a monkey or chimpanzee to discriminate weights or roughness except as a transitory phenomenon confined to the first postoperation weeks. Impairment, i.e., increased threshold, is all that remains after extensive lapse of time and retraining. Several mechanisms for such residual ability present themselves —(i) incomplete lesions, it being difficult to remove all the granular and transitory cortex from the floor of the central fissure without gravely interfering with voluntary movements required for testing; (ii) the motor cortex; (iii) the ipsilateral cortex; and (iv) the thalamus.

The possession of a strong thalamic projection makes areas 4 and 6 potentially a sensorimotor area, but the projection fibers may function in control of movement rather than in sensation. Stimulation of this region in man gives rise to conscious sensation, and the motor areas may play a part along with the parietal areas in the hopping reaction. The sensory function of the motor areas cannot be directly studied by weight and roughness discrimination technique because the ablations produce a disabling paralysis of voluntary movements requisite for manipulations involved in testing. However, it is evident from Figure 194 that the problem can be attacked by making lesions of the afferent tracts destined via the thalamus to end in the precentral and postcentral areas respectively. A section of the medial lemniscus and spinothalamic tract, but not encroaching on the more deeply situated dentatorubothalamic tract, permanently abolished hopping and placing reactions (24). Impairment of proprioceptive functions was manifested in failure to correct abnormal postures, and clumsiness and ataxia of stepping and manipulative movements, but very nearly complete recovery occurred. However, when the dentatothalamic fibers were also involved, more severe and more permanent deficits in proprioceptive functions resulted. The sensory pathway via the cerebellum to the motor area presumably was responsible for the recovery after section of medial lemniscus.

Cortical Function in Man (11, 12, 28). The status of sensation can be learned in much greater detail in man than in animals, but this advantage is offset in part by the fact that symptoms may be confused by increased intracranial pressure and that the lesions are incomplete or too extensive; their extent and location can only rarely be determined histologically. However, after the first World War the effects of gunshot wounds of the parietal cortex were studied exhaustively, especially by Sir Henry Head and Gordon Holmes, who used refined, quantitative methods of testing borrowed from the psychologists. But because such wounds destroy only portions of the sensory area, such studies show only the *kind* of sensory function carried on by the cerebral cortex and leave unanswered many of the problems of cortical localization, especially the question of the degree of "corticalization" of sensory functions.

Cortical lesions never produce anesthesia for any form of sensation except as a transitory phenomenon, and persisting anesthesia implies subcortical damage. Whether this means, as Head and Holmes believe, that the thalamus subserves sensation, or whether deep lesions are more effective because they interrupt projection fibers in the thalamus or internal capsule where they are concentrated, is an open question. Cortical lesions are manifested by an increase in the absolute threshold for elicitation of sensation, and the resulting sensation amounts to little more than recognition of the fact and kind of stimulation. Not all modalities of sensation are equally affected. Pain recovers most quickly and almost completely; pressure, warmth and cold recover next; and light touch and proprioceptive sensation are most severely and permanently damaged. Discrimination of intensity (relative threshold or the just noticeable difference) is subnormal for all modalities, as manifested by discrimination of lifted (proprioception) and supported (pressure) weights.

Perceptions having a strong spatial element—topognosis, two-point discrimination, figure writing and stereognosis—are especially affected by cortical lesions, and deficiencies in them may well be the first sign of damage to the parietal region. On the other hand, temporal perception as exemplified by vibratory sensibility is relatively little influenced by cortical lesions unless they extend into the white matter as in the case illustrated in Figure 175. Tactual and proprioceptive sensations and the perceptions built upon them are in general affected in much the same way by parietal and by posterior column lesions, but this is not so of vibratory sensibility which is greatly blunted by posterior column lesions but not by cortical lesions.

Because spatial and discriminative functions are severely damaged by cortical lesions, Head and others have given the impression that sensation has a thalamic representation and perception a cortical representation. Intensity and spatial functions have even been assigned different areas in the parietal lobes. Modern psychology teaches that, for example, the localization of a sensation or the ability to distinguish two points from one point cannot be separated from the sensation any more than an object and its location in space can be separated. The proper interpretation is that suggested in dealing with the posterior columns, namely, that the discrimination of fine differences in intensity probably requires a multitude of neurons such as the cortex possesses and the thalamus does not. Spatial functions are especially sensitive to cortical damage because refined discriminations demand not only many unit neurons but spatially organized fields of neurons. Therefore cortical remnants can support such functions only to a limited extent. Why else do regions having a high degree of spatial discriminative ability, e.g., the forefinger or the fovea of the retina, have a wide expanse of the cortex devoted to them? Thus even if the thalamus is capable of some form of sensation, it apparently does not possess the extensive apparatus necessary for fine discrimination and accurate localization, since only very few functional cells are left when the cortex is removed. Crude sensation of the type ascribed to the thalamus is "crude" in the sense that it is poorly located and capable of only coarse discrimination. Here, as in the discussion of epicritic and protopathic sensation, the same facts are open to two theories, one assuming qualitative difference and different neural substrata, the other stressing quantitative and topographical differences in the neuronal organization of tracts and projection fields.

Thalamus and Sensation (5, 8, 11, 28). While the function of the thalamus in the intact animal is inextricably bound up with the cerebral cortex and the two structures should always be thought of as a physiological unit, there remains the question whether and to what degree the thalamus has retained the ability to function in the absence of the sensory cortex. Before the advent of the cerebral cortex in phylogeny, the thalamus, together with subcortical motor centers, served the complex sensorimotor functions of which the lower animals—such as birds and fish—are indisputably capable. The motor functions have been very largely corticalized and progressively so. How far has the process of corticalization of sensation gone? The answer to this question must be provided by experiments on the higher primates and observations on man. At first sight, the recent cases of surgical hemidecortication in man would seem to offer a direct and conclusive answer to the question, namely, that whatever sensory capacity is retained is a function of the thalamus. The history of cortical localization justifies the rule that a given sensory or motor function should not be ascribed to subcortical regions until every possibility of cortical participation has been ruled out. The hemidecorticate man does not fulfill this requirement because only the cerebral cortex of one hemisphere is removed, and so any remaining sensory ability may be due to ipsilateral representation in the intact cerebral cortex.

The sensory disturbances produced by hemidecortication are less severe in the face than over the body. In the face, contralateral to the ablation, touch and pinprick are quite well appreciated and to some degree localized, but over the body all forms of sensation are lost except the appreciation of heavy touches and pinpricks, and localization of them is defective. It is agreed that in man and the primates, deep sensibility and probably all functions of the posterior column have no ipsilateral representation. However, ipsilateral representation of cutaneous sensations has been demonstrated in animals. Woolsey, Marshall and Bard recorded action potentials from the postcentral gyrus on the *same* side as the point stimulated, but only for *superficial stimulation in the region of the head;* and in Dusser de Barenne's experiments on strychninization of the cerebral cortex, ipsilateral representation was demonstrated for the body as well as the head but only for superficial stimulation.

While the respective share of ipsilateral representation and subcortical sensation in the recovery of sensation after hemidecortication is not yet fully known, considerable evidence of the latter exists. For example, if one cerebral cortex is removed in a monkey or baboon, sensation is temporarily completely abolished over the contralateral side for a few days, after which a limited recovery occurs. If the ipsilateral hemisphere subserves this recovery, removal of it should renew the state of complete anesthesia. Walker and Fulton (28) found that the regained sensory ability was not lost, indicating that it represented the activity of subcortical rather than ipsilateral cortical neurons. Other evidence comes from strychnine experiments.

The sensory phenomena which result from strychninization of the cortex are elicitable when all other portions of the sensorimotor area except that strychninized are rendered functionless by extirpation or novocainization (Dusser de Barenne). Apparently corticothalamic fibers activate the whole thalamic representation of one limb. Since a whole arm is rendered hyperalgesic by punctate strychninization when only a small fragment of cortical representation of the arm remains intact, the sensory process must have occurred in the thalamus. Furthermore, injection of minute amounts of strychnine into certain regions of the thalamus produces paresthesia and hyperalgesia. In the cat the same sensory phenomena occur unchanged after ablation of the cortex of both cerebral hemispheres, except that they are not so well localized. This appears to be critical evidence for "thalamic sensation," but it must be remembered that strychnine is a powerful excitant and perhaps magnifies the function of the thalamus.

Head ascribed to the thalamus the role of subserving the affective side of sensation and therefore of pain, which is a strongly affective experience. Affectivity was considered a primitive function which, in the course of evolution, has remained at a thalamic level despite development of the cerebral cortex. He pointed out that pain is only slightly and transiently affected by cortical lesions, and that clear-cut pain experiences have not been elicited by stimulation of the human cerebral cortex. Moreover, in one of the classic thalamic syndromes first clearly described by Déjerine and Roussy, spontaneous pain and subjective overresponse to pleasant and unpleasant stimuli are a prominent feature. This syndrome is usually caused by occlusion of a small blood vessel (thalamogeniculate branch of the posterior cerebral artery) which supplies the posterolateral portion of the lateral nuclear mass.

The so-called thalamic syndrome consists of the following (28):

1. *Fleeting hemiplegia or hemiparesis.* Paralysis or weakness of voluntary movement confined to one side of the body is due to slight involvement of the posterior internal capsule where it borders on the thalamus.

2. *Sensory disturbances of the cortical type.* Deep sensibility is abolished; superficial sensitivity is first abolished and then returns but in an altered form. Localization, two-point threshold and stereognosis are gravely affected, which is understandable since the relay nuclei are destroyed. The face often escapes because the relay nuclei for the face are the most medially situated and the lesion is more laterally placed. The superficial sensibility which returns is vague and poorly localized, and the stimuli may be confused.

3. *Overresponse and paresthesia.* Attacks of "spontaneous" or central pain of a severe, agonizing character are common, and pinprick or strong stimulation produces an intensely disagreeable, irradiating, diffuse sensation which is quite intolerable. One of Head's patients, a clergyman, complained that his trousers produced such disagreeable sensations that he was forced to remove them! Pleasant sensations are also magnified, and emotional responses to music give rise to excessive "feelings." Sensory overresponse is different from hyperesthesia because the threshold is often elevated; but once attained, the experience is overly intense. Irritation comes to mind as an explanation of these phenomena since lesions elsewhere than in the thalamus may give rise to pain, but irritation is not a satisfactory explanation for states which may last for many years. Head ascribed sensory overresponse to a release of the thalamus from a hypothetical cortical inhibition exerted by way of the corticothalamic fibers. However, cortical lesions produce these phenomena only in very slight degree, and stimulation of corticothalamic fibers activates rather than inhibits the thalamus as judged by action current studies (Dusser de Barenne, 5). Little definite can be said about the thalamic syndrome except that it is probable that spinothalamic fibers are especially well represented in fibers passing to the medial nuclei which are spared in thalamic syndrome, and that the ventrolateral relay nuclei are damaged. It is possible that spontaneous pain and overresponse have the same basis as dysesthesias produced by disturbances at lower levels. They are all instances in which a reduction of touch and deep sensibility is paralleled by a heightened response to painful stimuli. Perhaps all have a common explanation in the hypothesis that phylogenetically primitive functions of the midline nuclei are normally held in check (or prevented from receiving afferent impulses) when the phylogenetically newer lateral nucleus is activated.

That the medial thalamic group is concerned with the affective aspect of sensation is only an attractive hypothesis—attractive because the basic sensory and basic motor sides of emotion are integrated at the same level (diencephalic) and because the phylogenetically recent nuclei of the medial group are strongly connected with the prefrontal lobe, which, judging from clinical studies, is unquestionably related to the emotional life. Unfortunately, few definite facts are available in this field so important to the understanding of behavior, normal and abnormal.

REFERENCES

1. BARD, P. Studies on the cortical representation of somatic sensibility. *Harvey Lect.*, 1938, pp. 143–169.

2. BORING, E. G. *Sensation and perception in the history of experimental psychology.* New York, D. Appleton-Century Co., 1942, xv, 644 pp.

3. CLARK, D., HUGHES, J. and GASSER, H. S. Afferent function in the group of nerve fibers of slowest conduction velocity. *Amer. J. Physiol.*, 1935, *114:69–76.*

4. CLARK, W. E. Le G. and BOGGON, R. H. The thalamic connections of the parietal and frontal lobes of the brain in the monkey. *Philos. Trans.*, 1935, *B224:313–359.*

5. DUSSER DE BARENNE, J. G. Central levels of sensory integration. *Res. Publ. Ass. nerv. ment. Dis.*, 1935, *15:274–288.*

6. FOERSTER, O. The dermatomes in man. *Brain,* 1933, *56:1–39.*

7. FOERSTER, O. Symptomatologie der Erkrankungen des Rückenmarks und seiner Wurzeln. *Bumke u. Foersters Handb. Neurol.* 1936, *5:1–403.*

8. FULTON, J. F. *Physiology of the nervous system*, 2d ed. New York, Oxford University Press, 1943, ix, 614 pp.

9. GASSER, H. S. Pain-producing impulses in peripheral nerves. *Res. Publ. Ass. nerv. ment. Dis.*, 1943, 23:44–62.

10. HARRISON, F. and CORBIN, K. B. Oscillographic studies on the spinal tract of the fifth cranial nerve. *J. Neurophysiol.*, 1942, 5:465–482.

11. HEAD, H. *Studies in neurology*. London, Oxford University Press, 1920, 2 vols., ix & viii, 892 pp.

12. HOLMES, G. Disorders of sensation produced by cortical lesions. *Brain*, 1927, 50:413–427.

13. KEEGAN, J. J. Dermatome hypalgesia associated with herniation of intervertebral disk. *Arch. Neurol. Psychiat.*, *Chicago*, 1943, 50:67–83.

14. LANIER, L. H. An experimental study of cutaneous innervation. *Res. Publ. Ass. nerv. ment. Dis.*, 1935, 15:437–456.

15. LEWIS, T. *Pain*. New York, The Macmillan Co., 1942, xiii, 192 pp.

16. PEELE, T. L. Acute and chronic parietal lobe ablations in monkeys. *J. Neurophysiol.*, 1944, 7:269–286.

17. POCHIN, E. E. Delay of pain perception in tabes dorsalis. *Clin. Sci.*, 1938, 3:191–196.

18. POLLOCK, L. J. Nerve overlap as related to the relatively early return of pain sense following injury to the peripheral nerves. *J. comp. Neurol.*, 1920, 32:357–378.

19. RANSON, S. W. Cutaneous sensory fibers and sensory conduction. *Arch. Neurol. Psychiat.*, *Chicago*, 1931, 26:1122–1144.

20. RANSON, S. W., DROEGEMUELLER, W. H., DAVENPORT, H. K. and FISHER, C. Number, size and myelination of the sensory fibers in the cerebrospinal nerves. *Res. Publ. Ass. nerv. ment. Dis.*, 1935, 15:3–34.

21. RUCH, T. C. Cerebral cortex: the parietal lobes and somatic sensation. Chap. XIX in: FULTON, J. F. *Physiology of the nervous system*, 2d ed. New York, Oxford University Press, 1943, ix, 614 pp.

22. RUCH, T. C., FULTON, J. F. and GERMAN, W. J. Sensory discrimination in monkey, chimpanzee and man after lesions of the parietal lobe. *Arch. Neurol. Psychiat.*, *Chicago*, 1938, 39:919–937.

23. SHEEHAN, D. Some problems relating to the dorsal spinal nerve roots. *Yale J. Biol. Med.*, 1935, 7:425–440.

24. SJÖQVIST, O. and WEINSTEIN, E. A. The effect of section of the medial lemniscu on proprioceptive functions in chimpanzees and monkeys. *J. Neurophysiol.*, 1942, 5:69–74.

25. STEIN, M. H., WORTIS, H. and JOLLIFFE, N. Peripheral neuropathy: evaluation of sensory findings. *Arch. Neurol. Psychiat.*, *Chicago*, 1941, 46:464–470. Tabes dorsalis: evaluation of sensory findings. *Ibid.*, 471–476.

26. TROTTER, W. and DAVIES, H. M. Experimental studies in the innervation of the skin. *J. Physiol.*, 1909, 38:154–246.

27. TROTTER, W. and DAVIES, H. M. The peculiarities of sensibility found in cutaneous areas supplied by regenerating nerves. *J. Psychol. Neurol.*, *Lpz.*, 1913, 20, Ergänzungsheft 2, pp. 102–150.

28. WALKER, A. E. *The primate thalamus*. Chicago, University of Chicago Press, 1938, xxiii, 321 pp.

29. WALKER, A. E. Anatomy, physiology and surgical considerations of the spinal tract of the trigeminal nerve. *J. Neurophysiol.*, 1939, 2:234–248.

30. WALKER, A. E. Central representation of pain. *Res. Publ. Ass. nerv. ment. Dis.*, 1943, 23:63–85.

31. WALSHE, F. M. R. The anatomy and physiology of cutaneous sensibility: a critical review. *Brain*, 1942, 65:48–112.

32. WEDDELL, G., GÜTTMANN, L. and GUTMANN, E. The local extension of nerve fibres into denervated areas of skin. *J. Neurol. Psychiat.*, 1941, 4:206–225.

33. WOOLLARD, H. H., WEDDELL, G. and HARPMAN, J. A. Observations on the neurohistological basis of cutaneous pain. *J. Anat.*, *Lond.*, 1940, 74:413–440.

34. WOOLSEY, C. N., MARSHALL, W. H. and BARD, P. Representation of cutaneous tactile sensibility in the cerebral cortex of the monkey as indicated by evoked potentials. *Johns Hopk. Hosp. Bull.*, 1942, 70:399–441.

CHAPTER 18

TASTE

BY HARRY D. PATTON AND THEODORE C. RUCH

Taste and smell are usually classified together as the "chemical senses." The adequate stimulus for each is chemical in nature, that for smell being a gas, for taste, a liquid. Taste is also linked with smell because of the close psychological relation of the two senses as evidenced by the frequent subjective confusion between olfactory and gustatory sensations. Indeed, much of the "taste" of food is perceived by way of the olfactory end-organs. Starling has said, "The epicure with a fine palate has really educated his sense of smell and would be but little satisfied with the simple sensations derived from his tongue." This close functional and psychological relationship has thus led to the belief that taste and smell represent variants of a single morphological and physiological unit. The wide currency of this belief has led to the erroneous conviction that the central neural pathways of taste and smell coincide.

A different view of taste and smell is that of Börnstein (7, 8) who points out that our information about taste has been gained not so much by experimentation as by inference from known facts about olfaction. Furthermore, taste appears to be even more closely related to somatic sensation of the mouth and tongue than to olfaction. The evidence for Börnstein's hypothesis is as follows:

1. *Functional relations.* Although many foodstuffs stimulate gustatory and olfactory end-organs simultaneously, they also stimulate somatosensory receptors of the mouth and tongue. At physiological strengths many gustatory stimuli affect the end-organs of touch or pressure and temperature. Thus certain concentrations of salt activate simultaneously taste, touch and possibly pain receptors. Likewise, the alkaline taste of lye is a complex sensation composed of gustatory, olfactory, pain, temperature and touch components, while the astringent sensation derived from acids is a purely tactual sensation. In short, the sensory complexes which we commonly refer to as "tastes" are so inextricably commingled with somaesthetic sensations that it is extremely difficult to analyze them subjectively.

2. *Structure of receptor.* The olfactory end-organ, even in the highly developed primates, remains a primitive type of receptor which serves a double function of reception and conduction (Fig. 195). The cell body situated at the periphery acts at once as a receptor and a ganglion cell and unlike other sensory neurons has no proximally placed ganglion cell. Such "neurosensory cells" (Retzius) are commonly found in the lower animals (earthworm) but the olfactory receptors are the sole representatives of this type of cell in man. The gustatory end-organs, on the other hand, consist of two elements, (i) a peripherally placed end-organ which receives the stimuli, and (ii) centripetally conducting nerve fibers which originate in relation to the receptors and have *centrally* placed cell bodies or ganglion cells. In this respect, the neurons of the gustatory system are identical with those of the somatosensory systems and are unlike those of the olfactory system.

3. *Peripheral pathways.* The olfactory nerve is a special cranial nerve devoted purely to olfactory fibers, which are unmyelinated. The gustatory fibers, on the other hand, reach the brain via mixed cranial nerves and in their course accompany fibers which either conduct somatosensory impulses in man or did so in earlier phylogenetic stages (7).

4. *Central pathways.* Direct experimental evidence shows that the central course of the gustatory pathways through the brain stem (24) and thalamus (6, 25) and their termination

in the cerebral cortex (8) is coextensive with the pathways conducting somaesthetic sensory impulses from mouth and tongue. The widely accepted theory of contiguous central representation of taste and olfaction is discussed in more detail below.

It thus appears that the gustatory sensory system is derived from, and is therefore closely related to, the somaesthetic systems. For this reason, taste is discussed here in conjunction with the general sensory systems which were described in the preceding chapter.

Distribution of Receptors. In certain of the fishes, end-organs similar to taste receptors are widely distributed in the skin where they are accessible to stimulation by materials dissolved in the fluid in which the animal lives.

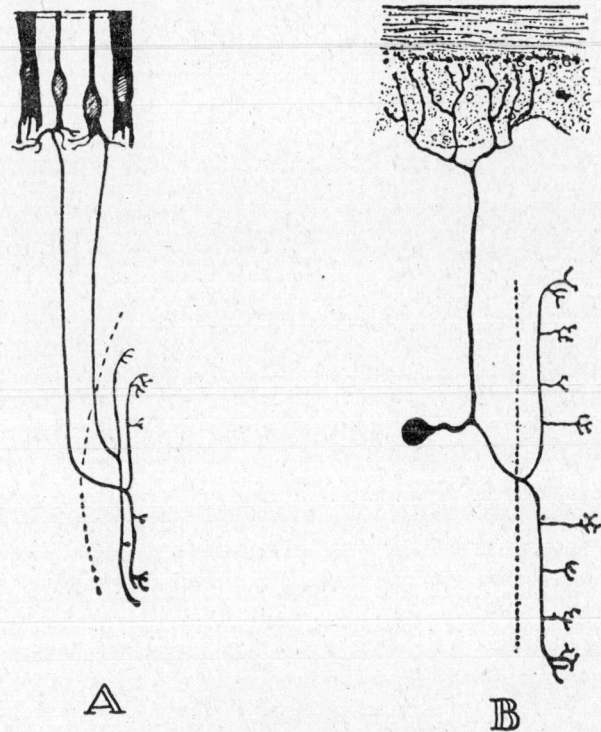

Fig. 195.—A gives an example of a primitive sensory neuron. The primary olfactory neuron in man resembles this neuron in possessing a peripheral bipolar cell body rather than a centrally placed ganglion cell of the type shown in B, which is a typical vertebrate sensory neuron. Human taste and somatosensory neurons are of this latter type. (After Cajal, *Histologie du système nerveux de l'homme et des vertébrés*, 1909–11.)

In the higher vertebrates and man the tongue constitutes the chief organ of gustation. However, taste sensations may sometimes also be aroused from the palate, pharynx, tonsils and epiglottis and more rarely from the mucosa of the lips and cheeks, the under surface of the tongue, and the floor of the mouth (8).

Four distinct gustatory modalities are recognized: sweet, salt, bitter and sour or acid. The complex sensations aroused by stimulation of the receptive areas of the oral cavity with mixed gustatory stimuli are the result of a fusion of these four primary gustatory sensations along with various somato-sensory and olfactory components as mentioned previously.

Regional examination of the tongue with pure solutions reveals that there are marked variations in sensitivity of different areas of the tongue to each of the four modalities. For such examinations the following solutions are most satisfactory because they minimize confusing extragustatory stimulation: sweet, cane sugar; salt, sodium chloride; bitter, quinine; and sour or acid, citric acid. If such solutions are topically applied to small areas of the tongue, the zonal character of gustatory sensitivity is apparent. The tip of the tongue is sensitive to all four modalities but mostly to sweet and salt. The lateral margins of the tongue are most sensitive to sour or acid stimuli but may also respond to salt. The basal portion of the tongue is sensitive to

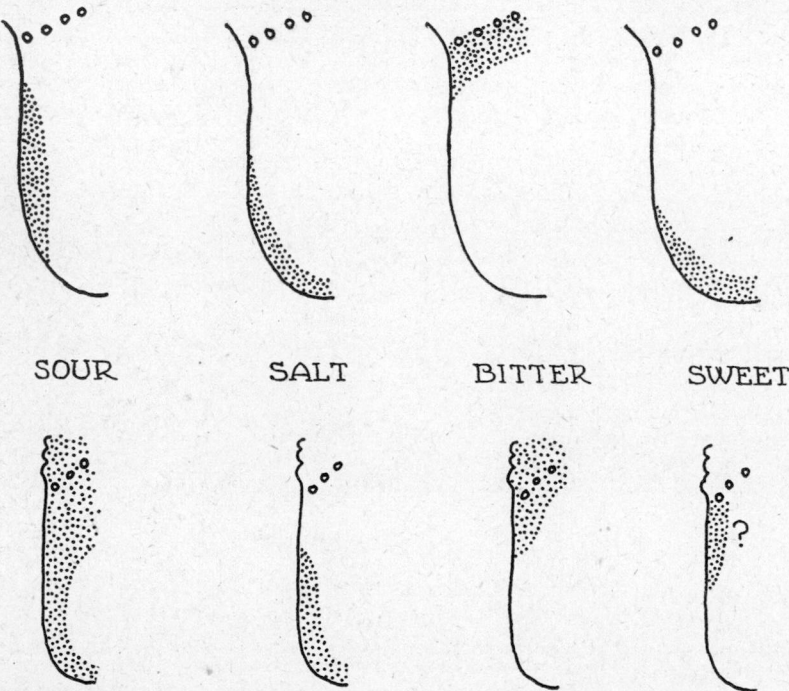

SOUR   SALT   BITTER   SWEET

Fig. 196.—Diagrams of the right half of the tongue of the human (above) and cat (below), illustrating areas of maximum sensibility to the four primary taste qualities as determined by punctiform exploration and electrical recording respectively. Electrical responses in cat to sweet stimuli were equivocal. (After Hänig, *Philos. Stud.*, 1901, *17*:576–623, and Pfaffmann, *J. cell. comp. Physiol.*, 1941, *17*:243–258.)

bitter stimuli. The dorsum of the tongue, particularly in the midline, is relatively insensitive.

Although these observations were made long ago on the human tongue, experimental proof of the zonal distribution of specific receptors has been accomplished only recently. Pfaffmann (27) recorded action potentials from the nerves of taste in the cat while stimulating the tongue with solutions of sucrose, dilute hydrochloric acid, sodium chloride and quinine. In Figure 196 the areas most responsive to each of these solutions in the cat are compared with those mapped out on the human tongue. With the exception of the area for sweet (sucrose) sensitivity, the similarity is striking. The localization of the sweet area for the cat's tongue was based on a few questionable results;

sugar usually failed to produce any discharge of impulses. This relative insensitivity of the cat's tongue to sweet solutions was also noted by Zotterman (35).

Thresholds for Taste. The zonal distribution of sensitivity complicates the determination of thresholds for the various modalities because the threshold varies with the region of the tongue being tested. For example, Kiesow (17) reported the following thresholds (grams per cent) for quinine sulfate on the various areas of the tongue:

Base of tongue	0.00005%
Tip of tongue	0.00029%
Right edge of tongue	0.00020%
Left edge of tongue	0.00021%

Similar regional variations in threshold can be demonstrated for the other taste modalities. Gustatory thresholds reported in the literature are consequently quite variable. For example, reported values for salt thresholds in the human have varied from 0.016 to 0.250 per cent (29).

Another factor which complicates the evaluation of threshold determinations is the rather marked individual variation which characterizes the gustatory threshold. An extreme example of this is the "taste blindness" displayed by some people for the aryl thiocarbamides and particularly phenyl thiocarbamide (13). This latter substance is distinctly bitter to most individuals, but about 5 per cent of a mixed population derive no gustatory stimulation from it. The inability to taste phenyl thiocarbamide is hereditary and appears to be a Mendelian recessive trait (5). In this respect taste blindness has been compared with color blindness.

The variability of thresholds, outlined above, need not interfere with the clinical examination of taste. Fortunately in most clinical neurological cases, gustatory disturbances are unilateral and a quantitative demonstration of a difference in sensitivity of the two sides of the tongue is of greater value than comparisons between the patient's threshold and reported values obtained on normal subjects (see below). In animal studies where the effect of experimental procedures on the taste threshold is sought, the animal serves as its own experimental control. This can be accomplished by testing the animal before and after introducing the experimental variable, for although there is great variation from animal to animal, the threshold of a single individual is remarkably constant from time to time (23).

Of the various general methods for testing sensation in animals, i.e., observational, conditioned reflex, discrimination, and preference methods, the latter is most satisfactory for taste studies. In essence, the method consists of presenting the animal with measured quantities of water and a taste solution such as quinine. No other drinking water is made available to the animal. An animal which consistently drinks water and avoids the quinine solution when all nongustatory cues are eliminated must be able to discriminate between the two liquids. When the concentration of quinine is reduced on successive days, more and more quinine is drunk until a concentration is reached at which quinine is drunk as readily as water. Plotting the quantity of quinine drunk relative to water (i.e., quinine drunk/total fluid drunk) against the concentration of quinine yields a threshold curve which is a remarkably stable measure of the animal's gustatory discriminative capacity.

This method has been of great value in the study of the central course of taste fibers in monkeys and chimpanzees (6, 25), and in studies of self-regulation of the diet in the rat (28).

Neural pathways for taste

End-Organs. The taste end-organs are the taste buds which were first described in man by Lovén (1867). These are ovoid structures found scattered throughout the areas which are responsive to taste stimuli, i.e., tongue, palate, anterior faucial pillars, pharynx, and larynx. They are, however, most numerous on the circumvallate, foliate and fungiform papillae of the tongue. Taste buds are absent from the mid-dorsal region of the tongue which, as mentioned previously, is insensitive. Strangely enough, taste buds are quite numerous in the larynx, particularly on the laryngeal side of the epiglottis and on the medial and lateral surfaces of the arytenoids. The functional

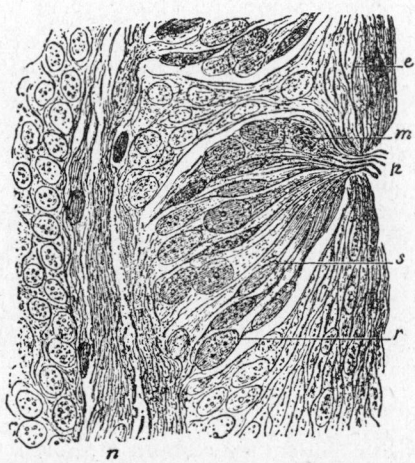

Fig. 197.—Section through one of the taste buds of the papilla foliata of the rabbit, highly magnified: *p*, Gustatory pore; *s*, gustatory cell; *r*, sustentacular cell; *m*, leukocyte containing granules; *e*, superficial epithelial cells; *n*, nerve fibers. (After Ranvier from *Quain's Elements of Anatomy*, 1909.)

significance of these laryngeal buds is unsettled; it has been suggested that they constitute part of a reflex mechanism involved in the closure of the larynx in deglutition (34). This appears unlikely, since their position is such that they would not normally come into contact with taste stimuli. Yet application of sapid substances by means of a laryngoscopic apparatus to the parts of the larynx containing these receptors arouses specific taste sensations for each of the four qualities (34).

Studies of the numbers of taste buds have been restricted largely to the tongue. Their numbers vary with age (4). From birth to 20 years of age the mean number per circumvallate papilla is about 245; in extreme old age (74 to 85 years) the number is reduced to 88 and many of these are highly atrophic and probably nonfunctional. It has long been recognized that gustatory acuity progressively diminishes with age.

All taste buds have with minor variations the same morphological structure (Fig. 197). They are embedded in the stratified epithelium and are composed of two types of cells, the gustatory cells and the sustentacular cells. The gustatory cells are fusiform in shape and occupy the interior of the bud, while the sustentacular cells are columnar and loosely arranged about the sides of the bud like the staves of a barrel. Between the gustatory cells and the sustentacular cells is a cavity which communicates with the oral cavity through a minute orifice, the gustatory pore. The peripheral ends of the gustatory cells are drawn into delicate processes which project through the pore and thus come into contact with the fluids covering the mucosa.

To the sustentacular cells is usually ascribed a supporting function, whereas the fusiform gustatory cells are usually regarded as the true sensory receptor cells. However, Kolmer (18) presents convincing evidence that both types of elongated cells are gustatory receptors but in different stages of development; both receive an innervation (34). There appears to be a constant turnover of cells, the degenerating fusiform cells being replaced by developing sustentacular cells. This may account for the frequent occurrence of leukocytes in taste buds.

The innervation of the buds arises from a subepithelial plexus of small myelinated and unmyelinated fibers. After traversing a plexus at the base of the taste bud, the fibers terminate (after loss of the myelin sheath, if present) on the cells of the bud either as delicate interlacing networks or as knoblike endings. These terminations are on fusiform and sustentacular cells alike, which supports Kolmer's hypothesis that both cell types subserve gustation. Some fibers likewise make their way into the epithelium surrounding the bud; they probably have somatosensory functions. Indeed, a single fiber may be seen to bifurcate, sending one branch to the bud and the other to an unencapsulated nerve ending quite removed from the bud (34). This is another manifestation of the close relationship between taste and general somatic sensation.

That these structures constitute the taste receptors is suggested by the fact that they appear in all parts of the mucosa known to be sensitive to gustatory stimuli and do not appear in any other part of the body. Furthermore, when the peripheral nerves known to conduct taste impulses are sectioned, the taste buds undergo atrophy and degeneration (21).

Morphologically all taste buds are fundamentally similar, irrespective of their position. Yet the existence of four psychologically distinct taste qualities and the zonal distribution of sensitivity suggests that four functionally, if not histologically, distinct types of receptors must exist. Lack of histological differentiation is no obstacle to belief in specific receptors; in the eye, cones are not morphologically differentiated into red, green, and blue receptive cones. The existence of specific receptors for the four taste qualities is suggested by the following facts: (i) Zonal distribution of taste qualities. (ii) Topical application of cocaine to the tongue abolishes taste sensibility in the following order: first bitter, then sweet, followed by salt, and finally sour (22). On the other hand, gymnemic acid (obtained from the leaves of *Gymnema sylvestre*) selectively abolishes sweet and bitter tastes, leaving sensitivity to salt and sour unimpaired (22). (iii) By punctate exploration of the tongue individual papillae can be found which respond to only sour, salt, sweet or bitter (20). Such papillae must be equipped with only one type of taste bud. (iv) Pfaffmann (27), working with the cat, recorded action potentials from single fiber preparations of the nerves of taste during stimulation of the tongue with solutions. He was able to isolate three types of single fiber preparations;. one gave action potentials only when the tongue was stimulated with sour solutions, another responded to sour and salt only, and the third to sour and bitter. No receptors for sweet were found in the cat. Pfaffmann points out the possibility that a single fiber innervates more than one bud, thus accounting for the mixed sensitivity of the latter two receptors. At any rate, his studies have shown that in the cat there are at least specific receptors for sour.

The basis for the specificity of the taste buds is unknown. Crozier (10) has suggested that each end-organ possesses a specific receptive substance with which the stimulating substance must combine to activate it.

Peripheral Pathways. The course of the fibers bearing taste impulses from the tongue to the central nervous system has long been disputed. The belief that the taste fibers, like those of other special senses, are all carried in a single cranial nerve did much to confuse the early investigators. Magendie and Claude Bernard were convinced that the trigeminal nerve carries the gustatory fibers and Sherrington (31) came to a similar conclusion from experimental studies on monkeys. Cushing (11), however, was unable to demonstrate significant gustatory alterations in patients in whom the sensory ganglion of the trigeminal nerve (Gasserian) had been resected. It is now generally agreed that the trigeminal nerves bear no taste fibers.

At least two cranial nerves are involved in the transmission of taste impulses from the tongue. The taste buds of the posterior one-third of the tongue are innervated by the *glossopharyngeal* nerve; those from the anterior two-thirds, by the chorda tympani branch of the *facial* nerve. To these may be added a few fibers in the vagus supplying the buds of the larynx and pharynx.

Taste fibers which enter the glossopharyngeal nerve continue with it into the brain. The course of the taste fibers leaving the tongue in the chorda tympani, however, is complicated; no less than four different peripheral pathways have been described for these fibers. These are described in detail in the article by Lewis and Dandy (19); only two need be described here. The first (Fig. 198, A) is a direct route through the chorda tympani as it leaves the tongue in company with the lingual nerve and thence in the facial nerve after the chorda tympani joins the latter. This pathway is supported by clinical studies of Lewis and Dandy (19). The alternative pathway (Fig. 198, B) is with the chorda tympani through the anastomoses of this nerve with the otic ganglion, and thence through this ganglion to the greater superficial petrosal nerve which bears the taste fibers to the geniculate ganglion of the facial nerve. According to Schwartz and Wedell (32), the former is the usual route but the petrosal nerve may be important in a few individuals. The course of the chorda tympani taste fibers is thus subject to individual variation.

The taste fibers in both facial and glossopharyngeal nerves are small fibers. This may be inferred from the small amplitude of the action potentials aroused by gustatory stimulation (27, 35). Zotterman (35) assigns the taste fibers a diameter of less than 4 μ. Since the smaller fibers tend to be unmyelinated, it is quite possible that many of the taste fibers lack myelin sheaths. This is of importance because many of the investigations of the central pathways of taste have involved studies of myelin degeneration by the Marchi method. Such studies obviously would yield no information as to the course of unmyelinated fibers.

Bulbar Nucleus. The afferent fibers of the seventh, ninth and tenth nerves after entering the medulla form a well defined common descending tract, the *tractus solitarius*. In this respect the taste fibers behave like the pain and temperature fibers of the trigeminal nerve which likewise pursue a descending course in the neighboring spinal trigeminal tract. The greater part of the

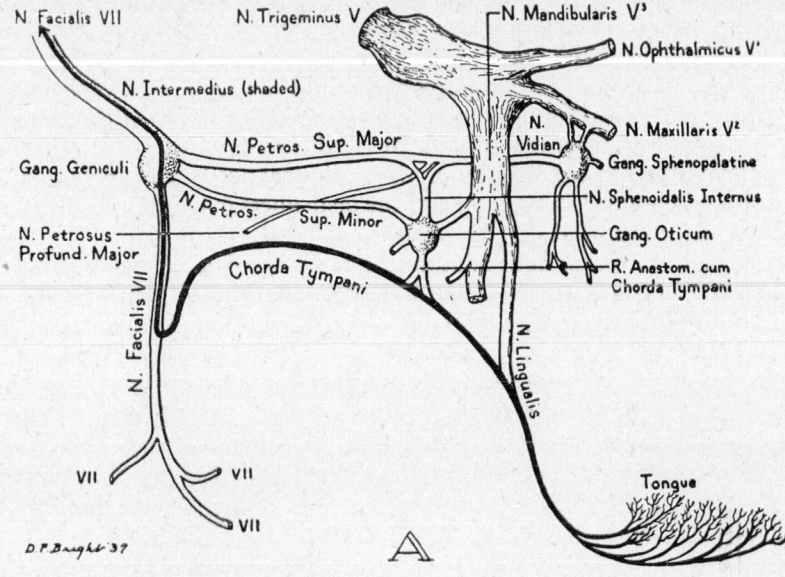

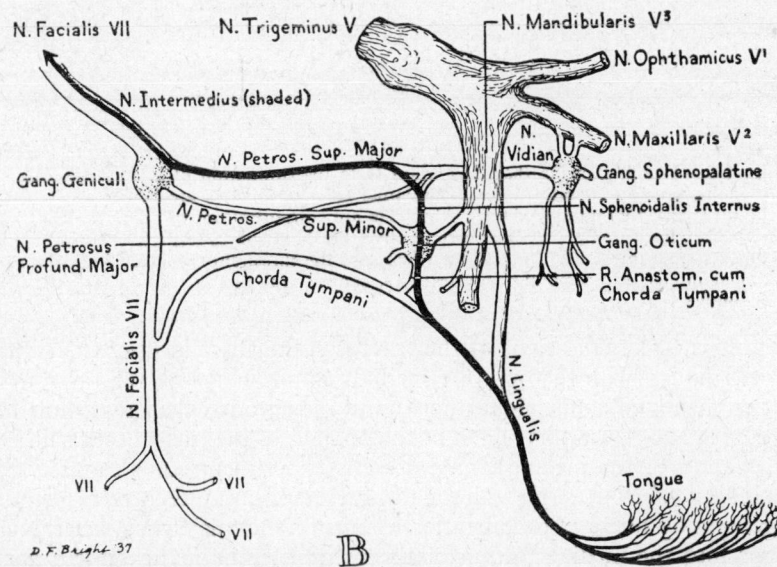

Fig. 198.—A, Course of taste fibers in the chorda tympani as determined by Lewis and Dandy. B, Alternative course of taste fibers in chorda tympani occurring in a limited number of cases. (From Schwartz and Wedell, *Brain*, 1938, *61*:99–115.)

taste and visceral sensory fibers terminate in the gray matter, adjacent to the solitary tract, the *nucleus of the tractus solitarius*. The fibers of the three nerves enter the tract and terminate in the nucleus at different levels; the rostral part of the nucleus thus receives fibers from the facial and glosso-pharyngeal nerves whereas the caudal portion receives only vagal fibers (2). Consequently, taste neurons probably have their cell bodies in the nucleus of the tractus solitarius and particularly in its rostral part. Kappers (16) has, however, suggested from purely comparative morphological studies that the bulbar taste center is in the nucleus intercalatus of Staderini. Allen (2) was unable to trace fibers from the seventh or ninth nerves to this nucleus; but as he employed the Marchi technique, his studies cannot be considered con-clusive, for, as mentioned above, some of the taste fibers may be unmyelinated or at best thinly myelinated.

Bulbothalamic Pathways. Both anatomical and physiological methods have been employed in tracing the course of the secondary taste pathways from the medulla to the thalamus. In the guinea pig Allen (3) made lesions of the

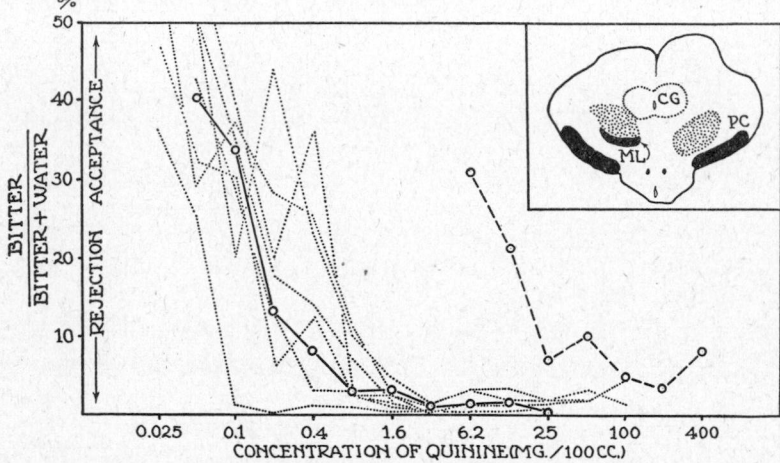

Fig. 199.—Graph showing the effect upon taste discrimination of bilateral lesions near the medial lemniscus and ventral trigeminothalamic tract. Ordinates are percentage of total fluid intake represented by bitter (quinine). Abscissae are concentrations of quinine. Heavy solid and heavy broken lines are the pre- and postoperative threshold curves respectively of rat with lesions shown in stipple in the inset. Fine dotted lines are the threshold curves of 7 normal rats. ML, medial lemniscus; PC, cerebral peduncles; CG, central gray matter. (Patton and Ruch, unpub-lished studies.)

rostral part of the nucleus of the tractus solitarius and traced degenerating fibers running with the opposite medial lemniscus to the ventral and lateral nuclei of the thalamus. He further found retrograde degeneration of the cells of the rostral ("gustatory") half of the nucleus of the tractus solitarius follow-ing section of the medial lemniscus. His experiments thus suggest that the secondary taste fibers run with the medial lemniscus. Gerebtzoff (14) followed degenerating fibers in rabbits after lesions of the nucleus of the tractus soli-tarius into the medial portion of the medial lemniscus in close association with the ventral trigeminothalamic path. This close parallel between taste and somatosensory pathways is consistent with the hypothesis of Börnstein.

Physiological evidence also supports this localization; the preference threshold for quinine is elevated by lesions in the region of the medial lem-niscus and ventral trigeminothalamic tract (24). In Figure 199 are shown the threshold curves of a rat before and after the Horsley-Clarke lesion shown in the inset. The fine dotted lines show threshold curves of seven normal rats. Along the abscissae is plotted the concentration of quinine, and on the ordinates the quantity of quinine drunk at each concentration expressed as a percentage of the total fluid intake. After operation the animal consistently drank relatively large quantities of quinine of a concentration which was left untouched preoperatively. The lesion on the right destroyed completely the medial lemniscus; on the left side only the dorsal fibers of this tract were damaged. This suggests that the taste fibers traverse the dorsal part of the medial lemniscus as do the ventral secondary trigeminal fibers.

Thalamic nucleus. Until recently the fact, to say nothing of the locus, of a thalamic center for taste was largely a matter of conjecture. There is now clear evidence that in the thalamus, as in the bulbothalamic pathways, the localization of taste is in close relation to that of somatic sensibility of the face. In Chapter 17 it was noted that the ascending somatic sensory systems (spinothalamic tract, medial lemniscus, dorsal and ventral secondary trigeminal tracts) are topographically projected upon the posteroventral thalamic nucleus, which is formed by two readily recognizable masses, the aterally situated nucleus ventralis posterolateralis and the medially situated nucleus ventralis posteromedialis or arcuate nucleus. Thus the fibers carrying sensory impulses from the leg terminate in the lateral part of the nucleus ventralis posterolateralis, those from the arm end in the medial part of the same nucleus near its junction with the arcuate nucleus, while the sensory fibers from the face synapse medially in the arcuate nucleus. It is in this latter nucleus that recent clinical, anatomical, and physiological observations have localized taste.

Clinically, discrete lesions in the region of the arcuate nucleus are rare, as are also careful tests of taste acuity. However, Adler (1) reported a human case with definite unilateral reduction of gustatory sensibility and cutaneous sensibility of the face. Microscopic examination of autopsy material revealed a tumor of the third ventricle which damaged the medial part of the arcuate nucleus on the side opposite the gustatory and cutaneous sensory disturbances.

In the rabbit Gerebtzoff (14) traced degenerating fibers to the medial part of the arcuate nucleus after damage to the nucleus of the tractus solitarius. Also after ablation of the cortical area which responds electrically to chemical stimulation of the tongue, retrograde degeneration was noted in the medial part of the arcuate nucleus (15). Direct evidence that the arcuate nucleus constitutes the thalamic locus for taste (6, 25) has been obtained from studies on monkeys by the preference method. Figure 200 shows threshold curves of a monkey before and after the Horsley-Clarke lesions of the thalamus shown in the inset. The two curves at the left, which are almost identical, represent two independent preoperative determinations of the taste sensibility. After operation the threshold curve was shifted to the higher concentrations, indicating that the monkey drank large quantities of intensely bitter solutions which were completely rejected before operation. A large portion of the arcuate nucleus was found destroyed by the lesion.

Cortical Representation. From what has been said of the subcortical course of the taste fibers, it may be predicted that the cortical center for taste must lie in or close to the area receiving somatic sensory impulses from the face. This area is situated in the region of the inferior end of the central fissure near the sylvian fissure. To this cortical area the arcuate nucleus, the taste nucleus of the thalamus, sends projection fibers (33). The first evidence that taste is localized not in the hippocampal region along with smell, as is widely held (Ferrier), but rather on the convexity of the hemisphere (Gad, Stcherbak), came from ablation studies by Bremer (9) and clinical observations by Börnstein (8). According to Bremer, gustatory impairment in rabbits follows ablation of those areas which on stimulation produce masticatory movements; in this species the area appears to be sensorimotor. Ectors (12) detected changes in the electrocorticogram of this area in unanesthetized rabbits when quinine solutions were placed on the tongue. More recently Gerebtzoff (15) has demonstrated retrograde degeneration in the arcuate

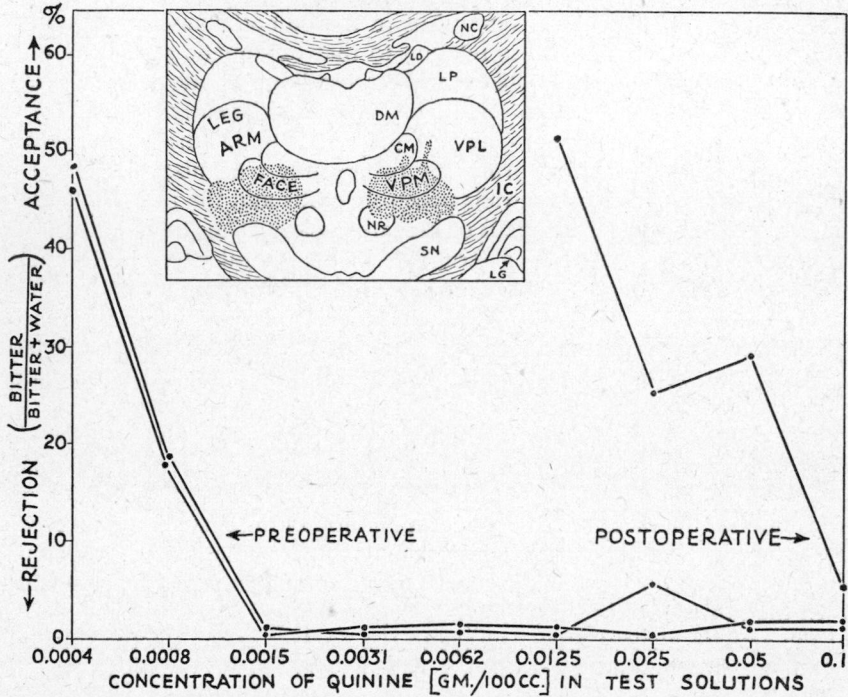

Fig. 200.—Graph showing the effect of bilateral lesions of the arcuate nucleus (stippled area of insert) on preference threshold curves in monkey. Ordinates and abscissae as in previous figure. CM, n. centrum medianum; DM, n. medialis dorsalis; IC, internal capsule; LD, n. lateralis dorsalis; LG, lateral geniculate body; LP, n. lateralis posterior; NC, caudate nucleus; NR, red nucleus; SN, substantia nigra; VPL, n. ventralis posterolateralis; VPM, n. ventralis posteromedialis (arcuate nucleus). (After Patton, Ruch, and Walker, *J. Neurophysiol.*, 1944, 7:171–184.)

nucleus of Bremer's rabbits in which the taste-masticatory areas had been extirpated.

In a series of human cases with bullet wounds of the inferior postcentral region, Börnstein demonstrated heterolateral reduction of gustatory and tactual sensibility of the tongue. A further line of evidence is provided by the observations of Penfield and Boldrey (26) who elicited gustatory sensations in conscious human patients by electrical stimulation of the lower end of the postcentral gyrus. Experiments carried out with the preference technique in both monkeys and chimpanzees reveal that bilateral lesions of face sensory area (inferior postcentral gyrus) and part of the face motor area (inferior precentral gyrus) does indeed produce significant elevation of the gustatory threshold. However, in contrast with the deficits produced by thalamic lesions, these deficits from cortical lesions are more transient and, after a period of time, taste acuity may reach the preoperative value. No explanation for this recovery phenomenon is available. In this respect, the disturbances of taste are not unlike the disturbances of somatic sensation which likewise are more severe and permanent after thalamic than cortical lesions. The possibility of both being incompletely corticalized must be reckoned with.

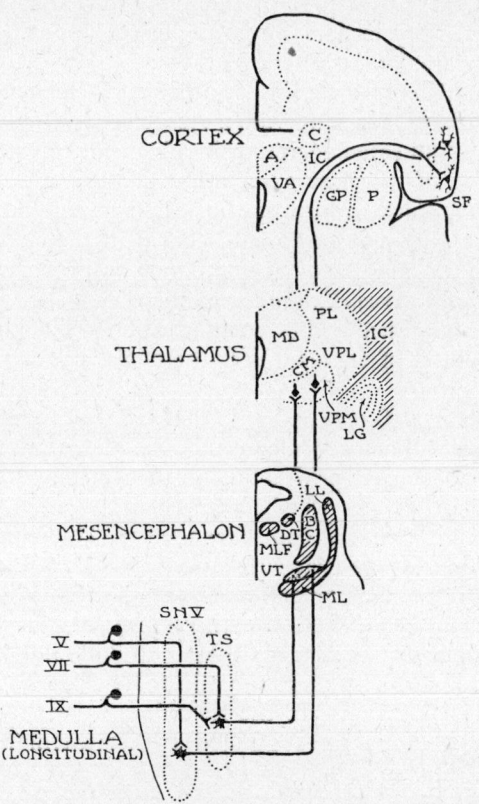

Fig. 201.—Summary diagram, highly schematic, representing taste and somatosensory pathways from the face. A, anterior thalamic nucleus; BC, brachium conjunctivum; C, caudate nucleus; CM, n. centrum medianum; DT, dorsal secondary trigeminal tract; GP, globus pallidus; IC, internal capsule; LG, lateral geniculate body; LL, lateral lemniscus; MD, n. medialis dorsalis; ML, medial lemniscus; MLF, medial longitudinal fasciculus; P, putamen; PL, n. lateralis posterior; SF, sylvian fissure; SNV, spinal nucleus of 5th nerve; TS, nucleus of tractus solitarius; VA, n. ventralis anterior; VPL, n. ventralis posterolateralis; VPM, n. ventralis posteromedialis (arcuate nucleus); VT, ventral secondary trigeminal tract. (Patton and Ruch, unpublished studies.)

Many details of the cortical representation remain in doubt, but the weight of evidence points away from the traditional hippocampal localization and suggests that taste and somatic sensation are closely related at cortical as they are at subcortical levels.

Summary of Taste Pathways. In Figure 201 is shown the central course of the taste pathways as determined from clinical, anatomical and physiological data. The somatosensory fibers from the face are also shown to stress the parallel between the two systems. The taste fibers of the chorda tympani and glossopharyngeal nerve enter the descending tractus solitarius just medial to the descending spinal nucleus of the trigeminal nerve bearing pain and temperature fibers from the face. The secondary taste neurons have their cell bodies in the nucleus of the tractus solitarius and send their fibers to the thalamus dorsal to the medial part of the opposite medial lemniscus. The ventral secondary trigeminal tract is shown just lateral to the taste fibers. The tertiary taste neurons lie in the arcuate nucleus of the thalamus, perhaps in the medial part, while the somatosensory fibers are shown terminating predominantly in the lateral part of the same nucleus. The fibers of both taste and somatosensory tertiary neurons project upon the inferior part of the somatosensory area of the cerebral cortex.

Clinical Examination of Taste. Detection of a taste deficit in a neurological case may be of definite localizing value. Associated with such a taste deficit one may expect to find some degree of involvement of cutaneous sensitivity of the face because of the close association of the pathways for these two types of sensibility. Furthermore, if the lesion is cortical, disturbances of chewing and of hearing may be found because of the closeness of the taste area to the precentral masticatory center and the primary auditory field in the superior temporal gyrus. Examples of the diagnostic value of such taste deficits have been published by Börnstein (8) and by Shenkin and Lewey (30). The following method of testing taste, therefore, has a place as a special sensory examination.

Reference to Figure 200 reveals that a large part of the gustatory pathway can be interrupted without completely abolishing gustatory discriminatory capacity; gustatory acuity is profoundly disturbed, but strong solutions are still distinguishable. In other words, neural lesions usually produce alterations in the taste threshold, not complete ageusia. Thus it is necessary to use several concentrations of the taste substance. Because of the zonal sensitivity of the tongue, corresponding areas on the two sides must be tested. Finally, since reliable normal values for taste thresholds in man are not available, significant alterations can be detected with certainty only by comparing the two sides of the tongue. This is possible in most cases since the deficits are usually unilateral (contralateral to the lesion).

The following solutions are suggested by Börnstein (8) as suitable for testing taste in the human:

	gm./100 cc.		
Cane sugar	4.0	10.0	40.0
Sodium chloride	2.5	7.5	15.0
Citric acid	1.0	5.0	10.0
Quinine monohydrochloride	0.075	0.5	1.0

Two drops of the solution are applied to the tongue with a pipette, and with the mouth open and the tongue still outstretched, the patient is asked to indicate on a card bearing the words *sweet*, *salty*, *sour* and *bitter* which quality he has perceived. Care should be taken to prevent the drop from rolling about on the tongue and stimulating areas other than that being tested; it is for this reason that the patient is asked to report by pointing to a word. Each area of the tongue (that is, the tip, sides, and base of each half) is tested several times with each concentration, the mouth being rinsed with tap water between each test. The solutions and the varying concentrations of each solution are applied in random order to prevent guessing. However, it is better to save the bitter (quinine) solution until the end because it produces an after-taste which may be sufficiently strong to mask the taste of other solutions subsequently applied.

Biological value of taste

Until recently there has been a tendency to consider the sense of taste as a relatively unimportant modality. To be sure, superficially taste appears to be something of a luxury which nature has bestowed upon the organism in order that it may enjoy its foodstuffs more thoroughly. Richter (28), however, has recently shown in a variety of experiments that the sense of taste plays a most critical role in nutrition and, indeed, in the maintenance of the constancy of the internal environment of the organism. Using the preference technique, he demonstrated that rats suffering from dietary or endocrine deficiencies selectively choose those foodstuffs or liquids containing the substances required to correct their deficiencies. For example, an adrenalectomized rat shows a marked appetite for saline, and if allowed to do so, will selectively drink sufficient sodium chloride not only to maintain life but to gain weight; adrenalectomized animals not offered saline die within a few days. Similarly, an animal in which the parathyroid glands have been extirpated displays an increased appetite for solutions containing calcium, and this can be abolished by parathyroid implants. Vitamin-deficient rats will also eat selectively those foods containing the necessary deficient vitamins. All these vitally important self-regulatory behavior patterns depend upon intact gustatory sensibility, for taste provides the sensory cue by which these discriminative selections are made. Richter has shown that animals deprived of the sense of taste by section of the peripheral taste nerves are no longer capable of regulating their diets to correct deficiencies, but tend to eat and drink indiscriminately. Thus, an adrenalectomized animal, deprived of its sense of taste, dies even though supplied with sufficient salt water to maintain life if it were selectively drunk.

Another series of experiments shows that animals on deficient diets are able to detect the needed elements in food or fluids in lower concentrations than are normal animals. In one experiment the average salt taste threshold for a group of normal rats determined by the preference method was found to be 0.055 per cent, whereas the average threshold for a group of adrenalectomized rats was 0.0037 per cent, or about 15 times lower. Richter suggested that such deficiencies produced some alteration in the taste buds which lowered their threshold to the required material. Another interpretation is based upon the fact that the preference threshold is not the same as the absolute threshold of gustatory sensibility (23). The fact that a normal rat does not preferentially drink salt solutions weaker than 0.055 per cent does not necessarily mean that the salt cannot be tasted, but rather that the motivation is not sufficiently great to force the animal to make such difficult discriminations. The adrenalectomized animal, on the other hand, is sufficiently motivated to increase the salt intake to explain the ingestion of large quantities of saline even at the low concentration of 0.0037 per cent without the hypothecation of chemical or structural alteration of the taste receptors.

Whatever may be the mechanism of these behavior patterns, Richter's experiments have demonstrated the importance of taste as a homeostatic mechanism and have profound implications for the physiology of infant nutrition.

REFERENCES

1. ADLER, A. Zur Topik des Verlaufes der Geschmackssinnfasern und anderer afferenter Bahnen im Thalamus. *Z. ges. Neurol. Psychiat.*, 1934, *149*:208–220.

2. ALLEN, W. F. Origin and distribution of the tractus solitarius in the guinea pig. *J. comp. Neurol.*, 1923, *35*:171–204.

3. ALLEN, W. F. Origin and destination of the secondary visceral fibers in the guinea pig. *J. comp. Neurol.*, 1923, *35*:273–311.

4. AREY, L. B., TREMAINE, M. J., and MONZINGO, F. L. The numerical and topographical relations of taste buds to human circumvallate papillae throughout the life span. *Anat. Rec.*, 1935, *64*:9–25.

5. BLAKESLEE, A. F. Genetics of sensory thresholds: taste for phenyl thio carbamide. *Proc. nat. Acad. Sci., Wash.*, 1932, *18*:120–130.

6. BLUM, M., RUCH, T. C., and WALKER, A. E. Localization of taste in the thalamus of *Macaca mulatta. Yale J. Biol. Med.*, 1943, *16*:175–191.

7. BÖRNSTEIN, W. S. Cortical representation of taste in man and monkey. I. Functional and anatomical relations of taste, olfaction, and somatic sensibility. *Yale J. Biol. Med.*, 1940, *12*:719–736.

8. BÖRNSTEIN, W. S. Cortical representation of taste in man and monkey. II. The localization of the cortical taste area in man and a method of measuring impairment of taste in man. *Yale J. Biol. Med.*, 1940, *13*:133–156.

9. BREMER, F. Centre corticale du goût chez le lapin. *C. R. Soc. Biol.*, Paris, 1923, *89*:432–433.

10. CROZIER, W. J. Chemoreception, Chap. 19 in: *A handbook of general experimental psychology*, ed. by C. Murchison. Worcester, Mass., Clark University Press, 1934.

11. CUSHING, H. The taste fibers and their independence of the N. trigeminus. Deductions from thirteen cases of Gasserian ganglion extirpation. *Johns Hopk. Hosp. Bull.*, 1904, *14*:71–78.

12. ECTORS, L. Étude de l'activité électrique du cortex cérébral chez le lapin non narcotisé ni curarisé. *Arch. int. Physiol.*, 1936, *43*:267–298.

13. FOX, A. L. The relationship between chemical constitution and taste. *Proc. nat. Acad. Sci., Wash.*, 1932, *18*:115–120.

14. GEREBTZOFF, M. A. Les voies centrales de la sensibilité et du goût et leurs terminaisons thalamiques. *Cellule*, 1939, *48*:91–146.

15. GEREBTZOFF, M. A. Recherches oscillographiques et anatomo-physiologiques sur les centres cortical et thalamique du goût. *Arch. int. Physiol.*, 1941, *51*:199–210.

16. KAPPERS, C. U. ARIËNS, HUBER, G. C., and CROSBY, E. C. *The comparative anatomy of the nervous system of vertebrates including man.* New York, Macmillan Co., 1936, 2 vols.

17. KIESOW, F. Beiträge zur physiologischen Psychologie des Geschmackssinnes. *Philos. Stud. (Wundt)*, 1894, *10*:329–368.

18. KOLMER, W. Ueber Strukturen im Epithel der Sinnesorgane. *Anat. Anz.*, 1910, *36*:281–299.

19. LEWIS, D., and DANDY, W. E. The course of the nerve fibers transmitting sensation of taste. *Arch. Surg.*, Chicago, 1930, *21*:249–288.

20. ÖHRWALL, H. Untersuchungen über den Geschmackssinn. *Skand. Arch. Physiol.*, 1891, *2*:1–69.

21. OLMSTED, J. M. D. Taste fibers and the chorda tympani nerve. *J. comp. Neurol.*, 1922, *34*:337–341.

22. PARKER, G. H. *Smell, taste, and allied senses in the vertebrates.* J. B. Lippincott, Philadelphia, 1922, xii, 192 pp.

23. PATTON, H. D., and RUCH, T. C. Preference thresholds for quinine hydrochloride in chimpanzee, monkey and rat. *J. comp. Psychol.*, 1944, *37*:35–49.

24. PATTON, H. D., and RUCH, T. C. The bulbo-thalamic taste pathway in the rat. (To be published.)

25. PATTON, H. D., RUCH, T. C., and WALKER, A. E. Experimental hypogeusia from Horsley-Clarke lesions of the thalamus in *Macaca mulatta. J. Neurophysiol.*, 1944, *7*:171–184.

26. PENFIELD, W., and BOLDREY, E. Somatic motor and sensory representation in the cerebral cortex of man as studied by electrical stimulation. *Brain*, 1937, *60*:389–443.

27. PFAFFMANN, C. Gustatory afferent impulses. *J. cell. comp. Physiol.*, 1941, *17*:243–258.

28. RICHTER, C. P. Total self regulatory functions in animals and human beings. *Harvey Lect.*, 1943, *38*:63–103.

29. RICHTER, C. P., and MACLEAN, A. Salt taste thresholds of humans. *Amer. J. Physiol.*, 1939, *126*:1–6.

30. SHENKIN, H. A., and LEWEY, F. H. Taste aura preceding convulsions in a lesion of the parietal operculum. *J. nerv. ment. Dis.*, 1944, *100*:352–354.

31. SHERRINGTON, C. S. Experiments in examination of the peripheral distribution of the fibers of the posterior roots of some spinal nerves. *Philos. Trans.*, 1898, *190B*:45–186.

32. SCHWARTZ, H., and WEDELL, G. Observations on the pathways transmitting the sensation of taste. *Brain*, 1938, *61*:99–115.

33. WALKER, A. E. *The primate thalamus.* Chicago, University of Chicago Press, 1938, xxiii, 305 pp.

34. WILSON, J. G. The structure and function of the taste buds of the larynx. *Brain*, 1905, *28*:339–357.

35. ZOTTERMAN, Y. Action potentials in the glossopharyngeal nerve and in the chorda tympani. *Skand. Arch. Physiol.*, 1935, *72*:73–77.

CHAPTER 19

VISCERAL SENSATION AND REFERRED PAIN

Langley in defining the sympathetic nervous system as an *efferent* system of nerves was fully aware that sympathetic nerves and the white rami carried sensory fibers from the viscera, but he chose by definition to "rule them out" because, apart from their origin, they resembled ordinary somatic afferents, whereas the sympathetic efferents were distinguished from somatic efferents by a peripheral synapse. So much of the rapidly developing field of autonomic surgery is directed to the control of pain that the modern tendency is to alter Langley's definition and to speak of sympathetic or autonomic afferents (Chap. 10). Alternatively the term *visceral nervous system* can be used to include both autonomic (motor) and visceral sensory (viscerosensory) fibers.

Sensory impulses arising from the structures of the abdominal and thoracic cavities may reach the central nervous system by three channels: (i) by the parasympathetic nerves, (ii) by the sympathetic nerves, and (iii) by the somatic nerves innervating the body wall and the diaphragm. Because of the latter, the sensory innervation of the viscera is a somewhat larger question than visceral sensation. On the basis of their central connections, visceral afferent impulses are divided into three groups: (i) reflex afferents which do not give rise to conscious sensation, e.g., those afferent fibers arising in the carotid sinus; (ii) organic sensation, which includes hunger, nausea, sexual sensations, sensations of bladder fullness, etc.; and (iii) pain afferents. These facts may be conveniently summarized in tabular form.

Sensory innervation of body cavities.

```
                                          ⎧ Reflex (unconscious)
                                          ⎪   1. Carotid sinus
                                          ⎨   2. Hering-Breuer
                                          ⎪   3. Bainbridge reflex, etc.
                                          ⎩
                      ⎧ Visceral afferents ⎫
                      ⎪ of the autonomic   ⎬
                      ⎪ nervous system     ⎭
                      ⎪                                    ⎧ Organic sensation
                      ⎪                                    ⎪   1. Hunger
                      ⎪                                    ⎪   2. Nausea
Thoracic, abdominal   ⎨                                    ⎨   3. Sexual sensation,
and pelvic cavities   ⎪                   Visceral sensation ⎪        etc.
                      ⎪                                    ⎪
                      ⎪                                    ⎩ Visceral pain
                      ⎪ Somatic afferents
                      ⎩ of the spinal nerves ..................Pain
```

Reflex Afferents. The afferent limbs of the reflex arcs which carry out the reflex control of vital visceral phenomena—cardiac reflexes, aortic and carotid sinus reflexes, Hering-Breuer reflexes, micturition, etc.—are without exception found in parasympathetic nerves. True, stimulation of the central end of the splanchnic nerve gives rise to visceral reflexes, notably an elevation of blood pressure, but these seem to resemble the reflexes resulting from stimulating somatic afferents and are connected with pain. The afferent fibers of the sympathetic nervous system, though abundant, are not essential to the reflex regulation of the visceral organs. Cannon's demonstration of the "dispensability" of the sympathetic nervous system is just as true of its afferent as of its motor functions. It will be shown later that the parasympathetic and sympathetic afferents come under the same generalization found to characterize the motor activities of the two systems. Reflexes from parasympathetic afferents are regulatory reflexes operative under normal conditions of life, whereas the reflexes from sympathetic afferents occur only under unusual and often pathological conditions.

It is not unlikely that minor exceptions to this generalization will come to light. For example, the pathway pursued by axons coming from the Vater-Pacinian corpuscles of the mesentery reach the nervous system by way of the splanchnic nerves. Sheehan has shown that all but a few of the mesenteric corpuscles are devoid of entering axons after removal of the 7–12th thoracic sympathetic ganglia, or section of the splanchnic nerves, but not after section of the vagus below the diaphragm. These sense organs, which tend to be distributed along blood vessels, respond to pressure changes of the pulse and the resulting discharges are recorded from the splanchnic nerve (Gammon and Bronk). Taken together, these two facts suggest that some kind of reflex concerned with control of the circulation is subserved by afferent fibers pursuing the splanchnic rather than the vagus nerve.

Organic Sensations. A similar generalization can be made with respect to the sensory functions of the sympathetic and parasympathetic afferents. *Sensory impulses underlying organic sensation are conducted to the central nervous system entirely by way of the parasympathetic nerves.* For example, interruption of the sympathetic nerve supply to the stomach, though interfering with its pain sensibility, does not block the sensory nerve impulses arising from hunger contractions. Similarly in the sacral division, sensations of bladder fullness are completely ended when the pelvic nerve or its roots are blocked. These organic sensations, like certain of the regulatory reflexes of the visceral organs, are elicited in the course of routine visceral activities. The specialization of function noted in the motor activities and in the reflex afferents of the parasympathetic and sympathetic nervous systems is also characteristic of the sensory function of the two divisions of the autonomic nervous system.

Hunger (3, 10). Hunger, defined behavioristically as those processes which lead to the ingestion of food, is made up of at least three components: appetite, hunger sensations, and a third unnamed physiological state of hunger-drive which leads to the ingestion of food.

Hunger sensation has been described "as a very disagreeable ache or pang or sense of gnawing or pressure which is referred to the epigastrium, the region just below the tip of the breast bone." Hunger pangs characteristically recur rhythmically, and with a fair degree of regularity. Previous to 1911 hunger sensation was considered to be a sensation of the depletion of bodily stores of foodstuffs in blood or tissues. Cannon was led to believe that hunger pangs were sensations derived from contractions of the empty stomach. A rubber balloon was swallowed and its tube led to a tambour writing on a smoked paper drum (Fig. 202). The subject, who was not permitted to observe the record, was instructed to depress a key when he felt sensations of hunger. To identify artifacts due to contractions of the abdominal musculature, a simultaneous pneumographic record of abdominal movements was made. Success of this experiment depended on the subject's being well accustomed to the presence of the balloon and tube. Figure 203 is a record obtained in the very first experiment of this type, and shows unmistakably that sensations of hunger coincided with vigorous contractions of the stomach. The hunger contraction was more vigorous than ordinary peristalsis and tended to occur in bouts in which contractions were successively more severe, followed by a period of relaxation and quiescence. They were stopped temporarily by sham chewing and swallowing, by smok-

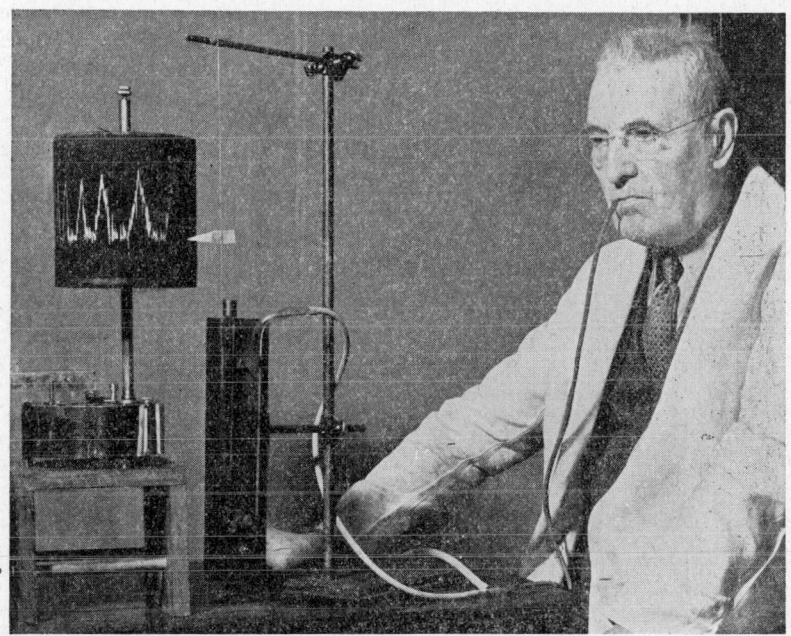

Fig. 202.—Apparatus for recording gastric hunger contractions of the human stomach. A tube attached to a balloon in the subject's stomach leads to a water manometer, with a pointer making a record of pressure fluctuations upon a kymograph. The subject is Dr. Anton J. Carlson; he and Dr. Walter B. Cannon were the pioneer investigators in this field. (From F. L. Ruch, *Psychology and life*, 2d ed., 1941.)

ing and by alcohol, or by tightening a belt; strong emotional states likewise abolished them. Sleep, however, did not inhibit them, and restlessness and dreams are associated with their occurrence as was proved by a simultaneous recording technique. Newborn infants show restlessness before feeding time as though disturbed by unpleasant internal sensations, and random activity of rats interpretable as food seeking is associated with the onset of hunger contractions. However, recent observations suggest that hunger sensations do not cause the increased random activity but that both are manifestations of some more deep-seated phenomena. (See also Chaps. 45 and 53.)

Appetite. Appetite has been carefully distinguished from hunger sensation. It may exist long after hunger has been satisfied. Appetite is highly specific for some one food or a slight variation in the preparation of food. Taste and smell stimuli afforded by food or the environment influence appetite, and it is largely the result of experience and training and culture. Dislike for food may be based on a single disastrous experience. Appetite varies in different parts of the world. As appetite has come to be defined, it is a higher cortical or conscious activity, and certainly not directly connected with sensation, though the appetite of the gourmet is the search for gustatory sensation rather than gastric satiety.

Hunger as a physiological state or drive (10). Hunger sensations are probably of some importance in determining *when* we eat, though the periodicity of eating is not interfered with by ending hunger sensations. However, they do not determine *what* we eat and especially *how much* is eaten. That additional

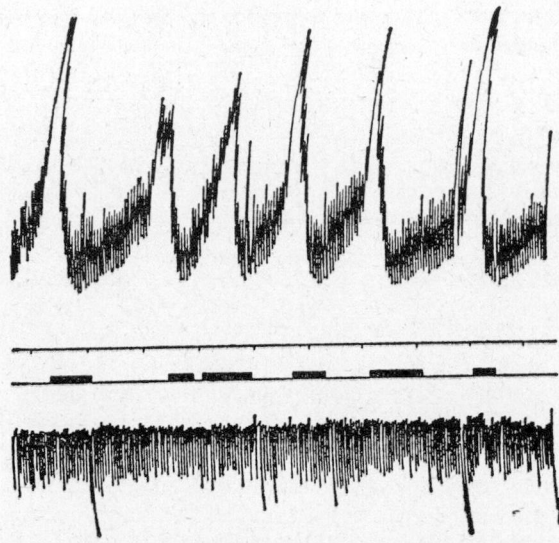

Fig. 203.—Record of the first experiment (W. B. Cannon) demonstrating the relation between hunger contractions and hunger sensation. The tracings in order from the top are: (i) intragastric pressure reflecting hunger contractions; (ii) time in 1 minute intervals; (iii) signal marker activated whenever hunger sensations are experienced; (iv) pneumographic record of breathing movements to prove that intragastric pressure changes were not artifacts. (From Cannon in: *Handbook of general experimental psychology*, C. Murchison, ed., 1934.)

factors are involved is shown by a variety of evidence. For one thing, hunger pangs cease promptly with the ingestion of a few mouthfuls of food, but eating continues. Rats, after removal of the stomach (Tsang), or section of the vagus (Bash, Morgan) which carries the sensory impulses from the stomach, continue to eat periodically, to exhibit periodic random activity, to evidence normal hunger drive, and to maintain body weight. Such animals were as strongly motivated by a food incentive to learn a maze or overcome an obstruction as were normal rats. Hunger, as a physiological state leading to the ingestion of food and in amounts adjusted to energy expenditure, is something different from hunger as a sensation. Just what hunger as a state consists of is less clear.

There is some evidence that the frequency and intensity of hunger pangs are related to the level of sugar in the blood; certainly insulin injections will increase gastric motility and induce hunger, provided the vagus innervation of the stomach is intact. The effect of insulin on food intake, however, is not solely dependent on the increased gastric motility, for food intake continues to be increased by insulin after vagotomy (Morgan). Administration of insulin therefore affects hunger as a physiological state. The self-selection experiments of Davis and of Richter, described in Chapter 18, prove that animals on a qualitatively defective diet will select from a choice of foods the one which will rectify the deficiency. Such hunger is more specific than that due to hunger sensations. The mechanism apparently requires no learning and is so closely connected with bodily needs that it can scarcely be grouped with appetite, which, rightly or wrongly, has become identified with conscious and learned behavior towards food rather than as instinctive drive essential for the preservation of the organism. To maintain the delicate balance between food intake and food requirements demands some more specific mechanism for the control of the kind and amount of food ingested than hunger contractions and hunger sensations. Lower organisms adjust food intake to energy requirements with great exactness (Chap. 53). Man without thought or other conscious activity does the same. Thus qualitative and quantitative dietary deficiency induces a physiological hunger state which motivates the animal to food seeking or to self-selection of a diet until the state is relieved. Whether the hunger state has a sensory basis or whether, as has been suggested (10), a hunger hormone acts upon the nervous system, is not known. Present evidence justifies the belief that three factors, distinct but not necessarily unrelated, are involved in hunger in the general sense—hunger sensations, appetite, and *hunger state or drive*.

Thirst (3, 10). Like the phenomenon of hunger, thirst is profitably considered both as a sensation and as a state of bodily need or drive. Cannon proved conclusively that sensations of thirst are locally generated by dryness of the mucous membranes of the mouth and throat. Thirst is relieved by procedures which alter the sensitivity of these regions (novocainization) or which temporarily relieve the dryness of the throat (chewing gum), and is induced by procedures which causes dryness of the throat (atropine) without altering the hydration of the body. Cannon's theory of thirst affords an explanation of the manner in which thirst acts to regulate water balance through water ingestion. Cannon suggested that reduction in water intake causes water to be drawn from the tissues into the blood, a depletion in which the salivary glands share. The resulting reduction of salivary secretion (not observed in the first few hours) results in thirst leading to drinking. Thirst, defined not as a conscious sensation, but behavioristically, as that which causes an animal to take water and to make strenuous efforts to obtain it, seems to involve factors in addition to local dryness of mouth and throat and local thirst sensation. For example, Montgomery has shown that removal of the salivary glands, leaving only mucous secretory glands to moisten the throat, does not prevent the animal from drinking an amount of water adequate to maintain water balance. Nor does bilateral section in different groups of animals of (i) the glossopharyngeal and chorda tympani (denervating the pharynx), (ii) the olfactory tracts, and (iii) the trigeminal nerve, alter normal drinking or prevent the increased drinking accompanying diabetes insipidus (Bellows and van Wagenen); unfortunately a more complete denervation of the mouth and throat by performing all three operations on the same dog was not attempted. Dehydration if sufficiently prolonged produces unpleasant sensations of dryness and malaise elsewhere than in mouth and throat which may substitute for local thirst sensation in motivating drinking behavior.

Certain phenomena discovered by Adolph and by Bellows are difficult to interpret on the basis of thirst sensations, local or general. Water deficits of different magnitudes were established in dogs by withholding water and the amounts of water drunk in the first 5 minutes after resumption of drinking were measured. This proved to be a linear function of the water deficit, indicating an ability of the dog to estimate the needs of the body by a process which is operative within the short space of 5 minutes, i.e., before absorption and rehydration occurred. Dryness of throat and mouth, being ended with the first gulp, does not motivate continued drinking nor cause it to stop at the "right" amount. Water introduced into the stomach of a dog in water deficit by means of an esophageal fistula did not immediately prevent the dog from drinking; but if thirst was tested 10 minutes after the water was introduced into the stomach, less than the predicted amount was drunk, and after 15 minutes none was drunk. Therefore mere presence of water in the stomach did not determine the amount drunk. The experiments indicate an immediate satisfaction connected with the act of drinking, which, in some way not understood, causes it to cease when the deficit is met, and a delayed satisfaction determined by the fact of drinking which requires about 15 minutes to develop.

Visceral Pain (7, 9, 16). A belief which has caused confusion in this field is that the "viscera are insensitive." It is noted by surgeons operating with local anesthesia that visceral organs can be handled, or even cut, crushed or burned without causing sensation so long as traction on the mesentery and stimulation of the body wall is avoided. And it is true that visceral nerves carry relatively fewer afferent fibers than do somatic nerves. Belief in the insensitivity of the viscera was supported by two misapprehensions. The first was that autonomic nerves contained no afferent fibers. The second mistake was a failure to take into account the principle of the adequate stimulus. The viscera, unlike the skin, are not exposed to and have not evolved sensitivity to the same forms of stimulation that are effective excitants of externally situated receptors. The adequate stimuli for visceral afferents appear to be those arising from their own environment and especially their own activities. Adequate stimuli include the following: (i) dilatation or distension, (ii) spasms or strong contractions, especially when accompanied by ischemia, (iii) chemical irritants. Normal contractions and relaxations of visceral organs apparently do not afford sufficient stimulus to discharge pain fibers though, as in the heart, normal activities may become painful if the blood supply is inadequate.

The generalization can be made that *impulses serving visceral pain are conducted in the sympathetic nerves, and rarely in the parasympathetic nerves.* The main exceptions to this rule are found in the pelvic region and are given in detail below. Because sympathetic nerves do not carry sensory or motor impulses essential for the regulatory reflexes of the visceral organs, sympathectomy can be resorted to for the relief of pain without disturbing seriously the functioning of the denervated organs. The pain pathway can be interrupted at several points, as can be seen by tracing the pathway from an abdominal organ. The free nerve endings in the walls of a viscus unite to form axons which follow the artery to the abdominal aorta where they traverse the collateral ganglia without synapse and enter the splanchnic nerve. The ganglion of the sympathetic chain is entered and traversed, again without synapse, and by way of the white ramus the fibers reach the spinal nerve close to the spinal ganglia. The cell body of the viscerosensory fiber is situated in the sensory ganglion and the central process enters the spinal cord by way of the dorsal root.* There they connect with somatic motoneurons, with preganglionic fibers, and with the neurons of the spinothalamic tract. A visceral organ can therefore be denervated of pain fibers by (i) stripping

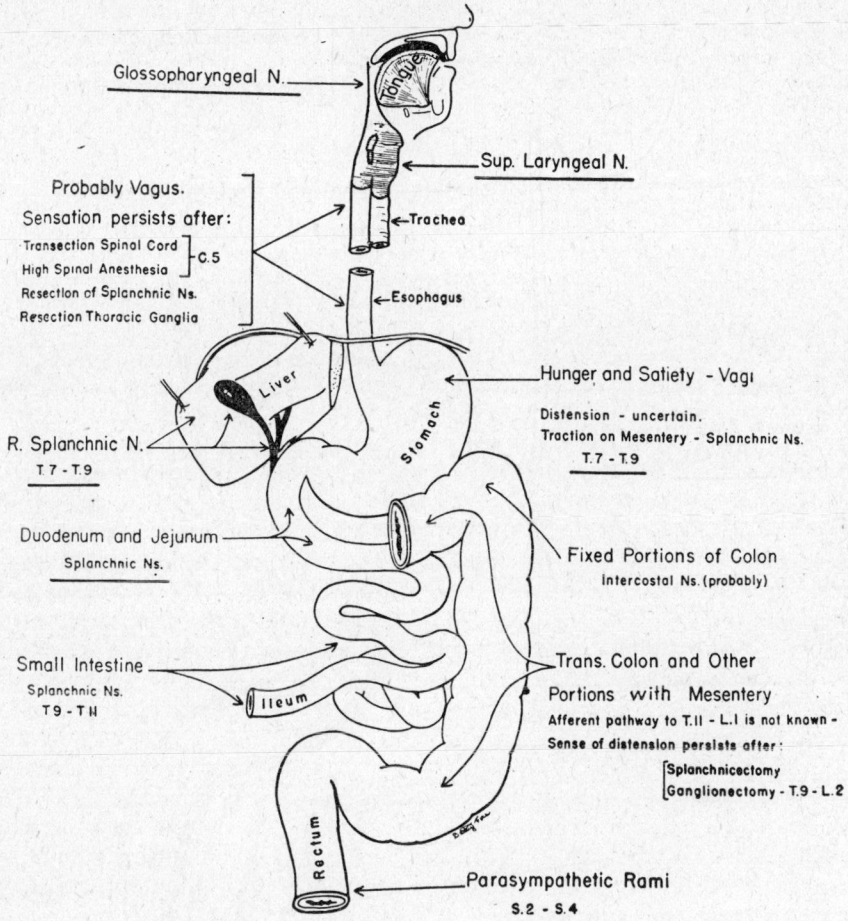

Glossopharyngeal N.

Sup. Laryngeal N.

Probably Vagus.
Sensation persists after:
Transection Spinal Cord
High Spinal Anesthesia ⎤ C.5
Resection of Splanchnic Ns.
Resection Thoracic Ganglia

←Trachea

←Esophagus

Liver

Stomach

Hunger and Satiety - Vagi

Distension - uncertain.
Traction on Mesentery - Splanchnic Ns.
T.7 - T.9

R. Splanchnic N.
T.7 - T.9

Duodenum and Jejunum
Splanchnic Ns.

Fixed Portions of Colon
Intercostal Ns. (probably)

Small Intestine
Splanchnic Ns.
T 9 - T 11

Ileum

Trans. Colon and Other
Portions with Mesentery
Afferent pathway to T.11 - L.1 is not known -
Sense of distension persists after:
⎡ Splanchnicectomy
⎣ Ganglionectomy - T.9 - L.2

Rectum

Parasympathetic Rami
S.2 - S.4

Fig. 204.—Summary diagram of the pathways of pain from the gastro-intestinal tract. The labels give the nerves conducting impulses for pain and the levels at which the impulses enter the spinal cord; where doubtful or fragmentary, the evidence is stated. (From White, *Res. Publ. Ass. nerv. ment. Dis.*, 1943, *23*:373–390.)

the artery supplying it (periarterial neurectomy), (ii) by removal of the sympathetic chain of ganglia at appropriate levels, (iii) by rhizotomy of several posterior roots, and (iv) by section of the spinothalamic tract (chordotomy). Impulses from a single visceral organ enter the spinal cord by several roots, necessitating extensive root sections.

* Removal of a ganglion of the sympathetic chain causes retrograde degenerative changes (chromatolysis, etc.) in the corresponding dorsal root ganglion. The affected cells were the small, deeply staining ones (Sheehan).

The generalization that impulses serving visceral pain are conducted in sympathetic nerves and not in the parasympathetic nerves has been considered true without qualification for the thoracic and abdominal vagus. By means of implanted electrodes, Bradford Cannon (2) stimulated the vagus below the recurrent laryngeal branches to avoid the pain fibers which it contains. Although the cat was fully conscious, no pain was exhibited. Recently

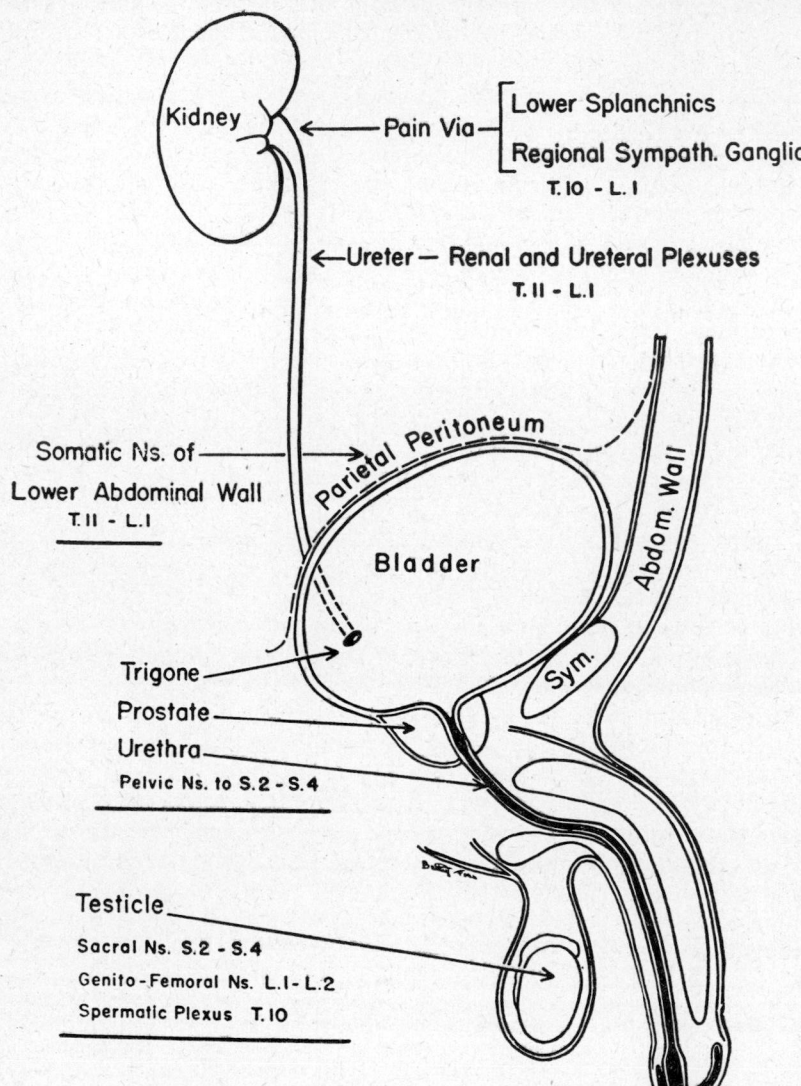

Fig. 205.—Summary diagram of the visceral and somatic pathways of pain from the genitourinary tract. Note the transition from "sympathetic" to "parasympathetic" sensory innervation at the distal end of the ureter. However, the testes, an organ which has migrated, are innervated in part from the lower thoracic and upper lumbar region. (From White, *Res. Publ. Ass. nerv. ment. Dis.*, 1943, 23:373–390.)

White (15) has suggested that in man some pain impulses from the esophagus and respiratory tract are conducted in the vagus nerve. The pain fibers of the gastro-intestinal tract (shown in Fig. 204) except at its lower end are conducted exclusively in the splanchnic nerves. Note, however, that pain from the lower part of the large intestine and from the rectum is not transmitted by the splanchnic nerves. The bladder constitutes a well recognized exception to the rule (Evans). Pain impulses traverse the pelvic nerve and enter the spinal cord by the sacral posterior roots, and surgical section of the hypogastric plexus (sympathetic) has failed in the relief of bladder pain. The proximal portions of the uro-genital system (kidneys, ureters, ovaries, Fallopian tubes and uterus) are served with pain afferents by way of sympathetic nerves, whereas pain impulses from the distal portions (the bladder neck, prostate, urethra and uterine cervix) enter the sacral region of the spinal cord (Fig. 205). Table 13 summarizes the sensory innervation of the viscera insofar as it is known in man.

Impulses arising in visceral structures characteristically give rise to pain localized to the surface of the body; and the point of apparent origin is not in the skin overlying the organ but often at a considerable distance. Such pain is said to be *referred*. The cause of the phenomenon is not known but what determines where the pain is referred is known. It is referred to the dermatomes supplied by the posterior roots through which the visceral afferent impulses reach the spinal cord (see Table 13). The pain of angina pectoris is referred to the chest and to a thin strip along the inner aspect of the upper arm. The highest root carrying pain fibers from the heart to the first thoracic posterior root and the upper border of the corresponding dermatome extends out along the inner aspect of the arm. Referred pain is only one of four associated signs of visceral disease.

Irritation of the viscera by a pathological process is manifested in four ways:

    i. referred pain, dermatomal in distribution.
    ii. hyperalgesia, hyperesthesia or tenderness also dermatomal.
    iii. autonomic reflexes, sweating, pilo-erection, or vasomotor changes.
    iv. somatic reflexes, muscular rigidity.

Types of Visceral Pain. As shown in the tabular summary (p. 385), two main types of pain must be recognized: (i) quasi visceral pain arising from stimulation of the inner surfaces of the body wall, and (ii) pain actually arising from the viscera. Both types may be either referred or unreferred. The former type is not strictly visceral pain but nevertheless is an important factor in visceral disease. Spread of inflammation, exudation, pressure, friction or invasion of the wall will cause pain impulses to reach the spinal cord via the somatic nerves which supply the walls of the visceral cavities. Moreover, the thoracic and abdominal cavities are deeply penetrated by a somatic nerve—the phrenic—in which one fiber in three is sensory and many are unmyelinated. The following expansion summarizes the role of the somatic afferents.

Role of somatic afferent fibers in sensibility of visceral cavities

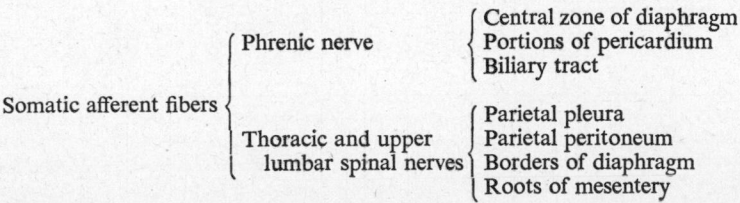

1. *Unreferred parietal pain.* This type of pain was studied by Capps and Coleman (4) in conscious patients. Taking advantage of the space afforded by collections of exudate or by injections of air into the body cavities to gain

Table 13.—Segmental Sensory Innervation of the Viscera*

Organ	Superficial Areas to Which Pain Is Referred	Segments at Which Visceral Afferent Axons Enter Spinal Cord																	Peripheral Visceral Pathway
		Thoracic												Lumbar		Sacral			
		1	2	3	4	5	6	7	8	9	10	11	12	1	2	2	3	4	
Heart	Precordium and inner arm	+	+	+	+	?													Middle and inferior cervical and thoracic cardiac nerves
Lung	No referred pain																		
Liver and Gall Bladder	Right upper quadrant and right scapula						?	+	+	?									Major splanchnic nerve
Stomach	Epigastrium						?	+	+	?									Major splanchnic nerve
Small Intestine	Umbilicus									+	+	?							Major splanchnic nerve
Colon { Ascending	Suprapubic										?	+	+	+					Lumbar chains and preaortic plexus
Colon { Sigmoid and Rectum	Deep pelvis and anus															+	+	+	Pelvic nerves and plexuses
Kidney	Loin and groin										?	+	+	+					Renal plexus via least splanchnic nerve and upper lumbar rami
Ureter	Loin and groin											+	+	+	+				Renal plexus and upper lumbar rami
Bladder { Fundus	Suprapubic											+	+	+					Superior hypogastric plexus
Bladder { Bladder Neck	Perineum and penis															+	+	+	Pelvic nerves and plexuses
Uterus { Fundus	Suprapubic region and lower back											+	+	+					Superior hypogastric plexus
Uterus { Cervix	Perineum															+	+	+	Pelvic nerves and plexuses

* From White and Smithwick, The autonomic nervous system, 1941, after Head, 1893.

space for maneuvering, they stimulated various internal structures. A wire was passed into the space by means of a trocar and pressure or friction was applied to visceral and parietal structures. The visceral peritoneum covering the visceral organs themselves was insensitive to this form of stimulation, but when the body wall was stimulated in this fashion, the pain was sharply localized and appeared to come from the body wall over the site of stimulation. The pain was not referred, presumably because the posterior root innervates superimposed areas on the internal and external surfaces of the body wall. The fact of unreferred parietal pain explains why pain from an

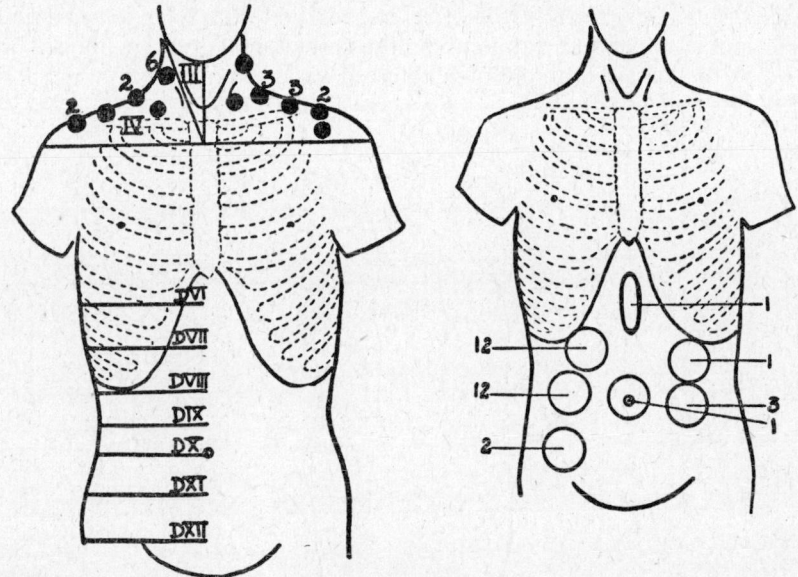

Fig. 206.—Superficial reference of pain from experimental stimulation of the diaphragm.

Left. Reference of pain from stimulating the *central zone* of the diaphragm. The black dots and the attached numbers represent the position and frequency of reference in a series of observations. Pain is also referred to corresponding territory on the dorsal surface of the neck and shoulders (not shown). Roman numerals identify boundary lines of the 3rd and 4th cervical and the 6th–12th thoracic segments (D).

Right. Reference of pain from visceral disease affecting the *margins* of the diaphragm. The circles represent the points of reference, the numbers the frequency of reference; in two cases pain was referred to the back. The margins of the diaphragm are innervated by the lower six thoracic posterior roots. Compare their cutaneous distribution shown in the figure at the left with the zones of reference shown in the figure at the right.

(From Capps and Coleman, *An experimental and clinical study of pain in the pleura, pericardium and peritoneum,* 1932.)

inflamed appendix may vary in position depending on the situation of the appendix.

2. *Referred parietal pain.* Pain arising from stimulation of the margins of the diaphragm which are innervated by the lower six intercostal nerves is referred to the anterior abdominal wall, which is innervated by the same thoracic nerves (Fig. 206). Pain from stimulation of the central zone of the diaphragmatic pleura or peritoneum was invariably referred and always to the point of the shoulder and the neck, as shown in the same figure. This reference is one well recognized clinically. Thus impulses ascending the phrenic nerve and entering the spinal cord via C.3-4-(5) were referred to the

dermatomes of these roots. The diaphragm is a muscle that has migrated caudally, carrying with it the nerve supply, and thereby makes possible such a wide discrepancy between the point of origin and point of reference of the pain. Morley (11) considers all referred pain from the abdomen to be derived from the body wall and suggests for it the unphysiological term "peritoneo-cutaneous reflex."

3. *Referred visceral pain.* In contradistinction to referred somatic pain, this type of pain results from impulses arising from the viscera and conducted over visceral nerves, usually sympathetic. The pain appears to come from the cutaneous surface of the body, often at considerable distance from the diseased organ. Despite the error of reference, the localization may be quite definite, and its apparent location obeys the dermatomal law. Angina pectoris is perhaps the classic example of a referred visceral pain. Pain originating

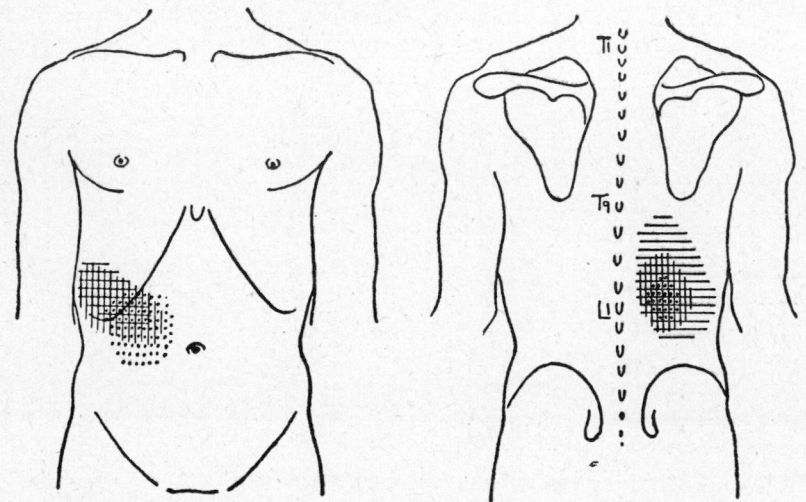

Fig. 207.—Diagram showing the reference of deep pain which was elicited by injections of hypertonic saline into muscles. The shading shows the coincidence of reference for pain elicited from three different deep structures supplied with pain fibers from the ninth thoracic posterior root. Horizontal hatching marks the reference of pain from stimulation of multifidus muscle; vertical hatching from stimulation of the intercostals; and dots from stimulation of rectus abdominus. (From Kellgren, *Clin. Sci.*, 1938, *3*:175–190.)

in the heart is referred to the chest wall with a characteristic extension along the underside of the arm, which is characteristic of the first thoracic dermatome. The pain from a renal stone descending the ureter does not move but has a fixed reference (to the groin, though the upper end of the ureter is beneath the last rib). An inflated balloon in the gut, which embryologically is a midline structure, gives rise to pain which has the same reference whether the stimulated portion of the gut is on the left or right side of the body. Stimulation of the central end of the splanchnic nerve in conscious patients gives rise to referred pain (Foerster). There seems little justification for Morley's contention that pain from the viscera is referred only when the body wall is involved.

4. *Unreferred visceral pain* (*splanchnic pain*). In anginal pain there is, in addition to superficially referred pain, a deep, substernal, agonizing com-

ponent. Such pain is therefore unreferred though it is poorly localized. Ross (12) in 1888 correctly recognized the double nature of visceral pain and named the unreferred component "splanchnic pain." MacKenzie's unphysiological pronouncement (8) to the effect that visceral pain afferents have no connection with the brain (see below) caused true splanchnic pain to be overlooked until quite recently. Clinical literature now stresses this form of pain.

Deep Pain and Referred Pain. The fact that pain conducted from the central zone of the diaphragm over somatic nerves is referred provides a clue to the nature of referred pain. So, too, does the common observation that pain arising in the teeth cannot be localized to the correct tooth, yet the sensory innervation of the teeth is somatic (trigeminal). Referred pain is therefore not a phenomenon associated exclusively with visceral pain, and the reference of visceral pain is therefore not due to any unique properties of the visceral pain pathways. The common denominator of referred visceral pain and referred muscular pain is that they both originate deep to the skin and in a general sense are deep pain. Faultiness of localization perhaps represents the failure to evolve a topographically organized neural apparatus necessary for localization. The faulty projection of deep pain to the surface is due to (i) infrequency of deep pain, (ii) inability to use vision to verify the source of stimulation and thus to develop a superficial projection. Lewis and Kellgren (7) studied the reference of pain from stimulation of deep structures by injection into them of small quantities of 5 per cent saline solution, which is highly irritating (Fig. 207). Localization was fairly accurate for injections into superficial fascia, and into superficial tendons or into the periosteum of superficial bones like the tibia. Pain from the same structures when deeply situated or from the belly of a muscle was diffuse and often referred to a distant area of the skin surface in a regular, reproducible fashion. As with visceral pain, deep somatic pain was referred to the dermatomes supplied by the posterior roots which conduct pain impulses from the muscle stimulated. Kellgren systematically worked out the segmental reference of pain by injecting successively the deep interspinous ligaments with hypertonic saline. Figure 208 shows the resulting maps. These differ in two ways from the dermatomes as obtained by the method of "remaining sensibility" (Fig. 179). On the trunk the reference of deep pain is concentrated near the mid-dorsal and midventral line and the fields of reference for the upper thoracic and upper lumbar segments extend farther upon the upper and lower limb respectively. Muscular rigidity and cutaneous tenderness accompany the referred pain of deep muscle stimulation. Further to emphasize the similarity of deep pain, Lewis and Kellgren induced pain in observers with experience of visceral pain (angina pectoris) by injection of the first thoracic interspinous ligaments. The observers recognized the similarity of the two types of pain.

Mechanism of Referred Pain. To account for the dermatomal reference of pain, MacKenzie (8) suggested that sensory impulses from the viscera were unable to pass directly to the brain, having no connection with the spinothalamic tract, but created an "irritable focus" in the segment at which they entered the spinal cord. Afferent impulses from the skin were thereby magnified, causing pain which was literally cutaneous pain. Similarly facilitation of proprioceptive impulses arising from muscles by the visceral impulses was thought to produce muscular rigidity. Reflex excitation of preganglionic

15

autonomic neurons accounted for pilo-erection changes and for vasomotor phenomena. Stated in modern language, MacKenzie's irritable focus amounts to the suggestion that visceral impulses facilitate somatic pain afferent impulses supposed to come from the skin in the absence of a cutaneous stimulus but in insufficient quantities to excite the spinothalamic tract fibers. Hyperalgesia and referred pain were the consequence. Wiggers (17) and Hinsey and Phillips (5) have stated the MacKenzie theory very clearly in modern

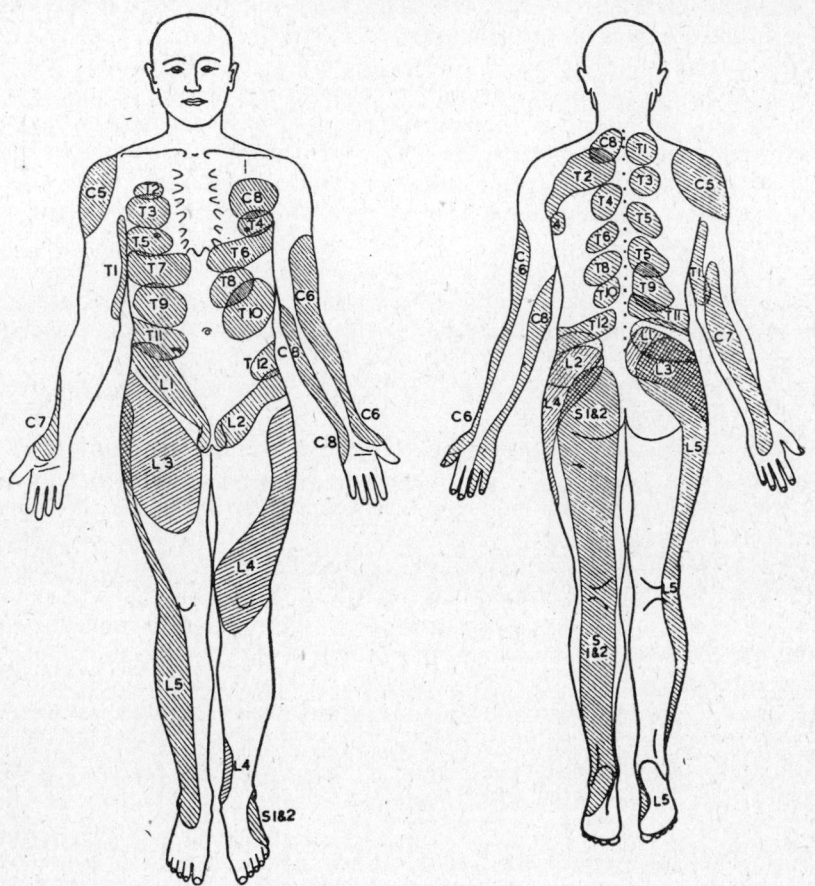

Fig. 208.—Maps showing the segmental reference of deep pain. The numbers identify the regions to which pain is referred from injecting hypertonic saline into the cervical (C), thoracic (T), lumbar (L), and sacral (S) interspinous ligaments. The segmental zones resemble but are not identical to the dermatomes as demarcated by other means. (Drawn by Lewis, *Pain*, 1942, from data by Kellgren, *Clin. Sci.*, 1939, *4*:35–36.)

physiological terms, in which form it can be known as the facilitation theory.

Convergence-projection theory. Facilitation, though it undoubtedly occurs, is not essential to the occurrence of referred pain and the three associated phenomena; in fact, it is a redundant assumption. Muscular rigidity is not due to facilitation of proprioceptive reflexes but is simply a flexion reflex elicited from visceral structures. Visceral afferents form reflex connections with anterior horn cells supplying motor innervation to the skeletal musculature.* Autonomic phenomena are viscerovisceral reflexes. Hyperalgesia of dermatomal distribution is probably the only element ascribable to facilitation. An adequate explanation of referred pain is that some visceral afferents converge with cutaneous pain afferents to end upon the *same* spinothalamic tract neurons, and the resulting impulses, upon reaching the brain, are interpreted as having come from the skin, the interpretation which has been learned from previous experience in which the same tract fiber was hitherto stimulated by cutaneous afferents. The same explanation serves equally well for referred parietal or diaphragmatic pain.

There are many more pain fibers in posterior roots than spinothalamic tract fibers, so that several pain fibers must converge upon one tract fiber. Therefore, it is likely that a share of the afferent pain fibers coming from the diaphragm converge with cutaneous pain fibers entering the same segment to end upon some of the spinothalamic tract neurons. Accord-

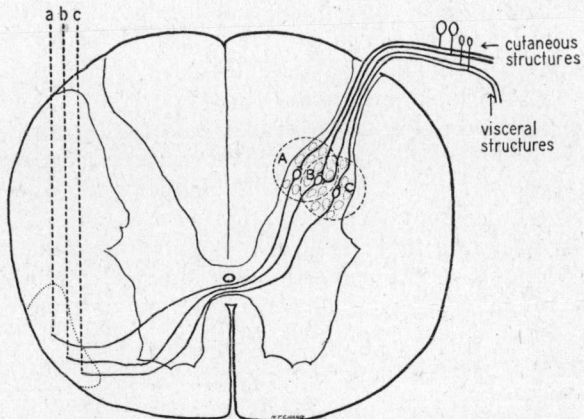

Fig. 209.—Convergence-projection mechanism of referred visceral and somatic pain based upon Sherrington's neuron-pool concept. *A*, *B*, *C* represent a neuron pool consisting of all the spinothalamic tract fibers originating in one segment of the spinal cord. *A* is the field of neurons having connections only with afferent fibers from cutaneous sense organs. *B* is the field of overlap constituted by neurons which receive impulses from *both* visceral and cutaneous afferents, and impulses in *b* will give rise to pain referred to the skin. *C* are those neurons of the pool which connect only with afferent fibers from the visceral cavities, and give rise to unreferred or true splanchnic pain. Only one neuron in each category is represented; others are indicated by "ghost cells." *a*, *b*, *c*, are fibers in the spinothalamic tract having cell bodies in fields *A*, *B*, and *C* respectively.

ing to the doctrine of specific nerve energies, impulses in a spinothalamic tract fiber are identical whatever their origin. On all previous occasions when these particular spinothalamic neurons have been activated, stimulation of the body surface was responsible, as verified by other senses. Thus when impulses of visceral origin reach the cerebral cortex, the interpretation is made which experience has built up—that of a pain arising from cutaneous pain neurons.

Figure 209 illustrates the convergence-projection theory of referred pain applied to visceral sensation. The spinothalamic tract fibers originating at one segment of the spinal cord are regarded as a pool of neurons. The visceral pain afferents entering the posterior root of that segment come into synaptic relation with one group of cells and the cutaneous pain afferents synapse with an overlapping field within the pool. Those spinothalamic tract neurons within the field of overlap, when stimulated by the visceral afferents, give rise to pain referred to the cutaneous surface. In Figure 209 there are certain spinothalamic tract fibers which are "private" to visceral afferent neurons. These fibers are responsible for splanchnic or unreferred visceral pain. Facilitation of cutaneous nerve impulses within the

* These connections are inhibitory as well as excitatory because the knee jerk is inhibited by bladder distension (Dusser de Barenne and Ward).

overlap probably accounts for hyperalgesia, but facilitation is not involved in referred pain. Thus is avoided the unphysiological and unnecessary supposition that cutaneous pain afferents are perpetually discharging at an amount inadequate to discharge spino-thalamic tract fibers unless facilitated.

The only evidence that facilitation is a necessary feature of referred pain lies in the experiments of Weiss and Davis (14) in which novocainization of the skin over the area of reference ended the referred pain or caused it to migrate. However, Carmichael for anginal pain and Livingston (5) for diaphragmatic pain find novocainization of an area of reference to be without effect upon the reference. White, Garrey and Atkins (16) denerv-ated the thoracic wall by section of the intercostal nerves in dogs and observed that ischemia of the myocardium continued to produce pain; Wolff (18) also finds that superficial anes-thesia in most instances does not prevent the superficial reference of deep pain experi-mentally produced.

Central Pathways of Visceral Sensation. Little is known of the spinal, thala-mic and cortical representation of visceral sensation. Visceral pain impulses are grouped with deep and cutaneous pain impulses to pass up the spinal cord in the anterolateral columns; chordotomy is commonly performed for the re-lief of visceral pain. Hyndman and Wolkin (6) have demonstrated this experi-mentally for testicular pain and for the pain produced by distention of the renal pelvis. With respect of other visceral sensations they find, in agreement with Foerster, that sexual sensations are lost in cases of anterolateral chord-otomy. On the other hand, sensations of bladder and rectal fullness are usually preserved even after bilateral anterior chordotomy. White (15) makes the interesting suggestion that the stretch impulses from the bladder, like those from muscle, ascend the posterior columns and thus escape section. Visceral pain presumably has the same thalamic and cortical localization as somatic pain. Like somatic pain it is rarely reported when the human cerebral cortex is stimulated. Little definite knowledge exists on this highly important subject in man.

REFERENCES

1. BELLOWS, R. T., and VAN WAGENEN, W. P. The effect of resection of the olfactory, gustatory and trigeminal nerves on water drinking in dogs without and with diabetes insipidus. *Amer. J. Physiol.*, 1939, *126*:13–19.

2. CANNON, B. A method of stimulating autonomic nerves in the unanesthetized cat with observations on the motor and sensory effects. *Amer. J. Physiol.*, 1933, *105*:366–372.

3. CANNON, W. B. Hunger and thirst, pp. 247–263 in: *A handbook of general experimental psychology*, ed. by C. Murchison. Worcester, Clark University Press, 1934.

4. CAPPS, J. A., with the collaboration of G. H. Coleman. *An experimental and clinical study of pain in the pleura, pericardium and peritoneum.* New York, The Macmillan Co., 1932, xiv, 99 pp.

5. HINSEY, J. C., and PHILLIPS, R. A. Ob-servations upon diaphragmatic sensation. (With a report of a case by W. K. Livingston.) *J. Neurophysiol.*, 1940, *3*:175–181.

6. HYNDMAN, O. R., and WOLKIN, J. An-terior chordotomy. Further observations on physiologic results and optimum manner of performance. *Arch. Neurol. Psychiat., Chicago*, 1943, *50*:129–148.

7. LEWIS, T. *Pain.* New York, The Mac-millan Co., 1942, xiii, 192 pp.

8. MACKENZIE, J. Some points bearing on the association of sensory disorders and visceral disease. *Brain*, 1893, *16*:321–354. See also his: *Symptoms and their interpretation.* London, Shaw and Sons, 2d ed., 1912, xx, 304 pp.

9. MOORE, R. M. Some experimental ob-servations relating to visceral pain. *Surgery*, 1938, *3*:534–555.

10. MORGAN, C. T. *Physiological psychology.* McGraw-Hill Book Co., 1943, xii, 623 pp.

11. MORLEY, J. *Abdominal pain.* New York, William Wood and Co., 1931, xv, 191 pp.

12. ROSS, J. On the segmental distribution of sensory disorders. *Brain*, 1888, *10*:333–361.

13. TSANG, Y. C. Hunger motivation in gastrectomized rats. *J. comp. Psychol.*, 1938, *26*:1–17.

14. WEISS, S., and DAVIS, D. The signifi-cance of the afferent impulses from the skin in the mechanism of visceral pain. Skin infiltra-tion as a useful therapeutic measure. *Amer. J. med. Sci.*, 1928, *176*:517–536.

15. WHITE, J. C. Sensory innervation of the viscera: Studies on visceral afferent neurones

in man based on neurosurgical procedures for the relief of intractable pain. *Res. Publ. Ass. nerv. ment. Dis.*, 1943, *23*:373–390.

16. WHITE, J. C., and SMITHWICK, R. H. *The autonomic nervous system. Anatomy, physiology, and surgical application.* New York, The Macmillan Co., 2nd ed., 1941, xx, 469 pp.

17. WIGGERS, C. J. The physiology of cardiac pain. Chap. 6 in: *Diseases of the coronary arteries and cardiac pain*, ed. by R. L. Levy. New York, The Macmillan Co., 1936, x, 445 pp.

18. WOLFF, H. G. Some observations on pain. *Harvey Lect.*, 1944, *39*:39–95.

CHAPTER 20

OLFACTION AND OLFACTORY PATHWAYS

BY HARRY D. PATTON

Olfaction is a phylogenetically old form of sensation. In many of the lower animals in which other sensory systems are but poorly developed, the olfactory brain is already conspicuously present, and, as might be expected, the olfactory sense is of considerable functional importance to such animals. In man and the higher primates, however, olfaction has become functionally less important than the other senses, and yet there remains in the human brain a complex structure the chief primary connections of which appear to be with the olfactory nerve. Furthermore, this so-called "primary olfactory structure" has extensive connections with brain stem nuclei. These connections are thought to subserve olfactory reflex functions. Knowledge of the functions of the olfactory brain or rhinencephalon is based largely on comparative anatomy; physiological studies of the functions of the various parts of the systems have only recently been undertaken and are as yet few in number.

End-organs. The olfactory end-organs have a limited distribution in the superior part of the nasal cavity (Fig. 210). The total area of this olfactory epithelium is only about 2.5 sq. cm. in each nostril (12) and includes the medial wall of the superior concha and the adjacent lateral face of the nasal septum. Because of this out of the way location, by far the greater part of the air passing through the nostrils fails to reach the olfactory epithelium. However, sudden forceful inspiration through the nose, as in sniffing, creates currents which carry air upwards into the crypt in which the olfactory mucosa is situated.

Histologically the olfactory mucosa consists of olfactory receptors imbedded in a mass of columnar epithelial cells. Some of the latter contain pigment granules which give the olfactory area a grossly recognizable yellowish brown color. As pointed out in Chapter 18, the olfactory receptors differ from all other sensory end-organs because they serve a double function of reception and conduction; i.e., they are at once receptor cells and ganglion cells. Indeed, they were once mistakenly called "nucleated fibers." This arrangement reflects the phylogenetic antiquity of olfaction, for such cells are a primitive type found widely in lower vertebrates (Fig. 195). The cells are ovoid with a tapered distal extension which terminates near the surface of the nasal cavity in a slightly swollen knob. From this knob project 2 to 12 delicate filaments which are thought to constitute the true olfactory surface. Proximally the olfactory cells send a fine unmyelinated fiber upward toward the brain. Ramifying among the epithelial cells of the mucosa are free nerve terminals which appear to belong to the trigeminal nerve and transmit somatic sensory impulses from the olfactory area.

Olfactory stimuli and olfactory threshold. Experimental studies of olfaction have been made on both human subjects and animals. The human studies have contributed information about the sensitivity of the olfactory receptors and the threshold changes of patients with neurological lesions.

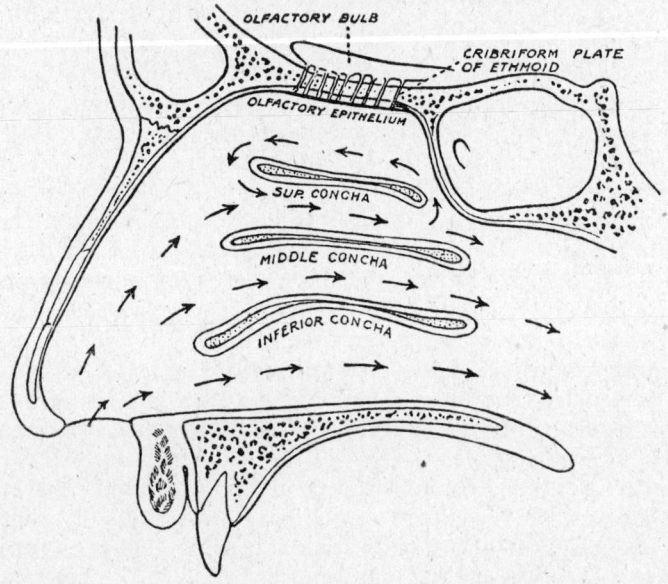

Fig. 210.—Diagram of the right nasal cavity with arrows showing the direction of the flow of air. Sniffing creates currents around the superior turbinate bringing olfactory stimuli to the olfactory epithelium. (From Evans, *Starling's principles of human physiology*, 1925.)

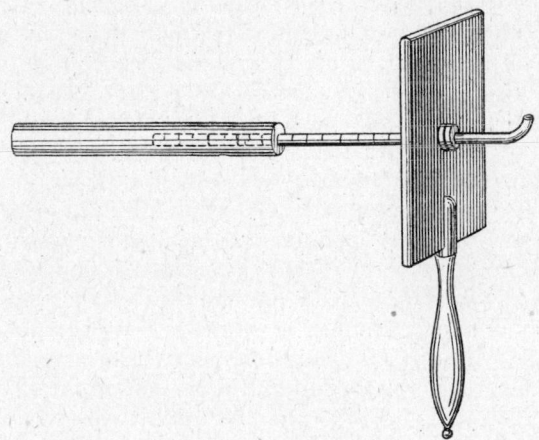

Fig. 211.—Zwaardemaker's olfactometer used for testing olfaction in humans. (From Zwaardemaker, *L'odorat*, 1925.)

The first apparatus for testing olfaction in the human was designed by Zwaardemaker (Fig. 211). It consists of a cylindrical tube the inner surface of which is composed of a porous material which can be saturated with a known strength of an odorous solution. Within this tube fits a second cylinder which is graduated in arbitrary units of length termed *olfacties* and may be inserted to any depth in the outer tube. The end of this tube is applied to the nostril and the subject inhales the olfactory substance. The strength of the stimulus depends on the distance to which the inner tube is pushed into the outer porous tube, i.e., the area of odorous material exposed. This apparatus has the disadvantage that the force with which the stimulus is inhaled is not controlled, and this may alter the threshold. To overcome this Elsberg (7) has designed an apparatus by which the odorous material is pumped into the nostril while the subject holds his breath. With this apparatus the minimum identifiable odor (MIO), or threshold, is determined as the least quantity of air saturated with the olfactory substance which can be smelled when injected with uniform force. The MIO is, within certain limits, the same for all normal individuals and for a given odorous substance, the normal for coffee being between 5 and 10 cc. and for citral between 4 and 9 cc. Variations are due largely to differences in the construction of the nasal passages which permits more or less stimulus-bearing air to reach the olfactory mucosa (7). For a given individual from time to time it is even more constant except that in women acuity increases just before and during the menstrual period. The significance of this is unknown, but it may be recalled that swelling and erythema of the nasal mucosa may be precipitated by administration of estrogenic hormones (11).

These olfactory testing methods have some limited application in clinical neurology because in 74 per cent of patients with tumors in or around the frontal lobes the MIO was found elevated (7). No changes were found in patients with lesions below the tentorium. Through lack of sufficient postmortem verification of the lesions, such studies have contributed little to the understanding of the functions of the various parts of the olfactory system.

The methods of Zwaardemaker and Elsberg yield relative thresholds only. Data for absolute thresholds vary considerably, depending on methods of measurement, but agree in indicating very small threshold quantities. For example, artificial musk can be detected at a concentration of only 0.00004 mg. per liter of air (5). Crozier (6) quotes Fischer and Penzoldt's demonstration that mercaptan can be recognized at a concentration of 0.00000004 mg. per liter of air.

Olfaction may be tested in animals by two methods, the conditioned reflex method and the discrimination method. In the conditioned reflex method presentation of the olfactory stimulus is accompanied by another stimulus which causes a motor response. Soon the animal becomes conditioned so that the motor response occurs on presentation of the olfactory stimulus although the conditioning stimulus is omitted. For example, Allen (2) presented dogs with olfactory stimuli simultaneous to electrical stimulation of the paw. Soon the animals learned to lift the paw when the olfactory stimulus was presented even though the electrical stimulus was omitted. Since such behavior depends on olfactory acuity and consequently on the integrity of the olfactory system, lesions of the latter should interfere with the habit. An interesting result of such studies is that many of the sensations which are commonly alluded to as olfactory are not entirely olfactory but partially trigeminal-borne (2). Such sensations have therefore, at least in the dog, a strong tactile component. Conditioned reflexes to inhalation of cloves, lavender, anise, asafetida, benzol and xylol are abolished by section of the olfactory nerves, and these substances are therefore true olfactory stimuli.

But conditioned responses to camphor, eucalyptus, pyridin, butyric acid, phenol, ether and chloroform persist after olfactory nerve section and can be abolished only after both olfactory nerve section and division of the maxillary and nasociliary branches of the trigeminal nerve. It follows that in studies of the olfactory system, stimuli of the first class, i.e., the purely olfactory stimuli, should be employed, for residual trigeminal-borne cues may be sufficient to provoke a response even though the olfactory pathways be completely divided.

In the discrimination method the animal is trained to discriminate between two food containers on the basis of an olfactory stimulus placed in one. If only one of the boxes contains food, an animal with intact olfactory sensation soon learns to respond appropriately and makes a correct olfactory discrimination in almost 100 per cent of the trials. If olfaction is destroyed by a neural lesion, the animal is no longer able to discriminate between the containers and chooses the food-bearing box on a purely chance basis only (50 per cent correct). Such methods have been employed with rats by Swann (15) and Lashley and Sperry (10).

For investigation of the central olfactory paths, human studies have the drawback that discrete lesions are rare and careful histological confirmation of their location is often unobtainable. On the other hand, animal studies are deficient in the lack of quantitative control of intensity of stimulus. Such control is of particular importance in studying the olfactory system because the central connections are so widespread and diverse that complete interruption of all pathways is impractical. This means that the deficit following ablations will not be complete abolition of function, but rather an elevation of threshold which can be detected only by careful quantitative pre- and postoperative testing.

Olfactory bulb. The axons issuing from the olfactory receptors pass upward and enter the cranial cavity through the cribriform plate of the ethmoid bone. On the ventral surface of the frontal lobes near the midline they enter an ovoid structure, the olfactory bulb. The bulb, like the retina, is a part of the brain proper, and in lower animals is quite prominent and possesses a cavity which communicates with the ventricular system of the brain. In man it is small and has the misleading appearance of a sensory ganglion; the central cavity is obliterated by a mass of neuroglia. Next to the neuroglia is a deep layer of myelinated fibers passing from the bulb to the olfactory tract. Superficially is a layer of unmyelinated fibers which are the terminations of the olfactory nerve, and situated between the two fiber layers is a mass of gray matter which contains three types of neurons, the tufted cells, the mitral cells and the granule cells. The tufted cells are most superficially placed, and the mitral cells form a compact layer just deep to them. The dendrites of both types of cells course toward the periphery of the bulb and break up into rounded, bushy terminals which form synapses with the primary olfactory fibers. These are the olfactory glomeruli. The axons of the mitral and tufted cells join the deep myelinated fiber layer of the bulb to pass into the olfactory tract. The granule cells are most deeply situated and send short axons toward the surface of the bulb.

Central olfactory pathways. The axons of the mitral and tufted cells, on leaving the bulb, are collected together in the olfactory tract which courses caudally on the base of the frontal lobes. Since both tract and bulb are derivatives of the brain, it is not surprising that the fibers are capped dorsally by gray matter continuous with the gray matter of the bulb. The tract is really a gyrus in which the gray matter has been greatly reduced. Just rostral to the optic chiasm the tract divides into two branches, the medial and lateral olfactory striae or (since they also possess gray matter) gyri. Often a less distinct intermediate gyrus is seen running directly into the anterior perforated substance. The lateral gyrus extends under the tip of the temporal lobe to join the hippocampal gyrus, forming with it the pyriform area. The fibers of the lateral gyrus terminate in the amygdaloid nucleus, the uncus and the anterior part of the hippocampal gyrus.

The medial gyrus curves medially into the inferior longitudinal fissure where its fibers terminate on the mesial surface of the hemisphere in the para-olfactory area. This occupies the inferior portion of the cingular gyrus just beneath the genu of the corpus callosum.

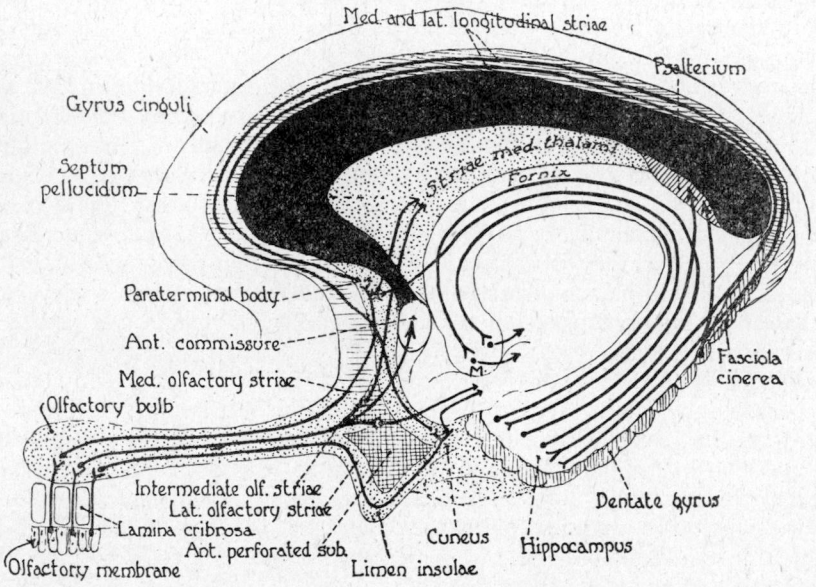

Fig. 212.—Diagram of the more important central and peripheral connections of the olfactory system. (After Rasmussen and Grinker in Fulton, *Physiology of the nervous system*, 1938.)

The cingular gyrus is a band of gray matter visible on the mesial surface of the hemisphere covering the corpus callosum. Posteriorly the cingular gyrus is continuous with the hippocampal gyrus. Anteriorly it is connected with the hippocampal gyrus by the diagonal band of Broca. Thus the olfactory cortex forms an almost complete ring around the medial surface of the hemisphere, and the gap is closed by a band of fibers.

The highest order of cortical olfactory center is thought to be the hippocampus. This structure is formed by a part of the hippocampal gyrus which is rolled into the temporal horn of the lateral ventricle. It receives fibers from the hippocampal gyrus and is thus an indirect connection with the lateral olfactory gyrus. Associated with the hippocampus is the dentate gyrus which has similar connections.

Unlike the other sensory systems, olfactory fibers have no known primary projection to the thalamus. Indirectly, however, such a connection is formed. Fibers from cells in the hippocampus and dentate gyrus are gathered together on the medial surface of the latter and pass caudally to form the fornix. The fornices of the two sides unite over the caudal part of the thalamus and proceed rostrally to encircle that structure and terminate in the mammillary bodies of the hypothalamus. These latter nuclei communicate with the anterior thalamic nuclei via the mammillothalamic tract of Vicq d'Azyr, and the anterior thalamic nuclei in turn project to the cingular gyrus. Numerous other connections of the olfactory system have been described, some of which are shown in Figure 212.

Experiments designed to determine the functions of the various parts of the central olfactory system have been of three types—ablation, stimulation, and electrical recording. In the ablation studies olfaction has been tested by the methods described above. For example, Swann (16, 17) studied the effect of neural lesions on the ability of rats to discriminate between two odors by digging through a pile of shavings saturated with the correct odorous substance to reach food. Lesions to the septum, amygdaloid complex, pyriform lobes, hippocampal complex, fimbria, fornix, habenula, and cortex around the central part of the corpus callosum were all without effect on the discrimination. Section of the olfactory tract was the only procedure which abolished the ability to make the discrimination. Using a similar testing technique, Lashley and Sperry (10) were unable to find alterations in olfactory discrimination in rats after section of the cortical projection fibers from the anterior thalamic nuclei. Allen (3) conditioned dogs to elevate the paw when the odor of cloves was presented. Bilateral temporal lobectomy, removal of the hippocampus, or destruction of the pyriform-amygdaloid complex had no effect on this habit. In more complex conditioned responses involving discrimination between cloves and asafetida, however, bilateral destruction of the pyriform-amygdaloid complex abolished the habit. All these studies are inconclusive, but it must be remembered that minimal cues even in the face of badly deranged function may allow a correct response.

Stimulation studies are poorly adapted to the study of any form of sensation because they necessitate the observer's subjective interpretation of the response. Rioch and Brenner (13) stimulated the basal olfactory areas in otherwise chronically decorticate cats. Such stimulation evoked chewing, swallowing, sniffing, salivation and chop-licking, i.e., produced responses which "appeared to be related to smelling and eating."

Electrical studies have been more fruitful. In the rabbit Hasama (9) detected electrical changes in the pyriform lobe when olfactory stimuli were presented to the animal and the responses were abolished by anesthetization of the nasal mucosa. Allen (4) obtained similar results in the dog and Adrian (1) in the hedgehog and cat. Rose and Woolsey (14), on faradic stimulation of the olfactory bulbs, detected conspicuous electrical alterations in the olfactory tract, the pyriform area, the amygdala and portions of the hippocampal gyrus. More recently Fox, McKinley and Magoun (8) have carried out similar experiments in the cat, placing the recording electrode in the brain with the Horsley-Clarke instrument, thus permitting investigation of deep structures not readily accessible from the surface. Stimulation of the bulb was accompanied by electrical potentials in the prepyriform cortex, anterior perforated substance, and the pyriform lobe. No responses were obtained from the para-olfactory area, the diagonal band of Broca, the amygdaloid nuclei, or the hippocampus. Absence of response in these latter areas may mean that they are connected with the bulb only after a long series of synapses.

REFERENCES

1. ADRIAN, E. D. Olfactory reactions in the brain of the hedgehog. *J. Physiol.*, 1942, *100*:459–473.

2. ALLEN, W. F. Olfactory and trigeminal conditioned reflexes in dogs. *Amer. J. Physiol.*, 1937, *118*:532–540.

3. ALLEN, W. F. Effect of ablating the pyriform-amygdaloid areas and hippocampi on positive and negative olfactory conditioned reflexes and on conditioned olfactory differentiation. *Amer. J. Physiol.*, 1941, *132*:81–92.

4. ALLEN, W. F. Distribution of cortical potentials resulting from insufflation of vapors into the nostrils and from stimulation of the olfactory bulbs and the pyriform lobe. *Amer. J. Physiol.*, 1943, *139*:553–555.

5. ALLISON, V. C., and KATZ, S. H. An investigation of stenches and odors for industrial purposes. *J. industr. Engng Chem.*, 1919, *11*:336–338.

6. CROZIER, W. J. Chemoreception. Chap. 19 in: MURCHISON, C., ed. *A handbook of general experimental psychology.* Worcester, Mass., Clark University Press, 1934.

7. ELSBERG, C. A. Olfactory tests. In: GLASSER, O., ed. *Medical physics.* Chicago, Year Book Publishers, 1944.

8. FOX, C. A., MCKINLEY, W. A., and MAGOUN, H. W. An oscillographic study of olfactory system of cats. *J. Neurophysiol.*, 1944, *7*:1–16.

9. HASAMA, B. Über die elektrischen Begleiterscheinungen an der Riechsphäre bei der Geruchsempfindung. *Arch. ges. Physiol.*, 1934, *234*:748–755.

10. LASHLEY, K. S., and SPERRY, R. W. Olfactory discrimination after destruction of the anterior thalamic nuclei. *Amer. J. Physiol.*, 1943, *139*:446–450.

11. MORTIMER, H., WRIGHT, R. P., and COLLIP, J. B. The effect of the administration of oestrogenic hormones on the nasal mucosa of the monkey (Macaca mulatta). *Canad. med. Ass. J.*, 1936, *35*:503–513.

12. READ, E. A. A contribution to the knowledge of the olfactory apparatus in dog, cat and man. *Amer. J. Anat.*, 1908, *8*:17–48.

13. RIOCH, D. McK., and BRENNER, C. Experiments on the corpus striatum and rhinencephalon. *J. comp. Neurol.*, 1938, *68*:491–507.

14. ROSE, J. E., and WOOLSEY, C. N. Potential changes in the olfactory brain produced by electrical stimulation of the olfactory bulb. *Fed. Proc. Amer. Soc. exp. Biol.*, 1943, *2*:42.

15. SWANN, H. G. The function of the brain in olfaction. I. Olfactory discrimination and an apparatus for its test. *J. comp. Psychol.*, 1933, *15*:229–241.

16. SWANN, H. G. The function of the brain in olfaction. II. The results of destruction of olfactory and other nervous structures upon the discrimination of odors. *J. comp. Neurol.*, 1934, *59*:175–201.

17. SWANN, H. G. The function of the brain in olfaction. The effects of large cortical lesions on olfactory discrimination. *Amer. J. Physiol.*, 1935, *111*:257–262.

CHAPTER 21

AUDITION AND THE AUDITORY PATHWAYS

In discussing the physiology of the ear it is necessary to consider the functional importance of its various parts; the external ear, consisting of the lobe or pinna, the external auditory meatus, and the tympanic membrane; the middle ear, with its chain of ossicles, its muscles and ligaments, and the eustachian tube; and the internal ear, with its cochlea, vestibule (utricle and saccule) and semicircular canals. The eighth cranial or so-called auditory nerve is distributed entirely within the internal ear; the fibers of the cochlear branch, which alone are concerned with hearing, end among the sensory nerve cells of the cochlea, while the vestibular branch supplies similar sense cells situated in the utricle, saccule, and the ampullae of the semicircular canals. We need consider only the functions of the ear in respect of the sensations of sound. The somewhat complicated anatomy of the middle and inner ear should be obtained from the special works on anatomy or histology. For the purposes of physiological presentation highly schematic diagrams (Figs. 213, 214) will suffice to portray the functional anatomy of the parts concerned in the transmission of sound waves from the exterior to the cochlea.

External Ear. The pinna leads into the external meatus by means of a cone-shaped depression, the concha. The whole organ, and especially the concha, may be considered as fulfilling more or less perfectly the function of collecting the sound waves and reflecting them into the meatus. The concave shape of the ear in lower animals and its motility make it much more useful in this respect than is the human ear. The external auditory meatus is not straight, but passes first somewhat backward and upward, and then turns forward and inward to end against the tympanic membrane. All sound waves that affect the drum of the ear must pass through this canal.

Middle Ear. The tympanic membrane completely separates the external auditory meatus from an air-filled chamber, the middle ear. The membrane, although not more than 0.1 mm. thick, consists of three coats: a layer of skin on the external surface, a layer of mucous membrane on the side toward the middle ear, and in between a layer of fibrous connective tissue. The middle layer gives to the membrane its peculiar structure and properties. In form the membrane has the shape of a shallow funnel with the apex or umbo somewhat below the center and directed inwards. The fibers of the fibrous layer are arranged partly circularly and partly in lines radiating from the umbo to the peripheral margin. The walls of the funnel are slightly convex outwardly. The peculiar form of the membrane, its funnel shape, its arched sides, and the eccentric position of the umbo are supposed to contribute to its value as a transmitter of the sound vibrations of the air.

Ear bones. The three ear bones—the malleus (hammer), the incus (anvil), and the stapes (stirrup)—taken together form a chain connecting the tympanic membrane with the membrane of the oval window (fenestra ovalis).

By this means the vibrations of the tympanic membrane are communicated to the oval window and thus to the fluid filling the osseus canals of the internal ear. The general shape and connections of the ossicles are illustrated in Figure 215. To understand the manner in which the chain of bones acts in conveying

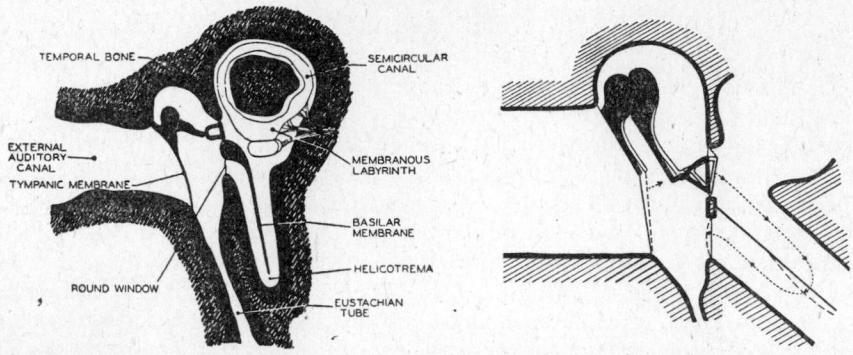

Fig. 213.   Fig. 214.

Fig. 213.—Highly schematic diagram of the middle and internal ear in which the cochlea is shown as though uncoiled. The oval window (unlabeled) lies just above the round window and opens into the vestibule and scala vestibuli, which is separated from the scala tympani by the basilar membrane. (After Békésy. Redrawn for Stevens and Davis, *Hearing. Its psychology and physiology*, John Wiley & Sons, Inc., 1938. Reprinted by permission.)

Fig. 214.—A highly schematic diagram of the auditory portions of middle and inner ear showing the position of the ossicles and various membranes at rest and following inward displacement of the tympanic membrane (shadow lines) by a sound wave. The dotted lines and arrows represent the path of the sound waves. (Reprinted by permission from Stevens and Davis, *Hearing*, John Wiley & Sons, Inc., 1938.)

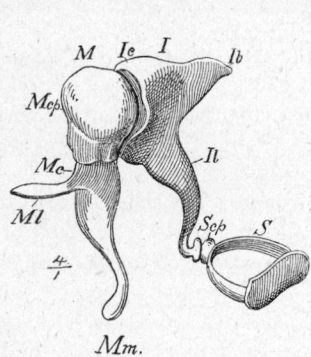

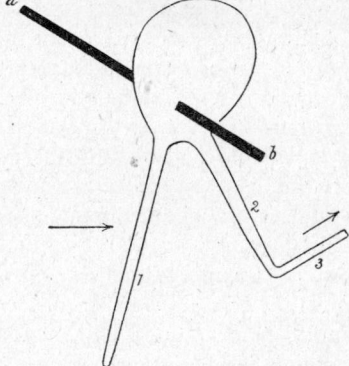

Fig. 215.—The bones of the middle ear in functional connection. *M*, malleus; *Mcp*, head; *Mc*, neck; *Ml*, processus gracilis; *Mm*, manubrium; *Ic*, body of the incus; *Ib*, short process; *Il*, long process; *S*, stapes. (From Helmholtz, *Die Lehre von den Tonempfinden*, 1896.)

Fig. 216.—Schema to illustrate the way in which the ear ossicles act together as a bent lever in transmitting the movements of the tympanic membrane to the cochlea. 1, handle of the malleus; 2, long process of the incus; 3, stapes; *a–b*, axis of rotation. The arrows indicate a movement inward of the tympanic membrane.

the vibrations from one membrane to the other some points in their structure and connections may be recalled. The long handle (manubrium) of the malleus is imbedded in the tympanic membrane, the tip reaching to the umbo. The large, rounded head of the hammer projects above the upper edge of the tympanic membrane and is so firmly bound to the incus that the two bones vibrate as a single unit. By means of several ligaments attaching it to the walls of the middle ear the malleus is held steadily in position even after its connections with the incus are loosened. The incus is somewhat more massive than the malleus, weighing about 25 mg. Its thicker portion articulates with the head of the malleus, and it has two processes nearly at right angles to each other. The shorter process extends posteriorly and is attached by a ligament to the posterior wall of the tympanic cavity; the long process passes downward parallel with the handle of the malleus, but is rounded and turned inward at its tip to articulate with the head of the stapes. The latter bone is extremely light, weighing about 3 mg., its oval base being attached to the margins of the fenestra ovalis by a short, stiff membrane, the annular ligament.

Mode of action of the ear bones. The movements of the tympanic membrane are communicated to the tip of the manubrium. As the handle moves in, the chain of bones acting as a unit makes a rotary movement around an axis passing through the attachment of the short process of the incus and the anterior ligament of the malleus. The general position of this axis is represented by the line a–b in Figure 216. This line passes through the neck of the malleus, so that as the handle moves inwards the head of the malleus and the upper part of the incus move in a direction opposite that of the movement of the handle, whereas the long process of the incus together with the stapes, being below the axis, moves in the same direction as the handle. The chain of bones, therefore, acts like a bent lever. The stapes does not move in and out of the oval window like a piston but rocks on a fulcrum as represented in Figure 214. At that point the annular ligament is short and thick, whereas at the upper margin it is thin and longer.

The function of the ossicular chain is clearly to increase the efficiency with which air waves falling on the tympanum produce oscillation in the fluid of the internal ear. Transfer of vibratory energy from air to water is quite inefficient; inability of a swimmer under water to hear loud air-borne sounds illustrates the inefficiency of this transfer. The factor most important in facilitating the critical step from air to fluid is the relative areas of tympanum and stapes. The tympanic membrane has a cross-sectional area of approximately 90 sq. mm. and the energy falling on that area is concentrated upon an area of 3.2 sq. mm. represented by the stapes. The fact that the stapes has a rocking rather than a piston-like motion with a pivot at the inferior margin of the oval window probably reduces the amplitude of its movement by a ratio estimated at 2 to 1, and hence increases its force. The ratios of the arms of the bent lever probably act in the same direction, i.e., a longer, less forceful movement of the manubrium is converted into a stronger but shorter movement of the stapes.

Muscles of the middle ear. Two small muscles are present in the middle ear: the *tensor tympani* and the *stapedius*. The former arises in a groove just above the eustachian tube, and its long tendon is inserted into the neck of the malleus just below the axis of rotation. The muscle is innervated by a branch of the trigeminal (5th) nerve and when it contracts the tympanic membrane is pulled inward and put under greater tension. An occasional person can contract this muscle voluntarily, when the pulling in of the tympanic membrane can be visualized with an otoscope. The stapedius muscle arises from the inner wall of the tympanic cavity, and its tendon is inserted into the neck of the stapes. This muscle is innervated through a branch of the facial (7th) nerve. Contraction of it tends to pull the stapes in a direction opposite to that of the inward movement imparted to the stapes by the long arm of the incus when positive pressure is applied to the tympanum by the sound wave. It also opposes the action of the tensor tympani muscle, which is to force the stapes into the oval window. The function fulfilled by these muscles has been the subject of controversy. According to a view first proposed by Johannes Müller, they act as a protective mechanism to the delicate auditory apparatus. By increasing the tension of the membranes the amplitude of their vibrations is reduced, particularly those produced by loud, low tones, and the delicate structures of the internal ear are protected from injury or possible rupture by the violent movements resulting from loud, explosive noises. Another view is that the contractions of the muscles adjust the membranes for the better reception of weak sound vibrations and thereby form a mechanism of accommodation similar in its general functions to the ciliary muscle of the eye. That contraction of the two muscles of the middle ear diminishes the transmission of low tones has become quite clear. The fact that the inner ear gives rise to electrical potentials (the cochlear microphonic) which are an accurate index of the responses of the inner ear to sound (see below) enabled H. C. Wiggers (18) to study this question in animals. Under light anesthesia the intra-aural muscles execute spontaneous rhythmic contractions. The threshold of hearing during these contractions was *increased* for low tones (below 1000 cycles per sec.), and was unchanged for all frequencies above 2000 cycles per sec. Since low pitched sounds are prone to dislodge or damage the organ of Corti, any device which reduces transmission of them would be protective in function.

The muscles of the ossicular chain are thrown into reflex contraction—the acoustic reflex—by two classes of stimuli: (i) sound, and (ii) irritation of the external auditory canal, pinna, or face. The latency of the reflex is 14 to 16 msec., only slightly less than that of the blink reflex. It is not improbable that the reflex contractions are more vigorous than the spontaneous ones observed by Wiggers which affected the threshold to the extent of 40 decibels.

The eustachian tube (3). Through the eustachian or auditory tube a communication is established between the cavity of the middle ear and the pharynx, and through this latter with the exterior. The obvious advantage of this arrangement is that it keeps the air within the middle ear under the same pressure as the outside air—that is, the pressure on the two sides of the tympanic membrane is kept the same. The slitlike pharyngeal opening of the tube is normally closed; otherwise the breath passing the orifice would be heard. It is opened reflexly by contractions of the tensor palati muscle in the acts of swallowing, yawning and sneezing, producing a characteristic "click." Without thinking we perform the act of swallowing whenever the sensations from the tympanic membrane warn us of an inequality in pressure upon the two sides. However, in upper respiratory infections the auditory tube may become closed as a result of inflammation and collection of mucous so that it cannot be reflexly opened. The air trapped within the middle ear is partly absorbed and the tympanum bulges inward with resulting discomfort and interference with hearing.

When one ascends in an airplane to levels at which the atmospheric pressure is sufficiently less than at ground level, the tympanic membrane would be bulged outward by the excess of pressure within the middle ear were it not for the existence of the eustachian tube. Under these conditions swallowing movements open the pharyngeal end of the tube and thus allow an equalization of pressure on both sides of the tympanic membrane. In nasal catarrh the tube may be occluded and prevent this equalization during ascent, and under such conditions, as is well known, the delicacy of hearing is much impaired and an uncomfortable sense of fullness results.

During ascent in an airplane or a decompression chamber the opening of the eustachian tube can occur periodically and automatically as a purely physical event, and is signaled by an unpleasant "click" due to the outward bulging tympanic membrane suddenly snapping back to its normal position. The tube first opens when the pressure within the middle ear reaches 15 mm. above sea level barometric pressure and remains open until the pressure falls to 3.6 mm. Hg; thereafter it opens with each increment of 11.4 mm. Hg. Periodic opening of the eustachian tubes by swallowing usually occurs during ascent, and is the *sole* mechanism for equalization of pressure during *descent*. In the absence of opening of the tube by muscular action, as may occur in the transport of wounded who are unconscious or anesthetized, the tube remains closed, or, in fact, is held more firmly closed by the pressure in the nasopharynx which is in excess of that of the middle ear. This is due to a flutter-valve action of the nasopharyngeal opening of the eustachian tube. If for any reason a marked negative pressure (about 80 or 90 mm. Hg) is allowed to develop within the middle ear, voluntary contraction of the muscles may be incapable of opening the tubes unless re-ascent is feasible. In airplane flights difficulty is therefore much more likely to develop in descent than in ascent. At negative pressures of 60–80 mm. Hg within the middle ear, pain is very severe and deafness, tinnitus, and vertigo are marked. Rupture of the ear drum occurs at negative pressures varying between 100 and 500 mm. Hg, and is marked by the sensation of a loud, explosive sound, piercing pain, nausea and even shock. It is reported that the patient feels "as though hit along the side of the head with a plank." Short of rupture, pressure differences are said to produce traumatic inflammation of the middle ear recently described as a clinical entity (aero-otitis media) by Armstrong and Heim (3). The ear drum is sometimes pierced by a fine needle to allow the trapped air to escape; small defects of the tympanum so produced quickly close and heal.

Inner Ear. The manner in which the ear analyzes complex sound waves into component frequencies (pitches) was originally deduced by Helmholtz from the anatomical structure of the internal ear; only recently has this shrewd deduction been vindicated by direct experiments. Helmholtz was struck by the fact that the ear contains a very large number of neurosensory units stretched out along a membrane interposed in the path of the sound wave. The arrangement seemed to him one which would result in a given unit being more vigorously stimulated by sound waves of given frequency. This would result in a different nerve fiber discharging more actively for each frequency within the audible range, and the discharge of this unit would be recognized by the cerebral cortex as a given pitch. The functional anatomy and the physiology of the inner ear are thus inextricably bound together.

The inner ear, like the middle ear, is housed in a system of cavities and tunnels known as the osseus labyrinth, and is partly concerned with hearing and partly with sensations of movement and position in space (Figs. 213, 217, 218). The cochlear portion of the osseus labyrinth consists of a fluid-filled tube approximately 3 cm. long, coiled in a spiral fashion not unlike the shell of a snail. The central pillar of the cochlea is known as the modiolus. A stout connective tissue membrane (the basilar membrane), stretching from the shelf-like, osseus, spiral lamina of the modiolus to the spiral ligament of the outer wall, completely divides the canal into two passageways except for a small opening (the helicotrema) at the apical end of the modiolus. This opening serves to equalize pressure differences and allow fluid to flow between the two divisions of the cochlea, but does so only slowly because of its small diameter. Sound waves enter the part of the cochlea *above* the basilar membrane (*scala vestibuli*) by way of the oval window and the *vestibule*—hence its name (Fig. 214). (The vestibule contains and connects with parts of the nonauditory apparatus of the inner ear.) The passageway *below* the basilar membrane, the *scala tympani*, communicates with the middle ear by way of the round window, which is closed by the *secondary tympanic membrane*. The osseous labyrinth contains perilymph and communicates with the subarachnoid space of the brain through the ductus perilymphaticus.

Within the osseous labyrinth lies the membranous labyrinth, a portion of which extending into the cochlea is variously known as the *cochlear duct* or

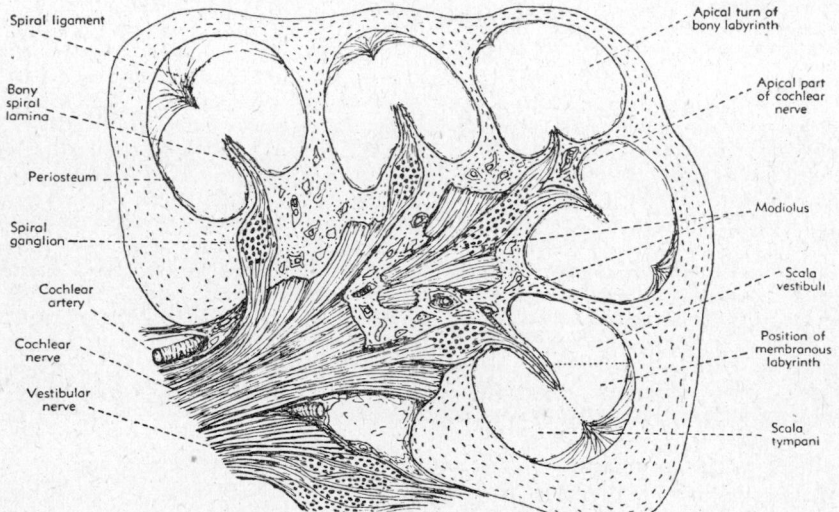

Fig. 217.—Vertical section through the middle of the human cochlea. The basilar membrane and the organ of Corti are not shown. The width of the basilar membrane (spiral lamina to spiral ligament) is less in the wide basal turns than in the more narrow apical turns; also the spira ligament is more massive in the basal turns. (From Rasmussen, *Outlines of neuro-anatomy*, 3d ed., 1943.)

the *scala media*. In a sense it occupies the lower third of the scala vestibuli, from which it is separated by a delicate layer of connective tissue, the *membrane of Reissner;* it is separated from the scala tympani by the spiral ligament, basilar membrane, and the extremity of the spiral lamina. The sleeve of connective tissue so formed is lined with epithelium, which, over the basilar membrane, is highly modified to form the organ of Corti, which contains the actual sound receptor cells. The cochlear duct resembles the finger of a rubber glove, which opens into the vestibule (palm) but ends blindly near the apex of the cochlea. Therefore Reissner's membrane is complete and separates the perilymph of the scala vestibuli from the endolymph of the cochlear duct. However, Reissner's membrane is so delicate that insofar as sound waves are concerned, the scala vestibuli and scala media probably function as a single tube in the transmission of sound. In fact, the term "scala vestibuli" is often used loosely to include the cochlear duct.

Sensory epithelium of the cochlea. The fibers of the cochlear branch of the auditory nerve arise in the nerve cells of the spiral ganglion situated within the modiolus of the cochlea. This ganglion resembles in structure the posterior

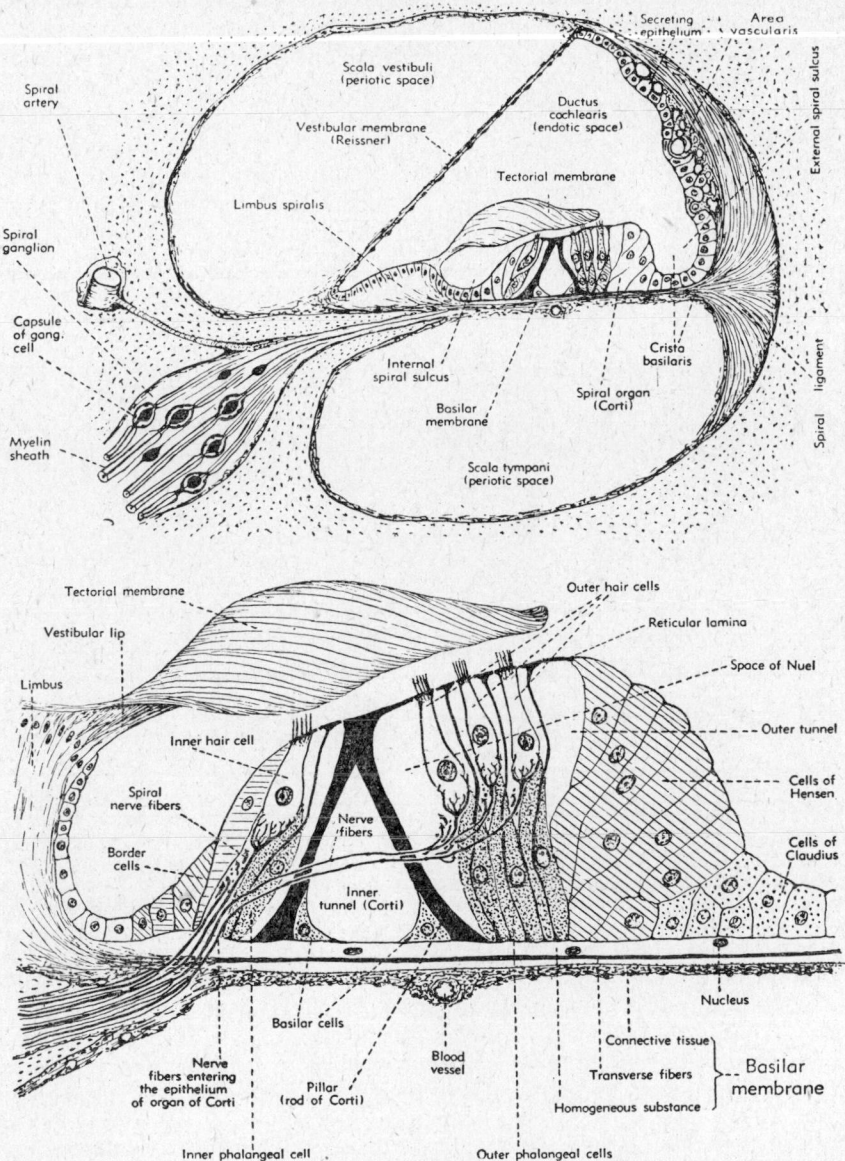

Fig. 218.—Upper: Vertical section of the human cochlea showing the organ of Corti and adjacent structures. Lower: The organ of Corti and the basilar membrane in greater magnification. (From Rasmussen, *Outlines of neuro-anatomy,* 3d ed., 1943.)

root ganglion of the spinal nerves. Each cell is bipolar, sending one fiber toward the brain in the auditory nerve, and one fiber to end in terminal arborizations around the sensory cells or *hair cells* of the *organ of Corti* in the cochlea. We have every reason to believe, therefore, that these hair cells form the apparatus which is affected by sound and by means of which nerve impulses are generated in the fibers of the auditory nerve. The general arrangement and the relations of these cells are indicated in Figure 218. They consist of short, more or less cylindrical cells, whose lower portion does not reach to the basilar membrane, but is supported by phalangeal Deiters cells. The upper ends of the cells project through the openings in the reticulate membrane and end in a number of short, stiff hairs. The hair cells are divided by a supporting arch of Corti (rods of Corti) into a single row of *inner hair cells* and three or four rows of the *outer hair cells*. Lying above, and, in the living state, possibly in contact with the hairlike processes of the sensory cells, is the nearly structureless tectorial membrane which is attached at one end to the spiral osseous lamina and free at the other.

Physical and Psychological Dimensions of Sound. Sound waves in air consist of vibrations of the air molecules, or alternate phases of rarefaction and con-

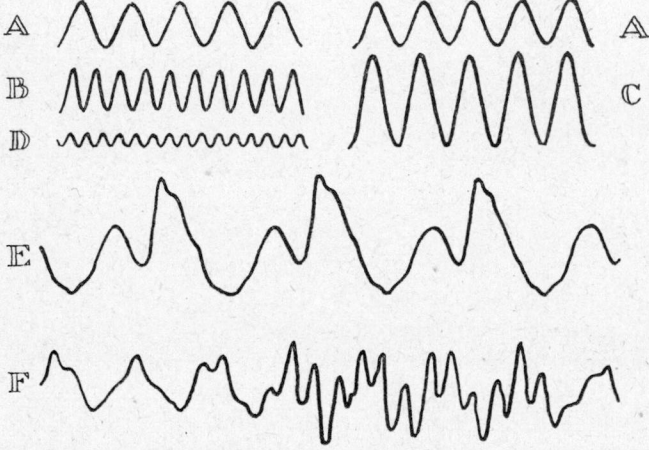

Fig. 219.—Diagram showing the dimensions of a sound wave. A and B differ in frequency (pitch). A and C differ in amplitude (loudness). D, though of smaller amplitude, is equal to A in loudness, showing that frequency is a factor in loudness. E and F illustrate the difference between a musical sound and a noise. Note that in E (from an organ pipe) the wave form is complex but is regularly repeated, whereas F, representing the sound of a bell, is irregular or nonperiodic. (After Miller, *The Science of musical sounds*, 1916.)

densation of the air. For the sake of convenience these waves are usually represented graphically, after the manner of water waves, by a curved line rising above and falling below a median zero line, the part of the curve above the zero line representing the phase of condensation, and the part below the phase of rarefaction. Force is exerted in the direction in which the wave is traveling and alternately pushes and pulls upon objects encountered. The simplest kind of sound wave—a sine wave—can vary in two ways, in frequency (and hence duration) and in amplitude. This is shown in Figure 219. But such simple sound waves are obtained only from tuning forks or other special devices. Most musical instruments produce *compound* sound waves (see Fig. 223). Even a single string does so because it vibrates as a whole, in halves, fourths, eights, etc. (overtones) (see Fig. 224). Therefore sound waves, if compound, can vary in form as well as in frequency and in amplitude. When these waves, whatever may be their form, follow each other with regularity—that is, with a definite period or rhythm—a musical sound is perceived provided the rhythm is maintained for a number of vibrations; regularity or periodicity of the sound waves may be considered as the underlying physical cause of musical sounds. Nonmusical sounds or noises, which constitute the vast majority of our auditory sensations, result from stimulation of the ear by nonperiodical vibrations. Waves of this kind may be due to the nature of the impulse given to the air by the sounding body— single pulses, for instance, or a series of such pulses following at a slow or irregular rhythm, or, more frequently, a mixture of very short and different rhythmical vibrations. As the case of musical sounds is far the simpler, the theory of the function of the cochlea has been based chiefly upon the results obtained from a study of waves producing these sounds.

Pitch. Sounds vary in pitch, i.e., "highness" and "lowness," and this difference finds its physical correlate in the frequency of the vibration of the sounding body and the sound waves produced by it. The pitch of compound sounds is determined by the frequency of the main wave or fundamental. The human ear is capable of perceiving vibrations ranging in frequency from 16 to 20,000 per second; below this range only a series of discontinuous pulsations is heard while above this range at moderate amplitudes no sound whatever is heard. The upper limit of hearing is higher for certain animals than it is for man, which is the physiological basis of the "silent dog whistle," a device that emits sound waves at a frequency above the range of frequencies perceptible by man but still within the range perceptible by dogs. Pitch, though primarily a correlate of frequency, is not wholly independent of the amplitude of sound waves. The pitch of a low tone is lowered by an increase of intensity, but the pitch of a high tone is raised by an increase of intensity of the sound stimulus (Stevens). However, this is true only of pure tones, not of compound tones, so that little disturbance of the pitch-frequency relationship is found in the sounds emitted by musical instruments.

It has been estimated that within the range of normal hearing 15,000 pitches can be discriminated (Stevens and Davis), an important fact which must be explained by any "adequate" theory of hearing.

Loudness and Intensity (14). In a general way it can be said that loudness of a sound is correlated with the amplitude of the sound wave, though several qualifications are necessary to make this an accurate statement. It must be remembered that loudness is a psychological reaction to the physical property, *intensity*, which is only very roughly synonymous with amplitude of sound waves. Certainly frequency as well as amplitude is a factor in determining the loudness of a sound, as can be seen in Figure 220. The determination of thresholds of hearing in terms of absolute physical quantities of force or energy at the tympanum is technically a difficult matter, but fortunately is unnecessary for many purposes. However, measurement of absolute quantities of energy at the threshold intensity of sound has brought out the fact that the minimum effective pressures and particle movement are extraordinarily minute. The calculated movement of the air particles (amplitude of sound wave) and the directly measured movement of the tympanum in the range within which the ear is most sensitive is less than 10^{-9} cm., and in terms of displacement of the basilar membrane must be less than 10^{-10} cm., which is less than the diameter of a hydrogen molecule. The sensitivity of the human ear is so great that it must approach the theoretical limit beyond which further sensibility would render audible the Brownian movement of air particles. Why pressure variations and vibrations of the blood vessels of the tympanum and cochlea do not produce disturbing sound becomes especially puzzling in view of the extreme sensitivity of the ear.

Audibility curve. Though one speaks of the threshold of hearing, there is not one threshold but many thresholds, one for each frequency within the audible range. Actually for each frequency there are two thresholds, one intensity at which the sound is first heard and one at which it is sufficiently intense to elicit a sensation of pressure, the threshold of feeling. The curve which shows the auditory sensitivity at various frequencies is analogous to the visibility curve in vision and is known as the *audibility curve* or *audiogram*. Sensitivity of the ear is expressed in relative terms (decibels, see below) or in

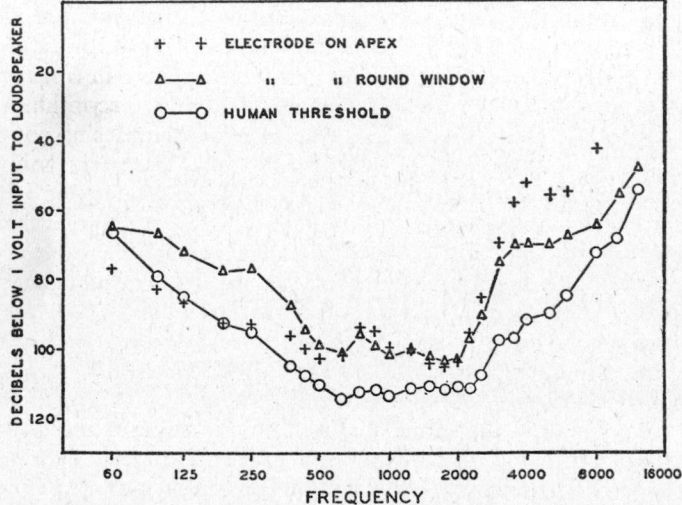

Fig. 220.—Audibility curves from eight human subjects and from 17 guinea pigs. For man the threshold of subjective sensation as related to frequency is plotted. For the guinea pig the intensity just sufficient at each frequency to elicit a detectable electric response from two positions on the cochlea (cochlear microphonic, described below) is plotted. The similarity of shape between curves suggests that the dependence of audibility upon frequency is due to the transmission properties of the middle ear. (From Stevens, Davis and Lurie, *J. gen. Psychol.*,1935, *13*:297–315.)

pressure of sound waves, which requires accurate measurement by physical instruments. The striking feature of the audibility curve is the degree to which the threshold depends upon frequency. Hearing is best at 1000 to 3000 cycles per sec. and decreases sharply for both low and high tones. The reverse holds for the threshold for feeling, which is lower for both high and low tones, so that increase in the intensity of the tones at the extremes of the curve results in nonauditory sensations before the vibration can be heard as sounds. It is interesting that the frequencies most important for perception of the human voice are just those which the human ear hears best. The audibility curve is largely determined by energy loss in transmission of the sound waves through the middle ear and cochlea—intra-aural muscles, the natural period of the ossicles, basilar membrane, etc.—rather than the nervous pathways. This is known because the audiogram plotted by measuring the threshold responses of the cochlea (by electrical methods) resembles that obtained by measuring the threshold for conscious sensation (Fig. 220).

Audiometry. The fact that the auditory threshold is so dependent upon pitch makes it evident that the rough and ready methods of testing hearing—the whispering or the ticking watch—do not measure but merely sample hearing ability. Testing of hearing has come to mean the determination of the audibility curve, usually called an audiogram. This is done by means of an apparatus specifically devised for this purpose, the audiometer, which consists of a vacuum tube oscillator arranged to produce a range of frequencies one octave apart. The intensity at which each of these frequencies is just barely heard is determined on a large number of normal individuals. The apparatus is so calibrated that the value thus obtained is "0" on the dial controlling

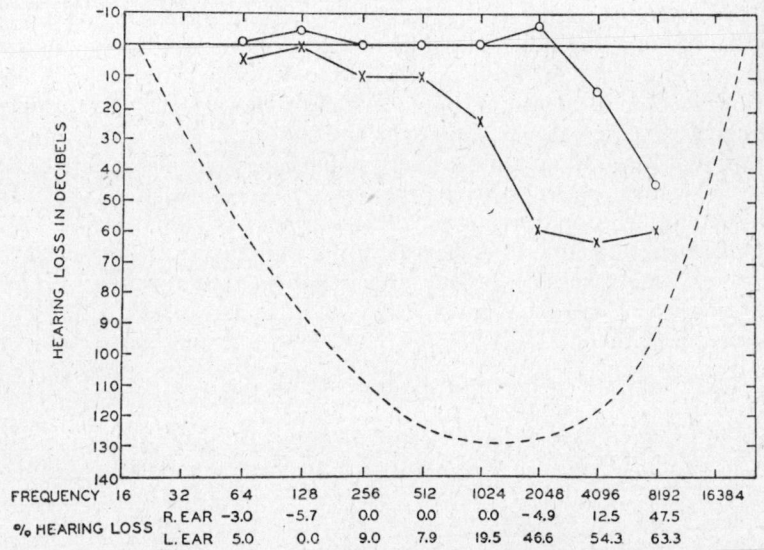

FREQUENCY	16	32	64	128	256	512	1024	2048	4096	8192	16384
% HEARING LOSS R. EAR		-3.0	-5.7	0.0	0.0	0.0	-4.9	12.5	47.5		
L. EAR		5.0	0.0	9.0	7.9	19.5	46.6	54.3	63.3		

Fig. 221.—A graphical representation of hearing ability (audiogram) of an individual suffering from high-tone deafness. Circles indicate the auditory sensitivity of the right ear, and crosses, the left ear. The figures at the bottom show the calculation of per cent hearing loss, with the broken line, the threshold of feeling, representing complete loss of hearing. For convenience, the normal threshold of hearing is taken as zero (or reference point) on a decibel scale. In absolute physical units threshold energy varies considerably throughout the audible range of frequencies. (Reprinted by permission from Stevens and Davis, *Hearing*, John Wiley & Sons, Inc., 1938.)

intensity, and therefore the 0 line on the audiogram represents normal hearing. The threshold of hearing is shown on the audiogram as though it were equal for all frequencies, but it is, as we have seen, very unequal (Fig. 220). The broken line in Figure 221 represents complete hearing loss: between 0 and the broken line each increase in intensity brings an increase in loudness up to the point beyond which a *tactual* sensation is experienced (threshold of feeling). The crosses and circles represent the thresholds of the left and right ears of an individual showing high-tone deafness, greater in the left than in the right ear. The test is conducted as follows. The patient holds a receiver to his ear and flashes a light whenever a sound is heard. A tone of a given frequency is intermittently sounded and steadily decreased until the intensity is found at which the patient is barely able to signal consistently the occurrence of the sound. The value is read from the dial controlling intensity, which is calibrated in decibels or sensation units, and entered on the audiogram. This fixes one point on the patient's audibility curve; the procedure is repeated for the remaining frequencies. In interpreting such curves the following points should be noted. Hearing loss may be stated in terms of decibels (see below), or it may be stated in terms of percentage loss of useful hearing. If at any point the patient's threshold coincides with the broken line representing the threshold for feeling, the loss of hearing is complete. If the threshold falls half way between the zero line and the broken line, the loss is 50 per cent.

The decibel. Intensity of sound, though a physical aspect of sound, is usually not stated in terms of the absolute pressures or energy of the sound wave. The commonly employed unit of intensity is the *decibel*, which states the intensity of a sound relative to the threshold of hearing of the given individual or of a group of individuals, or, better, in reference to an absolute value which is close to the average threshold of hearing. It is therefore a ratio of two sound intensities, one of which is chosen near the threshold of the human ear; the other is the sound intensity to be described. The reason for this practice is that the absolute magnitude of pressures or energy is inconvenient to measure, whereas the ratio of two intensities, for example, can be determined simply from the voltages applied to a loudspeaker. Because the range of sound intensities heard by the human ear is very extensive, a logarithmic scale is used to avoid large numbers. The formula, in terms of sound energy (E), in which E_2 is the reference sound, and E_1 is the sound to be described, is then:

$$N_{bel} = N_b = \log \frac{E_1}{E_2}$$

Since the bel* is inconveniently large, a *decibel* (db), which is one-tenth as large, has come into favor. The number of decibels is therefore ten times the number of bels, or:

$$N_{db} = 10 \log \frac{E_1}{E_2}$$

Since the energy of the sound wave is the square of the sound pressure and also of the voltage applied to a loudspeaker, the voltage or pressure ratio is squared by multiplying its logarithm by 2, to get the common form:

$$N_{db} = 20 \log \frac{V_1}{V_2} \text{ or } 20 \log \frac{P_1}{P_2}$$

To state the intensity of a sound in decibels, which is a ratio of two sounds, a reference intensity is required, and standard references have been established. When the threshold of the human ear is taken as the reference point, the decibel value of a sound is termed the *sensation level* and has no absolute physical meaning. When the standard reference is used the resulting value is described as the *intensity level*. The standard reference (0.0002 dyne/cm.²) is close to the human auditory threshold of hearing for a 1000-cycle tone, and is preferable because it has meaning in terms of absolute physical units. A useful scale of decibel values is shown in Figure 222. It will be noted that

---

* The bel which is 10 times as large as the decibel was named for Alexander Graham Bell, the inventor of the telephone.

the full range of sound from the threshold to the loudest tolerable to the ear, which is 1,000,000,000,000 times the threshold energy, can be expressed on the scale between 0 and 120 db.

Quality or Timbre. Besides pitch and loudness, musical sounds possess a third property, *quality* or *timbre*. The same note of the same amplitude, when given by different musical instruments, varies in quality, so that we have no difficulty in recognizing the note of a piano from the same note when given by a violin or the human voice. The underlying physical cause of variations in timbre is found in the form of the sound waves produced, and immediately, therefore, in the form of vibratory movement communicated to the perilymph and endolymph. Examination of the forms of sound waves produced by different sound producing instruments shows that they may be divided into

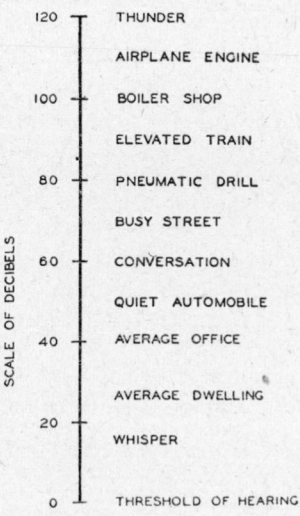

Fig. 222.—Evaluation of the decibel scale in terms of familiar sounds, e.g., conversation will not be heard if hearing loss exceeds 60 decibels. Observe that the scale spreads out the lower range of sounds and telescopes the upper range. Reprinted by permission from Stevens and Davis, *Hearing*, John Wiley & Sons, Inc., 1938.)

two great groups: (i) the simple or pendular form; (ii) the compound or nonpendular form. The *simple* or *sinusoidal* or *pendular* form of wave is given, for instance, by tuning forks. A graphic representation of this wave form may be obtained by attaching a bristle to the end of the fork and allowing it to write upon a "smoked drum." The vibrating body swings symmetrically to each side of the line of rest, and, inasmuch as this is also the form of movement that would be traced by a swinging pendulum, this form of wave is sometimes designated as pendular. It is more frequently called a sinusoidal wave, since the distance of the vibrating point to each side of the line of rest is equal to the sine of an arc increasing proportionally for the time of the phase. A *compound* (or nonpendular or nonsinusoidal) wave may have a very great variety of forms. The different phases follow periodically, but the movement of the vibrating body to each side of the line of rest is not perfectly symmetrical. Fourier has shown that any periodical vibratory movement, whatever may be its form, may be analyzed into a series of simple or pendular vibrations whose periods are 1, 2, 3, 4, etc., times as great as the vibration period of the given movement. That is, every so-called compound wave form may be considered as being caused by the fusion of a number of simple waves. Representing the wave movement of the air graphically as water waves, this composition of simple waves into compound ones is illustrated by the curves given in Figure 223. In this figure, 1, 2, and 3 are two simple vibrations such as would be given by three tuning forks of suitable frequency, the vibrations in 2 being double those of 1, and those in 3 being triple those of 1. If these three waves occur at the same time, the actual movement of air molecules will be the algebraical sum of the ordinates above and below the lines of rest, with the resulting compound wave form at the

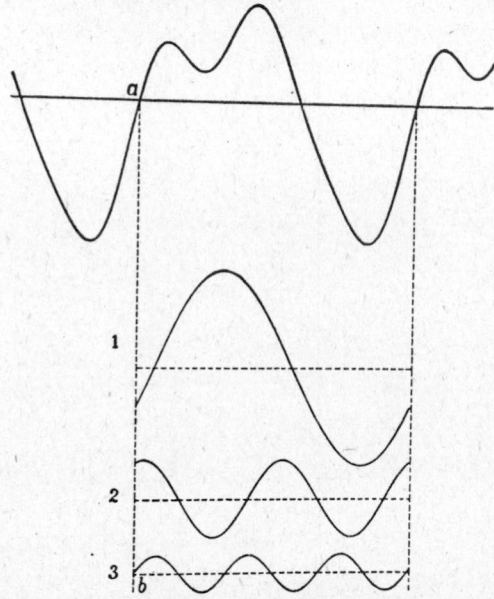

Fig. 223.—Diagram illustrating the physical basis of the timbre or quality of musical sounds. The upper curve represents sound waves of the type emitted by a violin. Curves 1, 2, 3 are the results of analyzing the upper curve into its components. The two vertical dotted lines enclose one cycle on the complex wave, one cycle of the fundamental (curve 1), and two and three cycles respectively of the overtones (curves 2 and 3). If n is the frequency of the fundamental tone, the harmonics are in the relation 2n, 3n, 4n, etc. Note the progressive decrease in amplitude of the overtones. (From Miller, *The science of musical sounds*, 1926.)

top. In this way a great variety of forms of compound waves may be supposed to be produced by the union of a series of simple waves of different periods of vibration. That compound waves differ from simple ones in being composed of several series of vibrations is indicated directly by our sensations. When we listen to the note of a tuning fork we hear only a single tone; when two or more tuning forks are sounded together, the trained ear can detect the tone due to each fork, and similarly when a single note is sounded by the human voice, a violin, or any other instrument that has a characteristic quality, the trained ear can detect a series of higher tones, variously termed the upper partial tones, or harmonics, or overtones, which indicate that the note is really compound, and not simple. The formation of these overtones is due to the fact that the sounding body vibrates not only as a whole, but also in its aliquot parts, as is represented in Figure 224. When the string is plucked, it vibrates as a whole (a), giving large waves which produce what is called the fundamental tone, but at the same time each half (b), third (c), fourth (d), etc., may vibrate, giving each its own simple tone. The combination of all of these simple waves forms a compound wave whose form, or t least whose composition, determines the quality of the tone heard. As ma y as ten or sixteen of these overtones may be detected from the vibrating strings of a violin or guitar. When the period of vibration of these overtones bears a simple ratio to that of the fundamental, a ratio that can be expressed by the simple numbers 1, 2, 3, 4, 5, they harmonize with it and form the harmonic overtones. It should be borne in mind that, so far as the tympanic membrane is concerned, it does not respond separately to the single tones which constitute the compound wave, but swings in unison with the movement of the

Fig. 224.—Diagram illustrating the mechanism of formation of overtones. In *a* the string vibrates as a whole, giving its fundamental tone; in *b, c,* and *d* its halves, thirds and fourths are shown vibrating independently, but the string in vibration executes all of these movements simultaneously. The combination gives a compound wave as in the previous figure.

compound wave. Nevertheless, the internal ear, according to the *acoustical law of Ohm*, is capable of analyzing the compound wave form into the series of simple or pendular waves of which it is composed, and of distinguishing the series of corresponding tones. While this analysis cannot be made consciously except by the trained musician, it is made unconsciously, as it were, by every normal ear, and in consequence of this analysis we recognize the variations in quality of different compound tones. The manner in which the cochlea acts in thus separating the compound tones into their elements is explained later.

Mechanism of the Cochlea. The cochlea as a whole may be viewed as a device whereby sound waves, transmitted through the fluid of the inner ear, are translated into nerve impulses. It is obvious from the arrangement of the cochlea that the vibration imparted to the basilar membrane by a pressure wave in the scala vestibuli is one stage in this process. This is directly shown by the fact that excessive vibrations produced by loud sounds may actually dislodge the organ of Corti from the basilar membrane. Moreover, there is conclusive evidence that the segment of the basilar membrane undergoing the widest excursion shifts progressively as the frequency of a sound wave is increased (14). Since the segments of the organ of Corti lying along the basilar membrane tend to be innervated by different nerve fibers of the auditory nerve, it follows that different nerve fibers will be the recipient of the greatest degree of stimulation as the point of maximal excursion shifts along the basilar membrane with change in the frequency of the sound waves. Direct evidence (2, 19) indicates that the nerve impulses remain canalized as they pass through the fibers of the auditory system, so that ultimately each tone results in a peak of activity at some definite point on the auditory cortex. Activity of each point of the cortex results in the psychological phenomenon of a pitch (doctrine of specific nerve energies). This view of the function of the cochlea is termed the "place theory" of hearing, which, however, has reached the status of a law. Because pitch ultimately depends on just *which* auditory fibers are most strongly stimulated, the place theory is somewhat irreverently known as the "pitch-is-which" theory.

Two general ways have been suggested whereby different frequencies activate different areas of the basilar membrane. The first is derived from the hydrodynamics of the cochlea, which unfortunately are very little understood. To activate the basilar membrane of the basal turns a short distance from the stapes and oval window, only a small column of fluid need be thrown into vibration. To activate the basilar membrane at a greater distance, near the helicotrema, a larger column of fluid must be moved. The base of the cochlea therefore forms a system with a high natural period (little mass), and consequently high frequencies should activate the basal region more strongly than the apical region. The second factor is a histological differentiation of the basilar membrane itself. There is no direct evidence that the fibers running from wall to wall of the cochlea and making up the basilar membrane are under tension; nevertheless, the following facts are suggestive. Although the diameter of the bony canal decreases from base to apex (somewhat more than is shown in Figure 217), the *basilar membrane is broadest near the apex* and narrowest near the oval window; moreover, the greater massiveness of the spiral ligament at the base suggests greater tension; and finally the cells on the underneath surface are less abundant at the basal turns and the organ of Corti is less massive. Histologically it appears that at the base of the cochlea the fibers making up the basilar membrane are shorter, under more tension, and less heavily loaded than those at the apex; and having a higher natural period they would respond more actively to high frequencies. On the other hand, the apical stretch of basilar membrane seems adapted to respond to low tones.

It was reasoning of this character which led Helmholtz to frame the *resonance theory* of hearing, which has developed into the modern *place theory* of hearing. Helmholtz was familiar with the fact that a series of strings like those of a piano will analyze a sound into its fundamental and principal overtones. A string having the same period as the fundamental will vibrate sympathetically, while adjacent strings with slightly different periods will be little affected. Similarly, the strings with the frequency corresponding to the overtones will vibrate. The compound wave is thus analyzed into component simple tones by the sympathetic vibrations of the corresponding strings of the resonator. Helmholtz assumed that the basilar membrane analyzed compound musical waves by an essentially similar method, which with certain modifications has been clearly established by recent physiological research. However, it is quite clear that the connective tissue strands of the basilar membrane are not piano strings and have not the opportunity to vibrate independently, because they are tied together and thus damp one another. Secondly, as pointed out above, differentiation of the basilar membrane is only one of the mechanisms making for selective tuning, i.e., for hydrodynamic reasons vibrations of different frequency do not affect all portions of the basilar membrane equally. Pure tone, especially if loud, will throw a long stretch of the basilar membrane into vibration, which, however, reaches a maximum at some point, and it is the detection of this point of maximum excursion which permits the appreciation of pitch. This point of maximum excursion shifts along the basilar membrane as the frequency is altered.

Electrical Activity of Cochlea. Until 1930 studies of the function of the cochlea were perforce largely confined to correlating the characteristics of the auditory stimulus and psychological response, and deducing the intermediate steps. With the advent of electrical recording, it has been possible to break into the chain of events linking sound waves and sound perceptions and in general to make a more analytical attack on physiological mechanisms involved. Two quite different kinds of electrical phenomena can be recorded from the ear: (i) the *microphonic response of the cochlea*, which can be called for its discoverers the *Wever and Bray effect*, and (ii) action potentials of the eighth nerve.

Because the cochlear microphonics were first recorded from the auditory nerve (16, 17), the potentials were mistaken for action currents. Analysis soon showed that the recorded electrical potentials originated in the cochlea and not from nerve fibers, and spread with an exponential decrement throughout the tissue surrounding the cochlea. The nerve in the original experiments was functioning not as an active conductor, as in the case of the nerve impulse, but as a passive conductor of a current originating in the cochlea. Subsequently it was possible to record the action currents of the auditory nerve separately from the microphonic potential (12). The following characteristics distinguish the microphonic effect of the cochlea from nerve impulses of the auditory nerve: longer latency, 0.1 msec. as opposed to 0.7 msec. for the nerve; absence of refractory period; resistance to fatigue, cold, anesthesia and ischemia; ability to follow notes close to the upper limit of hearing (16,000 per sec.); and ability to follow faithfully the form of the incident sound waves. These are not attributes of the nerve impulse (a trigger-like release of energy contributed by the reacting cell which does not vary in shape nor grade in amplitude), but they are characteristic of a passive transformation (technically, transduction) of mechanical energy of sound into electrical energy. Sound waves exert pressure upon the organ of Corti and the basilar membrane and produce distortion of cellular membranes. Several physical systems transduce pressure into electrical energy. Pressure upon the face of a section cut from a quartz crystal produces a potential difference between the two ends, while traction on the two faces reverses the polarity of the potential difference. The essential condition for this piezo-electric effect appears to be the orientation of the molecules, which is also a property of biological structures. Considerable evidence supports the theory that the potential generated within the cochlea arises in the hair cells of the organ of Corti in response to pressure. The polarity, as Figure 225 shows, is such that outward movement of the stapes, causing upward movement of the basilar membrane, induces electropositivity at the round window and electronegativity at the oval window; nerve impulses are initiated during the upward excursion of the basilar membrane. In view of these facts, it is tempting to believe that the microphonic potential is the means by which sound waves

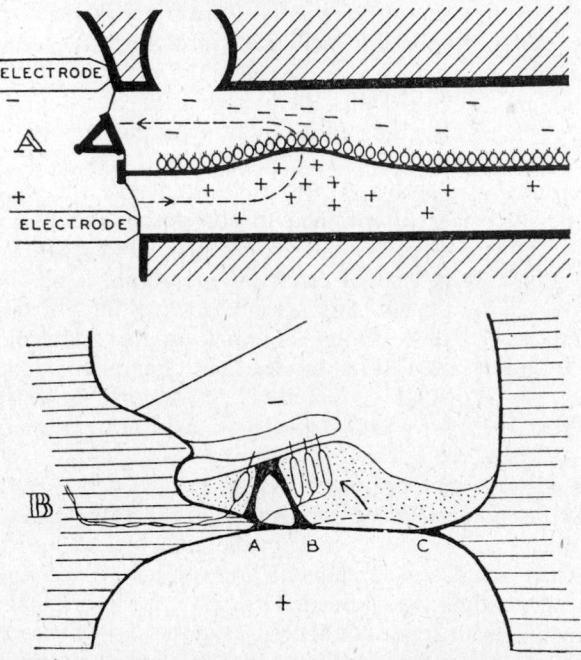

Fig. 225.—Diagrams of sections through the cochlea illustrating the generation of the cochlear potential. A, Longitudinal section showing the polarity of the microphonic in relation to an outward movement of the stapes. Fibers of the auditory nerve are excited during an upward movement of the hair cells. B, Cross section to scale, illustrating one view of the mechanics of the organ of Corti. Weak sounds will cause vibration of the basilar membrane between B and C, with pressure exerted against the *outer* hair cells in the direction of the arrow. A stronger sound wave will move the organ of Corti about the pivot A and thereby compress the *internal* hair cells. This view gives a rational explanation of the pillars of Corti and the inner and outer hair cells. (Reprinted by permission from Stevens and Davis, *Hearing,* John Wiley & Sons, Inc., 1938.)

stimulate nerve fibers, giving the sequence: Sound pressure → microphonic potential → nerve impulse. However, the time (0.6 msec.) elapsing between the first sign of the cochlear microphonic potential and the nerve impulse and several other features have never been satisfactorily explained. The microphonic effect may even be a mere by-product. If so, it is an exceedingly useful one for the experimental study of audition.

Action Potentials of Auditory Nerves. The action currents of the auditory nerve and of the auditory pathway and cortex, rather than the cochlear microphonics, provide the most direct information about the mechanisms of audition. As in other sensory spheres, much has been learned from studying whole nerve trunks, but more is learned from studying the discharges in single fibers in response to controlled stimuli. Galambos and Davis (6) have accomplished this by inserting micro-electrodes into the auditory nerve, which under favorable circumstances record the electrical events in only one nerve fiber. On the whole, the auditory mechanism has demonstrated no new properties not shared by some other sense organ. It shows the phenomenon of adaptation, the rate of discharge being initially high (400 per sec.) and within a few tenths of a second reaching a plateau rate of discharge

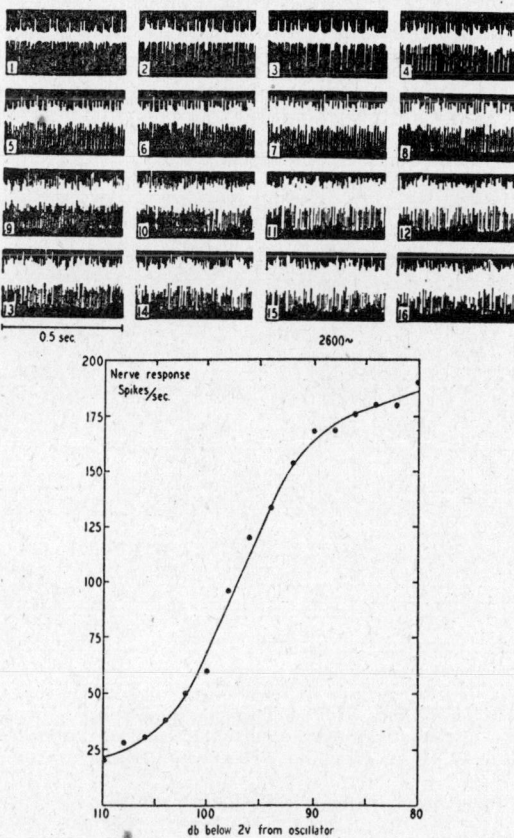

Fig. 226.—Curve showing the frequency of auditory nerve discharge as a function of sound intensity (2600 cycles per sec. tone), and oscillographic records made at 2 db. steps from which the graph was constructed. Single fiber recording. (From Galambos and Davis, *J. Neurophysiol.*, 1943, *6*:39–57.)

of 100 per sec. The spike height of the nerve impulse also decreases rapidly when the frequency is high (equilibration), just as occurs when a nerve trunk is electrically stimulated at rapid rates. The auditory receptor, like all other receptors so far examined, initiates more nerve impulses per second the more strongly it is stimulated. Frequency is the correlate of intensity. In Figure 226, the frequency of discharge is increased from 25 to nearly 200 impulses per sec. by increasing the intensity 30 db. Man can discriminate a difference of 3 db. of intensity in the frequency range between 3000 and 4000 cycles.

In the cat an intensity change of this sort is documented by a considerable change of frequency, so there is no obstacle to believing that frequency is the basis for intensity discrimination.

Studies of single auditory units demonstrate that *frequency* of the sound stimulus as well as intensity is a factor in determining the number of nerve impulses per second in a single-fiber preparation. This is brought out clearly by plotting the frequency of impulses against the number of cycles per second of the sound stimulus, intensity being constant. Repeating this for a number of intensities gives the family of iso-intensity contours shown in Figure 227. Either decrease or increase of the frequency of the sound stimulus from a critical value without changing the intensity decreases the number of discharges per second in a single auditory nerve fiber. Note that this is for high tones; for very low tones the frequency may be directly correlated with the rate of discharge of the auditory neurons. To test the place theory the follow-

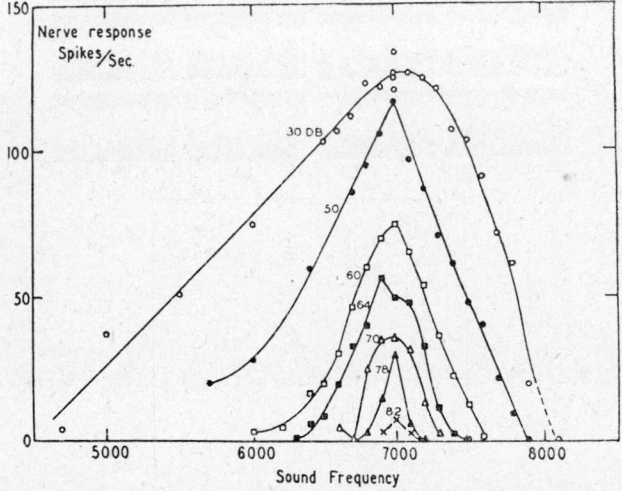

Fig. 227.—The relation of intensity and frequency to the discharge of a single auditory nerve fiber. As the intensity level is increased (numbers attached to the curves get smaller), a wider range of frequencies excite the fiber, and each frequency excites more discharges. Distance along abscissa is probably a function of distance along the basilar membrane. Intensity level equals db. *below* a reference level. (From Galambos and Davis, *J. Neurophysiol.*, 1943, 6:39–57.)

ing experiments were performed. With a different single auditory unit under observation in different experiments, the frequency was discovered at which the intensity threshold of the single unit was lowest. As demanded by the place theory of cochlear function, the minimal threshold was not found at the same frequency for all auditory fibers. For example, in Figure 228 is shown for four different nerve fibers the sound frequency at which the intensity threshold was lowest. This is evidence of the most direct character that the cochlea is so "tuned" that the hair cells innervated by each nerve fiber are especially liable to stimulation by some one band of sound frequencies. However, a single fiber is not activated exclusively by a single frequency or even by a narrow band of frequencies except at threshold intensity. The more the intensity is increased the wider is the band of frequencies which will cause the given fiber to discharge. In short, the basilar membrane is tuned to respond in different parts to different frequencies but is not sharply tuned, so that the basilar membrane vibrates over a wide extent to a given pure tone if the intensity is great.

The present-day concept—the place theory—allows for the fact that pure tone will throw a long stretch of the basilar membrane into vibration. But the vibration of the basilar membrane must have a maximum at some point and the nerve fibers leading from this point will discharge at maximum frequency (Fig. 227) and it is the evaluation of this maximum frequency which determines the pitch. This point of maximum shifts along the basilar membrane as the pitch of the sound is altered.

Tonal Localization in the Cochlea. That the apex of the cochlea is concerned with low sounds and the base with high sounds has been indicated. In an effort to prove this specialization or "tuning" of the cochlea, and especially to work out a detailed map of the cochlea, a variety of ingenious

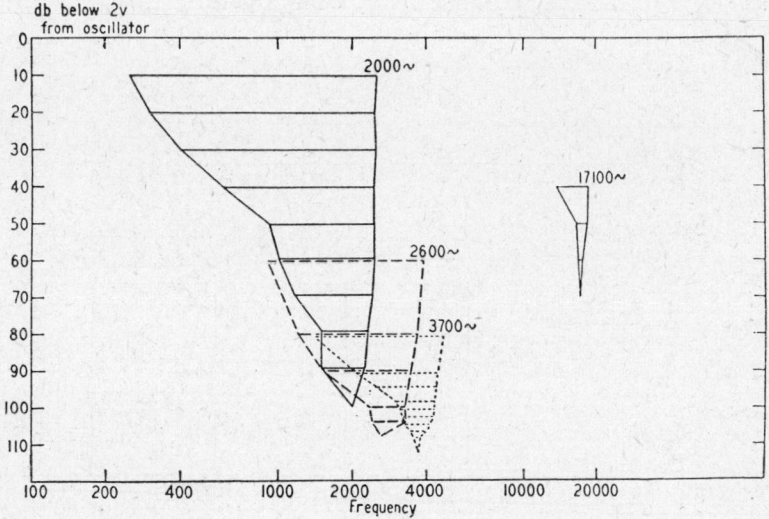

* Fig. 228.—Curves showing that the range of frequencies (horizontal lines forming an inverted triangle) capable of discharging an auditory nerve fiber widens with increase of intensity level. Four different auditory fibers are represented, and the maximum excitability of each lies at a different range of frequencies. (From Galambos and Davis, *J. Neurophysiol.*, 1943, *6*:39–57.)

and painstaking methods have been employed. For example, after prolonged exposure of the ear to loud sounds, the attempt is made to correlate the site of degeneration of the organ of Corti with the frequency of the damaging sound (Wittmack); and experimental production of tonal gaps—deafness to a narrow band of frequencies—by continued loud sounds has been attempted in animals, the conditioned reflex being used to determine the extent of deafness. Such methods fail to provide a detailed map because loud sounds throw into vibration a considerable extent of the basilar membrane.

The method which has yielded the most detailed maps of tonotopic localization along the basilar membrane is that employed by Stevens, Davis, and Lurie (14). In a series of guinea pigs the basilar membrane was disrupted by drilling into the cochlea at various points. The audibility curve was then determined, using the minimal cochlear microphonic as the threshold response (electrical audiograms); after histological verification the band of

16

frequencies affected was correlated with the position in the cochlea of the stretch of basilar membrane damaged. An electrical audiogram from such an experiment is shown at the top of Figure 229. Note that the loss of sensitivity is confined to two octaves and is not absolute, though the organ of Corti beneath the drilled hole is completely nonfunctional. The reason is presumably that sounds louder than 30 db. excited areas to either side of the damaged stretch. By relating the "tonal gaps" revealed by the audiograms to the areas of damage (determined by the histologist in ignorance of the audiograms), the map of the cochlea shown at the bottom of the figure was evolved. The curve for man was deduced from the experimental curve obtained from guinea pigs. In this reconstruction the octaves in different parts of the audible range of frequencies do not occupy equal extents on the

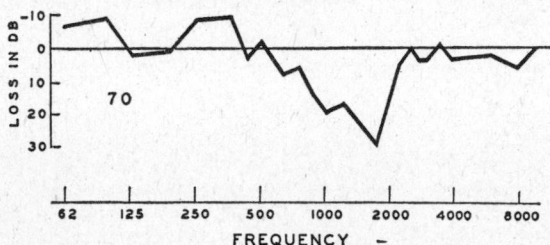

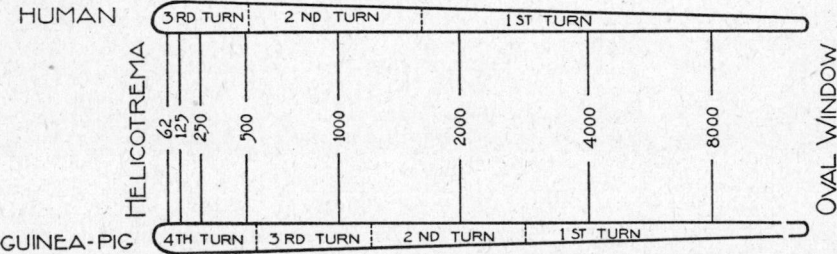

Fig. 229.—(Upper). An electrical audiogram as affected by a lesion to a portion of the basilar membrane. The threshold intensity for elicitation of a detectable microphonic response from the cochlea is increased for tones from the middle range of frequencies.

(Lower). A map of the cochlea of the guinea pig showing the localization of pitch reception on the basilar membrane. The map for the guinea pig is reconstructed from the results of 20 experiments like those shown in the upper part of the figure, together with histological data on the extent of the basilar membrane damaged. The map for man was deduced from the data on the guinea pig. (From Stevens, Davis and Lurie, *J. gen. Psychol.*, 1935, *13*:297–315.)

basilar membrane. The lower five octaves are crowded into little more than the short, apical turn of the cochlea. The upper four octaves, which include the frequencies essential to hearing human speech, occupy the balance of the basilar membrane. This apportionment apparently determines the fineness of pitch discrimination throughout the audible range. The minimal detectable difference in frequency appears to correspond to a constant distance on the cochlea. Therefore the long stretch of basilar membrane and organ of Corti devoted to the middle and upper range makes possible the discrimination of a large number of pitches which is characteristic of the middle portion of the audible range of frequencies. Thus, as in the case of cutaneous sensitivity and of vision, fine discriminations depending on a space factor appear to be gained by multiplication of sensory units.

The alternative to the place mechanism of cochlear function is some version of the "frequency theory," according to which the basilar membrane is not differentiated along its extent for differential frequency reception but responds as a whole to all frequencies of sound waves. The frequency of the sound wave is supposedly reproduced in the frequency of nerve discharge, and the cerebral cortex interprets different frequencies of discharge as different pitches. The problem of pitch perception is removed from cochlea to cortex. Since frequency of discharge is usurped by the signaling of pitch, intensity must be a function of the width of basilar membrane excited and the frequency of discharge within each pulse of action potentials. If the oscillations of the basilar membrane constitute the immediate stimulus to the hair cells, the nerve impulses would be discharged in a definite temporal relation to each pressure pulse of the sound wave. For the lower range of sound frequencies, the frequency of auditory nerve discharge therefore "follows" the frequency of the sound wave, a burst of impulses being produced by each pressure pulse of the sound wave. But the auditory nerve fibers, like other nerve fibers, are subject to the laws of excitability, one of which is that refractoriness follows a conducted nerve impulse. The ability to fire repetitively at high frequencies in step with the sound wave frequency is limited by the refractory period which, by direct measurement, is not longer than 1 msec. in duration. Thus a single auditory nerve fiber can be expected to conduct one nerve impulse per sound wave only for the lower frequencies of the audible range. Galambos and Davis (6) found that the critical rate at which the nerve impulses in single auditory nerve fibers ceases to bear a 1:1 relationship with the pressure pulse of the sound wave was only 400 to 500 per sec. at the onset of the sound, and soon falls to 200 to 300 per sec., due undoubtedly to a lengthening of the refractory period (equilibration). By recording the discharges of a single fiber and the cochlear microphonic simultaneously, it can be shown that (i) *when* a fiber fires, it fires in a definite temporal relationship to the microphonic (and by inference to the movement of the basilar membrane), but (ii) a nerve impulse is not originated by *each* sound wave when the ear is stimulated by a sound of high frequency. However, in recording from the auditory nerve as a whole, synchronization of impulses and sound waves ("following") is quite close for tones as high as 3000 cycles per sec., and some "following" is manifested as high as 4000 cycles per sec. The way in which this is accomplished within the limitation set by the refractory period is that at rates above 500 to 800 one group or squad of fibers fires in response to every other pulse of the sound wave and the remaining fibers fire to the intervening sound waves. In response to progressively higher tones, a given fiber comes to respond only to every third, then to every fourth, fifth, etc., wave. By dividing the total number of fibers into smaller and smaller squads, it is obviously possible for a volley to be fired synchronously with each pulse of the sound wave at quite high frequencies so long as the supply of fibers holds out. The volleys must necessarily decrease in size as though fired first by companies, then by platoons and finally by squads. Under certain conditions this can be demonstrated experimentally. Thus, if amplitude of action current, which reflects numbers of fibers firing, is plotted against cycles per sec. of the sound wave, successive sharp drops are apparent. The first occurs in the region of 700 to 800 per sec. and is presumably related to the refractory period; the other critical frequencies at which amplitude drops are multiples of 700 or 800.

Even with allowance for rotation of auditory nerve fibers in "firing-by-squads," it is improbable that the frequency of nerve impulses can signal the pitch of a sound to the cerebral cortex. As might be predicted from our knowledge of synaptic conduction, the secondary and tertiary neurons of the auditory pathway follow the frequency of the stimulating tone even less well than do the primary neurons making up the auditory nerve. Whether the auditory area can follow the frequency of the sound wave is the critical datum, and has not been demonstrated.

Routes of Conduction. Sound waves in the air reach the organ of Corti by three routes. The first may be termed the *physiological or ossicular route*. The vibrations are transmitted from tympanum → malleus → incus → stapes → oval window → scala vestibuli and scala media → organ of Corti and basilar membrane → scala tympani → round window. This route of conduction has already been discussed in some detail, and the role of the round window in this sequence of events will be discussed below.

The second path of conduction of sound waves through the middle ear may be termed the *air route* of conduction. The tympanum is common to this and the previous ossicular route, but here the waves traverse the air of the middle ear. Another difference is that the ossicular chain acts upon the oval window, while the sound waves traversing the air route are transmitted more efficiently through the round window into the scala tympani than through the oval window into the scala vestibuli. The reason is, of course, that the oval window is stoppered by the stapes and its relatively thick annular ligament, whereas the round window is covered only by a thin, soft membrane offering little obstruction to the air-borne sound waves. The air route of conduction has one significance when the ossicular chain is functioning, and another when the air route is the sole means by which sound waves traverse the middle ear.

The relative effectiveness of the ossicular and air routes is gauged by the hearing loss consequent to interruption of the ossicular chain. This amounts to a loss of 40 to 65 decibels in man and animals, which is the measure of the efficiency gained by having evolved a specialized means of translating air waves into fluid pressure waves—the ossicular chain. Although the air route of conduction supports some degree of useful hearing, it may in a measure hinder the hearing by means of the ossicular chain. Sound waves traveling through the round window and the scala tympani push the basilar membrane upwards during the phase of positive pressure while the same wave conducted by the ossicles to the oval window and scala vestibuli will push the membrane downwards. The two routes, acting out of phase, tend to neutralize one another in activating the hair cells. Hughson and Crowe (8) tested the question experimentally by placing pledgets of cotton wool in the round window or covering it with periosteal transplants, and used both the auditory threshold and the microphonic action of the cochlea to test the efficiency of transmission. Hearing was improved. This procedure should be viewed as merely shielding the round window from air-borne sound waves; rigid stoppering of the round window can be expected to produce the opposite effect. It is generally held that the function of the round window is to provide "give" in the hydraulic system represented by the cochlea. Deformation rather than compression from equal pressure acting from all directions is a requirement for the mechanical stimulation of skin receptors, and the hair-cells seem to behave likewise. For deformation to occur, the basilar membrane must actually move. The experimental evidence with respect to the effects of occlusion of the round window is unfortunately conflicting (7, 8). The cochlea is not a rigidly closed system; it is entered by blood vessels, it contains veins which are compressible at low pressures and is connected with the cranial cavity by the perilymphatic and endolymphatic ducts. However, no low resistance passageway other than the round window has been identified, and the value of "give" in the system is suggested by the following indirect evidence. Due to a pathological change in the temporal bone, the stapes may become rigidly fixed in the oval window (otosclerosis). Hearing is severely impaired since the ossicular route of conduction is lost. The theory that the function of the round window is to allow the perilymph actually to move suggests that another factor is involved besides immobilization of the ossicular chain, one which prevents the *air route* of conduction from functioning to maximum advantage—lack of provision for fluid movements. When the membrane of the round window becomes the entrance, as it were, to the inner ear, another "exit" is needed. This is sometimes provided surgically by drilling a small hole through the temporal bone into the portion of the bony labyrinth containing the horizontal semicircular canal, which is in continuity with the vestibule of the cochlea. Fascia is placed over this fistula and hearing is significantly improved as long as the passage remains patent. It is generally believed that the action of the fistula in the improvement of hearing is not to let sound waves into the inner ear but to provide a low resistance opening into the bony labyrinth such as the round window normally supplies.

The third route by which sound can reach the inner ear is by means of bone conduction or the *osseous route*. Neither the ossicular chain nor the air of the middle ear plays a part, but instead sound waves are conducted through the bone to the inner ear; the middle ear is, as it were, "short circuited" or "by-passed." Unlike the two previous routes discussed, bone conduction plays little if any part in normal hearing because of the great loss of energy in passage of a sound wave from air to the bones of the head. However, a tuning fork with its base held against the skull or a watch held between the teeth can be clearly heard, though the external meatus is well guarded. Bone conduction is important in discriminating between types of deafness and is employed for one type of hearing aid. It must be ruled out in testing one ear with sounds louder than 50-60 decibels, at which level sound may reach the normal ear by bone conduction. Ear plugs are of course useless, but hearing in the normal ear can be eliminated by introducing into it a masking noise.

The mechanism of bone conduction appears to be that tiny oscillations of the bone subject the fluid contents of the cochlea and the semicircular canals to alternate pressures. Both the scala vestibuli and the scala tympani are equally exposed to sound pressures. But the positive pressure phase of the sound wave causes a downward movement of the basilar membrane just as in normal hearing, because the round window presents relatively less resistance than the oval window. The round window bulges into the middle ear and allows the basilar membrane to move downward. By holding a watch in the teeth it is easily demonstrated that plugging the external auditory meatus with the index fingers increases the loudness of the sound conducted through the teeth and bones of the skull. By converting the auditory meatus into a closed cavity, the vibrations of the skull are able to compress the trapped air and thus act upon the tympanum and the ossicular chain. Experimental interruption of the ossicular chain has little effect on bone conduction.

Types of Deafness. Impairment of hearing is classified into three main types, according to the point in the chain of events at which the block occurs. *Transmission deafness* is any interference with the passage of the sound waves through the external or middle ear. Common causes are collections of pus, exudates or wax in the external or middle ear, inequality of pressure between the middle ear and the atmosphere, adhesions of the ossicles to the bony walls and thickening of the tympanum as a result of infection, and otosclerosis. Transmission deafness is often known as middle ear deafness and is characterized by a tendency for greater interference with the hearing of low tones than high tones as shown by the audiogram and by a greater interference with air routes of conduction than bone conduction. The reason for the latter is that the middle ear is "by-passed" in bone conduction. The former is far from invariable and the conduction of high tones is often at fault as well. The mechanism of the low-tone deafness in some cases seems to be the same as the functional low-tone deafness produced by the auditory reflex of the intra-aural muscles. Hearing aids which amplify sound may compensate for the defective transmitting mechanism by activating it more energetically. The second type of hearing impairment is ineptly termed *perception deafness;* a better designation is *nerve deafness,* since the defect is not in the cortical process of sound perception. The site of pathology is the auditory nerve or the hair cells of the organ of Corti. Examples of this type are the slowly progressive high-tone deafness which comes with age, a second form of high-tone deafness which is more abrupt in onset, so-called boilermaker's disease, tumors of the acoustic nerve, etc. Because the damage in these cases is in the portion of the hearing mechanism (hair cells or auditory nerve) common to air and bone conducted sounds, deafness to both is characteristic. Hearing aids are of little benefit.

The third type of deafness is *central deafness,* that due to interference with the central nervous pathways or their terminations in the cerebral cortex. It will be discussed in connection with these pathways.

AUDITORY PATHWAYS

The internal ear is served by the eighth cranial or acoustic nerve, which, however, is not concerned solely with audition but consists of one branch from the cochlea (the cochlear), and one (the vestibular) serving the saccule, utricle and semicircular canals. The constituent neurons follow the general plan of sensory neurons. The cell body is bipolar and lies outside the central nervous system in the *spiral ganglion* of the cochlea situated within the modiolus. A long central axon passes in the acoustic nerve to the pons. The other axon passes peripherally to end in relation to the receptor cells of the organ of Corti. There are sufficient numbers of neurons (about 25,000 ganglion cells) so that each neuron innervates only one or two inner hair cells, and an inner hair cell is innervated by only one or two nerve fibers. However, multiple rather than this 1:1 type of innervation obtains for the outer hair cells. One nerve fiber connects with many hair cells, extending over as much as one half a turn of the cochlea (Lorente de Nó, 10). This arrangement suggests that the inner hair cells are specialized for fine discrimination of pitch. It is an interesting detail that the fibers of the acoustic nerve are twisted, somewhat like a rope. The fibers of the acoustic nerve enter the dorsolateral border of the pons at its junction with the medulla oblongata and follow the rule, "synapsis before decussation" (Fig. 230). The primary neuron bifurcates, one branch terminating in the *ventral cochlear nucleus* and the other in the *dorsal cochlear nucleus,* which shows on the external surface of the pons as a prominent elevation, the tuberculum acusticum. Second order neurons having their cell bodies in these two nuclei pursue quite varied pathways across the pons to take up a position in a well-defined bundle, the *lateral lemniscus,* which ascends to the inferior colliculus of the midbrain. The tract is continued as the brachium of the inferior colliculus to the medial geniculate body, where the final neuron conducts the impulses to the auditory area of the cerebral cortex, situated in the temporal lobe.

The neuronal structure of the lateral lemniscus is complex. Collaterals are given off or the axon terminates at several nuclear masses en route to the cerebral cortex. The crossing fibers of the ventral nucleus loop under the superior olive and form a conspicuous plate of fibers called the *trapezoid body*. Second order neurons relay in nuclei associated with the trapezoid body, or in the superior olivary nucleus, or in a nucleus of the lateral lemniscus, or in the inferior colliculus of the midbrain; few, if any, pass the whole distance to the medial geniculate body without synaptic interruption. Therefore the neurons reaching the medial geniculate body are at a minimum third order neurons. Finally, not all of the second and third order fibers are

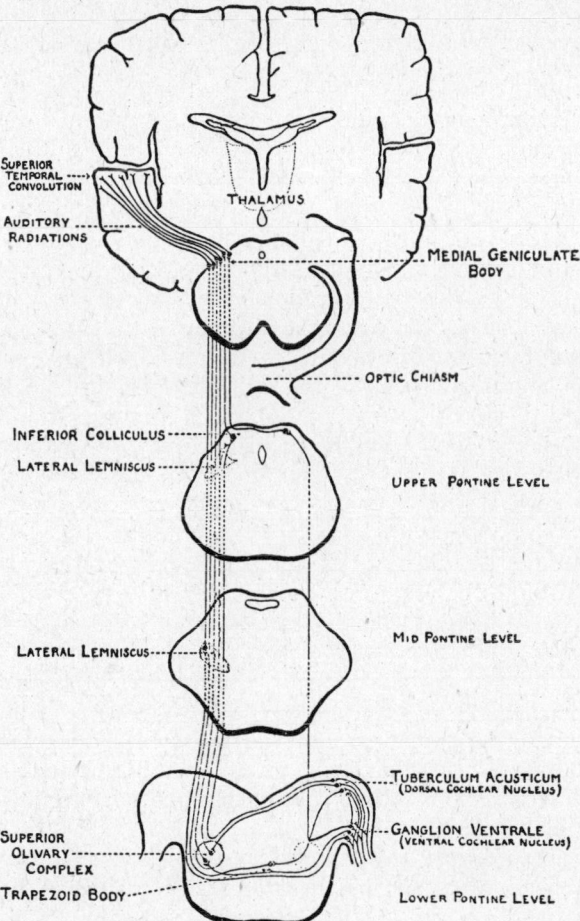

Fig. 230.—The auditory system as known from anatomical studies, showing typical connections of one auditory nerve. Functional studies modify this in two respects: (i) all neuron chains are interrupted at each of the four synaptic levels, and (ii) fibers equal in number to those shown pass to the ipsilateral temporal lobe. (From Davis, in Murchison, *Handbook of general experimental psychology*, Clark Univ. Press, 1934.)

crossed, but many ascend in the lateral lemniscus and collicular brachium of the *same* side that they entered. The ipsilateral pathway is known more on a physiological than on an anatomical basis.

According to the studies of Lorente de Nó (10), the auditory tract as described constitutes the arterial highway; in the cochlear nucleus, and presumably at other relay stations, there are many byways and alternative routes like the streets of a town, represented by complex chains of neurons entirely confined to making intranuclear connections. The existence of chains of fibers suggests that the pathways of four neurons serve primarily to conduct impulses to the cortex, while the multiple neuron chains and the intranuclear neurons serve reflex connections and subcortical integrations. Chains of short fibers are difficult to follow by the degeneration method, since Wallerian degeneration does not continue across synapses. Physiological methods, therefore, are often used to elucidate the details of anatomical organization of a sensory pathway.

Kemp, Coppée and Robinson (9) recorded action potentials from the auditory pathways at various levels. The decreasing ability of second, third and fourth order neurons to follow the frequency of sound waves has been mentioned. To determine the number of neurons involved in the auditory pathway, the time required for nerve impulses to reach various levels of the auditory pathway was measured. The latency of the first impulse in response to a click stimulus was 1.0 msec. at the round window (auditory nerve), 2.2 msec. at the trapezoid body, 3.6 msec. at the lateral lemniscus. Allowing for conduction time and 0.8 msec. for transmission across the synapse, this indicates that there are two synapses between the auditory nerve fibers and the medial geniculate body. Contrary to anatomical teaching, this means that all fibers are interrupted by a synapse in the contralateral olivary complex or the nucleus of the lateral lemniscus as well as in the ipsilateral cochlear nucleus, making the neurons of the lateral lemniscus at a minimum third order fibers. Fibers do not pass directly from the cochlear nucleus into the lateral lemniscus of the *same* side, but have a synapse in the superior olivary complex (Barnes, Magoun and Ranson); the commissure connecting the inferior colliculi appears not to be a factor in bilateral representation of the cochlea (Ades).

Electrical studies establish the existence in the lateral lemniscus of fibers from the ipsilateral cochlea, since action currents are recorded from the ipsilateral as well as from the contralateral tract when one cochlea is stimulated. In experimental animals the number of ipsilateral fibers, judging from the size of electrical disturbance, equals the number of contralateral ones. The intermingled impulses from the two cochleas reach a given point in the lateral lemniscus at the same time, confirming the anatomical finding that the ipsilateral pathway is also interrupted by two synapses below the lemniscus. Further evidence comes from interrupting various portions of the auditory path and will be described later.

Thalamocortical auditory radiations (15). All auditory fibers destined to reach the cerebral cortex synapse in the medial geniculate body, which is situated in the posterior part of the thalamus at the same level as the lateral geniculate body. The cortical projection fibers pass from here to a small area of highly granular cortex (koniocortex) of the typical sensory type situated in the inferior lip of the sylvian fissure, with no part appearing on the free surface. This region in man is marked by several gyri running roughly at right angles to the sylvian fissure, one of which, the anterior transverse temporal gyrus or Heschl's gyrus, contains the auditory cortex. In the monkey it is confined to an area of about one-quarter of a square centimeter in area, lying on the superior temporal gyrus, in the mesial portion of area 22 of Brodmann. Removal of this small area causes complete retrograde degeneration of the cell bodies making up the medial geniculate body (Walker).

Deductions from anatomical data are confirmed by mapping in animals

of the area which becomes electrically active in response to brief aural stimulation (cat, Bremer and Dow, 4; monkey, Ades and Felder). By this procedure Woolsey and Walzl (19) have discovered two auditory areas in the
cat's cerebral cortex. A sound if sufficiently intense activates besides the
familiar auditory area a distinct, more inferiorly placed area which they
term the secondary auditory area. It differs from the primary area in cytoarchitecture and receives a projection from a different (magnocellularis)
portion of the medial geniculate body.

The portions of the temporal lobe adjacent to the granular cortex are
concerned with audition, but it is now believed that the temporal lobe is not
in its entirety auditory in function (see p. 542).

Bilaterality of the auditory pathway (9, 11). The auditory system is unique
in the degree to which the cochlea is bilaterally represented in the cerebral

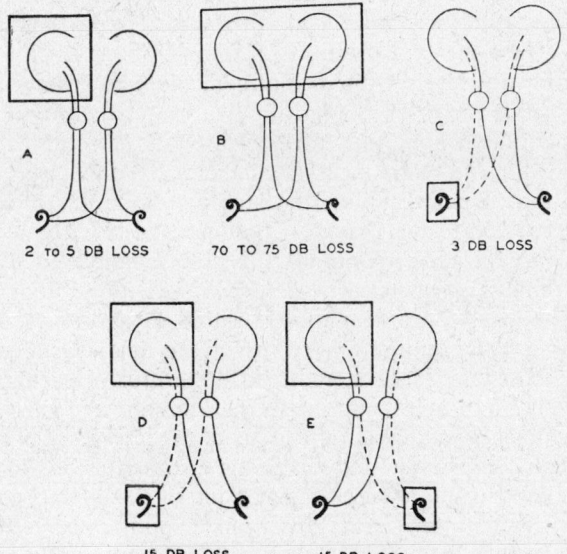

Fig. 231.—Summary diagram of a series of experiments demonstrating bilaterality of the
auditory pathway in the dog. The number below each diagram is the hearing loss in decibels and
a box around the symbol for cerebral cortex or cochlea indicates destruction of it. Observe that
in D hearing depends on the *uncrossed* fibers of the left lateral lemniscus while in E hearing
depends upon the crossed fibers of the right lateral lemniscus; the hearing loss is equal in the two
cases. (Experiments by Mettler, Finch, Girdon and Culler, *Brain*, 1934, *57*:475–483; diagram
after Stevens and Davis, *Hearing*, 1938.)

cortex. That impulses are conducted in both lateral lemnisci is proved by
electrical methods. Some of these impulses may cross at the inferior colliculus,
but none crosses above the thalamus; otherwise lesions of the auditory area
would produce retrograde degeneration in the medial geniculate body of
the other side. That the impulses in the lateral lemniscus arising from the
ipsilateral labyrinth remain uncrossed to the cerebral cortex is shown by an
ingenious experiment of Mettler, Finch, Girden and Culler (11) summarized
in Figure 231. Various components of the auditory pathway were interrupted
in dogs and the degree of hearing loss determined by the conditioned reflex
method. Removal of one cerebral cortex causes only 2 to 5 db. loss of hearing, about that produced by destruction of one cochlea. That this means a

bilateral representation of hearing rather than a thalamic localization follows from the magnitude of the loss when both cortices are ablated (70–75 db.). Only the very loudest sounds can be heard. An idea of the relative importance of the crossed and uncrossed fibers of the lateral lemniscus is gained by destroying one cochlea plus the ipsilateral cortex in one experiment and one cochlea plus the contralateral cortex in a second. The hearing loss was found to be 15 db. in both cases, indicating equal "acoustical value" of the crossed and uncrossed components of the auditory pathway. Nearly complete bilaterality of representation also characterizes the auditory system of man. The effects of unilateral cortical lesions on the threshold of hearing is very slight, and since the auditory areas of the two sides are rarely involved in the same pathological process, deafness is rarely produced by lesions of the cerebral cortex.

Topographical organization. The auditory system is highly organized topographically. The spiral organ of Corti is projected upon the auditory cortex in such a way that the "localization of tones" observed at the cochlea is preserved both at the level of the medial geniculate body and in the cerebral cortex. That such is the case is a logical extension of the place-mechanism of audition. A peripheral apparatus for the analysis of complex sound waves and a signaling of the component frequencies by different auditory nerve fibers are without meaning unless the streams of impulses remain distinct until the cerebral cortex is reached. Evidence of the requisite degree of topographical organization to permit this is impossible to obtain by anatomical techniques but is clearly demonstrated physiologically. In cats trained to respond to tones near the threshold of audibility, Ades, Mettler and Culler (2) destroyed minute portions of the medial geniculate body by means of the Horsley-Clarke stereotaxic apparatus. Hearing was reduced for a restricted band of tones, and the frequencies affected varied in a systematic fashion with small changes in the locus of the lesion. They were thus able to map the medial geniculate body in terms of tone localization.

An orderly, point-to-point type of projection of the medial geniculate body upon the superior temporal gyrus has been demonstrated by the technique of retrograde degeneration (15). At best, only relatively large portions of the auditory area can be dealt with in this fashion. However, electrical recording from the cerebral cortex provides a means of mapping the topographical localization of tone (tonotopic organization). One difficulty to be surmounted is that threshold tones produce only small cortical action currents, difficult to distinguish from background activity, while loud tones activate a wide expanse of the basilar membrane and hence excite a correspondingly large area of the auditory cortex. This difficulty was circumvented by Woolsey and Walzl (19) who broke down the wall of the cochlea and tore away the basilar membrane, leaving exposed the spiral lamina along which the nerve fibers from the organ of Corti enter the modiolus. By means of fine electrodes, a few fibers at a time could be stimulated, and a change in the point of maximal electrical activity on the auditory cortex was occasioned by shifting the electrodes along the row of nerve fibers. Stimulation of the smallest possible group of nerve fibers activated a vertical band, not a point or area, of cortical tissue in the temporal lobe. Stimulation at the base of the cochlea, which responds preferentially to high tones, caused activity in the most forward bands, while the apex (low tones) projected to the bands nearest the occiput;

intermediate cochlear regions were also intermediate at the cortex. Results of this character suggest that the doctrine of specific nerve energies applies not only to a whole modality of sensation but to each pitch in the case of hearing. Thus, what pitch is heard depends upon what group of cells in the cerebral cortex is thrown into activity.

REFERENCES

1. Ades, H. W. A secondary acoustic area in the cerebral cortex of the cat. *J. Neurophysiol.*, 1943, 6:59–63.

2. Ades, H. W., Mettler, F. A., and Culler, E. A. Effect of lesions in the medial geniculate bodies upon hearing in the cat. *Amer. J. Physiol.*, 1939, 125:15–23.

3. Armstrong, H. G. *Principles and practice of aviation medicine*, 2d ed. Baltimore, The Williams & Wilkins Co., 1943, xiv, 514 pp.

4. Bremer, F., and Dow, R. S. The cerebral acoustic area of the cat. A combined oscillographic and cytoarchitectonic study. *J. Neurophysiol.*, 1939, 2:308–318.

5. Bunch, C. C. Age variations in auditory acuity. *Arch. Otolaryng.*, Chicago, 1929, 9:625–636.

6. Galambos, R., and Davis, H. The response of single auditory-nerve fibers to acoustic stimulation. *J. Neurophysiol.*, 1943, 6:39–57.

7. Hallpike, C. S., and Scott, P. Observations on the function of the round window. *J. Physiol.*, 1940, 99:76–82.

8. Hughson, W., and Crowe, S. J. Immobilization of the round window membrane: a further experimental study. *Ann. Otol., etc.*, St Louis, 1932, 41:332–348.

9. Kemp, E. H., Coppée, G. E., and Robinson, E. H. Electric responses of the brain stem to unilateral auditory stimulation. *Amer. J. Physiol.*, 1937, 120:304–315. (See also: *Ibid.*, pp. 316–322.)

10. Lorente de Nó, R. Anatomy of the eighth nerve. The central projection of the nerve endings of the internal ear. *Laryngoscope*, St Louis, 1933, 43:1–38.

11. Mettler, F. A., Finch, G., Girden, E., and Culler, E. Acoustic value of the several components of the auditory pathway. *Brain*, 1934, 57:475–483.

12. Saul, L. J., and Davis, H. Action currents in the central nervous system. I. Action currents of the auditory tracts. *Arch. Neurol. Psychiat.*, Chicago, 1932, 28:1104–1116.

13. Stevens, S. S., and Davis, H. *Hearing: its psychology and physiology*. New York, John Wiley & Sons, Inc., 1938, xv, 489 pp.

14. Stevens, S. S., Davis, H., and Lurie, M. H. The localization of pitch perception on the basilar membrane. *J. gen. Psychol.*, 1935, 13:297–315.

15. Walker, A. E. *The primate thalamus*. Chicago, University of Chicago Press, 1938, xxiii, 321 pp.

16. Wever, E. G., and Bray, C. W. Action currents in the auditory nerve in response to acoustical stimulation. *Proc. nat. Acad. Sci.*, 1930, 16:344–350.

17. Wever, E. G., and Bray, C. W. The nature of acoustic response: the relation between sound frequency and frequency of impulses in the auditory nerve. *J. exp. Psychol.*, 1930, 13:373–387.

18. Wiggers, H. C. The functions of the intra-aural muscles. *Amer. J. Physiol.*, 1937, 120:771–780.

19. Woolsey, C. N., and Walzl, E. M. Topical projection of nerve fibers from local regions of the cochlea to the cerebral cortex of the cat. *Johns Hopk. Hosp. Bull.*, 1942, 71:315–344.

CHAPTER 22

THE EYE AS AN OPTICAL INSTRUMENT

BY FRANK W. WEYMOUTH

The eye is the peripheral organ of vision. By means of its physical structure rays of light from external objects are focused upon the retina and there set up nerve impulses that are transmitted by the fibers of the optic nerve and optic tract to the visual area in the cortex of the brain. In this last organ is aroused that reaction in consciousness which we designate as a visual sensation. In studying the physiology of vision we may first consider the eye as an optical instrument physically adapted to form an image on the retina and provided with certain physiological mechanisms for its regulation; secondly, we may look into the properties of the retina in relation to its reactions to light; and, lastly, we may study the visual sensations themselves, or the physiology of the visual cortex.

Formation of an Image by a Convex Lens. That the refractive surfaces of the eye form an image of external objects upon the retinal surface is a necessary conclusion from the physical structure. The fact may be demonstrated directly, however, by observation upon the excised eye of an albino rabbit. The thin coats of such an eye are semitransparent, and if the eye is placed in a tube of blackened paper and held in front of one's own eyes it can be seen readily that a small, inverted image of external objects is formed upon the retinal surface, just as an inverted image of the exterior is formed upon the ground glass plate of a photographic camera. This image is formed in the eye by virtue of the refractive surfaces of the cornea and the lens. The curved surfaces of these transparent bodies act substantially like a convex glass lens, and the physics of the formation of an image by such a lens may be used to explain the refractive processes in the eye. To understand the formation of an image by a convex lens the following physical facts must be borne in mind. The most common form of lens is a piece of glass with polished spherical surfaces surrounded by air. Such lenses are of two types, the thick-in-the-middle or converging lens with convex surfaces, and the thin-in-the-middle or diverging lens with concave surfaces. The *principal axis* of a lens with two spherical surfaces is a line passing through the centers of curvature and therefore perpendicular to these surfaces where it pierces them. Real images that may be caught on a screen are formed only by convex or converging lenses. Light coming from a point on the principal axis so distant that its rays are parallel when it strikes the lens will, on emerging, converge to a point, the *principal focus*, on the principal axis behind the lens (*F*, Fig. 232, I).* The distance of the principal focus from the lens is the *principal focal distance*. This distance, which is a measure of the refractive power or "strength" of the lens, depends upon the curvatures of the lenticular surfaces and the refrac-

---

* In all such diagrams it must be remembered that the curvatures and thicknesses of the lenses are greatly exaggerated. Statements concerning the course of rays are strictly true only for an ideally thin lens and for a small area about the principal axis.

tive index of the glass. Parallel rays are given theoretically by a source of light at an infinite distance in front of the lens, but practically objects not nearer than about 20 feet give rays so little divergent that they may be considered as parallel, so far as the optical apparatus of the eye is concerned. On the other hand, if a luminous object is placed at F the rays from it that strike upon the lens will emerge from the other surface as parallel rays of light. If a luminous point (f, Fig. 232, II) is placed in front of such a lens at a distance greater than the principal focal distance, but not so far as to give practically parallel rays, the cone of diverging rays from it that impinges upon the surface of the lens will be brought to a focus (f') farther away than the principal focus. Conversely, the rays from a luminous point at f' will be brought to a focus at f. These points, f and f', are, therefore, spoken of as

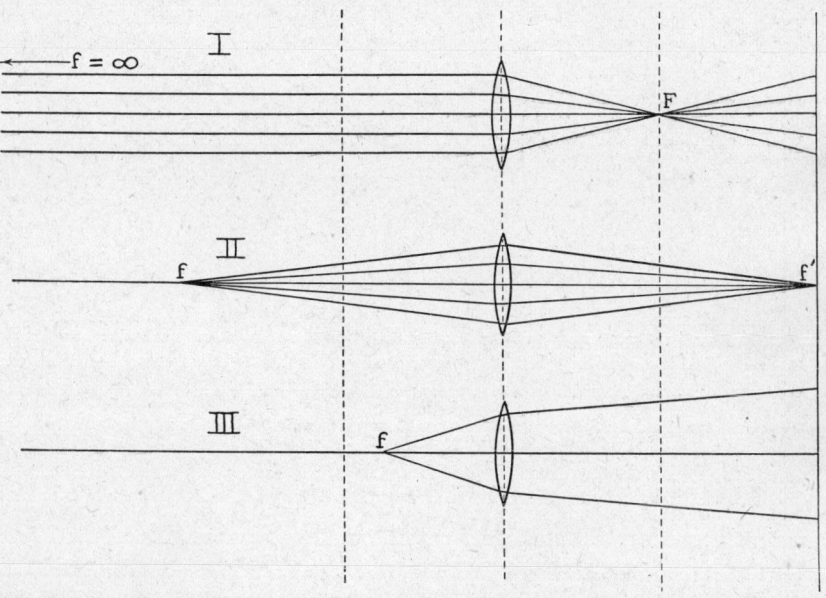

Fig. 232.—Diagrams to illustrate the refraction of light by a convex lens. I, refraction of parallel rays; II, refraction of divergent rays; III, refraction of divergent rays from a luminous point nearer than the principal focal distance. F, principal focus; f, luminous point; see text for further explanation.

conjugate foci. All luminous points within the limits specified will have their corresponding conjugate foci, at which their images will be formed by the lens. Lastly, if a luminous point is placed nearer to the lens than the principal focal distance, as at f in Figure 232, III, the cone of strongly divergent rays that falls upon the lens, although refracted, is still divergent after leaving the lens on the other side and consequently is not focused and forms no real image of the point.

In a biconvex lens with equally curved surfaces there is an *optical center* or nodal point on the principal axis equidistant from the surfaces. In the ideally thin lens, it should be remembered, the surfaces and the optical center are supposed to coincide. In Figure 233, *DE* is the principal axis and *o* the optical center. All other straight lines passing through the optical center are known as *secondary axes.* Rays of light coincident with any of these secondary axes suffer no change in direction in passing through the lens. Moreover, any luminous point not on the principal axis will have its image (conjugate focus) formed somewhere upon the secondary axis drawn from this point through the optical center. The exact position of the image of such a point can be determined by the following construction: Let *A* represent the luminous point in question. It will throw a cone of rays upon the lens, the limiting rays of which may be represented by *Ab* and *Ac*. One of these rays, *Ap*, will be parallel to the principal axis, and will therefore pass through the principal focus, *F*. If this distance is determined and is indicated properly in the construction, the line *Ap* may be drawn, as indicated, so as to pass through *F* after leaving the lens. The point at which the prolongation of this line cuts the secondary axis, *Ao*, marks the conjugate focus of *A* and gives the position at which all of the rays will be focused to form the image, *a*. In calculating the position of

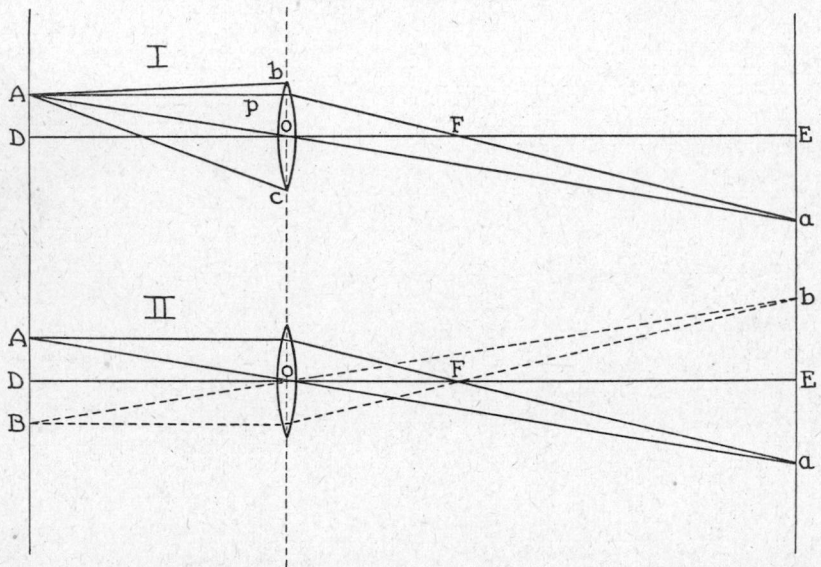

Fig. 233.—Diagram to illustrate the formation of an image by a convex lens. *A, B*, luminous points; *a, b*, images of points; *F*, principal focus; *o*, optical center of lens; *DE*, optical axis; see text for further explanation.

the image of any object in front of the lens the same method may be followed, the construction being drawn to determine the images for two or more limiting points, as shown in Figure 233, II. Let *AB* be an arrow in front of the lens. The image of *A* will be formed at *a* on the secondary axis *Ao*, and the image of *B* at *b* along the secondary axis *Bo*. The images of all the intervening points will, of course, lie between *a* and *b*, so that the image of the entire object will be that of an inverted arrow. This image may be caught on a screen at the distance indicated by the construction if the latter is drawn to scale. The principal focus of a convex lens in air may be determined experimentally or it may be calculated from the formula

$$\frac{1}{p} + \frac{1}{p^1} = \frac{1}{f},$$

f representing the principal focal distance and *p* and *p*¹, the conjugate focal distance for an object farther away than the principal focus. That is, if the distance of the object from the lens, p, is known, and the distance of its image, p^1, is determined experimentally, the principal focal distance of the lens, f, may be determined by the formula.

Formation of an Image by the Eye. As stated above, the refractive surfaces of the eye act essentially like a convex lens. As a matter of fact, these refractive surfaces are more complex than in the case of the biconvex lens. In the latter the rays of light suffer refraction at two points only; where they enter the lens they pass from a rarer to a denser medium and where they leave the lens they pass from a denser to a rarer medium. At these two points, therefore, they are refracted. In the eye there is a larger series of refractive surfaces. The light is refracted at the anterior surface of the cornea where it passes from the air into the denser medium of the cornea; at the anterior surface of the lens, where it again enters a denser medium; and at the posterior surface of the lens, where it enters the less dense vitreous humor. The relative refractive effects of these various surfaces have been studied, and in texts of oph-

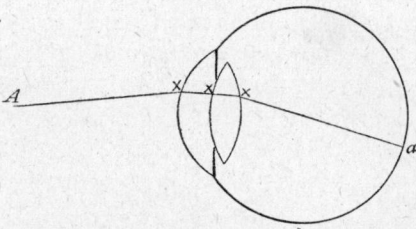

Fig. 234.—Diagram to illustrate the chief interfaces at which light rays are refracted.

thalmology (Duke-Elder, 6; Helmoltz, 8) may be found data including the curvatures and the indices of refraction* of the various media of the eye.

The three points at which the light is refracted are indicated in the accompanying diagram (Fig. 234). The refractive surfaces of the eye may be considered as being composed of a concavo-convex lens, the cornea and aqueous humor, and a biconvex lens, the crystalline lens. In a system of this kind, composed of media of differing indices of refraction separated by surfaces of varying curvatures, it is possible, but laborious, to trace accurately the entire path of the light. As far as the eye is concerned, it has been shown that the course of the light rays may be followed with sufficient accuracy by employing what is known as the reduced eye. This useful simplification of the optical system of the eye was introduced by Listing and later modified by Donders (3). Although not exact, it is accurate enough for ordinary purposes and has the additional merit that the round numbers are easily remembered. In the

* The index of refraction is the ratio of the velocity of light in the substance considered to the velocity of light in the air, or more exactly, in vacuum; it is commonly measured by the ratio between the sine of the angle of incidence and the sine of the angle of refraction.

$$\text{index of refraction} = \frac{\text{velocity in air}}{\text{velocity in X}} = \frac{\text{sine } i}{\text{sine } r}$$

The following illustrate the data on the index of refraction.

air	= 1.000
water	= 1.333
aqueous and vitreous	= 1.336
crystalline lens (index of an equivalent thin lens)	= 1.413

Because of the greater difference between the index of refraction of air and of the cornea as compared with that between the lens and its surroundings, light is more strongly bent on entering the eye than in its passage through the lens.

reduced eye all refraction is supposed to take place at a single interface be-tween air and the contents of the eye, here assumed to be homeogeneous and to have the index of refraction of water, 1.333. This interface (*c*, in Fig. 235), corresponding to the surface of the cornea, has a radius of 5 mm. and its center of curvature is the optical center or nodal point of the system (*n*). The retina lies 15 mm. posterior to the nodal point or 20 mm. from the cornea; this point is also the principal focus of the system so that in the reduced eye at rest, distant objects are focused on the retina. The anterior principal focus, to which rays parallel within the eye would converge on emerging, lies at a distance of 15 mm. in the air before the cornea. This apparent asymmetry of focal distance is due to the fact that from the object to the cornea the light is traveling in the air while from the cornea to the retina the light is in the more dense medium of the eye; if this second focal distance of 20 mm. is divided by the index of refraction of the reduced eye, it will equal the anterior focal distance, $20/1.333 = 15.0$.

In the completely relaxed ideal eye the surfaces and distances are so related that the posterior focal point coincides with the retina and distant objects are focused on the retina. To show the formation of the image of an external

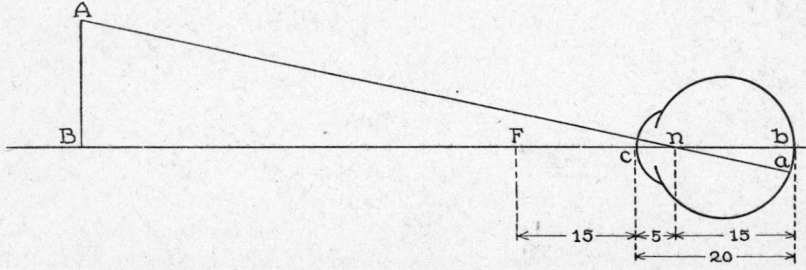

Fig. 235.—Diagram of the reduced eye (Donders) with dimensions and the construction required for the location and size of the retinal image. *AB*, object; *ab*, image; *n*, nodal point; *F*, principal focus (anterior); *c*, corneal surface.

object on the retina it suffices, therefore, to use a construction such as is represented in Figure 235. Secondary axes are drawn from the limiting points of the object — *A* and *B* — through the nodal point. Where these axes meet the retina, the retinal image of the object will be formed. That is, all the rays of light proceeding from *A* that penetrate the eye will be focused at *a*, and all proceeding from *B* at *b*. The image on the retina will therefore be inverted and will be smaller than the object. The angle formed at the nodal point by the lines *An* and *Bn* (angle *AnB* or *anb*) is known as the *visual angle;* it varies inversely with the distance of the object from the eye.

Retinal Image and Spatial Perception. Although the images of external objects on the retina are inverted, we see these objects in their correct posi-tions in space. This purely verbal paradox of "inverted" image and "erect" seeing has been magnified by some into a physiological "problem." We neither "see" our retinae nor the images upon them; the stimulation of a particular point on the retina is the sign of an object in a particular position in the outside world agreeing with our other sense reports, particularly those of touch and muscle sense. Experience in the growing child builds up such an agreement. Experience in the adult maintains such an agreement; in cases where abnormal movement or position of an eye causes the stimulation of its retina to indicate a position not in agreement with other sensations, including that of the fellow eye, the afferent impulses from this eye are, after a short period of confusion, excluded from our consciousness and the nonconforming eye becomes, for all practical purposes, "blind."

The apparent position of objects is related to their retinal images by the physical process of image formation. The stimulation of retinal point a (Fig. 235) indicates an object at A, the position in the outside world from which light would normally come to a focus on a. If point a is stimulated in some other manner, say mechanically, the sensation still appears to be due to an "object" in the direction of A. This may easily be demonstrated by producing pressure phosphenes. If the tip of the little finger is pressed against the eyeball through the closed lids in a position as far as possible either nasally or temporally, the eye being turned in the opposite direction, the slight bending of the sclera will stimulate the retina mechanically. The visual sensation produced, a *phosphene*, is that of a dark blue spot surrounded by a light or yellow halo. The "object" appears to lie in a direction opposite to the stimulating finger, a position from which light would have to come to form an image on that part of the retina beneath the finger.

Another illustration is afforded by Lecat's experiment. This experiment is performed as follows: if a card, pierced by a pinhole, is held about 2 cm. from the eye, and the head of a pin interposed between it and the cornea, they may be so adjusted that in the circle of light from the pinhole is seen an inverted pinhead. Light from the pinhole at this distance, which is within the near point of distinct vision, becomes nearly parallel within the eye and therefore casts an erect shadow of the pinhead on the retina. Each point of this shadow appears to come from a corresponding point of an "object" in such a position that its image would coincide with the shadow actually stimulating the retina; the "object" obviously must be inverted to do this.

Size of the Retinal Image. The size of the retinal image of an object may readily be calculated if the size of the object and its distance from the eye are known. As will be seen from Figure 235 the triangles AnB and anb are similar; consequently we have the following equality of ratios

$$\frac{AB}{ab} = \frac{An}{an} \quad \text{or}$$

$$\frac{\text{size of an object}}{\text{size of image}} = \frac{\text{distance of object from nodal point}}{\text{distance of image from nodal point}}$$

To take a concrete example: suppose it is desired to find the size of the retinal image of a tree 40 m. high at a distance of 2 km. (2000 m.). Reducing all measurements to meters to avoid confusion and substituting in the above equation we have

$$\frac{40}{\text{image}} = \frac{2000}{0.015}$$

$$\text{image} = \frac{0.6}{2000} = 0.0003 \text{ m. or 0.3 mm.}$$

The image of the tree is thus about the size of the fovea. Obviously the ratio of object size to image size is the same as the ratio of object distance to image distance or

$$\frac{2000}{0.015} = 133.333$$

Accommodation of the Eye for Objects at Different Distances. The emmetropic or ideal refractive state of the eye is one in which, at rest, parallel rays are brought to a focus on the retina. That is, in the relaxed eye the refractive media have such densities and such curvatures that infinitely distant objects are clearly imaged on the retina. Many eyes approach this ideal condition closely enough to permit us to say that a distant far point is normal. When objects are brought closer to the eye, however, the rays proceding from them become more and more divergent. If the eye remains unchanged, the refracted rays strike the retina before coming to a focus; in consequence each luminous point in the object, instead of forming a point upon the retina, forms a circle, known as a diffusion circle. As this is true for each point of the object, the retinal image as a whole is blurred. We know, however, that up to a certain point at least this blurring does not occur when the object is brought closer to the eyes. The eye, in fact, *accommodates* itself to the nearer object so as to obtain a clear focus. In a photographic camera this accommodation or focusing is effected by moving the ground glass plate farther away as the object is brought closer to the lens. In the eye the same result is obtained by increasing the curvature and therefore the refractive power of the lens. That a change in

Fig. 236.—Reflected images of a candle flame as seen in the pupil of an eye (A) at rest and (B) accommodated for near objects. (Williams)

the lens is the essential factor in accommodation for near objects is demonstrated by a simple and conclusive experiment utilizing the Purkinje images. The eye to be observed is relaxed; that is, gazes into the distance. A lighted candle is held to one side and the observer takes a position on the other where he can see the light of the candle reflected from the observed eye. With a little practice and under the right conditions of illumination the observer will be able to see three images of the candle reflected from the observed eye as from a mirror: one, the brightest, is reflected from the convex surface of the cornea (image *a*, Fig. 236, *A*); one, much dimmer and of larger size, is reflected from the convex surface of the lens (image *b*). This image is larger and fainter because the reflecting surface is less curved. The third image (*c*), is inverted and is smaller and brighter than the second. This image is reflected from the posterior surface of the lens, which acts, in this instance, like a concave mirror. If, now, the observed eye gazes at a near object, it will be noted (Fig. 236, *B*) that the first image does not change at all, the third image also remains practically the same, but the middle image (*b*) becomes smaller and approaches nearer to the first (*a*). This result can only mean that in the act of accommodation the anterior surface of the lens becomes more convex. In this way its refractive power is increased and the more divergent rays from the near object are focused on the retina. Helmholtz has shown that the curvature of the posterior surface of the lens is also increased slightly; but the change is so slight that the increased refractive power is referred chiefly to the change in the anterior surface. The means by which the change is effected was first satisfactorily explained by Helmholtz. The structures involved and their action as envisioned by this theory will be described briefly.

The tiny *ciliary muscle* lies in the thickened anterior portion of the vascular layer called the *ciliary body*, which lies like a collar between the anterior

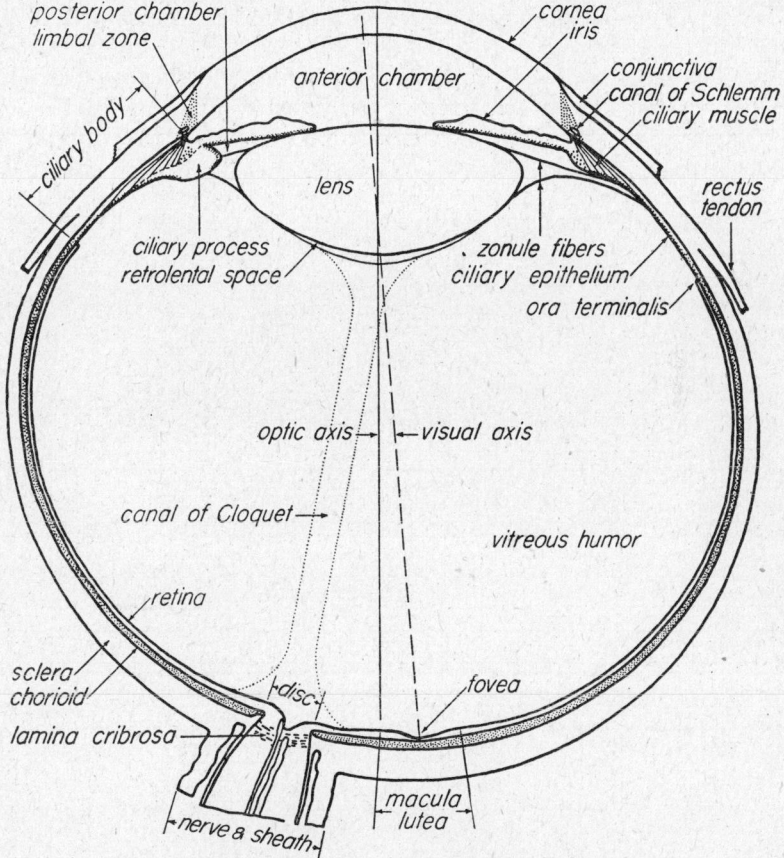

Fig. 237.—Horizontal section of the human eye (right). Due to the level of section, a ciliary process partly conceals the zonule fibers on the left, but on the right their full extent can be seen. (From Walls, The *vertebrate eye*, 1942, modified from Salzmann, *The anatomy and histology of the human eyeball in the normal state*, E. V. L. Brown, translator, 1912.)

margin of the functional retina and the root of the iris, surrounding the lens. Some of the smooth fibers of which it is composed take a radial or meridional course, having their origin in the sclera near the margin of the cornea and their insertion in the chorioid* near the posterior margin of the ciliary body. Other fibers lying central to these have a circular course like the fibers of a sphincter muscle, although all fibers are so intimately related that they cannot be separated into distinct portions.

* The spelling *chorioid* is preferred to *choroid* as etymologically more correct and closer to the intended meaning, "resembling the chorion."

The lens is suspended by the *zonula* consisting apparently of delicate transparent membranes and fibers attached on the one hand to the inner surface of the ciliary body and on the other to the elastic capsule covering the lens. At rest this zonula is under tension and in consequence of the pull on the equator of the lens, the latter assumes a flattened form. When the ciliary muscle contracts it pulls the ciliary body in towards the lens, stretching the chorioid in so doing, and relaxing the zonula. The tension which held the lens in its flattened form having been abolished or reduced, the elasticity of the capsule, like the rubber of a toy balloon, tends to mold the plastic lens into a more convex form, varying in degree with the degree of contraction of the ciliary muscle.

Other theories have been proposed both before and since that of Helmholtz but, although recent work, particularly that of Fincham (7), has led to minor changes, his view of the mechanism of accommodation is still the most adequate.

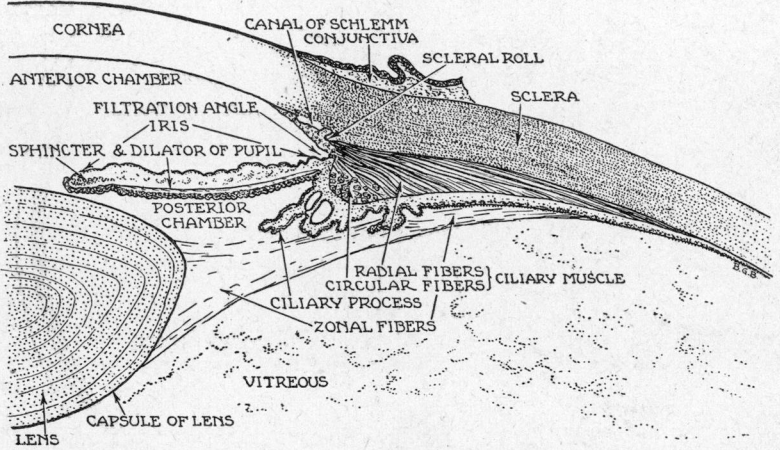

Fig. 238.—Detail of the anterior segment of the human eye. The retina begins just beyond the right hand margin. The ciliary process is distorted by the sectioning knife. The scleral roll is a narrow shelf of scleral tissue, on the under side of which the radial or meridianal fibers of the ciliary muscle take their origin. (Redrawn from Maximow and Bloom, *A textbook of histology*, 1931).

Other mammals accommodate in the same way as man, but this is not true for all groups of vertebrates. In most bony fish, for example, the mechanism is wholly different. The cornea has no demonstrable refractive effect since the intra-ocular fluids do not differ appreciably in refractive index from the surrounding water. The lens is more curved, in fact spherical, and of higher refractive index than in man. At rest it lies close to the cornea and far from the retina so that the eye is focused for near objects. In accommodation a special muscle, the *retractor lentis*, moves the lens backward and toward the retina, thus focusing the eye for more distant objects (1, 17).

Limit of the Power of Accommodation—Near Point of Distinct Vision. When an object is brought closer and closer to the eye a point will be reached at which it is impossible by the strongest contraction of the ciliary muscle to obtain a clear image of the object. The rays from it are so divergent that the refractive surfaces are unable to bring them to a focus on the the retina. Each luminous point makes a diffusion circle on the retina, and the whole image is indistinct. The nearest point at which an object can be distinctly seen, with full accommodation, is called the *near point*. The distance of the near point from the eye increases with age, slowly in early life, most rapidly in the early forties and very slowly after fifty. The general features of this decline are shown in Figure 239. The distance of the near point from the emmetropic eye at various ages is shown in Table 14. This recession of the near point is usually ascribed to a progressive loss of plasticity of the lens, so that although the ciliary muscle contracts and reduces the tension of the zonula, the lens is less and less capable of being molded into a more convex form. The process starts as early in life as satisfactory measurements of the near point can be made, and is one of the many facts which show that senescence begins practically at birth. This decline in the power of accommodation is little noticed until it begins to interfere with reading, usually between the

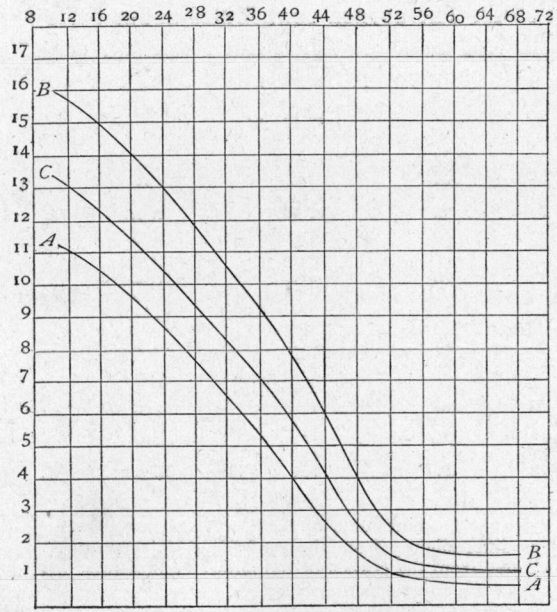

Fig. 239.—Changes in amplitude of accommodation with age. Abscissae, age in years; ordinates, accommodation in diopters calculated from a point 14 mm. in front of the cornea. Line *CC* represents the average of over 1000 cases; *AA* and *BB* give the extremes. (Duane, *Ophthalmoscope*, 1912, *10*:486–502.)

fortieth and fiftieth years, when the condition is called *presbyopia* or oldsightedness. If no other defect exists in the eye, this deficiency of the lens is readily overcome by using suitable convex glasses to aid the eye in focusing the rays. It is obvious that in such cases the glasses need not be used except for near work.

Far Point of Distinct Vision. The normal eye is so adjusted that parallel rays are brought to a focus on the retina. The far point is therefore theoretically at infinity. Objects at a great distance are seen distinctly, as far as their size permits, without accommodation—that is, with the eye at rest. Practically it is found that objects at a distance of six meters (20 feet) send rays that are sufficiently parallel to focus on the retina without muscular effort on the part of the eyes, and this distance, therefore, measures the practical far point of the normal eye.

Refractive Power of the Eye and Amplitude of Accommodation. The refractive power of lenses is expressed usually in terms of their principal focal distance. A lens with a distance of one meter is taken as the unit and is designated as having a refractive power of one diopter, 1 D. Compared with this unit, the refractive power of lenses is expressed in terms of the reciprocal of their principal focal distance measured in meters; thus, a lens with a principal focal distance of 1/10 meter is a lens of 10 diopters, 10 D., and one with a focal distance of 10 meters is 1/10 diopter (0.1 D.). As pointed out above, the reduced eye at rest has a refractive power of $66\frac{2}{3}$ D. This value is the reciprocal of the focal distance in air when measured in meters ($1/0.015 = 66\frac{2}{3}$ D.) or the reciprocal of the focal distance within the medium of the eye multiplied by the refractive index of that medium ($1.333/0.020 = 66\frac{2}{3}$ D.). This is somewhat greater than the power based on the more exact measurements, which is about 58 D. The cornea contributes about twice as much to this power as does the lens although this is not commonly recognized. Thus the loss of the lens, as in cataract operations, does not lessen the refractive power

Table 14

Age YRS.	Amplitude D.	Near point CM.
8	11.6	8.6
10	11.3	8.8
15	10.5	9.5
20	9.6	10.4
25	8.7	11.5
30	7.8	12.8
35	6.6	15.2
40	5.4	18.5
45	3.4	20.4
50	1.9	52.6
55	1.3	76.9
60	1.2	83.3
65	1.1	90.9
70	1.0	100.0

Table giving for each age the amplitude of accommodation and the near point. Data from Duane (5). The values differ slightly from those of Fig. 239 in representing more cases (over 4000) and being calculated from the cornea of the reduced emmetropic eye rather than from a point 14 mm. before the cornea of the actual eye.

as much as does the abolition of the action of the cornea which occurs, for example, when the eye is opened under water.

In accommodation the greater curvature of the lens increases the total refractive power of the eye. Thus when a 20 year old emmetrope, with a near point of 1/10 m., accommodates, the eye not only brings to a focus parallel rays ($66\frac{2}{3}$ D.) but overcomes in addition the divergence of light from the near point (10 D.). It is as though the eye were left at rest and a glass lens of 10 D. were placed before the cornea. The amplitude of accommodation may thus be expressed by the number of diopters which may be added to the refractive power of the eye by the action of the ciliary muscle. In Table 14 are given the amplitudes of accommodation corresponding to the near points at various ages. Its values and those plotted in Figure 239 are derived from data collected by Duane (4, 5).

Optical Defects of the Emmetropic Eye. In the eye as in other optical systems spherical, chromatic, and other aberrations are present but they seldom appreciably affect vision. For this there are several reasons of which space permits only brief mention. The shape and structure of the cornea and lens are usually such as to reduce aberrations, as is also the strategic location of the iris which enables it to act advantageously as a diaphragm. In addition to these physical reasons there are certain physiological elements favorable to clear vision. The most marked distortions fall, of course, on the peripheral retina where visual acuity is low; in consequence the aberrations pass unnoticed and they do not interfere with the important "finder" function of this part of the retina. The distribution of spectral sensitivity in the retina is also important. The central part of the spectrum, the yellow, has by far the greatest stimulating power and both the extreme red and the extreme blue, which of course show the greatest chromatic aberration, play little part in vision. Again, light that is out of place and tends to destroy the clearness of images, scattered light, diffraction fringes, and the like, are of low intensity and thus tend to fall below the retinal threshold. For these reasons what may be called the "physiological image" is more satisfactory than the physical image.

Abnormalities in the Refraction of the Eye: Ametropia. The length of the globe and the refractive curvature of the eye vary from person to person as do height, weight, or other physical measurements. As a result, not all eyes show that relation between axial length and refractive power which is called *emmetropia*, in which, at rest, parallel rays are brought to focus on the retina. If we take the deviation from the emmetropic condition as measured by the lens needed to focus the rays in each case, we will find that these positive and negative values are distributed in an approximately normal curve as in the case of other human measurements. The departure from emmetropia in many eyes is so slight as to have no appreciable effect on vision, while the greater and greater degrees of departure occur less and less commonly. At one time these biological variations shut out a man or woman from occupations requiring good vision and the higher degrees made the person pitifully clumsy at all tasks requiring skill. Now the great majority of defects may be so satisfactorily remedied by glasses that they are hardly noticed. For this reason it is worth while to discuss the fundamental nature of these defects although more detailed treatment will have to be sought in special treatises.

Emmetropia may be defined as that refractive state of the eye in which, without accommodation, parallel rays are focused on the sensitive layer of the retina, or in which the far point is infinitely distant; a person with such eyes is often called an *emmetrope*. Any deviation from this condition is called *ametropia*. Obviously these deviations must be of two types; in one, parallel rays will come to a focus before reaching the retina and in the other they will reach the retina before coming to a focus. In the first the refractive power is relatively too great for the axial length; in the second the refractive power is relatively too small. Of course, either or both may depart from the average values, but the axial length is apparently more often at fault and for the purposes of discussion we may assume that this is always true. In either case an inequality of refraction in different meridians may, in addition, give astigmia, which will be discussed below.

The form of ametropia in which, as we have supposed, the axis is too long, is called *myopia;* that in which it is too short, *hyperopia* (hypermetropia). At birth the great majority of eyes are hyperopic, indicating that the axial length is relatively less than required to match the refractive power. During growth, particularly from about five years to the late teens, the increase of length is relatively more rapid than the decrease of refractive power. As a result, there is a shift of the refractive state toward myopia. Hyperopic eyes, depending upon the degree, become less hyperopic, emmetropic, or myopic; emmetropic eyes become myopic and myopic eyes, more markedly myopic, until in the adult the proportions of the two defects are more nearly equal (2, 9, 12, 14, 15).

In myopia, without accommodation, parallel rays of light come to a focus in the vitreous and diverge again to form diffusion circles on the retina, thus giving blurred vision. In any degree of myopia there is some point, nearer than that giving parallel rays, from which the light is sufficiently divergent to come

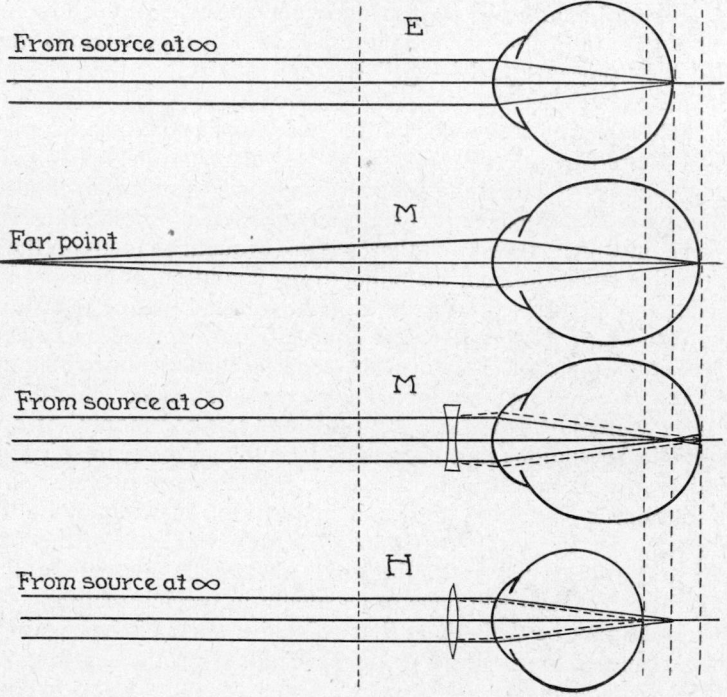

Fig. 240.—Diagram of emmetropia (E) (reduced eye to scale), myopia (M), and hyperopia (H); showing by the dotted lines, in the two lower diagrams, the effect of proper correcting lenses.

to a focus on the retina of the unaccommodated eye; this is the myopic far point. The distance of this far point may be only a few centimeters and all more distant objects will appear in some degree blurred, the more so the more distant they are. This condition is represented by diagram *M* in Figure 240. The obvious remedy is to use concave lenses for distant vision. By this means, if the lenses are properly chosen, the rays will be given such an amount of divergence that the focus will be thrown accurately on the retina. Since the myopic eye at rest is capable of focusing rays of some degree of divergence, it can, in full accommodation, focus on very near objects, i.e., its near point is nearer than that of an emmetropic eye with equal amplitude of accommodation. This has led to the term *near-sightedness*. Wearing his distance correction, however, both the near and the far point of the myope correspond to those of an emmetrope of similar age.

The condition in *hyperopia* is represented in diagram *H* of Figure 240. In the eye at rest the retina is reached before the light has come to a focus, and each point source of light is represented by a diffusion circle; vision is thus blurred in proportion to the degree of the defect. A converging lens of the proper strength will obviously bring light to the eye with that additional amount of convergence required to bring it to a focus on the sensitive layers of the retina. Since no point in nature gives off converging rays there is no real far point for the hyperopic eye, although we may consider the point toward which light is converging from the correcting lens as a virtual far point.

We have so far considered the hyperopic eye at rest, but it is obvious that the necessary additional convergence of the light rays may be furnished by accommodation. Thus the uncorrected hyperope may see distant objects clearly by the use of his accommodation provided that its amplitude is greater than the defect. We should not hastily consider this an advantage, however, since the constant excessive accommodation exerted in an abnormal relation to the convergence of the eyes is a serious cause of eye strain. Since some accommodation is used in seeing even distant objects, there is less available for viewing near things and in consequence the near point is more distant than in an emmetrope with equal amplitude of accommodation. The double effort required for near work, therefore, makes close application possible for short periods only, and even these periods are painful. The term *far-sightedness* is unfortunately misleading. The vision of a hyperope for distant objects is indeed better than that of the more reasonably named near-sighted person, but it is not better than that of the emmetrope and when it equals that of the latter it is, as we have just seen, at the cost of serious eye strain.

Presbyopia has already been mentioned as a consequence of the decline in the amplitude of accommodation with age. The near point of distinct vision recedes farther and farther from the eye until near work is difficult or impossible. From what has been said above it is clear that, because of his more distant near point, the uncorrected hyperope will experience difficulty with near work before the emmetrope and that the uncorrected myope will find reading difficult late or perhaps never. A myope with a near point of 20 or 30 cm. can see near objects even should no accommodation remain; those people who can read fine print at 80 or 90 are, in all cases, myopes. All properly corrected eyes will become presbyopic at about the same time, at an age of approximately 45, after which an additional convex lens will be necessary for comfortable reading

Astigmia or Astigmatism. In an ideal eye the refractive surfaces of the cornea and lens might be expected to be, for practical purposes, spherical surfaces in which the curvature along all meridians would be equal. Such an eye would bring the cone of light falling upon it from a distant luminous point to a focal point on the retina, barring the effect of spherical and chromatic aberration. In many eyes, however, the corneal surface is not spherical but toric, a shape similar to the outer surface of an auto tire. In such a case there will be one meridian of least curvature and a second, at right angles to the first, of greatest curvature. Rays from a luminous point refracted in passing through such a surface will not form a point image, since rays falling along the meridian of greatest curvature will tend to reach a focus before those falling along the meridian of least curvature and may be already diverging when the latter reach a focus. The effect may be illustrated by the diagram forming Figure 241, which represents the refraction of rays from a distant luminous point by a lens in which the curvature along the vertical meridian is greater than that along the horizontal. The rays along the vertical meridian are brought to a focus first (G) while those from the horizontal meridian are still converging, so that a screen placed at this point will give an image having the shape of a horizontal line (a–a'). The rays along the horizontal meridian are brought to a focus at B, but those from the vertical meridian, having passed through the focus at G, are by this time spread out vertically, so that a screen placed at this point will show the image as a vertical line (b–b'). In between, the image of the point may be elliptical or circular, as represented in the diagram.

In the eye, astigmia may be due to a toric cornea or to the decentering of the cornea or of the lens. Such a condition, producing the image forms just

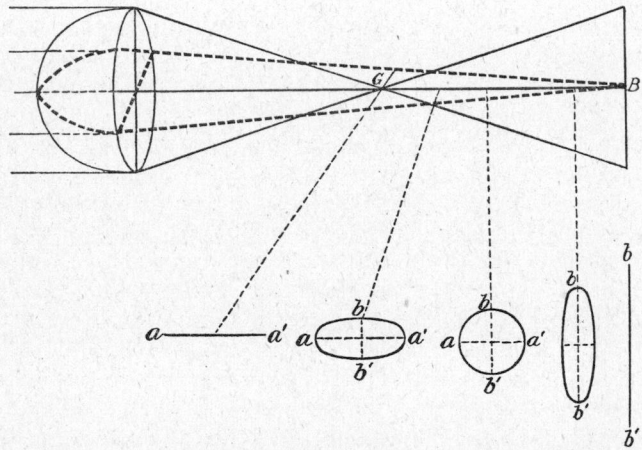

Fig. 241.—Diagram of conoid of light emerging from an astigmatic lens. The lower row of figures represent the cross sections of the light at the indicated points; it should be noted that nowhere is the image of the distant light source a point.

described, is called *regular astigmia*. Regular astigmia may be corrected by a cylindrical lens or by a combination of spherical and cylindrical lenses of such strength and so placed as to equalize the refraction in the meridians of greatest and least curvature and give a point image on the retina of the unaccommodated eye receiving parallel rays from a distant point. Since in a markedly astigmatic eye the image of a point is an ellipse or line, the image of a line, which may be considered as a series of points, will consist of a series of small image lines. If these image lines have the same direction as the entire image, this image will be dark and clear (except for a slight blurring at the ends), but if the image lines are transverse, the entire image will appear broad, gray, and indistinct. Because of this fact a chart like Figure 242 may be used to detect astigmia and locate the axes of least and greatest curvature. If the lines appear to differ in clearness, astigmia is present and the two axes, at right angles, correspond to the blackest and grayest sets of lines.

What is called *irregular astigmia* deserves mention merely. The marked degrees of this defect, due to irregularities of the cornea following injury, seriously affect vision and cannot easily be corrected. A slighter degree, resulting from inhomogeneities, particularly of the lens, is almost universally present and passes unnoticed except in the case of very small images. The stars which furnish accurate point sources of light do not give rise in the human eye to point images but to radiate figures, the exact form of which varies from eye to eye. The "star" form is thus not characteristic of the heavenly bodies but of our eyes.

Iris and Pupil. The iris, arising from the anterior surface of the ciliary body, lies between the cornea and the lens and in contact with the latter; it is pierced by a central opening, the pupil. It forms the characteristically colored portion of the eye and, as seen through the cornea, is magnified by about one-eighth. The stroma of the iris contains, besides the visible pigment, a rich network of blood vessels and the posterior surface is covered with black pigment. Because of the abundant pigment the iris is impervious to light and

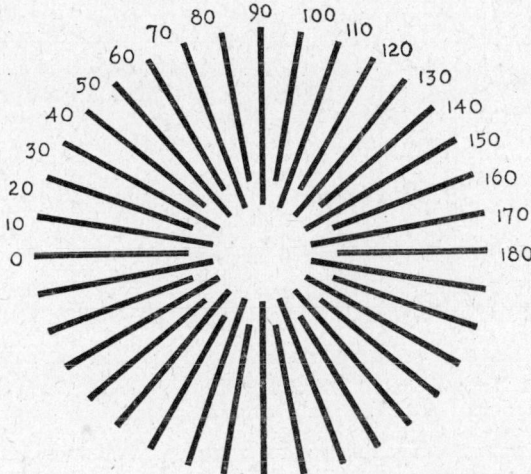

Fig. 242.—Astigmatic chart of Lancaster-Regan.

forms an excellent diaphragm. Between the layers mentioned lie the muscles of the iris, the larger and better developed sphincter near the pupillary margin and the smaller and less completely differentiated dilator.

The iris has important optical and sensory functions: it is the diaphragm in a complex optical system, by constriction in near work it increases the depth of focus, it regulates the intensity of the light reaching the retina; these functions will be considered briefly in the present section.

The iris is innervated from two divisions of the autonomic: the parasympathetic reaching the constrictor and the sympathetic, the dilator. These long and indirect pathways are exposed to lesions in a number of locations so that the abnormal reactions of the pupil have a surprisingly important diagnostic significance; this aspect is considered in other chapters.

As an optical diaphragm the iris is strategically located between the elements of the compound lens system. For this reason it has the maximum effect in producing clear images, since it excludes, when light is abundant, the peripheral optical portions of both the lens and the cornea. Because of their innervation the two pupils in man are always of the same size, at least as nearly as may be seen with the naked eye, unless a lesion has interrupted some of the widespread conduction paths. In consequence a light stimulus to either eye will cause the same change in size of both pupils. When looking at a near object the pupil constricts along with the contraction of the ciliary muscle; this is called the *near reflex*. It greatly increases the depth of focus in near work, giving clear images of objects that would otherwise be out of focus because of their position.

Light reflex. A change in the intensity of the light, provided it is rapid enough or great enough, causes a change of the size of the pupil, which constricts to an increase and dilates to a decrease in light intensity. Because of the innervation as pointed out above, an increase of light in one eye leads to changes in size of both pupils. The reaction of the pupil of the eye illuminated is called the *direct* light reflex and of the opposite eye the *consensual* light reflex. Over a considerable range of ordinarily encountered illumination the pupil of any individual has a nearly constant average or habitual

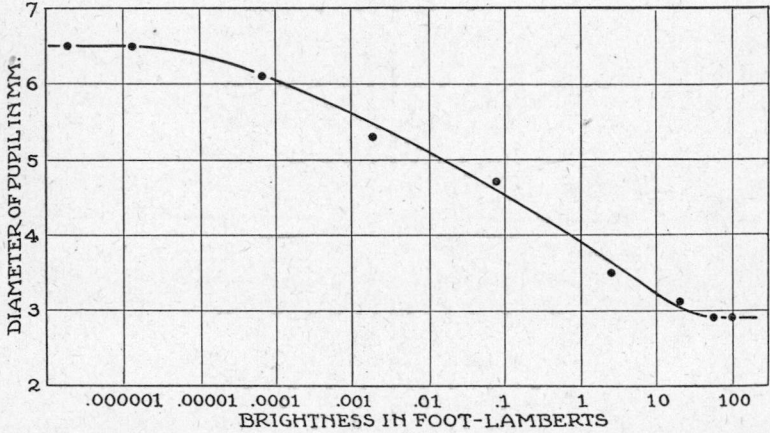

Fig. 243.—Relation of pupil diameter to illumination. Data obtained by infrared photography. (From Wagman and Nathanson, *Proc. Soc. exp. Biol., N. Y.*, 1942, *49*:466–470.)

size, varying with age, state of refraction, and perhaps other factors. It is against this background of habitual size that the reflex changes in the size of the pupil occur. A slight increase in light intensity causes a slight constriction of the pupil which then gradually dilates again as the retina adapts to the new higher level of illumination, and in a short time the pupil has resumed its habitual size.

When exposed to greater variations of intensity the changes in pupillary size persist. This is illustrated by Figure 243, which shows the average pupil diameter of six subjects exposed to illuminations covering a range of 100,000,000-fold (16). It will be seen that at both ends of this huge range of illumination, the pupil has reached a constant size, representing its limit of possible dilation or constriction. The diameters are approximately 2.9 and 6.5; there has been, therefore, a fivefold change of area. Obviously such a small change of area is utterly inadequate to compensate for the enormous range of experimental intensities or even the smaller one met in the daily range of light. The pupil is, therefore, clearly incapable of explaining the great variation of sensitivity found in adaptation (Chap. 23). A fivefold alteration of area, however, is useful in meeting the sudden light changes of moderate extent to which the eye is constantly exposed. If the light is decreased, the dilation of the pupil, though far less effective than adaptation, is more prompt and gives within 15 or 20 seconds an appreciable improvement in the ability to see in dim light. If the light is increased, the still more rapid constriction of the pupil, in 3 or 4 seconds, shields the retina, or better, perhaps, the state of adaptation of the retina, from light too intense for the existing level of sensitivity.

Intra-ocular Pressure and the Nutrition of the Eye. Certain other aspects of the eye as an optical instrument remain to be considered. In the first place, the position of the refracting surfaces with relation to each other and to the retina must be maintained with great exactness. As stated above, variations in the axial length cause ametropia; the small extent of the variations is not as well recognized. Of 1000 school children, 12 years and older, whose refraction was carefully measured, 47 per cent showed ametropia of 0.50 or 0.25 D. (9). The change in axial length necessary to produce these degrees of ametropia is 0.187 mm. or less. Clearly if there is to be any constancy in the refraction, even of an individual eye, the constancy of size and shape of the globe must be assured.

A second problem is presented by the fact that the eye contains the largest nonvascular mass in the body. No blood vessels are found in the cornea, aqueous, lens, or vitreous after the early fetal period of rapid growth. Obviously blood vessels would seriously interfere with the optical function of all these structures. Although the metabolism of none of these tissues is high and that of the aqueous and vitreous negligible, yet interference with the oxygen supply, for example, of the cornea is promptly followed by loss of transparency. These two problems will be considered in this section.

Intra-ocular pressure. The fixed distance of the refractive surfaces from the retina is maintained because the inelastic scleral envelope is under a constant intra-ocular pressure of 20 to 25 mm. Hg. The intra-ocular pressure results from a balance between the production and escape of the intra-ocular fluid. The vitreous is relatively constant in volume although it may absorb or lose water to some extent; the chief changes occur in the aqueous. The mechanism of intra-ocular pressure is complex and although much studied is not completely agreed upon; the following appears to be the most satisfactory view. The aqueous contains about 1 per cent of solids, or about one-eighth of that of the serum. Traces at least of all the constituents of the serum are found in the aqueous; the proteins are little more than traces but the electrolytes about equal those of the serum, the anions being clearly more abundant while, according to recent work (13), the total osmotic activity is above that of the blood. The material of the aqueous is derived from the blood, chiefly in the ciliary body, although to some extent in the iris, partly by secretion and partly by diffusion, and it escapes by leakage into the canal of Schlemm nonselectively at a rate of 5 or 6 cc. per day (Kinsey and Grant, 11). It is claimed that the hypertonicity is due to secretion of the electrolytes. Interference with the outflow leads to a rise of intra-ocular pressure which may damage the fibers of the optic nerve where they pass out of the globe.

Nutrition of the lens and cornea. The lens has a low metabolic rate, but like other organs of epithelial origin it continues to grow throughout life, and must maintain an interchange with the blood. It does this through the intra-ocular fluid, which, as pointed out above, contains at least a trace of all the constituents of the blood.

The transparency of the cornea, so necessary to its optical function and impaired in so many pathological conditions, has attracted much study. Histologically its stroma shows no striking difference from that of the opaque white sclera. The corneal stroma, however, differs in its osmotic relations from that of the sclera, since it is covered by closely investing semipermeable membranes, epithelium on the exterior and endothelium on the inner surface.

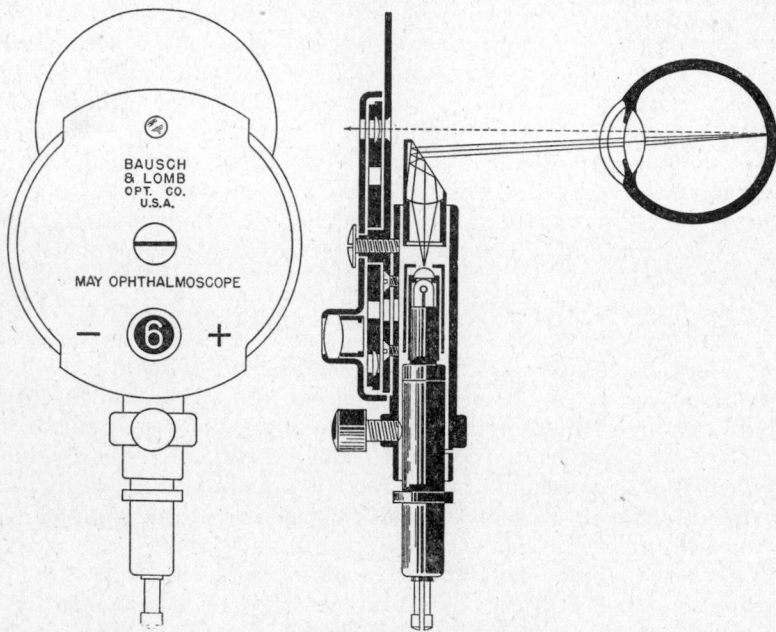

Fig. 244.—Ophthalmoscope head seen from the examiner's side and in section; the handle containing the battery is not shown. Note the course of light from the lamp to the observed eye (continuous lines), and from the retina to the observer (dotted line). A series of lenses is set into a concealed disc which can be rotated by its exposed margin. Directly across from each lens is a number giving in diopters the strength of that lens. When a given lens is at the upper aperture through which the user looks, its dioptric strength appears at the lower window. The minus sign is red, the plus sign, white, so that a red number showing means that one of the series of negative or concave lenses is in position, and a white number denotes the same for a convex or magnifying lens. Note provision for light to reach the window so that the numbers (slightly magnified by a lens) can be read easily in the dark. (Courtesy of F. W. Jobe, the Bausch & Lomb Optical Company.)

The normal transparent cornea is markedly dehydrated; when excised and placed in water it swells to three or four times its normal thickness and becomes opaque. If the uninjured surface of the cornea is placed in contact with a hypertonic solution, it loses water rapidly enough to remain dehydrated and transparent. Under normal conditions the water of the cornea is derived from the vascular margin, slowly diffuses toward the center and is lost through both surfaces to the hypertonic tears and aqueous rapidly enough to maintain the dehydration and transparency of the cornea (Kinsey and Cogan, 10). This slow circulation of fluid from the periphery and the diffusion from the aqueous supply the slight metabolic needs of the cornea. In addition, oxygen reaches it directly from the external air.

Chief Instruments for Examining the Eye. Among the instruments designed to study the eye two have proved of outstanding usefulness and will be described briefly. The ophthalmoscope makes visible the interior of the eye and is useful both to the specialist in the eye and to the general practitioner. The retinoscope presents an objective and accurate method of determining the refraction of the eye. In addition the ophthalmometer should be mentioned. Designed to measure corneal curvature, the ophthalmometer has been a valuable source of data on the optical constants of the eye, but is too limited in usefulness for modern practice to justify a description. The accounts here given are of necessity brief

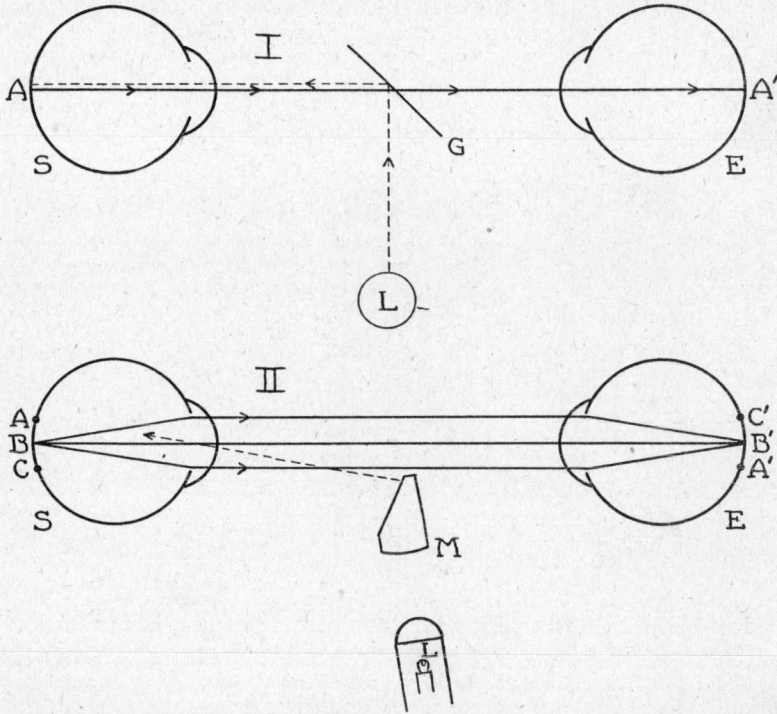

Fig. 245.—Course of light in the ophthalmoscope; *S*, eye of subject; *E*, of examiner. I. Diagram of original model of Helmholtz. *L*, light; *G*, unsilvered glass; *A* illuminated point in observed eye; *A'*, image in examiner's eye. II. Diagram of ophthalmoscope with May prism; *L*, electric bulb in handle; *M*, May prism. The entering light is indicated by dotted line. *A*, *B*, and *C*, three illuminated points in observed eye, here assumed to be emmetropic; *A'B'C'*, images in examiner's eye, also emmetropic.

and general; for the numerous practical details necessary to their successful use reference must be made to special manuals.

Ophthalmoscope. The light that enters the eye is largely absorbed by the black pigment of the retina and chorioid but a part is reflected, chiefly by the blood vessels, and, in leaving the eye, approximately retraces the course by which it entered. Merely holding a light near the eye does not, therefore, enable us to see the interior, since to catch this emerging light in our eye it is necessary to place the head where it blocks the entering light. If, however, we could arrange the light to enter the observed eye as though it proceeded from our own eye, then the returning rays might be utilized to give a view of the retina and its blood vessels, or the *fundus*, as it is called. Arguing in this way, Helmholtz devised the ophthalmoscope in 1851. The principle of the instrument is well represented by the original form as shown schematically in Figure 245, I. *S* represents the observed eye and *E* the eye of the observer. Between the two eyes is placed a piece of glass inclined at an angle. Rays falling from a source of light upon this glass are in part reflected from the surface to enter eye *S*, and these rays emerging from the eye along the same course in part pass through the glass and enter eye *E*. The glass plate of Helmholtz was soon replaced by a mirror either with a small hole in the center or with a small area of the silvering removed to permit the returning light to reach the observer's eye. The source of light was later placed in the handle of the instrument, and at the present time light is thrown into the observed eye not by a mirror but by a prism of special form. By this prism the light is directed into the lower half of the pupil while the returning rays emerge through the upper half and reach the observer's eye over the top of the prism (Fig. 245, II). Irrespective of the manner in which the light reaches the fundus, this surface becomes a luminous object sending out rays of light. Taking any three objects on the retina, *A, B, C*, it is apparent that if eye *S* is an emmetropic eye, these points are at the principal focal distance, and the rays sent from each after emerging from the eye are in parallel bundles. These rays enter the observer's eye as though they came from distant objects. If the observer's eye is also emmetropic, or is made so by suitable glasses, these bundles of rays will be focused on his retina without an act of accommodation. He must, in fact, in looking through the ophthalmoscope, gaze, not at the eye before him,

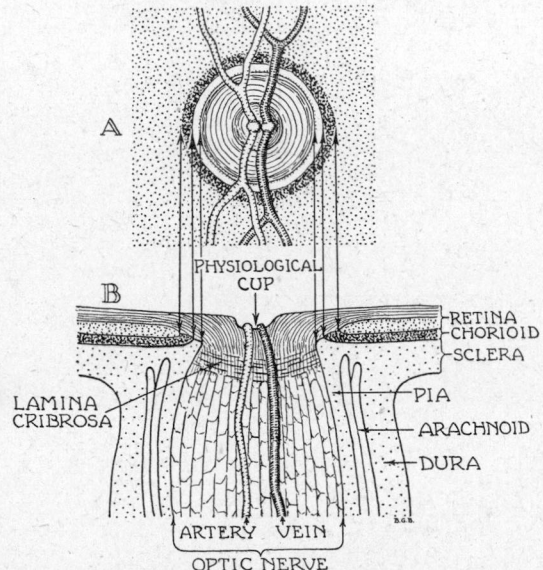

Fig. 246.—Ophthalmoscopic appearance of the optic disc (A) correlated with a histological section through it (B). The arrows indicate corresponding points on the two views. The pigmented ring is emphasized in A to show the manner of its formation.

but, relaxing his accommodation, through the eye, as it were, into the distance. In this way he will see the portion of the retina illuminated, the images of the objects seen being inverted on his own retina and therefore appearing erect. If the observed eye is myopic, its retina is farther back than the principal focus of its refracting surfaces; consequently the rays sent out from the illuminated retina emerge in converging bundles and cannot be focused on the retina of the observer's eye. By inserting a concave lens of proper power between his eye and the mirror, the observer can render the rays parallel and thus bring out the image. Just the reverse happens if the observed eye is hyperopic. In such an eye the retina is nearer than the principal focal distance of the refractive surfaces; consequently the light emitted from the retina emerges in bundles of diverging rays which cannot be brought to a focus on the retina of the observer unless he exerts his own power of accommodation or interposes a convex lens between his eye and the mirror. From the power of the lens used the degree of ametropia may be estimated. This method of estimating the refractive state of the eye is so uncertain as to be of little value and has been displaced by the use of the retinoscope. Despite this fact the battery of lenses in the ophthalmoscope is valuable in estimating the degree to which objects lie above or below the general level of the fundus. For example, the optic disc normally shows a slight conical pit, the *physiological depression,* or *cup* (Fig. 246). When the intra-ocular pressure has been greatly elevated, as in glaucoma, this depression may be transformed into an *excavation* in consequence of the weakness of this part of the scleral envelope. The difference in the power of the lenses required to bring the bottom of this *cup* into sharp focus as compared with that required for its margin may be recorded in diopters. Thus the progress of the cupping may be followed and the depth estimated by remembering that 3 D. correspond to about 1 mm. The usefulness of the ophthalmoscope is twofold. First, it renders visible conditions within the eye as clearly as if the structure were on the surface and in the second place the blood vessels of the retina are a sample of those in all parts of the body and reveal certain general circulatory conditions.

Retinoscope or skiascope. The retinoscope or skiascope is the most valuable of the objective methods of determining the refraction of the eye. It is similar in plan to the ophthalmoscope and the principle on which it operates is relatively simple, but the details are numerous and cannot all be presented here. If the retina of the observed eye is illuminated by light from a plane perforated mirror, the light moves, when the mirror is tilted, in the same direction as does the spot of light falling on the face. This is true for all refractive states of the eye. As in the case of the ophthalmoscope, the illuminated fundus may now be considered a source of light and the emerging rays will be found to take a course dependent on the refraction of the eye. If the observed eye is emmetropic, the rays will be parallel in the air; if myopic, the rays will converge to the far point in the air in front of the eye; if hyperopic, they will diverge as if coming from the virtual far point behind the eye. If the observer is seated at one meter from the observed eye (the more convenient distance of $\frac{2}{3}$ m. will not alter the argument) he will receive from an emmetropic eye parallel rays, and, as is diagrammed in Figure 245, II, for the ophthalmoscope, will see the retina in its true position. At this distance and through so small an aperture as the pupil, no details can be observed, but the light, or more exactly, the boundary between the lighted and the unlighted parts of the retina, will be seen as the light moves. If the mirror is now tilted, the spot of light seen through the pupil will seem to move in the same direction as that on the face, or the light is said to move "with." If the examined eye is hyperopic, the light will also move "with" although the observer must accommodate somewhat to see it clearly. If the observed eye is myopic, two possibilities exist. The far point may be beyond the observer (myopia of less than 1 D.) or between the observer and the observed eye (myopia of more than 1 D.). In the first case, as in emmetropia and hyperopia, the light will move "with"; in the second case the observer sees an aerial image at the far point of the more myopic eye which will of course show a movement opposite to that on the retina or "against" the light on the face. If the observer is located exactly at the far point of the observed eye, which obviously must have a myopia of 1 D., the light, on movement of the mirror, will disappear so rapidly that the direction cannot be told; this is the "point of reversal." In determining the state of refraction of an unknown eye, various lenses are placed before it until a combination of eye and lens is obtained giving the point of reversal. The combination is now known to be myopic 1 D., and if a 1 D. diverging lens is added to the combination it will be emmetropic. The algebraic sum of the lenses will then be the patient's correction.

REFERENCES

1. BEER, T. Die Accommodation des Fischauges. *Pflüg. Arch. ges. Physiol.,* 1894, *58:* 523–650.

2. BROWN, E. V. L. Use-abuse theory of changes in refraction versus biologic theory. *Arch. Ophthal., N. Y.,* 1942, *28:*835–850.

3. DONDERS, F. C. *Anomalies of accommodation and refraction.* London, 1864. xvii, 635 pp.

4. DUANE, A. Studies of the accommodation. *Ophthalmoscope,* 1912, *10:*486–502.

5. DUANE, A. Studies in monocular and binocular accommodation with their clinical applications. *Amer. J. Ophthal.,* 1922, *5:*865–877.

6. DUKE-ELDER, W. S. *Text-book of ophthalmology,* St. Louis, C. V. Mosby Company, 1934, Vol. I, xxix, 1124 pp.

7. FINCHAM, E. P. The mechanism of accommodation. *Brit. J. Ophthal.,* 1937 (Monog. Suppl. VIII).

8. HELMHOLTZ, H. VON. Treatise on physiological optics. Rochester, N. Y., Optical society of America, 1924–1925, 3 vols.

9. KEMPF, G. A., COLLINS, S. D. and JARMAN, B. L. Refractive errors in the eyes of children as determined by retinoscopic examination with a cycloplegie. *Publ. Hlth Bull., Wash.,* No. 182, 1928, 56 pp.

10. KINSEY, V. E. and COGAN, D. G. The cornea; hydration properties of the whole cornea. *Arch. Ophthal., N. Y.,* 1942, *28:*449–463.

11. KINSEY, V. E. and GRANT, W. M. The secretion-diffusion theory of intraocular fluid dynamics. *Brit. J. Ophthal.,* 1944, *28:*355–361.

12. KRONFELD, P. C. and DEVNEY, C. Ein

17

Beitrag zur Kenntnis der Refractionskurve. *v. Graefes Arch. Ophthal.*, 1931, *126*:487–501.

13. ROEPKE, R. R. and HETHERINGTON, W. A. Osmotic relation between aqueous humor and blood plasma. *Amer. J. Physiol.*, 1940, *130*:340–345.

14. TRON, E. Über die optischen Grundlagen der Ametropie. *v. Graefes Arch. Ophthal.*, 1934, *132*:182–223.

15. TRON, E. J. The optical elements of the refractive power of the eye. Pp. 245–255 in: *Modern trends in Ophthalmology*, F. RIDLEY and A. SORSBY, Ed. New York, 1940.

16. WAGMAN, I. H. and NATHANSON, L. M. Influence of intensity of white light upon pupil diameter of the human and the rabbit. *Proc. Soc. exp. Biol., N. Y.*, 1942, *49*:466–470.

17. WALLS, G. L. *The vertebrate eye.* Bloomfield Hills, Michigan, Cranbrook Institute of Science, 1942, xiv, 785 pp.

CHAPTER 23

VISION

In the previous chapter the eye was portrayed as an optical instrument, capable of focusing light rays from objects at variable distances and of regulating the amount of light allowed to fall upon the retina. The formation of a physical image on the retina of the eye is of no value unless that physical image is translated into a pattern of nerve impulses from which the cerebral cortex can reconstruct a reasonably accurate perception of the external world. In this perception, color, fineness of detail, and sharpness of contours all play a part. Vision therefore includes the formation of an image by a system of lenses, the stimulation of receptor cells by light waves, and the conduction of the resulting impulses to the brain, where a "mental image" is formed.

The eye is not a single end-organ but is two end-organs, specialized for quite different visual functions, though closely knit together anatomically. One system of receptors and nerve fibers is specialized to function in daylight when the surroundings are brightly illuminated. Objects are then seen clearly, with much detail, and exhibit grades of color. Visual acuity is at a premium. A second system of receptors is specialized for twilight and night vision. A low threshold is at a premium. By a process of dark adaptation the eye becomes many times more sensitive to light, and by dilation of the pupil more light is admitted to the eye. Utilization of the slightest light energy afforded by the environment is achieved to an extraordinary degree by the human retina, which has nearly attained the theoretical lower limit of sensitivity— being sensitive to one quantum of light. But specialization in one direction has meant loss of capacity in another. The apparatus for night vision does not provide a record of the color of objects or of fine details and sharp boundaries. Yet the perception of objects as dark, indistinct masses at night makes the difference between blindness and visual orientation to the environment. Never is the ability to see at night valued so highly as in wartime, when the safety of a ship or of a body of soldiers may depend upon this primitive capacity to "see in the dark."

The fact that the eye is a double mechanism is encountered in the provision of a pupil, which by constricting adjusts the eye for detail vision but requires a high level of illumination, or by dilating makes the utmost of what light is present at low intensities of illumination. Two kinds of receptor cells—rods and cones—are specialized respectively for night and for day vision. The retina is specialized into a fovea centralis for color and detail vision and a periphery for light and dark vision. The neural pathways give further evidence of a double function. The "duplicity" theory of vision is, then, the organizing principle to be used in describing vision. Orginally the duplicity theory or law referred only to the existence of two types of receptor cells, but as more is learned of the retinal and central mechanisms of vision, a wider application of the theory is justified.

Visual Stimulus. The eye is sensitive only to a narrow band of wave lengths, the visible spectrum (723 mμ – 397 mμ) consisting of wave lengths lying between the long, infra-red heat waves and the short, ultra-violet "chemical" waves. Within this range not all wave lengths are equally effective in stimulating the retina. The wave length of light, the prism teaches us, determines hue or chroma, but wave length also influences the intensity of light necessary to elicit a sensation. The curve which expresses that relation is the *visibility curve* (Fig. 247). But before any curve or other quantitative data can be understood the nature of the visual stimulus and the units in which it is measured require definition.

In dealing with the audibility curve the abscissa was frequency; for the visibility curve it is wave length. The reason for this is largely a matter of custom. The wave length is the

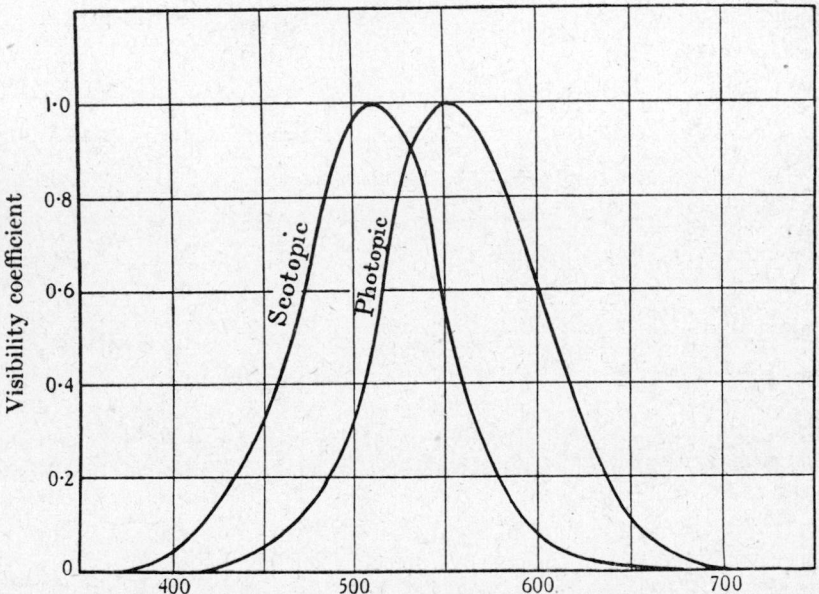

Fig. 247.—Visibility or luminosity of a bright spectrum as seen by cones (photopic) and of a dim spectrum as seen by rods (scotopic). The ordinates are the reciprocal of the energy which is just visible for each wave length of light (scotopic) or which matches a moderately bright standard light (photopic). The curves were adjusted to a common scale by making the maximum of each curve equal to one. On an absolute scale of intensities, the rod curve would fall far below that for the cones, which are much less sensitive than rods. (From Rawdon-Smith, *Theories of sensation*, 1938, after Hecht and Williams, *J. gen. Physiol.*, 1922, 5:1–34.)

inverse of the frequency or number of waves per sec., being the speed of light divided by its frequency. A wave length is stated in terms of Ångstrom units (1 Å = 1/10,000,000 mm.), or more usually in millimicrons (1 mμ = 1/1,000,000 mm.). For the ordinate is needed a unit for expressing the intensity of the light. As in audition, the physical unit most useful is one which has a psychological reference. The basic unit is the *international candle*, which is the total luminous energy emitted in all directions by a standardized candle approximately equivalent to an ordinary candle with a flame one inch in height. To state the amount of light *falling upon* an object, or the illumination—a more usual requirement— the distance of the object from the candle must be defined because, as the total energy is spread over a large sphere, it becomes less per unit area. The *foot-candle* is the amount of light falling on a square foot of area when placed one foot from the standard candle. But not all of the light falling on a surface is reflected, and only the reflected light can be seen. A convenient unit of *brightness* of an object, which is the amount of light reflected from it, is the millilambert, the amount of light reflected by an ideal surface one foot square and illuminated by 0.93 foot-candle. And since the size of the pupil of the eye affects the amount of light entering the eye, a unit of brightness, the photon, has been devised which takes that factor into account. The photon is the number of millilamberts $\times$ mm.^{2} of pupil area. In experiments this is easily calculated because an artificial pupil—a screen with an aperture smaller than the pupil—is usually employed.

The visibility curve is affected by the distribution of energy among the different wave lengths, which varies with the kind of light source employed, daylight, carbon lamp, etc. For this reason the data are usually calculated and expressed in terms of an equal energy spectrum. Finally to be taken into account is the filtering of light by cornea, lens, and vitreous body analogous to the way in which the properties of the middle ear influence the audibility curve. When these physical factors are properly accounted for, the visibility curve becomes an index of the manner in which the retina utilizes light of different wave lengths. The visibility curve expresses one of the fundamental parameters of visual sensation whether aroused by colored or uncolored light, namely, luminosity.

Intensity Functions. The intensity of a visual stimulus as measured by physical instruments is distinguished from the intensity of the resulting visual experience. The two are related in a causal sequence of stimulus-response, but photochemical and neural processes intervene and may considerably alter the correlation between the two. For example, the visibility curve shows that wave length is a factor determining the intensity of the psychological response. *Luminosity*, *brilliance*, or *apparent brightness* always refers to the response, and *brightness* is restricted to the intensity of the physical stimulus. In vision three main intensity functions are distinguished: (i) the *absolute threshold*, or the minimal intensity of light that can be seen; (ii) the *difference threshold*, or the least discriminable difference between two intensities; and (iii) the *flicker fusion frequency*.

The principal factors which affect the absolute threshold will be discussed in detail separately, but may be enumerated as follows: (i) intensity of light, (ii) wave length of light, (iii) size of illuminated area, (iv) duration of exposure, (v) state of the retina (dark adaptation), etc., and (vi) the region of retina stimulated. Much the same factors influence the difference threshold, which is basically little different from the absolute threshold. The Weber fraction is not constant for brightness discrimination. The curve for $\dfrac{\Delta I}{I}$ rises sharply for weak and strong stimuli and is constant for the middle range of intensities only if small changes are ignored (by coarse plotting). The absolute threshold under the most favorable conditions for vision has been calculated in terms of absolute physical units (quanta) by Hecht, Shlaer and Pirenne (7). As few as 54 quanta of light incident upon the cornea are perceptible and an estimated half of these are reflected or absorbed by the ocular media and do not reach the retina. Of the 27 quanta remaining, perhaps only 5 are absorbed by the visual purple of the rods, and these, spread over an area of the retina containing an estimated 500 rods, are so few that at threshold a given rod must rarely receive more than one quantum of energy, which, according to Einstein's photochemical equivalence law, will break down one molecule of visual purple. The evolution of the eye has progressed to the theoretical maximum of sensitivity, i.e., individual receptors are sensitive to one quantum of light.

The critical fusion frequency is determined as follows. A sectored disc, placed in front of a light source, is so arranged that its rate of rotation is controlled by the observer. At slow rates of rotation intermittent flashes of light are experienced, but at some rate for any intensity a sensation of continuous brightness is experienced, the *critical fusion frequency*, or c.f.f. The higher the intensity the higher the c.f.f., or more exactly, at least for middle range of intensities, c.f.f. = log I + k (Ferry-Porter law). The duality of the visual mechanism manifests itself in the flicker phenomenon by a sharp break or inflection in the curve relating c.f.f. to log I (Fig. 248) when the light falls on the periphery of the retina. For the fovea the curve of relationship shows no inflection. For the areas outside the fovea the curve has two limbs, one part related to low intensities of illumination in which there is an increase in the c.f.f. up to a maximum which is then maintained, and a second part

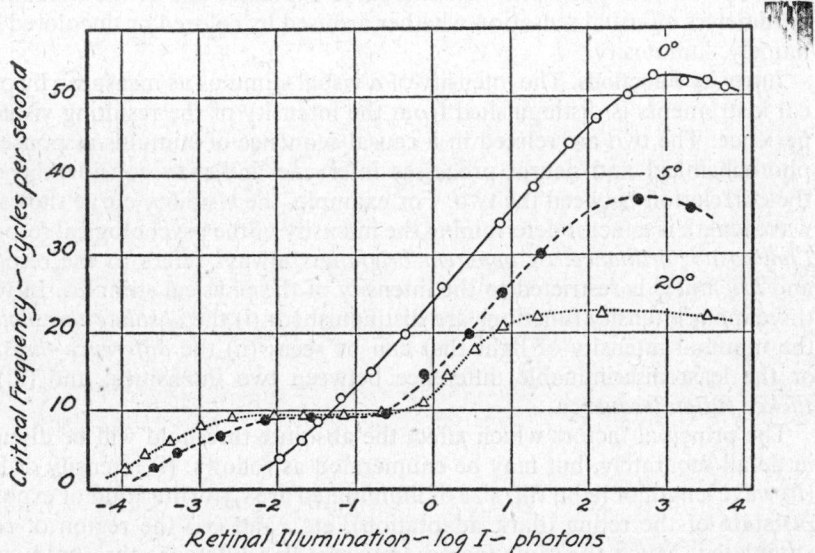

Fig. 248.—Curves showing the relation between the critical fusion frequency (c.f.f.) and the logarithm of intensity for three retinal locations; fovea, and 5° and 20° from the fovea. (From Hecht and Verrijp, *J. gen. Physiol.*, 1933–34, *17*:251–268.)

related to the higher intensities. The first part of the duplex curve is interpreted as a response of the rods and the second as a response of the cones. The Ferry-Porter law applies to both rods and cones with a change in the constant k, but only over a restricted range of intensities.

Flicker fusion is the basis of a method of photometry useful in measuring or equating the brightness of colored lights or objects. This is difficult to do by a matching technique because the hue of the color leads one astray. The critical frequency of flicker is not influenced by color.

PHOTOCHEMICAL BASIS OF VISION

Visual Purple—Rhodopsin. The change that takes place in the rods and cones whereby the energy of light waves is translated into nerve impulses is unknown. The general view, however, is that one step in the process is photochemical—that is, the light waves set up chemical changes in the rods or cones which in turn give rise to nerve impulses that are transmitted to the brain. In the retina itself a basis for such a view is found in the existence of a red pigment which is bleached by light. This interesting discovery was made by Boll in 1877, and the facts were afterwards carefully investigated by Kühne. The red pigment, known usually as visual purple or rhodopsin, is histologically demonstrable only in the external segments of the rods; the cones probably contain another pigmented substance. The existence of visual purple in the retina may be demonstrated very easily. A frog is kept for some time in the dark; it is then killed and an eye removed and bisected equatorially. If the vitreous is removed from the posterior half, the retina may be detached by means of a pair of forceps. When the operation is performed in

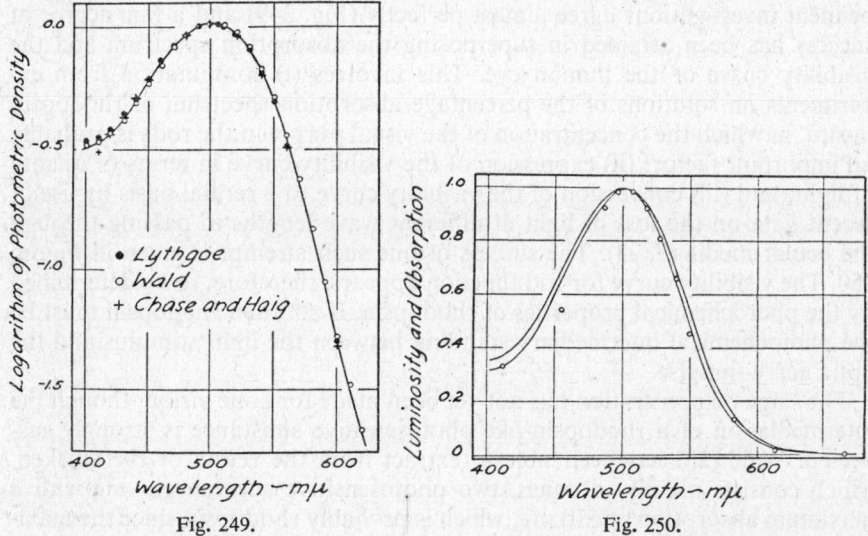

Fig. 249.   Fig. 250.

Fig. 249.—Absorption spectrum of the visual purple from the frog. The data obtained by three independent observers were made equal at 500 mμ. The ordinates show the degree to which each wave length is absorbed, with 0.0 representing maximal absorption. (From Hecht, *Amer. Scientist*, 1944, *32*:159–177.)

Fig. 250.—The relation of the subjective brightness of the spectrum (luminosity, circles) to the absorption curve of visual purple (frog). The visibility curve is corrected for transmissional losses, quantum effectiveness, etc., and therefore is not identical with that shown in Figure 247. The two solid lines give the absorption spectrum calculated by assuming that 20 and 5 per cent of light is absorbed by visual purple. (From Hecht, Schlaer and Pirenne, *J. gen. Physiol.*, 1942, *25*:819–840.)

red or yellow light, as in photographic work, the detached retina on examination by daylight is found to be a deep red color; but after a short exposure it fades rapidly, finally becoming colorless. Visual purple has been extracted from the rods by solutions of bile salts, which have the power to discharge the pigment from its combination in the rods in the same way that it releases hemoglobin from red corpuscles. The solutions thus obtained are also bleached upon exposure to light. We have in the visual purple, therefore, an unstable substance readily decomposed or altered by the mechanical effect of the light waves, and there can be little doubt that the substance plays an important part in the response of the rod elements to light and forms, as well, the basis of dark adaptation. If rhodopsin is the chemical intermediary standing between light and nerve impulses, then its photochemical properties should be reflected in the visibility curve.

Rhodopsin and the Visibility Curve. Why is light at 510 mμ wave length so much more effective as a visual stimulus than the shorter and longer wave lengths? That the shape and position of the visibility curve is due to the photochemical properties of rhodopsin was first suggested by Kühne (1878) on the basis of rather simple experiments in which the effectiveness of light of different wave lengths in bleaching the rhodopsin of the dark adapted retina was determined. According to Draper's law, the photochemical effect of light of a given wave length is proportional to the degree to which light of that wave length is absorbed. Pure solutions of visual purple have been obtained from the frog's retina since the absorption spectra determined in three independent investigations agree almost perfectly (Fig. 249) and a fair degree of success has been attained in superposing the absorption spectrum and the visibility curve of the human eye. This involves (i) computation from experiments on solutions of the percentage absorption spectrum of rhodopsin in situ, in which the concentration of the visual purple in the rods is probably an important factor; (ii) expression of the visibility curve in terms of quanta of light; and (iii) conversion of the visibility curve to a retinal basis by use of recent data on the loss of light at different wave lengths in passing through the ocular media (7, 23). The success of one such attempt is given in Figure 250. The visibility curve for rod function appears, therefore, to be determined by the photochemical properties of rhodopsin. If so, then rhodopsin must be the photochemical intermediary standing between the light stimulus and the optic nerve impulse.

The same demonstration has not yet been made for cone vision, though the intermediation of a rhodopsin-like photosensitive substance is strongly suspected. Wald (23) has been able to extract from the retina of the chicken, which consists mainly of cones, two photosensitive substances, one with a maximum absorption of 510 mμ, which is probably rhodopsin since the maximum sensitivity of the dark adapted eye lies near this point, while the other has its maximum absorption at 570 mμ which corresponds with the point of maximum sensitivity of the light adapted eye. He believes that this second substance belongs to the cones and proposes for it the name *iodopsin* (visual violet).

Dark Adaptation. The retina possesses to a remarkable degree the ability to become more sensitive in dim light and thereby to make the maximum use of the weak light reflected from objects. This is especially true of the periphery of the retina. When one passes from daylight into a dark room, vision is at first very imperfect, but within a few minutes it rapidly improves "as the eye becomes accustomed to the dark." This change is known as dark adaptation. Loss of the sensitivity attained through dark adaptation occurs upon exposure of the eyes to light and is called "*light adaptation*." In the change from the brightness of full sunlight to the darkness of night, the eye must adjust itself to an extremely large range of light intensities. Taking the minimum amount of light which will stimulate the fully dark adapted retina as 1, the ratio of night and daylight intensities under extreme conditions is 1 to approximately 10 billion.

A curve of dark adaptation is plotted by repeated determination of the absolute threshold, the least amount of light which is visible. Stimuli of low intensity and short duration are used; otherwise adaptation is retarded by the light stimulation necessary for testing sensitivity. The rate of dark adaptation for rods is initially rapid though not so rapid as light adaptation, and is about 60 per cent accomplished in the first five minutes and virtually completed in 20 minutes, after which the curve is asymptotic. A curve with this simple form is obtained by starting from low levels of illumination in order not to stimulate cones, and observing with the peripheral portions of the retina where cones are absent or few in number. It is therefore the rod adaptation curve. The dark adaptation curve obtained when the whole eye is tested, thus stimulating both cones and rods, is made up of two curves (Fig. 251). The first part of the curve consists of an initial rapid fall in threshold which tends to strike a plateau. After approximately 7 minutes of darkness a further drop occurs which is not so rapid but is quantitatively much greater than the initial fall in threshold. Analysis shows that the curve previous to the inflection is

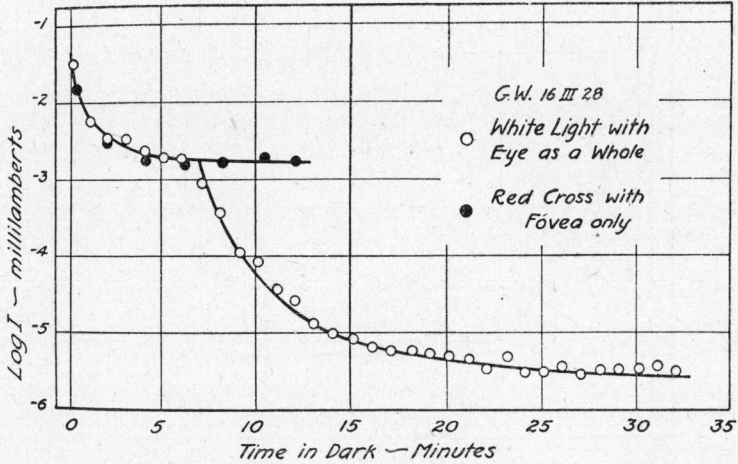

Fig. 251.—Curve of dark adaptation obtained by plotting visual threshold against the time spent in darkness. The initial limb of the curve for the whole eye (circles) is due to cones ;the lower portion is due to rods. To obtain the complete curve for cones alone (black dots), stimulation of the more sensitive rods was avoided by employing red light and foveal fixation. (From Hecht, *A handbook of general experimental psychology*, C. Murchison, ed., 1934.)

due to dark adaptation of the cones. With red light which stimulates rods only weakly (see visibility curve) directed at the fovea which contains only cones, the initial curve can be explored completely without exciting the more sensitive rods and obtaining the rod curve. Dark adaptation is therefore not a phenomenon peculiar to the rods; adaptation of the cones also occurs. Cone adaptation is a much more rapid process and produces a small lowering of the threshold relative to that accomplished by rod adaptation.

Factors Influencing Dark Adaptation. The extent and rapidity of dark adaptation is critical in many military and civilian activities. Several factors are involved.

Avoidance of light. Perhaps the most effective means of securing dark adaptation is to prevent light adaptation from overilluminated instrument panels or by other unnecessary exposure to light. Obvious as this principle is, it has often been overlooked in the design of aeroplane cockpits. The introduction by Miles (14) of red goggles as an aid to the acquisition of dark adaptation illustrates the effective application of visual physiology (the visibility curve) to a practical situation. A tedious 20 to 30 minute wait in a completely dark room, and the problem of retaining the dark adapted state while reaching the point of operations, are avoided by the simple procedure of wearing red goggles, which allow cone vision to continue at the same time that dark adaptation of the rods is proceeding. The principle involved, which stems from the visibility curve, is that wave lengths longer than 640 mμ stimulate rods only very weakly. The red goggles, by shutting out the portions of the spectrum which do stimulate the rods, prevent light adaptation of them, while permitting the use of cone vision.

Pre-adaptation illumination. The more intense the illumination and the longer the time during which the eye is light adapted, the longer is the period

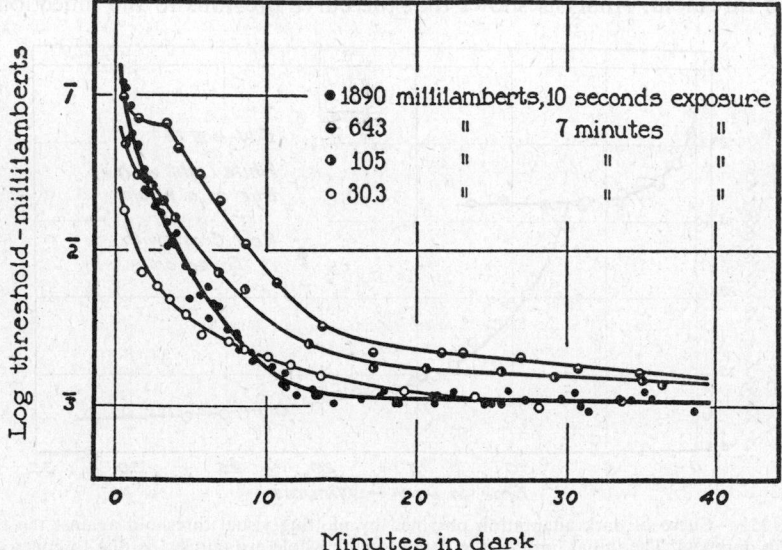

Fig. 252.—Curves of the visual threshold showing the effect upon the rate of dark adaptation of different degrees of preceding light adaptation. Three intensities of the light adapting stimulus, acting for 7 minutes, are represented. A much more intense light (filled circles), acting for a briefer period, has the highest initial effect on the threshold but retards dark adaptation less than weaker, more prolonged, stimuli. (From Wald and Clark, *J. gen. Physiol.*, 1937, *21*:93–105.)

necessary to attain complete dark adaptation (8, 24). Figure 252 shows the effects of different intensities of illumination prior to the dark adaptation period. There is no *one* curve of dark adaptation; a family of curves is necessary for a full description of dark adaptation when preceding light adaptation is also a factor. These curves will be discussed more fully in considering light adaptation.

Hemeralopia. This is a rare, organic, often hereditary abnormality in which rod function is seriously disturbed or, in extreme cases, absent. Dark adaptation is correspondingly reduced in extent and greatly slowed or absent, with resulting *night blindness*. Color vision is normal. There is no evidence that vitamin A therapy will affect the congenital form of hemeralopia.

Vitamin A deficiency. Severe vitamin A deficiency experimentally induced interferes with the mechanism of dark adaptation, of which vitamin A is probably a part. In fact, irreversible changes can be produced by severe and prolonged deprivation of vitamin A. Dark adaptation of cones as well as rods is affected. The discovery of the connection of vitamin A with visual function is a striking scientific accomplishment. The same cannot be said for the uncritical manner in which dark adaptation physiology has been applied in the field of vitamin research, with little regard for the physical, the physiological, and the psychological pitfalls. Whether or not vitamin A deficiency of sufficient severity to affect dark adaptation exists in the population is an open question, and not one to be answered by indiscriminate surveys using inadequate adaptometers. The value and limitations of the adaptometer in this connection have been carefully studied by Hunt and Hayden (10).

Anoxia and metabolic factors. McFarland and Evans (13) have shown that the visual threshold of the completely dark adapted eye is elevated as a result of anoxic anoxia. Exposure to an oxygen pressure equivalent to an altitude of 15,000 feet increased the threshold 2.5 times. Glucose administration neutralized the effects of anoxia and insulin intensified them. Hyperventilation at sea level by forced breathing improved visual sensitivity, causing the threshold to fall approximately to half value (25). This effect was abolished by adding 5 per cent CO_2 to the mixture breathed, suggesting that the effect was due to alkalosis; and CO_2 added to air doubled the threshold. The retina except for rods and cones is a part of the brain, and in fact has one of the highest metabolic rates of any portion of the brain; therefore, it is to be expected that the retina is sensitive to anoxia, etc. The same relationships have been encountered when the effects of anoxia, hyperventilation and CO_2 on various cerebral functions were studied. Because of the rapidity with which they occur and because photochemical changes are relatively slow, it is believed that the effects on the visual threshold are exerted on the synaptic apparatus rather than on the photochemical mechanisms of the retina. Such changes, though small in relation to the whole range of dark adaptation, may be significant under circumstances such as the night operation of airplanes.

Curve of Light Adaptation. After a period of darkness, exposure to light of moderate intensity elicits at first an intense, dazzling, or even painful light sensation, but after a few minutes the eye becomes less sensitive. In other words, the sensitivity gained by dark adaptation is lost as a result of stimulation of the eye by light. Light adaptation is, therefore, simply the absence of dark adaptation and hence the expression is somewhat misleading. It is an active process inasmuch as the rhodopsin accumulated during dark adaptation is bleached during light adaptation.

The time course of the loss of dark adaptation is different from the acquisition of dark adaptation. Light adaptation is more rapid and follows a curve different from that for dark adaptation. Light adaptation is largely completed in a very few minutes. The curve of light adaptation, as Hecht pointed out, resembles that characteristic of a chemical reaction involving the splitting of a single molecule into two end products, while the curve of dark adaptation resembles that characteristic of the reaction of two molecules to form a compound.

Mechanism of Rod Stimulation and Dark Adaptation (6, 23). Rhodopsin is the intermediary in the excitation of rods by light, and changes in its concentration are believed to be the basis of dark adaptation. The simplest possible photochemical mechanism employing rhodopsin is as follows:

Light → rhodopsin → excitatory decomposition product → nerve impulse

Rhodopsin, must be resynthesized or the system would soon be exhausted, and the excitatory decomposition product must be removed quickly; otherwise, visual sensation would greatly outlast the stimulus. Hecht has had considerable success in accounting for the quantitative aspects of the excitation process by using the equations of photochemistry. Light is conceived of as breaking down the photosensitive material at a rate dependent on several constant factors and two variable ones: the intensity of light and the amount of photochemical substance present. The process is represented by the equation,

$$\frac{dR}{dt} = k. \, a. \, I. \, R.$$

The amount of rhodopsin (dR) bleached in a unit time (dt) is a function of the per cent of light absorbed (a) and the product of the light intensity I times the concentration of rhodopsin (R). If only threshold sensitivity to light is involved, dR is always the same, so that it is unnecessary to know the relationship between amount of decomposition and visual effect. The manner in which this equation fits such facts of vision as the reciprocity law (that the energy needed for a threshold effect or to produce a just noticeable difference between two light stimuli for short exposures must be reciprocally increased if the duration is decreased) is given by Wald (23) as follows: "When the wave length and state of adaptation (hence a and R) are held constant, the product $I. \, dt$ is constant: the reciprocity law. When the wave length and duration of exposure (a and dt) are kept constant, the term $I. \, R$ is constant: the rhodopsin concentration is inversely proportional to the threshold intensity, or is directly proportional to the reciprocal of the threshold, the sensitivity or visibility. On exposure of the eye to light, as the concentration of photopigment falls, the threshold reciprocally rises, eventually to some steady-state value. This is light adaptation. In the dark the concentration of photopigment rises to a maximum and the threshold reciprocally falls to a minimum; this is dark adaptation."

In addition to the rapid changes represented by bleaching and re-formation of visual purple are certain slower processes involved in the photochemical process of the retina.

Photochemical Cycle of the Retina. That rhodopsin plays a part in the long-term changes in retinal excitability has been recently demonstrated by chemical methods. Using a spectrographic technique to follow the changes in the photochemical substances, Wald (22, 23) has established the broad outlines of the photochemistry of the visual cycle. Three main reactions were observed. The first is a rapid reaction:

$$\text{Rhodopsin} \underset{\text{dark}}{\overset{\text{light}}{\rightleftarrows}} \text{Retinene} + \text{Protein}$$

The molecular weight of visual purple is very high, 270,000. It is a conjugated protein of the same type of structure as hemoglobin, that is to say, it consists of a protein molecule united to a pigment group which is designated *retinene* and is related to the carotene compounds. Rhodopsin is stable except when exposed to light, when it bleaches owing to a dissociation into protein and retinene. In the dark it is reconstituted (Fig. 253). Because the rate and extent of decomposition depend on the intensity of light and duration of exposure, this phase is believed to be the photochemical basis of light and dark adaptation. Proceeding much more slowly is a thermolabile reaction in which rhodopsin is re-formed with vitamin A as an intermediate step. Vitamin A of blood is also a source for restoring the retinal level of vitamin A and rhodopsin. These reactions therefore form the photochemical cycle which may be divided into a photodynamic and a thermolabile phase. The length of line in Figure 253 connecting the substance indicates roughly the speed of the reaction.

The effect of pre-adaptation illumination on the rate of dark adaptation (Fig. 252) is explained by the fact of a "slow" and a "fast" synthesis of rhodopsin. If the completely dark adapted retina, charged with rhodopsin, is light adapted by a *short exposure to intense light*, much retinene and little

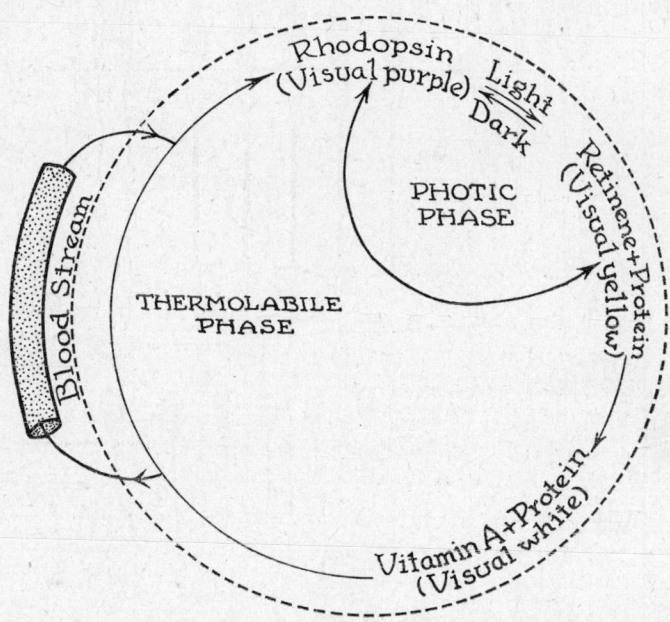

Fig. 253.—The retinal photochemical cycle according to Wald. The length of the arrows suggests the speed of the reaction.

vitamin A is produced. Therefore, subsequent dark adaptation is rapid because rhodopsin is re-formed by the "fast route" from retinene. Exposure to weaker adapting lights for a seven minute period is followed by a slowed adaptation curve, because more retinene has gone to vitamin A and must be resynthesized by the slower route.

In addition to visual functions which seem interpretable on the basis of photodynamic action are certain processes which depend on the neural mechanisms of the retina.

NEURAL BASIS OF RETINAL FUNCTION

Functional Anatomy of the Retina (20). The neural layers of the retina consist of three strata of densely packed cell bodies and two intervening synaptic layers consisting of intertwining dendritic and axonic brushes (Figs.

254, 255). The retinal layer nearest the chorioid consists of pigmented cells believed to be concerned with the production or storage of visual purple. The layer next to the pigment cells consists of two kinds of neurons, one bearing a cone-shaped process, the other a rod-shaped process. The rods and cones are believed to be the structures actually sensitive to light. Packed closely together, they form the layer of rods and cones. In some animals the distinction between rods and cones is not sharp, but in the primates there are apparently no intermediate forms, and the rods and cones can easily be dis-

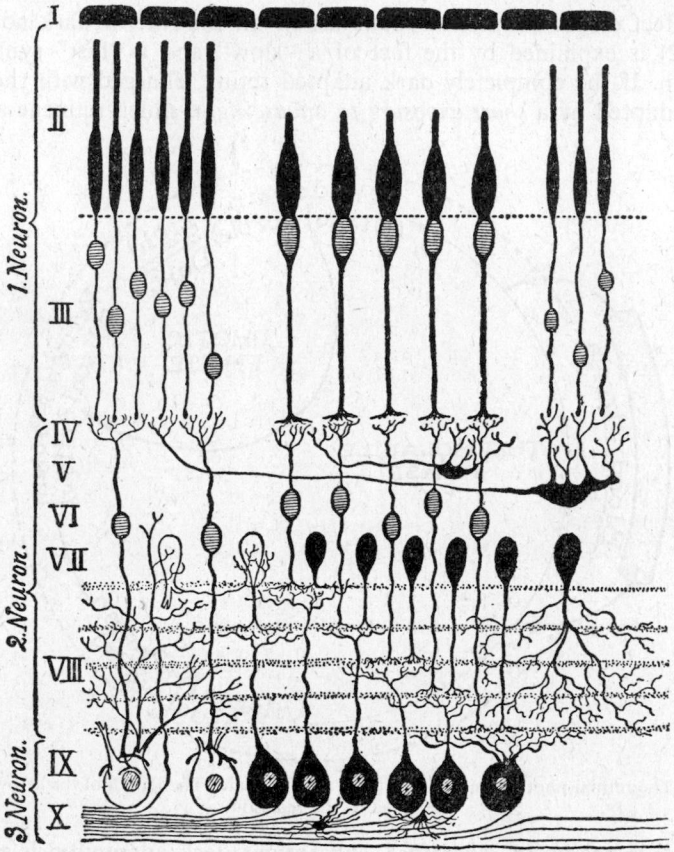

Fig. 254.—Simplified schema of the structure of the human retina: *I*, pigment layer; *II*, rod and cone layer; *III*, outer nuclear layer; *IV*, external plexiform layer; *V*, layer of horizontal cells; *VI*, layer of bipolar cells (inner nuclear); *VII*, layer of amacrinal cells (without axons); *VIII*, inner plexiform layer; *IX*, ganglion cell layer; *X*, nerve fiber layer. "Inner" means toward the interior of the eyeball; light passes through the retina from inwards to outwards. (After Greeff.)

tinguished. The axons of the rod- and cone-bearing neurons end upon the dendrites of the middle layer of bipolar cells forming the external plexiform layer and the axons of the bipolar cells end in the inner plexiform layer upon the dentrites of ganglion cells. The axons of the latter sweep to a point just slightly to the nasal side of the center of the retina and there pierce the chorioid and sclera in company with blood vessels and make up the optic nerve; they are the axons of third order neurons. It is an instance of nature's lack of wisdom that light must pass through the retinal blood vessels, nerve fibers, and cell bodies of the retina to reach the rods and cones. The rod and cone neurons are the receptor cells; the bipolar and ganglion cells are respectively second and third order neurons. This makes them a part of the brain, and, like the brain, these neurons form complex synaptic relations (20).

Polyak's study of the human and simian retina employed the Golgi technique, the uncertainties of which are offset by the fact that only occasional neurons are fully impregnated, so that the cell body and the dendritic and axonic ramifications of single neurons can be

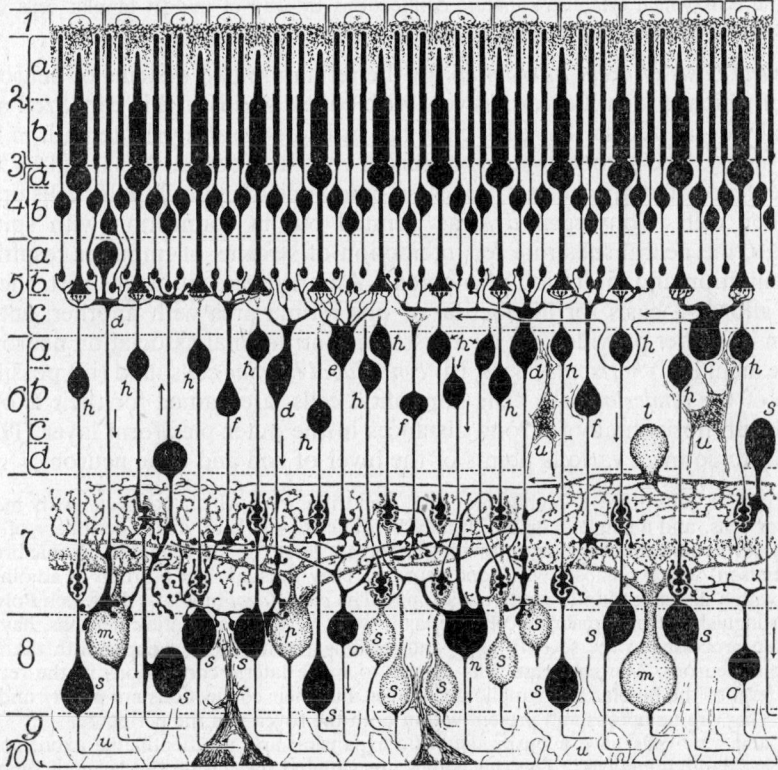

Fig. 255.—Reconstruction of the primate retina, based on Golgi impregnations, showing the principal neuron types and their synaptic relations. The layers are: 1, pigment epithelium; 2a, outer segment of rods and cones; 2b, inner segment of rods and cones; 3, outer limiting membrane; 4, outer nuclear layer; 5, outer plexiform layer (cone-pedicles and rod-spherules); 6, inner nuclear layer; 7, inner plexiform layers; 8, ganglion cells (origin of optic nerve fibers); 9, layer of optic nerve fibers; 10, inner limiting membrane. Various cell types are: c, horizontal cells; d, e, f, diffuse or polysynaptic bipolar cells; h, individual cone (midget) bipolar cell; i, l, "amacrine cells"; m, n, o, p, r, s, ganglion cells of which s is the individual or monosynaptic ganglion cell. (From Polyak, *The retina*, 1941.)

made out. The distinctness of rod and cone systems clearly marked insofar as the receptor cell is concerned breaks down at the level of the bipolar cells. As seen in Polyak's preparations, many bipolar cells synapse with both rod and cone neurons. This is not an occasional variation, but is typical of the commonest form of bipolar cell. The observation means that rod and cone systems are incompletely separated in the pathways to the brain. This finding obviously embarrasses the theory of specific receptors and specific nerve energies, but its exact significance is yet to be realized.

Polyak recognizes two types of bipolar cells on the basis of the number and extent of their dendritic processes and hence of their synaptic connections. The first type, which is the most common, is variously termed the *diffuse*, *polysynaptic*, or *rod and cone* bipolars because of their widely spread dendritic branches whereby they receive impulses from a group, sometimes large, of rods and cone neurons. The dendritic ramifications overlap, so that a single receptor neuron connects with more than one bipolar cell. Two forms of this type of bipolar cell are distinguished, the *mop* bipolar and the *brush* bipolar. The second main type of bipolar cell is termed variously the *individual, monosynaptic, cone,* or *midget* bipolar cell. Rods never connect with these bipolars; the midget bipolars are related only to the cones and in the fovea centralis each bipolar receives impulses from only one cone. The third order neurons fall into two broadly similar categories: (i) *diffuse* ganglion cells which connect with a great number of bipolar cells and exhibit to a considerable degree the phenomenon of partially shifted overlap; and (ii) *monosynaptic* or *individual* ganglion cells which establish synaptic connections by way of midget bipolar cells with only one or two cones.

Neural basis of areal interaction. In the retina are two systems of neurons, one of which is identified exclusively with cones, and is highly canalized and spatially organized so that each cone has at its disposal a private path in the optic nerve. The second system, of mixed rods and cones, is marked by the convergence of many rods and cones on bipolar cells and of bipolar cells upon ganglion cells. Convergence is, as pointed out in connection with spinal reflexes, the neural substrate for interaction of streams of impulses resulting in facilitation and inhibition phenomena. An arrangement of this sort, therefore, affords a basis for interaction of one retinal area with another. Interaction is further provided for by a system of intraretinal association neurons. These include (i) *horizontal* cells, (ii) *centrifugal bipolar* cells, and (iii) possibly some of the *amacrine* cells. The horizontal cells, are named for their axons, which run horizontally for long distances in the outer plexiform layer. They appear to connect various points of the layer of rod and cone neurons.

Horizontal cells have a highly branched dendritic tree, which connects with many receptor cells, and a single axon which may be quite long (1 mm. in the periphery of the retina). At its end the single axon divides to form a large, highly branched, axonic brush (teledendron) which synapses with cone neurons. They thus connect a group of adjoining cones with a distant group of contiguous cones. The *centrifugal* bipolar cells which Polyak has distinguished from amacrine cells are, as it were, vertical association neurons, having dendritic processes in the seventh layer and sending the axons to synapse with the rod and cone neurons. The amacrine cells appear to make lateral connections in the retina at the level of the bipolar and ganglion cell layer, but their connections are poorly understood. They are numerous and present within both the fovea and the periphery.

The amacrine cells have a bushy dendritic expansion and no identifiable axon; some resemble "daddy-long-legs." The cell bodies are situated just inside the layer of bipolar cells, and their dendrites ramify in the inner plexiform layer. They are numerous, and are present both within the fovea and the periphery of the retina. Since their axons cannot be made out, their connections cannot be known, but they are in a position to make lateral connections at the level of the bipolar and ganglion cells. This involves the assumption that they are primitive cells, without functional polarity, and conduct in both directions.

Regional variations of the retina (20). The portion of the retina stimulated is a common variable in experiments on vision. By confining the stimulus to the fovea, cone function can be studied in isolation; by confining it to the extreme periphery, rod function can be studied almost free of cone activity. However, there are important differences between cortical and peripheral vision besides the ratio of cones to rods, e.g., the synaptic relationships.

The primate retina extends through roughly 180 degrees. In this roughly hemispheric field four regions are recognized: (i) the *papilla,* disc or optic nerve head, (ii) the *macula lutea,* a yellow pigmented spot in the line of the visual axis, which encompasses the *fovea centralis,* (iii) the *extramacular area,* and (iv) the anterior serrated margin, the *ora serrata.* Polyak has proposed a more detailed subdivision of the retina to keep pace with present physiological and histological knowledge. A central area (area centralis) focused about the fovea centralis is a region 6 mm. wide, roughly coinciding with the maximum extent of the pigmented area (macula lutea). The critical distinguishing feature separating the central area from the periphery is the piling up of ganglion cells of the eighth layer reflected away from the central foveal area. The area centralis is divided into the fovea centralis and two concentric bands, the parafovea and the perifovea. The fovea centralis is a small, round, pitlike depression in the retina on the floor of which a second, slighter depression can be discerned, the foveola, containing the finest cones (see Table 15). From margin to margin the foveal pit measures 1500 μ or 2 degrees 30 minutes of arc on each side of the fixation point. In man the fovea is entirely rod-free over an area of only 600 μ diameter (2 degrees of arc), the rods first appearing at the margin of the fovea centralis; it contains approximately 34,000 cones.

To summarize, the fovea is specialized in four ways for detail vision: (i) the cones are more slender and densely packed, especially in the foveola; (ii) its central area is rod-free so that the cones are not "diluted" by rods; (iii) blood vessels detour around it and even capillaries are absent from the foveola; (iv) the cellular layers and nerve fibers are deflected to the side. The last two features serve to reduce the scattering of light falling on this region. The fact that foveal cones are long would for optical reasons increase depth of focus. And finally Polyak has shown that the cones of the fovea centralis have a "private line" through the layers of the retina.

In passing along a meridian through the three extrafoveal regions, two principal changes occur. The cone-to-rod ratio steadily decreases, though a few cones (6 to 8 per 100 μ linear distance) are found even in the outermost district. Figures for cone size and intercone distance are given in Table 15. Another difference is an increase in the degree of convergence of receptor elements on single ganglion cells. Such information can be gained by studying the synaptic relationships in Golgi preparations (Polyak) or by counting the number of ganglion cells per unit length or area, which is probably reliable for the periphery though difficult near the fovea because of the piling up of ganglion cells; and also because cones are lumped with rods in stating such a ratio. The ideal ratio of one cone to a ganglion cell is probably attained or approached in the fovea centralis. In the periphery (beyond 10 degrees from the fovea) Chievitz counted as high as 250 rods and cones per ganglion cell. Polyak gives the number of cells in the outer nuclear layer per 100 μ linear distance—parafoveal region 20, perifoveal 14, near periphery 9–10.

Electrical Activity of the Retina. Three types of potential changes are recorded from the retina: (i) a steady corneoretinal potential, (ii) phasic potentials produced by light stimuli, and (iii) action potentials of optic nerve fibers. A galvanometer connected to the cornea and to the back of the eye records a steadily maintained potential, with the posterior aspect of the eye negative to the cornea. The potential is recordable from the tissues surrounding the eye. If the leads are from temple to temple, movements of the eyes laterally cause the lead at which the eyes look to record positive; movements upwards and downwards or convergence of the eyes are without effect. It is as though the eye possesses an electrical axis coinciding with the visual axis, which influences the galvanometer maximally when in line with the leads, and least or not at all when at right angles to the leads. Advantage is taken of the potential to record eye movements. The characteristics of the potential are as follows: it is steadily maintained; it occurs on passive movement of the eyeball in deeply anesthetized animals; destruction of the retina ends it; and it persists when no light is falling on the retina. For these reasons, the potential probably originates in the retina and not in the eye muscles and is a resting as opposed to an action potential (16).

Electroretinogram (ERG). This is a phasic potential change superimposed upon a resting potential, induced by stimulation of the retina with light. The electroretinogram which, like potentials in physical science, is recorded so that an upward deflection denotes positivity, commences with a small, brief, downward or negative deflection (A wave) followed by a large positive wave (B) which declines, and in turn is followed by a prolonged positive wave (C). Upon cessation of the stimulus, a slight hump (D wave) may be seen breaking the slow decline of the potential. The retinogram is shown by the thick line in Figure 256. The ERG is compounded of at least three potential waves due to different retinal processes, which vary considerably in shape with the intensity and duration of the light stimulus. Granit, principally by the use of drugs and anesthetics, has analyzed the ERG into three components, P I, P II and P III, as indicated in the figure. The origin of P I, a slow positive wave contributing most of the C wave, is quite unknown. P II is probably associated with activity of bipolar and ganglion cells and P III, coming early, may reflect activity of the rods and cones.

Optic Nerve Potentials and Retinal Interaction (3, 4). Sherrington, on the basis of Cajal's histological studies of the retina, drew a parallel between retinal function and spinal reflex activity. The layer of rods and cones is a highly compressed field of receptors, and the inner synaptic layers, being second and third order neurons, are comparable to the interneurons of the

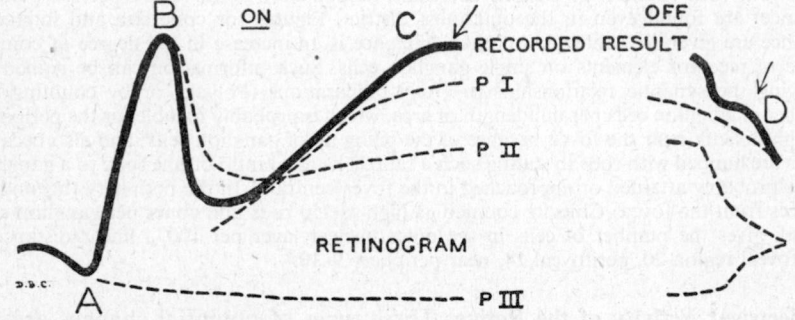

Fig. 256.—The compound electrical potential (heavy line) recorded from the retina (electro-retinogram, ERG) in response to stimulation by light. Upward deflections indicate electropositivity. A, B, C, D, are potential waves of the ERG, and the broken curves, P I, P II, P III, are one analysis (Granit) of the compound potential into its components. (From Bartley, *Psychol. Rev.*, 1939, 46:337–358.)

spinal cord and afford abundant opportunity for convergence and interconnections. It is desirable to separate the functional characteristics of the receptors from those of the bipolar and ganglion layers. In the lateral eye of the horse-shoe crab (*Limulus*) the optic nerve is made up of the axons of the receptive cells; there are no lateral connections. The visual receptor reacts in a fashion broadly similar to other sense organs. One of the types of receptors, however, appears to react not to the incidence of light but to the cessation of light, the "off type." Another type reacts to light with an initial rapid discharge which slowly declines to a steady state at which a constant frequency of discharge is maintained. In a third type the discharge occurs at the beginning and the end of stimulation: "on-off type." Frequency appears to be the correlate of intensity; the stronger the stimulus the more rapid the initial rate of discharge and the higher the frequency at which a steady state is reached. A single visual unit is capable of an enormous range of response. The total number of discharges to a flash of light of different intensities ranges from 1 to 100,000. The Weber-Fechner law applies to the discharge of the visual end-organ for moderate intensities, the frequency of discharge increasing not linearly with the strength of the stimulus but in proportion to the logarithm of intensity. Despite the chemical step in the excitation of visual receptors their discharge is not unlike that of skin and muscle receptors.

Interaction between retinal elements has been amply demonstrated for the human visual apparatus. That the site of the interaction is in part retinal was first demonstrated by Adrian and Mathews. The conger eel was chosen because of the accessibility of its optic nerve for recording, and the latency for the appearance of action potentials in the nerve was the principal factor studied. As in spinal reflexes, the latency here is shorter for more intense

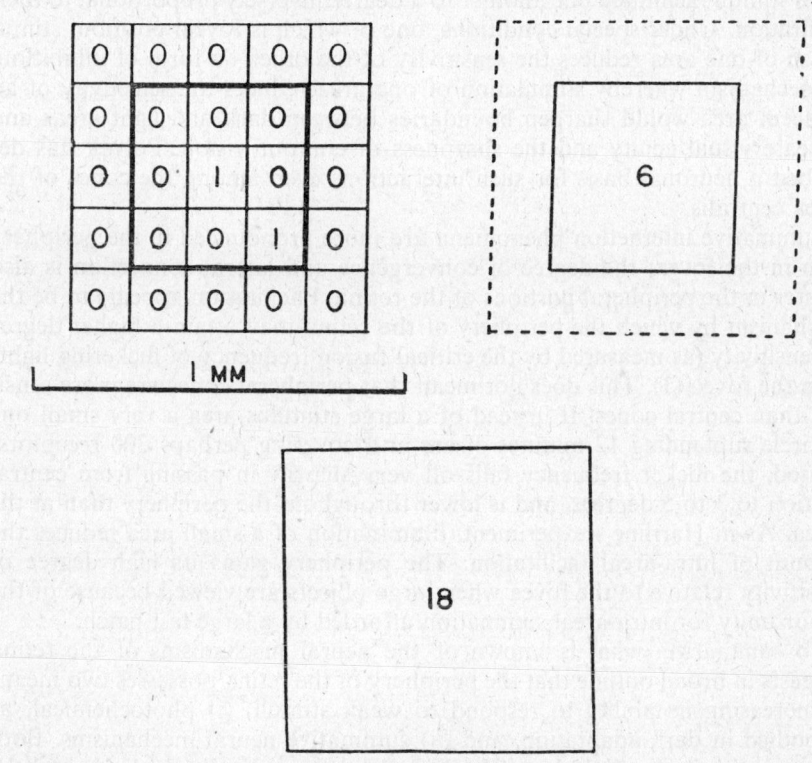

Fig. 257.—Diagrammatic explanation of an experiment showing intra-areal facilitation in the retina. The large square is the field of receptors in a frog's retina served by the optic nerve fiber under observation. In upper left, each small square was separately stimulated by a point of light adjusted so that only two squares responded and with only one discharge. When a light of the same intensity was made to cover the central nine squares (upper right), the nerve fiber discharged six times; when all 25 squares were illuminated, 18 discharges occurred. (From Hartline, *Amer. J. Physiol.*, 1940, *130:*700–711.)

stimuli (reduction of summation time). Increase of the retinal area stimulated, with intensity held constant, also shortens the latency. It is well known that the threshold for the human fovea is inversely proportional to the area of the test object (Ricco's law) in the case of small objects. Such areal effects represent a mutual facilitation between the units occupying the field of stimulation, just as the fibers within a nerve trunk facilitate one another.

Using the frog's retina, which possesses lateral connections, Hartline divided the retinal field served by a single ganglion cell into 25 squares and adjusted the stimulus so that upon stimulating each square separately only two squares gave a discharge (Fig. 257). However, when the middle 9 of the small squares were illuminated simultaneously with the same intensity as before, the ganglion cell responded with 6 discharges, and when all 25 were illuminated at once the ganglion cell discharged 18 times. The impulses arriving at the ganglion cell following stimulation of the small areas were clearly subliminal for most squares, but through convergence impulses from more than one square can summate and discharge the ganglion cell. Granit, using the flicker technique, demonstrated summation between two retinal areas by throwing two illuminated half circles upon the retina and varying their separation. The two areal stimuli facilitated one another to a degree inversely proportional to their separation. Under special conditions, one of which is foveal position, stimulation of one area reduces the sensitivity of the other—a form of inhibition. A mechanism whereby stimulation of one area reduces the sensitivity of an adjacent area would sharpen boundaries between dark and light areas and increase visual acuity and the sharpness of contour vision. Polyak has described a neuronal basis for such interactions even among the cones of the fovea centralis.

Summative interaction phenomena are more pronounced in the periphery than in the fovea; the degree of convergence and lateral connection is also greater in the peripheral portions of the retina. Facilitation appears to be the mechanism by which the periphery of the retina may attain a higher degree of sensitivity (as measured by the critical fusion frequency of flickering light) than the fovea (1). This does not mean that peripheral cones are more sensitive than central cones. If instead of a large stimulus area a very small one (a circle subtending 12 minutes of arc and covering perhaps 300 receptors) is used, the flicker frequency falls off very sharply in passing from central fixation to 3 to 5 degrees, and is lower throughout the periphery than at the fovea. As in Hartline's experiment, illumination of a small area reduces the amount of intra-areal facilitation. The periphery gains its high degree of sensitivity relative to the fovea when large objects are viewed because of the opportunity for intra-areal summation afforded by a large test patch.

To summarize: what is known of the neural mechanisms of the retina suggests in broad outline that the periphery of the retina possesses two means of increasing its ability to respond to weak stimuli: (i) photochemical, as embodied in dark adaptation, and (ii) summative neural mechanisms. Both are operative in dim light but only the latter is operative in daylight, and the latter is probably a factor in endowing the scattered rods of the extreme periphery of the retina with good perception of movement. Neural interactions of an inhibitory character occur in the foveal region and are of significance to detail vision.

VISUAL ACUITY AND DETAIL VISION

Visual acuity can be defined in two ways. Biologically, it is the sharpness with which detail and contours are perceived, and constitutes the basis for form or object vision. From the point of view of testing, visual acuity is measured by the smallest distance by which two lines may be separated without appearing as a single line. This distance is the *minimum separable*. Visual acuity is thus the *resolving power* of the eye, i.e., the ability to resolve two lines. Lines or contours of solid fields placed closer together than the minimum separable blur into one another and if sufficiently close present a homogeneous appearance. So, too, if visual acuity is low, the fine details of the environment are blurred and the intricate pattern of detail and contour gives way to structureless masses with fuzzy outlines. Visual acuity can also be expressed in terms of the *minimum* visible, the narrowest line or the finest thread that can be discriminated from a homogeneous background. Tests of visual acuity are simply standardized and quantified means of sampling a basic physiological function—detail vision—just as the Bárány chair affords an artificial test of a mechanism fundamental for the maintenance of visual orientation and the position of the body in space.

In testing visual acuity experimentally, a grid of alternating lighted and unlighted bands, the widths of which are adjustable, may be used (Ives grating); or simply a series of incompleted circles resembling the letter C, the problem being to locate the break, the width of which is variable; or two black bars separated by a white line serve the purpose. The least distance of separation at which a discontinuity between black areas is observed, the *minimum separable*, is expressed in seconds or minutes of visual angle (see Chap. 22). It is closely analogous with the two-point threshold of the skin, and somewhat similar factors affect the two measures. The traditional value for the minimum separable is 1 minute of visual angle, though for some individuals it is as low as 44 seconds.

Factors Determining Detail Vision. Dioptric Factors. The minimum separable varies with many conditions, which are of two main kinds. The first have to do with the physical formation of a sharply focused image on the retina (Chap. 22). Under this heading come (i) the "normal errors" of the dioptric mechanism: spherical and chromatic aberration, diffraction by imperfections in the ocular media, and scattering of light by reflection from the retina; (ii) pathological errors of refraction: myopia, hypermetropia, astigmatism; (iii) pupillary size with constriction making for increased visual acuity by minimizing factors (i) and (ii), although undue constriction hinders detail vision by increasing diffraction (a myopic individual can demonstrate the first factor by looking at a brightly illuminated, distant object through a pin hole); (iv) the composition of the light, monochromatic light increasing visual acuity by decreasing chromatic aberration; (v) random variations of fixation, which occur even when control of eye muscles is normal, causing a slight shifting (30 mins. of visual angle) of the image on the retina with consequent blurring of the image. Detection of errors of refraction is the main clinical purpose for testing visual acuity.

Stimulus Factors. With a black letter printed on a white card as the stimulus, there are four ways in which the stimulus can be altered to make its recognition more difficult (12). The letter might be reduced uniformly in size; the ink might be bleached to the white of the background or the latter darkened; the light falling on the card could be diminished; and finally the time allowed for observation could be shortened. *Size of detail*. Whether a detail is seen depends upon its size. Since visual acuity is usually expressed in terms of size of detail which can be resolved, one does not usually think of size as a factor in visibility. Size of detail is obviously an important factor in visibility since the detail of an object must be seen in order for the object to be correctly recognized. *Brightness contrast*. The relative brightness of the background and of the stimulus letter is of considerable influence in determining whether the detail of the letter is clearly seen (see Fig. 258).

This is not surprising, because complete inability to see the white line in a test for visual acuity is preceded by a stage in which the intervening white space is filled with gray that progressively darkens until the whole figure appears homogeneous. Perception of detail involves brightness discrimination, so that any reduction in the brightness difference between the letter and the background would be expected to reduce acuity. *Time of exposure* of the test object to view also affects acuity, shortening of the exposure acting to reduce visual acuity. *Intensity of illumination* has a very decided influence on visual acuity, especially when contrast is low. On the other hand, excessive illumination may reduce visual acuity by producing *glare*. The quantitative relationship between illumination and acuity is shown in Figure 261, and the explanation of this relationship is given below.

Retinal Grain. The second group of factors determining visual acuity is the anatomical and physiological grain of the retina, and comparable character-

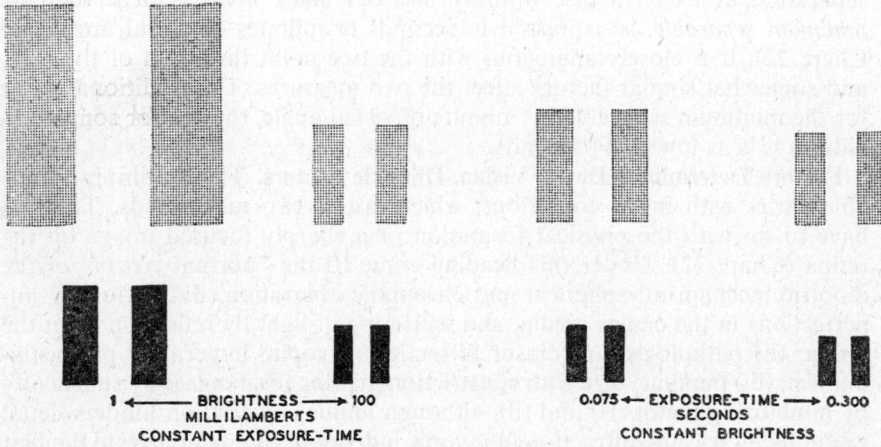

1 ◄——— BRIGHTNESS ———► 100   0.075 ◄— EXPOSURE-TIME ——► 0.300
MILLILAMBERTS   SECONDS
CONSTANT EXPOSURE-TIME   CONSTANT BRIGHTNESS

Fig. 258.—A diagram summarizing the factors determining visibility in terms of how large the test object must be for the presence or absence of the intervening space to be recognized. The test object consists of two parallel black bars upon a white background made by eliminating the middle third of a black square. Two objects in each of the four vertical columns are of equal threshold visibility and illustrate the influence of contrast. Comparison between members of the pair gives the relative size which the object must have for the intervening line to be recognized under two different illuminations (left) and two different exposures (right). (From Luckiesh and Moss, *The Science of seeing*, 1937.)

istics of the visual pathway. Just as one factor in obtaining detail in photography is fineness of grain in the film, so is the grain of the retina a factor in visual acuity. The general plan of the retina—the dense packing together of exceedingly minute receptor elements—is undoubtedly based upon the need for a finely grained receptive mechanism.* The minimum separable, converted from seconds of visual angle to retinal distance, and the diameter of a cone, are of about the same order of magnitude. At first sight this suggests that the condition which limits visual acuity is attained, for example, when the width between *striae* of an Ives grating is such that an unstimulated

* Numerous analogies to the retina can be drawn besides that of the photographic film. Color and half tone printing of pictures are made up of fine dots, the number to the square inch determining the fineness of detail that can be shown. The illuminated signs on Broadway; pictures drawn on the typewriter; paintings of the French pointilist school; the card spectacles at football games—these are all utilizations of the principle on which the retina operates in the recording of detail.

cone separates two stimulated ones. In short, two white lines on a black field could not be seen as two unless an unstimulated row of cones intervened between the stimulated ones. In Figure 259 this situation is labeled "Ideal retinal illumination" because it would demand a perfect optical system. (Such calculated ideal images are sometimes called geometrical images.) The mechanism is more complex than this, because the accuracy of the lens system, diffraction by the pupil, the steadiness of fixation, etc., do not allow two rows of cones to be illuminated and an intervening row to be wholly dark. Diagrams C and C′ represent more nearly the actual state of affairs. A band of light which in a perfect optical system would have a width at the retina equal to the diameter of a cone, is spread over the adjacent row of cones in a random fashion C′. If the striae of the test-grating are narrowed, the normal frequency curves representing the random distribution of light will be drawn together

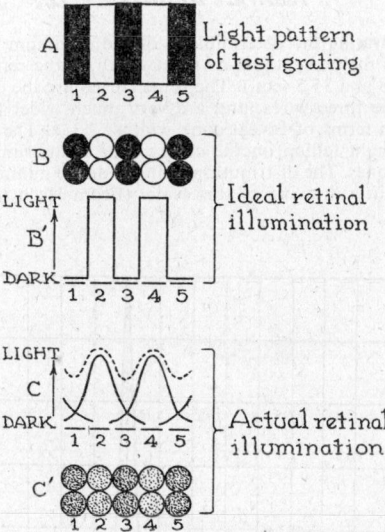

Fig. 259.—Diagram illustrating the mechanism of detail vision or visual acuity. A is the test grating; B and C are receptors with intensity of the illumination represented by shading; B′ and C′ are plots of the intensity of illumination, with the dotted line in C′ representing an algebraic summation of the two underlying curves. For further explanation see the text.

until the summated stimulus on the center cone equals that on the neighboring cones. So long as there is a discriminable difference in intensity of illumination between cones 3 and cones 2 or 4, the minimum separable has not been attained and a dark stria is visible.

These factors have been treated quantitatively in connection with the minimum visible, the finest line which can be distinguished when viewed against a homogeneous field. This value is very much smaller than the minimum separable. Hartridge obtained a figure as low as 3 *seconds* of visual angle for the minimum visible, which Hecht and Mintz (9) by attention to obtaining a perfectly homogeneous background reduced to 0.5 seconds or less. The geometrical image (assuming perfect lens system, etc.) of the narrowest wire which could be seen is barely 0.04 μ wide or 1/60 the width of a foveal cone 2.0 to 2.6 μ in diameter. A computation of the light or shadow distribution

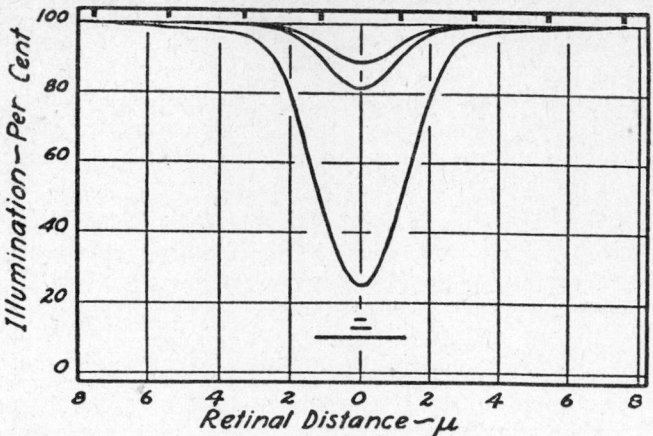

Fig. 260.—Curves illustrating the determinants of the minimum visible. The horizontal lines below the curves indicate the geometrical or ideal width of the retinal image of three wires of different diameter (4.1, 6.8 and 35.5 secs.). The three curves are the calculated *actual* distribution of the shadow cast by the three wires, and are very much wider than the geometrical image. The scale at the top is in terms of foveal cone widths, 2.3 μ. The three wires shown are seen because the intensity of light falling on the center cone is discriminably less than that falling on the two neighboring cones. The distribution of light for the minimum visible 0.5 secs. is so flat that it cannot be shown in a drawing of this scale. (From Hecht and Mintz, *J. gen. Physiol.*, 1939, *22*:593–612.)

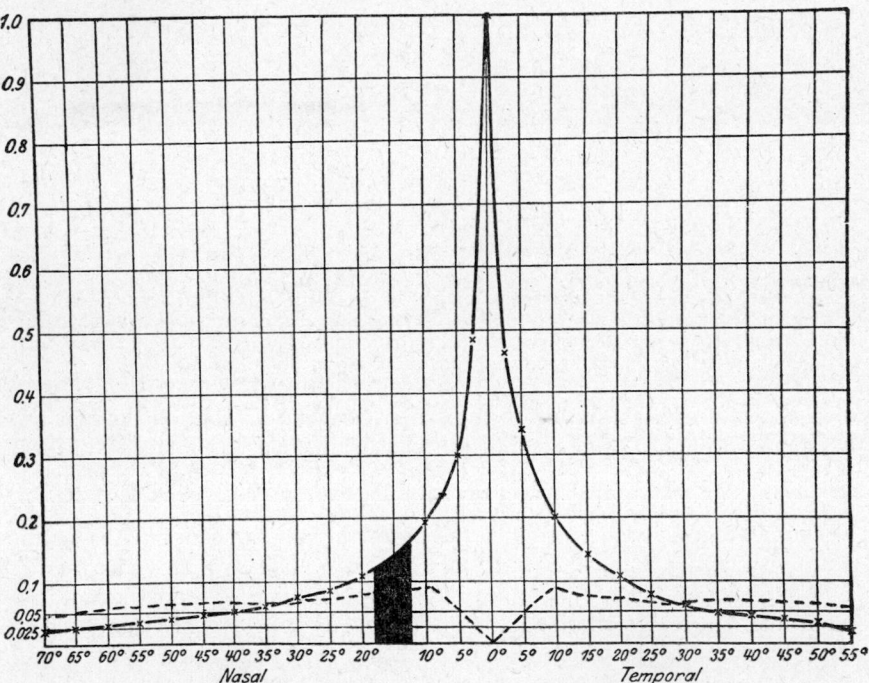

Fig. 261.—Curve of the relative acuity of vision in central and peripheral fields of the retina. The solid line represents acuity of cone vision (light-adapted eye) and the dotted line the acuity of rod vision (approximate). The black area is the blind spot. (After Wertheim, *Z. Psychol.*, 1894, *7*:177.)

actually occurring at the retina is shown in Figure 260 for wires of three diameters. The shadow extends considerably beyond the width of a cone. The scale along the top shows foveal cone width and by calculating the area under the curve for each cone the relative amount of light falling on each cone becomes known. The three wires shown are easily discriminated. For a wire which is just barely visible, 0.5 secs. of angle, it works out that the central row of cones is illuminated by 98.83 per cent of general retinal level of illumination, the two adjacent rows by 99.78 per cent, a difference of 0.95 per cent. This corresponds closely with the discriminable difference (Δ I/I) in light intensities. These fine wires are seen, therefore, because they cast a shadow, which reduces the light on one row of cones to a value just perceptibly less than the light falling on the row of cones on either side. The illumination of the cones on either side of the central row is not discriminably different from the general illumination. Hecht and Mintz conclude that a line becomes recognizable when the light distribution which it produces on the retina is such that only one row of cones is just perceptibly shaded by it. Visual acuity therefore resolves on analysis into a light-dark discrimination of a pattern. With these facts in mind, the retinal factors influencing visual acuity may be enumerated.

Table 15.—*Polyak's Data on Cone Diameter and Density*

RETINAL REGION	DISTANCE FROM CENTER OF FOVEA	DIAMETER OF CONE	VISUAL ANGLE SUBTENDED	NUMBER OF CONES PER 100 μ OR 20° OF ARC
Center of foveola	0	1 μ	12–15 sec.	83
Fovea centralis	0–20′	2 μ	24 sec.	50
Edge of rod-free area	1°	3.3 μ	40 sec.	30
Parafoveal region	3° 20′			15
Polyak's region III	7°–8°			12

Retinal region. Visual acuity is far from uniform over the entire retina. The fovea centralis is a region specialized for high visual acuity and is the portion of the retina employed for accurate inspection of fine detail. The concentric zone immediately surrounding the fovea in turn possesses greater capacity for detail vision than does the periphery, and the falling off in acuity in passing from fovea to periphery is quite abrupt (Fig. 261). Taking the foveal visual acuity as 1, the acuity at the edge of the macula (2.5°) has fallen to one half; at 7.5° from the fovea it is one-fourth, and in the extreme periphery is only one-fortieth. At least two factors operate to produce this result. Extrafoveal cones are both larger in diameter and fewer per unit area because of dilution by rods which at high illumination supposedly do not take part in vision. Secondly, more cones probably converge on a single ganglion cell in the periphery than in the central zones.

Table 15 contains data from Polyak and gives the change in size of the cones from the center of the fovea to the beginning of the rod-free area, beyond which cones are separated by rods and the pertinent value is the number of rods per 100 μ of retinal distance. Division of 100 by the number of cones in the last column gives the size of the "functional cone unit," or the distance

from the center of the cone to the center of the adjacent cone. Further values
may be determined from Polyak's graph (Fig. 262) which shows the manner
in which visual acuity and the average distance between cones measured from
center to center change in passing from fovea to periphery. The minimum
separable increases (the curve falls off) rather more abruptly than does the
intercone distance. The decrease in acuity is therefore not accounted for by
the actual cone grain of the retina. The difference between the two curves is
undoubtedly due to the second factor, the convergence of more than one
cone upon a bipolar cell, i.e., the functional grain of the bipolar cell layer.

Another striking feature of visual acuity, illustrated in Figure 261, is the
marked difference between visual acuity of the rod and cone mechanisms. The
curve for the rods is obtained by studying acuity at levels of illumination too

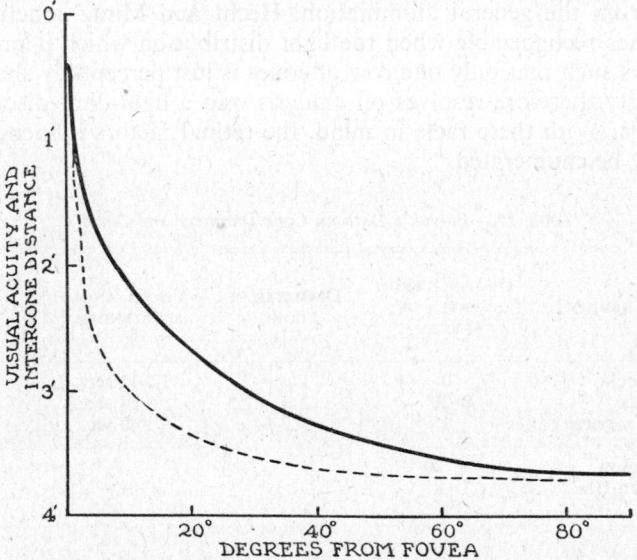

Fig. 262.—A comparison of visual acuity and cone density for the central and peripheral
portions of the retina. Dotted line shows the visual acuity in minutes of visual angle. Note that
the lower the curve the larger is the minimum separable. Heavy line shows the cone gradient
of the retina in terms of intercone distance for the periphery and the cone width for the rod-free
areas, plotted on the same ordinate as visual acuity. Failure of the curves to correspond proves
that factors other than density and diameter of cones determine the minimum separable. (After
Polyak, *The retina*, 1941.)

low to excite cones. Under such conditions the fovea and the area immediately surrounding it become the least sensitive region and the peripheral
regions the most sensitive. This is the physiological basis for one element in
the training for night vision—teaching observers to use the parafoveal regions
of the retina. The acuity of rod vision increases throughout 10 degrees due
to the increasing proportion of rods, i.e., less dilution of active rods by
the inactive cones. The acuity of rod vision at its best is far inferior to that
of cone vision within a 30 degree zone surrounding the fovea. This cannot
be charged to the rod grain of the retina, for the rods are densely packed at
the periphery where they are very little "diluted" by inactive cones. The reason
is certainly that many rods converge upon brush and mop bipolars which in
turn converge upon a single ganglion cell and are represented by a single

fiber of the optic nerve. The comparison of acuity of peripheral rods and central cones therefore proves that it is not merely the anatomical grain of the receptor elements which matters but that the number of "lines" available to carry information to the brain is important. Actually there is good reason to believe that the fineness of "grain on the optic cortex" is the determining factor in visual acuity (Chap. 24).

To test the theory of "functional grain" Hecht assumed that cone thresholds are distributed according to a normal frequency curve, like heights or weights of individuals. By integrating* such a curve, the black line in Figure 263 is

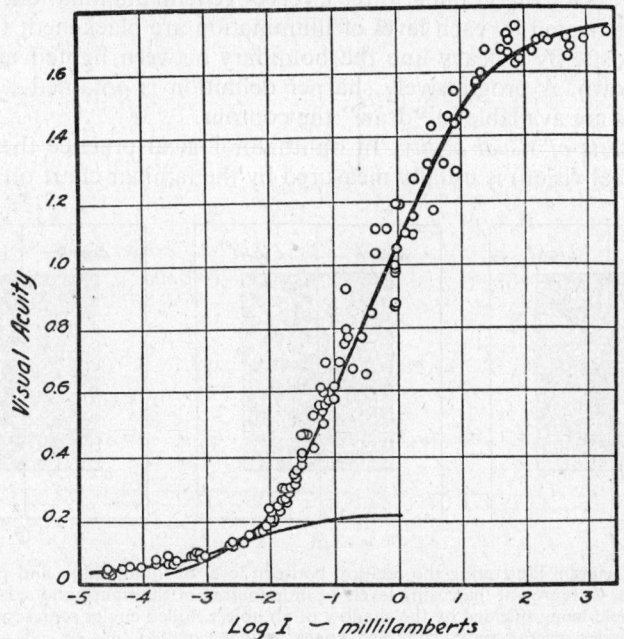

Fig. 263.—Curves showing the relation between visual acuity and level of illumination. The circles represent experimental determinations by König of visual acuity (reciprocal of the minimum separable on the ordinates) for a wide range of intensities of illumination (abscissae). The two solid lines, one for the rods (lower) and one for the cones (upper), show the success with which a normal probability integral can be fitted to the data. According to Hecht's theory, the curve represents the number of receptor units whose threshold is attained by a given intensity of illumination, the thresholds of the receptors being distributed according to the normal probability curve. (From Hecht, *A handbook of general experimental psychology*, C. Murchison, ed., 1934.)

obtained, and the agreement of the theoretical and the experimental curves justifies the assumption.

* This can be done graphically. A graphic integration of the normal frequency curve means merely that the first point on the integrated curve is established by the class of cones having the lowest threshold; the second point is the number in the first class plus those in the class of next most sensitive cones; the third point is the sum of the frequencies in the first three classes; etc. This is a logical procedure since one wishes to know the number of cones active at each intensity of illumination, and of course an intensity which stimulates high threshold cones also stimulates more sensitive ones. The whole hypothesis is in general agreement with known properties of sense organs which ascribes signaling of intensity in part to the number of end-organs active. However, frequency of discharge, the main correlate of intensity, is neglected in this formulation, and if units are classed according to frequency of discharge, a normal frequency curve would also result (Crozier). Both factors may be involved, since it is certainly not grain at the retina but functional grain of occipital cortex that determines acuity. Frequency of discharge, for example, might ultimately be translated into grain on the occipital cortex.

Functional grain and contour vision. In Figure 264 is illustrated the manner in which decreasing illumination results in fuzzy or blurred contours as opposed to sharp boundaries seen in good illumination. For convenience of illustration Hecht's theory of cone thresholds is adopted. Circles represent the anatomical grain of the retina, the filled circles the cones active at the given illumination. The same diagram illustrates the difference in contour vision in central and peripheral regions of the retina under conditions of bright illumination, the unfilled circles then being considered rods (inactive), the filled circles, cones. The diagram represents a shadow cast upon the retina by viewing a black object under three levels of general illumination. The cones which are activated by each level of illumination are blackened; those inactive are ghosts. By a heavy line the boundary between lighted and shaded cones is shown. A progressively sharper definition is obtained when many active cones are available to "draw" the contour.

Clinical tests of visual acuity. In ophthalmological practice the acuity of vision (central vision) is usually measured by the familiar chart on which the

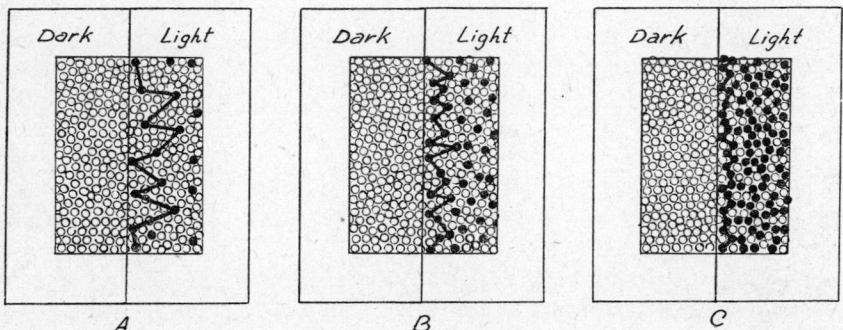

Fig. 264.—Diagram illustrating the relation between level of illumination and perception of contours. A, B, C, represent increasing levels of illumination of the right-hand side of the field, the left-hand field being shielded by the shadow of an object. Filled circles represent active units and unfilled circles inactive units, rods and cones, retinal ganglion cells or cells of the striate cortex. Where many units are active the contour is quite sharply defined, but when few units are active the contour is fuzzy. The same diagram serves to compare contour vision of peripheral (A), intermediate (B), and macular (C) regions of the retina, with the filled circles representing active cones, and the unfilled circles the inactive rods.

letters in each line are smaller than in the previous line of test type. The chart is viewed from a standard distance of 6 meters (20 feet), the practical far point of vision at which no accommodation is needed. At the end of each row of type is a number, which is the distance in feet or meters at which a whole letter of the size found on that line subtends on the retina an angle of 5 minutes, while the width of the lines composing the letter and of the intervening spaces subtends a visual angle of 1 minute. Snellen (1876), in constructing the chart, was of the belief that the component strokes of a letter should be separated by a distance equal to the minimum separable for the exact form of the letter to be perceived. The test is far more complex than this. For example, the letters employed differ considerably in legibility; if B, the hardest letter to distinguish is taken as 1, G and H are next hardest at 0.92 and L the easiest at 0.71. However, the shortcomings of the test appear to compensate for one another, and the test serves its purpose very well.

If at 20 feet the individual succeeds in reading the letters of the line marked

20 feet, visual acuity is stated as 20/20 and is considered normal. If an individual can read only those letters that a normal eye can read at 100 feet, his visual acuity, V, is equal to 20/100. The general expression used is:

$$V = \frac{d}{D},$$

in which V indicates the visual acuity; d, the distance at which the test is made; and D, the distance at which the normal eye can read the smallest letters recognized by the person examined at distance d. Attention must be paid to proper illumination of the chart. Obviously, each eye must be tested separately. Lines of test-type smaller than the 20/20 line are provided and are rated 20/15, 20/13 and 20/10. Such ratings mean that the individual has better than normally acute vision and do not mean that the individual is hypermetropic. As pointed out in the previous chapter, the hypermetrope does not see better than the emmetrope at a distance but sees normally only when objects are at a distance. It is apparent that such fractions cannot be reduced to percentages; so the common statement that a person with 20/40 vision has half normal visual acuity is incorrect. (Such an operation is equivalent to saying that a temperature of 80 degrees is twice as hot as a temperature of 40 degrees.) In another form of the Snellen test chart (A.M.A. chart), an attempt has been made to evaluate the numerical ratios in terms of percentage of useful vision.

COLOR VISION

The sensations resulting from the stimulation of the retina with the successive wave lengths of the visible spectrum, together with certain *extraspectral* colors (purple), form the *chromatic series*. It is paradoxical that the series of whites and grays—which in common parlance denotes a lack of color—is most conveniently considered as a form of color vision, the *achromatic series*.

Achromatic and Chromatic Series. Our standard white sensation is that caused by sunlight. Objects reflecting to our eye all the visible rays of the sunlight give us a white sensation. This sensation, therefore, is due primarily to the combined action of all the visible rays of the spectrum, each of which, taken separately, would give us a color sensation. White or gray may be produced also by the combined action of certain pairs of colors—complementary colors—as described below. Black, on the contrary, is the sensation caused by withdrawal of light. It must be emphasized that in order to see black a retina must be present. In the region of the blind spot one does not see black, but sees nothing. That black is a sensation connected with a definite retinal activity is not improbable. Both in the electroretinogram and in the optic nerve discharge a burst of electrical activity occurs in association with turning off the light stimulus—the so-called "off-response." In fact, some fibers of the vertebrate optic nerve appear to fire only in response to extinction of light. Blackness, therefore, is a sensation produced by withdrawing light from the retina, and a black object is one that reflects no light to the eye. Further reason for believing that black is a sensation is that black may be combined with white to produce the series of grays, and when combined with the spectral colors it gives a series of modified color tones; thus the olives of different shades may be considered as combinations of green and black in varying proportions.

The *chromatic series* consists of those qualities of visual sensation to which we give the name of colors. They consist of the colors of the spectrum and the extraspectral color, purple, together with the light-weak and light-strong hues obtained by combining the colors with white or black. In the spectrum many different colors (technically hues) may be detected—some observers record as many as 160—but in general we give specific names only to those that stand sufficiently far apart to represent quite distinct sensations, namely, the red, orange, yellow, green, blue, indigo, and violet. The limiting wave lengths (mμ) of these colors according to Listing are: red, 723–647; orange, 647–585; yellow, 585–575; green, 575–492; blue, 492–455; indigo, 455–424; violet, 424–397. When light is taken from a definite, limited portion of the spectrum we have a monochromatic light that gives us a distinct color sensation varying with the wave length of the portion chosen.

Color saturation. The term "saturation" as applied to colors is meant to designate their freedom from accompanying white sensation. Pale or pastel shades is the nontechnical name for unsaturated colors. A perfectly saturated color would be one entirely free from mixture with white. On the objective side it is easy to select a monochromatic bundle of rays from the spectrum without admixture of white light, but on the physiological side it is not probable that the color sensation thus produced is entirely free from white sensation, since the monochromatic rays may initiate in the retina not only the specific processes underlying the production of its special color, but at the same time give rise in some degree to other color processes which mix, causing white sensations (see below). Even the spectral colors are therefore not entirely saturated.

In accordance with these definitions our color sensations may be said to have three characteristics, namely, apparent brightness or luminosity, hue, and saturation. Luminosity is determined by the intensity or brightness of the stimulus, hue and saturation by the spectral distribution of the stimulus.

Laws of Color Vision. The phenomena of color are perhaps less the province of physiology than is the mechanism underlying these psychological responses. We must therefore content ourselves with a brief statement of the main facts of color vision which an adequate theory of color vision must explain.

Color mixture. Perhaps the phenomenon which tells most of the mechanism of color vision is that of color mixture or color fusion. Two or more colors falling upon the same retinal area result in a sensation which is often quite different from the sensation aroused by each wave length falling separately. Many different means have been employed to throw colors simultaneously upon the retina, the most perfect being a system of lenses or mirrors by which different portions of a spectrum can be superposed. The usual method employed in laboratory experiments is that of rotation of discs of colored paper. Each disc has a slit in it from center to periphery so that two discs can be fitted together to expose more or less of each color. If a combination of this kind is attached to a small electrical motor it can be rotated so rapidly that the impressions of the two colors upon the retina follow at such a short interval of time as to be practically simultaneous.

It must be borne in mind that color fusion upon the retina is quite a different thing from color mixture as practiced by the artist. A blue pigment, such as Prussian blue, for instance, owes its blue color to the fact that when sunlight falls upon it the red-yellow rays are absorbed and only the blue, with some of the green, rays are reflected to the eye. So a yellow pigment, chrome yellow, absorbs the blue, violet, and red rays and reflects to the eye only the yellow with some of the green rays. A mixture of the two upon the palette will absorb all the rays except the green and will therefore appear green to the eye. If, however, by means of a suitable device, we throw simultaneously upon the retina a blue and a yellow light, the result of the retinal fusion is a sensation of white.

Primary colors. By the methods of color fusion it can be shown that three wave lengths may be selected from the spectrum, one from the red end, one from the blue end, and one from the middle, whose combinations in differen₁ proportions will give a sensation of white, or of any of the intermediate color shades, or of extraspectral purple, obtained by mixing the two ends of the spectrum. It is permissible to designate these three wave lengths as primary colors* only if it is remembered that color is a term used to indicate a reaction in consciousness and is, therefore, not strictly applicable to the physical stimuli, the light waves, which fall upon the retina. From Newton, 1794, through Helmholtz, the attempt has been made to identify three specific receptors having luminosity curves which, when summed, will reproduce the photopic visibility curve of the spectrum. The thought behind such attempts is that there are certain more or less independent photochemical processes or receptors which give rise to our fundamental color sensations, and by combined action, the intermediate and achromatic colors.

Complementary colors. It has been found by the methods of color fusion that certain pairs of colors when combined give a white (gray) sensation. It may be said, in fact, that for any given color there exists a complement such that the fusion of the two in suitable proportions gives white. Because the colors of the spectrum differ in saturation, widely differing intensities may be necessary. For a mixture of yellow and violet to yield a gray, the ratio of luminosities must be approximately 40 to 1. If we confine ourselves to the spectral colors we recognize such complementary pairs as the following:

> Red and greenish blue.
> Orange and cyan blue.
> Yellow and indigo blue.
> Greenish yellow and violet.

The complementary color for green is the extraspectral purple, made by mixing red and violet. Colors that are closer together in the spectral series than the complementaries give on fusion some intermediate color which is more saturated—that is, less mixed with white sensation—the nearer the colors are together. Thus, red and yellow when fused give orange. Colors farther apart than the distance between the complementaries give some shade of purple. On the physical side, therefore, we can produce a sensation of white in two ways: either by the combined action of all the visible rays of the spectrum (sunlight) or by the combined action of pairs of colors whose wave lengths vary by a certain interval. It is probable that in the retina the processes induced by these two methods are qualitatively the same, the wave lengths represented by the complementary colors setting up by their combined action the same photochemical processes that normally are induced by sunlight.

After-images. As the name implies, this term refers to images that remain

* There are many combinations of three wave lengths with which the spectrum can be matched.

in consciousness after the objective stimulus has ceased to act upon the retina. They are doubtless due to the fact that the changes set up in the retina by the visual stimulus continue, with or without modification, after the stimulus is withdrawn. After-images are of two kinds: positive and negative. In the case of positive after-images the visual sensation retains its normal colors. If one looks at an incandescent electric light for a few seconds and then closes his eyes he continues to see the luminous object for a considerable time in its normal colors. In the case of negative after-images the colors are reversed—that is, they take on the complementary color. White becomes black, red, a bluish green, and vice versa. Negative after-images are produced very easily by fixing the eyes steadily upon a given object for an interval of twenty seconds or more and then closing them. In the case of colored objects the after-image is shown better, perhaps, by directing the gaze toward a white surface after the period of fixation is over.

Color contrasts. By color contrast is meant the influence that one color field has upon a contiguous one. If, for instance, a piece of blue paper is laid upon a larger yellow square, the color of each of them is heightened by contrast. A piece of blue paper on a blue background does not appear so saturated as when placed against a yellow background. The influences of contrast may be shown in a great variety of other ways. It is evident that in all artistic and ornamental employment of colors this influence must be considered, and empirical rules are established which indicate for the normal eye the sharpening or the dulling effect of different colors upon each other when brought into juxtaposition.

Theories of Color Vision. A number of theories have been proposed to explain the facts of color vision. None of them has been entirely successful. Two of these theories contain most of the ideas that have been advanced and may be described briefly. The first is now almost universally accepted.

Young-Helmholtz theory. This theory, proposed by Thomas Young in 1801 (27) and afterward modified and expanded by Helmoltz in his *Treatise on physiological optics* (which is available in English translation), rests upon the assumption that there are three fundamental color sensations—red, green, and violet—and corresponding with these there are three classes of cones containing three different photochemical substances. By the decomposition of each of these substances different nerve fibers are stimulated and impulses are conducted to different systems of nerve cells in the visual cortex. The theory, therefore, assumes specific nerve fibers and specific cortical cells corresponding respectively to the red, green, and violet photochemical substances, and the peculiar qualities of the resulting sensations are ascribed in the original theory to the different reactions in consciousness in three corresponding centers in the brain.*

When these three cone types are equally excited a sensation of white results, of greater or less intensity according to the extent of the excitation. White therefore, on this theory, is a compound sensation produced by the combination or fusion in consciousness of the three equal fundamental color sensations. The sensation of black, on the other hand, results from the absence of stimulation, from a state of inactivity in the retina and in the correspond-

---

* Helmholtz's hypothesis of zonal representation of color in the cerebral cortex has not proved justified. Le Gros Clark, however, has made the interesting suggestion that the three layers of the lateral geniculate body are related to the three receptors of the trichromatic theory.

ing nerve fibers and nerve centers. All other color sensations, including yellow, are compound sensations produced by the combined stimulation of the three receptors in different degrees. It is assumed, furthermore, that each of the photochemical substances is acted upon more or less by all of the visible rays of the spectrum, but that the rays of long wave lengths and smaller frequencies at the red end of the spectrum affect chiefly the red substance, those corresponding to the green of the spectrum chiefly the green substance, and the rays of shortest wave length and highest frequencies chiefly the violet substance.

Because it is impossible to stimulate any one of these substances entirely alone, a perfectly saturated color sensation cannot be obtained. Even the extreme red or the extreme violet rays act more or less on all of the substances, and the resulting red or violet sensation is, therefore, mixed to some extent with white—that is, is not entirely saturated. The theory, as stated by Helmholtz, held strictly to the doctrine of specific nerve energy, in assuming that each photochemical substance serves simply as a means for the excitation of a nerve fiber, and that the quality of the sensation aroused depends on the ending of this fiber in the brain. The phenomenon of negative after-images finds a simple explanation in terms of this theory. If we look fixedly at a green object, for example, the corresponding photochemical substance is chiefly acted upon, and if subsequently the same part of the retina is exposed to white light, the red and violet substances, having been previously less acted upon, now respond in greater proportions to the white light, and the after-image takes a red-violet—that is, purple—color. Many objections have been raised to the Young-Helmholtz theory. It has been urged, for instance, that we are not conscious that white or yellow sensations are blends or compound color sensations; we perceive in them none of the supposed component elements that we do in such undoubted mixtures as the blue-greens or the purples. The theory explains poorly or not at all the fact that the periphery of the retina is color blind and yet can perceive white or gray; and it is not clear why yellow is seen more peripherally than green or red if it results from the combined stimulation of the red and green receptors. The theory, according to some, fails to explain the facts of partial and complete color blindness.

Hering's theory of color vision. This theory also assumes the existence in the retina of three photochemical substances, but of such a nature as to give us six different qualities of sensation. A white-black substance is assumed to be broken down by the visible rays of light, and thereby sets up nerve impulses that arouse in the brain the sensation of white. On the other hand, when not acted upon by light this same substance is built up and sets up nerve impulses which in the brain give us a sensation of black. There are in the retina also a red-green and a yellow-blue substance as shown in the table.

Photochemical substance	Retinal process	Sensation
Red-green	—	red
	+	green
Yellow-blue	—	yellow
	+	blue
White-black	—	white
	+	black

It will be observed that the theory gives an independent objective cause for the sensations of white, black, and yellow. In the latter condition one may assume, in terms of this theory, that in complete color blindness the white-black substance is present, while red-green

18

blindness is explained on the view that in such persons a red-green substance is deficient or lacking. On this theory, complementary colors—red and blue-green, yellow and blue—are in reality antagonistic colors. When thrown on the retina simultaneously their effects neutralize each other, and there remains only the effect on the white substance which is exerted by all the visible rays. For this reason it is sometimes called the opponent color theory. To this theory, also, a number of objections may be made. For example, red and green as an antagonistic pair should extinguish each other when thrown simultaneously on the retina. As a matter of fact, such a combination gives us a sensation of yellow, unless a blue-green and a blue-red are selected. There is no known way by which the same receptor rod can signal two different hues to the brain, and the hypothesis therefore does not conform to the doctrine of specific nerve energies.

Site of Color Mixture. Colored lights produce white, gray, spectral and nonspectral colors when allowed to fall in proper combinations upon the retina. But where does this mixing of colors occur? According to the Hering

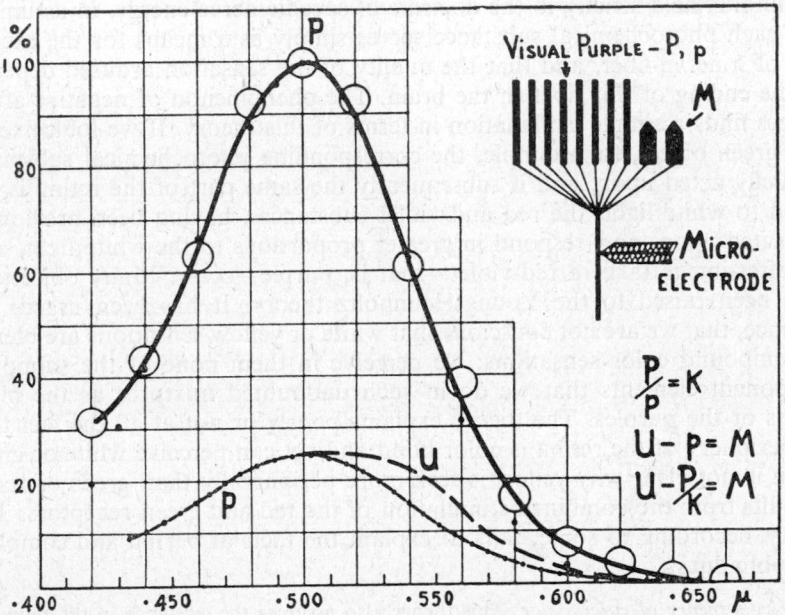

Fig. 264A.—Average sensitivity curve (large circles) of the receptors connected with a single ganglion cell of the cat's retina when dark-adapted. Black dots are Lythgoe's curve for the absorption of light by visual purple. U is the experimentally obtained curve from which curve P in appropriate magnitude (p) is subtracted to give the sensitivity of the specific color receptor. (From Granit, *J. Neurophysiol.*, 1945, 8:195-210.)

theory lights interact by producing opposite effects on the receptors. According to the Young-Helmholtz theory each of three postulated receptors may be stimulated in varying degrees by different wave lengths, but the impulses each initiates give rise to *only one* hue sensation regardless of the wave length stimulating it. Roughly speaking, the resulting primary "sensations" or cerebral events fuse to produce *fusion colors* or white and gray. The critical experiment is to have two lights fall upon corresponding points of the two retinas (impulses from which cause a fused mental image). Binocular fusion of color, though once doubted, does occur, and many of the color mixture phenomena of monocular color fusion can be reproduced in binocular fusion (5). The interaction of light with light is therefore not a chemical one in the receptors, nor a neural one in the deeper layers of the retina. The lateral geniculate body is the first point at which nerve fibers from corresponding points on the retina converge, so that binocular fusion of color must occur either there or in the cerebral cortex.

Binocular color fusion is critical in another respect. The Hering theory postulates a retinal process for yellow; the trichromatic theory dispenses with a yellow receptor because yellow sensations result from a mixture of red and green lights. This can also be accomplished by binocular color fusion, showing that yellow is sensory fusion produced in the brain. For the same reason Hering's postulated "white" receptor is unnecessary. The trireceptor theory therefore accounts for the retinal process of vision.

Specific Color Receptors. The number and sensitivity characteristics of the

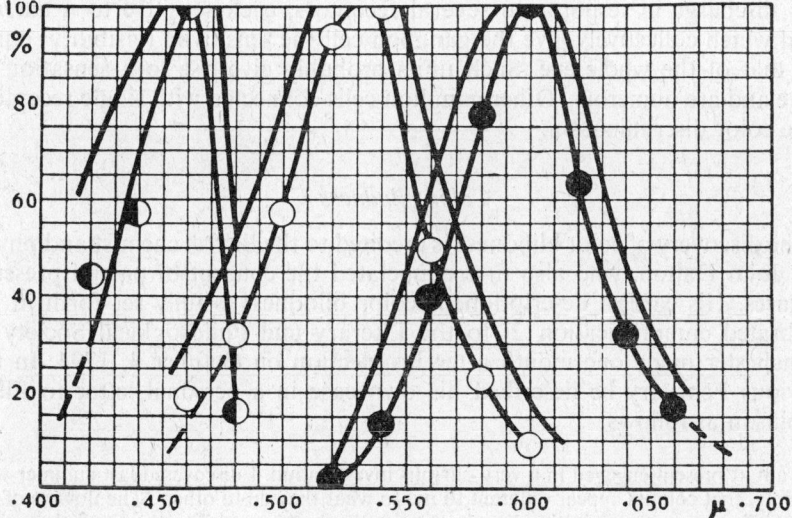

Fig. 264B.—The sensitivity curve for blue (left), green (middle), and red (right) color receptors. These were obtained by selective adaptation and by averaging the curves of several individual receptors, which varied from the average by the amount indicated by the outer contour. (From Granit, *J. Neurophysiol.*, 1945, 8:195-210.)

hypothetical color receptors have been deduced from data on color mixture, hue discrimination, and the luminosity of the spectrum when the eye is adapted to certain wave lengths in an effort to eliminate or reduce the action of the corresponding receptors. The procedures and calculations are highly technical. Recently (May 1945) Granit has succeeded in recording impulses from single ganglion cells of the mammalian retina by means of micro-electrodes. The least amount of light at different wave lengths adequate to discharge the ganglion cell was determined, i.e., a sensitivity curve analogous to the visibility curve was obtained for single functional retinal units. All units studied exhibited sensitivity to a wide band of wave lengths, the curve of sensitivity obtained in the dark-adapted eye agreeing closely with the absorption curve of visual purple (Fig. 264A). Under conditions of light adaptation, a curve with a different maximum, resembling the photopic visibility curve shown in Figure 265, was often obtained. Polyak (20) has shown that both rods and cones converge through bipolar cells upon the same ganglion cell. The shift from the scotopic to the photopic curve presumably means that rods cease to function at the intensities that stimulate the cones. Granit terms this response the *scotopic and photopic dominator* response.

In addition to these dominator responses, analysis reveals in the light-adapted eye units having sensitivity to a *narrow* band of wave lengths, which are termed *modulators*, and may represent individual cones. The sensitivity curves tend to vary slightly, but cluster into three groups (Fig. 264B) falling in the following regions: red-yellow (580–600 mμ), green (520–540 mμ) and blue (450–470 mμ). From these curves can be reconstructed a visibility curve which agrees satisfactorily with that of the human eye. This direct evidence therefore indicates that Helmholtz's trireceptor theory may be true in the statistical sense that the cones fall into three groups within which the receptors are similar though not identical in sensitivity. Apparently many ganglion cells discharge in response to several receptors, each sensitive to a narrow band which collectively give the ganglion cell the sensitivity (visibility) curve like that of the whole eye. Such units probably give rise to a sensation of white and are numerous. Other ganglion cells connected with single receptors serve color discrimination.

Color blindness

The discovery of color blindness is credited to the British chemist and physicist, John Dalton, who also first enunciated the concept of partial pressure of gases. His earliest description of color blindness is fully set forth in his celebrated communication (2) to the Literary and Philosophical Society of Manchester made one month after his election on October 3, 1794. In the previous February he described his own case in a personal letter to Elihu Robinson as follows:

"I am at present engaged in a very curious investigation. I discovered last summer with certainty, that colours appear different to me to what they do to others. The flowers of the Cranesbills appear to me in the day almost exactly sky-blue, whilst others call them deep pink; but happening once to look at one in the night by candle-light I found it of a colour as different as possible from daylight; it seemed then very near yellow, but with a tincture of red; whilst nobody else said it differed from the daylight appearance, my brother excepted, who seems to see as I do. . . . The primary colours, *orange, yellow,* and *blue,* appear to me much the same in the night as they do in the day, and I always distinguish them and call them by their proper names, as well as several drabs, and other mixed colours; some reds—for instance vermilion—appear the same or alike day and night; but others, and more especially the different shades of *pink,* confound me most completely in the day, they all appearing *light blue;* all the dyed *greens* seem to have little or no green about them; they appear inclining to *red* or *brown* in the day, and almost *blue* in the night; the *pinks* and *light blues,* which appear almost of the same piece in the day, are as opposite as black and white in the night, or by candlelight."(15)

Classification of Color Blindness. The conventional classification of color blindness derives from the Young-Helmholtz theory of three specific receptors, color blindness being ascribed to an alteration in one of them. Color anomalies are no longer described in terms of red, green, and violet blindness, because, for example, the individuals Helmholtz called red blind and green blind are actually both red and green blind. Instead are employed the more noncommittal categories suggested by von Kries: protanopia, deuteranopia, and tritanopia, implying merely a defect in the first (*protos*), second (*deuteros*) receptor, etc. The conventional classification is as follows:

I. TRICHROMATS	II. DICHROMATS	III. MONOCHROMATS
1. normal color vision	1. protanopia	
2. protanomaly	2. deuteranopia	
3. deuteranomaly	3. tritanopia	

This classification, like the parent Young-Helmholtz theory, characterizes adequately the objective phenomena of color mixture in the color blind and is not meant to describe the appearance of the spectrum. The protanomalous and deuteranomalous, like those with normal color vision, require three primary colors with which to match the spectrum and hence are trichomats, but they use the color from the red and from the green parts of the spectrum in different proportions from the normal and in different proportions from each other. In matching yellows by mixing red and green wave lengths, they employ quite different ratios, as first noticed by Lord Rayleigh in 1882; the protanope requires more of the red and the deuteranope more of the green. Their defect may be quite slight or may be nearly as severe as in dichromatism. Dichromats are so named because they can match the spectrum as they see it with only two primary colors, a blue and a red for the deuteranope and a blue and a green for the protanope. These two conditions are believed to be reduction systems representing the loss of one or other of the three Young-Helmholtz color receptors. Tritanopia is an extremely rare form of color blindness in which a wave length from the long end and one from the middle of the spectrum suffice to duplicate the spectrum. The monochromat duplicates the spectrum with only one wave length by suitably adjusting its intensity. Apparently only grades of light and dark are seen. Though only a few cases have been studied, it is an interesting condition which strengthens the duplicity theory of vision.

Total color blindness, achromatopsia or monochromatic vision. Of all the forms of color disability this is the only one which can be accurately termed color *blindness*, for it is an inability to see color extending to all degrees of all hues. In the complete form only black, white and gradations of gray are seen. Achromatopsia is congenital and extremely rare; only 130 cases were reported up to 1934. Typically, it is accompanied by photophobia, lowered visual acuity, failure of foveal vision (central scotoma), and a fine nystagmus resembling miners' nystagmus. The curve relating visual acuity to illumination shows only the rod-limb (Fig. 263), as does the flicker frequency-intensity curve (Fig. 248). The visibility curve is that of rod vision, and dark adaptation is normal. These symptoms can have only one interpretation—that the cones, though anatomically present and not necessarily pathological in appearance, are functionless; the subject is forced to employ exclusively the mechanism for night vision.

Luminosity of the spectrum in color blindness. To the protanope-protanomalous the luminosity of the spectrum is distinctly abnormal; to the deuteranope-deuteranomalous it is virtually normal. For the former the spectrum is shortened; the longer (red) wave lengths are not even appreciated as light; it is as though they did not reach the retina. The shortening of the spectrum explains why a protanope can confuse a red with a black and appear at a funeral wearing a red tie. The point at which the spectrum seems brightest is shifted from 552 mμ to approximately 540 mμ and the curve for longer wave lengths is similarly shifted. No intermediate forms linking the protanope with the normal

are found (Fig. 265), and the visibility curves for protanopes and protanomalous are identical. The term *scoterythrous* has been suggested for this state.
The visibility curve of the deuteranope shows no such abnormality, hence
is a form of pure color blindness while protanopia is a *color plus light*
blindness.

Color confusions. The color blind person is satisfied with the appearance
of his visual world, rarely misnames a colored object or even a color, and is
often tardy in discovering his abnormality. His deficiency is usually first
manifest because he confuses certain colors, and tests of color vision depend
on these confusions. The confusion of the color blind can, as Clerk Maxwell
showed in 1855, be stated in terms of a color triangle or diagram, as in Fig-

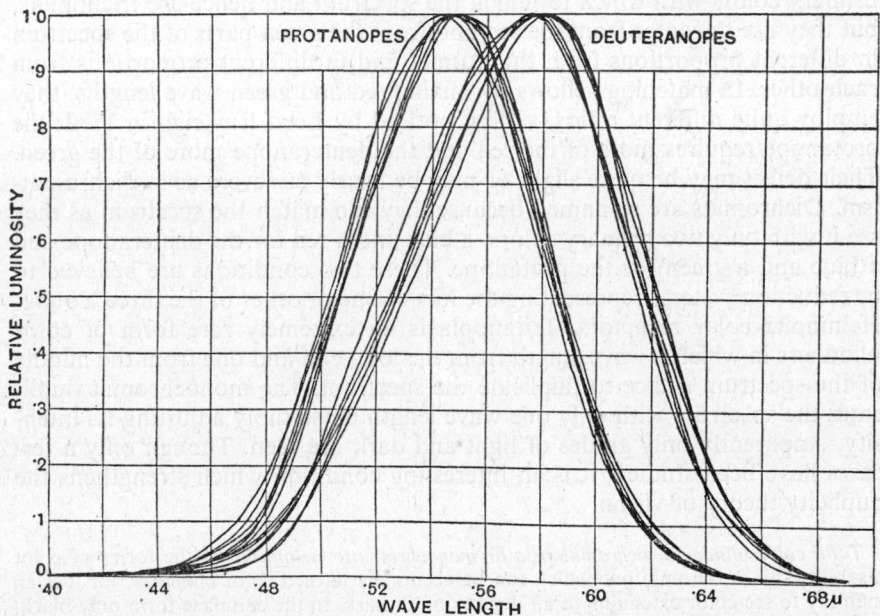

Fig. 265.—Visibility curves of six protanopes and six deuteranopes. The curves are adjusted
to the same height. Observe the similarity of curves within each group and that there are no intermediate cases. The curves for deuteranopes are very similar to those for persons with normal
color vision (cf. Fig. 247); but a band of the long wave lengths (red), normally visible, cannot
be seen or is poorly visible to the protanope, whose point of maximum brilliance is shifted to
the short wave lengths. (From *Spec. Rep. Ser. med. Res. Council*, 1935, no. 200, 58 pp. By permission, the Controller, His Britannic Majesty's Stationery Office.)

ure 266. Each point on one of the dotted lines is a different color obtained
by mixing a wave length from the y-axis with one from the x-axis in the proportions indicated by the scale of coefficients. (A fact of considerable practical and military importance is that any spectral or extraspectral color can
be "specified" by stating the proportions—coefficients—of *three* primary
colors required by the normal individual to mix that color.) Along the line
forming the blunt-ended triangle are arranged the colors of the spectrum.
All colors falling on the line running from 500 to 750 mμ will appear the same
as spectral color of 500 mμ, the wave length at which the line intersects the line
representing the spectrum. Using these diagrams, Judd (11) shows how the
fact that Dalton suffered from protanopia can be deduced from one of his

descriptions of his color difficulties—"woolen yarn, dyed crimson or dark blue, is the same to me." Harvard crimson is found by the Munsell system of color notation to have the color specification: $x = 0.48$, $y = 0.25$; Navy blue similarly is: $x = 0.27$, $y = 0.25$; the two colors are indicated by crosses (x) on the diagrams. On the chart for the protanope, these two colors fall on the same dotted line and hence are confusion colors for the protanope, but the two colors fall upon different lines on the diagram for the deuteranope, and hence are distinguished.

Subjective phenomena. Certain subjective phenomena are less well explained than are color mixture and color matching, and the luminosity of the spectrum. How does the spectrum appear to the color blind? To the dichromat,

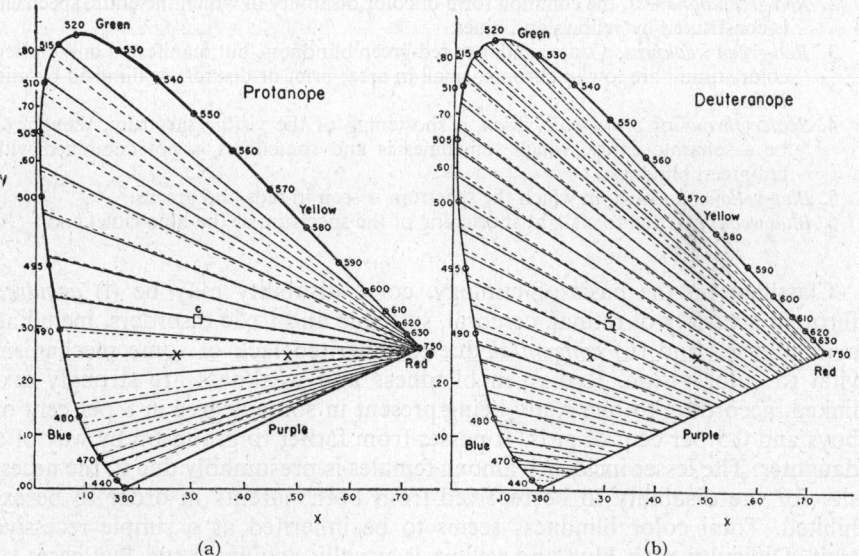

(a)   (b)

Fig. 266.—Charts describing the color confusion in two kinds of color blindness (protanopia and deuteranopia). The periphery of the pyramid and its attached numbers represent the wave lengths (mμ) of the spectrum. The y- and x-axes are coefficients giving the proportions of two primary colors by which the dichromat can match all of the colors contained within the color pyramid. Colors along the horizontal dotted lines are confused by the color blind. The use of the diagram and the meaning of the two x's are explained in the text. (From Judd, *J. opt. Soc. Amer.*, 1943, *33*:293–307, after Pitt.)

protanope and deuteranope, the spectrum is divided into two halves by a band of gray in the neighborhood of 493–497 mμ (greenish blue), the so-called neutral point, above which all wave lengths seem yellow and below which they seem blue. Dalton described the spectrum as follows: "My yellow comprehends the red, orange, yellow and green of others; and my blue and purple (dark blue?) coincide with theirs." The few cases of monocular color vision examined confirm this description of the spectrum. So, too, the color confusions of deuteranope and protanope are only subtly different. From the point of view of their subjective experiences protanopes and deuteranopes are both instances of red-green color blindness but of slightly different character, with protanopia being characterized by a shortening of the spectrum and a decreased luminosity of the longer (red) wave lengths.

The explanation which accounts best for the fact that the spectrum appears to be made up of yellow and blue, rather than red and blue, and green and blue, is as follows. In protanopia the "red receptor" is supposed to change its sensitivity so that it is excited by the same wave lengths as the "green receptor" but retains its central reaction unaltered. Therefore, neither green nor red are ever separately experienced, their receptors being always excited together, resulting in a color mixture. The spectrum corresponding to the whole red and green range appears as yellow or orange, the hues resulting from mixing red and green wave lengths. Deuteranopia may consist of a change in the cone normally most sensitive to the green wave length so that it has the same sensitivity as the red sensitive cone. For explanations of other subjective phenomena of color blindness the reader is referred to Walls (6) and for the objective phenomena to Hecht (26). Some believe that the whole classification of color disability on a trireceptor basis as now used should be discarded in favor of one which associates yellow with blue and green with red, as in the Hering theory. A substitute classification has been suggested by Murray (17):

1. *Total color blindness* or *achromatopsia.*
2. *Red-green blindness*, the common form of color disability in which the entire spectrum is constituted by yellows and blues.
3. *Red-green weakness*, a state similar to red-green blindness, but manifested only "when color stimuli are low in chroma, small in area, brief or distant, or dimmed by rain or fog."
4. *Scoterythrous* or *protanopic vision*, a shortening of the visible spectrum, thought to be a separate entity, which sometimes is and sometimes is not combined with red-green blindness.
5. *Blue-yellow blindness*, in which the spectrum is seen in reds and greens.
6. *Blue weakness*, due to a slight shortening of the spectrum at the blue-violet end.

Classified on the basis of etiology, color disability may be (i) *acquired* through a variety of retinal, cerebral, systemic and toxic disorders, including avitaminosis, and (ii) *congenital* due to inherited lack of some mechanism vital to color vision. Red-green blindness and weakness are strongly sex-linked, according to one study being present in some degree in 8 per cent of boys and 0.5 per cent of girls. It passes from father to grandson by way of a daughter. The lesser incidence among females is presumably due to the necessity for the disability to be received from both parents in order to be exhibited. Total color blindness seems to be inherited as a simple recessive trait. Difficulty with blue and yellow is usually acquired; too few cases of congenital forms have been discovered to learn much of its genetics.

Tests of Color Blindness. A great number of methods have been proposed and used to detect color blindness. The simplest for the purpose of explanation of the principles involved is that of Holmgren. A number of skeins of wool are used and three standard colors are chosen, namely, standard *I*, a pale pure green skein, which must not incline toward yellow green; standard *II*, a medium purple (magenta) skein; and standard *III*, a vivid scarlet skein. The person under investigation is given skein *I* and is asked to select quickly from the pile of assorted colored skeins those that have approximately the same color. Those who are dichromatic will see the test skein as a gray with some yellow or blue shade and will select, therefore, not only the green skeins, but the grays or grayish yellow and blue skeins. To ascertain whether the individual is a protanope or a deuteranope, standards *II* and *III* may then be employed.

With standard *II* (medium purple) the protanope will select, in addition to other purples, only blues or violets; the deuteranope will select as "confusion colors" only greens and grays.

With standard *III* (red) the protanope will select as confusion colors greens, grays, or browns less luminous than the standard color, while the deuteranope will select greens, grays, or browns of a greater brightness than the standard.

The second test of color vision in common use is the Ishihara or other version of Stilling's (1876) pseudo-isochromatic charts. This test, familiarly known as the "hidden digit" test, consists of a book of plates containing a digit made up of spots of color set in a field composed of spots of the confusion color (Fig. 267). Spots of several shades are used because the luminosity of certain hues is altered for color deviates. In constructing the original tests, Stilling was guided in choice of colors, etc., by a red-green blind painter and a blue-yellow blind school teacher. In the Ishihara test one number is

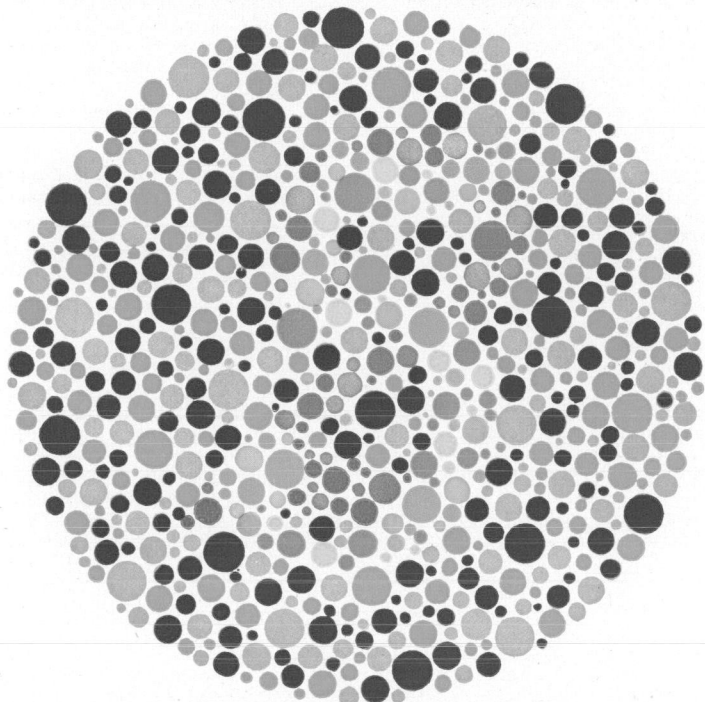

Fig. 267.—Hidden-figure chart for the detection of color blindness. The normal eye sees the figure 5, the color blind eye sees the figure 2. (Copied by permission from Ishihara's *Series of plates designed as tests for color blindness*, Tokio, 1920.)

seen by the normal eye, and another by the color-weak eye. By appropriate choice of colors and chroma levels the test can be made qualitatively and quantitatively diagnostic.

REFERENCES

1. CREED, R. S., and RUCH, T. C. Regional variations in sensitivity to flicker. *J. Physiol.*, 1932, *74*:407–423.

2. DALTON, J. Extraordinary facts relating to the vision of colours, with observations. *Mem. Manchr lit. phil. Soc.*, 1794, *5*:28–45.

3. GRAHAM, C. H. Vision: III. Some neural correlations. Pp. 829–879 in: *A handbook of general experimental psychology*, C. MURCHISON, ed. Worcester, Clark University Press, 1934.

3a. GRANIT, R. The colour receptors of the mammalian retina. *J. Neurophysiol.*, 1945, *8*: 195–210. Also: A physiological theory of colour perception. *Nature, Lond.*, 1943, *151*:11–14.

4. HARTLINE, H. K. The neural mechanisms of vision. *Harvey Lect.*, 1941, pp. 39–68.

5. HECHT, S. On the binocular fusion of colors and its relation to theories of color vision. *Proc. nat. Acad. Sci., Wash.*, 1928, *14*: 237–240.

6. HECHT, S. Vision: II. The nature of the

photoreceptor process. Pp. 704–828 in: *A handbook of general experimental psychology*, C. MURCHISON, ed. Worcester, Clark University Press, 1934.

7. HECHT, S. Energy and vision. *Amer. Scientist*, 1944, *32*:159–177. *Idem:* Pp. 1–21 in: *Visual mechanisms*, H. KLÜVER, ed. Lancaster, Pennsylvania, Jaques Cattell Press, 1942.

8. HECHT, S., HAIG, C., and CHASE, A. M. The influence of light adaptation on subsequent dark adaptation of the eye. *J. gen. Physiol.*, 1937, *20*:831–850.

9. HECHT, S., and MINTZ, E. U. The visibility of single lines at various illuminations and the retinal basis of visual resolution. *J. gen. Physiol.*, 1939, *22*:593–612.

10. HUNT, E. P., and HAYDEN, K. M. Medical evaluation of nutritional status. IX. The reliability of visual threshold during dark adaptation as a measure of vitamin A deficiency in a population group of low income. *Milbank mem. Fd quart. Bull.*, 1942, *20*:139–168.

11. JUDD, D. B. Symposium on color-blindness. Facts of color blindness. *J. opt. Soc. Amer.*, 1943, *33*:294–307.

12. LUCKIESH, M., and MOSS, F. K. *The science of seeing.* New York, D. Van Norstrand Co., Inc., 1937, viii, 548 pp.

13. MCFARLAND, R. A., and EVANS, J. N. Alterations in dark adaptation under reduced oxygen tensions. *Amer. J. Physiol.*, 1939, *127*:37–50.

14. MILES, W. R. Red goggles for producing dark adaptation. *Fed. Proc. Amer. Soc. exp. Biol.* 1943, *2*:109–115.

15. MILLINGTON, J. P. *John Dalton.* London, J. M. Dent & Co., 1906, xii, 225 pp.

16. MOWRER, O. H., RUCH, T. C., and MILLER, N. E. The corneo-retinal potential difference as the basis of the galvanometric method of recording eye movements. *Amer. J. Physiol.*, 1936, *114*:423–428.

17. MURRAY, E. Color vision tests. Pp. 275–282 in: *Medical physics*, O. GLASSER, ed. Chicago, The Year Book Publishers, Inc., 1944.

18. PARSONS, J. H. *An introduction to the study of colour vision.* Cambridge, Cambridge University Press, 1924, x, 323 pp.

19. PITT, F. H. G. Characteristics of dichromatic vision (with an appendix on anomalous trichromatic vision). *Spec. Rep. Ser. med. Res. Council,* 1935, no. 200, 58 pp.

20. POLYAK, S. L. *The retina.* Chicago, University of Chicago Press, 1941, x, 607 pp.

21. RAWDON-SMITH, A. F. *Theories of sensation.* Cambridge, Cambridge University Press, 1938, xiii, 137 pp.

22. WALD, G. Carotenoids and the visual cycle. *J. gen. Physiol.*, 1935, *19*:351–371.

23. WALD, G. Vision: photochemistry. Pp. 1658–1667 in: *Medical physics*, O. GLASSER, ed. Chicago, The Year Book Publishers, Inc., 1944.

24. WALD, G., and CLARK, A.-B. Visual adaptation and chemistry of the rods. *J. gen. Physiol.*, 1937, *21*:93–105.

25. WALD, G., HARPER, P. V., Jr., GOODMAN, H. C., and KRIEGER, H. P. Respiratory effects upon the visual threshold. *J. gen. Physiol.*, 1942, *25*:891–903.

26. WALLS, G. L. *The vertebrate eye and its adaptive radiation.* Bloomfield Hills, Michigan, Cranbrook Institute of Science, 1942, xiv, 785 pp.

27. YOUNG, T. On the theory of light and colours. The Bakerian Lecture. *Philos. Trans.*, 1801, *92*:12–48.

CHAPTER 24

BINOCULAR VISION AND CENTRAL VISUAL PATHWAYS

The dioptric and neural mechanisms making for accurate vision at the central portions of the retina are rendered more useful and flexible by a provision for training this efficient portion of the visual apparatus upon whatever portion of the environment requires close examination. The gaze can be transferred quickly from point to point, or it can be fixated steadily on a single detail. Two types of movements are executed: (i) convergence-divergence movements occurring when the eye is fixated upon near and far objects, and (ii) conjugate movements in which the eyes sweep from side to side, or up and down, etc., in unison so that a light from an object, no matter where its position, falls always upon the fovea, making possible the fusion of images from the two eyes.

EYE MOVEMENTS

Movements of the Eye. Each eyeball is moved by six extrinsic, striated muscles which are innervated by three cranial nerves. The third or oculomotor nerve controls the medial rectus, the superior rectus, the inferior rectus, and the inferior oblique; the fourth cranial nerve (*n. trochlearis*) innervates the superior oblique alone; and the sixth (*n. abducens*) the lateral rectus alone. By means of these muscles the eyeballs execute various movements, all of which may be considered as *rotations* of the eyeball around various axes. The common point of intersection of these axes is designated as the center of rotation of the eyeball; it lies about 13.5 mm. back of the cornea in the emmetropic eye. The various axes of rotation all pass through this point, and we may classify them under four heads: (i) The horizontal, or sagittal, axis is the line passing through the rotation point and the object looked at—the fixation point. This axis corresponds practically with the visual axis. Rotations around this axis give a wheel movement or torsion to the eyeballs. (ii) The transverse axis is the line passing through the rotation points of the two eyes. Rotations around this axis move the eyeballs straight up or down. (iii) The vertical axis is the vertical line passing through the rotation point and perpendicular at this point to the horizontal and transverse axes. Rotations around this axis move the eyeball to the right or the left. (iv) The oblique axes include all the axes of rotation passing through the rotation point at oblique angles to the horizontal axis. These axes all lie in the equatorial plane of the eye, and rotations around any of them move the eyeball obliquely upward or downward.

The share of the individual eye muscles in producing rotation of the eyeball around the various axes is shown in Figure 268, which indicates the paths traversed by the visual axis when each muscle separately moves the eyeball. Starting from the primary position, rotations of the eyes about the vertical axis—that is, movements directly to right or left—may be made by the contraction of the medial or the internal rectus, as the case may be. Rotations around the transverse axis—that is, movements directly up or down—require in each case the cooperation of two muscles. In movements upward the superior rectus, acting alone, would, in rotating the eyeball upward, also give it a slight torsion so as to turn the upper part of the vertical meridian inward. To obtain a movement directly upward (rotation around the transverse axis) the superior rectus and inferior oblique must act together. For a similar reason rotation directly downward requires the combined action of the inferior rectus and superior oblique. From its name, the superior oblique might be expected to move the eyeball obliquely upwards, but because the tendon passes through a "pulley" (trochlea) situated well forward in the orbit and turns back and laterally to attach to the sclera at the back of the

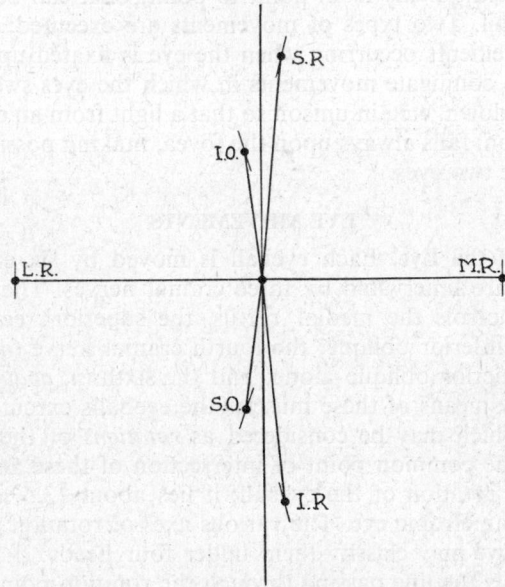

Fig. 268.—Hering's diagram showing the actions of individual eye muscles. The lines radiating from the primary fixation point show the path which the visual axis would describe on a screen placed in front of the eyes when they are rotated by each muscle acting singly. The short line through the terminus of each line represents the tilt of the eyes from the vertical imparted by the action of each eye muscle in executing each movement. The abbreviations are: *I.O.* and *S.O.*, inferior and superior oblique; *I.R.* and *S.R.*, inferior and superior recti; *L.R.* and *M.R.*, lateral and medial recti. (From Martin and Weymouth, *Elements of physiology*, 1928.)

eyeball, its contraction rotates the eye downwards as well as outwards. The inferior oblique arises from the front of the orbit on the medial side and runs backwards and laterally beneath the eyeball to attach to the sclera at the back of the eye; contraction of it rotates the eye upwards and laterally.

Rotations of the eyeballs around oblique axes require the cooperation of three of the muscles: movements upward and outward—the superior rectus, inferior oblique, and lateral rectus; movements upward and inward—superior rectus, inferior oblique, and medial rectus; movements downward and outward—inferior rectus, superior oblique, and lateral rectus; movements downward and inward—inferior rectus, superior oblique, and medial rectus. Most of the movements of the eyes are of the latter kind—namely, rotations around an oblique axis—and the position of the axis for each definite movement of this character may be determined by Listing's law, which may be stated as follows: when the eye passes from a primary to a secondary position it may be considered as having rotated around an axis perpendicular to the positions of the two visual axes. In so doing rolling movements or arching pathways, which would hinder localization and space perception, are successfully avoided.

As already mentioned, the eyes ordinarily make only such movements as will keep the visual axes of the two eyes parallel or will converge them upon a common point (conjugate deviation movements and convergence). In movements of convergence the medial recti of the two eyes are associated, while in symmetrical lateral movements the medial rectus of one eye acts with the lateral rectus of the other. Under normal conditions it is impossible for us to diverge the visual axes beyond the parallel—that is, to associate the action of the lateral recti. A movement of this kind would produce useless double vision (diplopia). The eyes can be moved sufficiently to fixate on objects within a circular area 100 degrees in diameter. Rotation to the left and right are approximately equal in extent but vertical upward movements are more limited (40 degrees) than vertical downward movements (60 degrees). Rotation around the anterior-posterior axis in man is rarely more than 10 degrees in extent.

Coordination of the Eye Muscles—Muscular Insufficiency—Strabismus. In order that the eyeballs may move in absolute unison as is necessary for binocular vision, a beautifully balanced or coordinated action of the opposing muscles is necessary. The object of these movements is to bring the point looked at into the fovea of each eye and thus prevent double vision, diplopia (see following paragraphs). This goal is attained when the eyeballs are so moved that the visual axes unite upon the object or point looked at. In viewing an object or in reading we keep readjusting the eyes continually to bring point after point at the junction of the visual axes. When we look before us at a distant object the muscles in each eye should be so adjusted that without any contraction the antagonistic muscles will just balance each other—that is, when the eye muscles are entirely relaxed, except for their reflex tone, the visual axes should be parallel. If this balance does not exist, we have a condition designated as *heterophoria*.

In this condition a constant contraction of one or more muscles is required, even in far vision, to prevent diplopia. When the eye at rest tends to drift toward the temporal side, owing to the fact that the pull of the lateral rectus overbalances that of the medial rectus, the condition is known as *exophoria*. If, for the opposite reason, there is a tendency to drift to the nasal side, the condition is described as *esophoria*. A tendency to drift up (*hyperphoria*) or down (*hypophoria*) is further specified as right or left according to the eye which deviates. A lack of resting balance of this kind may make itself felt also in near work, particularly in reading, sewing, etc., since it will require a constantly greater innervation of the muscle whose antagonist overbalances it. Under some conditions the resulting muscular strain causes much uneasiness or distress. The heterophorias are easily detected and measured by the use of prisms, but they do not show the same constancy as the refractive errors of the eye, owing probably to the fact that they involve the variable factor of muscular tonus.

The defect may be remedied by surgical operations upon the muscles, or by the use of proper prisms with their bases so adjusted as to help the weaker muscle. In exophoria, for example, the greater pull of the lateral rectus rotates the front of the eye outward, while the back of the eye with the fovea is moved inward toward the nose. A prism of the proper strength placed before the eye with its base toward the nose will throw the image of an external object on the fovea, without necessitating a contraction of the medial rectus to bring the fovea back into its normal position. When the lack of balance between the opposing muscles is so great that the visual axes cannot by muscular effort be brought to bear upon the same points, we have the condition of squint, or *strabismus: exotropia, esotropia, hypotropia* or *hypertropia*. Such a condition may result from a deficiency in strength or from actual paralysis of one or more of the muscles, or from an overaction in some of the muscles as contracted with their antagonists.

VISUAL FIELDS AND BINOCULAR VISION

Visual Fields—Perimetry. By the visual field of each eye is meant the entire extent of the external world which can be seen without change of fixation of that eye. From what has been said in Chapter 22 regarding the dioptrics of the eye it is obvious that the visual field is inverted upon the retina, and that, therefore, objects in the upper visual field fall upon the lower half of the retina, and objects in the right half of the visual field fall upon the left half of the retina. Assuming that the retina is sensitive to light out to the ora serrata, it is evident that if the eye were protruded sufficiently from its orbit its projected visual field, when represented upon a flat surface, would have the form of a circle, the center of which would correspond to the fovea centralis. As a matter of fact, the configuration of the face is such as to cut off a considerable part of this field, in any fixed position of the eyes, and to give to the field as it actually exists an irregular outline. The bridge of the nose, the projecting eyebrows, and the cheek bones serve thus to limit the field; and, in addition, the sensitivity of the peripheral portion of the retina may not extend equally far toward the ora serrata in different eyes or in different meridians of the same eye. To obtain the exact outline and extent of the visual field in any given case it is only necessary to keep the eye fixed and then to move a small object inward along the different meridians, keeping it at the same distance from the eye. The limits of vision may be obtained in this way for each meridian and the results combined upon an appropriate chart. An instrument, the perimeter, has been devised to facilitate the process of charting the visual field, which is useful for the peripheral fields. For plotting the central region of the visual field in detail, use is made of a large flat screen marked off in degrees of visual angle which is viewed from a distance of 1 meter (Bjerrum screen). The shape of the visual fields in the normal eye is represented in Figure 269. The field of vision measured from the fixation point or center of the fovea is more extensive on the temporal side (90 degrees) than on the nasal side (60 degrees), and is more extensive downwards (80 degrees) than upwards (50 degrees). The field of vision is broken at 15 degrees to the temporal side by the blind spot, which is an absolute scotoma corresponding to the optic nerve head. Radiating from the blind spot are irregular shaped areas of complete and relative blindness due to interruption of light by the larger retinal vessels. Exact mapping of the size of the optic nerve head and of the blood vessels issuing from it (angioscotometry, Evans) is sometimes of diagnostic value (5). The determination of the visual fields has its main importance in suspected cases of brain lesions, and is a routine diagnostic procedure.

Visual fields for color. The outer zone of the retina has no color sensitivity, at least as ordinarily tested with reflected light at moderate levels of illumination; the colored object gives rise only to an achromatic sensation. In passing toward the fovea the color sensitivity develops gradually, the blue colors being perceived first and the greens last—that is, nearest to the fovea— so that in a zone close to the margin of the retina the normal eye is red-green blind. The zonal sensitivity of the retina to color may be plotted conveniently by means of a perimeter. It will be found to vary somewhat with each individual and in the two eyes of the same individual. The outlines of the different fields usually show many irregularities, and in some cases it will be found that bright green is perceived over a larger area than the red. As a rule, the fields are more extensive upon the nasal than upon the temporal side of the retina. Of the three primary colors, blue usually has the most extensive field and

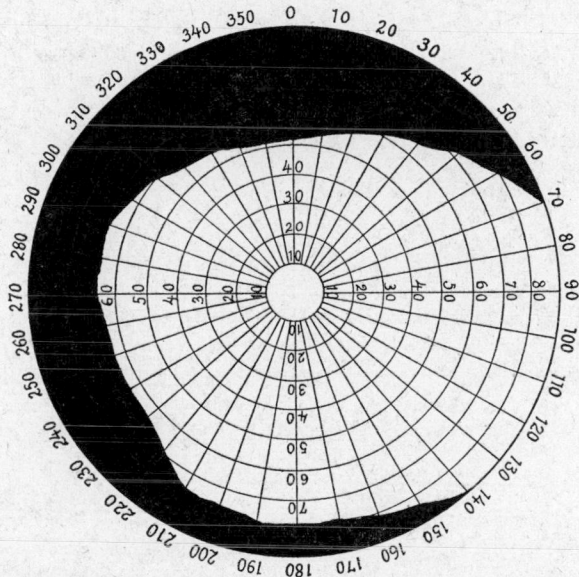

Fig. 269.—Perimetric chart to show the field of vision for the *right* eye when the eye looks straight ahead and does not move. The temporal field is to the right, the nasal to the left of the chart. The numbers along the vertical and the horizontal meridians are degrees of visual angle from the center of the fovea.

green the least. If the green chosen is blue green (490 mμ)—that is, the complementary of the red—it is stated that their fields are coextensive. From this standpoint the retina presents three concentric zones: an extreme peripheral zone devoid of color vision, an intermediate zone in which yellow and blue are perceived, and a central zone sensitive to red and green. Ferree and Rand (6) state that the color blindness of the periphery of the retina is relative and not absolute. With a sufficient intensity of stimulation they find that the fields for red, blue, and yellow are coextensive with that of white. Green has a more restricted field, the periphery of the retina being entirely devoid of this sense.

Binocular Vision. When the two eyes are fixed upon a point straight ahead, each eye has its own visual field that may be charted by means of the perimeter. But the two fields overlap for a considerable portion of their extent, and this overlapping area constitutes the field of binocular vision (see Fig. 270). At both sides of this field is a region which can be seen only by one eye and is known as the monocular crescent or the temporal half-moon. Every point in the binocular field forms an image upon the two retinas. The most interesting fact about the binocular field is that some of the objects contained in it are seen single in spite of the fact that there are two retinal images, while others are seen or may be seen double when one's attention is directed to the fact. Whether any given object is seen single or double depends upon whether its image does or does not fall upon corresponding points in the two retinas.

Corresponding points. By definition corresponding points in the two retinas are those which when simultaneously stimulated by the same luminous object give a single sensation, while noncorresponding points are those which when so stimulated give two visual sensations. It is evident, from our experience,

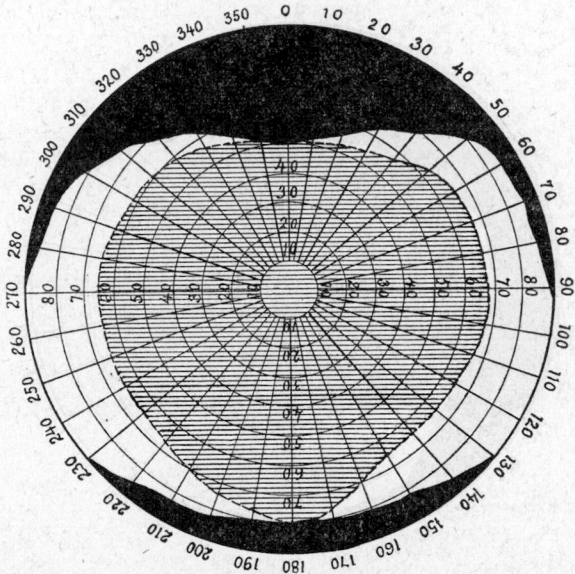

Fig. 270.—Perimeter chart to show the extent of the binocular visual field. The shaded area is the portion of the visual field seen by both eyes; the white areas at both sides are the monocular crescents seen only by the extreme nasal portion of the homonymous retina.

that the foveae form corresponding points or areas. When we look at any object we so move our eyes that the images of the point observed shall fall upon symmetrical parts of the two foveas; the visual axes of the two eyes converge upon and meet at the point looked at. If, while observing an object, one eyeball is gently pressed upon from the side, two images are seen and they diverge farther and farther from each other as the pressure upon the eyeball is increased. Experiment shows, also, that, in a general way, portions of the retina symmetrically placed to the right side of the foveae in the two eyes are corresponding, and the same is true for the two left halves and the two upper and lower halves. The right half of the retina in one eye is noncorresponding to the left half of the other retina, and vice versa; and the same relation is true of the upper and lower halves, respectively. If we imagine one retina to be lifted without turning and laid over the other so that the fovea and vertical and horizontal meridians coincide, then the corresponding points will be superposed throughout those portions of the retina that represent the binocular field.

The doubling of objects that do not fall on corresponding points (physiological diplopia) is most readily demonstrated for objects that lie either closer or farther away than the object looked at. If, for instance, one holds the two forefingers in front of the face, in the median plane, one hand being at about the near point of distinct vision and the other as far away as possible, it will be noticed that when the eyes are fixed on the far finger the near one is seen double, and vice versa. Or if a long stick is held horizontally in front of the eyes the end near the face will be doubled when the eyes are directed to the far end, and vice versa. Moreover, by a simple experiment it may be shown that objects nearer the eyes than the point looked at are doubled heteronymously—that is, the right-hand image belongs to the left eye and the left-hand one to the right eye. This is easily demonstrated by closing the eyes alternately and noting which of the images disappears.

The reason for the cross-projection of the images is made apparent by the construction in Figure 271 I, bearing in mind the essential fact that in projecting our retinal images we

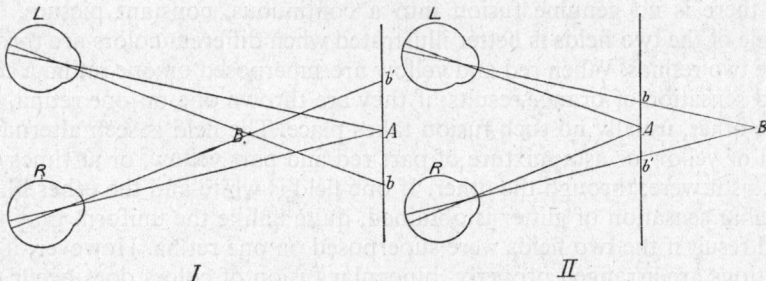

$$I \qquad\qquad II$$

Fig. 271.—Diagrams to show homonymous and heteronymous diplopia: In *I* the eyes are focused on *A;* the images of *B* fall on noncorresponding points—that is, to different sides of the foveae—and are seen double, being projected to the plane of *A*, giving heteronymous diplopia. In *II* the eyes are focused on the nearer point, *A*, and the farther point, *B*, forms images on noncorresponding points and is seen double—homonymous diplopia—the images being projected to the focal plane *A*.

always project to the plane of the object upon which the eyes are focused. In the figure the eyes are converged on *A;* the images of point *B* fall to the opposite sides of the visual axes and are seen double and are projected to the plane of *A*, the image on the right eye being projected to *b'* on the left of *A* and that on the left eye to *b* on the right of *A*. In a similar way it may be shown that objects farther away from the eye than the point looked at are doubled homonymously—that is, the right-hand image belongs to the right eye, and the left-hand one to the left eye. The fact is explained by the construction in Figure 271 II, in which *A* is the point converged upon and *B* the more distant object. In all binocular vision, therefore, the series of objects between the eye and the point looked at are doubled heteronymously, and those extending beyond the point in the same line are doubled homonymously. Normally we take no conscious notice of this fact, our attention being absorbed by the object upon which the eyes are fixed. It is usually assumed that the explanation of corresponding points is to be found in the anatomical arrangement of the central visual pathways. Fibers from the right halves of the two retinas, which are corresponding halves, reach the right side of the brain, while the fibers from the left halves go to the left side of the brain. The basis of the single sensation from two retinal images is to be found probably in the fact that the cerebral terminations through which the final visual act is mediated lie close together or possibly unite.

Suppression of visual images. When an image of an object falls upon noncorresponding points in the two retinas, one of the images is usually ignored or suppressed. This peculiarity is exhibited especially in the case of persons suffering from "squint" (strabismus). In this condition, for one reason or another the visual axes of the two eyes cannot be made to converge upon the same object. The image of the object falls upon noncorresponding points and should give double vision, diplopia. This would undoubtedly be the case if the condition came on suddenly, just as double vision results when we dislocate one eyeball by pressing slightly upon it. But in cases of long standing one of the images, that from the abnormal eye, is usually suppressed. The act of suppression seems to be a case of a stronger stimulus prevailing over a weaker one in consciousness, just as a painful sensation from stimulation of one part of the skin may be suppressed by a stronger pain from some other region.

Binocular rivalry. When the images of two dissimilar objects are thrown one on each retina, the mind is presented, so to speak, simultaneously with two different sensations. Under such circumstances what is known as binocular rivalry ensues. If the image on one eye consists of vertical lines and on the other of horizontal lines, only one field is seen at a time, first one, then the other; or the field is broken, vertical lines in part and horizontal lines in part; there is no genuine fusion into a continuous, constant picture. The struggle of the two fields is better illustrated when different colors are thrown on the two retinas. When red and yellow are superposed on one retina a compound sensation of orange results; if they are thrown one on one retina, one on the other, usually no such fusion takes place. The field is seen alternately as red or yellow or as a mixture of part red and part yellow, or at times one color, as it were, through the other. If one field is white and the other black, a peculiar sensation of glitter is obtained, quite unlike the uniform gray that would result if the two fields were superposed on one retina. However, if the conditions are arranged properly, binocular fusion of colors does occur (see Chap. 23).

*Judgments of solidity and depth.** Vision gives us knowledge not only of the surface area of objects, but also of their depth or solidity—that is, from our visual sensations we obtain conceptions of the three dimensions of space. The visual sensations upon which this conception is built are of several different kinds, partly monocular—that is, such as are perceived by one eye alone— partly binocular. If we close one eye and look at a bit of landscape or a solid object we are conscious of the perspective, of the right relations of foreground and background, and those individuals who have the misfortune to lose one eye are still capable, under most circumstances, of correct visual judgments concerning three-dimensional space. Nevertheless, it is true that with binocular vision the perception of depth and solidity are far more perfect. This difference is shown especially in the combination of stereoscopic pictures, and in ordinary vision when the light is dim, as in twilight, or in exact judgments of perspective in the case of objects close at hand. If, for example, we close one eye and attempt to thread a needle, light a pipe, or make any similar coordinated movement that depends upon an exact judgment of the distance of the object away from us, it will be found that the resulting movement is far less perfectly performed than when two eyes are used.

* Depth perception is measured by the Howard-Dolman apparatus. A short, upright rod is mounted 20 feet from the observer on a wire passing around a pulley. The two ends of the wire are manipulated by the observer until this rod and a stationary rod appear to be equidistant. The error is then measured and the average of repeated tests is made.

CENTRAL VISUAL PATHWAYS

Retina, Optic Nerve and Chiasm (10). The fibers composing the optic nerve originate in the ganglion cells of the inner layer of the retina, converge to form the optic nerve, and pierce the chorioid and scleral coats of the eyeball. Morphologically the point of convergence forms the optic nerve head, disc, or papilla; physiologically it produces a *blind spot* in the visual field because only nerve fibers are present at that point. The nerve head lies 15 degrees to the nasal side of the fovea centralis; because the lens reverses spatial relationships the blind spot is 15 degrees to the temporal side in the visual field. Fibers from the macula lutea are numerous and form a distinct bundle running horizontally to the nerve head (Fig. 272), the *maculopapillary bundle*.

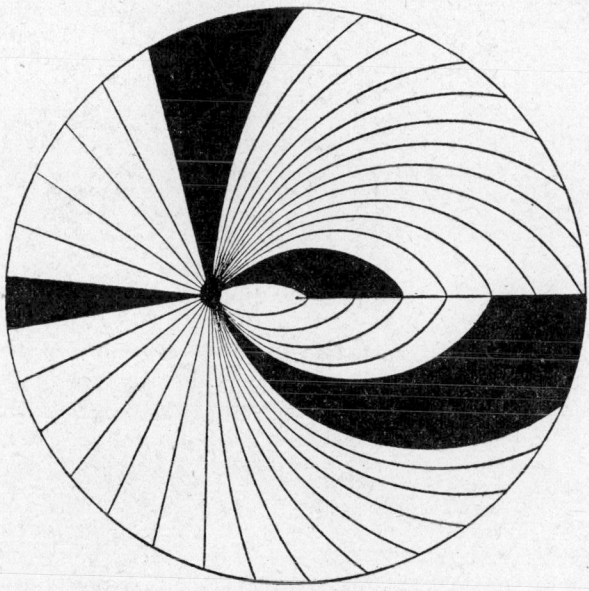

Fig. 272.—Highly schematic diagram of the arrangement of fibers coursing across the retina of the left eye to form the optic nerve. The arching and radiating lines are the path taken by nerve fibers converging to the optic nerve head. The black areas represent four types of defect which result from interruption of nerve bundles at the optic nerve head. Note the horizontal raphe running from the macula to the temporal margin of the retina. (From Traquair, *Clinical perimetry*, 1927.)

Fibers to the nasal side of the nerve head pursue a direct course like the spokes of a wheel. No fibers pass through the fovea. Therefore, to reach the nerve head, fibers from the temporal portion of the retina arch above or loop below the fovea centralis, forming a geometrically sharp "water-shed" along a horizontal line drawn through the fovea to the temporal margin of the retina. In this fashion the temporal retinal fibers (and some of the fibers of the nasal half) become separated into an upper and a lower quadrant by the interposition of the macular fibers,* an arrangement continued throughout the central visual pathways.

* In discussing the central visual pathways, the terms "macula" and "macular" do not always mean the region of the macula lutea as defined anatomically in the previous chapter. As used in clinical literature, it is almost a synonym for "central," and it denotes any central zone less than about 10 degrees of visual angle.

A vertical line drawn through the center of the macula divides the retina into two hemimaculas and hemiretinas, the fibers of which pursue different pathways to the brain. Fibers from the temporal hemiretina of the left eye continue through the *optic chiasm* and without crossing pass in the optic tract to the *lateral geniculate body* of the left side; those from the temporal side of

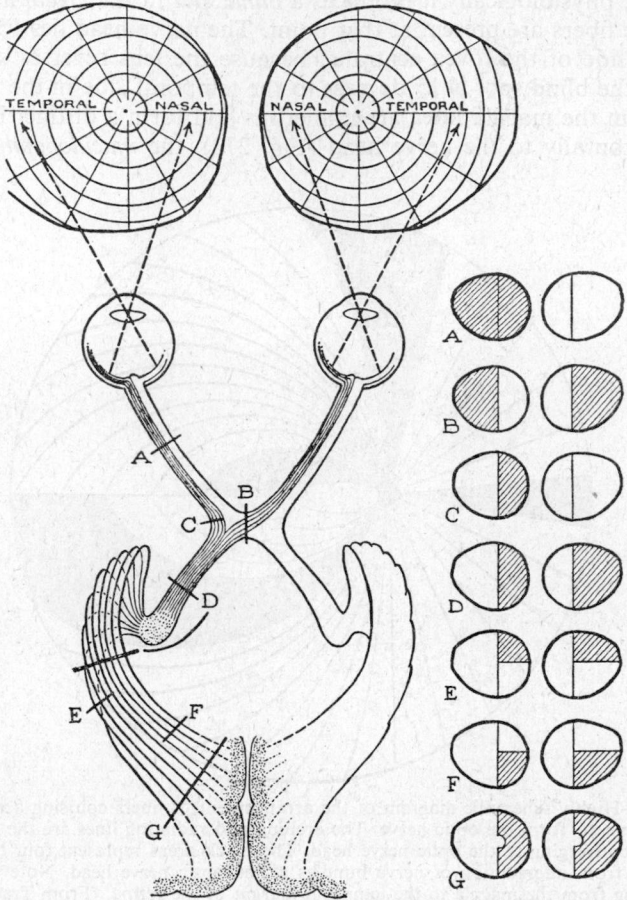

Fig. 273.—Diagram of the central visual pathways passing to the left hemisphere. The shaded areas in the inserts indicate the visual field defects resulting from lesions at the point indicated by the corresponding letter on the left-hand figure. For convenience, the visual fields for the two eyes are shown separated, but actually they superimpose so that the vertical meridians coincide: *A*, complete blindness of left eye; *B*, bitemporal hemianopsia; *C*, unilateral nasal hemianopsia; *D*, right homonymous hemianopsia—interruption of either the optic tract or the geniculocalcarine projection; *E* and *F*, right upper and lower quadrant hemianopsias; *G*, right homonymous hemianopsia from a large lesion of occipital lobe. (From Homans, *A text-book of surgery,* 5th ed., 1941.)

the right eye enter the right optic tract. Fibers from the nasal half of each retina decussate in the optic chiasm and enter the optic tract of the opposite cerebral hemisphere where they join the uncrossed fibers from the temporal half of the other eye to end in the contralateral geniculate body. The effect of this regrouping of fibers is that lesions of the optic chiasm, or central to it, cause visual defects different from those induced by lesions of the retina or optic nerve. The effects upon visual fields of lesions at various points in the visual system are shown in Figure 273. From complete interruption of only one optic nerve there is only a slight, lateral narrowing of the binocular visual field, on the same side as the lesion. This is due to loss of vision in the temporal half-moon, the extreme lateral portion of the visual field which is seen only by the extreme nasal portion of the ipsilateral retina. However, interruption of the visual pathway central to the chiasm on one side blocks impulses from *both eyes* conveying impressions from one half the binocular visual field. The result of such a lesion in, for example, the right hemisphere, is a visual field defect known as *left lateral homonymous hemianopsia*—half blindness because the blindness extends over a geometrical half of the visual field, homonymous because the corresponding halves of the two retinas are blinded, lateral because nothing to one side is seen, and left because the disturbance is named for the side of the visual field defect, not for the side of the "retinal blindness." The lesion is always on the side opposite the visual field defect. Occurring less commonly, an expanding tumor of the pituitary body, the stalk of which is located in the bay formed by the two optic tracts, may split the decussating fibers from the nasal half of each retina, producing a *bitemporal hemianopsia;* then only the nasal half of each visual field is seen. Similarly, a pathological expansion of both internal carotid arteries lying in the angle formed by the optic nerve and tract of each side may interrupt the fibers from the two temporal hemiretinas, yielding a *binasal hemianopsia.* These are *heteronymous* because noncorresponding retinal fields of the two eyes are affected.

Between the optic chiasm and the lateral geniculate bodies a *functional* regrouping of fibers occurs. Fibers or collaterals of the optic tract fibers representing every portion of the hemiretinas pass to the pretectal region lying just rostral to the superior colliculus and constitute the afferent limb of the pupillary reflexes to light. Until the observations of Ranson and Magoun (15, 22), these fibers were believed to end in the superior colliculus; it is now known that they end in the pretectal region. Hemianopsia, with retention of the light reflex, therefore characterizes lesions central to this regrouping. The "visual fibers" continue to the lateral geniculate body of the diencephalon where they enter synaptic relations with the fourth order neurons which continue on to the occipital lobe.

Lateral Geniculate Bodies and Striate Cortex. This nucleus is made up of six layers of cells separated by layers of fibers giving the structure its conspicuous laminated appearance. Alternate layers of fibers are contributed by the hemiretinas of the two eyes (Minkowski). Crossed fibers end in laminae 1, 4 and 6, and uncrossed fibers end in the intervening layers of cells; impulses from corresponding retinal points presumably first converge in the occipital cortex. Glees and Le Gros Clark (8) have further shown that in the monkey each optic nerve fiber breaks up into a spray of five or six branches. In degenerating preparations each branch ends by means of a *single* degenerating bouton related to the cell body (never the dendrites) of a neuron of the lateral geniculate body. This is a remarkable instance of *divergence*, and the only known instance in which a cell is excited by single synapse stimulation; the absence of convergence is probably the reason why transneuronal degeneration is so striking in the lateral geniculate body.

By making lesions of the retina and tracing the resulting Marchi degeneration of optic tract fibers into the geniculate bodies (Brouwer and Zeeman, 2), or, better, by studying the transneuronal degeneration of the cells of the geniculate body resulting from lesions of the retina (Le Gros Clark and Penman, 3), the projection of the retina upon the lateral geniculate body has been established. Note in Figure 274 that the macular sector is interposed between sectors containing fibers from the upper and lower extramacular quadrants and that the lower retinal quadrant is lateral. Note also that, relative to its small retinal area, a disproportionate amount of the nucleus is devoted to representation of the macula. The oral-caudal relationship is the same as in the retina, i.e., the macular region is posterior to the periphery in both.

Fourth order neurons constituting the geniculostriate bundle, especially the inferior part, swing forward and around the ventricle of the temporal

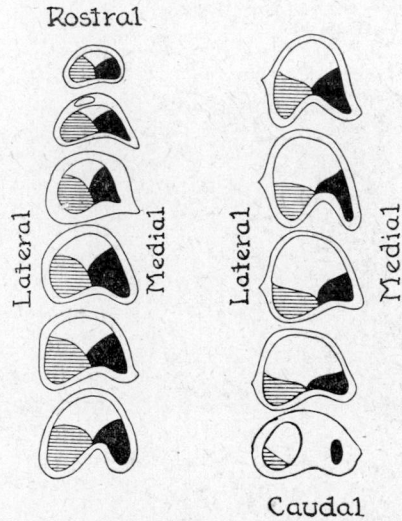

Fig. 274.—Sections through the left lateral geniculate body of the monkey. The terminations of fibers from the retina are indicated as follows: cross hatching, lower peripheral quadrant; white, macula, upper and lower quadrants; black, upper peripheral quadrant. According to the work of Le Gros Clark and Penman, this diagram shows too much macula at the rostral end and too much peripheral representation at the caudal end. (After Brouwer and Zeeman, *Brain*, 1926, *49*:1–35.)

lobe before running posteriorly to the striate area of the occipital lobe (Fig. 279). Meyer's loop or detour so formed accounts for the occurrence of of visual field defects from lesions well forward in the temporal lobe (Cushing). Within the geniculostriate bundle, the macular fibers continue to separate those from the upper and lower quadrants. Those originating in the mesial sector of the geniculate body and representing the upper quadrant of the retina pass above the tip of the posterior horn and end in the superior lip of the calcarine fissure; those from the lateral sector (lower retinal quadrant) pass below the horn and end on the lower lip of the calcarine fissure. The macular fibers swing around the end of the ventricle and can be traced mainly to the posterior part of the calcarine fissure. The interposition of macular fibers between peripheral ones explains how a quadrant visual field defect having a sharp horizontal border can occur (Fig. 279). An irregular shaped pathological process can produce a quadrant defect with a geometrically sharp inferior boundary only if the fibers from the two quadrants are to some degree topographically separated, as they are by intervening macular fibers.

The cortical visual area in man is almost completely concealed from view in a longitudinal infolding on the mesial and cerebellar surfaces of the occipital lobe, the *calcarine* fissure. It begins near the splenium of the corpus callosum, extends nearly to the occipital pole forming a flat, inverted V the rostral branch of which indents the posterior horn of the lateral ventricle. In the monkey the visual area extends over the free surface of the occipital lobe but is focused on the calcarine fissure. Cytoarchitecturally the region is characterized by a conspicuous line of Gennari, visible to the naked eye without staining, and so is often called the *striate area*. The cellular structure (Fig. 275) is the highly granular type associated elsewhere in the cerebral cortex with

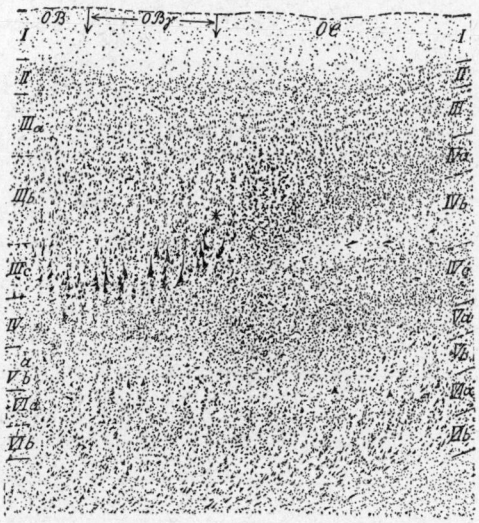

Fig. 275.—Cytoarchitecture of the transition zone (asterisk) between area 17 (right) and area 18 (left) of the upper lip of the calcarine fissure. On the right (striate area) note that the inner and outer layers of pyramidal cells are virtually absent. The almost clear area, *IVb*, corresponds to the line of Gennari. Observe the band of large pyramidal cells in layer *IIIc* of area 18. Cell stain and 44× magnification. (From von Economo, *Zellaufbau der Grosshirnrinde des Menschen*, 1927.)

sensory function. The outer and inner granular layers are made up of small granular cells, densely packed, and the two layers almost merge, the intervening layer of pyramidal cells being thin and the cells small. The striate area, which is area 17 in Brodmann's numeration, is surrounded by a concentric band, area 18 or the *parastriate* cortex, and between them is an exceedingly abrupt transition in cytoarchitecture. A second more anterior concentric zone is the *peristriate* area, Brodmann's area 19. The optic radiations terminate in area 17; none passes to areas 18 and 19.

Topographical Organization of the Visual Area. Knowledge of the manner in which the fibers of the optic radiations terminate in the cerebral cortex is gained in three main ways: (i) correlation of visual field defects with the locus of restricted lesions of the occipital lobe; (ii) correlation of the site of retrograde degeneration in the lateral geniculate bodies from restricted striate lesions with the site of transneuronal degeneration or tracing Marchi degeneration in the same nuclei from experimental lesions of the retina (monkey); and (iii) recording action potentials from the cortical fields in response to systematic stimulation of the various retinal regions (monkey).

As shown in Figure 276, the representation of the upper quadrant of the *retina* is on the upper lip of the calcarine fissure; that of the lower retinal quadrant is on the lower lip of the calcarine fissure, so that, for example, lesions of the lower lip produce a visual field defect in the upper quadrant of the field of vision. Much evidence (12, 20) indicates that the anterior-posterior dimension of the striate area corresponds to the periphery-macula (meridianal) dimension of the retina. The rule is that the macula is posterior in the eye, and its representation is posterior in the lateral geniculate body and

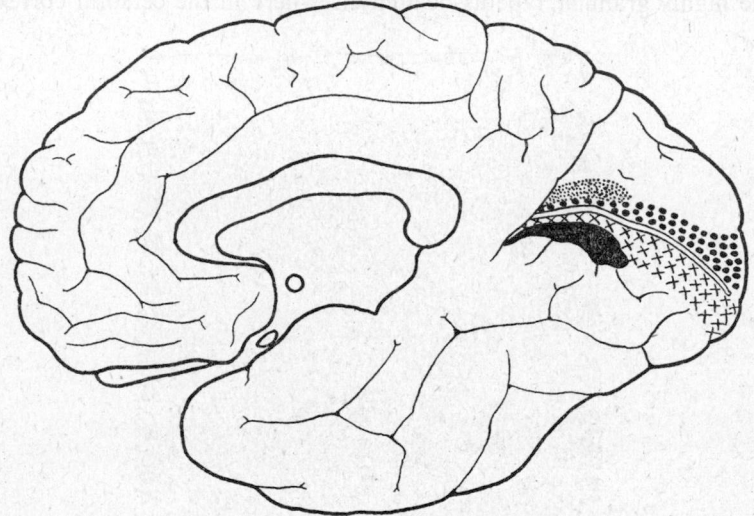

Fig. 276.—Projection of the retina upon the calcarine fissure of man. Fine dots and black are respectively the representation of the upper and lower *peripheral* quadrants of the retina; heavy dots and crosses are respectively the representation of the upper and lower quadrants of the *macula*. The rostral extension of the macular representation is hypothetical. (Modified from Brouwer, *Res. Publ. Ass. nerv. ment. Dis.*, 1934, *13*:529–534.)

posterior in the occipital lobe. The periphery is most anterior at these three levels. As in the geniculate body, a very large area of the cortex is devoted to the macula relative to the small area devoted to the periphery.

How this arrangement comes about may be easily visualized as follows. Imagine the left hemiretinas of the two eyes superposed with their foveae coinciding. They are then folded forward from top to bottom along the horizontal meridian and inserted into the calcarine fissure with the fold coming at the bottom of the fissure and the point (fovea) posterior. If the meridians are imagined as closing like the blades of a Japanese fan, it becomes clear that the periphery will be located anteriorly. But this fails to suggest that a larger cortical area is devoted to the fovea than to the periphery. The ribs at the handle end of the fan must be made farther apart, to have the relations that exist in the cortex. Note that the free edges of the infolded retinas are the two halves of the vertical meridian, which are vis à vis to the vertical meridian of the right hemiretinas located in the opposite hemisphere. This explains why midline lesions affecting both occipital lobes may produce a confluent midline scotoma of the right and left visual field.

If this arrangement is correct, it means that at the occipital lobe the macular fibers for the first time cease to lie interposed between the upper and lower peripheral quadrant fibers. Such a rearrangement is to some degree unlikely. It is possible that the macular fibers do not all pass to the posterior end of the calcarine fissure, but form a wedge, the point of which is directed forward, separating the upper and lower quadrant, as shown in Figure 276. Some evidence demands that a portion of the macular fibers extend even further forward than the peripheral fibers.

Functional significance of topographical organization. What is the significance of the topographical organization of the occipital lobe? It is generally believed that a high degree of topographical organization is the neural basis for detail vision, for the vision of forms and patterns and for visual localization. To what degree is it possible to think of the pattern of light being translated into a pattern of impulses on the occipital cortex, with each unit holding its topographical position relative to other units? That this is the case is suggested by the fact that minute injuries of the cortex produce contiguous areas of blindness of the visual field. That the retina is projected point-to-point on the retina is confirmed anatomically within the limits of our techniques. Thus Polyak (20) finds that a lesion of the occipital cortex 1 sq. mm. in extent causes a degeneration confined to a single band of cells in the geniculate body only 4 to 5 cells in width. Moreover, the extent of the striate cortex devoted to the fovea justifies the belief that the fineness of grain of the occipital cortex is the basis for the high degree of visual acuity exhibited by the fovea.

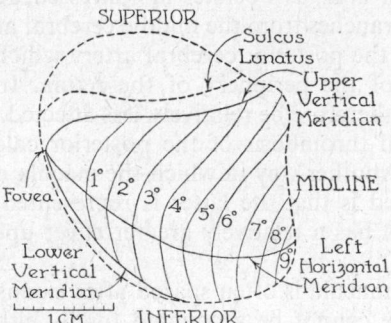

Fig. 277.—Map showing the projection of the retina upon the occipital lobe of the monkey as charted by electrical methods. The left occipital lobe is shown as viewed from behind so that foreshortening decreases the apparent size of the central representation. (Redrawn from Talbot and Marshall, *Amer. J. Ophthal.*, 1941, 24:1255–1264.)

For the monkey this has been demonstrated in a quantitative fashion by Talbot and Marshall (19, 26), who recorded the points of maximal electrical activity in the striate area while systematically exploring the retina with a point of light. The foveal representation of the monkey is situated at the anterior border of the striate area on the lateral surface of the occipital lobe, which places it about 5 mm. below the tip of the simian or lunate sulcus (external parieto-occipital sulcus), not far from the ear (Fig. 277). This region becomes posterior when the striate area largely disappears from the free surface of the cortex in chimpanzee and man as a result of expansion of the parietal association area. Even in the monkey only 8 degrees of the periphery (little more than the macular area) is on the wide expanse of the free surface of the occipital cortex. The first 8 degrees are arranged in concentric bands medial to the fovea. The portion of the striate area devoted to the hemifovea is an area 6 mm. in radius. Retinal distance and cortical distance compare as follows: within the foveal representation 1 mm. of cortex is devoted to only 2 minutes of visual angle, whereas at 5 degrees from the fovea, 18 minutes of visual angle are crowded into 1 mm. of cortex. Much greater ratios than 9:1 must obtain for the extreme peripheral regions of the retina. Another outcome of these studies is a quantitative estimate of the degree to which the retina is magnified upon the occipital cortex.

Talbot and Marshall calculate that a circular area on the fovea of the retina 1 minute in diameter (5 μ, or the width of 2 foveal cones) is represented by a cortical region 100 times as wide (0.5 mm.) with an area 10,000 times as great. With nerve cells spaced at 20 μ, the ratio between cone and cortical cell is 1:100. In the physical transmission of light to the retina, the energy tends to spread over a wide region, and in neural transmission there is a further tendency for lateral spread of excitation, yet the cortical grain is finer than retinal grain. Since, as Figures 177 and 259 show, acuity is a question of discrimination of intensity differences between peaks and valleys of excitation, discriminations much less than cone width are theoretically possible because of the fine cortical grain. An offset in a line of only 2.5 seconds of visual angle (Vernier acuity or "aligning power") is discriminable. Perhaps the fine cortical mosaic is used for such discriminations, or in registering the slight differences in two images as seen by two eyes which form the basis for stereoscopic vision. On the other hand, the multiplicity of units may be significant for intensity discrimination, numbers of active units being one of the ways of reflecting intensity.

Macular Sparing (21). A hemianopsia which includes macular vision is relatively infrequent from lesions of the occipital lobe. More often the vertical or median border of the blind area is not a straight line splitting the macula but is indented so that the macula is "spared." Usually 3 to 5 degrees of central vision in the otherwise blind hemiretinas are retained. The explanation of this fact is a neurological puzzle which has successfully defied solution for decades, though few neurologists have refrained from attacking it.

The tendency of the macula to escape is probably due to several different factors. The macular area, as Foerster first stressed, receives a blood supply from anastomotic branches from the middle cerebral artery in addition to the calcarine branch of the posterior cerebral artery which is the sole supply for the representation of the periphery of the retina. In vascular disease the macular fibers may therefore be relatively less affected. In a recently reported case (14) of bilateral thrombosis of the posterior calcarine artery, macular vision was spared. Another way in which the macula escapes though peripheral vision is affected is that the latter is represented by so few fibers that pressure or ischemia has a relatively greater effect upon the peripheral field of vision.

The fact that the macula is often spared after extensive surgical resections of the occipital lobe cannot be accounted for by either of the two factors mentioned above. Two explanations have been advanced: (i) that the macular region is bilaterally represented in the cerebral cortex, and (ii) that the macula is extensively localized throughout the striate area so that only rarely is the whole macular representation destroyed. A bilateral representation would result if some fibers from the nasal half of each macula pass to the ipsilateral occipital cortex, i.e., fail to decussate in the optic chiasm, and if some fibers from the temporal half of the macula cross instead of entering the optic tract of the same side. No evidence exists for this at an anatomical level. That bilateral representation is accomplished at a retinal or a chiasmal level is obviously impossible; otherwise, lesions of the optic tract, optic radiations and occipital lobe could never produce a macular splitting hemianopsia as they indisputably do. If bilateral representation is accomplished, central to the optic chiasm, a crossing of temporal fibers and a *recrossing of nasal fibers* of the macula must occur (Fig. 278). The suggestion has been made that fibers or collaterals leave the optic radiation near the posterior horn of the lateral ventricles and cross through the splenium of the corpus callosum to the striate area of the opposite hemisphere (Fig. 278). Anatomical descriptions of such a path have not been confirmed, and Polyak has conducted a critical experiment which disproves its existence. Complete occipital lobectomy in the monkey caused no retrograde degeneration in the opposite geniculate body, and no normal cells remained in the ipsilateral geniculate body that might send fibers to the contralateral undamaged lobe. Finally, Fox and German (7) have shown (Fig. 279) that surgical lesions in the optic radiations well anterior to the occipital lobe spare the macula when only a small

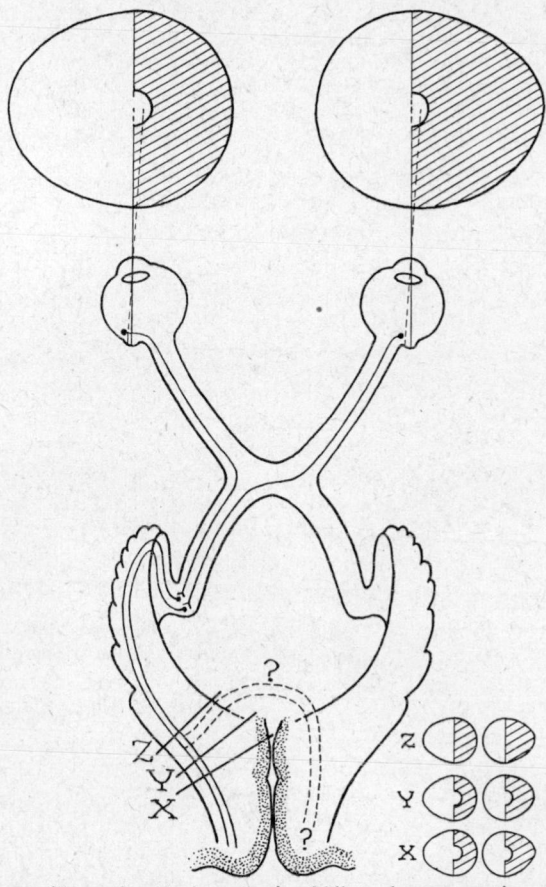

Fig. 278.—Diagram illustrating the hypothesis of bilateral representation of the macula. The solid line represents the same neurons that are shown in Figure 273, but coming from the macula rather than the periphery. The dotted line represents a *hypothetical* crossing of fibers from the temporal side of the ipsilateral hemimacula and a recrossing of fibers from the nasal half of the macula of the contralateral retina. These fibers are presumed to escape section Y, producing a macular sparing hemianopsia, but are interrupted by section Z, producing a macular splitting hemianopsia. The existence (and the termination) of collaterals, indicated by the dotted line, is hypothetical. By another hypothesis, macular sparing is due to a section such as X, which leaves the anterior extent of the striate area intact.

amount of the inferior portion of the radiation escapes. This portion is rostral to the point of hypothetical decussation shown in Figure 278.

By recording action potentials from the macular representation, electrical activity is detectable in the left occipital lobe (7) only when light is flashed upon the left hemimaculae of the two eyes. Electrical responses of both striate areas suggestive of bilateral representation were never observed (26).

The remaining possibility is that the macular region is more extensively localized than is suggested in the previous section. That the representation of the macula is situated at the polar end of the calcarine fissure is firmly grounded anatomically, and is confirmed by the mapping of the visual cor-

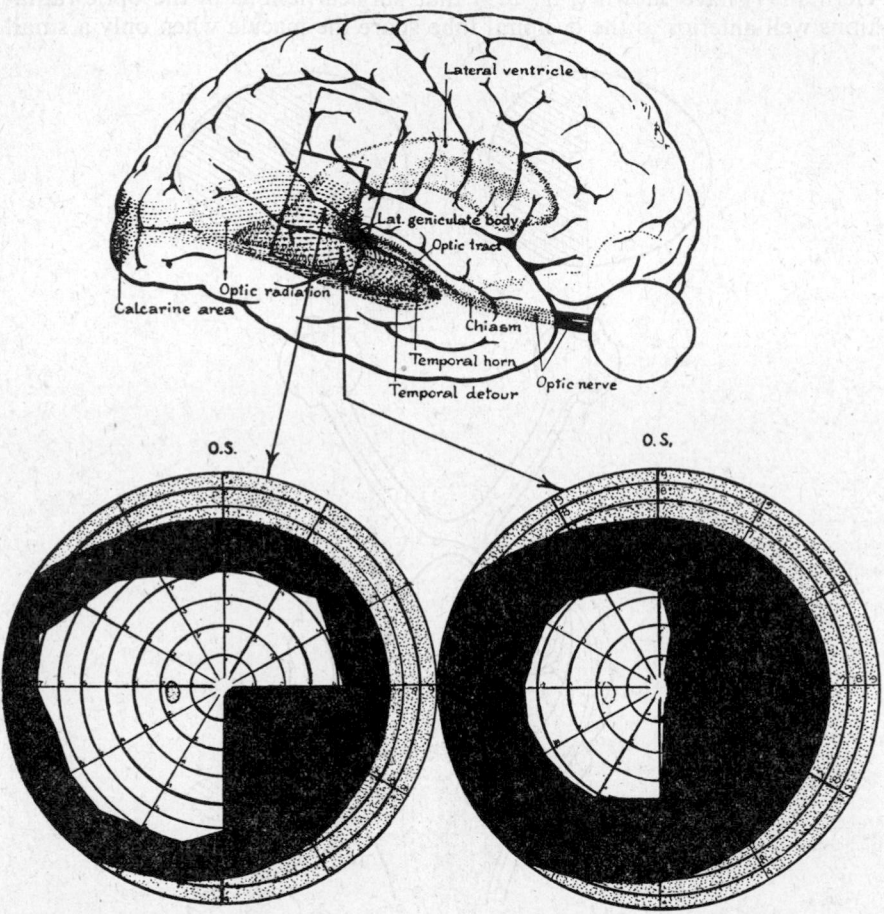

Fig. 279.—Effects upon vision of two successive surgical resections involving increasing amounts of the visual radiations. In the upper diagram the position of the cerebral ventricles and of the optic radiations are represented by stippling and fine dashes. The small rectangle shows the limits of the first and the large rectangle the limits of the second resection. The perimetric charts are both for the left eye, those for the right eye being closely similar. Each circle represents 10 degrees of visual angle. Observe that the first resection produced a quadrantic, macular sparing field defect (lower left diagram). Extension of the resection to include all but the inferior fascicles of the radiation extended the field defect to the upper quadrant apart from a few degrees along the vertical meridian, but the macula was still spared. Note also the geometrical inferior border of the quadrant defect. (After Fox and German, *Arch. Neurol. Psychiat.*, *Chicago*, 1936, *35*: 808–826.)

tex (26) in monkeys. Yet lobectomies which fall short of destroying the whole extent of the calcarine fissure tend to spare the macula, whereas if the resection is carried out further forward to include the extreme anterior tip of striate area, the macula is usually split. It is almost necessary to suppose that the macular area extends further forward than the representation of peripheral retinal zones and that the foveal representation extends further forward than the extrafoveal region of the macula. The evidence of Fox and German that the macular fibers overlap the peripheral fibers in the radiations is consistent with this point of view. It is not necessary to suppose that macular fibers are intermingled with peripheral ones in cortex or radiations. Such a departure from topographical projection in the most highly organized sensory system of the brain seems unlikely. Every supposed fact of the visual system is in question until the mechanism of macular sparing is elucidated.

The following observations cannot be fitted into either of the above interpretations of macular sparing. Evans and Browder (5), basing their conclusions on especially complete perimetric examination with control of fixation, find that sagittal splitting of the chiasm produces bitemporal hemianopsia with a relative scotoma (visual acuity reduced by half) of the whole visual field for the fovea, as though some fibers had not crossed and hence were not sectioned.

Halstead, Walker and Bucy (9), using elaborate perimetric techniques and controlling fixation by the corneoretinal potential technique of recording eye movements, report a case of macula splitting in which the anterior end of the striate area was intact, and a case of macular sparing in which the whole of the striate area was included in a block resection. The latter is critical. It has been suggested that the spared macular vision represents subcortical visual sensation. This is unlikely, since not even monkeys have subcortical visual ability except under conditions in which only rods are operative, and these are absent from the center of the macular region.

Visual Function of the Striate Area. The role of the cerebral cortex in vision is shown by cortical ablations to increase steadily throughout the phylogenetic series. And as a corollary, the cerebral cortex is necessary for certain types of visual function, whereas other functions can be carried on by subcortical structures. The high degree of visual ability (especially acuity) possessed by birds and fishes is legendary, but is subserved entirely by subcortical mechanisms (the superior colliculus and adjacent regions). Throughout the mammalian series, visual function has become progressively corticalized or encephalized so that in the primates the midbrain centers serve largely reflex functions.

In rats, cats and dogs, brightness discrimination can be tested by establishing the habit of choosing between two differently illuminated alleys or stimulus objects in order to receive food. Discrimination of light from dark is possible in all three animals after complete removal of the striate areas of the cerebral cortex. The ability to discriminate may be temporarily lost, but it seems to be merely the discriminatory habit which is upset because the discrimination is readily relearned. The fineness of discrimination is decreased but not greatly so. In monkeys the disturbance is more severe and in man vision for light and dark is apparently completely lost.

When discrimination of two moderately bright lights is tested, quite different results are obtained. In fact, it now seems that the duality of the visual system so apparent at the retinal level is in evidence at the cortical level as well. Whereas rod functions (discrimination of light from dark), as mentioned above, continues after occipital lobectomy, cone vision is dependent upon the cerebral cortex. The original demonstration by Marquis (17) of discriminatory ability after bilateral occipital lobectomy in the dog involved discrimination of a dimly lighted alley from an unlighted alley. K. U. Smith (25) confirmed this for cats, and added the observation that cats, after occipital lobectomy, lose, and are unable to regain, the ability to discriminate between two moderately bright lights. That monkeys can learn to discriminate when the conditions call forth rod vision was shown by Klüver (13), who, however, believes the discrimination is based on total illumination rather than brightness. A conditioned response in monkeys to a change from darkness to light, a rod function, persists after occipital lobectomy (18). The clinching evidence is based on the fact that the monkey exhibits rod and cone visibility curves not unlike those shown in Figure 247 for man. After removal of the occipital lobes, the visibility curve even at high illumination is that characteristic of rods (16). Color discriminations are not possible after destruction of the striate area. The conclusion, therefore, is that rod vision is not corticalized to the same extent as cone vision, and even in the monkey rod vision can be carried out at subcortical levels of the brain. In man both rod and cone vision appear to be subserved by the occipital cortex.

Pattern vision. Perception of two-dimensional forms or patterns is a higher level of visual function than brightness discrimination. Even the rat is rendered incapable of pattern vision by occipital lobectomy, and no amount of retraining restores the ability. Pattern vision demands a topographically organized system of fibers consisting of multiple, discrete units, such as the foveal cones and their central connections provide. Since cone vision depends on the cerebral cortex, little pattern vision can occur after destruction of the cortex. However, under low illuminations a low order of pattern vision, such as might be expected from the rod mechanism, survives occipital lobectomy in the cat. Optokinetic reflexes—pursuit movements of the eye occurring when a striped field is rotated around the animal's head—are elicitable after bilateral destruction of the striate area. Considerable visual acuity, as judged by the fineness of lines which will elicit such pursuit movements, is manifested.

Interconnection of visual areas (1). The visual cortex in the broadest sense includes areas 18 and 19, area 17 being the primary sensory zone and the sole recipient of the optic radiations. Areas 18 and 19 are of considerable size. In man these areas together are three times greater in extent than area 17, whereas in the orang the ratio is less than two to one and in the monkey is still less. Being association areas, they have undergone the same phylogenetic development in the primate series exhibited by the posterior parietal association areas, with which they are closely related. Electrical study of the transmission of "strychnine spikes" to remote areas as a result of local strychninization gives some idea of the interconnections between areas and of their potential associative functions. Strychninization of area 17 leads to activity only in the region of application and in the bordering parastriate area (Brodmann's area 18). In a region corresponding roughly with area 18, strychninization results in widespread electrical activity in all three occipital zones and in the inferior and middle temporal gyrus of the same side, and in area 18 itself of the opposite hemisphere. Only adjacent sectors of 17 are fired, but the whole of area 18 may be activated. This area seems to be the "efferent zone," i.e., it possesses the widest outgoing connections. The most anterior band (area 19) fires only itself, but can originate a slow suppressor wave which travels over the whole cortex. Area 19 is fired by strychninization from many other areas, and appears to integrate the other sensory systems with the visual impulses by way of area 17 which seems to be more purely visual.

The effects of electrical stimulation of areas 17, 18 and 19 in human subjects are described in Chapter 13.

Higher levels of visual sensation in man (11, 24). Visual disturbance occurs as a result of large injuries to the free surface of the occipital lobe and especially to the posterior parts of the parietal lobe, but only the higher levels of visual sensation are affected. Perceptions of light and dark, of color and of pattern, are retained, apart from visual field defects due to interference with the underlying optic radiations. Objects are recognized visually so that the disturbance is not a visual agnosia. Holmes (11), who described the symptoms, characterized the syndrome as *visual disorientation*, and described it as follows. Spatial localization is markedly defective and the patient finds it particularly difficult to coordinate the movements of the hand in relation to an object. The estimation of distance towards and away from the patient presents more difficulty than side to side localization, possibly because the latter is simply a matter of retinal local sign, whereas the former involves many factors. The patient in good faith will reach out for an object five or six feet away. Length and size are inaccurately judged. Asked to divide a line into halves, the patient may make one part several times as long as the other. The fact of movement of an object is appreciated, but to say whether the movement is up or down, or towards or away, presents difficulty.

Occasionally stereoscopic vision is lost, objects appearing flat. Visual inattention is also characteristic. By this is meant that objects, though seen, are not reacted to, as though mechanism for translating sensory impressions into action is damaged. Whether lesions of the posterior part of the brain producing these disturbances of the higher visual processes do so by destroying areas 18 and 19, or by interrupting the long association pathways linking the visual cortex with other regions of the brain, is not yet clear. The functions of the association areas and the intercortical systems are the subject of the next chapter.

REFERENCES

1. VON BONIN, G., GAROL, H. W. and MC-CULLOCH, W. S. The functional organization of the occipital lobe. Pp. 165–192 in: *Visual mechanisms*, H. KLÜVER, ed. Lancaster, Pennsylvania, Jaques Cattell Press, 1942, viii, 322 pp.

2. BROUWER, B. and ZEEMAN, W. P. C. The projection of the retina in the primary optic neuron in monkeys. *Brain*, 1926, *49*:1–35.

3. CLARK, W. E. LE GROS and PENMAN, G. G. The projection of the retina in the lateral geniculate body. *Proc. roy. Soc.*, 1934, *B114*: 291–313.

4. EVANS, J. N. Classic characteristics of defects of the visual field. *Arch. Ophthal., Chicago*, 1939, *22*:410–431.

5. EVANS, J. N. and BROWDER, J. A problem of split macula: study of the visual fields. *Arch. Ophthal., Chicago*, 1944, *31*:43–53.

6. FERREE, C. E. and RAND, G. Chromatic thresholds of sensation from center to periphery of the retina and their bearing upon color theory. *Psychol. Rev.*, 1919, *26*:16–41; 150–163.

7. FOX, J. C., JR. and GERMAN, W. J. Macular vision following cerebral resection. *Arch. Neurol. Psychiat., Chicago*, 1936, *35*: 808–826.

8. GLEES, P. and CLARK, W. E. LE GROS. The termination of optic fibres in the lateral geniculate body of the monkey. *J. Anat., Lond.*, 1941, *75*:295–308.

9. HALSTEAD, W. C., WALKER, A. E. and BUCY, P. C. Sparing and nonsparing of "macular" vision associated with occipital lobectomy in man. *Arch. Ophthal., Chicago*, 1940, *24*:948–966.

10. HINES, M. Recent contributions to localization of vision in the central nervous system. *Arch. Ophthal., Chicago*, 1942, *28*:913–937.

11. HOLMES, G. Disturbances of visual orientation. *Brit. J. Ophthal.*, 1918, *2*:449–468; 506–520.

12. HOLMES, G. and LISTER, W. T. Disturbances of vision from cerebral lesions, with special reference to the cortical representation of the macula. *Brain*, 1916, *39*:34–73.

13. KLÜVER, H. Functional significance of the geniculo-striate system. Pp. 253–299 in: *Visual mechanisms*, H. KLÜVER, ed. Lancaster, Pennsylvania, The Jaques Cattell Press, 1942, viii, 322 pp.

14. MCDONALD, P. R. Bilateral thrombosis of posterior calcarine arteries with sparing of macular vision. *Arch. Ophthal., Chicago*, 1943, *29*:92–97.

15. MAGOUN, H. W. and RANSON, S. W. The central path of the light reflex: a study of the effect of lesions. *Arch. Ophthal., Chicago*, 1935, *13*:791–811. See also: *Ibid.*, pp. 862–874.

16. MALMO, R. B. Effects of removal of the visual cortex on brightness discrimination and spectral brightness distribution in the rhesus monkey. *Psychol. Bull.*, 1940, *37*:497–498.

17. MARQUIS, D. G. Effects of removal of the visual cortex in mammals with observations on the retention of light discrimination in dogs. *Res. Publ. Ass. nerv. ment. Dis.*, 1934, *13*:558–592. See also: *Arch. Neurol. Psychiat.*, *Chicago*, *1935*, *33*:807–812.

18. MARQUIS, D. G. and HILGARD, E. R. Conditioned responses to light in monkeys after removal of the occipital lobes. *Brain*, 1937, *60*:1–12.

19. MARSHALL, W. H. and TALBOT, S. A. Recent evidence for neural mechanisms in vision leading to a general theory of sensory acuity. Pp. 117–164 in: *Visual mechanisms*, H. KLÜVER, ed., Lancaster, Pennsylvania, Jaques Cattell Press, 1942, viii, 322 pp.

20. POLYAK, S. Projection of the retina upon the cerebral cortex, based upon experiments with monkeys. *Res. Publ. Ass. nerv. ment. Dis.*, 1934, *13*:535–557.

21. PUTNAM, T. J. and LIEBMAN, S. Cortical representation of the macula lutea with special reference to the theory of bilateral representation. *Arch. Ophthal.*, *Chicago*, 1942, *28*:415–443.

22. RANSON, S. W. and MAGOUN, H. W. The central path of the pupilloconstrictor reflex in response to light. *Arch. Neurol. Psychiat.*, *Chicago*, 1933, *30*:1193–1202.

23. RIDDOCH, G. Dissociation of visual perceptions due to occipital injuries with especial reference to appreciation of movement. *Brain*, 1917, *40*:15–57.

24. RIDDOCH, G. Visual disorientation in homonymous half-fields. *Brain*, 1935, *58*:376–382.

25. SMITH, K. U. Visual discrimination in the cat: V. The postoperative effects of removal of the striate cortex upon intensity discrimination. *J. genet. Psychol.*, 1937, *51*:329–369.

26. TALBOT, S. A. and MARSHALL, W. H. Physiological studies on neural mechanisms of visual localization and discrimination. *Amer. J. Ophthal.*, 1941, *24*:1255–1264.

ASSOCIATION AREAS AND THE CEREBRAL CORTEX IN GENERAL

Sensory and motor functions are the beginning and the end of cortical activity. Coming between sensation and action are cerebral processes difficult to characterize on a physiological basis but which include such functions as learning, memory, language, symbolic processes, etc. These functions are traditionally ascribed to the "association areas." In extent the primary sensory and motor areas constitute but a small fraction of the cerebral mantle; in the present chapter the functions of the remaining cortical regions are discussed after certain basic cerebral functions pertaining to the cortex as a whole have been considered.

ELECTRICAL ACTIVITY OF CEREBRAL CORTEX

Electroencephalogram (5, 6, 14). It was first reported in 1929 by Hans Berger, a German psychiatrist, that electrodes applied to the human head and led to an oscillograph through suitable amplifiers pick up irregularly rhythmical potentials. The record of these is known as the electroencephalogram, EEG, the Berger rhythm, or simply "brain waves." The voltages are extremely small, usually 50 microvolts or less, and are amplified as much as 10 million times. In practice ink-writing recorders are used, since very long records at a fast rate (3 cm. per sec.) are required; as a result of the mass of the moving parts, frequencies above 100 per sec. are not followed faithfully. The electrodes, usually eight in number, consist of metallic cups or discs, fixed to the scalp by collodion or other means. Monopolar leads (one on ear and one over cortex) or bipolar leads (both over cortex) are employed and they are symmetrically located on both sides of the head in the frontal, parietal, temporal and occipital regions. The apparatus records various artifacts, such as loose leads, muscle potentials, eye blinks and other eye movements, the artifacts from the latter being due to corneoretinal potentials described in Chapter 23.

An example of a "normal" EEG is shown in Figure 280. It is apparent that the record represents the blend of many frequencies; it can, in fact, be subjected to Fourier's analysis. In evaluating such records, frequency, i.e., the duration of the potentials, has proved of more importance than their amplitude. By convention the duration of the electrical potentials is described in terms of frequency per sec., or as "slow" and "fast" waves, and this is done even though a deflection of a given duration is not repeated for a full second. In the early days of electroencephalography, the designation of frequency by Greek letters was introduced. *Alpha* waves, the predominant frequency, are approximately 10 per sec. (8 to 12); *beta* waves are of higher frequency, 14 to 60 per sec., and may be seen superimposed on the slower waves; and *delta* waves are those slower than 5 per sec. This terminology is analogous to that used for radiant energy—light waves, infra-red, etc. But since the number of waves per second must be measured, it is just as simple and more exact to state the frequency or a frequency range, as is done for the visible spectrum. The amplitude of the potentials tends to be inversely proportional to the frequency, with beta waves being smaller than alpha waves. Wave form, i.e., whether the excursions are "spiky," flat-topped, serrated, etc., has significance.

The factors, normal and pathological, which affect the pattern of the EEG are as follows: (i) *Cortical region*. Records from the occipital region contain more activity in the frequencies neighboring on 10 per sec., whereas the frontal and parietal regions tend to show more 15 to 30 per sec. waves. This is not invariable. (ii) *Individual differences*. These are marked and the pattern of the EEG is stable and characteristic of the individual. The records

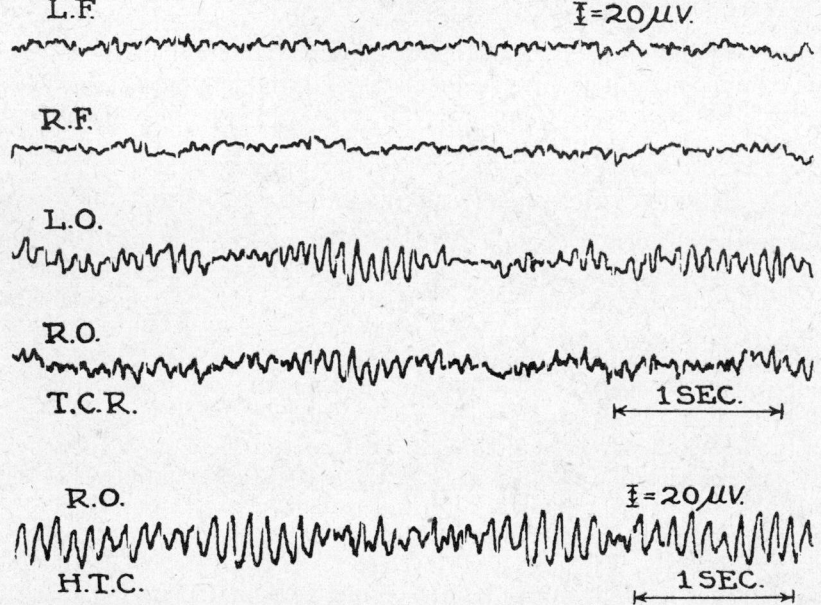

Fig. 280.—A normal electroencephalogram of the frontal and occipital areas as recorded by a Grass ink-writing electroencephalograph. L.F. and R.F. are the record for left and right frontal region and L.O. and R.O. the record for the left and right occipital region. Amplification was equal (see upper right-hand corner of record for calibration) for all leads. Notice the greater amplitude and lower frequency in the occipital record. The lowest record, from the occipital region of a different subject, shows a more pronounced 10 per sec. rhythm (alpha). (Records courtesy of Dr. Margaret Lennox.)

from identical twins are as similar as two records taken at different times from the same person. (iii) *Age*. At birth the electroencephalogram consists of irregular, slow waves, 0.5 to 2 cycles per sec., and fast waves, 20 to 50 per sec. With maturation of the cerebral cortex, the waves become more regular and more rapid. The occipital record shows the adult 10 per sec. rhythm at 9 years, but the adult pattern is not attained in all leads until 14 to 19 years of age. (iv) *Attention or sensory stimulation*. This tends to replace the normal preponderant 10 per sec. rhythm with a faster rhythm of greatly reduced amplitude (Fig. 281). As the sensory stimulus ceases to hold the attention the slower rhythm reasserts itself. Emotional excitement or concentration on mental arithmetic, etc., also abolishes the 10 per sec. rhythm. (v) *Sleep*. A slowing of the frequency characterizes sleep; in deep sleep, waves of 3 per sec. or longer are seen (Fig. 281). In moderately deep sleep, so-called sleep spindles occur and are bursts of 15 per sec. waves. (vi) *Drugs*. Apart from a few hypnotics and narcotics, drugs have surprisingly little effect upon the electrical activity of the cerebral cortex. The barbiturate hypnotics produce changes characteristic of sleep, or they may produce other abnormalities which are in evidence when the subject is awake (M. A. Lennox). Deep anesthesia induces slow waves. Cerebral excitants are without marked effect until the convulsant dosage is approached, when the changes resemble those of epilepsy. (vii) *Metabolic factors*. These are important because of their suspected relationship to epilepsy. Interruption of the blood or oxygen supply of the brain results in a prompt slowing or cessation of the

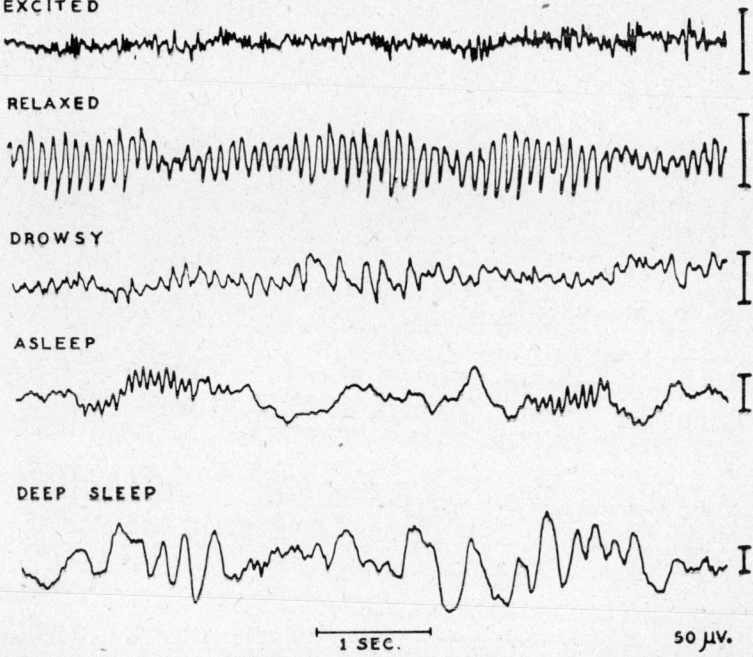

EXCITED

RELAXED

DROWSY

ASLEEP

DEEP SLEEP

1 SEC.   50 μV.

Fig. 281.—Electroencephalographic records during excitement, relaxation and varying degrees of sleep. In the fourth strip the runs of 14 per sec. rhythm, superimposed on slow waves, are termed "sleep spindles." Note that excitement is characterized by a rapid frequency and small amplitude and that varying degrees of sleep are marked by increasing irregularity and by the appearance of "slow waves." (From Jasper in *Epilepsy and cerebral localization*, 1941, by Penfield and Erickson.)

electrical activity. The critical level for slowing is 30 per cent oxygen saturation at the venous end of the cerebral capillaries. Similar slowing occurs when the blood sugar level is lowered to the region of 35 mg. per cent. A CO_2 level of 48 vols. per cent in jugular blood induces slow waves of 2 to 4 per sec., and increase in CO_2 tension of the cerebral cortex produces "fast" activity. In both cases the effect of CO_2 on cerebral blood vessels is to minimize changes in the cerebral CO_2 level and therefore in the electroencephalographic pattern. However, forced overbreathing may reveal a latent abnormality of the EEG, and is standard procedure in the electroencephalographic examination. (viii) *Epilepsy*. According to Gibbs, Gibbs and Lennox (7), the three major types of epilepsy present distinctive electroencephalograms during the attack

(Fig. 282), and also present briefer and less pronounced abnormalities between attacks. The latter are sometimes subclinical or larval seizures. *Grand mal* epileptic attacks are accompanied by an increase in the amount of fast activity often detectable before onset of the overt seizure and obtain through the tonic period. The clonic phase is marked by slow waves synchronous with the clonic jerks, and the postseizure stupor by high voltage slow waves (1 to 3 per sec.). The epileptic attack is therefore manifested by high frequency, followed by slow waves of large amplitude. *Petit mal* attacks consist of frequent momentary lapses of consciousness, often accompanied by blinking and chewing. They are evidenced electroencephalographically by alternating

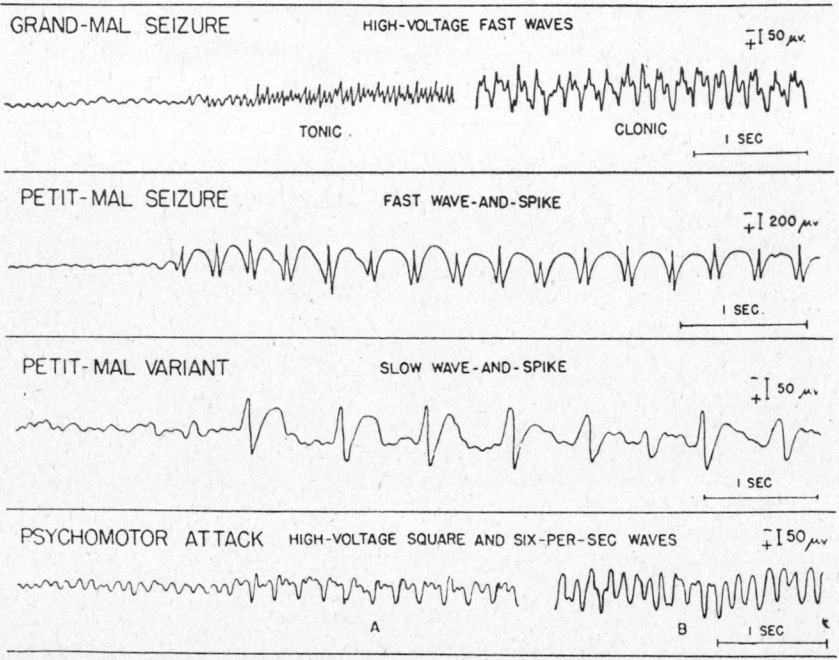

Fig. 282.—Electroencephalographic patterns typical of three major forms of epileptic attack. The amplitude and time calibration is given at the right of each strip. At the left of each strip a small amount of the pre-attack record is shown. In the fourth strip A is the initial phase of the attack in which the patient was dazed and quiet, and B is a later phase in which the patient was talking excitedly and making coarse voluntary movements. (After Gibbs from Davis, *Res. Publ. Ass. nerv. ment. Dis.*, 1939, *19*:50–80.)

single fast and slow waves at the rate of 3 doublets per sec., which have been called wave and spike formations, and other more fanciful names (even perisphere and trylon). The clonic contractions of petit mal, usually confined to the muscles of the eyes or jaws, are synchronous with the spike. In *psychomotor epilepsy* which takes the form of a stereotyped behavior pattern, perhaps an emotional outburst, the attack is distinguished by runs of slow waves which are characteristically flat-topped, or serrated. The occurrence of any of these waves between attacks is diagnostic of epilepsy but not of a particular type of epilepsy. (ix) *Cortical lesions*. Focal damage to the cerebral cortex is difficult to localize clinically when it occurs elsewhere than in sensory and motor areas. Localization by the electroencephalograph depends upon the existence of irregular and abnormal electrical activity (usually slow waves) in the neighborhood of the lesion. Since these abnormalities occur locally, they will not appear equally in all leads but will affect one or two leads more strongly than the others. Asymmetry of the records from corresponding po-

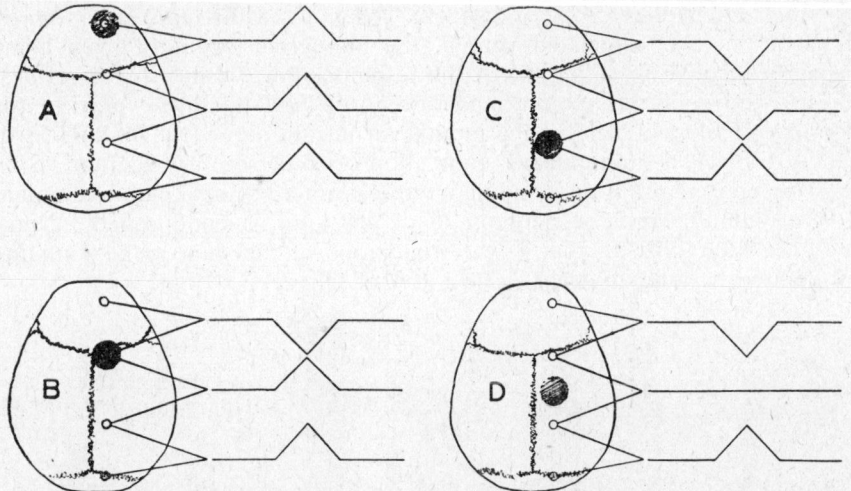

Fig. 283.—Localization of a focal area of damage or focal epileptic discharge by means of phase reversals. The shaded circles represent the area of abnormal electrical activity, the converging lines leading from the head represent bipolar leads, and the horizontal line is the record obtained from each pair of leads. In A, the amplitude would be greater in the first pair of leads than in the third, which is also an aid in localization. (From Jasper in *Epilepsy and cerebral localization*, 1941, by Penfield and Erickson.)

sitions over the two hemispheres is suggestive of focal damage. In localizing regions of abnormal electrical activity use is also made of "phase reversals," the principle of which is shown in Figure 283.

LEARNING

The motor functions which have been the chief concern of physiologists are mostly inborn or unlearned activities. However, since the pioneer work of Pavlov and S. I. Franz, and later of Lashley, *learned* activities have come within the scope of physiological analysis. Learned activities are studied by a variety of means, namely, (i) the conditioned response technique, (ii) the Yerkes-Watson discrimination apparatus or some modification of it (see Chaps. 16 and 17), (iii) mazes, and (iv) apparatuses calling forth learning, problem solving, or awareness of abstract relations. For the sake of brevity only the first of these will be considered in any detail.

Conditioned responses (11, 18, 23). The reflexes of the spinal cord and brain stem are relatively fixed. Light thrown upon the retina always causes constriction of the pupil; a touch applied to the cornea always an eye blink, etc. These and similar reflexes are essentially invariable responses to appropriate stimuli; and the mechanism involved, the reflex arc, is an inherited structural pathway already elaborated for use. Pavlov designates these inborn acts as *unconditioned reflexes*. In contrast to them he describes a class of responses obtained largely through the cortex of the cerebrum which he calls *conditioned reflexes,** because they are elaborated under certain fixed, stimulus conditions. They are established by a process of training or learning, and they are subject to various forms of inhibition. The formation of conditioned responses takes place in general whenever an indifferent stimulus, which in itself causes no response, is repeatedly associated with another stimulus which does evoke a response. After a certain number of repetitions of the two associated stimuli, the indifferent stimulus given alone becomes effective in calling forth the response. Pavlov and his coworkers, in their studies on this subject, made use of the flow of saliva evoked by the presence of food or acid in the mouth, an unconditioned reflex, and associated with this a simultaneous stimulation of some sensory receptor, as by pressure upon the skin or sounding a musical note. By this kind of combination of stimuli, repeated perhaps 30 or 40 times, a conditioned salivary response is established; that is, the stimulation of the skin or the sounding of a note will alone, in itself, cause a flow of saliva.

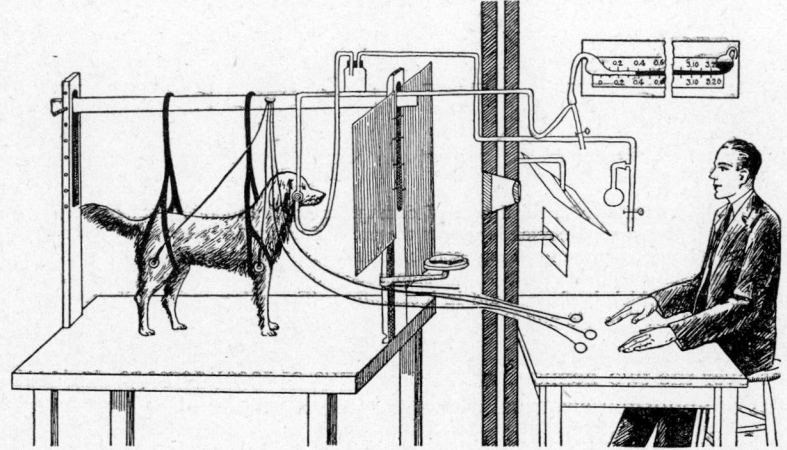

Fig. 284.—The figure represents a dog in the apparatus used by Pavlov for establishing or experimenting upon conditioned responses. The observer is in a separate room with three keys to manipulate. With one of the keys he controls the injection of acid into the mouth, the resulting flow of saliva being indicated by the scale (greatly enlarged) above his head. With the other two keys he can stimulate mechanically the skin of the dog at two points, one on the foreleg and one on the hindleg. (After Pavlov, *Lectures on conditioned reflexes*, London, Martin Lawrence, Ltd., 1927.)

For technical reasons certain other responses are now preferred to salivation, e.g., the eye blink in response to a puff of air, leg flexion to electric shock applied to the paws, or changes in the breathing rhythm to a painful stimulus. Closer scrutiny of conditioned responses has shown them not to be the unconditioned response attached to a new stimulus, as Pavlov supposed. The two responses are often similar but are not identical (see Fig. 285). When the total response in Pavlov's original situation is studied, it is often found to conform to the pattern of a preparatory response—preparation for reacting to the food (unconditioned stimulus), e.g., orientation towards the food box, chop licking, etc.

* It is now recognized that conditioned responses are not reflexes. The minimum latency of more than 100 msec. for conditioned responses of striate musculature is longer than the latencies of reflexes and about equal to those of voluntary activities. Pavlov has so modified the word reflex that it is synonymous with behavior, e.g., "a reflex of slavery,"

Establishment of conditioned reflexes. Repetition of the conditioned and unconditioned stimuli in association is a prime factor in the formation of a conditioned response. The time relations of the two stimuli are another. If the conditioned stimulus *follows* the unconditioned stimulus, the resulting "backward conditioning" requires a great many trials, and the association

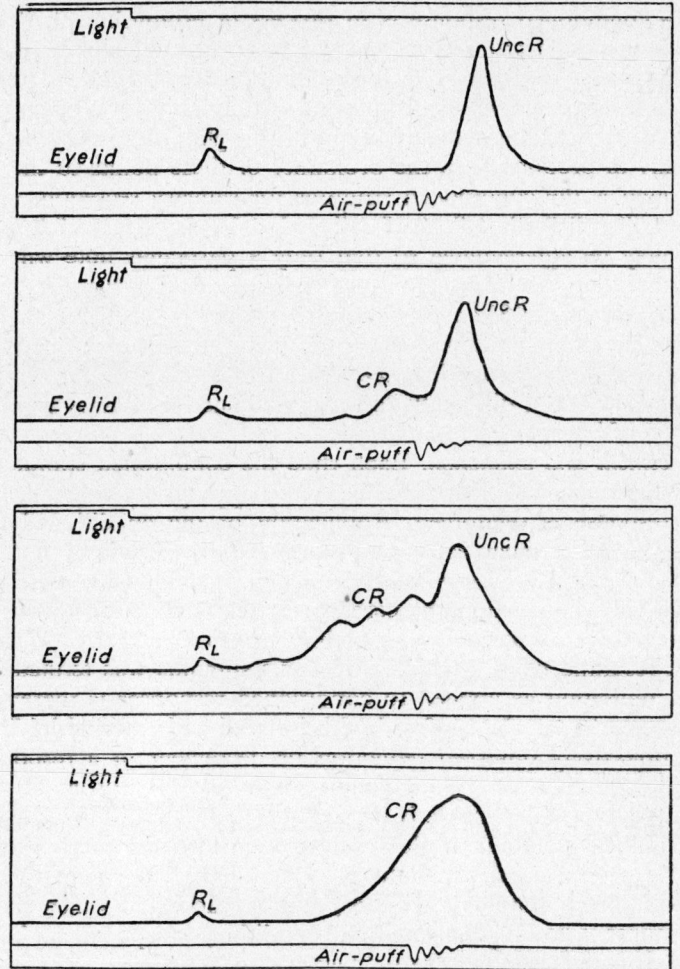

Fig. 285.—Diagram showing the differences between conditioned and unconditioned eye blinks The upper record, before conditioning, shows the reflex blink, RL, to light (the conditioned stimulus) and the unconditioned blink response, UncR, to a puff of air. The three lower records were made during the acquisition of the conditioned response, CR. Observe that the form of the CR curve is quite different from the UncR curve, and that the latency of CR is longer than either RL or UncR. (From Hilgard and Marquis, *Conditioning and learning*, 1940.)

is weak. On the other hand, if the conditioned stimulus *leads* by an interval longer than a few seconds, the acquisition of a conditioned reflex is retarded. A slight lead of the conditioned stimulus over the unconditioned stimulus is more advantageous than simultaneous presentation of the stimuli, a fact which strengthens the interpretation of conditioned responses as an anticipatory response.

Special types of responses—trace responses—are established by prolongation of the interval between the cessation of the conditioned stimulus and the beginning of the unconditioned stimulus. After such training the unconditioned response does not begin at the onset of the conditioned stimulus but is delayed in that it occurs at about the time at which reinforcement ordinarily occurs. Trace responses are difficult to establish.

When a conditioned response is in process of establishment, it tends at first to be nonspecific with respect to the kinds of stimuli evoking it. Related stimuli which have not themselves been reinforced will be adequate to elicit the response. For example, if a response to stimulation of a given point on the skin has been established, stimulation of neighboring points is effective, and roughly in proportion to the proximity of these points to the original one. If sound is the conditioned stimulus for salivary secretion, a note of any pitch will call forth a flow of saliva, but by a process of training the response may be *differentiated* so that only a particular note will elicit it. Pavlov found that a differentiation may be established in the dog between a note of 800 and one of 812 cycles per sec., one being effective and the other ineffective. The differentiation is accomplished by combining one note with the act of feeding and sounding the other from time to time without this association. The act of differentiation was explained by Pavlov as being due to a process of internal inhibition.

Reinforcement and extinction. Each time the conditioned stimulus is followed by the unconditioned stimulus at the appropriate interval, the conditioned response is reinforced. Application of the conditioned stimulus without this reinforcement leads to a progressive suppression of the response, which Pavlov termed *experimental extinction.* This Pavlov ascribed to a process of inhibition within the cerebral cortex. Extinction through unreinforced repetition of the conditioned stimulus was termed *internal inhibition;* extinction resulting from a third, extraneous stimulus was termed *external inhibition.* Inhibition as applied to conditioned responses is therefore used in a dual sense (not to be confused with internal and external inhibition)—first, the objectively observed reduction or decrement in a response, and second, a hypothetical central or synaptic inhibitory process underlying that decrement. Only the first usage is justified since no direct knowledge of the centrally inhibitory state is available. Extinction through internal inhibition is an active process, and cumulative; by continuing to repeat the unreinforced conditioned stimulus after the point is reached at which the conditioned response is no longer elicited, the conditioned response can be further weakened. It is reduced, as it were, "below zero" since more reinforcements are required to re-instate the response than if extinction stops with disappearance of the conditioned response. This suggests that central inhibition is capable of existing in some form other than a decrement in central excitation. Extinction is not a spontaneous decay, for conditioned responses show little signs of weakening even after months have elapsed without reinforcement. However, the process underlying internal inhibition is subject to rapid spontaneous decay. After an interval of several hours an experimentally extinguished response undergoes a spontaneous recovery. Also a third stimulus, to which the animal is unaccustomed, will revive an extinguished conditioned response—*disinhibition.* Hilgard and Marquis (11) suggest the terms *habituation* or *negative adaptation* for the extinction of a conditioned response by repetition of the conditioned stimulus without reinforcement, and point out that this extinction is also a property in lesser degree of unconditioned reflexes. They also note that Pavlov's concept of inhibition as a cortical process adds nothing to the basic facts of extinction, and its relationship to central inhibition as known in spinal reflexes is uncertain.

External inhibition (Pavlov) or *interference* (Hilgard and Marquis) results when a new stimulus is combined with a conditioned stimulus, especially when the new stimulus elicits investigatory behavior, i.e., conflicting behavior. Such inhibition lasts for a matter of only a few minutes, and on repetition the inhibitory effect is weakened or lost. External inhibition resembles reciprocal inhibition, described in Chapter 6.

Neurophysiological basis of conditioning (11). From Pavlov's early observations it was believed that modifiability of behavior as exemplified in the conditioned response was a function unique to the cerebral cortex. The learned connection of responses to new stimuli is a capacity exhibited in some degree by the simplest nervous system, and by the subcortical structures of the complex mammalian nervous system. The ability of decorticate dogs to form new stimulus-response connections has been investigated by using the so-called motor type of conditioned response, i.e., one in which the unconditioned response is a flexion of the forelimb in response to electric shock applied to the paw, and the leg withdrawal to the conditioned stimulus enables the animal to escape the painful stimulation. The response was learned as quickly in a nearly completely decorticate dog as in a normal dog, but never attained the same discreteness. The first sign of acquisition of a conditioned limb flexion in a normal dog is the occurrence of generalized escape movements which later narrow down to a discrete limb flexion. The decorticate dog never progresses to this second stage, the conditioned response continuing to be diffuse escape movements despite protracted conditioning (3).

Consistent is the result of extirpating the sensory areas of the cerebral cortex. In animals high in the evolutionary scale (monkeys) conditioned responses to light may be retained without retraining after destruction of the cortical representation of vision, which is a highly encephalized function. As pointed out previously, certain conditioned responses to light persist after removal of the cortical visual area, and no other part of the brain assumes the function. Neither is the rate of acquisition, nor the form and latency of the response, altered by removal of the visual cortex (Marquis and Hilgard). Similarly the motor area can be ablated without abolishing conditioned responses. Though the formation of a learned connection between stimulus and response at a subcortical level must be conceded, this capacity is quite limited. According to a simple schematic view of cortical function, removal of sensory areas or motor areas should be roughly equivalent to decortication in limiting ability to form conditioned reflexes. For some reason such is not the case. Since the so-called association areas are projection areas, it is possible that they aid the subcortical reflexes in the acquisition of learned responses.

For the dog and the rat, the postoperative retention of visual conditioned reflexes is not due to the vicariation of other cortical areas, and salivary and blink conditioned reflexes (though possibly not limb flexion) survive removal of the appropriate portions of the motor area. The significance of the cerebral cortex is not that it alone is capable of learning but that through it a wide range of discrete and individual motor responses can be conditioned to slight differences in complex stimulus patterns, e.g., small variations in visual forms.

In the initial chapters were described the results of separately stimulating the components of the reflex arc, sense organ, axon, synapse, etc. In an effort to discover the locus of the stimulus-response association in learned responses the conditioned response has been subjected to the same type of analysis. For this purpose a device was needed for stimulating various parts of the nervous system in the intact, unanesthetized animal. This stimulation was ingeniously accomplished by Loucks (19), who buried beneath the skin of a dog's neck a small coil of insulated wire with its two ends running to the structure to be stimulated. A current is induced in it by making and breaking the circuit through a primary coil held close to the buried coil which therefore acts as a secondary coil. Wires passing through the skin were thus avoided. For the conditioned stimulus, artificial stimulation anywhere along the sensory pathway, including the cerebellum, can be substituted for sense organ stimulation. For example, Loucks was able to obtain a conditioned response to stimulation of the striate area of the occipital lobe. For the *unconditioned* response, the movements produced by stimulation of the dorsal roots, of the dorsal columns, or of the cerebellum can be substituted for stimulation of sensory receptors. The motor pathway of the unconditioned response has been eliminated as the site of conditioning; the unconditioned response must be elicited reflexly via the central nervous system. If an unconditioned stimulus is followed by a limb movement elicited by stimulation of a motor nerve, the stimulus and response do not become associated. Responses to peripherally acting drugs, e.g., histamine, cannot be conditioned, unlike those to centrally acting ones, e.g., morphine. Responses from stimulation of the motor cortex by the buried coil technique cannot be conditioned while movements elicited by cerebellar stimulation can (2), presumably because in the latter case afferent impulses by way of the dentatorubrothalamic tract to the cerebral cortex are involved. According to Masserman's observation (21), a well-integrated pattern of movement elicited by stimulation of the hypothalamic nuclei by implanted electrodes cannot be linked to a visual or auditory stimulus even when associated several hundred times. Hilgard and Marquis (11) conclude from these experiments, "The available evidence, although not conclusive, indicates that the locus of the conditioning association lies outside the regular pathways of the conditioned stimulus, the unconditioned stimulus, and the unconditioned response. The obvious alternative is the assumption of an association pathway . . . "

It is generally though not universally believed that learning is a synaptic phenomenon. The nature of the synaptic modification by which a response pathway is made accessible to a new stimulus is at present a matter of unjustified speculation. The synaptic change, whatever it is, lasts for hours, days, and months; facilitation phenomena of spinal reflexes come to mind, but the difference in time scale, milliseconds vs. months, is an obstacle which has not been successfully overcome.

Limits of conditioning (18). A feature of deep importance to psychosomatic medicine is that processes quite beyond voluntary control can nevertheless be attached to new stimuli by means of the conditioned response technique.

In this category come various autonomic functions, salivary secretion, changes in skin resistance, pupillary reflex; various humorally controlled functions such as diuresis to increased water intake—mere presentation of the apparatus for administration of water may be sufficient to cause increased secretion of urine; and pharmacological and immunological reactions such as nausea and vomiting from morphine injection. Such simple reflexes as the knee jerk can be conditioned, though with great difficulty. In short, activity in kind or degree inappropriate to the situation (stimulus) can result from conditioning. In this it is not difficult to see a potential mechanism for the so-called functional disorders of the vascular and digestive system. A related fact is that emotional reactions can be so conditioned that neutral or symbolic stimuli may elicit them. Such responses may develop with astonishing rapidity, and display considerable fixity, but one trial conditioning is not easy to demonstrate experimentally. In such a mechanism may lie the explanation in whole or part of the phobias exhibited by some neurotic patients. Emotional reactions amounting to neurotic behavior can also be induced in animals by eliciting incompatible conditioned responses.

Experimental neurosis (11, 18, 21). In the conditioned response and other experimental situations, behavior can be produced in animals which bears a strong resemblance (its identity is not yet proved) to neurotic behavior in man. The classic experiment in which this was first observed was conducted in Pavlov's laboratory in 1914, and involved the discrimination of a circle from an ellipse. A dog was trained to salivate on appearance of the circle, but not of an ellipse. The ellipse was then made progressively more circular until the difference was no longer discriminable. When this point was reached, continued training failed to bring improvement of discrimination, and, in fact, the habit deteriorated. The animal displayed neurotic behavior which Pavlov described as follows:

"At the same time the whole behaviour of the animal underwent an abrupt change. The hitherto quiet dog began to squeal in its stand, kept wriggling about, tore off with its teeth the apparatus for mechanical stimulation of the skin, and bit through the tubes connecting the animal's room with the observer, a behaviour which never happened before. On being taken into the experimental room the dog now barked violently, which was also contrary to its usual custom; in short, it presented all the symptoms of a condition of acute neurosis."

Experimental neurosis is not merely a momentary emotional response. Chimpanzees in a somewhat similar situation exhibit violent emotional behavior resembling a severe temper tantrum (13), but in addition assume a negligent, lackadaisical attitude toward the discrimination task, or refuse entirely to give attention to the stimuli. In sheep, the neurosis affects behavior of animals outside of the experimental situation (18). Twenty-four hour records of spontaneous activity, or respiratory rhythm, and of the heart beat yield objective evidence of an excited state persisting outside of the experimental room. Another element in neurotic behavior is anxiety, i.e., a continuous or recurring emotional response to stimuli not present in the immediate environment. Memories of past events or expectance of future events appear to take the place of immediate stimuli. The occurrence of such behavior is closely linked to the functions of the frontal lobule of the cerebral cortex.

ASSOCIATION AREAS

The so-called association areas are three in number: (i) the frontal, (ii) the temporal, and (iii) the posterior parietal areas. Though there are slight cytoarchitectural differences within these areas permitting subareas to be established, the cortex comprising association areas is relatively unspecialized or homotypical cortex. All six layers are well developed. The association areas are myelinated later than the primary sensory and motor areas (Flechsig), which is consistent with a late phylogenetic development and which is especially marked in the primate series. As pointed out previously, the conventional term "association area" fails to convey the full scope of the activity of these regions, and is therefore inadequate or even misleading. (Personality changes, hyperactivity, etc., are certainly not disturbances of associative functions.) Though they lie between the various sensory and motor areas, a fact suggestive of an association function, it is now realized that *these regions are also proiection areas* (Chap. 17); they receive numerous fibers directly from the thalamus and hence are not solely concerned with integrating or elaborating impulses from the cortical sensory areas. One of the largest of the thalamic nuclei, n. dorsomedialis, projects exclusively to the frontal association area; the pulvinar, also a large and recently developed thalamic nucleus, projects to the parieto-occipitotemporal association area, the common ground between the respective lobes. The temporal lobe, exclusive of the auditory area, alone is without a known thalamic projection.

Prefrontal Area. Occupying the frontal pole anterior to the premotor area, the frontal association area is sometimes known as the "prefrontal area" or the prefrontal lobule. Its posterior border, area 8, is transitional, in some functions resembling the premotor area and in others the prefrontal area. The anterior border of the prefrontal area, it is now realized (25), extends fully upon the orbital surface of the frontal lobe and merges posteriorly with olfactory structures. Ablation of the frontal association areas produces definite disturbances, in *behavior*, units of behavior, i.e., reflexes, posture and discrete movement, being unaffected. This is consistent with the fact that the frontal lobule, exclusive of areas 8 and 13 (Fig. 157), is electrically inexcitable. Unlike the language functions, the behavior disturbances described below are marked only when both prefrontal areas are damaged.

As recently as 1922 the results of extirpating the prefrontal areas in animals, were described by Bianchi in purely mentalistic terms from "naked-eye" observation. Since that time certain definite, objectively demonstrable disturbances of behavior have been discovered.

Hyperactivity (15, 23). Complete ablation of the prefrontal lobule or of subareas of that region (e.g., area 13) induces a state of hyperactivity manifested by incessant walking or pacing in a stereotyped fashion, resembling the pacing of a caged lion. It appears aimless and without goal, yet the animal is *driven* in the sense that this activity is continued for hours, scarcely without pause, and in the extreme form is almost maniacal; it is not continued in darkness. For some unknown reason, the hyperactivity of monkeys after prefrontal lesions, like the hyperactivity of certain problem children, is stopped by benzedrine and certain other cerebral excitants. Hyperactivity is also induced in cats and rats by removal of the prefrontal area, but has not yet been demonstrated in chimpanzee or man. To some degree the whole prefrontal cortex, including area 8, is concerned with the regulation of activ-

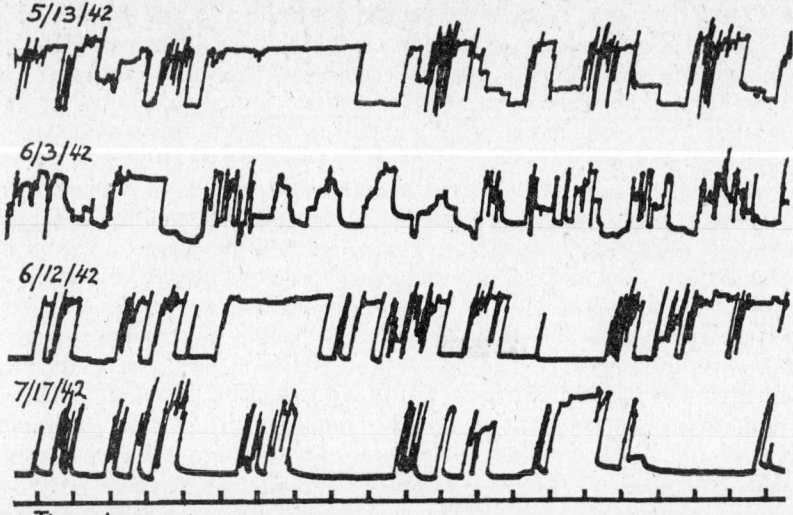

Fig. 286.—Records of normal activity of a monkey. The freely movable bottom of an oblong activity cage rests on a pneumatic pad connected to a tambour which records upon a long-paper kymograph in ink. Any movement toward or away from the end resting on the pad causes an excursion of the pen, and the height roughly reflects the extent of the animal's movement within the cage. Notice the varied pattern of the activity and the frequency of small movements indicated by small excursions of the pen. These records show that craniotomy with ablation of the tip of the frontal pole (between first and second record) does not significantly alter activity. (From Ruch and Shenkin, *J. Neurophysiol.*, 1943, 6:349–360.)

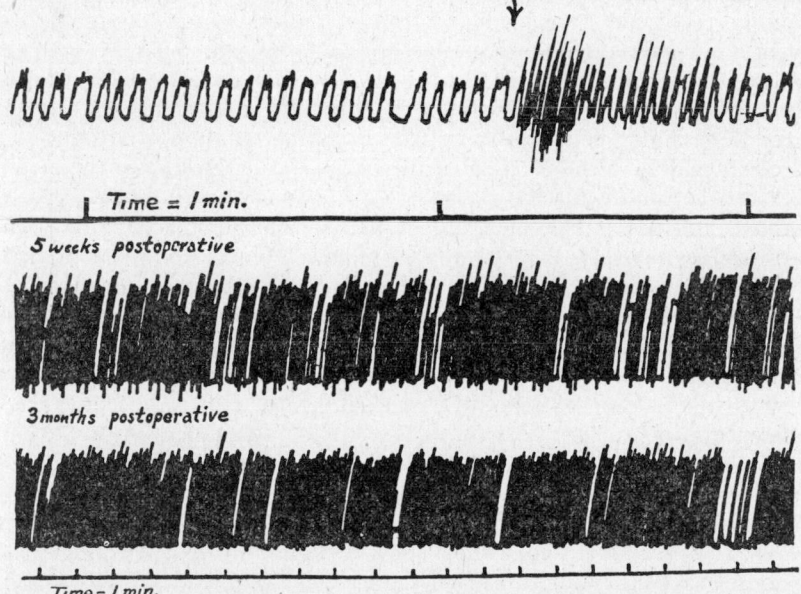

Fig. 287.—Records showing hyperactivity consequent to lesions of the frontal lobe. First record, made with a fast drum, shows the regularity and speed of the walking (16 "round trips" per minute in a cage 4 feet long) and the effect of the observer entering the room (at the arrow). The second and third strips show hyperactivity induced by bilateral ablation of the posterior orbital gyrus (area 13). Observe the absence of pauses longer than a few seconds and that the hyperactivity presented undiminished three months after operation. (From Ruch and Shenkin, *J. Neurophysiol.*, 1943, 6:349–360.)

ity (15). Lesions which include the posterior portions of the orbital surface (area 13) can produce nearly maximal hyperactivity, and lesions which spare this region sometimes fail to produce marked hyperactivity. Lesions of the head of the caudate nucleus are said to produce forced locomotion (cursive hyperkinesis, Mettler), but lesions confined to the cerebral cortex produce maximal hyperactivity (15, 24).

Paradoxically, the period of hyperactivity is preceded by a sharply contrasting state. The immediate consequence of prefrontal ablations is apathy, drooping of the head, sluggishness of movement, a blankness of expression, and a tendency to sit staring into space and to ignore human presence. This state persists for several days and sometimes for as long as three weeks. It is then interrupted by "bouts" of stereotyped pacing punctuated by periods of inactivity, the former increasing at the expense of the latter. Later, when hyperactivity is marked, there is a distinct reduction of random activity, i.e., the varied pattern of manipulations and posturings and the play of grimacing and head and eye movements give way to stereotyped walking or quiescence.

Delayed response (12, 13, 20). Many reactions are responses to the temporally and spatially immediate environment. However, a problem can be set, the solution of which depends on sensory information gained previously and not available at the time of response. In a *delayed reaction** test the monkey or chimpanzee is allowed to view through a glass door a piece of food being deposited beneath one of two cups (Fig. 288). An opaque door is lowered in front of the animal for a chosen interval, after which both doors are raised, permitting the animal to reach the food. Food is obtained only if the "correct" cup is remembered. Delays as long as 1.5 minutes do not prevent a normal animal from successful reactions. After bilateral prefrontal ablation the slightest delay, i.e., less than 5 seconds, completely prevents the animal from responding successfully; the animal is at complete loss to select the food-containing cup. Unilateral frontal lobule ablation is without effect, as are extirpations of other areas of the brain. No other part of the cerebral cortex can substitute for the prefrontal areas since the problem cannot be relearned, and this is true of infant monkeys which tend to exhibit greater postoperative recovery than do adult animals. Nor is complete failure in the delayed reaction test due to a general impairment of intelligence or ability to learn. After prefrontal lobectomy monkeys retain or relearn a visual discrimination quite as well as normals. Furthermore, successful performance of the "stick and platform problem," which tests the animal's ability to solve configurational problems, indicates that a defect of general intelligence is not responsible for failure in the delayed reaction. A chimpanzee placed in a barred experimental cage is confronted with a platform on which is placed a piece of food and a stick or rake, the food being out of arm's reach but within reach if the rake is used. After this is mastered, a series of sticks is introduced, a short stick being used to secure a longer stick, etc., until one long enough to reach the food is obtained. A prefrontal lobectomized chimpanzee is able to grasp these relations and organize a serial

* Ability to delay a response is not to be confused with ability to respond after a delay or delayed reaction. Finan tested the former by training a monkey to cross from one electrified platform to another, using estimated lapse of time as the cue; since premature as well as tardy crossing was punished, ability to inhibit the tendency to cross was tested. Bilateral prefrontal lobectomized monkeys were able to perform this task efficiently.

response involving four sticks, but this is true only if the whole problem is within the animal's view at one moment. If the sticks are arranged on two platforms so that it is necessary to carry a stick from one platform to the other in order to secure the next longer stick, etc., the frontal lobe animal fails totally and experiences great difficulty when only one stick is involved, provided stick and food are on different platforms. Correct solution of this problem, like that of delayed response, demands that behavior be determined by memory of what occurred previously, a memory for recent sensory experience. Much the same type of ability is required in the performance of *delayed alternation*, in which the animal (usually a rat) is taught to make alternate right and left turns and to remember which turn comes next, despite an

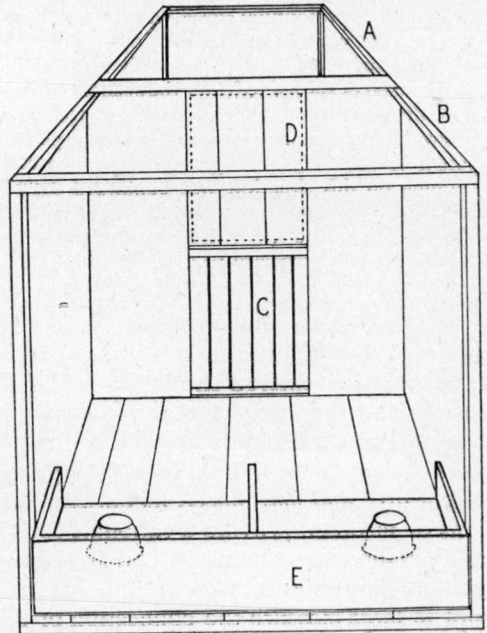

Fig. 288.—Apparatus for eliciting delayed responses. The monkey, in the delay compartment, A, observes through grill door C, one of the food cups E, being baited. After a delay interval in which opaque door D is lowered, both doors D and C are raised, allowing the monkey into reaction or choice compartment B where it obtains access to the food if the correct cup is remembered. (From Jacobsen, *Comp. Psychol. Monogr.*, 1936, *13:* no. 3, 3–60.)

enforced delay after each turn is completed. Rats show definite deficiencies in this problem after bilateral injury to the frontal poles (Loucks; Morgan and Wood).

The analysis of the factors responsible for the loss of immediate memory is not yet completed. One factor in the loss of immediate memory lies in the greater susceptibility of animals with prefrontal lesions to interference from extraneous sensory experience (in clinical parlance, *distractibility*). Malmo (20) trained monkeys in delayed response, using a flash of light rather than the sight of the food to indicate which of two boxes contained food. Inability of monkeys which lack the prefrontal lobes to perform delayed reactions with this arrangement was confirmed, but it was discovered that the same animals were able to perform successfully when the delay period was spent in darkness. Hyperactivity which decreases in darkness was recorded during the delay period and was ruled out as a factor. Interpolation of a light for a period of only two seconds' duration prevented correct delayed response. Visual sensory experience appears to interfere with memory traces or "set" which makes delayed reaction possible.

Experimental neurosis and prefrontal lobotomy. Monkeys and chimpanzees tend to exhibit neurotic behavior under somewhat the same conditions as those employed by Pavlov. In a highly emotional chimpanzee which was unable to perform delayed reactions successfully in preoperative tests, Jacobsen observed the following behavior:

"This animal was extremely eager to work and apparently well motivated; but the subject was highly emotional and profoundly upset whenever she made an error. Violent temper tantrums after a mistake were not infrequent occurrences. She observed closely loading of the cup with food, and often whimpered softly as the cup was placed over the food. If the experimenter lowered or started to lower the *opaque door* to exclude the animal's view of the cups, she immediately flew into a temper tantrum, rolled on the floor, defecated and urinated. After a few such reactions during the training period, the animal would make no further responses to this test, although she responded eagerly if examined on different problems. Training on this situation was continued daily for three weeks. At the beginning, the animal had been eager to come to the experiment room, and when released from the living quarters ran to the transfer cage, opened the door and entered. But by the end of this period it was necessary to drag the animal from the living cage to the transfer cage, and in turn force her into the experimental cage. It was as complete an 'experimental neurosis' as those obtained by Pavlov's conditioned reflex procedures."

After bilateral prefontal lobectomy there occurred a profound change in the animal's behavior. She now entered the experimental room and worked with alacrity. Mistakes and failures to obtain food caused no emotional manifestation, though many more errors were made than before operation. "It was," in Jacobsen's words, "as if the animal had gained the 'happiness cult of the Elder Micheaux,' and had placed its burdens on the Lord."

These observations of Jacobsen provide a rationale for the recently introduced neurosurgical operation upon the prefrontal area. In 1935 Egas Moniz, a Portuguese neurologist, introduced an operation—prefrontal lobotomy—designed to interrupt in large measure the connection of the prefrontal area with the deeper portions of the brain. A special device was invented whereby the fibers passing in the white matter to and from the prefrontal cortex could be sectioned through a trephine opening in the skull. The design is to break the connection of this region with the thalamus without completely isolating it from the remainder of the cerebral cortex. Certain neurotic symptoms of man, like those experimentally engendered in the chimpanzee, are altered by lobotomy. The effects of this procedure are most favorable in disorders characterized by emotional tension, e.g., anxiety neuroses, involutional depression and manic-depressive psychosis. This does not mean that the patient becomes incapable of experiencing emotion; he may even be emotionally over-reactive. But the force of the emotion or its connection with imagination and thought processes is reduced.

Frontal Lobe Function in Man (1, 4). A conspicuous feature of the disturbances consequent to damage of the prefrontal area is the diversity of symptomatology and the marked variation in symptoms from patient to patient. The manner of damage is important, whether by lobotomy or lobectomy, by trauma or tumor. The extent and location of damage is a factor; the degree to which it is bilateral is certainly important. Lobectomy cases provide the best evidence with respect to the physiology of the prefrontal lobule in man, but in evaluating such evidence it must be remembered that other brain areas may be affected through vascular damage, and the scar rather than the loss of cerebral tissue may be the source of abnormal frontal lobe activity (10) which is the cause of the behavioral abnormalities. Contributing to the diversity of symptomatology is the fact that the symptoms have not been reduced to objective description, and different investigators have emphasized different phases of the symptomatology. The following are some of the more frequently encountered disturbances.

Intelligence and intellectual functions. Loss of intelligence as tested by familiar mental tests is not conspicuous in cases of prefrontal lobectomy, though some decrease in general intelligence is observed. An I.Q. approaching 100 (normal) has been obtained from a bilaterally lobectomized patient (10). According to one study (4), lobotomy improved rather than hindered performance in tests of intelligence. The frontal lobes are clearly not the "seat of intelligence," and intellectual disturbances are manifested only in subtle ways. The type of intellectual function which is likely to be disturbed is exemplified by the ability to categorize (8). Spread out before the patient in a random fashion is a large number of heterogeneous objects. After the patient is familiar with the objects, he is asked to "place those together which seem to you to belong together." Ability to recall the objects in each group after an interval of five minutes is then tested, and the basis on which each group is formed is discovered by seeking to withdraw objects or by offering additional objects for inclusion. When compared with normal individuals or those with cortical damage elsewhere in the brain, cases of unilateral frontal lobectomy (i) grouped fewer objects spontaneously and created fewer categories, (ii) recalled fewer objects after an interval of five minutes, and (iii) were less assisted in recalling the objects by the fact that they had been thrown into groups. Another recent study demonstrates objectively slowed perceptual reactions. Earlier studies emphasized failure to analyze and synthesize, failure of planned foresight, etc. Undoubtedly, close examination would reveal subtle changes in many of the higher levels of mental activity.

Emotional behavior and personality. Since the famous "crow-bar" case of Phineas P. Gage in 1848 in which the anterior pole of the brain was traumatized, the prefrontal area has been related to the emotional life and personality. These are not changed in any consistent direction in all cases but some form of personality alteration is frequently though not invariably reported.

Phineas P. Gage, an "efficient and capable" foreman, was injured on September 13, 1848 when a "tamping iron" was blown through his frontal region during the building of the Rutland and Burlington Railroad. He suffered the following change in personality, according to the physician, J. M. Harlow, who attended him. "He is fitful, irreverent, indulging at times in the grossest profanity (which was not previously his custom), manifesting but little deference to his fellows, impatient of restraint or advice when it conflicts with his desires, at times pertinaciously obstinate yet capricious and vacillating, devising many plans for future operation which are no sooner arranged than they are abandoned in turn for others appearing more feasible. . . . His mind was radically changed, so that his friends and acquaintances said he was no longer Gage." (Harlow, *Boston med. surg. J.*, 848, *39*:389.)

The alterations in the *continuity of behavior* in this classic description are characteristic of many cases of damage to the prefrontal area. The patients are highly distractable, as are the monkeys after prefrontal lobectomy, turning from one activity to another, according to the novelty of fresh stimulation rather than any plan. Lack of foresight and planned activity, and inability to anticipate future events on the basis of past experience, an intellectual function, contributes to a lack of continuity in behavior. Another character change is *Witzelsucht*, a tendency towards frivolous and sometimes stupid joking, often at the expense of others. This frequently takes the form of good-humored criticism of others. Such patients often react with a light remark to situations of considerable gravity, and the ebullient spirits may conceal an emotional dulling. In some cases unresponsiveness, inertia, apathy, masking of the face are characteristic of lobotomy, especially in the early stages, and may alternate with restlessness. This calls to mind the sequence of events observed in the monkey after prefrontal lobectomy and in lesions of area 13, i.e., first apathy, followed by an excess of activity, which in both cases is likely to be perseverative and stereotyped. It is equally certain that the personality changes following extensive bilateral lobectomies may be slight and transitory, as in the well-studied case of Hebb and Penfield (10). Personality changes are possibly more marked from lobotomy, severing the frontal region from connection with the dorsomedial nucleus of the thalamus, whereas lobectomy interferes more with intellectual function.

Temporal Lobes. Apart from the small area on the superior surface devoted to audition (Heschl's gyrus) and a convolution on its inferior border (hippocampal gyrus), having olfactory function, the temporal lobe represents a wide expanse of cerebral cortex to which no function can be assigned with certainty. A recent investigation (16, 17) of bilateral temporal lobectomy in the monkey sparing the primary auditory areas reported widespread disturbances of behavior, not related to the auditory sphere.

Some of the observed phenomena were as follows. (i) *"Psychic blindness"* was manifested by inability to recognize objects visually. To find a familiar edible object in a series of inedible ones, all must be brought to the mouth and tested instead of the bit of food being picked out immediately by visual examination. A snake, which monkeys ordinarily fear, was manipulated freely and apparently not recognized. Object vision at the higher levels is therefore disturbed by lesions in three different areas of the cerebral cortex in addition to the striate area: area 19, area 8 and the temporal lobe. (ii) *Oral exploration*, i.e., examination of objects by sniffing or by biting or touching them with the lips appears to be compulsive rather than a mere substitute for vision. (iii) *Compulsive manipulatory reactions* or hypermetamorphosis takes the form of excessive attraction to objects, which were examined closely. (iv) *Emotional changes* in the direction of docility and emotional unresponsiveness were pronounced. (v) *Sexual activity* was augmented. The temporal lobectomy included a portion of the olfactory system, which some believe to be concerned with emotional behavior, and the posterior portion of the region removed lies close to area 19, and may therefore possess a visual function. Tentatively it may be concluded that the nonauditory portions of the temporal lobe are concerned with the control of behavior rather than simple motor or sensory function; in this respect they broadly resemble the prefrontal lobule.

AGNOSIA, APRAXIA, APHASIA

The loss of the memory of learned reactions, sometimes referred to as intellectual functions, as a result of cortical damage takes three principal forms—agnosia, apraxia and aphasia.

Agnosia. By this is meant a loss of the ability to recognize common objects, i.e., to perceive the significance of sensory stimuli. Recognized forms of agnosia are: (i) *astereognosis*, or tactile agnosia, the failure to recognize common objects by palpation of them; (ii) *auditory agnosia*, or *psychic deafness*, which verges into aphasia; (iii) *visual agnosia*, inability to appreciate the meaning of objects seen, or of colors, or of visual space in the absence of primary visual defect; and (iv) *finger agnosia*, or *autotopognosia*, failure to recognize the parts of the body, or to differentiate right and left, and in general the relationship of objects to the body.

Apraxia. In 1886 Hughlings Jackson described a selective disturbance of the higher levels of voluntary motor function now known as apraxia. His patient could not protrude the tongue when asked to do so, but used it well in semi-automatic acts such as chewing and swallowing. There was no paresis or paralysis typical of pyramidal tract damage. Several types of apraxia are recognized: (i) *limb-kinetic apraxia*, in which there is no loss of motor power on the one hand, nor on the other hand failure to appreciate the nature of the movement required, but movements are not carried out with normal skilfulness; (ii) *ideokinetic apraxia*, inability to predetermine individual movements; (iii) *ideational apraxia*, a faulty conception of the movement as a whole, with confusions with respect to the spatial and temporal relations of the parts in the movement sequence, which might, for example, be manifested by inability to strike a match and light a cigarette properly—the wrong end of the match or even the cigarette being struck on the box—etc.; and (iv) *constructive apraxia*, in which the spatial relations of drawings or constructions with blocks are incorrect despite the fact that the patient is visually aware of the errors.

Aphasia (26). The term aphasia means literally the loss of the power of speech. It was used originally to indicate the condition of those who from accident or disease affecting the brain had lost in part or entirely the power of expressing themselves in spoken words, but the term is now extended to include any marked interference with the ability either to use or to comprehend symbolic expressions of ideas by spoken or written words or by gestures or interference with the use of language in thinking. Formerly a sharp distinction was made between sensory and motor aphasia. By the latter term was meant the condition of those who were unable to speak, although there was no paralysis of the muscles of articulation; and by sensory aphasia, those who were unable to understand the written, printed, or spoken symbols of language, although there was no loss of vision or of hearing. These terms are still used in describing the symptoms of aphasia, but later work indicates that the clean-cut separation formerly claimed rarely if ever exists in clinical cases; intermediate forms are far more numerous.

Motor or expressive aphasia. The first definite statement of the portion of the brain involved in motor aphasia seems to have been made by Bouillaud (1825), who, as the result of numerous autopsies, attributed the defect to lesions of the frontal lobe.

It is a curious fact that Bouillaud's observations were inspired by the work of Gall, the founder of phrenology. Gall having observed, as he thought, that individuals who are fluent speakers are characterized by projecting eyes, concluded that this peculiarity is due to the larger size of the lower part of the frontal lobe, and he therefore located speech in this region of the brain. In spite of the vagaries into which he was led by his false methods, Gall made some contributions to our knowledge of the anatomy of the brain and the cord. The discovery of the location of the center of speech, however, cannot be rightly placed to his credit, since his reasons for its location were, as far as we know, entirely unjustified.

Broca located the lesions of the brain involved in motor aphasia in the posterior part of the third or inferior frontal convolution. This region is, therefore, frequently known as Broca's convolution or Broca's area. Subsequent observations tended to confirm this localization, and what is designated as the "motor speech area" is placed in the inferior frontal convolution in the gyrus surrounding the anterior or ascending limb of the lateral fissure, region S in Figure 289. This region has a characteristic cytoarchitecture and is known as area 44. Many authors insist that this localization is too limited, and that defects in the power of speech may result not only from injuries to this region, but also from lesions of contiguous areas, including the anterior portion of the island of Reil and the opercular portion of the central convolution. This Broca's region is not the direct cortical representation of the muscles of speech; it lies just anterior to the portion of area 4 devoted to the face and laryngeal musculature and is possibly a development of the portion of area 6 from which vocalization can be produced by stimulation in monkeys. As a result, aphasia can exist without paralysis of these

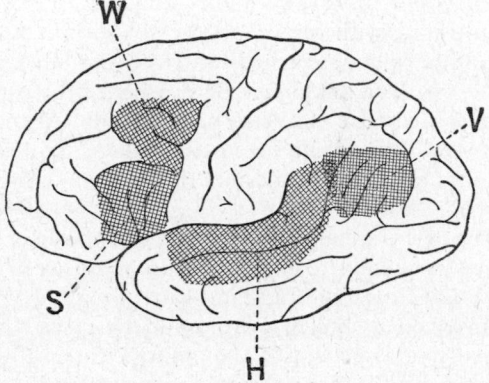

Fig. 289.—Lateral view of a human hemisphere representing one view of the localization o the language areas: cortical area *V*, damage to which produces mainly word-blindness; cortical area *H*, damage to which produces mainly word-deafness; cortical area *S*, damage to which causes the loss of articulate speech; cortical area *W*, damage to which particularly affects ability to write. (After Donaldson.)

muscles. On the other hand, the motor act of speech may be disturbed with relatively little influence on the symbolic aspect of language.

Broca's area appears to be the region in which are organized complex motor innervations necessary to form appropriate sounds and words with which we have learned to express certain concepts. Lesions of any kind affecting this area destroy more or less the ability to use spoken words appropriately, and clinical experience shows that motor aphasia may be exhibited in all degrees of completeness and in many curious varieties. The individual may retain the power to use a limited number of words, with which he expresses his whole range of ideas, as, for instance, in the case described by Broca, in which the individual retained for the expression of numbers only the word "three," and was obliged to make this word do duty for all numerical concepts. Not infrequently the last words spoken before a cerebral accident alone survive. Thus an intelligent woman stricken while ordering her lunch had available for expressing her whole range of ideas but one word—"Horseradish." Automatic word series, e.g., the days of the week, or counting, tend to survive, as does reactive speech demanded by a particular situation, e.g., "Hello" or "Good-bye." When no words can be commanded for the expression of ideas (propositional speech), speech expressive of emotion—ejaculations or swearing—may persist. Usually associated with disturbance of speech is a loss of ability to write (agraphia), whether spontaneously, to dictation, or from copy. Since writing involves a different set of muscles, it was natural to assume that a different cortical area is responsible for this form of expression, as in Figure 289. Although pure agraphia is a questionable entity, in some aphasics the expression of thoughts by writing is more definitely affected than is speech. When the difficulty is in finding the word and writing it correctly, agraphia is considered comparable to aphasia; when the errors are in forming the letters, the disturbance is related to apraxia.

Sensory or receptive aphasia. In this form of aphasia the individual suffers from an inability to *understand* spoken or written language. Lesions in the cortex of the temporal or temporoparietal region (*H* and *V*, Fig. 289) are held responsible for disturbances of this kind, and, as in the case of motor aphasia, the lesion is usually on the left side in right-handed individuals. Since the cortical areas for hearing and seeing are situated in different parts of the brain, it is to be expected that the mechanism for the association, in one case of visual impressions with certain concepts, and in the other case of auditory impression, should also be located in separate regions. Inability to understand spoken language, or word-deafness, has been, in fact, attributed to a lesion involving the superior or middle temporal convolution contiguous to the cortical center of hearing (*H*, Fig. 289), while loss of power to understand written or printed language, word-blindness (alexia), is traced to lesions involving the inferior portion of the posterior parietal lobule, the gyrus angularis, contiguous to the occipital visual center (*V*, Fig. 289). More recent writers find that this separation is too schematic. Weisenberg and McBride (26) found that some patients have greatest difficulty in comprehending spoken words, and others the greatest difficulty with written language, while many patients have equal trouble in both spheres. It is possible that cases of reputed pure word-blindness and word-deafness are in reality special manifestations of visual and auditory agnosia. Furthermore, these writers find little evidence of a pure sensory aphasia. Because of the associated expressive difficulties they refer to this group as "predominantly receptive aphasics."

Aphasia as an intellectual defect. Aphasics once labeled "expressive" or "receptive" have, on close examination, disturbances of language as a symbolic function and disturbances of intellectual functions in general. An example of a disturbance of the language mechanism at a high level is *amnesic aphasia*, which may exist in relatively pure form.

In this form of aphasia the articulation of words is normal, and the understanding of language is not gravely affected. Nevertheless the patient finds it difficult to name objects and in speaking often hesitates while searching for words. Often some words are recognized when supplied by the examiner and are well spoken by the patient under certain circumstances. According to Goldstein, there are disturbances of intellectual character, e.g., in the ability to categorize—to sort miscellaneous collections of objects according to classes. The lesion in these cases is supposed not to affect the speech areas but to result from widespread though not severe cortical damage.

The modern tendency in the investigation of aphasia is to neglect the problem of cortical localization and to concentrate upon the nature of the aphasic disorder, and to emphasize its intellectual components. Head (9), for example, has advanced the following classification of aphasia based not upon sensory and motor dichotomy but upon language processes: (i) *verbal aphasia* is similar to classic motor aphasia; (ii) *nominal aphasia*, difficulty in naming objects, is similar to amnesic aphasia; (iii) *syntactical aphasia* is so named because the structure of sentences is distorted (agrammatism), sometimes to the point that jargon is spoken; when pronunciation is affected, the speech resembles baby talk. Speech is voluble, and the words may or may not be well pronounced, but essential prepositions, conjunctions and inflections are omitted; (iv) *semantic aphasia* is almost purely a defect in the comprehension of the meanings of language, with little difficulty in speaking, or understanding the actual words.

In Head's scheme language is considered more or less as a total function involving the cerebral cortex as a whole. His categories are levels of language function. At the low level, receptive aphasia merges with agnosia, expressive aphasia merges with apraxia, and at high levels aphasia is probably the manifestation in the sphere of language of intellectual defects of a more general character.

REFERENCES

1. BRICKNER, R. M. *The intellectual functions of the frontal lobes.* New York, The Macmillan Company, 1936, xvi, 354 pp.
2. BROGDEN, W. J. and GANTT, W. H. Intraneural conditioning: cerebellar conditioned reflexes. *Arch. Neurol. Psychiat., Chicago*, 1942, *48*:437–455.
3. CULLER, E. and METTLER, F. A. Conditioned behavior in a decorticate dog. *J. comp. Psychol.*, 1934, *18*:291–303.
4. FREEMAN, W. and WATTS, J. W. *Psychosurgery. Intelligence, emotion and social behavior following prefrontal lobotomy for mental disorders.* Springfield, Ill., Charles C Thomas, 1942, xii, 337 pp.
5. GIBBS, F. A. Electroencephalography. Pp. 361–370 in: GLASSER, O., ed. *Medical physics.* Chicago, The Year Book Publishers, Inc., 1944, xlvi, 1744 pp.
6. GIBBS, F. A. and GIBBS, E. L. *Atlas of electroencephalography.* Cambridge, Mass., privately printed, 1941, 221 pp.
7. GIBBS, F. A., GIBBS, E. L. and LENNOX, W. G. Cerebral dysrhythmias of epilepsy. *Arch. Neurol. Psychiat., Chicago*, 1938, *39*:298–314.
8. HALSTEAD, W. C. Preliminary analysis of grouping behavior in patients with cerebral injury by the method of equivalent and non-equivalent stimuli. *Amer. J. Psychiat.*, 1940, *96*:1263–1294.
9. HEAD, H. *Aphasia and kindred disorders of speech.* New York, The Macmillan Company, 1926, 2 vols.
10. HEBB, D. O. and PENFIELD, W. Human behavior after extensive bilateral removal from the frontal lobes. *Arch. Neurol. Psychiat., Chicago*, 1940, *44*:421–438.
11. HILGARD, E. R. and MARQUIS, D. G. *Conditioning and learning.* New York, D. Appleton-Century Co., 1940, xi, 429 pp.
12. JACOBSEN, C. F. Studies of cerebral function in primates. I. The functions of the frontal association areas in monkeys. *Comp. Psychol. Monogr.*, 1936, *13*, no. 63:3–60.
13. JACOBSEN, C. F., WOLFE, J. B. and JACKSON, T. A. An experimental analysis of the functions of the frontal association areas in primates. *J. nerv. ment. Dis.*, 1935, *82*:1–14.
14. JASPER, H. H. Electroencephalography. Chap. 14 in: PENFIELD, W. and ERICKSON, T. C. *Epilepsy and cerebral localization.* Springfield, Ill., Charles C Thomas, 1941, x, 623 pp.
15. KENNARD, M. A., SPENCER, S. and FOUNTAIN, G., JR. Hyperactivity in monkeys following lesions of the frontal lobes. *J. Neurophysiol.*, 1941, *4*:512–524.
16. KLÜVER, H. and BUCY, P. C. Preliminary analysis of functions of the temporal lobes in monkeys. *Arch. Neurol. Psychiat., Chicago*, 1939, *42*:979–1000.
17. KLÜVER, H. and BUCY, P. C. An analysis of certain effects of bilateral temporal lobectomy in the rhesus monkey, with special reference to "psychic blindness." *J. Psychol.*, 1938, *5*:33–54.
18. LIDDELL, H. S. The nervous system as a whole: the conditioned reflex. Chap. 26 in: FULTON, J. F. *The physiology of the nervous system.* New York, Oxford University Press, 2d ed., 1943, ix, 614 pp.
19. LOUCKS, R. B. The experimental delimitation of neural structures essential for learning: the attempt to condition striped muscle responses with faradization of the sigmoid gyri. *J. Psychol.*, 1935, *1*:5–44.
20. MALMO, R. B. Interference factors in delayed response in monkeys after removal of frontal lobes. *J. Neurophysiol.*, 1942, *5*:295–308.
21. MASSERMAN, J. H. *Behavior and neurosis; an experimental psychoanalytic approach to psychobiologic principles.* Chicago, The University of Chicago Press, 1943, xv, 269 pp.
22. MORGAN, C. T. *Physiological psychology.* New York, McGraw-Hill Book Co., Inc., 1943, xii, 623 pp.

23. PAVLOV, I. P. *Conditioned reflexes: an investigation of the physiological activity of the cerebral cortex.* London, Oxford University Press, 1927, xv, 430 pp.

24. RUCH, T. C. and SHENKIN, H. A. The relation of area 13 on orbital surface of frontal lobes to hyperactivity and hyperphagia in monkeys. *J. Neurophysiol.*, 1943, 6:349–360.

25. WALKER, A. E. A cytoarchitectural study of the prefrontal area of the macaque monkey. *J. comp. Neurol.*, 1940, 73: 59–86.

26. WEISENBERG, T. and McBRIDE, K. E. *Aphasia, a clinical and psychological study.* New York, Commonwealth Fund, 1935, xvi, 634 pp.

SECTION IV

PROPERTIES AND CONSTITUENTS OF THE BLOOD

BY DAVID I. HITCHCOCK

CHAPTER 26

GENERAL PROPERTIES OF BLOOD: THE FORMED ELEMENTS

BY JOHN H. FERGUSON

GENERAL PROPERTIES OF BLOOD

Functions of the Blood. Claude Bernard (1878) pointed out that the evolution of the highest forms of life could only have been made possible by the substitution for the fickle outer environment of a more equable internal environment (*milieu intérieur*) composed of the ensemble of tissue fluids which bathe the living cells of multicellular organisms (Chap. 10). The primary function of the blood and circulatory system of animals is to maintain the constancy of the internal environment by continuously renewing the tissue fluids, serving thus as the connecting link between tissue cells and the body's external surroundings. Although chemical substances and biological cells are continuously entering and leaving the blood, its overall composition is remarkably constant. The blood is usually spoken of as the nutritive liquid of the body, but its detailed functions must be stated more explicitly.

The respiratory function of the blood, so attractively elucidated by Barcroft (1), consists in bringing oxygen from the lungs to the tissues and carbon dioxide from the tissues to the lungs. The mode of carriage of these gases by the blood is discussed below in the section on respiration.

Blood is also the transport highway for digested foodstuffs, some of which are carried to reserve depots where they are again mobilized for blood transport as tissue needs arise. The blood-borne foodstuffs include both energy resources and building materials for growth, repair and renewal of tissues. Certain metabolic functions undoubtedly proceed in the circulating blood. Carbon dioxide, lactic acid, nonprotein nitrogenous substances and other metabolites are carried by the blood to organs which deal with them in various ways. Some metabolites are reconverted into useful forms, e.g., blood lactic acid into liver glycogen. Others are detoxified and the so-called waste products are eliminated by the excretory organs. The *buffer* mechanisms of the blood assist in the preservation of the acid-base equilibrium of the body, which is dealt with in Chapter 27. The blood also conveys excess of buffered acid or base to organs, like the lungs and kidneys, where they are taken care of by excretion and other forms of physiological buffering.

Water balance and fluid distribution throughout the body depend upon the mobile water content of the blood. Fluid balance must always be considered in relation to salts and other solutes, which have nonspecific osmotic effects in determining fluid distribution. In the regulation of fluid shifts between the blood and tissue fluids, and in the filtration process in the kidneys (Sect. VII), the small colloidal osmotic pressure of the plasma proteins is of great physiological significance. Many physiological functions are dependent upon the normal balance between the concentrations of various cations (H^+, Na^+, K^+, Ca^{++}, Mg^{++}) and anions (OH^-, Cl_7^-, HCO_3^-, $H_2PO_4^-$, $HPO_4^=$, $SO_4^=$) and between electrolytes and colloids, especially proteins.

Life requires a restricted temperature range, and the blood is significantly concerned with temperature regulation. Water, of which the blood and indeed the whole body is so largely composed, tends to retain heat. The flow of the blood assists in conducting and intermingling the heat produced during the chemical processes of metabolism and the various bodily activities. The blood circulating at the body surface is especially important in controlling the loss of heat by radiation and evaporation, the latter largely through the sweat secretion. Warm blooded (homoiothermic) animals have thermostat devices, particularly the heat-regulating centers of the central nervous system, for balancing heat loss and heat production in order to maintain the body temperature within narrow limits. The mechanisms of temperature regulation are dealt with in Chapter 11. The blood of man is ordinarily at a temperature about a degree higher than the average mouth temperature of 37° C. (98.6° F.).

Cells, Plasma and Serum. In its fluid state, which can be maintained outside the body only by artificial anticoagulant measures, the blood is separable into the microscopically visible *formed elements* and the liquid *plasma* in which they are suspended. The formed elements are the red cells or erythrocytes, the white cells or leukocytes, and the blood platelets. The leukocytes are true cells with nuclei and powers of active movement, but mammalian erythrocytes and platelets are non-nucleated cell remnants. The plasma is a complex watery fluid containing colloids, electrolytes, and other substances. The process of coagulation, which is so characteristic of shed blood, is primarily a plasma phenomenon, although ordinarily modified by the presence of platelets and other formed elements. A plasma protein fraction termed fibrinogen is the soluble precursor of the jelly-like fibrin of the blood clot. Corpuscles and platelets in various stages of disintegration are commonly entangled in the filamentous meshwork of the fibrin clot. After coagulation, the clot typically undergoes retraction, separating from the wall of the containing vessel and shrinking in volume, thereby squeezing out a straw-colored fluid termed *serum*. Serum may be regarded as the liquid part of blood *after* clotting has taken place, whereas plasma is the liquid part of blood *before* clotting has occurred. The serum from a fasting person or animal is generally clear and transparent. Milky or lipemic serum is due to submicroscopic fatty particles (chylomicrons, hemoconia, or "blood dust") which are best seen under the dark-field microscope, where they are conspicuous because of their Brownian movement. A pink or reddish tinge in the serum indicates faulty technique; it is due to the presence of hemoglobin released by breakdown of some of the red blood corpuscles. The pigments which give the serum its normal yellowish or greenish tinge are chiefly porphyrins related to the degradation of hemoglobin on the one hand and to the synthesis of the bile pigments on the other.

In order to obtain plasma, fresh blood is first mixed with an anticoagulant and then centrifuged (or allowed to stand until the cells have settled). The supernatant plasma is drawn off by means of a pipette or siphon tube. In referring to plasma, the anticoagulant which it contains is often designated by a prefix, as citrate-plasma, oxalate-plasma, magnesium sulfate-plasma, heparin-plasma, etc.

The fluidity may also be maintained by stirring freshly shed blood with a glass rod or similar object. The fibrin adheres to the rod as it forms, while the main bulk of the blood remains free from coagulation. If care is taken not to rub the rod against the sides of the container, most of the red cells remain intact and are now suspended in noncoagulating serum. Blood that has been treated in this way is known as "defibrinated" blood. Anaerobic defibrination may be accomplished by collecting the blood over mercury in a special glass vessel; the blood displaces all except 1 or 2 cc. of the mercury, which is made to defibrinate the blood by repeatedly inverting the tube.

Viscosity of Blood. The viscosity of a liquid is its internal friction, or the resistance offered to a force which tends to make one layer in the liquid slide past another. Numerical values of the viscosity are commonly obtained from measurements of the rate of flow of the liquid through a glass capillary tube; the rate varies inversely as the viscosity. According to Poiseuille's law, the rate of flow is proportional to the difference in pressure which causes the flow, but the viscosity is independent of the pressure difference. This law applies exactly to the results obtained for water and many other liquids, including true solutions, if suitable instruments are used. The viscosity of a liquid is usually decreased about 2 per cent by a rise in temperature of 1° C., but for any one temperature the viscosity of a liquid which exhibits true viscous flow is a definite physical constant. The relative viscosity of a liquid is the ratio of its viscosity to that of water at the same temperature.

The viscosity of many colloidal solutions and suspensions increases markedly with the concentration, and the flow of such liquids often fails to follow Poiseuille's law. In that case the apparent or effective viscosity will depend on the method of measurement. The plasma of normal blood has a fairly definite relative viscosity of about 1.6. Because of the large fraction of the total volume occupied by the cells in whole blood or defibrinated blood, widely different figures for viscosity are obtained under different conditions of measurement. With the Hess technique, figures ranging from 3.9 to 5.3 were obtained for the relative viscosity of blood from normal men and women, but these figures may well be twice as large as the viscosity which is effective in the circulation (Chap. 30).

Specific Gravity and Sedimentation. The specific gravity of whole blood (see p. 585) is somewhat variable (1.041–1.067), but 1.060 is a fair average for the normal male human adult. The specific gravity of plasma or serum (average, 1.026) is less than that of the corpuscles, especially the red cells (average, 1.097). Hence the formed elements in shed blood tend to settle out under the influence of gravity, provided that the fluidity is maintained. If no anticoagulant measures are taken, clotting usually occurs before appreciable sedimentation of the corpuscles has taken place. In the old days of bloodletting, observant physicians sought to establish some significance for the so-called "size" or "buffy coat" (crusta phlogistica) which often appeared. We now dismiss this as merely a result of sufficiently rapid sedimentation to enable the separation of a relatively cell-free upper layer of plasma, in which coagulation often occurs before clotting of the red cell layer. Modern methods separate the phenomena of red blood cell sedimentation from the coagulation process.

Fåhraeus (1918, 1921) found that the rate of sedimentation of red blood cells is markedly increased in pregnancy and in many conditions of disease. Numerical values of this rate depend on the method used to measure it as well as on the nature of the blood specimen. Various techniques have been proposed in an effort to increase the value of the measurement as a clinical test (9). The type of anticoagulant used is especially important. Fåhraeus diluted blood with a citrate solution, but others have obtained good results with a dried mixture of ammonium and potassium oxalates. It has been shown that a 6:4 mixture of these salts has little or no effect on the relative cell volume. Coagulation is adequately prevented if the blood is received in a tube or bottle containing a dried film of the oxalates, in the proportion of 2 mg. per cc. of blood, and gently stirred by a swirling motion while the salts are dissolving.

From physical principles the rate of sedimentation would be expected to depend on the size and specific gravity of the cells and the specific gravity and viscosity of the plasma. Fåhraeus pointed out that the observed range of sedimentation rates is too wide to be explained by known variations in any or all of these quantities. There is a definite effect of the concentration or relative volume of cells, and sedimentation rates are often corrected to a standard value of the relative cell volume (hematocrit, see below); this effect is largely responsible for the fact that sedimentation is faster in the blood of normal females than of males. While there is not much variation in the volumes of individual erythocytes, there is a marked difference in the tendency of the cells in different bloods to agglutinate or form aggregates, and this tendency appears to be responsible for the wide variations observed in the rate of sedimentation.

Physiological variations occur to a greater extent in women than in men, with minor fluctuations related to menstruation and a definite acceleration during pregnancy. Pathological variations are numerous and represent a nonspecific reaction having much the same general significance as fever, pulse acceleration, and leukocytosis. The sedimentation rate is not an accurate nor a specific measure of any blood constituent, but it may have a significant correlation with the plasma fibrinogen level (p. 590) and with the concentration of alpha globulins.

Relative Volumes of Cells and Plasma. The centrifuge affords a rapid method for separating the corpuscles from the plasma. Quantitative techniques date back to 1890–91 (Hedin, Blix, Daland); more modern methods are described in Wintrobe's book (18). The *hematocrit* is a small graduated centrifuge tube in which the relative volumes of corpuscles and plasma are quickly and accurately determined. It is necessary to use an anticoagulant, requiring a correction factor except in the case of the dry oxalate mixture previously referred to. The Wintrobe hematocrit tube is a simple, flat-bottomed, narrow (3 mm. diam.) glass tube graduated in mm. up to 100 mm. from the bottom. It is a common clinical laboratory routine to leave the

Wintrobe tube in a vertical holder for the first hour after it has been filled to the 100 mark. The sedimentation rate in mm./hr. is taken as the distance between the upper surface of the plasma and the top of the column of sedimenting cells. The tube is then centrifuged at 3000 rev./min. for 30 minutes, after which the percentage corpuscular volume is read. In normal blood the red cells occupy nearly all of the observed cell volume, but in abnormal conditions (leukocytosis, leukemia) it is important to distinguish between the red cell volume and the total volume of all cells. The average normal hematocrit volumes are 47 ($\pm$7) per cent red cells in the blood of men, and 42 ($\pm$5) per cent for women (18). Hematocrit readings may be a few per cent higher than the true cell volumes, because of incomplete separation of the plasma from the column of cells. This does not detract from the value of hematocrit determinations in clinical work if a standard procedure is used. With a centrifuge operating at 2500 rev./min., 60 minutes may be required for adequate packing of the cells.

In the separation achieved by the centrifuge, the white blood corpuscles, together with the platelets, form the so-called "leukocyte cream" on top of the red cell layer. This should not be confused with the "buffy coat" (see above). The yellow color of the plasma layer can be compared with a colorimetric standard to obtain the icteric index, which is a measure of the concentration of bile pigments in plasma. Gross degrees of lipemia are readily detected by the milky appearance of the plasma or serum.

Total Blood Volume. The blood in healthy adults probably makes up about 6 to 8 per cent of the body weight. The blood volume is higher in men than in women and is subject to considerable individual variation. The *direct* method for blood volume determination, employed by Welcker (1854) on animals and by Bischoff (1855) on two condemned human criminals, consists in bleeding, washing out the blood vessels, extracting the minced tissues with water, and matching dilutions, colorimetrically, against an original blood sample in order to determine the total hemoglobin and hence the total volume of blood which this represents. Values averaging 7.7 per cent of body weight were obtained by these methods (15).

The carbon monoxide method (3) consists in rebreathing a known small volume of carbon monoxide gas mixed with oxygen in a bag, until the CO is all absorbed. The concentration of CO in the blood is determined, and the blood volume is given by the ratio of the known amount of CO to its concentration in the blood. The calculation is based on the assumptions that all of the CO is in the blood, and that it is uniformly distributed throughout the total blood volume. This method is infrequently used nowadays and gives values (averaging 6 to 7 per cent of body weight) consistently lower than the dye methods. It does, however, offer a "corpuscle" method with which to check the results obtained with the "plasma" methods.

The dye method (15) involves the injection of a known amount of a harmless dye into a vein, and the determination of the concentration of dye in the plasma after it has become well mixed by the circulation. If all of the dye remains in the plasma, the plasma volume is the ratio of the total amount of dye to its concentration. The method has been improved by using a blue dye (T-1824, Evans blue) instead of the original red dye.* The blood volume

---

* Gregersen (6) has described a convenient modification of the dye method, developed primarily for the armed forces.

is obtained by dividing the plasma volume by the fractional volume of plasma in the blood, as given by the hematocrit. In this way Gibson and Evans found average blood volumes of 77.7 cc. per kg. body weight for normal men, and 66.1 cc. per kg. for women. As blood is 1.06 times as heavy as water, these figures imply that the total mass of the blood is about 8.2 per cent of the body weight in men and 7.0 per cent in women. Since the average plasma volumes were nearly the same, 43.1 cc. per kg. in men and 41.5 in women, the difference between the blood volumes per unit body weight is largely a reflection of the usual difference in the hematocrit readings of men and women. There is still a question whether *indirect* methods account for a fraction of the blood volume which is believed to be sequestered by stagnation in "reservoir" areas.

THE FORMED ELEMENTS

As stated above, the formed elements in blood include the erythrocytes, the leukocytes and the platelets (Fig. 290). The red color of blood is due entirely to hemoglobin in the erythrocytes, but when single red cells are observed under the microscope their color appears only as a faint yellowish red. When seen in mass, the red cells in arterial blood have a bright scarlet color, but in venous blood their color is a purplish red; this variation in color depends on the extent to which the hemoglobin is saturated with oxygen.

Hemocytometry. In making a blood count, a minute measured volume of blood is accurately diluted with a solution appropriate for the particular formed element which is to be enumerated, and counts of the corpuscles in the ruled areas of a special hemocytometer chamber are made under suitable magnification with the microscope. The conventional "normal" red cell count of 5,000,000 per cu.mm. is approximated in women (4.9 ± 0.6 millions) but is usually exceeded by about half a million in men (5.4 ± 0.8 millions) in current data on American adults. The normal white cell count of 7000 (5000–10,000) per cu.mm. is now known to be subject to considerable variations, particularly in infants and young children. The basal level in adults, under conditions of perfect health and complete physical and mental rest, may be regarded as 5000–7000 per cu.mm. Platelet counts vary considerably with different methods and with the type of sampling (finger-prick, venous, or arterial blood). The usually accepted normal range is 250,000–400,000 per cu.mm.

Morphology of the Formed Elements. Observations in this field require the best microscopical methods. For study of blood cells in the living state, the dark-field microscope is especially recommended (5). Full cytological investigations include supravital staining techniques, especially with neutral red, Janus green (for mitochondria), and brilliant cresyl blue (for reticulocytes). For differential leukocyte counts and routine examinations, blood films are dried on slides or coverslips and stained with one or other of the numerous modifications (e.g., Wright's) of the Romanowsky eosin-methylene blue-azur method.

The normal human erythrocyte is a nearly circular biconcave disc, averaging close to 7.5 μ (6–9 μ) in diameter. Its width is about 1 μ in the center and 2–2.4 μ at the widest points. These values are best obtained, by ocular micrometry, on fresh blood films in which the red corpuscles are commonly adherent in rouleaux, like piles of coins. A statistical analysis of red cell diameters is

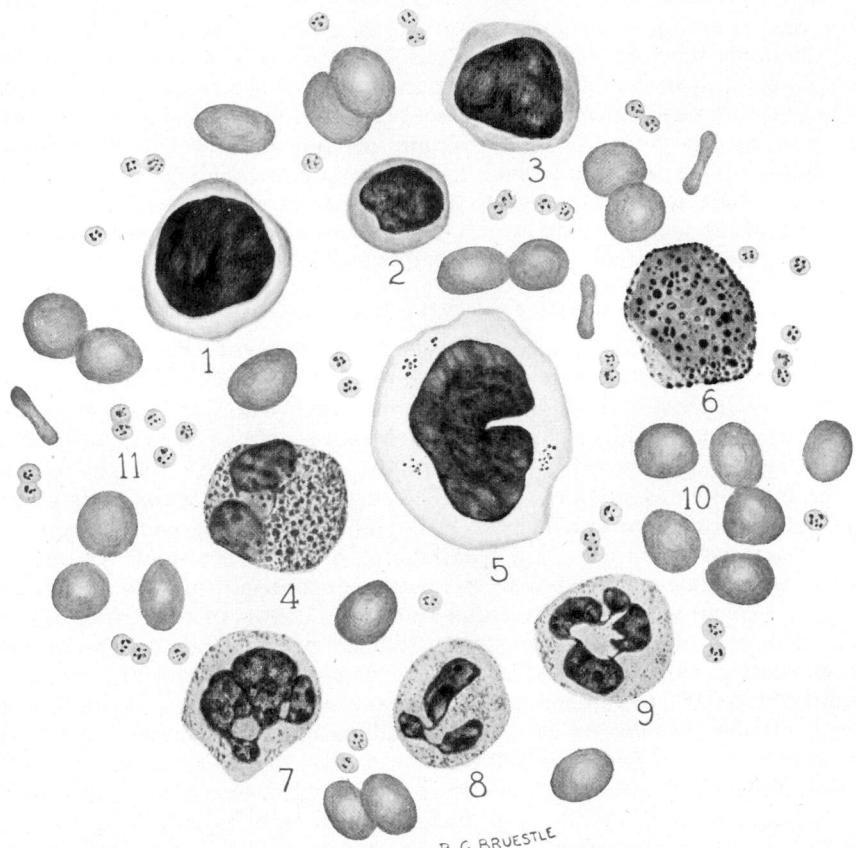

B. G. BRUESTLE

Figure 290.—Normal blood cells stained with May-Grünwald Giemsa. These cells are magnified approximately 1500 times.

1, 2, 3: *Lymphocytes.* Cells of this type are variable in size (10 to 20 μ) and constitute 25 to 33 per cent of the leukocytes of normal blood.

4: *Eosinophil.* These cells have bilobed nuclei and large discrete granules which stain a bright yellowish-red color. They are 10 to 15 μ in size and make up 1 to 3 per cent of the leukocytes of normal human blood.

5: *Monocyte.* The monocytes are the largest (12 to 20 μ) of the leukocytes in normal blood and constitute from 3 to 7 per cent of the white blood cells. They are distinguished by the more open structure of the nucleus and the slate-gray cytoplasm which contains dustlike granules.

6: *Basophil.* Basophils contain water-soluble bluish-black granules which usually hide much of the nucleus. These cells are 10 to 15 μ in size and are very few in normal blood (0 to 0.75 per cent).

7, 8, 9: *Mature polymorphonuclear neutrophils.* The nuclei of these cells normally are divided into from 2 to 4 lobes which are connected one to the other by small strands of chromatin. The cytoplasm is a faint yellowish-pink and contains fine violet-pink granules. These cells are 10 to 15 μ in size and constitute 54 to 62 per cent of all leukocytes.

10: *Erythrocytes.* These are biconcave discs which are approximately 7.5 μ in diameter. There are 4.8 millions of red cells per c.mm. in the female and 5.4 millions in the adult male.

11: *Platelets.* Platelets are fragments of megakaryocytes and contain azur granules. They vary from 2 to 4 μ in diameter, and there are usually said to be 250,000 per cu.mm. although some methods give a higher value.

(From Dr. Thomas F. Dougherty, Department of Anatomy, Yale University School of Medicine.)

the basis of the Price-Jones curves, which have largely been superseded by volume index determinations, especially in the clinical diagnosis of the anemias (7). The volume index is the red cell hematocrit volume (as percentage of normal) divided by the red cell count (as percentage of normal).

Under the dark-field microscope, human erythrocytes are highly refractile at their margins but show no structural contents. Supravital staining (brilliant cresyl blue) reveals a few reticulocytes, normally 0.5–1.5 per cent of all erythrocytes. In the adult human, nucleated red cells (erythroblasts) are rarely seen in the peripheral blood.

The leukocytes are of five types. The dark-field microscope permits excellent observation of their appearances and behavior (e.g., ameboid movements and phagocytosis) in the living state (5). In fixed, stained films they are easily differentiated by the Romanowsky techniques (Fig. 290). The granulocytes are characterized by specific cytoplasmic granulations, classed according to their staining reactions as *neutrophil*, *eosinophil*, and *basophil*. The non-granular types should be classed separately as *monocytes* and *lymphocytes*.

About two-thirds of the white cells in normal blood are the polymorphonuclear neutrophilic leukocytes. The lymphocytes normally constitute about one-quarter of the white cells. The other white cells are usually present in much smaller proportions; the normal order of decreasing frequency is monocytes, eosinophils and basophils.

The platelets are much altered in stained films. Preserved by citrate or other anticoagulants, they are seen to change from their normal form of a small oval disc to stellate and similar forms characterized by delicate protrusions, suggestive of myelin figure formations at water-phospholipid interfaces. In the absence of preservatives, the platelets undergo swelling and a peculiar lytic alteration (see below), which is a partial disintegration. In Wright-stained films, they are merely little granular bodies, often in agglutinated masses, with a few central azurophile granules and an indefinite outline of blue-staining hyaloplasm.

Hematopoiesis (the formation of blood cells) in the embryo as well as in the adult organism is an important part of a complete biology of the blood. Knowledge of this subject has been helpful in understanding the morphological abnormalities of blood cells in disease, but this field is too extensive to be treated here. Reference may be made to works on hematology (4, 18), histology, and embryology.

Erythrocytes

The physiological importance of the red blood corpuscles in man is obviously due to the fact that they are essential for the respiratory function of the blood. Oxygen must be brought to all the cells of the body if life is to persist, and in the mammals this gas is carried almost entirely by the hemoglobin in the red blood cells.

Life History of the Erythrocyte. It has been shown satisfactorily that in the adult the organ for the production of red corpuscles is the red marrow of bones. In this tissue the formation of red blood cells goes on continually, the process being much increased after hemorrhages and in certain pathological conditions. It has long been known that acclimatization to high altitudes is accompanied by a rise in the red cell count; a rapid rise of this sort is ascribed to the release into the circulation of red corpuscles previously held in reserve in the spleen or other reservoirs. A subsequent slower increase in the red cell count supports the belief that low oxygen pressure is a physiological stimulus to the production of red blood cells by the bone marrow.

Since the number of erythrocytes normally in circulation is fairly constant, and new cells are continually being produced, it follows that there must also be a continual loss or destruction of the red corpuscles in normal individuals. Such destruction is reasonable on general biological grounds, for the non-nucleated human red cell is a mere cell remnant. From this viewpoint one may regard the normal life of the erythrocyte as surprisingly long. Large numbers of transfused red cells have been detected after 25 to 50 days, and some after 100 days. It has been computed that some ten million erythrocytes are normally removed from the circulation every second. Their destruction liberates, daily, about 25 gm. of hemoglobin (85 mg. Fe), which is the amount normally contained in 160 cc. of blood. This can well be spared from the total blood volume of 5.5-6 liters, containing some 950 gm. of hemoglobin (3.2 gm. Fe), but it does indicate a considerable turnover of the iron-containing pigments. When hemoglobin is broken down in the body, the porphyrin part of the molecule goes to form other pigments, including those of the bile.

Iron in relation to hemoglobin formation (8). It is an important fact that the body jealously conserves the iron from its hemoglobin. Recent studies (8) with an isotope of iron (Fe^{59}) indicate that earlier estimates of adequate iron in the diet were too high. The normal adult excretes only about 4.5 mg. of iron in the daily urine. While there are appreciable amounts of iron in the feces, practically all of this is now believed to be unabsorbed iron from the food. Traces of iron are excreted in the bile and intestinal secretions, but the body reabsorbs this, together with sufficient food iron to prevent depletion of the iron stores. The adult daily requirement is probably 5 to 15 mg. and is supplied by an average mixed diet yielding 10 to 80 mg. Fe. Any excess of dietary iron is not absorbed. Of course, there are important conditions requiring extra iron intake, especially in the young, growing animal (infant), for hemoglobin regeneration after hemorrhage (including menstruation), and in the anemias. Growing children require 0.6 to 0.76 mg. of iron daily per kg. of body weight, and females need about four times as much as males. To be absorbed from the gut, iron must be in the ferrous state, and inorganic iron is absorbed as well as, if not better than, iron in organic combination. Much depends upon the digestion. Ferrous carbonate is effective in the presence of gastric achlorhydria (absence of HCl); many food iron and ferric preparations are much less so. Meats, especially red meats, are valuable for their available iron. Liver is very good and so are egg yolks. Milk is notoriously poor in iron.

Experiments with anemia induced in young rats fed a basal milk ration, deficient in iron, show that traces of copper, under certain circumstances, are of distinct aid in the full utilization of therapeutic iron. These circumstances require preliminary depletion of the body's copper stores (especially in the liver) since only very minute amounts of copper are needed and careful experimentation is required to produce the deficiency. Of other metals investigated, none has proved significant in hemoglobin formation.

The body seems well able to synthesize, if necessary, the porphyrin portion of the hemoglobin molecule. Normally, porphyrins are abundant in the food and such sources are undoubtedly used. The fact that chlorophyll is a magnesium porphyrin, while hemoglobin contains an iron porphyrin, has supported the belief that a diet rich in chlorophyll would promote the formation of hemoglobin in the body. Eating spinach and other chlorophyll-rich foods promotes hemoglobin formation provided the diet contains available iron, but recent evidence shows that much of the vegetable iron is nonavailable and is poorly mobilized by the digestive processes. The administration of chlorophyll preparations, after a period of medication with comparable amounts of iron, was followed by an increase in the concentration of hemoglobin in cases of chronic hypochromic anemia.

The globin (protein) portion of hemoglobin constitutes 96 per cent of the molecule and may be a limiting factor in hemoglobin regeneration. The body can synthesize this protein, if the iron factors are adequate. In starved animals, hemoglobin synthesis even takes precedence over the plasma proteins, but the response is inadequate as soon as the limited amount of protein reserve has been depleted. Adequate dietary protein for hemoglobin formation is supplied on a good mixed diet, but whole liver, kidneys, and chicken gizzards are excellent for this purpose.

Maturation of the erythrocyte and the antipernicious anemia principle. In the so-called pernicious types of anemia, the defect is not primarily in the hemoglobin content of the individual red cells, but in the maturation of sufficient numbers of these cells. According to Castle (2) an extrinsic factor, probably a food protein, is acted upon by an intrinsic factor, probably an enzyme in the gastric juice, to form the "maturation principle" responsible for the regeneration of red cells. This agent is then absorbed, partly via the stomach (since extracts of stomach wall, or "ventriculin," are effective therapeutically), but probably via the intestines chiefly. Storage occurs in the liver, with other minor reserves, especially in the bone marrow. Liver and liver extracts are good sources of the active maturation principle. The bone marrow gets the maturation principle via the blood and, in some unknown manner, the red cells are thereby enabled to develop through the successive stages to normal erythrocyte maturity. Deficiency of the maturation factor results in erythropoiesis being held back in the more primitive phases. The typical large size (macrocytic) red cells of pernicious anemia can perhaps be attributed to continued growth of their bone marrow precursors, whereas normocytes (and normoblasts) have their growth arrested by the earlier completion of the maturation phenomena. In pernicious anemia the individual red cells may be well hemoglobinized, as shown by the hyperchromia or color index in excess of unity. The color index is the hemoglobin (percentage of normal) divided by the red cell count (percentage of normal). A lowering of the red cell count (oligocythemia) shows that the number of new cells formed is inadequate to maintain the normal quota of circulating erythrocytes, especially under the conditions of increased red cell destruction due to the abnormal character of many of the cells. Liver extract therapy has been remarkably successful in the treatment of pernicious anemia, but a few "achrestic" cases seem to have some fundamental defect in the metabolism of the bone marrow cells themselves, so that they are unable to use the maturation principle even when it is adequately provided.

Achlorhydria, or lack of free HCl in the stomach, is an almost universal finding in cases of pernicious anemia, and is of major diagnostic significance. It is difficult to correlate this with failure of the stomach to elaborate the maturation principle, especially since the pyloric regions of the stomach yield most of the active factor but do not secrete acid. It is true, however, that extensive surgical resection or widespread destructive lesions of the stomach are frequently followed by macrocytic anemia.

The aplastic anemias are characterized by a failure of bone marrow erythropoiesis, often secondary to a toxic cause, and must represent failure of red cell formation due to impaired vitality of the blood-forming cells. The classification of the anemias is excellently presented by Haden (7).

Stimulus to erythropoiesis. The physiological stimulus to the bone marrow function of forming new red cells is a lowering of the blood oxygen content (anoxemia). This may be secondary to blood loss (hemorrhage) or to anemia (oligocythemia) of deficiency (see above) or of hemolytic origin. Except in the aplastic and achrestic anemias, the anoxemic stimulus is quite adequate. The anemia problem, therefore, is one of red cell replacement, either urgently, by blood transfusion, or gradually, by keeping up the supply of protein, iron, and maturation factor. The anoxemia may be primary, in which case the red cell count may rise considerably above the normal (*polycythemia*). Idiopathic polycythemia (vera) may be due to narrowing (sclerosis) of the nutrient vessels to the bone marrow, thus producing a localized anoxia. In obstructive lung diseases and congenital anomalies of the heart and pulmonary circulations the anoxemia is due to deficient aeration of the blood. Chronic exposure to high altitudes (Monge's disease) causes anoxia because of the low barometric pressure of oxygen. Chronic poisoning with carbon monoxide and some other agents may produce polycythemia by minor degrees of interference with the oxygen-carrying capacity of the blood hemoglobin. Cobalt polycythemia is a result of chemical stimulation of the bone marrow, but cobalt has no rational use in treating the anemias.

Normal Mechanisms of Red Blood Cell Destruction. It is probable that the buffetings which the erythrocytes get in the normal wear and tear of the circulation play a major role in the considerable physiological destruction previously noted. Microscopic observation of normal blood films reveals no hemolysis but some evidence of fragmentation of red cells. Much more of this breaking up, however, goes on in the spleen, and to some extent in the bone marrow and other reticulo-endothelial tissues. Phagocytosis of both fragments and whole red cells is evident in these tissues.

Abnormal Mechanisms of Red Blood Cell Destruction. These include various types of hemolysis, hemoglobin alterations, and red cell destruction by parasites (e.g., malaria). Hemolysis or laking of blood is a process whereby hemoglobin escapes from the red cells into the surrounding fluid. That the process is not simple is indicated by the fact that mere fragmentation is often insufficient to release the hemoglobin. The term "cell membrane" comes closest to factual reality in the "ghost" or *stroma* of the red cell, which is left after the simpler forms of hemolysis, e.g., in water or hypotonic salt solutions. Accepting at face value the statement that the red cell membrane is permeable to water but not to the cations of salts, osmotic hemolysis can be explained as a water shift from a salt-poor outer environment into the relatively salt-rich interior of the cell. At the isotonic or isosmotic concentration (for NaCl, about 0.9 per cent, in the case of mammalian erythrocytes) no change in corpuscle volume is evident by hematocrit and similar tests.

An isotonic solution of sodium chloride (0.9 gm. per 100 cc. for mammalian tissues, but 0.65 gm. for those of frogs and turtles), is not, in general, adequate for keeping tissues in a state of normal activity. It was shown by Ringer (1880–83) that small amounts of potassium and calcium salts, together with a little bicarbonate, were also needed to maintain normal beating of the isolated frog heart. Formulas for Ringer solutions suitable for work with mammalian tissues are given in Table 16. A Ringer-Locke solution without glucose or oxygen can be used in some mammalian experiments.

Table 16.—Modified Ringer Solutions for Mammalian Tissues

SUBSTANCE	GM. PER 100 CC. IN	
	LOCKE'S SOLUTION FOR RABBIT HEART	TYRODE'S SOLUTION FOR RABBIT INTESTINE
NaCl	0.9	0.8
KCl	0.042	0.02
$CaCl_2$	0.024	0.02
$MgCl_2$		0.01
$NaHCO_3$	0.015 (0.01 to 0.03)	0.1
NaH_2PO_4		0.005
Glucose	0.1	0.1
Oxygen	Saturated	Saturated

Although a modified Ringer's solution is useful in experimental work with other tissues, it is not adequate for the preservation of blood. When blood or plasma is to be used for transfusions, it is desirable to dilute it as little as possible, but coagulation must be prevented. This is accomplished by the use of solutions containing sodium citrate. In the preparation of plasma, usually about 500 cc. of blood are collected in a bottle containing 50 cc. of a 4 per cent solution of this salt (3.2 per cent if the dihydrate is used). The mixture is kept cold until the cells are centrifuged down or allowed to settle, and the plasma is then drawn off. Citrate alone is not adequate for the preservation of whole blood for very many days, as the cells undergo hemolysis even in an isotonic solution. It was found by Rous and Turner in 1916 that this hemolysis could be greatly delayed by the addition of a considerable amount of an isotonic (5.4 per cent) solution of glucose. Later workers have employed mixtures of citrate and glucose in which the blood is kept at two-fifths to two-thirds of its original concentration. Although trisodium citrate solutions have an alkaline reaction (pH 8.5 to 9.0), the pH of the blood in the mixtures is not far from the normal value of 7.4. It has been reported, however, that the cells are better preserved in a slightly acid medium. Good results have been obtained by collecting 420 or 430 cc. of blood in a mixture of 100 cc. of a 2 per cent solution of disodium citrate (or of a solution containing corresponding amounts of trisodium citrate and citric acid) with 20 cc. of 15 per cent glucose. This acid citrate-dextrose mixture has a pH of 4.9, which is raised to 6.5 or more on the addition of the blood. The recommendation of this mixture for the preservation of blood for transfusions is supported by experimental determinations of the period of survival in vivo of transfused erythrocytes (10). Other solutions which have been used for the preservation of blood, as well as full details of the operation of a blood bank, were described in a report by Canadian workers (14).

With a hypotonic solution outside the red cell, water accumulates in the corpuscle, causing it to swell. If the swelling exceeds a certain limit, hemoglobin escapes and forms a clear reddish solution in the surrounding fluid. On examination with the dark-field microscope, the residual envelope, "ghost" or stroma is readily seen as a spheroidal, feebly refractile outline, which changes its shape under mechanical stress and, under certain conditions, undergoes a disintegration called stromatolysis. Stromatolysis is said to resemble the so-called myelin figures observed when phospholipids swell in certain salt solutions. Such a resemblance in the case of blood platelets has also been noted, and similar formations from intact red cells under artificial conditions have been observed. It may be significant that chemical analyses reveal an abundance of phospholipids in both red cell stromata and washed blood platelets. Recent data stress the importance of cephalin.

Hypertonic salt solutions (e.g., over 0.9 per cent NaCl) containing a non-penetrating ion withdraw water from the erythrocyte, causing it to shrink and wrinkle (crenate). On restoring to isotonicity, some degree of swelling (spherocytosis) and hemolysis frequently occurs, showing that the hypertonic solution has damaged the cell membrane. The so-called "reversal of hemolysis" produced by transferring red cells from hypotonic to hypertonic solutions is simply an osmotic shrinkage of partially hemolyzed cells and not a true reversal.

Osmotic fragility test. On placing human red cells in a series of NaCl dilutions in small centrifuge tubes we can detect the degree of hypotonicity necessary to produce (i) start of hemolysis, i.e., lysis of the more susceptible cells, as shown by the pinkish red tint of liberated hemoglobin in the supernatant liquid after centrifugation, and (ii) complete hemolysis, when the subsequent centrifugation shows no red cell layer but merely a trace of stroma debris below a clear red solution. This is the osmotic *fragility test;* normal values are (i) 0.45 to 0.39 per cent, (ii) 0.33 to 0.30 per cent NaCl. Comparison with isotonicity (0.9 per cent NaCl) shows that there is a very considerable reserve of protection against sudden osmotic shifts of fluid between plasma and corpuscles. The fragility test is of considerable clinical diagnostic value, e.g., the increase in familial acholuric jaundice. Younger and less mature red cells are generally more resistant to saline hemolysis and the fragility is often lessened, for example, in pernicious anemia. Older cells and abnormal forms are usually more fragile, examples being seen in sickle cell anemia, spherocytosis, etc.

The term "isotonicity" is not strictly applicable to solutions whose solutes penetrate the red cell membrane, e.g., ammonium salts, urea, glucose, etc. In these instances any fluid balance is only temporary and water is not restrained from entering and rupturing the cell. The permeability of the cell membrane varies with pH and other conditions and the influence of specific cations and anions depends upon dissociation, ion exchange, and other factors.

Toxic hemolysis. Hemolytic agents of a second group act by damaging the red cell membrane. This group includes a number of physical agents, such as shaking, freezing and thawing, heat, light in the presence of certain photochemical sensitizers (hematoporphyrin, eosin, rose bengal, etc.), ultraviolet, roentgen and radium radiations, and electric currents. Toxic hemolysis is also caused by a number of chemical agents, including alkalis, soaps and higher fatty acids, saponin, bile salts, numerous organic solvents, certain glucosides (sapotoxin, solamin, digitalin, etc.), "toxalbumins" (ricin, abrin, crotin), some proteolytic enzymes, certain venoms (cobra, scorpion, centipede, etc.), extracts of some parasitic worms (hookworm, fish tapeworm), and the hemolytic bacteria. Deserving of special classification because of their serious effects in vivo are the immunological hemolysins.

Serological agglutination and hemolysis (17, 18). The sera of many species possess the property of agglutinating and hemolyzing the erythrocytes of other species both in vivo following a transfusion and in vitro. To such phenomena may be attributed in large part the reactions and fatalities following attempts to use a "foreign" blood for transfusion.

Of more practical importance in medicine is the fact that human erythrocytes differ in their antigenic makeup and human sera in their agglutinin content. The existence of these "iso" antigens and antibodies was discovered by Landsteiner, who found that human bloods could be divided into four main groups based upon such differences. His classification, together with those of Jansky and of Moss, is as follows:

LANDSTEINER (INTERNATIONAL)		JANSKY	MOSS
RED CELL FACTORS (AGGLUTINOGENS)	SERUM FACTORS (AGGLUTININS)		
O	$\alpha\beta$	I	IV
A	β	II	II
B	α	III	III
AB	0	IV	I

It will be noted that in every case an individual contains in his serum the antibodies for the antigens lacking in his erythrocytes. Since transfusion with blood from a person of another group may result in reactions sometimes terminating fatally, it is essential always to type the bloods prior to such a procedure. Typing is performed by mixing on a glass slide drops of red cell suspensions of the unknown type with drops of known α and β sera. No agglutination with either serum denotes a blood of group O, agglutination with the α serum of group A, with the β serum a B blood, and with both sera an AB blood. Transfusions should always be made with a blood of the same group, and as a further safeguard for complete compatibility a "crossmatching" test should be performed, in which the patient's red cells are mixed with the donor's serum, and the donor's cells with the patient's serum.

It is apparent that the cells of a group O individual will not be agglutinated by the sera of any of the other groups, while his own serum, unless extremely potent in α and β agglutinins, will be so diluted in a recipient's blood stream that the titer may fall to an ineffective level. (It is for this latter reason that plasma, usually pooled, can be safely used). Group O individuals are, therefore, sometimes regarded as "universal donors." Conversely, Group AB members may be considered "universal recipients." However, transfusions of whole blood based on these principles are, except in emergencies, regarded unfavorably in modern practice.

In addition to these so-called major antigens of the human erythrocyte, others have been revealed. For example, all bloods can be further divided into three groups, M+N+, M+N−, and M−N+, depending upon the presence or absence of the M and N antigens. The serum normally contains no antibodies for these substances.

Recently another antigen, present in the erythrocytes of about 85 per cent of the white population, has been disclosed. This is the *Rh substance*, so called because it was first detected by the use of antibodies produced in guinea pigs following injections of rhesus monkey red cells.* An Rh+ individual may have one of several "Rh" antigens more or less similar to that found in monkeys. Human serum ordinarily contains no corresponding antibody, so that detection of the antigen depends upon the use of specially prepared animal sera or of serum from an Rh− person who has unwittingly been exposed to Rh antigen. The importance of this antigen lies in the fact that Rh− individuals can develop antibodies as a result of transfusions with Rh+ blood, so that subsequent transfusions with blood containing this factor may give more or less pronounced reactions. Moreover, since the Rh factor is heritable, an Rh− mother may have a child which is Rh+ through inheritance from the father. In such a case during pregnancy the mother may become sensitized by means of the antigen in the fetus, and to the reaction between the antibodies so produced with the red cells of the fetus have been ascribed some hematological abnormalities such as erythroblastosis foetalis. Furthermore, if the mother should receive a transfusion of Rh+ blood she herself might suffer a reaction. For these reasons it would seem highly desirable that in every pregnancy the Rh characteristics of the two parents be determined, and that in every case of transfusion the blood be compatible in Rh group as well as in the O, A, B and AB type.

In the field of forensic medicine, also, the existence of these antigenic differences in man, all inherited according to the laws of genetics, is of increasing importance, particularly in cases involving the proof of non-paternity. For example, if a child has the A factor in his erythrocytes, that factor must have been inherited from one of the parents. If the mother is an O or a B individual, then the real father must be an A or an AB. Presence of the A factor in the man obviously cannot establish paternity, but its absence is evidence that he is not the father. By use of the subgroups A_1 and A_2, the M and N types and the several Rh types, the value of such a test is correspondingly increased.

Chemical alteration of hemoglobin. Methemoglobin formation occurs in

---

* Literature concerning the Rh factor is meager, since the recognition is recent. The important paper of L. K. Diamond appeared in the *New England Journal of Medicine* in December 1942 (*227*:857–862; 932). Attention should also be directed to editorials on the subject (*J. Amer. med. Ass.*, 1944, *125*:495, and *New Engl. J. Med.*, 1944, *230*:816). There is a valuable report by L. E. Young and D. H. Kariher of the University of Rochester (*J. Amer. med. Ass.*, 1945, *127*:627–632) which contains an up-to-date bibliography.

vitro when blood is treated with an oxidizing agent. In vivo, methemoglobinemia is encountered in poisoning with phenylhydrazine, pyrogallol, nitrobenzene, and other nitro- and amide-compounds, especially acetanilide, sulfanilamide, and with nitrites, methylene blue, sulfonal, potassium chlorate, etc. Sulfhemoglobin seems to require preliminary formation of methemoglobin and is more important as a postmortem phenomenon than during life, for instance, in hydrogen sulfide and similar poisonings. Only small amounts of SH-hemoglobin are formed (along with methemoglobin) by the sulfonamides. Arsine (AsH_3) and nitric oxide (NO) (e.g., from explosives) also combine with hemoglobin. Carbon monoxide forms CO-hemoglobin, which is serious because of the nonavailability of the hemoglobin for oxygen transport.

Red Blood Cells in Relation to Spleen. In addition to a temporary embryological role in red cell formation and the important function, throughout life, of removing effete erythrocytes, the spleen has a "reservoir" function of considerable physiological significance. It is estimated that the spleen of the cat can accommodate one-quarter of the red blood cells or one-sixth of the total blood volume. Under resting conditions, the blood flow through the spleen is so sluggish that this amount of blood, for all practical purposes, is out of effective circulation; the spleen serves as a *reservoir* (Barcroft, 1925) for the prompt replenishment of red cell and whole blood volume, such as is normally required in exercise, emotional stress, and adjustment to cold environmental temperatures and to anoxia. The spleen reservoir is also important in pathological conditions, especially hemorrhage and shock. Splenomegaly (enlargement of the spleen) is common in the hemolytic anemias, malaria and other conditions in which its phagocytic functions are overworked.

Leukocytes

Ameboid Motility and Chemotaxis. The leukocytes "crawl," like an ameba, but do not "swim," and therefore need for their motion some surface, such as strands of fibrin, connective tissue fibers, etc. The rate of motion seems to depend solely upon conditions within the living cell, but its direction is largely determined by external stimuli called chemotactic. *Chemotaxis* (11) may be positive, attracting the leukocytes, or negative, repelling them. Chemotaxis is best studied in cell cultures or explants, in which it is possible to observe the behavior of large numbers of one particular kind of leukocyte. Substances used in testing for chemotaxis are classified as: (i) positive test substances (e.g., collodion particles, bacteria, tissue proteins, some carbohydrates, etc.), (ii) negative agents (e.g., aluminum silicate, some streptococci —after initial attraction), (iii) indifferent substances (e.g., carbon particles). In such tests the *granulocytes* (neutrophil, eosinophil; data are lacking for basophils) are found to give positive chemotaxis with (i), negative chemotaxis with (ii), and an indifferent response to (iii); the *monocytes* are largely indifferent but may be slightly positive with (i) and slightly negative with (ii); and the *lymphocytes* are definitely indifferent to chemotaxis. It is very difficult, in view of the extreme insolubility and chemical inertness of most of the test substances, to offer any adequate explanation for chemotaxis. Menkin (12) has crystallized from inflammatory exudates a dialyzable polypeptide, termed *leukotaxine*, which affords a partial explanation of the attraction of leukocytes to areas of injury and inflammation. It induces early aggregation (margination) of leukocytes in capillaries of the inflamed region, and they quickly migrate ("diapedesis") through the endothelial wall out into the tissue spaces to engage upon their phagocytic and other functions.

Functions of Leukocytes. Cells of the monocyte type (of both blood and tissue origin) are active in the repair and remodeling of tissues. Possibly the leukocytes and related cells provide building and nutritive materials, especially of protein and lipid nature. The best evidence for this lies in the demonstration that leukocytes can provide growth-promoting substances or *trephones* for cells growing in tissue cultures.

Phagocytosis (13). *Neutrophil* and *eosinophil* polymorphonuclear leukocytes actively devour bacteria and other "foreign" agents with which they come into contact, especially aided by their ameboid movement under positively chemotactic influences. The presence of protein-digesting enzymes in leukocytes and the protein nature of the agents which commonly undergo phagocytosis point to a correlation, details of which are obscure. The frequent association of localized eosinophil accumulation in affected tissues and sometimes *eosinophilia* (increase in blood *eosinophils*) suggest that the sensitization to foreign proteins characteristic of *allergic conditions* may involve this type of leukocyte. The eosinophilia of skin diseases and of parasitic worm infections may have an essentially similar significance. The *monocytes* have an especially wide range of phagocytic powers. They ingest many bacteria and other micro-organisms, including types which are not attacked by the microphages (polymorphonuclear leukocytes). Like the rest of the reticulo-endothelial system, they may contain pigment (e.g., malarial), fragments of dead cells and necrotic tissue, etc., and all sorts of inert foreign materials. A special phagocytosis of dyes and other materials (e.g., India ink) in fine suspension or colloidal solution is a characteristic vital staining reaction of the reticulo-endothelial system.

Opsonins are substances which appear in the serum of immunized animals, and, in some manner, sensitize the bacterial, or other, antigen to phagocytosis by leukocytes. We are far from clear whether the leukocytes play some role in the production of antibodies in general. The evidence is more convincing in the case of the relatively fixed cells of the reticulo-endothelial system and has recently been advanced in the case of the lymphocyte.

Other functions of leukocytes are insufficiently elucidated. A suggested role in intestinal absorption (especially of fats) is currently in much doubt. The *lymphocyte* is especially a problem. It is not truly phagocytic. It has a characteristic type of ameboid mobility and accumulates in the tissues in large number in the later stages of acute inflammations, in chronic inflammations, and around degenerative and neoplastic (cancerous) lesions. Some have claimed that resistance of the tissues to cancer and tuberculosis varies with the degree of mobilization of the lymphocytes.

Fate of the Leukocytes. The circulating white blood cells are really en route to the tissues into which they ultimately migrate in order to carry on their functions, although in blood stream infections (septicemia) phagocytosis occurs in the blood itself. The evident phagocytosis of leukocytes by macrophages in the spleen, bone marrow, Kupffer cells of the liver, etc., strongly suggests that the *reticulo-endothelial system* plays the leading role in disposing of leukocytes, just as it does for the red cells. This applies, presumably, to effete, senile, and abnormal forms. Damaged and degenerated leukocytes are the chief forms of *pus* cells, especially in acute septic inflammations. Fatty degeneration is of some importance in relation to certain lipid inhibitors (e.g., antitrypsin) of proteolytic phenomena. *Enzymes* liberated by degenerating leukocytes and other cells are largely responsible for proteolytic liquefaction of dead (necrotic) tissue, fibrinous exudates (e.g., in pneumonia), etc. In addition, there are always leukocytes in various stages of degeneration to be found in the excretions, especially the saliva and the secretions of the respiratory, alimentary, and genito-urinary tracts. It is possible that the ordinary bacterial flora of these various excretory channels may exert a positive chemotaxis which could be largely responsible for the leukocytic migration. It is now believed that the fatty particles in leukocytes in the mucosa of the alimentary canal—once thought to be evidence of a role of lymphocytes in fat absorption—are merely a result of fatty degeneration of transmigrating leukocytes.

More *lymphocytes* enter the blood stream via the thoracic duct* than can be accounted for by the white cell count at any time. Hence it is probable that their life span is very brief, perhaps less than 24 hours. It is suggested that the myeloid leukocytes survive for a few days, but the evidence is far from convincing. For details of variations in the white cell count and the morphological appearances of leukocytes, the reader is referred to the hematological literature (4, 18).

Blood platelets (16)

The identification of the blood platelets as a third type of formed element in mammalian blood survived a number of early attempts to dismiss them as various artifacts. Their origin in the fragmentation of cytoplasmic processes (pseudopods) of *megakaryocytes*, or histiocytic giant cells of bone marrow, spleen, lungs, etc., is unique, in all probability, only because of the degenerative (necrobiotic) character of the parent cells.

The *life span* of the platelet is thought to be about three to five days, but this guess is the result of the indirect evidence of recovery periods after induced thrombocytopenia. The arterial blood entering an organ consistently has a higher platelet count than the venous blood leaving it, especially in the lungs. It is suggested that the macrophages of the spleen, and other reticulo-endothelial macrophages, are the physiological mechanisms for platelet removal. As in the case of other formed elements, the platelet *count* represents the overall balance between removal on the one hand and new formation, in bone marrow, etc., on the other.

Under artificial conditions (e.g., living blood films kept under observation with the dark-field microscope), leukocytes may, at times, lose fragments of their protoplasm and erythrocytes may bud off the so-called *erythroplastids*. Further, the peculiar disintegration of the platelets in shed blood is only a more conspicuous and regular example of a phenomenon which has essentially similar counterparts in mammalian (intact) megakaryocytes, the thrombocytes of lower animals, and red cell "stromatolysis." The resemblance of these phenomena to myelin-figure formations is fundamental, in view of the high phospholipid (especially cephalin) content of platelets, red

---

* It has been reported (Reinhardt and Li, *Science*, 1945, *101*:361) that the administration of adrenocorticotrophic hormone to rats produced a decrease (50 per cent or more) in the number of lymphocytes in the thoracic duct lymph. The authors conclude that the lymphocyte level of the circulating blood is under direct adrenal cortical control.

cell stroma, and probably of cell membranes in general. The specific role of calcium ions in platelet lysis can be referred to lipid-water phase relations. Studies of myelin-figure formation in the presence of various salts showed that Ca was unique in favoring penetration of the water into the lipid phase. It is believed that the platelet, which is normally a little disc composed chiefly of protein and lipid in a highly condensed film, is thus enabled to undergo partial liquefaction, with the appearance of characteristic little vesicles, and thereby liberates a portion of its contents.

Antiplatelet sera may be obtained by active immunization. *Heparin* preserves platelets in addition to its anticoagulant effect. Platelet breakdown is very slow in *hemophilia*. Micro-organisms adhere to and clump around platelets ("platelet loading") in the presence of plasma or serum, and so do foreign red cells, India ink, carmine and other colloidal dyes; these phenomena resemble the process of opsonization (which precedes phagocytosis in the case of leukocytic functions) and are probably important in removing foreign agents such as bacteria from the circulation by anchoring them in the capillaries, especially of lung, liver and spleen, where the leukocytes can take care of them. These and other facts suggest that the platelet surface has important functions as a site for colloidal adsorption and that protein as well as lipid factors must be considered. It may very well be that some of the factors in blood coagulation (possibly serum tryptase) are equally important in aiding platelet disintegration, and that the two phenomena must often be regarded as coincidental rather than as directly related. The chief function of the platelets has been thought to be their share in the formation of blood clots (*thrombi*) in vivo (Chap. 28).

REFERENCES

1. BARCROFT, J. *The respiratory function of the blood*, 2d ed. Cambridge, University Press, 1925 and 1928, 2 vols.

2. CASTLE, W. B. The etiology of pernicious and related macrocytic anemias. *Harvey Lect.*, 1934–35, *30*:37–48.

3. CHANG, H. C., and HARROP, G. A., JR. The determination of the circulating blood volume with carbon monoxide. *J. clin. Invest.*, 1928, *5*:393–405.

4. DOWNEY, H. *Handbook of hematology*. New York, Paul B. Hoeber, 1938, 4 vols.

5. FERGUSON, J. H. Living human blood cells under the dark-ground microscope. *Trans. roy. Soc. S. Afr.*, 1930, *18*:317–323.

6. GREGERSEN, M. I. A practical method for the determination of blood volume with the dye T-1824. *J. lab. clin. Med.*, 1944, *29*:1266–1286.

7. HADEN, R. L. *Principles of hematology*, 2d ed. Philadelphia, Lea & Febiger, 1940, 362 pp.

8. HAHN, P. F. The metabolism of iron. *Medicine, Baltimore*, 1937, *16*:249–266.

9. HAM, T. H. and CURTIS, F. C. Sedimentation rate of erythrocytes. *Medicine, Baltimore*, 1938, *17*:447–517.

10. LOUTIT, J. F. and MOLLISON, P. L. Advantages of a disodium-citrate-glucose mixture as a blood preservative. *Brit. med. J.*, 1943, *2*:744–745.

11. MCCUTCHEON, M. Chemotaxis. *Arch. Path.*, 1942, *34*:167–181.

12. MENKIN, V. The role of inflammation in immunity. *Physiol. Rev.*, 1938, *18*:366–418.

13. MUDD, S., MCCUTCHEON, M., and LUCKÉ, B. Phagocytosis. *Physiol. Rev.*, 1934, *14*:210–275.

14. RHEA, L. J., DENSTEDT, O. F., BERTRAND, A., VAN DORSSER, G. J. E. and GREEY, P. H. Procedures recommended for the organization and operation of a blood bank. *Canad. med. Ass. J.*, 1944: *50*:403–410; *51*:144–166.

15. ROWNTREE, L. G., BROWN, G. E. and ROTH, G. M. *The volume of blood and plasma in health and disease*. Philadelphia, W. B. Saunders Co., 1929, 219 pp.

16. TOCANTINS, L. M. The mammalian blood platelet in health and disease. *Medicine, Baltimore*, 1938, *17*:155–260.

17. WIENER, A. S. *Blood groups and blood transfusion*, 3d ed. Springfield, Charles C Thomas, 1943, 438 pp.

18. WINTROBE, M. M. *Clinical hematology*. Philadelphia, Lea & Febiger, 1942, 792 pp.

Thanks are due to Dr. P. B. Cowles, Dept. of Bacteriology, Yale University School of Medicine, for help on serological agglutination and hemolysis, pp. 560–561.

CHAPTER 27

CHEMICAL ASPECTS OF THE PHYSIOLOGY OF BLOOD

The quantitative chemical analysis of blood has yielded information of considerable value in the study of physiology as well as in clinical medicine. Blood contains a great many different substances, and their detection and estimation constitute an important part of analytical biochemistry. Details of technique, and an indication of the significance of these studies in normal and abnormal physiology, may be found in special works on physiological or clinical chemistry (9). The present chapter will be limited to a broad outline of the chemical composition of blood, a statement of some chemical principles which have been applied in the explanation of physiological phenomena mediated by the blood, and a short account of the properties of the proteins in blood. The discussion of many important substances, such as lipids, enzymes, hormones, and other organic molecules, must be left for biochemical texts.

CHEMICAL COMPOSITION OF BLOOD

As a first approximation, it may be said that blood is about 80 per cent water. The proteins constitute about 18 per cent of blood, leaving 2 per cent for other solutes. About half of these are inorganic salts, the rest being organic molecules smaller than proteins. The important blood gases, oxygen and carbon dioxide, amount to little more than 0.1 per cent of the total mass of the blood.

The total concentration of all dissolved substances in blood, including ions as well as molecules, is about 0.3 mol per liter. The results of blood analyses are often expressed in mg. per 100 ml.; concentrations in these units are also commonly (though illogically) designated as milligrams per cent. Such data may be translated into millimols (mM.) or milliequivalents (mEq.) per liter by multiplying by 10 and dividing by the molecular or equivalent weight of the substance in question. For example, if blood plasma contains 370 mg. Cl per 100 ml., its chloride concentration is $3700/35.46$ or 104 mEq./l.; that is, 0.104 N. If the chloride concentration is reported as 610 mg. per cent of NaCl, the concentration of this salt is also $6100/58.45$ or 104 mM./l., which is 0.104 M.

In attempting to apply the physicochemical laws of dilute solutions to the blood, chemists have found that simpler results are obtained if the concentrations are referred to unit mass of the solvent, water, rather than to unit volume of solution. Such units of concentration, the weight normality and molality, are commonly employed by physical chemists, especially in dealing with concentrated solutions. For dilute solutions of small molecules, the molality and the ordinary volume concentration (molarity) are practically identical. For blood plasma, however, and especially for the cells, the values are quite different, because the proteins occupy an appreciable portion of the total volume. According to Peters (8), one liter of average plasma or serum contains 935 gm. of water, while a liter of red blood cells contains only 707 gm. of water. A plasma concentration of 0.104 N may also be expressed as 104/935 or 0.111 equivalents per kg. of plasma water, while a concentration of 0.052 N in blood cells means that there are 52/707 or 0.074 equivalents per kg. of cell water. In any calculation involving osmotic pressure or other colligative properties of solutions, concentrations are best referred to 1 kg. of the solvent.

Distribution of Substances Between Cells and Plasma. Many of the constituents of blood are very unequally distributed between the cells and the plasma, as shown in Table 17.

Table 17.—*Distribution of Solutes between Cells and Plasma of Normal Human Blood*

	MOLS (OR EQUIVALENTS) PER KG. H_2O IN	
	SERUM	CELLS
Protein	0.001	0.007
Base neutralized by protein, equivalents	0.018*	0.062
Urea	0.007	0.007
Glucose	0.004	0.004
Other neutral organic solutes	?	?
Bicarbonate + carbamino CO_2	0.028	0.027
Chloride	0.111	0.074
Acid soluble organic phosphate	trace	0.021*
Base neutralized by organic phosphate	unknown*	unknown*
Inorganic phosphate	0.002	0.002
Base neutralized by inorganic phosphate, eq.	0.003	0.003
Sulfate	0.001	?
Base neutralized by sulfate, eq.	0.001	?
Calcium	0.003	0
Equivalents of calcium	0.005	0
Magnesium	0.001	0.003
Equivalents of magnesium	0.001	0.005
Potassium	0.004*	0.135*
Sodium	0.147*	0.027*
Sum of equivalents of base	0.157	0.167
Sum of equivalents of acid	0.161	0.166
Sum of molal concentrations, including ions	0.309	0.307

* Most of the data in Table 17 are reproduced from Peters' *Body Water* (1935), by courtesy of Charles C Thomas, publisher, Springfield, Illinois. The figures marked with an asterisk are revised values kindly supplied by Dr. Peters. The estimate of the serum protein concentration and the summations in the last three lines were made by the present writer.

The unequal distribution of proteins is qualitative as well as quantitative in nature. The protein of the cells is almost entirely hemoglobin, which constitutes about 32 per cent of their weight. The stromata or "ghosts" of the red cells, which represent structural elements in the cells, also contain some protein, probably about 1 per cent of the wet weight of the cells. These cell proteins are not found in plasma, and the plasma proteins are absent from the cells. Plasma contains about 7 gm. of protein per 100 ml. Of this, about 0.2 to 0.4 gm. is fibrinogen. The remaining plasma proteins are the serum proteins, which are classified as albumins and globulins on the basis of the concentrations of ammonium sulfate or other salt required to precipitate them. The albumin: globulin (A/G) ratio shows considerable variability in normal sera, and it also varies somewhat with the particular salting-out technique which is adopted; the normal ratio runs from about 1.5 to 2.0.

Another marked instance of unequal distribution is that of the principal cations or bases,* sodium and potassium. In human blood the greater part of the potassium is found in the cells, while most of the sodium is in the plasma. These cations, as well as the proteins of the blood, are in some way restrained from free diffusion between the cell contents and the plasma. Yet the impermeability of the cells to potassium cannot be absolute, for the injection into the plasma of a salt solution containing a radioactive isotope of potassium has been followed by the detection of radioactivity in the cells. The mechanism responsible for the unequal distribution of cations is not known, but under most conditions the cells behave as if they were impermeable to all cations, with the possible exception of the hydrogen ion.† The situation with respect to anions is quite different, since the human red cell is freely permeable to chloride, bicarbonate and hydroxyl ions, although not to various other anions. It is also readily permeable to water and to many undissociated molecules, such as those of dissolved carbon dioxide or carbonic acid, ammonia or ammonium hydroxide, urea and glucose.

It will be noted that Table 17 shows a small discrepancy between the amounts of total base and total acid in each phase. This is not due to the omission of hydroxyl and hydrogen ions, for their concentrations lie in the seventh and eighth decimal places. If the analytical data were complete and the figures represented the equivalent concentrations of actual ions, the sums would have to agree, for any solution must be electrically neutral with respect to ionic charges. The table is admittedly incomplete; organic acids (other than proteins) are not included, and the amount of base neutralized by organic phosphate is unknown. The actual concentrations of bicarbonate ion are less than the figures given, since these include carbon dioxide bound to proteins in carbamino complexes. It is possible that sodium and potassium proteinates are not completely ionized, there is good evidence that this is true of calcium proteinates, and there may be some un-ionized chloride in combination with lipids. In view of these uncertainties, the discrepancies between the totals in each column of the table are not unexpected, and it is quite possible that serum and cells may have the same total number of equivalents of ions per 1000 gm. of water.

OSMOTIC EQUILIBRIUM

Total Osmotic Pressure of Blood. It has long been known that red blood cells can be made to swell or shrink by placing them in slightly hypotonic or hypertonic salt solutions. Because of the ease with which water is driven into or out of the cells in this way, it is inferred that the cell contents and the plasma must have the same total osmotic pressure. Hematocrit experiments have shown that human red cells retain their original volume in a sodium chloride solution containing slightly less than 0.9 gm. of NaCl per 100 ml. (0.154 molar). The results of thermo-electric measurements, which

---

* Physiological and medical chemists use the term "base" to include metallic radicals or cations, as well as all compounds which can react with acids to form salts. This older usage should not be confused with the more recent definition of a base as a proton acceptor.

†The apparent permeability of the red cell to NH_4^+ has been ascribed to penetration by NH_3 or NH_4OH.

detect differences in vapor pressure or rate of evaporation of water, indicate that sera from normal men have the same osmotic activity as sodium chloride solutions of molal concentrations between 0.152 and 0.159. These results are consistent with the belief that a 0.9 per cent solution of sodium chloride (0.155 molal) is isotonic with either cells or plasma. Since the salt is believed to be completely dissociated into ions, the osmotically effective (osmolal) concentration of an isotonic salt solution is 0.310, a figure which agrees well with the totals in the last line of Table 17.

The total osmotic pressure of a solution is approximately related to its total concentration by the same equation which applies to gas pressure:

$$P = 0.082 \ TC.$$

Here P is the pressure in atmospheres, T the absolute temperature, and C the concentration of the gas or the dissolved substance in mols per liter. (In the case of aqueous solutions, the equation fits better if C is mols of solute per 1000 gm. of H_2O.) Accordingly the osmotic pressure of blood plasma at 38° C. should be $0.082 \times 311 \times 0.31$, or about 7.9 atmospheres. This figure does not represent an actual pressure in the blood. It will be recalled that osmotic pressure is defined as the excess pressure which must be imposed upon a solution to prevent the entrance of pure solvent into the solution through a membrane permeable only to the solvent. Because the membranes of the body are permeable to most of the dissolved substances as well as to water, they do not fit the physical chemist's definition of a perfect semi-permeable membrane, and the total osmotic pressures of body fluids are not manifested as actual pressures in the body. However, since natural membranes are more readily permeable to water than to most other substances, a comparison of total osmotic pressures or concentrations serves to indicate the direction in which water tends to flow. This flow results from the diffusion of water away from a region in which its own concentration (more exactly, its escaping tendency or vapor pressure) is high. Accordingly osmosis is directed towards a solution which is initially more concentrated with respect to dissolved substances. If the membrane is permeable to all solutes as well as to the solvent, the liquids on both sides will be identical at equilibrium, and they will be at the same pressure. If the membrane is impermeable to any solute but permeable to the solvent, the concentrations on both sides need not be the same at equilibrium, but the solvent on both sides of the membrane must have the same vapor pressure. In an osmometer this is achieved by the excess pressure on the solution, the osmotic pressure, which raises the vapor pressure of the solvent in the solution.

The belief that osmotic equilibrium prevails in the animal body is supported by thermo-electric comparisons of the rates of evaporation of body fluids from the dog. It was found (by Gilman et al. in 1933) that blood, lymph, aqueous humor, gastric juice, hepatic bile and pancreatic juice were practically isotonic with one another.

Colloid Osmotic Pressure of Plasma. A small fraction of the total osmotic pressure of plasma consists of the partial osmotic pressure of the plasma proteins. This colloid osmotic pressure has a more direct physiological significance than the total osmotic pressure. Colloid osmotic pressure was first measured in 1895 by the English physiologist Starling, who was also the first to recognize its importance in physiology. According to the Starling theory, the exchange of fluids between the tissue spaces and the blood stream is regulated by a balance between two opposing forces, the hydrostatic pressure in the blood capillaries and the partial osmotic pressure of the plasma colloids. These colloids consist almost entirely of the serum proteins, and the tissue fluids contain very little protein. The thin walls of the capillary blood vessels are membranes readily permeable to water and ordinary molecules or ions in solution, but essentially impermeable to proteins. If this impermeability is maintained, fluid should be absorbed from the tissue spaces into the blood whenever the hydrostatic pressure head is less than the colloid osmotic pressure. When the hydrostatic pressure exceeds the colloid osmotic pressure, fluid should be filtered from the blood into the tissue spaces.

Starling (12) measured the colloid osmotic pressure by placing serum in an osmometer on one side of a membrane, with a 1 per cent salt solution on the other. The membrane was permeable to salt and water, but impermeable to proteins, and it was supported rigidly by a wire mesh. He found that the pressure increased on the side containing the serum, reaching an equilibrium value of 30 to 40 mm. Hg, which was close to the accepted value for the capillary blood pressure. More recent figures for the colloid osmotic pressure of normal human serum fall between 22 and 30 mm. Krogh found about the same pressure when serum was equilibrated against an isotonic sodium chloride solution, Ringer's solution, or a protein-free ultrafiltrate obtained from another sample of the same serum. The early measurements of colloid osmotic pressure required several hours or days for the establishment of osmotic equilibrium, but improvements in technique have reduced the time to 15 minutes.

The validity of Starling's theory has been confirmed by Landis's measurements of the hydrostatic pressure in capillaries, although some difficulties have arisen because of incomplete knowledge of the permeability of the capillaries and the composition of tissue fluids.

MEMBRANE EQUILIBRIUM

Distribution of Ions across a Membrane. Although the colloid osmotic pressure, as measured by Starling's method, is useful in the interpretation of physiological facts, the name of this quantity is somewhat misleading, for in most cases it is not identical with the true osmotic pressure of the colloidal material. If the latter carries an electric charge, as it usually does, some of the measured pressure is due to an unequal distribution of diffusible electrolytes. Whenever a colloidal electrolyte is present on one side of a membrane through which it cannot pass, it is found that other ionized substances, to which the membrane is freely permeable, tend to become more concentrated in the solution on the opposite side of the membrane. This unequal distribution of ions at equilibrium is known as the Donnan effect; it was discovered in 1911 by Donnan and Harris, and explained by Donnan's theory (5) of membrane equilibrium.*

In a form applicable to a system composed of dilute solutions of a colloidal electrolyte and of sodium chloride, the Donnan principle may be stated by the simple equation

* Some writers call this condition the Gibbs-Donnan equilibrium, because Donnan's equations can be derived from a more general equation which had been deduced by J. Willard Gibbs. Gibbs did not refer to concentrations nor to ions; his paper was written before the ionic theory was formulated.

$$[Na^+]_I [Cl^-]_I = [Na^+]_{II} [Cl^-]_{II}$$

in which the brackets signify molal concentrations at equilibrium and the subscripts refer to the two solutions separated by the membrane. If solution I contains an ionized salt, NaR, whose anion cannot diffuse through the membrane, the fact that each solution is electrically neutral may be expressed by the additional equations:

$$[Na^+]_I = [Cl^-]_I + [R^-]$$

$$[Na^+]_{II} = [Cl^-]_{II}.$$

These three equations may be combined to give the relation

$$([Cl^-]_I + [R^-]_I) [Cl^-]_I = [Cl^-]_{II}^2.$$

This shows that $[Cl^-]_{II}$ must be greater than $[Cl^-]_I$, as was found in experiments in which solution I contained a sodium salt with a nondialyzable anion.

For a system containing a number of diffusible ions of unit valence, Donnan's equation may be written in the form of an equality of ratios of ion concentrations, as

$$\frac{[Cl^-]_I}{[Cl^-]_{II}} = \frac{[HCO_3^-]_I}{[HCO_3^-]_{II}} = \frac{[Na^+]_{II}}{[Na^+]_I} = \frac{[K^+]_{II}}{[K^+]_I}.$$

This equation holds only for those ions to which the membrane is freely permeable.

Colloid Osmotic Pressure and Donnan Equilibrium. The Donnan equilibrium has the effect of making the observed colloid osmotic pressure of serum greater than that due to the colloidal material alone, but much less than that due to the colloidal anions plus their equivalent cations. This may be shown by the following approximate calculations.

If normal serum contains 7 gm. of protein per 100 ml., it contains 75 gm. of protein per kg. of water. With an albumin: globulin ratio of 1.5, 1000 gm. of water contains 45 gm. of albumin and 30 gm. of globulin. Studies with the ultracentrifuge have indicated that the molecular weight of serum albumin is about 70,000, while that of the globulins is 150,000 to 175,000. Accordingly the molal concentration of the proteins in serum is about $0.0006+0.0002$, or 0.0008. Titration experiments have shown that at pH 7.4 these proteins have neutralized 0.018 equivalents of base. If the alkali proteinates are completely ionized, the concentration of cations equivalent to the protein anions is also 0.018 equivalents per kg. H_2O. When serum is placed in an osmometer and equilibrated against a physiological salt solution, the principal ions in the inner solution will be Na^+, Cl^- and the nondialyzable protein ions. The rule of electroneutrality requires that $[Na^+]$ must be greater than $[Cl^-]$ by 0.018. The outer solution will consist of 0.155 molal NaCl, which may be renewed to keep its concentration constant. The molal concentrations of ions at equilibrium may be represented by the numbers in the following diagram:

Serum	Saline
0.0008 R^{n-}	
y Cl^-	Cl^- 0.155
$y + 0.018$ Na^+	Na^+ 0.155

According to Donnan's principle, the concentrations of Na^+ and Cl^- at equilibrium are related by the equation,

$$y(y + 0.018) = (0.155)^2,$$

From this equation it turns out that the value of y is 0.14625. The sum of the total concentrations of ions in the serum is therefore 0.3113, while that in the saline is 0.3100. It is the difference between these concentrations, 0.0013, which is responsible for the observed colloid osmotic pressure. The osmotic pressure of a dilute solution at 38° C., when expressed in atmospheres, is equal to $0.082 \times 311 \, C$, or $25.5 \, C$. If the pressure is to be expressed in mm. Hg, the factor 25.5 must be multiplied by 760, which makes it 19,400. The colloid osmotic pressure is therefore calculated to be the product of 19,400 and 0.0013, or about 25 mm. Hg, in good agreement with observed values.* If our assumptions are correct, the protein particles alone are responsible for only about 16 mm. of this pressure, and the remainder is due to the Donnan equilibrium. Since the total concentration of the ions of the sodium proteinates is 0.0188, the total osmotic pressure of these salts should be 365 mm. Hg, a pressure which is never obtained by the use of a membrane permeable to ions.

It is characteristic of the Donnan equilibrium that the ion ratios approach unity if the concentration of diffusible salt is made much greater than that of the colloid. In that case the colloid osmotic pressure is reduced towards the partial osmotic pressure of the colloidal ions alone, but the approach to this lower limit is gradual. Although this discussion shows that colloid osmotic pressure is usually greater than the partial osmotic pressure of colloidal particles which bear electric charges, it is the measured pressures themselves which are significant in physiology, without correction for the Donnan effect.

Distribution of Ions between Cells and Plasma. The value of Donnan's theory of membrane equilibria in the interpretation of experiments with proteins and electrolytes was firmly established by the work of Jacques Loeb (7). Other workers tried to apply this theory to the distribution of ions across membrane in living systems. Here a difficulty appears, for the theory was deduced for a condition of equilibrium. The internal environment of a living organism is not in a condition of equilibrium, in the sense in which this word is used by physical chemists. The processes of the body are not balanced reactions, taking place at equal rates in opposite directions, but they do result in a more or less steady state in the blood, with equal rates of inflow and outflow. It seems likely that Donnan's equation for ion ratios may apply to systems in a steady state as well as to those in equilibrium. In a few experiments with cellophane membranes it was found by Teorell in 1937 that the continuous diffusion of one electrolyte across the membrane resulted in the unequal distribution of another. The ions accumulated in such a way as to simulate the Donnan effect without the presence of a nondialyzable ion.

Of the ions in blood cells and plasma, the protein anions and the principal cations, Na^+ and K^+, are unable to pass freely across the cell membrane. Diffusible ions whose ratios might fit the theory are Cl^-, HCO_3^-, and H^+ or OH^-. Definite ratios of the concentrations of the latter pair cannot be obtained by present methods of measurement, but it is inferred that the concentration of hydrogen ions in the cells is greater than that in serum because this is true of a mass of hemolyzed cells. The chloride concentration in the cells is definitely less than that in serum, as shown in Table 17, but the bicarbonate concentrations do not show the difference found in earlier work. Van Slyke (13) reported that the bicarbonate as well as the chloride ratios could be altered by changes in the carbon dioxide content of the blood,

---

* It has been concluded by others (3) that such good agreement of observed and calculated values is accidental, since it is not obtained for human serum albumin if the pH differs much from 7.4.

and the direction of these shifts fitted the predictions of the theory. It seems likely that a quantitative agreement of these ratios would be found if the hydrogen ion concentration in the cells could be measured, and if the analytical concentrations of chloride and bicarbonate could be accurately corrected by subtracting the amounts not in ionic form.

In some cases a qualitative agreement has been found between the ratios of chloride and bicarbonate concentrations, and the inverse ratio for sodium or for hydrogen ion, in serum and its ultrafiltrate or a pathological transudate.

ACID-BASE EQUILIBRIUM

Hydrogen Ion Concentration and Buffer Action. The reaction of normal blood is remarkably constant; an average figure is pH 7.40, with normal deviations of only a few hundredths of a pH unit. Since present methods for measuring pH do not give access to the interior of the cells, the pH of whole blood is really that of the plasma. If fresh blood is handled carefully, with precautions against loss of carbon dioxide, identical pH values are obtained for whole blood, plasma, and serum.

The symbol pH was originally defined as the logarithm of the reciprocal of the hydrogen ion* concentration, $\log \frac{1}{[H^+]}$ or $-\log [H^+]$. It is now recognized that this definition is not strictly consistent with the accepted methods of measuring pH. One may think of pH as $-\log a_H$, where a_H is the activity or effective concentration of hydrogen ions but not necessarily their actual concentration. In pure water a_H and $[H^+]$ are identical, but in ordinary dilute solutions the activity is less than the concentration. The activity coefficient, which is the ratio of activity to concentration, is about 0.75 for the ions of a physiological salt solution. It is the activities rather than the concentrations of the ions of water in dilute aqueous solutions which are related by the law of the constancy of the ion product,

$$a_H \, a_{OH} = K_w.$$

For any one temperature K_w is a true constant, independent of the acidity or alkalinity of the solution. Because of this relation, pH values can be used to describe the reaction of alkaline as well as neutral or acid solutions. For 25° C. the value of K_w is 1.0×10^{-14}, but for 38° C. it is about 2.5×10^{-14}. In pure water the values of a_H and a_{OH} are equal to each other and to the square root of K_w, which is 1.6×10^{-7} for 38° C. The pH of a neutral solution at body temperatute is the negative logarithm of this number, $-(0.20-7.00)$ or 6.80. Since pH of normal blood is higher than this by 0.6, the blood is a slightly alkaline liquid. The hydrogen ion activity in blood is the antilogarithm of -7.40 or of $0.60-8.00$. Since the antilogarithm of 0.60 is 4.0, the value of a_H is 4.0×10^{-8}.

In dealing with pH values it should be remembered that an increase in pH means a decrease in acidity. If the pH of a solution is increased by one unit, its actual acidity, or the value of a_H, is reduced to 1/10 of its former value. If the acidity of a solution is doubled, its pH is decreased by the logarithm of 2, which is 0.30.

The measurement of pH in blood, as in other solutions of moderate acidity or alkalinity, is most conveniently made by means of the glass electrode (4). A colorimetric method requiring only 0.1 cc. of blood was described by Shock and Hastings in 1934. The theory and practice of pH measurements in general were discussed in detail by Clark (1).

Blood plasma has a high buffer capacity, and that of whole blood is still higher. This means that considerable amounts of a strong acid or base may be added to these liquids without producing great changes in pH.

* In this discussion it seems unnecessary to use a special name or formula to emphasize the hydration of hydrogen ions in all aqueous solutions.

A buffer solution is one which possesses reserve acidity and alkalinity; this results from the presence in the solution of a weak (i.e., slightly ionized) acid or base, together with a highly ionized salt of the same acid or base. If the formula HA is used to represent any weak acid, buffer action may be seen to be a consequence of the mobile equilibrium,

$$HA \rightleftharpoons H^+ + A^-.$$

If an alkali is added, hydrogen ions are removed to form water, with the production of more A^- ions from the weak acid. If a strong acid is added, its hydrogen ions combine with A^- ions, furnished by the buffer salt, to form undissociated HA. Such an equilibrium may be described by the law of mass action in the form

$$K' = a_H \frac{[A^-]}{[HA]}.$$

The K' of this equation is called the apparent dissociation constant of the weak acid. For any one acid the value of K' varies, not only with the temperature, but also with the total concentration of dissolved substances, especially ionized salts. In the case of blood and many common buffer solutions, there is enough salt present to keep the ionic environment essentially constant, and K' is then independent of the ratio $[A^-]/[HA]$. If the proper value of K' is known, the value of a_H may be calculated from the composition of the buffer.

The pH of a solution containing buffer substances may be calculated from the ratio of the components of any one buffer system by means of the equation,

$$pH = pK' + \log \frac{[BA]}{[HA]}.$$

This modified form of the law of mass action is known as the Henderson-Hasselbalch equation. Here [HA] is the concentration of a weak acid and [BA] is the concentration of an ionized salt of this acid. Each buffer system may be characterized by its own pK' value, but this is a constant only under certain conditions. The temperature and the concentrations of dissolved substances, especially ionized salts, must be nearly constant and the concentrations of H^+ and OH^- ions must be much less than [HA] and [BA]. These conditions are satisfied for the buffer systems in blood.

Buffer equilibria are shown graphically as dissociation curves of the buffer acids. The abscissas are pH values and the ordinates represent the fraction of the total buffer substance of each system which has been transformed into the more alkaline form, $[BA]/([HA] + [BA])$. Figure 291 shows such curves for two buffer acids, H_2CO_3 and NaH_2PO_4. Each of these curves shows the pH values which are obtained by mixing the more acid and more alkaline components of one buffer system in the proportions indicated. Such a curve may also be regarded as a titration curve. The phosphate curve could be nearly reproduced, if the scale of ordinates were adjusted in the proper proportion, by plotting against pH the number of cubic centimeters of a sodium hydroxide solution added to a fixed amount of NaH_2PO_4. Even better agreement would be obtained by plotting against pH the amounts of a hydrochloric acid solution added to a fixed amount of Na_2HPO_4; in this case the curve would have the same shape if the ordinates were plotted downwards from the top of the figure.

The curves for the two buffers are identical in form, differing only in their location along the pH axis. When the buffer acid is exactly half neutralized, the concentrations of the acid and its salt are equal and the pH is equal to the pK' of the buffer acid. At this point the dissociation curve has its steepest slope and the buffer capacity of the system is at a maximum. The addition of any acid or base causes some change in the proportions of the buffer constituents, but the resulting change in pH is least at the midpoint of the curve. The slope of the curves becomes decidedly less at both ends; the buffer capacity is rather poor if the buffer acid is less than 15 per cent or more than 85 per cent neutralized. For very efficient buffering, the ratio [BA]/[HA] should lie between 1/5 and 5. A concentrated buffer solution is, of course, more effective in controlling pH than a dilute solution having the same buffer ratio.

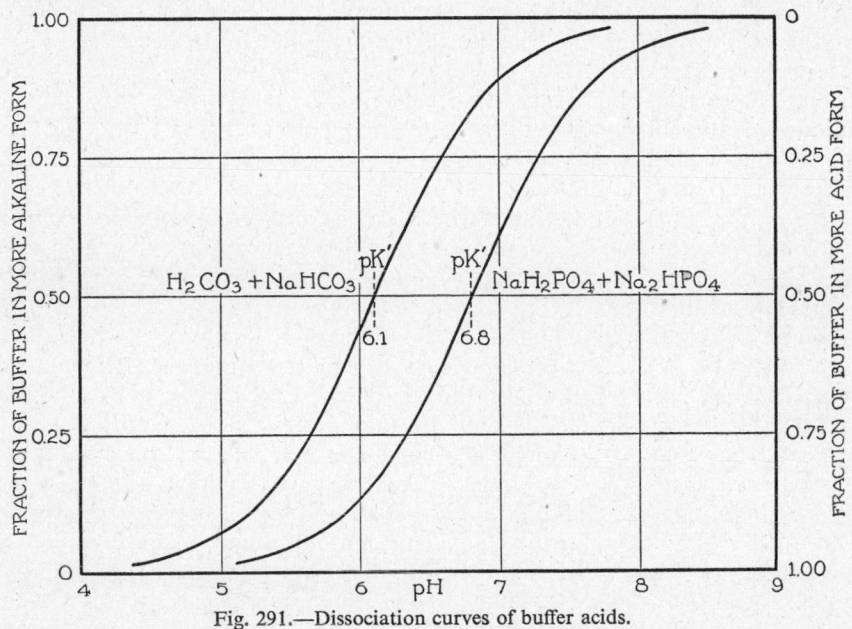

Fig. 291.—Dissociation curves of buffer acids.

Buffers in Blood. The buffers of the blood include the phosphate, bicarbonate and protein buffer systems. Inorganic phosphate, in solutions within the physiological range of pH values, cannot exist in significant amounts as the free acid, H_3PO_4, nor as the trivalent anion, $PO_4^{\equiv}$; it is present as $H_2PO_4^-$ and $HPO_4^=$. These two ions constitute a buffer system whose behavior may be represented by the equation

$$pH = 6.8 + \log \frac{[B_2HPO_4]}{[BH_2PO_4]}$$

in which B stands for Na or K. Since these salts are regarded as completely ionized into B^+, $HPO_4^=$ and $H_2PO_4^-$, the latter ion is the weak acid of the buffer system. At pH 7.4 the logarithmic term is 0.6, and the ratio $[B_2HPO_4]/[BH_2PO_4]$ is 4.0. This ratio is favorable for efficient buffer action, but the inorganic phosphates in blood are present at such low concentrations that they cannot account for much of the total buffer capacity.

Most of the carbon dioxide in blood is present as bicarbonate ions, HCO_3^-. In the physiological range of pH the concentration of carbonate ions, $CO_3^=$, is negligibly small. The distribution of carbon dioxide in blood plasma or serum at body temperature is quantitatively described by the equation

$$pH = 6.10 + \log \frac{[BHCO_3]}{[H_2CO_3]}$$

if $[BHCO_3]$ represents the concentration of bound CO_2, which is largely bicarbonate ions, while $[H_2CO_3]$ is the concentration of free CO_2, including dissolved CO_2 and un-ionized H_2CO_3. According to this equation, the ratio of free to bound CO_2 at pH 7.4 is only 1/20. This is a very poor buffer ratio, and the total concentration of carbon dioxide in blood is not large, about 0.029 M. One might be tempted to conclude that the buffer action of the bicarbonate system in blood would be unimportant, but such a conclusion would be quite erroneous, because of the facts which are discussed in the following pages.

The proteins in blood exist as negatively charged particles or colloidal anions. On the alkaline side of its iso-electric point, a protein behaves as a multivalent acid. Because of the large number of ionizable groups in the protein molecule, the buffer action of a protein cannot be described by a single pK' value. The proteins of the body are powerful buffers; they may give off hydrogen ions, becoming more negatively charged, or they may take up hydrogen ions, becoming less negatively charged. At physiological pH values the net charge of the blood proteins is negative.

Because of the predominantly acid nature of the substances formed in physiological processes, the buffers of the body are usually called upon to resist increases in acidity rather than alkalinity. It was estimated by Peters and Van Slyke (9) that the distribution among the buffers of normal blood of the alkali which is physiologically available for the neutralization of acids other than carbonic acid is about as follows, in milliequivalents per liter: bicarbonate, 18; hemoglobin, 8; other buffers, principally serum proteins, 2. These figures are less than the equivalent concentrations of the same buffer substances, as given in Table 17, because they apply only to a change in pH from 7.4 to 7.0. If the total volume of the circulating blood is 6 liters, these buffers could neutralize 6 × 28, or 168 ml. of a 1.0 N solution of a strong acid. This is by no means the total buffer capacity of the body. In experiments in which a solution of a strong acid was injected into the circulating blood of a dog, it appeared that about five times as much acid was neutralized by other tissues as by the blood. Most of this buffer action is probably due to tissue proteins, although organic phosphate may also be of importance. According to these estimates (9), it seems possible that the body of an average man might neutralize one equivalent (i.e., 1 liter of a 1.0 N solution) of a strong acid such as HCl before the blood pH fell below 7.0, which is almost the lowest value found for blood from a living subject. The upper limit of blood pH compatible with life appears to be close to 7.8.

Physiological Buffer Action of Carbon Dioxide. The buffer system composed of carbon dioxide and bicarbonate is especially important in physiology. Carbon dioxide is continually being produced in the body, and unless it were eliminated the ratio of the concentrations of free and bound CO_2 would soon rise far above the normal value of 1/20. It is, of course, the lungs which constitute the path by which this tremendous excess of acid is removed from the body. The regulation of respiration is so sensitive to small changes in the concentration of free carbonic acid or dissolved carbon dioxide in the blood that this concentration is held nearly constant. As L. J. Henderson pointed out in 1908, this physiological or heterogeneous buffer action transforms the carbonic acid-bicarbonate system from a rather poor buffer into a very good one (6). Since carbonic acid is a weaker acid than most of the other acids produced by metabolic processes, the bicarbonate of the blood can neutralize these acids. This tends to decrease the numerator, $[BHCO_3]$, in the buffer equation, but because CO_2 is removed by respiration this decrease is not accompanied by an equal increase in the denominator, $[H_2CO_3]$. The change in pH is therefore less than it would be in an ordinary, homogeneous buffer system.

Because of the availability of bicarbonate as a means of defending the body against excess acid, the bicarbonate of the blood was called by Van Slyke and Cullen the alkaline reserve of the body. This name is generally accepted because a disturbance of the acid-base balance, if it is due to retention or loss of nonvolatile acids or bases, is indicated by a change in the plasma bicarbonate content. Actually, the bicarbonate is not the only reserve of alkali in the body or even in the blood. Considerable amounts of alkali are combined with the proteins of the blood, especially hemoglobin. Carbonic acid can react with an alkali proteinate, which takes up hydrogen ions and leaves the ions of the alkali bicarbonate in solution. Such a reaction may be written in the form

$$H_2CO_3 + Protein^= \rightleftharpoons HCO_3^- + H\ Protein^-$$

if it is understood that the valence of the protein anions in blood is certainly more than 2, and that a single protein anion can combine with several molecules of carbonic acid without losing all of its negative charge. This buffer action of the proteins provides an explanation for the fact that the pH of venous plasma is only 0.02 or 0.03 less than that of arterial, although the concentration of free CO_2 in venous blood is some 15 per cent greater. When blood gains carbon dioxide from the tissues, some of the dissolved gas diffuses into the red blood cells. Here its hydration to form carbonic acid is hastened by the action of an enzyme, carbonic anhydrase, and some of the CO_2 is bound to hemoglobin as a carbamino protein complex. Carbonic acid reacts with hemoglobin anions according to the chemical equation given above; this reaction is possible because some of the acid groups in hemoglobin are weaker acids than H_2CO_3, and it is favored by the removal of oxygen from the hemoglobin, since reduced hemoglobin behaves as a weaker acid than oxyhemoglobin. The resulting bicarbonate ions tend to diffuse out into the plasma. They cannot do this without some other change, because of the electrostatic forces between oppositely charged ions. Because of the peculiar impermeability of the red cell, cations cannot accompany the bicarbonate ions into the plasma. The diffusion of bicarbonate ions is made possible by the simultaneous diffusion of chloride ions from plasma to cells. The chloride-bicarbonate shift proceeds in the reverse direction when the blood reaches the lungs and loses CO_2.

Special form of buffer equation for carbon dioxide. Because of the fact that carbon dioxide is a gas, the Henderson-Hasselbalch equation is sometimes written in a special form, applicable only to the ionization of carbonic acid. No distinction is made between dissolved CO_2 and undissociated H_2CO_3. The sum of their concentrations, [free CO_2], is proportional to the partial pressure of CO_2 in the gas mixture with which the solution is in equilibrium (Henry's law). The solubility of the gas is expressed as the (Bunsen) absorption coefficient; its value for CO_2 in serum, acidified to prevent the formation of any bicarbonate, is 0.51

for 38° C. This means that 1 liter of serum at 38° C. could hold 0.51 liters of CO_2 (measured at 0° C. and 760 mm. Hg) if the partial pressure of the CO_2 were 760 mm. Since 1 mol of CO_2 occupies 22.26 liters under standard conditions, 0.51 liters represents 0.51/22.26 or 0.0229 mols. If the partial pressure of CO_2 is p mm. instead of 760, the solubility becomes 0.0229 p/760, which is $3.01 \times 10^{-5} p$ mols or 0.0301 p millimols per liter. It is this quantity which is used in place of [HA] or [free CO_2] in the Henderson-Hasselbalch equation. The difference between the concentrations of total CO_2 and free CO_2 is [bound CO_2] or [BA]. If [total CO_2] is expressed in millimols per liter, the equation becomes

$$pH = 6.10 + \log \frac{[\text{total } CO_2] - 0.0301\, p}{0.0301\, p},$$

since the value of pK' is 6.10. In this form, the equation is used to calculate the pH of serum or plasma from measurements of CO_2 content and CO_2 tension. Some workers have measured pH and CO_2 content and then solved the equation to get values for the CO_2 tension. Once the value of pK' has been established, any one of the three variables may be obtained from experimental measurements of the other two.

It is recognized that the difference between [total CO_2] and [free CO_2] is greater than the true value of [HCO_3^-] in blood serum, because some of the CO_2 is bound in the form of carbamino protein complexes. However, the equation is still valid because the numerical value of pK' was determined by applying the equation in this form to experimental measurements of the three variables.

Kidney Action and Neutrality of Blood. The constant pH of the blood is maintained, not only by physicochemical buffer action and the elimination of CO_2 in the lungs, but also by the action of the kidneys. Excess acid may leave the body in the form of weak organic acids, acid phosphates or ammonium salts in the urine; excess alkali may be eliminated as bicarbonate in the urine.

Since urine is usually more acid than blood, the ratio [BA]/[HA] is generally decreased for each buffer system whose constituents pass from the blood to the urine. For example, the ratio [$HPO_4^=$]/[$H_2PO_4^-$] is 4 in blood of pH 7.4 but only about 0.16 in urine of pH 6.0. This decrease in the phosphate buffer ratio, together with other similar changes, is ascribed to a selective action of the kidneys, especially in the reabsorption in the renal tubules of the fluid which has been filtered from the blood in the glomeruli. The protein-free ultrafiltrate is believed to contain the crystalloidal buffer substances in essentially the same proportions as the blood. Most of the water in the filtrate, much of the alkali bicarbonate, and certain other solutes are reabsorbed through the tubules into the blood. It has been assumed that carbonic acid or dissolved carbon dioxide is not actively reabsorbed, but becomes concentrated as water is reabsorbed. This would explain the fact that urine often has a partial pressure of CO_2 much higher than that in blood. It was calculated in 1934 by Sendroy, Seelig and Van Slyke that the glomerular filtrate provides enough CO_2 to account for the acidity of the urine by reaction with other buffer systems, as:

$$H_2CO_3 + Na_2HPO_4 \rightleftharpoons NaHCO_3 + NaH_2PO_4.$$

Such a reaction might be driven nearly to completion by the reabsorption of bicarbonate. In 1945, however, this hypothesis was found inadequate to explain some quantitative experiments of R. F. Pitts. He worked with dogs which had received dilute hydrochloric acid by mouth and neutral sodium phosphate by intravenous infusion. Pitts calculated that the glomerular filtrate contained less than one-fourth as much CO_2 as the titratable acid found in the urine. He concluded that the CO_2 of the ultrafiltrate is largely reabsorbed in the tubules, but that additional CO_2 is formed by metabolic processes in cells of the distal tubules. According to Pitts the urine acquires its acidity by a quasi-secretory process in which the urine exchanges Na^+ from Na_2HPO_4 for H^+ from H_2CO_3 provided by these tubule cells.

Acid is also eliminated in the urine as ammonium ion. This ion is present in blood only in small amounts, and at pH 7.4 the concentration of free ammonia (NH_3 or NH_4OH) must be extremely low. The immediate source of urinary ammonia has in the past been thought to be urea, or possibly amino acids. Experiments reported in 1943 by Van Slyke et al. indicate that the kidney obtains ammonia by the hydrolysis of the amide group in glutamine, which is brought to the kidney by the blood. The ammonia combines with H^+ to form NH_4^+, which is excreted in the urine with equivalent amounts of an anion such as Cl^-. In this way acid is removed while adequate amounts of HCO_3^- and Na^+ are retained in the blood.

The greater part of the nitrogen of protein foods is removed from amino acids by a process of deamination. The resulting ammonia does not appear in the blood because the liver converts it to urea, a neutral substance. If intermediate steps and necessary catalysts are disregarded, the chemical reaction for this conversion may be written in the form

$$2 NH_3 + CO_2 \rightarrow CO(NH_2)_2 + H_2O.$$

The normal excretion of urea may therefore be regarded as a means of removing ammonia and preventing a change in the reaction of the blood.

Experimental Shifts in the Acid-Base Balance. When a person hyperventilates his lungs by rapid and deep breathing, a good deal of acid is lost from the body as CO_2. In one experiment on a human subject, it was found by Shock and Hastings (11) that twenty minutes of intentional overbreathing caused the pH of the plasma to rise from 7.36 to 7.69, producing a temporary condition of CO_2 deficit or respiratory alkalosis. The reverse of this condition, CO_2 excess or respiratory acidosis, could be produced by rebreathing through a closed system of about 35 liters of oxygen for 15 to 18 minutes; in one case the pH of the plasma fell from 7.37 to 7.19 as the CO_2 content of the gas rose to 9 per cent. A condition of acid excess or metabolic acidosis was produced by having the subjects take 5 or 10 gm. of NH_4Cl, dissolved in water, by mouth. In one such experiment the plasma pH fell from 7.45 to 7.22 in three hours, while there was also a marked drop in the plasma bicarbonate concentration. The acidity produced by NH_4Cl in the body may be explained on the assumption that some of its NH_3 is converted to neutral urea, leaving an excess of H^+ ions to disturb the buffer equilibria. When subjects received 10 or 20 gm. of $NaHCO_3$ by mouth, their condition became one of temporary alkali excess or metabolic alkalosis. In one case the plasma bicarbonate was nearly doubled within one hour, during which the free CO_2 also rose somewhat and the plasma pH rose from 7.35 to 7.50.

These four types of experiments illustrate what the authors (11) termed four primary paths of acid-base disturbance. These paths were drawn, from theoretical considerations, as the labeled diagonal lines in Figure 292. This graph is a plot, on triaxial coordinates, of the three variables of the Henderson-Hasselbalch equation, plasma pH, plasma bicarbonate, and CO_2 tension. The scales are so adjusted that any point on the graph fits the equation; that is, if pH and $[BHCO_3]$ are plotted, the value of the CO_2 tension can be read correctly from the third scale. This method of plotting gives equal emphasis to each of the three variables, and it makes it possible to show the changes in acid-base equilibrium at various times. The small hexagon in the center

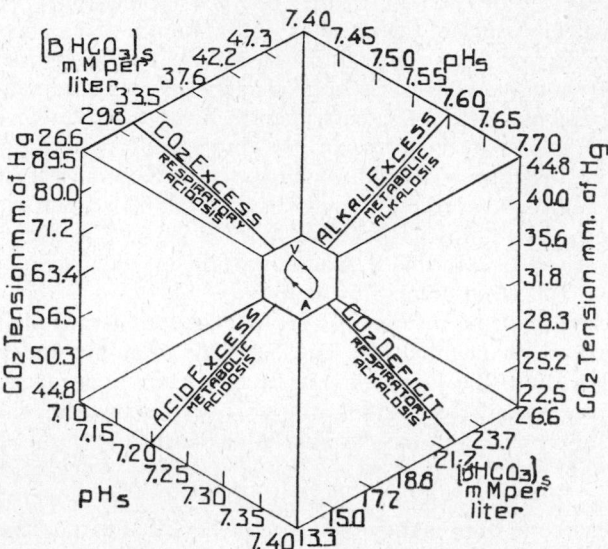

Fig. 292.—Theoretical acid-base chart showing four primary acid-base paths. (From Shock and Hastings, *J. biol. Chem.*, 1935, *112*:239–262).

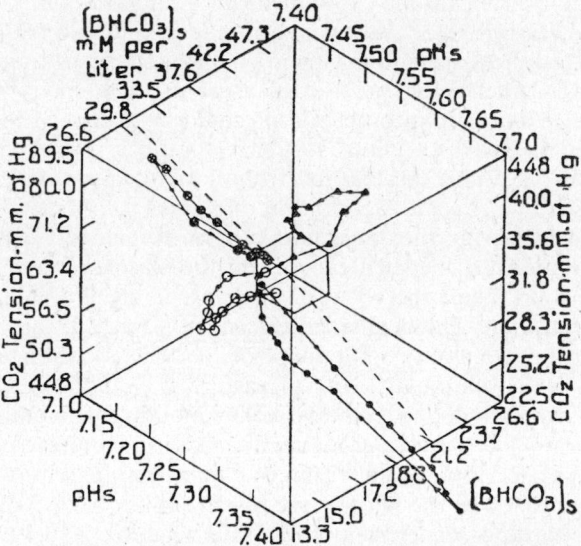

Fig. 293.—Four primary acid-base paths of displacement and recovery determined on normal human subjects. (From Shock and Hastings, *J. biol. Chem.* 1935, *112*:239–262)

encloses points obtained for subjects in normal condition, and the smaller closed curve marked A and V indicates average values during the normal respiratory cycle.

Figure 293 is a similar plot of the results of experiments of the four types. The points which lie NW and SE from the center were obtained by rebreathing and overbreathing, while those which lie to the NE and SW were the result of giving $NaHCO_3$ and NH_4Cl, respectively. Evidently these experimental treatments produced results which fall close to the lines of the theoretical paths. The authors were able to produce more complex acid-base paths by combining two of the experimental procedures, and they suggested that the rates of recovery from experimental displacement of the acid-base equilibrium might be of clinical value. Shock and Hastings were not the first to plot these variables on a single chart, but to those who can become adjusted to the use of triaxial coordinates their plots seem simpler than the earlier graphs (9, vol. 2, p. 944).

PROTEINS OF THE BLOOD

Properties of Hemoglobin. Hemoglobin is a readily crystallizable protein which contains iron and has the unusual property of combining, rapidly and reversibly, with oxygen. This useful property is easily lost when the protein is dried, subjected to the action of an oxidizing agent, or even kept in the laboratory; the best crystalline preparations have only about 95 per cent of the oxygen-combining capacity of the same amount of hemoglobin in fresh blood. The maximum amount of oxygen which can be made to combine with native hemoglobin approaches 401 ml. for each gram of iron contained in the hemoglobin, as shown by R. A. Peters in 1912. Since the atomic weight of iron is 55.84, it follows that the amount of hemoglobin which contains one gram-atom of iron can combine with 0.401×55.84 liters of oxygen; this is 22.4 liters or 1 mol of the gas. The iron content of human hemoglobin (crystallized, dialyzed and dried to constant weight at 105° C.) is 0.340 per cent, as reported by Bernhart and Skeggs in 1943. The weight of hemoglobin which contains one gram-atom of iron is therefore 55.84/0.00340 or 16,400 grams. This amount of hemoglobin (its minimal molecular weight) is commonly represented by the symbol Hb, or HHb when the acidic nature of the protein is under discussion. The actual molecular weight of human hemoglobin in aqueous solutions, as determined from its osmotic pressure or from the study of its sedimentation in the ultracentrifuge, is about 67,000 or 63,000; these figures indicate that the molecule contains 4 atoms of iron ($4 \times 16,400 = 65,600$).

The combination of oxygen with hemoglobin is not an oxidation in the electrochemical sense; studies of oxidation-reduction potentials (summarized by Conant in 1923) have indicated that the iron in oxyhemoglobin as well as in reduced hemoglobin (ferrohemoglobin) is in the ferrous condition. There is some evidence that normal blood contains about 5 per cent of its iron in a form which cannot combine with oxygen. The true oxidation of hemoglobin by chemical reagents such as ferricyanide results in the formation of a brown substance, methemoglobin (ferrihemoglobin), in which the iron is ferric and the oxygen-binding capacity is lacking. If oxyhemoglobin or methemoglobin is first reduced by sodium hydrosulfite ($Na_2S_2O_4$), the maximum amount of carbon monoxide which can be bound agrees quite well with the total iron content, as shown by Taylor and Coryell in 1938. The combination of hemoglobin with carbon monoxide, like that with oxygen, is a reversible reaction, but the affinity of hemoglobin for CO is about 210 times as great as its affinity for O_2. Carbon monoxide can therefore displace oxygen from combination with hemoglobin, and this accounts for the well known facts of carbon monoxide poisoning. In this connection it may be noted that carefully measured, small amounts of carbon monoxide have been breathed without untoward results by physiologists experimenting upon themselves; this procedure is involved in one of the methods for determining total blood volume (see p. 552).

Hemoglobin resembles other proteins in its amphoteric nature. Oxyhemoglobin is iso-electric at about pH 6.7, and reduced hemoglobin at 6.8. Since both of these values are below the pH of circulating blood, hemoglobin in vivo is negatively charged or combined with base. Although it seems unlikely that the 32 per cent of hemoglobin in the red cells can be in true solution, the hemoglobin may be regarded as a large, colloidal anion of an ionized potassium salt. The valence of this anion, or the number of equivalents of base bound per mol of hemoglobin, is variable, being increased by a rise in pH or an increase in the degree of oxygenation.

Hemoglobin is a conjugated protein; it can be broken down into a nonprotein fraction and a protein called globin. Globin is classified as a histone; it has none of the color of hemoglobin, does not combine with oxygen, and contains no iron. Globin has a rather high content of the basic amino acid, histidine, and an alkaline iso-electric point, pH 8. The nonprotein fraction of hemoglobin has been called reduced hematin, reduced heme or ferroheme; it contains all of the iron of hemoglobin. The name heme (haem in British publications) is used to describe a class of iron-porphyrin complexes which includes the nonprotein parts of hemoglobin, cytochrome and other derivatives of animal or plant origin. The nature of the chemical linkages which hold the iron atom in the porphyrin nucleus of the heme compounds, and of those which unite ferroheme and globin in hemoglobin, has aroused the interest of both physical and organic chemists. It appears that each iron atom in hemoglobin is linked in some way to six other atoms, as in the ferrocyanide ion. These atoms include the four nitrogens of the porphyrin structure and one in globin, probably an imidazole nitrogen of histidine. In reduced hemoglobin the sixth group may be a second histidine residue in the globin, while in oxyhemoglobin it is oxygen. Measurements of magnetic susceptibility (reported by Pauling and Coryell in 1936) have shown that reduced hemoglobin is strongly paramagnetic while oxyhemoglobin has zero magnetic moment; it is inferred that the bonds about the iron are electrostatic in the former case but covalent in the latter. This difference in the type of bonding is associated with the more strongly acid nature of oxyhemoglobin.

Because hemoglobin and its derivatives have characteristic and specific absorption spectra, the spectroscope has been a valuable tool in the study of these substances. The concentration of hemoglobin in blood is usually determined by colorimetry, or the comparison of the intensities of light transmitted by known and unknown solutions. Visual colorimetry is greatly improved by the use of a suitable light filter (green in this case), and a photoelectric colorimeter with monochromatic or filtered light is even better. One instrument of this sort, described by G. A. Millikan in 1942, gives an estimate of the degree of oxygenation of circulating blood by means of a photo-electric cell responding to light transmitted through the lobe of the human ear.

Plasma Proteins. The plasma proteins, because of their colloid osmotic pressure, play an important part in the regulation of the distribution of water in the body; this osmotic pressure is due largely to the albumins. Fibrinogen and other proteins, present in smaller quantities, are responsible for the coagulability of blood. The antibodies of immunology, which constitute an important defense of the body against disease, appear to be protein in nature and are associated with certain of the globulins of plasma, the gamma globulin fraction.

The classical separation of the plasma proteins involved their fractional precipitation by the addition of salt solutions. Fibrinogen can be precipitated from oxalated plasma by adding an equal volume of saturated sodium chloride solution. It may also be removed, as fibrin, by adding calcium chloride to neutralize the anticoagulant salt and allowing the plasma to coagulate, either with or without stirring. The results of this procedure are a fibrin clot and a noncoagulable serum, free from fibrinogen. Globulins may be precipitated from serum by adding an equal volume of saturated ammonium sulfate; if the filtrate is saturated with this salt by adding a sufficient amount of solid ammonium sulfate, the albumins are precipitated and the last filtrate is free from protein. These separations are not absolutely sharp and definite, and they are not even reproducible unless the temperature, pH and other conditions are carefully controlled. Another method of separating albumins and globulins (suggested by P. E. Howe in 1921) involves the use of a specified concentration of sodium sulfate instead of ammonium sulfate. Sodium sulfate does not interfere with the determination of nitrogen in the protein fractions, but because its solubility is relatively low it must be used at 37° C. Other precipitation methods make use of concentrated buffer solutions of the phosphates of potassium, and of graded concentrations of alcohol at low temperatures (2).

Although globulins are usually said to be insoluble in pure water but soluble in salt solutions, an appreciable fraction of the globulins of serum does not precipitate when the salts are removed by dialysis. These more soluble globulins are termed pseudoglobulins. The globulins which can be precipitated by dialysis, or by simple dilution and acidification of serum with carbon dioxide, are called euglobulins, Still other fractions have been separated by adjusting the pH of dialyzed solutions for iso-electric precipitation; serum globulins have iso-electric points in the vicinity of pH 5 or 6.

Serum albumins from horse blood and human blood have been crystallized from concentrated salt solutions. Albumin from horse serum has been crystallized in two forms, one free from carbohydrate and another containing 5.5 per cent of such material. The iso-electric point of human serum albumin at 0° C. is pH 4.6 in a buffer of 0.1 ionic strength, but recent work indicates that its iso-ionic point in 0.15 M NaCl at 25° C. is pH 5.4 (Cohn et al., 3).

New information about the plasma proteins has been obtained by subjecting plasma and its fractions to electrophoresis. It has long been known that dissolved proteins would migrate in an electric field, but the phenomenon of electrophoresis became useful for the quantitative characterization and analysis of protein mixtures only after the technique was improved by A. Tiselius in 1937. The electrophoretic velocity depends principally on the number of charges carried by the particle, and different proteins can usually be made to move with different velocities by conducting the experiment in a medium of suitable pH. By means of ingenious optical systems it is possible to obtain photographic records which show not only the mobilities of the different constituents in a protein solution but also their relative amounts. In this way it has been found that the most rapidly moving protein component of human plasma is the albumin. In order of decreasing mobilities, the next are two globulin fractions designated as alpha 1 and alpha 2. These are followed by beta globulin, fibrinogen, and gamma globulin. The albumin comprises about 55 per cent of the total plasma proteins, of which the globulins amount to about 38 per cent and the fibrinogen, 7 per cent or less.* According to the results of this electrophoretic analysis, the albumin:globulin ratio in normal plasma is slightly less than 1.5. Since the procedure involves only the addition of a weakly alkaline buffer solution and the passage of a small electric current at a low temperature, it seems likely that electrophoretic analysis gives a better idea of the proteins as they exist in plasma than does any of the precipitation methods. Because the technique is quantitative and reproducible, electrophoresis has been extensively employed in the characterization of the fractions obtained by large-scale methods from human plasma (3).

The fractions of human plasma proteins which have been tested in clinical work include albumin, gamma globulin, and fibrinogen. The albumin has been injected intravenously as a 25 per cent solution in 0.3 M (1.7 per cent) NaCl, with the object of restoring plasma volume in cases of shock. The intramuscular injection of a gamma globulin preparation has been used in the prophylaxis and treatment of measles. "Fibrin foams," impregnated with a thrombin solution, have a rapid hemostatic action (3).

Specific gravity and protein concentration. The classical method of estimating the amount of protein in plasma is based on a total nitrogen determination by the Kjeldahl method. After a small correction for nonprotein nitrogen, the nitrogen content is multiplied by 6.25, since the plasma proteins contain about 16 per cent of nitrogen. Because Kjeldahl determinations are slow, approximate methods which can be carried out more rapidly have often been used for clinical purposes. It was shown by Moore and Van Slyke in 1930 that the specific gravity of serum or plasma is essentially a straight line function of its protein content. The specific gravity can be determined, with a single drop of plasma or serum, by the falling drop method, which was described by Barbour and Hamilton in 1926 and modified by Kagan in 1938. These methods are rapid and can be made very accurate, but they require some skill and practice. An extremely simple method, of accuracy adequate for clinical work, has been described (10). A series of copper sulfate solutions is prepared, differing by 0.001 or 0.004 in specific gravity, and a small drop (not measured) of plasma is allowed to fall into the solution from a height of about 1 cm. above its surface. The drop is observed for 15 or 20 seconds, during which it remains intact because of the formation of a film of copper proteinate. If the drop continues to fall during this time, it is heavier than the standard; if it rises, it is lighter. The specific gravity can be estimated

---

* Electrophoretic analyses of normal human plasmas by V. P. Dole (*J. clin. Invest.*, 1944, 23:708–713) indicate that albumin makes up about 60 per cent of the total plasma proteins; serum globulins, 35 per cent; and fibrinogen, 5 per cent. According to G. E. Perlmann and D. Kaufman (*J. Amer. chem. Soc.*, 1945, 67:638–641), the apparent percentage of albumin decreases from about 57 to 54 (with a corresponding increase in gamma globulin) as the salt concentration of the sample in the electrophoresis cell is raised from 0.1 to 0.3 N; they conclude that the lower figure for albumin is more nearly correct.

with an accuracy equal to about $\frac{1}{4}$ of the difference between successive copper sulfate solutions. The determination may be carried out without temperature control, because the coefficient of expansion of the copper sulfate solutions approximates that of plasma. The protein concentration, P, in gm. per 100 ml., is given by the equation (corrected by Van Slyke in 1944),

$$P = 360\,(G - 1.0070),$$

in which G is the specific gravity of the plasma.

The same procedure, with more concentrated copper sulfate solutions, can be used to obtain the specific gravity of whole blood, and the authors (10) have shown that approximate values for hematocrit and hemoglobin concentration may be calculated graphically from the specific gravities of whole blood and its plasma. According to this work, the average specific gravities of samples obtained from 20 normal men were 1.0264 for plasma, and 1.0595 for blood. The average hematocrit was 46.9 per cent cells, while the oxygen capacity of the blood samples averaged 21.62 volumes per cent. These figures correspond to 6.98 gm. of protein per 100 ml. of plasma, 15.9 gm. of hemoglobin per 100 ml. of blood, and 1.0970 for the average specific gravity of the cells in normal blood.

The specific gravities of blood and its plasma or serum have served as a guide in the treatment of patients in whom the blood volume has been diminished by injury, as in shock.

REFERENCES

1. CLARK, W. M. *The determination of hydrogen ions*, 3d ed. Baltimore, Williams and Wilkins Co., 1928, 691 pp.
2. COHN, E. J. The properties and functions of the plasma proteins, with a consideration of the methods for their separation and purification. *Chem. Rev.*, 1941, *28:* 395–417.
3. COHN, E. J., *et al.* Chemical, clinical, and immunological studies on the products of human plasma fractionation.I–XXIII. *J. clin. Invest.*, 1944, *23:*417–606.
4. DOLE, M. *The glass electrode.* New York, John Wiley and Sons, 1941, 317 pp.
5. DONNAN, F. G. The theory of membrane equilibria. *Chem. Rev.*, 1924, *1:*73–90.
6. HENDERSON, L. J. *Blood: a study in general physiology.* New Haven, Yale University Press, 1928, 390 pp.
7. LOEB, J. *Proteins and the theory of colloidal behavior*, 2d ed. New York, McGraw-Hill Book Co., 1924, 371 pp.
8. PETERS, J. P. *Body water.* Springfield (Ill.), Charles C Thomas, 1935, 396 pp.
9. PETERS, J. P., and VAN SLYKE, D. D. *Quantitative clinical chemistry.* Baltimore, Williams and Wilkins Co., 1931–32, 2 vols.
10. PHILLIPS, R. A., *et al.* Copper sulfate method for measuring specific gravities of whole blood and plasma. *U. S. Navy Dept., Bumed News Letter*, 1943, *1:*1–16. *Bull. U. S. Army Med. Dept.*, 1943, *71:* 66–83.
11. SHOCK, N. W., and HASTINGS, A. B. Studies of the acid-base balance of the blood. IV. Characterization and interpretation of displacement of the acid-base balance. *J. biol. Chem.*, 1935, *112:* 239–262.
12. STARLING, E. H. On the absorption of fluids from the connective tissue spaces. *J. Physiol.*, 1895–96, *19:*312–326.
13. VAN SLYKE, D. D. *Factors affecting the distribution of electrolytes, water and gases in the animal body.* Philadelphia, J. B. Lippincott Co., 1926, 62 pp.

CHAPTER 28

COAGULATION OF BLOOD: TRANSFUSION PROBLEMS IN HEMORRHAGE AND SHOCK

BY JOHN H. FERGUSON

Loss of blood endangers the circulatory functions by which the tissues are kept supplied with the internal environment of the fluids they need. There are several physiological reactions which help to counteract the effects of blood loss. Vasoconstriction, which is discussed in Chapter 33, helps locally to lessen the escape of blood, and at distant sites serves to redistribute the blood remaining in the circulation in order to maintain the more vital functions of the organism. The formation of a hemostatic plug or *thrombus* eventually checks the hemorrhage by closing the leak in the damaged blood vessel. A thrombus is made up partly of formed elements and partly of fibrin clot. There are also mechanisms for the temporary restoration of the effective blood volume after hemorrhage, as well as for the more gradual return of the blood proteins and corpuscular elements to the normal levels. Severe bleeding resembles the simpler forms of cardiac and vasomotor disturbance (e.g., fainting or syncope) in that the circulatory mechanisms are thrown off balance and require readjustment. In the more serious condition called shock they are thrown out of gear, so to speak. A modern understanding of the physiology of the blood in relation to its circulatory functions paves the way for the rational treatment of hemorrhage and shock by means of blood transfusion and its recent modifications.

COAGULATION OF BLOOD

One of the most striking properties of blood is its power of coagulating, or clotting, shortly after it escapes from the blood vessels. The gross changes in shed blood have been noted in Chapter 26. The essential part of the clot is the *fibrin* gel, which is derived from a soluble precursor, *fibrinogen*, that makes up about 3 to 7 per cent of the plasma proteins. Under certain abnormal conditions, e.g., pneumonia, pleurisy, pericarditis, etc., fibrin may be deposited intravascularly or in pathological (fibrinous) exudates. As best seen under the dark-field microscope, fibrin is deposited in the form of delicate needles which elongate and fuse to form a meshwork of fibrils or threads (Fig. 294).

In some invertebrate bloods and even in mammalian blood if excess of alkali is added, a nonresolvable jelly may be formed instead. Nevertheless, the quasi-crystalline needles or threads, in which electron microscopy, x-ray, and other optical studies clearly indicate a definite molecular orientation, are highly characteristic of the true fibrin gel and serve to distinguish it from other types of coagulation (irreversible) and precipitation (reversible) of fibrinogen solutions. During normal clot retraction, the formed elements are entangled in the fibrin meshwork, leaving a clear *serum*, from which the few remaining cells, etc., may be removed with the aid of the centrifuge. Coagulation does not alter the pH and is largely independent of the minor pH changes which occur in shed blood, although there is an optimal pH range (6.5–8.0) for blood clotting.

The chief, but not necessarily the only, physiological function of blood coagulation is hemostatic. In the evolution of mechanisms for protecting against loss of blood, adherence and agglutination of certain types of the *formed elements* undoubtedly preceded the more specialized chemical processes of the plasma fibrin-forming system. The importance of the cell factor in thrombus formation depends upon mechanical factors, which may be expressed in terms of *surface properties* of the formed elements. The thrombocyte of lower animals and the blood platelet of the mammal are formed elements in which these surface properties are well developed and they are,

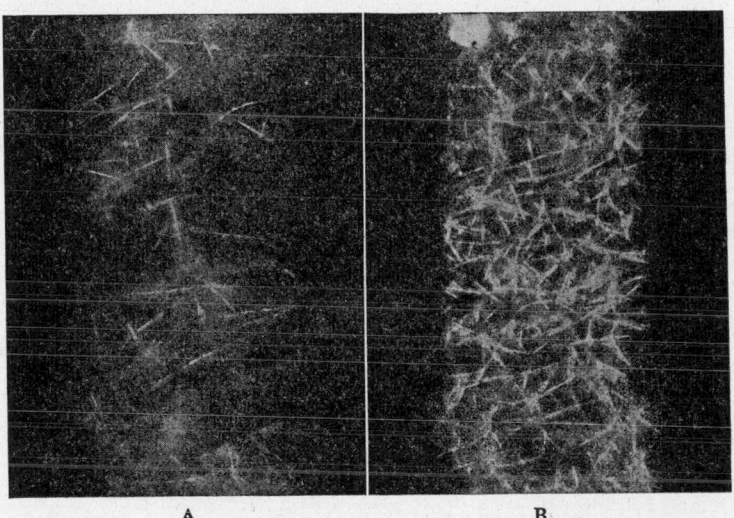

A   B

Fig. 294.—The fibrin needles formed in the clotting of blood. Plasma of oxalated dog's blood clotted by thrombin. The photographs show the needles as seen with the ultramicroscope. A, photographed by sunlight; B, by arclight. Only the needles lying in the focal plane are seen distinctly (Howell).

therefore, of major importance in thrombus formation, especially when the blood flow is rapid. A primitive form of the fibrin gel occurs in a few present day invertebrates, but the process reaches its most effective and typical form in the higher vertebrates. The fibrin meshwork is an efficient mechanical buttress for the cellular portion of the thrombus. In man, the need for both elements is emphasized by the bleeding tendencies which appear in (i) platelet deficiencies (thrombocytopenic purpura) and in (ii) coagulation defects (hypoprothrombinemia, afibrinogenemia [rare], hemophilia, anaphylactic shock, etc.).

Clinical tests for bleeding tendency (*hemorrhagic diathesis*). Determinations of bleeding time and clotting time, observation of clot retraction, and tests for capillary fragility are in common clinical use (23). According to the simple method of Duke, the *bleeding time* is determined by pricking a finger or an ear and absorbing the blood on filter paper at half-minute intervals. Ivy recommends the use of a sphygmomanometer armlet cuff at a pressure of 40 mm., pricking the skin of the forearm and absorbing the blood, as in the

Duke method. In these tests bleeding normally stops in 1 to 3 minutes. By raising the cuff pressure to midway between diastolic and systolic (p. 710) and keeping up the pressure for 8 minutes, undue *fragility of capillaries* may be detected by the appearance (within 15 minutes) of tiny hemorrhages or petechiae below the elbow region. Other capillary tests employ a suction cup, or the intradermal injection of moccasin venom.

Methods for determining *coagulation time* are numerous and varied, and the "normal" values depend upon many technical variables. Limited value attaches to data obtained by capillary tube, wire loop, slide drop, and similar methods which use skin prick blood that is not controlled for contamination with tissue juices. Arm vein blood is much preferred and, in the simple method of Lee and White, 1 ml. of such blood is allowed to clot in a small (8 mm. diam.) test tube. Temperature is a variable, said to be of minor practical importance, and the "normal" range of 5 to 15 minutes refers to average room temperature (70° F.). After coagulation, the tubes are re-examined from time to time in order to note the subsequent appearance and character of *clot retraction*. An example of the application of the above tests is seen in the differential diagnosis of (i) thrombocytopenic purpura (the low *platelet count* is an additional feature), (ii) scurvy, and (iii) hemophilia.

Scope of the coagulation problem

The inherent difficulties of the coagulation problem lie in the complexities of the chemical and physical phenomena involved. Water, pH, specific salt ions (Ca^{++}), proteins (fibrinogen and fibrin, prothrombin and thrombin), fatty substances (especially the phospholipid, cephalin), carbohydrate derivatives (heparins), and enzymes (tryptases) are all clearly implicated, and their modes of action extend into the farthest reaches of chemistry, including many approaches through the avenues of colloid chemistry (9). A satisfactory explanation must account not only for the phenomena in shed blood but likewise for the fluidity normally maintained by the circulating fluids in the body and for the coagulation (and related) anomalies of pathological conditions.

It is now established that the fundamental reactions of blood clotting proceed in two stages or phases, although these are partly concurrent in ordinary coagulation. The *first phase* is the conversion of prothrombin into active thrombin. In the *second phase*, this coagulant (thrombin) causes the specific conversion of fibrinogen into fibrin. We shall have to discuss the chemical factors involved, but it should be stressed at the outset that the two phases of the clotting mechanism are subject to both favoring and inhibitory influences, partly physical (e.g., temperature) and partly chemical (e.g., pH, certain salt ions, and many other factors varying in their degree of specificity).

Cooling and freedom from contact with foreign ("wettable") surfaces retard the clotting processes. Warmth, shaking with foreign materials, contact with injured tissues, and other influences accelerate blood clotting. The blood of some species (birds, horse) is frequently slow to coagulate. The coagulation process shows anomalies in a number of conditions of disease.

The rather obvious fact that active thrombin does not exist in the circulating blood is further indicated by the experimental finding that intravascular coagulation promptly follows the intravenous injection of a potent thrombin preparation. The cause of the fluidity of the circulating blood, therefore, is the absence of active thrombin. However, its failure to form from the plasma prothrombin in vivo is by no means easily elucidated, and the same is true of the formation of thrombin when blood is shed.

The simplest method for keeping the blood from clotting outside the body is to decrease the calcium ion content of the blood by such agents as oxalates, citrates, fluorides, etc. Blood treated in this way is not entirely free from deterioration but can often be preserved for several days and may be made to clot by the subsequent addition of a suitable amount of a calcium salt. Oxalates (0.1 per cent) and fluorides (0.4 per cent) are useful anticoagulants for work in vitro (e.g., biochemical analyses) but these agents are toxic in vivo. Blood preserved with one-tenth volume of isosmotic trisodium citrate (3.8 per cent $Na_3C_6H_5O_7.5\frac{1}{2} H_2O$) is safe for human transfusions, even after cold (2°–5° C.) storage for 7 to 10 days. Heparin is a special type of anticoagulant which has been used both in vitro and in vivo.

Individual factors in the coagulation mechanism

Fibrinogen. If blood plasma is heated to 56° C., the fibrinogen is removed as a heat coagulum and the power of clotting (fibrin formation) is lost. The best evidence that fibrinogen exists in plasma as a separate entity (protein fraction) is the separation of its specific moving boundary in the electrical field of the electrophoresis apparatus. Determinations of the fibrin obtainable from pooled human plasmas at the Harvard Laboratories (4) indicate an average fibrinogen content of 0.28 gm. per 100 ml. of (undiluted) plasma. This agrees very well with the value of 0.25 (0.19–0.33) gm. per 100 ml. obtained in other laboratories by precipitation methods (10). One method consists in clotting the plasma fibrinogen and determining the nitrogen content or dry weight of the washed clot. Howe in 1921 used selective precipitation by Na_2SO_4 (at 37° C.); the use of this salt permits N analyses on the recovered precipitate. Other modifications of this technique differ only in the choice of the salting agent.

The step by step precipitation of proteins by neutral salts and testing of solubilities in specified salt solutions have long been standard techniques in plasma fractionation (3). Fibrinogen is precipitated by half saturation with sodium chloride: use of the same procedure in the cold (2° C.) and at acid pH (6.0) yields a protein of constant and reproducible solubility. One-quarter saturation with ammonium sulfate is preferred by many investigators. The use of 10 per cent ethyl alcohol, *in the cold* (0° C.), is a new means of preparing (human) fibrinogen, obtained as a stable dry powder by lyophile methods (4, 29). That the new preparations are purer than hitherto is attested by the ability to account for over 90 per cent of the protein in electrophoretic analysis and in the fibrin (clottable N). The preparation of pure fibrinogen is especially difficult because of the ease with which it becomes denatured, hydrolyzed by proteolytic enzymes (e.g., serum tryptase) or clotted to fibrin (by contaminating thrombin). The significance of small amounts of impurities, particularly prothrombin, serum tryptase, and other factors concerned with the mechanisms of coagulation, must be evaluated very carefully in determining the properties of fibrinogen.

It is now certain that fibrin formation does not occur "spontaneously" but requires a specific coagulant. The latter is normally thrombin, but a thrombin-like action can be obtained with the proteolytic enzyme papain and with certain snake venoms (*Bothrops*, *Crotalus*, sp.). The characteristic fibrin "needles" (Fig. 294) are produced in the case of the thrombin and papain clots, but not in the pseudoclots formed by ninhydrin, etc.

Physicochemical data. Fibrinogen has an iso-electric point close to pH 5.4. This value obtains at (i) the null point of electrophoresis, (ii) the flocculation maximum (minimum of suspension stability) in *electrolyte-poor* solutions, (iii) the iso-ionic point in electrometric titration. Thus, fibrinogen is a typical protein, ampholytic in its electrical behavior. At the blood or plasma pH (average 7.4) it is on the alkaline side of its iso-electric point and forms salts (fibrinogenates) with the cations (Na, Ca, etc.) present. Physicochemical studies indicate a molecular weight close to 500,000 and molecular dimensions of approximately 900 × 33 Ångstrom units. The fibrinogen molecules are believed to be miniature rodlets or fibrils of about the same thickness as the molecules of the serum proteins but very much longer (4). In flowing solutions, such molecules tend to arrange themselves "like logs in a stream" and this accounts for anomalies of optical properties (streaming double refraction) and peculiar fluid properties, including viscosity behavior. Although the fibrinogen molecule is relatively long, it is much smaller than the microscopically visible fibrin needles (Fig. 294), which average 10 μ to 30 μ (100,000–300,000 Å) in length. Electron microscopy and x-ray spectroscopic studies indicate that *fibrin* resembles fibrinogen in its molecular characteristics. The individual fibrin molecules are believed to be fine fibrils which aggregate into larger units or micelles that can be discerned by the electron microscope within the fibrin needles.

Physiological significance of fibrinogen. A variety of experimental procedures and the evidence of clinical disorders establish the importance of the liver as the chief site for the formation of fibrinogen. The average normal fibrinogen level in human plasma is 250 (190–330) mg. per 100 ml. (10). Pathologically, it can fall to about 20 mg. before any bleeding tendency appears. Lack of fibrinogen, therefore, is a very rare cause of hemorrhagic disease, although a few cases have been described and some of them are familial (pseudohemophilia). Elevation of the plasma fibrinogen is one of the commonest nonspecific responses of the body to a variety of disease conditions. It has somewhat the same clinical significance as leukocytosis and fever. It may be of diagnostic and prognostic value in following the course of tuberculosis, rheumatoid conditions, and various low grade infections. Higher fibrinogen levels are the chief, but not the only, concomitant of an increase in the red blood cell sedimentation rate (Chap. 26). Some practical uses of modern fibrinogen preparations (4) are mentioned later.

Prothrombin. It is very difficult to obtain prothrombin in a pure state. Despite a considerable excess in plasma over the amount needed to clot all the fibrinogen, the yields are extremely small, not exceeding 0.6 per cent of the total plasma protein. Prothrombin is very easily converted to active thrombin during the process of purification.

Potent prothrombin preparations may be obtained by Mellanby's method, which is an iso-electric precipitation (pH about 5.3) from well diluted, cooled plasma. According to Seegers, further purification is best effected by adsorption procedures. Fractional salting-out with 0.45 saturated ammonium sulfate is also recommended. Useful tests may be made with the cruder prothrombin papers long used by Howell and others (11).

In serum, plasma, and in most ordinary preparations, prothrombin is unstable; this may be due to the digestive action of an accompanying enzyme, serum tryptase. According to most reports, 62° C. represents the temperature of thermal denaturation. However, enzyme-free preparations are more stable and, particularly in salt-poor solutions, can retain the ability to produce considerable amounts of thrombin when activated even after several minutes of boiling.

There is a tendency for many prothrombin preparations to pass over into thrombin, either "spontaneously" or under the influence of simple treatment such as acidification, dialysis, shaking with chloroform, etc. The best prothrombin preparations do *not* behave thus. The reasonable explanation is that traces of the necessary activators persist in most prothrombin preparations. These activators include calcium salts, cephalin (phospholipid factor), thromboplastin or thrombokinase (crude aqueous tissue extracts), and proteolytic enzymes (tryptase).

Physiological significance of prothrombin. The relative amounts of prothrombin in different bloods may be estimated by the Quick test (20), in which oxalated plasma is clotted with an arbitrarily fixed amount of calcium and an excess of thromboplastin (brain extract). Normal plasma, by this test, clots in 10 to 12 seconds. The more complicated two stage procedure of the Iowa workers (2) gives similar results in many important variations but does not always agree with the Quick test. There are also "bedside methods" which employ whole blood (22). None of the prothrombin tests (unmodified) is reliable on heparinized plasma, and they are all open to certain technical criticisms which do not invalidate their success in clinical practice.

Hypoprothrombinemia (plasma prothrombin deficiency) is now accepted as a clinical entity, thanks to these modern tests. It occurs chiefly in such pathological conditions as obstructive jaundice and other liver disorders, in some intestinal dysfunctions, and in hemorrhagic disease of the newborn. Experimental evidence has confirmed the importance of the liver in the formation of prothrombin and the dependence of this function upon the adequate supply, absorption, and utilization of K vitamins (Koagulation-Vitamin of Dam, 5). The K vitamins are substituted naphthoquinones with complicated side chains. Related synthetic forms (e.g., menadione or 2-methyl-1,4-naphthoquinone) are being used therapeutically; some, being insoluble, are taken orally and require bile salts for their absorption, while others (e.g., menadione bisulfite, synkamin, etc.) are in aqueous solution ready for parenteral injection. It is not known how these naphthoquinones help the liver to produce prothrombin. They do not participate in the blood clotting reactions proper, but the hypoprothrombinemia, which occurs when the K vitamin function is deficient, greatly prolongs the coagulation time and predisposes to bleeding conditions.

Dicumarol (dicoumarin). A bleeding disease of cattle was traced to a toxic agent in spoiled sweet clover hay (15). The isolated agent is a derivative of coumarin, the chemical structure of which has certain similarities to the naphthoquinones. The synthetic substance dicumarol (3,3'-methylene bis-4-hydroxycoumarin) can be used, orally, in human cases of threatened thrombosis and embolism, to lower the plasma prothrombin level and thus reduce the tendency to form clots in the body. The action is seen only in vivo and is due to an effect upon the liver, which is just the opposite of that evoked by vitamin K. There is little tendency to damage the liver, but a rather specific action upon the unknown mechanism of prothrombin production. Overaction of dicumarol is not well antagonized by vitamin K but requires blood transfusions.

Thrombin. Thrombin may be obtained from blood which has clotted normally, or it may be prepared by the activation of previously isolated prothrombin. It can be extracted by sodium chloride from the washed fibrin clot, upon which it has presumably been adsorbed. The thrombic activity of *fresh* serum indicates that much remains in solution, but serum is not a good source material because of factors which rapidly inactivate the thrombin. Preparation via prothrombin is the modern method for obtaining really potent thrombin and attempts at further purification are currently being made.

Thrombin preparations with highest coagulant potency (2) are protein in nature, but do not yet appear as a single component in solubility tests or in the electrophoresis apparatus. Thrombin is said to differ from prothrombin in being soluble in 0.45 saturated ammonium sulfate. Thermal denaturation of thrombin may commence as low as 40° C., with complete destruction in five to ten minutes at 56° C. In the absence of rigid control of a contaminating proteolytic factor (serum tryptase), these and other stability data must be accepted with great caution. The best thrombin preparations have no proteolytic activity. Some chemical analyses have revealed the presence of sulfur, probably as SH groups, and of a carbohydrate fraction (about 5 per cent), but these data are of unknown significance. The ability to prepare thrombin free from (phospholipid) phosphorus is in agreement with a recent finding that only insignificant traces of radioactive P, supplied with the thromboplastin activator, are transferred to the final thrombin. Preparations free from calcium have also been reported.

Hemostatic uses of thrombin. Thrombin should never be injected intravenously because of the danger of intravascular clotting. It may be used locally to control bleeding from small vessels. Some preparations are applied in the form of a solution, as a spray or on gauze packing, cotton pledgets, etc. Others consist of a dried powder. Parfentjev's "hemostatic (rabbit) globulin" is essentially a thrombin, of excellent potency. The new dried (lyophilized) forms keep much better than the older solutions. Successful applications of human thrombin, impregnated on to "fibrin foams" and "fibrin films," have been reported from the Harvard Laboratories (4). It is sometimes best to combine thrombin and fibrinogen solutions immediately prior to application in order to form a fibrin gel which molds on to the surface, e.g., (i) formation of covering for burns, (ii) skin grafts, (iii) coagulum pyelolithotomy (i.e., removal of kidney stones, surgically, with the aid of an artificial clot). Plasticized fibrin films are better for more rigid support, e.g., artificial dura. The hemostatic action of thrombin-fibrin is especially useful in brain surgery. These are only a few of the practical uses of the new blood clotting protein preparations.

Calcium and Blood Clotting (7). The ability to prevent clotting by means of oxalates, citrates, fluorides, and other agents known to depress the ionization of calcium, together with the restoration of clotting on subsequent addition of an ionizable calcium salt, have long given evidence of the importance of calcium. Some careful studies of the rather complex circumstances controlling the ionization of calcium in the presence of proteins, oxalates, citrates, etc., make it clear that the action is quantitatively determined by the concentration of *active* Ca-ions available. This is why several times the chemical equivalent of the blood calcium is needed before enough oxalate (or citrate, etc.) has been added to prevent clotting and, conversely, why much less ionizable calcium than the amount of decalcifying agent present will suffice to restore coagulation.

Calcium is not necessary for the clotting of fibrinogen by thrombin. The role of Ca-ion is to aid in the conversion of prothrombin to thrombin. Fully formed thrombin is active in the presence of a considerable excess of oxalate (etc.) and some purified thrombins have been prepared completely calcium-free. There is, however, an intermediary stage in prothrombin activation, during which the thrombin (up to a short time after the mixture has reached its maximal coagulant potency) can be progressively inactivated by oxalate or citrate. Addition of Ca-ions restores thrombin formation. These experimental facts, together with the dependence of the thrombin yield upon the amount of ionizable Ca present, below a certain optimum, clearly indicate a calcium-containing *intermediary complex* in thrombin formation. Excess of calcium, as of many other salts, delays or inhibits the thrombin-fibrinogen interaction.

Blood calcium and bleeding conditions. The optimal calcium ion concentration for plasma clotting is approximately equal to that in normal blood. The minimum necessary, however, is well below any level encountered clinically, even in the severest hypocalcemias. Blood clotting is not modified in hypercalcemias. The therapeutic administration of calcium salts in bleeding conditions, therefore, is not rationalized by any possible effect on the coagulation mechanisms. This does not rule out the possibility that calcium may have an action on capillary permeability, although it has yet to be proved that this can influence capillary bleedings.

Thromboplastic Substances. The best preparations of prothrombin will not form active thrombin unless they are treated with *both* calcium *and* an additional activating substance. One such activator is *cephalin*, as little as one part in a million (of the pure phospholipid added to recalcified prothrombin solution) having significant thromboplastic effects. In the minimal range, the concentration of cephalin determines the amount of thrombin formed. *Phospholipids* are of ubiquitous distribution along with body proteins. In normal plasma there is little, if any, free cephalin, and the addition of a simple solution of the phosphatide to plasma or serum (even in hemophilia) quickly results in a combination between the proteins and the phospholipid. Since thrombin can be obtained free from phospholipid, cephalin would appear to have an *intermediary* role, analogous to that of calcium. Lecithin, sphingomyelin, and other known phospholipids do not affect blood clotting to any significant extent.

Crude aqueous tissue extracts, long known to accelerate blood coagulation, have been designated *thrombokinase* (Morawitz) or *thromboplastin* (Howell). Typically, their action is thermolabile, in contradistinction to the thromboplastic action of cephalin or crude alcoholic tissue extracts. When Howell in 1912 identified cephalin as the thermostable factor, he was fully aware that this did not account for all the clot-promoting activity of aqueous tissue extracts. Howell's suggestion, that a *lipoprotein* (cephalin-protein combination) might be involved, receives a measure of support from recent ultracentrifuge and electrophoretic studies on lung thromboplastin. These data should be accepted tentatively, with due regard to other facts: (i) the plasma itself (free from all material of platelet, cell, or tissue origin) can provide abundant thromboplastin, (ii) proteolytic enzymes (tryptases), also ubiquitous in body cells and fluids, when freed from inhibitory influences, have important thromboplastic actions. Evidence is currently appearing for a "kinase" type of activator of serum tryptase (8).

Thromboplastic extracts have been prepared from brain, lungs, and other tissues (thymus, testis, muscle, etc.). The material from blood platelets is essentially thromboplastic in nature and is rich in cephalin and other phospholipids. Recently there has been considerable interest in certain "globulin" preparations from placenta, plasma or serum. These have been tried, with some success, in hemophilia and other deep-seated bleedings, being given by intramuscular injection. Generally speaking, thromboplastic preparations should be used only for *local* hemostasis, and they are usually disappointing. Intravenous injections are highly dangerous because of intravascular clots and foreign protein reactions. The use of human products may minimize the latter. The crude globulins, however, are a mixture of clotting agents, in

21

which prothrombin, thrombin, and proteolytic enzymes ("fibrinolysin" *or* serum tryptase) have, at times, been identified.

Proteolytic Enzymes. Some old observations, with crude enzyme preparations, record the coagulant effect of pancreatic trypsin and also the loss of coagulability when the protease digests away the clotting proteins. Crystalline trypsin digests, but does not clot, purified fibrinogen solutions. Papain (an enzyme from pawpaw fruit, used in "tenderizing" meat) gives a fibrin clot, which is subsequently lysed. The clot formed by papain is indistinguishable from that produced by thrombin, except that the latter, in the absence of contaminating serum tryptase (or "fibrinolysin"), is stable for many days. Trypsin acts in the conversion of prothrombin to thrombin, resembling (according to Eagle) a mixture of calcium salt and platelets (or other thromboplastin). The inhibition of this "thromboplastic" action by a sufficient excess of oxalate or citrate suggests that it is not independent of the ordinary (Ca *plus* cephalin) mechanism of prothrombin activation.

Early in the century, Nolf (17) made extensive investigations of the phenomenon of fibrinolysis or the dissolving of fibrin clots, which is conspicuous when clotting occurs under certain conditions. Shaking oxalated or citrated plasma with a little chloroform is especially effective both for inducing coagulation and for the subsequent lysis of the clot. The term *fibrinolysin* has been widely used for the proteolytic enzyme believed to be involved. Enzyme chemists, however, are strict in allocating specific names and prefer to use general terms when more than one substrate can be attacked. According to Oppenheimer, *tryptases* are proteases which, like pancreatic trypsin, act in an alkaline medium. Such tryptases have long been recognized in the blood (serum tryptase) and in various cells and tissues. They are not active normally because of excess of *inhibitors* (antitrypsins), or possibly because a necessary activator is lacking. Shaking with chloroform is said to release tryptases from the accompanying inhibitors. Northrop and Kunitz (18) crystallized a trypsin inhibitor from pancreas and found it to be a polypeptide capable of forming a definite, crystallizable *trypsin-inhibitor* compound. Heparin (p. 598) can inhibit crystalline trypsin and also the lytic actions in blood clotting systems. An artificial system composed of calcium salt, cephalin and crystalline trypsin activates prothrombin to thrombin in a manner closely resembling that of tissue thromboplastin. Trypsin works in two systems, namely, (i) heparinized prothrombin solutions and (ii) hemophilic plasma, where cephalin often fails. Intravenous injection of trypsin is very dangerous and can kill a rabbit within a few minutes from extensive intravascular coagulation or phenomena resembling anaphylactic shock.

Hemophilia. This "bleeder's disease," sometimes called "the curse of the Hapsburgs," is a serious hereditary disorder. True hemophilia, as a rule, affects only the male but is transmitted only through the female. That is to say, a man who is hemophilic does not have overtly hemophilic children. His sons are free from the taint, but his daughters carry the defect in a latent form and transmit it actively to some of their sons. The mortality from this condition is high; simple bruising or a nosebleed or tooth extraction, which would hardly bother a normal person, may threaten the life of one who is hemophilic. Blood analyses (including calcium, fibrinogen, prothrombin, phospholipids) are normal in the hemophilic and there does not appear to be any increase in clot inhibitory factors. The platelet count is normal, but it has been observed that the platelets are unusually stable and slow to undergo the breakdown processes ordinarily seen in shed blood. This has led to a suggestion that failure of a platelet factor is responsible for the coagulation delay. The arguments against this will be presented later. The main fact, well substantiated by suitable tests, is that the conversion of prothrombin to thrombin is retarded in hemophilic blood, and the best explanation is a deficiency in the (plasma) thromboplastic mechanism. The ability of crystalline trypsin to restore thrombin formation, together with the data of several investigators who claim a diminished tryptase (or fibrinolytic) activity in preparations from hemophilic plasma, strongly indicate both (i) that hemophilia is due to deficiency of plasma tryptase and (ii) that this tryptase is an important part of the normal thromboplastic system of plasma (8). Isolated hemophilic platelets, on the other hand, show normal thromboplastic behavior and the frequent finding of a normal "bleeding time" in hemophilia indicates that the tissue thromboplastin is not impaired.

Blood platelets in relation to coagulation. Platelet suspensions or extracts accelerate blood clotting. Platelet-free (Berkefeld filtered) plasma sometimes, not always, clots poorly on recalcification but clots normally if platelets are added. The platelets are unusually stable in hemophilia (see above). Factors which prevent platelet alterations (e.g., cold, non-wettable surfaces, citrates, oxalates, heparin, cocaine, etc.) are also anticoagulant. Dark-field microscopy shows the deposition of fibrin needles, often, though not universally, in relation to foci of disintegrating platelets. These facts have long been regarded as evidence for a significant role of the platelets in blood coagulation. The fallacies of the arguments, however, are clear to the careful student. The bulk of the platelets is so small relative to the plasma that their total content of cephalin, tryptase (or other thromboplastic agent)*, is negligible compared with the plasma's contribution. There is no coagulation defect but merely a prolonged "bleeding time," in severe thrombocytopenias (pp. 587, 588). Platelet-free citrated plasma, obtained experimentally, often clots normally on simple recalcification.

By their mechanical adherence and agglutination, especially in small vessels, platelets do have an important physical function (along with a variable number of the less "sticky" leukocytes and red cells) in forming the *cellular* thrombus. As previously mentioned (p. 587), lack of this function results in a bleeding tendency. This can be explained as the inadequacy of the fibrin meshwork, alone, to check the oozing of blood from injured capillary and other vessels.

It is often postulated that *clot retraction* (p. 596) is partly responsible for the firmness of the thrombus plug. Platelets have been shown experimentally to aid in clot retraction; this may be associated with their demonstrated content of tryptase enzyme.

Fibrinolysis and other lytic actions. In natural clotting systems and in protease-free reagents to which crystalline (pancreatic) trypsin is added, the optimal pH being in the alkaline region (7.5–8.0), it is easy to demonstrate a progressive proteolytic destruction of the protein factors in the clotting system. Thus we find prothrombinolysis, thrombinolysis, fibrinogenolysis, and fibrinolysis. There is every reason to believe that these proteolytic phenomena play a large part in the notorious instability of the isolated blood clotting reagents and, indeed, of many other products of plasma origin. The elimination of contaminating *serum tryptase* (and possibly of other proteases) is by no means easy but is a major achievement in the purification of plasma protein products. Until the enzyme is fully controlled, it is difficult to be certain about the properties of the isolated materials. This is particularly true of their role in the coagulation reactions. In the presence of proteolytic enzyme, other possible causes of protein instability (e.g., "denaturation") can hardly be evaluated.

The amounts of tryptase needed for the lytic phenomena are greater than the small quantities which suffice for the previously considered "thromboplastic" action. This can easily be demonstrated by introducing known amounts of crystalline trypsin, by which means the natural phenomena can be accurately duplicated.

* The platelets are now believed not to supply prothrombin, but only the analytically demonstrable thromboplastic agents.

Lysis of fibrin, followed turbidimetrically, or lysis of fibrinogen, followed by loss of clotting power when tested with a stable thrombin, are two practical methods for the assay of active tryptase. The fibrinogenolytic method is easily sensitive to 1 : 1,000,000 trypsin. Problems of quantitative separation of natural tryptases from their accompanying inhibitors (as possibly by shaking with chloroform) have to be solved before these new methods can be put to extensive application.

Clot retraction. The curious phenomenon of clot retraction or syneresis offers many data consistent with the major role of a proteolytic enzyme. In enzyme-free systems, the fibrin clot undergoes no retraction or lysis in many days. The addition of crystalline trypsin readily induces both these phenomena and, if a suitable small quantity of enzyme is chosen, the retraction occurs without visible digestion. Retraction of clot and fibrinolysis occur if the thrombin or the fibrinogen solution is contaminated with serum tryptase. The previously noted favoring influence of platelets on clot retraction may be a tryptase effect.

When blood or plasma is allowed to clot in a wide test tube paraffined down a longitudinal *half* of its inner surface, care being taken to avoid shaking, the clot typically retracts away from the glass and adheres to the smooth paraffin. This may be explained on the assumption that the wettable glass adsorbs and thus concentrates a proteolytic enzyme (tryptase) which loosens the fibrin filaments from their attachments to the glass, causing elastic retraction, because they were originally deposited under conditions of mechanical stretching. There are some other considerations with respect to the adhesiveness of fibrin clots and relationships to platelets, but none offer as simple an explanation as the above.

Surface Factors. It is well known that coagulation is accelerated by many kinds of surfaces which are chemically inert but "wettable" in the physicochemical sense. Thus blood clots more readily in a dry glass test tube than in one whose inner surface is coated with oil, petrolatum, or paraffin or in a vessel made of nonwettable plastic (e.g., "athrombit" or "lusteroid").

Surface phenomena undoubtedly play an important part in the breakdown of platelets (p. 564) and it is just possible that platelets ordinarily initiate blood clotting by the greater ease with which they liberate thromboplastin as compared with plasma sources. However, the arguments given in a preceding section minimize this possibility.

Contemporary opinion inclines toward the view that a foreign surface disturbs the equilibrium between the colloids that make up the blood plasma and in some way makes thromboplastic factors available from plasma sources, rather than from the platelets or other formed elements. More specifically, concentration of serum tryptase by surface adsorption may account for its removal from the influence of the natural enzyme inhibitor, and the local mobilization of the mechanisms for thrombin production then initiates the process of clotting. This may very well explain the ability of trypsin to clot plasma in which the calcium ionization is depressed by a not too great excess of oxalate or citrate and in which the cephalin is tied up in combination with the proteins present. The calcium-cephalin-prothrombin interaction does not require tryptic enzyme in a system of purified materials, but in the natural clotting of plasma the enzyme and surface actions on the colloids may be very important in controlling the availability of the factors required for thrombin formation.

Fibrin and the thrombin-fibrinogen interaction. The conversion of fibrinogen (sol) into fibrin (gel) is best interpreted along the lines of colloid chemistry (9). This introduces questions of *suspension stability* about which satisfactory information is meager, but many diverse agents can modify coagulation by altering colloidal conditions during the thrombin-fibrinogen interaction. The effects of pH, numerous cations, anions, hydrotropic (i.e., solubility increasing) substances, organic compounds, and various types of colloids may be mentioned. It is very doubtful if the clot is ever composed of pure fibrin; it is always accompanied by salts, lipids, other proteins (including some thrombin) and other substances in a state of colloidal *adsorption.* The suggestion of some workers that coagulation proceeds via an intermediary phase ("soluble fibrin" or "profibrin") is controversial, especially in view of evidence that fibrin possesses a certain degree of solubility. It is not known whether any chemical change accompanies the conversion of fibrinogen to fibrin or how thrombin causes the change in colloidal properties. Many attempts have been made to follow the course of the formation of fibrin, both in plasma and in isolated materials, in the hope of shedding some light upon the way in which thrombin acts. Coagulation chemistry suffers a great handicap in not being able to identify and measure the products of the reaction. Important advances have been made recently in the development of turbidimetric methods. Nygaard's (19) "photelgraph" obtains a continuous photographic record of the relative turbidity of clotting solutions as measured with the photo-electric cell. The *coagelgram* can be used to indicate the varying amounts of fibrin and also for timing the clot. The new data confirm older conclusions that the clotting time of fibrinogen-thrombin mixtures depends (though perhaps not in a simple manner) upon the relative concentration of thrombin, whereas it is not altered by varying the fibrinogen concentration until very low levels of fibrinogen are reached. For normal recalcified human plasmas, using the coagelgraph technique, average clotting times (at 37° C.) are 178 ± 3.6 seconds with citrate, and 161 ± 3.1 seconds with oxalate. Ordinary timing of coagulation, which offers approaches of at least a semiquantitative character in the analysis of clotting problems, is subject to many experimental variables, some uncertainties as to "end points," and considerable difficulty in interpretation, so that the first requisite is a rigid standardization of all the test conditions.

Clot Modifying Mechanisms. Blood clotting, it may be re-emphasized, occurs in two phases:

1. Prothrombin $+$ Ca^{++} $+$ "thromboplastic" factor (e.g., cephalin) $\rightarrow$ thrombin;
2. Fibrinogen $+$ thrombin $\rightarrow$ fibrin.

In order to avoid the persistent confusion of terms which imply chemical entities but are actually based merely upon experimental circumstances that modify the clotting processes, it is proposed to use certain words only descriptively, to denote aiding and inhibiting the two clotting phases, respectively. Thus, the adjective *thromboplastic* (rather than the noun "thromboplastin") refers to the process, other than the action of calcium, involved in the conversion of prothrombin to thrombin. *Antiprothrombic* (in Howell's original sense) merely means inhibition of thrombin formation (first phase of clotting), and *antithrombic*, likewise, signifies any interference with the thrombin-fibrinogen interaction (second phase of clotting). The term *fibrinoplastic* may be used for aid, usually nonspecific, in fibrin formation. The value of the suggested nomenclature, uncommitted to theoretical and controversial interpretations, is exemplified in the presentation of the data on clot-inhibitory influences.

Active thrombin is absent in at least four common situations: namely, (i) in plasma (unaltered prothrombin) or prothrombin-containing systems in the presence of inhibitors (antiprothrombic) of thrombin formation; (ii) in thrombin-containing systems in the presence of inhibitors (antithrombic) of the thrombin-fibrinogen interaction; (iii) in serum which has lost its thrombic activity but can be made active again by treatment with alkali and acid (see "metathrombin"); (iv) in serum and other systems containing proteolytic enzyme (tryptase) which irreversibly digests away the thrombin protein (thrombinolysis).

Heparin. When Howell's pupil McLean, in 1916, tested a crude liver "phosphatide" and found it *inhibitory* to clotting, he opened the way for the discovery of *heparin.* The singular is often used for convenience but there are actually a number of heparins, having the composition of mucoitin-polysulfuric-esters. That is, they are carbohydrate derivatives and not related to the phospholipids. The molecular building stones are hexuronic (glycuronic) acid, glucosamine, acetic acid (?), and a variable number of sulfonic (sulfuric acid) groups, ester-linked to the sugar OH-radicals. Howell's researches (12) went a long way towards establishing the chemistry of heparin and its chief modes of action on blood coagulation mechanisms. Purification of heparin, as a lung rather than a liver product, was advanced at the Connaught Laboratories (Toronto) and by several groups of European workers (14).

The barium salt of heparin is most easily crystallized. Heparin itself is strongly acidic, readily combining with proteins and their basic split products, e.g., protamines. Proteins acted upon by heparin are altered with respect to their electrolytic dissociation, colloidal properties, and combining powers (Fischer). Two chemical data are of special relevance to coagulation: (i) heparin dissociates (or deviates) cephalin from its protein combinations, and (ii) heparin inhibits trypsin and tryptase actions in natural clotting and lytic systems.

Heparin originates in the metachromatic-staining basophilic granules of the Ehrlich "mast" cells (tissue basophils). The well-known ability of the blood to remain fluid in an excised ligated stretch of blood vessel may depend upon the presence of these basophil cells in the tissues of the vessel wall (14).

The actions of heparin on the blood clotting system are highly complex. It does act, in vivo as well as in vitro, by delaying or inhibiting the clotting reactions. There is evidence that heparin does not act by itself but only in conjunction with a *cofactor* (heparin-complement), which has tentatively been identified with some fraction (not the crystallizable portion) of serum albumin. In the presence of this cofactor, heparin is both "antiprothrombic" and "antithrombic." This statement does not offer a full explanation, however, since the underlying mechanisms remain to be elucidated. The deviation of cephalin and the antitryptase actions of heparin suggest important "antithromboplastic" modes of action, but we shall not go deeper into this technical problem. An important characteristic of the clot-inhibitory actions of heparin is that they are completely reversible by salmine.

Salmine is a basic protamine (from fish roe) which can also combine with proteins and modify their characters (see protamine-zinc-insulin). In contrast to heparin, salmine unites with the acidic groups of the proteins. By itself, salmine is "antiprothrombic." This action is quantitatively opposed by heparin although heparin alone is also antiprothrombic (see above). In the second phase, salmine is markedly "fibrinoplastic" (over a wide pH range) and this action antagonizes the antithrombic effect of heparin (*plus* cofactor). The antiheparin action of salmine occurs in vivo, as well as in vitro, and the more rapid clotting time observed after the intravenous injection of small amounts of salmine is one of the best pieces of evidence (though not unequivocal) for the existence of traces of heparin in normal blood. A salmine titration method (described by Jaques, Charles and Best in 1938) is very useful for following the changing levels of blood heparin, in vivo. The protamine would be a good agent for combating overdosage of administered heparin, were it not for the danger of allergic reactions from the injected foreign protein derivative.

Clinical uses of heparin. Heparin injections have been employed therapeutically in the prevention and palliative treatment of thrombosis and embolism (1). Repeated or even continuous intravenous injections are recommended, although a new subcutaneous method, said to give more lasting effects, is now available. The action of intravenous heparin is prompt but its degree and particularly its duration of action are very variable. Excretion occurs via the kidneys but there is also an unpredictable amount of destruction within the body, which is attributed to an enzyme (*heparinase*) in the blood and tissues.

Other anticoagulants. The blood of animals after an injection of *peptone* or in the so-called "negative phase" of *anaphylactic shock* is typically incoagulable and its serum has a greatly enhanced power of inactivating thrombin. Howell associated these phenomena with an increased outpouring of heparin and recent data prove that such bloods do contain considerable amounts of heparin and are also markedly antitryptic. The anticoagulant actions of *hirudin* (a crude extract from leeches) and of certain *venoms* (e.g., viperine snakes) have long been known but are still in need of further investigation, with particular reference to the thrombinolytic role of proteolytic enzymes. In addition to the anticoagulants which immobilize the calcium ion needed for the conversion of prothrombin to thrombin, numerous inorganic and organic compounds are capable of inhibiting blood clotting. Mention may be made of the chlorazole dyes (e.g., chlorazole fast pink, Chicago blue, etc.), "liquoid," "germanin," cysteine, etc. A biological *trypsin inhibitor* (p. 594), the crystalline polypeptide isolated from beef pancreas, has distinct anticoagulant effects. There is evidence for the existence of a similar inhibitor in the blood but it has not yet been isolated nor have its possible relationships to heparin been investigated. The plasma tryptase (and its inhibitor) system is not connected with the analogous pancreatic enzyme, since it persists in the depancreatized animal.

Fate of thrombin in serum. Much confusion continues as to the fate of thrombin in serum. The progressive character of the loss of thrombic activity, which is retarded by excess of heparin, suggests a process of *thrombinolysis* by serum tryptase. Such proteolytic destruction also occurs in impure thrombin preparations and is irreversible. The term *metathrombin* is used for the hypothetical substance in aged (inactivated) serum which can be restored to active thrombin by treatment with (N/10) alkali and acid. Several early workers tried to link "metathrombin" formation with the adsorption of thrombin by certain plasma proteins, including serum albumin. Howell and his pupils (Weymouth, Rich, Gasser) advanced the view that metathrombin is a combination of thrombin and "antithrombin." But *antithrombin* is a vague term inadequately identified as heparin *plus* an insufficiently characterized serum cofactor. It is important to rule out the mere persistence of *unaltered prothrombin*, which can be activated by the simple addition of cephalin or other thromboplastic agent, ionized calcium already being available.

Interpretations of the data on blood clotting

There have been numerous and divergent attempts to weld the mass of facts and alleged facts about blood coagulation into a comprehensive viewpoint. Detailed information and discussion may be found in a number of excellent reviews, including those by Morawitz (16), Wöhlisch (24, 25), Howell (13), Eagle (6), and Quick (20). A brief account by Taylor, Davidson and Minot (21) may also be recommended.

The Howell theory (13). The role of heparin as a natural clot inhibitor was fundamental to Howell's viewpoint. The inhibition of the conversion of prothrombin to thrombin ("antiprothrombic" action of heparin) was particularly emphasized, together with the overcoming of this type of inhibition by cephalin and tissue thromboplastins. Howell persistently denied the earlier (Morawitz) view that thromboplastin (thrombokinase), or its phospholipid component cephalin (identified by Howell, as well as by Zak, in 1912), is needed for the actual conversion of prothrombin to thrombin. This, according to Howell, merely requires calcium salts, once prothrombin has been released (by the thromboplastic factors) from "combination" with its antiprothrombic inhibitors.

Modern data re-emphasize *Morawitz's view* as to the need for the thromboplastic factor, as well as ionized calcium, in the activation of prothrombin to thrombin. Granting this, it is more logical to look upon heparin as an inhibitor of the thromboplastic mechanisms. Recent work has confirmed Howell's claim that thrombin can be obtained free from calcium and phosphorus. This is reconciled with the Morawitz concept by the evidence (Ferguson) pointing to an *intermediary*, not final, prothrombin-cephalin-calcium complex (or compound). The misplaced emphasis on platelets and tissue materials as sources of the thromboplastic factors must yield to recognition of the fact that the plasma itself is a sufficient source of all the clotting factors. Maintenance of the fluidity of the blood within the normal cardiovascular system is sufficient evidence that not all of the factors necessary for thrombin formation are ordinarily available. Confirmation is afforded by the prompt intravascular coagulation that follows the intravenous injection of potent thrombin or thromboplastin.

Eagle's view. Eagle (6) must be credited with the modern revival of interest in proteolytic enzymes in relation to blood coagulation. Much older work, done in a variety of connections, gave evidence that the blood contains proteolytic enzymes. The best recent work on enzymes in relation to blood clotting has come from Tagnon and colleagues in Taylor's laboratories in Boston. Eagle did not actually study the enzymes of natural clotting systems but argued, from experiments with crystalline (pancreatic) trypsin, that calcium *plus* platelets (or their thromboplastin) might be considered an enzymic activator of a mother substance (prothrombin), in much the same way as Northrop and his colleagues had shown crystalline trypsin to activate the precursor of another pancreatic enzyme, chymotrypsinogen. Besides being speculative, Eagle's view is committed to an enzymatic concept of the action of thrombin. This is not objectionable, per se, provided that the ordinary type of protease is not envisioned, as it seems to be in Eagle's continued analogies with papain and certain proteolytic snake venoms.

Nolf's views (17). Nolf and his colleagues, several decades ago, compiled a series of experimental data in an effort to relate blood clotting and fibrinolytic (proteolytic) phenomena. The heterodoxy of Nolf's views is due to his placing the proteolysis in a central theme (thus displacing the orthodox thrombin theory), instead of in its rightful role as subsidiary to, and in many actions independent of, the clotting processes proper.

Ferguson's views (8, 9). To the present writer it seems more logical to stress the ability of natural serum tryptase, freed from its inhibitors, to act like experimentally employed pancreatic trypsin in the display of both thromboplastic and proteolytic powers. The first refers to catalysis of the prothrombin-cephalin-calcium interaction. The enzyme does not appear to be necessary in artificial systems composed of these isolated thrombic factors. The natural plasma system, however, is believed deficient in the availability of its phospholipid factor and, in the presence of citrate or oxalate, etc., also in the availability of calcium. A normal role for the thromboplastic action of plasma tryptase, therefore, is postulated in terms of making available these activators of prothrombin. The ability of trypsin to clot hemophilic and heparinized plasmas is highly significant. The former suggests that the cause of hemophilia is lack of the ordinarily required plasma tryptase. The latter suggests that trypsin inhibitors may have much to do with the lack of active enzyme in the normal circulating blood. The anticoagulant effects of crystalline trypsin inhibitor, and the known antitryptic action of blood and other biological materials, afford confirmatory evidence. The exact nature of the plasma enzyme system needs further elucidation, along the lines opened up by Schmitz in 1937. It seems possible that the activation of serum tryptase in shed blood is due to disruption of the colloidal stability of the plasma system by adsorption ("wetting") and related physical phenomena. The appearance of active tryptase initiates the thrombin-forming reactions. Proteolytic actions of excess of serum tryptase afford a satisfactory explanation for (i) clot retraction, (ii) fibrinolysis, and (iii) deterioration of prothrombin, thrombin, fibrinogen and other plasma protein products.

TRANSFUSION PROBLEMS IN HEMORRHAGE AND SHOCK

A large portion of the entire quantity of blood in the body may be lost suddenly by hemorrhage without a fatal outcome. Experiments with dogs and cats indicate that the loss of an amount of blood equal to 3 per cent of the body weight is usually not fatal, and the same may be true of a healthy human being. After severe hemorrhage, and in cases of shock, physicians attempt to restore physiological balance by giving intravenous transfusions of the whole blood, red cell suspensions, plasma, or blood substitutes of various kinds. The problems of hemorrhage and shock are difficult and there are many angles and many urgent needs for practical solutions, based upon rational physiological principles (27).

After *hemorrhage* the immediate response of the vasomotor system (Chap. 33) is one of vasoconstriction in certain regions, whereby the blood is redistributed to the more vital organs (e.g., brain, heart, lungs) with only a limited fall in the general systemic blood pressure. However, a fall of merely 1 or 2 mm. Hg in the capillary blood pressure is sufficient to give a definite imbalance, resulting in the transfer of tissue fluids into the circulating blood. In this compensatory drawing upon the reserve of tissue fluids, it is only water and salts which enter the blood stream. Thus the blood is diluted and the colloid osmotic pressure of the plasma is reduced. This imposes a definite limit to these secondary compensating mechanisms. As there is a considerable reserve of hemoglobin function, the most urgent problem in acute hemorrhage is the maintenance of an effective blood volume and an adequate circulation. The poor blood supply (ischemia) of the vasoconstricted regions and the dehydration of the tissues, limiting nutritional interchanges, must be urgently combated. In the more severe bleedings, where the hemoglobin is much reduced, and especially because of the aggravation of this by the hemodilution, it also becomes important to combat the anoxemia (lowered oxygen content of the blood). The therapeutic suggestions are obvious. Some good undoubtedly accrues from simple infusions of physiological saline, especially with glucose. Since this merely dilutes the plasma colloids still further, it is rapidly lost into the tissue spaces, its effect in maintaining blood volume and blood pressure is brief and disappointing, but it helps to relieve the tissue dehydration and to improve blood flow in vasoconstricted regions by lessening the viscosity of the blood. There are a number of objections to the use of foreign colloids such as gum acacia (introduced by Bayliss during World War I), although better (immediate) results have been reported for more recent agents (29), e.g., pectin, isinglass, gelatin, hemoglobin (which may damage the kidneys) or globin alone. However, the best blood substitutes are those which are creating remarkable records in World War II, namely, preserved blood plasma, frozen plasma, and especially dried ("lyophilized") plasma and serum. Some special advantages (e.g., reduced bulk) and some disadvantages (possibly, slower convalescence) characterize the use of the isolated albumin fraction of plasma. Casein and other protein "digests" are not helpful for the emergency problems but may aid in the restoration of the normal plasma protein level. It does appear that we should now think, not only of the immediate problem of restoring plasma colloid, but also of ultimate recovery based upon physiological normality of the blood, both in composition and distribution. Transfusion of compatible whole blood is the logical emergency treatment of severe hemorrhage.

Whole blood was used on a large scale by Loyalist physicians in the Spanish Civil War (1936), and it had also been recommended by the British at the beginning of the second World War. In 1939–40 they developed blood banks and mobile transfusion units designed for whole blood, but on account of difficulties in typing, preserving and shipping whole blood, and owing possibly also to the fact that most of their mobile transfusion equipment was lost at Dunkirk, the British reverted for a time to the use of plasma for war casualties, among both troops and civilians. The United States Army and Navy, on advice from the National Research Council, followed suit, and a highly profitable four-year research program on the processing of various plasma fractions was launched for our armed forces. Following our North African and Italian campaigns and operations in the Pacific theater, particularly Bougainville, it became evident that plasma would not restore the severely wounded, especially those who had suffered severe hemorrhage, and that in any war theater it is imperative to have whole blood available as well as plasma. During the year 1944 the Surgeons General of the United States Army and Navy developed a far-flung service for distributing whole blood. In the Pacific theater in operations such as those at Saipan and Iwo Jima, whole blood was available scarcely 48 hours after it had been drawn from donors on the west coast of the United States. The Russians developed a similar service on the Eastern front in 1944–45.

The *shock* problem is especially complex and confusing. The earlier summarizations of data by Cannon (26) and Wiggers (32) characterized shock as an "irreversible circulatory failure." Moon (28) made valuable contributions in pointing out the significance of capillary damage and leakage of the plasma proteins into the tissues, with resulting hemoconcentration. This is especially true of burn shock, where the local fluid loss is undoubtedly of major importance. A recent review by D. W. Richards (30) of a very careful and intensive clinical and experimental study by a large group of New York authorities serves to emphasize the multiplicity of factors involved. *Traumatic* shock, first in importance in war casualties and in civilian accident cases, is apparently too closely connected with concomitant hemorrhage to permit of any hard-and-fast separation of shock from hemorrhage.

The fundamental physiological difficulty in these conditions is in the capacity of the circulation to be effective in supplying tissue needs. In the face of the emergency, major calls are made upon the mechanisms of adjustment and the more "vital" functions have often to be maintained at the expense of what may be termed the "luxury" functions, important as some of these are for the everyday processes of life. When the mechanisms of adjustment are taxed to the limit, there is imminent danger of breakdown, not only *early*, but also *later* ("secondarily"), as the result of accumulating deficits leading to a vicious circle, which is no less serious because the final breakdown is delayed. It is this sort of thing that is at the heart of the shock problem, and it is to prevent and thwart these dangerous circulatory failures that modern medical science steps in with the weapons of transfusions and ancillary measures. In all shock cases, the primary disturbance is a marked reduction in the venous return (Chap. 38) and hence in the effective circulating blood 'volume. Despite compensatory mechanisms (see below) this leads, typically, to a distinct fall in the blood pressure.

The term *primary* shock is sometimes used for the earliest phases, which differ from simple fainting (syncope) and other forms of "vasomotor collapse," chiefly in the tendency to progress into the classical form usually referred to as true or *secondary* shock. It does seem, from recent data, that the initial disturbances must be regarded minutely and every effort made to find out the manner and extent of their contributions to the final picture. It is not necessary to postulate any significant widespread vasodilatation, which would be implied by early vasomotor failure. Rather, the excessive *vasoconstriction* (in physiological compensation for the diminished venous return) may be directly involved, in areas such as the skin and splanchnic regions, by causing tissue ischemia and anoxic cell damage. The pallor of the skin is an obvious example of the adrenosympathetic response mediating some of these vasoconstrictor mechanisms. It is not rational to expect much of adrenaline and other vasoconstrictor drugs (e.g., pituitrin) when there is evidence that the body is not only already responding by vasoconstriction but, in some cases, is even carrying this response too far. In the kidney, for example, the blood flow may be reduced to one-twentieth of normal. Thus, to lowered blood pressure and reduced renal blood flow, lessening the urine formation in the first place, we add ischemic diminution in the oxygen supply and so lower the functional capacity of this vital excretory organ that nitrogenous wastes may accumulate and the patient die in uremia. Similar functional disorders may develop in other organs, especially the brain, liver, and lungs. Acute pulmonary edema may occur in shock cases.

The evidence is too conflicting at this time to make it profitable to discuss the possibility of systemic "toxic factors" in shock. We can, however, emphasize the importance of *tissue anoxia*. Not all contributions to this impasse are circulatory. In cases of hemodilution, such as hemorrhagic and traumatic shock, there is loss of oxygen transport because of the oligocythemia (reduction in red cells). Saline and plasma transfusions may even aggravate this. There may be deficient aeration of blood in the lungs, which brings in the whole gamut of respiratory disturbances. There is clear evidence that the *oxygen consumption* of the tissue is reduced in shock. It is all part of a vicious cycle, and the cells cannot even get the full benefit of such oxygen as can be supplied. The practical use of oxygen therapy is limited by the oxygen-carrying capacity of the patient's blood. In all cases where there is anemia or hemodilution, red blood corpuscles should be supplied. In some instances, there is a definite advantage in using *saline suspensions* of red cells, rather than whole blood, because of the undue viscosity of the latter, which may add to the burden of the heart in trying to force blood through a vascular system narrowed, in many regions, by the compensatory vasoconstriction.

The *peripheral resistance* is increased in shock, both because of the widespread vasoconstriction and because of other factors, especially the increased viscosity in cases where there is hemoconcentration (e.g., burns, abdominal shock). In most cases, it takes some time for capillary damage to occur, particularly in sites remote from the original injury.

As the cutaneous vasoconstriction in shock is protective, it must not be broken down by undue warming of the patient or by vasodilator agents, amongst which alcohol is a bad offender. Exposure aggravates shock, so the body temperature must not be allowed to fall. It is best, therefore, to keep the trunk covered and have the extremities open to a moderately cool room temperature. The *vasomotor adjustment* may be supported by having the patient lying on his back with the foot of the bed somewhat elevated. He should not be allowed to raise himself suddenly, as the onset of acute vasomotor failure is greatly to feared and guarded against.

There are disturbances in *electrolyte balance* and a tendency to *acidosis* in shock, which are further evidence of tissue damage and metabolic difficulties. Some recent experimental data (31) and clinical experiences (e.g., burn cases) point to benefits, particularly in terms of lowered mortality rate, of giving large quantities of *sodium* salts, even orally. It does not seem rational to recommend saline in late cases where there is gross capillary leakage, but in *early* shock, intravenous saline is often valuable, especially if immediately follqwed by plasma transfusion. The probable explanation is that the hemodilution and reduced viscosity, aided by the saline, counteract to some extent the high peripheral resistance due to vasoconstriction. In burns, and some other cases, plasma seepage may be controlled by pressure bandages. Adrenal cortical extract has *not* proved valuable in the practical handling of permeability problems. With dried plasma, serum, or plasma albumin, it is sometimes recommended that the reconstituted solution be double or even four times the original protein strength, but the usefulness of this is debatable. Human plasma albumin has been supplied as a 25 per cent solution in hypertonic saline. This has the practical advantage of small bulk, and its viscosity is about the same as that of plasma. When this concentrated solution is used, it may be injected with or without dilution. It is generally regarded as safest to use solutions approximating the normal values of 5 to 7 per cent plasma protein or 4 to 5 per cent albumin. Any threatened vasomotor collapse is a strong indication for prompt additional plasma transfusion. The emergency period is protracted in nearly all shock cases owing to the profound disturbances in the bodily economy. The significant points mentioned serve to indicate how difficult it is for the physiologist and pathologist to explain these disturbances. Even in cases where the immediate dangers and complications have been circumvented, there is necessarily a long period of supportive treatment and intelligently ordered convalescence.

REFERENCES

Coagulation

1. BEST, C. H. Heparin and thrombosis. *Harvey Lect.*, 1940–41, *36*:66–90.
2. BRINKHOUS, K. M. Plasma prothrombin; vitamin K. *Medicine, Baltimore*, 1940, *19*:329–416.
3. COHN, E. J. Properties and functions of plasma proteins, with consideration of methods for their separation and purification. *Chem. Rev.*, 1941, *28*:395–417.
4. COHN, E. J., *et al.* Chemical, clinical, and immunological studies on the products of human plasma fractionation. I–XXIII. *J. clin. Invest.*, 1944, *23*:417–606.
5. DAM, H. Vitamin K, its chemistry and physiology. *Advances in Enzymology*, 1942, *2*:285–324.
6. EAGLE, H. Recent advances in the blood coagulation problem. *Medicine, Baltimore*, 1937, *16*:95–138.
7. FERGUSON, J. H. The blood calcium and the calcium factor in blood coagulation. *Physiol. Rev.*, 1936, *16*:640–670.
8. FERGUSON, J. H. A new theory of blood clotting. *Science*, 1943, *97*:319–322.
9. FERGUSON, J. H. The modern outlook on blood coagulation. Vol. 5, pp. 951–957 in: J. ALEXANDER, ed., *Colloid chemistry; theoretical and applied.* New York, 1944.
10. HAM, T. H. and CURTIS, F. C. Plasma fibrinogen response in man. *Medicine, Baltimore*, 1938, *17*:413–445.
11. HOWELL, W. H. The coagulation of blood. *Harvey Lect.*, 1916–17, *12*:273–324.
12. HOWELL, W. H. The problem of coagulation. *Proc. Chicago Inst. Med.*, 1925, *5*:139–163.
13. HOWELL, W. H. Theories of blood coagulation. *Physiol. Rev.*, 1935, *15*:435–470.
14. JORPES, J. E. *Heparin: its chemistry, physiology and application in medicine.* London, Oxford University Press, 1939, 87 pp.
15. LINK, K. P. The anticoagulant from spoiled sweet clover hay. *Harvey Lect.*, 1943–44, *39*:162–216.
16. MORAWITZ, P. Die Chemie der Blutgerinnung. *Ergebn. Physiol.*, 1905, *4*:307–422.

17. NOLF, P. The coagulation of the blood. *Medicine, Baltimore,* 1938, *17*:381–411.
18. NORTHROP, J. H. *Crystalline enzymes: the chemistry of pepsin, trypsin, and bacteriophage.* New York, Columbia University Press, 1939, 176 pp.
19. NYGAARD, K. K. *Hemorrhagic diseases: photo-electric study of blood coagulability.* St. Louis, C. V. Mosby Co., 1941, 320 pp.
20. QUICK, A. J. *The hemorrhagic diseases and the physiology of hemostasis.* Springfield, Illinois, Charles C Thomas, 1942, 340 pp.
21. TAYLOR, F. H. L., DAVIDSON, C. S. and

MINOT, G. R. The physiology of blood coagulation. *Nelson Loose Leaf Living Medicine,* 1944, *4*:105–115D.
22. WARNER, E. D. Current methods for estimating prothrombin. *West. J. Surg.,* 1942, *50*:408–415.
23. WINTROBE, M. M. *Clinical hematology.* Philadelphia, Lea & Febiger, 1942, 792 pp.
24. WÖHLISCH, E. Die Physiologie und Pathologie der Blutgerinnung. *Ergebn. Physiol.,* 1929, *28*:443–624.
25. WÖHLISCH, E. Fortschritte in der Physiologie der Blutgerinnung. *Ergebn. Physiol.,* 1940, *43*:174–370.

Transfusion, Hemorrhage, Shock

26. CANNON, W. B. *Traumatic shock.* New York, D. Appleton Co., 1923, 201 pp.
27. FERGUSON, J. H. The physiological basis of treatment in shock and hemorrhage. *N. C. med. J.,* 1944, *5*:493–496.
28. MOON, V. H. *Shock: its dynamics, occurrence and management.* Philadelphia, Lea & Febiger, 1942, 324 pp.
29. MUDD, S. and THALHIMER, W. *Blood substitutes and blood transfusion.* Spring-

field, Illinois, Charles C Thomas, 1942, 407 pp.
30. RICHARDS, D. W., JR. The circulation in traumatic shock in man. *Bull. N. Y. Acad. Med.,* 1944, 2d ser., *20*:363–393.
31. ROSENTHAL, S. M. Experimental chemotherapy of shock and burns. *Publ. Hlth. Rep., Wash.,* 1943, *58*:513–522; 1429–1436.
32. WIGGERS, C. J. Present status of the shock problem. *Physiol. Rev.,* 1942, *22*:74–123.

SECTION V

PHYSIOLOGY OF THE ORGANS OF CIRCULATION OF THE BLOOD AND LYMPH

BY DONALD H. BARRON, HAROLD LAMPORT AND

JOHN F. FULTON*

The blood of the body is contained in a closed but elastic system of vessels composed of the arteries, arterioles, capillaries and veins through which it is circulated by the action of the heart. During its passage through the tissue capillaries of the body, the composition of the blood is altered by the diffusion of materials from the plasma into the tissue spaces and vice versa. Through these exchanges between the tissue spaces and the blood, the temperature and the composition of the fluid environment about the individual tissue cells is held relatively constant, and it is toward this end—the maintenance of the constancy of the internal fluid environment—that the action of the entire circulatory apparatus appears to be integrated and directed. For this reason consideration of the physiology of the circulatory system begins with the blood flow through the capillaries, Chapter 29. Attention is next turned to the mechanics and hydrodynamics of blood flow through the elastic tubes of varying diameter—arteries, arterioles and veins—to and from the capillaries, Chapters 30, 31 and 32. The movement of the blood through the capillaries and the normal exchange of materials between extracellular fluids and plasma depend upon an adequate pressure gradient between the arteries and veins; the regulation of the arterial pressure and the blood flow through particular organs of the body are considered in Chapters 33–34 and 38 respectively. Finally the physiology of the heart itself, the organ which must serve to establish the gradient of pressure, is presented in Chapters 35, 36 and 37.

* Editorial responsibility for the chapters in this Section has been assumed as follows: Chapters 29, 31–34, 38,—Dr. Barron; Chapter 30, Dr. Lamport; Chapters 35–37, Dr. Fulton.

CHAPTER 29

THE CAPILLARIES AND THE LYMPHATICS

BY ERIC PONDER

CIRCULATION THROUGH THE CAPILLARIES

The circulation in the capillaries can easily be observed by examining the web or mesentery of the frog or the mesentery of the mouse under moderate powers of the microscope. The small arterioles will be seen to terminate, by quite a rapid transition in structure, in the capillaries; the endothelium becomes thinner, the muscular and fibrous walls disappear, and there remains only the delicate capillary wall, anchored in place by connective tissue fibers, which here and there may produce sharp kinks in the vessels.

The most striking feature of the capillary bed is that not all of the capillaries are open at one and the same time, so that in resting tissue the number along which blood can be seen to flow is much smaller than the number which open up as the tissue becomes active. Krogh's (4) observations on the capillaries of living muscle show that under resting conditions only a few capillaries are open, and that these are often so constricted that red cells can make their way through them only after considerable distortion. In stimulated muscle, on the other hand, large numbers of previously invisible capillaries open up, with the result that the rate of blood flow through the tissue, and therefore its oxygen supply, is greatly increased. By injecting India ink into the circulation and stimulating the muscle, 190 capillaries per sq. mm. were counted, as compared with 5 capillaries per sq. mm. in a resting muscle used as a control. In some resting tissues, accordingly, it is not uncommon to find that only 1/20 to 1/50 of the total capillary bed is open to the circulation. In the case of other tissues, however, e.g., the human skin, the same number of capillaries is open, whether the blood flow is great or small.

These changes in the amount of the capillary bed which is occupied by actively circulating blood are the result, in part, of the peculiar anatomical arrangement of the capillaries into two types of vessel. First, direct continuations of small arterioles can be traced through to the venous circulation, and these "a-v capillaries," which are direct short circuits between the arterial and the venous circulation, are the ones which always remain open, even when the tissue is resting. These a-v capillaries have a distinct, although not extensively developed, muscular coat. Secondly, true capillaries arise as extensions of the arterioles (metarterioles) near the junction of the arteriole with the a-v capillary, and anastomose with each other to form the bulk of the capillary network, rejoining the a-v capillary near its venous end (Fig. 295). The metarterioles, like the a-v capillaries, possess muscular elements in their walls. There is always a vigorous circulation through the a-v capillaries because they are a direct pathway from the arterioles to the venules, and offer little resistance to the flow of blood; the true capillaries, on the other hand, are abrupt offshoots of the arterioles, and so are readily cut off from the rapid circulation through the a-v trunk by a contraction of the musculature of the metarterioles. This arrangement allows of the utilization of the two types of vessel at different times according to the level of activity of the tissue (9).

The average length of a capillary is from 0.4 mm. to 0.7 mm., while its diameter may vary from 15 or 20 μ to 5 μ or even less. In these narrow vessels there is no rapidly moving axial stream such as is seen in arterioles, in which the red cells are hurried along in the middle of the vessel while the

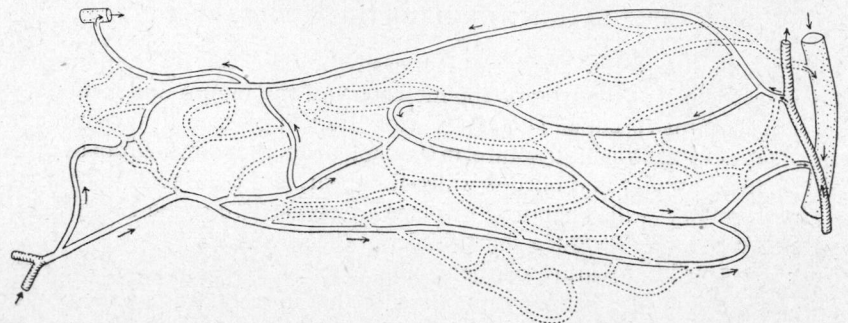

Fig. 295.—Capillaries (dotted), a-v capillaries (full line), and their relations to arterioles (shaded) and venules (stippled). (From Zweifach, *Amer. J. Anat.*, 1936–1937, *60*:473–514.)

white cells remain in the more slowly moving fluid near the walls. The narrower capillaries, indeed, can scarcely accommodate the red and white cells which flow through them, and the cells have to get through as best they can, often with temporary stoppages and by being squeezed out of shape. The red cells thus come into very close contact with the capillary endothelium.

It has been estimated that the total area of the walls of the capillaries of the voluntary muscle of man is about 6,000 sq. meters, and that each ml. of blood which passes through them comes into contact with about 6,000 sq.

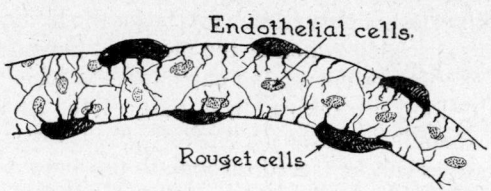

Fig. 296.—The structure of a typical capillary.

cm. of capillary surface. Such a situation is very favorable to the rapid diffusion of gases and other substances from the blood in the capillaries to the tissues which lie beyond their walls.

The Capillary Wall. The wall of the typical capillary is composed of plate-like endothelial cells held together by an "intercellular cement substance," and of larger cells with long cytoplasmic processes arranged in a saddlelike manner along the endothelial tube (Fig. 296). These are called Rouget cells, and require special histological methods for their demonstration. They have been considered by some to be homologues of plain muscle fibers, and at one time it was thought that they were responsible for the contraction of capillaries; other observers, with more probability, have identified them with the wandering cells of the tissues which have adapted themselves to the shape of the capillary wall. There is now general agreement that the endothelial cells themselves are contractile, and, although the matter cannot be said to be altogether settled, we no longer look upon the Rouget cell as an important contractile element. The subject has been reviewed by Zweifach (8).

The endothelial cells are thin flat plates with homogeneous cytoplasm and a long, granular nucleus. When the capillary is collapsed the cells may be wrinkled into folds; the folds disappear when capillary dilatation occurs, and still further degrees of dilatation must result in stretching of the capillary wall. Such stretching probably results in an increase in permeability.

The fact that red cells, white cells, and inanimate particles such as India ink can escape from apparently uninjured capillaries into the surrounding tissue spaces has recently directed attention to the spaces between the endothelial cells and to the properties of the intercellular cement substance which normally fills them. Not only red cells but even larger objects can pass through the endothelium without damaging it; microfilariae, for example, pass from the blood to the lymph although they measure some 40 μ in length and 5 μ in breadth. Observations of this kind suggest that the particles traverse the capillary wall at points where transit is relatively easy, and the existence of actual holes or stomata between the endothelial plates was once postulated. Recently, however, Chambers and Zweifach (2) have emphasized the importance of the junctions between the endothelial plates as the most likely points of passage of large particles and of leakage of smaller ones, such as the molecules of the plasma proteins.

In experiments in which frog capillaries were perfused with Ringer-gelatin solutions, Chambers and Zweifach (2) arrived at conclusions which are best given in their own words:
"*The inter-endothelial cell cement during normal blood circulation.*

"1. The endothelial lines can be stained, under viable conditions, by spraying 10 per cent $AgNO_3$ on the outer surface of the capillaries with a micropipette. The blackened surface of the cement is gradually washed away by the blood stream and replaced by fresh cement.

"2. Carbon, suspended in the blood stream, adheres to the sticky cement without adhering to the exposed surfaces of the endothelial cells. In this way the carbon-deposit outlines the endothelial cells.

"3. When the capillary is prodded with a micro-needle, there occurs an immediate flattening of red cells against the irritated wall and a local accumulation of carbon. This indicates an excessive leakage of fluid through that region of the capillary.

"*The effect of perfusion of physiological salt solutions containing ash-free gelatin* (0.5%) *on the inter-endothelial cell-cement.*
"A. By varying the calcium content of the perfusate.

"4. The capillary bed can be perfused with a normal Ringer-gelatin solution for over 100 minutes with no visible abnormalities.

"5. With solutions lacking calcium, a softening of the cement is indicated by its increased stickiness and by its being washed away.

"6. With solutions containing double the amount of calcium, the stickiness of the endothelial lines becomes intensified and later the entire inner surface of the endothelial wall becomes sticky.

"B. By varying the pH.

" 7. An increase in acidity of the medium induces early and intense stickiness followed by pronounced leakiness of the capillary wall.

"*The relation between the induced changes in the endothelial cement and the extrusion of particulate matter and the appearance of edema.*

"8. The lack of calcium and increase in acidity soften the cement (evidenced by increased stickiness to carbon) and enchance its dissipation. These conditions favor the extrusion of formed elements of the perfusate (e.g., carbon, leucocytes, and red cells) and accelerate the outward diffusion of the perfusate."

Zweifach (9) has farther shown that the rate at which edema appears in the frog mesentery when the pH is varied is also dependent on the calcium content of the perfusion fluid, and summarizes the experimental evidence by saying,

"The physical state of the capillary wall depends on the calcium content of the perfusate. The conditions produced are reversible, and appear closely analogous to those in epithelial membranes in which the intercellular cement reacts to inorganic salts as if it were itself a salt. The absence of calcium from the medium serves to increase the instability of the cement substance through the replacement of the relatively stable but reversible calcium salt by the soluble sodium or potassium salt. Increased acidity acts to increase the ionization of the cement and thereby to enhance its dissipation. An important role of the endothelial cell appears to be the continual secretion of the intercellular cement, the chemical stability of which controls the permeability of the blood capillary."

The possibility that capillary permeability depends on the nature and integrity of the interendothelial cement substance rather than on the permeability of the membranes of the endothelial cells themselves is a new and important conception in capillary physiology.

Capillary Reactions. It is now recognized that the vessels of the capillary network have the inherent ability to contract and dilate, and that these changes are not mere passive accompaniments of pressure changes in the arterioles, as was once believed. Although the adjustment of the capillary circulation to the requirements of tissue metabolism is apparently dependent to a far greater extent on chemical than on nervous stimuli, the capillaries are to some extent under nervous control, and both vasoconstrictors and vasodilators have been described.

Most of the changes in capillary diameter which occur when a tissue passes from a resting to an active state are the result of the lack of oxygen and the accumulation of metabolites. Investigations as early as those of Gaskell in 1877 and Roy and Graham Brown in 1879 led to the following conclusion: "There is a local mechanism, independent of centers in the medulla and spinal cord, by which the degree of dilatation of the vessels (capillaries) is varied in accordance with the requirements of the tissues." This view has been confirmed by many observers. Bayliss first showed that CO_2 has a local vasodilator effect, and subsequently Ebbecke, Barcroft and Kato, Gesell, and many others found capillary dilatation to be dependent on anoxia or the presence of metabolic products of tissue activity. Krogh and Rethberg, for example, placed rabbits in respirators from which the CO_2 could be absorbed with soda lime and in which the O_2 content could be controlled; as the O_2 tension in the animal's blood fell, cyanosis developed and was accompanied by capillary dilatation, which might be due either to the low O_2 content of the blood or to the accumulation of metabolites such as lactic acid. Further determinations showed that the pH changes in the blood were themselves insufficient to produce the capillary dilatation, which was finally attributed to the anoxemia itself. This experiment is typical of many of the same general kind.

While the results of experiments like this are not at all in question, there is now a tendency, initiated by Lewis (6), to look upon the changes in capillary diameter as due to the action of a *specific substance* rather than as the direct result of diminished O_2 tension, increased CO_2 tension, accumulation of lactic acid, and so on. Lewis's view is that the agent causing the capillary dilatation when the tissue passes from the resting to the active state ("functional hyperemia") is a histamine-like substance, a normal metabolite of cells which is released by them in proportion to their activity, and that it is this same substance ("H-substance") which is released by tissue cells when they are injured mechanically. Anrep (1) has reviewed the subject in so far as it relates to the regulation of the circulation in muscle, and has presented evidence both for the effects of a specific histamine-like substance and for the effects of accumulated acid metabolites and anoxemia.

While capillary dilatation is controlled by local conditions and by substances produced locally, there is evidence that the tone of the capillaries, in the amphibia at least, is maintained by the action of a hormone derived from the pituitary. Rethberg first observed that the capillaries of the frog become dilated after removal of the pituitary, and this aspect of capillary control has been extensively investigated by Krogh. Assuming for the moment that the results obtained in the amphibia are not peculiar to that vertebrate class, we arrive at a hypothesis of this kind: The capillaries of resting tissue are maintained in a state of contraction by the action of a pituitary hormone. When the tissue becomes active, the cells use up O_2 and produce metabolites (H-substance and others); these tend to bring about capillary dilatation. As the capillaries dilate, fresh blood flows through the tissue, removing the metabolites and bringing a new supply of the pituitary hormone; the capillaries then contract until another accumulation of metabolites produces dilatation, and the cycle of events is repeated again and again in proportion to the activity of the tissue. This is a valuable hypothesis for enabling us to understand how the blood supply of a tissue is adapted to its needs; too much insistence, however, should not be placed on the role of the pituitary hormone, for which the evidence is not nearly as convincing in the mammal as it is in the amphibian.

Vascular reactions in the skin (*The "triple response"*). The study of the vascular reactions of the skin is important for an understanding of capillary responses and the mechanisms underlying them. The observations can easily be made on the skin on the front of the forearm.

If the skin is lightly stroked with a blunt instrument, a line of pallor appears in about 15 to 20 seconds along the path of the instrument. The pallor increases in intensity for about 30 to 60 seconds and then gradually fades (3 to 5 minutes). This *"white reaction"* is due to capillary contraction following on direct stimulation, and the capillaries will remain closed, at the height of the pallor, against a pressure of as much as 100 mm. Hg.

If the instrument is drawn over the skin more firmly, a red instead of a white line appears after a shorter latent period (3 to 15 seconds), and may last for several minutes or even half an hour. This *"red reaction"* is dependent, in duration and intensity, on the intensity of the stimulus provided by the blunt instrument, and is due to capillary dilatation. It occurs with full intensity even when the circulation to the skin area is cut off with a tourniquet, and even when all nerves to the skin area have degenerated. The reaction is accordingly an active process, not dependent on pressure in the arterioles, and not dependent on nervous mechanisms.

If the stimulus is still stronger or repeated sufficiently often, a bright red flush or flare spreads outwards from the border of the red line, usually within 15 to 30 seconds after the first appearance of the red reaction. This *"red flare"* reaction does not occur if the circulation to the part is cut off, and is due to a dilatation of the arterioles. It occurs when the nerves to the skin area are cut, but not when they have degenerated, and so is due to a local axon reflex mechanism (see p. 830).

If the stimulus is still more intense, the local red reaction grows paler and begins to become raised above the surface of the surrounding skin. This *local edema* or *wheal formation* is due to the escape from the injured capillaries of a fluid similar in composition to blood plasma. In some sensitive skins the wheal formation occurs unusually readily, so that letters and words, lightly traced on the skin with a blunt point, appear written on the skin as wheals which may persist for half an hour or more. This is known as *dermographism*. After a variable length of time the wheals lose their sharpness by becoming wider and less raised, and finally they disappear altogether.

The succession of events, red reaction, flare, and wheal formation, is called the *"triple response,"* and it is believed that these three reactions are brought about by the diffusion of a substance liberated by the cells of the skin along the path traced by the instrument. The hypothetical diffusible substance bears a close resemblance to histamine in its effects (production of capillary dilatation by direct action, of arteriole dilatation by means of an axon reflex, and of the wheal by increasing capillary permeability), and Lewis speaks of it as the *H-substance;* it may actually be histamine itself. While the reactions which constitute the triple response are most easily studied in the skin, they can also be demonstrated in the viscera (liver, spleen, and kidney).

Vascular reactions in inflammation. The vascular changes which occur in an inflamed area involve reactions similar to those of the triple response, and like them are independent of all except local innervation. Injury, due to direct trauma or to bacterial toxins, causes a liberation of a histamine-like substance from the tissue cells, and the diffusion of this substance is followed by capillary dilatation and an increase in capillary permeability (see Moon, 7). As in the case of the triple response, there is an increased transudation of fluid from the dilated and highly permeable capillaries, the walls of which now permit not only water and solutes, but also proteins, to pass readily into the extracellular spaces. In this way the inflamed tissue becomes filled with a protein-rich edema fluid. The process is aided by two additional factors: the dilatation of near-by arterioles, brought about by axon reflexes and resulting in a still greater blood flow into the dilated capillaries, and an obstruction, probably by clots of fibrin, of the lymphatics draining the area. As a result of the increased blood flow the inflamed area becomes red and warm, as a result of the transudation of edema fluid it becomes turgid, and as a result of the turgor there is pain; these constitute the classical signs of inflammation.

The leukocytes in the dilated capillaries of inflamed tissue tend to adhere to the endothelial walls and then to pass through them into the extracellular spaces surrounding the tissue cells. Red cells may accompany them, and within a few hours the white cell count in the edema fluid of an inflamed area (e.g., the fluid of a blister) may be as high as 30,000 per cu. mm. This tendency for leukocytes (principally polymorphs) to collect in regions of inflammation is called leukotaxis. Menkin has brought forward evidence that it is due to a nitrogenous substance which he calls leukotaxin, and which has properties quite different from those of histamine.

Capillary Permeability. The rate of penetration of a substance through the capillary wall is measured in terms of the amount of the substance dS which passes across the capillary wall in time dt. It is directly proportional to the area A of the wall, the difference of pressure (mechanical or osmotic) between the inside and the outside of the capillary, and the diffusion constant for the substance, and is inversely proportional to the thickness of the capillary wall.

If the thickness is considered as being constant, its value may be incorporated into the diffusion constant to give a "permeability constant, k," so that the rate of penetration becomes

$$\frac{dS}{dt} = kA(C_i - C_o)$$

where C_i is the total pressure (mechanical and osmotic) inside the capillary and C_o the total pressure outside. In the case of the permeability to water, the amount which penetrates is measured as the volume in μ^3 which filters across each μ^2 of membrane per second, under a pressure difference of 1 atmosphere. To determine it, we require an experiment in which capillary pressure, capillary diameter (and hence area), and transudation of fluid from the capillary are all measured simultaneously. Such experiments were carried out by Landis (5), a fine tube, connected to a manometer, being inserted into a capillary of the mesentery of the frog and perfused with a weak solution of toluidine blue in Ringer. The amount of fluid passing through the capillary wall in known times under known pressures was then measured. The figure which Landis obtained for the rate of penetration of water was about 60 μ^3 per μ^2 per second per atmosphere of pressure, which is so much greater than the value obtained for any other type of cell as to lead to the conclusion that the water passes through fairly large pores into the capillary wall. Possibly most of its passage takes place through the intercellular junctions and the cement substance; at all events, there is virtually no resistance to its movement.

Comparatively little is known about the permeability of the typical capillary to the electrolytes and nonelectrolytes of plasma, although there is evidence that substances penetrate in the order water > urea > glucose > sucrose. Even if substances such as these were to diffuse freely, there would be differences in their diffusion rates, because of differences in their molecular size. In the absence of precise information, it is usually assumed that all the constituents of plasma except the proteins can pass across the capillary wall without difficulty. This simplification of the situation led Starling (1895) to make his classical statement about the conditions in the capillary which regulate the transfer of water; the force of capillary pressure, which tends to drive water outwards, was supposed to be balanced by the osmotic pressure of the plasma proteins, which draws water inwards from the extracellular fluid outside the capillary. Putting the hypothesis into symbols, what is required by Starling's theory is that at equilibrium there shall be a balance between the "effective" blood pressure CP within the capillary and the "effective" osmotic pressure of the plasma. The effective osmotic pressure of the plasma is the difference between the osmotic pressure of the plasma, OP_{plasma}, inside the capillary, and the osmotic pressure of the extracellular fluid, $OP_{e.f.}$, outside the capillary. It has also to be borne in mind that the capillary pressure is to some extent offset by the pressure in the tissues outside the extracellular space, or by the "tissue turgor pressure," TP. Collecting these various quantities, we require to have, at equilibrium,

$$CP - TP = OP_{plasma} - OP_{e.f.}$$

If either side of the equation is greater than the other, water will move out of the capillary (when the left-hand side is larger), or into the capillary (when the right-hand side is larger), until the balance is attained. All the pressures, mechanical and osmotic, have to be measured in the same units, usually atmospheres (1 atmosphere = 760 mm. Hg).

One of the simplifications which was introduced into the original statement of Starling's theory is that the difference between the osmotic pressure of the plasma and that of the extracellular fluid is the same as the osmotic pressure produced by the plasma proteins. This would be true if the typical capillary wall were completely impermeable to protein, but it is now recognized that it is not. Some leakage of protein is the rule, and the cases of the glomerular membrane and the walls of the capillaries of the choroid plexuses, across which protein does not normally pass, are the exceptions. Fibrinogen, albumin, and globulin are all able to pass through most capillary walls, their restricted rate of diffusion being sufficient to reduce their osmotic effect to 70 to 90 per cent of what it would be under conditions of free diffusion. In the case of the very large molecules of antisera, their slow and incomplete diffusion results in the concentration of antiserum in the lymph being quite small. Antisera are accordingly not very effective when given intravenously, and lymph is a fluid of low bactericidal power. Since bacteria can leave the capillaries just as many inanimate particles do, they may flourish in the lymph without being agglutinated or lysed by it.

Only in a very few cases has the permeability of the capillary wall been analyzed in terms of area and of the total pressures, mechanical and osmotic, on the inside and the outside of the vessel. It is usually impossible to obtain the necessary data with sufficient accuracy, and even Starling's theory does not rest on a basis of unimpeachable experiment. The theory, however, allows us to make predictions which can be approximately verified by the limited experimental methods at our disposal. It should be kept in mind, in this connection, that experiments on capillary permeability in the intact animal are semiquantitative at the best. Part of the reason for this is that theory speaks of "permeability" and "effective capillary pressure," whereas experiment shows that both the permeability and the capillary pressure are not only very variable in themselves, but are variable from point to point along the vessel. This makes it very difficult to be sure that the terms of the theoretical concepts correspond to the results of the experiments.

Some substances are absorbed directly into the capillaries of the mucous membrane of the nasopharynx and the gastro-intestinal tract. In the case of the nasopharynx, the substance is painted on the mucous membrane, and its appearance in the lymph of the cervical lymph ducts is watched for. Substances of low molecular weight, such as potassium iodide, a number of dyes (Prussian blue, trypan blue, Evans blue, etc.), and even substances such as egg albumin and serum albumin, have been shown to be directly absorbed (3). It is believed that the substances of smaller molecular weight pass directly into the capillaries, whereas those of higher molecular weight are absorbed through the lymphatics. In the case of the gastro-intestinal tract, carbohydrates and amino acids make their way, for the most part, through the capillary walls, whereas the absorption of fat involves the lymphatics. Cholesterol and other lipids do not pass through capillary walls to any appreciable extent.

Capillary pressure. The pressure in the typical capillary is sometimes above, and sometimes below, the effective osmotic pressure of the plasma proteins.

It may be measured directly (5) by inserting a micropipette connected with a manometer into the lumen of a capillary of the animal (frog, mouse, dog: the mesenteric capillaries are usually used), or indirectly by observing the pressure necessary to cause the collapse of the capillaries of the skin. This is done by placing a cover glass of known area on the surface of the skin and adding weights until the skin begins to blanch, or by placing a small glass-roofed chamber connected to a manometer over an area of skin and raising the pressure until blanching occurs. Alternatively, pressure may be applied in the region of the nail bed and the collapse of individual capillaries observed with the low powers of the microscope. All the indirect methods, although suitable for use in man, give results which are difficult to interpret; indeed, they probably measure the pressure in the venous plexuses of the skin rather than capillary pressure.

The results of attempts to measure capillary pressure vary within wide limits, and values from 0.5 to 54 mm. Hg have been recorded. A few of the results are shown in Table 18. All these were obtained by the direct cannulation of a vessel, and are expressed in cm. of H_2O. The values obtained by indirect methods are still more variable.

Table 18. Capillary Pressure

INVESTIGATOR	ANIMAL	VESSEL OBSERVED	CAPILLARY PRESSURE CM. OF H_2O
Landis	Frog	Mesentery:	
		Average arteriolar capillary	14.5
		Average venous capillary	10
		Normal variation	5–22
	Rat	Mesentery	13–49
	Man	Skin of hand:	
		Arteriolar limb	28–65
		Top of loop	20–43
		Venous limb	8–24
	Guinea pig	Mesentery	13–49
Königes and Otto	Cat	Intestinal villus:	
		Capillary	42

In general, constriction of the arterioles causes the pressure in the capillaries fed by them to fall, and dilatation of the arterioles causes capillary pressure to rise, but in addition to these passive effects there may be increases or decreases in capillary pressure as a result of the ability of the endothelial wall to contract independently. An increase in venous pressure, however, has the constant result of increasing capillary pressure, and so of increasing the rate of filtration of fluid from the capillary into the extracellular spaces. Hemorrhage, on the other hand, decreases capillary pressure, and so increases the passage of fluid *from* the extracellular spaces into the capillary bed, as Starling's theory requires.

Table 18 shows that the pressure at the arterial end of a capillary tends to be higher than that at the venous end, and it is generally agreed that there is a gradient of decreasing pressure as we move from one end of a capillary to the other. This gradient has important implications from the standpoint of Starling's theory, for if the pressure at the arterial end is higher than the effective osmotic pressure of the plasma and the pressure at the venous end is lower than the effective osmotic pressure of the plasma, fluid will pass out of the capillary at its arterial end and be absorbed back into the capillary at its venous end. In this way a circulation of fluid, from the capillary to the extracellular spaces and back again, is set up. The briskness of this circulation, moreover, will depend on the difference between the pressures at the arterial end and at the venous end, and any factor which tends to abolish the difference will tend to abolish the movement of fluid. Thus an increase in venous pressure raises the mean capillary pressure and so increases passage of fluid out of the capillary, while at the same time it raises the pressure at the venous end of the capillary and so decreases reabsorption. There is accordingly a double reason for the accumulation of fluid in the tissue spaces (edema) when there is obstruction of the venous return from some area of the body.

Gradient of capillary permeability. Rous, McMaster, and their associates have made observations on the permeability of capillaries to a series of dyes of increasing molecular size, and have found that there is a continuous gradient of permeability which increases as one goes from the arterial to the venous end of the vessel. This gradient is not dependent on capillary pressure; indeed, the permeability is greatest at the venous end where the pressure is smallest. Zweifach has recently confirmed the observations, and has found that the extent of the gradient varies with the length of the vessel, so that considerable differences in the rate of diffusion of dyes and in the molecular size of the dyes which diffuse are observed only in long capillaries. If the flow in the capillary is reversed, as can be done by compressing the proper side channels and venules with microdissection needles, the gradient of permeability is reversed also, now being greatest near the arterial end. This leads Zweifach to attribute the existence of the gradient to some factor which is present in the blood of the venous end of the vessel rather than to permanent structural differences in the endothelial wall.

The principal facts relating to the permeability of various kinds of capillaries to dyes is excellently summarized in Figure 297 (Zweifach). Because there is a permeability gradient for dyes, it does not follow, of course, that the same gradient exists for water and dissolved substances. There may be one gradient for large molecules and another for water and crystalloids.

Variations in capillary permeability. What is known about the variations in capillary permeability in the intact animal is largely the result of experiments in which the increase in lymph flow or the accumulation of edema fluid is taken as evidence of an increase in the rate of filtration through the capillary walls of the part affected.

The least doubtful of the effects are those produced by the *lack of O_2*, but the experimental production of anoxemia and tissue anoxia is so regularly accompanied by changes in the CO_2 tension, the accumulation of other metabolites, changes in pH, and alterations in capillary pressure that it is impossible at present to disentangle their effects. In the individual capillaries of the frog, Landis found that the rate of filtration is increased threefold or fourfold by a short period of oxygen deprivation, and that prolonged oxygen lack renders the capillary wall so permeable that even protein molecules pass through with ease. Restoration of the O_2 tension is followed by a return of the permeability to something near its original value, provided that the period of anoxia is not so long as to produce irreversible changes. Compared with the effects of O_2 lack, the effects of the accumulation of CO_2 and of the accompanying pH, changes are relatively small. More recently, Saslow showed that the web of the frog can be perfused for hours provided the perfusion fluid contains red cells to carry oxygen for the use of the tissues; in the absence of the red cells, the relative anoxia renders the capillary wall more permeable, and the web becomes edematous.

In the dog, Maurer has shown that the lymph flow from the cardiac lymphatic trunk begins to be increased when the O_2 saturation falls to about 75 per cent, and that it reaches a maximum when the saturation is about 50 per cent of normal. When the CO_2 content of the blood was approximately doubled, the lymph flow was found to be doubled. Such experiments as have been done in man, however, have not shown that either a decrease in O_2 tension or an increase in CO_2 tension have much effect on capillary per-

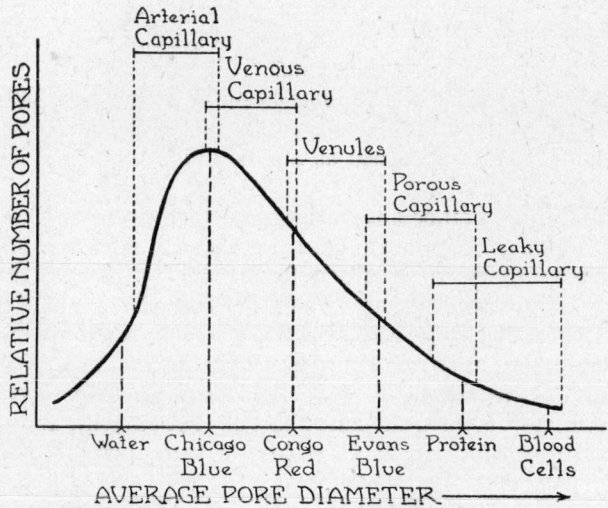

Fig. 297.—Diagram to illustrate the approximate porosity of different capillary subdivisions and of abnormal capillaries. The curve shows the distribution of different sizes of pores. (From Zweifach, *Cold Spr. Harb. Symp. quant. Biol.*, 1940, *8*:216–223.)

meability. The rate of swelling of a human arm, constricted by a sphygmomanometer cuff and enclosed in a plethysmograph, is not appreciably altered by the O_2 content or the CO_2 content of the inspired air, even though both are varied considerably. It may reasonably be asked whether this failure to observe effects of changes of O_2 and CO_2 tensions in the intact animal is not largely due to the relative crudeness of the experimental methods employed.

During activity, the tissues require more oxygen, glucose, and other substances in solution than they do when at rest. This is provided for by the capillary dilatation which accompanies tissue activity and which results in a great increase in the area of the wall through which diffusion can take place (p. 607). There is no evidence that the greater supply is the result of an increase in the permeability of the capillary endothelium itself. Histamine and the H-substance, for example, have not been shown to increase the permeability of the capillary wall except in so far as capillary dilatation increases the area of the wall and the pressure on it.

Since variations in the ionic *composition of the environment* have such marked effects on the permeability of many cells, it is likely that similar effects can be produced on the cells of the capillary endothelium. The work of Chambers and Zweifach on the importance of the pH and ionic composition of the fluid circulating through the capillaries has already been referred to (p. 609). In addition to the changes produced by variations in pH and in Ca content, Zweifach has described an effect of the plasma proteins which is due to their clogging the pores in the intercellular cement and making it less permeable. Colloidal perfusion fluids are known to be greatly superior to fluids such as Ringer's solution, and it is possible to continue the perfusion of a tissue for hours without edema developing if one uses Ringer-gelatin or Ringer to which serum proteins have been added, instead of Ringer's solution alone. This is explained in part by the osmotic pressure of the colloid producing reabsorption of water at the venous ends of the capillaries (Starling's theory, p. 613), but part of the explanation is that fluids such as Ringer's solution wash the cement substance away from the endothelial junctions and render the capillaries more permeable. This washing-away is prevented by the addition of colloids such as acacia, gelatin, or the serum proteins, which are absorbed as a colloidal layer on the inside of the capillary wall.

It is very doubtful whether any variations which occur in the ionic constitution of the blood of the intact animal are great enough to produce changes in capillary permeability. In severe malnutrition the plasma protein concentration may fall to levels (4.5 to 5.5 gm. per 100 ml.) at which generalized edema occurs, but this is largely because of diminished reabsorption of fluid by the capillaries, as would be expected on Starling's theory.

Both increase in *temperature* to 45°C. and decrease to 5°C. cause an increase in the lymph flow from the nasopharynx (McCarrell), and an increase in temperature from 14°C. to 45°C. results in a doubling of the filtration from the capillaries of the arm (Landis and Gibbon). Because of the effects of higher temperature on the filtration of the skin capillaries, swelling of the feet and hands and increase in any pre-existing edema is commonly observed when a person moves from a temperate to a tropical climate.

Because whole blood, or even a fluid containing red cells or some plasma protein, is so much better a perfusion fluid than any saline solution, it has been supposed that blood may normally contain *specific chemical substances* which keep the capillary wall from becoming unduly permeable, just as the hormone of the pituitary maintains capillary tone. Variations in the amount of such substances, were they shown to exist, might then be responsible for variations in capillary permeability. Experiments designed to demonstrate the existence of these specific substances have failed to do so except perhaps in a single instance. In observations on the edema which occurs in the skin around the genitals and anus of monkeys in relation to the menstrual cycle, Arkroyd and Zuckerman found that the administration of estrone increases the amount of extracellular fluid in the tissues, giving rise to a local edema. This may be due to a local change in capillary permeability, but the demonstration is as yet incomplete.

There is some evidence that vitamin C, and especially the fraction known as P (a flavone glucoside present in Hungarian red peppers, fresh lemon juice, etc.) is necessary for the normal maintenance of the capillary wall, and that various degrees of deterioration of the endothelium and cement substance, with increases in capillary fragility, develop in its absence. This deterioration occurs particularly in scurvy, which is due to vitamin C deprivation.

Capillary poisons. While the presence of specific chemical substances which control capillary permeability has not been demonstrated, we know of a large number of drugs and druglike substances which have profound effects on the integrity of the capillary wall. Some of these effects are *direct*, e.g., if solutions of saponin or of the bile salts are perfused through a limb, the cells of the capillary endothelium are subjected to a direct cytolytic action, and the perfusion fluid leaks out of the capillaries in proportion to the amount of injury to their walls. The active principles of the venoms of poisonous snakes and spiders, of bees, and of certain marine animals probably act in the same sort of way (7). If these substances gain access to the blood stream in sufficient concentration, they produce widespread injury which results in edema and hemorrhages. If the escape of edema fluid is great enough, the blood may become so concentrated and viscous that the heart cannot force it through the vessels; the blood pressure then falls, and death results. Mercuric chloride, gold chloride, arsenicals, and the salts of many heavy metals may have similar direct effects on the capillary wall.

Other effects may be *indirect*, and it is often very difficult to distinguish between these and the direct effects. A substance such as histamine, for example, probably has no effect on capillary permeability per se, but it produces capillary dilatation, which leads in turn to stasis of the blood in the capillary, anoxemia, anoxia of the cells of the endothelial wall, and, finally, to an increase in capillary permeability as a result of the anoxia.

Pathology furnishes many instances of deterioration of the capillary wall as a result of the action of various kinds of toxins. Hemorrhages of varying size take place at the points of injury or deterioration, and appear as purplish spots in the skin (purpura). If they do not appear spontaneously, they can be made to occur by raising the pressure in the capillaries of the arm by applying a tourniquet or the cuff of a sphygmomanometer in which the pressure is raised to midway between the systolic and diastolic pressures. The pressure is maintained for eight minutes, and the number of petechial hemorrhages which occur within fifteen minutes in a 5 cm. circle on the skin of the front of the forearm is counted. In a normal adult the number is ten or less. Alternatively, a small suction cup can be applied to the skin of the forearm, and the negative pressure required to produce petechial hemorrhages determined. Tests such as these are referred to as capillary fragility tests.

Exemia in wound shock (see Chap. 28). Extensive tissue injury has frequently been observed to be followed by a concentration of the blood (hemoconcentration), the red cells occupying as much as 80 per cent of the total volume instead of the normal 40 to 45 per cent. This hemoconcentration results from loss of fluid from the blood vessels (*exemia*), the red cells, for the most part, being left behind. There has been much discussion as to whether the loss of plasma occurs because of a local or a general increase in capillary permeability, and those who believe that the increase in permeability is general have made many attempts to isolate or identify a substance, produced at the point of injury, which can be held responsible for it. Histamine-like substances and substances derived from the breakdown of proteins were at one time considered as possibilities. The evidence now points to the loss of fluid being primarily a local one. When such an injury as a fracture of a femur occurs, for example, as much as 1500 ml. of fluid may be lost into the tissues of the thigh as edema develops; since this amount is about half the plasma in circulation, the degree of hemoconcentration which results is very great (volume occupied by red cells = 70 per cent, instead of 40 per cent). The possibility of a general effect being involved in addition has recently been revived, and it has been suggested that the "general factor" in wound shock is due to the wound becoming infected with anaerobic organisms. These produce toxins which enter the circulation and are responsible for many of the "general" effects observed, but whether they act as capillary poisons and produce increases in capillary permeability in parts remote from the wound has not yet been decided. Adenosine triphosphate and related compounds have also been suggested as the "general factor."

In this connection, it should be observed that inhalation anesthetics tend to increase the permeability of capillaries. During a long anesthesia with ether, for example, the increased rate of filtration is sufficient to give rise to an appreciable increase in hemoconcentration. Possible effects of the anesthetic must always be considered in experiments on capillary permeability and lymph flow which involve the use of anesthetized animals.

Lymphagogues. About seventy years ago Heidenhain and other investigators of the same period found that a variety of substances (extracts of crayfish muscle, extracts of leech heads, extracts of strawberries, histamine, peptone, and many different proteins) produce an increase in both the rate of flow and the solid content of lymph from the thoracic duct of dogs. Heidenhain called these substances "lymphagogues of the first class," and thought that they act on the endothelial cells of the lymphatics, which he believed to have true secretory properties. We now recognize that all the substances included under the term "lymphagogues of the first class" are capillary poisons, and that the increased flow of lymph is due to an increased filtration and loss of proteins through the damaged capillary walls.

Atypical capillaries. The capillaries of the *liver sinusoids* are atypical in that their wall is reduced to an endothelial sheet so thin, and so closely applied to the surface of the liver cells, that there has been doubt as to its very existence. At intervals along the wall there appear the highly phagocytic Kupffer cells, which are stellate cells with processes which extend around, and even across, the liver sinusoids. The permeability of the walls of the liver sinusoids is very high, and proteins are able to pass across them easily. This results in the protein content of the lymph from the liver being almost as high as that of plasma itself.

The capillaries of the *spleen* resemble those of the liver sinusoids in being very permeable to all the components of plasma. The permeability is so great that at one time it was thought that the walls of the splenic capillaries were fenestrated, i. e., interrupted at intervals by holes.

The capillaries of the *choroid plexuses*, of the *ciliary body*, and of the *glomerulus* of the kidney are atypical in that they are normally completely impermeable to protein. The urine contains no protein (in man), and the cerebrospinal fluid only traces. The glomerular capillaries are reinforced by the epithelial cells of Bowman's capsule, and those of the choroid plexuses are similarly reinforced by an epithelial layer. Fluid leaving these capillaries has thus to pass through two layers of cells.

THE LYMPHATICS

Arrangement and Structure of the Lymphatics. Just as the extracellular space surrounding the tissue cells is supplied with water and dissolved substances through the walls of the capillary network, so is it drained by a network of lymphatics (Fig. 298). The lymphatic network is about as extensive as that of the capillaries, and begins as a series of blind, closed tubes which converge on one another to form first a series of lymphatic plexuses, and then smaller, and finally larger, lymphatic vessels and trunks. In the skin, for example, there are two such plexuses, the more superficial of the two, in which the lymph can move in all directions, connecting with the deeper, which has valves and in which the lymph moves in one direction only. Valves are present in all the larger lymphatic trunks, which have smooth muscle in their walls, and which are contractile (unlike the smaller lymphatics, which are not). In particular anatomical situations the course of the larger lymphatics is interrupted by lymph glands or nodes, a number of lymphatics converging on the periphery of the gland and breaking up into lymphoid sinuses, separated by masses of lymphoid tissue and supporting trabeculae. The sinuses lead into one or more afferent lymphatics, by which the lymph leaves the gland. Ultimately, all the lymphatics converge on the lymph duct

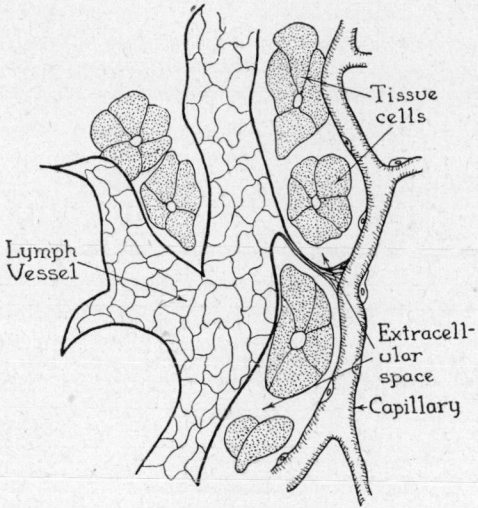

Fig. 298.—A capillary and an adjacent lymph vessel.

and the thoracic duct, which empty their contents into the right and left subclavian veins respectively. In the case of the limbs at least, it seems to be a rule that lymph never reaches the blood without passing through at least one lymph node, one of the principal functions of which is to act as a filter for micro-organisms.

Some structures e.g., the bone marrow, the alveoli of the lung, and the pulp of the spleen, have no lymphatics. The lymphatic drainage of voluntary muscle is probably confined to the fascial planes between groups of fibers, and it is very doubtful if the central nervous system is provided with lymphatics at all.

The walls of the lymphatic capillaries are composed of very thin endothelial cells, held together by an intercellular cement substance similar to that of the blood capillaries. Except in the case of the lacteals and of the larger lymph trunks, the lymph vessels lack the power of contractility. As a result they are unaffected by the many drugs which cause constriction and dilatation of the blood capillaries. The cells of the lymph vessel walls have little, if any, phagocytic activity, and particles as large as bacteria can pass through or between them, just as in the case of the blood capillary wall.

Formation of Lymph. The old idea that the cells of the lymph capillary have secretory properties has been completely abandoned, and we now regard the formation of lymph as an entirely passive process. The pressure in the blood capillaries produces a filtration of water, solutes, and a small amount of protein into the extracellular space surrounded by the tissue cells, and in the simple statement of Starling's theory the outwardly directed capillary pressure is just balanced by the effective osmotic pressure of the plasma proteins plus the tissue turgor pressure (p. 613). A more complete description of the situation would include the fact that the extracellular space is provided with a series of drainage channels, so that increased filtration from the capillaries is relieved by increased lymphatic drainage instead of producing as great a tissue pressure as it would if the extracellular space were entirely closed. Under ordinary circumstances, indeed, the amount of lymph

Table 19. *Average Composition of the Cervical Lymph of the Dog* (Heim, *Amer. J. Physiol.*, 1933, *103*:553.)

	PROTEIN GM./ 100 ML.	SUGAR MG./ 100 ML.	N.P.N. MG./ 100 ML.	UREA MG./ 100 ML.	CREATININE MG./ 100 ML.	CL AS NACL MG./ 100 ML.
Serum	6.18	123	32.6	21.7	1.37	411
Lymph	3.12	132	34.8	23.5	1.40	431

	URIC ACID MG./100 ML.	AMINO ACIDS MG./100 ML.	PHOSPHORUS MG./100 ML.		CALCIUM MG./100 ML.	pH
			TOTAL	INORG.		
Serum	Trace	4.90	22.0	5.6	11.7	7.34
Lymph	Trace	4.84	11.8	5.9	9.8	7.41

drainage from an area is equal to the amount filtered from the capillaries at their arterial ends minus the amount reabsorbed at their venous ends, and the tissue turgor pressure remains substantially constant. If the lymph vessels draining an area are obstructed, however, the capillary filtration results in the accumulation of fluid in the extracellular space (edema), and the tissue turgor pressure rises. It might be supposed that the lymphatics in such edematous tissue would collapse as a result of the increased tissue turgor pressure, but there are connective tissue attachments which apparently support them and keep them open.

Most studies on the composition of lymph and on lymph flow are based on experiments in which cannulae are placed in the larger lymphatic trunks. These are the thoracic duct, the right lymph duct, the cervical lymph ducts, and the larger lymph trunks draining the limbs. By cannulizing individual lymphatics from the heart, lungs, liver, etc., lymph from these organs can be obtained.

The *total volume of the lymph* in the body is not known. The attempts which have been made to estimate it indicate that it is not greater than the total volume of the blood, and probably considerably smaller.

Composition of lymph. From the manner of its formation we would expect lymph to have approximately the same composition as the fluid which filters through the capillary walls, i.e., to contain water and most solutes in about the same proportion as they exist in plasma, but considerably less protein. Table 19 shows the average composition of the cervical lymph of the dog.

The principal conclusion to be drawn from these data is that the ionic pattern of the lymph is similar to that of the plasma, all the differences being in a direction which can be accounted for by the lower protein content of the lymph and the existence of a Donnan equilibrium between lymph and plasma.

The lymph contains a number of enzymes (amylase, maltase, diastase, lipase, cholesterinase, protease, and catalase, among others). These may be derived either from the blood stream or from the tissue cells. Although lymph coagulates, very little is known about the clotting mechanism. Presumably it is similar to that in blood, for fibrinogen, calcium, and thromboplastin are all present. Considerable variation exists as regards the protein content of the lymph derived from different regions. That from the liver has the highest protein content (about 5 per cent), as one would expect from the fact that the capillaries of the liver sinusoids are very freely permeable to protein. Next in order comes the lymph from the thoracic duct (about 4 per cent), then the lymph from the heart, kidney, and intestine, then that from the lungs and from the cervical regions, and, finally, that from the skin and subcutaneous tissues (1–2 per cent). These differences no doubt correspond to differences in capillary permeability to proteins. As regards the amount of other substances present in the lymph, there are no great variations, except that the lymphatics draining the intestine (lacteals) may contain large amounts of fat after meals. The lacteals are believed to be completely permeable to fat, and it is the suspended fat droplets which give the intestinal lymph (chyle) its milky appearance. When they reach the blood stream these small fat droplets are called chylomicrons.

Flow of lymph. Since the lymphatics are, for the most part, noncontractile, the movement of lymph in the mammal must depend on forces outside the lymphatic system. These are of two kinds: (i) contraction of the muscles of the region, and (ii) the pressure generated by filtration of fluid from the capillaries. McMaster and Hudack have shown that there is a flow of lymph even in a quiescent part, by injecting small quantities of dye into the skin of the human forearm and observing its appearance, as far away as 15 cm. from the point of injection, within five minutes. The amount of lymph which can be collected from a lymph duct draining a limb, however, is very small when the limb is at rest. If the limb is in active movement, or if it is moved passively or even massaged, the lymph flow is greatly increased and tends to become constant with continued activity. This can be shown by cannulating a lymph duct in the leg of the dog, and observing the rate of flow during various phases of activity (3). The contractions of the limb muscles squeeze the lymph along the lymphatics, and the effect of passive motion and of massage is about the same.

In the case of the heart and of many of the viscera, a similar squeezing of lymph along the lymphatics results from the contractions of the heart muscle and from the peristaltic movements of the plain muscle in the visceral walls. As might be expected, the lymph flow from the heart varies, in a general sort of way, with the rate and amplitude of the contractions, i.e., with the work done by the heart. The flow from the intestines can be greatly increased by injecting pilocarpine, muscarine, or pituitrin, all of which increase the contraction of smooth muscle. The movement of the lymph in the lacteals is also aided by the rhythmic contractions of the lacteals and by contractions of the intestinal villi from which the lymph originates.

Anything which increases the rate of filtration of fluid from the capillaries tends to increase the flow of lymph. Raising the venous pressure, and with it the mean pressure in the capillaries, is particularly effective. If the inferior vena cava, for example, is obstructed above the entry of the hepatic veins, there is a great increase in the flow of lymph in the thoracic duct as a result of the increase in pressure in the hepatic capillaries. Similarly, ligation of the portal vein, which causes an increase in the pressure in the capillaries of the intestine, results in a four- to fivefold increase in the flow of lymph from the intestine. Increases in the arterial pressure are much less effective, while any considerable decrease in arterial pressure is followed by a diminution in lymph flow or even by its cessation. Both increases (to 45°C.) and decreases (to 5°C.) in temperature result in an increased filtration from the capillaries and therefore in an increased lymph flow. Again, the flow of lymph from the heart rises to a maximum when the O_2 tension of the blood is reduced to about 70 per cent of saturation (Maurer's experiments, p. 617), and the effects of changes in O_2 and CO_2 tension on the rate of capillary filtration are in general closely paralleled by their effect on lymph flow.

The question as to whether an increased flow of lymph results from increased tissue activity has been the subject of many classical experiments. Most of these support the conclusion that an increase in lymph flow begins shortly after the tissue (gland, muscle) responds to stimulation and that its maximum coincides with the period of greatest tissue metabolism. The increased formation of lymph is attributed to the production of metabolites which diffuse out of the active tissue into the extracellular space. This results in an increase in osmotic pressure in the extracellular fluid; fluid then moves from the blood stream through the capillary walls, to restore the equilibrium, and the entry of this fluid into the extracellular space is followed by an increased flow of lymph. The metabolites may also increase the permeability of the capillary endothelium, and so make the lymph flow all the greater. In active tissues there are more open capillaries, and consequently a greater area of capillary wall across which fluid transfers can take place. This increase in area permits very rapid movements of fluid. In the case of muscle, the increased amount of lymph produced is squeezed along the smaller lymphatics by the muscular contractions, and this too increases the flow of lymph. In the case of a stimulated gland, e.g., the submaxillary, the cells empty their secretion into the ducts, and then draw on the surrounding extracellular fluid for water with which to restore their volume; this produces a concentration of the extracellular fluid, an increase in its osmotic pressure, and a transfer of fluid from the blood stream through the capillary wall to restore the equilibrium. These movements of water result in an increased formation of lymph and in an increased lymph flow.

It must be admitted, however, that the results of the classical experiments have not been wholly confirmed by more recent investigations, and some of the explanations which seemed to be reasonable at the time are not so convincing now. Drinker and Yoffey (3) review a number of experiments, more or less recent, on the lymph flow from the liver, pancreas, salivary glands, and kidneys, during activity as compared with rest. In all of these the results were negative, inconclusive, or disputed.

The action of "lymphagogues of the first class" has already been discussed (p. 620). These are essentially capillary poisons which act by increasing the permeability of the capillary endothelial wall. Heidenhain also described "lymphagogues of the second class," of which hypertonic NaCl and hypertonic glucose (50 per cent) are examples. When injected into the blood stream these substances pass rapidly across the capillary wall into the extracellular space and raise its osmotic pressure; water then leaves the cells of the tissues (intracellular space) to restore equilibrium, and in doing so increases the volume of fluid in the extracellular space. Since this space is drained by the lymphatics, an increased flow of lymph results. The effect is to produce a redistribution of water, which moves from the intracellular space into the extracellular space, the tissues becoming relatively dehydrated. The water which is transferred to the extracellular space eventually reaches the blood stream *via* the lymph, and is excreted. The lymph flow, meanwhile, is greatly increased.

Edema. When the flow of lymph drains the extracellular space inadequately, an excessive amount of fluid collects in the tissue spaces and becomes visible as edema. Edema can arise in many ways, an enumeration of which would virtually constitute a review of the material of this chapter.

1. When the mean capillary pressure is increased, the filtration of fluid from the capillaries is increased, and the balance between filtration at the arterial end of the capillary and absorption at the venous end is upset in the favor of filtration into the extracellular space. If the lymphatic drainage is unable to cope with the increased transudation from the capillaries, fluid collects in the extracellular space and gives rise to edema. Since the most usual cause of an increase in mean capillary pressure is an increase in venous pressure, while the most common cause of an increased venous pressure is a failing power of the heart muscle, *cardiac edema* is associated with heart failure. Aided by gravity, fluid collects in the extracellular spaces of dependent parts, such as the ankles when the individual is upright, and the back and sacrum when he is in bed. Accumulations of fluid may also be found in the peritoneal cavity (ascites), the pleural cavities, etc.

Any mechanical obstruction of the veins leading from a part, as by tumors or by the formation of clots in the lumen of a vein (thrombosis), raises the venous pressure and produces local edema in just the same way. Obstruction of the portal vein, draining the intestines, may produce large accumulations of fluid in the peritoneal cavity.

2. A reduction in the concentration of plasma proteins below a certain critical value (4.5-5.5 gm./100 ml.) results in edema because the absorbing power of the capillaries at their venous ends, which depends on the effective osmotic pressure of the plasma proteins, is reduced. Filtration then exceeds absorption, and edema tends to develop, particularly in dependent parts. The principal causes of a reduction in the concentration of plasma proteins are malnutrition, in which sufficient protein is either not supplied or fails to be synthesized in the body, and conditions in which protein is lost from the body through abnormal paths, usually by hemorrhage or through damaged kidneys.

3. Any factor which increases capillary permeability tends to produce edema. Both heat, ("tropical edema") and cold (as in frostbite) act in this way. A number of capillary poisons,

22

such as the salts of heavy metals, the toxins of certain bacteria, and the histamine-like substances liberated in inflammatory conditions and in anaphylactic responses, tend to produce edèma by increasing local, and even general, capillary permeability. It is believed that the edema of malnutrition ("prison camp edema") is contributed to by vitamin deficiencies and a resulting deterioration of the capillary wall.

4. Obstruction of the lymphatics results in edema, although the intercommunication between the lymphatic plexuses is so free in the mammal that it is very difficult to produce complete obstruction. This may occur, however, when the lymphatic trunks are blocked with tumor cells or with organisms such as filariae, and some lymphatic obstruction always occurs in local inflammatory processes. While the turgor of the inflamed part is due essentially to increased filtration through dilated and injured capillaries, it is aggravated by the local lymphatic obstruction.

Rate of lymph flow. The quantity of lymph in circulation and the rate of flow are not large in the mammal under ordinary physiological conditions. In the dog, the lymph flow from the heart is only 0.005 to 0.025 ml./minute. There is no correlation between the weight of the animal or the weight of the heart and the rate of lymph flow. The lymph flow in the leg lymphatics is about 0.06 ml./minute when the dog walks; when the animal is at rest, it is very difficult to obtain lymph at all. The flow in the thoracic duct is about 0.6 ml./minute in the dog, and 1.0 to 1.5 ml./minute in man (fasting).

The pressure which can be recorded by inserting a cannula in lymphatic vessels is very variable. It amounts to some 2 to 4 cm. of water in the lymphatics of the skin, 15 cm. of water in the thoracic duct and in the lymphatics of the beating heart, and as much as 40 cm. of water in the lymphatics of the intestinal villi. It will be clear from these figures that the circulation of lymph in the mammal is not very brisk. In the amphibian it is much less sluggish, because the lymphatic system possesses lymph hearts which drive the lymph along the larger lymphatics.

Cell Content of Lymph. The number of cells found per cu.mm. of lymph depends very largely on the number of lymph nodes the lymph has passed through. Lymph draining the extracellular space in peripheral regions and not having passed through any nodes has a cell count of about 500 cells per cu.mm., whereas the lymph of the thoracic duct and right lymph duct, having traversed many nodes, has about 40,000 cells per cu.mm. as an average figure, and sometimes three or four times as many.

Nearly all the cells are lymphocytes, although there are occasional eosinophils and still more occasional monocytes. A few red cells are found even in peripheral lymph, especially during activity; apparently they make their way across the capillary wall into the extracellular space, and from there through the lymph vessel wall into the small lymphatics. The lymphocytes are derived from the lymph nodes and other lymphoid tissue (e.g., Peyer's patches in the intestine), and probably all the lymphocytes of the blood stream are delivered to it through the lymphatics. Ligation of the thoracic duct and the right lymph duct results in a fall of the number of lymphocytes in the blood stream to virtually zero. About 200 million lymphocytes enter the blood of the dog each hour through these great lymphatic ducts. Most of them remain in the blood stream for less than a day, their fate being either disintegration or extrusion through the mucous membranes of the alimentary canal; a few, however, pass through the capillary walls into the extracellular space and thence into the lymph again.

The controversial question of "digestion leukocytosis," about which a large literature has accumulated, is closely related to the subject of the cell content of lymph. The evidence points, somewhat uncertainly, to there being a mechanical "flushing out" of the lymphoid tissue of the intestine during a meal, particularly if the meal is rich in protein. This, together with the increased flow in the lymph channels leading from the alimentary tract, results in a pouring of a larger number of lymphocytes than usual into the blood stream and in a "digestion leukocytosis" in the course of which the white cell count in the blood may increase several fold. While the consensus of opinion is that no such increase occurs after a meal in man, there is evidence for its occurrence in the dog and other mammals.

Lymphoid Tissue. In the mammal, lymphoid tissue exists as masses of cells, principally lymphocytes, held together in a supporting framework of reticulum cells, fibrous and elastic tissue, and sometimes plain muscle fibers. Anatomically speaking, it can be divided into the lymphoid tissue of the lymph nodes or glands, that in the mucous membranes, particularly of the alimentary canal (tonsils, Peyer's patches, etc.), and that of the spleen. By dissection and weighing all the recognizable masses of lymphoid tissue, it has been estimated that it constitutes about 1 per cent of the body weight.

The lymph enters the typical lymph gland through a number of afferent lymphatics which converge on its periphery and leaves it through a few efferent lymphatics which emerge near the hilum. As the lymph passes through the node, it has to traverse a meshwork of sinusoids, lined by phagocytic cells and divided by a reticulum which acts as a mechanical barrier to the passage of particles, as well as being phagocytic. The primary function of the node is thus that of acting as a filter of bacteria. While this function is exercised principally when the lymph is infected, there is some disputed evidence that a state of "subinfection" exists even in health, and that the lymph nodes filter out bacteria which have entered the lymph stream through minute "physiological defects" in the skin and mucous membranes.

A number of suggestions have been made as to what other functions the lymphoid tissue may have in health, and it is understandable that some function other than that of defense against invading bacteria should be sought for a tissue which makes up so large a proportion of the body weight. Among the additional functions which have been considered are (i) the metabolism and transport of fat and protein, (ii) the storage of vitamins, (iii) the production of hormones and antihormones, and (iv) the destruction of, and sometimes the production of, red cells. The one function about which there is no doubt is the production of lymphocytes, and recently White and Dougherty have established the presence in lymphocytes of a protein identical with the gamma globulin of serum. Antibodies (modified globulins) have also been demonstrated in the lymphocytes obtained from immunized animals. The rate of release of the normal and modified globulins from the lymphocytes is influenced by the hormones of the adrenal cortex, the action of which is dependent on a stimulation of the adrenal cortex by pituitary adrenotrophic hormone. The adrenal hormones produce an increase in the rate of dissolution of the cytoplasm of the cells of the lymphoid tissue, and also a destruction of circulating lymphocytes in large numbers.

ADDENDUM: CLINICAL APPLICATIONS—PRESSURE BANDAGES AND THE CLOSED PLASTER TREATMENT OF BURNS, FROSTBITE AND FLESH WOUNDS

Surgeons since time immemorial have set fractures in splints or plaster casts. Following the first World War, Winnett Orr (13) of Nebraska recommended the use of closed plaster for treating any type of open flesh wound of the extremities, whether the limb were fractured or not. The recommendation was little heeded until the Loyalist surgeon, Juan Trueta of Barcelona, used closed plaster with remarkable success upon some 20,000 cases of injury sustained during the Spanish Civil War (15). So impressive were Trueta's figures that the British adopted the procedure at the time of the evacuation from Dunkirk. Three other quite different clinical entities have also responded to closed plaster management, namely crush injuries of the extremities, burns and frostbite. By 1941 the British had begun to find that if a severe crush injury of an extremity were associated with a fracture and therefore put in plaster, the patient almost invariably did well (14); if, on the other hand, the extremity was crushed to a corresponding degree but the bone was unfractured, the patient invariably did badly if not put into plaster. The extremity swelled unduly, local circulation became cut off by edema, urine became suppressed, and a general vasomotor collapse ensued. Much the same has happened with severe burns of the extremities or frostbite when not put in pressure bandages.

From the physiological standpoint, plaster does not serve to reduce swelling, but rather to prevent it. Once an extensive edema has developed, it is too late for plaster to be effective. Burns and crushing injuries cause capillary damage with the result that protein escapes freely into the tissue spaces through the capillary wall. The rate at which fluid accumulates depends, as pointed out earlier in this chapter, upon several factors: (i) extent of the capillary injury, (ii) hydrostatic pressure, (iii) temperature, and (iv) tissue pressure. The importance of tissue pressure is seldom stressed and it clearly deserves wider emphasis. Duncan and Blalock (10) found that animals after an experimental crush responded favorably if the injured extremity were placed in a pneumatic cuff under a pressure of 40 mm. Hg. Drinker (11, 12) and his colleagues in a series of classic studies find that when an extremity of an anesthetized dog is subjected to a standard burn (one minute in boiling water to a height of six inches up the leg), edema rapidly develops, local circulation is greatly cut off by the edema, the skin sloughs, the leg becomes infected, and the animal generally dies within three to four days; if, on the other hand, the extremity so burned is immediately placed in a plaster cast, edema fails to develop, the local circulation remains good, the burned epidermis quickly regenerates, and the animal emerges with a surprisingly healthy extremity within a period of eight to ten days. With war wounds, especially those made by high velocity missiles (bullets or shell fragments), tissue contusion is inevitably great and extensive edema may be anticipated. If, however, such open wounds are placed immediately in plaster, edema is prevented and healing occurs at an accelerated speed (15).

The use of plaster has an important secondary effect, namely, that the resulting immobilization reduces lymph flow, and by so doing tends to keep infection localized; it also reduces the speed of absorption of toxic products into the general circulation. Trueta finds that virulent pathogenic organisms can be injected locally into the extremity, and the infection remains local if the extremity is promptly immobilized by plaster (15). It was highly important, therefore, that surgeons, and especially medical officers in the war theaters, appreciate the twofold physiological basis of the closed plaster management of wounds: i.e., (i) through prevention of local edema normal circulation is assured; (ii) through immobilization the spread of infection is eliminated and the rate of absorption of toxic products by the lymphatics is reduced. Some believe that the widespread use of plaster in burns and flesh wounds represented one of the most significant advances in medicine during the war period.

REFERENCES

1. ANREP, G. V. *Studies on cardiovascular regulation.* Lane Medical Lectures. Stanford University, Stanford University Press, 1936. 118 pp.
2. CHAMBERS, R. and ZWEIFACH, B. W. Capillary endothelial cement in relation to permeability. *J. cell. comp. Physiol.,* 1940, *15*:255–272.
3. DRINKER, C. K. and YOFFEY, J. M. *Lymphatics, lymph, and lymphoid tissue.* Cambridge, Harvard University Press, 1941. 406 pp.
4. KROGH, A. *The Anatomy and physiology of capillaries,* revised ed. New Haven, Yale University Press, 1929. 422 pp.
5. LANDIS, E. M. Capillary pressure and capillary permeability. *Physiol. Rev.,* 1934, *14*:404–482.

6. LEWIS, T. Mechanism of the flare and of the wheal, Chap. 5 in his: *The blood vessels of the human skin and their responses.* London, Shaw and Sons Ltd., 1927. xv, 322 pp.
7. MOON, V. H. *Shock and related capillary phenomena.* London, New York, Toronto, Oxford University Press, 1938. 442 pp.
8. ZWEIFACH, B. W. The structure and the reactions of the small blood vessels in amphibia. *Amer. J. Anat.,* 1936–1937, *60*:473–514.
9. ZWEIFACH, B. W. The structural basis of permeability and other functions of blood capillaries. *Cold Spr. Harb. Symp. quant. Biol.,* 1940, *8*:216–223.

Addendum

10. DUNCAN, G. W. and BLALOCK, A. The uniform production of experimental shock by crush injury: possible relationship to clinical crush syndrome. *Ann. Surg.,* 1942, *115*:684–697.
11. GLENN, W. W. L., GILBERT, H. H. and DRINKER, C. K. The treatment of burns by the closed-plaster method, with certain physiological considerations implicit in the success of this technique. *J. clin. Invest.,* 1943, *22*:609–625.
12. GLENN, W. W. L., MUUS, J. and DRINKER, C. K. Observations on the physiology and biochemistry of quantitative burns. *J. clin. Invest.,* 1943, *22*:451–460.
13. ORR, H. W. Wounds and fractures; a clinical guide to civil and military practice. Springfield, Ill., C. C Thomas, 1941. x, 227 pp.

14. PATEY, D. H. First-aid prophylactic treatment of the compression syndrome ("crush syndrome"). *Brit. med. J.,* 1942, *2*:212–215.
15. TRUETA, J. *Treatment of war wounds and fractures with special reference to the closed method as used in the war in Spain. With a foreword by Ernest W. Hey Groves.* London, H. Hamilton, 1939. xiii, 146 pp. Also: New York, Paul B. Hoeber, Inc., 1940.
16. TRUETA, J. *The principles and practice o war surgery, with reference to the biological method of the treatment of war wounds and fractures. With introduction by O. H. Wangensteen.* St. Louis, C. V. Mosby Co., 1943. 441 pp.

CHAPTER 30

HEMODYNAMICS

BY HAROLD LAMPORT

The heart and the blood vessels form a closed assemblage of tubes, the vascular system, through which the blood is circulated primarily by the action of the heart. The main function of this system, as discussed in the previous chapter, is to bring blood to the capillaries in amounts and at pressures which permit them to fulfill their role as a semipermeable membrane between tissue fluid and blood. The amount and pressure of blood delivered to the capillaries is adjusted locally as well as throughout the body, in accordance with its changing biological requirements. Hemodynamics is the study of the manner in which the physical properties of the blood and the tubes through which it circulates affect blood flow and pressure, often through a fairly indirect and complicated chain of interrelated variables. The stimuli which initiate the changes, for example chemical or neurogenic constriction of arterioles, are considered in subsequent chapters of this Section.

In order to study the relationships between the physical characteristics of the vessels and the blood flowing through them, it is necessary to turn to the physical laws concerning the flow of liquids in tubes to form a background for understanding the more complicated situation in human vessels. So that these physical laws may be considered in the light of the problems to which they are to be applied, the brief outline of the facts concerning the circulation (Chap. 29) should be borne in mind. Aside from the differences due to the lower discharge pressure and short pulmonary artery as compared to the longer aorta, the hemodynamics of the pulmonary (or lesser) circulation are probably quite like those of the systemic circulation; the relative inaccessibility of the pulmonic system has interfered with its detailed study. We shall not consider it separately in this chapter.

PHYSICAL PRINCIPLES OF LIQUID FLOW

Essentially, if training in the basic subjects underlying physiology were as broad as could be conceived, study of the circulation would be resolved into an immediate application, so far as has yet been accomplished, of the fundamental physicochemical sciences to the biological system. However, the facts concerning flow of liquids in mechanical systems have not been widely studied and some of those which should be applied to the circulation are fairly obscure and relatively recently discovered in the rapidly expanding field of rheology, the science of flow and elasticity. Rheology has been given new impetus by the industrial need for knowledge of the flow characteristics of oils, paints, colloids, plastics, foams, emulsions, suspensions, and so on. We shall therefore present some of the pertinent principles of rheology, beginning with the simpler systems and progressing to the more complex. It is of historical interest that the father of rheology, Poiseuille (1799–1869), was a French physician whose interest in the circulation of the blood prompted him to determine experimentally with great skill and acumen the law of flow of fluids through capillary tubes. His experiments were performed with such unusual precision that his data are still useful, and the law describing viscous flow through capillaries bears the name of Poiseuille (18).

A homogeneous fluid contains no other material, whether droplets of another immiscible fluid (an emulsion), solid particles (a suspension), or bubbles (a foam). A viscous fluid is one which flows whenever there is any difference in pressure within it and which shows no tendency to return to its previous position when the pressure difference is discontinued. Some liquids are not truly viscous; they behave somewhat like elastic solids in that they flow very little until the propelling force exceeds some minimal value. Such liquids are said to behave like plastic substances, being inter-mediate between the perfectly elastic solids and the perfectly viscous fluids.

Actually, no solid is perfectly elastic, since it does not return exactly to the place it started from after stress is withdrawn. An example of this phenomenon is seen in sensitive gal-vanometers, which do not return to their starting point, after current stops flowing, but come to rest at whichever side of the zero point they were last swung to. In time, however, elastic solids which are not overstressed return to their original position, unlike the situ-ation after true flow. However, even rigid solids, such as metals, exhibit true flow when the propelling force is large enough. Some "solids" are actually viscous fluids and flow un-der every pressure difference.

Our attention will be confined to viscous liquids, suspensions in viscous liquids, and to plastic fluids, since they are most helpful in understanding the circulation. We are concerned not only with the fluid and how its proper-ties affect its flow, but also with the influence of the tubular system—the influences of the rigidity of its walls, the size and shape of the bore, its rough-ness, and the way in which the tubules are interconnected. We shall outline the principles underlying the instruments used in measuring blood pressure and flow rate. And lastly, the effects of a pulsating pressure will require analysis.

Steady flow of a homogeneous viscous fluid in rigid tubules

Strangely enough, the flow of a viscous fluid in large bore tubes is more complex than flow in small bore tubes. In small tubes the flow, under con-stant pressure, soon becomes steady so that conditions at any point are invariant: dynamic equilibrium is established.

Turbulence. In large tubes turbulence arises, with variable eddy currents, so that the flow, its direction, and its pressure vary with time. The conditions which produce turbulence involve the characteristics of both the tube and the fluid as well as the perfusing pressure and rate of flow. Turbulent flow is often called hydraulic flow, while viscous flow is sometimes called *stream-line* or *linear*. Reynolds (1842–1912) is perhaps the most outstanding of those who analyzed turbulence and the critical regime, in which turbulent and stream-line flow alternate cyclically (20). Reynolds concluded that tur-bulence should arise in a fluid of viscosity v and density D flowing with mean linear velocity V through a tube of radius R, when the following equation is satisfied:

$$\frac{RVD}{v} = \text{constant}$$

The quantity evaluated by the formula* has since been called the *Reynolds number;* when it exceeds a critical value turbulence arises, as has been widely confirmed. It can be seen that rapidly flowing fluids of low viscosity in large bore tubes are likely to be turbulent, having Reynolds numbers greater than the critical value for turbulence. A greater increase in perfusion pressure is needed to increase flow rate a given amount when turbulence replaces viscous flow.

Wetting. If fluid wets a tube through which it flows in viscous fashion, then there is a cylindrical layer of liquid which adheres to the tube and does not flow. Inside this layer another cylindrical fluid layer flows, rubbing against it; and inside it there is another, flowing faster, and so on, until the central axial core of fluid is reached, which has the maximum velocity. In Figure 299 we see in diagrammatic form a representation of the relative fluid velocity at different points within the tube.

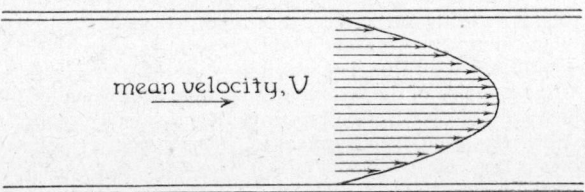

Fig. 299.—Velocity of fluid in viscous flow through round tube. The mean velocity, V, is indicated on the same scale as the velocities at different points in the cross-section of the tube. The curve enveloping the velocities is a parabola.

If the tube is not wetted, there will be a layer of air or vapor separating the fluid from the tube. If this layer were thick or had a viscosity very different from that of the fluid, it would be important whether or not wetting occurred. However, experiments with tubes coated and treated in various ways and with mercury in glass tubes demonstrate that absence of wetting is not consequential, apparently because the intervening layer between tube and fluid is only of molecular dimensions. Electrical and magnetic effects also seem unimportant where they have been studied.

Energy of Fluid. The energy of matter is composed of kinetic energy, due to its motion, and potential energy, which can be converted into kinetic or some other form of energy, such as heat. Considering only heat and energy due to position or motion (since usually they are the only forms of energy involved in the flow of fluids through tubes) the energy relations involved in viscous flow are these:†

Potential energy at
reservoir leading   =
to tube

Potential energy of fluid leaving tube
+   kinetic energy of fluid leaving tube
+   loss of energy due to friction in tube

Kinetic energy‡ is measured by ½ mass × velocity². For fluids, unit mass is used throughout. For measuring the friction loss due to viscous flow, the change in potential energy of the fluid is obtained. (The kinetic energy is

* The formula given here is actually an application of a more generalized formula of Reynolds·

† If we start, not at the reservoir, but at the entrance to the tube, then kinetic energy of the fluid entering the tube must be added to potential energy at the reservoir, on the left side of the equation. If the tube has the same bore at the two points chosen, so that the velocity of the fluid is unchanged, the kinetic energy will be identical at these two points and will be dropped from both sides of the equation.

‡ More precisely, since the velocities of the lamellae of fluid of different radii differ, the integrated sum of their kinetic energies is required. It is not much different from the result obtained by using the average velocity, which is half of the maximum velocity reached in the axial stream (Fig. 299), but the integration for kinetic energy drops the one half, yielding: mass × average velocity² (18a).

made negligible, or it is converted back into potential energy, or allowance is made for it.) Pressure (force per unit area) is the usual measure of the potential energy of fluids.

Pressure measurement. In estimating potential energy, care must be taken that the observation is made in such a way that the kinetic energy of the fluid does not contribute to the measurement. If a fluid is at rest, there is no problem, since it has no kinetic energy. As seen in Figure 300, fluid pressure can be measured by balancing it against that exerted on it by a piston, whereupon the force per unit area of the piston required to obtain balance gives the pressure. The pressure of the fluid can also be balanced by that produced by the weight of the liquid itself. In our example, the source of the pressure is itself gravity—the fluid's weight—so that the height H to which fluid must rise in the tube shown in Figure 300 to balance pressure

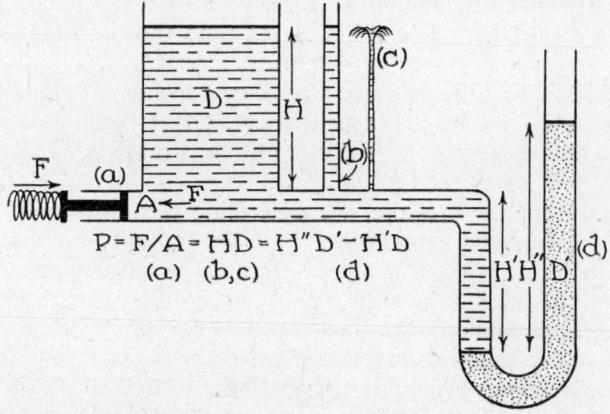

Fig. 300.—Pressure measurement. D and D' are the densities of the two fluids shown; A is the area of the piston and F is the force of the spring.

is also the height of the level in the reservoir. Irrespective of the source of pressure, use of gravity as its measure is convenient. Spinal fluid pressure is often determined in this way, since the pressures are not so high as to make a long tube necessary. Stephen Hales, in 1733, used this method in making the first measurement of blood pressure (9). A more convenient method is to balance pressure with a heavy inert liquid, such as mercury. A shorter column is then adequate and a U-shaped tube prevents mixing of the two fluids and decreases the length of tube needed. The relationships are shown in Figure 300. Pressure is often given, not in terms of force per unit area, but in terms of the equivalent pressure of vertical columns (heads) of a fluid. Thus arterial blood pressure is usually given in millimeters of mercury, venous pressure in centimeters of water.

Frequently it is not realized that the pressures given by a mercury manometer connected to a much lighter fluid should be corrected for the displacement of the mercury by the fluid, as the pressure rises. In Figure 300 the method of correction is indicated. For a uniform bore mercury manometer connected to blood, omission of the correction involves approximately a 4 per cent error, which is usually negligible, especially when small relative pressure changes are of primary interest. Another method of measuring pressure is to convert the potential energy back to kinetic energy which is then measured. In Figure 300 this type of conversion is illustrated, with the fountain of fluid rising to a level, H, at which point the kinetic energy has been reconverted back into potential energy. This method is not of practical importance.

Aside from the methods of pressure measurement here referred to, other methods, often called indirect, are used. They are discussed in Chapter 31. When fluid is flowing, the mode of connection between the pressure measuring device and the stream affects the pressure indicated. If a manometer is connected to the tube at an acute angle, pointing upstream, some of the kinetic energy is converted back into potential energy, which is added to the lateral pressure reading obtained when the manometer is connected at right angles to the tube. Conversely, if the manometer is connected pointing downstream, then some potential energy is converted into kinetic energy, and the manometer will indicate less than lateral pressure. For exact measurement of the potential energy of the fluid in the tube, lateral pressure readings alone are desired. Compare tubes *d* and *e* with tubes *a*, *b*, *c*, *f*, and *h* in Figure 301.

Measurement of Flow. The simplest method for determining flow rate is to collect all of the fluid flowing in a given time and measure its volume. A modification consists in diverting for short intervals all or a fixed fraction of the whole flow for this purpose. Accuracy depends on not disturbing the steady flow conditions by the measurement. Other methods are less direct but are of value because they give a continuous reading with little disturbance of flow.

If, in measuring the pressure, we determine the difference between upstream end pressure and lateral pressure in the center of the stream or some fixed point within it, without much disturbance to the flow, the value of the kinetic energy of the fluid at that point can be obtained (see tubes *d* and *e* in Fig. 301). A manometer in which these two pressures are applied to the two arms (a differential manometer), so that the pressure difference is read directly, gives readings which are proportional to the square of the velocity of flow. Since the velocity at different points varies in the parabolic manner shown in Figure 299, such a device serves to indicate the velocity of flow through the tube and, if the dimensions of the tube are fixed, the rate of flow, in addition. This device, the Pitot tube, is in widespread use as an air speed indicator in airplanes and has physiological application.

Other devices for measuring flow are based on the complementary changes between kinetic and potential energies when fluid passes through a short stream-lined constriction in a uniform tube.* Within the constriction, where flow is faster and kinetic energy is therefore greater, the fluid side-pressure (potential energy) is correspondingly reduced. The differential manometer measures this decrease in side-pressure at the constriction so that the initial velocity of flow can be determined. If the dimensions of the tube and constriction are fixed, the rate of flow is proportional to fluid velocity. The method outlined is illustrated diagrammatically by tubes *f* and *g* in Figure 301.

When fluid flows through a fixed resistance, such as an orifice in a plate, the small drop in lateral pressure thereby produced by the friction developed is proportional to flow rate, as will be explained more fully below. Tubes *f* and *h* in Figure 301 illustrate this kind of device. Some methods of flow measurement depend on other physical properties besides pressure and kinetic energy. In studies of the circulation, the rate of dissipation of heat by flowing blood, the rate of dilution of chemical solutes in the blood stream,

---

* This is Bernoulli's Principle, the basis for the Venturi tube used in gasoline carburetors, in jet-propelled airplanes, and in the common laboratory water suction pump.

and the electrical potential induced across an artery—a conductor of electricity—by virtue of the movement of the blood across a magnetic field have all been utilized. The practical application of the various methods of flow measurement here outlined is found in the next chapter.

Resistance to Flow—Poiseuille's Law. When fluid flows in viscous fashion through a tube, as the fundamental equation indicated (p. 632), energy is lost in the form of friction (heat) within the fluid. If the tube is round and uniform in size, and flow is kept constant, the loss in potential energy equals the heat developed in the fluid* and is best measured as the difference in fluid pressures at the opposite ends of the part of the tube under consideration. The kinetic energy of the fluid does not enter, since in a uniform round bore tube, the velocity and the kinetic energy are unchanged at any two

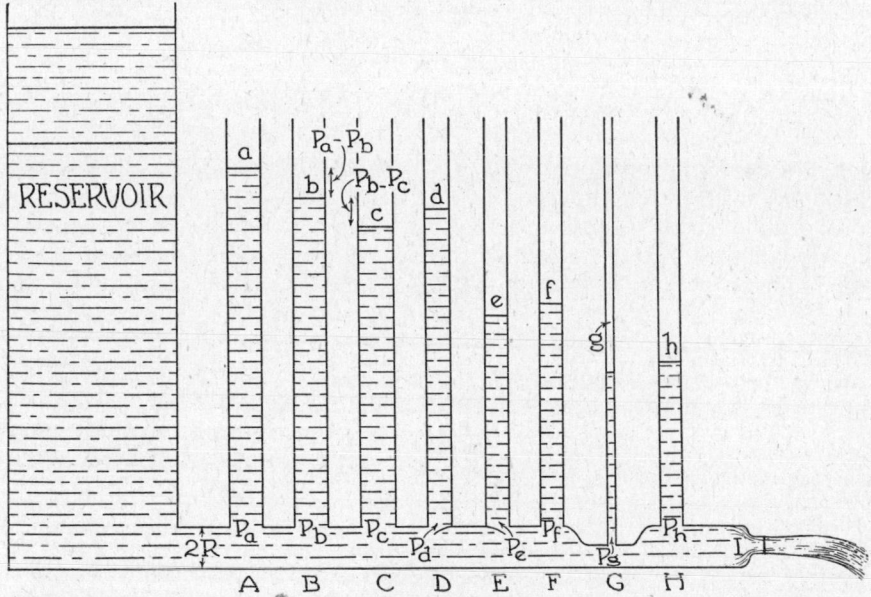

Fig. 301.—Pressure along a tube during viscous flow under various conditions: applications to measurement of flow rate.

points. Clearly, the fall in pressure alone is involved. This fact is important, since pressure measurements for studying flow need not therefore take account of barometric pressure. In physiology, circulatory pressure measurements are relative and are always given in terms of pressure above (or below) atmospheric pressure.

Length of tube. In Figure 301 the difference in pressures at A and B is the difference in the heights of the columns of fluid a and b, or $P_a - P_b$. Poiseuille demonstrated that, for viscous flow in the situation illustrated with a tube of uniform bore, the pressure drop along it is proportional† to the length of tube between the points of measurement. Thus:

* We have here assumed that the properties of the fluid—its viscosity and density primarily—do not change. Viscosity, especially, often varies considerably with temperature, so that we must assume here either that the temperature does not rise significantly, due to dissipation of heat through the walls of the tube, or that the flow is not changed by the temperature rise.

† The symbol ∝ means *proportional to.*

$$\frac{P_a - P_b}{P_b - P_c} = \frac{\overline{AB}}{\overline{BC}}, \text{ or } P_a - P_b \propto \overline{AB}$$

Caliber of tube. If the caliber of the tube is changed, while flow is held constant, the fall in pressure per unit length of tube is changed very considerably; it varies inversely as the fourth power of the diameter:

$$P_a - P_b \propto 1/R^4$$

The caliber of the tube is clearly of greater importance in determining the frictional loss (pressure drop) in the tube than is its length.

Pressure and flow. With a given tube, the flow produced by the perfusing pressure source is found to be proportional to the pressure drop along that tube:

$$P_a - P_b \propto I \text{ (the rate of flow)}.$$

These facts can be summarized as:

$$P_a - P_b = \text{Constant} \times \frac{\overline{AB}}{R^4} \times I.$$

Or, the pressure drop along a uniform bore tube during viscous flow is proportional to the rate of flow and to the length of the tube, and it is inversely proportional to the fourth power of the radius of the tube. It immediately follows that mean velocity of flow is inversely proportional to the square of the radius.

The constant depends only on the frictional properties of the fluid and is proportional to the coefficient of viscosity. It is of physiological interest that the expression is unchanged when the bore is elliptical instead of circular, if the proper geometrical considerations are used to get the equivalent radius R from the axes of the ellipse. For precise results, the pressure drop must not be measured where the fluid comes into contact with another medium, such as air, since surface tension effects then enter complexly. Fortunately for our analysis, the blood circulates in a closed system. Corrections for kinetic energy need to be made only when flow velocity is different at the two points, A and B, in our example. The correction is simple, as has been described, as long as the fluid is within the tube and neither of the points of pressure measurement is that at which the fluid enters a reservoir from the end of the tube, a situation not important in the circulation. Our knowledge is not sufficiently precise to warrant discriminating between the simple and correct forms for the kinetic energy correction. In fact, we shall find the kinetic energy correction negligible, except occasionally in pathological aortic blood flow.

The formula given above for the pressure difference between A and B in Figure 301 is Poiseuille's Law for viscous flow of a fluid of fixed viscosity. A correction for kinetic energy along the tube was added later. In more general terms, where P is the pressure difference, v the fluid viscosity, and L the length of tube between the points of pressure measurement, Poiseuille's Law is:

$$P = \frac{8L}{\pi R^4} v I$$

Viscosity. Poiseuille's Law really separates into discrete components the contributions to the production of friction in the fluid to be ascribed to the nature of the tube and to the characteristics of the fluid. Thus, the way in which pressure will fall along different narrow tubes and for different flow rates of the same liquid is given; the constant v is the same as long as the properties of the fluid are unchanged. When a more viscous fluid is used, the constant is found to be increased. If there were no theoretical derivation of Poiseuille's Law, one would be forced to treat this constant as an empirical one. However, this is not the case; Poiseuille's Law has been repeatedly confirmed and has been theoretically derived on firm ground: the constant developed from the empirical relationships discovered by Poiseuille is the viscosity of the liquid, which is defined in other terms than those of flow through tubes. Viscosity (or the coefficient of viscosity) is the force required to slide tangentially a unit area of a smooth flat surface at unit velocity with respect to another such surface parallel to it but separated from it by a unit layer of the viscous substance. It is, in other words, the force required per unit area to produce unit rate of shear, since rate of shear is the difference in velocity of slipping between layers of viscous fluid per unit separation of the layers. This rate of shear is the same throughout a fluid, which explains why viscosity is so basic an index in rheology. Its units in the C.G.S. system are grams per centimeter per sec. One *poise* is the name given to this prime unit and one-hundredth of a poise, the *centipoise*, is the commonly used submultiple. The viscosity of water at 20°C. is 1 centipoise within less than 1 per cent so that viscosities expressed in centipoises are close approximations of the relative viscosities, referred to water at 20°C. as the standard.

Viscosity can be measured, as should now be clear, from evaluation of Poiseuille's Law where all of the quantities involved, except the viscosity, are known. (Pressure, in the equation given, must be in dynes per cm.) Instruments of many types have been developed for determining the viscosity, aside from those employing the perfusion of tubes.

Fluidity. In many ways, especially in biological applications, the reciprocal of viscosity, the *coefficient of fluidity*, is a more useful entity. It is likely that *fluidity* will be found with increasing frequency in medical and physiological literature. Its unit is the reciprocal of the poise and is called the *rhe*.

$$\text{Fluidity} = 1/\text{Viscosity}$$
$$\text{or} \qquad f \quad = 1/v$$

The relationship of fluidity and viscosity to temperature and to the concentrations and character of the constituents of the fluid has been of both practical and theoretical interest, casting considerable light on the physical chemistry of liquids. Fluidity (and so, *not* viscosity) is theoretically proportional to the temperature for an ideal fluid. But the effect of temperature on fluidity is still better described mathematically (Batschinski's Law) by the constant proportionality between fluidity and the *free molecular volume*, i.e., the difference between the volume occupied by a mol of fluid at the temperature considered, less its apparent limiting value (a constant for any liquid as the fluidity approaches zero).*

Resistance. Just as Ohm's Law in electricity (the ratio of the electrical potential along a conductor to the electrical current this potential causes to flow is a constant) leads to the definition of this proportionality constant characterizing the opposition of the conductor to current flow as resistance, so does Poiseuille's Law, in rheology, lead to the definition of viscous resistance as the ratio between pressure difference (corresponding to potential difference) and rate of flow (electrical current) times viscosity. In Ohm's Law a term corresponding to viscosity does not enter, since only one kind of "fluid" (electrons) is involved. In rheology the resistance characterizes the

---

* The effects of pressure on fluidity can also be predicted from Batschinski's Law, when the change in molecular volume caused by the pressure is utilized as the parameter.

opposition by the tube to fluid flow. Calling the resistance r, and the pressure difference P,

$$r = \frac{P}{vI} \left(\text{as ohms} = \frac{\text{volts}}{\text{amperes}} \right).$$

It is this equation based on Poiseuille's research which permits one to measure the tubular resistance directly. One of the methods of flow measurement described above and illustrated by tubes f and h in Figure 301 where the resistance is kept constant depends on the following form of this equation:

$$I = \frac{P_f - P_h}{rv}.$$

If the constants of the tube are known, r is then known without flow studies since v is determined by the character of the fluid. If r is known in this way or by some other method, absolute measurement of I can then be made. From the previous discussion, it is apparent that for the uniform bore tube Poiseuille's Law gives:

$$r \propto \frac{L}{R^4}$$

If all the units are C.G.S., summarizing the above facts arising from Poiseuille's Law (without kinetic energy correction):

$$r = \frac{8L}{\pi R^4}, \quad \text{and} \quad v = \frac{\pi R^4 P}{8LI} = \frac{P}{rI}.$$

If the length of tube being perfused is kept constant, *and if* the liquid always flows linearly and has a known viscosity, measurements of flow and pressure fall give an indication of the changes in the bore of the tube, even if the actual fixed length of tube is not known. That is to say, resistance evaluation by means of flow-pressure measurements then can give, in this instance, knowledge of the relative bore of the tube.* This possibility is one of the reasons for the increasing interest in measuring resistance to blood flow: resistance to flow is desired as an index of the degree of vasoconstriction.

So far, we have confined our attention to a single tube of uniform bore. The effects of having several different tubes connected in series or in parallel and with efflux at more than one point must also be considered. It can be shown that Poiseuille's Law, like its analogue in electricity, leads to the conclusion that many resistances in series are equivalent to a single resistance of the same value as the sum of the resistances in series; and that parallel resistances, where flow divides into several streams to be reunited into one, can be considered replaced by a single resistance of a value such that its reciprocal (the conductance) is equal to the sum of the reciprocals of the parallel resistances. In Figure 302 the currents, I, through each of two outlets A and B from the reservoir, are equal, as are their terminal pressures,

---

* We have: $R_1^4 = (8Lv/\pi) \dfrac{I_1}{P_1}$; $R_2^4 = (8Lv/\pi) \dfrac{I_2}{P_2}$. $\dfrac{R_1}{R_2} = \sqrt[4]{\dfrac{I_1 P_2}{I_2 P}}$

P_6. The resistances r_s and r_p in series at A are equivalent, respectively, to the series and parallel resistances shown connected at B:

$$r_s = r_1 + r_2 + r_3 + r_4; \quad \frac{1}{r_p} = \frac{1}{r_5'} + \frac{1}{r_6''}.$$

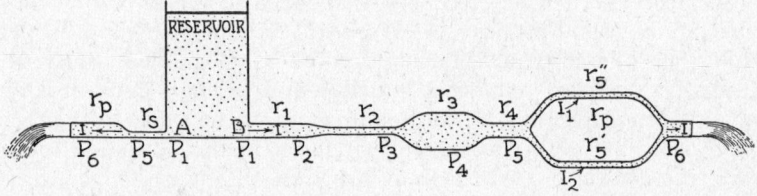

Fig. 302.—Resistances equivalent, for viscous flow, to a series of resistances and to resistances connected in parallel. The tubes connected at A have the same resistance as those connected at B:

$$r_s = r_1 + r_2 + r_3 + r_4; \quad \frac{1}{r_p} = \frac{1}{r_5'} + \frac{1}{r_6''}.$$

Steady flow of colloidal fluids: viscous flow

A colloidal solution, like blood plasma, is found to obey Poiseuille's Law for viscous flow, if the tubes are not so large that turbulence arises, if the concentration of solute does not exceed a critical value,* and—very likely— if the perfusion pressure is not too small. It is probable that there is, in addition, some minimal bore for the tube below which plastic rather than viscous flow must be considered to occur, just as when the concentration exceeds the critical value. However, it appears that the flow of the protein solution under consideration, blood plasma, conforms well to Poiseuille's Law, both in vitro and in vivo throughout the ranges in which we are interested (4, 5, 26).

The fluidity of mixtures of noncolloidal inert fluids is the mean of their separate fluidities, weighted for their respective volume fractions; that of colloidal solutions, whether suspensions or sols, while also proportional to the volume fraction of the dispersed substance, approaches zero as the volume fraction (b) approaches (b'), the critical value mentioned above. Thus, if f_0 is the fluidity of the solvent alone, and f is the fluidity of a volume fraction, b, of the substance in colloidal solution, then

$$f = \left(1 - \frac{b}{b'}\right) f_0$$

(1, 2, 24). This formula applies remarkably well to blood serum and plasma. Bingham and Roepke (5), using data of Nageli (14) from in vitro studies of dilutions of a sample of human serum, found an average deviation of only 0.3 per cent between observation and the formula (temperature 37°C.):

$$f = 129.6 - 5.72b.$$

These same workers have also demonstrated that the fluidity of blood plasma can be derived with modest precision (for lack of adequate experimental data) from the known fluidities of solutions of each of the component fractions of the blood proteins. The fluidity of human blood plasma outside the body, at 37°C., is about 70 rhes.†

* The critical concentration is independent of the temperature. It is likely that the transition from viscous to plastic flow is more gradual than, for the sake of simplicity, it is here represented. As far as the author is aware, blood plasma has not actually been studied in concentrated form so that it is included in these statements by deduction alone.

† More complex formulas have been derived and to some extent verified, but they will not be given here since the simpler form is quite successful for plasma and serum.

Steady flow of suspensions: plastic flow

When the concentration of suspended particles in the fluid exceeds the critical concentration, we have said that plastic flow arises. There is disagreement as to how critical this transition is as well as over the type of expression which best describes the flow of plastic substances. Our special purpose is to consider the effect of the red cells suspended in blood. While they can bend and are not solid particles, they are still more nearly like a suspension of a solid than like an emulsion composed of liquid globules which, during shear, can be stretched into long lamellae and perhaps even broken into smaller globules, depending on the relationship of the shear to their surface tension. Accordingly, we confine our attention to the flow of suspensions. However, the elasticity of red cells is probably of some significance in the capillaries, where red cells are comparable in size with the lumen.

Some suspensoids at low perfusion pressures act like simple viscous fluids, but at higher pressures their apparent fluidity starts to rise rather sharply. Such colloids are called superfluid. Later we shall see that blood is not a superfluid. Completely different are the characteristics of "elastic" suspensoids; while considerable perfusion pressure is required for low flow rates, smaller increments of pressure are needed to obtain a given increase in flow as it reaches higher levels at which the apparent fluidity approaches a constant value. Blood falls in this class of plastic elastic fluids and actual elastic rebound of blood when pressure is released has been demonstrated.

For some plastic fluids, Bingham's modification of Poiseuille's Law, which includes another constant p', the yield pressure, serves well, especially for certain inorganic sols and dyestuffs, and, under certain conditions, for blood (3, 6). His formula is:

$$I = \frac{\pi R^4 m}{8L} \left(P - \frac{4}{3} p' + \frac{p'^4}{3P^3} \right).$$

Here m, the *mobility*,* replaces the fluidity as the index of opposition to flow by the fluid; m is $1/r$ times the slope of the straight-line asymptote, approached for large values of P; and $\frac{4p'}{3}$ is the pressure intercept of this straight line for zero flow. In practice, the last term is negligible. In Figure 303 these relationships are indicated. Bingham's formula reduces to:

$$I = \frac{\pi R^4 m}{8L} (P - p),$$

where $\frac{4}{3} p' = p$, the indicated yield pressure, the value indicated for zero flow by extrapolation from large perfusion pressures, P. This is the equation of the straight line asymptote and has had some usefulness in studying the circulation, as will be shown later; the more complex form helps very little in fitting the observed data and, in our opinion, the equation should be treated as an empirical one, since its theoretical derivation is open to question.

The likelihood that the expression offered by Bingham is an approximation, a special case of a more general and widely applicable formula, has been advanced by Nutting (15) and others (22, 23). Where Bingham regards slippage and seepage as the cause of deviations from his formulas, near the yield pressure, others regard them as phenomena which are always present to a varying degree and which are characteristics of plastic flow. Nutting's formula,† while initially empirical, has been derived on thermodynamical grounds (16). It is said to fit various reported data, including that for paints observed by Bingham and Green (3), better than other formulas in use. In general:

$$S = at^n F^k.$$

---

* Just as the reciprocal of fluidity is the viscosity, the reciprocal of mobility is the consistency, which corresponds to viscosity; it is not widely used.

† Others have previously advanced an exponential expression like Nutting's, but not on such general grounds.

Here S is the total strain produced in time t by a stress F in a material characterized by the positive constants a, n, and k. A perfectly elastic body (or a gas under adiabatic expansion) has n = 0 and k = 1, so that the formula reduces to the familiar Hooke's Law: stress is proportional to strain. For the perfusion of fluids this formula becomes, where Q is the quantity of fluid flowing in time t, $Q = at^n P^k$.

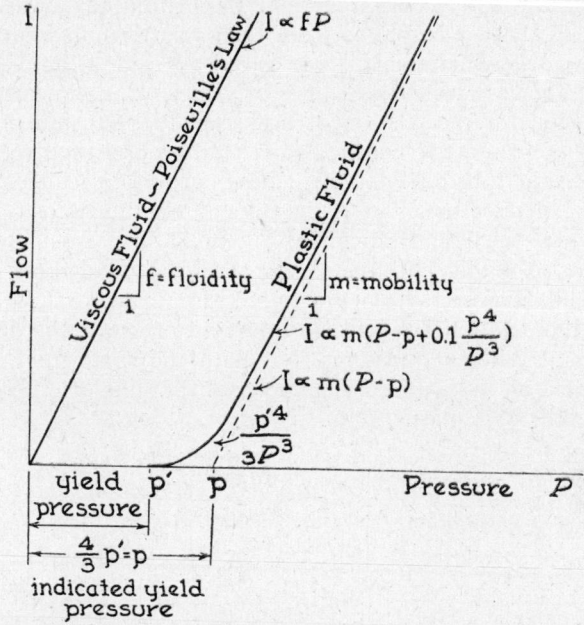

Fig. 303.—Comparison of pressure-flow curves for a viscous and a plastic fluid, where the respective fluidity and mobility are equal. Unit resistance has been assumed for convenience in illustration.

For perfectly viscous fluids n = 1 and k = 1, and Poiseuille's Law results, since $\frac{Q}{t} = I$, in steady flow. The constant a is then the reciprocal of the product of viscosity and resistance. A plastic fluid of the elastic type in which flow rate under constant pressure head P does not vary with time—blood appears to be in this class—is characterized by n = 1. Where the apparent viscosity (proportional to perfusion pressure ÷ rate of flow after a long time interval) decreases as perfusion is raised, k > 1. This is the condition that is of most interest to us, since blood acts in this way. The Bingham expression may be a special limiting case* of the Nutting equation where n = 1 and k > 1 (15, 22, 23):

$$I = aP^k.$$

The Nutting and Bingham formulas have been included here because they both have applicability to the circulation. The rheology of the blood is still too unsettled to warrant elimination among these forms, each of which still serves a useful purpose.

* There is a difficulty in attempting to demonstrate that the Bingham formula is a special case of the Nutting formula. The rate of change of rate of flow with pressure $\left(\frac{dI}{dP}\right)$, in Bingham's formula, is a constant, independent of pressure; but in Nutting's formula this quantity is not a constant—it increases progressively with pressure so that the Nutting formula for pressure-flow gives a curve with *no* asymptote. In view of the limited pressure in the circulation, this difficulty need not concern us; we shall see that within our pressure range the Bingham formula and Nutting's may, under certain conditions, give similar results.

Resistance to the Flow of Suspensions: Hindrance. In our consideration of the circulation we are of course concerned with the changes in blood flow resulting from physiological alterations in the characteristics of the blood. However, we are also interested both in blood flow changes caused by variations in the caliber of vessels and in estimates of these variations. Measurements of blood flow and perfusion pressure in portions of the vascular system are necessary so that we can learn from their relationship what the relative variations in vessel caliber are. It is our only way, aside from direct observation, to determine changes in the caliber of vessels. Consequently, in obtaining an expression for the relation of flow rate to perfusion pressure, it is desirable that the respective contributions to the opposition to flow due to the fluid and to the tube be separable, as they are in Poiseuille's Law. There the resistance expressed the effect of the tube alone; the viscosity (or fluidity) characterized only the fluid. In Bingham's formula for plastic flow, the mobility corresponds to fluidity, but the yield pressure depends both on the tube and on the fluid. However, from Bingham's simplified form for the asymptotic straight line relationship between flow and pressure, the determination of two points at different pressures, but with the same fluid and tubular system, can yield an index to the relative contributions of different tubes to opposing the flow of a plastic fluid.

Referring to the two observations needed by the subscripts 1 and 2, and the change in the tube by a "primed" superscript, Bingham's formula gives:

$$I_1 = \frac{\pi R^4 m}{8L}(P_1 - p); \qquad I_2 = \frac{\pi R^4 m}{8L}(P_2 - p)$$

$$\frac{\pi R^4}{8L}m = \frac{I_2 - I_1}{P_2 - P_1}.$$

And similarly,

$$\frac{\pi R'^4}{8L'}m = \frac{I'_2 - I'_1}{P'_2 - P'_1},$$

so that

$$\frac{\pi R^4/8L}{\pi R'^4/8L'} = \frac{P'_2 - P'_1}{P_2 - P_1} \cdot \frac{I_2 - I_1}{I'_2 - I'_1} = \frac{r'}{r}.$$

The Nutting formula cannot yet be treated like the Bingham one for estimating changes in the opposition to flow offered by different tubes. The relationship between the constant a and the other constants of the fluid, m and k, and of the tube R and L, on which a is dependent, has not yet been reported. When it is known, the estimation of changes in opposition to flow by different bore tubes should merely require the determination of a from pressure-flow measurements under the different conditions, but with the same fluid.

Both of the equations given for plastic flow reduce to Poiseuille's Law, when a viscous fluid replaces the plastic one. In Bingham's form, the mobility m becomes the fluidity f and the yield pressure p becomes zero; in the Nutting formula,

$$k = 1 \text{ and } a = \frac{f}{r} \cdot$$

Thus we see that in each case the resistance, r, to viscous flow as given in Poiseuille's Law enters the equation and characterizes the opposition of the tube to the flow of plastic fluids.* In geometric terms,

$$r = \frac{8L}{\pi R^4} \cdot$$

* In the Nutting formula, while we can say that $a = f/r$ for $k = 1$, we cannot be sure that the constant r will explicitly enter the function defining a when $k > 1$; the length and bore of the tube may not maintain their same interrelationship in the equation. At our suggestion, Dr. Nutting is seeking the unknown function relating a to the constants characterizing tube and fluid.

However, if the word "resistance" is defined in terms of pressure drop and resulting flow (r = fP/I), while it will be identical with the geometric expression given above *so long as viscous fluids are used*, it will certainly differ from it when plastic fluids are substituted. Since "resistance" has come to be thought of as equal to $\frac{fP}{I}$, irrespective of the fluid, we shall keep *resistance* to mean this quantity, dependent, as it is, on the nature of nonviscous liquids, and to avoid confusion* we use the word *hindrance* to mean the geometric quantity, $\frac{8L}{\pi R^4}$, which characterizes, in the Bingham formula for plastic flow, the opposition of the tube to fluid perfusion. For viscous fluids, because of the applicability of Poiseuille's Law, the hindrance becomes identical with the resistance. Using h, for hindrance, Bingham's formula gives:

$$h = \frac{m\,(P - p)}{I},$$

while its value from Nutting's formula unfortunately is still not known. There have been those who have preferred to use *apparent viscosity* or apparent fluidity (7, 17, 26), while retaining resistance as a constant defined above. The apparent viscosity or fluidity is considered a variable which shifts so that resistance, in the equation defining it, stays constant. This seems to serve no useful purpose, except that of description and discussion, unless only the properties of the fluid are of interest. The method used here has the virtue that both the fluid and the tube can be separately characterized.

Nonrigid tubes and steady flow

If the tube is not rigid, both its length and bore change with pressure. As a consequence, its hindrance becomes dependent on the pressure. Since, for a uniform bore,

$$h = \frac{8L}{\pi R^4},$$

we must substitute whatever the proper relationship is between R, L, and the actual pressure. In the Bingham formula the indicated yield pressure is related to the length and the bore of the tube, so that yield pressure would also be affected by the elasticity of the tubes. The mathematical procedure for allowing for nonrigid tubes is complex (19). Whether there is need for attempting this correction in analyzing the blood vascular system will be discussed later.

Pulsatile pressure

Rigid Tubes. If the tubes are rigid, a rapid change in the pressure of the fluid as it enters the tube will produce a wave front of increased pressure (a compression wave, like that of sound in liquids) which travels with the velocity of sound through the fluid (*ca.* 5000 feet per sec.) to the efflux point. Whenever there is a sudden change of resistance to flow along the perfusion system—division of one tube into two, a constriction, etc.—a pressure wave will be reflected which travels back, upstream. The suddenly increased pressure will cause increased flow, but the rate of increase of the flow will not increase as fast as the pressure because of the inertia of the fluid in the tube; it takes time for the fluid in the system to be accelerated to the new flow velocities.

* The author has previously applied the Bingham formula to the circulation (12), but did not call the quantity, h, by a new term, simply redefining resistance as h, when plastic fluids are used. Considerable confusion was found to have been caused by this shift which, it is hoped, a new term will avoid.

Elastic Tubes. If the tubes are elastic, as blood vessels are, so that the pulsating pressure makes them pulsate in caliber and length, the pressure wave is transmitted more slowly through the fluid than in rigid tubes, and it is damped out faster by the imperfect elasticity of the tubes. The velocity of propagation of the pressure wave, M, in meters per sec., where the fluid is blood, is given by:

$$M = \frac{3.57}{\sqrt{E}},$$

where E is the per cent volume elasticity coefficient of the tube perfused: per cent increase in volume per millimeter of mercury pressure increase. Pulsatile flow in elastic tubes corresponds closely to the circulation of the blood. As in rigid tubes, reflections of the pressure waves occur whenever there is sudden change of hindrance along the length of the elastic tube, irrespective of the type of fluid. The propagation in elastic tubes of pressure waves in plastic fluids has not yet been worked out; we expect that for fluids which are only moderately plastic (almost viscous), it will not differ markedly from that for viscous liquids.

HEMODYNAMICS: APPLICATION OF PHYSICAL PRINCIPLES OF FLOW TO THE CIRCULATION

It must be stated immediately that hemodynamics has not mastered many of its main problems so that the application to the circulation of the principles of rheology, itself in considerable flux, is still in need of critical analysis. Reference to the preceding portion of this chapter will frequently be necessary if this part is to be understood.

Blood

Blood wets the endothelium lining the vessels. For the purpose of rheology it is a colloid protein solution, buffered by inorganic salts; it is an emulsion of lipid globules with a suspension of cells, mainly erythrocytes.

Turbulence. Turbulence is a condition of instability in which flow and pressure vary rapidly and spontaneously. These variations, if they occur in blood, cause vibrations in the vessel and surrounding tissues such that sounds can be heard through a stethoscope. From the previous discussion of turbulence, we see that turbulence is to be expected when the Reynolds number exceeds a critical value:

$$RVD/v > \text{critical constant for turbulence.}$$

That is to say, a large blood vessel (R large), with rapidly moving blood of low viscosity, should be the most likely situation for the occurrence of turbulence.* Auscultation over large blood vessels normally reveals no turbulence. However, in anemia where the viscosity is lowered murmurs over the heart and at the branchings of the largest vessels can often be heard. The physician discounts some of the murmurs arising in the heart in the presence of anemia, calling them "functional," since they do not arise from an anatomical abnormality. In conditions of rapid blood flow, other functional

---

* The density of blood varies little; viscosity, or mobility, is much more variable. We use viscosity here freely since in the large vessels in which turbulence alone may arise the viscosity of blood serves well, for blood behaves there as a viscous fluid.

murmurs can also be heard, and sometimes, on the contrary, they disappear. During exercise, in association with the elevated metabolism of hyperthyroidism and in aortic insufficiency, increased velocity of blood flow occurs and murmurs may be heard. The rapid velocities produced when blood flows through small irregular orifices also can cause turbulence. The "organic" murmurs resulting from stenosed or leaking cardiac valves are such examples. Pressure by the stethoscope on a vessel can cause a sound due to turbulence and mislead the physician. The present-day method of indirect blood pressure determination depends on hearing the turbulence arising just at systolic pressure, when blood is barely able to pass through the brachial artery, collapsed during the rest of the pulse cycle.

Forces maintaining the circulation

The heart is the prime mover of the blood. It empties itself at each beat into the aorta which stores a portion of the blood received so that the pressure and flow do not fall to very low levels before the next heart beat. In this way a pulsatile pressure is exerted on the blood which reaches the arterioles where the greatest drop in pressure occurs. If the cardiac output of blood is unchanged while the heart rate increases, the pulsation produced by the heart will be reduced. It will pump less blood at each stroke so that aortic pressure will not rise so high, and during the shorter diastolic time less blood will flow from the aorta, causing a correspondingly increased diastolic pressure. The inverse relationship between pulse pressure and pulse rate is one with protean clinical examples.

At the capillaries the pulsatile pressure normally has been fairly well damped out by the arterioles. However, after exercise, at high environmental temperatures, and in hyperthyroidism, the decreased arteriolar resistance permits pulsation to reach the capillary and venule beds where it is seen clinically by the examining physician. While the heart is the main source of pressure in moving the blood in the capillaries, variations in tissue pressure have some effect. In the muscles, whether striated or smooth, variations in muscle tension make extracapillary pressure fluctuate and help to fill or empty them.

In the venules external tissue forces become more influential. The color of the skin is determined primarily by the amount of blood in the venules and by the amount of reduced hemoglobin present. The cyanosis (blue color) of the skin and mucous membranes in polycythemia and congestive heart failure result from the large absolute (not relative) amount of reduced hemoglobin contained in the venules and visible through the skin. The force of gravity plays a minor role, since it promotes flow in venules carrying blood in the direction of gravity but opposes flow in those oppositely directed.

From the venules blood flows into the veins where valves aid the flow of blood by preventing reflux whenever the forces of gravity or of muscular contraction would otherwise promote peripheral flow. The closing of the valves forces the blood to flow centrally whenever external pressure increases about the veins. Our many changes in posture and in muscular tone, whether we are sleeping or awake, help in returning venous blood to the heart. If the tissues or veins lack tone, inadequate cardiac return may ensue so that the heart cannot maintain sufficient pressure to keep the brain supplied with blood. Well-trained soldiers standing rigidly at attention, with inadequate change of posture, have been known to faint as a consequence.*

The pressure changes produced in the thorax and abdomen by respiratory movements contribute to maintaining the circulation. The visceral contents of the abdomen can be considered, hemodynamically, as fluid (this has been proven experimentally), so that the net extravascular pressure on abdominal veins is that of the uppermost portion of the abdomen, and the effects of gravity on the venous return to the heart from the abdomen are thereby partially nullified. However, the elevation of pressure in the abdomen because of its fluid content necessitates somewhat higher pressures in the veins entering the abdominal cavity from the lower extremities. There, however, variations in muscle tension and the presence of valves promote flow. During inspiration intra-abdominal pressure rises while intrathoracic pressure falls, thus aiding the flow of blood from abdomen to thorax. The partial emptying of the vena cava and iliac veins occurring during inspiration then enhances flow into them from the lower extremities when next intra-abdominal pressure falls, during expiration.

Relation of pressure to flow: peripheral resistance or hindrance

Aorta. The aorta offers little resistance† to the steady flow of blood. Its great elasticity, however, amounts to a variable resistance to blood flow, depending on the rate at which blood pressure is changing. Thus, when the pressure rises suddenly, as it does when the heart contracts, the considerable increase in aortic volume which results amounts to a flow of blood into a new space, just as though a new reservoir had opened up into the aorta opposing the pressure rise. When the pressure falls it is as though this reservoir reinjected blood back into the aorta, thus tending to maintain its pressure despite the lack of flow from the heart. The elastic recoil of the aorta is therefore of importance in providing the pulsatile circulation with an elastic reservoir.

It is found that the distensibility of the aortic wall decreases with advancing age. The consequence of this phenomenon, if there were no changes in the size of the aorta, would be to reduce aortic storage capacity for the blood ejected by the heart so that, other things being equal, systolic pressure would rise but diastolic pressure would drop. Such a finding is frequent in persons with uncomplicated arteriosclerosis of the aorta and large vessels; they must be distinguished from patients suffering from hypertension due to arteriolar constriction, in whom the diastolic pressure is characteristically elevated.

However, the usual increase of aortic rigidity with age is also accompanied by increasing diameter of the aortic lumen. Its effect is to offset the rigidity. The volume of a tube is proportional to its cross-sectional area (its diameter squared), while the amount of increase in the diameter, for a given rigidity and increase in pressure, is itself proportional to the diameter. Thus the

---

* Persons placed on a tilt-table, at an angle of about 70 degrees, show a similar manifestation, especially if they have also received sodium nitrite, which reduces venous tone. Runners immediately after a race, if they remain standing, may faint because their dilated blood vessels pour large quantities of blood into the distensible veins, unsupported any longer by muscular contractions. "Black-out" from acceleration in aviation, while somewhat similar, requires a more elaborate explanation.

† In vessels larger than arterioles, hindrance and resistance are identical, since blood then behaves like a viscous fluid.

volume increase, for given increase in pressure and fixed wall rigidity, is proportional to the square of the diameter of the lumen. Consequently, omitting consideration of changes in the length of the aorta, it is apparent that an increase in rigidity would be offset by a corresponding increase in the diameter of the aorta. These facts are illustrated in Figures 304 and 305 (10). Figure 304 shows the per cent increase in volume of isolated segments of human thoracic aortas as a result of increasing pressure. The effects of changes in both length and diameter are thereby included. It is seen that the per cent volume-pressure elasticity of the aorta is approximately constant at physiological pressures. In Figure 305 is shown the results of measurements on human aortas obtained at autopsy, for different age groups. The

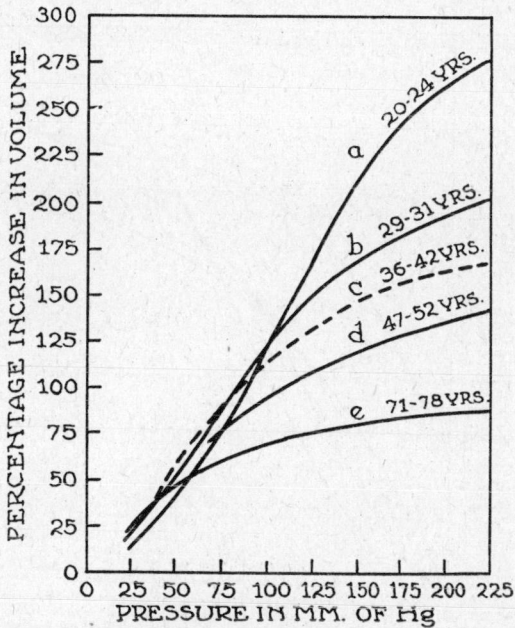

Fig. 304.—The effect of age on the per cent increase in volume of isolated human thoracic aortas obtained at autopsy for varying pressure. Note that elasticity decreases as age advances, but that the elasticity is fairly constant in the physiological pressure range—the curves passing through almost the same elasticity point in this region. See Figure 305. (Redrawn from Hallock and Benson, *J. clin. Invest.*, 1937, *16*:597.)

slopes of the curves at the same pressure give the relative elasticity of the aorta; the curves (excepting that for 71–78 years), despite their wide spread at zero pressure, are fairly close together in the physiological zone.

The aorta also increases in length with age, becoming slightly tortuous, which adds to the effect of the increased lumen in opposing the influence of the increased rigidity. Just as the pulse wave traveling down the aorta distends it laterally, so, also, does it cause elongation. However, the many large branches of the aorta with their connective tissue sheaths tend to act as anchors, opposing aortic elongation.

The application of the physical principles of pulsating pressure in elastic tubes to the form and propagation of the arterial pulse is given in more detail elsewhere (Chap. 32). We shall consider here only some of the broad, quali-

tative facts. The inertia of the blood and elasticity of the aorta, or, put another way, the low resonant frequency of the aorta, act so that the pulse
wave caused by the contraction of the heart travels through the aorta and
large vessels much faster than the rate at which the ejected blood effectually
flows toward the periphery. The discrepancy between the velocity of blood
flow and the pressure of the blood becomes considerable in the abdominal
aorta and the large arteries of the lower extremities. It is in the smaller arteries
and the arterioles that the discrepancy disappears as a natural consequence
of the conversion of a pulsatile pressure to a steady pressure and flow; peak
pressure must be retarded relative to velocity of flow to accomplish this

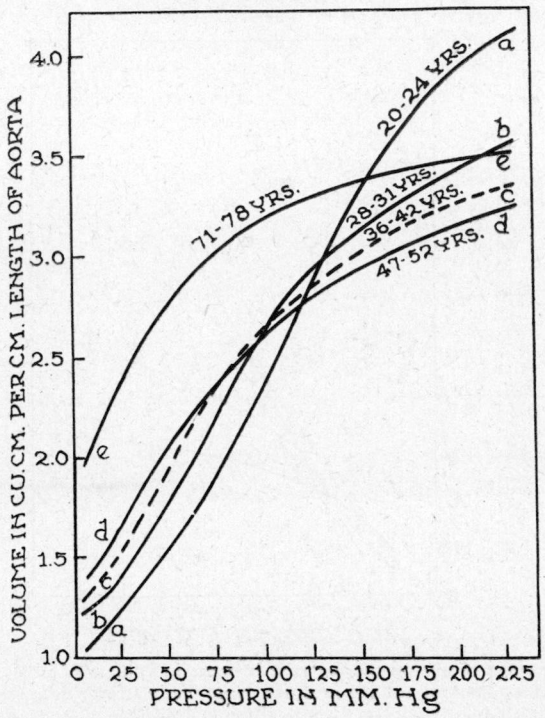

Fig. 305.—The effect of the increased volume of the aorta with advancing age on the capacity
of the aorta to store blood between heart beats and so to convert pulsatile pressure into steady
pressure. Compare with Figure 304. In the physiological arterial pressure range, the increasing
aortic rigidity caused by age (Fig. 304) is offset to a considerable extent by the concomitant
dilatation. (Redrawn from Hallock and Benson, *J. clin. Invest.*, 1937, *16*:599.)

result. Figure 306 shows the discrepancy referred to. Notice that the direction
of flow actually reverses itself during part of the cycle, due to reflux of blood
from the large elastic vessels back into the aorta. The presence of reflux
depends in part on the rate of flow through the arteries: if flow is fast, reflux
is prevented by the rapid run-off of blood into the tissues; if there is considerable vasoconstriction, however, the vessels act like elastic pouches,
returning to the aorta some of the blood which first flowed into them at
higher pressures.

   This explanation, while correct, amounts to a description of the reflection
of pressure (and flow) waves in tubes when their resistance changes suddenly.

Pressure waves are reflected in the aorta and its branches and are superimposed on each other in a complex way. Systolic pressure measured near the iliac bifurcation is actually higher than at the root of the aorta.

In certain diseases in which the peak velocity of aortic blood flow is increased, the systolic pressure measured in the thigh is exaggerated. In aortic insufficiency, because diastolic pressure is reduced by reflux of blood back into the heart through the leaking semilunar valves, the heart maintains the circulation by increasing its stroke volume so that the net output, after subtracting reflux, is sufficient. As a result, velocity of flow is abnormally high during the early part of the pulse cycle and the end pressure of the blood in the iliacs is elevated. When blood pressure is measured in the clinical manner, using an inflated cuff about a limb, the systolic pressure is the end pressure of the occluded artery at the level where it branches from a larger trunk. If the artery leaves the main trunk at an acute angle, the pressure obtained is partly end pressure at the trunk and, as has been explained (see Fig. 301, d),

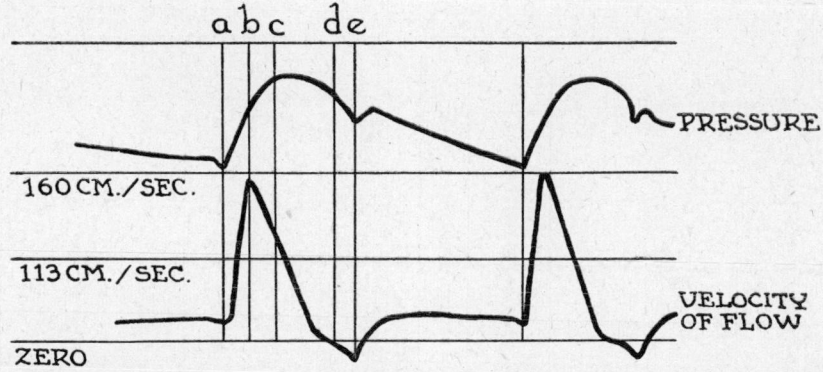

Fig. 306.—Pressure and velocity of flow in the abdominal aorta during the cardiac cycle. (Redrawn from Wiggers, *Physiology in health and disease*, 1944, p. 565. Schematized from Broemser.)

will be higher than the lateral pressure on the walls of this larger vessel. Brachial measurement of systolic pressure does not include much error due to the end effect, but femoral systolic pressure is more subject to it because of the acute angle of the bifurcation of the aorta into the iliacs. The functional importance of leaking semilunar valves is sometimes estimated clinically by determining the amount by which femoral systolic pressure exceeds brachial systolic pressure.

Dimensions of Vessels. After the blood leaves the aorta, it enters many large arteries of various sizes, which progressively subdivide. To understand the relationship between pressure and flow, the number of vessels in each size category and their lengths are of central significance. Unfortunately, the estimates of number, caliber and length of the different vessels are not consistent enough for a comparison between actually observed pressure and the calculated pressure drop to be expected along them. Such a comparison would be of great value in confirming the theoretical basis used in computing the pressure drop along the different calibers of vessels. To make such estimates it is essential that there be a valid method for substituting an equivalent single uniform bore tube for a series of different sized ones and for a set of parallel ones, connected in shunt. If, as has been noted previously, Poiseuille's

Law does not apply to blood without substantial correction, resistance as customarily determined (pressure per unit flow rate times viscosity) is not independent of pressure and so cannot be used in determining the equivalent single tubular system under varying pressure conditions for the complicated blood vascular system, with its series and shunt connections. A constant depending solely on the tube dimensions, which measures its influence on pressure drop for a given flow, becomes necessary—the hindrance, measured by whatever relationship replaces Poiseuille's Law for blood in the vascular system.

Arterioles. The fall in blood pressure along the arterial circulatory route, as vessels subdivide, depends on the relative numbers of the different sizes of vessels. Thus, while capillaries are the narrowest vessels, their short length and great number combine to make them offer relatively less opposition to blood flow than the arterioles which, because of their small number in relation to the narrow bore (its influence varies as the fourth power of its diameter), are the site of the largest pressure drop: in them the conversion into heat

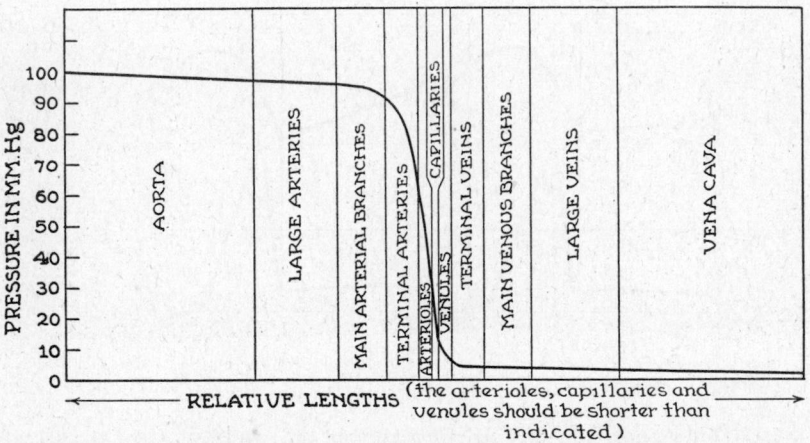

Fig. 307.—Pressure at the different anatomical divisions of the vascular system in relation to their relative lengths. Notice that most of the fall in pressure is arteriolar. (Modified from Green, *Medical physics*, 1944, p. 221.)

of the potential energy, represented by pressure, is greatest. The arterioles are the prime controllers of systemic blood pressure and of local blood flow. The disease syndrome, essential hypertension, is due to excessive constriction of arterioles and exemplifies their vital importance as pressure regulators. The routing of blood to the different regions and organs of the body depends mainly on the pressure drop in their arterioles. If these vessels are constricted in one region, as they are, for example, in the chilled skin, the pressure drop in them increases so that the pressure remaining to perfuse the capillaries (even if unchanged in caliber) is reduced and so, therefore, is the flow of blood through them. The manner in which pressure declines along the blood vascular system is shown in Figure 307. The control of blood pressure and local blood flow is discussed in more detail in Chapter 38.

One of the principles referred to briefly in the previous section of this chapter was that of Bernoulli. Because of the law of the conservation of energy, the lateral pressure is reduced when fluid speeds up in flow through a constriction in a tube. However, in the circulation the velocity of blood, even at its maximum in the aorta, is so low that most of the energy of the blood is potential energy and very little is kinetic energy. In the aorta, kinetic energy is normally only about 0.5 per cent of total energy. Consequently, little change in pressure is to be expected as the result of change in velocity of blood flow in the circulatory system except in a highly pathological condition. In the glomerulus, for example, where blood flows from several capillaries into a single efferent arteriole, so that it is speeded up, computation shows that the decrease in pressure is infinitesimal.

Capillaries. The relation of capillaries to control of blood flow is only partially understood. They are capable of active contraction, but more than other vessels they reflect into the blood stream the pressure of the tissue fluid which bathes them. Their distensibility is great for small increments of pressure. Many capillaries rupture or increase their permeability with increased pressure, as when a tourniquet blocking venous flow is placed on an extremity in the clinical test of capillary fragility.

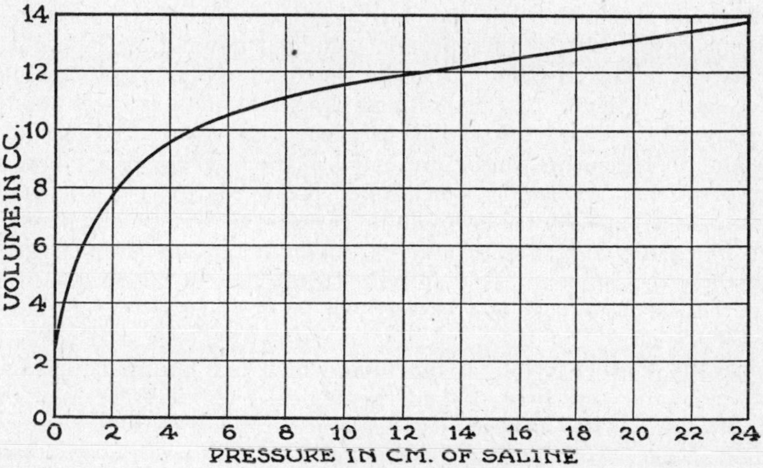

Fig. 308.—The pressure-volume relationship in the inferior vena cava of a dog. While highly distensible at pressures near normal, the vessel becomes fairly rigid at higher pressures. (Redrawn from Green, *Medical physics*, 1944, p. 213.)

Venules and Veins. The role of venules and veins in controlling blood flow depends less on their opposition to flow than on their volume capacity at the pressure existent. The fact that venules and small veins are not normally distended means that slight changes in venous pressure greatly increase the capacity of the whole circulation. Even the vena cava is quite distensible, as is shown in Figure 308. It is to be noted, though, that the distention is limited when the pressure becomes high. This reservoir action of the venous side of the circulation has already been discussed; it is fundamental for an understanding of the way in which the circulation, closed system though it be, is adjusted to varying conditions, both physiological and pathological.

When the circulation is subnormal because of narrowing and obliteration of the arteries in disease, the influence of the size and shape of the veins can become vital. If a limb suffering from narrowed, diseased arteries is elevated, intravenous pressure may fall to that of the tissues so that the veins collapse and blood trickles through them with more difficulty than if they were distended. On the other hand, depression of the limbs may require more venous pressure (and so capillary pressure) for circulation than the narrowed arteries can maintain along with adequate flow and capillary function. Therefore, in these conditions there is an optimal position for the limb at which the veins are not quite collapsed and blood flow and capillary function are most nearly normal.

Serum and Plasma: Their Lack of Plasticity. Blood serum and plasma, while colloids, behave like viscous fluids, to which Poiseuille's Law applies, both in glass tubes and other viscometers, and in animal perfusion experiments (4, 5, 26).

Elasticity of vessels. A result of the applicability of Poiseuille's Law to colloids flowing steadily through the nonrigid tubes of the circulatory system is the conclusion that the vessels must stretch in length enough, as their caliber expands with increase in pressure, so that the net resistance to flow is unchanged.* Thus it would appear that a rigid tubule system of some size can be considered as the equivalent of the elastic blood vessels for the purposes of calculating plasma flow in response to slow (nonpulsatile) pressure changes. While this result, obtained for protein solution, may not at first sight seem to apply to the flow of blood, it can be shown to apply, if the contributions of the vessels to the drop in pressure resulting from flow are separated from that of the blood in such a way that the effects of a network of tubes in series and shunt arrangements can be evaluated in the same way for blood as for serum or plasma. As has been mentioned previously for a plastic fluid, the hindrance, evaluated by the law relating pressure to flow for the plastic fluid —it is equal to the resistance if a viscous fluid replaces the plastic one— fulfills these requirements. Thus, for the steady flow of blood as well as for plasma and serum, the blood vessels can be considered to act as though they were rigid.

Blood: Its Plasticity. Blood, the fluid which first prompted Poiseuille's classical research, has been studied rheologically for many years. Unfortunately the relationship between its rheological properties in glass tubes and in blood vessels is still not clear; we shall give an outline of the present status of the problem as we view it.

In vitro properties. Some of the difficulties in the study of the flow of blood outside the body are its rapid clotting, necessitating the use of defibrinated or otherwise stabilized blood or substitutes for blood; the formation of stacks of clumped red cells, called *rouleaux;* rapid settling of the cells, if flow rates are low, as they are in the body in the smaller vessels; the fragility of red cells, which, on leaking, increase the viscosity markedly; the tendency of fine capillary tubes to clog; the problem in obtaining satisfactory tubes of sizes small enough to compare with the arterioles and capillaries in the body. Most of the studies of blood have been made on large bore tubes. Bingham and Roepke (6) have gathered many of the observations on human and animal blood. In vitro, whole blood behaves as a viscous fluid—Poiseuille's Law applies—until the diameter of the glass capillary is less than

---

* An alternative hypothesis is that the individual elastic tubes, in the branching system of parallel and series tubes comprising the vascular system, act so that the ratio between pressure and flow of serum or plasma through them remains statistically invariant. This alternative is more difficult to handle rigorously, but appears to lead to the same conclusion. (Application of experimental data is evidently required.) In any case, since it is shown below that the Bingham and Nutting formulas, developed for plastic flow through a single rigid tube (or similar viscometer), describe blood flow in the elastic circulatory system, it is clear that analysis of that system as though it were rigid can be fruitful.

0.20 mm. Then the apparent viscosity of the blood becomes progressively *less* with decreasing capillary diameter, if perfusion pressure is fixed. But with a given tube of small caliber, the apparent viscosity *rises* as the pressure falls below a fairly critical value. This increase in apparent viscosity, reported especially by Hess (11) and Rothmann (21), is almost certainly due to the plastic properties of whole blood. We have found that the most frequently quoted data, those of Rothmann, fit well the Nutting formula for plastic flow. The magnitude of the shifts in apparent viscosity increases as the concentration of red corpuscles rises. Of two tubes, the one with the finer bore will be the first to show a falling off in apparent viscosity compared with the viscosity in large bore viscometers, as the red cell concentration is raised; and the increases in apparent viscosity are larger and occur at higher critical pressures as pressure is reduced with the finer bore capillary.

The fall in apparent viscosity with decreased lumen is not in accord with observations on the viscosity of another suspension. Colophonium in turpentine displays increasing apparent viscosity as tubes with lumens smaller than a critical value are used (1). Thus a 90 per cent suspension has a critical bore of 1.6 cm.; an 80 per cent suspension one of 0.2 cm., using the same pressure. Since flows were very low with the pressure employed, it seems likely that they correspond to the increase in apparent viscosity occurring at low flows with blood, where it deviates from Poiseuille's Law. Still, the apparent viscosity of blood falls rapidly, as smaller lumen viscometers are used, and it is difficult to reconcile this finding with the constancy of viscosity found for the colophonium suspensions before Poiseuille's Law starts to fail. It is likely that the results stated for blood are correct and the differences mentioned will be reconciled.

The influence of shear on suspensions is to rotate the suspended particles as though they were ball bearings, with the axis of the stream rolling on them. Like the ball resting on the jet of a fountain, which serves as a target in shooting galleries, the particles move towards the center of the stream, away from the wall of the tube. As a result of these facts, which have been confirmed experimentally, suspended particles flow axially, in the center of the stream, while the more slowly flowing peripheral stream is almost clear of the suspension. Red cells, in glass capillaries and in living ones, also flow only in the axial stream, as has been frequently noted. Following Poiseuille's original observation, these facts have been utilized to explain the falling off of the apparent viscosity of blood in small tubes: the red cells flow through faster than the plasma, the discrepancy being more pronounced for smaller bore tubes, so that the apparent viscosity is reduced in tubes in which axial streaming is prominent. In them the red cell concentration is considerably reduced from its value in the blood reservoir.

The rheology of blood, in vitro, can be summarized as follows: deviations from Poiseuille's Law occur in the direction of an increased apparent viscosity as perfusion pressure falls; they are more pronounced with smaller tubes and larger concentrations of cells. At higher pressures, while Poiseuille's Law appears to apply to a given tube, the apparent viscosity falls as tubes with bores smaller than a critical size are chosen, and this phenomenon is also accentuated by increased corpuscular concentration.

In vivo properties. Perfusion of animals with whole blood requires careful technique, if conclusions are to have validity. Whittaker and Winton observed the relationship between pressure and blood flow rate in the isolated hindlimb of a dog using a pump-lung preparation and a vasodilator drug, which caused large flows (28). They found that Poiseuille's Law applied to serum quite well, but that, when blood of different erythrocyte concentrations was used, Poiseuille's Law did not apply. Flow was found to be proportional to the difference between perfusion pressure and a constant which depended on the red cell concentration. Their results are represented in Figure 309. The implications of their findings,* which are in complete accord with the simple version of Bingham's formula for the flow of plastic fluids, are that blood must be treated as a plastic fluid, at least in the circulation, and that the vascular resistance, defined as pressure per unit blood flow times viscosity, must be replaced by an index of vessel caliber determined from the appropriate factor in Bingham's formula (or whichever one ultimately is found best), which we now call the hindrance (12).

Other workers have succeeded in obtaining reliable measurements of perfusion in living tissue. Difficulties due to the need for avoiding chilling of blood and tissue, interference from collateral blood vessels, development of edema, settling and agglutination of red cells particularly at low flow rates, change in concentration of proteins and cells in passing through tissue, tox-

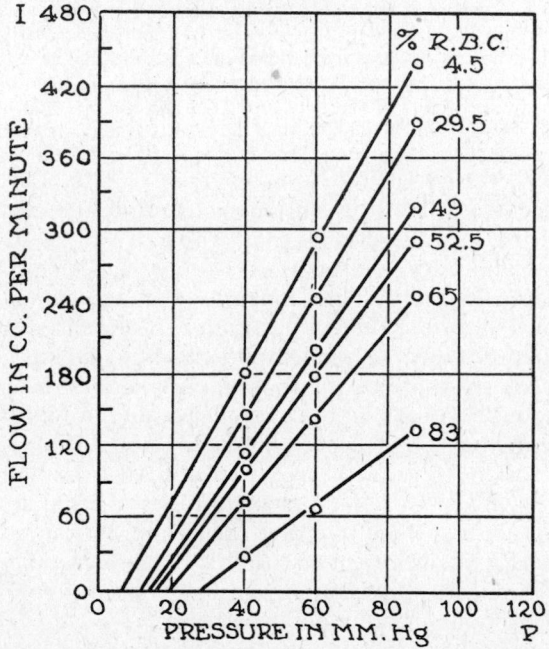

Fig. 309.—The pressure-flow relationship for blood of different hematocrits in the pump-lung perfusion of the hindlimb of a dog. The data fit the equation: $I \propto P - p$, where $p_h = P$ when $I = 0$, for the hematocrit of the blood used. (Redrawn from Whittaker and Winton, *J. Physiol.*, 1933, 78:353.)

icity of manipulated blood, variations in vessel tone,† all have in good part been overcome. Unlike the straight lines found by Whittaker and Winton for the relation between pressure and flow, fairly marked curvature at low pressures has been obtained. It is likely that the flow rates of Whittaker and Winton were abnormally high and were not varied to low enough levels.‡

* Whittaker and Winton note that L. E. Bayliss, in unpublished work, had succeeded in using blood in glass viscometers of a bore comparable to that of arterioles, and had obtained about the same viscosities as those found in their limb preparations (26).

† Green *et al.* (8) have shown clearly that results require interpretation. If pressure is dropped below normal and maintained there, the results shown in Figure 310 are not obtained; instead, a sigmoid curve arises, probably because of reactive hyperemia and possibly, also, because of the number of vessels opened to perfusion changes.

‡ However, in one of Whittaker and Winton's experiments vasoconstriction was caused by pitressin without shift from the linear relationship.

Pappenheimer and Maes (17) and Green and his coworkers (8) report data which are summarized in Figure 310 (a) and (b). It is seen that the curves in Figure 310 (a) asymptotically approach a straight line, which does not pass through the origin: they resemble the curve for plastic flow in Figure 303. The curves in Figure 310 (b) are more curvilinear than those in Figure 310 (a) but show the same general features. The greater the vasoconstriction (or the less the mobility of the blood), the less steep the straight line asymptote and the larger the indicated yield pressure—the pressure to which the straight

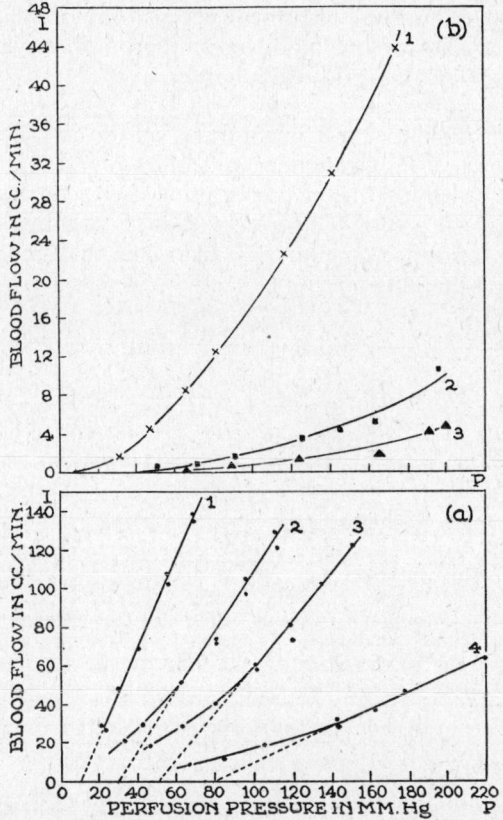

Fig. 310.—Pressure-flow curves for blood perfusion of isolated regions of the dog. (a) Skin and muscle of hindlimb with increasing amounts of adrenaline in the perfusion liquid (2–4); 1 is the control. (Redrawn from Pappenheimer and Maes, *Amer. J. Physiol.*, 1942, *137*:187.) (b) Skin supplied by the saphenous artery during spontaneous changes in vasomotor activity. 1 is the control; 2 is 6 hours later; 3 is 8½ hours after 1. (Little change in the hematocrit occurred.) (Redrawn from Green, Lewis, Nickerson and Heller, *Amer. J. Physiol.*, 1944, *141*:522.)

line asymptote is projected for zero flow. Clearly, Bingham's simplified straight line formula is a good approximation to Pappenheimer and Maes' curves (Fig. 310 (a)) at pressures above 100 mm. Hg and a fair approximation at pressures between 80 and 100 mm. Hg. These results have been criticized by Green and his collaborators on the ground that the blood flow rate considerably exceeded what they consider to be normal values. However, as in Whittaker and Winton's experiments vasoconstriction due to adrenaline produced low flow rates with similar results (Fig. 310 (a)).

In the first hemodynamic application of formulas for plastic flow, Lamport found an indicated yield pressure proportional to the red cell concentration to be a fair approximation (12). In many situations indicated yield pressure can be observed directly from the intercept of the pressure-flow curve. Bingham's formula, using the symbols previously described,

$$Ih = m (P - p),$$

can then be evaluated for p, P, and I. The ratio m/h is the slope of the asymptote of the curves in Figure 310 (a), but with this formula two sets of experimental observations are at present necessary to obtain separate relative values for the mobility of the blood m or the hindrance h, as will be discussed further in the last part of this chapter.*

While the apparent viscosity varies with both pressure and hindrance, it seems that blood mobility, on the contrary, varies very little, as the blood vessels are constricted. Pappenheimer and Maes found that the mobility did not change when their perfusion preparations were constricted with adrenaline,† using perfusion with Ringer's solution as a control to separate the change in vessel resistance or hindrance from any that might have been due to a shift in blood mobility (17).

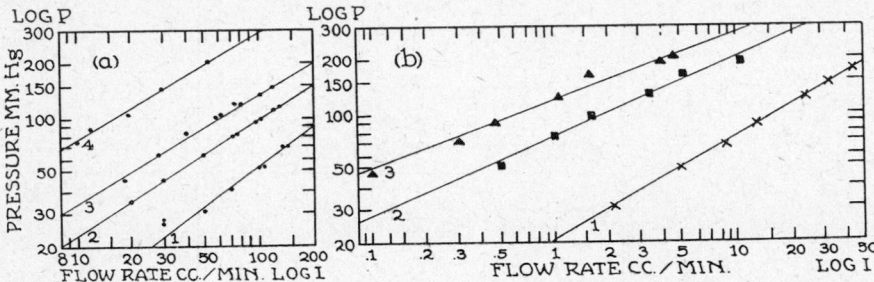

Fig. 311.—This figure corresponds to Figure 310, except that pressure and flow are graphed logarithmically and ordinates and abscissae are interchanged. It is apparent that log I = log constant + k log P fits the data well in both (a) and (b). The lines in (b) are almost parallel (k = 1.41, 1.59, 1.68, 1.78 respectively in 1–4), which indicates that the plasticity of the blood was fairly independent of the vessel tone. The value of the flow I for the extrapolation, P = 1, gives the value of the constant. (Redrawn from Green, Lewis, Nickerson and Heller, *Amer. J. Physiol.*, 1944, *141*:526.)

Green and his collaborators (8) have shown that their pressure-flow data and also Pappenheimer and Maes' can be described by the formula:

$$I = aP^k.$$

The data of Figure 310 are seen in Figure 311, where the linear relationship between log I and log P was demonstrated by Green *et al*. This equation has not been recognized by these workers as the special case of the Nutting formula which applies to plastic flow and which has already been discussed. It does not have the limitations of the Bingham form to pressures above 100 mm. Hg, and must be regarded as the basic equation, replacing Poiseuille's Law, for the flow of whole blood in the vascular system. In certain

* If the evaluation of the indicated yield pressure were accurate enough and an equation relating it to mobility and hindrance were known, the value of m/h from the slope could be solved simultaneously with this equation, thus avoiding the need for two sets of experiments and obtaining absolute values for m and h.

† Some of the observations in this experiment are shown in Figure 310.

applications, where perfusion pressures are high enough or where there is not marked vasoconstriction, Bingham's formula can be used more conveniently as a good approximation; the precise conditions permitting the application of the Bingham form have not yet been elucidated. As we have previously seen, in order for the Nutting formula to reduce to Poiseuille's Law, the constant a must be equated to m/h for $k=1$ (viscous flow). Our fundamental law for blood flow is, then:

$$I = aP^k, \text{ where } a = \text{function of m, h, and k; } a = \frac{m}{h} = \frac{f}{r}, \text{ when } k = 1.$$

The approximation, under conditions which are not yet sharply delineated (in general, for large pressures, low hematocrit, and vasodilation), is:

$$I = \frac{m}{h} (P - p).$$

Unfortunately, the lack of the functional relationship between a and the constants characterizing the blood (mobility m and plasticity k) and the vessels (hindrance, or else the radius and length of the equivalent tube), interfere with the easy applicability of the Nutting formula. Still, in its present form, the Nutting equation must be considered the basic one, replacing Poiseuille's, for describing the flow of whole blood in the vascular system. In certain applications where perfusion pressures are high enough or where there is no marked vasoconstriction, Bingham's formula can be used more conveniently as a good approximation; the precise conditions permitting the application of the Bingham expression have not yet been formulated.

PERIPHERAL RESISTANCE AND HINDRANCE: VASOMOTOR TONE

Peripheral resistance. The resistance of the peripheral blood vessels, defined as the pressure drop along them per unit flow *for blood of given composition*, measures the opposition to blood flow offered to the pumping action of the heart by the blood vessels. It is the functional index of opposition to blood flow. Since the viscosity of blood is less in the vascular system than it is in a large bore glass viscometer and there is no constant proportion between the two, their ratio depending on the hematocrit (26) (and very likely also depending on the viscosity itself and on the degree of vasoconstriction), peripheral resistance can be defined independently of the composition of the blood only when crude approximations are sufficient. In this case, where *blood viscosity* refers to its value in the large bore viscometer,

$$\text{Resistance} = \frac{\text{Pressure drop in blood vessels}}{\text{Blood viscosity} \times \text{Flow rate of blood}}.$$

Since Poiseuille's Law does not apply to blood in the body, the ratio of pressure to flow rate is not constant, even though the vessels do not change in size. Consequently, the peripheral resistance to the circulation of blood is seen to be a variable quantity, dependent both on blood pressure and vessel caliber. While serving as a measure of the relationship between pressure and flow at a particular instant, peripheral resistance cannot be used to predict flow under other conditions of pressure or blood viscosity and it does not measure vessel changes in physical size.

23

Vasomotor tone. The state of the vessels as channels for the passage of blood has been estimated by direct observation. Windows in the skull, the ear of the rabbit, the abdomen—transparent tissues, such as the human nail bed, the intestinal mesentery, the web of the toes of the frog, the eye, all have permitted direct examination of blood vessels and estimations of changes in their caliber—i.e., their vasomotor tone—under various conditions. While having the virtue of being direct, these methods have the disadvantage of utilizing only a very small and special part of the vascular bed. Furthermore, the anatomical changes found are small (Poiseuille found viscous fluid resistance varied inversely as the fourth power of the diameter of the tube) in comparison with their physiological consequences.

If the perfusion pressure is kept constant, changes in vasomotor tone are reflected as changes in blood flow. While qualitative judgments can thereby be formed of shifts in vasomotor tone, quantitation requires the use of a valid formula to replace Poiseuille's Law.

Hindrance. Bingham's formula for flow of plastic substances has been applied to the kidney, for which clinical methods of measuring blood flow are well developed, so that the vasomotor tone of the afferent and efferent arterioles can be estimated. (See *Blood flow through the kidney* in Chap. 38.) This application probably permitted a good approximation, since arterial blood pressure was in the physiological range and because the kidney normally has a very high blood flow rate. It gave the hindrance in terms of measurable or estimable quantities:

$$h = \frac{m\,(P - p)}{I}.$$

The changes in hindrance, being dependent solely on changes in vessel caliber (approximations for indicated yield pressure are available), provided a measure of vascular changes under various physiological and pharmacological circumstances (12, 13).

Pappenheimer and Maes (17), in their pump-lung perfusion of blood through the limb of a dog, in effect used hindrance in the Bingham formula in measuring vasomotor activity, since they took the ratio of increments of pressure to flow, approached asymptotically as pressure increased, which corresponds to the hindrance.

Green and his coworkers (8), while similarly regarding the slope of the asymptote of the pressure-flow curve for the individual's blood (proportional to the hindrance) as the best available measure of vessel tone, suggest that the ratio of the pressures required to obtain a given flow rate with the same blood through the same portion of the circulation under control and experimental conditions estimates approximately the relative vessel tone under these two conditions. When the function defining a in the Nutting equation is known, it may well simplify the estimation of relative hindrance, since two observations determine a and k, and, if the same blood is used, relative changes in vessel tone should probably be determined more simply than is now possible by either of the methods described.

Despite the many complexities inherent in the circulation, an approach to understanding the circulation in terms of physical principles is quite possible. Expanding knowledge of plastic flow will no doubt further elucidate the complicated special case of the pulsating flow of the elastic plastic suspension, blood, in the branching elastic vessels of the living body in which our interest lies. Rapid progress should be possible, since newly designed instruments for measuring easily and accurately the pressure and rate of flow of blood should facilitate experimentation.

REFERENCES

1. BINGHAM, E.C. *Fluidity and plasticity.* New York, McGraw-Hill, 1922. 440 pp.

2. BINGHAM, E. C. and DURHAM, T. C. The viscosity and fluidity of suspensions of finely-divided solids in liquids. *Amer. chem. J.*, 1911, 46:278–298.

3. BINGHAM, E. C. and GREEN, H. Paint, a plastic material and not a viscous liquid; the measurement of its mobility and yield value. *Proc. Amer. Soc. Test. Mater.*, 1919, 19:640–676.

4. BINGHAM, E. C. and ROEPKE, R. R. The rheology of the blood. II. The effect of fibrinogen on the fluidity of blood plasma. *J. Amer. chem. Soc.*, 1942, 64:1204–1206.

5. BINGHAM, E. C. and ROEPKE, R. R. The rheology of the blood. III. *J. gen. Physiol.*, 1944, 28:79–93.

6. BINGHAM, E. C. and ROEPKE, R. R. The rheology of the blood. IV. The fluidity of whole blood at 37° C. *J. gen. Physiol.*, 1944, 28:131–149.

7. GREEN, H. D. Circulation: physical principles. Pp. 208–232 in: GLASSER, O., ed. *Medical physics.* Chicago, Year Book Publishers, 1944.

8. GREEN, H. D., LEWIS, R. N., NICKERSON, N. D. and HELLER, A. L. Blood flow, peripheral resistance and vascular tonus, with observations on the relationship between blood flow and cutaneous temperature. *Amer. J. Physiol.*, 1944, 141:518–536.

9. HALES, S. *Statical essays: containing haemastaticks; or, an account of some hydraulick and hydrostatical experiments made on the blood and blood-vessels of animals.* London, W. Innys and R. Manby, 1733. Vol. 2.

10. HALLOCK, P. and BENSON, I. C. Studies on the elastic properties of human isolated aorta. *J. clin. Invest.*, 1937, 16:595–602.

11. HESS, W. R. Gehorcht das Blut dem allgemeinen Strömungsgesetz der Flüssigkeiten. *Pflüg. Arch. ges. Physiol.*, 1915, 162: 187–224.

12. LAMPORT, H. Formulae for afferent and efferent arteriolar resistance in the human kidney: an application to the effects of spinal anesthesia. *J. clin. Invest.*, 1941, 20:535–544; Charts for osmotic pressure of blood. Application of formulas for renal arteriolar resistance. *Fed. Proc. Amer. Soc. exp. Biol.*, 1942, 1:48; Improvements in calculation of renal resistance to blood flow. Charts for osmotic pressure and viscosity of blood. *J. clin. Invest.*, 1943, 22:461–470.

13. LAMPORT, H. The effects on renal resistance to blood flow of renin, angiotonin, pitressin and atropine, hypertension, and toxemia of pregnancy. *J. clin. Invest.*, 1942, 21:685–695.

14. NAGELI, O. *Blutkrankheiten und Blutdiagnostik*, 4th ed. Berlin, Walter de Gruyter und Co., 1919. xvi, 666 pp.

15. NUTTING, P. G. A new general law of deformation. *J. Franklin Inst.*, 1921, 191:679–685; A study of elastic viscous deformation. *Proc. Amer. Soc. Test. Mater.*, 1921, 21:1162–1168; A general stress-strain formula. *J. Franklin Inst.*, 1943, 235:513–524.

16. NUTTING, P. G. [Personal communication, 1945.]

17. PAPPENHEIMER, J. R. and MAES, J. P. A quantitative measure of the vasomotor tone in the hindlimb muscles of the dog. *Amer. J. Physiol.*, 1942, 137:187–199.

18. POISEUILLE, J. L. M. Recherches sur les causes du mouvement du sang dans les vaisseaux capillaires. *C. R. Acad. Sci., Paris*, 1841, 7:105–175; Recherches experimentales sur le mouvement des liquides dans les tubes de très-petits diamètres. *Ibid.*, 1846, 9:433–544.

18a. RALSTON, H. T. and TAYLOR, A. N. Streamline flow in the arteries of the dog and cat. *Amer. J. Physiol.*, 1945, 144:706–710.

19. RASHEVSKY, N. A problem in the mathematical biophysics of blood circulation: I. *Bull. Math. Biophysics*, 1945, 7:25–33; A problem in the mathematical biophysics of blood circulation: II. Relation between pressure and flow of a viscous fluid in an elastic distensible tube. *Ibid.*, 35–39.

20. REYNOLDS, O. An investigation of the circumstances which determine whether the motion of water shall be direct or sinuous, and of the law of resistance in parallel channels. *Philos. Trans.*, 1883, 174:935–983.

21. ROTHMANN, M. Ist das Poiseuille'sche Gesetz für Suspensionen gültig? *Pflüg. Arch. ges. Physiol.*, 1914, 155:318–348.

22. SCOTT BLAIR, G. W. and COPPEN, F. M. V. The measurement of the "firmness" of soft materials in industrial use. *J. Soc. chem. Ind., Lond.*, 1941, 60:190–196.

23. SCOTT BLAIR, G. W. and CAFFYN, J. The classification of the rheological properties of industrial materials in the light of power-law relations between stress, strain and time. *J. sci. Instrum.*, 1942, 19:88–93.

24. TREFFERS, H. P. The viscosity-fluidity relations of proteins. *J. Amer. chem. Soc.*, 1940, 62:1405–1409.

25. WEZLER, K. and BÖGER, A. Die Dynamik des arteriellen Systems. Der arterielle Blutdruck und seine Komponenten. *Ergebn. Physiol.*, 1939, 41:292–606.

26. WHITTAKER, S. R. F. and WINTON, F. R. The apparent viscosity of blood flowing in the isolated hindlimb of the dog, and its variation with corpuscular concentration. *J. Physiol.*, 1933, 78:339–369.

CHAPTER 31

THE VELOCITY AND PRESSURE OF BLOOD FLOW

BY ERIC PONDER

The Circulation as Seen under the Microscope. By selecting a suitable region in the web of the frog's foot, the frog mesentery, or the mesentery of a small mammal such as the mouse, it is possible to observe the flow of blood in arteries and arterioles, capillaries, and veins in the same low power field of the microscope. The first thing which strikes the observer is the different rate of flow in the various vessels. In the arteries and arterioles the rate is very rapid and somewhat intermittent; there is a slight acceleration, or pulse, corresponding to each heart beat. In the capillaries, which branch off from the smaller arterioles in various directions, the flow is much slower and its rate more variable; in open capillaries one can see the red cells moving along at a more or less uniform rate, whereas the few red cells contained in the closed capillaries remain motionless. Under ordinary conditions, no pulsation is observed in the capillaries. In the veins the rate of flow becomes rapid again, and the larger the vein the more rapid the flow. Normally there is no indication of a pulse, and the velocity of flow is uniform.

In both arteries and veins, the red cells accumulate in a column in the middle of the vessel, and move in an *axial stream* which is separated from the walls of the vessel by a much more slowly moving *inert layer* of clear plasma containing no cells except an occasional leukocyte or platelet. This results from the fact that the velocity of flow in arteries and veins, like that in any tube, is greatest in the axis of the stream and slowest near the walls, because there the frictional resistance is greatest. The red cells (density 1.10), being heavier than the plasma (density 1.027), are drawn into the rapidly moving axial stream, while the lighter leukocytes (density 1.060) remain near the periphery. Under conditions of inflammation, leukocytes may be found in the inert layer in large numbers because the stickiness of the vessel wall becomes increased, and the white cells tend to adhere to it.

There is no axial stream in the capillaries, which are often so narrow that they can scarcely accommodate the red and white cells which have to pass along them. The red cells, carrying their oxygen, thus come into very close contact with the capillary endothelium.

Velocity and Volume of the Blood Flow. These microscopical observations show that the velocity of blood flow varies widely, being rapid in the arteries and veins and slow in the capillaries. Special experimental methods are necessary for finding the velocity of flow in the larger vessels, and these employ a variety of *stromuhrs* or flowmeters. The simplest stromuhr is that devised by Ludwig in 1867. The principle used is that of cutting an artery or vein of known size and determining the amount of blood which flows out in a given time. This cannot, of course, be done on the living animal without some special device, for, quite apart from the continuous blood loss first modifying the beat of the heart and eventually proving fatal, no peripheral resistance would be encountered by the blood as it issued from the cut vessel, and so the experimental conditions would be highly artificial. What can be done, however, is to allow the blood to flow from one end of the cut vessel into the stromuhr and to return it from the stromuhr into the other end of the cut vessel. In this way no blood is lost, and the flow, from vessel to stromuhr and from stromuhr to vessel again, encounters the full peripheral resistance offered by the vascular bed.

Ludwig's stromuhr (Fig. 312) consists of two glass bulbs which communicate with each other at the top, and which are supported by a spindle mounted on a movable horizontal plate which can be turned on a lower fixed plate

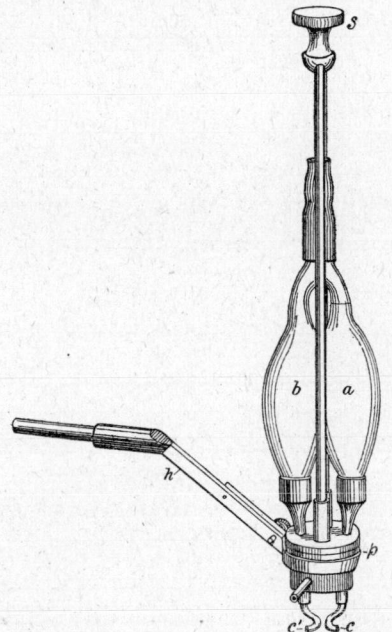

Fig. 312.—Ludwig's stromuhr. *a* and *b*, the glass bulbs; *c* and *c'*, the cannulae inserted into the cut ends of the vessel; *p*, the movable plate upon which the stromuhr is turned by twisting the screw *s*; *h*, the holder. For a description of the use of the instrument, see text.

by twisting the spindle through 180 degrees. From the lower fixed plate go two tubes which end in cannulae; one of these communicates with one of the bulbs, and the other with the second, through apertures in the fixed and moving plates. The cannulae are inserted into the two ends of the cut vessel through which the velocity of the blood flow is to be measured, the cannula communicating with bulb *a* of the stromuhr being connected to the proximal end of the vessel. The ends of the vessel are temporarily clamped off. Before use, one of the bulbs (*a*) of the stromuhr is filled with oil to a mark engraved near its top; the volume of the oil (and of the blood which is to replace it) is exactly 5 cc. The other bulb (*b*) and the remainder of the communicating neck are filled with saline. The clamps are then removed from the vessel, and blood flows from the proximal end of the vessel into the bulb *a*, displacing the oil over into the neck and bulb *b* and pushing the saline out of bulb *b* into the distal end of the vessel. At the moment when the blood reaches the engraved mark at the top of bulb *a*, the bulbs are switched around by twisting the spindle; bulb *b*, containing the oil, is now where bulb *a* was, and bulb *a*, containing the blood, is on connection with the distal end of the vessel. Now blood flows from the proximal end of the vessel into bulb *b* and drives its oil into bulb *a*, and the blood in bulb *a* is driven out into the distal end of the vessel. When the inflowing blood again reaches the mark, the stromuhr is rotated again; this brings the bulbs back into their original position, with bulb *a* containing the oil and connected to the proximal end of the vessel and bulb *b* connected to the distal end. The process of turning the instrument every time the entering blood reaches the mark at the top of the bulb which is receiving it is repeated again and again. In this way blood is transferred in 5 cc. portions from the proximal end of the vessel to the distal end.

Suppose that the stromuhr has to be turned 10 times in 50 seconds; 10 × 5 cc. of blood have then flowed through it in 50 seconds, or 1 cc. per sec. Now the velocity of blood flow at any point is defined as the length of the column which flows past that point in a second, and the length of a column is equal

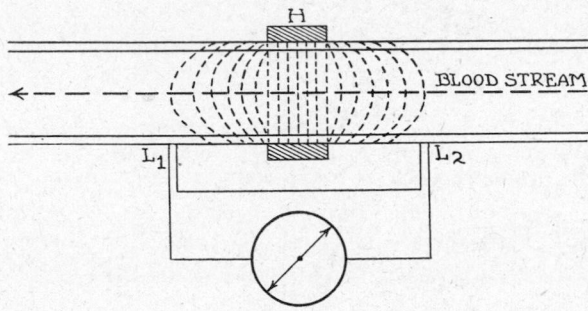

Fig. 313.—Diagram of Rein's thermostromuhr. *H*, the heating electrodes applied to the outside of the vessel; L_1 and L_2, the two thermojunctions leading to a galvanometer. Description in text.

to its volume divided by its cross-sectional area. The cross-sectional area of the vessel through which the blood flows can be found by measuring its radius r, the cross-sectional area being πr². Suppose that the radius is 1 mm.; the cross-sectional area then is 3.14 mm.² As the volume passing through the stromuhr in 1 second is 1 cc. or 1000 mm.³, the length of the column is 1000 mm.³/3.14 mm.², or 317 mm. The velocity of the blood flow in this case is accordingly 317 mm. per sec.

Other types of stromuhr. Several types of stromuhr based on the same principle as Ludwig's stromuhr, some of them driven electrically, have been devised. In addition to these, there are several kinds of stromuhr which depend on quite different principles.

In *Rein's thermostromuhr* (15), which is applied to the outside of the unopened vessel, a small diathermy unit heats the blood lying between two heating electrodes (*H* in Fig. 313). Two thermojunctions, one placed upstream and the other downstream, record the temperatures at L_1 and L_2 through a recording galvanometer. The difference in temperature is a function of the velocity of blood flow, and becomes smaller as the rate of flow increases. An improved form of the instrument, designed for use with unanesthetized animals and for continuous observation, has been described by Baldes, Herrick and Essex (1).

The *hemodromograph* of Chauveau (Fig. 314, A) consists of a rigid tube *ab* which is placed in the course of the vessel through which the rate of the flow of blood is to be measured.

The tube is provided with a side tube *c*, the end of which is covered with a piece of rubber dam *r*. A needle *n*, the lower end of which terminates in a plate *p* lying in the tube broadside to the direction of flow, passes through the rubber dam, and the movements of its upper end *e* can either be measured directly on a scale or transmitted to a tambour *t* and thence to recording apparatus. The flow of blood through the tube *ab* gives rise to a pressure on the plate *p* and deflects the needle, which turns on its insertion through the rubber dam as a fulcrum. The deflection is a function of the rate of flow, being great when the rate of flow is great, but if the velocities are required in absolute units, the instrument has to be calibrated for known rates of flow of liquids of the same viscosity as that of blood. The hemodromograph possesses an advantage over a stromuhr such as Ludwig's in that it measures small variations in velocity of flow associated with the heart beat, rapid changes in peripheral resistance, etc., instead of only mean velocities over periods of time amounting to half a minute or more.

The *photohematachometer* of Cybulski is illustrated diagrammatically in Figure 314, B. The end *a* of a right-angled tube *ab* is attached to the proximal end of a cut vessel, and the end *b* to the distal end of the vessel. The tube *ab* has side tubes *c* and *d* connected with each other at their upper ends. The connecting tube has an inlet at the top through which

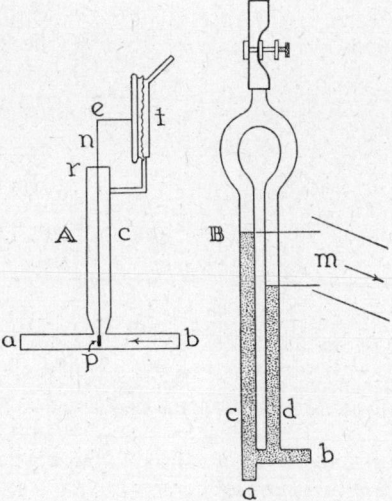

Fig. 314.—A, Chauveau's hemodromograph; B, Cybulski's photohematachometer. For description see text.

the instrument can be partially filled with saline. Because the momentum of the flowing blood is added to the lateral pressure in tube *c*, whereas only the lateral pressure is exerted in the direction of the tube *d*, the pressure in *c* will exceed that in *d*. This will result in fluid in *c* rising to a greater height than that in *d*, the difference in height being proportional to the velocity of blood flow. By means of a narrow slit of light, the images of the fluid menisci in *c* and in *d* are thrown on moving photographic paper *m* to give a permanent record from which the differences in fluid level can be measured. If absolute values of velocity of flow are required, the instrument requires to be calibrated. Like the hemodromograph, the photohematachometer records small and rapid variations in the rate of flow.

The *electromagnetic flowmeter* (13), developed by Kolin and independently by Wetterer, depends on the principle that when an electrical conductor, in this case the column of blood in the vessel, moves across the lines of force of a magnetic field, a potential difference is developed in the conductor, and under certain conditions which can be fulfilled in practice this potential difference is proportional to the rate of blood flow. A uniform magnetic field is applied to the outside of the unopened vessel either by an electromagnet or a permanent magnet, and the potential developed is drawn off from the walls of the vessel through nonpolarizable electrodes. As the potential is small, it has to be amplified by a suitably constructed amplifier, which is coupled to a recording galvanometer or oscillograph. The hemodromograph and the photohematachometer are now largely of classical interest, while the thermostromuhr and the electromagnetic flowmeter are becoming more and more widely used.

Mean Velocity of Blood Flow in Arteries, Veins and Capillaries. It can be observed that the velocity of blood flow in the arteries becomes smaller the further one goes from the heart, and that it reaches its minimum value at the point where the arterioles pass into the capillaries (Fig. 315). Thus in the arteries of the horse we have the following figures for the rate of flow per sec.: carotid, 300 mm.; maxillary, 232 mm.; metatarsal, 56 mm.

The flow in the carotid and other large arteries, however, is not uniform, for there is an acceleration or pulse at each ventricular systole. During systole the velocity may reach 520 mm. per sec., while it may fall to 150 mm. per sec. during diastole. It is also found that this difference between rate of flow during systole and that during diastole tends to disappear as the arteries become smaller, so that it disappears altogether when the capillary regions are reached, and no pulse is observed there normally. The smaller the artery, therefore, the more uniform is the rate of blood flow in it.

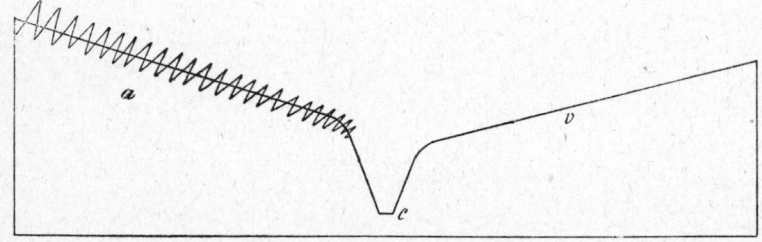

Fig. 315.—Diagrammatic representation of the relative velocities of the blood flow in different parts of the vascular system. *a*, the arterial side, showing the variations of velocity with each heart beat and the fall in mean velocity as the bed widens; *c*, the capillary region, with a great diminution in velocity corresponding to the great widening of the bed; *v*, the venous side, showing the gradual increase in velocity in the direction of the heart.

The flow in the large veins is approximately uniform as one approaches the heart, although the velocity in the large veins near the heart is somewhat less than that in the large arteries of the same region because the total area of the venous bed is larger than that of the arterial bed. As in the case of the arteries, the smaller the vein the smaller the velocity of flow of the blood in it (Fig. 315); we have, for example, the following values for various sized veins in the dog: jugular, 147 mm./sec.; femoral, 61.6 mm./sec.; mesenteric, 84.9 mm./sec., and renal, 63 mm./sec. The mean rate of blood flow in the capillaries is estimated as being from 0.5 mm. to 1.0 mm. per sec., but is very variable from capillary to capillary. The values are usually obtained by measuring the time taken by individual red cells to traverse known lengths of capillary.

An ingenious method for measuring the rate of the blood flow in the capillaries of the human retina is due to Vierordt. Under certain conditions of illumination, the movement of the red cells in the retina can be perceived because they cast shadows on the rods and cones. The images thus produced can be seen by the individual as projected images if he looks at a surface such as a white wall. The distance covered by a moving red cell in the retina can then be calculated from the relation

$$ab = \frac{AB \times an}{An}$$

where *ab* is the distance traversed on the retina, *AB* the distance covered by the projected image, *An*, the distance of the surface from the nodal point of the eye, and *an* the distance of the retina from the nodal point (Fig. 316). Using this method, Vierordt calculated the velocity of the blood flow in the capillaries of the human retina to be about 0.6 to 0.9 mm. per sec.

Explanation of differences in velocity of flow. The principal reason for the velocity of the blood flow being so different in different blood vessels is that there are differences in the total width of the vascular bed at different distances from the heart, and that (as in the case of a river) the flow becomes slower as the bed widens. At this point, the student must be careful not to confuse the width of *individual* vessels with the *total* width, or cross-sectional area, of all the vessels of the same kind, and it is the latter which determines the mean velocity. Thus in the systemic circulation the main stem, the aorta, branches into arteries which, taken individually, become smaller and smaller as we approach the capillaries, but each time an artery branches the sum of the cross-sectional areas of the two branches is *greater* than that of the vessel from which they are derived. The arterial system, indeed, may be compared to a tree, in which the sum of the cross-sectional areas of all the little twigs is much greater than that of the trunk. In flowing towards the capillaries,

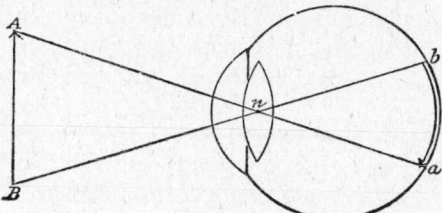

Fig. 316.—Diagram of the eye to show how the size of the retinal image is found from the size of the projected image. For description see text.

the blood accordingly flows through a bed which becomes wider and wider, and similarly, as it returns from the capillaries towards the heart, it flows through a bed which becomes progressively narrower. For this reason the mean velocity of flow decreases as we go from the large vessels towards the capillaries, and increases again as we go from the capillaries towards the large veins (Fig. 315). The sum of the cross-sectional areas of all the capillaries of the systemic circulation has been estimated to be about 800 times as great as that of the aorta, and so the rate of flow in the aorta would be expected to be about 800 times as rapid as that in the capillaries. This is approximately true (rate in aorta, 320 mm./sec.; rate in capillary, 0.4 mm/-sec.; ratio, 1 to 800).

While this is the explanation of the major differences in the rates of flow in arteries, capillaries and veins, the velocity of flow in any given vessel varies whenever any of the conditions affecting the blood flow vary. The average velocity in the large arteries, for example, depends on the force and rate of the heart beat, and also on the peripheral resistance to the blood flow offered by the smaller arteries and arterioles. In 1881 Marey summarized the effect of these factors as follows: whatever increases or diminishes the force with which the blood is driven from the heart towards the periphery causes the velocity of the blood and the pressure in the arteries to vary in the same sense;

whatever increases or diminishes the resistance offered to the blood in passing from the arteries (or veins) causes the velocity and the arterial pressure to vary in an inverse sense as regards each other, i.e., an increased resistance diminishes the velocity in the arteries and increases the pressure, and vice versa.

Circulation Time. In many physiological investigations it is necessary to have an approximate idea of the length of time which the blood takes to make a complete circuit of the vascular system, i.e., how long it takes the blood which leaves one spot to return again to the same spot. Unfortunately the problem is complicated by the fact that there are many paths by which the blood may go, so that the time required for a complete circulation depends on the route followed. For example, blood leaving the left ventricle may pass through the coronary vessels to the right side of the heart and then through the pulmonary system to the left ventricle again, or it may go to the extremities of the toes before returning to the heart, or it may pass through the vessels of the intestines, in which case it has to traverse three sets of capillaries (intestinal, hepatic, and pulmonary) before reaching the left ventricle. If we were to inject a substance such as a dye into the ventricle and await its re-appearance in the ventricle, the "circulation time" which would be measured would be that corresponding to the shortest circuit. For this reason, the term "circulation time" is usually qualified by stating the points between which the measurement is made, e.g., "vein to tongue circulation time," and the normal values which are obtained depend on the points selected.

Circulation time in man is measured by injecting a dye (usually fluorescein) into a vein in one arm, and observing the time taken for it to appear in samples of blood withdrawn every 5 seconds from a vein in the opposite arm. In this case the dye traverses the heart, the pulmonary circulation, and the arteries and capillaries of the arm in succession before it appears in the venous sample. The average circulation time obtained by this method is 21 seconds, with a variation of from 12 to 26 seconds. The circulation time from arm to foot and vice versa is from 1 to 2 minutes. Alternatively, one can inject histamine into an arm vein and measure the time which elapses before flushing of the face begins (18), or one can inject glucide or decholin into an arm vein and measure the time required for the drug to travel to the tongue in which it produces a sudden sensation of sweetness. This gives the "vein to tongue" circulation time (10). In this case, as in the case of the method in which histamine is injected, the drug circulates through the heart, the pulmonary vessels, and the vessels of the neck and face, the response (flushing or the sensation of sweetness) signaling its arrival in the capillaries of the face or tongue. The circulation time as measured in this way averages 24 seconds. Other methods (2) employ the injection of a radioactive substance into a vein and its detection, by a Geiger counter, as it arrives in an unopened artery in the other arm; this arm vein to arm artery circulation time averages 18 seconds.

The pulmonary circulation time, or the time taken by the blood to pass through the pulmonary circulation, is measured by injecting a radioactive substance into the vein of one arm and determining the time taken for it to reach the brachial artery at the elbow of the other arm. From this is subtracted the "arm vein to heart" circulation time (about 6 seconds), and, since the time taken for the blood to pass from the heart through the aorta and subclavian artery to the brachial artery at the elbow is not more than 1 second, the remainder is taken as being a very good approximation to the pulmonary circulation time. The average value is 11 seconds. Alternatively, a small quantity of cyanide may be injected into the vein of the arm and the time taken for its arrival at the carotid sinus measured. The arrival of the drug at the carotid sinus is signaled by a sudden stimulation of respiration (16).

Volume of Blood Flowing through an Organ. If there is a single vessel taking blood to or from an organ, the blood flow through the organ can be measured by inserting a stromuhr in the vessel and observing the rate of flow of blood in it. Table 20 gives the blood supply per minute per 100 grams of tissue for a variety of organs and regions (5). The figures are arranged in order of increasing magnitude.

Table 20. Volume of Blood Flowing through an Organ

Posterior limb	5 cc.	Spleen	58 cc.
Skeletal muscle	12 cc.	Liver (venous)	59 cc.
Head	20 cc.	Liver (total)	84 cc.
Stomach	21 cc.	Brain	136 cc.
Liver (arterial)	25 cc.	Kidney	150 cc.
Intestines	31 cc.	Thyroid	560 cc.

The total volume of blood which flows through an organ in a given time should not be confused with the rate of flow in the individual vessels. The former varies directly with the fourth power of the radius of the vessel, whereas in a vessel of varying radius the latter varies inversely with the square of the radius. Under conditions of vasodilatation, the total volume of blood flowing through an organ is in general increased, but the velocity of flow in the small arterioles and in the capillaries may be decreased.

In the *plethysmographic method* of Brodie (3), the organ is enclosed in a plethysmograph (p. 693), and the venous return is occluded for a short period of time. During this time the blood continues to flow into the organ, the volume of which increases. The increase in volume can be measured by the plethysmograph, and is obviously equal to the amount of blood which has flowed into the organ during the brief period of venous occlusion. The method has been applied to the human hand and forearm, the venous return being cut off by a cuff placed around the upper arm.

Pressure in the Vascular System. It has long been known that the blood in the vascular system is under pressure and that the pressure is different in different parts. When an artery is cut, the blood flows out in a forcible jet with spurts corresponding to each heart beat; when a vein is cut, on the other hand, the flow shows no pulsations and has little force. Measurements of the hydrostatic pressure of the blood were first published by the Reverend Stephen Hales (12), an English clergyman, in 1733. He describes one of his experiments as follows:

"In December I caused a Mare to be tied down alive on her Back, she was fourteen Hands high, and about fourteen Years of Age, had a Fistula on her Withers, was neither very lean, nor yet lusty: Having laid open the left crural Artery about three Inches from her Belly, I inserted into it a brass Pipe whose Bore was one sixth of an Inch in Diameter; and to that, by means of another brass Pipe which was fitly adapted to it, I fixed a glass Tube, of nearly the same Diameter, which was nine Feet in Length: then untying the Ligature on the Artery, the Blood rose in the Tube eight Feet three Inches perpendicular above the Level of the left Ventricle of the Heart. . . When it was at its full Height, it would rise and fall at and after each Pulse two, three, or four Inches; and sometimes it would fall twelve or fourteen Inches, and have there for a time the same Vibrations up and down at and after each Pulse, as it had, when it was at its full Height; to which it would rise again after forty or fifty Pulses."

A similar experiment made on a vein showed a rise of only 12 inches. Hales drew the following inference from his experiment: "The real Force of the Blood in the Arteries, depends on the Proportion, which the Quantity of blood thrown out of the left Ventricle in a given time, bears to the Quantity which can pass through the capillary Arteries [arterioles and capillaries] into the Veins, at that time." As we would put it, the arterial pressure depends on (i) the rate and force of the heart beat, and (ii) the peripheral resistance.

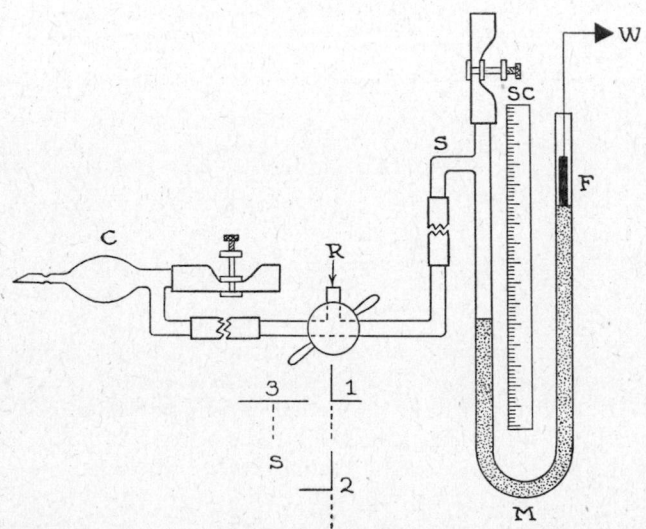

Fig. 317.—Recording mercury manometer and its connections. *M*, the manometer with float *F* and writing point *W*. The levels of the mercury are read off on a scale *sc*. *S*, details of the stopcock which is connected by rubber tubing to the side tube of the manometer *s*. The stopcock is connected to a reservoir of citrate solution *R*, about 6 feet above the level of the manometer. Three positions of the stopcock are shown: *1*, for raising the pressure in the manometer; *2*, for flushing out the cannula; and *3*, for recording. *C*, the cannula, connected to the stopcock by a length of rubber tubing.

Methods of recording blood pressure. The disadvantages of Hales' method are the length of the tube and the liability of the blood to clot in it. Poiseuille in 1823 overcame both these difficulties when he attached a mercury manometer, instead of a straight tube, to the artery by means of a cannula and connecting tube filled with an anticoagulant (sodium bicarbonate). Since mercury is 13.5 times as heavy as blood, the column of mercury which the blood pressure would support in Hales' experiment would be $\dfrac{8 \text{ ft. } 3 \text{ in.}}{13.5}$, or 7.3 inches (183 mm.) instead of the 8 foot 3 inch column of blood in his straight vertical tube. In 1847 Carl Ludwig added a float with a writing point to one limb of the mercury manometer, and, by arranging for the point to write on a moving surface, recorded the movements of the mercury, i.e., the variation in blood pressure, on the first *kymograph*.

Figure 317 shows a recording mercury manometer and its connection with the artery. One limb of the U-shaped manometer and the tubes connecting it with the vessel are filled with sodium citrate (or bicarbonate), while the other limb carries the writing point. The connecting tube leads to a three-way stopcock and thence to a cannula, which is constructed so that small clots can easily be washed out. The pressure in the artery displaces the mercury in the limb connected to it and raises it in the other limb. The difference in height between the two mercury levels measures the blood pressure in mm. Hg. The difference can be read either directly on a scale or from the permanent kymographic record (Fig. 318). To find the height of the column of blood which would be supported at any blood pressure, the pressure as recorded in mm. Hg would have to be multiplied by 13.5.

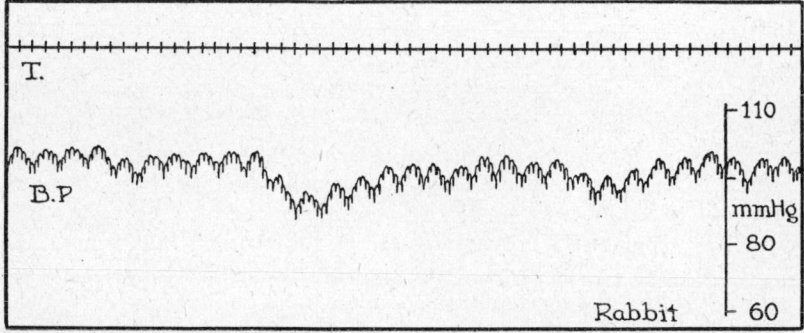

Fig. 318.—Typical blood pressure record with mercury manometer. *B.P*, the record showing the heart beats and the larger curves due to the respiration (respiratory waves of blood pressure) and still longer waves due to vasomotor changes; *T*, the time line, giving the time in seconds. The actual arterial pressure at any moment is the distance from the base line—that is, the line of zero pressure—to the blood pressure line, multiplied by two. These values are indicated in the vertical line drawn to the right, which shows the average pressure at the time of the experiment was 100 mm. Hg. The small size of the variations in pressure due to each heart beat is altogether a false picture due to the inertia of the mercury and its inability to follow the quick change completely. Each heart beat, instead of being lower, should be higher than the respiratory waves.

The blood pressure record (Fig. 318) usually shows large rhythmic variations corresponding to the respirations, and smaller waves due to the heart beat. Because of the inertia of the heavy mercury column, however, the waves in the records obtained with mercury manometers do not correspond faithfully to the smaller blood pressure variations. When the heart is beating slowly, the maximum arterial pressure as read with this instrument is too high and the minimum pressure too low; while when the heart is beating rapidly, the maximum pressure recorded is too low and the minimum pressure too high. As a result, the oscillations of the mercury manometer do not give true values for the maximum and minimum pressures, i.e., for the systolic and diastolic pressures respectively. The extent of the larger pressure variations, however, are recorded with entire accuracy. For this reason, mercury manometers are most useful for recording the considerable variations in pressure which result from vasoconstriction and vasodilatation; and when we require to follow the rapid pressure changes accompanying the heart beat (the "pressure pulse"), we use a different kind of recording instrument.

The effects of inertia are largely done away with by arranging for the changes in blood pressure to produce movements of a small membrane instead of the heavy mercury column. A cannula is tied into the artery and connected by a rigid tube to a very small chamber roofed in with a rubber membrane (Fig. 319). The cannula, connecting tube, and chamber are filled with an anticoagulant fluid (3 per cent sodium citrate), and the movements of the membrane are magnified by a system of levers which works against a spring to prevent "overthrow." The membrane manometer must be calibrated in order to give absolute values to the records obtained. The earliest manometer of this type was introduced by Hurthle in 1891, and the original design has undergone many modifications. In the present day pressure pulse manometers (p. 685), the dimensions of the chamber and the mass and elastic properties of the membrane (now made of thin sheet metal) are arranged so as to give maximum fidelity of recording, and the system of levers is replaced by a mirror attached to the membrane, a beam of light reflected from it, and photographic recording.

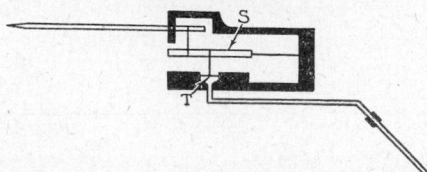

Fig. 319.—Construction of Hurthle's manometer. T, tambour with membrane of rubber; S, compound lever working against a spring (not shown).

Systolic, diastolic and mean arterial pressure. The arterial blood pressure undergoes rapid and extensive changes at each heart beat, and it is these changes which produce the smaller waves seen in the blood pressure tracing (Fig. 318). The maximum pressure caused by the systole of the heart is called the *systolic pressure;* this is synchronous with the apex of the pulse wave in the artery in which the measurement is made. The minimum pressure, which occurs at the bottom of the pulse wave, is called the *diastolic pressure.* In man the systolic pressure as measured in the brachial artery is about 120 mm. Hg, while the diastolic pressure is about 70 mm. The difference between the systolic and diastolic pressures, about 50 mm., is called the *pulse pressure*, and measures the variation in pressure, in any given artery, caused by the heart beat. So far as that artery is concerned, it also gives the force of the heart beat except for a small component used to accelerate the column of blood; each cardiac systole accordingly extends the brachial artery by a sudden increase in pressure equal to the weight of a column of mercury about 50 mm. high. As we go outwards along the arterial tree the pulse pressure becomes less and less and the oscillation in pressure with each heart beat smaller and smaller, until finally when we come to the smallest arteries and the capillaries, there is no pulse wave and no pulse pressure.

The arithmetical mean of the systolic and diastolic pressures, e.g., (120 + 70)/2 = 95, is called the *mean pressure*. It can also be obtained by adding half the pulse pressure to the diastolic pressure, e.g., 70 + 50/2 = 95. It is of some interest in physiological experiments, because it is an approximation to the pressure which would assure a *steady* flow of the same amount of blood as actually passes through a vessel under the variable pressure conditions associated with the cardiac cycle. The mean pressure is obviously largely determined by the diastolic pressure, and usually varies with it.

The arithmetical mean of the systolic and diastolic pressures during any one heart beat does not give the mean pressure exactly, because of the form of the pulse wave. If the rise from diastolic to systolic pressure and the succeeding fall took place uniformly, so that the pulse curve was a triangle, the true mean pressure would be the mean of the diastolic and systolic pressures. The descending limb of the pulse curve, however, is not a straight line but a curve broken by secondary waves, and so the true mean pressure during any one heart beat is dependent on the form of the pulse wave.

Data as to the mean pressure in arteries, veins and capillaries. The mean pressure in the aorta has been determined for many mammals, and varies greatly according to the conditions (particularly as regards anesthesia) under which the experiments are done. The following values give an idea of the range of variation:

Horse	321 mm. to 150 mm. Hg	
Dog	172	104
Sheep	206	156
Cat	150	..
Rabbit	108	90

There seems to be no relation between the size of the animal and the mean arterial pressure, although the pulse pressure may vary with the size of the animal's heart.

As we pass from the aorta to the smaller arteries, the mean pressure decreases, although not very rapidly, and at the same time the pulse pressure decreases. When the arterioles are reached, the mean pressure falls off rapidly and the pulse pressure becomes much reduced. Finally, when we reach the capillaries, we observe a great decline in mean pressure (20–30 mm. Hg), and the pulse pressure disappears altogether. Figure 320 illustrates these general relations of mean pressure and pulse pressure to the part of the vascular system in which they are measured.

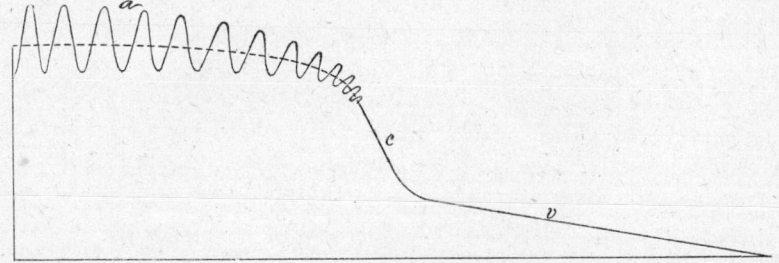

Fig. 320.—Diagrammatic representation of the relations of blood pressure in different parts of the vascular system. *a*, arteries; *c*, capillaries; *v*, veins. The variations in pulse pressure, growing less as the arterioles are approached, are indicated by the oscillating line.

The pressure in the veins is lowest in the vena cava and increases as we go toward the capillary regions; it has been estimated that the fall in pressure from the periphery towards the heart is at the rate of 1 mm. Hg for every 35 mm. of distance. In the great veins near the heart the lateral pressure of the blood on the vessel walls is accordingly very small, and as these great veins lie in the thoracic cavity in which the pressure is 2 to 6 mm. Hg below that of the atmosphere, the blood pressure in them is characteristically negative with respect to that of the atmosphere. This negative pressure acts as a factor which favors the flow of blood towards and into the heart, and at each inspiration, during which the negative pressure in the thorax and therefore in the great veins becomes still more negative, the blood is sucked from the extrathoracic veins into the intrathoracic veins.

The pressure in the capillaries (see p. 615) may be measured either directly by inserting a micropipette into the vessel and connecting it to a manometer, or indirectly by observing the pressure required to cause the collapse of the skin capillaries. The indirect methods are none too exact, but all the results of methods which attempt to measure capillary pressure show that it varies within wide limits. Pressures of from 0.5 mm. to 54 mm. Hg have been recorded. Much of the variation is due to the fact that there is a very steep pressure gradient between the arteriolar end of the typical capillary and its venous end. The difference in pressure may amount to 20 mm. or more, and

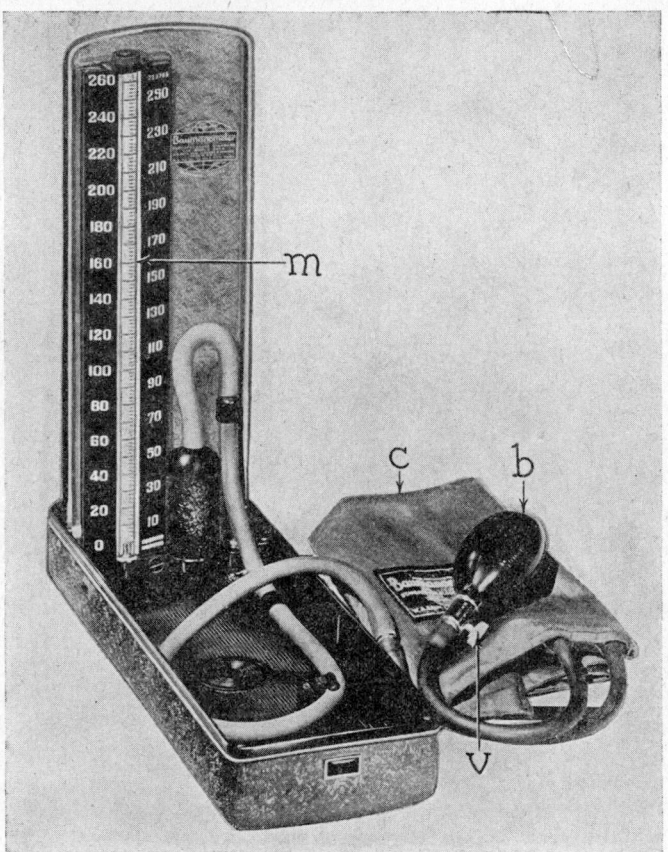

Fig. 321.—A modern sphygmomanometer. *m*, mercury column and scale; *b*, pressure bulb; *v* needle valve; *c*, cuff. (Photograph through the courtesy of W. A. Baum Co., Inc., New York.)

so the capillary pressure recorded depends on the distance along the capillary, starting from the arteriolar end, at which the measurement is made.

Blood pressure in the large arteries of man. Since an artery has to be opened in order that the blood pressure may be recorded by the mercury manometer or any of the various forms of pressure pulse manometers, these instruments are rarely used for measuring the blood pressure and its variations in man except for observations under experimental conditions (6). The instrument universally used for the purpose is the *sphygmomanometer*, of which there are many different models. Essentially, the instrument (Fig. 321) consists of an inflatable cloth-covered rubber bag b, which fits snugly around the upper arm, and which is held in position by wrapping an extension of the cloth covering over the bag and about the arm like a bandage. The bag communicates with a mercury manometer m, and can be inflated by a pressure bulb p. On the tube leading from the bulb to the bag there is a needle valve v which can be opened gradually to allow air to escape and the pressure in the bag to fall.

To measure the blood pressure by the *auscultatory method*, the bag is secured in position on the upper arm and the pressure in it is raised to a point well above the systolic blood pressure. The pressure in the bag, outside and pressing on the brachial artery, is then greater than the systolic pressure within the artery, and so the lumen of the vessel is completely obliterated. A stethoscope is now applied over the brachial artery just below the lower edge of the bag, and the needle valve is slowly opened so as to let the pressure in the bag fall. At the moment the pressure in the bag falls to a point at which a pulse wave can break through the compressed artery, a distinct tapping sound is heard with the stethoscope at each pulse beat, and the level of the mercury manometer at this moment indicates the systolic pressure. As the pressure in the bag falls, the sounds heard in the stethoscope undergo changes in character and intensity.

In the normal individual, the changes in the sounds heard as the pressure in the manometer falls occur in four phases, known as the *sounds of Korotkow*, after the physician who first described them in 1905 (8). The sounds in the successive phases are described as follows:

Phase 1. Sudden appearance of a clear, sharp, tapping sound, which becomes louder during the first 10 mm. fall in pressure. Its first appearance corresponds to the *systolic* pressure.

Phase 2. The sound becomes softer, like a murmur, during the next 15 mm. fall in pressure.

Phase 3. The sound becomes louder again during the next 15 mm. fall in pressure.

Phase 4. The sound becomes suddenly reduced in intensity and develops a muffled quality. This corresponds to the *diastolic* pressure.

If the pressure in the bag is lowered still further, the sounds disappear altogether. There has been considerable discussion as to whether the true diastolic pressure corresponds to the abrupt drop in intensity of the sound in the fourth phase, or to its complete disappearance. The sudden muffling and the complete disappearance may occur at two quite different pressures, in which case the diastolic pressure corresponds to the sudden muffling rather than to the disappearance. It may be remarked that there is little practical value in trying to record the pressures at which each of the auscultatory phases pass into each other. It is usually sufficient to ascertain the systolic and the diastolic pressures, and these only. We conventionally write the systolic and diastolic pressures as 120/70, 130/90, and so on.

In the *palpatory method*, the pressure cuff is secured around the upper arm as before, and the pressure in it raised until the radial pulse, as felt at the wrist, is obliterated. The pressure is then slowly lowered by opening the needle valve, and the point at which the radial pulse reappears is taken as the systolic pressure. The method is not exact, and the true systolic pressure is usually 5 to 10 mm. higher than that at which the reappearance of the pulse takes place. Further, the diastolic pressure cannot be measured by the palpatory method. It is standard practice, however, first to find the systolic pressure roughly by the palpatory method, and then to use the stethoscope to determine the systolic and the diastolic pressures.

The *oscillometric method* depends on the following principle. When the pressure in a cuff applied to a limb, outside the artery, exceeds the systolic pressure in the artery itself, the artery collapses and there are no oscillations of its walls. As the outside pressure is lowered, a point is reached at which the pressure inside the artery is just greater than that outside in the cuff, and at this point oscillations in the pressure begin to appear. This marks the systolic pressure. As the pressure in the cuff is still further lowered, the oscillations become larger and larger until they suddenly disappear when the pressure in the cuff is less than the smallest pressure in the artery, i.e., less than the diastolic pressure.

In the Pachon oscillometer (14), the oscillations of the arterial walls are measured by the use of a special cuff containing two rubber bags, one for varying the pressure on the artery and the other for transmitting the oscillations to an aneroid manometer. In the Tycos oscillometer the oscillations are recorded by a writing device on a moving circular chart, thus providing a permanent record.

Unfortunately the appearance and disappearance of the oscillations are often not sudden, but gradual, so that there is great difficulty in determining the systolic pressure, the diastolic pressure, or both. The method finds its principal use in the study of obstructive arterial disease of the extremities.

These modern oscillometers are derived from the apparatus designed by Erlanger (7) for measuring the systolic and diastolic arterial pressures by recording the pulsations of an artery under a pressure cuff on the smoked surface of a kymograph. The Erlanger apparatus employs a cuff which is applied to the upper arm and which can be inflated to above the systolic pressure. With the pressure in the cuff above the systolic level, the artery is completely compressed, but the pulsations in the stump above the cuff are transmitted to a tambour by a lever writing on the moving smoked surface, thus giving a record of the pulse waves. The pressure in the cuff is then reduced 5 mm. at a time by opening a stopcock, and records of the pulse are taken at each pressure level. As in the case of other oscillometers, the systolic pressure level is marked either by a sudden increase in the size of the pulse wave, or (as there is an actual tracing of it) by a spreading of its limbs. On lowering the pressure in the cuff further, larger and larger pulse waves are recorded, and the level at which the waves are maximal (or just beginning to decline) marks the diastolic pressure. The Erlanger apparatus has been replaced by modern oscillometers largely because of its bulk.

Normal arterial blood pressure. At birth the arterial blood pressure is only about 20 to 60 mm. Hg, but at the end of the first month it is 70 to 80 mm. It increases steadily thereafter, so that the average normal systolic pressure of young male adults, as measured in the brachial artery, is about 120 mm. Hg, while the average diastolic pressure is about 80 mm. Hg. The values vary under a variety of physiological conditions.

The influence of *age* on the systolic, diastolic and pulse pressures is shown in Table 21, which is compiled on the basis of Hunter's observations of the average values in healthy Americans (9).

It will be noticed that there is a sharp increase in the systolic pressure about the time of puberty. After the age of 20 there is a steady rise in both systolic and diastolic pressures as age advances. Sex differences in the way in which the arterial pressure varies with age have been observed. In girls the sharp increase at puberty is less marked and is often followed by a decrease until the eighteenth year, after which the increase is steady as age advances, although the absolute values are about 10 mm. less than in the male. After the menopause the systolic pressure tends to be a little higher than that in the male.

Emotional states, such as fear, excitement, and worry, increase the arterial pressure. The increase affects the systolic pressure particularly, but also the diastolic pressure. The effect is due to the increased rate and stroke volume of the heart, to peripheral vasoconstriction, or to both, and may be partly accounted for on the basis of an increased output of adrenaline. During restful sleep, on the other hand, the systolic pressure falls some 10 to 30 mm. Anxiety or excitement is frequently responsible for the first of a series of blood pressure determinations being spuriously high.

Table 21. Influence of Age on Blood Pressure

Age	Systolic Pressure	Diastolic Pressure	Pulse Pressure
10	103	70	33
15	113	75	38
20	120	80	40
25	122	81	41
30	123	82	41
35	124	83	41
40	126	84	42
45	128	85	43
50	130	86	44
55	132	87	45
60	135	89	46

Exercise raises both the systolic and the diastolic pressures, but more particularly the former. To some extent, the increase is of the same nature as that which occurs as a result of excitement, for it may begin as soon as the individual even thinks of exerting himself. The maximum increase in pressure is roughly proportional to the severity of the exercise, the minute output of the heart being roughly proportional to the O_2 consumption of the individual during the period of exertion. When the exercise ceases, there is a sudden drop in the systolic pressure, probably due to the relaxation of the abdominal muscles, and this is followed by a secondary rise, which again is roughly proportional to the exertion and which continues for several minutes. The increases in arterial pressure are accompanied by a general increase in the rate of the circulation, and in the rate of supply of oxygen to the active, and recovering, tissues.

The diastolic pressure is always lower when the individual is lying down than when he is standing, and, when in the upright position, the pressure in the femoral artery is greater than that in the brachial artery. This is a gravitational effect (see below). When the individual stands or sits up, the systolic pressure usually increases less than does the diastolic, so that the pulse pressure becomes somewhat less. A small increase in the systolic pressure (5–10 mm.) occurs after meals.

Essential hypertension: hyperpiesia. This is a condition characterized by an abnormally high blood pressure, both systolic and diastolic, in persons in whom inflammatory kidney disease, urinary obstruction, and other known causes of high blood pressure can be eliminated. The term probably covers a number of conditions. In hyperpiesia the systolic pressure may rise to between 200 and 300 mm. Hg, and the diastolic to 140 mm. Hg or more. Diagnosis of the condition rests on the blood pressure measurements.

Hypertension can be produced experimentally in animals by impairing the renal circulation by means of a clamp applied to the renal artery and tightened up gradually so as to produce progressive degrees of ischemia (deprivation of blood supply) in the kidney concerned. Moderate interference with the blood supply results in hypertension, while severe deprivation is followed by impairment of kidney function as well (11). The hypertension results from peripheral vasoconstriction, brought about by the action of a pressor substance circulating in the blood. This pressor substance is called *angiotonin* or *hypertensin*, and is believed to be produced by the interaction of *renin*, an enzyme-like substance from the kidney, and an activator, *renin-activator*, present in plasma. Angiotonin is a crystalline substance which produces a rise in blood pressure when injected into the intact animal; the response to its injection, however, is greater in animals with an ischemic kidney than in those with intact kidneys, and so it is inferred that there is also an *anti-angiotonin* or an *angiotonin-inhibitor*. Substances antagonizing the effects of angiotonin can be extracted from the normal kidney. The extent to which essential hypertension in man is dependent on this renal pressor mechanism is not yet settled, for there is evidence that certain types of essential hypertension are neurogenic in origin.

Gravitational effects. The arterial blood pressure in man is almost always measured in the brachial artery. While this artery is selected for convenience, it also happens that it is situated at the level of the heart when the arm is hanging by the side. At any level other than that of the heart, the weight of the column of blood in the vessel acts in the same direction as the arterial blood pressure if the level is below the heart, and opposes it if the level is above the heart. For example, when a person is standing up, the pressure in the femoral artery is greater than that in the brachial artery, and the difference (50–60 mm. Hg) is the same as the pressure of an imaginary column of blood which would reach from the one artery to the other. When the person lies down, the difference disappears.

In the case of the arteries above heart level, the expected difference in pressure due to gravity is not usually observed because the effects of gravity are compensated for in the upper part of the body, so that the brachial or carotid pressures are as great (or even greater) when the individual is erect as when he is lying down. The principal compensatory mechanism consists in vasoconstriction of the vessels of the splanchnic area, and in this way an adequate blood pressure in the vessels of the brain is assured. In some animals, however, the compensatory mechanisms are poorly developed or lacking altogether. A rabbit, which is an animal accustomed to walk on all fours, can be killed by simply holding it in the vertical position for some minutes. The blood flows into the vessels of the splanchnic area under the effect of gravity, and neither splanchnic vasoconstriction nor the contraction of the lax abdominal walls are sufficient to prevent it from accumulating there until the animal dies of cerebral anemia or from an insufficient return of blood to the heart.

In some otherwise normal individuals, the compensatory splanchnic vasoconstriction mechanism is less active than usual, and these persons are very sensitive to the sudden assumption, or the prolonged maintenance, of the vertical position. They feel giddy and faint as a result of a fall in blood pressure, which may amount to from 25 to 30 mm. Hg and produce a momentary unconsciousness. Persons who have been confined to bed experience the same symptoms when first they try to walk. When an individual is unconscious or under an anesthetic, the normal compensatory mechanisms may be in abeyance, and raising him to the vertical position may then result in such a reduction in the amount of blood returned to the heart as to prove fatal.

In the venous system the effects of gravity are even more striking than they are in the arterial system. This is partly because the venous pressure is much lower than the arterial, partly because the veins are much more distensible than the arteries, and partly because the venous columns upon which gravity

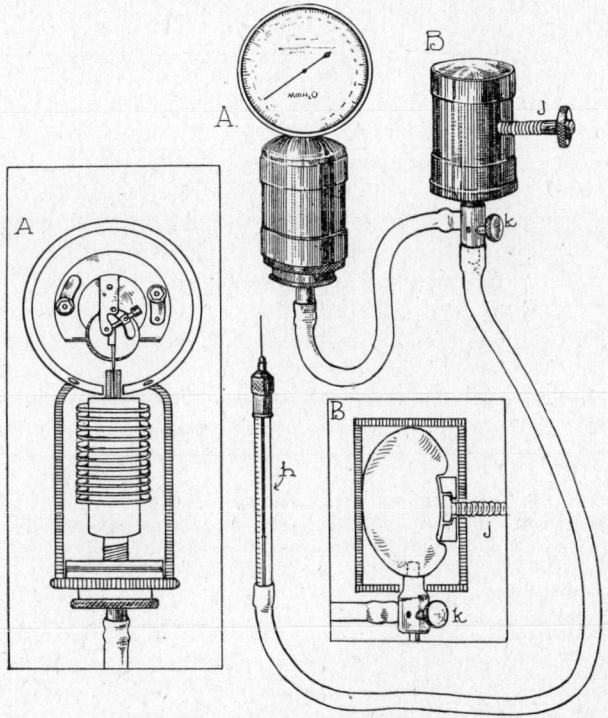

Fig. 322.—Diagram of the phlebomanometer. *A*, the aneroid manometer; *B*, pressure chamber with screw *j* for varying the pressure; *k*, needle valve; *n*, glass adapter holding hypodermic needle. (Through the courtesy of Dr. G. E. Burch, School of Medicine, Tulane University.)

acts to impede the blood flow (feet to head) are greater than the corresponding arterial columns in which gravity acts to impede arterial flow (heart to head). Again we have a number of compensatory mechanisms which operate to offset the effects of gravity on the venous pressure of man and most mammals, although in some animals these are poorly developed or lacking. Thus the distensibility of the venous walls is reduced by their being supported by the pressure arising from the contraction and tonus of the muscles of the abdominal walls and of the lower limbs, while the vasomotor tone of the veins and venules of the splanchnic area tends to prevent blood from accumulating there. In addition, the gravitational effect is opposed by the sucking effect which results from the increase in negative pressure in the thorax during inspiration, and to this may be added the "massaging effect" of the contraction of voluntary muscle, though the importance of the latter has recently been questioned (17). If these compensatory mechanisms fail, the force of gravity tends to prevent the flow of blood from the dependent parts towards the heart, and the venous system of the body and the lower limbs tends to become distended and engorged. The greater part of the gravitational effect disappears, of course, when the individual is recumbent.

Measurement of venous pressure. The simplest method for measuring venous pressure in man is that described by Gaertner in 1903. The arm is allowed to hang by the side until the veins fill with blood, and is then slowly raised until the veins on the back of the hand just begin to collapse. The height above the level of the heart at which this collapse occurs gives the venous pressure in mm. of blood (which is very nearly the same as mm. of water) in the right auricle, since the arm vein is substantially a manometer tube ending in the auricle. The venous pressure as measured in this way is usually about 50 mm. of water, or $50/13.5 = 3.7$ mm. Hg.

More satisfactory measurements are obtained with a venous pressure manometer such as that of von Recklinghausen described in 1906, or the modification suggested by Hooker in 1908. A small glass chamber, sealed with collodion to the skin overlying a vein in such a way as to be airtight, is connected to a pressure bulb and a water manometer. The pressure in the chamber is raised until the vein collapses; the pressure registered by the water manometer then equals the venous pressure. Even more satisfactory results can be obtained by inserting a hypodermic needle, connected to a water manometer, directly into the vein, and with an apparatus such as the *phlebomanometer* (Fig. 322) the pressure in various superficial veins, both large and small, can be measured.

In Burch and Winsor's phlebomanometer (4) a very sensitive aneroid barometer is used to measure the pressure. A rubber tube leads to a glass adapter which holds the hypodermic needle, and the tube also communicates with a small pressure chamber, the pressure in which can be varied by turning a screw. By reducing the pressure in the chamber, a little sodium citrate solution is drawn up into the needle to form a meniscus in the glass adapter. The needle is then inserted into the vein, the pressure in which causes blood to enter the needle and move the meniscus further along the glass adapter. The pressure in the pressure chamber is increased until the meniscus assumes its original position; the pressure as registered on the aneroid barometer now measures the venous pressure.

In the venous system the gravitational effects are very marked, and the venous pressure measured by any of the manometric methods depends on the position of the vein. Thus when the hand hangs by the side, the pressure in its veins is greater than when it is at heart level, the difference being the pressure of the column of blood reaching, vertically, from the heart level to the level of the hand vein in which the measurement is made. To minimize the gravitational differences, measurements of venous pressure are usually made with the subject lying down, and are referred to heart level by determining the vertical distance of the vein from the level of the heart and subtracting, or adding, this distance in cm. from the venous pressure as measured in cm. of water. "Heart level" for the recumbent individual is the level of a plane parallel to the anterior surface of the body and passing midway between the dorsal aspect of the thorax and the xiphoid process (19); if the individual is sitting up, the reference level is a plane passing horizontally through the fourth intercostal space at its junction with the sternum.

Measurement of venous pressure in man under basal conditions, i.e., lying down for at least 15 minutes before the measurement is made, show that there are considerable variations in different individuals. The pressure in the median basilic vein, for example, varies between 40 and 100 mm. of water after being corrected for differences from the reference plane of the heart. Conditions under which the blood flow is increased cause only a temporary rise in venous pressure, for normally the heart meets the greater demand by increasing its rate, its diastolic volume, and its stroke volume, and thus is able to transfer a greater amount of blood from the venous side of the circulation to the arterial side. A sustained elevation of venous pressure points clearly to myocardial insufficiency.

Venous pressure in heart failure. When the cardiac muscle is unable to transfer the usual amount of blood (normally about 60 cc. per stroke) from the venous side of the circulation to the arterial side, there results (i) a deficit of blood on the arterial side, and (ii) an accumulation of blood on the venous side. Under some circumstances ("forward failure" as in fainting or other forms of syncope) it is the deficit on the arterial side which gives rise to symptoms (low blood pressure, unconsciousness, and sometimes sudden death), but more frequently symptoms are due to the accumulation of blood on the venous side; the condition is then known as "backward failure" or *congestive heart failure*.

Suppose that this failure begins at the left ventricle, which becomes unable to transfer the usual amount of blood from the pulmonary veins to the aorta and the systemic circulation. Blood then accumulates in the veins and capillaries of the lungs, and this gives rise to *dyspnea* or shortness of breath, due to impulses which pass up to the medulla through the afferent vagi and stimulate the respiratory center. Along with the dyspnea goes a diminution in *vital capacity*, because the accumulated blood prevents the filling of the lungs with air, and *cyanosis* because oxygen cannot diffuse sufficiently rapidly to oxygenate the blood in the congested lung capillaries. Sometimes the venous pressure in the pulmonary capillaries becomes so great that the dyspnea passes into *pulmonary edema*, in which the alveoli of the lungs are filled with edema fluid. If the congestion and pressure in the pulmonary circuit is so high that the right ventricle cannot adequately transfer blood from the venous side of the circulation to the pulmonary vessels, a new set of symptoms, all due to the accumulation of blood in the systemic veins, make their appearance. These are congestion of the veins of the neck and of the liver and spleen, *peripheral edema* due to an increase in the venous pressure, and therefore of the filtration pressure in the capillaries, in dependent parts such as the ankles, scanty urine because so much of the body water is immobilized in the form of edema fluid, and sometimes the extreme forms of edema, *ascites* (accumulation of fluid in the peritoneal cavity) and *hydrothorax* (accumulation of fluid in the pleural cavities).

Accessory factors aiding the circulation. While the circulation of the blood is primarily dependent on the force of the heart beat, this and this alone could scarcely maintain the blood flow as it occurs in the intact animal. The force of the heart is almost entirely spent in overcoming the frictional resistance in the arterioles and capillaries, so that the blood issuing from the capillaries into the veins does so under a pressure of only some 40 to 80 mm. of water (3–6 mm. Hg), while that arriving at the right auricle is under a pressure of only about 5 mm. of water. The flow of blood towards the heart is aided in the intact animal by three factors which operate on the venous side of the circulation: (i) the respiratory movements, (ii) the tonus and contraction of voluntary muscle, and (iii) the contraction of the involuntary muscle of the viscera.

(i) During inspiration the pressure in the thoracic cavity falls to about

80 mm. of water below that of the atmosphere, and this negative pressure acts as a force which stretches the thin walls of the intrathoracic veins and draws blood into them. At the same time the downward movement of the diaphragm during inspiration puts pressure on the abdominal viscera and their veins; the arrangement of the valves in the femoral veins at their entry into the pelvis prevents the venous blood from being forced backwards into the lower extremities, and so the increased abdominal pressure pushes the blood from the abdominal veins towards the thorax at the same time as the inspiratory sucking force is at its greatest. This sucking force is not so great during expiration, at the end of which the intrathoracic pressure is only about −35 mm. of water, but it is always present as a force which tends to move the blood in the venous system towards the heart. One speaks, indeed, of the *effective venous pressure* in the thoracic veins, this being the sum of the negative pressure within the thoracic cavity (e.g., −80 mm. of water at the end of inspiration) and the pressure which would be measured in the thoracic veins themselves (e.g., 5 mm. of water) if the thorax were open and its contents at atmospheric pressure. It is this compound force which is the force causing the blood to move towards the heart.

The system of large veins in the thorax and abdomen, i.e., the superior and inferior venae cavae and the innominate, hepatic, renal and iliac veins, constitute a *venous cistern*, the capacity of which is about 500 cc. This cistern is shut off, so far as the blood flow away from the heart is concerned, from the veins of the arms by the valves in the subclavian veins, from the veins of the head and neck by the jugular valves, and from the veins of the lower extremities by the valves in the femoral veins. On inspiration blood is sucked from this venous cistern into the intrathoracic veins, and the valves prevent backflow during expiration.

A similar but oppositely directed effect of the changes in intrathoracic pressure on the venous inflow ought to be demonstrable in the arterial system. Each inspiration, with its fall in intrathoracic pressure, should retard the flow of blood from the intrathoracic arteries into the extrathoracic ones. The effect, however, is exceedingly small, because of the thickness and rigidity of the arterial walls in comparison with those of the veins.

(ii) When voluntary muscle contracts, the thickened fibers press on the capillaries and venules and empty them into the veins. When the muscles relax, blood enters them from their arterial side because the blood pressure on the arterial side is high, whereas that on the venous side is low; reflux of blood from the veins is also prevented by the valves in the veins. Each contraction of the muscle accordingly propels blood along the venous system so that the contracting muscle acts as a kind of accessory heart. This pumping action of the muscles is important in returning blood from the lower extremities and in counteracting the gravitational effect, for the venous pressure in a foot vein is not more than a fraction of the pressure of the column of blood which it supports. During exercise, the pumping effect of the muscles is greater than at rest because their contractions are more frequent and extensive, but even the steadily maintained tonus of the resting muscle is a factor aiding the circulation, in that it opposes the dilatation of the smaller venous channels which would otherwise occur under the action of gravity.

(iii) The contraction of the involuntary musculature of the stomach and intestines, particularly during digestion, also squeezes blood out in the direction of the heart and so assists the circulation, at least locally. The musculature of the spleen is supposed to aid the circulation through that organ by its rhythmical contractions.

REFERENCES

1. BALDES, E. J., HERRICK, J. F. and ESSEX, H. E. A modification in the thermostromuhr method of measuring flow of blood. *Proc. Soc. exp. Biol., N. Y.*, 1933, *30*:1109–1111.

2. BLUMGART, H. O. and YENS, O. C. Studies on the velocity of blood flow. I. The method utilized. *J. clin. Invest.*, 1927, *4*:1–31.

3. BRODIE, T. G. and RUSSELL, A. E. On the determination of the rate of blood-flow through an organ. *J. Physiol.*, 1905, *32*:xlvii–xlix.

4. BURCH, G. E. and WINSOR, T. The phlebomanometer: a new apparatus for directing measurement of venous pressure in large and small veins. *J. Amer. med. Ass.*, 1943, *123*:91–92.

5. BURTON-OPITZ, R. The vascularity of the liver. III. The effect of stimulation of single nerves of the hepatic plexus upon the flow in the hepatic artery. *Quart. J. exp. Physiol.*, 1911, *4*:103–125.

6. DAMESHEK, W. and LOMAN, J. Direct intra-arterial blood-pressure readings in man. *Amer. J. Physiol.*, 1932, *101*:140–148.

7. ERLANGER, J. A new instrument for determining the minimum and maximum blood-pressures in man. *Johns Hopk. Hosp. Rep.*, 1904, *12*:53–110.

8. ERLANGER, J. Studies in blood pressure estimation by indirect methods. II. The mechanism of the compression sounds of Korotkoff. *Amer. J. Physiol.*, 1916, *40*:82–125.

9. GAGER, L. T. *Hypertension*. Baltimore, Williams & Wilkins, 1930. 158 pp.

10. GARGILL, S. L. The use of sodium dehydrocholate as a clinical test of the velocity of blood flow. *New Engl. J. Med.*, 1933, *209*:1089–1093.

11. GOLDBLATT, H. Experimental hypertension induced by renal ischemia. *Harvey Lect.*, 1937–38, *33*:237–275.

12. HALES, S. *Statical essays: containing haemastaticks; or, an account of some hydraulick and hydrostatical experiments made on the blood and blood-vessels of animals.* London, W. Innys and R. Manby, 1733. vol. 2.

13. KOLIN, A. An electromagnetic flowmeter. Principle of the method and its application to blood flow measurements. *Proc. Soc. exp. Biol., N. Y.*, 1936, *35*:53–56. An a-c induction flowmeter. *Ibid.*, 1941, *46*:233–239.

14. PACHON, V. Sur la methode des oscillations et les conditions correctes de son emploien sphygmomanometrie clinique. *C. R. Soc. Biol., Paris*, 1909, *64*:733–735.

15. REIN, H. Die Thermo-Stromuhr. Ein Verfahren zur fortlaufenden Messung der mittleren absoluten Durchflussmengen in uneröffneten Gefässen in situ. *Z. Biol.*, 1928, *87*:394–418.

16. ROBB, G. P. and WEISS, S. The velocity of pulmonary and peripheral venous blood flow and related aspects of the circulation in cardiovascular disease. *Amer. Heart J.*, 1934, *9*:742–763.

17. ROBERTS, FF. Return of blood to the heart. *Lancet*, 1945, *248*:209–211.

18. WEISS, S., ROBB, G. P. and BLUMGART, H. L. The velocity of blood flow in health and disease as measured by the effect of histamine on the minute vessels. *Amer. Heart J.*, 1929, *4*:664–691.

19. WINSOR, T. and BURCH, G. E. Phlebostatic axis and phlebostatic level, reference levels for venous pressure measurements in man. *Proc. Soc. exp. Biol., N. Y.* 1945, *58*:165–169.

CHAPTER 32

THE PULSE

BY WILLIAM F. HAMILTON

When the pressure generated by cardiac contraction forces some 60 cc. of blood into the aorta, room must be made for the additional volume either by moving the whole mass of blood forward and pushing an equal amount out through the capillaries into the venous side of the circulation, or by an enlargement of the arteries and a stretching of their elastic walls. Less pressure is required to enlarge the arteries than to move the whole mass of blood forward under the conditions which normally exist in the body, and so the walls of the aorta become stretched as soon as the column of blood leaves the ventricle and enters the aorta through the open semilunar valves. The column of blood, however, is still under pressure, and this is transmitted rapidly along the whole arterial system. At every point in its progress it is accompanied by a stretching of the arterial walls and by a local enlargement of the vessel, as well as by an acceleration in the onward flow of blood. At the end of the contraction of the ventricle, all the arteries are beginning to enlarge, and with the closure of the semilunar valves the elastic recoil of the stretched aortic wall continues to drive the column of blood onwards. As the aorta returns towards its original size during diastole, the more distal portions of the arterial system are undergoing their distension; and after being stretched to a certain point these, too, return to their diastolic size as the excess of blood streams through the capillaries into the veins. In this way the distension caused by the emptying of the contents of the ventricle into the aorta spreads peripherally throughout the whole arterial system in the form of a wave, which may be felt as the pulse.

If the blood vessels were rigid tubes instead of being extensible and elastic, the pressure created by the contraction of the ventricle would be transmitted almost instantaneously through the system, and an equal quantity of blood would be displaced from the vena cava into the right auricle at almost the same instant as the left ventricle delivered its contents into the aorta. The flow of blood in the vessels would then take place in a series of spurts during each of which the pressure would suddenly rise during systole and fall to zero during diastole. A pulse would be observed in such a rigid system, but it would occur simultaneously in all of its parts, and the pressure would be maintained only during the contraction of the heart. It is the extensibility and elasticity of the walls of the blood vessels which determines that the pulse is transmitted as a wave, modifies the abruptness of the pressure changes and converts what would otherwise be an intermittent flow of blood into a continuous flow.

The pulse pressure, for reasons to be considered later, increases as the pulse wave approaches the arterioles. Beyond the arterioles the flow ceases to be pulsatile and the flow through the capillaries is steady, although if the arterioles are sufficiently dilated the pulse may spread through the capillary bed and be visible in the veins. A venous pulse produced in this way may sometimes be observed on the back of the hand during sleep (11).

Velocity of the pulse wave. The pulse wave would spread virtually instantaneously through all parts of a system of vessels with rigid walls, while in a system of vessels with distensible walls it spreads as a much more slowly propagated wave; by an extension of the same idea, we now find that the *velocity of the pulse wave* depends on the *degree* of distensibility of the arterial walls. Thus it comes about that the rate of pulse transmission is usually regarded as a measure of the distensibility of the artery, for the more rapidly the pulse is transmitted, the more rigid the artery must be. If D is the percentage distensibility of the artery per mm. Hg increase in pressure and V_p the velocity of the pulse wave in meters per second, the relation between D and V_p is, approximately (2),

$$D = \frac{12.7}{(V_p)^2}$$

The fact that the pulse wave in man is propagated from the heart outwards can be determined by simple palpation. If one feels the pulse in the carotid and radial arteries, it is obvious that the wave arrives first in the artery nearer

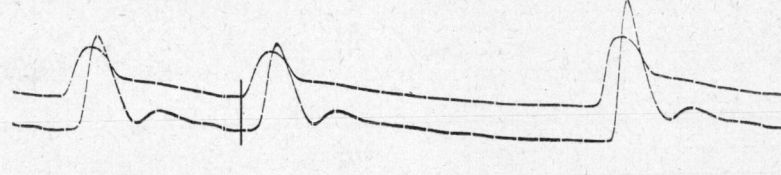

Fig. 323.—Optical tracings of pressure pulsations in the femoral and dorsalis pedis artery. The records are interrupted 12 times per sec. The vertical line marks the rise of the femoral pulse which is followed by the rise in the dorsalis pedis pulse. Diastolic pressure is alike in the two arteries but systolic pressure is 35 mm. Hg higher in the dorsalis pedis. Note dropped beat.

the heart. In the case of the blood vessels of man as they exist at any particular moment, the velocity of the pulse wave can be estimated by a very simple method. Two arteries are selected at different distances from the heart, e.g., the femoral and the dorsalis pedis, and the pulse wave as it passes by a given point on each artery is recorded on a rapidly moving photographic surface. The distance between the two points is measured, and the time lag in the arrival of the pulse measured as indicated in Figure 323. The light beams making the three lines are interrupted simultaneously every 1/12 second and the lower beam for a longer time every second. The time lag is thus 0.05 second, and the distance between points 75 cm. The pulse wave velocity through the leg arteries of this subject is then approximately 15 meters per sec. The unusually high velocity in this subject is due to arteriosclerosis and hypertension.

The velocity of the pulse wave varies between 5 and 9 meters per sec. in normal man, and is greater in the peripheral vessels than in the aorta, being 7.5 meters per sec. and 4.5 meters per sec. respectively (1). It is slowest of all in the arch of the aorta, which appears to be the most distensible part of the vascular system (1, 5). Howell's determinations in medical students show that the velocity in the leg (femoral and anterior tibial arteries) is 6.1 meters per sec. when the records are taken from the same leg, but 7.4 meters per sec. when the record for the femoral is taken from one leg and that for the anterior tibial from the other. This difference would no doubt have been minimized if the femoral receiver had been placed highly enough so as not to obstruct flow in the artery and hence reduce its pressure. Any condition which renders the arteries more rigid increases the velocity of the pulse wave. The velocity accordingly increases with age, and Bramwell, Hill and McSwiney (3) found a speed of 5.2 meters per sec. at the age of five years and one of 8.6 meters per sec. at the age of eighty-four. Elevation of the blood pressure as a result of exercise stretches the blood vessels nearer to their elastic limits, and so the velocity of the pulse wave is increased; vasodilatation or low blood pressure, on the other hand, has just the opposite effect. The condition of arteriosclerosis, in which the rigidity of the arteries and arterioles is increased, is accompanied by an increase in the velocity of the pulse wave.

Sphygmographs. The pulse wave may be felt on any superficial artery in consequence of the distension of the vessel, and by the tactile sense alone the experienced physician can distinguish some of the characteristics of the wave—its regularity, its frequency, its force, etc. The details of the form of the wave, however, are made evident only when the variations in the size of the artery are recorded graphically.

A sphygmograph may be defined as an instrument designed to record the movements of the skin which are due to the pulsations of the artery beneath. The pulsations of the artery are due to changes in pressure in its lumen but are not quantitatively proportional to the pressure because at high pressures the artery is less distensible than at low pressures. The upper parts of the surface pulse is therefore a foreshortened replica of the pressure pulse. The pressure pulse is measured by a manometer (see below) as distinguished from a sphygmograph which is used to record the surface pulse.

Mechanical sphygmographs were in use during the nineteenth century in research laboratories, but at present they should be used only to get qualitative impressions in student laboratory work. The defect of these instruments consists in the large inertia of the writing lever which can be lessened only at the expense of shortening the lever and decreasing the sensitivity of the instrument.

The inertia of the lever causes each quick movement to be delayed in its recording and to be followed by an overfling, often by two or more afterswings of the lever. These distortions have no real meaning in the form of the pulse, but unfortunately this fact was not recognized by the earlier workers. They developed an elaborate nomenclature for the waves which were superimposed upon the pulse curve by their inadequate instruments. Thus, an anacrotic pulse was one with distinct undulations on the upstroke; a catacrotic pulse was one with distinct undulations on the descending limb. A dicrotic pulse was one with two peaks. Speculations were even ventured as to the height of the blood pressure from the degree of dicrotism and the flatness of the diastolic part of the curve.

Modern sphygmographs use optical levers instead of mechanical levers. The sensitivity of the apparatus can be increased indefinitely without increasing the inertia. It is customary to hold a small funnel (Fig. 324) over the pulsating artery. As the artery bulges the skin into the funnel, the air within the system is compressed slightly, which causes the delicate rubber membrane tied over the end of the capsule to bulge and the mirror to tip, giving a deflection of the light beam which records the movements of the skin over the artery. The greatest inertia which exists in such a system is that of the air in the tube. This inertia can be reduced and the record made less subject to lag and overfling by filling the system with hydrogen instead of air (4, 7).

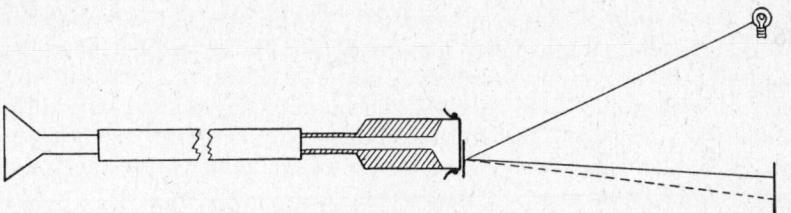

Fig. 324.—Optical capsule for the recording of surface pulsations. Light beam is reflected from a source onto a moving photographic surface. The mirror tips as the rubber membrane bulges.

Manometers. These are instruments designed to register in absolute terms the pressure that is found in some blood vessel or other body cavity. The mercury and water manometer are discussed elsewhere. Because of the great mass of the moving column of fluid, these manometers cannot be used to follow the details and extent of the arterial or venous pressure pulse. If the

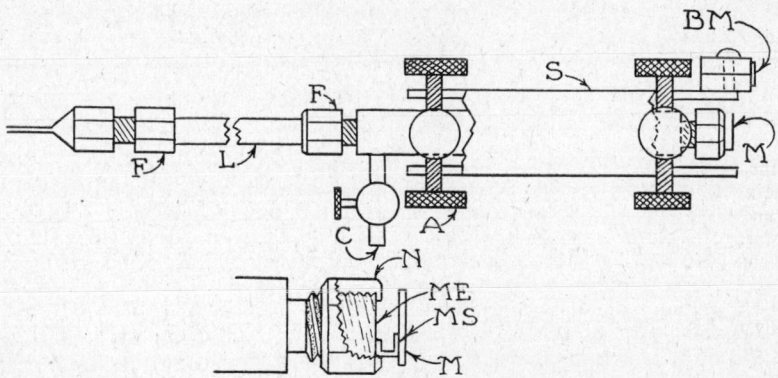

Fig. 325.—Details of manometer: A, eight adjusting screws to control the position of the light beam focused by the manometer mirror; BM, base line mirror (a steady base line indicates that the manometer has not been jarred); C, cock for filling the manometer with anticoagulant solution; F, tight brass to brass fittings with no air pockets; L, leaden tube which communicates the pressure from the needle in the artery to the manometer; M, mirror made from a 0.5 diopter planoconvex lens, silvered on the flat side; ME, "membrane" of beryllium copper rolled 0.09 inch thick and shaped into the form of a pie plate; MS, brass mirror support soldered to the membrane and cemented to the mirror; N, nut carefully machined to hold membrane to the manometer; S, shell to support the manometer in the clamp.

systolic pressure is 120 mm. Hg, and the diastolic 80, the mean pressure will be about 105. The mercury manometer will register this mean pressure with fluctuations of 3 or 4 mm. above and below this figure. In spite of this obvious fact, it is very difficult to get most students and some instructors to refrain from calling the fluctuations of the mercury manometer record, "systolic and diastolic pressure."

The mean pressure as recorded by the mercury manometer is of greatest accuracy and use in following slow changes in the blood pressure. The quick changes which are the result of the pressure pulse can be recorded only by quickly responding optical manometers. In essentials such manometers consist of a tube which may be inserted into an artery the end of which is covered by a flexible membrane carrying a mirror. The membrane bulges under the pressure to be recorded and the light beam reflected by the mirror is deflected to a degree that is proportional to the pressure. The path of the light beam is photographed on a moving film or photo-sensitive paper, giving a record of the pulsations as seen in Figure 323.

The quickness and sensitivity of such manometers depend upon the distensibility of the membrane and the dimensions of the tube. These factors are related mathematically in the design of manometers in the following manner (14).

Manometer design. The design of modern manometers is based on principles laid down by Frank (6, 7). The inertia of the fluid system in the manometer depends on the amount of fluid which must enter it in order to move the mirror and register the pressure. Frank called this the "volume elasticity coefficient E'," defined by $\Delta P / \Delta V$, where ΔV is the volume of fluid which enters the manometer system per unit of pressure rise ΔP.

When fluid enters the manometer system it must move all of the fluid in the tube through a certain distance. If the manometer is narrow, the distance through which the average particle of fluid moves will be greater than if the manometer is wide, and it is more difficult to accelerate the movement of fluid in a long tube than in a short one. We express this by saying that the "effective mass M'" of the manometer is proportional to L/A, where L is the length of the fluid column and A its cross-sectional area.

The natural period $1/N$, which is the measure of the quickness of the response of the manometer, is now given by

$$\frac{1}{N} = 2\pi \sqrt{\frac{M'}{E'}}.$$

N is the number of free vibrations which the manometer will make per sec., and for a very quickly responding instrument we require to have M' small and E' large, i.e., to have a small effective mass and a high volume elasticity coefficient. This means that the ideal manometer should be as short, wide and rigid as possible. In the development of the instruments from the time of Frank until 1934 it was customary to design them with as small an effective mass as possible; this made them so short, and with cannulae so wide, that a surgical operation was necessary to insert them into a blood vessel. Modern manometers (8, 10) are designed to have a very high volume elasticity coefficient by using a highly rigid but elastic membrane to support the mirror. The membrane of the manometer shown in Figure 325 is of beryllium copper 0.09 inch thick and shaped to resemble a tiny pie plate. The stiffness of this membrane makes E' so great that the effective mass may be greatly increased without getting a manometer that responds too slowly to record the quickest arterial pulsations. The advantage of being able to work with a large effective mass is that the cannula may be small and the connection between the cannula and the membrane long and flexible provided it is not distensible. An ordinary hypodermic needle may be used as a cannula that can be inserted into an artery through the skin of unanesthetized man and experimental animals, and a long leaden tube may be used to make a convenient flexible connection to the manometer.

Form of the pulse. The pressure pulse wave can be divided into a systolic portion and a diastolic portion. The two are separated by the *incisura*, a small notch succeeded by one or more after-vibrations which marks the closure of the semilunar valves separating the left ventricle from the aorta.

The incisura is due to an increase in the capacity of the aorta which is produced suddenly as the ventricle begins its isometric relaxation and the aortic valves are forced to bulge back toward the ventricle in closing. The incisura and its after-vibration are often exaggerated by inadequate pulse recorders, and, merging with the second reflected wave (see below), give rise to a phenomenon of mixed causality called the dicrotic notch, or the dicrotic wave by the older authors.

The systolic portion of the pulse is not a simple graphical representation of the relation of ventricular ejection to arteriolar drainage. In addition is the fact that as the pulse wave progresses, a larger reach of aorta is being distended by the blood ejected from the heart. This tends to make the later parts of the systolic curve flatter than the earlier parts, and gives rise to the shoulder seen on most central pulse curves. The contour of the later part of the systolic curve which is recorded after the pulse wave has spread over the aorta may be rising, falling, or may be held at a level. If it is rising, ejection is continuing at a greater rate than drainage; if it is falling, drainage is the greater; and if the late systolic pressure pulse contour is horizontal, ejection and drainage are balanced.

The shape of the systolic portion of the pressure pulse wave is quite variable because the three factors which determine it, i.e., ventricular ejection, pulse wave transmission time, and arteriolar drainage, are themselves variable. Vasoconstriction tends to make the later parts of the systolic pressure pulse wave rise more steeply because it reduces the rate of drainage, whereas vasodilatation often produces a rounded pressure pulse wave with a relatively long descent during late systole. Delay in pulse wave transmission time delays the shoulder. Factors which increase the venous return to the heart increase the amount and rate of ejection, so that a pressure pulse which has been rounded becomes plateau-like or shows a steady rise throughout systole. For these reasons, it is impossible to decide what the "normal" contour of the systolic portion of the arterial pressure pulse wave may be.

The diastolic portion of the pressure pulse wave occurs after ejection has ceased, and is determined by the rate of drainage in relation to the changes in arterial elasticity which occur as the pressure decreases. The diastolic portion of the pulse usually appears as a smooth curve which falls rapidly at first, and then less rapidly as the pressure decreases. It has the same form in all animals, whether they have high or low blood pressure, and whether they have slow or rapid hearts (15). The rate of drainage is proportional to the pressure above 20 mm. Hg (13), and so a given amount of fluid tends to drain through the arterioles more rapidly at high pressures than at low; the rate of pressure fall is thus greatest when the pressure is high and least when the pressure is low. The changes in the rate of pressure fall are exaggerated by the arteries being much less distensible at high pressures than at low ones (12).

The simple filling and emptying curve just described can be seen in arterial pressure records from the mouse, the rat, the bird, and many cold-blooded animals (15). In the larger laboratory animals (dog, cat, rabbit) and in man, however, a series of reflected waves which arise in the arteries themselves are superimposed on the fundamental filling and emptying curve.

Reflected waves. When the pulse wave is transmitted to the terminal arterioles, resistance to flow increases and the wave is reflected back over the arterial tree. This second wave is reflected again from the closed semilunar valves, and in this way a highly complex system of standing waves is generated with each pulse beat.

The standing wave system in the aorta is illustrated by Figure 326. The lowest curve (marked 0) is the pulse pressure record taken from the root of the aorta near the heart; the other curves (marked 10, 20 and 30) are pulse pressure records taken 10, 20, and 30 cm. respectively further down the aorta. The dip in the lowest curve is simultaneous with peaks in the other records. This means that the record from the aorta has been taken from a point on one side of a node of the standing wave system, whereas other records (20 and 30) taken in the descending aorta have been taken at points on the other side of the node. (Pressures on either side of a node show waves which are reciprocally related, and reflected pressure waves are absent at the node itself.) In this case the node is in the neighborhood of 10 cm. from the root of the aorta, where the record marked 10 was taken. If a record were taken exactly at the node, a true filling and emptying curve would result.

The most important standing wave system is that in the aorta, and in the dog the same system extends peripherally as far as the saphenous artery. In man, however, the leg arteries have a standing wave system which is sep-

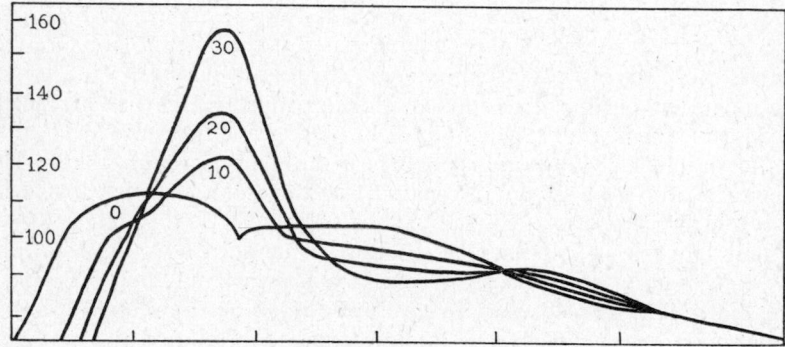

Fig. 326.—Contour of arterial pressure pulse in various parts of the aorta. At 0 the pulse was taken near the root of the aorta. At 10, 20 and 30, it was taken at 10, 20 and 30 cm. farther down the aorta.

arate from that of the aorta, and considerable emphasis has been placed on these differences between the *central pulse*, as recorded in the aorta and the arteries near the heart, and the *peripheral pulse* as recorded in an artery such as the radial (9). The peripheral pulse has the same fundamental form as the aortic pulse at the point of origin of the branch artery. Upon this fundamental pulse are superimposed standing waves which are the result of the reflection of the pulse wave from the terminal arterioles of the artery in question. The pulse transmission time over the carotid artery is relatively short, that over the brachial artery somewhat longer, and that over the leg system of man longer still; in each case the natural period of the standing wave is approximately twice the transmission time.

The presence or absence of standing waves is of interest in relation to the degree of vasodilatation present in hypotension. It has been shown that when the blood pressure falls as a result of hemorrhage, the arterioles constrict to maintain the blood pressure at as high a level as possible. Constriction of these vessels accentuates standing waves and gives rise to the situation shown in Figure 327A, when records are made simultaneously from the root of the aorta and the femoral artery. The interlacing of the two curves seen during diastole shows that forceful reflected waves are present. When, on the other hand, the low blood pressure is due to dilatation of the peripheral arterioles, reflected waves are absent (Fig. 327B). There is no interlacing of the pressure tracings during diastole and no evidence of standing waves at all. Standing waves can also be eliminated from the peripheral arteries by the administration of vasodilator drugs (9).

Characteristics of the pulse in health and disease. By palpation of the pulse the physician obtains valuable information regarding the heart and the circulation. The frequency of the heart beat is at once determined, at least so far as the ventricle is concerned. One may observe whether the frequency is above or below normal, and whether the rhythm is regular or irregular. By the same means one can determine whether the pulse is large or small, whether

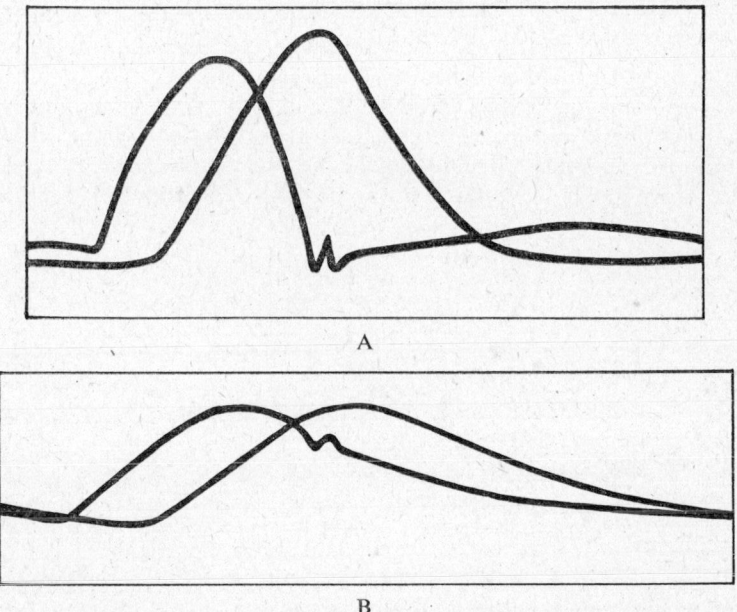

A

B

Fig. 327.—A, a record of the hypodynamic pulse which shows reflected waves indicating vasoconstriction. B, a similar hypodynamic pulse record showing the absence of a reflected wave and indicating vasodilatation.

the wave rises and falls rapidly (the "water-hammer" pulse of aortic insufficiency), or whether one phase or another is unduly prolonged. An experienced observer develops great skill in recognizing changes in the form of the pulse wave by mere palpation. By pressure on the artery one can also estimate whether the blood pressure is high or low.

Venous pulse. Under usual conditions the pulse wave is lost before entering the capillary regions, although as a result of arteriolar dilatation the pulse may spread through the capillaries and appear in the veins. The rhythmical flow of blood from an opened vein is a familiar instance. The term "venous pulse," however, is generally applied to a quite different phenomenon, i.e., to a pulse observed in the large veins (jugular) near the heart. In this case the pulse is not due to a pressure transmitted through the capillaries, but to pressure changes of both a positive and a negative nature occurring in the

24

in the heart or neighboring arteries and transmitted to the great veins. The records are usually taken from the external or internal jugular vein, where it is of considerable magnitude; under certain pathological conditions, however, it is plainly discernible at a further distance from the heart, and may even cause a noticeable pulsation of the liver ("liver pulse"). The venous pulse curve provides us with a means of determining the rate of the auricles, just as the arterial pulse curve enables us to count the contractions of the ventricles, and for this reason venous pulse records are of importance in the interpretation of various irregularities in the heart beat.

Tracings of the typical venous pulse in the jugular veins show three positive main waves, labeled *a*, *c*, and *v* in the same manner as the waves in the auricular pressure curve are labeled, and three negative waves, *x*, *x'*, and *y*. Many tracings, however, are far from typical, and in disease it may be impossible to identify the waves unless one has a simultaneous record of the arterial pulse from which one can determine the beginning of ventricular systole. The polygraph, designed by Mackenzie, makes the tracing of the venous pulse and the carotid pulse simultaneously, and synchronous points on the records are marked with arcs drawn on stationary paper by the respective writing points ("alignment marks"). The positive wave in the venous pulse record immediately preceding the beginning of ventricular contraction

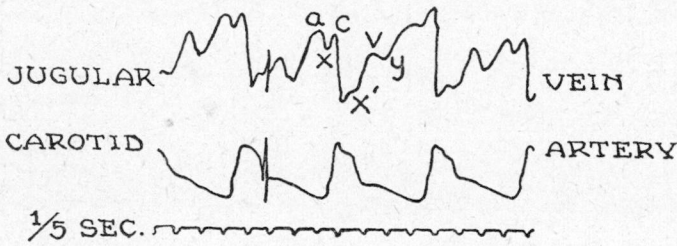

Fig. 328.—The upper tracing records the pulse of the jugular vein; the lower tracing is from the carotid artery. (After Best and Taylor, *The physiological basis of medical practice*, 1937.)

is the *a* wave due to auricular contraction. Following this is the first negative wave *x*, which marks the beginning of auricular relaxation. Next comes the positive *c* wave, which is due primarily to a rise of pressure in the auricle synchronous with ventricular contraction and the bulging of the atrioventricular valves into the auricle. Contributing to the *c* wave may also be a transmission of the pulse from the neighboring carotid artery. The *c* wave is followed by a negative wave *x'* which is attributed to the shortening of the ventricle from base to apex, resulting in a drawing-down of the atrioventricular septum and the closed atrioventricular valves. This negative wave is followed by the positive *v* wave, which reflects the rise in auricular pressure as that chamber is filled by the steady inflow of venous blood. The last negative wave *y* is due to the pressure in the auricle falling when the atrioventricular valves open and the blood is emptied into the ventricle. This passes into the positive *a* wave, and the cycle is repeated.

Figure 328 shows a record of the carotid and jugular pulses, taken simultaneously, in which the various waves can easily be recognized. The venous pulse tracing, however, is often atypical; frequently successive waves are merged together, and sometimes subsidiary waves, as to the explanation of which there is still incomplete agreement, make their appearance. For the variations in the form of the venous pulse under pathological conditions of the heart, reference must be made to the clinical literature.

REFERENCES

1. BAZETT, H. C. and DREYER, N. B. Measurements of the pulse wave velocity. *Amer. J. Physiol.*, 1922, *63*:94–116.

2. BRAMWELL, J. C. and HILL, A. V. The velocity of the pulse wave in man. *Proc. roy. Soc.*, 1922, *B93*:298–306.

3. BRAMWELL, J. C., HILL, A. V. and McSWINEY, B. A. The velocity of the pulse wave in man in relation to age as measured by the hot-wire sphygmograph. *Heart*, 1923, *10*:233–256.

4. BREWER, G., HAMILTON, W. F. and BROTMAN, I. Analysis of the pulse contour in relation to sound production by means of the hydrogen transmission pulse-recorder. *Amer. J. Physiol.*, 1934, *107*:420–426.

5. DOW, P. and HAMILTON, W. F. An experimental study of the velocity of the pulse wave propagated through the aorta. *Amer. J. Physiol.*, 1939, *125*:60–65.

6. FRANK, O. Kritik der elastischen Manometers. *Z. Biol.*, 1903, *44*:445–613.

7. FRANK, O. Theorie des Lufttransmissions Sphygmographen. *Z. Biol.*, 1929, *89*:274–296.

8. GREGG, D. E., ECKSTEIN, R. W. and FINEBERG, M. H. Pressure pulses and blood pressure values in unanesthetized dogs. *Amer. J. Physiol.*, 1937, *118*:399–410.

9. HAMILTON, W. F. The patterns of the arterial pulse. *Amer. J. Physiol.*, 1944, *141*: 233–241.

10. HAMILTON, W. F., BREWER, G. and BROTMAN, I. Pressure pulse contours in the intact animal. 1. Analytical description of a new high frequency hypodermic manometer with illustrative curves of simultaneous arterial and intracardiac pressures. *Amer. J. Physiol.*, 1934, *107*:427–435.

11. HOOKER, D. R. Observations on the venous blood pressure in man. *Amer. J. Physiol.*, 1914, *35*:73–86.

12. McWILLIAMS, J. A. On the properties of the arterial and venous walls. *Proc. roy. Soc.*, 1902, *70*:109–153.

13. WHITTAKER, S. R. and WINTON, F. R. The apparent viscosity of blood flowing in the isolated hind limb of the dog and its variation with corpuscular concentration. *J. Physiol.*, 1933, *78*:339–369.

14. WIGGERS, C. J. *The pressure pulses in the cardiovascular system.* New York, Longmans, Green and Co., 1928. xi, 200 pp.

15. WOODBURY, R. A. and HAMILTON, W. F. Blood pressure studies in small animals. *Amer. J. Physiol.*, 1937, *119*:663–674.

CHAPTER 33

VASOMOTOR REGULATION

BY DONALD H. BARRON

The pressure on the blood in the arteries is a function of the volume of blood in the arterial system, and that volume is in turn the resultant of two variables, (i) the rate at which blood is forced into the aorta by the action of the heart, and (ii) the rate at which it escapes into the capillaries. The rate of escape into the capillaries is determined principally by the tone of the arterioles, i. e., their diameter. The various factors, chemical as well as nervous, which alter the diameter of the arterioles, vasoconstriction and vasodilatation, thus modifying blood pressure, must now be considered in some detail. To simplify the presentation, the rate at which blood enters the arteries is assumed to be constant.

Before entering directly upon the discussion of the vasomotor mechanisms, some consideration must be given to the methods by which variations in the tone of the arterioles may be followed and their magnitude estimated.

METHODS USED TO DETERMINE VASOMOTOR ACTION

The simplest and most direct method is mere inspection when this is possible. The blanching of an organ is usually an indication of an increase in the tone of its arterioles, whereas flushing and congestion are indices of a decrease. This method is applicable in only a few instances and does not lend itself to quantitative study. The state of the arterioles may be inferred by measuring the flow of blood from the veins; a decrease in flow implies an increase in the resistance provided by the arterioles, an increase in flow, a reduction. The state of the arterioles may also be inferred from variations in arterial and venous pressures. When arteriolar constriction occurs, there is a rise in the pressure in the artery supplying the organ and a fall of pressure in the veins which emerge from it. The diminution in the size of these vessels by increasing the peripheral resistance augments the internal pressure on the arterial side and causes a fall of pressure on the venous side. If the area involved is large enough, the increased resistance will produce a perceptible difference in pressure, not only in the organ under consideration, but in the aorta as well; there will be a general rise (diastolic) of blood pressure. On the other hand, arteriolar dilatation in any organ is accompanied by changes of the opposite character. Peripheral resistance being diminished, there will be a fall of pressure on the arterial side and a rise of pressure on the venous. In fact, any abrupt rise of arterial pressure which cannot be ascribed to an increased cardiac output, must, by inference, be the result of vasoconstriction. If the method is applied to a definite organ —the brain, for example—the evidence that vasomotor changes are taking place is made decisive when simultaneous observations upon the pressure in the artery and the vein of the organ indicate that the pressures in these vessels vary in opposite directions.

Other conditions remaining the same, vasoconstriction in an organ is accompanied by a diminution in its volume; vasodilatation, by an increase. This method of studying the state of the peripheral resistance by following changes in the volume of organs is called plethysmography, and any instrument designed to record the changes in the volume of an organ is a plethysmograph (Fig. 329). Plethysmographs have been designed for special organs, and in such cases they have sometimes been given special names. Thus the plethysmograph used upon the kidney and the spleen has been designated an oncometer, that for the heart a cardiometer. The precise form and structure of a plethysmograph varies, of course, with the organ studied, but the principle involved is the same in all cases. The organ under observation is enclosed in a container with rigid walls which have but one opening. Through this opening the container is connected by pressure tubing with a device which will record the changes in volume. The connections between the recorder and the plethysmograph, and the space in the interior of the

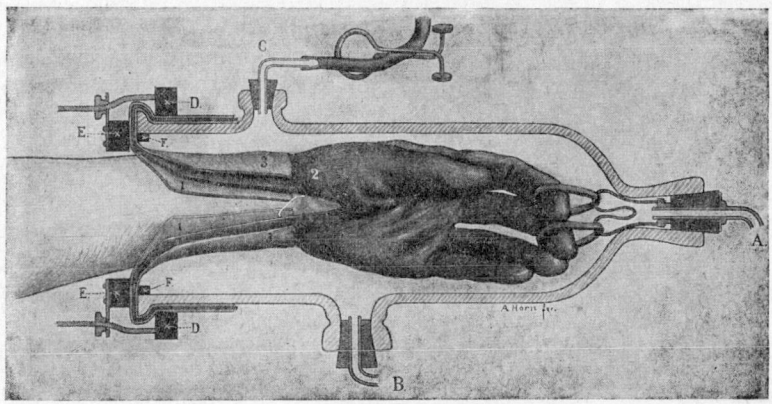

Fig. 329.—Detailed drawing of the glass plethysmograph with the arrangement of rubber glove to prevent leaking without compressing the veins. 2, the glove with its gauntlet reflected over the end of the glass cylinder; 1 and 3, supporting pieces of stout rubber tubing; D and E, sections of outer and inner rings of hard rubber to fasten the reflected rubber tubing and reduce the opening for the arm.

latter not occupied by the organ, may be filled with air, or, as is more often the case, with *water*. The principle of a plethysmograph may be illustrated by the skull, which forms a natural closed container for the brain. If a hole is bored through the skull at any point and a connection is then made with a recording device such as a tambour, the volume changes may be registered successfully.

Arteriolar dilatation in the skin, muscle, gland or brain, and the resultant increased blood flow, other circumstances remaining the same, are accompanied by a rise in temperature; conversely, vasoconstriction is followed by a fall in the temperature of the affected organ. These changes in temperature, as recorded by means of the thermocouples embedded in the tissue, afford a ready means for following the variations in the state of the arterioles. Finally, appropriate use of any of the methods for measuring the volume of blood flow in the artery supplying the organ (see Chap. 31, pp. 661–663) serves to indicate the variations in the degree of resistance to flow offered by the arterioles and the capillaries.

By the application of the methods which have been just described, it has been shown that under normal conditions the arterioles are in a state of moderate tone or constriction, which may continue even after all their connections with the nervous system have been severed. This inherent tone is undoubtedly a normal characteristic of the smooth muscle found in the tunica media of the arterioles, but that characteristic is maintained by the opposition of the muscle to the distending force exerted by each beat of the heart and by the effect of internal secretions, such as angiotonin and epinephrine. These methods have further demonstrated that rapid alterations in this inherent tone of the arterioles are wrought by two distinct mechanisms, nervous and chemical. The chemical mechanism includes metabolites as well as hormones.

NERVOUS REGULATION OF THE ARTERIOLES

The control over the tone of the arterioles by the nervous system is exercised through two functionally antagonistic sets of nerve fibers: first, the vasoconstrictor fibers, the action of which increases the tone of the smooth muscle of the arterioles and causes a diminution in the size of the vessels; second, the vasodilator nerve fibers: their action is followed by an increase in the diameter of the lumen of the blood vessels, due to a relaxation (inhibition) of the tonic contraction of the muscular coats of the arteries (9).

Claude Bernard first discovered the existence of vasoconstrictor nerve fibers to the blood vessels in 1851, when he observed that on cutting the sympathetic nerve in the neck of the rabbit the blood vessels in the ear on the same side became very much dilated. He and other observers later showed that if the peripheral end of the severed nerve is stimulated electrically the ear becomes blanched, owing to a vasoconstriction of the blood vessels. Bernard was doubly fortunate in being the first to demonstrate the existence of a second class of nerve fibers, which, when stimulated, cause a dilatation of the blood vessels and are therefore called vasodilators. This discovery was made in connection with the chorda tympani, a branch of the facial, which sends secretory fibers to the submaxillary gland. When this nerve is cut and the peripheral end is stimulated, a secretion of saliva results and at the same time, as Bernard showed, the blood vessels of the gland dilate and the flow of blood is greatly increased in the efferent vein and may even show a pulse.

The activity of these two groups of fibers and the functional balance between them is regulated by a vasomotor center in the medulla which works through subsidiary centers situated in the spinal cord. The activity of the medullary center is modified by impulses which arrive via (i) special afferent fibers from the blood vessels themselves through the depressor, carotid sinus, and vagus nerves, (ii) general somatic and visceral afferents, and (iii) the higher centers of the brain—the hypothalamus and the cerebral cortex.

General Distribution and Course of the Vasoconstrictor Nerves. The fibers which by their direct action increase the tone of the arterioles are nonmedullated postganglionic sympathetics (see Chap. 10) arising from cell bodies situated either in a prevertebral ganglion or in one of those that belong to the vertebral chain. Those that arise from the cell bodies in the vertebral chain join the segmental spinal nerves via the gray rami communicans to be distributed chiefly to the vessels in the skin and muscles; whereas the axons of cells in the prevertebral ganglia, for example the celiac and the superior mesenteric, continue to the blood vessels in the splanchnic region, without joining the segmental nerves (Fig. 330). The vessels of these two regions, the skin and the viscera are the most richly supplied with constrictor fibers though they are distributed to the arterioles in skeletal muscle and to the mucous membranes of the mouth and nasopharynx.

The cell bodies of the vasoconstrictor fibers are activated by medullated preganglionic fibers which arise from neurons situated in the intermedio-lateral column of the spinal cord to emerge through the ventral roots of the

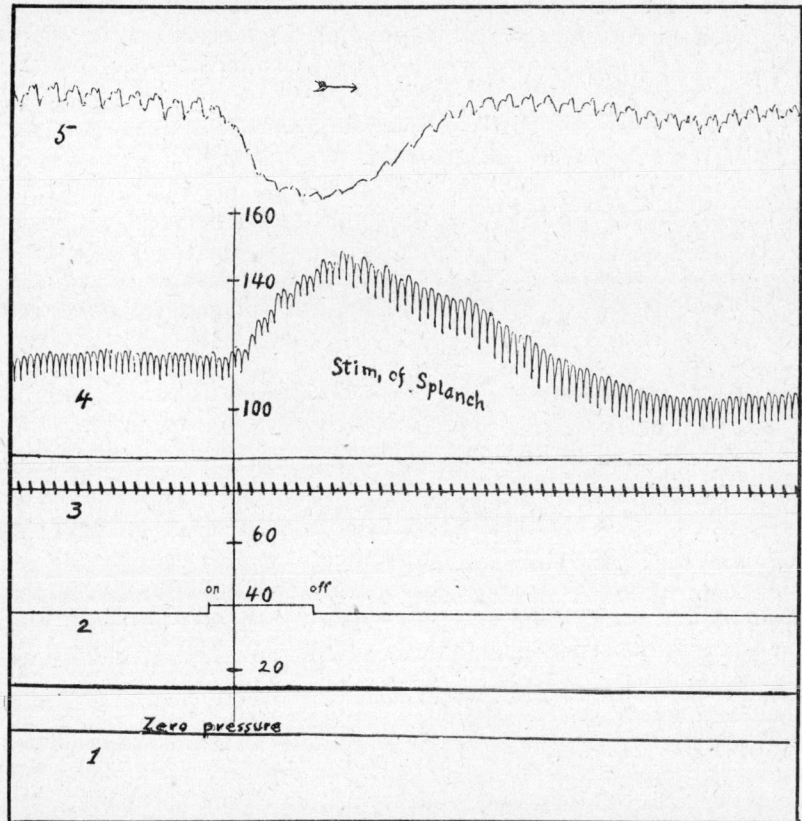

Fig. 330.—Vasomotor effect of stimulation of the splanchnic nerve—peripheral end—in the dog (Dawson): 1, the line of zero pressure; 2, the line of the stimulating pen; *on* and *off* mark the beginning and end of the stimulation; 3, the time record in seconds; 4, the blood pressure record (stimulation causes a marked rise of blood pressure due to stimulation of vasoconstrictor fibers); 5, plethysmographic tracing of the volume of the kidney (oncometer); stimulation of the splanchnic causes a diminution in volume of the kidney owing to the constriction of its arterioles.

first thoracic to the second or third lumbar segment inclusive. The pregang-lionic fibers which form synaptic connections with the vasoconstrictor nerves to the skin and skeletal muscle do so within the ganglia of the vertebral chain which they join via the white rami communicans. Some, it appears, form synapses in the ganglia of the corresponding spinal segment from which they emerge; others seem to extend forward or backward in the chain before terminating in some distant ganglion. As an illustration, preganglionic fibers emerging from the anterior five thoracic segments end about cells in the superior cervical ganglion. Unlike those which activate the vasoconstrictors of the skin, the preganglionics which control the vasoconstrictors of the splanchnic viscera leave the vertebral chain and combine to form the splanchnic nerves with branches to the prevertebral or collateral ganglia.

A more precise statement of the location of the cell bodies of the vasoconstrictor fibers to specific regions of the body and their relation in turn to the segmental position of the preganglionic neuron in the intermediolateral of the spinal cord can be made on the basis of the researches of Bradford and of Langley. The following table illustrates the relations of the motor nerves to the blood vessels in an animal with seven lumbar vertebrae.

Location of Vessels	Position of Ganglion Cell	Ventral Roots Containing Preganglionic Fibers
Head and neck	Superior cervical ganglion	1st to 4th thoracic
Heart	Stellate and inferior cervical ganglia	1st to 5th thoracic
Anterior extremity	Stellate ganglion	4th to 9th thoracic
Posterior extremity	6th and 7th lumbar and 1st sacral ganglia	11th to 13th thoracic, 1st to 3rd lumbar
Kidney	Renal ganglion	4th to 12th thoracic, 1st to 3rd lumbar
Spleen	Semilunar ganglion	3rd to 12th thoracic, 1st to 3rd lumbar
Abdominal viscera	Semilunar and superior mesenteric ganglia	6th to 12th thoracic, 1st and 2nd lumbar
Pelvic viscera	Inferior mesenteric ganglia	1st to 3rd lumbar

This table brings out the striking fact that the vasoconstrictor supply to the arterioles is practically continuous from one end of the thoracolumbar outflow to the other. Further, it emphasizes the fact that the vasoconstrictor neurons to the arterioles are situated in the prevertebral as well as the vertebral ganglia. The former supply the fibers to the blood vessels in abdominal and pelvic viscera; the latter are devoted entirely to the supply of vasoconstrictor nerves to the structures innervated by the segmental nerves, both spinal and cranial, including the central nervous system and the viscera of the thorax.

General Course and Distribution of the Vasodilator Fibers. The distribution pattern of the neurons and axons which dilate the arterioles lacks the simplicity and uniformity that mark the organization of the vasoconstrictors. Whereas all the vasoconstrictor neurons belong to the sympathetic division of the autonomic nervous system, vasodilator neurons are not, as might have been expected, confined to the parasympathetic system as it is usually described. In addition to the parasympathetic vasodilators, there is a second group of fibers which leaves the spinal cord in the thoracolumbar region, commingled with the preganglionic vasoconstrictor fibers (4). A third group of neurons, the activity of which is followed by vasodilatation, is found in the somatic division of the nervous system. The neurons of the first two groups—the vasodilators in the sympathetic and parasympathetic outflows—are efferents whereas the cells of the somatic system which evoke vasodilatation are generally agreed to be afferent neurons, with their cell bodies in the spinal ganglia, though the question cannot be regarded as settled.

The demonstration of the existence of vasodilator fibers in mixed nerves has been difficult, for the stimulation of a nerve in which both constrictors and dilators are present may give only a constrictor effect. Several methods have been used to avoid this masking of vasodilatation by vasoconstrictors. Pharmacological agents such as ergotinine which paralyzes the endings of the vasoconstrictor fibers without inhibiting the action of the vasodilators have been employed. Advantage has also been taken of the fact that vaso-constrictor fibers degenerate much more rapidly after separation from their cell body than do vasodilators; the vasodilators retain their excitability for some six to ten days after division, whereas the vasoconstrictor fibers lose their excitability on the third or fourth day. Further, the vasoconstrictor fibers are paralyzed by cooling in some nerves before the vasodilators. By selective paralysis of nerve fibers and the employment of the recording devices described above, vasodilator nerves have been traced to the blood vessels by the following routes.

Via the parasympathetic outflow. Vasodilator fibers to the vessels of the sublingual and submaxillary glands are found in the chorda tympani branch of the facial, whereas the glossopharyngeal nerve contains the vasodilator fibers to the parotid gland, the posterior third of the tongue, the tonsils and the pharynx. The vagus is said to contain vasodilator fibers to the coronary arteries (12). The sacral portion of the parasympathetic outflow contributes through the second, third and fourth sacral nerves the dilator fibers which go to the vessels of the clitoris or the penis. These fibers join the hypogastric plexus at the nervi erigentes.

Via the sympathetic system. Vasodilator fibers to the vessels in mucous membrane of the mouth (lips, gums and palate), the nostrils and the skin of the cheeks may be activated by stimulation of the cervical sympathetic. The fibers are distributed to the individual vessels via branches of the trigeminal nerve. In the dog, at least, there appear to be vasodilators to the coronary arteries included in the branches of the stellate ganglion, and the vessels of the skeletal muscles of the limbs receive vasodilator fibers from the thoracolumbar outflow via the branches of the brachial and lumbar plexus, whereas the sympathetic vasodilators to the abdominal viscera are components of the splanchnics.

Via the somatic nervous system. Vasodilator fibers reach the vessels in the skin of the extremities via the dorsal spinal roots.

This interesting exception to the Bell-Magendie law was first pointed out by Stricker in 1876 following his discovery that stimulation of the dorsal roots of the spinal segments contributing to the sciatic resulted in a rise in temperature and a marked reddening of the foot. Stricker's observations made on dogs, though confirmed by Gärtner in 1889, were not generally accepted until the subject was reinvestigated by Bayliss, who found that reddening of the skin, a rise in the temperature of the toes, and an increase in the volume of the hindlimb occurred where the dorsal roots of the fifth, sixth, and seventh lumbar and first sacral nerves were stimulated. Further experiments by Bayliss demonstrated that the trophic centers of these fibers are in the dorsal root ganglion. As these fibers in both structure and their course resembled ordinary sensory nerve fibers, Bayliss drew the conclusion that they were identical; the vasodilatation of the skin vessels was brought about by impulses which passed centrifugally or antidromically in them.

It is difficult to understand how impulses conveyed antidromically to the peripheral termination of sensory fibers can affect the blood vessels; the hypothesis is advanced that sensory fibers near their termination in the skin give off collaterals that go to the cutaneous arterioles. Thus local stimulation, such as the application of irritants to the skin, sets up an axon reflex which acts upon the arterioles. Similarly, stimulation of the sensory nerve at its central termination or anywhere along its course would set up impulses which reach the arterioles via the same collateral and cause vasodilatation. Hinsey and Gasser (11) have shown that the fibers concerned in the dorsal root belong to the small medullated group (3 to 5μ) and they suggested that the action of the fibers was due to the liberation of acetylcholine at their peripheral terminals, a suggestion which has been confirmed experimentally by Wybau.

Bayliss established the fact that active vasodilatation of the vessels of the skin of the extremities via the dorsal roots could be brought about reflexly by stimulation of the depressor nerve and his observations were independently confirmed by Fafanow and Tschalussow in 1913. Hence there appears to be no reason to doubt that the dorsal root vasodilators play a role in the normal regulation of the state of the vessels in the skin of the extremities. The question which remains unsettled is how the central terminations of the sensory fibers are reflexly excited to set up impulses which travel outward. Some evidence on this point has been accumulated (1, 18), but it is impossible to offer any final interpretation at present.

There are some who claim (7) that the cell bodies of the fibers responsible for vasodilatation via the dorsal root are located in the spinal cord rather than in the ganglia, but the results of careful degeneration studies by Tower *et al.* and Hinsey *et al.* lend no support to this view.

VASOMOTOR CENTERS

Spinal Vasomotor Center. The portions of the vasomotor neurons, dilator as well as constrictor, which lie within the cord may be described as elements of the spinal vasomotor center. This description is justified, for there is a certain amount of integration of afferent impulses which occurs at spinal levels before the impulses are expressed in vasomotor action—integration which may be observed in segmental vasomotor reflexes. Reflexes of this type were first described by Lovén in the ear and in the hindleg of the rabbit and hence are called Lovén reflexes. Since then, similar reflexes have been demonstrated in a variety of organs, so their occurrence may be fairly regarded as general. Briefly stated, when the afferent nerve from any particular organ is excited, a general rise in blood pressure is produced, due in part to vasoconstriction; at the same time there is a local vasodilatation in the organ itself. The dilatation, as Bayliss (2) has shown for the limb, is due to inhibition of the local vasoconstrictors as well as excitation of the local dilators, an effect comparable to the reciprocal innervation seen in skeletal muscles. By this combination of circumstances, the organ is furnished a maximal blood supply.

Medullary Vasomotor Center. In addition to the impulses which arrive via segmental afferents, the vasomotor center of the spinal cord is regulated by impulses from cells situated in the medulla. The existence of the control by medullary cells was first suggested when it was found that a fall in blood pressure due to vasodilatation in the skin and splanchnic region followed transection of the spinal cord at any cervical level. The vasodilatation is the result of a paralysis of the spinal vasomotor centers and the inference is that the paralysis is a consequence of the removal of a tonic control by cells situated in the brain.

When the spinal cord is sectioned in the lower thoracic region, there is a similar paralysis of the portion of the spinal vasomotor center caudal to the cut, illustrated by vasodilatation in the caudal extremities. If, however, the animal is kept alive, the spinal centers and the vessels gradually recover their tone, although they are not in connection with the vasomotor centers in the brain. The return of the tone in this case may be attributed to the vasomotor neurons of the lower thoracic and upper lumbar segments, since vascular paralysis is again produced when this portion of the cord is destroyed or the splanchnic nerves are sectioned. The time required for the restoration of vasomotor tone by the autonomous action of the special centers varies from one animal form to another. The loss of tone and the recovery are a part of a larger phenomenon, spinal shock.

The exact position of the medullary cells has not been determined, though the majority appear to be located in the tegmentum of the medulla caudal to the midpoint of the pons, for sections ahead of that level do not produce any effect on the vasoconstrictors. Progressively more caudal slices cause a greater and greater fall in blood pressure until the upper part of the cord is reached. Thereafter, no further effect is produced.

The different cells within the vasoconstrictor center appear to be connected by axons in the ventrolateral column with specific preganglionic vasoconstrictor fibers to the different regions of the body. Some cells, for example, control the activity of the fibers distributed to the intestinal area; others govern the neurons with axons to the vessels of the skin.

Ludwig and his pupils, Dittmar and Owajannikow, were the first to localize the vasoconstrictor center—a center in this sense is a portion of the nervous system in which afferents make connections with efferent neurons. They found that, whereas section of the brain just behind the corpora quadrigemina did not produce any noteworthy change in arterial pressure, the pressure fell progressively with each successive cut caudally through the medulla until the fall equaled that which follows transection of the cord. By experiments of this character, the center was localized in the rabbit to a region—bilaterally represented—3 to 4 mm. long, beginning 1 to 2 mm. below the quadrigeminal bodies and terminating about 4 mm. above the tip of the calamus scriptorius. The location of the vasoconstrictor center has recently been re-investigated (17) by using three techniques, i.e., chemical stimulation with acetylcholine, electrical stimulation, and localized destruction of the floor of the fourth ventricle. The results indicate that the center lies within or near the vestibular nuclei, and the spinal path—chiefly uncrossed—is in the ventrolateral column. This area includes the pressor center of Ranson and Billingsley (16) located at the inferior fovea and Dittmar's center in the lower part of the pons in the region of the facial nucleus and the superior olive.

The demonstration of the existence in the medulla of neurons, the activities of which are essential to the normal maintenance of vasoconstriction in the skin and splanchnic regions, raises the question: are there similar cells in the medulla, which, by their activity, directly regulate the vasodilators? A final answer cannot be given, but there is good reason to believe that there are, even though their location remains undetermined. Their existence is inferred from the fact that a fall in blood pressure which results from the stimulation of a sensory nerve—the depressor—is accompanied by a vasodilatation in regions deprived of vasoconstrictor nerves. Further, Rosenblueth, Cannon, and their associates have furnished evidence that the vasodilators in the dorsal roots are activated by stimulating the depressor point —an area in the floor of the fourth ventricle just lateral to the pressor center of Ranson and Billingsley (16). This suggestion implies that efferents to vasodilators in the medulla, as well as the efferents to vasoconstrictors, can be activated via the depressor point.

Like other motor type cells, those of the medullary vasoconstrictor and vasodilator centers are capable of being stimulated reflexly; functionally they resemble antagonistic motor centers: as the activity of one increases the activity of the other declines, and by this balance the total peripheral resistance is regulated. Moreover, the cells of these two centers are in a constant state of activity, due, very likely, to the constant inflow of afferent impulses from a variety of peripheral and central sources.

Records of the impulses which reach the arterioles via vasoconstrictor nerves indicate that the activity of the cells in the medullary vasoconstrictor center, though continuous, is expressed by rhythmic bursts of impulses. The rhythm of the impulse groups is often associated with the respiratory rhythm; at other times it is related to the pulse, though not infrequently it bears

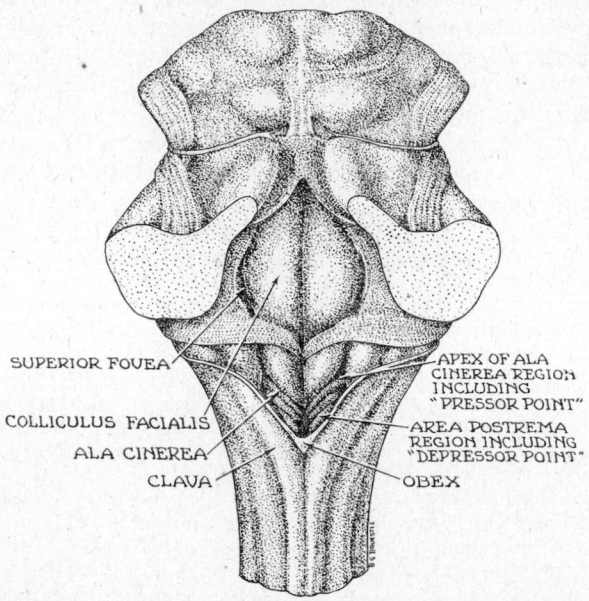

SUPERIOR FOVEA

APEX OF ALA
CINEREA REGION
INCLUDING
"PRESSOR POINT"

COLLICULUS FACIALIS

AREA POSTREMA
REGION INCLUDING
"DEPRESSOR POINT"

ALA CINEREA

CLAVA

OBEX

Fig. 331.—The floor of the fourth ventricle of the human brain; the areas described by Ranson and Billingsley as pressor and depressor points respectively in their studies on the cat are indicated.

no obvious relation to any other observable cyclical phenomenon in the body. Under certain unusual conditions the "centers" may exhibit other rhythmical variations in activity which make themselves visible in a periodic

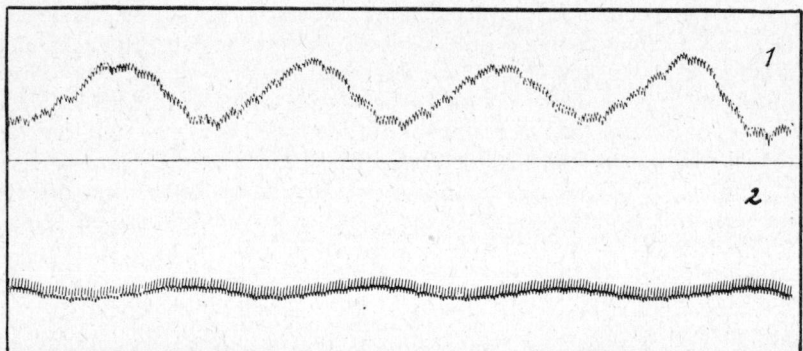

Fig. 332.—Rhythmical vasomotor waves of blood pressure in a dog (Traube-Hering waves). The upper tracing, 1, is the blood pressure record as taken with the mercury manometer; the lower tracing, 2, is taken with a Hürthle manometer. Seven distinct respiratory waves of blood pressure may be recognized on each large wave. (Dawson.)

waxing and waning of the general arterial pressure (Fig. 332); the waves are much longer than those associated with respiratory movements. These periodic variations in the blood pressure are occasionally observed in experiments upon animals, though their ultimate cause is not understood. They are usually designated as Traube-Hering waves, although this term, strictly speaking, should be reserved for the waves synchronous with the respiratory movements which Traube observed in animals with the thorax open and the diaphragm paralyzed. These waves, too, are due to rhythmical variations in the activity of the vasoconstrictor center. During sleep, certain much longer wavelike variations also occur, which are doubtless due to a rhythmical change of tone in the vasomotor centers.

Nervous control of the vasomotor centers

For purposes of description the afferent fibers, the action of which serves to modify the balance between the vasoconstrictor and vasodilator centers at the cord and medullary levels, may be divided into two functional groups:

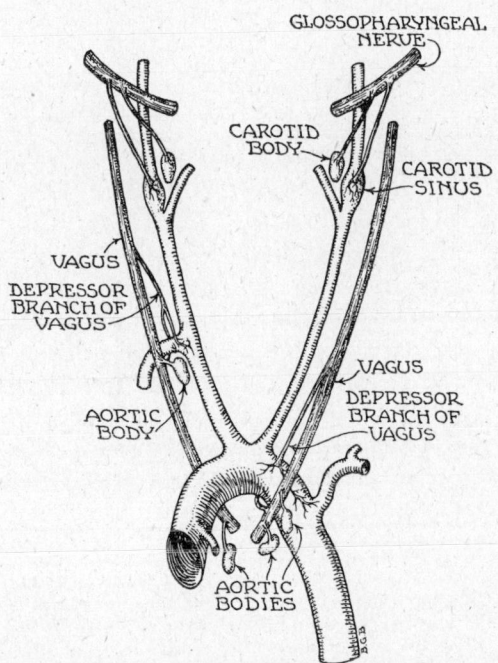

Fig. 333.—A diagram illustrating the position and the nerve supply of the carotid sinuses and the aortic arch, together with the carotid and aortic bodies.

(i) those which by their activity inhibit the vasoconstrictor center and stimulate the vasodilator—the depressor fibers, and (ii) those which excite the vasoconstrictor center and inhibit the vasodilator—the pressor fibers.*

Depressor afferents. The adventitia and media of the arch of the aorta, the root of the innominate, and the proximal portions of the internal carotid arteries are supplied with nerve endings similar to Golgi tendon organs by the aortic branches of the vagi and the sinus branches of the glossopharyngeal nerves respectively (Fig. 333). These endings are stimulated by an increase in the internal pressure within the vessels upon which they lie (Fig. 334A).

* This concept of the reciprocal relations of the medullary vasomotor centers was first introduced by Bayliss in 1893 and subsequently established by him in a series of studies which were finally presented as a small monograph in 1923, about a year before his death (2).

The greater the internal pressure the more rapidly do the individual endings fire and the greater the number of individual endings which are excited. At all pressures in the normal living rabbit, for example, some nerve endings of the sinus fibers are discharging, and in the rise in pressure which accompanies the systolic discharge the impulse frequency per second and the number of active units increase (3). Though the impulse activity in the depressor has not been studied in the same detail, there, too, some endings appear to be stimulated at all normal pressures.

The central effects of these impulse discharges can be illustrated by electrical stimulation of the central cut end of either the depressor or carotid sinus nerve. They are: (i) a pronounced fall of pressure due in part to a slowing and weakening of the heart rate, (ii) an inhibition of the vasoconstrictor center with a concomitant dilatation in the splanchnic vessels (Fig. 335B),

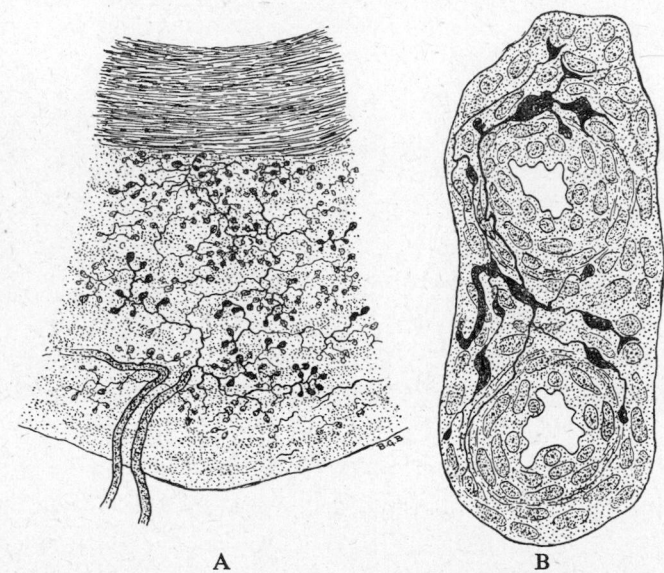

A   B

Fig. 334.—A diagram showing the characteristics of the afferent endings in (A) the carotid sinus and (B) the carotid body. (After de Castro.)

and (iii) an increase in the activity of the vasodilator center, manifested by a vasodilatation in the skin, the salivary glands and the skeletal muscles (Fig. 335A). Similar effects can be produced by a compression of the internal carotid to increase the pressure in the sinus, by electrical stimulation of the walls of the sinus, or by artificially increasing the pressure within the vessel.

A reduction in the number of impulses normally reaching the vasomotor center from the aortic and sinus endings, due either to a local reduction in the pressure within the carotid sinus or as the result of section of the sinus and depressor nerves, is accompanied by a rise in the systemic blood pressure. The rise in pressure appears to be due to an increase in the activity of the vasoconstrictor center expressed by a constriction of the arterioles in the splanchnic region. There is some evidence to indicate that the vasodilator center is inhibited at the same time, for under these circumstances Bayliss found the blood flow through the submaxillary gland was decreased even though the cervical sympathetic had been sectioned earlier.

Evidence is slowly accumulating which indicates that, in addition to these special nerves to the aortic arch derivatives, there are fibers intermingled in other nerves to blood vessels, the skin and the viscera—the peritoneum, the anus, the vagina and spermatic cord—which, if activated, bring about a fall in blood pressure through vasodilatation in the splanchnic region. Thus by stimulation of the sciatic and other mixed nerves, vasodilatation may be obtained if the nerves are (i) cooled, (ii) stimulated at a particular stage in regeneration, (iii) activated by weak stimuli or mechanically. These depressor fibers in the spinal nerves make connections centrally with internuncial neurons to end in the medulla.

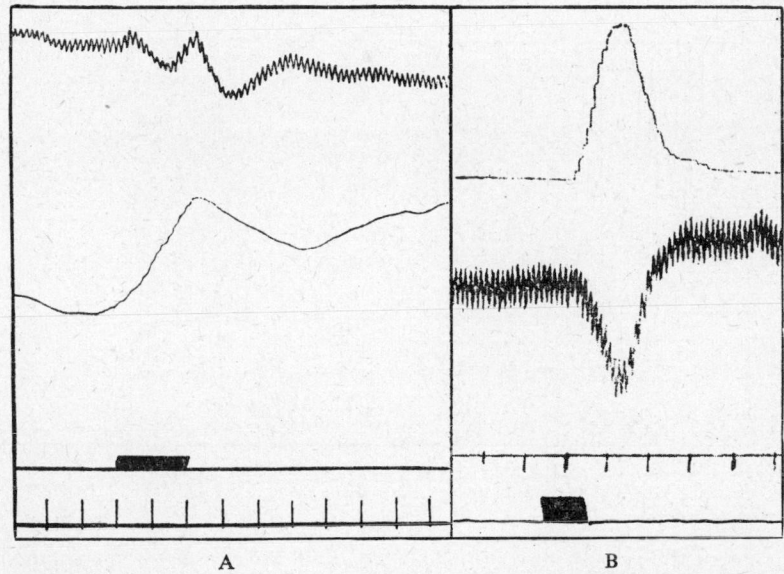

A   B

Fig. 335.—A: Excitation of the vasodilators as illustrated by the increase in the volume of the ear—middle curve—during stimulation of the depressor fibers of the vagus. Upper curve, blood pressure. Cervical sympathetic cut. Time in 10 sec. intervals. B: Intestinal volume—upper curve— increases during stimulation of the central end of the vagus (depressor) due to inhibition of vasoconstrictors as the blood pressure—lower curve—falls. Time in 10 secs. (From Bayliss, *Proc. roy. Soc.*, 1908, *B80*:339–375; and Bayliss, *The vaso-motor system*, New York, Longmans, Green and Co., 1923.)

Pressor afferents. With the exception of the depressor and the carotid sinus nerves, all afferent nerves appear to contain fibers which, if excited, provoke a rise in arterial pressure, neither dependent upon cardiac effects nor upon the secretion of adrenaline. The impulses which reach the cord via these fibers ascend in the spinal cord via Lissauer's tract, a fact which is in accord with the suggestion that the pressor fibers are in reality protopathic pain fibers. Whatever their source and route to the vasomotor centers, the impulses appear to work their effect by stimulation of the vasoconstrictor centers and inhibition of the vasodilator.

Impulses reaching the vasomotor center via afferent vagal fibers with their peripheral terminations in the roots of the great veins and the right auricle have been shown by McDowall (13) to excite the vasoconstrictor center. The vagal afferents are stimulated when the pressure in the great veins and the right auricle falls, as in severe hemorrhage. As a consequence of their activity, the arterial pressure either fails to fall or declines moderately, for if the vagi are severed the pressure does fall, or if it has fallen, drops still further (Fig. 336). It is obvious that this reflex will be of importance in the maintenance of blood pressure in any circumstance in which the venous pressure is reduced due to actual or relative loss of blood. Further studies by McDowall have demonstrated that when the venous pressure is high the vasoconstrictor center is stimulated just as the cardio-accelerator center is stimulated in the Bainbridge reflex. This (Chap. 35, p. 790) auriculopressor reflex may be of value in opposing the depressor and aortic reflexes, thus permitting a rise of pressure which would be of value during exercise, for example.

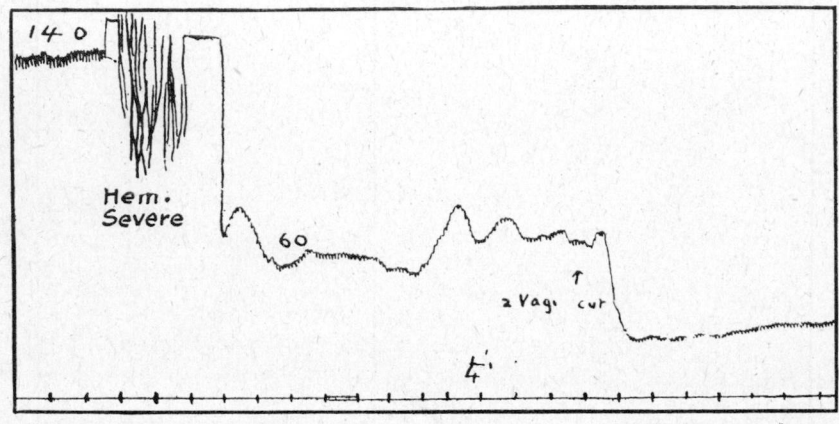

Fig. 336.—McDowall's kymograph tracing illustrating the fall in systemic pressure which follows the section of the vagi after severe hemorrhage. (From McDowall, *J. Physiol.*, 1924, *59*:41–47.)

In view of the important role played by the blood vessels of the splanchnic region in the regulation of the total peripheral resistance, it might be expected that the vessels there would be supplied by sensory fibers which regulated their tone reflexly after the fashion of the proprioceptors in skeletal muscle. With this in view, Gammon and Bronk (8) recorded the impulse discharges in the peripheral end of the splanchnic nerve and found that impulses are set up in its afferent fibers by distension of the vessels. The impulses arise from Pacinian corpuscles of the mesenteries as a result of their mechanical deformation by the distension of neighboring as well as intrinsic vessels. Increasing the distension of the vessels increases the frequency of impulse discharge, and vice versa. The reflex effects of those discharges have not been finally determined, but there is some evidence to indicate that they activate the vasoconstrictor fibers to the gut.

Control by higher centers. The vascular bed of the skin plays such an important role in regulating heat loss that it is not surprising to find that the activity of the medullary and spinal vasomotor centers is controlled in part by centers in the hypothalamus. Ranson and his coworkers have repeatedly demonstrated that direct stimulation of cells located in the posterior and lateral hypothalamic nuclei results in a rise in blood pressure. The rise is due in the main to vasoconstriction but there may be an undiscovered decrease in vasodilator tone at the same time. Certainly the vasodilatation in the skin which accompanies activation of the hypothalamic centers controlling heat loss is due not only to a decrease in vasoconstrictor tone but to an increase in the activity of the vasodilators. The details of the interaction of the hypothalamus and the medullary vasomotor centers remain to be worked out.

This same statement may be extended to the relations between the cerebral cortex and the vasomotor centers, though cortical stimulation has been observed to increase blood pressure and the vascular responses in the skin are altered by lesions in the contralateral premotor cortex. So far as man is concerned, experiments with the plethysmograph and other recording devices demonstrate clearly that the centers are affected in a pressor or depressor manner by psychical states and activities. Mental work, especially mental interest, however aroused, is followed by a constriction of the blood vessels of the skin—a pressor effect (Fig. 337), and an explanation of the value of the

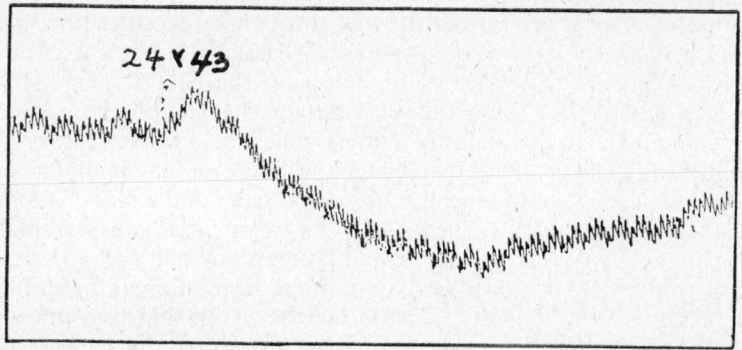

Fig. 337.—Plethysmographic curve of forearm. The volume of the arm was recorded by means of a counter weighted tambour and the record shows the pulse waves. A problem in mental arithmetic—the product of 24 by 43—caused a marked constriction of the arm.

reflex may lie in the supposition that the rise of arterial pressure thus produced forces more blood through the brain. On the other hand, feelings of embarrassment or shame may be associated with a depressor effect, a dilatation in the vessels of the skin manifested, for example, in the act of blushing. In both cases it must be assumed that there are intracentral nerve paths between the cortex and the center in the hypothalamus to the medulla, the impulses along one path exciting the center, while those along the other inhibit its tone and excite the vasodilator center.

CHEMICAL REGULATION OF THE ARTERIOLES

Via the carotid and aortic bodies. Associated with and in part derived from the remnants of the embryonic system of aortic arches are the carotid, aortic and paraganglionic bodies. Within those bodies afferent fibers of the glossopharyngeal nerves in the case of the carotid bodies, and the vagi in the aortic and paraganglionic, arborize about the intrinsic epithelial cells to end in reticulated swellings (Fig. 334B). These reticulated endings appear to be activated when the composition of the blood which perfuses the local vessels is altered. Specifically, an increase in the CO_2 pressure in the blood perfusing the carotid sinus region and the body causes an increase in the frequency of impulse discharge in individual fibers of the carotid sinus nerve as well as an increase in the number of active fibers (10). Conversely, a reduction in CO_2 tension in the perfusate is accompanied by a reduction in both the frequency of discharge and the number of active units. The effects of altering the composition of the blood perfusing the carotid sinus region—including the carotid body—on the vasomotor center have been demonstrated by isolating the sinus region from the rest of the circulation and perfusing it either by means of a pump or as a part of the circulation of a second animal. Under such conditions, perfusion of the sinus region with a fluid of acid pH augments reflexly the arterial pressure, whereas the arterial pressure falls when the perfusate is alkaline, other conditions remaining the same. Similarly, an increase in the CO_2 tension, without altering the pH of the perfusate, increases the tone of the vasoconstrictor center; conversely, a decrease in the CO_2 tension is sufficient of itself to bring about a fall in pressure. Further perfusion of the carotid sinus region of one animal as a part of the circulation of a second breathing a gas mixture poor in oxygen, results in an augmentation of arterial pressure in the first through vasoconstriction.

Direct action on the vasomotor centers. Variations in the carbon dioxide and oxygen pressures in the blood perfusing the central nervous system exercise a direct effect upon the activities of the neurons comprising the spinal and medullary vasomotor centers much as the respiratory centers are influenced (Chap. 42). Thus when the lungs of an animal are overventilated with pure air, the carbon dioxide pressure in the blood is decreased and the blood pressure falls, due in part to a vasodilatation in the splanchnic region (Fig. 338A). When excessive ventilation is stopped and a slow rate of artificial respiration is substituted or natural respiration is permitted, the blood pressure rises with the increase in carbon dioxide pressure and the intestinal volume decreases (5). Artifically increasing the carbon dioxide content of the alveolar air, and so the pressure in the blood, results in a vasoconstriction in the splanchnic area accompanied by a rise in blood pressure. With the fall in the carbon dioxide pressure, the volume of the intestine increases, indicating a vasodilatation; at the same time the blood pressure returns toward normal. Compared with the medullary vasoconstrictor center which responds to 5 per cent carbon dioxide—decerebrate cat—the spinal vasomotor centers are much less sensitive, for they are effected in a spinal cat only by the inhalation of gas mixtures containing 25 per cent and upwards. The blood pressure changes are in the same direction, however, and appear to be similarly exercised through the action of the vasoconstrictor nerves to the splanchnic region.

The changes in arterial pressure wrought by altering the carbon dioxide pressure in the blood so closely parallel the changes in the hydrogen ion concentration of the blood—they fall and rise together—that it might be thought the alterations in pressure are consequences of the change in the H-ion concentration. However, Dale and Evans found that wide variations in the reaction of the blood produced surprisingly little effect upon the circulation in cats provided the variations were brought about by adding fixed acid or base to the blood. The characteristic fall in blood pressure occurred only when the carbon dioxide pressure in the blood was reduced; and though the reduction of the carbon dioxide pressure entailed an increase in the alkalinity of the blood, it is quite as effective when the reaction was initially acid (so that the removal of the carbon dioxide increased the alkalinity of the blood toward normal) as it was when the blood was initially alkaline. In other words, the fall in blood pressure due to the reduction of the carbon dioxide in the blood is due to acapnia—a marked diminution in the amount of carbon dioxide in the blood—rather than to an alkalosis, a condition in which the blood is unduly alkaline. An increase above the normal oxygen pressure in the blood leaving the lungs does not affect the vasomotor centers directly; however, a reduction in the oxygen pressure in the inspired air, such as may be brought about by giving a decerebrate preparation nitrogen to breathe,

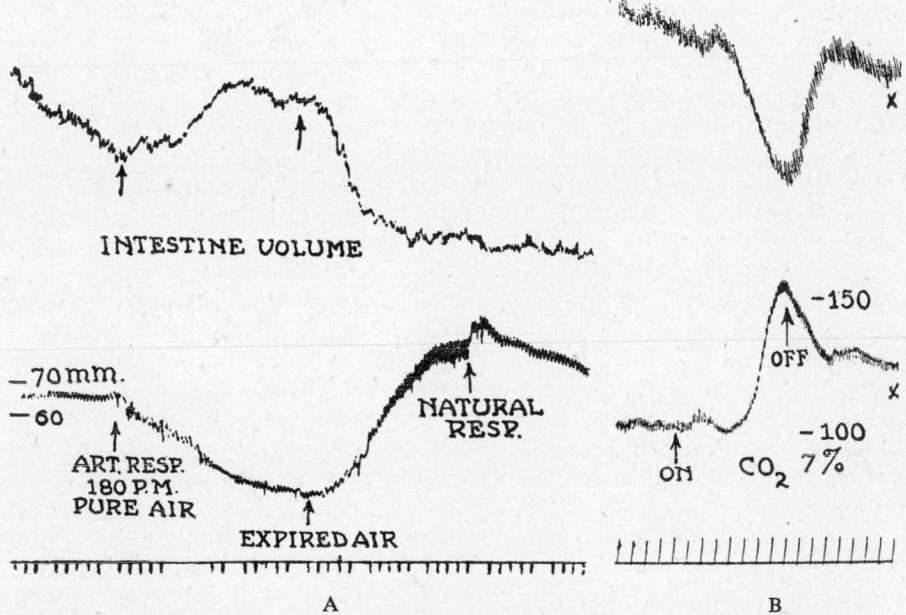

Fig. 338.—Kymograph records illustrating (A) the fall in systemic blood pressure which accompanies hyperventilation (Dale and Evans) and (B) the rise in blood pressure—lower curve—and the fall in intestinal volume—upper curve—when 7 per cent of CO_2 is added to the inspired air (Mathison). (From Dale and Evans, *J. Physiol.*, 1922, *56*:125–145; and Mathison, *Ibid.*, 1911, *42*:280–300.)

is accompanied by a vasoconstriction in the splanchnic region and a rise in blood pressure (Fig. 338B). Both the spinal and medullary vasomotor centers are affected, for a similar decrease in volume follows when the lungs of a spinal preparation are ventilated with nitrogen. There is, however, this difference: the spinal centers are less sensitive. The medullary center of the cat, according to Mathison (15), is affected by a period of oxygen lack of 40 seconds' duration, whereas the spinal vasomotor centers do not alter the vascular bed of the intestine under similar circumstances until the oxygen has been withheld for two minutes (14).

By direct action on the arterioles. The chemical substances which bring about arteriolar constriction and relaxation by direct action upon them may, for purposes of description, be divided into two groups: (i) the metabolites and (ii) the hormones. In the first group carbon dioxide, oxygen, hydrogen and hydroxyl ions may be included; in the second epinephrine, sympathin E and I, pituitrin and renin. The latter exercise a general effect on the arterioles, the former, a local one.

Metabolites. Experiments in which portions of the vascular system were perfused with Ringer's solution or blood have demonstrated that a rise in the hydrogen ion concentration, an increase in the carbon dioxide pressure, or a reduction in the oxygen pressure of the perfusing fluid tends to relax the arterioles by direct action and to increase the flow for the same head of pressure. Conversely, a rise in the concentration of the hydroxyl ion or an increase in the oxygen pressure has a constricting effect. Under normal conditions the hydrogen ion concentration tends to rise in an active tissue due to the increased production and local accumulation of carbon dioxide or lactic acid; simultaneously the oxygen pressure in the tissue diminishes. Both circumstances favor arteriolar dilatation and a compensatory increase in blood flow. Thus the local effects of a rise in the carbon dioxide pressure and the fall in oxygen are the opposite of those which are exercised through the carotid and aortic bodies or directly on vasomotor centers. Nevertheless, the two actions are complementary; the action via the nervous system, general arteriolar constriction, by raising the blood pressure increases the rate of flow through the locally dilated arterioles.

Hormones. The addition of small amounts of epinephrine—the active principle of the medulla of the adrenal gland—to the circulating blood either by intravenous injection or increased activity of the gland has a differential effect upon the arterioles. The effects produced are just those which would follow stimulation of the sympathetic supply to the arterioles of the organ or tissues in question. The arterioles of the skin, the mucous membranes, and the splanchnic bed constrict; at the same time the coronary arteries—in the dog, at least—dilate, as do the arterioles in the skeletal muscle.

The constrictor effect of epinephrine on the arterioles of the splanchnic bed, the skin, and mucous membranes parallels and serves to reinforce the action of the sympathin E which, according to Cannon and his collaborators, is liberated through the activity of fibers of the sympathetic system which constrict arterioles; the dilator effect on the coronary arteries and the arterioles of skeletal muscle parallels the action of sympathin I. Sympathin I appears to be the active agent liberated through the activity of sympathetic fibers which dilate blood vessels. As these two substances, sympathin E and I, are not rapidly destroyed, they circulate in the blood and may act some distance from the site of their production. For this reason they have been grouped under the hormones rather than the metabolites.

Though any participation by the pituitary gland in the normal control of the arterioles remains to be discovered, extracts of the posterior lobe—the pars nervosa—yield a substance, pituitrin, which, if introduced into the circulation in appropriate amounts, produces a vasoconstriction in the systemic arterioles and the coronary and pulmonary vessels. Compared with epinephrine, the effect is of shorter duration, and a second injection soon after the first is usually followed by vasodilatation.

In addition to the metabolites and hormones, there are some other substances affecting the arterioles directly that merit consideration though they are not easily classified, i. e., histamine and adenylic acid. Histamine (beta-imidazolylethylamine), derived from the acid, histidine, is present in all mammalian tissues in a bound and inactive form. It produces arteriolar dilatation in man, monkey and dog, and the suggestion has been made that the release of histamine in excessive amounts when tissues are mutilated may account for the fall in blood pressure and the marked capillary dilatation observed in traumatic shock. Adenylic acid is one of the substances—phosphate is the other—formed when adenyl-pyrophosphate breaks down during muscular activity and has been found in extracts of cardiac and skeletal muscles, the spleen, the kidney and the brain. When injected intravenously, it produces general dilatation of the arterioles and a slowing of the heart. The importance of adenylic acid, like that of histamine, rests on the possibility that it may be released into the circulation as a result of tissue damage.

Yet another substance of interest because of its action on the arterioles is angiotonin. An extract that may be obtained from the kidney, renin, acts as an enzyme on a subtrate associated with the pseudoglobulin fraction of the blood to produce a pressor substance, angiotonin. The principal action of this substance appears to be to increase the peripheral resistance by vasoconstriction through a direct action on arteriolar muscles. In normal individuals angiotonin is quickly inactivated, and does not appear to have any role in the maintenance of normal blood pressure. But it remains active in the circulation of hypertensives for longer periods and may play a considerable part in the maintenance of a high peripheral resistance and thus keep the blood pressure at hypertension levels.

REFERENCES

1. BARRON, D. H. and MATTHEWS, B. H. C. Dorsal root potentials. *J. Physiol.*, 1938, *94:* 27–29P.

2. BAYLISS, W. M. *The vaso-motor system.* New York, Longmans, Green and Co., 1923. 163 pp.

3. BRONK, D. W. and STELLA, G. Afferent impulses in the carotid sinus nerve. *J. cell. comp. Physiol.*, 1932, *1:*113–130.

4. BURN, J. H. Sympathetic vasodilators. *Physiol. Rev.*, 1938, *18:*137–153.

5. DALE, H. H. and EVANS, C. L. Effects on the circulation of changes in the carbon-dioxide content of the blood. *J. Physiol.*, 1922, *55:*125–145.

6. FAFANOW, L. L. and TSCHALUSSOW, M. A. Über die Beziehungen des N. depressor zu den vasomotorischen Zentren. *Pflüg. Arch. ges. Physiol.*, 1913, *151:*543–582.

7. FOERSTER, O. The dermatomes in man. *Brain*, 1933, *56:*1–39.

8. GAMMON, G. D. and BRONK, D. W. The discharge of impulses from Pacinian corpuscles in the mesentery and its relation to vascular changes. *Amer. J. Physiol.*, 1935, *114:*77–84.

9. GASKELL, W. H. *The involuntary nervous system.* New York, Longmans, Green and Co., 1916. 178 pp.

10. HEYMANS, C. and BOUCKAERT, J. J. Les chémo-récepteurs du sinus carotidien. *Ergebn. Physiol.*, 1939, *41:*28–55.

11. HINSEY, J. and GASSER, H. S. The Sherrington phenomenon. *Amer. J. Physiol.*, 1928, *87:*368–380.

12. KATZ, L. N. and JOCHIM, K. Observations on the innervation of the coronary vessels of the dog. *Amer. J. Physiol.*, 1939, *126:* 395–401.

13. McDOWALL, R. J. S. *The control of the circulation of the blood.* New York, Longmans, Green and Co., 1938. 619 pp.

14. MATHISON, G. C. The action of asphyxia upon the spinal animal. *J. Physiol.*, 1910, *41:*416–449.

15. MATHISON, G. C. The effects of asphyxia upon medullary centres. Part I. The vasomotor centre. *J. Physiol.*, 1911, *42:*283–300.

16. RANSON, S. W. and BILLINGSLEY, P. R. Vasomotor reactions from stimulation of the floor of the fourth ventricle. Studies in vasomotor reflex arcs. III. *Amer. J. Physiol.*, 1916, *41:*85–90.

17. SUH, T. H., WANG, C. H. and LIM, R. K. S. The effect of intracisternal applications of acetylcholine and the localization of the pressor tract and center. *Chin. J. Physiol.*, 1936, *10:*61–78.

18. TOENNIES, J. F. Reflex discharge from the spinal cord over the dorsal roots. *J. Neurophysiol.*, 1938, *1:*378–390.

CHAPTER 34

REGULATION OF ARTERIAL PRESSURE

BY WILLIAM F. HAMILTON

The arterial pressure varies with the systole and diastole of the heart. Each systolic discharge effects an increase in the pressure from 80 to 120 mm. Hg; during diastole the pressure falls to 80 mm. Hg. The rise in pressure is due to the increased rate at which blood enters the arterial system during ventricular systole over that of arteriolar drainage; the fall results from the escape of blood through the arterioles. The elastic recoil of the arterial wall maintains the pressure and the flow through the arterioles during diastole.

Methods for measuring the systolic and diastolic pressure have been discussed in Chapter 31. The mean pressure is best recorded by the mercury manometer. As it is ordinarily used, the record of the mercury manometer fluctuates above the mean pressure during systole and below that pressure during diastole. The amplitude of these fluctuations varies with the length of the interval between heart beats rather than with the pulse pressure. The use of a very small cannula or of a constriction in the tubing leading from the cannula to the mercury manometer reduces the size of the fluctuations until the tracing approaches one of the mean pressure. The tracing then represents a ballistic integration of the arterial pulse pressure contours, recording their average height. The mean arterial pressure is subject to physiological regulation so that in conditions which involve a wide variation in blood flow there is a mean pressure head, within physiological limits, for the distribution of blood to the various organs. During exercise, blood flow —cardiac output—may increase fivefold with but a small change in the arterial pressure (24, 26); hence there must be a simultaneous fivefold decrease in the peripheral resistance with the rise in blood flow. This decrease in resistance is the result of the dilatation of the arterioles in the skeletal muscles.

The regulation of the mean arterial pressure involves, then, striking a balance between the cardiac output and arteriolar drainage. When the activity of any one of the several organs of the body increases, there is an increase in the local metabolic requirements which is met by an increased blood flow. These requirements are satisfied by means of local nervous and hormonal mechanisms discussed in Chapters 29 and 33, which dilate the arterioles in the vascular bed of the active organ and permit increased arteriolar drainage locally. The increased rate of drainage tends to reduce the arterial pressure, and if a sufficient number of organs is active at one time the tendency toward a reduction in arterial pressure is further increased. To offset this tendency, additional reflex adjustments are required. The adjustments which occur are of two varieties: first, an increase in the output of the heart brought about by nervous acceleration of its rate, and second, a constriction of the arterioles in the inactive organs, for the peripheral resistance is controlled through constriction and dilatation of the arterioles.

The peripheral resistance may be expressed as varying directly with pressure and inversely with flow, in accordance with the formula:

$$R = \frac{P}{F}$$

If P is expressed as dynes per cm.² and flow as cm.³ per second, the expression becomes:

$$R = \frac{\dfrac{dynes}{cm.^2}}{\dfrac{cm.^3}{sec.}}$$

which may be simplified into:

$$R = \frac{dyne\ secs.}{cm.^5}$$

When values for arterial pressure and blood flow are used in this formula, the peripheral resistance is expressed in absolute units with numerical values which differ widely in different organisms. The value is of the order of 2000 absolute units in normal man and it may be as high as 5000 in hypertensive disease, for the pressure increases but the flow remains normal. In smaller animals—dogs, for example—the figure in absolute units is much larger than it is in man and the flow is very much less. In very small animals such as mice and rats, the figure assumes astronomical values and the variation within the species, depending as it does upon the size of the individual, is so wide that figures from normal individuals are difficult to interpret.

The reason for the difficulty is quite apparent. The large number of arterioles in a large animal offers a great deal less resistance to flow than the smaller number of arterioles in a small animal. This is true even if the arterioles in both animals are in the same degree of constriction and are completely normal. It may be better, therefore, to correct any formulation for peripheral resistance by a factor which introduces the size of the animal. The surface area is the measurement which is most closely correlated with blood flow and metabolism (7). Hence it has been suggested (2) that the resistance be formulated as follows:

$$R = \frac{3\ M}{\dfrac{F}{A}}$$

where M is the mean pressure in mm. Hg, F is the cardiac output in liters per minute, and A is the surface area in square meters. This expression provides a value which in normal man and most other normal animals varies less widely than the figure expressed in absolute units. During experimental procedures a rise or fall in the peripheral resistance value calculated in this manner is similar in all organisms.

As stated above, the peripheral resistance resides predominantly in the arterioles, for the resistance to flow is inversely proportional to the fourth power of the diameter of the channel through which flow takes place. As the arteries subdivide, their cross-sectional area increases; together the two branches of an artery have a cross-sectional area of about one and one-third that of the trunk from which they spring. But the resistance to flow in the smaller vessels is somewhat greater than it is in the larger vessels. As branching continues, this increase in the resistance to flow is negligible until the arterioles are reached. Thus the mean pressure in the dorsalis pedis artery is quite the same as it is in the aorta, an indication that the frictional losses in the great vessels between these two regions are very small and a consequence of the fact that as the blood slows up in the peripheral vessels some of the energy which had existed at the root of the aorta as kinetic energy, or velocity, has become transmuted into pressure energy in the peripheral vessels. When the pressure is measured in the capillaries just below the arterioles, the mean figure is much lower than it is in the prearteriolar vessels, whereas the drop between the arterial and venous ends of the capillaries is small. A marked drop in pressure is associated, therefore, with the movement of blood across the arteriolar bed. This drop in pressure is greater when the arterioles are constricted and less when they are dilated. Further, the fact that the great drop in pressure occurs in the arterioles justifies our statement that the peripheral resistance resides in these vessels, and it points to the conclusion that the peripheral resistance is regulated by controlling their average diameter.

The regulation of the peripheral resistance is brought about by hormonal and nervous mechanisms, which act on the arteriolar musculature. In normal man the resistance is due fundamentally to the natural or myogenic tone of the arteriolar walls. This normal muscular tone of the arterioles may have, and probably does, a hormonal genesis because in renal hypertension the basic blood pressure level is much higher than it is in a normal individual. The higher basal level is attributed to the presence, in abnormally large amounts, of a renal vasotonic principle which circulates in the blood and is elaborated by a precursor secreted into the blood by the kidney. Antagonistic substances have been extracted which destroy this hormone or its precursor and which set the basic blood pressure level at a lower figure (normal or below). Since these renal pressor principles operate without producing striking changes in blood flow, it is to be assumed that they react upon the arterioles, changing the fundamental myogenic tone of their musculature. The blood flow to each of the several organs is regulated by local oxygen requirements, and since there is no great change during renal hypertension in the oxygen consumption, neither is there any in the total blood flow or in the manner in which the blood flow is distributed to the several organs of the body.

Nervous influences acting through the sympathetic and parasympathetic systems also affect the peripheral resistance. In general, the activity of the parasympathetic system, together with the outflow through the dorsal roots, tends to decrease it, whereas the activity of the sympathetic system serves to increase the resistance. It is generally held that the tone of the arterioles is the algebraic sum of the simultaneous activity of both divisions of the autonomic nervous system. This is probably true in the case of an anesthetized animal which has been subjected to extensive surgical manipulations, but it may not be in an animal that is in a normal physiological state. That nervous influences play a small role in the control over the state of the arterioles is indicated by the fact that paralysis by spinal anesthesia of a major portion of the vasoconstrictor nerves of a normal recumbent man produces little or no change in his average blood pressure or in the distribution of the blood to the several organs (21). If, while he is under the influence of the spinal anesthetic, the man is tipped into an upright or partly upright position, his blood pressure falls to a very low figure and he faints. The inference is that, although the tone of his blood vessels is such as to maintain a normal arterial pressure when he is recumbent and the venous return is large, when he is tipped to a vertical position the caudal vasoconstrictor nerves are paralyzed and no response can be made to the fall in blood pressure resulting from a diminished venous return (9, 15, 16). This experiment further demonstrates that the paralysis of vasoconstrictor activity does not decrease the peripheral resistance, though it will do so in an animal which is under an anesthetic and has suffered from a severe operation such as a laminectomy. Further, there is no increase in the peripheral resistance when the parasympathetic endings of an animal are paralyzed by atropine; nor is there any great decrease when a sympatholytic drug is administered or when the animal is totally sympathectomized. It appears, therefore, that nervous influences affect the peripheral resistance in response to definite stimuli and to situations which resemble an emergency.

The action of nervous influences can be illustrated by consequences of increased activity in an organ or system of organs. This activity produces a local arteriolar dilatation and increase in blood flow. If the increase in flow is great enough, it will result in a reduction of pressure in the great arteries. In certain of these vessels, i. e., the carotid sinus, the aortic arch and the mesenteric blood vessels, there are stretch receptors. When the pressure is reduced the walls are stretched to a lesser degree, and there is a diminution in the number of impulses sent out by these receptors (4, 11). The diminution in the number of impulses reaching the vasomotor centers permits an increase in the tone of the sympathetic system and results in cardio-acceleration which empties the blood depots in the lungs and the liver, thereby augmenting the venous return and hence cardiac output. The increase in cardiac output restores the pressure toward normal and a new balance is struck with a greater output then before. As soon as the augmented flow through the active bed has had time to return to the heart there is no further depletion of the central blood depots.

If an increase in cardiac output brought about in the manner described is insufficient to maintain the blood pressure, there is further excitation of the sympathetic system which results in a constriction of the arterioles to such organs as are not active; the decrease in blood flow through these organs results in a net shunting of blood from the inactive to the active organ. The visceral organs are those which are primarily deprived of blood during very violent exercise. This deprivation may be so severe as to cause ischemic damage to these organs and to result in irreversible changes, leading to insufficiency of the circulation (heat stroke, shock).

An impending emergency likewise results in a generalized increase in sympathetic activity (5, 6). Such an emergency, accompanied by the emotions of fright or anger, may be elicited by a variety of painful stimuli. The sympathetic activity evolves cardio-acceleration, a generalized increase in the peripheral resistance and a rise in blood pressure. This rise is immediately moderated by the stimulation of the stretch receptors which have been mentioned above. Impulses which arise in the stretch receptors as a result of the increased blood pressure cause the heart to slow by their action in the vasomotor center, and later, if the increased blood pressure continues, a generalized peripheral vasodilatation follows. Any rise in blood pressure, whether it be produced by psychic influences as mentioned above or by the injection of vasoconstrictor drugs, will increase the activity of the stretch receptors in the aorta and carotid sinus and slow the heart, thus permitting the blood pressure to return toward normal. These stretch receptors may therefore be regarded as a safety valve or moderating influence. Whenever the blood pressure is high, they are stimulated to increase the number of impulses which reach the cardiac and vasomotor centers, slowing the heart by stimulating the vagus center and inhibiting the accelerator center. They bring about at the same time a decrease in peripheral resistance by inhibiting the vasoconstrictor apparatus, and stimulate to greater activity the mechanisms which bring about vasodilatation. When the blood pressure is reduced impulses are fewer in number, the sympathetic system assumes greater activity, the parasympathetic system less activity, the heart is accelerated, and the arterioles constrict. This response as a whole tends to maintain the blood pressure within physiological limits.

Denervation of the carotid sinus and aortic arch (section of the moderator nerves) leads to hypertension. This form of hypertension is not asymptomatic as is the form which is due to an interference with the blood supply to the kidney. In experimental renal hypertension, the peripheral resistance is increased equally in all parts of the body, the heart is regulated at a normal rate, and the high arterial pressure may be the only sign of anything amiss. This is in marked contrast to neurogenic hypertension which is produced by destruction of the moderator reflexes. Both the heart rate and blood pressure are unstable and tend to rise together. Blood flow is shunted away from those regions which have the most active vasoconstrictor supply. Both forms of hypertension are seen clinically and many patients suffer from derangements of both mechanisms. Obviously sympathectomy is of more use in neurogenic than in renal hypertension, though in the latter the operation may increase kidney blood flow and result in clinical improvement. One of the problems of the future is to learn to diagnose these two forms of hypertension (3, 13, 14, 25).

The cardiac regulation of the venous pressure is also due to a reflex mechanism in which the stretch receptors play an important role. An increase in venous pressure causes an inhibition of the vagus center (and perhaps a stimulation of the sympathetic center via the Bainbridge reflex) which results in acceleration of the heart and augmentation of its beat. This serves to pump blood out of the great veins and to reduce the activity of the stretch receptors which are situated at the roots of the great veins and in the right auricle (1). This is not a prepotent reflex as compared with the reflex described above, the receptors of which are in the walls of the arteries, because as soon as the arterial pressure rises to any considerable degree the heart is slowed even though the venous pressure be excessive. For this reason it is not easy to repeat experiments giving clear evidence of the reflex. Impulses from the receptors in the great veins and auricle may exercise vasomotor effects, though the final proof is wanting (17, 18).

The venous pressure is fundamentally related to the volume of blood which distends the vascular system. It is never permanently or generally elevated except when the blood volume is increased and the static pressure which distends the vascular tree (postmortem) is increased. The static pressure rises to the same degree after death from congestive heart failure as the venous pressure does during life (22, 23). After death from hemorrhage or shock the static pressure is very low. Before death the venous pressure is about as much below normal as the static pressure is after death. These low pressures indicate a low blood volume in proportion to the size of the vascular tree.

The veins, venules and capillaries can be greatly distended by very small changes in pressure. This is due to physical relationship as well as to physiological responses. Over the range of stretch, in which the walls of veins or capillaries have a constant elastic modulus, the walls can be distended indefinitely with no great rise in internal pressure. More and more tension must be applied to them to give them progressively more stretch, but as the hollow shape is enlarged, the area over which the pressure acts increases (27). A rubber balloon may be blown up to various sizes with small differences in pressure. Similarly the venous and capillary beds may be distended by very large volumes of fluid with little increase in pressure (19). Receptive relaxation of smooth muscle tone is usually regarded as the mechanism which permits hollow organs to be distended while the contents remain at a constant pressure. It must be recognized also that over ranges where Young's modulus remains constant, large increases in volume may occur with surprisingly small increases in pressure as a result of simple physical relationships.

The blood vessels are also responsive to chemical stimulation. The local effects of decreased oxygen tension, of increased carbon dioxide tension and of accumulated metabolites has already been discussed in terms of the regulation of blood flow to the several organs. When the oxygen transport to the brain is interfered with there results an increase in blood pressure. This is true whether the stimulus be an increase in intracranical pressure tending to collapse the brain blood vessels (8) or whether it be simple asphyxia through some interference with the respiratory process (20). In any case, this asphyxia leads to an increased activity of the vasoconstrictor centers and a marked rise in blood pressure. This rise in blood pressure may bring about a stimulation of the receptors in the aortic arch and carotid sinus and result in a slowing of the heart. Increased intracranial pressure, however, stimulates the vagal centers directly and produces a cardiac slowing whether the blood pressure rises or not (10).

The vasomotor and cardiac centers therefore differ from other tissues of the body in that they become more active under conditions in which the oxygen pressure falls rather than less so, as is the case with muscular tissue and most glands (12). This property is shared by the receptors for internal pain. Thus, when the heart is receiving an inadequate oxygen supply as a result of sclerosis of the coronary arteries, anginal pains develop. Pains similar in origin develop in skeletal muscles when they contract in the absence of a proper blood supply. This can be shown experimentally by inflating a cuff around the arm to a pressure above systolic and then moving the fingers. A severe pain in the forearm results. Ischemic pains in the legs are a prominent complaint of individuals suffering from senile arterial sclerosis, a consequence of the fact that such individuals are unable to increase the blood supply to their leg muscles.

REFERENCES

1. BAINBRIDGE, F. A. The influence of venous filling upon the rate of the heart. *J. Physiol.*, 1915, *50*:65–84.

2. BAZETT, H. C., COTTON, F. S., LAPLACE, L. B. and SCOTT, J. C. The calculation of the cardiac output and effective peripheral resistance from blood pressure measurements with an appendix on the size of the aorta in man. *Amer. J. Physiol.*, 1935, *113*:312–334.

3. BLALOCK, A. Experimental hypertension. *Physiol. Rev.*, 1940, *20*:159–193.

4. BRONK, D. W. and STELLA, G. Afferent impulses in the carotid sinus nerve; the relation of the discharge from single end organs to arterial blood pressure. *J. cell. comp. Physiol.*, 1932, *1*:113–130.

5. CANNON, W. B. *Bodily changes in pain, hunger, fear and rage.* New York, Appleton, 1915, xii, 324 pp.

6. CANNON, W. B. and ROSENBLUETH, A. *Autonomic neuro-effector systems.* New York, The Macmillan Company, 1937, xiv, 229 pp.

7. CLARK, A. J. *Comparative physiology of the heart.* London, Cambridge University Press, 1927. v, 157 pp.

8. CUSHING, H. Concerning a definite regulatory mechanism of the vasomotor center which controls blood pressure during cerebral compression. *Johns Hopk. Hosp. Bull.*, 1901, *12*:290–292.

9. EDHOLM, O. G. Effect of gravity on the blood pressure of the cat. *J. Physiol.*, 1940, *98*:79–96.

10. EDHOLM, O. G. The relation of heart rate to intracranial pressure. *J. Physiol.*, 1940, *98*:442–445.

11. GAMMON, G. D. and BRONK, D. W. The discharge of impulses from pacinian corpuscles in the mesentery and its relation to vascular changes. *Amer. J. Physiol.*, 1935, *114*:77–84.

12. GELLHORN, E. *Autonomic regulations, their significance for physiology, psychology and neuropsychiatry.* New York, Interscience Publishers, Inc., 1943. xii, 373 pp.

13. GRIMSON, K. S. Role of sympathetic nervous system in experimental neurogenic hypertension. *Proc. Soc. exp. Biol., N. Y.*, 1940, *44*:219–221.

14. HEYMANS, C. Some aspects of blood pressure regulation and experimental arterial hypertension. *Surgery*, 1938, *4*:487–501.

15. HILL, L. The influence of the force of gravity on the circulation of the blood. *J. Physiol.*, 1895, *18*:15–53.

16. MAYERSON, H. S. Effect of gravity on the blood pressure of the dog. *Amer. J. Physiol.*, 1942, *135*:411–418.

17. McDOWALL, R. J. S. A vago-pressor reflex. *J. Physiol.*, 1924, *59*:41–47.

18. McDOWALL, R. J. S. The effect of the peripheral resistance on the responses to the intravenous injection of fluid. *J. Physiol.*, 1941, *99*:5P.

19. MEEK, W. J. and EYSTER, J. A. E. The effect of plethora and variations in venous pressure on diastolic size and output of the heart. *Amer. J. Physiol.*, 1922, *61*:186–202.

20. SCHMIDT, C. F. Functions of carotid and aortic bodies. *J. Lab. clin. Med.*, 1940, *26:* 223–231.

21. SMITH, H. W., ROVENSTINE, E. A., GOLDRING, W., CHASIS, H. and RANGES, H. A. The effects of spinal anesthesia on the circulation in normal, unoperated man with reference to the autonomy of the arterioles, and especially those of the renal circulation. *J. clin. Invest.*, 1939, *18*:319–341.

22. STARR, I. and RAWSON, A. J. Role of the "static blood pressure" in abnormal increments of venous pressure, especially in heart failure. I. Theoretical studies on improved circulation schema whose pumps obey Starling's law of the heart. *Amer. J. med. Sci.*, 1940, *199*:27–39.

23. STARR, I. Role of the "static blood pressure" in abnormal increments of venous pressure, especially in heart failure. II. Clinical and experimental studies. *Amer. J. med. Sci.*, 1940, *199*:40–55.

24. TAYLOR, C. Studies in exercise physiology. *Amer. J. Physiol.*, 1941, *135*:27–42.

25. THOMAS, C. B. Experimental hypertension from section of moderator nerves: relationship of the acute pressor response to the development and cause of chronic hypertension. *Johns Hopk. Hosp. Bull.*, 1944, *74*:335–377.

26. WHITE, H. L. and MOORE, R. M. Circulatory responses to static and dynamic exercise. *Amer. J. Physiol.*, 1925, *73*:636–648.

27. WINTON, F. R. and BAYLISS, L. E. *Human physiology.* Philadelphia, P. Blakiston and Son, 1931. xiv, 583 pp.

CHAPTER 35

EVENTS OF THE CARDIAC CYCLE

BY HEBBEL E. HOFF

ORIGIN OF THE HEART BEAT

The sequential pattern of excitation in the heart is made possible by the fact that, physiologically, the heart is a single unit. An excitation arising in any part of a normal heart will be conducted to all other regions, whether conduction in any single pathway travels in the normal direction or antidromically. It is thus possible to initiate rhythms experimentally which start in the ventricles and later involve the auricles, and such reverse beats are frequently observed in man. In fact, all parts of the heart possess the ability to develop rhythmic discharges, as William Harvey first demonstrated in 1628 by cutting an excised heart into small bits and noting that each portion continued to beat by itself. He noticed, however, that the auricular portions beat much more frequently than the ventricular elements, and all observers since that time have agreed that there is a definite gradient in the frequency of isolated portions of the heart, starting with the highest rates in the sinus venosus, and terminating with very low rates, or even arrest, in the isolated ventricular apex.

These observations strongly suggest that the sequence of contraction in the various chambers of the heart is determined by the part of the heart which possesses the highest degree of spontaneous automaticity. An impulse arising in this part of the heart will be conducted to contiguous regions and excite them, and will continue to progress in like fashion over the entire heart, differing from an impulse passing over a nerve fiber only in the anatomical complexity of the pathways it follows and in the variations in rate of conduction associated with them.

Normally, in amphibia and reptiles, the cardiac impulse begins in the sinus venosus. This may be demonstrated by the fact that cooling or warming this region of the heart produces an appropriate change in the frequency of the heart beat, while local cooling and heating of the atria, or portions of the ventricle, fail to influence the rate of the heart. Dilute solutions of drugs known to influence the heart rate, such as acetylcholine, may be applied to various portions of the heart by means of small squares of filter paper soaked in the test solution. Only when they are placed over the sinus venosus do they alter the rate of the heart beat.

Pacemakers in the Embryo. The region of the sinus venosus, which can appropriately be termed the pacemaker of the heart, has for some time been regarded as being endowed with its particular properties because it was supposed that this was the first part of the embryonic heart to beat: according to Haller's aphorism, "primum movens, ultimum moriens." This concept has been thoroughly disposed of through the work of Patten and Kramer (20), who have made an extensive study of the developing heart of the chick by means of motion-picture photography. By mounting a developing chick embryo in a specially designed chamber on a microscopic stage, it was possible to photograph for later study the first beats of a developing heart. These beats occurred in embryos of 9 somites, after approximately 29 hours of incubation. The heart at this time was a simple, straight tube which was made up only of the bulboventricular portions. The atria and sinus venosus were as yet unformed, and were represented only by paired, unfused primordia which had no myocardial investment. The first contractions were isolated fibrillary twitches, restricted to the convex right side of the ventricle. In another hour (30 hours of incubation, 10 somites) these had coalesced to produce concerted movement of the entire right margin of the bulbo-ventricular region. Next came a similar involvement of the left side, and the entire ventricle showed synchronized contractions. These early contractions were not regular, but were interrupted by rest periods which became progressively shortened as a slow rhythm was established in embryos of 12 somites, after 32 hours of incubation.

During this time myocardium was slowly extending over the atrium, and after a time it, too, began to contract. Its rate of contraction, however, was higher than that of the ventricular myocardium, as could plainly be seen when an incision was made between them. The atrium thereby assumed the function of a pacemaker, the rate of the whole heart increased, and impulses could be seen starting in the atrium and sweeping forward over the ventricle. After 38 to 40 hours of incubation, in embryos possessing 16 to 17 somites, the atrial rate was strong and regular, blood was set in motion and a circulation began. The sinus venosus was still unformed and had little myocardium.

Several hours after circulation of the blood began, the sinus venosus was finally formed behind the atrium, and began to contract after it had been invested with myocardium. Its intrinsic rhythmicity was in turn greater than that of the atrium, and as it became incorporated into the heart it usurped the position of pacemaker, and further increased the rate of the heart (42 hours, 19 somites).

Structure of the pacemaker in mammalian hearts

In the mammalian heart the pacemaker has been found to be located in the sino-auricular node, a mass of modified muscle tissue situated near the termination of the great veins in the right atrium, which has been thought to represent the remnants in the mammalian heart of the sinus venosus itself. It is known, after its discoverers, as the node of Keith and Flack (13), whose original description is worth quoting:

"There is a remarkable remnant of primitive fibres persisting at the sino-auricular junction in all mammalian hearts examined [man, mole, porpoise, dolphin, kangaroo, wallaby, whale, mouse, shrew-mouse, rat, kitten, ram, pig, cart-horse, pony, fetal gibbon]. These fibres are in close connection with the vagus and sympathetic nerves, and have a special arterial supply; in them the dominating rhythm of the heart is believed normally to arise.

"The higher one ascends in the vertebrate scale, the less becomes the amount of the sinus musculature, but the greater the closeness of its connection with the canalar and auricular musculature. It therefore appears to us that sino-auricular 'block' cannot be due to an anatomical lesion of a narrow bridge of fibres, but must arise from the depression, probably of vagal origin, of the muscular tissue in this region. . . . Our search for a well-differentiated system of fibres within the sinus, which might serve as a basis for the inception of the cardiac rhythm, has led us to attach importance to this peculiar musculature surrounding the artery at the sino-auricular junction. In the human heart the fibres are striated, fusiform, with well-marked elongated nuclei, plexiform in arrangement, and embedded in densely-packed connective tissue—in fact, of closely similar structure to the Knoten [A–V node]. The amount of this musculature varies, depending on how much of the sinus has remained of the primitive type; but in the neighbourhood of the taenia terminalis there is always some of this primitive tissue found. Macroscopically, the fibres resemble those of the a.-v. bundle in being paler than the surrounding musculature, i.e., in being of the white variety. . . .

"The nature of this remnant is perhaps best exemplified in the heart of the mole. Here it is seen that at the sino-auricular junction there is a mass of remarkable tissue. It appears to the eye as a very intimate network of palely stained undifferentiated fibres with a large number of well-stained nuclei. It is totally different from the surrounding musculature, and contains but little fibrous tissue. Although the mass by its connections is undoubtedly muscular, the nerves in the neighbourhood of the superior vena cava appear to come into very intimate connection with it, so much so that we feel justified in stating that a highly-differentiated neuro-muscular junction occurs at this point. In this heart also the bundle [A-V node] is of absolutely identical structure."

A view somewhat at variance with this concept of the fibers of the sino-auricular node as constituting a unique group of myocardial cells quite distinct in histological structure and embryological origin from the associated atrial musculature has been expressed by Glomset and Glomset (8). They consider the sino-auricular node to be an integral part of the muscular sheet known as Bachman's bundle. This is a stout, transverse band of muscle which runs between the bases of the right and left auricular appendages. From the right of this band, a sheet of muscle spreads out fanlike to envelop the superior vena cava posteriorly and anteriorly, to form the bottom and the sides of the sulcus terminalis, and to form a part of the wall of the right appendage. The part of this sheet which happens to lie in the bottom of the sulcus and its immediate neighborhood is what has been described as the node of Keith and Flack. The fact that the muscle fibers in this region become a little more slender and are less distinctly striated is to be ascribed, Glomset and Glomset think, to their environment. Hence, "nodal" muscle fibers exist on both sides of the caval entrance as well as below and above it. Glomset and Glomset were also impressed by the abundance of nerve fibers and ganglion cells found in the immediate vicinity of the nodal tissue.

The two views are not inconsistent as far as two salient features are concerned. There is agreement that the node is essentially muscular, being woven into the surrounding musculature by countless branching fibers if it is not, in fact, an integral part of the myocardium of this region. It is also clear that the region is particularly richly supplied by nerve fibers and ganglion cells. These two facts provide the background for our understanding of the origin and regulation of the heart beat in this region.

Experimental localization of the pacemaker

Local heating and cooling, local injury, and local application of drugs may be employed, as in the cold-blooded heart; by these means the heart beat may usually be found to originate in the region of the sino-auricular node. Two techniques which permit of more precise localization have been proposed by Lewis (15). The first involves recording the action potentials arising in the atria with each heart beat. When two electrodes connected to an electrocardiograph are placed at random on the surface of the heart, the direction of the initial deflection will indicate which region of the heart first became negative. By inference, this region (electrode A) must have been excited before the region under the other electrode (B). Electrode B is then moved, in an attempt to find a region which shows negativity before the area under electrode A. If one is found, electrode A is moved to find a region which is activated still earlier. Finally, a region is found which shows negativity in advance of any other area. In the dog, this is usually a small region a millimeter or so square, at the cephalic end of the sino-auricular node. The other method is to elicit extrasystoles by stimulation of various parts of the heart, and to record them by means of the usual electrocardiographic leads. Since the electrocardiogram reflects the particular sequence of excitation in the heart, the complex described by the extrasystole will not be exactly the same as the normal complex unless the pathway of the extrasystole reproduces precisely the normal beat. This can only occur if the extrasystole starts in exactly the same place as the normal beats, namely, in the pacemaker. A third method, which agrees entirely with the two methods of Lewis, makes use of the observation of Rijlant that when electrodes leading to a suitable amplifier and recording system are placed over the pacemaker, a wave of low amplitude will be found to precede the action potential of the sino-auricular node. This "presinus wave" can be found only in records taken from a small area at the head of the S-A node in the normally beating heart.

Neurogenic and Myogenic Theories of the Heart Beat. The discussion among physiologists as to whether the initial impulse starting the heart beat originates in the heart muscle itself, or in nerve cells, has almost entirely ceased, with the vast majority of physiologists in agreement with the myogenic doctrine as far as the heart of vertebrates is concerned. Inasmuch as the centuries-old problem served as a direct or indirect stimulus for much of the basic information about the heart that we now possess, the outstanding features of the development of the modern concept are worth recounting. It will be seen that although the heart beat originates in muscle tissues, the essential physiological properties of pace-making myocardial cells which make possible the rhythmic beat of the heart are little if any different from those of nerve fibers, nerve cells, sense organs, and even skeletal muscle fibers, which can and under the proper circumstances do act like the pacemaker to set up autogenic rhythms.

The ancients, especially Galen, recognized that the heart is a muscle, and, since Galen clearly recognized that skeletal muscle is controlled by nerves, it is only natural that the assumption was made that the heart, too, owed its contraction to nervous influences. The first complete statement of this supposition was probably made by Willis, who explained the fact that the heart was obviously far less under the control of the nervous system than skeletal muscles, by dividing muscular action into two divisions, voluntary and involuntary. The voluntary functions were directed from the cerebral hemispheres, while the involuntary functions were subject to the control of the cerebellum. In proposing this, Willis was impelled by two mistaken observations; he thought that the vagus nerves originated in the cerebellum, and he had noticed that attempts to remove the cerebellum were invariably fatal, not realizing that death was in fact due to damage to the underlying medulla. Haller summarized the evidence against this view, calling particular attention to the failure of the heart to stop when the vagus nerves were cut, or even when the heart was entirely removed from the body. He proposed that the heart was itself irritable, that is, able to contract when stimulated (he used the term "irritability" in its restricted sense, meaning by it exactly what we now mean by "contractility"), and was stimulated to contract by the inflow of venous blood.

Haller's views never completely disposed of the neurogenic theories, and in fact Haller himself admitted the possibility that a local nervous reflex might equally well account for many of the observations in favor of the myogenic theory. The neurogenic theory was soon supported by Le Gallois who in 1812 reported that decapitated animals maintained by artificial respiration invariably died when the spinal cord was destroyed. He argued that the heart depends for its continued contraction upon the presence of at least a portion of intact spinal cord, and assumed that the sympathetic nervous system, which was associated with the cord, was the mediator of the influence it exerted upon the heart. Le Gallois was obviously unaware of the work of Fontana, who had destroyed completely the central nervous system of frogs without killing them, or of Whytt, who even earlier than Fontana had remarked that the regular alternate contraction of the hearts of frogs persisted for five or six hours after decollation and destruction of their spinal marrow.

These objections to Le Gallois' view, and those that subsequently demonstrated that even in the mammal the heart will continue to beat after complete destruction of the spinal cord, were unable to dislodge the neurogenic doctrine because of a new development. Unzer and Prochaska, in their development of the doctrine of reflexes, in which, incidentally, they introduced the term "reflex," postulated that excised hearts continued to beat because of intrinsic nervous reflexes, and Bichat extended this view by suggesting that the ganglia of the sympathetic system are not only reflex centers but true centers of involuntary action, in the same sense that the brain is the center of voluntary activity. Remak concluded the evidence by discovery of the ganglion named after him, which he described in these words, "Because of this one must assume that the movements of the heart depend especially upon sympathetic nerve fibers, and thus upon the ganglia. This view receives a confirmation amounting almost to certainty through a second observation, which I take this opportunity to report, that along the peripheral branches of the cardiac nerves there are to be found countless tiny, almost microscopic ganglia lying partly superficially and partly buried in the muscle fibers."

The structure of the neurogenic doctrine, soon greatly fortified by the discovery, by the Webers, of the inhibitory influence of the vagus nerves, dominated physiological thinking for over half a century. During this period two isolated observations were made that pointed the way to the work of Gaskell and others who have re-established the myogenic doctrine. The first was the report by Purkinje, who wrote, "On the inner walls of the ventricles of sheep's hearts, I saw, first with the naked eye, a network of fine, flat, jelly-like fibers lying just under the endocardium, which continued partly into the papillary muscles and around other fiber bundles, and partly bridged over single folds and fissures of the heart wall." This was, of course, the Purkinje system of modified muscle fibers which in mammals serves for the rapid distribution of the cardiac impulse within the ventricles. The second was the rediscovery by Bidder of the protoplasmic intercommunications between individual fibers in the myocardium, which serves as the anatomical basis for the physiological concept that the whole heart is in fact a single functional unit in which its functions of genesis of rhythm and intracardiac conduction may be carried out without recourse to external agencies.

The present myogenic theory had its inception in the elucidation by Gaskell of the true function of the ganglia of Bidder, Remak and Ludwig, namely, that they are the ganglia of the vagus nerves, and function solely to transmit to the heart muscle impulses arriving via these nerves. The clear demonstration that heart muscle can beat rhythmically in the absence of nerve cells, whether excised from intact hearts, or in the embryo before neuroblasts reach the heart, or in tissue culture, adds to the impression that in the normal vertebrate heart the impulse that starts the heart beat originates in the muscle cell itself, and that the action of the nerves is to modify the beat to meet the ever-changing conditions with which the heart and circulation must cope. It is equally clear that automaticity in heart muscle requires no new concepts, and that in acting as a pacemaker, cardiac muscle behaves very much like nervous tissue.

Refractory period and rhythmic discharge

When Haller postulated that the heart beats because it responds, by virtue of its inherent irritability, to the stimulus of inflowing blood, his suggestion was countered by the demand for an answer to the question of why it relaxed, rather than remaining contracted, for it was never really emptied of blood, and in fact could be shown to relax even when blood was prevented from flowing out by the ligation of pulmonary and systemic aortae. The first to come forward with an adequate answer was Fontana (see 12), who suggested that it relaxed because the act of contraction exhausted its store of irritability, and this required a given time for restoration. Only when its irritability was sufficiently re-established could the heart again respond to the ever-present stimulus of the blood in its cavities. This suggestion was supported by the observation that once a frog's heart contracted in response to a mechanical stimulus, it could not be maintained in a state of contraction by further stimulation, and, in fact, would respond to a second stimulus only after it had fully relaxed from the first contraction. This observation, which is probably the earliest recognition of the refractory period in any tissue, was no doubt inspired by the generally held notion that all active organs need periods of rest and recuperation, and that since the heart cannot obtain such rest during the hours of sleep, it must get its rest between beats. It is interesting that this suggestion goes at least as far back as Senac, the famous French cardiologist of the early eighteenth century, who wrote:

25

"A physician has suggested that the animal spirit is subject to exhaustion, and that time is required for its re-accumulation. The muscles throughout the body are capable of exerting only a certain degree of energy, and this force being exhausted, sleep is necessary

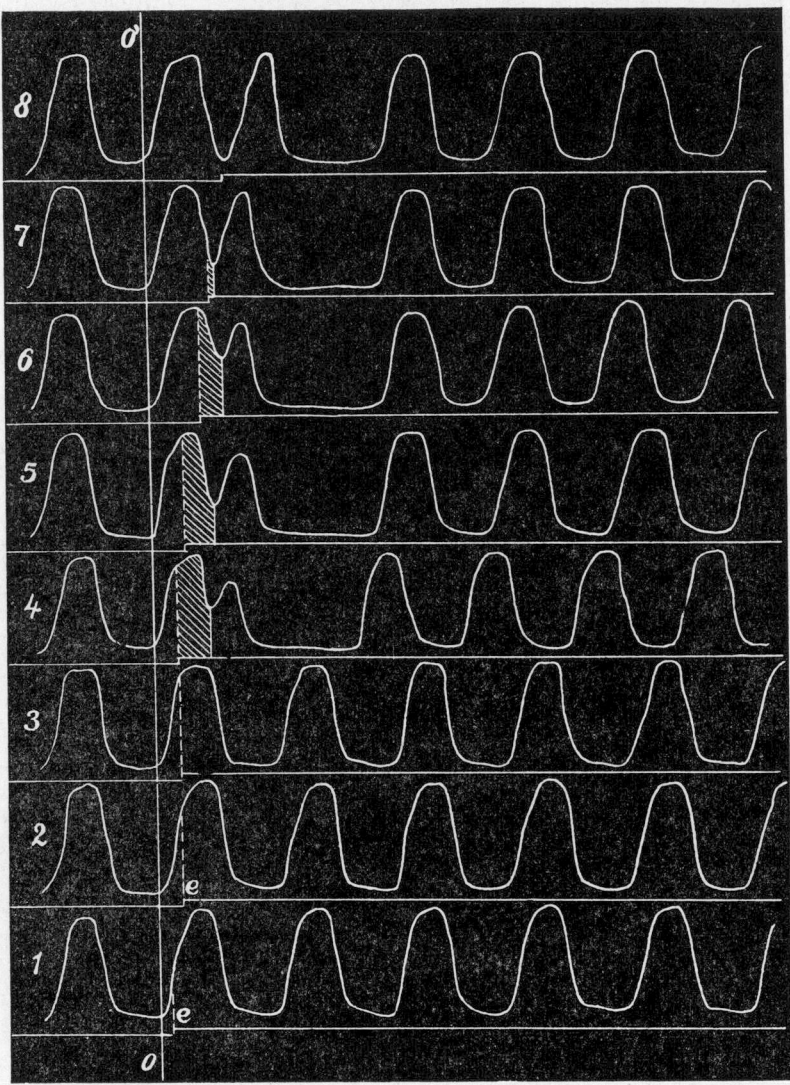

Fig. 339.—Marey's original figure illustrating the refractory period. The record is taken from the frog's heart. In 1, 2, and 3 the stimulus (e) falls in the heart during systole (refractory period) and has no effect. In 4, 5, 6, 7, and 8 the stimulus falls toward the end of systole or during diastole, and is followed by an extra systole and corresponding compensatory pause. It will be noted that the latent period (shaded area) between the stimulus and the extra systole is shorter the longer diastole has proceeded before the stimulus is applied.

to repair them. The heart also requires repose like other muscles, but this repose cannot be continuous as in other muscles, which is why it is divided into instants, and the sum of these instants is equal to the duration of sleep. Thus according to this opinion the heart is under the necessity of sleeping."

Later workers, particularly Marey, contributed much to the precise knowledge of the subject by showing that during the greater part of systole the heart shows no response to stimulation, however intense; it is "absolutely refractory," to employ the term used first by Carlson (Fig. 339). Following the absolutely refractory period, the heart will respond to a stimulus, but at a threshold higher than normal; the heart is now "relatively refractory." The duration of the relatively refractory period, during which the threshold falls gradually toward normal, is variable. It may be long, extending up to the next beat, or it may be, and usually is, quite short, leaving a fairly long interval of level threshold.

The presence of such an interval of unchanging threshold effectively disposes of any such simple theory as that mentioned above. Obviously, the heart rhythm cannot evolve from the simple interplay of some constantly acting "inner stimulus" and the refractory period. Were these two factors alone operative, a heart beat would be expected each time the refractory period of the pacemaker reached its normal level. Even more difficult to explain by any such theory is the fact that the pacemaker, like other portions of the heart in mammals as well as other forms, shows, following the relatively refractory period, a period of supernormal recovery during which the threshold is significantly lower than normal. The recognition of a subnormal period as a fourth and final stage of recovery accounts for the slow autogenous rhythms of certain motoneurons where beats are separated by intervals far greater than the absolutely refractory period, but this mechanism can hardly be postulated for the heart, in view of the failure to find any progressive changes in threshold in the pacemaker. *To summarize*, it can be stated that although the heart, and particularly the pacemaker, shows a classical recovery curve characterized always by an absolutely and a relatively refractory period, often by a supernormal period (and there seems no reason to doubt that a subnormal period of recovery will be found eventually), such threshold changes are themselves insufficient to account for the rhythmic beat of the heart.

Pacemaker potentials

The fact that a constant "inner stimulus" cannot account for the rhythmic discharge of the pacemaker, and the implication to be drawn from it that the "inner stimulus" to pacemaker activity in the heart is therefore a phasic affair, has certain direct evidence to support it, largely furnished by the work of Bozler (2, 3). Supporting evidence is found in studies of pacemaker activity in a variety of other tissues. In the ureter Bozler found that the rhythmic waves of contraction which sweep over this organ start in a restricted area at the renal end of the ureter. In this area of a ureter made quiescent with adrenaline, slow phasic swings of electric potential could be recorded, associated with "tonus waves" or small changes in muscular tension. These waves were purely local, were nonpropagated, and appeared at a frequency equal to that of the propagated contractile waves in the uninhibited ureteral pacemaker. In these, the slow, localized potentials could also be recorded, but now, at the negative peak of each wave (i.e., the time during which the pacemaker was most negative to nonpacemaking regions) a propagated disturbance was set up. Studies of the sinus venosus of the turtle heart, and of isolated tissue of the auricles and ventricles of mammalian hearts which beat spontaneously, reveal the presence in them, too, of rhythmic, slow, nonpropagated potential shifts. These, if they attain an intensity great enough (roughly one-fiftieth of the spike potential) and if the tissue has recovered adequately from a preceding response, act as a stimulus and set up a propagated discharge. Much the same results were obtained by Harris and Moe (11), who created ectopic pacemakers in the dog's ventricle by polarizing regions of the ventricles with low-voltage constant currents. With subthreshold polarization, the same type of slow, nonpropagated waves appeared that Bozler observed in spontaneous pacemakers. With increasing intensity of polarizing currents the amplitude of the rhythmic potential swings increased, until the threshold for a propagated discharge was reached, at which time a propagated beat appeared at the height of negativity at the pacemaker. Bozler calls these slow potential shifts which characterize pacemaker activity "prepotentials" because they initiate the much larger spike action currents characteristic of propagated discharges, and has shown that their intensity, as well as frequency, serves as an index of the inherent automaticity of any given tissue. This concept of rhythmic discharge is, of course, applicable to the intact mammalian heart, and appears to explain adequately the major problems. As yet, there are no reports of "prepotentials" at the mammalian pacemaker, unless we infer that these are actually what Rijlant recorded and called "presinus waves."

The influence of pH and calcium-potassium balance upon rhythmic behavior of isolated nerve and muscle tissue, as described by Lehman (14) and Adrian and Gelfan (1), affords some insight into the metabolic factors which determine rhythmic activity. Lehman noted in isolated mammalian nerve fibers, and Adrian and Gelfan observed in striated muscle, that pacemaker activity, developing out of the appearance of slow, spontaneous oscillations in potential, could be produced in a nerve by exposing it to an environment deficient in calcium ions, or strongly alkaline. On the contrary, the phenomenon could be repressed by high calcium or by acidity. A reciprocal activity between calcium and potassium was also found, an increased concentration of potassium having much the same effect as low calcium. While the influence of ions on the heart, especially in the mammal, is by no means as simple as reported in these experiments, it can thus be seen that the spontaneous action of pacemaker tissues is very directly influenced by the chemical composition of the surrounding medium.

The supernormal period

A third mechanism for the production of rhythmic discharge is that involving the supernormal period. While this mechanism plays no part in the normal beat of the heart, there is evidence that it may operate in the production of abnormal rhythms. The prototype of this reaction is a phenomenon observed by Wedensky. When a nerve fiber showing a supernormal period is stimulated near the muscle it supplies, with a slightly subliminal tetanizing current, no muscular response naturally takes place. When, then, a single threshold shock is applied to the nerve while the subliminal tetanus is continued, the muscle responds, not with a single twitch, but with a tetanus which continues as long as the previously subliminal stimulation is maintained. What has occurred is that following the first propagated disturbance set up by the single liminal shock, the stretch of nerve under the tetanizing current recovered via a supernormal period, during which the threshold was lowered sufficiently for the previously subliminal shocks to become effective. In response to one of them the nerve was excited a second time, only to pass again through supernormality, and again be stimulated by a shock which was below the threshold of a completely recovered nerve. In the heart this mechanism may be responsible for the "coupling" of extra-systoles to a previously normal beat to set up what is known as a "bigeminus" rhythm. Presumably a certain subliminal level of "inner" stimulation builds up in the ventricle, which is ordinarily not sufficient to initiate a beat. If the ventricle passes through a supernormal period, the stimulus may at this time be adequate to meet the lowered threshold, and the ventricle sets up a beat of its own. A general rise in threshold, possibly associated with the subnormal phase, interferes with a repetition of the ventricular beat until after another normal beat, when another complete ventricular beat occurs. Thus a regular alternation of normal and ectopic beats develops, with the ectopic beat occupying the position in the cycle in which supernormality is known to occur. This hypothesis is reinforced by the observation that agencies which are known to favor the development of supernormality, such as acid and veratrine, also facilitate the appearance of bigeminus rhythms.

In summary, it can be said that there are at least three means whereby rhythms may develop. In the first two the stimulus may be taken as constant, and the rhythm is determined by the refractory period. Relatively slow rhythms develop when the governing factor is the subnormal period; relatively rapid ones appear when the supernormal period is a marked feature of the recovery cycle. Apparently the first of these mechanisms cannot account for the rhythm of the vertebrate heart, while the second mechanism may be found only in certain abnormal rhythms. The third mechanism assumes the importance of all the classic changes in excitability during the recovery cycle as vitally influencing the threshold, but recognizes the presence of an intermittent stimulus, in the form of slow, nonpropagated potential swings at the pacemaker.

DISTRIBUTION OF THE CARDIAC IMPULSE

Just as the origin of the cardiac impulse in the mammalian heart is clearly myogenic in origin, so also it is almost universally agreed that the distribution of the impulse throughout the heart takes place solely through the myocardium itself without the mediation of nerves. Periodically, attempts to demonstrate a nervous factor are made. The general view is that conduction occurs along the fibers of the myocardium in much the same manner as along nerve fibers, at rates varying with the size of the fiber, i.e., the greater the diameter of the fiber the more rapid the transmission. At points of branching, an impulse is sent along each branch as in a branching axon. It is often considered that the fibers of the heart branch to such an extent that there is actual protoplasmic continuity throughout the heart. While this may be true in the amphibian and reptilian heart, it may not necessarily be the case in the mammalian heart. This does not constitute an unsurmountable barrier to the myogenic theory—in fact, one view of auriculoventricular conduction (see p. 726) postulates a protoplasmic discontinuity at this region.

Intra-auricular conduction

Within the auricle the cardiac impulse is conducted by the contractile elements themselves at a rate close to 1 meter per sec. (in the dog). Fibers lying around the S-A node are thus the first to be excited and the impulse travels by progressive activation of more and more distal regions. Fairly direct fibers passing to the left auricle and to the A-V node excite these regions somewhat in advance of the more distal regions of the right auricle itself simply because of the length of the pathway and not by virtue of any increased conductivity. The whole of the auricle in the dog is excited within 30 to 45 msec.

Auriculoventricular conduction

Conduction from the auricles to the ventricles is, from even superficial study, quite a different affair. The relative frequency with which A-V conduction is disturbed, and the delay between auricular and ventricular systoles, suggest the existence of a region of subnormal conductivity without the possibility of accessory pathways. This concept is reinforced by anatomical study of the region, which indicates that in mammals the auriculoventricular connections are restricted to a single muscular connection, the node of Tawara and the bundle of His. The node of Tawara, or the A-V node, is described as a small nodule of modified muscular tissue resembling that in the S-A node, situated in the septal wall of the right auricle immediately above the opening of the coronary sinus. The bundle of His is a continuation of this node, which runs forward on the septum, passes through the fibrous atrioventricular junction, and appears beneath the endocardium of the right ventricle under cover of the medial cusp of the tricuspid valve. Thence it extends forward along the posterior and lower border of the membranous upper part of the ventricular septum, and divides into right and left branches. It is said to be constituted of nodal fibers, and, especially lower down, of more and more large, pale staining fibers of the Purkinje type.* The delay between auricular and ventricular systoles may be taken as an evidence of some degree of block existing even under normal conditions (7). The usual explanation is that conduction in this region is unusually slow, in keeping with the small size of the fibers making up the node.

Another ingenious suggestion has been made that merits attention, however. This is the view that at the junction between the auricle and the node all protoplasmic continuity ceases, and a form of "synaptic" transmission occurs across a region of inexcitable tissue by virtue of electrotonic spread, much as takes place in transmission across blocked nodes in nerve fibers. The node is not, however, stimulated by the onset of the monophasic action potential of the near-by auricular musculature but by its declining phase. In a general way, this amounts to saying that it is the auricular T wave that stimulates the node rather than the auricular R wave, much as a rheoscopic frog preparation placed in contact with the heart will contract twice with each systole, being stimulated first by the potential changes responsible for the R wave and secondly by potentials which cause the T wave. Such a suggestion does not account easily for the fairly marked and progressive delays in A-V conduction that can often be observed.

Another indication that the A-V node and bundle are regions of depressed conduction is seen in the fact that conduction from ventricle to auricle does not take place as readily as conduction from auricle to ventricle. In a great proportion of instances, in fact, impulses arising in the ventricles (e.g., premature ventricular extrasystoles) fail to reach the auricles, while equally premature auricular extrasystoles do reach the ventricles. This may be il-

* Some recent studies (8) have suggested that in man the node and bundle are far less clear-cut anatomically and histologically than they are in some animals such as the sheep, and are much more closely related to ordinary myocardium. This view, which awaits confirmation in most of its details, tends, if anything, to emphasize the myocardial nature of the bridge between auricle and ventricle and does not require any fundamental reorganization of views of A-V conduction.

lustrated in the laboratory by stimulating the turtle's auricle with faradizing currents from a Harvard inductorium, producing a rapid irregular beat in the auricles, which will be transmitted to the ventricles, causing them to beat in much the same manner. When the ventricle is similarly stimulated, it alone will respond, while the auricles will continue to beat normally. Similarly, in auricular fibrillation, the ventricles may contract with abnormal rapidity, following a great number, at least, of the impulses that reach the node. In ventricular fibrillation, on the other hand, the auricles beat at their own rate, uninfluenced by the events in the ventricle. This fact is in keeping with present views on the transmission of impulses along normal tissue as well as across regions of block. According to them, stimulation occurs by electrotonic spread of the spike action potential ahead of the advancing wave front. The distance over which any particular impulse will stimulate will depend upon the size of the spike potential, other factors being equal. Thus, if an impulse from normal tissue, yielding a full sized action potential, arrives at a region of block it might be expected to stimulate tissue across the area of block, while another impulse, arriving at the same block along partially depressed tissue, which did not give as great a spike potential, might fail to cross it.

There is evidence that accessory pathways may exist for conduction between auricle and ventricle. Kent some time ago called attention to accessory muscular connections in laboratory animals, and these have been found to exist in man, although the frequency with which they may be found in man is unknown. If they exist, they apparently must be almost universally nonfunctional. It will be seen in a subsequent section that auricular and ventricular fibrillation may develop in the presence of alternative conducting pathways, so that an impulse may be conducted away from a point of stimulation by one pathway, only to return by another, restimulate the point of origin and so continue to travel around and around in the closed anatomical circuit, thus exciting the tissue at the starting point and initiating another impulse. The fact that auricular fibrillation never excites fibrillation in the ventricles and vice versa, may be taken to indicate that a single conductive pathway exists between the auricles and ventricles.

There may, however, be an exception to this rule. In rare instances in man electrocardiograms are seen which show more rapid A-V conduction than normal, and a somewhat prolonged ventricular excitation time. One of the most interesting suggestions as to the cause of the condition postulates an accessory muscular bridge between auricles and ventricles, by which A-V conduction is mediated at an accelerated rate. The accessory bridge excites the ventricles in an abnormal sequence, which is reflected in the abnormal appearance and delay in the ventricular part of the electrocardiogram. An individual showing the condition was noticed to suffer from attacks of rapid heart action, and died in the course of one of them. Careful histological study of the A-V junctional region revealed the presence of the accessory muscular connection postulated on the basis of the electrocardiogram and the attacks of tachycardia (26).

Intraventricular conduction

Once the region of block in the A-V node and bundle has been surmounted, the impulse spreads with great rapidity (5–6 meters per sec.) along the branches of the bundle and into the finer ramifications of the Purkinje network distributed throughout the endocardium of both ventricles. Although studies on this subject are incomplete, there is evidence that the whole of the endocardium may be fully activated within 6 to 7 msec. (right ventricle in the dog). From here on out to the surface, it was formerly supposed that impulses traveled in the ordinary heart muscle at a greatly reduced rate (400 mm. per sec.), but more recent histological study suggests that the ventricular walls are penetrated almost to the epicardium by fibers closely resembling the endocardial Purkinje fibers. These extend perpendicularly outward in the right ventricle, and more obliquely in the left. The supposition is that they constitute extensions of the endocardial Purkinje system, and provide for rapid extension of the impulse through the ventricular wall. However the impulse reaches the external surface of the heart, points on the surface are activated some 1 to 20 msec. later than their endocardial counterpart—never simultaneously or before. In the thinnest part of the right ventricle the interval ranges from 1 to 5 msec., while the longer times apply to the conus and the left ventricle.

Almost certainly because of the thinner muscular wall in the right ventricle, the impulse breaks through to the surface in this ventricle first, appearing over the anterior surface contiguous to the interventricular groove. Within the next 5 to 10 msec. practically the whole of the right ventricular surface has been activated in the dog (Fig. 340). The left responds slightly later, on

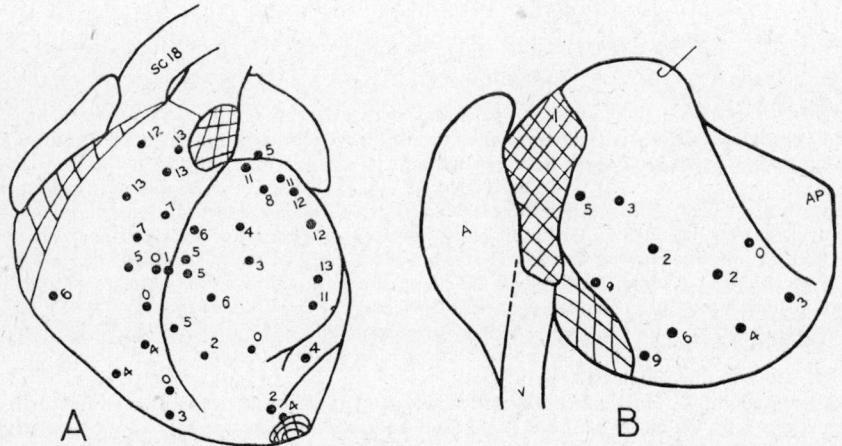

Fig. 340.—The spread of surface excitation in the monkey's heart. A, dorsal surface; B, ventral surface. Figures give intervals in milliseconds after earliest ventricular point recorded (labeled as 0). (From Harris, *Amer. J. Physiol.*, 1941, *134:*319.)

the whole, with the exception of regions contiguous to the right ventricle in the dog and toward the apex in the monkey, which become active from 2 to 5 msec. after the first appearance of activity in the left ventricle. Last of all, in many hearts, the conus region of the right ventricle responds. The total sequence of surface activation in the dog lasts for 18 to 23 msec., according to the most accurate measurements at present available. In the smaller heart of the monkey (Fig. 340) the whole space is in the neighborhood of 15 msec., and it may be presumed that in man the total duration will be in the neighborhood of twice that in the dog. It is significant that most studies of the excitation of surface areas fail to show any evidence of progression from point to point across the surface of the heart, as is seen in the auricle, in keeping with the concept that the walls of the ventricles, with the possible exception of the conus region, are excited from within outward.

There is, however, another and alternative account of the intraventricular course of the cardiac impulse. This is the suggestion by Robb (23) that the individual muscle bundles of which the heart is made up may be considered, like skeletal muscle, to have a separate blood supply and "innervation." Each muscle, which is considered to be anatomically isolated and without myocardial interconnections with other bundles, receives branches from the Purkinje system, and thereafter the impulse is distributed within the muscle bundle, either along the fibers themselves or by Purkinje fibers running along with the muscle fibers. This theory has been invoked to account for the tardy excitation of the conus region; the weight of the evidence, however, favors the radial spread of the impulse from endocardium to epicardium.

MECHANICAL EVENTS OF THE CARDIAC CYCLE

Auricular Systole. As each portion of the myocardium is excited by the spreading impulse, it begins to contract. As far as can be detected, the onset of electrical activity precedes by a very short interval any signs of contraction. The exact relationship between the two is, however, obscure. This develops in part because of the difficulty in distinguishing between so called "extrinsic" and "intrinsic" portions of the electrogram, with a resultant uncertainty as to when the electrical activity of a small localized area really begins, and is contributed to by the response characteristics of the myographs usually employed, which tend to follow rapid changes in tension less faithfully than the electrical system records the action potential. The most satisfactory studies suggest, however, that shortening begins nearly coincidentally with the main peak of the so-called "differential" electrogram (e.g., two closely placed leads on the region to be studied).

In the auricle there is, in consequence, a progressive wavelike spread of contraction from the S-A node in all directions, reproducing the spread of the action current.

Inasmuch as the total duration of contraction in any one fiber is of the order of 50 msec., while the time required for spread of the impulse is only very little less, the whole of the auricular musculature has barely come into full contraction before relaxation begins near the S-A node, and auricular pressure rises to its maximum at this moment, and then gradually falls away, as more and more fibers relax. Because the A-V valves are open throughout all stages of auricular systole, auricular contraction is largely isotonic, and the pressure increment is not great. It is enough, however, to produce a small rise in ventricular pressure, and a similar increment in venous pressure, which is registered in the record of the venous pulse (phlebogram) as the A wave.

The contribution made by auricular systole to ventricular filling is a dispensable but not unimportant factor in the dynamics of the circulation. The greater part of ventricular filling (Fig. 341) occurs during the rapid filling stage of each diastole, and, as frequently occurs in cases of auricular fibrillation in man, auricular systole may be completely dispensed with for long periods without prejudice to circulatory competence. Auricular systole may therefore be considered as an accessory mechanism to insure that adequate filling of the ventricles takes place, particularly when the heart rate is more than usually rapid.

The termination of auricular systole contributes in some measure to the closure of the A-V valves. The eddy currents set up by the flow of blood through the A-V orifices tend to bring the valve leaflets into position, as well as does the wave of negative pressure developing behind a jet of fluid when it

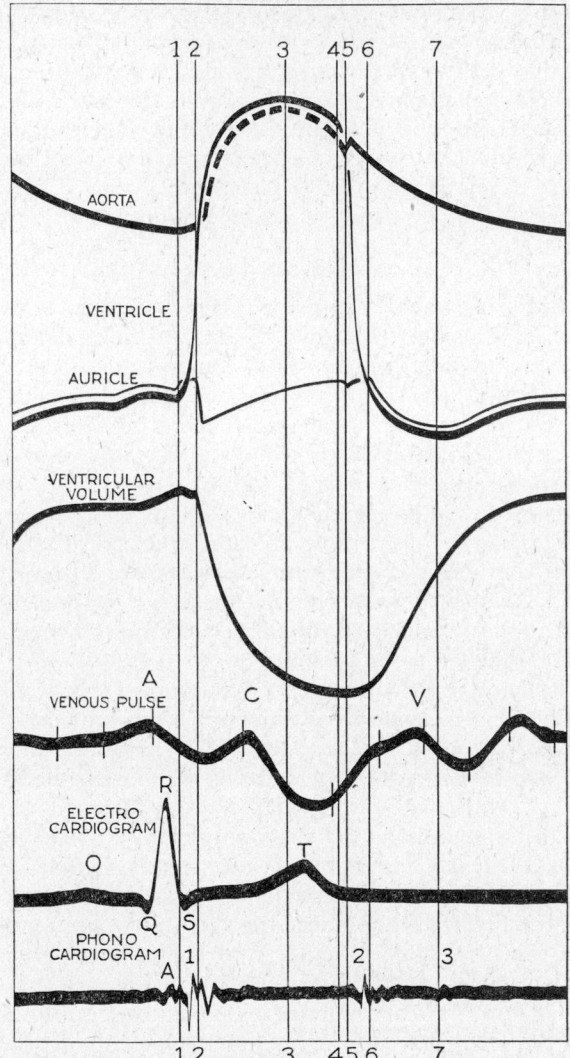

Fig. 341.—A correlation of the events of the cardiac cycle. The venous pulse, electrocardiogram, and heart sounds are given as actually recorded in man (Rappaport and Sprague). Curves of aortic pressure, auricular pressure, ventricular pressure, and ventricular volume are adapted from the dog and cannot therefore be accepted without reservation as applicable to man. For this reason actual pressures cannot be given, but it can be assumed that peak pressures within the left ventricle will be in the neighborhood of 20 mm. Hg above systolic pressures in the brachial artery. 1, closure of the A-V valves and the beginning of ventricular contractions, which is *isometric* until the opening of the aortic valves at 2; 2–3, maximal ejection phase; 3–4, reduced ejection phase; 4–5, protodiastolic phase with closure of aortic valves at 5; 5–6, isometric relaxation, opening of A-V valves at 6; 6–7, the phase of rapid filling; and from 7 to auricular systole, the phase of diastasis. Time marks 0.10 sec. which apply to the lower three curves are shown on the venous pulse curve. Average durations of the various phases in seconds have been suggested as follows: isometric contraction 0.05; maximum ejection 0.09; reduced ejection 0.13; total systole 0.27; protodiastole 0.04; isometric relaxation 0.08; rapid inflow 0.11; diastasis 0.19; auricular systole 0.11; total diastole 0.53.

is suddenly interrupted. Whatever mechanism is responsible, the end of auricular systole finds the A-V valves floated into position, ready to be firmly closed by ventricular systole. With prolongation of A-V conduction time the valves may again slacken and float apart, and this alteration in their position has been evoked to account for the fact that the first heart sound, to which the closure of the A-V valves in all probability contributes, is intensified when the A-V interval is short, and attenuated when the interval is prolonged.

Ventricular Systole. The contraction of the ventricular musculature follows the sequence of excitation as does auricular contraction, beginning at any one locality at the peak of the differential electrogram. According to the conventional view, therefore, the musculature of the interventricular septum is the first to contract, followed shortly by endocardial regions of the outer walls near the apex and later at the base. Finally, the full thickness of the two ventricles is brought into contraction as the impulse is conducted outward through the ventricular walls. The alternative view suggests that the four fundamental structural masses of myocardium are excited much as are skeletal muscles, by their own proper Purkinje fibers, and that distribution of the wave of contraction takes place along or parallel to the fibers of each muscle bundle.

The net effect of this asynchronous onset of ventricular contraction is reflected in the gradual slope by which intraventricular pressure at first begins to ascend. The first effect of this gradually increasing pressure is to insure the full closure of the A-V valves, sealing off the two ventricular cavities. The papillary muscles are presumably among the very first parts of the ventricles to contract, and serve to retain the edges of the valve and prevent their eversion into the auricles. The slow initial rise in intraventricular pressure is rapidly transformed into a steeper and steeper ascent, as, within a few msec., the whole of the ventricular musculature is brought into play. During the whole of this period in which intraventricular pressure is approaching that in the aorta, there is no change in ventricular volume, barring a small change due to some ballooning out of the A-V valves, so that this period has been designated the *isometric* phase of systole. The outward thrust of the A-V valves transmits a small rise in pressure to the auricles, and the growing pressure within the ventricles is transmitted in a similar way to the aorta via the semilunar valves, causing a slight rise in intra-aortic pressure just before the valves actually open. There is some difference of opinion as to whether the small rise in auricular pressure is transmitted to the veins to cause the C wave. Most workers seem to regard this wave as the result of the transmission to the veins of an arterial pulse with but a small representation of the isometric phase.

The isometric phase is terminated by the opening of the semilunar valves, and ejection of blood from the ventricles begins. The flow is at first slow, during the period of steepest rise of the aortic pressure, and is then almost completed during the period of slower pressure rise to the summit of the aortic and intraventricular pressure curves, which rise and fall together as long as the aortic valves remain open. A final increment of blood is ejected during the terminal phase of systole, when, because the quantity ejected is exceeded by the outflow of blood from the great vessels, the pressure within the aorta and ventricle begins gradually to diminish. The highest point in the pressure curve of the aorta or ventricle thus serves to subdivide the ejection period into a phase of maximum ejection and one of reduced ejection.

This period is characterized by a marked fall in the auricular pressure as the base is pulled downward by the changing position of the heart, and this may be transmitted to the venous pulse. Here, however, this phase may be obscured by a large positive wave (C) in the venous pulse resulting from the transmission of the arterial pulse from nearby large arteries. The changing position of the heart, involving a rotation of the heart to the right, brings the apex in forcible contact with the anterior chest wall, and causes the *apex beat*.

The end of ventricular systole abruptly transforms the ventricular and aortic pressure curves, which show a rapid decline that is checked in the aorta by the closure of the aortic valves at the *incisura*. This is the earliest stage of diastole, the protodiastolic period, and lasts only 0.02 to 0.04 sec. Ventricular pressure continues to fall rapidly until it is exceeded by pressure within the auricles, and the A-V valves open. This event marks the end of the period of isometric relaxation, lasting 0.05 to 0.08 sec. During this period auricular pressure may rise as the result of accumulation of blood in the auricles, and the compression of these chambers as the base rises with relaxation. This is communicated to the venous pulse as the rising limb of the V wave.

The opening of the A-V valves permits the blood, under relatively high pressure in the auricle, to flow rapidly into the ventricles, which now rapidly increase in volume. This feature gives the name to the period: the phase of rapid filling. Auricular pressure falls, and the venous pressure declines from the summit of the V wave. Finally, in hearts beating at a normal (or slower) rate, filling proceeds more and more slowly, and comes virtually to a standstill during the stage of *diastasis*, which is finally interrupted by the onset of auricular systole and the commencement of a new cardiac cycle.

HEART SOUNDS

"With each beat of the heart," wrote Harvey, "when there is the delivery of a quantity of blood from the veins to the arteries, a pulse takes place and can be heard within the chest." There are, in fact, as Laënnec recognized in 1819, two major heart sounds associated with each heart beat, while a third sound of much lower intensity can often be heard, especially in persons in the lower age groups. A fourth sound can occasionally be distinguished, particularly in cases of total heart block, and even when it cannot be heard separately it probably contributes to the first heart sound (Fig. 342).

First Heart Sound. This sound is heard best over the apex (mitral area) and over the sixth rib at the right sternal border (tricuspid area). It is, at the apex, the loudest sound heard, and it has the longest duration of any sound (0.05 to 0.165 sec., depending upon the means by which it is recorded). The sound as heard in the stethoscope is dull and booming; when it is recorded by a system capable of recording all the vibrations as they present themselves at the surface of the chest (a phonocardiograph of "linear" characteristics), it is found to consist of five or more vibrations at frequencies varying from 25 to 40 per sec. They usually begin with one or two small initial variations at the lower frequency, lasting 0.035 to 0.04 sec. (component 1), followed by two groups of larger vibrations at higher frequencies (components 2 and 3), and a final group of smaller, slower vibrations (component 4). The first vibrations begin as much as 0.02 to 0.04 sec. before the onset of ventricular systole, and are clearly associated with auricular contraction (the A wave in the venous pulse, Fig. 341). The second phase begins at or just after the apex of the R wave, and is coincident with the isometric phase of ventricular systole. It ends before the beginning of the ejection phase of ventricular systole (C wave in the venous pulse). The third component is coincident with the onset of the ejection phase (the beginning of the C wave of the venous pulse). The vibrations of the fourth component are associated with the maximum ejection phase.

It is apparent from this graphic analysis that auricular systole contributes in a small way to the first sound, and so also does the maximum ejection

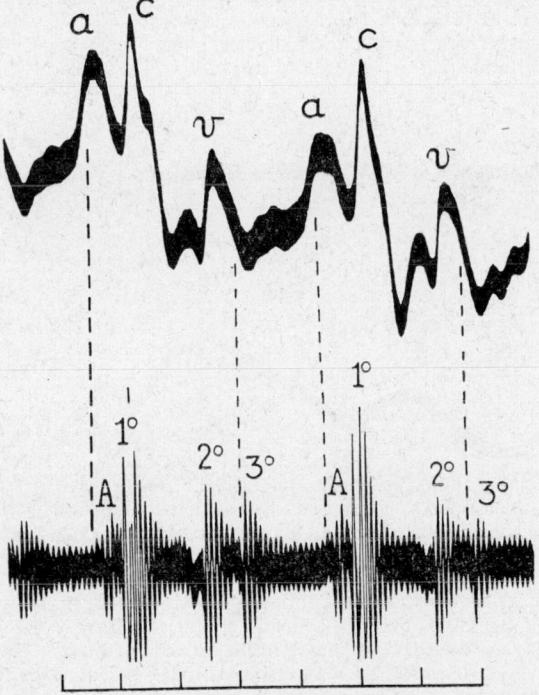

Fig. 342.—The four normal heart sounds, showing their relation to the venous pulse (above); below, phonocardiogram. A, auricular sound; 1°, 2°, 3°, the first, second and third sounds respectively. Time in $\frac{1}{5}$ sec. (From Orias and Braun-Menéndez, *The heart sounds in normal and pathological conditions*, 1st ed., London, Oxford University Press, 1939.)

phase. These auricular and vascular factors are attenuated in phonocardiographic recordings which have response characteristics similar to the ordinary stethoscope-ear system (which attenuates low-pitched sounds), and may not contribute significantly to the first sound as heard by auscultation. This factor is undoubtedly responsible for the spread in values given for the duration of the first sound. Thus, the maximum duration of the first sound, as recorded by a system recording the sounds as attenuated by the stethoscope (stethoscopic phonocardiogram), was 0.165 sec., with a minimum of 0.105 sec. On the other hand, a phonocardiograph designed to record the sounds as they would be further attenuated by the normal ear (a "logarithmic" phonocardiogram), which further diminishes the lower pitched sounds, reduces the above limits to 0.135 sec. and 0.08 sec. respectively. As far as the ear is concerned, therefore, the first and fourth components are greatly attenuated, but still contribute somewhat to the first sound.

The first heart sound is therefore a conglomerate of random vibrations arising from four events in the cardiac cycle: (i) an auricular component, (ii) a component associated with isometric contraction, and (iii) and (iv) two "vascular" components, which are presumably due respectively to the opening of the aortic valves and the acceleration of blood in the arterial vessels during the maximum ejection phase. There is, however, lack of agreement as to the causation of the second component. The first suggestion was that of Rouanet (1832) who wrote, "From many experiments I have learned that any membrane passing from flaccidity to tension always makes a sound. The auriculo-ventricular valves present conditions which are most favorable for the production of the first heart sound. They are thin and tough, do not stretch, and they pass from the most complete flaccidity to sudden and violent tension." This viewpoint is reinforced by numerous experiments which indicate that the first heart sound fails or is greatly weakened by immobilization of the A-V valves (through ligation of the A-V ring).

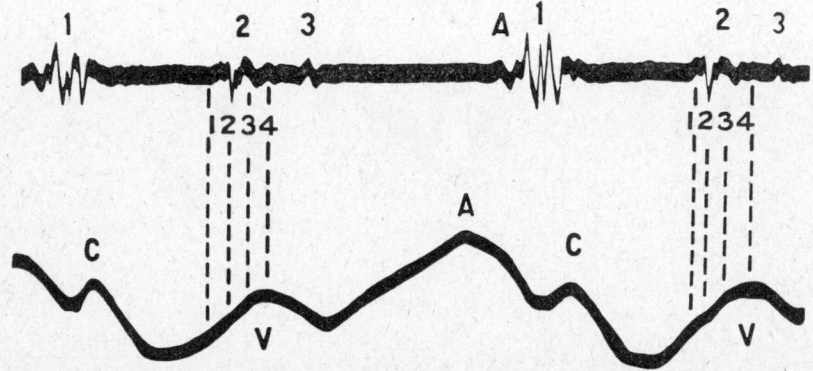

Fig. 343.—The four components of the second heart sound. Upper record, phonocardiogram showing, above the line, sounds 1, 2 and 3, and below, the four phases of the second sound; bottom record, the venous pulse. (From Rappaport and Sprague, *Amer. Heart J.*, 1942, 23:591–623.)

Other investigators have held that the sound is solely muscular in origin, calling attention to the low-pitched sounds that can be heard in contracting skeletal muscle (this can easily be heard by placing the index finger snugly in the external auditory meatus and vigorously contracting the arm muscles). These workers point to the fact that the first sound persists if the action of the A-V valves is supposedly suppressed by placing the finger in the A-V orifices or by inflating balloons in the auricles. The obvious contradiction between the experiments performed by adherents of the "valvular" theory and those by protagonists of the "muscular" theory remains to be resolved. Study of their experimental methods reveals many uncontrolled factors as well as significant differences in recording; it is probably wisest in the present state of knowledge to agree with Hope (1840) that "the first sound was shown by evidence verging on demonstration and which I have subsequently corroborated to be occasioned partly by sudden extension of the auricular valves and chordae tendinae, and partly by violent extension of the muscular wall at the moment the valves close."

Second Heart Sound. This may be heard best over the second interspace near the right sternal border (aortic area) and over the second rib near the left sternal border (pulmonic area) where it is louder, of higher pitch and of shorter duration than the first sound. At the apex it is less loud, but retains its higher pitch. When recorded by a stethoscopic phonocardiograph, its duration ranges between 0.085 and 0.145 sec., but, as recorded by a logarithmic phonocardiograph, further attenuation of low frequency vibrations reduces its duration to between 0.080 and 0.110 sec. Presumably this latter figure represents the duration of components that would be transmitted by the normal ear. The second sound as recorded in the stethoscopic phono-cardiogram is also a conglomerate of four components (Fig. 343): (i) an early vibration of low amplitude, coincident with the beginning of relaxation and the fall of pressure within the ventricle, (ii) a component of great amplitude coincident with closure of the semilunar valves, (iii) vibrations of lower amplitude presumably due to vibrations in the arterial walls and in the column of blood in the aorta, and (iv) a fourth component synchronous with the apex of the "V" wave in the venous pulse, and therefore presumably due to the opening of the mitral and tricuspid valves. The first of these components is attenuated, but recorded by the logarithmic phonocardiogram, which also records preponderantly the higher frequencies in the second or valvular component. The third and fourth components are usually not recorded in this type of record, so they fail to contribute to the sound as heard by a normal ear through a stethoscope.

Third Heart Sound. This sound may be heard on the apex and in the neighboring mesocardiac area, and appears to best advantage with the subject lying on his left side. It is weak, low-pitched, and dull when compared with the first two heart sounds. Table 22 indicates the frequency with which it

Table 22

Age	1–10	10–20	20–30	30–40	40–50	50–60
Number of persons	39	90	55	26	14	7
Frequency with which the third sound was heard	58.9	84.4	5.09	42.3	14	0

has been heard in the various age groups. When recorded by the stethoscopic method its duration ranged between 0.03 and 0.085 sec., and when recorded by the logarithmic method its duration lay between 0.015 and 0.05 sec. While the stethoscopic method recorded the sound in 85 per cent of 33 normal subjects, it was present in only 30 per cent when studied by the logarithmic method. It is generally accepted that this sound is caused by vibrations of the ventricular walls due to their sudden distension by the onrush of blood from the auricles in the period of rapid ventricular filling, appearing, as it does, in front of the lowest portion of the descending limb of the V wave (see Fig. 343).

Auricular Sound. As has already been seen, auricular systole sets up vibrations which in normal circumstances fuse with ventricular components in the formation of the first heart sound. There seems to be no doubt that in addition the auricle, when contracting, produces vibrations which may occasionally be heard as an independent sound in normal subjects under ordinary conditions of auscultation. In cases of prolonged A-V conduction and especially in complete heart block, this sound may, of course, be detected more readily (Fig. 344). The low frequency of the auricular sound favors its attenuation in the stethoscope and in the ear; thus the stethoscopic phonocardiograph recorded auricular components in 88 per cent of 33 normal young subjects, while it was detected in but 21 per cent of the same individuals by the logarithmic method. The sound appears to consist of components from (i) the auricular musculature, (ii) vibrations in the ventricles produced by the distension of their walls by blood forced in by auricular systole, and (iii) vibrations at the end of systole due to the transient and incomplete closure of the auricular ventricular valves that takes place at that time. The first of these factors may not contribute significantly to the sound as heard in auscultation of the chest.

Abnormalities. *Splitting of heart sounds.* In a number of circumstances a dissociation of the component vibrations of a sound takes place, dividing it into separate parts, each of which is heard or recorded as a separate entity.

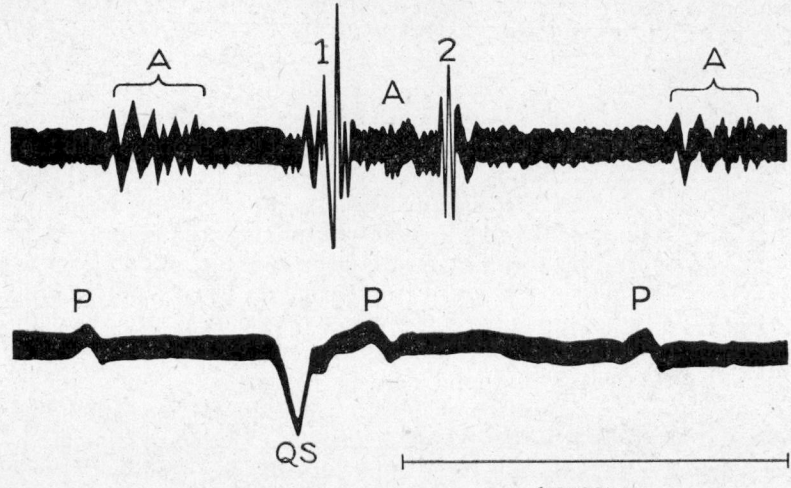

Fig. 344.—Auricular sounds more clearly identifiable because of total heart block. Above, phonocardiogram; below, electrocardiogram. (After Orias and Braun-Menéndez, *The heart sounds in normal and pathological conditions,* 1st ed., London, Oxford University Press, 1939.)

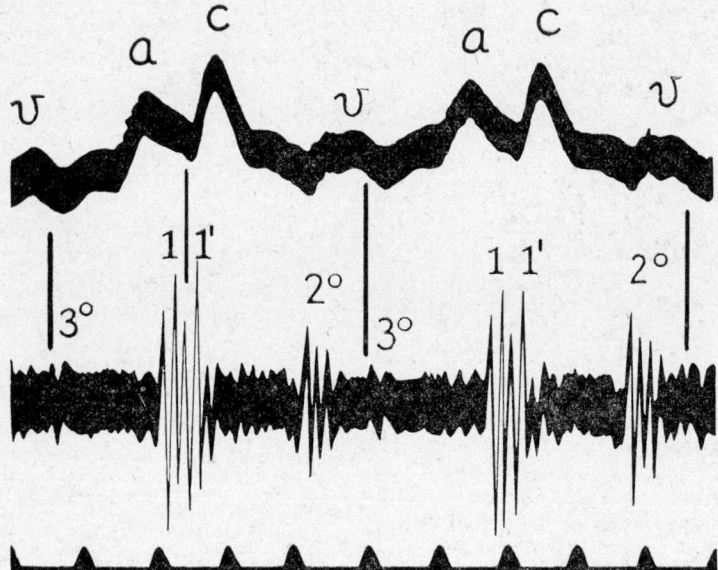

Fig. 345.—Splitting of the first sound by an exaggerated separation of the second and third components of the first sound. Above, venous pulse; below, phonocardiogram. Time in $\frac{1}{5}$ sec. (From Orias and Braun-Menéndez, *The heart sounds in normal and pathological conditions,* 1st ed., London, Oxford University Press, 1939.)

As far as the first sound is concerned, this may be a purely physiological event, and can be recorded frequently as an exaggerated separation of the two major components of the first sound, the isometric phase and the ejection phase components; this may often occur at the end of expiration. The total duration of the first sound is not, however, prolonged (Fig. 345).

Splitting of the second sound proceeds from quite a different cause, namely, asynchrony in closure of the aortic and pulmonary valves, whereby the sound

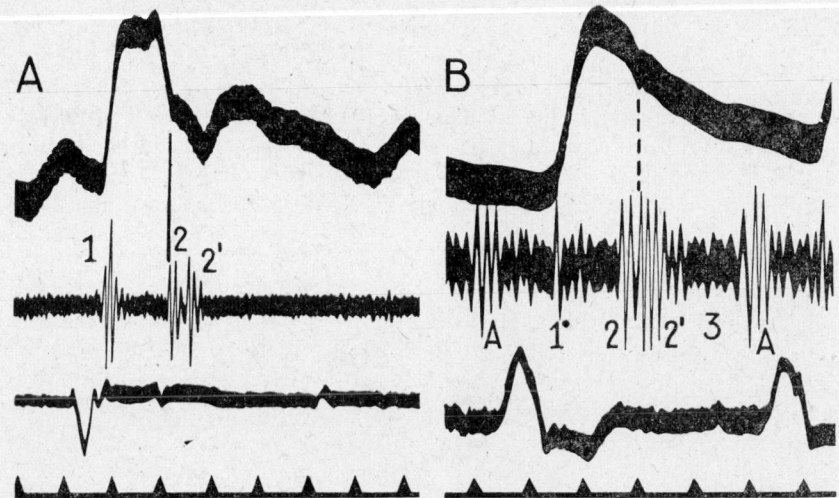

Fig. 346.—A, splitting of the second sound in right bundle-branch block. Arterial pulse, phonocardiogram, electrocardiogram from lead I, and time in ⅕ sec. The second component of he split second sound, 2′, comes after the incisura so it must represent the closure of the pulmonary aortic valves. This is consistent with the expected delay in activation of the right ventricle. B, splitting of the second sound in left bundle-branch block. The second component is now synchronous with the incisura of the systemic arterial pulse. In this case the contraction (and hence the relaxation) of the left ventricle is delayed. (From Orias and Braun-Menéndez, *The heart sounds in normal and pathological conditions*, 1st ed. London, Oxford University Press, 1939.)

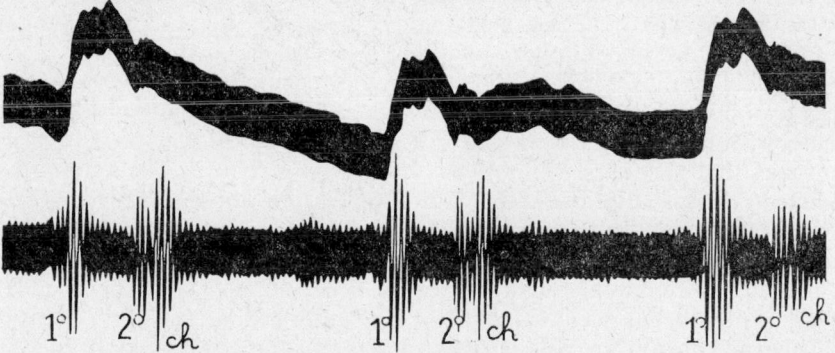

Fig. 347.—Opening snap of the mitral valve in mitral stenosis. The snap (ch) represents an increase to an audible stage of vibrations normally present but inaudible. Above, central arterial pulse; below, phonocardiogram. (From Orias and Braun-Menéndez, *The heart sounds in normal and pathological conditions*, 1st ed. London, Oxford University Press, 1939.)

is, in fact, reduplicated. The phenomenon occurs occasionally in normal subjects, but is understandably more frequent in bundle-branch block where the interval between right and left ventricular contraction is abnormally prolonged (Fig. 346). The second sound associated with ventricular extrasystoles may also be split for the same reason.

Opening snap of mitral valves. In mitral stenosis a third sound is heard, and, when it is recorded phonocardiographically, it is found to begin at the apex of the V wave of the venous pulse. It is coincident in time, therefore, with the opening of the A-V valves, and represents an abnormal intensification of the fourth component of the normal second heart sound, which, because of attenuation in the stethoscope-ear combination, is not normally heard (Fig. 347).

Gallop rhythms. When a loud third sound is heard in a rapidly beating heart, the resulting triple rhythm has a cadence resembling the sound of a galloping horse. The loud third sound can be shown phonocardiographically to represent (i) an intensified third sound (rapid filling gallop), (ii) an intensified auricular sound (presystolic or auricular gallop), or (iii) a combination of summation of third and the auricular sounds, when the rapid filling phase and auricular systole occur more or less simultaneously (summation gallop). Such gallop rhythms are heard most frequently in cases of serious disease of the heart, and it is presumed that the abnormal intensification of the third or auricular sounds is related in some way to an altered ventricular response to rapid filling or auricular systole. A systolic gallop may occasionally be heard when there is marked splitting of the first heart sound.

Murmurs. When fluid flows slowly through a smooth tube of uniform diameter, no sound may be heard through a stethoscope placed on the tube. If, however, the velocity of flow is greatly increased or the viscosity of the fluid reduced, flow is no longer smooth, but becomes turbulent, i.e., eddy currents are set up, and these produce vibrations which may be audible. The velocity at which turbulence begins is greatly diminished by the presence in the tube of annular expansions or constrictions or inequalities of the surface, and these factors therefore favor the development of murmurs.

In the normal heart, with altered diameters at the orifices and the presence of valves as impediments to streamline flow, the critical velocities for turbulent flow are not quite attained in average circumstances. In strenuous muscular exercise and in other conditions in which cardiac output is increased and the velocity of flow augmented in consequence, systolic murmurs may appear in normal hearts. Increased velocity of blood flow during the ejection phase, with resulting turbulence, is probably also responsible for the systolic murmurs that may appear in anemia and in thyrotoxicosis. The murmurs of a patent ductus arteriosus, the hum over arteriovenous aneurysms, the Korotkow sounds, and Duroziez sign (systolic and diastolic murmurs heard over the femoral artery in aortic incompetence and modified by the degree of pressure exerted by the stethoscope), are other examples of the production of sounds by turbulence at constrictions in smooth tubes.

Abnormal narrowing of an orifice such as occurs in mitral or aortic stenosis will lower the velocity at which turbulence occurs, and accounts in the main for the murmurs heard in these conditions, although the roughening of the walls of the orifice by scarring and partial destruction of the valves undoubtedly also contributes in some measure. In mitral stenosis the murmurs will be diastolic, occupying typically the periods of rapid filling and auricular systole (Figs. 347 and 348), although the murmur may be continuous throughout diastole owing to overlapping of the two phases (Fig. 349). The typical murmur of aortic stenosis occurs in systole during the phase of ejection.

It is understandable that in the presence of valvular incompetence, in addition to stenosis, murmurs may be heard during systole in mitral valvular disease and during diastole in aortic valvular disease, due in part to the regurgitation of blood through the narrow orifice. Another mechanism may

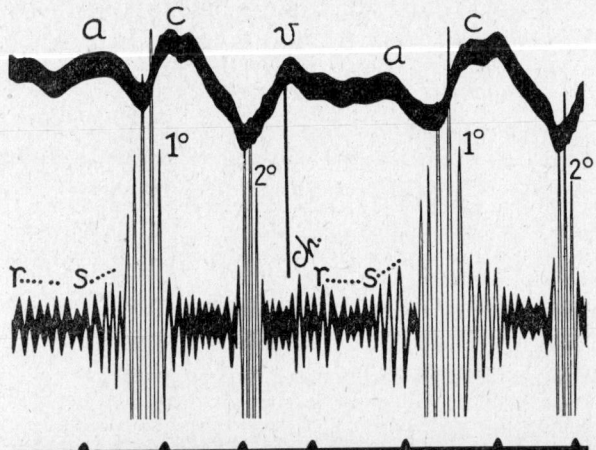

Fig. 348.—The classical murmurs of mitral stenosis: (1) an opening snap of the mitral valve (ch). (2) a diastolic murmur during the rapid filling stage (r), continuing into a presystolic murmur with auricular systole. Time in $\frac{1}{5}$ sec. (From Orias and Braun-Menéndez, *The heart sounds in normal and pathological conditions*, 1st ed. London, Oxford University Press, 1939.)

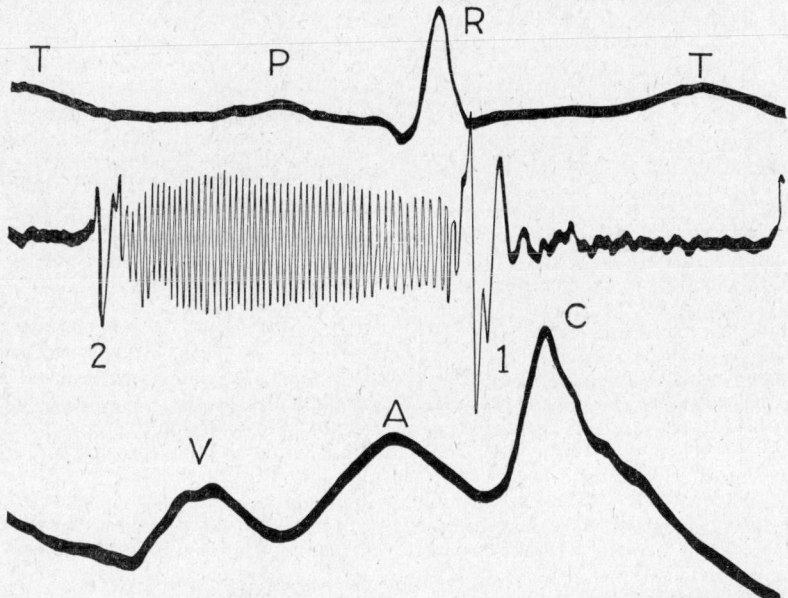

Fig. 349.—A musical diastolic murmur occupying the whole of the diastole. Electrocardiogram, phonocardiogram, and venous pulse from above down. (After Orias and Braun-Menéndez, *The heart sounds in normal and pathological conditions*, 1st ed. London, Oxford University Press, 1939.)

also contribute to the murmur heard in these circumstances; the regurgitated column of blood may set up vibrations in structures upon which it may impinge and thus produce sounds not related to turbulent flow. In mitral incompetence the auricle itself may be set in vibration by the blood forced back during ventricular systole, causing a "collision" murmur, while the regurgitation of blood against the anterior mitral valve leaflet in aortic incompetence is thought to give rise to the presystolic murmur of aortic stenosis, the "Austin Flint murmur."

THE ELECTROCARDIOGRAM

Historical note. With the general recognition that electrical currents are generated in association with the contraction of skeletal muscle, developing out of the suggestive experiments of Galvani in 1791 and the direct experimental verification of Matteucci, it was natural that attempts be made to demonstrate a similar phenomenon in the heart. The first of these to succeed was that of Kölliker and Johannes Müller in 1858. They had connected a frog's heart to the leads of the slow-moving, coil-type galvanometer of the period, and believed that they were able to detect a movement coincident with the heart beat. To confirm this equivocal evidence thay had recourse to Matteucci's rheoscopic frog preparation and, looping the nerve over the ventricle, noted that the muscle contracted with each heart beat much as does the diaphragm from stimulation of the phrenic nerves as it descends over the pericardium. With particularly excitable rheoscopic preparations, Kölliker and Müller noted *two* contractions in the testing muscle for each beat of the ventricle.

From this point on, the more exact study of the action currents of the heart has depended in large measure upon technical advances in recording devices. The nature of the action currents generated by the heart demanded an electrical recording system that was, at the same time, sensitive to extremely small voltages and rapid in its inherent period of vibration to follow faithfully the quickly changing sequence of events in the heart. Failing such an instrument, Marchand was able to provide the first accurate graphic representation of the time-voltage course of the heart beat in the frog by the employment of a sensitive, but slow, galvanometer in conjunction with a "rheotome." This instrument was, in its essentials, a mechanically controlled arrangement of two shutters, one of which opened an electrical circuit at a given instant while the other interrupted the flow of current a moment later. A frog's ventricle arrested with a Stannius' ligature could then be stimulated electrically, and the potential across apex-base electrodes could be determined at a chosen interval of time thereafter. By progressively lengthening this interval, the whole heart cycle could be "scanned." The curves so obtained were diphasic, i.e., they consisted of an initial deflection indicating negativity of the basal with respect to the apical electrode, followed by a deflection in the opposite direction. It is apparent that the double response of the rheoscopic frog preparation was evoked by the double electrical discharge with each beat of the heart.

This simple apparatus, which is important because its use by Burdon-Sanderson led to a fundamental understanding of important phases of the electrophysiology of the heart, was soon supplanted by the capillary electrometer. The operation of this instrument depends upon the fact that the surface tension of mercury in contact with dilute acid will alter with changes in electrical potential across the interface. If this junction is established in a capillary tube, the level of the mercury will rise and fall with change of potential between two electrodes which lead to the acid and to the mercury. Despite the slowness of response inherent in a system which depends on movement of mercury, this instrument is of importance, historically, in two ways; in the first place, it permitted photographic recording, and consequent magnification of the deflections by the simple arrangement of a near-by light source which threw the shadow of the mercury column upon a more distant, moving photographic plate. It was, moreover, the apparatus used by Waller to record for the first time the electrical activity of the human heart by taking leads from the front and back of the chest of a normal subject.

Einthoven finally solved the problem in a definite way by constructing a galvanometer in which a fine quartz fiber no more than a few micra in diameter, gold-plated to make it a conductor, was suspended in the intense magnetic field created by a powerful electromagnet with an extremely small interpolar distance. The string now acted like the armature of an electric motor, moving one way or another in the electromagnetic field when a current passed through it. The tension of the string ensured an adequate rapidity, while its small mass and the intensity of the electromagnetic field endowed it with a sufficient sensitivity. Magnification and optical recording were made possible by means of a lens system and source of illustration which projected on the slit of a camera the shadow of the quartz fiber. With the development of thermionic valve amplification, it has become possible to record the electrocardiogram by means of the cathode ray oscillograph or other oscillographs with adequate speed of response characteristics.

Conventions

Whatever type of instrument is employed, the conventions established by Einthoven are in a large measure retained. The sensitivity of the galvanometer is adjusted to give a deflection on the record of 1 cm. per millivolt. The recording paper travels 2.5 cm. per sec., and the illumination is interrupted by a shutter 25 times per sec. to give cross lines at an interval of 0.04 sec. Lines etched in the cylindrical lens of the camera also interrupt the light to produce white lines running horizontally against the dark background 1 mm. apart. Records are usually taken from a variety of leads. In almost every instance the original leads devised by Einthoven are first recorded: lead I from the right and left arms, lead II from right arm to left leg, and lead III from left leg to left arm. Because these leads at times failed to reveal signs of myocardial damage, particularly at the apex, chest leads came to be employed. In these, an electrode at the apex was paired with the right arm (4R), the left leg (4F), left arm (4L), or with the three limb leads combined through resistances (V). The desirability of exploring other points on the chest has led to standardization of six chest positions as follows: C1, right sternal margin in the fourth interspace, C2, left sternal margin in the fourth interspace, C3, midway between C2 and the midclavicular line in the fifth interspace (all the remaining leads are in this interspace), C4 at the midclavicular line, C5 at the anterior axillary line, and C6 in the midaxillary line. These leads may be combined with the right arm (CR) left leg (CF) left arm (CL) or with the combined limb leads through resistance (CV). Leads are arranged so that positivity of the chest electrode produces an upward deflection in the record.

Normal standards. "The interpretation of an electrocardiogram," write Graybiel and coworkers (9), "ordinarily involves three distinct steps, namely, (i) the actual measurement of the various component parts, (ii) the recognition of any deviations from the normal, and (iii) a proper evaluation of the significance of the findings. The first step is essentially objective, if carried out in accordance with established procedure. The second step requires a thorough knowledge of the normal electrocardiographic patterns gained from past experience. The third step requires a full knowledge of the significance of the various deviations from the normal, together with a careful correlation with the other findings in the case. This part of the interpretation is largely subjective and reflects the judgment of the interpreter. The need for information regarding the normal has led to an extensive study of the electrocardiograms obtained from healthy persons. Early studies were carried out on only a small number of subjects, and the results did not disclose the full extent of the normal range. This, not infrequently, led the electrocardiographer wrongly to regard a particular measurement as abnormal and, as a consequence, to err in assessing its significance."

The studies of these workers and of others—studies largely of healthy young men in the armed services—have shown more completely the normal range, and indicate that even in such an extremely carefully selected group of young men with unquestionably sound cardiovascular systems, variations within wide limits may exist. There is obviously need for further studies in women, and in the various age groups.

Taking first the *duration* of the various components of the electrocardiogram (Fig. 350), the first measurable interval of significance is the P-R or P-Q interval, which extends from the beginning of the P wave to the beginning of the QRS complex. (The duration of the P wave is commonly not considered to be particularly significant because it varies so greatly with changes in amplitude. It varies between 0.05 sec. and 0.10 sec. in all but a very small proportion of instances.) In the 1000 young healthy aviators studied by

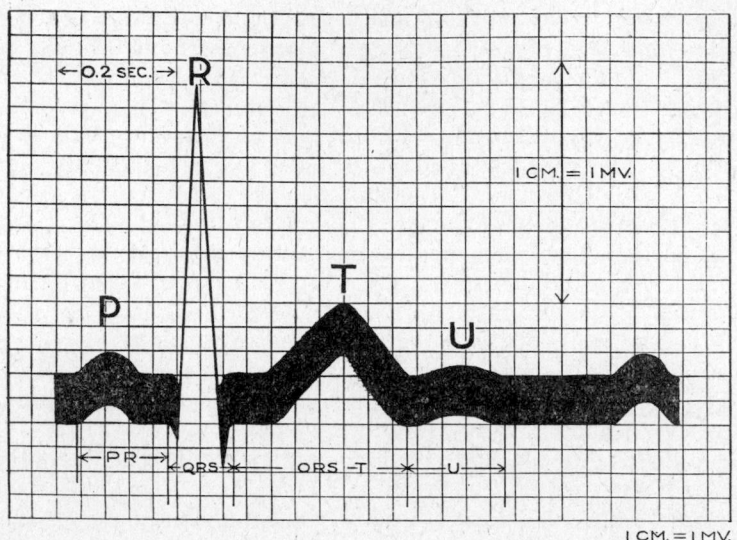

Fig. 350.—A single complex from lead II drawn to scale and to proportions taken from the mean amplitudes and durations reported by Graybiel *et al.* (From Graybiel *et al., Amer. Heart J.,* 1944, 27:524–549.)

Graybiel and collaborators, the P-R interval varied from 0.09 to 0.28 sec.; with a mean of 0.154 sec. In all but 82 instances the value lay between 0.12 and 0.18 sec. as shown in Table 23. An interval greater than this was found in 68 instances, and less in 13, not counting one case with an A-V nodal

Table 23.—*Duration of the P-R Interval* (From Graybiel *et al., Amer. Heart J.,* 1944, 27:524–529.)

P-R INTERVAL (SEC.)	NUMBER OF INSTANCES
0.10	6
0.11	7
0.12	76
0.13	83
0.14	211
0.15	117
0.16	249
0.17	95
0.18	84
0.19	19
0.20	33
0.21	4
0.22	8
0.24, 0.25, 0.26, 0.28 (one instance each)	4
Total =	996

rhythm with a P-R of 0.09 sec. The limits set by twice the normal standard deviation as determined by Stewart and Manning are from 0.11 to 0.21 sec.

The duration of QRS was found by Graybiel to vary from 0.06 to 0.14 sec., with a mean value of 0.087; Table 24 gives the values for the entire range. Stewart and Manning (24) set the upper limit of QRS as determined by twice the standard deviation at 0.10 sec., and this figure has been generally regarded as the upper limit of normal. The Graybiel studies appear to justify the following modifications of this view: (i) QRS complexes as long in dura-

Table 24.—*Duration of QRS* (From Graybiel *et al., Amer. Heart J.,* 1944, 27:524–549.)

DURATION OF QRS (SEC.)	NUMBER OF INSTANCES
0.06	7
0.07	68
0.08	431
0.09	295
0.10	161
0.11	27
0.12	8
0.13	1
0.14	2
	Total = 1,000

tion as 0.13 sec. may be observed in young persons without any evidence of heart disease; (ii) a QRS duration of 0.11 sec. is found with sufficient frequency in young healthy persons to suggest that it is not necessarily of pathologic significance; (iii) apparently "faulty" conduction may occur as a temporary functional condition, and it is not therefore necessary to explain

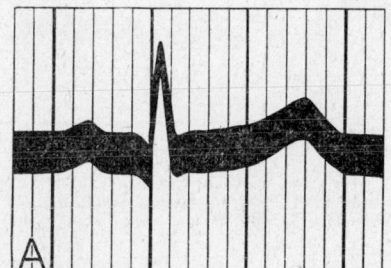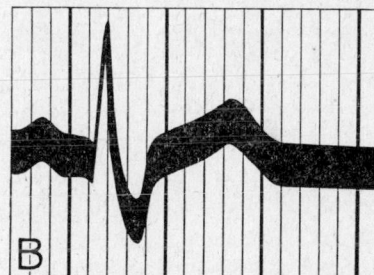

Fig. 351.—A, A single complex from lead I with subject under basal conditions. B, 10 min. after a pistol had been fired near him. Change in intraventricular conduction occurred within 30 sec. of the detonation and the abnormality remained for two days. (From Graybiel *et al., Amer. Heart J.,* 1944, 27:524–549.)

all disturbances of intraventricular condition on an anatomical basis (see Fig. 351).

The Q-T interval varies so greatly with the heart rate that uncorrected measurements have little significance. Bazett has found that the relation of Q-T interval to the rate may be expressed by the formula:

$$Q\text{-}T = K\sqrt{R\text{-}R} \text{ (cycle length),}$$

where K has the value of 0.37 for males and 0.4 for females. The duration of the U wave is extremely difficult to measure with any accuracy because of its low amplitude; it may, however, add as much as 0.2 sec. to the electrical events of the cardiac cycle.

The Q wave was present in lead I in 511 of the 1000 electrocardiograms studied by Graybiel, and varied from −0.1 to −3.0 mm., with a mean value of −0.54. Stewart and Manning, on the other hand, found it in but 29 per cent of instances in their study of 500 R.C.A.F. aircrew. A Q_2 was found by Graybiel in 681 out of 1000 instances, and in 58 per cent of Stewart and Manning's cases. It had an amplitude of from -0.6 mm. to -3.5 mm. with a mean of -0.73 mm. A Q_3 was present in 677 of Graybiel's 1000 cases and in 61 per cent of Stewart and Manning's. Its amplitude varied from -0.1 to -4.5 mm. with a mean of -1.04 mm.

An R wave was always present in lead I in the cases studied by Graybiel, excepting for three cases of abnormal rhythms. It ranged in amplitude from 1 to 16.5 mm. with a mean value of 5.9 mm. An R_1 over 10 mm. in amplitude was found in 6.2 per cent of cases. Stewart and Manning's cases fall within somewhat narrower limits: 1.2 to 12 mm. In lead II an upright R was also found without exception, ranging in amplitude from 1.3 to 26 mm., with a mean value of 11.6 mm. There were 152 instances in which the amplitude was from 15 to 19.9 mm., and 29 instances in which it was from 20 to 26 mm. Stewart and Manning's measurements ranged from 6.1 to 22 mm.

In lead III, the R wave failed to be clearly present in 61 instances, but was measurable in the remaining electrocardiograms. It ranged in height from 0.5 to 24 mm. with a mean of 7.2 mm. Stewart and Manning set similar levels: 0 to 18.7 mm.

The S wave was present, according to Graybiel, in 856 instances in lead I, where it had a mean amplitude of -1.74 mm., with a range of -0.1 to -6.3. Its amplitude equalled nearly 40 per cent of that of R_1, with a range of 0.9 to 266.7 per cent. In lead II an S was present in 749 instances, averaging -1.78 mm., with a range of -0.1 to -9. Its amplitude averaged 20 per cent of R, varying from 0.6 to 200 per cent. In lead III detectable S waves were found in 527 out of the 1000 cases, and they varied in amplitude from -0.1 to -12 mm., with a mean of -1.48 mm. This represented, on the average, 43.5 per cent of the amplitude of the R wave in the same lead, and again there was a wide range of proportionality, ranging from 0.6 to 500 per cent. In a very few instances there was a second upright

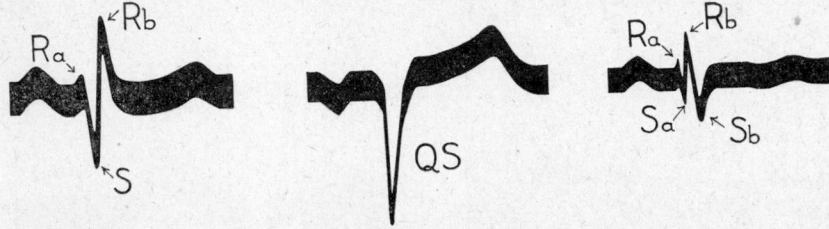

Fig. 352.—Illustrations of recommendations for nomenclature of unusual QRS complexes. (From Pardee, *Amer. Heart J.*, 1940, *20*:655–666.)

wave following the main QRS deflection; this may be called R^b, according to the suggestions of Pardee (19). (Pardee recommends that in complexes showing more than one positive peak, they should be designated as R^a, R^b, R^c, etc. Only when a negative deflection occurs before any positive wave can it be called Q. Negative deflections occurring after an R should be designated S^a, S^b, etc. When only a downward wave appears it is to be called QS; see Fig. 352.)

The T wave is normally upright in lead I, and almost always so in lead II. Graybiel reported no inverted T wave in lead I and only two instances of inversion in lead II. In lead III, however, the T wave was inverted or diphasic in over one-fifth of all records. It is necessary to remember, however, that the T wave is extremely susceptible to changes in posture, diminishing in amplitude or inverting as the position is changed from recumbent to upright. Thus in a study of a control group of 26 young healthy medical students carried out at McGill University, mean recumbent amplitudes were as follows: T_1 2.4 mm., T_2 3.3 mm., and T_3 1.1 mm., comparing closely with the mean values given by Graybiel. After these individuals had been tilted to 70 degrees for 10 minutes, the following values were obtained: T_1 1.7, T_2 1.3, and T_3 -0.65 mm.

Inversion was noted in half of all T_3's. No inverted T waves were noted in lead II during recumbency, but two became inverted when the subject was tilted. Inverted T waves were not found in lead I at any time. Whatever the mechanism (i.e., change in position of the heart in the chest, the influence of the sympathetic nervous system on the recovery cycle of the myocardium exerted as part of the circulatory reflex adaptations to the change in posture or simple change in rate per se), it is apparent that such diminution in amplitude of the T wave in all the limb leads, which may entail an actual inversion of T_2 and T_3, is in no way abnormal.

The U wave is present most commonly in lead II as is seen in Table 25, and never has an amplitude greater than 1 mm. in the limb leads.

The S-T segment is that portion of the electrocardiogram lying between the QRS complex and the T wave. It is considered in idealized representations as a flat segment at the same level as that prevailing during diastole. Actually, however, it is rarely flat, and not often does it arise at the diastolic base line. It may, in fact, as is shown in Table 26, be found to rise in occasional instances as much as 1.0 to 2.0 mm. above the P-Q reference level. It is depressed much less often. In form it is more frequently concave or ascending rather than flat (Table 27).

Table 25.—Incidence and Amplitude of U Waves in the Standard Leads

INCIDENCE OF U WAVES	
LEAD	NUMBER
1	268
2	448
3	141
1 and 2	131
1 and 3	14
2 and 3	66
1, 2, and 3	50
One Lead Only	284
No Leads	438

AMPLITUDE OF U WAVES				
	N	MEAN (mm.)	RANGE (mm.)	NUMBER INVERTED
Lead I	268	+0.12	+0.1 to +0.3	0
Lead II	448	+0.14	+0.1 to +1.0	0
Lead III	141	+0.13	+0.1 to +0.3	2

Table 26.—Displacement of the S-T Junction in the Standard Leads

		N	MEAN (mm.)	RANGE (mm.)	NUMBER GREATER THAN 1 mm.
Lead I	upward	854	+0.41	+0.1 to +1.5	5
	none	137			
	downward	9	−0.64	−0.1 to −1.2	1
Lead II	upward	890	+0.62	+0.1 to +2.0	30
	none	98			
	downward	12	−0.46	−0.1 to −1.0	0
Lead III	upward	460	+0.43	+0.1 to +1.5	7
	none	463			
	downward	77	−0.33	−0.1 to −1.5	1

Table 27.—Form of S-T Segment in the Standard Leads

	PERCENTAGE		
FORM OF S-T SEGMENT	LEAD I	LEAD II	LEAD III
Ascending	13.4	12.9	3.5
Concave	76.9	79.7	45.4
Convex	0.2	0.0	2.3
Flat	9.5	7.4	48.8

Table 28 summarizes a valuable study of the amplitude of the various components of the electrocardiogram in the various decades of life. Pre-

Table 28.—Measurements of P, Q, R, S, and T Waves in Normal Subjects (amplitude in millimeters).
(From Chamberlin and Hay, *Brit. Heart J.*, 1939, *1*:105–115.)

	P	Q	R	S	T
		FIRST DECADE; 8 CASES			
Lead I					
Average	0.9	1.0	8.2	1.7	3.1
Range	0.0–1.6	0.6–3.6	5.6–11.6	0.0–7.6	1.6–4.6
Lead II					
Average	1.5	0.5	12.5	1.7	2.2
Range	0.5–3.0	0.0–4.0	7.5–19.5	0.5–2.5	0.5–5.5
Lead III					
Average	−0.2	0.4	4.1	0.8	−0.5
Range	−0.5–1.5	0.0–3.5	1.5–10.5	0.5–1.5	−1.5–1.5
		SECOND DECADE; 25 CASES			
Lead I					
Average	1.0	0.9	8.8	2.3	3.3
Range	0.0–2.5	0.0–3.5	2.0–18.6	0.0–8.0	1.5–4.5
Lead II					
Average	1.7	1.1	11.8	2.6	3.0
Range	0.5–2.6	0.0–2.5	6.6–23.6	0.0–11.5	1.6–6.5
Lead III					
Average	0.2	0.5	6.0	1.6	1.1
Range	−4.4–2.5	0.0–4.5	1.5–14.4	1.5–8.5	−2.0–3.5
		THIRD DECADE; 136 CASES			
Lead I					
Average	0.6	0.4	9.0	1.6	3.1
Range	0.0–1.5	0.0–2.6	2.5–18.6	0.0–7.5	1.1–6.5
Lead II					
Average	1.7	0.5	15.6	3.0	4.2
Range	0.5–2.7	0.0–2.5	6.5–23.5	0.0–10.6	0.5–12.5
Lead III					
Average	0.7	0.5	9.3	1.5	−0.3
Range	−3.5–2.5	0.0–3.6	1.5–20.5	0.0–8.5	−5.5–6.5
		FOURTH DECADE; 36 CASES			
Lead I					
Average	0.8	0.1	6.4	2.2	2.1
Range	0.0–1.5	0.0–0.5	2.0–10.5	0.5–4.5	1.5–3.6
Lead II					
Average	2.4	0.7	14.6	3.5	2.4
Range	0.5–5.0	0.5–1.5	7.5–18.5	0.5–8.5	−3.5–6.6
Lead III					
Average	1.5	0.9	11.2	1.5	0.1
Range	−0.5–3.0	0.0–3.0	4.5–18.5	1.5–8.6	−4.5–4.6
		FIFTH DECADE; 42 CASES			
Lead I					
Average	1.0	0.1	7.5	1.9	2.5
Range	0.5–2.6	0.0–2.0	2.6–13.5	0.0–3.6	0.6–3.5
Lead II					
Average	2.0	0.6	12.4	3.0	2.7
Range	0.0–2.6	0.0–2.6	4.5–16.4	0.0–5.0	0.6–4.6
Lead III					
Average	1.0	0.4	6.8	2.2	0.0
Range	−4.0–2.6	0.0–4.0	1.6–13.4	0.0–4.5	−5.0–2.5
		SIXTH DECADE; 33 CASES			
Lead I					
Average	0.6	0.7	7.8	1.2	2.0
Range	0.0–1.5	0.0–2.5	1.5–13.6	1.5–6.5	0.0–3.5
Lead II					
Average	1.9	1.3	11.3	2.3	3.0
Range	0.5–3.5	0.0–4.5	5.5–16.5	1.5–9.5	0.5–7.5
Lead III					
Average	1.4	1.2	5.9	2.2	0.5
Range	−1.5–3.0	0.0–4.5	0.0–14.6	1.5–10.5	−4.5–4.5

Table 28 (*Continued*)

	P	Q	R	S	T
SEVENTH DECADE; 13 CASES					
Lead I					
Average	0.9	1.2	8.4	1.4	2.1
Range	0.0–1.5	0.0–2.5	2.5–13.6	0.5–2.5	0.5–3.5
Lead II					
Average	1.5	1.5	10.4	2.0	2.8
Range	0.5–2.5	0.0–3.0	3.6–17.6	0.0–4.5	1.5–5.5
Lead III					
Average	0.2	0.5	4.6	2.0	−0.7
Range	−1.5–1.5	0.0–2.5	0.5–18.6	0.0–7.5	−4.5–3.5

sumably these records were taken with the subject in the sitting position. Standards for the chest leads are less well established, due as much to the variation that occurs with small deviations in placement of the chest electrode as to the number of chest leads for which standards must be provided, recommended by various workers. As far as leads 4F and 4R are concerned, Graybiel finds that there is little to choose between them, except that 4F gives at conventional sensitivity a record not quite so large as 4R, and this affords a more convenient normal range. In 4F the P wave was visible in 969 out of 994 records, being upright in 508 instances, with a mean amplitude of 0.43 mm. It was inverted in 126 instances, diphasic in 249 and small and bizarre in shape in 71 cases. QRS duration ranged from 0.06 to 0.14 sec. with a mean of 0.086, and did not vary significantly from its counterpart in the standard limb leads. The Q wave was absent in 795 records, was clearly present in only 120 records, and was of an amplitude greater than −1 mm. in only 22 instances. An R wave was always present, ranging in amplitude from 1 to 29 mm., with a mean of 10.4. The S wave failed to appear in only six instances. It varied in amplitude from −0.2 to −28 mm., with a mean of −9.3. The S-T segment was upwardly displaced in 977 out of 994 records, ranging from 0.1 to 5 mm. with a mean of 1.14 mm. The T wave was upright in all but two instances in which it was diphasic. Its mean amplitude was 5.9 mm., with a range of 1 to 15 mm. The U wave was found in 915 out of 994 records, was never inverted, and ranged in amplitude from 0.1 to 1.2 mm., with a mean of 0.24 mm.

Auricular and ventricular components

An immediate insight into the nature of the electrocardiogram is gained by placing it in its proper temporal relationship with other events of the cardiac cycle, as in Figure 341. Inspection of such a chart indicates immediately that the P wave must be associated with auricular systole, while the whole of the QRS-T complex accompanies ventricular systole. The P wave is related to the rise in ventricular pressure brought about by auricular systole, with the A wave of the venous pulse, and, when one is present, with the fourth or auricular heart sound. In all circumstances a measurable interval exists between the beginning of the P wave and the mechanical events of auricular systole. The initial wave of the QRS complex begins somewhat before the first indication of increased intraventricular pressure (0.01 to 0.035 sec. in the dog), and precedes also the beginning of the first heart sound (0.004 to 0.029 sec. in the dog, and 0.009 to 0.039 sec. in man). In general this agrees with the concept that the electrical response of a muscle is an expression of the wave of excitation which sets the contractile mechanism into motion after a short latent period.

The end of the T wave does not, however, bear any constant relationship to the end of mechanical systole. It may, according to Lewis (15), terminate as much as 0.028 sec. before the beginning of the second heart sound, or as much as 0.035 sec. after the second sound has begun. Inferences as to the duration of mechanical systole are not therefore to be drawn from the length of the QRS-T portion of the electrical cycle.

A variety of other evidence confirms the division of the electrocardiogram into auricular and ventricular portions. Local damage, application of drugs, etc., affect the P wave when applied to the auricles, and evoke changes in the QRS and T when restricted to the ventricles. Auricular fibrillation involves fragmentation of the P wave, leaving the QRS-T complex essentially unchanged. Ectopic auricular beats show aberrant P waves and normal QRS-T complexes, while the electrocardiogram of an ectopic ventricular beat begins directly with a modified QRS-T complex without any P wave.

The P wave may therefore be considered to represent the electrical correlate of auricular systole just as the QRS-T complex represents the electrical accompaniment of ventricular systole. This view is strengthened by the observation, in favorable circumstances such as A-V delay or total A-V block, of an end-deflection following P as a counterpart to the T wave of the ventricular complex. The major problem in the further interpretation of the electrocardiogram becomes, therefore, the problem of explaining the diphasic nature of the ventricular complex; i.e., the nature of QRS on the one hand, and of the T wave on the other.

Electrical Activity of Cardiac Muscle. *Membrane and dipole hypotheses.* There is general agreement that in its essential features the electrical activity of cardiac muscle has close affinities with that of nervous tissue. When it becomes active in response to an external stimulus or to the normal conducted wave of excitation, the active region is found to be electronegative to neighboring resting areas. An injured region is electronegative to adjacent noninjured, resting regions. Speaking in other terms, the physiologically active and the injured tissues, as Bernstein originally showed, become sinks, to which current flows from the surrounding resting and noninjured areas. In explaining the intimate nature of the events responsible for these phenomena, another viewpoint has been proposed which ignores the classical membrane theory (Chap. 1). This is the so-called "dipole hypothesis."

This hypothesis differs from the membrane hypothesis in three essential postulates: (i) there is no "resting" polarization or membrane potential, (ii) polarization appears only during activity or injury, and (iii) the polarization so appearing is perpendicular to the long axis of the fiber and is confined to the area of transition between resting and active or injured tissue, the negative charge being on the active or injured side of the interface. Thus a wave of excitation passing along a fiber will present to an exploring electrode first a positive charge, and then a negative charge as the wave of excitation approaches and passes the electrode; and then, as the tissue recovers (if it does so in the same sequence), a negative and then a positive charge will pass the electrode. It is now most generally conceded that the electrical activity of excitable tissues develops at the surface membrane, and not as is postulated in the dipole hypothesis. Figure 354A presents schematically the salient features of the dipole and membrane theories as they can be applied to the explanation of the electrogram of nerve and a strip of cardiac tissue as recorded by direct leads. It is seen that the dipole hypothesis, although it can no longer be seriously considered as an explanation of the genesis of action potentials, provides a simple notational system by which the advance and retreat of the wave of excitation may be represented, and it is only this feature of the hypothesis which is retained in the elucidation of the electrocardiogram.

Interference theory. Marchand, who was the first to demonstrate the diphasic character of the electrogram of the frog heart, explained it in terms of the diphasic electrogram of skeletal muscle, namely, that the first deflection represented the arrival of the impulse at the proximal recording electrode, while the second deflection, which was in the opposite direction, indicated the arrival of the wave of excitation at the distal electrode. This explanation was shown to be inadequate by Burdon-Sanderson, who called attention to the fact that the two deflections were separated from one another by an interval amounting to a half second or more, while the time for conduction of the impulse between the two electrodes (base and apex) could be measured in hundredths of a second. He noted, too, that the end-deflection occurred at the end of systole, and in association with the end of the refractory period, and concluded:

"As regards the terminal phase, its coincidence in time with the relaxation of the ventricle appears to me to indicate that, as the initial phase certainly corresponds with the beginning of the period of electrical change, so its cease is marked by the opposite electrical condition; in other words, it seemed probable that the equipotentiality of the surface during the greater part of the ventricular contraction does not mean, as Engelmann supposed, that all is over, and that the electrical disturbance merely precedes the systole and ceases with its commencement, but only that during the period in question the electromotive forces in action are nearly balanced, this state of equilibrium persisting until, toward the end of systole, they again manifest themselves in an electrical difference between the two contacts opposed in sign to that by which the systole was ushered in. It further appeared to be probable that the occurrence of the terminal phase at the end of the period of excitation might be explained on the supposition that at that time, electrical activity has ceased at the contact nearest the point of excitation, but continued at the one more remote."

He reinforced this conclusion by demonstrating that the amplitude, and even the direction of the end-deflection, could be altered by changing the rate at which the regions under the two electrodes recovered. Normally, with homogeneous tissue, the recovery would proceed with equal rapidity under both electrodes, and consequently the region that was excited first would naturally be the first to recover. The natural or simplest form of the electrogram is thus one in which the end-deflection is directed in the opposite direction to the initial deflection. By the simple expedient of cooling the electrode at the base of the heart (the first part to become active) or warming the apex where the "distal" electrode was placed, the apex could be made to recover earlier than the base. Thus the part which was first to respond was also the last to recover, and the end-deflection was necessarily upright and in the same direction as the initial deflection.

Speaking physiologically, therefore, the initial deflection of the cardiac electrogram is a reflection of the sequence of excitation at the recording electrodes, while the end-deflection represents the sequence of recovery of the tissue under the recording electrodes. In terms of the membrane theory, the initial deflection develops from asynchronous depolarization at the recording electrodes, and the end-deflection arises from the asynchronous repolarization of these regions. It may also be said that the electrogram represents the interference between the monophasic action currents underneath the two recording electrodes, developing asynchronously and subsiding asynchronously, but not necessarily in the same order (Fig. 353).

Electrocardiogram and the interference theory. It is almost universally agreed that the electrocardiogram, as recorded from the limb and chest leads, has the same fundamental meaning as the electrogram, namely, that the initial portion, QRS, is an indication of the sequential excitation of the heart (period of invasion) and that the iso-electric portion of the S-T segment represents the interval when the whole heart is excited but before any part has begun to recover (period of possession), while the T wave is the result of the unbalanced recovery of the heart (period of retreat). In other words, the electrocardiogram pictures the sequence of activation and recovery in the heart. It is apparent that no one lead follows the entire sequence of excitation within the heart; it reflects only the march of events in those parts to which it has access, either because of its orientation with respect to the potential differences which develop within the heart or because of its ability, from the standpoint of sheer sensitivity, to record the potentials arrayed between its terminals.

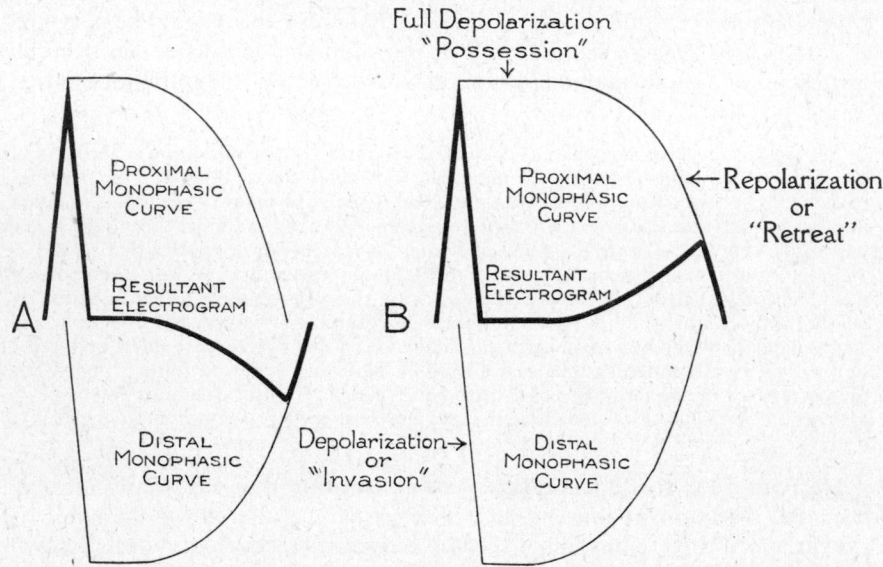

Fig. 353.—Another conventional way of expressing the origin of a cardiac electrogram, in terms of the algebraic summation of two monophasic action currents which develop and regress asynchronously. In A, the basic type is depicted, in which the tissue under the two electrodes is homogeneous, so that recovery takes place at the same rate under each electrode. The order of recovery will repeat the order of excitation, and the second phase will be inverted. In B, the recovery under the proximal electrode is delayed (or recovery under the distal electrode might be accelerated), producing an upright end-deflection. The monophasic curves may be considered as simple graphic representations of the development of excitation and recovery therefrom without regard to the electrical theory involved.

Geographical Representation. *Significance of leads.* As a result of experience with the correlation of electrocardiographic findings with postmortem observations, as well as from animal experimentation, cardiologists have come to recognize that no single lead can suffice to give a full picture of the electrical events within the heart, but that each lead does, however, record from some favored region or regions of the heart. It is universally recognized that in man damage to the anterior quadrant of the left ventricle results in characteristic distortion of the electrocardiogram in lead I, while damage to the posterior left ventricle is revealed by the appearance of the same changes in lead III. This is in keeping with accepted theory, for it is recognized that electrodes placed across volume conductors fail to be influenced by potentials which develop along an axis perpendicular to the line joining the leads, and are, on the other hand, maximally affected when the axis of developing potentials lies parallel with the axis of the leads.

As far as the limb leads are concerned, therefore, lead I records those potentials which develop along a horizontal axis, while lead III records potentials aligned along a more or less vertical axis. Whether lead III actually records along a strictly vertical axis at a right angle to the axis of lead I is debatable. The classical Einthoven triangle represents lead II and lead III as forming the two sides of an equilateral triangle with lead I, thus forming an angle of 60 degrees with the horizontal. This is in line with Einthoven's view that the left leg represents in reality a pubic lead, and that the right leg might be therefore used interchangeably with the left leg. This is probably not strictly true, and lead III, when recorded from the left leg, probably represents

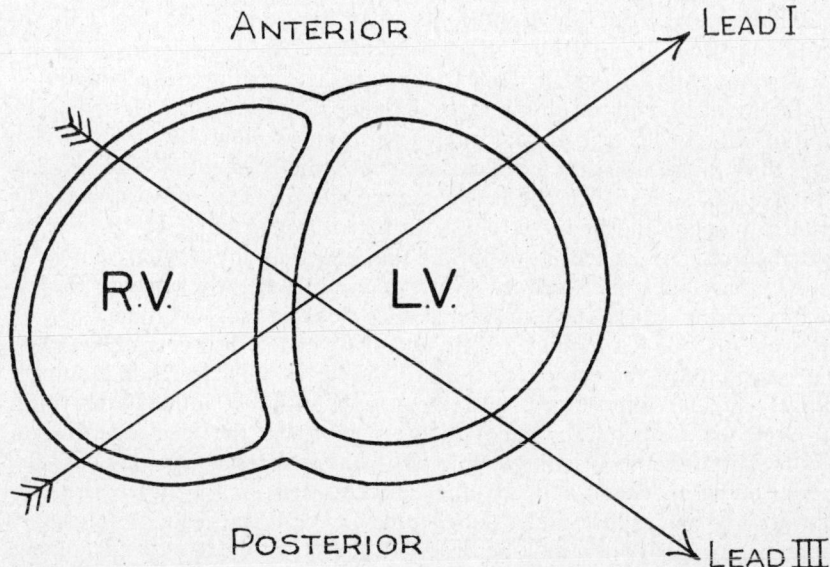

Fig. 354.—Topographical representation of the heart in leads I and III. Lead I records preponderantly from the posterior surface of the right ventricle and the anterior surface of the left ventricle, while lead III records from the anterior surface of the right ventricle and the posterior surface of the right ventricle. In each lead the electrocardiogram may be considered to be formed from the summation of an upright dextrocardiogram and an inverted levocardiogram, as in Fig. 357.

an angle somewhere between the extremes of 60 degrees and 90 degrees. Whatever the exact angle formed, it does not invalidate the facts as to geographical representation outlined above, nor affect essentially the concept of the Einthoven triangle to be outlined later. Potentials recorded maximally by lead I are recorded minimally or not at all by lead III, and vice versa. The horizontal axis of lead I in the dog passes through the posterior quadrant of the right ventricle and the anterior quadrant of the left ventricle, while the vertical axis of lead III passes through the anterior quadrant of the right ventricle and the posterior quadrant of the left ventricle. It is thus to be expected that potentials developing normal to the surfaces of the anterior right and posterior left ventricles would be recorded in lead III, while potentials so developing in the anterior left and posterior right ventricles would be recorded in lead III (Fig. 354). This is, in fact, the case, and it can be amply demonstrated in the case of externally applied potentials, damage by burns, KCl, coronary artery ligation, or by localized warming and cooling.

The standard limb leads in the dog, therefore, record in each instance across approximately equal portions of right and left ventricles. Because of the arrangement of leads, negativity oriented toward the right ventricle results in an upward deflection in the resultant electrocardiogram, while a potential which develops with negativity oriented toward the left ventricle causes a downward deflection. Thus an electrical change produced in the right ventricle will evoke a response in the electrocardiogram just opposite in direction to that which would be produced by the same physiological or pathological event in the left ventricle.

Evidence at present available indicates that in man the limb leads have in general the same localizing significance that they do in the dog. The distribution in leads I and III of changes produced by damage, local cooling and warming, and by ventricular extrasystoles is essentially the same in the dog, the monkey, and the chimpanzee. The localization by the electrocardiograph of infarcts due to coronary occlusion in man follows the same patterns that it does in the dog and monkey, and the same is essentially true of ventricular extrasystoles when the heart is normally situated and normally surrounded by lungs and an intact chest wall. It is particularly worth mentioning that there is no evidence to support the view that any standard limb lead records a base-apex interference, a view derived from early work on the frog and turtle heart, where such an interference does, in fact, take place.

The chest leads have quite a different significance, however. Due to the close proximity of the chest electrode to the heart, this electrode assumes a relatively greater importance, and the region of heart immediately under this electrode contributes proportionately more to the electrocardiogram than do distal regions of comparable size. The interference in this case may be considered to occur between the concentrated area beneath the chest electrode and the diffuse areas represented in the distal lead. Whatever the theoretical explanation, it may be observed that in all the chest leads, marked electrocardiographic changes may be induced by appropriate treatment of the restricted area of the heart beneath the chest electrode (usually near the apex) and similar changes, of opposite polarity, are caused by similar treatment of a much larger, distal area, often lying near the base of the heart. The interference areas of the chest leads approach, therefore, the apex base interference of the cold-blooded heart.

Theory of limited potential differences. The most generally accepted concept of the genesis of the electrocardiogram follows the line laid down by the late Sir Thomas Lewis, based upon the dipole hypothesis. It is clearly understood by most modern exponents of the view, however, that the theory is used only as a notational system to indicate and to calculate mathematically the presumptive current flow within the heart as the wave of excitation advances and regresses, and that the membrane theory is to be invoked to account for the actual development of the electrical potentials. This position is expressed most clearly in the following statement by Wilson *et al.* (25).

"The resting cardiac muscle fiber is surrounded by a 'membrane' which has a very low electrical conductivity. Across this membrane there is an electromotive force which makes its inner surface strongly negative in comparison with its outer surface. The passage of the excitatory process along the fiber is associated with a sudden and very great increase in the conductivity of the resting membrane and a sudden decrease in the electromotive force; in other words, with the sudden development of a short circuit between the inside and

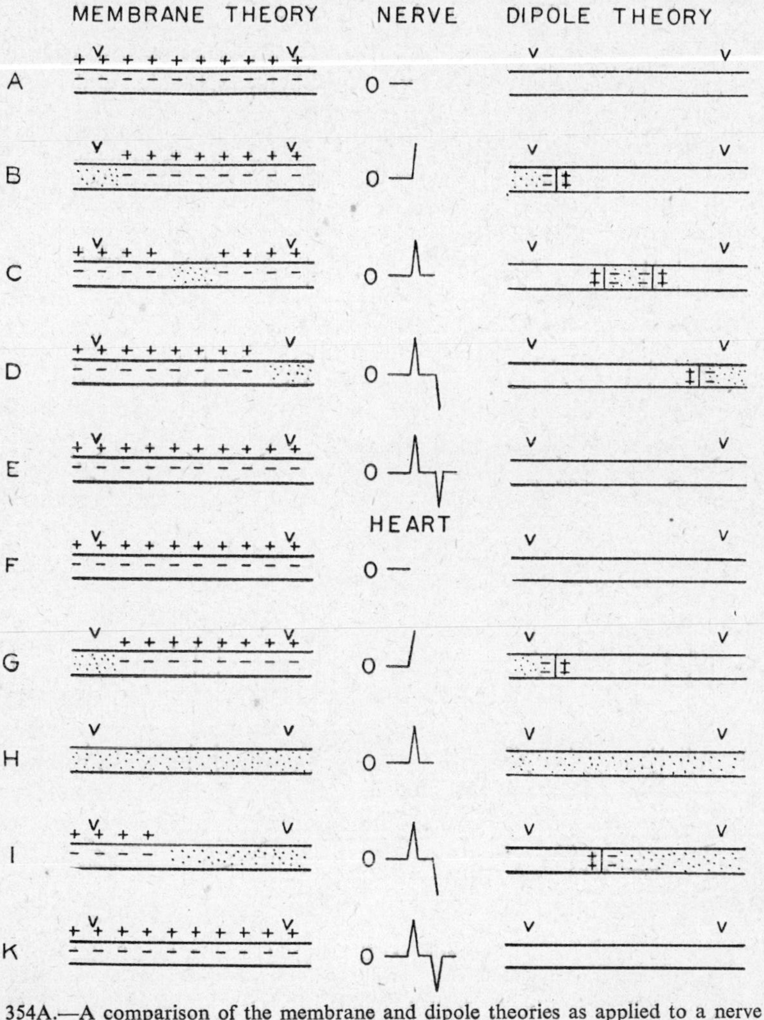

Fig. 354A.—A comparison of the membrane and dipole theories as applied to a nerve fiber (A-E) and to a strip of cardiac tissue such as a Purkinje fiber (F-K), suspended in a nonconducting medium. In the resting state the membrane potential postulates that the surface membrane of the tissue is polarized (A), while, according to the dipole hypothesis, no potentials exist. The appearance of a wave of excitation (denoted by stippling) is associated with disappearance of surface polarization according to the membrane theory, and by the development of polarization according to the dipole theory. The current flow between active and inactive tissue would be the same whatever theory is invoked, and for this reason the dipole system may be employed as a valid system of notation. It is to be noted that the second phase of the diphasic potential of the nerve action potential represents the arrival of the impulse at the distal electrode, while in the heart the second phase represents the onset of recovery at the proximal electrode when tissue at the distal electrode is still active.

26

the outside of the fiber. Current flows out of the resting part of the fiber adjacent to the short circuit and re-enters the fiber through the short-circuited region. *The effect in the medium outside the fiber is the same as if the cardiac impulse were immediately preceded by the positive pole, and accompanied by the negative pole, of a battery.* In other words, we may say that, across the boundary between active and resting muscle, there is an electromotive force which makes the potential of points toward which the excitation wave is advancing positive, and the potential of points which lie behind it negative."

The simplest application of this concept is found in the explanation of the chest leads, particularly the CV leads (Fig. 354B). Here the view is expressed that the upward deflection of the R wave, with which normal electrocardiograms taken with this lead almost always commence, is caused by the outward travel of the wave of excitation from endocardium to epicardium immediately under the chest electrode. The excitation dipoles in

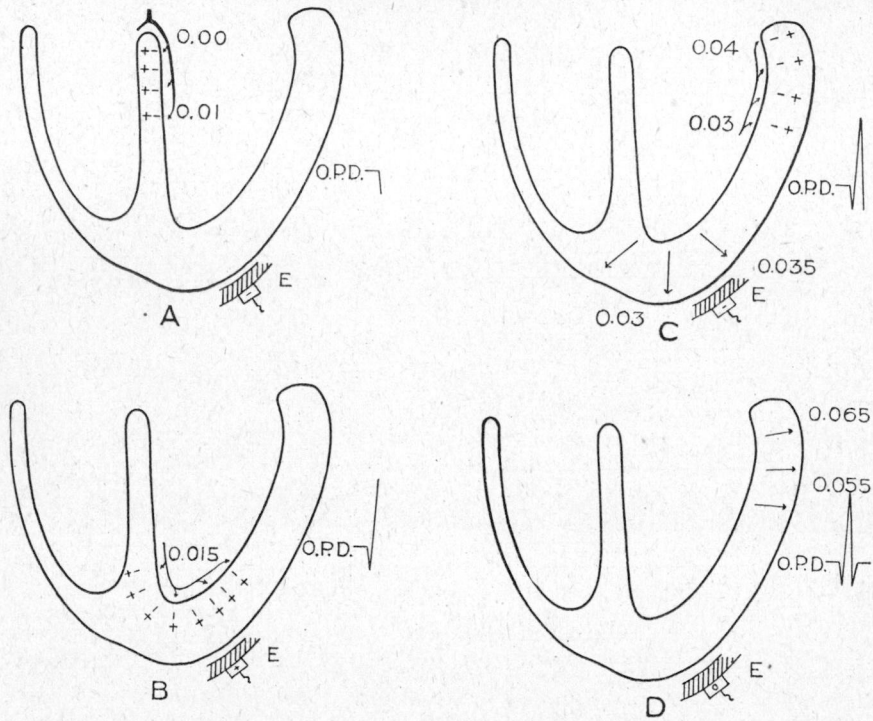

Fig. 354B.—An illustration of the genesis of QRS in a chest lead over the left ventricle according to the theory of limited potential differences, and in conformity with the spread of the impulse as postulated by Lewis. According to this view, the first activation of the left ventricle (A) involves the septum, resulting in a relative negativity of the cavity, which being transmitted to the chest electrode causes the downward excursion of Q from the line of zero potential difference. Some 0.015 sec. later, (B), the septum is fully activated and all potentials disappear from this area, to be replaced by beginning excitation in the endocardium of the apex. This produces an outwardly traveling wave-front which reverses the polarity of the chest electrode and is responsible for the upswing of R. The situation 0.03 to 0.035 sec. after the start of ventricular excitation is depicted in C. The apex is now fully activated, no differences of potential exist within it, and the downstroke of R is inscribed. The wave of excitation is still penetrating the ventricular wall at the base, however, so the cavity again becomes negative, and this is transmitted to the chest electrode to produce the downstroke of S. Finally, in D, the left ventricle is completely excited, all potential differences are extinguished, and the upstroke of S is inscribed.

such an event would progress from within outward, with their positive pole outwardly oriented. In terms having less specific implications, the endocardium would act as a sink and the external epicardium as a source; the chest electrode would record this as a positivity, and the record would show an upward deflection.

When the whole thickness of the ventricular wall is activated, the potential across the

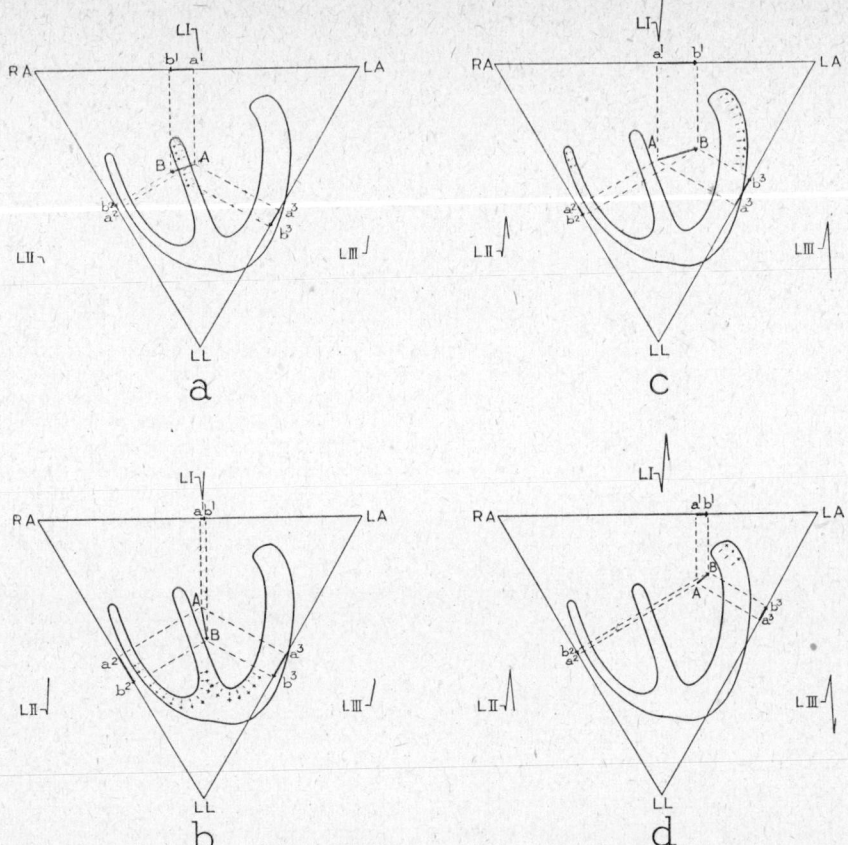

Fig. 354C.—a, an illustration of the genesis of QRS according to the theory of limited potential differences as adapted from Gardberg and Ashman. The heart is considered to lie in the chest with approximately the orientation depicted with relation to the horizontal axis of lead I (RA-LA). Lead II (RA-LL) and lead III (LA-LL) are supposed to form the other two limbs of an equilateral triangle (LL representing in effect a pubic lead). The first excitation of the ventricles occurs at the base of the interventricular septum; in reality it affects both sides, but it is assumed that that of the left side progresses somewhat faster than that of the right side, so that the preponderant effect is an oriented "front" of dipoles with the positive charges facing to the right. The effect of all these small dipoles can be summated into a single electromotive force (represented by the arrow A-B) having an intensity represented by the length of the arrow and bearing an orientation represented by its inclination to the horizontal. The influence of such a potential on the limb leads could be indicated graphically by the length and direction of its projections along the three sides of the triangle by means of perpendiculars dropped from its extremities (a^1-b^1, a^2-b^2, a^3-b^3). If this be done it will be seen that a rather large Q wave would be produced in lead I while a somewhat smaller R_3 would result. A small Q_2 is also produced.

b, The impulse has now reached the endocardium of the apex and two "shells" of dipoles are found, that on the right being somewhat more extensive. Summation of individual dipoles gives a single potential A-B which has rotated somewhat to the left and is of greater amplitude as compared to Figure 354C, a. The projection of this electromotive force on the axis of lead I would produce a beginning R, while in lead III R would reach its maximum.

c, As the apex is activated throughout its full thickness, all potential differences in this region disappear and are replaced by a shell of dipoles around the base. That on the left is more extensive because through-and-through activation of the right ventricle proceeds more rapidly on account of the thinner musculature of the right ventricle. For this reason, the resultant "manifest potential" A-B will be directed still more to the left, bringing R_1 to its apex. R_3 will diminish and eventually change to an S_3. R_2 will be in its declining phase.

d, Only a few dipoles remain at the base of the left ventricle as the heart is almost fully activated. There being now no opposing forces, the remaining dipoles produce a summated potential directed well to the left but of smaller amplitude. The declining phase of R_1 will therefore be described, S_3 will begin to ascend, and a small S_2 will be inscribed. In a few milliseconds even these dipoles will disappear, and the iso-electric state be re-established. Finally, as dipoles of recovery begin to appear, the T wave will be inscribed.

755

ventricular wall disappears and the downward deflection of the R wave is described. If the excitatory process is still spreading through some part of the ventricular wall when this "intrinsic" deflection occurs, the negativity of the ventricular cavity outlasts the R deflection and an S wave is produced. If the subendocardial muscle of some part of the ventricular wall passes into the active state earlier than the subendocardial muscle which lies between the chest electrode and the ventricular cavity, the initial negativity of the cavity is transmitted to this electrode and a Q deflection occurs.

The possibilities in regard to the standard leads of the electrocardiogram are considerably more complicated and despite a general assumption of the validity of the concept, no careful analysis of the implications of the theory had been made until the impressive attempt of Gardberg and Ashman (6) to visualize the electrocardiogram in terms of the advance and retreat of localized dipoles.

According to this analysis, the Q wave in lead I begins when the septum is first excited. It postulates that the left side is excited somewhat in advance of the right side, producing a local "front" or "shell" of dipoles with the predominant orientation of negative charges on the left side of the septum. This local difference in potential would be recorded in lead I as the downstroke of the Q wave and in lead III as the upstroke of the R wave. With full activation of the septum the septal dipoles disappear, to be replaced by dipoles lined up along the endocardial surfaces of the heart near the apices of both ventricles. These, it is presumed, produce a change in the orientation of electrical forces in a manner to produce the rising phase of R in lead I and to continue it in lead III. Lead II naturally represents the algebraical summation of leads I and III.

Since, next, the full thickness of the right ventricular walls is activated, except for a region of the conus, the left ventricle becomes the major site of potentials, which are arranged in such a manner that R reaches its apex, while an S wave develops in lead III. When, finally, the remaining portion of the ventricles are excited, the upstroke of S is inscribed and the iso-electric portion of S-T begins.

The order of recovery is first of all determined by the sequence of excitation. It is also, however, influenced by the local metabolic state in each and every fiber of the myocardium. Thus the sequence of recovery, with its resultant recovery dipoles, does not necessarily reproduce the sequence of excitation. Furthermore, the tissue does not pass from excitation to recovery with the same abruptness with which excitation was initiated, but the process is much more gradual, as is best visualized in the recovery phase of a monophasic curve. Thus the orientation of the dipoles of recovery does not undergo the rapid and extreme changes which occur during excitation, and the consequence is that the T wave is a much smoother, far less complicated, and temporally more extended curve. This view, which attributes the T wave to repolarization in septal, subepicardial and subendocardial laminae, and even in different parts of single muscle fibers or between closely adjoining parts of small syncytial masses, makes analysis of the T wave from the standpoint of topography extremely difficult. In fact, the advocates of the view state that "attempts to determine the metabolic or other effect of certain agents upon the heart muscle from a study of the electrocardiogram of the intact animal is [sic] almost futile." (1a).

In attempting to decide as to the validity of the above view of the genesis of the electrocardiogram, three questions must be answered: (i) Does the impulse spread through the heart in the manner postulated? (ii) Would potentials oriented in the manner pictured be recorded in the several leads of the electrocardiogram as here portrayed? and (iii) Is the electrocardiogram of the standard and chest leads able to record the potentials that accompany the cardiac impulse as it is distributed throughout the ventricular musculature?

The first question is probably to be answered in the affirmative. As has been pointed out previously, however, the alternative view put forward by Robb (23) cannot be readily dismissed. The second question must be answered with a definite negative. The view that excitation restricted to a single ventricle will cause deflections in leads I and III of opposite directions (see Fig. 354C, d) is based upon interpretation rather than direct evidence. Direct experimental evidence makes it quite clear that excitation (or injury) restricted to a single ventricle produces deflections in leads I, II and III in the same direction.

The experimental validation of this hypothesis and the presumably affirmative answer to the third question rest largely upon Lewis's work. Recognizing the implications of the hypothesis, Lewis predicted that the initial complexes of ventricular extrasystoles induced by stimulation of the endocardium should be just the reverse of the complex initiating an epicardially induced extra-systole. This is illustrated in Figure 355. In four experiments performed by

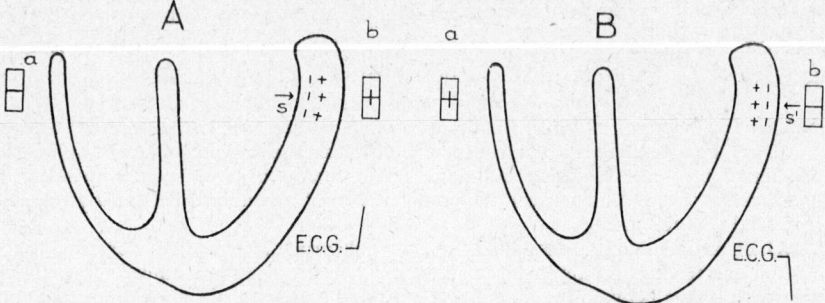

Fig. 355.—An illustration of the rationale of experiments designed to test the theory of limited potential differences as applied to the electrocardiogram. In A, a stimulus is applied to the endocardium of the outer wall of a ventricle, creating an outwardly traveling impulse. An epicardial stimulus S^1 in B would presumably result in an inwardly traveling impulse. According to the theory of limited potential differences, there would in consequence be created wave fronts of dipoles oriented in exactly opposite directions in the two cases. Therefore the initial deflections of the resultant electrocardiogram as recorded from leads a-b would be expected to be directed downward in one case and upward in the other, providing, of course, that such potentials are of recordable magnitude.

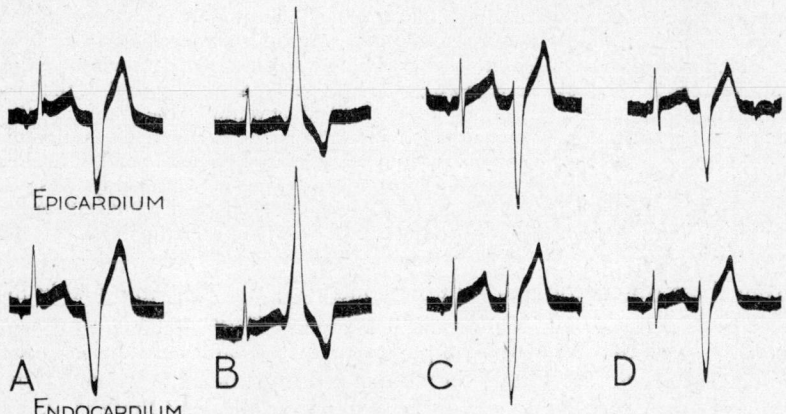

Fig. 356.—Experimental results for comparison with theoretical postulates of theory of limited potential difference in Fig. 355. Records were taken with CV leads, with the chest electrode over the right ventricle in the dog. Extrasystoles induced from the epicardium are above, with endo-cardial extrasystoles below. In each instance the epicardial and endocardial electrodes were directly opposite each other on the two sides of the ventricular wall. Identical results were obtained with the standard limb leads I, II, and III, with 4F, 4R, and 4L in addition to CV, and from the left ventricle as well as the right. A, when the stimulating electrodes are directly beneath the chest electrode. No distinction between epicardial and endocardial extrasystoles can be made out. Both extrasystoles show a simple QS configuration. B, when the stimulating electrodes are as far as possible away from the chest electrode (usually but not necessarily on the opposite ventricle). Again no difference between epicardial and endocardial extrasystoles, but a simple R is seen instead of a QS. C, when points intermediate between A and B are stimulated intermediate stages are seen, showing a small R and a large S when near A, and the contrary when near B. D, occasionally, near A, an endocardial extrasystole will show an RS while the epicardial extra-systole shows only a QS. It is most likely that this R represents the same factors as are responsible for the RS seen in B and C, rather than an externally traveling dipole.

Lewis on the right ventricle in the dog and using transthoracic leads, this was, in fact, found to occur.

A more recent study of the configuration of endocardial extrasystoles and their epicardial counterparts, carried out in the author's laboratory, employing not only transthoracic leads but also the standard limb leads I, II and III, as well as 4F, 4R and CV leads, and covering a large number of points on the right and left ventricles, has led to an opposite conclusion (Fig. 356). Briefly, the results are these (16):

(i) When, using standard leads, the points stimulated are well in the "center" of each ventricle, as far as possible removed from the septa so that the ectopic impulse must traverse a maximum course in the ventricle stimulated before the opposite ventricle is involved, no difference whatsoever exists between the configuration of an endocardial extrasystole and its epicardial counterpart.

(ii) When, using any of the chest leads, the chest electrode is immediately external to the stimulating electrodes, or, employing transthoracic electrodes, the stimulating electrodes are on a line drawn between the recording electrodes, there is again no difference of configuration between endocardial and epicardial extrasystoles. In situations (i) and (ii) the initial complex is a simple R or QS wave.

(iii) Should the stimulating electrodes be shifted to the center of the opposite ventricle when the standard leads are used or to some distal point (usually the base of the same or the opposite ventricle) when chest leads are employed, the extrasystoles are again identical, showing a simple R or QS configuration just opposite to that seen in (i) and (ii).

(iv) When, finally, points intermediate between the proximal areas (i) and (ii) and distal regions (iii) are stimulated, the complex becomes diphasic, showing a QR or RS form, in all stages of transition between the simpler states just described in paragraphs 1, 2, 3. In this intermediate zone, particularly near the "proximal" area, points may be found on the endocardium which will give the diphasic QR or RS pattern while the epicardial points give the simpler R or QS configuration. Presumably, when the endocardium in this region is stimulated the Purkinje system is more quickly activated, and the spread of the impulse to distal areas is hastened. This presumption is fortified by warming the distal area, thereby hastening its full activation, whereby the R or Q wave becomes larger. The initial R or Q waves which usher in the main complex are not, therefore, restricted to endocardial extrasystoles but are, in the majority of instances, found also in epicardial extrasystoles. Whenever they are present, the evidence is that they represent the activation of "distal" or distant regions of the heart and not the outward travel of the wave of excitation.

From these observations it may be concluded that it is impossible in the electrocardiogram, either in the standard leads or in the chest leads, to detect the existence of the impulse as it passes from the endocardium to the epicardium. It is therefore the writer's conclusion, despite the weighty *a priori* arguments in favor of the theory of limited potentials, that there is as yet no satisfactory direct experimental evidence that the electrocardiogram is developed in the manner originally outlined by Lewis and secondarily espoused in this country by Wilson (25) and others.

Dextro- and levocardiograms. It therefore appears worth while to present an alternative account of the genesis of the electrocardiogram which is in more complete agreement with experimental facts as they may be observed in the electrocardiogram. This alternative view, which is modified from earlier suggestions and was largely disregarded after the general acceptance of the theory of limited potential differences, postulates that, as far as the indirect leads by which the electrocardiogram is recorded are concerned, imbalance in potential between them does not occur during the period of invasion of the ventricular septum or muscular wall, but comes into being only when the wave of excitation breaks through the surface of the heart in one region, while it has not yet done so in the distal regions of interference of the lead in question. The electrocardiogram thus represents the sequential pattern of surface activation and recovery in the respective regions of the heart represented in any given lead.

As far as the standard limb leads are concerned, the interfering surfaces are in all cases segments of the right and left ventricles, lead I representing the anterior left ventricle and the posterior right ventricle, while lead III represents the anterior right ventricle and the posterior left ventricle. The chest leads apparently represent a restricted area of the heart lying immediately beneath them and a very diffuse area distal to this area. This diffuse zone may include portions of the same ventricle or of the opposite ventricle, or both. The general interference thus appears to be between base and apex rather than between right and left ventricles as in the limb leads.

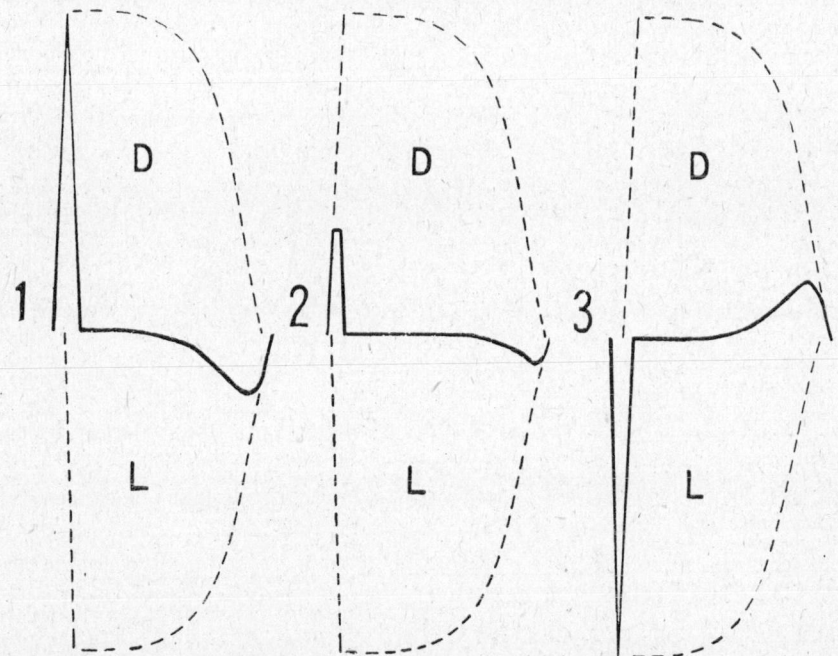

Fig. 357.—Alteration in the height and direction of the QRS complex according to the degree of priority in the excitation of the right and left ventricles. A monophasic-like curve represents the depolarization and repolarization of each ventricle. The dextrocardiogram (D) is upright, while the levocardiogram (L) is inverted.

The electrocardiogram may therefore be graphically represented as the result of the interference resulting from the asynchronous development and regression of two monophasic curves showing the course of depolarization and repolarization of the major interfering surfaces represented in each. Because of the conventions employed, relative negativity of the right ventricle with respect to the left results in an upward deflection in the record in the standard limb leads. The contribution of the right ventricle to the electrocardiogram may thus be pictured as an upright monophasic curve, while the contribution of the left ventricle may be represented as a similar but inverted monophasic curve. These may be termed "dextrocardiogram" and "levocardiogram" respectively. The mutual interference of these two factors may then be assumed to occur as in Figure 357. Accordingly, the ascending limb of the R wave may be taken to represent activation in the right ventricle, while the downstroke of R results from the activation of the left ventricle. An upright T may be interpreted as an indication of repolarization in the right ventricle after that process has been completed in the left ventricle. This view of the development of the ventricular portion of the electrocardiogram may be verified experimentally in a number of ways. By warming the heart, the rapidity with which the impulse reaches the surface might be expected to be accelerated, while cooling might be expected to retard it. Warming the right ventricle or cooling the left should therefore increase the amplitude of the R wave by increasing the interval separating right and left ventricular excitation, thus permitting greater development of the dextrocardiogram. Cooling the right ventricle or warming the left ventricle should, on the other hand, reduce the R wave by allowing less time for the unopposed development of the dextrocardiogram. These predictions are, in fact, borne out experimentally as seen in Figures 357 and 358. When warming or cooling

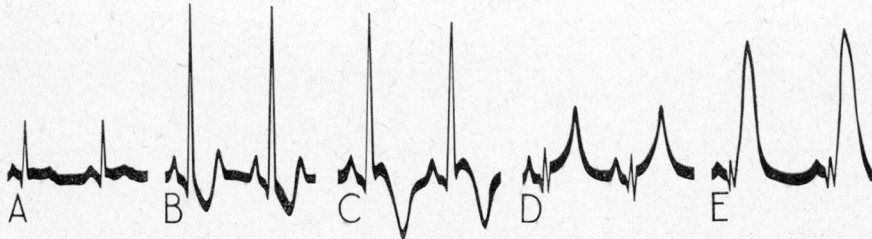

Fig. 358.—Regulation of the amplitude of R and T by varying the time of excitation and recovery in the right and left ventricles by local warming and cooling. Lead III. *A*, control. *B*, warming the right ventricle accelerates the full excitation of the right ventricle and thus permits a greater development of the dextrocardiogram before it is antagonized by the levocardiogram. *C*, the same effect produced by cooling the left ventricle and thus delaying its excitation. Note in both cases the inversion of the T wave caused by the relative prolongation of recovery in the left ventricle with respect to the right (cf. Fig. 357). *D* and *E*, diminution in R caused by cooling the right ventricle and warming the left ventricle, respectively, thus hastening the activation of the left ventricle with respect to the right. Recovery in the right ventricle now continues l onger than in the left ventricle and an upright T wave results.

are restricted to the anterior part of the right ventricle or the posterior part of the left, lead III alone is involved, while lead I alone participates when the anterior part of the left ventricle or the posterior part of the right ventricle is so treated.

A further application of the theory may be utilized in a study of the configuration of ventricular extrasystoles. If activation of the right ventricle occurs before that of the left ventricle, the initial deflection of the complex should be upward, while the initial deflection will be downward if activation of the left ventricle precedes that of the right. If the right ventricle is stimulated at its lateral margin, the impulse will spread over much of the right ventricle before the left ventricle is activated. The initial deflection will consequently be a simple R wave in both leads I and III. Stimulation of a similar region on the lateral margin of the left ventricle will insure primary activation of the left ventricle, producing a downward initial complex, or QS, in both leads I and III. Anterior extrasystoles involve primary right ventricular excitation in lead III and primary left ventricular activation in lead I. A QS_1 and an R_3 will consequently be produced. Posterior extrasystoles which entail primary right ventricular activation in lead I and primary left ventricular activation in lead III will exhibit an R_1 and QS_3 (Fig. 359).

Change in the temperature of a restricted region of the heart will also alter the rate of repolarization of that area. Warming will hasten and cooling will delay repolarization, which will in turn alter the T wave in a predictable manner. Cooling the left ventricle as well as warming the right ventricle will cause an actual or relative prolongation of the repolarization of the left ventricle with respect to the right ventricle, and will result in a diminution in the amplitude of the T wave. Cooling the right ventricle or warming the left ventricle will retard the repolarization of the right ventricle relative to that of the left ventricle, and the T wave will consequently become more and more upright. These predictions may also be confirmed experimentally and the changes will occur in T_1 if the anterior left or posterior right segments

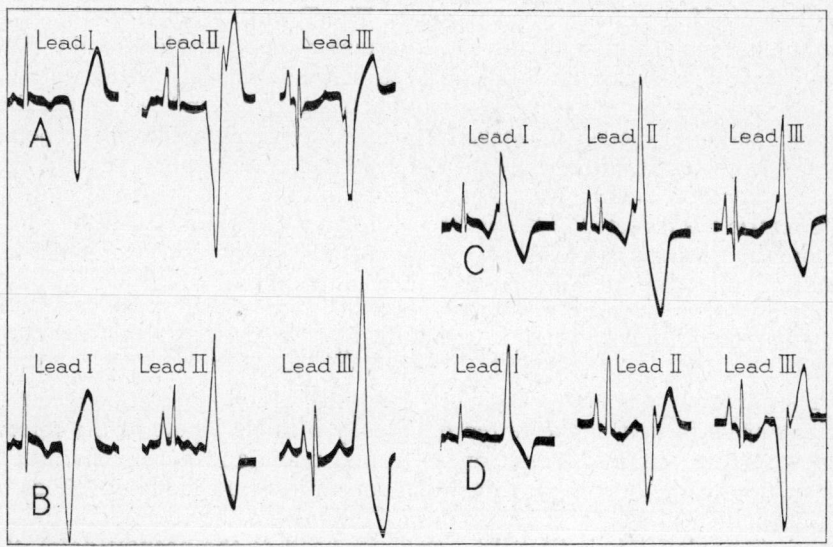

Fig. 359.—Configurations of ventricular extrasystoles in leads I, II and III. A, a left ventricular extrasystole. B, an "anterior" extrasystole. C, a right ventricular extrasystole. D, a "posterior" extrasystole. (From a dog.)

are treated, and in T_3 if the posterior left and anterior right quadrants are treated (Fig. 358).

The Q wave, according to this formulation, must arise from the early activation of some region of the left ventricle, before the main sequence of right and left ventricular excitation responsible for the R wave. Q_1 must arise somewhere in the anterior quadrant of the left ventricle and Q_3 from the posterior segment of that ventricle. This suggestion is in keeping with the observation that portions of the left ventricle near the septum are often the very first parts of the surface of the heart to be excited. The view is strengthened by the observation that Q may be abolished by damage to the appropriate part of the left ventricle, may be increased in amplitude by warming the left ventricle or be diminished by cooling it. Extrasystoles having Q waves may be produced by stimuli placed so that primary activation of the left ventricle is quickly followed by excitation of the right.

The S wave must be expected to occur where the whole of the left ventricle has been excited while some part of the right ventricle remains at rest, and the final return to the base line which constitutes the upstroke of S must occur when this region of the right ventricle finally responds. The frequent presence of an S_3 in the dog is accounted for by the fact that the region of the conus of the right ventricle is frequently the last part of the heart to be excited. S_3 is abolished by damaging this region, and can be increased in amplitude by cooling the area to delay further its excitation. Warming the region of the conus, on the other hand, diminishes or abolishes S_3 by hastening its activation.

In summary it may be stated that the QRS portion of the electrocardiogram is a reflection of the asynchronous excitation of the surface of the heart, in which all upward deflections (upstroke of QRS) result from the excitation of portions of the right ventricle, while all downward deflections reflect the excitation of left ventricular components. The T wave arises from the asynchronous repolarization of the same surfaces; repolarization of the right ventricle now evokes a downward deflection, while that of the left ventricle results in an upward deflection. An upright T wave thus indicates the earlier repolarization of the left ventricle. An inverted T wave signifies that repolarization in the right ventricle preceded that in the left. The interplay of events in the anterior surface of the right ventricle and the posterior surface of the left ventricle is reflected in the electrocardiogram from lead III, while lead I records the counterpart of this sequence at the anterior surface of the left ventricle and the posterior surface of the right ventricle.

Calculation of the electrical axis

The effect on the limb leads of electrical potentials existing within the heart at any given instant might be reproduced by a single dipole of the correct voltage, lying within the chest on its frontal plane and having the proper inclination to the horizontal axis which constitutes lead I. If the voltage of this hypothetical single dipole, or *manifest potential*, be represented by its length (its polarity is indicated by an arrowhead at the positive pole), the amplitude of the potential recorded in each lead would be indicated by the length of the projection of the manifest potential by perpendiculars dropped to the line of each lead. The usual convention is to consider these lines as forming an equilateral triangle, the so-called Einthoven triangle. The direction of each deflection will be indicated by the direction in which the arrow points, granting that positivity of the left arm with respect to the right arm causes an upright deflection in lead I, that positivity of the left leg with respect to the left arm gives an upright deflection in lead III, and positivity of the left leg with respect to the right arm gives an upright deflection in lead II.

If the amplitude of the deflections in any two leads of the electrocardiogram is known at a given instant, the orientation of the manifest potential may be calculated, and thus the general orientation of electrical forces within the heart at that time may be calculated. It is understandable that this orientation is not constant throughout the cycle, but varies greatly with the spread of the wave of excitation through the heart. The illustrations of Gardberg and Ashman (6) indicate how the manifest potential might at first show a marked deviation of its positive pole toward the right, and then move progressively in a counter-clockwise manner far to the left. It is equally apparent from these figures that the apex of a given part of the complex, such as the R wave, does not appear at the same instant of time in all leads, so that errors will occur in using the apex of the main deflections for calculation of the angle the manifest potential makes with the horizontal, or the *electrical axis*.

It is nevertheless worth while to ascertain the so-called electrical axis at the moment the major amplitudes of the QRS waves are reached, and this calculation has the greater validity if the algebraic sum of the deflections in leads I and III is found to equal the amplitude of the deflection in lead II. This test constitutes a rough test of simultaneity, because necessarily the potential difference between the right arm and left leg is measured directly by lead II and in two steps by leads I and III.

While the angle may be measured trigonometrically, it may also be calculated graphically by numerous methods, the most useful being that of Carter, Richter, and Greene (5), which is illustrated in Figure 360, A, B and C. The amplitudes of the major deflections in leads I and III are measured and laid off along the side of the triangle representing the lead in question, according to their polarity. Perpendiculars dropped from the ends of the line, representing the measured amplitude, will meet within the triangle and thereby delimit a line representing the magnitude and orientation of the manifest potential difference. The angle this line makes to the horizontal is read off the protractor encircling the triangle; this is the electrical axis of the heart at the moment the summits in question were reached.

White has suggested a simple guide to the degree of electrical axis deviation which may be employed without formulae or graphic analysis. The amplitude in millimeters of R_3 and S_1 are added, and subtracted from the sum of the amplitudes of R_1 and S_3. If the remainder is greater than 30, abnormal left axis deviation may be presumed to exist. If, on the other hand, the remainder is less than -15, abnormal right axis deviation is present.

It is obvious that two major factors regulate the electrical axis. One is, of course, the sequence of excitation within the heart, while the other is the position of the heart in the chest. Thus in a long chest with low diaphragm the heart will tend to hang vertically, giving a right deviation to the axis, while in a short chest with a high diaphragm the heart will be swung upward to the left, and the picture of left axis deviation will be produced. Often fairly marked changes of this nature will occur in respiration, with a tendency toward right axis deviation in inspiration and left axis deviation during expiration. Similar but less marked deviations will occur in changes from the lying to the standing position. For these, and for other as yet unrecognized reasons, wide variations in the electrical axis are found in normal individuals, the usually accepted limits being from 0 degree to 90 degrees. Graybiel and his associates have found even wider normal limits, varying from -36 degrees to $+120$ degrees, with a mean inclination of 64.2 degrees.

Hypertrophy of the right or left ventricles may produce, although not invariably, right or left axis deviation respectively, and here one may speak justifiably of right or left ventricular preponderance. Right axis deviation is, in addition, noted in the so-called "discordant" type of "right" bundle-branch block and in "left" ventricular extrasystoles, while left axis deviation is found in "discordant left" bundle-branch block and "right" ventricular extrasystoles.

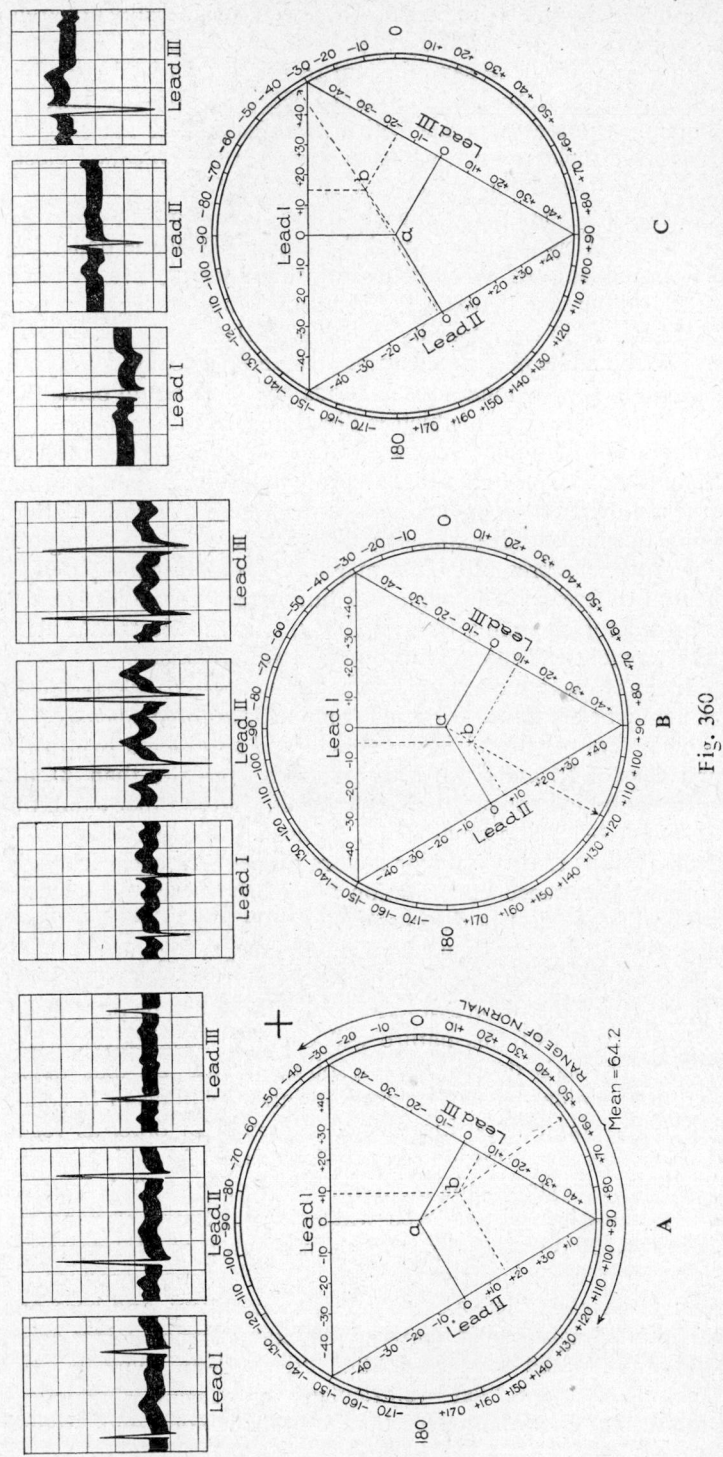

Fig. 360

Experimentally, right axis deviation may be produced, not by a "left" ventricular extrasystole, but by one arising along the anterior septum. It may also be produced by warming the anterior surface of the heart over the septum involving both right and left ventricles. Remembering that the anterior surface of the right ventricle is represented in lead III, it can be understood that hastening the onset of excitation in this region or eliciting its early response by stimulation will produce a large upright R_3, while the early activation of the adjoining left ventricle will produce a diminution in R_1 or even an inverted QS complex, depending on how early that region is activated. Left axis deviation may be produced by hastening the activation of the posterior segment of the right and left ventricles by warming them, or by eliciting ventricular extrasystoles from along the posterior septum. In this event the early right ventricular activity will again produce a large R wave, this time, however, in lead I, while the early activation of the left ventricle will produce, in lead III, a QS complex. True, or "concordant," extrasystoles, in which the initial complexes are consistently upright or inverted in both leads I and III, do not fit into the category of either right or left axis deviation. The same is true of "concordant" bundle-branch block. It is therefore wiser, in the present state of knowledge, not to infer anatomical localization from axis deviations or to interpret right or left axis deviations in terms of right and left ventricles.

Conduction disturbances. At practically every stage in its distribution from the pacemaker to the ventricular musculature, the cardiac impulse may be subject to delay or complete interruption from a variety of causes. The electrocardiograph serves as the chief means for the identification of most of them. Sino-auricular block has been produced experimentally by incisions partly surrounding the S-A node and by intoxication with digitalis and quinidine, and is seen in man in circumstances in which vagal overactivity is present. If the block is total, no evidence of its presence exists, for the pacemaker then shifts to the auricle and a completely normal electrocardiogram may result. If the block is partial or intermittent, it may be recognized by the periodic absence of a complete complex, a "missed beat," leaving a pause equal to exactly twice the normal interval between beats. This exact relationship of the cycle to two normal cycles serves to distinguish the condition from sinus arrhythmia.

Intra-auricular block may be recognized by the excessive prolongation, flattening, and notching of the P wave and by the consequent prolongation of the P-R interval. It may be noticed as the result of mitral stenosis, often as

Fig. 360.—The graphic method of determination of the electrical axis illustrating a normal inclination (Carter, Richter, Greene). A, the amplitude of lead I, +9 mm., is laid out along the horizontal arm of the triangle to the right of the zero point and a perpendicular dropped from it. Similarly the amplitude of lead III, +6.5 mm., is laid out along the axis of lead III and a perpendicular dropped. The two perpendiculars intersect at b, delimiting a line a–b which makes an angle of +55 degrees to the horizontal. The line a–b represents graphically a single dipole of such an amplitude (represented by its length) and such an orientation (represented by its inclination) as would produce in the three standard leads the deflections recorded at the heights of the R waves. While the normal range of the electrical axis is usually taken as from 0 to 90 degrees, the range noted by Graybiel *et al.* in normal young men is far greater, i.e., −36 to +120 degrees. B, an example of right axis deviation as used by Carter, Richter and Greene to illustrate their graphic method of calculating the electrical axis. In this case they recommend that lead I be considered to be the major deflection minus the lesser deflection (−5 mm.) and lead III be similarly treated (+10 mm.). These two leads are laid off as in the preceding figures and perpendiculars are dropped to intersect at b. A potential of amplitude a–b, with the orientation noted (+120 degrees), would produce deflections in the three leads as delimited by perpendiculars dropped to the three sides of the triangle. C, left axis deviation as used by Carter, Richter and Greene to illustrate their graphic method for calculating the electrical axis. Here R_1 and S_3 are laid out according to their direction and amplitude, and perpendiculars dropped to delimit a single "manifest potential" a–b, which in this case is directed to the left, forming an angle of −33 degrees with the horizontal. Note that the projection of a–b on the axis of lead II does not agree with the amplitude of S_2 actually recorded. This indicates that the peak of R_1 and of S_3 were not actually simultaneous, but that R_1 must have preceded S_3 by a short interval. (Adapted from Carter, Richter and Greene, *Johns Hopk. Hosp. Bull.*, 1919, *30*:162–167.)

a precursor to auricular fibrillation, and may be produced experimentally by increasing the level of serum potassium to a level toxic to the auricle (7–9 mEq./1).

Auriculoventricular block reflects by its frequency the general low level of conductivity of the A-V node and bundle of His evident in the normal P-R interval. In fact, even in the normal state, the A-V node and bundle appear to function as a region of partial block, and it is understandable that the normal limits for the P-R interval should be wide, and pass off almost imperceptibly into the abnormal. This situation is contributed to by the rich innervation of this region by the vagus, which acts further to impede conduction in it. The region is also highly susceptible to local or generalized anoxemia (as by arteriosclerotic occlusion or narrowing of the vessels which supply it, or by generalized anoxemia), to pressure from nearby inflammatory lesions, edema, tumors or hemorrhages, to toxins, as of diphtheria, and to a number of drugs such as acetyl-beta-methylcholine, digitalis, etc.

In its earliest stages, A-V block takes the form of simple prolongation of the P-R interval, exceeding 0.2 sec., but a QRS-T complex follows each R wave, and is initiated by it. Intervals as long as 0.35 sec. may be observed in this stage. As block deepens, some of the auricular impulses fail to pass

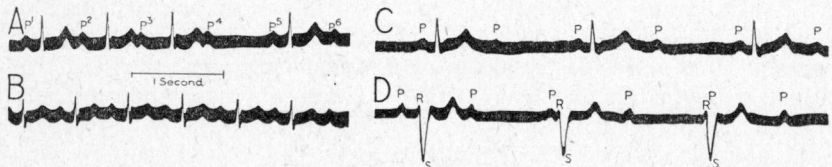

Fig. 361.—A, A-V delay in man progressing (p^1, p^2, p^3) to the point where an impulse is blocked (p^4). The subsequent impulse (p^5) is conducted as a normal interval and the process is repeated (Wenkebach phenomenon). The phenomenon is suppressed by atropine, B, indicating its vagal origin. (After Levy, *Ann. intern. Med.*, 1939, *12*:1525–1529.) C, 2:1 block; D, total A-V dissociation in man. (Courtesy of Dr. C. F. Moffatt.)

the region of block, so that P waves are seen which are not followed by ventricular complexes (Fig. 361). This is the stage of *partial block*, and it can be recognized by the regular procession of P waves, with a regular dropping out of a portion of the QRS complexes. Commonly, every other ventricular complex is missing; i.e., the block is 2:1, although 3:1, 4:1, and 3:2 blocks are not unusual. In all of them, however, the presence of a definite proportionality indicates that the ventricle is still contracting solely in response to supraventricular stimulation.

In the final stage, block becomes total, and the auricles and the ventricles beat independently of each other. The condition can be recognized by the appearance of P waves at regular normal intervals, and by the appearance of ventricular complexes at a completely independent rate, which is usually, but not always, much slower than that of the auricles.

When one of the branches of the bundle of His is severed in an experimental animal, or conduction in it interrupted reversibly by pressure, important alterations take place in the distribution of the cardiac impulse. The part of the heart served by the intact bundle is supplied in an entirely normal manner. The rest of the heart will receive its impulse excitation from contiguous areas of normally activated myocardium, and will consequently be late in responding. This does not necessarily imply, as has often been assumed, that all of one ventricle is excited in advance of the other. For example, the left bundle-branch may be assumed to supply the anterior portion of the left ventricle near the septum. This region is known to be excited in advance of almost every other part of the heart. This being the case, in right bundle-branch block this region will retain its early activation, and, as a consequence, contiguous areas of the right ventricle will also be excited with almost equal rapidity, perhaps well in advance of regions on the posterior aspects of the left ventricle. Such a state of events would be expected to reproduce the electrocardiogram characteristic of early anterior activation, namely, a downward deflection (QS) in lead I and an upright initial deflection (R) in lead III. In

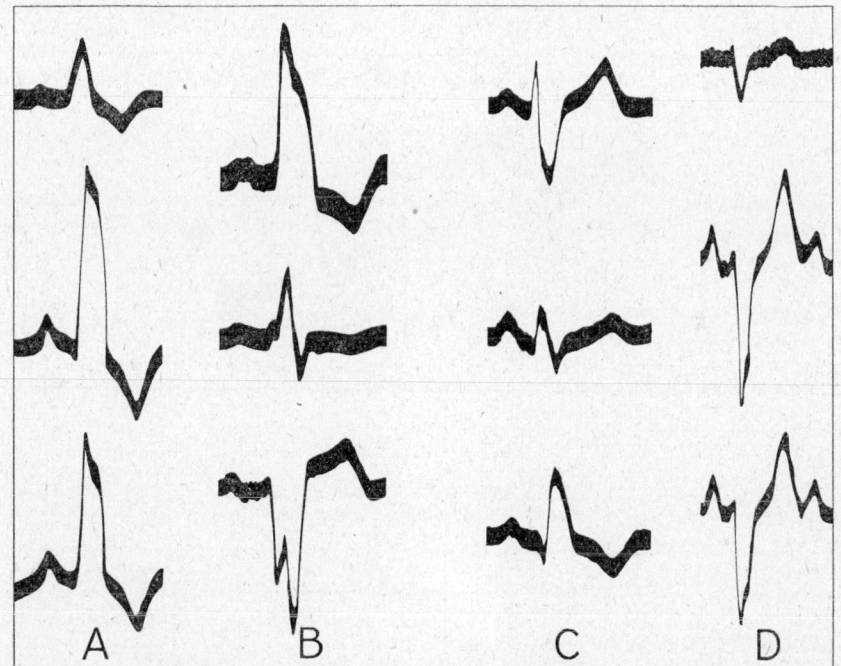

Fig. 362.—"Concordant" and "discordant" types of bundle-branch block. A, "concordant" left bundle-branch block in the dog. B, "discordant" left bundle-branch block in man. C, "discordant" right bundle-branch block in man. D, "concordant" right bundle-branch block in the dog. (Records in man by the courtesy of Dr. C. F. Moffatt; in the dog after Foster, *Amer. Heart J.*, 1935, *10*:1042–1046.)

experimental animals, a type of electrocardiogram also occurs in which the initial deflection is downward in both leads I and III. This "concordant" pattern is understandably due to early activation of the left ventricle as a whole before the right ventricle responds (Fig. 362).

On the contrary, damage to the left bundle-branch would affect the activation of the right ventricle. This might result in the primary activation of most of the right ventricle before the impulse spreads to the left ventricle, which would yield a "concordant" pattern in which the initial deflection of the complex is upright (R) in both leads I and III. By analogy, it might also result in early posterior activation, yielding a "discordant" type of complex with an R_1 and a QS_3. In any event, this is the pattern most frequently observed in

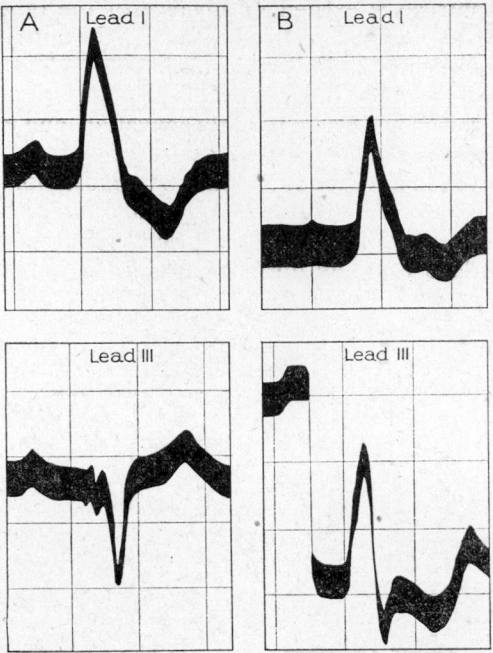

Fig. 363.—Shift from a "discordant" left bundle-branch pattern, A, to a "concordant" type'
B, in man, when patient was moved from back to left side. This affords some confirmation of
the suggestion that the "discordant" type represents a left sided lesion. (From Kissin, Ackerman
and Katz, *Amer. J. med. Sci.*, 1933, *186*:721–723.)

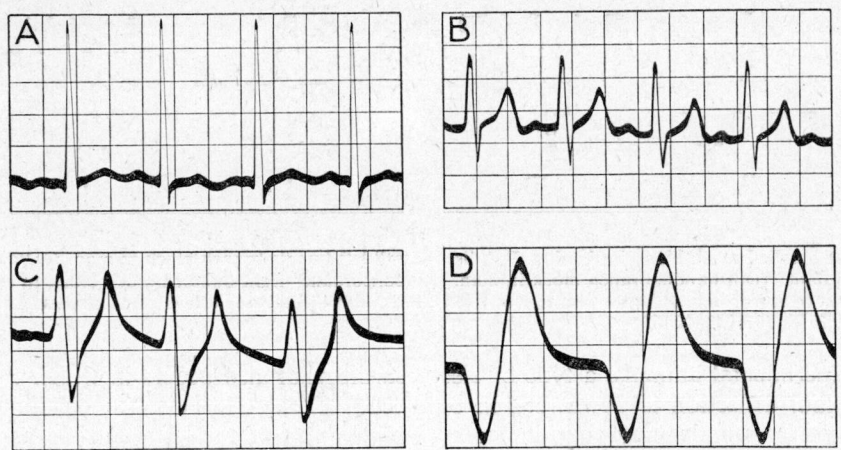

Fig. 364.—Progressive intraventricular block developing in man in the course of spontaneous
potassium poisoning in uremia. A, B and C are from Keith, King and Osterberg, *Arch. intern.
Med.*, 1943, *71*:675–701, and show the progressive widening of QRS at potassium levels of 7.1
mEq. per 1 (B) and 10.4 in C. The control in A is presumably at a normal level (4–5 mEq. per
1). In D is shown an even later stage 30 min. before death in another similar case reported by
Finch and Marchand, *Amer. J. med. Sci.*, 1943, *206*:507–520.

cases of bundle-branch block, and it is at present attributed to interruption
of conduction in the left bundle-branch (Fig. 363).

Thus far it is seen that a small lesion strategically located may disturb conduction in a striking manner. Once the impulse has reached the Purkinje system and is ramifying through it and the ventricular musculature itself, however, only more generalized agencies may impede its course. This is illustrated in the intraventricular block produced by diphtheria toxin, and that caused by intoxication with potassium (Fig. 364).

Ectopic beats

Attention has already been called to the fact that all parts of the musculature of the heart are inherently capable of autogenic rhythmic discharge, and that the normal sequence of excitation is made possible only because the S-A node possesses this capacity in a higher degree than any other region. By its greater frequency it suppresses the automaticity of the other centers, which are regularly forced to discharge by reason of a conducted wave of excitation before their own inherent automaticity has time in which to express itself. There are occasions, however, in which a subsidiary rhythmic center is able to establish itself as a pacemaker, and when it does, ectopic beats appear. According to circumstances they may appear as single beats only, or may entirely replace the normal rhythm to constitute ectopic rhythms lasting from a few seconds to weeks or months. They may arise in any portion of the heart—in the auricles, in the A-V node, or in the ventricles.

The site from which ectopic beats arise may be determined in the electrocardiogram. Ectopic auricular beats are characterized by certain salient features: (i) A full sequence of auricular and ventricular components is present, the QRS-T portion being in general completely normal, while the P wave is abnormal in amplitude and in contour, being often inverted, notched or diphasic. The altered appearance of the ectopic P wave reflects its abnormal origin and distribution over the auricle. Once the A-V node is reached, however, the subsequent pathway of the impulse is completely normal, and the electrocardiographic record of its course will be normal (unless, by virtue of its prematurity, it finds the ventricular conducting system still partially refractory). (ii) The ectopic impulse is conducted antidromically to the S-A node and discharges it prematurely. Thereafter the pacemaker must pass through its complete recovery cycle, and repeat all the processes involved in the production of an impulse before it can again initiate a new beat. This takes the usual time, or possibly a very short additional interval. An auricular extrasystole is therefore followed by an interval little if any longer than normal, the rhythm being in this manner "reset." When the A-V node or the bundle of His above its bifurcation becomes the seat of ectopic impulse formation, the wave of excitation so generated will naturally travel in two directions simultaneously: toward the auricles and toward the ventricles. If the impulse starts in the region nearest the auricle, that chamber will be first to respond, and a P wave will be the first deflection recorded, followed after an abnormally short interval by the QRS-T complex which will be normal in all respects. If the impulse arises well down in the bundle of His, the ventricles will be excited before the auricles and the initial deflections of the resulting complex will be ventricular. The P wave may then be detected in the S-T interval.

Extrasystoles originating in the Purkinje system or in the myocardium of the ventricle may be identified in a number of ways: (i) The complex will commence with the ventricular components, and P waves will seldom be seen except in those cases in which the A-V node will have recovered sufficiently to conduct the antedromic impulse. In these circumstances retrograde P waves will appear. (ii) In all but rare cases the retrograde impulse will encounter the normally descending impulse somewhere en route between the S-A node and the bundle of His, and the two will be mutually blocked. The S-A node will therefore not be disturbed by the ectopic ventricular beat and the basic rhythm of this heart will be unaffected. For the same reason, also, the ventricle will have to wait for the next normally descending impulse, so that the ventricular cycle following the ectopic beat will be abnormally long and will make up exactly for the prematurity of the ectopic beat. It is therefore termed the "compensatory pause." The abnormally long pause permits more than normal filling of the heart, and the first normal beat after the extrasystole will be unusually forceful and may be felt by the subject. For this reason ectopic ventricular beats are much more often recognized by the subject than are auricular extrasystoles, which are not followed by a compensatory pause. Very occasionally, the ectopic beat originates early enough in the cycle so that the refractory period of the ventricles has had time to pass off by the time the normal supraventricular complex, which is usually blocked, arrives in the ventricle. In this circumstance the ventricle responds normally, and the ventricular beat will be seen to be "interpolated" between two normal complexes. (iii) The electrocardiographic configuration of a ventricular extrasystole reflects, as does that of a normal beat, the particular sequence of excitation within the heart. Starting, as the ventricular extrasystole does, without previous excitation from the auricles, the complex begins with ventricular components. Inasmuch as the impulse will radiate locally through muscular tissue, and reach Purkinje tissue and be distributed more rapidly only after a certain delay, the duration of the QRS portion of the electrocardiogram will be generally prolonged and of greater than normal amplitude. Because of the same delay in distribution, recovery will often have begun in those regions which were first excited even before excitation of the entire ventricular musculature is complete. For this reason the S-T take-off will appear elevated or depressed, there will be no iso-electric S-T segment, and its T wave will, in most instances, have a direction opposite to that of the QRS portion of the complex.

As far as the experimental animal is concerned (dog, cat, monkey), if adequate precautions are taken to restore the normal relationship of the chest (full expansion of lungs, closure of chest wound, spontaneous respiration) following the operation to place stimulating electrodes, the site of origin of extrasystoles can be determined by the configuration of the ectopic beat in leads I and III by application of the localizing principles outlined on pages 760–761 (cf. Fig. 359). An impulse originating along the lateral margin of the right ventricle, either on the epicardium or in the endocardium, will presumably be conducted locally to near-by regions of the right ventricle before the left ventricle is excited. The anterior portion of the right ventricle would thus be excited in advance of the posterior quadrant of the left ventricle, producing a simple R in lead III. The primary activation of the posterior quadrant of the right ventricle over the anterior quadrant of the left ventricle would similarly produce an R wave in lead I. This is, in fact, what occurs.

Stimulation of the corresponding area on the lateral margin of the left ventricle would ensure that an impulse would have to traverse and thus activate most of the left ventricle before the right ventricle were involved. This priority of excitation in both anterior and posterior quadrants of the right ventricle would be expected to produce a downward initial deflection or a simple QS in both leads I and III. When, however, the general region of the septum is stimulated, the wave of excitation might be expected to spread to adjacent regions of right and left ventricles, thus producing oppositely directed initial complexes in leads I and III. Anterior septal extrasystolic waves therefore exhibit a QS and an R_3 configuration, while posterior extrasystoles should display an opposite configuration, an R_1 and a QS_3. These predictions are also borne out experimentally. Transitional points from anterior to right lateral are by way of a diminishing Q_1 and an increasing R_1 and the same transition occurs in lead III between right lateral and posterior zones. Intermediate points between anterior septal and left lateral, and posterior septal and left lateral, show transitions involving R and S in leads III and I respectively. The apex is naturally the zone of transition between all regions; an extrasystole starting here would spread to all quadrants of the heart with almost equal velocity, and on theoretical grounds one might expect to obtain complexes from this region having very small deflections in no fixed direction. Stimulation of the apex does, in fact, produce almost formless M- or W-shaped complexes of small amplitude.

Extension to man of the results of these findings in dogs, cats and monkeys must, however, be postponed until further evidence is at hand. What information there is at present available is derived from two kinds of experiments: (i) direct stimulation of the human heart exposed as the result of surgical intervention, such as for pericarditis, and (ii) stimulation of the heart in situ and covered by skin and subcutaneous tissue after successful rib resection. The first type of observation suffers from the fact that a large part of the heart is uncovered and therefore does not contribute to the electrocardiogram, while in the second type of experiment the localization of the point of stimulation is necessarily faulty. In both types of experiment, however, there is general agreement that stimulation of the anterior surface of the heart evokes the anterior pattern, viz., QS_1 and R_3, while more lateral left ventricular stimulation yields complexes showing the concordant left type with QS deflections in both leads I and III. Concordant right ventricular complexes have not been reported following direct stimulation of the right ventricle, but rather the discordant "posterior" type is most generally reported. This may be due to the fact that in most of such reports the right ventricle has been exposed more than the left.

While it is not possible in every case fully to explain the physiological mechanisms by which ectopic foci develop as pacemakers, a considerable number of them fall into one of three general categories. The first of these may be termed the "escape" mechanism. This may be illustrated in its most physiological form by stimulation of the vagus nerve to cause slowing or arrest of the heart. If stimulation is not excessive, it is observed that the pacemaker shifts from the S-A to the A-V node, and it may be presumed that the inhibition of the normal pacemaker permitted the A-V node, which was not so inhibited, to escape from the domination of the S-A node and display its own rhythmicity. With more vigorous vagal stimulation, the A-V node is inhibited as well as the S-A node, and in these circumstances foci in the ventricles have an opportunity to act as pacemakers. Another example of the same type of mechanism is seen in total A-V block, where maintenance of circulation is made possible only because, or only when, the ventricles assume the role of pacemaker.

In all circumstances of this nature, the ectopic beats come at an interval greater than the normal cycle, and if time is permitted for an ectopic rhythm to be established, this rhythm is always at a lesser frequency than the normal pacemaker rhythm. Thus the ventricular rate in total A-V block in man is ordinarily about half that of the auricular rate. If, furthermore, A-V block is established suddenly, a considerable period may often elapse before a ventricular rhythm is established. During this period syncope and death may occur because of the failure of ventricular systole.

An important factor in the maintenance of rhythmicity in the centers ordinarily subsidiary to the S-A node appears to be the sympathetic nervous system. The frequency of ventricular "escape" on vagal stimulation is drastically reduced when the sympathetic fibers to the heart are cut and the adrenal glands removed. This serves to call attention to a second stage in the development of ectopic pacemakers, in which a measure of "escape" mechanism persists but in which, in addition, a definite enhancement of the automaticity of ectopic pacemakers exists.

The prototype of this mechanism is observed when adrenaline is given intravenously. Two reactions occur: the blood pressure is raised, and as a result, the heart is slowed by reflex stimulation of the vagus. The vagus, however, supplies the S-A node, auricle, and A-V node primarily, and sends few if any fibers to the ventricle. The injected adrenaline may therefore act directly on the uninhibited ventricle, enhance its automaticity, and thus produce ectopic beats and even short bursts of ventricular tachycardia which may have a more rapid rate than the S-A nodal rhythm they displace. Simultaneous stimulation of the vagus and the sympathetic nerves to the heart will also produce ventricular extrasystoles by the same mechanism, i.e., inhibition of the normal pacemaker and enhancement of the automaticity of subsidiary centers not accessible to the vagus.

If the vagus nerve has been cut or put out of action by atropine, the S-A node would not have been inhibited; it would have responded to the adrenaline by an increase in rate, and would therefore have remained the pacemaker. At times, in this way, ventricular extrasystoles in healthy young persons may be caused to disappear by small doses of atropine.

The above mechanism, which may well be the causal factor in the ventricular extrasystoles experienced by many normal individuals in the course of emotional stress, is probably also involved in the production of ectopic impulse formation at the pathological level. The prototype of this modification is seen in chloroform anesthesia. In the course of anesthesia with chloroform it is noted that ventricular extrasystoles often appear, especially when the anesthesia is light, during induction and recovery. These may proceed to runs of ventricular tachycardia, which are dangerous because they may terminate in ventricular fibrillation which is almost always fatal. These ectopic rhythms, which may be produced most readily in the cat, do not appear in the absence of circulating adrenaline and sympathetic nervous activity, and are on the contrary greatly increased in frequency, rate, and likelihood of termination in ventricular fibrillation by intravenous injection of adrenaline. (In the dog rather more than physiological doses of adrenaline are required, but there seems no reason to doubt that the mechanism is found in all common laboratory animals to some degree, and is in some measure, at least, applicable to man.) The suggestion has therefore been made that chloroform "sensitizes" the myocardium to adrenaline or sympathetic nerve discharge and thus potentiates the action of adrenaline insofar as its action to increase automaticity in the heart is concerned. A similar action is exhibited by a number of other anesthetic agents such as cyclopropane, ethyl chloride, and by benzene. Digitalis, which has a vagus stimulating property but which also sets up ectopic rhythms, may operate by this means; so also may calcium salts, whose injection in the mammal causes first vagal stimulation and then ectopic rhythms (see p. 821). It may be that in this group are to be found many of the cases of paroxysmal tachycardias in man, where no known pathological course may be assigned but in which emotional stress acting through the sympathetic and parasympathetic nervous system may play an important part, along with unidentified toxic or metabolic factors.

Finally are those circumstances in which neither of the preceding factors is paramount, but in which a direct change takes place in the metabolic processes responsible for the automaticity of the myocardium. The best example of this is found in coronary artery occlusion. Here the anoxemic myocardium, particularly that lying between normal tissue and that so deeply anoxemic as to be completely inactive, becomes hyperexcitable and almost invariably sets up ectopic beats in some degree, ranging from a few isolated extrasystoles to continuing ventricular tachycardia leading eventually to ventricular fibrillation. Polarizing (galvanic) currents and local cooling operate in this manner also, and so, possibly, do local mechanical or thermal injury, certain ions such as barium, calcium, mercury, toxins in diseases such as diphtheria, and alkalosis.

Bigeminy. When, for some of the reasons outlined above, the extrasystoles arise with a very definite relationship to a normal beat, the phenomenon is

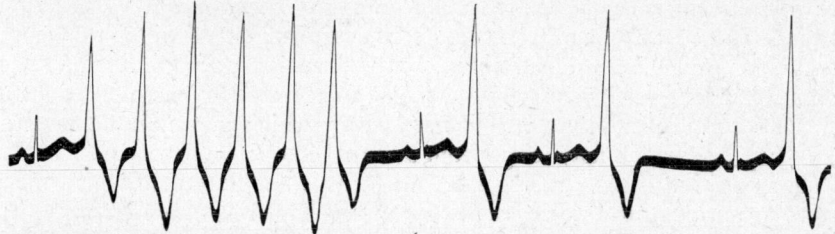

Fig. 365.—Bigeminus rhythm and short run of ventricular tachycardia produced in the dog by local injury and injection of acid to produce a supernormal period. (From Hoff and Grant, *J. Neurophysiol.*, 1944, *7*:305–322.)

recognized as a "bigeminus" or "coupled" beat. The same phenomenon may be extended to "tripling" in which a third beat, possibly from a second ventricular focus, is coupled to the preceding beats, and even to runs of tachycardia. The precise linkage of the "coupled" beats in these circumstances has led many investigators to suggest that in this case, and as well perhaps in many tachycardias, the cause lies in the "re-entrant excitation," or circus motion soon to be discussed. According to this view, pathways exist in which the impulse may continue to travel, to emerge later and re-excite the heart over again. In all probability, this mechanism does not play a part in such circumstances. The best argument in favor of this view is that of Harris (10), who calls attention to the fact that incomplete and continuing excitation within the heart is signalized by a wide and continuing QRS complex. In cases of bigeminus, the QRS complexes are clear-cut, and are clearly completed before the T wave begins. Even in tachycardias it is usually possible to establish that one QRS complex is at an end before the other begins.

The factor responsible for the linkage is more probably the presence of a supernormal phase in the recovery cycle of the supraventricular beat, during which the threshold drops to a level at which the ectopic focus is able to discharge. This phenomenon is illustrated in Figure 365 in which a minor injury (affixing stimulating electrodes) constituted a normally subthreshold stimulus which was able to evoke a short run of ventricular tachycardia and a series of coupled beats when a supernormal period was invoked by inject on of acid. It is just possible that supernormality may proceed to such a degree that ectopic beats arise even without any other precipitating factor; this may account for the ventricular extrasystoles in veratrine poisoning, since the drug is known to enhance supernormality, but this is improbable in most cases, and the function of supernormality in this connection appears to be restricted to creating a period of low threshold and thus determining the time at which ectopic beats may appear.

Auricular fibrillation

Lewis describes auricular fibrillation as "a condition of the auricle in which some parts of its muscle are constantly contracting, but in which the movement as a whole is more or less incoordinate, and therefore ineffectual." It is characterized by (i) lack of the auricular component (A wave) in the venous pulse, (ii) a rapid ventricular rate in which there is absolute irregularity in rate and force of ventricular contractions, (iii) a "pulse deficit," i.e., not all ventricular beats are forcible enough to open the A-V valves and produce a pulse wave, and (iv) by an electrocardiogram showing (a) a supraventricular type of ventricular complex, (b) variation in amplitude of R, (c) complete absence of P waves and (d) their replacement by fine oscillations of low amplitude and rapid rate, which are never regular in amplitude, form or frequency and which may range from 500 to 1000 per minute.

The condition is closely associated with auricular flutter, in which the P waves are broken up into segments which appear with some regularity at a frequency of about 300 per minute. In this condition the ventricular rate is regular and there is almost always some degree of A-V block, usually 2:1 to 4:1. The condition may be converted into fibrillation by a number of means (see p. 776) and it passes through stages of progressive fragmentation of the auricular components into coarse and finally fine fibrillation.

Auricular fibrillation is perhaps the most important, and certainly the most common, of the major cardiac arrhythmias, and is found most frequently in rheumatic heart disease (contributing approximately 50 per cent of all cases), in chronic nonvalvular myocarditis (largely of hypertensive origin) in middle-aged or elderly people, and in thyrotoxicosis. It is not infrequently seen in paroxysmal attacks in persons in whom no evidence of heart disease can be disclosed. It may become permanently established and persist for years, or it may appear paroxysmally. It may exert surprisingly little harmful influence on the dynamics of the circulation once the rapid rate is controlled by digitalis, although when the rate is not so controlled it may contribute to heart failure by reducing the time available for diastolic filling. In general, auricular fibrillation may be considered to be a sign of heart disease rather than a cause of it.

The appearance of an auricle when fibrillating—ceaselessly in motion yet fully dilated with countless tiny waves of contraction passing over the auricles in an ever-changing pattern—suggests the perpetual travel of impulses through irregular channels, always returning to their source to start again. This suggestion of "re-entrant excitation" was made first on the basis of studies on the circular umbrella of the Medusa, in which it was possible to set a wave in motion around and around the circle of tissue without stop. Similar results were later obtained in loops of auricular tissue.

The genesis of auricular fibrillation may therefore be formulated as follows: the auricle is made up of loops of muscle surrounding the great veins, and ventricular orifices; within these sheets of muscle smaller loops are potentially present. For the purposes of exposition a single ring will serve, if it be remembered that an anatomical ring or loop is not necessarily required. The pacemaker excites one portion of this loop, and impulses set out along both arms; on reaching the other side these mutually extinguish themselves by running into each other's refractory period. If, now, the refractory period of one arm be lengthened, a second normal impulse might find one pathway temporarily blocked, so that an impulse would be started along only one arm. On reaching the former meeting point, it would not now be blocked because it would meet no impulse coming up from the other side. It would in consequence be able to continue down to the region of prolonged refractoriness, and, if the circus path had been long enough, the blocked region might by now have recovered. In this case the impulse would continue on around a second time, and so on indefinitely, provided the pathway were long enough to permit recovery between circuits.

Another possibility is that the refractory period be locally shortened, and an early extrasystole evoked. An impulse might again be started on one limb of the circuit and not on the other, and circus motion begun. This is of interest because it fits in with the major clear-cut factors involved in auricular fibrillation: extrasystoles and vagus stimulation.

Experimentally, auricular fibrillation may be stimulated by faradic stimulation of the auricles. Often fibrillation persists after the stimulation has stopped, and it apparently tends to persist longer if the vagus nerve is stimulated at the same time. (Direct stimulation of the auricles very probably stimulates vagal endings in them.) When, however, a compound related to acetylcholine but more resistant to destruction by esterase, acetyl-beta-methylcholine, is applied to the surface of the auricle in high dilution, or the locally liberated acetylcholine potentiated by topical application of physostigmine, auricular fibrillation may appear spontaneously, being ushered in by a P wave or be evoked in response to stimulation, and will persist for considerable periods. It appears that acetylcholine shortens the refractory period and delays conduction; both of these are factors that favor the development of circus motion.

That acetylcholine, released as the result of vagal stimulation, may be the "trigger" mechanism by which auricular fibrillation is precipitated in otherwise susceptible individuals has a measure of confirmation in the observation that, in man, acetyl-beta-methylcholine will convert auricular flutter into auricular fibrillation and will, in patients with thyrotoxicosis, precipitate transient auricular fibrillation (Fig. 366). Search for other factors which may act to increase the susceptibility of the auricles to fibrillation with acetylcholine derivatives reveals that stretching the auricles (such as might occur in mitral stenosis or in congestive failure) and anoxemia will both act in this manner. Presumably other factors operate in the same way, but there is no evidence that vagal stimulation is an indispensable factor in all cases in man, however important it may be in the experimental production of auricular fibrillation. It is of interest to note, however, that the drug that is most clearly implicated in the precipitation of auricular fibrillation in man is digitalis, which has both a vagus stimulating and myocardial stimulating action. Adrenaline has been noted to precipitate attacks of auricular fibrillation in thyrotoxic dogs, and in this case, too, we recognize the presence of a direct myocardial stimulant which produces in addition strong reflex vagal stimulation.

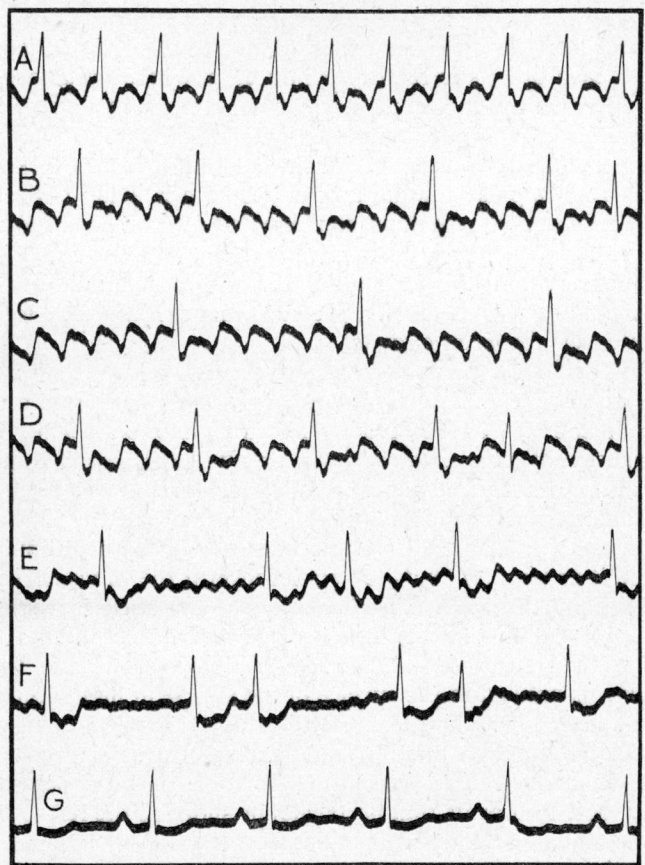

Fig. 366.—A, auricular flutter with 2:1 A-V block in a hyperthyroid patient. B, within five minutes after subcutaneous injection of 50 mg. acetyl-beta-methylcholine chloride, block increased to 4:1. Subsequent records are at five minute intervals. C, 6:1 block. D, beginning fragmentation of large regular auricular components seen in flutter. E, coarse auricular fibrillation. F, fine auricular fibrillation. G, reversion to normal rhythm 1 hour later.

Ventricular fibrillation

Closely allied to auricular fibrillation as far as its fundamental nature is concerned, ventricular fibrillation differs from its auricular counterpart in the manner in which it develops and in the consequences of its appearance. In the fibrillating ventricle one sees the same ceaseless but incoordinate and aimless spread of ineffective waves of contraction, and the electrocardiogram testifies to the same effect by its lack of regular ventricular complexes, which are displaced by ceaseless irregular waves of small but varying amplitude and rate. Just as auricular fibrillation is never seen to spread to the ventricles, so ventricular fibrillation is confined to the ventricles, and the auricles continue to beat in a normal manner. While auricular fibrillation is not directly a threat to life, ventricular fibrillation in man is almost invariably fatal, and only rarely does the heart revert to normal rhythm. (In the dog this is also true, while in the cat spontaneous recovery is possible, and will happen

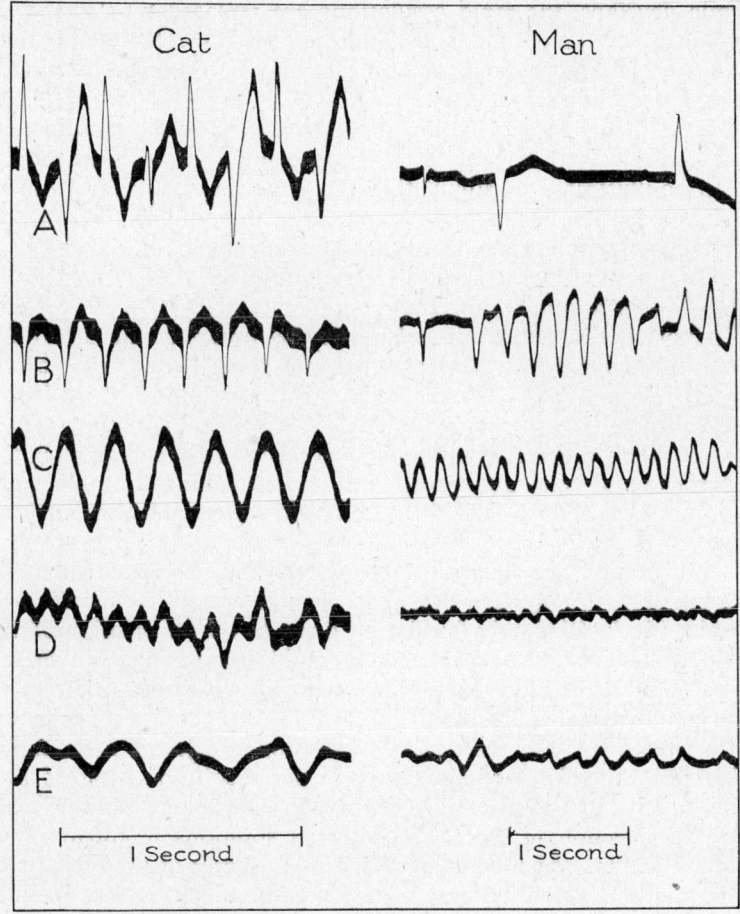

Fig. 367.—Stages in the development of ventricular fibrillation in the cat and man; A, ventricular extrasystoles from multiple foci. B, ventricular tachycardia from one or more foci. C, ventricular flutter. D, fine ventricular fibrillation. E, terminal slow fibrillation. Fibrillation in cat produced by chloroform and adrenaline, that in man in patient with A-V and intraventricular block. (Human case reported by Gertz, Kaplan, Kaplan, and Weinstein, *Amer. Heart J.*, 1938, *16:225–234*.)

in almost all cases if the heart is rhythmically compressed to maintain circulation.)

Ventricular fibrillation almost invariably develops in a definite sequence (Fig. 367). First ventricular extrasystoles appear, singly at first, and then in multiples. They may arise from a single or many foci, usually the latter. These then develop runs of ventricular tachycardia, first from one focus and then from another, faster, center. This center discharges faster and faster, until it is noted that the complexes are no longer discrete and easily separable from each other, but are replaced by smooth oscillations of fairly large amplitude and rapid rate. This stage, which might be termed ventricular flutter, marks apparently the onset of circus motion, and soon passes into the stage of rapid small irregular vibrations characteristic of fully established ventricular fibrillation. Later, as the effects of circulatory failure begin to be noticeable and anoxemia develops, the rapid oscillations are replaced by slower waves of somewhat greater amplitude, and if the heart is inspected at this time it is seen that quite large portions of the heart may be occupied by each slowly traveling contraction wave.

The most plausible explanation of what occurs is that the increasingly rapid ectopic pacemaker finally overtaxes the ability of the heart to follow it. This can be illustrated by stimulating the ventricle electrically by induction shocks at an accelerating tempo. At first the heart responds to each stimulus, and, in fact, as stimulation proceeds becomes capable of following even faster rates of stimulation by virtue of a shortening in its refractory period. This serves only over a limited range, and soon stimuli begin to fall very near to the refractory period and the impulses they set up are conducted away from the point of stimulation at slower and slower rates. If now a wave is set up and meets fully refractory tissue all around it, it is totally blocked and is of no consequence. If, on the contrary, the wave is blocked in one region, but because of minor differences in the recovery rate of the surrounding tissue is able to excite and be conducted away at another point, it becomes possible for the impulse to return later to the blocked region and thus set up circus motion.

This explanation accounts satisfactorily for the observation that the development of ventricular fibrillation in man is greatly facilitated by intraventricular block. Obviously fibrillation depends on the creation of areas of physiological block due to increasingly rapid stimulation, and these areas will be set up all the more readily in a heart in which intraventricular conduction is already at fault due to disease or drugs. Injection of potassium chloride will also evoke ventricular fibrillation if injected intravenously at a rapid rate, while if it is run in slowly in dilute solution it rarely results in fibrillation, but causes only extreme intraventricular block and cardiac arrest. With rapid injection in more concentrated solutions it apparently has a stimulating action, which combines with its property of producing block to cause fibrillation, which, because of the extreme block, is of a much slower type than that found in a normal heart.

The fibrillation that develops following ligation of a coronary artery is of the same type. While complete deprivation of oxygen very quickly depresses all functions in the myocardium, partial deprivation enhances the inherent rhythmicity of the affected tissue. All the myocardium affected by coronary ligation passes through such a stage when the vessel is first occluded, and all of it emerges through this stage if circulation is re-established before irreversible damage is done; these are times when the heart is particularly liable to fibrillation. Even when the occlusion has been established for some time, zones of partial damage exist around the region of dead tissue, and they may serve as foci of extrasystoles and ventricular tachycardia, and, if they discharge rapidly enough, may set up ventricular fibrillation. The variable degrees of anoxemia in this zone may also create varying degrees of block, which will facilitate the creation of circus motion.

Fibrillation by electric currents follows the same pattern. Low voltage alternating current operates in all likelihood just as does overly rapid stimulation with induction shocks. Each change of phase constitutes a stimulus, and it is obvious that sooner or later the vulnerable part of the cycle will emerge in which an impulse will be started, only to be blocked in one direction while proceeding in another. Fibrillation can also be produced by single shocks with direct (galvanic) current, and here another factor comes into play. Single induction shocks, unless exceedingly strong, rarely, if ever, precipitate ventricular fibrillation in a normal heart but *galvanic* stimulation, in addition to calling forth a ventricular extrasystole, also polarizes the myocardium at the point of stimulation and renders the region unstable to such a degree that it begins to show the potential swings characteristic of pace-

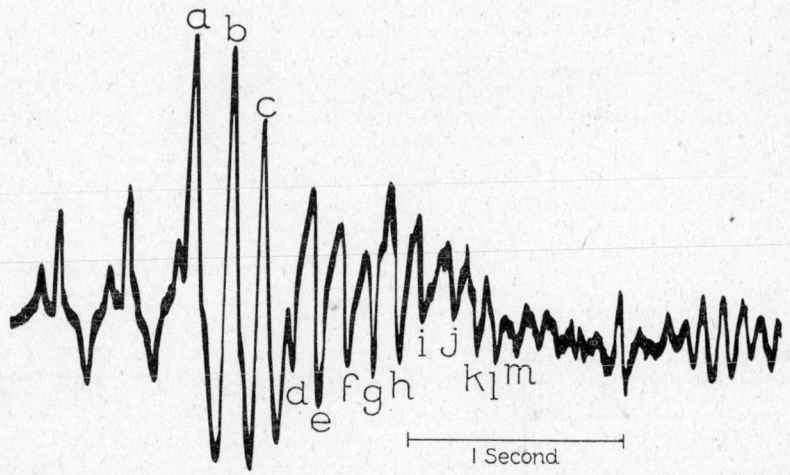

Fig. 368.—Development of ventricular fibrillation from the accelerating tachycardia developing from an irritable focus created by cooling a small area on the left ventricle. It was induced to begin to fire by three mechanically induced extrasystoles originating in the right ventricle (a, b, c), and gives a series of beats in accelerating tempo (d–m); but it is difficult to be certain of the exact moment when tachycardia ends and fibrillation begins.

maker tissue. The extrasystole excited by the stimulus also plays an important part. If it is early enough, the stimulated region for some reason begins to act as pacemaker and a ventricular tachycardia is generated which increases in frequency beat by beat and shortly culminates in fibrillation.

The same mechanism is illustrated in Figure 368. Here the two factors are separated. The unstable myocardium with potential pacemaker ability is provided for by local cooling below 10°C., as in nerve, while the stimulus was produced mechanically in a region of the heart not subjected to cooling. Three mechanically evoked extrasystoles are seen, arising in the right ventricle. They are followed by a series of spontaneous extrasystoles arising in the cooled zone on the left ventricle which discharges at a shorter interval with each beat, until, after the eighth or ninth beat, all distinction between beats is lost and fibrillation commences.

REFERENCES

1. ADRIAN, E. D. and GELFAN, S. Rhythmic activity in skeletal muscle fibres. *J. Physiol.*, 1933, *78*:271–287.

1a. ASHMAN, R., FERGUSON, F. P., GREMILLION, A. J., and BYER, E. The effect of cycle length upon the form and amplitude of the T deflections of the electrocardiogram. *Amer. J. Physiol.*, 1945, *143*:453–461.

2. BOZLER, E. The activity of the pacemaker previous to the discharge of an impulse. *Amer. J. Physiol.*, 1942, *136*:543–552.

3. BOZLER, E. The initiation of impulses in cardiac muscle. *Amer. J. Physiol.*, 1942–43, *138*:273–282.

4. BOZLER, E. Tonus changes in cardiac muscle and their significance for the initiation of impulses. *Amer. J. Physiol.*, 1943, *139*:477–480.

5. CARTER, E. P., RICHTER, C. P. and GREENE, C. H. A graphic application of the principle of the equilateral triangle for determining the direction of the electrical axis of the heart in the human electrocardiogram. *Johns Hopk. Hosp. Bull.*, 1919, *30*:162–167.

6. GARDBERG, M. and ASHMAN, R. The QRS complex of the electrocardiogram. *Arch. intern. Med.*, 1943, *72*:210–230.

7. GILSON, A. S., Jr. The locus and nature of the A–V pause in the spread of cardiac activation. *Amer. J. Physiol.*, 1942–43, *138*:113–125.

8. GLOMSET, D. J. and GLOMSET, A.T.A. A morphologic study of the cardiac conduction system in ungulates, dog, and man. *Amer. Heart J.*, 1940, *20*:389–398; 677–701.

9. GRAYBIEL, A., McFARLAND, R. A., GATES, D. C. and WEBSTER, F. A. Analysis of the electrocardiograms obtained from 1000 young healthy aviators. *Amer. Heart J.*, 1944, *27*:524–549.

10. HARRIS, A. S. The spread of excitation in turtle, dog, cat and monkey ventricles. *Amer. J. Physiol.*, 1941, *134*:319–332.

11. HARRIS, A. S. and MOE, G. K. Idioventricular rhythms and fibrillation induced at the anode or the cathode by direct currents of long duration. *Amer. J. Physiol.* 1942, *136*:318–331.

12. HOFF, H. E. The history of the refractory period. *Yale J. Biol. Med.*, 1942, *14*:635–672.

13. KEITH, A. and FLACK, M. The form and nature of the muscular connections between the primary divisions of the mammalian heart. *J. Anat.*, 1907, *41*:172–189.

14. LEHMAN, J. E. The effect of changes in pH on the action of mammalian A nerve fibers. *Amer. J. Physiol.*, 1937, *118*:600–612.

15. LEWIS, T. *The mechanism and graphic registration of the heart beat*, 3rd ed. London, Shaw and Sons, Ltd., 1925. xx, 530 pp.

16. NAHUM, L. H. and HOFF, H. E. The localization of ventricular extrasystoles. *Yale J. Biol. Med.*, 1945, *17*:539–554.

17. NONIDEZ, J. F. The structure and innervation of the conduction system of the heart of the dog and rhesus monkey, as seen with a silver impregnation technique. *Amer. Heart J.*, 1943, *26*:577–597.

18. ORIAS, O. and BRAUN-MENÉNDEZ, E. *The heart sounds in normal and pathological conditions*, 1st ed. London, Oxford University Press, 1939. xx, 257 pp.

19. PARDEE, H. E. B. Nomenclature and description of the electrocardiogram. *Amer. Heart J.*, 1940, *20*:655–666.

20. PATTEN, B. M. and KRAMER, T. C. The initiation of contraction in the embryonic chick heart. *Amer. J. Anat.*, 1933, *53*:349–375.

21. RAPPAPORT, M. B. and SPRAGUE, H. B. Physiologic and physical laws that govern auscultation, and their clinical application. *Amer. Heart J.*, 1941, *21*:257–318.

22. RAPPAPORT, M. B. and SPRAGUE, H. B. The graphic registration of the normal heart sounds. *Amer. Heart J.*, 1942, *23*:591–623.

23. ROBB, J. S. and ROBB, R. C. The normal heart. *Amer. Heart J.*, 1942, *23*:455–466.

24. STEWART, C. B. and MANNING, G. W. A detailed analysis of the electrocardiograms of 500 R. C. A. F. aircrew. *Amer. Heart J.*, 1944, *27*:502–523.

25. WILSON, F. N., JOHNSTON, F. D., ROSENBAUM, F. F., ERLANGER, H., KOSSMANN, C. E., HECHT, H., COTRIM, N., MENZIES DE OLIVEIRA, R. and SCARSI, R. The precordial electrocardiogram. *Amer. Heart J.*, 1944, *27*:19–85.

26. WOOD, F. C., WOLFERTH, C. C. and GECKELER, G. D. Histologic demonstration of accessory muscular connections between auricle and ventricle in a case of short P-R interval and prolonged QRS complex. *Amer. Heart J.*, 1943, *25*:454–462.

CHAPTER 36

CARDIAC OUTPUT: REGULATION AND ESTIMATION

BY HEBBEL E. HOFF

THE HEART RATE AND ITS REGULATION

Normal Standards and Physiological Variations. When counted while the subject is under basal conditions (recumbent, in the postabsorptive state, before breakfast), the average pulse rate in healthy men lies between 61 and 64 beats per minute (Fig. 369), although the range may extend from as low as 38 (1 case in 1000) to as high as 110 (3 out of 1000 were between 100 and 110). The range of normalcy accepted by the American Heart Association

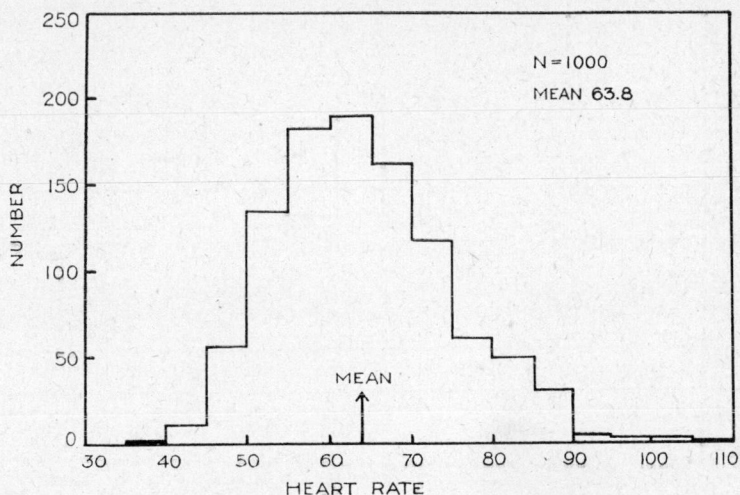

Fig. 369.—Mean heart rates under basal conditions in 1000 healthy young aviators. (From Graybiel *et al.*, *Amer. Heart J.*, 1944, 27:524–549.)

extends from 50 to 100 beats per minute. Figures for women are 7 to 8 beats higher in the basal condition, although data for women are not as extensive as for men.

There is said to be a tendency for individuals in good physical condition to have lower pulse rates than nontrained subjects; this is probably reflected in the high proportion of heart rates below 60 (38 per cent) in Graybiel's study of the heart rate in 1000 young aviators. Other tabulations of heart rate as related to physical fitness fail to show any clear relationship, if certain exceptionally slow rates in highly trained athletes are excepted (Brouha). The generally elevated resting pulse rates in neurocirculatory asthenia illustrated the other side of the same inverse relationship between heart rate and physical fitness.

781

While there is an apparent inverse relationship between size of the animal and the frequency of heart beat and while the differences in pulse rate between men and women are often considered to depend upon differences in size, there seems to be little relationship between heart rate and body weight, stature, or body type in man. There are indications of a slower heart rate in individuals showing lower diastolic blood pressures.

During sleep there is a progressive slowing of the heart beat during the first 7 hours, followed by an increase before awakening. The average diminution in frequency is very close to 7 beats a minute in both men and women, the greatest fall taking place during the first two and a half hours of sleep

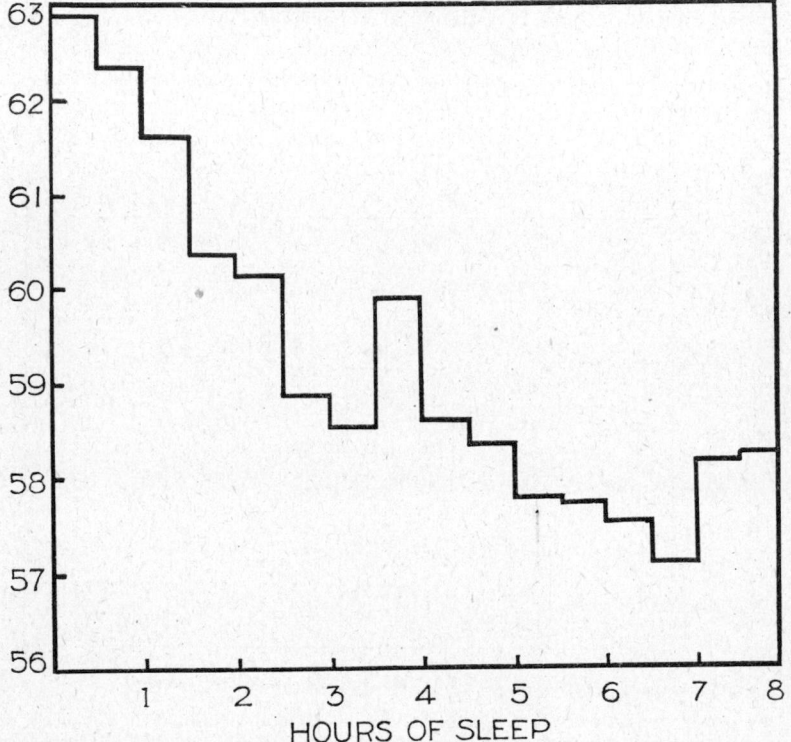

HOURS OF SLEEP

Fig. 370.—Chart showing composite record of heart rates during successive hours of sleep in 49 men. (From Boas and Goldschmidt, *The heart rate*. C. C Thomas, 1932.)

(Fig. 370). In waking hours wide variations occur, and frequencies range from below the basal figures to maximum rates very close to 200 beats per minute, the average of rates during the day being nearly 78 beats per minute in men and 84 beats per minute in women: In individuals in good physical condition the heart beat increment at a given work load is less than in nonfit individuals (Table 29), but in the performance of exhausting work, maximal rates in the neighborhood of 200 beats per minute are attained by fit as well as nonfit subjects (Figs. 371A and B).

The rapidity with which the heart rate returns to normal after cessation of exercise is also considered to be an indication of physical fitness (Fig. 371B) and is incorporated into many of the tests purporting to measure physical fitness. (The score in the "Harvard step test" ignores the rate during the exercise and calculates that the physical fitness index = duration of exercise in seconds times 100 ÷ twice the sum of the pulse counts 1 to 1.5, 2 to 2.5

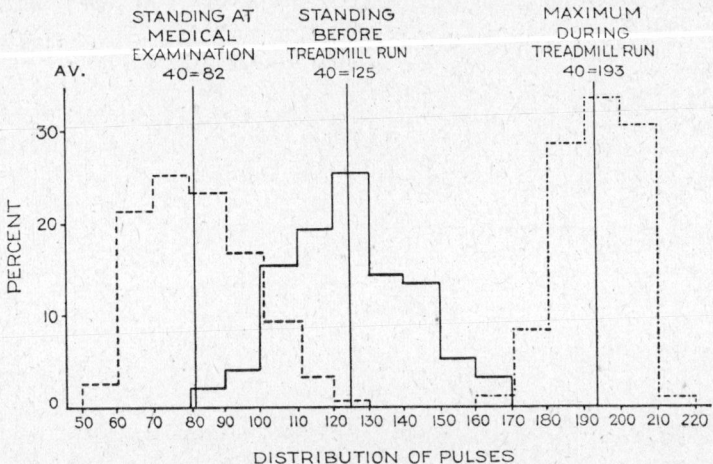

Fig. 371A.—Distribution of pulse rates in young men before and during exhausting physical activity. (From Brouha.)

and 3 to 3.5 minutes after cessation of exercise.) Emotional disturbances may cause an increase in the heart rate equal to all except the most strenuous types of muscular exercise. Heart rates between 130 and 140 have been noted

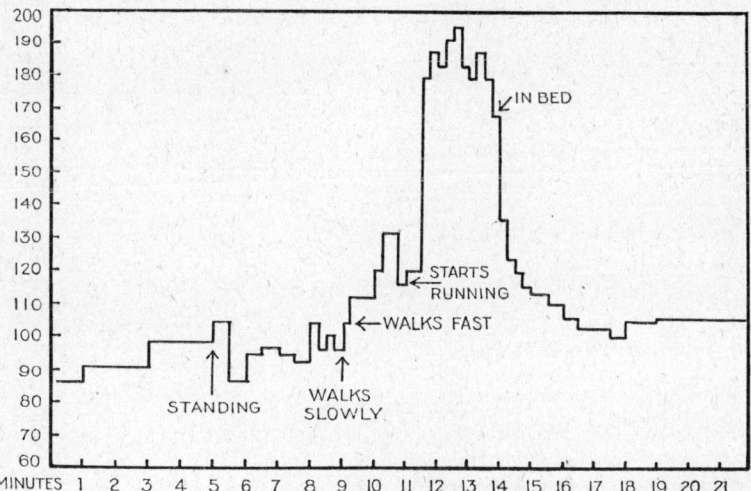

Fig. 371B.—The heart rate in a boy of 13 during exhausting physical exercises. (From Boas and Goldschmidt, *The heart rate.* C. C Thomas, 1932.)

in patients anticipating operations, and under other circumstances involving intense emotional excitement. This may also be seen in Table 30A, in which heart rates in tamed and untamed rats are compared, and in Table 30B, in which are compared rates in restrained, conscious rats and in rats lightly anesthetized with nembutal (which gives heart rates comparable with quiet, nonrestrained, conscious rats). The extreme range of heart rates found in the so-called "basal" state (Fig. 369) suggests the presence of unrecognized emotional factors even though the subject is supposedly at rest.

Table 29.—*Measurements on Young Men of Various Degrees of Physical Fitness. (Running on treadmill at 7.0 m.p.h. with an 8.6 per cent grade.) It is apparent that a maximal effort was not required in groups A and B.*

GROUP	MAXIMUM PULSE RATE DURING RUN (AVERAGE)	MAXIMUM BLOOD LACTATE (AVERAGE)	DURATION	WORK INDEX* (ARBITRARY UNITS)
A. (10 oarsmen)	179 (range 171–185)	97	4 min., 55 sec.	+ 22
B. (10 men in good condition)	189 (range 178–202)	121	4 min., 55.5 sec.	− 11
C. (10 men in average condition)	196 (range 182–208)	123	3 min., 32 sec.	−106
D. (10 men in poor condition)	194 (range 183–205)	131	2 min., 18 sec.	−169

* Work index = (duration of run in seconds) − (maximum pulse in beats per minute) + (maximum lactate in mg. per cent).

Pathological Variations. An increased heart rate is found in hyperthyroidism (Fig. 372), congestive heart failure, myocarditis (Fig. 373), fevers and secondary shock, while a slow pulse may be noted during labor, during convalescence from acute fevers, in diseases of the gastro-intestinal system such as gallbladder disease, in myxedema and in anemia. Diseases of the central

Table 30A.—*Heart Rates in Tamed and Untamed Rats at 30 and 120 Days of Age*

| SEX | 30 DAYS | | 120 DAYS | |
	TAMED	UNTAMED	TAMED	UNTAMED
Male	355 ± 35.6	496.5 ± 57	422 ± 30.7	506.7 ± 35
Female	413 ± 45.5	491 ± 43	484 ± 18	483 ± 42.2

Table 30B.—*Influence of Thyroxine on the Heart Rate in White Rats when Restrained and when Anesthetized*

GROUP No.	NUMBER OF ANIMALS	TREATMENT	HEART RATE NEMBUTAL BEATS PER MIN.	HEART RATE RESTRAINED BEATS PER MIN.	DIFFERENCE
1	10	Normal Controls	379 ± 9	431 ± 21	+52
2	9	Thyroidectomized	265 ± 12	339 ± 11	+74
3	4	Thyroidectomized plus 30 gamma thyroxine daily	478 ± 13	527 ± 10	+49
4	8	Thyroidectomized plus 300 gamma thyroxine daily	505 ± 17	558 ± 18	+53
5	2	Thyroidectomized plus 3000 gamma thyroxine daily	574	647	+73

(From Leblond and Hoff, *Amer. J. Physiol.*, 1944, *141*:32–37.)

nervous system may be associated with a slow pulse. Cooling the body, as in exposure or as a therapeutic measure, slows the heart markedly, and pulse rates of 50 and below have been reported in patients cooled to 80° in such circumstances. Table 30B illustrates the magnitude of variations that may be produced experimentally by deficiency or excess of the thyroid hormone.

The heart rate may therefore be considered to reflect the metabolic rate of the pacemaker. The particular steps by which the various metabolic activities of these cells gain final expression in periodic alterations in the electrical polarization of the surface membrane are almost completely unknown. Reference to the influence of inorganic ions in the genesis of rhythmic discharge will be made in the next chapter. Figure 374 emphasizes in a somewhat

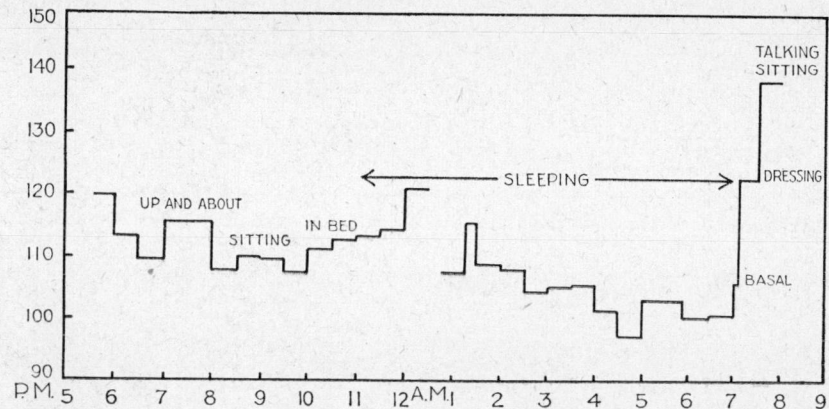

Fig. 372.—The heart rate in a patient with hyperthyroidism. (From Boas and Goldschmidt, *The heart rate*. C. C Thomas, 1932.)

different manner the intimate relationship between rate of the heart beat and metabolism by demonstrating the similarity between curves relating oxygen consumption and temperature on the one hand and heart rate and temperature on the other. While the heart rate is thus basically regulated by the metabolism of the pacemaker and while this factor is directly implicated in the alterations that occur in fevers, in cooling and in hyper- or hypothyroid-

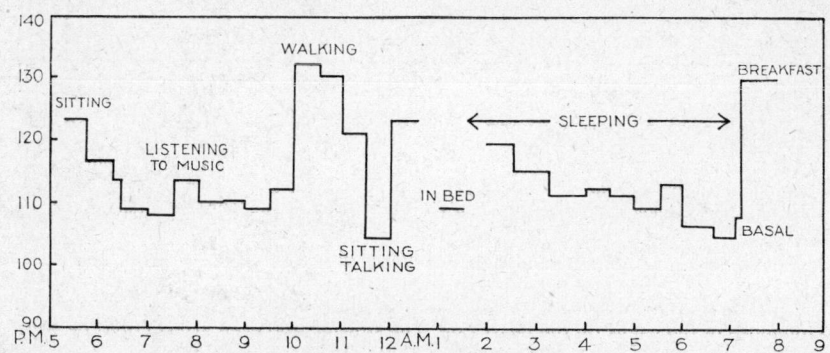

Fig. 373.—Heart rate in a case of subacute rheumatic myocarditis. (From Boas and Goldschmidt, *The heart rate*. C. C Thomas, 1932.)

ism, the heart rate in most physiological circumstances is regulated by the parasympathetic and sympathetic nervous systems.

Parasympathetic Control: The Vagus. It is now recognized that a single effective stimulus to the right vagus nerve will exert a measurable inhibitory effect upon the heart rate if accurate recording and timing systems are employed, but this influence is completely unappreciated in simple visual ob-

27

servation of the exposed heart. It is not surprising, therefore, that the inhibitory action of the vagus nerves on the heart was for so long unnoticed, or
unappreciated in the rare occasions when it was seen as the nerve was cut
or ligated, despite the great interest which centered around the functions of
the vagi. Once the discoveries of Oersted and Faraday made possible the
construction of the rotating armature inductorium, a series of stimuli could
be delivered at variable frequencies and thus unequivocal evidence of vagal
inhibition could be obtained.

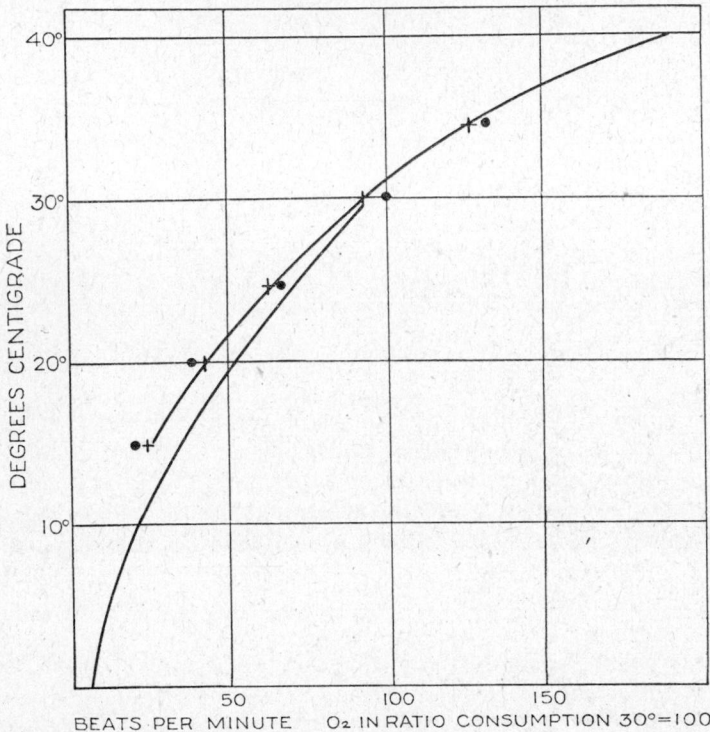

Fig. 374.—The action of temperature on the frequency of the frog's heart (lower curve) and the
rabbit's auricle (crosses), and on the oxygen consumption of the guinea pig's uterus (circles).
(From Clark, *The comparative physiology of the heart*. Cambridge, The University Press, 1927.)

The first physiologist in Europe to avail himself of this instrument was Edward Weber
who made use of it to elucidate the nature of tetanus, and then, with his brother Ernst
Heinrich, to discover the inhibitory action of the vagus nerves. The Webers reported only
the influence of the vagus on the heart rate. The slowing and even arrest could be appreciated by inspection alone, but it was later apparent that, in addition, vagal stimulation could
(i) weaken the force of the heart beat, (ii) depress conduction within the heart (chiefly within
the auricles and A-V node where it might produce all grades of A-V delay and dissociation),
and finally, (iii) reduce markedly the refractory period of auricular musculature. Statistically,
stimulation of the right vagus is found to influence the S-A node more importantly, while
the left vagus has a preponderant influence upon the A-V node; but in most cases both right
and left vagi can be shown to have some degree of influence upon both the S-A and A-V
nodes.

In the mammalian heart the vagus nerves ramify most extensively amongst
the fibers of the S-A node, the auricular musculature, and the A-V node and

along the bundle of His down into its two bundle-branches. The A-V node is considered by some observers to be even more richly supplied than the S-A node. The Purkinje fibers in the ventricles proper, and the ventricular musculature itself, are not thought to receive any innervation from the vagus. For this reason ectopic ventricular rhythms cannot be inhibited by vagal reflexes as can tachycardias of auricular and nodal origins, nor can the force of ventricular contraction or the refractory period of the ventricles be influenced by the vagi. It is commonly stated that structures in the heart which are not innervated by the vagi show no response to acetylcholine; nevertheless ventricular tachycardias may be arrested by acetyl-beta-methylcholine.

Concerning the mechanism of vagal inhibition, one fact at least is clear; it takes place through the mediation of acetylcholine liberated at the postganglionic nerve endings. How this substance operates is largely unknown, but the most likely supposition is that it acts to alter the electrical behavior of the cell membrane. Pointing in this direction is the old experiment of Gaskell in which it could be demonstrated that the injury potential, as recorded between an injured point and an uninjured point on the surface of the tortoise heart, was diminished when the vagus was stimulated.

Reflex Regulation of the Vagus. The major regulation of the activity of the vagus nerve occurs through its participation in the depressor reflexes of the arch of the aorta and carotid sinus. As Bronk has pointed out, these and associated vasopressor receptors are in constant activity, with a resulting constant discharge of the vagus fibers to the heart. Thereby the heart is kept under a constant vagal restraint, or in a state of vagal "tone" which varies from species to species and from individual to individual. In dogs as well as in man, this vagal "tone" may be pronounced, and great increase in heart rates will consequently be observed after administration of atropine in these species. In fact, almost all of the increase in heart rate that takes place with exercise in the dog and in man may be ascribed to a central inhibition of vagal tone in the course of the exercise. The remarkably slow pulse in certain highly trained athletes is also apparently a reflection of tonic vagal control. In infancy and in old age (man), vagal "tone" is at a minimum, while it is at a maximum during adolescence and early adulthood. Other afferent systems appear to be relatively unimportant as indicated by the fact that the heart rate after denervation of the carotid sinus and aortic receptors is almost as rapid as after section of the vagi. Through the operation of the same mechanism, the heart also participates in the depressor reflex in circumstances in which more rapid fluctuations in the blood pressure may occur. Increased vagal discharge as the result of increased arterial blood pressure serves to diminish cardiac output and prevent excessive rise in pressure; this constitutes the mechanism for the functioning of *Marey's law of the heart*, which states that the heart rate varies inversely as the blood pressure.

In almost all individuals the carotid sinus reflex may be elicited mechanically by pressure over the sinus; but occasionally hypersensitive individuals are encountered in whom relatively light pressure will elicit a strong response (in which partial or total heart block and temporary arrest of the heart will occur) with resultant syncope (Figs. 375 and 376).

A second important receptive zone for vagal reflexes is the respiratory tract. The inhalation of irritating vapors may produce marked slowing of the heart, which is particularly noticeable in the application of certain anesthetics such as chloroform. In fact, atropine was first introduced as a premedication in anesthesia to suppress this reflex, which was at one time thought to be responsible for the sudden deaths in chloroform anesthesia. The reflexogenic zone is mainly the nasal mucosa, supplied by the trigeminal nerve, but the reflex may be observed in a measure when the nasopharynx is by-passed,

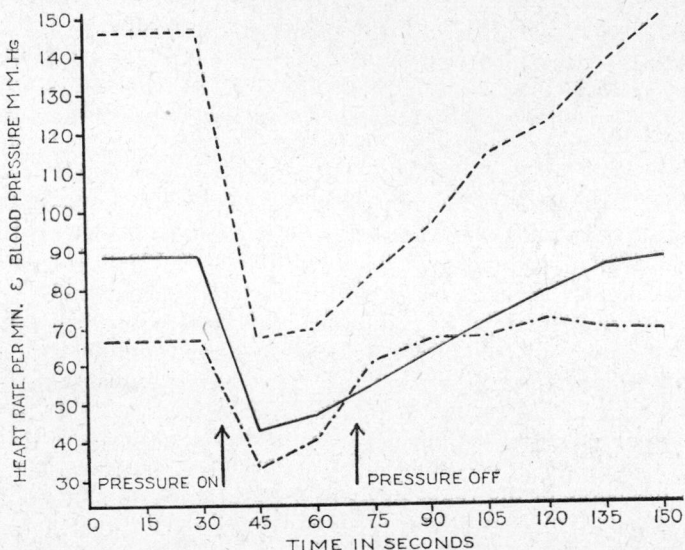

Fig. 375.—Systolic blood pressure (dashes, top line), diastolic blood pressure (solid line) and heart rate (dots and dashes) during carotid sinus pressure in a sensitive subject. Note that heart rate is practically normal at 75 secs. while systolic and diastolic do not return to the control value until 150 secs. This emphasizes the fact that slowing of the heart is but one manifestation of the carotid sinus reflex, and as a means of governing blood pressure is less important than the vascular component of the reflex. (From Weiss and Baker, *Medicine, Baltimore*, 1933, *12*:297–354.)

and the lower reaches of the respiratory tree are stimulated alone. The reflex is particularly well-developed in diving and burrowing animals and is best demonstrated in the rabbit, where it is associated with a well-marked response to laryngeal pressure. It has been suggested that the reflex serves to reduce the circulation and lower oxygen requirements in diving or in burrowing.

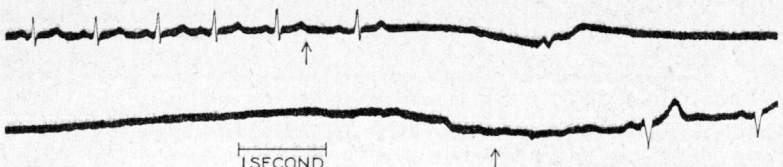

Fig. 376.—Cardiac arrest by carotid sinus pressure in a sensitive subject. Arrows mark beginning and end of pressure. (From Weiss and Baker, *Medicine, Baltimore*, 1933, *12*:297–354.)

In man the response assumes some importance during operations on the neck and pharynx, and during procedures in anesthesia such as intubation.

Another association between the respiratory center and the vagus is seen in the phenomenon of sinus arrhythmia, in which inspiration is accompanied by a temporary diminution in vagal tone which is reflected in an acceleration of the heart. During expiration the heart again slows, giving rise to a phasic irregularity in the rate of the heart. This phenomenon is almost invariably observed in the resting dog, and it is also seen in children and adolescents while at rest. It appears to result in part from reflex inhibition of the vagal center by impulses originating in pulmonary receptors which are stimulated by expansion and in part from central connections between the cardiovascular and respiratory centers, by which the inspiratory activity of the latter has an inhibitory effect on the vagus center.

Reflex discharge of the vagus occurs also on stimulation of the gastro-intestinal tract by mechanical stimulation or by distension, particularly of the gallbladder. Excessive stimulation of the labyrinthine mechanism, as in sea-sickness or other measures designed to produce nausea and vomiting, and pressure on the eyeballs, will often evoke marked vagal slowing of the heart, and these reflexes are often employed to terminate attacks of paroxysmal auricular tachycardia.

While it is not necessary to review the general pharmacology of acetyl-choline as applied to the heart, it is advisable to recall that many substances in common use have a definite influence on the vagal mechanism. Thus mor-phine, chloralose, chloroform, and chloral increase the sensitivity of the cardio-inhibitory mechanism, while the barbiturates depress it. Digitalis exerts a vagal stimulating action while quinine and quinidine have an atropine-like action. Increased potassium and a lowered pH augment vagal effects, while injection of calcium salts may stimulate the vagus strongly and even produce temporary asystole and syncope in man. The vagus center in the medulla is probably stimulated directly to produce the slow pulse associated with increased intracranial pressure.

Sympathetic Control: Adrenaline. Sympathetic fibers reach the heart by a variety of pathways: (i) via the superior, middle and inferior cardiac nerves, (ii) via branches to the vagi in all probability, and (iii) via direct fibers from the upper four or five thoracic ganglia. In the dog and cat the fibers which arise in the stellate ganglion form the largest single nerve supplying the heart. They are distributed not only to the S-A node, auricle and A-V node, but supply in addition the ventricle itself, in marked contrast to the vagi. Their stimulation results in (i) an accelerated and more vigorous beat, (ii) a diminu-tion of A-V conduction time, (iii) a shortening of the refractory period and mechanical and electrical systole, and (iv) an increase in the automaticity of all normally nonpacemaking tissues, at times to the point of production of ectopic beats (see p. 772).

The action of the sympathetic nerves on the heart is mediated, as elsewhere, by the liberation of an adrenaline-like substance, sympathin, if not adrenaline itself, and the general relations of sympathomimetic and sympatholytic drugs apply in the heart as elsewhere. As in the case of acetylcholine, the influence of the sympathetic hormone may be to alter metabolism (increase it) or to affect the polarization of surface membranes. In this regard it can be recalled that stimulation of sympathetic fibers supplying the heart has been claimed to augment the injury current in the heart while vagal stimulation diminishes it.

As in the case of the parasympathetic, the sympathetic nervous system exercises a tonic action upon the heart, which may be recognized in the persistently slow heart rate in totally sympathectomized dogs, in the enhanced vagal tone after removal of the stellate ganglia, and in the infrequency of "vagal escape" in such animals when the vagi are stimulated. It is obviously a manifestation of a generalized sympathetic tone recognized also in the peripheral vascular system. The source of such tone is not clear, as is the source of vagal tone in the carotid sinus and aortic arch mechanisms; for this reason, spontaneous discharge of the sympathetic center in the medulla or higher levels has been postulated. The maintenance of a normal or elevated blood pressure in the decerebrate animal suggests that the mechanism is in its essentials medullary or spinal.

In the reflex regulation of the heart rate, the sympathetic and parasympathetic nervous systems are reciprocally linked in their central representation, and thus, for example, reflex slowing of the heart will still take place in a vagotomized animal by virtue of central inhibition of sympathetic tone. The reflexes that stimulate the sympathetic are, on the whole, far less clear-cut than are the parasympathetic reflexes, and in most circumstances the heart is only one of many participants in a generalized sympathetic discharge. Such discharge also occurs in responses to stimuli such as cold, pain, etc., and in more complex reactions involving physical exercise, emotional states, and postural adjustments. For this and other reasons there is a tendency to avoid laying too great emphasis on the Bainbridge reflex, whereby increased venous pressure sets up a reflex via receptors in the great veins and auricles and afferent fibers in the vagi; this reflex accelerates the heart in exercise, etc., and thus makes possible an increased cardiac output.

The effects of sympathetic stimulation are reinforced by the secretion of adrenaline which, reaching the heart via the coronary circulation, reproduces the effects of locally liberated sympathin. The heart beat is increased in rate and force, and conductivity is improved. The systolic rise in blood pressure is steeper and the isometric phase is greatly shortened. The duration of mechanical and electrical systole is curtailed out of proportion to the curtailment of the whole cycle. Extrasystoles may appear because of the enhancement of automaticity of ectopic pacemakers. (Topical application of adrenaline to the surface of the ventricle has been reported to evoke ventricular extrasystoles.) The metabolism of the heart is markedly augmented, and the utilization of glucose and lactic acid is increased. It is, however, necessary to point out that not all these events can be observed when adrenaline is injected intravenously in a normal subject. In man as well as in the dog, injection of adrenaline in moderate doses will almost always cause a slowing of the heart due to stimulation of the vagus via the depressor reflex. The hyperdynamic action of adrenaline on the heart is marked in such circumstances, however, being intensified by the slower rate and by the increased blood pressure.

Influence of Heart Rate upon Cardiac Output. If a heart-lung preparation be employed for the sake of simplicity and the venous pressure and peripheral arterial resistance are kept constant, the effect of variations in heart rate may be studied by altering the rate by vagal stimulation. It will be found that, at rates below 60 per minute, cardiac output falls off because filling of the heart is largely completed in a total cardiac cycle of one second (Fig. 377), and further lengthening of diastole adds little to the diastolic volume of the heart and consequently to the output of the heart per beat. Hence the cardiac output per minute, which is the product of the stroke volume and the heart rate per minute, will tend to fall. At rates above 100 per minute, under these conditions, cardiac output will begin to fall because of encroachment on the

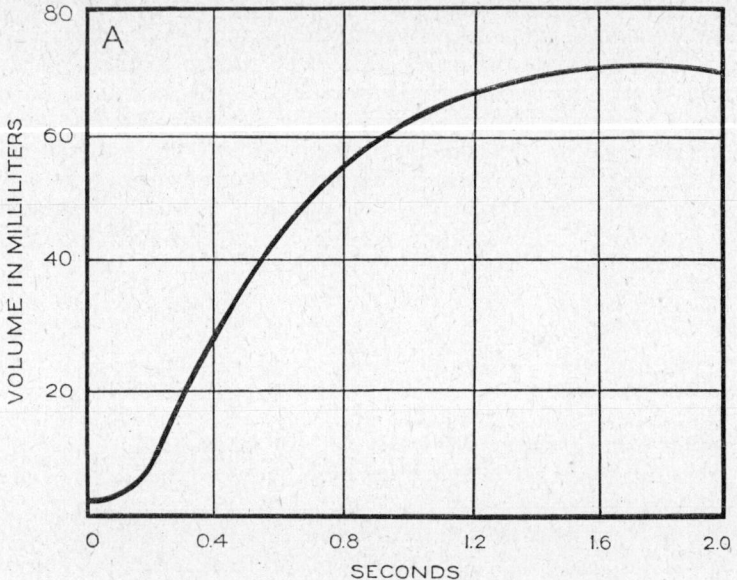

Fig. 377A.—Diastolic volume of the heart at various cycle lengths, when venous pressure is kept constant in a denervated heart.

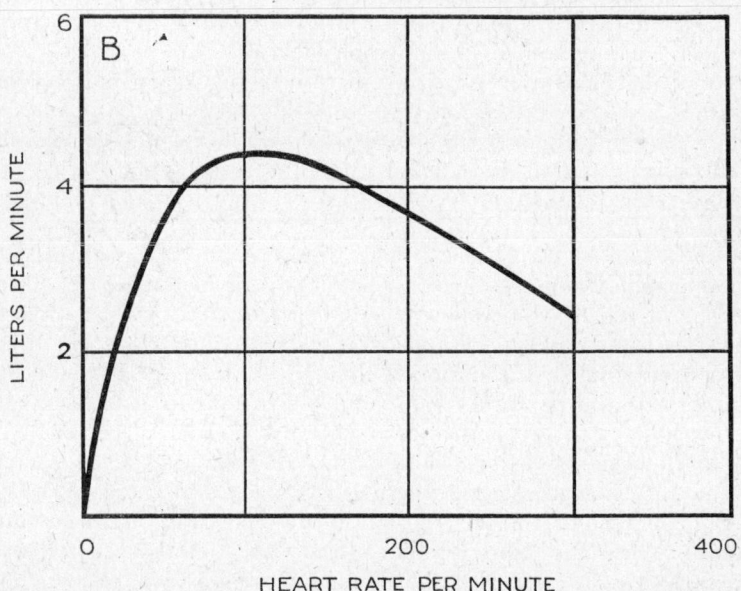

Fig. 377B.—Influence of rate of the heart on output calculated from diastolic volume times rate. (From Landowne and Katz, pp. 578–588 in: *Medical physics*. Year Book Publishers, Inc., 1944.)

period of diastolic filling; this phenomenon does not become marked until rates somewhat above 200 are reached. Between 60 and 200 beats per minute, however, changes in cardiac output are not great (Fig. 377B).

Such relations do not, however, apply to the heart in situ. Most importantly, venous pressure is not constant, but changes with varying activities. The cardiac output in the intact organism is therefore regulated by the volume of venous return, and change in heart rate within wide limits will have no influence whatever on cardiac output (Table 31). The finding of basal pulse rates as low as 40 to 50 per minute indicates that even at these low rates a normal cardiac output can be maintained. When during exercise, the rate of venous inflow is vastly increased, the rate of ventricular filling must be

Table 31.—*Regulation of Cardiac Output by the Amount of Venous Return. Data from a heart-lung preparation in which venous return was limited to 650 cc. per min. Increase in heart rate is accompanied by reduction in stroke volume and venous pressure. (From Markwalder and Starling, J. Physiol., 1914, 48:348–356.)*

Time	Tempera-ture	Rate of Heart per Minute	Arterial Pressure	Systemic Output	Coronary Sinus Output	Total Coronary Output (Calculated)	Total Output (Calculated)	Output per Heart Beat	Venous Pressure
	C		MM. HG	CC. PER MINUTE	CC. PER MINUTE	CC.	CC.	CC.	CM. WATER
2:20	28.2	72	119	612	24.20	40.3	652.3	9.05	11.0
2:28	30.2	90	119	612	20.62	34.4	646.4	7.20	9.0
2:37	33.4	114	119	612	18.46	30.8	642.8	5.63	6.2
2:42	35.0	126	119	625	19.74	32.9	657.9	5.2	5.0
2:50	37.0	144	117	612	21.20	35.3	647.3	4.47	4.2
2:58	39.0	156	116	612	22.90	38.1	650.1	4.16	3.8

greatly accelerated, and consequently increase in heart rate would make possible a greater increase in cardiac output than when venous pressure is kept constant. Acceleration of the heart therefore becomes an important factor in the adaptation to strenuous physical exercise, and finds expression in the fact that maximum physical exertion in highly trained athletes with maximum cardiac output is achieved with pulse rates of 200 or more. When venous return is not increased, as in paroxysmal auricular tachycardia, output may begin to fail at rates as low as 180 beats per minute.

REGULATION OF STROKE VOLUME

Starling's Law of the Heart. It has been pointed out previously (p. 38) that the vigor of contraction of skeletal muscle increases with increasing initial length. This phenomenon is equally characteristic of cardiac muscle and may be restated in more appropriate terms: the output per beat is directly proportional to the diastolic filling (Fig. 378). Thus to the extrinsic regulation of output by variation in heart rate is added an intrinsic regulation made possible by the properties of the cardiac musculature itself. Not only is the mechanism operative in all circumstances in which venous return is augmented, such as in exercise where it provides for an increased output per beat, but it plays a part in the adaptation of the heart to increased peripheral resistance. When the heart is confronted with an increase in the arterial blood pressure with which it must contend in the isometric and ejection phases of systole, it fails to empty itself as completely as before. This residue is added to the normal inflow from the auricles, increases the diastolic size of the heart, and makes possible a more vigorous systole in the course of which a more nearly normal quantity of blood is ejected. During the subsequent 8 or 10 beats the process is repeated, until a steady state is re-established in which the normal quantity of blood is ejected at each beat, but in which a

residue constantly remains to give an enlarged diastolic volume. With reduction in peripheral resistance the reverse occurs; the vigorous systole
meets less resistance and ejects a greater volume of blood, reducing its diastolic volume and weakening the subsequent beats to the point where a
normal volume of blood is again put out at a lowered pressure and at a
diminished diastolic volume.

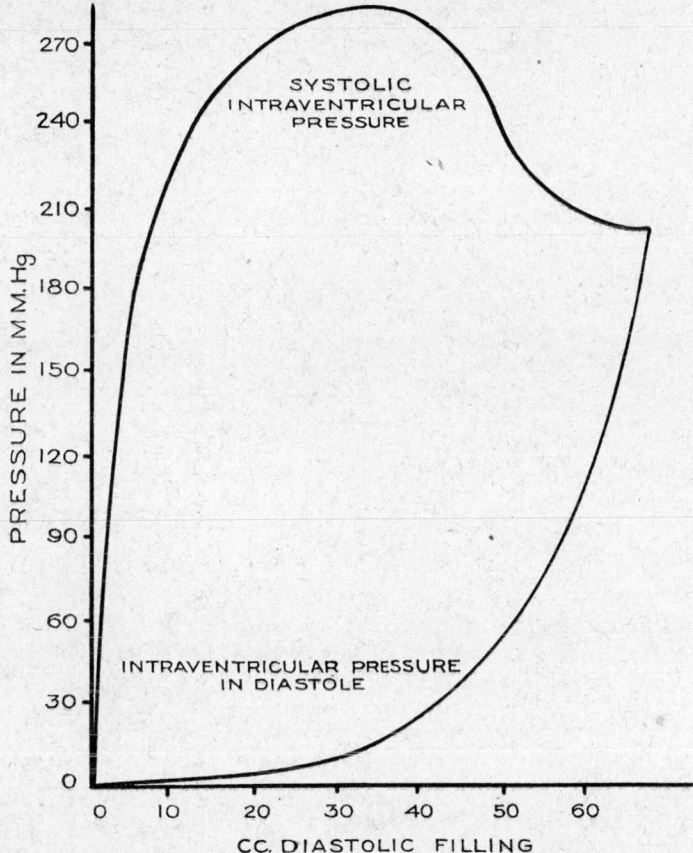

Fig. 378.—Influence of diastolic filling upon force of ventricular contraction as shown by
systolic intraventricular pressure (upper curve) and the diastolic pressure within the ventricle.
After the elastic limits of the ventricle are reached at about 30 cc., contractions begin to weaken
until finally the two curves meet, when systole is incapable of adding to the pressure within the
ventricle. (Copied from a diagram representing measurements on the frog and relabeled to indicate
capacity of left ventricle in relation to its systolic and diastolic pressure in a healthy dog's heart
weighing 70 grams. By Patterson, Piper and Starling, *J. Physiol.*, 1914, *48*:465–513.)

Finally, the mechanism is involved in the adaptations to diminution in
the contractile power of the myocardium. Primarily this occurs as the result
of failure of the energy-liberating systems of the myocardium to meet the
demands placed upon them, and ordinarily results from inadequacy of the
blood supply or from toxic or metabolic factors which affect the functional
ability of the heart. Whatever the cause, the heart responds in much the same
fashion as to an increased peripheral resistance. The weakened heart is
unable to empty itself completely and a variable residue remains to increase

the diastolic size of the heart and thus to increase the vigor of contraction. The greater the impairment of contractile power the greater will be the diastolic volume required for the performance of a given amount of work. Thus the diastolic volume of a patient with extreme myocardial weakness may be as great as that of an athlete performing to the maximum of his ability. In the first instance, however, the output per beat will be normal or less than normal, while in the latter case the output per beat will be tremendously augmented.

The long continuance of an augmented contraction based on increased initial length leads, as it does in skeletal muscle, to *hypertrophy*, or increase in the size of contractile elements. In this manner the amount of contractile material, as well as the quantity of substances required to furnish energy for contraction, may be increased, and provision thus be made for more effective performance of required tasks. The existence of increased stretch and dilatation of the ventricle as the primary factors in hypertrophy can be recognized in the various clinical types of hypertrophy: those developing from constant increased work as (i) in hypertension, valvular lesions, etc., (ii) in impaired blood flow, and (iii) in toxic and inflammatory states.

Whether or not the increased work output of athletes and those engaged in daily occupations requiring long-continued strenuous exercise ever leads to hypertrophy has been much discussed, and no completely satisfactory answer has been found. X-ray studies suggest that while the diastolic size of the heart in athletes may be increased, in keeping with the lower pulse rates and consequent greater diastolic filling, the systolic size is not greatly (if at all) increased. The probability is that the bulk of the heart will reflect the load which it carries, it being therefore larger in the athlete and in the hard worker than in a person of sedentary habits. The increased output associated with participation in athletics and with the strenuous occupations is relatively insignificant (as compared with the constant and inescapable load of a valvular lesion or elevated arterial blood pressure) when considered in terms of duration times intensity, and it is not to be expected that the increase in heart size in the former would in any way approach that seen in pathological conditions. The mechanism underlying the two phenomena would be the same, however much they might differ quantitatively.

Cardiac Reserve and Heart Failure. The ability of the heart to meet an increased work load or to maintain a normal output in the face of failing contractile powers depends upon the full utilization of all three adaptive mechanisms previously outlined: (i) increase in heart rate, (ii) increase in stroke volume, and (iii) hypertrophy. The degree to which any heart is still able to utilize any or all of these measures can be called the *cardiac reserve*. The heart rate and the diastolic and systolic size of the heart, which are determinable factors, thus serve as an index of the degree to which the heart is forced to encroach upon its reserve, and give warning of the approach of the failure that occurs when the reserve of the heart is no longer able to meet the demands of ordinary activities.

Failure occurs when the limit of cardiac reserve is reached, for a limiting factor exists for each of the adaptive mechanisms that together constitute the cardiac reserve. For the heart rate it is reached by the excessive curtailment of diastolic filling that occurs at rates of 200 and above. Increasing initial length ceases to be profitable when the elastic limits of the fiber are overstrained and diastolic pressure begins to rise, and output begins to fall with further increments to diastolic filling (Fig. 378). The time then comes in a failing heart when a vicious circle is established in which the rapid and dilated heart contracts less and less effectively because of its very rapidity and distension, and when slowing of the rate and relief of distension become important therapeutic aims to be sought, along with improvement in the primary contractile defect. Finally, the limit to hypertrophy is reached when the blood supply, which does not increase, begins to be insufficient to meet the needs of the hypertrophied muscle.

ESTIMATION OF CARDIAC OUTPUT

Fick Principle. It is apparent that the output of the right ventricle equals that of the left ventricle over any considerable period of time. The volume of blood passing through the lungs in a given unit of time may be calculated if the amount of carbon dioxide given off or oxygen taken up is known, together with the arteriovenous difference of either gas. In an experimental animal these are determinable factors. The oxygen utilization or carbon

Table 32A.—*Cardiac Output in Five Normal Unanesthetized Dogs as Determined by the Direct Fick Method.* (From Marshall, *Amer. J. Physiol.*, 1926, 77:459–473.)

Dog	Weight	Surface Area	Cardiac Output	Cardiac Index (Output per Sq. Meter of Body Surface)
	KG.	SQ. METERS	LITERS PER MIN.	LITERS PER MIN.
Brownie ♂	18.0	0.77	2.61	3.39
Hound ♂	14.5	0.67	1.76	2.64
Liz ♀	20.0	0.83	2.19	2.66
Misch ♀	12.0	0.59	1.62	2.76
Blackie ♀	16.0	0.71	2.86	4.02

dioxide production is determined by one of the standard methods, and samples of arterial and mixed venous bloods are obtained for analysis of their carbon dioxide or oxygen contents. In the case of arterial blood, puncture of any artery will yield a true sample, while the sample of mixed venous blood may be obtained by direct puncture of the right ventricle or by passing a catheter down the external jugular vein into the right ventricle. (The most

Table 32B.—*Successive Determinations of Cardiac Output in the Same Trained Unanesthetized Dog.* (From Marshall, *ibid.*)

Date	Oxygen Consumption	Arteriovenous Difference	Cardiac Output	Pulse Rate	Stroke Volume
	CC. PER MIN.	VOL. PER CENT	LITERS PER MIN.	BEATS PER MIN.	CC. PER BEAT
Feb. 21	92	4.95	1.86	80	24
" 26	101	5.20	1.94	63	31
" 26	109	5.70	1.91	77	25
Mar. 7	98	5.62	1.75	76	23
" 7	85	5.40	1.58	81	20
" 10	101	5.29	1.91	74	26
April 4	65	4.81	1.35	66	20
June 30	74	4.13	1.80	87	21
July 3	76	4.43	1.72	85	20

convenient practice is to make a venepuncture with a needle with a gauge large enough to accommodate a ureteral catheter or a length of fine "spaghetti" used as insulation in radio construction. The needle may then be removed, leaving the tubing in place for serial samples.)

The cardiac output may be calculated according to the formula:

$$M.V. \text{ (minutes volume)} = \frac{O_2 \text{ consumption per min.}}{\text{arteriovenous } O_2 \text{ difference}} = \frac{CO_2 \text{ production per min.}}{\text{arteriovenous } CO_2 \text{ difference}} \cdot$$

Table 33.—*Cardiac Output in Seven Normal Humans as Determined by the Direct Fick Method,*
Riley, *J. clin. Invest.,*

SUBJECT	CO_2 OUTPUT	O_2 INTAKE	CO_2 MIXED VENOUS BLOOD	CO_2 ARTERIAL BLOOD	CO_2 DIFF.	O_2 ARTERIAL BLOOD
	CC./MIN.	CC./MIN.	VOLS. %	VOLS. %	VOLS. %	VOLS. %
P. H.	183	235	55.0	50.1	4.9	13.1
F. K.	252	273	61.5	57.2	4.3	13.3
W. O'Br.	221	263	52.8	48.8	4.0	13.0
H. W.	223	240	54.1	50.1	4.0	11.8
W. O'Bo.	243	296	52.6	48.0	4.6	11.7
J. L.	244	311	54.9	51.3	3.6	13.0
J. B.	199	242	51.3	47.6	3.7	14.3

Division of this value by the pulse rate gives the output per beat or the stroke volume. Results of such determination in a trained unanesthetized dog over a period of several months indicate the general stability of the output in a normal animal at rest, and suggest something of the reliability of the method (Table 32). Experience has shown, however, that the method is not equally reliable in circumstances in which repeated determinations must be made in a short period.

In man the method has been now employed in numerous circumstances, largely as an indispensable means of checking the accuracy of other methods (Table 33). Although the literature does not reveal any reports of harm resulting from the catheterization of the right ventricle in man, it is apparent that its usefulness will be limited. For this reason a number of measures have been developed to ascertain the arteriovenous oxygen or carbon dioxide difference without the necessity of obtaining blood samples.

Indirect Fick Method. *CO_2 technique.* It is known that the alveolar air is in equilibrium with the arterial blood; a determination of the alveolar CO_2 content will make it possible to calculate the alveolar CO_2 tension, and, by consultation with a CO_2 dissociation curve for arterial blood (a "standard" curve, or one prepared from the subject's own blood), the volumes per cent of CO_2 carried in arterial blood may be calculated. The mixed venous CO_2 is arrived at by a variety of techniques. The method of Douglas and Haldane is to prepare bags containing various concentrations of CO_2 in the expected range of the venous alveolar concentration. The lungs are emptied as far as possible by a maximum expiration and filled by the gas mixture from the bag, and the procedure is repeated once or twice with each expiration to the room air and each inspiration from the bag. The last breath is held for 2 seconds and half of it is exhaled to give an alveolar CO_2 sample. The other half is exhaled 2 to 3 seconds later and another sample is taken. If the second sample has neither gained nor lost CO_2 it may be considered to be in equilibrium with the venous blood. If it gains CO_2, a second trial is made with a gas mixture with a higher concentration of CO_2; if it loses CO_2 the second trial is made with a lower concentration.

Another less cumbersome method consists in expiring maximally and then inspiring the contents of a bag containing 6 to 10 per cent CO_2 and the rest oxygen, and thereafter holding the breath or rebreathing back and forth in the bag for 10 to 15 seconds. It will be found that the CO_2 content in the bag or lungs will first rise or fall to come into equilibrium with the venous blood, and then remain constant for 3 or 4 seconds before it begins to rise as blood is recirculated through the lungs. The CO_2 content during the plateau is utilized to calculate the venous CO_2 content.

Acetylene technique. If a mixture of a foreign gas (acetylene) and oxygen is rebreathed, the relative rate of disappearance of the two gases can be determined by two analyses spaced a few seconds apart. The concentration of acetylene being known from these analyses, and its coefficient of solubility being known, it can be calculated how much acetylene is carried away by each liter of blood—in other words, the arteriovenous acetylene difference. From the ratio of acetylene to oxygen disappearance the O_2 arteriovenous difference may be calculated. The oxygen consumption having been determined previously, the cardiac output can be calculated. The individual steps in the calculation are as follows:

a. The rate of disappearance of acetylene (Ac diff) equals the difference in concentration in sample 1 and sample 2, corrected for volume changes in the lung bag system by multiplying by the inverse ratio of the nitrogen concentration. As nitrogen is neither absorbed nor given

Compared with Output as Determined by the Ballistocardiograph. (From Cournand, Ranges and 1942, *21*:287–294.)

O_2 MIXED VENOUS BLOOD	O_2 DIFF.	CARDIAC OUTPUT CO_2	CARDIAC OUTPUT O_2	PULSE	STROKE VOL. FICK*	STROKE VOL. BALLISTO-CARDIOGRAPH
VOLS. %	VOLS. %	L./MIN.	L./MIN.	BEATS/MIN.	CC.	CC.
19.1	6.0	3.74	3.92	56	68.4	61.6
17.8	4.5	5.86	6.07	61	97.8	84.8
17.9	4.9	5.53	5.33	80	68.0	57.1
16.3	4.5	5.58	5.34	75	72.8	63.4
17.2	5.5	5.29	5.37	64	83.1	73.1
17.7	4.7	6.76	6.69	96	69.7	52.2
19.0	4.7	5.38	5.27	65	81.1	62.2

* Average of outputs by O_2 and CO_2 calculations divided by the pulse rate.

off, the total quantity will remain unchanged and will reflect the change in volume which results because the CO_2 produced does not equal the oxygen and acetylene absorbed. Therefore,

$$\text{Ac diff} = \frac{N_2}{N_1} \times (Ac_I - Ac_{II})$$

b. In a like manner,

$$O_2 \text{ diff} = \frac{N_2}{N_1} \times (O_{2I} - O_{2II})$$

c. The relative rates of disappearance of O_2 and acetylene equal

$$\frac{O_2 \text{ diff}}{Ac \text{ diff}}$$

d. Since one liter of blood at body temperature absorbs 740 cc. of acetylene at a tension of one atmosphere, the amount of acetylene absorbed per liter in the experiment will be

$$740 \times \frac{\frac{(Ac_I + Ac_{II})}{2}}{100} \times \frac{\text{Barometric pressure} - 48.1 \text{ (water vapor)}}{760} = \text{Ac (average)} \times$$

$$(B - 48.1) \times (0.00974)$$

e. The amount of O_2 absorbed per liter will equal

$$d \times \frac{O_2 \text{ diff}}{Ac \text{ diff}} = \frac{O_2 \text{ diff} \times Ac \text{ (average)} \times (B - 48.1) \times (0.00974)}{Ac \text{ diff}}$$

f. This value may then be substituted in the formula,

$$\text{cardiac output} = \frac{O_2 \text{ consumption}}{\text{arteriovenous } O_2 \text{ diff}}$$

According to the method as applied by Grollman (5) in which the two samples are taken within 23 seconds, cardiac outputs in the basal state in healthy young men range from 2.96 to 4.61 liters with an average value of 3.87 liters. The cardiac index (output per sq. meter of body surface) ranges from 1.90 to 2.49 liters per sq. meter, with a mean of 2.21 (Table 34). In view of the fact that the circulation in the kidneys alone may account for somewhat over one liter, consideration of these figures (especially in comparison with the values for the cardiac index in the dog) suggests that these values are too low. The reason may be that recirculation of blood through the coronary circulation may begin within 10 seconds, so that when samples are taken after this period, acetylene absorption is altered by the presence of some acetylene in the recirculating blood. The calculated acetylene arteriovenous difference will consequently be too high, as will that for oxygen, and the cardiac output will be abnormally low. When the two samples are both taken within the recirculation time of 10 seconds, significantly higher cardiac outputs are obtained, reflecting the lower arteriovenous oxygen differences given by the shorter rebreathing method.

Table 34A.—The Cardiac Output of Fifty Normal Young Adults in the Basal Resting Condition. (From Grollman, *The cardiac output of man in health and disease.* Charles C Thomas, 1932.)

	PULSE RATE	CARDIAC OUTPUT	ARTERIO-VENOUS OXYGEN DIFFERENCE	CARDIAC OUTPUT PER SQ. METER OF BODY SURFACE (CARDIAC INDEX)	CARDIAC OUTPUT PER KG. OF BODY WEIGHT	OUTPUT PER BEAT
	BEATS PER MIN.	LITERS PER MIN.	CC. PER LITER	LITERS PER MIN.	CC. PER MIN.	CC.
Range	49–78	296–4.61	55–67	1.90–2.49	50–75	38–84
Average	64	3.87	59	2.21	60	62

Dilution Method. If a nondiffusible substance be injected intravenously at one time, it will appear in a systemic artery along a rising and falling curve of concentration from which the cardiac output as well as the volume of blood in the heart, lungs and great vessels may be calculated.

The following example serves to illustrate the application of the method. Three hundred mg. of dye were rapidly injected into a normal human and frequent samples of arterial blood were taken thereafter. Twenty-three seconds after injection the dye appeared in the arterial blood, reaching a maximum concentration at 31.5 seconds, and declining steadily

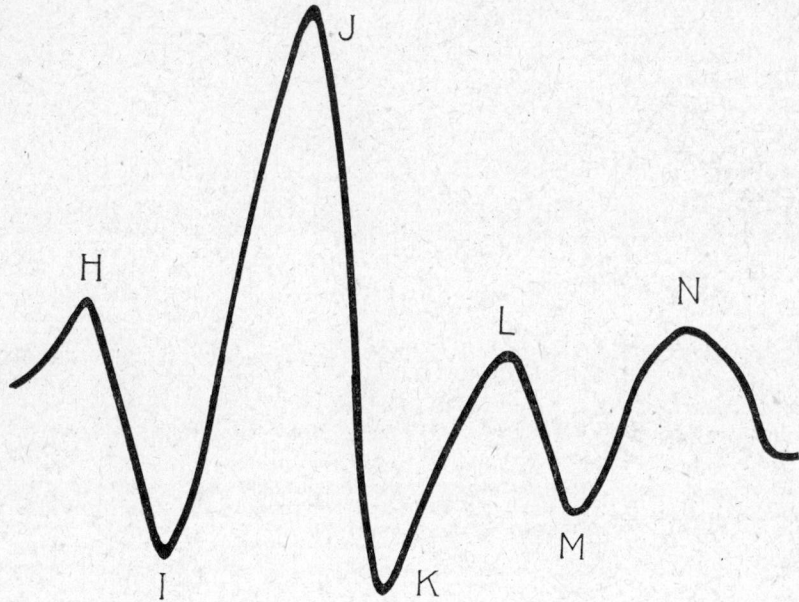

Fig. 379.—A typical record obtained by the ballistocardiograph, covering 1 cardiac cycle. A headward movement gives an upward deflection in the record. Although it might be supposed that the first movement would be footward (recoil from ventricular ejection), it is in fact headward (H). A suggested formula for calculation of output per stroke is:

$$\text{Stroke volume} = 7\sqrt{(3I + 2J)} \, AC^{\frac{3}{2}},$$

in which I and J are amplitudes in mm., A is the aortic cross-section in sq. cm., and C is the length of 1 heart cycle in secs.

during the next 20 to 22 seconds, at which point a secondary rise occurred, presumably due to recirculation of blood. By extrapolation it was concluded that the whole of the injected material would have been ejected in 27 seconds had there been no recirculation. The average concentration of the dye was 12.7 mg. per cent. To put out 300 mg. of the dye at an average concentration of 12.7 mg. per cent would require 2.36 liters of blood, and since this was accomplished in 27 seconds, a cardiac output of 5.22 liters per minute must have been attained.

Ballistocardiograph. With each beat of the heart a series of movements are imparted to the body, which are found to have a relationship to the stroke volume of the heart (Fig. 379). The instrument by which they are recorded consists of a table (on which the subject lies) suspended so as to be relatively free to move in the headward or footward directions, but as stable as possible in he others. The movements of the table are amplified optically and are recorded photographically as a series of waves, beginning with a headward movement. While the exact explanation for each move is unknown, it is surmised that the main factors involved in their production are the recoil of the heart during ejection, which would impart a footward movement, and the headward impact from the blood as it strikes the arch of the aorta and reverses its flow to pass down the aorta. Based on the presumption that these forces would vary in magnitude with the cardiac output and with the aortic cross-sectional areas, formulae have been devised which relate these factors in the calculation and which involve measurement of the area or the amplitude of one or more of the waves of the ballistocardiogram. The cross-section of the aorta is estimated from data prepared from measurements in cadavers, and cardiac outputs so calculated are lower than those obtained in the same individual by the direct Fick method (Table 32). When values obtained by visualization of the aorta in the x-ray are substituted, a much closer fit is obtained; but when this procedure cannot be carried out, it has been suggested that the values obtained by the original formula be increased by 18.5 per cent.

Calculation of Output from Pulse Pressure and Other Measurements. Calculations of this kind, of which the formula of Bazett *et al.* (1) is given as an example, are based upon the logical premise that the fall in blood pressure during diastole is proportional to the quantity of blood leaving the arterial system during that period. Therefore, if one knew the volume of the great arterial vessels, their distensibility (i.e., the relation of pressure to volume), and the fall in pressure during diastole, the diastolic outflow could be computed. Then, from the relative durations of systole and diastole and the relative mean pressures during systole and diastole, the systolic outflow could be determined. The sum of the two would naturally represent the input during systole.

It has been stated that the distensibility of an artery is related to the pulse wave velocity, an increase in pressure of 1 mm. Hg causing an increase in volume, V, of $\frac{12.7}{v^2}$ per cent, where v is the pulse wave velocity in meters per sec. The pulse wave velocity, v, is determined for the following segments of the arterial tree: v_1, heart to subclavian; v_2, subclavian to brachial; v_3, subclavian to femoral; and v_4, subclavian to dorsalis pedis. The volumes (at the end of diastole) of arteries contained in these respective segments are calculated as follows: V_1 = Q (cross-section of aorta) $\times$ 0.12 H (height of body in cm.), V_2 = Q $\times$ 0.15 H, V_3 = A (surface area of the body in sq. meters) $\times$ 0.065 H, and V_4 = A $\times$ 0.34 H. The diastolic pressure fall is the difference between pressure at the incisura (dicrotic pressure, Z_p) and at the end of diastole (D_p). The diastolic outflow, Vd, can then be calculated as:

$$Vd = \frac{12.7}{100} \times Z_p\text{-}D_p \times \frac{V_1}{(v_1)^2} + \frac{V_2}{(v_2)^2} + \frac{V_3}{(v_3)^2} + \frac{V_4}{(v_4)^2}$$

Bazett (1) then determines the systolic outflow, Vs, according to the formula,

$$Vs = Vd \times \frac{s}{d} \times \frac{(Ms - 20)}{(Md - 20)},$$

when $\frac{s}{d}$ is the ratio of the durations of systole and diastole, and Ms and Md are respectively mean systolic and mean diastolic blood pressures in mm. Hg. The stroke volume would then equal Vs + Vd.

Values so obtained check closely with values obtained in the same subject by the acetylene method, and are therefore in all probability somewhat low.

PHYSIOLOGICAL AND PATHOLOGICAL VARIATIONS IN CARDIAC OUTPUT

As may be judged from statements made concerning individual methods for determining cardiac output, there is no general agreement as to the

Table 34B.—Measurements of Cardiac Output under Standard Conditions in Seventeen Subjects with Normal Circulation.
(From Cournand, Ranges and Riley, J. clin. Invest. 1942, 21:287–294.)

	AGE	BODY SURFACE	WT.	OXYGEN ARTERIO-VENOUS DIFF.	CARDIAC OUTPUT		OXYGEN INTAKE	PULSE RATE	RESP. RATE	COMMENT
					L. PER MIN. PER SQ. M.	PER BEAT ML.				
	YEARS	SQ. M.	KG.	VOLUMES PER CENT			ML. PER MIN. PER SQ. M.			
A. Thirteen Normal Males under Standard Basal Conditions										
P. H.	52	1.80	68.0	6.0	2.12	68	128	56	12	
F. K.	41	1.71	61.0	4.5	3.55	98	160	61	14	
W. O'B.	44	1.70	56.0	4.9	3.17	69	155	78	17	
H. W.	37	1.74	61.0	4.5	3.14	71	138	77	14	
W. O. B.	49	1.88	71.5	5.4	2.71	78	147	65	22	
J. B.	32	1.81	68.0	4.7	2.91	81	134	65	17	
J. T.	21	1.82	69.5	3.5	4.01	108	151	67	17	
H. P.	26	2.02	79.5	3.5	3.38	100	118	68	14	
I. M.	44	1.48	49.5	4.3*	2.93	85	126	51	10	
O. E.	32	1.97	79.0	3.6*	3.54	103	127	68	18	
J. P.	35	1.38	42.0	4.4	2.75	53	121	72	14	
A. H.	43	1.79	65.0	4.0*	3.47	99	139	63	18	
P. McK.	39	1.77	67.0	5.2	2.86	74	149	68	15	
Average	38	1.77	64.5	4.5	3.12	84	138	66	16	
Standard deviation	±9.1	±0.19	±10.6	±0.7	±0.40	±17.0	±13.7	±7.6	±3.02	
B. Four Normal Males with Increased Oxygen Consumption and/or Pulse Rate										
L. K.	58	1.60	54.5	5.2	2.99	44	155	108	20	Rapid pulse
J. K.	53	1.35	44.0	5.3*	3.10	35	164	120	25	Rapid pulse
J. L.	39	1.68	57.0	4.7	3.99	70	187	96	12	Rapid pulse. Elevated oxygen consumption.
D. M.	40	2.00	90.0	4.8*	3.65	107	175	68	15	Elevated oxygen consumption
Average	48	1.66	61.4	5.0	3.43	64	170	98	18	

* Mixed venous samples from right ventricle.

acceptability of figures thus far obtained. The aceytelene and the ballisto-cardiographic methods are in close agreement, but the impression is gaining ground that the values they give are too low. This is particularly apparent from the recent report by Cournand and associates (4a), summarized in Table IIA of their article. Cardiac outputs were determined in 13 normal males in basal conditions by the direct Fick principle, and an average cardiac index of 3.12 liters per minute was found, which is 26.8 per cent higher than Groll-man's average figure of 2.21 liters. An average pulse rate of 66 beats per minute and normal oxygen consumption and rate of respiration suggest that in these individuals the procedure did not entail a significant emotional response which might result in abnormally high values (Table 34B).

In most individuals circulatory adjustments are successful in preventing excessive changes in cardiac output where posture is altered, although one can assume a reduction in cardiac output of approximately 25 per cent on change from the recumbent to the upright posture. Individuals exist in whom compensatory mechanisms are much more inadequate, particularly in quiet standing, and cardiac output falls, blood pressure is not maintained, and fainting occurs. There appears to be no significant change in the cardiac output in sleep, the menstrual cycle, moderate alterations in external environmental temperature, and moderate tobacco smoking. On the other hand, moderate (up to 30 to 40 per cent) increase in cardiac output is noticed after meals, after ingestion of quantities of fluids or moderate quantities of alcohol, after rapid and vigorous cigar smoking, and in emotional disturbances. In pregnancy, fever, anemia, hyperthyroidism and arteriovenous anastomosis, the cardiac output may be very nearly double, as it may also be in exposure to low oxygen tensions. Comparison of output in aortic insufficiency as measured by the acetylene method (which gives only the net output) with the value as calculated by the pulse pressure method (which includes the total output) enables one to estimate the amount of regurgitation. This may amount to as much as a third of the total quantity ejected, and thus will entail an increase in cardiac output by 50 per cent. The most marked variations are those which may be recorded in muscular exercise, where all gradations are found from insignificant increases with light exercise to outputs as great as 35 liters or more in all-out exertion by trained athletes.

Cardiac output will be reduced in the tachycardias, when the rate reaches the neighborhood of 200 per minute and the period of rapid filling is curtailed. It will be found diminished in heart failure, in myxedema, in constrictive pericarditis, and in primary and secondary shock.

Drugs which cause vasodilatation will increase cardiac output; so also will adrenaline which increases metabolism. Digitalis will increase the output of a failing heart but will produce only minor alterations in a normal person. Atropine increases cardiac output significantly in man by some mechanism whereby venous return is facilitated, for unless this factor were altered, simple cardiac acceleration could not by itself be effective.

REFERENCES

1. BAZETT, H. C., COTTON, F. S., LaPLACE, L. B. and SCOTT, J. C. The calculation of cardiac output and effective peripheral resistance from blood pressure measurements with an appendix on the size of the aorta in man. *Amer. J. Physiol.*, 1935, *113*:312–334.

2. BOAS, E. P. and GOLDSCHMIDT, E. F. *The heart rate*. Springfield, Ill., C. C Thomas, 1932, xi, 166 pp.

3. BEUTNER, R. Bioelectricity. Pp. 35–38 in: GLASSER, O., Ed. *Medical physics*. Chicago, Year Book Publishers, Inc., 1944.

4. COURNAND, A., RANGES, H. A. and RILEY, R. L. Comparison of results of the normal ballistocardiogram and a direct Fick method in estimating the cardiac output in man. *J. clin. Invest.*, 1942, *21*:287–294.

4a. COURNAND, A., RILEY, R. L., BREED, E. S., BALDWIN, E. DE F. and RICHARDS, D. W., JR. Measurement of cardiac output in man using the technique of catheterization of the right auricle or ventricle. *J. clin. Invest.*, 1945, *24*:106–116.

5. GROLLMAN, A. *The cardiac output of man in health and disease.* Springfield, Ill., C. C Thomas, 1932, xiv, 325 pp.

6. HAMILTON, W. F. Heart output. Pp. 575–578 in: GLASSER, O., Ed. *Medical physics.* Chicago Year Book Publishers, Inc., 1944.

7. LANDOWNE, M. and KATZ, L. N. Heart: work and failure. Pp. 578–588 in: GLASSER, O., Ed. *Medical physics.* Chicago, Year Book Publishers, Inc., 1944.

8. MCDOWALL, R. J. S. *The control of the circulation of the blood.* London, New York, Toronto, Longmans, Green and Co., 1938, xv 619 pp.

9. MORRISSEY, M. The measurement of the cardiac output; an investigation of the carbon dioxide method. *Med. J. Aust.*, 1942, *1*:543–555.

10. STARR, I., RAWSON, A. J., SCHROEDER, H. A. and JOSEPH, N. R. Studies on the estimation of cardiac output in man, and of abnormalities in cardiac function, from the heart's recoil and the blood's impacts: the ballistocardiogram. *Amer. J. Physiol.*, 1939, *127*:1–28.

11. STARR, I. and SCHROEDER, H. A. Ballistocardiogram. II. Normal standards, abnormalities commonly found in diseases of the heart and circulation, and their significance. *J. clin. Invest.*, 1940, *19*:437–450.

12. WEISS, S. and BAKER, J. P. The carotid sinus reflex in health and disease. Its role in the causation of fainting and convulsions. *Medicine, Baltimore*, 1933, *12*:297–354.

CHAPTER 37

THE NUTRITION OF THE HEART

BY HEBBEL E. HOFF

CARDIAC CIRCULATION

Arterial Supply. The arterial blood supply of the heart comes from the two coronary arteries, right and left. In about 34 per cent of individuals the two arteries may be said to be "balanced," that is, the right coronary artery supplies the right ventricle and the posterior half of the interventricular septum, while the left coronary artery supplies the left ventricle and the anterior half of the interventricular septum. In another 48 per cent the right coronary artery preponderates, and supplies not only the whole of the posterior septal region but makes a contribution to the blood supply of the posterior region of the left ventricle. The remaining 20 per cent fall into the category of left predominance; here the circumflex branch of the left coronary artery supplies all of the posterior septum as well as some of the contiguous portions of the right ventricle. Apparently this latter type of coronary architecture is physiologically the least sound, for the incidence of arterial occlusion is unusually high in this group and infarcts resulting from such occlusions generally result in death. In contrast, almost all infarcts found in hearts with a balanced circulation are healed infarcts, and two-thirds of those with right coronary artery preponderance are likewise healed (22a).

The generally accepted view of the distribution of the coronary vessels is that it follows a purely topographical pattern, i.e., the coronary artery ramifies within the substance of the region to which it runs, and supplies the full thickness of the wall of the heart at that point. This is borne out (i) by the location of the infarcts within the region into which an occluded vessel is observed to run, (ii) by the general course of the finer ramifications of the coronary arteries as visualized by Roentgen rays after injection of radiopaque injection masses, and (iii) by the reproduction of certain electrocardiographic signs of myocardial infraction by other means of injury such as injection of corrosives, burns, and surface application of KCl solutions. In such cases the pattern characteristic of occlusion of a chosen coronary artery may be duplicated by other types of injury applied to the region over which the occluded vessel is seen to ramify, and which is seen to become ischemic when the vessel is occluded.

It should be pointed out that this conventional concept is at variance, and perhaps irreconcilably so, with the view outlined in Chapter 35 (Robb and Robb), according to which the distribution of the coronary arteries follows no such simple topographical pattern. Instead, the arterial distribution is, in the first instance, to the various separate muscle bundles of which the ventricular musculature is composed, and all ramifications take place within these muscle bundles. It is apparent that many observations are difficult to

803

reconcile with the concept; but the decision as to its validity should not be made on a priori grounds.

The finer ramifications of the coronary arterial tree are, in a physiological sense, "end-arteries" in that they form the sole blood supply to the capillaries into which they ramify. This is attested to by the fact that when normal human hearts at any age are injected at pressures comparable to normal blood pressure with injection masses of a viscosity approaching that of blood, little or no mixing of perfusates from the right and left coronary arteries occurs. Thus, from studies of this nature reported by Blumgart, Schlesinger and Davis (2a), it can be concluded that in the normal heart no anastomoses occur between arteries which are as large as 40 μ (the size of small terminal arterioles) or larger. Experimental evidence points in the same way: sudden occlusion is invariably followed by infarction in the area supplied by the ligated artery.

If, however, a *watery* injection solution is employed, material injected into the left coronary artery readily finds its way into the right coronary artery, and vice versa, and the entire heart may be injected from a single artery. If, too, the occlusion of the vessel takes place slowly, an entire right or left coronary artery may be occluded with minimum and even no necrosis. The injection of such hearts demonstrates an extraordinarily rich network of anastomotic vessels and all semblance of end-arteries is lost. Apparently, therefore, the ultimate ramifications of the coronary arterial tree are end-arteries only in normal circumstances. An anatomical substrate capable of development into an extremely effective anastomotic network does exist and does often develop when the narrowing and final occlusion of a coronary artery takes place slowly enough. Absent in a normal heart, it appears only *when* and *where* it is needed.

While on the subject of anastomoses between coronary arteries, which occur not only between branches of the right and left arteries but also between adjacent branches of the same artery, attention should be given to the anastomoses between coronary vessels and extracoronary arteries. These may develop with branches of the aortic vasa vasorum, with branches from vessels in the mediastinum, lungs, parietal pericardium, and the diaphragm. Surgical methods have been designed to increase the numbers and effectiveness of these extracardiac anastomoses in attempts to create a blood supply in the face of increasing narrowing of the coronary arteries, and it may be that the survival of hearts in which it was found postmortem that both coronary arteries were occluded at their orifices is due to the effective development of adequate extracardiac anastomoses.

As far as the capillaries of cardiac muscle are concerned, little is known except that the richness of the capillary network surrounding the muscle fibers in all dimensions is not exceeded in any other issue—there is at least a one to one relationship existing between capillaries and muscle fibers. This intimate anatomical relation between capillary and muscle fiber must contribute significantly to the ability of the fiber to utilize oxygen in the presence of a considerable diminution in the oxygen saturation of the blood.

Cardiac Veins and the Thebesian Vessels. The venous drainage of the heart is also of physiological interest. The usual arrangement is found in the heart whereby capillaries drain into venules and these into even larger veins. The veins follow roughly the distribution of the major arteries, joining finally into a single trunk which empties into the right auricle via the coronary sinus. There is in addition, however, an accessory channel for venous drainage via the so-called Thebesian vessels.* These vessels pass directly from the capillaries and veins to the lumen of the ventricles; they are most numerous in the right ventricular side of the interventricular septums. Two other structures should also be mentioned, the arterioluminal and the arteriosinusoidal vessels, which form direct communications between the arteries or arterioles and the ventricular or auricular cavities. The first of these maintain their arteriolar character to the very end of their course; the latter break up shortly into sinusoids which lie between the muscle bundles. These vessels resemble capillaries in possessing thin walls made up of endothelium only, but differ from capillaries in their larger diameter, which varies from 50 to 250 μ.

The function of the Thebesian vessels is still obscure. In the dead heart ready communication exists between the ventricular cavities and the coronary veins via these channels, and the supposition is that the Thebesian vessels constitute an alternative route for venous drainage. This view gained support from a comparison of the amount of blood perfused through the coronary vessels in a heart-lung preparation with the quantity that could be collected through a cannula in the mouth of the coronary sinus. Earlier work indicated that approximately 60 per cent of the total coronary flow passed through the coronary sinus, the other 40 per cent, by implication, entering the ventricular cavities via the Thebesian vessels. More recent work indicates that the partition between coronary sinus flow and other pathways is by no means constant and a much smaller proportion than this may be drained by the coronary sinus. The vigor of the heart beat and the pressure within the right ventricle appear to be major determining factors. The general impression is gained that the blood flow from the right coronary artery is drained largely through Thebesian channels, while the left coronary blood returns in the veins via the coronary sinus.

Recently Gregg, Shipley and Bidder (15a) have called attention to a source of error in previous measurements that alters radically the whole picture. They painstakingly cannulated the greater part of the numerous anterior cardiac veins that are seen to pass to the base of the right ventricle and empty directly into the auricle, and found that the amount of blood collected from them was almost sufficient to account for all the coronary outflow not collected from the coronary sinus flow. The unsuspected magnitude of the flow in these hitherto neglected veins, will demand, if these results are corroborated, a significant downward scaling of our concept of the role of the Thebesian vessels in the venous drainage of the heart. Their summary is worth quoting in full.

"The number and anatomical distribution of the major anterior cardiac veins of the dog's heart have been studied from roentgenograms of specimens injected immediately postmortem. Inspection alone reveals that the greater portion of the subepicardial surface of the right ventricle is traversed by many small branches which emerge to form, in different hearts, from two to five major anterior cardiac veins. Each major vein empties separately and directly into the right atrium about 4 to 8 mm. superior to the border of the tricuspid valve. Other small veins are invariably present.

"The functional importance of the anterior cardiac veins, virtually ignored by previous investigations, is demonstrated. In 16 anesthetized open chest dogs with different body

* After Adam Christian Thebesius, who first described them in his *Dissertatio medica de circulosanguinis in corde*, Leyden, 1708 (2d ed., 1716).

weights and blood pressures, the flow from all the major anterior cardiac veins cannulated ranged from 8.5 to 26.5 cc. per minute. The flow could be increased greatly by various procedures. It was established that flow from the anterior cardiac veins is almost if not entirely derived from the coronary arteries, and its magnitude generally approaches and not infrequently exceeds the simultaneously measured right coronary inflow.

"The major portion (50–92 per cent) of right coronary inflow was found to drain via the anterior cardiac veins into the right atrium. This finding makes completely untenable the conventionally accepted belief that nearly all of the right coronary inflow drains by way of the Thebesian vessels into the right ventricle."

Equally unsatisfactory is the status of another hypothetical function of the Thebesian vessels—that of nourishment of the heart in the presence of coronary insufficiency. This possibility was suggested by Pratt to account for the survival of an isolated cat's heart kept alive and beating by perfusion with defibrinated blood through the ventricular cavities. The occasional finding of human hearts that had apparently survived occlusion of both coronary arteries clearly indicates the existence of some extracoronary source of nutrition. A variety of experiments have failed to demonstrate any significant flow of blood from the ventricular cavities into the coronary arterial tree, and the suggestion has been made that ebb and flow in the myocardial sinusoids accounts for much of the extracoronary nourishment of the heart.

Nervous Control of the Coronary Vessels. The nerve supply to the coronary arteries is so abundant that at one time anatomists were led to believe that the heart itself received no nerves, and that the so-called cardiac nerves were present only for the innervation of the coronary arteries. While this extreme view was in the course of time demonstrated to be incorrect, it serves to emphasize a richness of innervation which, according to Anrep (1), is unsurpassed in any other artery in the body. Both sympathetic and parasympathetic fibers are present, in approximately equal representation in the larger vessels but with a preponderance of parasympathetic fibers in the finer arterioles.

The functions of the two subdivisions of the autonomic nervous system, as regards their peripheral influence as well as their central regulation, are still in some measure unclear. The cause for this lies in the difficulty with which coronary blood flow may be measured. Flow in the isolated heart can be measured with considerable accuracy, but the applicability of such results to the intact animal is naturally open to question. On the other hand, the methods applicable to intact unanesthetized animals, such as the thermostrohmuhr of Rein, have been criticized on the basis of their accuracy. Newer flowmeters are being devised to meet the double requirements of applicability to normal conditions and of accuracy, and should add much to the fundamental knowledge of this subject. It has also been difficult to separate with certainty the direct effect of stimulation or section of a nerve from indirect influences arising from alterations in the rate and force of the heart beat and in the aortic blood pressure.

Notwithstanding the above-mentioned difficulties, it appears to be fairly well established that the parasympathetic fibers serve as vasoconstrictors while the sympathetic fibers are vasodilators. Gregg and Shipley (15) have reported that stimulation of the stellate ganglion may in some instances double the inflow via one or the other coronary arteries. Apparently the influence is more marked on left coronary artery inflow, where increases in flow from 27 to 45, 18 to 39, 14 to 30, and 16 to 32 cc. per minute were obtained as against the following increments in the right coronary: 27 to 32, 10 to 15, 23 to 44, and 25 to 37 cc. per minute. An increase in flow was noted when blood pressure and heart rate were maintained at a constant value or did not increase spontaneously, indicating that alterations in heart rate or blood pressure are not indispensable parts of the mechanism.

The most significant studies on the function of the parasympathetic innervation appear to be those of Anrep and Segall (1) and of Essex, Herrick, Baldes and Mann (5). Anrep and Segall studied the coronary blood flow in heart-lung-brain preparations in which the vagus nerves could be left intact or be cut. They found that the flow in the denervated heart was almost twice that of the innervated heart, but that it was relatively fixed, showing no change with alterations in heart rate or in the strength of the cardiac contraction as produced by variation in the stroke volume. On the other hand, the innervated heart did respond to increase in the minute output of the heart by an increase in coronary flow which then equalled that of the denervated

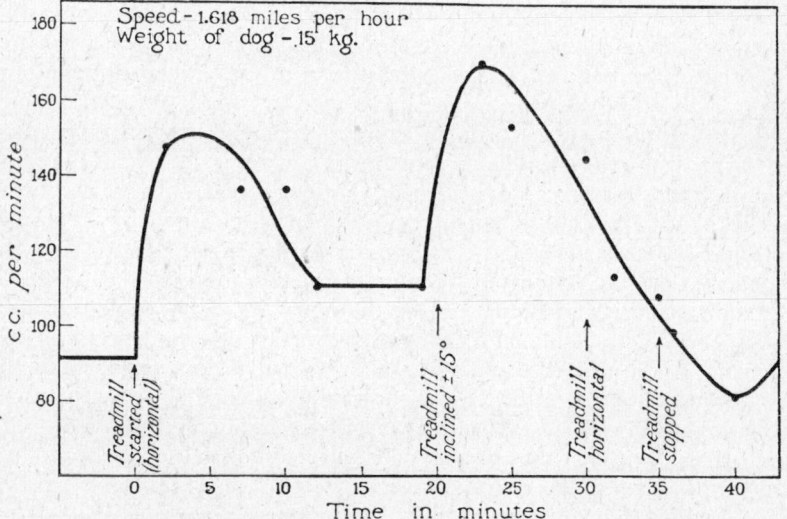

Fig. 380.—Blood flow in the circumflex branch of the left coronary artery before and during exercise on a treadmill. The subject is a normal trained dog after full recovery from the operation at which the flowmeter was placed on the artery. (From Essex, Herrick, Baldes and Mann, *Amer. J. Physiol.*, 1943, *138*:687–697.)

heart. Stimulation of the peripheral stump of the vagus in the denervated heart reduced the coronary flow even when precautions were taken to maintain a constant heart rate (rhythmic electrical stimulation or small doses of atropine). Anrep and Segall concluded that the increased coronary blood flow which accompanies an augmented cardiac output in the innervated heart is due to the reflex inhibition of vagal tone, which maintains vasoconstriction in the coronary arteries of an unstressed heart.

Much the same conclusion is arrived at by Essex, Herrick, Baldes and Mann (5) in studies by the thermostromuhr method in trained unanesthetized dogs after recovery from the operation in which the apparatus was applied to the coronary artery (Fig. 380). Their conclusions are worth quoting:

"With all the limitations acknowledged with respect to the present experiments, which have been in progress for a number of years, we submit that sufficient data are presented in this report to indicate rather conclusively the dominant role of the vagus in control of cardiac circulation. In not a single instance has there been any evidence that the sympathetic nerves exercised a tonic action on the heart or coronary vessels. A sympathectomized heart was indistinguishable from a normal heart as to rate and coronary blood flow. In every series of experiments the tonic action of the vagus was strongly evident. A dramatic change of rate and coronary flow was not seen except when the heart was deprived of both vagus nerves. So long as one vagus supplied the heart its reaction to exercise as respects rate and coronary flow was indistinguishable from that of the fully innervated heart. In the absence of the cardiac sympathetic nerves the sectioning of the remaining vagus nerve was followed by marked acceleration of heart and augmentation of coronary blood flow. The response of the rate and coronary blood flow of the totally denervated heart to moderate exercise was in many instances completely negative whereas the fully innervated heart showed marked acceleration and increased coronary blood flow with the same rate of exercise. The results of our experiments on the trained dog strongly support the findings of Anrep and Segall on the innervated and denervated heart-lung preparation as regards the tonic vagal control of coronary blood flow and likewise our results support the findings of Samaan with regard to the influence of the vagus on the heart rate of exercising dogs."

It has been observed that increase in the pressure in the carotid sinus is followed by a reduction in coronary blood flow which can be shown to be independent of alterations in blood pressure and heart rate, although it was normally associated with them. The phenomenon results, in all probability, from the constriction of the coronary arteries, presumably as the consequence of reflex vagal stimulation. The present concept of tonic activity of the carotid sinus and other pressoreceptors suggests that these receptors are responsible for the tonic vagal influence on the coronary arteries observed by Anrep and Segall, and by Essex, Herrick, Baldes and Mann.

Chemical Control: Autonomic Hormones. Determination of the influence of adrenaline and acetylcholine on the coronary vessels is made difficult by the additional indirect influence exerted by virtue of their effects on heart rate, aortic blood pressure, and vigor of myocardial contraction, and these difficulties are reflected in the widely variant statements made by the numerous investigators who have studied the subject. The consensus of opinion seems to be, however, that the action of adrenaline is to excite a moderate dilating influence on the coronary arteries. This effect may be partly or perhaps even completely masked by a reduction in systolic flow due to the increased vigor of ventricular contraction. It may be aided, on the other hand, by the vasodilating action of metabolic products liberated by virtue of the increased metabolism induced by the drug. It has been suggested that the angina produced by injection of adrenaline in susceptible subjects occurs because the increase in metabolism, and the consequent demand for oxygen, far outstrips the increase in flow made possible by the direct vasodilating action of the adrenaline.

As far as acetylcholine is concerned, most workers find that the drug dilates the coronary vessels, quite contrary to what might be expected from the vasoconstriction which follows vagal stimulation. On the other hand, electrocardiographic studies after injection of acetylcholine and associated drugs suggest the existence of myocardial ischemia, though there is no proof that this results from coronary vasoconstriction.

There is complete agreement that pitressin reduces coronary flow, with more or less proportional reduction throughout the cardiac cycle. This reduction, which is sufficient to bring about well marked electrocardiographic signs of myocardial ischemia, is antagonized by adrenaline. Green, Wegria and Boyer (11) found in the dog, in confirmation of the original observation by Melville and Stehle, that 0.1 cc. of a 1:1000 solution of adrenaline promptly restored the coronary flow and the vigor of cardiac contraction which had been depressed by 1 to 2 units of pitressin.

Amyl nitrite, nitroglycerin, aminophylline, histamine, acetyl-beta-methyl-choline, papaverine, pyridine-beta-carbonic acid, diethylamide (coramine), and atropine have been noted to increase coronary blood flow, and coronary vasodilatation has been recognized as responsible, at least in part, for the phenomenon.

Oxygen, Carbon Dioxide, and Other Metabolites. Much more pronounced than the influence of nervous factors or of the vasodilating drugs mentioned above is the action of anoxemia (Fig. 381). An increase in blood flow to as

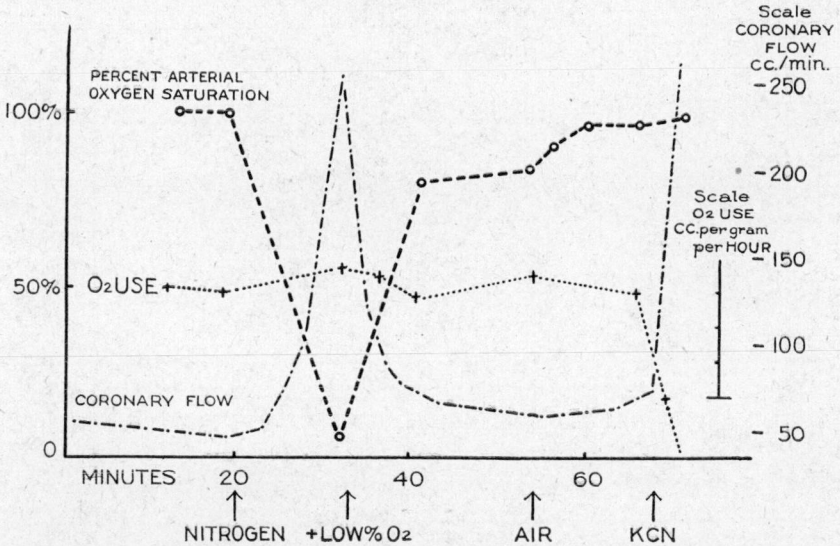

Fig. 381.—Graph showing the great increase in coronary blood flow in a heart-lung preparation when ventilated with nitrogen or when KCN was administered. The oxygen consumption remains constant. (From Hilton and Eichholtz, *J. Physiol.*, 1924–25, *59*:413–425.)

much as five times the control value has been observed. Injection of cyanide reproduces the effects of general anoxia. On the other hand, increase in the CO_2 content of the inspired air, or injection of lactic acid, has a much smaller effect, increasing flow by approximately 50 per cent (Fig. 382). It is apparent, therefore, that the increased coronary blood flow in anoxia must be due to the influence of anoxia per se, and not to metabolites liberated as the result of oxygen lack. This view is supported by the observations of Hilton and Eichholtz that the vasodilatation produced by anoxemia occurs without reduction in oxygen consumption. There would in such a case be no oxygen debt and no abnormal production of metabolites.

The rapidity with which oxygen lack operates has impressed many observers. Green and his coworkers (10) noticed that local ischemia caused by temporary ligation of a coronary artery would produce a marked vasodilatation in the ramifications of the artery occluded. Occlusion of an artery for as short a time as from 3 to 5 secs. was followed by an increase of up to 200 to 250 per cent, although no influence on blood pressure or the vigor of myocardial contractions could be detected. Maximal dilatation, producing an increase in flow of as much as 500 per cent, was obtained before myocardial contractions began to fail, while the increased coronary circulation was maintained for as long as 1.5 minutes after full recovery of the force of contraction in experiments where occlusion was maintained to the point of failure.

Mechanical Regulation of Coronary Blood Flow. *Aortic pressure.* "It is a priori evident that the aortic blood pressure must constitute the main factor in the control of the coronary circulation" (1). In the heart-lung preparation increases up to fivefold occur when aortic blood pressure is raised from 40–60 mm. Hg to 130–140 mm. Hg. A fall in perfusion pressure caused a reduction in coronary inflow from 67 cc. per minute to 19 cc. per minute in an experiment on an isolated heart preparation. In experiments on the heart in situ

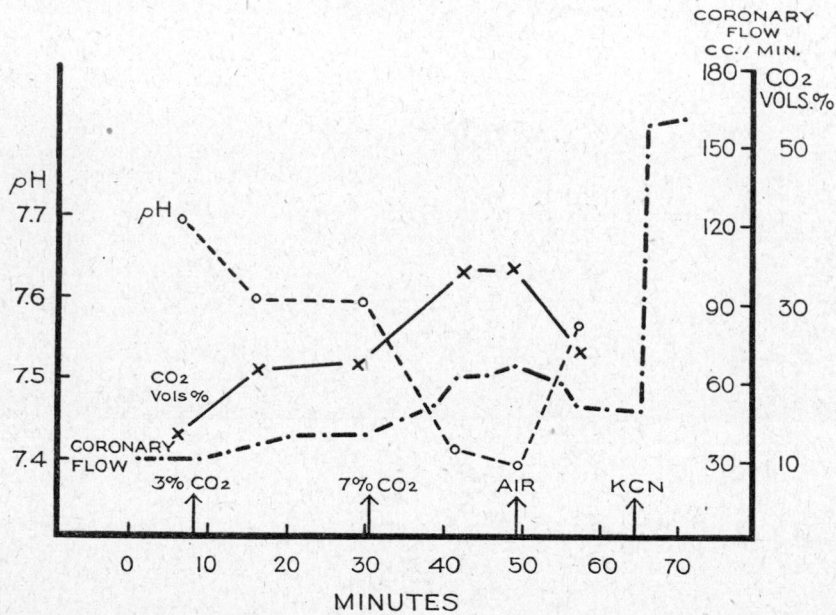

Fig. 382.—An illustration of the influence of CO_2 on coronary flow. Comparison with Figure 381 indicates that CO_2 is much less effective as a vasodilator than O_2 lack. (From Hilton and Eichholtz, *J. Physiol.*, 1924–25, *59*:413–425.)

in the anesthetized animal much the same results are obtained, but they are complicated by alterations in blood pressure and in the vigor of cardiac contractions. When the elevation in pressure is produced by compression of the aorta, systolic blood flow per beat is increased, but the total systolic flow per minute is only moderately increased because of the reflex slowing of the heart which reduces the total time occupied by systole in a minute.

Diastolic flow per beat is also increased, and the relative contribution of diastolic flow to the total increase in minute flow is augmented by the fact that the diastolic interval is prolonged by the slowing of the heart. When the increased blood pressure is evoked by injection of adrenaline, one effect of the drug is to increase the vigor of myocardial contractions which, as will be explained later, reduces the systolic flow. In this case all of the increase in flow takes place during diastole.

Heart rate. Within fairly wide limits, and in a variety of preparations, alterations of heart rate are without influence on coronary circulation. With abrupt slowing of the heart rate, increase in coronary circulation has been recorded, however. An acceleration of the coronary circulation has also been noted during short periods of cardiac arrest and during ventricular fibrillation.

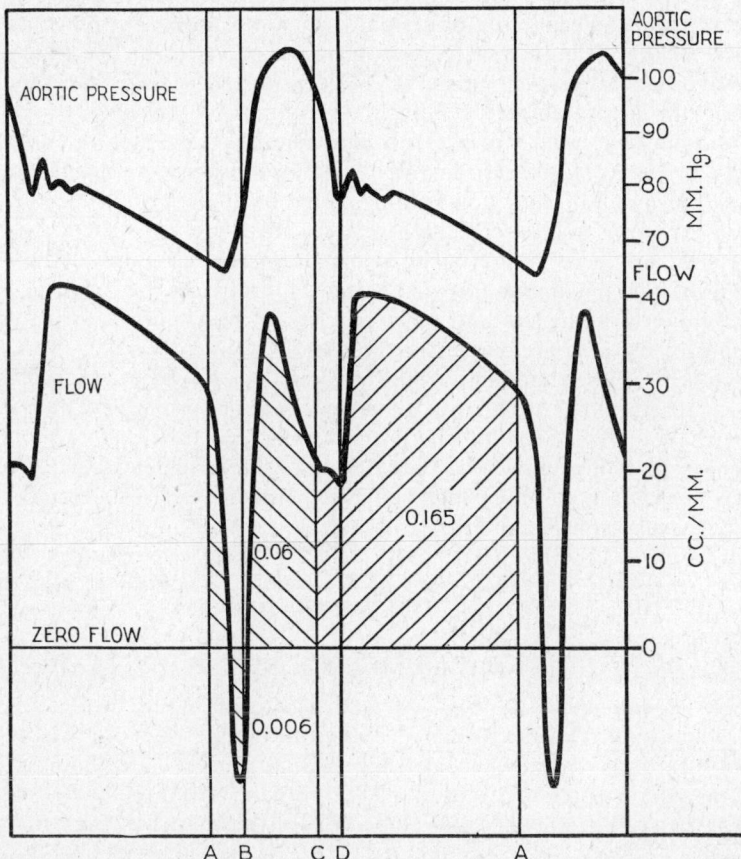

Fig. 383.—Blood flow in the anterior descending branch of the left coronary artery, synchronized with the aortic pressure curve. At the end of diastole, A, blood is flowing into the coronary artery at a rate of 28 cc. per minute. At the onset of isometric contraction, A, the rate of flow abruptly diminishes and a backflow is established momentarily. With the beginning of ejection, flow recommences and reaches a maximum of 40 cc. per minute shortly before the peak of the aortic pressure curve. It then declines somewhat in parallel with the fall of aortic pressure, only to increase again after the closure of the aortic valves, D. Finally, it declines with declining diastolic pressure until the next systole begins. The total blood flow during each phase can be calculated from the area enclosed by each curve (rate × time). The net flow in systole equals 0.06 minus 0.006 or 0.054 cc., while that during diastole is 0.165 cc. Since the heart rate was 131 per minute, the total flow is 29 cc. per minute. (From Gregg and Green, *Amer. J. Physiol.*, 1940, *130*:114–125.)

On the other hand, increase in heart rate to abnormally high rates has been found to reduce coronary flow. The implication of these observations is that systole may interfere in some measure with coronary circulation, causing a reduction in total flow in conditions such as in tachycardia, where the diastolic interval is excessively curtailed and systole occupies the greater part of the cardiac cycle.

Mechanical Interference with Blood Flow during Systole. Circulation in the frog's heart is apparently a simple in and out motion of blood which enters the sinusoids of the heart during diastole and is squeezed out during systole. A somewhat similar view has been held regarding the mammalian heart. According to this view, the contraction of the ventricles is strong enough to stop arterial flow throughout systole and to increase venous flow by squeezing blood from the capillaries and small veins into the larger veins and into the right atrium. The different views that have prevailed at one time or another have been almost completely a reflection of the technical difficulties attending the measurement of flow in the coronary arteries throughout a single cardiac cycle. At present the evidence suggests that the following sequence of events (Fig. 383) most probably occurs during a normal cardiac cycle. At the end of diastole flow is approximately 70 per cent of its maximum velocity. During isometric contraction flow into the coronary arteries stops completely, and there may even be some back flow at a rate of nearly 20 per cent of the maximum forward speed. During the period of ejection forward flow recommences and soon reaches its maximum forward rate at the height of the pressure curve. By the end of systole, flow has again fallen to 50 per cent of its maximum, which, however, is soon again reached during isometric relaxation. Throughout diastole there is a progressive fall in rate of flow to about 70 per cent of maximum by the time the next systole begins.

When, instead of rate of flow, the volume of flow is calculated—as can be done by measuring the area inclosed by the graph of rate changes—it is seen that a very considerable net forward flow occurs during systole, even though during a very brief part of systole flow may cease entirely. Recent figures on the ratio of total flow during systole to total flow during diastole range from 1:1.75 to 1:7.4 with an average of 1:2.4.

OXYGEN METABOLISM

Oxygen Requirement. *Cardiac efficiency.* Oxygen requirements in heart-lung preparations are of the order of magnitude of 2 to 5 or more cc. O_2 per gram of heart per hour, when average cardiac outputs are maintained at mean aortic blood pressures close to 100 mm. Hg. Given the energy equivalent of oxygen (2 kg. m. per cc.), the efficiency of the heart can be estimated by calculating the work output by means of a formula which includes the two major ways in which the heart performs work: creating pressure and imparting a kinetic energy to the flowing blood. One example of such a formula is:

$$W = VP + \frac{MV^2}{2g},$$

where W = work in kg. meters, V = minute volume in liters, P = mean aortic pressure in meters of blood, M = weight of blood, V^2 = square of mean velocity, and g = acceleration due to gravity. The total work of the heart requires such a computation for both ventricles. The kinetic factor constitutes but a small proportion of the total work in most circumstances and is usually neglected. In these circumstances the efficiency of the heart is usually in the neighborhood of 3 to 7 per cent.

Increase in the work of the heart demands additional oxygen but not necessarily a directly proportioned increment, since the efficiency of contraction may change. Augmentation of the work load required by increase in arterial resistance lowers efficiency by approximately 20 per cent so that a greater than proportioned rise in oxygen consumption must occur. Efficiency is lowered when the heart rate increases. Even where the output is unaltered, the oxygen consumption varies in an almost linear fashion with heart rate which can be expressed mathematically in the following formula: O_2 (cc. per gram per hour) $= 0.0187R$ (rate per min.) $+ 2.23$. This increase in oxygen requirements without alteration in output entails, of course, a reduction in efficiency that may be a critical factor in a failing heart. On the other hand, increase in work load imposed by greater diastolic filling and consequent greater stroke volume, without change in heart rate or mean arterial pressure, is attended by a marked increase (to almost 30 per cent) in efficiency of contractions (Fig. 384). The opinion of some workers is that the output is abnormally low in heart-lung preparations operating at efficiencies of 3 to 10

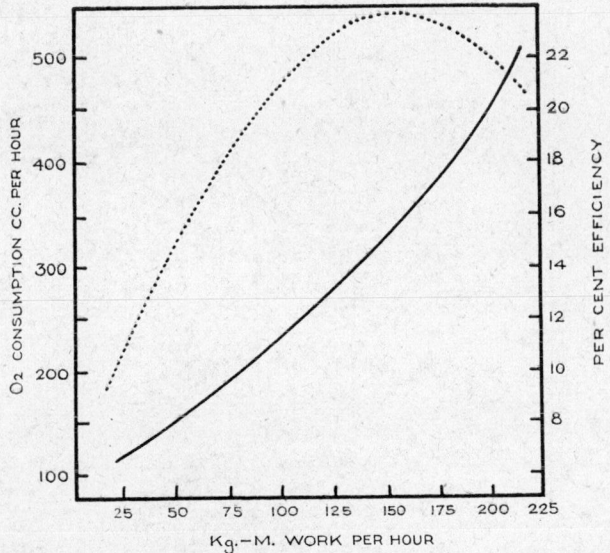

Fig. 384.—Graph showing rise in efficiency (dotted line) when increased output is mediated by enlargement of stroke volume, without change in rate or mean arterial pressure. Efficiency finally begins to fail as the limits of diastolic distensibility are approached. Continuous line = oxygen consumption.(From Evans, *J. Physiol.*, 1918–19, *52*:6–14.)

per cent, and that the efficiency of the human heart in the basal state may be in the neighborhood of 12 to 20 per cent. Calculations based on these figures suggest that the oxygen utilization in the human heart may constitute 4 to 5 per cent of the total consumption.

The conclusions to be drawn from these studies are: (i) the efficiency of the heart is lowered when the demand for increased output is met by an increased heart rate, but is raised where the stroke volume is increased without change in rate; (ii) because of these two opposing tendencies it is not possible to predict the net change in efficiency that might occur in strenuous exercise, because both factors are involved, but since the trained individual performs the same work at a lower heart rate than the nontrained person, it follows that the trained person is operating at a higher level of cardiac efficiency; (iii) increase in arterial resistance forces the heart to work at a lessened efficiency, unless the heart rate is slowed (Marey's law) to accommodate the same output with a more efficient contraction.

Despite even the most favorable changes in efficiency, the consumption of oxygen in the heart increases markedly in strenuous physical exertion, and figures as high as 200 to 250 cc. of oxygen per minute have been suggested as the requirements of the heart in man in exhausting physical exertion. In meeting this demand, the heart has access to a number of mechanisms already described, including extensive vasodilatation in the coronary tree and increase in the mean aortic pressure. In addition, the heart has the ability to increase its oxygen utilization coefficient to an even more marked degree than skeletal muscles. Thus in Figure 381 it can be seen that oxygen consumption may be

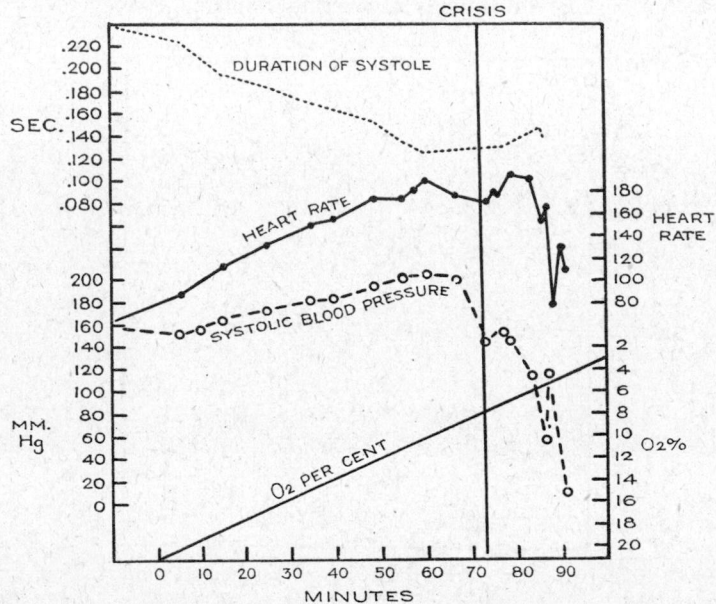

Fig. 385.—Duration of systole (dots), heart rate (solid line with solid circles), systolic pressure (dashes with open circles), and oxygen content of respired air in dog during progressive anoxia (solid line). Until crisis at approximately 8 per cent O_2, all cardiovascular functions are stimulated. Crisis appears to be precipitated by fall in blood pressure. A respiratory crisis occurs at the same time. (From Sands and DeGraff, *Amer. J. Physiol.*, 1925, 74:416–435.)

maintained at a constant level despite a most drastic reduction in the oxygenation of the coronary blood supply. The time may nevertheless come when the demand for oxygen exceeds the supply and the heart becomes anoxemic, either as it participates in *general* anoxemia affecting the whole body or as it suffers from *localized* anoxemia affecting only part of the heart. To each condition characteristic reactions take place.

General Anoxemia. The progressive development of generalized anoxemia involves the heart directly and indirectly. In the early stages of anoxemia or hypoxia the general response is one of stimulation, with increased blood pressure, heart rate and cardiac output. The duration of systole is shortened (Fig. 385), the minute volume of respiration increases and a relative alkalosis develops because of excessive loss of CO_2 by hyperventilation. This stage, in which it is clear that the heart is operating with normal or even increased efficiency, is terminated classically in a cardiovascular-respiratory crisis; the blood pressure falls abruptly, respiration becomes slower and stops altogether, while the heart slows markedly and shows signs of A-V block of varying degree. If adequate oxygen is not rapidly made available and artificial respiration instituted, death will soon follow.

In man and experimental animals this sequence has been followed electrocardiographically to the very moment of collapse and two findings are almost universally noted: a progressive diminution in the height of the T wave in all leads, beginning at oxygen concentrations of around 14 per cent, and a moderate depression of the S-T segment, rarely exceeding 1 mm. The R wave has also been reported to suffer a progressive diminution. This latter change results from a progressive increase in chest volume resulting from the gradual augmentation in inspiratory tone as anoxemia develops. At the crisis, A-V dissociation may appear in man as well as in the dog. Once the crisis has appeared, the T wave shows a rapid reversal to the upright. The T wave continues to grow in amplitude, and may exceed the amplitude of R. Arrest may occur at this stage, or the ventricles may continue to beat until widespread intraventricular block develops. All these events occur after the arrest of respiration and may therefore be considered to represent agonal changes. They undoubtedly reflect the direct effect of anoxemia upon the myocardium as well as changes due to the large outpouring of potassium from anoxemic tissues throughout the body.

The question is frequently raised as to the extent to which the precrisis changes in the electrocardiogram indicate the presence of myocardial anoxemia, resembling as they do the T wave changes following acute myocardial infarction. While the question cannot be considered to be fully settled, there are certain arguments to favor the view that they do not indicate the existence of myocardial anoxemia. These may be summarized as follows.

(i) The heart can continue to maintain its oxygen consumption at extremely low levels of oxygen saturation in the coronary circulation by means of vasodilatation and by increasing its oxygen utilization coefficient (Fig. 381). (ii) If anything, the heart is stimulated during this period, contracts more efficiently, and maintains an increased cardiac output. (iii) Changes in the T wave can be in a large measure prevented by addition of CO_2 to the gas mixture being breathed to produce anoxemia. Inasmuch as similar T wave changes are produced by alkalosis (hyperventilation, $NaHCO_3$ ingestion) and since there occurs a diminution in the CO_2 tension with the progress of anoxemia, it is probable that the T wave changes seen in these circumstances reflect the increase in pH rather than an anoxemia of the myocardium. There is even some evidence that the crisis is precipitated by some factor other than myocardial failure. Keys and coworkers (18) fail to find any signs of change in heart volume, immediately before and after anoxemic syncope in young men. Lorber (20) observes that in perfused hearts dilatation and failure does not occur until the oxygen content of the perfusing blood is reduced significantly below that tolerated by the intact animal.

As a balance to this generally optimistic view of the ability of the heart to survive generalized anoxemia, it must be remembered that permanent damage can be produced by long exposure to low oxygen tensions—as may happen in nitrous oxide anesthesia, carbon monoxide poisoning, and when resuscitation is not carried out immediately after the crisis in anoxemia of whatever cause. Lesions in these cases consist of small focal areas of necrosis scattered throughout the myocardium, especially in the papillary muscles. In a recent report they were produced in kittens by exposure to atmospheres containing 4 to 5 per cent O_2 for at least three days. Complete bibliographies on the influence of generalized anoxemia on the heart are to be found in E. C. Hoff and Fulton's *Bibliography of aviation medicine* (16, 17).

Localized Anoxemia. Occlusion or excessive narrowing of a coronary artery, taking place with such abruptness that an adequate collateral circulation cannot develop in time to be of assistance, will produce, in the area of myocardium it supplies, an area of almost complete oxygen lack surrounded by a zone of reduced oxygenation improving by degrees to normal myocardium at its periphery. Within the zone of oxygen deficiency certain physiological processes are altered: (i) the force with which the affected muscles contract, (ii) the ability with which they conduct the cardiac impulse, and (iii) the irritability of the anoxemic tissue as shown in its threshold, its rate of repolarization, and the degree of its automaticity. Many of these factors produce changes in the electrocardiograph by which the course of events may be followed.

Diminution in *contractility* is perhaps the most significant alteration that occurs. Partial deficiency in oxygen supply, when carried beyond the compensatory ability of the myocardium, is soon followed by weakening of contraction and dilatation; complete deprivation of oxygen is followed within 30 seconds by complete cessation of contractions. The most common cause of death in acute attacks of coronary occlusion is probably failure of muscular force, while progressive congestive heart failure is the most important complication in individuals who recover from the acute attacks with insufficient functional myocardium to maintain an adequate cardiac output. The very act of occlusion favors the establishment of collateral circulation, but in myocardium that is totally deprived of oxygen for more than 30 minutes recovery cannot take place; an *infarct* is produced which is later replaced by noncontractile tissue.

Disturbances of conduction that take place with anoxemia are especially important when the anoxemic area includes specialized conductile tissue such as the A-V node, bundle of His, or one of the bundle-branches. In these circumstances a further burden is placed on the heart in addition to the direct loss of contractility insofar as the ventricular rate is slowed to levels where cardiac output falls or the distribution of the impulse within the ventricles is delayed to such a degree that summation of the fractionate contributions of the individual muscular elements can no longer yield a vigorous contraction.

Changes in irritability of paramount importance are those which develop in partially anoxemic areas, particularly soon after the anoxemia begins. As has been seen, generalized anoxemia stimulates the heart during the pre-crisis stages, as much via the sympathetic nervous system as by direct action on the myocardium. Other irritable tissues are equally hyperexcitable at certain stages of oxygen want. In heart muscle this stage of hyperirritability expresses itself in an increased tendency to spontaneous discharge and a shortened refractory period, and serves as the physiological background for the ectopic beats that almost invariably arise after occlusion of a coronary artery. These range all the way from isolated extrasystoles arising within the anoxemic area to runs of tachycardia which may ultimately lead to ventricular fibrillation and death. Even when they do not terminate in fibrillation, such tachycardias are of clinical importance because cardiac output may thereby be reduced.

The electrocardiogram reflects certain of these changes in the following sequence: (i) the period of stimulation through which all the myocardium passes as it becomes anoxemic, and which persists in the outlying zone for some period; (ii) the current of injury that develops when anoxemia proceeds to a degree such that the integrity of the surface membrane can no longer be maintained, (iii) the more lasting changes which persist in myocardium which survives but which has an insufficient blood supply: this change is principally one of delayed recovery from excitation; and (iv) the lasting changes in distribution of the cardiac impulse brought about by the permanent loss of myocardial elements.

During the initial stage of stimulation, seen as the first event after acute occlusion of a coronary artery in a normal heart, the refractory period is shortened, and this is manifested in the electrical behavior of the tissue as an increased rate of repolarization. This *shortens* the duration of the mono-

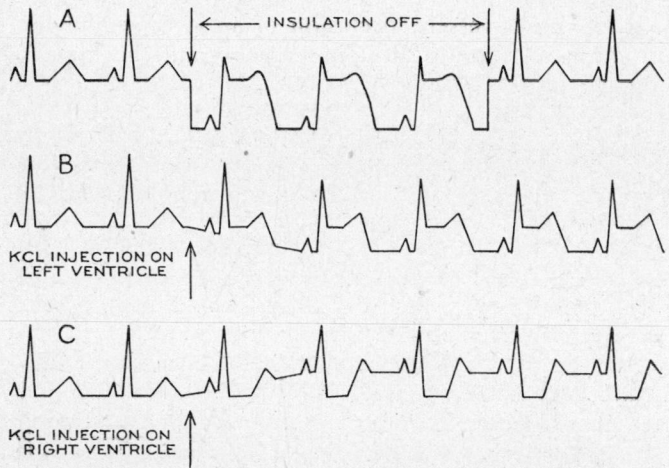

Fig. 386.—A, injury current produced by injury (KCl) of the left apex in Lead II. The region of injury was insulated from surrounding tissue by a rubber dam and dry blotting paper, which could be short-circuited by forming a circuit between two metal plates placed on either side of the insulation and connected to a switch by means of fine insulated wires. Between the arrows the insulation was short-circuited, revealing an injury current which produced a downward shift of the diastolic baseline. During the S-T interval the injury current disappears with the full excitation of the heart. B, the injury current revealed by injecting a minute amount of isotonic KCl solution onto a small square of blotting paper placed on the left ventricle. C, the injury current in the right ventricle produced as in B. (Drawn semidiagrammatically from records of experiments reported by Nahum, Hamilton and Hoff, *Amer. J. Physiol.*, 1943, *139:*202–207).

phasic curve from the damaged region. In the electrocardiogram this shows up as an increase or a decrease in the amplitude of the T wave (which depends upon relative recovery rates in the regions recorded by any given lead).

As far as leads I, II and III alone are concerned, such a change in the left ventricle shows up as an *increase* in the amplitude of T, while it appears as an inversion of T where the right ventricle is involved. (The electrocardiographic changes characteristic of acute coronary occlusion in experimental animals can be reproduced in every essential by appropriate damage of the external surface of the heart in the area supplied by the occluded artery, which can be seen to become cyanotic when the vessel is occluded. The early changes in repolarization may therefore be represented as reductions in the duration of the dextro- or levocardiogram, with consequent terminal preponderance of the opposite phase.)

28

The *injury current* is the next change to develop. When anoxemia reaches a critical level, repolarization can no longer take place, and an injury current is set up between the injured region and adjacent noninjured areas. When the noninjured region is depolarized, the injury current disappears. This produces in the electrocardiogram an apparent shift of the S-T segment.which is in reality a shift of the diastolic baseline in the opposite direction (Fig. 386). The direction of the shift in baseline is as though the damaged ventricle were electronegative with respect to the undamaged ventricle. Occlusion of an artery supplying the left ventricle, which can be reproduced by any other kind of damage to the external surface of the ventricle, causes therefore a downward movement of the diastolic baseline; but when the noninjured regions of the ventricle are excited (during the S-T interval) the beam moves back to the isopotential line, giving the appearance of an "elevated" S-T segment (Fig. 386). Conversely, occlusion of an artery supplying the right ventricle produces an upward shift in baseline and the appearance of a

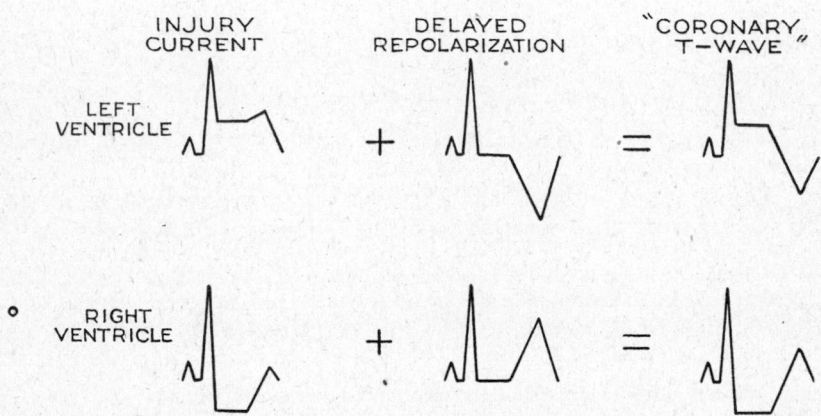

Fig. 387.—Illustrating the production of the classical S-T segment and T wave changes in myocardial function as the combination of two factors: the injury current, and delayed repolarization in the partially damaged but excitable tissue surrounding the injury. These changes may be produced experimentally by injuring a small area by KCl or by burning, and cooling the viable tissue around the area of injury.

"depressed" S-T segment. It will be seen that in this early stage the T wave deviates in the same direction as the apparent S-T deviation. After a variable period, the injury current will begin to disappear, partly because some tissue will eventually receive an additional supply of blood through collaterals and recover, and partly because the junction between dead and viable tissue will be "sealed off" by the formation of new cell membranes. The phase of stimulation will have passed off quite soon, leaving viable tissue with a slow recovery phase. This will, understandably, cause the T wave to move in the opposite direction to the S-T deviation, giving rise to the classical electrocardiogram of myocardial infarction (Fig. 387).

Eventually, even these changes may pass away with the progressive development of collaterals, leaving only the more or less permanent changes depending upon alterations in the path of the impulse. Inasmuch as infarcts of any size are almost universally restricted to the left ventricle, electrocardiographic changes will be restricted to left ventricular effects. These can best be explained by supposing that the net effect of extensive scarring will be to reduce the effective thickness of the ventricle and hasten the arrival of excitation at the ventricular surface. This results in an increase in the amplitude of the Q wave.

The location of the lesion will determine the leads in which these changes will occur according to the principles of representation outlined earlier (p. 751). Damage to the anterior surface of the left ventricle will lead in succession, therefore, to an increase in the amplitude of T_1 followed shortly by an "elevation" of $S-T_1$, and later, by the development of an inverted T which grows as the S-T interval returns to normal. Last of all, a large Q wave will be seen in this lead, persisting after all other changes may have disappeared. Similar changes in lead III are indicative of a posterior left ventricular lesion.

Inasmuch as the arteries most commonly involved are the anterior and posterior descending branches, the right ventricle will also be involved, and therefore the changes characteristic of left ventricular damage will have their reciprocal, or mirror-image counterparts, in lead III with anterior damage and lead I with posterior damage.

INORGANIC IONS AND THE HEART

Ringer's Solution. This eponym serves as an enduring reminder of Sidney Ringer's contributions to our understanding of the mineral requirements of the heart (22). Perfusing the frog's heart with artificially constituted fluids of differing constitutions, Ringer came to the following conclusions:

(i) "Saline is incapable of maintaining the contractions of the heart, for when blood is replaced by saline, the contractions speedily grow weaker, and in some cases contractility ceases altogether, for no contraction can be excited by even a strong break shock. . . ."

(ii) "Calcium bicarbonate, or calcium chloride in physiological doses, or even in smaller quantities than are present in the blood, restores good contractions, even when contractility has been lost for seven or eight minutes, and the ventricle no longer responds to strong induction shocks. . . . I conclude therefore that a lime salt is necessary for the maintenance of muscular contractility. . . ."

(iii) "But whilst calcium salts are necessary for the proper contraction of the heart, yet if unantagonized by potassium salts the beats would become so broad and diastolic dilatation so prolonged that much fusion of the beats would occur and the ventricle would be thrown into a state of tetanus. . . ."

(iv) "If these two salts are not present in the correct proportions then the trace becomes abnormal. If too little potassium is present the contractions become broader, etc., and there results fusion of the beats. If too much potassium is present, or too little lime salts, then the contraction of the ventricle is imperfect, and by increasing the quantity of potassium salt the beat becomes weaker and weaker till it stops. . . ."

(v) "A small quantity of calcium bicarbonate or calcium chloride (of chloride 1 in 19,500 parts), added to saline solution [0.75 per cent] with 1 part of potassium chloride in 10,000 parts, makes a good artificial circulating fluid and the ventricle will continue beating perfectly for more than four hours, with calcium bicarbonate."

These simple relationships are naturally modified in mammals, where a great many accessory factors must be considered, and it is therefore advisable to review the action of these ions in the dog and cat, and in man as far as it is possible.

Sodium. The main function of sodium in the blood plasma (140 mEq. per liter) appears to be that of maintaining osmotic pressure, and it may not have any other specific function as far as the heart is concerned. The maximum level compatible with life in the dog is approximately 200 mEq. per liter in animals made hypertonic by withdrawal of drinking water or by intravenous or intraperitoneal injections of 5 per cent saline. In these animals the peripheral pulse is slow and vigorous until the very end, and in both acute and chronic animals nonprotein nitrogen does not rise and urine excretion continues, testifying to the adequate maintenance of circulatory efficiency. The electrocardiogram deviates insignificantly in the course of the rise in serum sodium, and is essentially normal immediately before death. Death invariably occurs from respiratory failure while the heart is still beating. Reduction in sodium, on the other hand, is followed by develop-

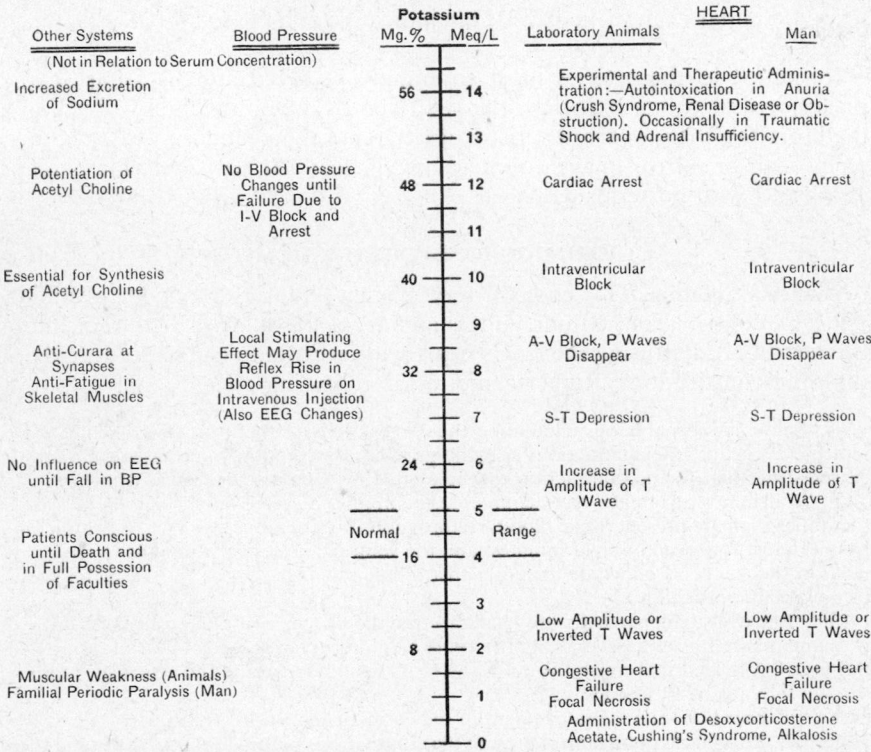

Fig. 388A.—The influence on the heart and associated systems of alteration in the serum concentration of potassium.

ment of marked signs of cardiovascular inefficiency: rapid, weak pulse, low cardiac output and falling blood pressure, resulting in cardiovascular collapse. Insofar as the heart is concerned, however, there is no evidence of any direct influence; all the cardiac manifestations appear to be secondary to the reduced plasma volume.

In summary it can be said that although the sodium of the plasma forms the backbone of the electrolyte structure and is therefore the major determinant of the osmotic value of the plasma, it has little if any direct influence upon the heart, within the limits of hypo- and hypertonicity compatible with life, but that by its influence upon the plasma volume sodium exerts an important effect upon cardiovascular efficiency.

Potassium. In the mammalian heart potassium acts much as it does in the frog; its main effect is to promote relaxation and when present in excess to arrest the heart in diastole. In addition, it alters the sequence of recovery in the heart to cause a conspicuous alteration in the amplitude of the T wave, and produces widespread, progressive intracardiac block, noticeable first in the auricle, than at the A-V node, and finally in the ventricle. In man as well as in experimental animals, blood pressure is well maintained, falling only when intraventricular block becomes pronounced. It may well be, therefore, that potassium does not weaken cardiac contraction per se, but so disperses the fractionate contractions contributed by individual fibers that their net effectiveness is lost. An impairment of contractility is, on the contrary, clearly seen in circumstances in which the serum concentration is lowered (Figs. 388A and 388B).

Responsiveness of the heart to acetylcholine is markedly augmented by increments in serum potassium which are well within limits of spontaneous variability, and it appears from other evidence that the presence of potassium

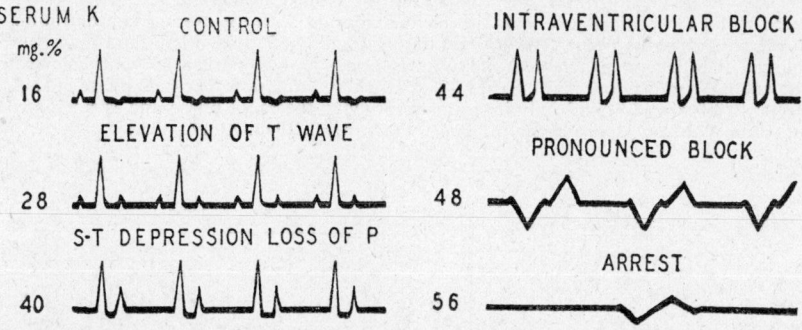

Fig. 388B.—Diagram showing the progressive changes that occur in the electrocardiogram of the dog (lead II) as an isotonic solution of potassium chloride is injected at a slow rate. At the left is given the average level of serum potassium at which the various changes occur. The P wave diminishes in amplitude and widens progressively, and just before it disappears (not shown here) various stages of A-V block may be seen. (From Winkler, Hoff and Smith, *Yale J. Biol. Med.*, 1940, *13*:123–132.)

is required for the synthesis of acetylcholine. It is particularly appropriate in this book to recall the pioneer work of Howell in directing attention to the intimate relationship between potassium and the parasympathetic system, which probably extends also to all cholinergic mechanisms.

The importance of the understanding of the syndrome of intoxication with potassium has grown with the recognition that the condition may occur in man in circumstances when anuria or oliguria exists, especially where this state is accompanied by increased tissue breakdown as in the crush syndrome (anuria following extensive crush injury, particularly to muscles).

Calcium. In the dog, three phases of calcium activity are found as the serum concentration rises progressively (Figs. 389 and 390): (i) initial vagal bradycardia occurring at serum calcium levels of 13 to 35 mg. per cent, (ii) a phase of tachycardia and ectopic beats terminating in approximately 50 per cent of cases in ventricular fibrillation (30 to 60 mg. per cent), and (iii) a final stage of slowing (not of vagal origin) in animals surviving the second stage, at concentrations greater than 60 mg. per cent. In applying these facts to man it will be seen that spontaneous elevation never proceeds to

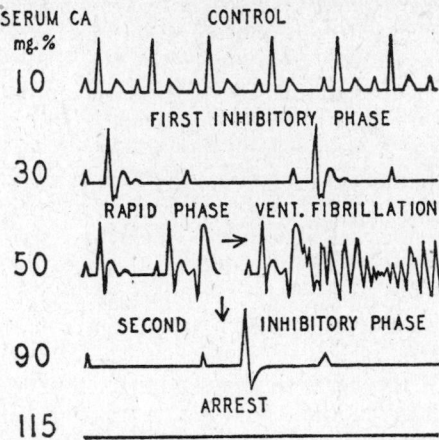

Fig. 389.—Diagram illustrating the changes in the electrocardiogram (lead II) of the dog produced by the slow infusion of isotonic calcium chloride, with the average concentrations at which the several events occur. The first inhibitory stage is of vagal origin, and may be very pronounced. The second phase of acceleration is nearly always marked by ventricular extra-systoles and tachycardia, and may end in fatal ventricular fibrillation. The final phase of slowing and arrest is, of course, found only in animals surviving the rapid phase and is not of vagal origin. (From Winkler, Hoff and Smith, *Yale J. Biol. Med.*, 1940, *13*:123–132.)

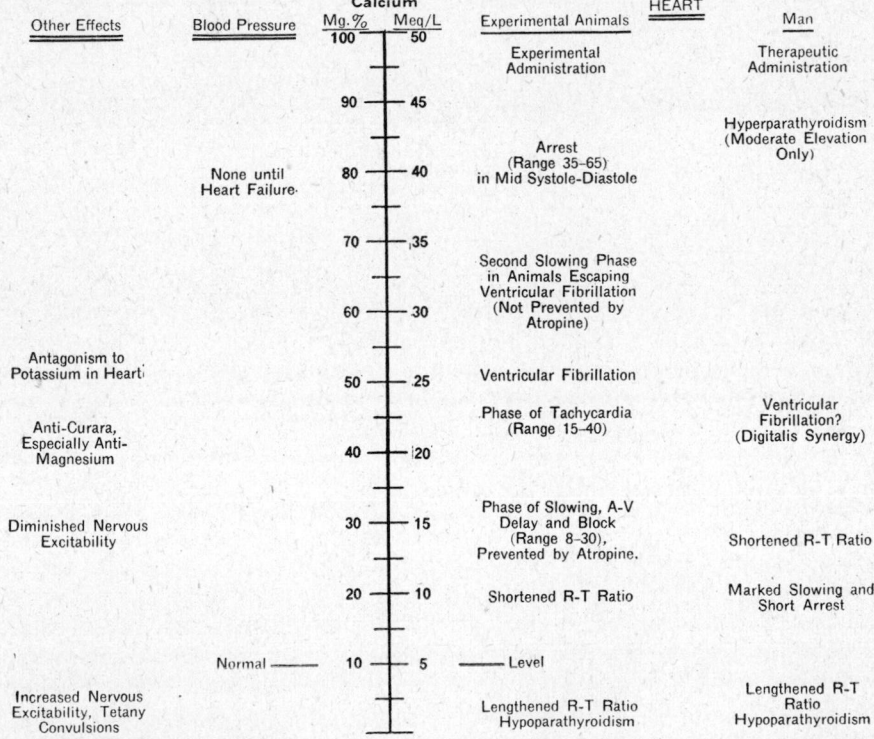

Fig. 390.—A summary of the important systemic effects of elevated serum calcium, especially with reference to the heart.

levels at which the heart is placed in jeopardy, as can and does occur in the case of potassium. The main consideration must therefore be given to the therapeutic use of calcium salts by intravenous injections. The usual therapeutic dose injected at one time is one gram (of calcium chloride) which can hardly produce a serum concentration exceeding 20 mg. per cent unless given with extreme rapidity—therefore the first two stages only need be considered: the early bradycardia and the stage of rapid ectopic beats. An interesting example of the first effect is in all probability seen in the report of a long period of arrest (with syncope) in man, following injections of a very small amount of calcium. It is unlikely that this vagal effect can ever be intense enough to cause death, so that in all probability the cause of fatalities

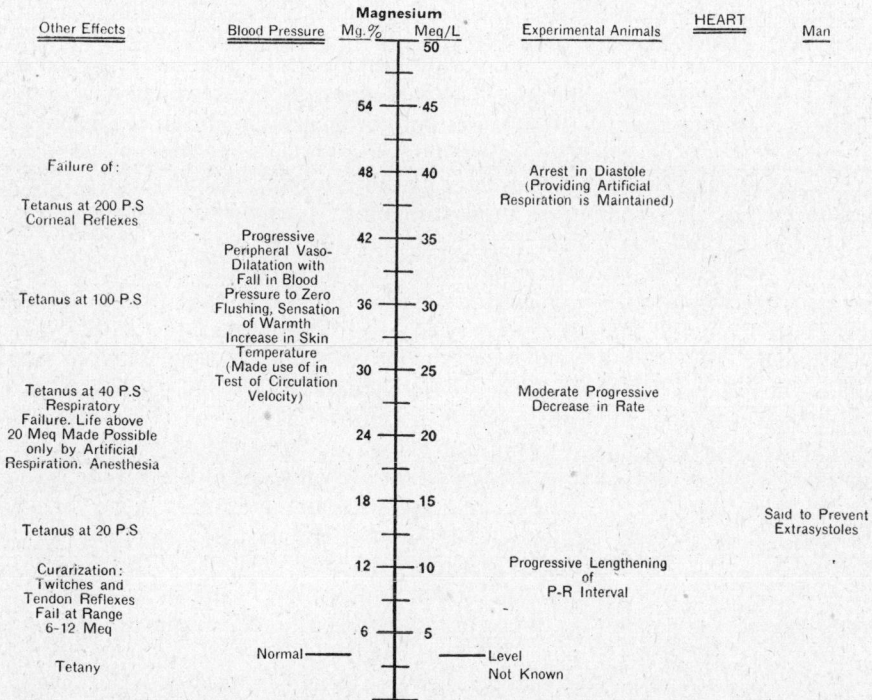

Fig. 391.—An illustration of the influence of magnesium on the cardiovascular and other systems with progressive increase in its concentration in the serum.

in therapeutic injections in man is ventricular fibrillation. The lowest concentration at which this was observed in dogs was 30 mg. per cent, a concentration considerably greater than obtained in man by the injection of the customary therapeutic dose of calcium salts. Presumably very occasionally, fibrillation may occur at a lower level or a rapid injection may temporarily elevate the concentration in arterial blood to toxic levels. The danger from ventricular fibrillation seems to be increased in some measure in digitalized patients either because of some uncomfirmed digitalis synergism or because of the underlying disease in these patients.

Magnesium. Within limits consistent with life, alteration in the concentration of magnesium in the serum has very little influence upon the heart beyond a moderate prolongation of the P-R interval and a variable influence on the heart rate, depending upon the balance between a direct effect to slow the heart and a reflex increase in rate due to fall in blood pressure (Fig. 391). It has been claimed that magnesium salts reduce the excitability of the ventricle, and thus serve to suppress ventricular ectopic beats. The main cardio-vascular effect of magnesium salts is to dilate arterioles, thus reducing the systemic blood pressure. This property is utilized in tests of circulation velocity, where a sudden flushing and sensation of warmth serve to time the arrival of the substance in the periphery. This property may also contribute, at least in part, to the effectiveness of the material in nephritis and eclampsia by improving cerebral circulation. Magnesium may also dilate the veins much as do the nitrites, and produces syncope by reduction of venous return because of excessive pooling of blood in relaxed venous reservoirs.

Beyond this, magnesium operates to block myoneural junctional transmission much as does curare, and it will ultimately stop respiration by curarization of muscles of respiration. This it does at levels which have little influence on the heart, so that arrest of the heart can never occur unless respiration be maintained by artificial respiration. Finally, magnesium acts as an anesthetic, but only at levels very close to those which also produce myoneural block so that it is at times difficult to distinguish between the two.

Acid-base equilibrium. The frog heart is rather remarkably resistant to changes in the acid-base composition of its perfusate, and beats have been reported to persist with perfusates as acid as pH 5.5 and as alkaline as pH 10. In the mammal the subject has been much less studied; in fact, most of our reliable information on the subject derives from the reports by Andrus and Carter on the influence of acid-base changes in dog and cat hearts perfused with mammalian Ringer's solution. On the basis of these reports it is widely assumed that the lower limit of pH is reached at 7.0 where A-V block and arrest occur. When it is considered that pH values as low as this or lower have been reported in diabetic acidosis without any remarkable cardiac manifestations, it may be concluded that the Ringer-perfused mammalian heart is far more sensitive to pH changes than is the intact heart. Investigation of this problem by injection of a variety of acids intravenously in the intact anesthetized dog reveal that this is in fact the case, and that quite a different sequence of events takes place: (i) The lethal pH level is very close to pH 6.0 (range 6.6 — 5.5) and is independent of the acid employed (lactic, HCl). (ii) Changes in A-V or intraventricular conduction are practically non-existent; there is a slight progressive P-R delay, reaching a maximum in the dog of no more than 0.15 sec., and a 1:1 auriculoventricular rhythm is maintained to the point of death. (iii) Rate is well maintained to the very end, with only moderate slowing; arrest comes suddenly as the terminal event. (iv) There is a progressive increase in the amplitude of the T wave, and just preterminally a marked progressive drop in the S-T segment in all leads which can be interpreted as due to right ventricular failure. Blood pressure falls precipitously and respiration fails. The heart is found to be arrested in extreme diastole. It is therefore concluded that the primary effect of low pH is to abolish suddenly the contractibility of the heart at a critical level, before any serious changes have occurred in the rate, rhythm or conduction of the cardiac impulse, but the rapidity with which this event is followed by arrest of the heart and respiratory failure suggests that these systems were overtaxed. Difficulties in conduction are not a significant part of the picture of acid intoxication in the mammalian heart in situ.

CARBOHYDRATE METABOLISM

Lactic Acid. The carbohydrate metabolism of the heart takes the same general course as it does in skeletal muscle, and most if not all of the events described in Chapter 3 transpire in the heart. It is therefore necessary to point out only certain aspects in which cardiac metabolism differs, at least quantitatively, from that of skeletal muscle. The most significant of these differences is perhaps the importance assumed in the heart by the oxidation of lactic acid. This has been emphasized in a number of ways: (i) Himwich, Koskoff and Nahum found that whereas in skeletal muscles venous blood has a higher lactic acid concentration than arterial blood, coronary sinus blood has a lower lactic acid content than arterial blood. This indicates that while skeletal muscle liberates lactic acid, cardiac muscle, when well oxygenated, removes lactic acid from the blood perfusing it. (ii) In perfusion experiments in which the lung is replaced by an artificial oxygenating device to avoid the glycolysis that can occur in the lungs, the utilization of lactic acid, when present in normal or slightly higher concentrations, is greater than that of glucose (200 mg. per 100 gm. of heart per hour of lactic acid against 70 mg. per 100 gm. per hour of glucose). The utilization of lactate is increased by adding to the work load of the heart. (iii) When heart-lung preparations begin to fail, the addition of glucose to them produces little if any effect while the addition of sodium lactate brings about a definite improvement in performance. (iv) The diabetic heart can still utilize lactate, although its ability to consume glucose is drastically curtailed. Similarly, the well oxygenated heart can still oxidize lactic acid after poisoning with iodo-acetic acid.

This concept of lactic acid as the most important normal fuel of the heart is at variance with an older view that lactic acid is harmful to the heart, and that the ability of the myocardium to withstand its toxic effects is less than that of skeletal muscle. It has been suggested that accumulation of lactic acid in heart muscle causes extrasystoles, arrhythmias and eventual arrest, and that failure of the anoxemic heart results from excessive liberation of lactic acid. These views appear to be largely groundless. Lactic acid may be injected intravenously in the dog with a striking lack of any influence apart from its effect on blood pH. The progressive electrocardiographic changes, the events at death, and the lethal pH limit are the same with lactic as with hydrochloric acid, namely a moderate progressive increase in amplitude of the T wave, slight slowing of rate and A-V conduction, and sudden arrest, after a premonitory S-T depression in some cases. The final complex before death is frequently indistinguishable from normal. The levels of lactic acid that can be attained by the time the lethal pH (6.0 average) is reached are considerable, and range from 175 to 350 mg. per cent. If, on the other hand, the lactic acid is neutralized before injection and given as sodium lactate, there appears to be no easily attained toxic level, and all cardiovascular functions remain unchanged until death occurs from water intoxication from the fluid in which the lactate is administered. Levels as high as 500 mg. per cent are apparently without effect. The conclusion is inescapable that the lactate ion is completely nontoxic to the heart, at least in any concentration likely to be found in the body.

Glycogen and Glucose. In anoxemia, especially when the oxygen saturation falls below 25 per cent, lactic acid utilization fails, and it is produced instead of absorbed by the heart. Production is associated with disappearance of myocardial glycogen, and ceases when the glycogen stores have been exhausted. The process is presumed to be the chief source of energy available to the anaerobic heart. However this may be, the anaerobic energy supplies of the heart are extremely limited and the heart is capable of accumulating an oxygen debt of but small proportions and little significance. The heart is instead adapted to function on an aerobic basis, and in anatomical arrangement and physiological properties it is designed to receive and make use of a large uninterrupted oxygen supply.

The heart can and does utilize glucose directly, in proportion to its concentration in the blood and in inverse proportion to the quantity of available lactic acid. When the utilization of glucose is increased by addition of glucose to the blood, utilization of lactic acid falls off, as it does also when the consumption of glucose is increased by administration of insulin to the diabetic heart. While, therefore, glucose and lactic acid are in a measure interchangeable in supplying the carbohydrate requirements, they are not completely so. As has been mentioned, lactic acid appears to be of greater benefit in the hypodynamic heart, and is fully utilizable in the iodo-acetic acid poisoned heart. On the contrary, glucose is indispensable in the synthesis of glycogen. When the heart-artificial lung preparation is forced to work at a high level and given 0.3 mg. adrenaline per hour, the heart performs well for approximately two hours and then suddenly fails as its glycogen becomes fully depleted. If administration of adrenaline is stopped and the work load reduced just before failure, the heart can survive in a hypodynamic state for some time. While lactic acid can improve its condition, it will not restore its glycogen which can, however, be restored by glucose. It has been suggested on the basis of this and similar experiments that glycogen serves mainly as an emergency substance available when the supply of other carbohydrates is exhausted or when they cannot be utilized.

The heart is, finally, able to utilize fat as shown by (i) its ability to survive for considerable periods without glucose, lactic acid or glycogen, (ii) the low respiratory quotient at times observed, particularly in the diabetic heart, and (iii) the direct observation of utilization of beta-hydroxybutyric acid.

REFERENCES

1. ANREP, G. V. and SEGALL, H. N. The regulation of the coronary circulation. *Heart*, 1926, *13*:239–260.

2. BARKER, P. S., SHRADER, E. L. and RONZONI, E. The effect of alkalosis and of acidosis upon the human electrocardiogram. *Amer. Heart J.*, 1939, *17*: 169–186.

2a. BLUMGART, H. L., SCHLESINGER, M. J. and DAVIS, E. Studies on the relation of the clinical manifestations of angina pectoris, coronary thrombosis, and myocardial infarc-

tion to the pathological findings. *Amer. Heart J.*, 1940, *19*:1–91.

3. CLARKE, N. E. On the action of calcium on the human electrocardiogram. *Amer. Heart J.*, 1941, *22*:367–373.

4. ESSEX, H. E., HERRICK, J. F., BALDES, E. J. and MANN, F. C. Blood flow in the circumflex branch of the left coronary artery of the intact dog. *Amer. J. Physiol.*, 1936, *117*: 271–279.

5. ESSEX, H. E., HERRICK, J. F., BALDES,

E. J. and MANN, F. C. Effects of exercise on the coronary blood flow, heart rate and blood pressure of trained dogs with denervated and partially denervated hearts. *Amer. J. Physiol.*, 1942–43, *138*:687–697.

6. EVANS, D. L. Metabolism of the heart. *Edinb. med. J.*, 1939, *46*:733–749.

7. GRAYBIEL, A. A consideration of the effects of oxygen lack on the cardiovascular system from the standpoint of aviation. *J. Aviat. Med.*, 1941, *12*:183–193.

8. GREEN, H. D. and GREGG, D. E. The relationship between differential pressure and blood flow in a coronary artery. *Amer. J. Physiol.*, 1940, *130*:97–107.

9. GREEN, H. D. and GREGG, D. E. Changes in the coronary circulation following increased aortic pressure, augmented cardiac output, ischemia and valve lesions. *Amer. J. Physiol.*, 1940, *130*:126–129.

10. GREEN, H. D. and WEGRIA, R. Effects of asphyxia, anoxia, and myocardial ischemia on the coronary blood flow. *Amer. J. Physiol.*, 1941–42, *135*:271–280.

11. GREEN, H. D., WEGRIA, R. and BOYER, N. H. Effects of epinephrine and pitressin on the coronary artery inflow in anesthetized dogs. *J. Pharmacol.*, 1942, *76*:378–391.

12. GREENE, C. W. and GILBERT, N. C. Studies on the response of the circulation to low oxygen tension. *Arch. intern. Med.*, 1921, *27*:517–557.

13. GREGG, D. E. and GREEN, H. D. Effects of viscosity, ischemia, cardiac putput and aortic pressure on coronary blood flow measured under a constant perfusion pressure. *Amer. J. Physiol.*, 1940, *130*:108–113.

14. GREGG, D. E. and GREEN, H. D. Registration and interpretation of normal phasic inflow into a left coronary artery by an improved differential manometric method. *Amer. J. Physiol.*, 1940, *130*:114–125.

15. GREGG, D. E. and SHIPLEY, R. E. Changes in right and left coronary artery inflow with cardiac nerve stimulation. *Amer. J. Physiol.*, 1942, *141*:382–389.

15a. GREGG, D. E., SHIPLEY, R. E. and BIDDER, T. G. The anterior cardiac veins. Their functional importance in the venous drainage of the heart. *Amer. J. Physiol.*, 1943, *139*:732–741.

16. HOFF, E. C. and FULTON, J. F. *A bibliography of aviation medicine*. Springfield, Ill., and Baltimore, C. C Thomas, 1942. xv, 237 pp.

17. HOFF, P. M., HOFF, E. C. and FULTON, J. F. *A bibliography of aviation medicine. Supplement.* Washington, D. C., National Research Council, 1944. viii, 109 pp.

18. KEYS, A., STAPP, J. P. and VIOLANTE, A. Responses in size, output and efficiency of the human heart to acute alterations in the composition of inspired air. *Amer. J. Physiol.*, 1942–43, *138*:763–771.

19. KATZ, L. N., JOCHIM, K., LINDNER, E. and LANDOWNE M. The effect of varying resistance-load and input-load on the energetics of the surviving mammalian heart. *Amer. J. Physiol.*, 1941, *134*:636–644.

20. LORBER, V. and EVANS, G. T. Mechanical response of the isolated mammalian heart to anoxia. *Proc. Soc. exp. Biol., N. Y.*, 1943, *54*:1–4.

21. NAHUM, L. H., HAMILTON, W. F. and HOFF, H. E. The injury current in the electrocardiogram. *Amer. J. Physiol.*, 1943, *139*:202–207.

22. RINGER, S. A further contribution regarding the influence of the different constituents of the blood on the contraction of the heart. *J. Physiol.*, 1883–84, *4*:29–42.

22a. SCHLESINGER, M. J. Relation of anatomic pattern to pathologic conditions of the coronary arteries. *Arch. Pathol.*, 1940, *30*:403–415.

23. WEGRIA, R., ESSEX, H. E., HERRICK, J. F. and MANN, F. C. The simultaneous action of certain drugs on the blood pressure and on the flow in the right and left coronary arteries. *Amer. Heart J.*, 1940, *20*:557–572.

24. WINKLER, A. W., HOFF, H. E. and SMITH, P. H. Cardiovascular effects of potassium, calcium, magnesium, and barium. An experimental study of toxicity and rationale of use in therapeutics. *Yale J. Biol. Med.*, 1940, *13*:123–132.

CHAPTER 38

CIRCULATION THROUGH SPECIAL REGIONS

BY WILLIAM F. HAMILTON

REGULATION OF BLOOD FLOW TO THE SEVERAL ORGANS

The blood which is pumped out through the aorta is distributed to the various organs in accordance with their needs. These needs are concerned with their oxygen supply, with the elimination of waste products, and with the dissipation of heat from the body. In addition, the blood flow through the several organs is so regulated as to maintain within physiological limits the pressure of the blood in the great arterial reservoir (arterial pressure). These two functions, maintenance of local supply and regulation of reserve pressure, make contradictory demands. A generalized increase in the blood flow to the individual organs reduces the pressure in the great distributing arteries. This is balanced by an increase in the output of the heart which will suffice if conditions are not extreme (40). If through some interference the cardiac output cannot be increased or if the local demand for blood is extreme, central regulation shuts off the blood supply to the organs the participation of which in the emergency is not essential. The function of the gut, and to some extent the kidney, can be suspended during short-lasting stresses, and central regulation often shunts blood away from these visceral fields during extreme emergencies.

The total blood flow (cardiac output) is governed by peripheral vasomotor action rather than by heart action. This can be illustrated by the differing effects upon the cardiac output of drugs which act primarily upon the peripheral vessels and drugs which act primarily upon the heart. Small doses of atropine have little or no effect upon the peripheral blood vessels, but, by paralyzing the cardiac vagus endings, produce a marked acceleration of the heart. The total blood flow is not increased by this increased heart action. The output per beat is decreased in proportion to the increased heart rate (51). Acetyl-beta-methylcholine, the depressing effect of which upon the heart is evanescent, produces a strong dilatation of the arterioles. The cardiac output increases to two to three times the resting figure, with an increased stroke volume, unless the heart is reflexly accelerated (10, 33).

These and many other facts can be adduced to show that the volume of the circulation as measured in liters per minute is governed by the state of the arterioles in the various organs of the body and that the heart is governed merely to maintain a physiologically adequate differential in pressure between the arterial and venous systems.

The mechanisms which govern the peripheral blood flow and whose aggregate action governs the cardiac output may be classed as nervous, hormonal or chemical. The *nervous* mechanisms are the axon reflexes, the local reflexes and the general reflexes. The *hormonal* mechanisms act parallel to the general reflexes in the sense that they act upon blood vessels widely distributed over the whole body. They include the production and action of angiotonin, of epinephrine and of sympathin. Acetylcholine probably does not act as a hormone in the normal presence of cholinesterase. *Chemical* mechanisms result from anoxia and from metabolites during inadequate oxygen supply to produce an increase in blood flow which is independent of nerve supply. It has been difficult to show that specific metabolites have a vasodilator action which can function physiologically, and it may be that uncomplicated subnormal oxygen tension acts to produce local vasodilatation which is self-compensatory.

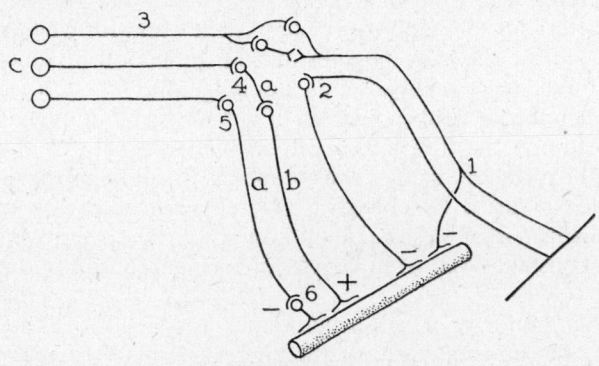

Fig. 392.—Possible nervous influences which control the caliber of arterioles. 1: Axon reflex-collaterals from sensory fibers which make a simple receptor-effector connection with blood vessels 2: Local reflexes of the Lovén type. 3: Reflexes through dorsal root fibers (central connections questionable). 4: Reflex sympathetic path. 5 and 6: Reflex parasympathetic path. a: Preganglionic fibers. b: Postganglionic fibers. c: Vasomotor centers. In addition, chemical mechanisms act directly upon the arteriolar wall. Epinephrine, sympathin and angiotonin are constrictor hormones, while the products of metabolism produce dilatation. + = constriction; − = dilatation.

In the various organs considered below, these nervous, hormonal and chemical mechanisms control the blood flow. The role of each is similar in all organs with slight differences in the importance of the several mechanisms. These differences will be brought out in the discussion.

BLOOD FLOW TO THE SKIN

The blood flow to the skin, in addition to providing for the metabolic needs of its tissues, plays a prominent role in the regulation of the body temperature. The changes in flow associated with the metabolic needs are governed predominantly by local mechanisms; those associated with the regulation of heat loss are under the control of centers in the hypothalamus.

Chemical mechanisms. Of the local mechanisms which maintain the blood flow in accordance with metabolic needs of the skin, the action of locally formed metabolites directly upon the arteriolar wall is the simplest because it is an independent effector (55); that is to say, the dilatation produced by metabolites is not dependent upon the integrity of any nervous connection (48). The most striking illustration of the action of this mechanism is seen in reactive hyperemia. When, for example, the blood flow to the arm is arrested, the arterioles gradually dilate, with the result that when blood is again permitted to flow the skin becomes flushed, hot, and begins to throb. Plethysmographic evidence indicates that an increase in the blood flow, as compared with that prior to the arrest, is manifest with the first pulse beat after the release of the occlusion; hence, the arterioles appear to have dilated during the period of ischemia. The evidence also indicates that the degree of dilatation is proportional to the duration of the period of ischemia.

The substance which accumulates during ischemia may be lactic acid, but lactic acid cannot be found in sufficient quantities to explain the dilatation; it may be histamine, but histamine is known to produce capillary dilatation by direct action and arteriolar dilatation indirectly through the axon reflex. This and other evidence make it doubtful that histamine is responsible for reactive hyperemia. On the other hand, the reaction may be the result of a lessening of arteriolar tone due to simple oxygen want, for when pure oxygen is allowed to diffuse through the skin during the period in which the circulation is arrested, reactive hyperemia no longer follows the ischemia (30). Moreover, when the nervous regulation of cutaneous blood flow is eliminated by sympathectomy, the flow of blood through the paw of the cat is determined by the metabolic rate of the cutaneous tissues. Specifically, when the metabolic rate is varied by changing the temperature of the paw, a non-nervous mechanism regulates the blood flow so that the arteriovenous oxygen difference is constant over wide ranges of oxygen consumption and blood flow (26).

The vasodilating factor which accumulates as a result of ischemia acts in opposition to the inherent tone of the smooth muscles of the walls of the arterioles. This inherent tone is also independent of the presence of nerves, for it is regulated by a hormone present in the body fluids, i.e., angiotonin, a substance which is derived from renin, an internal secretion of the kidney (see above). Thus maintained, the inherent tone of the arterioles serves to keep the peripheral resistance at different overall levels in different species and in different individuals.

Nervous mechanisms. The local regulation of blood flow through the skin is also wrought by means of the axon reflex. The vascular reactions which follow injury serve to illustrate the operation of the axon reflex (48). If a drop of weak histamine solution is laid on the skin and the underlying region is pricked with a needle, the subcutaneous tissues are injured by the chemical. A similar injury is produced by pricking alone in a sensitive (urticarial) skin without the histamine. The injured area is characterized by a local redness due to capillary dilatation, which is followed by a swelling which obscures the color of the dilated capillaries, producing a pale wheal. A red flare, which is due to arteriolar dilatation, surrounds the wheal. If the skin has been anesthetized, the red flare is absent. A nervous element is therefore necessary for the response. If, however, the cutaneous nerve trunk is narcotized or has only recently been cut, the flare is present. The response is, therefore, not mediated by a reflex through the central nervous system, though the peripheral nerve fiber is necessary because the red flare is no longer seen if the cutaneous nerve has been cut long enough to have degenerated.

The usually accepted hypothesis to account for the above facts is that the afferent fiber from the receptor in the skin gives off a collateral to the blood vessel; activation of this collateral causes dilatation of the arterioles responsible for the red flare. The anatomical background for such a mechanism was worked out by Woollard in 1926 (66). Further evidence that collaterals from sensory nerves have a vasomotor function has been provided by plethysmographic studies which indicate that, when the peripheral end of a severed dorsal root is stimulated, the vessels in the corresponding skin area dilate; and there is some evidence to indicate that this path plays a role in the reflex adjustment of cutaneous blood flow (6).

The importance of the axon reflex and the direct responses of arterioles in the regulation of the circulation can be illustrated by the fact that peripheral blood vessels deprived of their connection with the central nervous system by sympathectomy (6, 11), by spinal anesthesia (57), or even by the complete destruction of the spinal cord (50, p. 353), can still respond by dilating and constricting as the occasion demands. Furthermore, the finer adjustments of the circulation which result in the local regulation of temperature are said to depend on local cutaneous mechanisms and short reflexes, whereas the center for temperature regulation in the hypothalamus serves to prevent gross changes in the temperature of the blood (7).

Stimulation of the afferent end of the auricular nerve brings about a dilatation of the ear vessels. This reflex response was first described by Lovén in 1866 (49), and similar reflexes in which a dilatation is produced in a field localized about the site of the stimulus are now commonly spoken of as "Lovén reflexes" (6). The same stimulus which evokes a Lovén reflex is followed by axon and general reflexes as well. The general reflexes may be considered as responses to superficial pain, for they give rise to a generalized vasoconstriction which is part of the emergency mechanism, and consequently to a rise in blood pressure. Thus two effects from painful stimulation can be recognized—a local dilatation which may be aimed toward local repair of injury, and a generalized constriction which is a part of the response to emergency and which fits the whole organism for combat or flight.

Hormonal mechanisms. These also serve to control the circulation through the skin during an emergency. Epinephrine mimics the action of the sympathetic endings in the sense that it reduces the blood flow to the skin, diverting blood from this organ to others where the more acute need may be. Epinephrine is secreted by the medullary cells of the adrenal gland which are innervated by preganglionic sympathetic nerves.

The sympathetic endings in all parts of the body including the skin secrete small quantities of an epinephrine-like substance which is known as sympathin (12). This substance appears in the blood stream after sympathetic excitation and serves in this way to augment the action of the sympathetic fibers. It is held by some (12) that there are two forms of sympathin. One form—sympathin I—is supposed to be liberated by those sympathetic fibers whose activation is followed by inhibitory effects; the other, sympathin E, is thought to be liberated by sympathetic fibers whose action brings about excitation. As might be expected, the action of the blood-borne sympathin I is restricted to effectors which are normally inhibited by sympathetic action; similarly, sympathin E affects only those tissues that are excited by the action of sympathetic fibers. Epinephrine differs from sympathin in that it mimics the effects of both the inhibitory and excitatory endings.

An analogous substance is secreted by the parasympathetic endings, by the endings of the somatic nerves on skeletal muscle, and by ganglionic synapses. This substance, acetylcholine, may serve as a chemical intermediary for the transmission of excitation in the regions mentioned, but its function as a hormone is limited by the fact that it is rapidly destroyed by enzymes present in the body fluids. Only in the presence of eserine or similar drugs which inactivate the destructive enzymes can the systemic effects of normally produced acetylcholine be demonstrated.

Two hormonal mechanisms, then, can be clearly distinguished in control of the circulation to the skin and elsewhere: first, the angiotonin which is elaborated in response to the secretion of renin by the kidney and which serves to regulate the myogenic tone of all of the arterioles in the body; and second, the sympathetic hormone, epinephrine, which, together with sympathin, mimics the action of sympathetic endings and produces specific and adaptive constrictions in response to emergency situations.

The regulation of body temperature is managed in part by varying the balance of the cutaneous circulation. Activity, particularly if it is accompanied by certain emotional disturbances, brings about cutaneous vasoconstriction and a reduction of blood flow through the skin. As soon as heat is produced by the activity, the blood flow through the skin is at once augmented through the action of centers in the hypothalamus. This increase in blood flow serves to bring warm blood to the surface of the body where it can lose heat through the skin by conduction to the atmosphere, by radiation into surrounding space, and by the evaporation of sweat. This avenue of heat loss is reduced in cold weather by vasoconstriction which lessens the blood flow near the body surface and permits only a small amount of blood to enter the cooler cutaneous tissue.

Cutaneous vasodilatation in response to a rise in body temperature is a prepotent reflex. Blood will flow through the skin of an overheated individual in spite of the fact that his circulation may fail to meet the demands of the body's activity. This failure to meet the demands of the active tissues precipitates a fall in blood pressure which, in cool environments, would give rise to cutaneous vasoconstriction. In the overheated individual the constriction is not achieved, with the result that the fall in blood pressure in heat exhaustion is often shocklike in its intensity (16). If the environmental temperature increases to a moderate degree, generalized cutaneous vasodilatation is not accompanied by a fall in blood pressure. The widened vascular bed is filled by a movement of tissue fluids into the vascular space with a resulting increase in the blood volume of from 10 to 20 per cent (4, 9).

In addition to its role in temperature regulation and in local metabolism. the vascular bed of the skin—in particular the subpapillary venous plexus— is thought by some to serve on occasion as a blood store. A dog may be infused with a volume of blood equal to its own circulating volume without raising its arterial or venous pressures beyond physiological limits (53). Microscopic examination of the skin of a dog so infused reveals that the subpapillary venous plexus is much engorged. The implication is, of course, that a fraction of the infused blood has been stored in the plexus. This blood in the venous plexus can be returned to the active circulation by a reduction of the venous pressure through cardiac acceleration and perhaps by an active contraction of the venous walls.

The color of the skin is determined to a great extent by the nature of the cutaneous circulation. This relationship is of importance in the diagnosis of anemia, anoxia (cyanosis) and emotional disturbance, as well as being an indication of the nature of a cutaneous inflammation. It is interesting that certain minnows mimic the color of a reddish background by cutaneous vasodilatation (14).

BLOOD FLOW THROUGH THE KIDNEY

Modern work on kidney blood flow is based upon clearance of substances from the blood into the urine. From this work it appears that the kidneys possess a very rich blood supply, amounting to 1.3 liters per minute. As a consequence of this rapid blood flow, the kidney receives blood very much in excess of its metabolic needs, and the AV oxygen difference is very low. That local metabolic needs regulate kidney blood flow has not been proven. In any case, blood flow through the kidney is relatively constant (13, 56, 57). Changes in the peripheral resistance of the kidney are much less than the changes in the peripheral resistance of the body as a whole. The normal tone of the renal blood vessels is not dependent upon the vasomotor system because when a normal man is subjected to spinal anesthesia no increase in the kidney blood flow occurs (57). This does not mean that the kidney is not subject to sympathetic vasoconstriction. Injection of epinephrine into the renal artery will momentarily stop renal blood flow, and the renal blood vessels are richly supplied with sympathetic nerve fibers.

That the normal tone of the renal arterioles is not dependent upon the vasomotor system is in contrast to some animal experiments which indicate that denervation of the kidney or spinal anesthesia (immediately after laminectomy) does cause an increase in kidney blood flow. The best interpretation of these facts, however, is that the general anesthetic, postural regulation, or emotional excitement has established an active background of constriction against which is compared that following denervation. The kidney has a rich supply of vasomotor nerves and these enable the kidney to participate in emergency and natural blood pressure regulation. That there is a continuous resting vasomotor tone in the kidney arteries will, pending further evidence, have to be decided in the negative. That there are reflexes which regulate the relative resistance of afferent and efferent arterioles so as to maintain an efficient filtration pressure is a notion that lacks clear evidence in its support. When the blood flow to the kidney is interfered with, the kidney secretes renin into the blood stream. Renin was discovered by Tigerstedt and Bergmann in 1893, but its physiological role has not been recognized until recent years. This substance in the blood, renin, reacts with the globulins there to form a compound, angiotonin, which stimulates the smooth muscles of the vascular system to a tonic contraction. By this tonic contraction, peripheral resistance is increased equally in all parts of the body and the blood pressure is raised, though there is no change in the distribution of blood flow. The regulation of the blood pressure through the hormonal action of the kidney serves the needs of the body when the blood pressure is low and when a general increase in peripheral resistance would be in the direction of normal regulation. It does this by the increased elaboration of angiotonin (32). If, however, the kidney blood flow is interfered with more than that of the resting organism, the excess renin secreted into the blood stream gives rise to hypertension in the body so that the kidney itself may have an adequate blood supply. This has been experimentally shown by placing small clamps on the renal arteries. These clamps reduce the blood supply to the kidneys and cause production of renin and a rise in pressure with symptoms that are very similar to those seen in clinical hypertension of man (29). Hypertension, whether it be experimental or clinical, finally results in failure of the circulation and death. The kidney, therefore, in maintaining its own blood supply exercises a ruthless regulation over the blood supply to other parts of the body.

BLOOD FLOW TO THE VISCERA

The blood flow to the viscera is controlled in essentially the same fashion as blood flow to the skin except that it is not controlled by the hypothalamic centers concerned with temperature regulation. The direct effect of locally produced metabolites on the flow to the viscera can be illustrated by the fact that reactive hyperemia is very evident in the visceral circulation and has been shown to be completely independent of nervous influences (46).

Chemical control. Increased activity of the visceral muscles or glands is always accompanied by an increase in blood flow. It is often said that the parasympathetic system which produces an increase in visceral activity also contains vasodilator fibers. Whether this vasodilatation is the result of nerve impulses acting directly on the blood vessel walls or whether these impulses produce vasodilatation indirectly through increased production of metabolites is a question that is difficult of solution (3).

Nervous control. That axon reflexes play an important role in the regulation of visceral blood flow is exemplified by the fact that if the gut is stretched by overfilling the blood flow is maintained in spite of the increased interstitial pressure. Further, if the gut is stretched in a fashion which does not increase the interstitial pressure, the blood flow is augmented. Cocainization of the stretched part eliminates the increase in blood flow, but it is not altered by severing the central nervous connections (46). Segmental reflexes of the Lovén type may also play a role in the control of visceral blood flow.

The vasomotor centers of the central nervous system exert a control upon the visceral blood flow in the regulation of the general blood pressure. During an emergency, the blood flow to the viscera is reduced. Visceral functions can be postponed until the emergency is over, and hence the need for blood by the viscera is not acute. Thus in violent exercise, heat exhaustion and shock, blood flow to the viscera may be reduced by an amount sufficient to produce definite changes in visceral function, and, under some circumstances, irrevocable damage to visceral capillaries (24, 25).

Hormonal control. Hormonal control of the visceral circulation is dependent upon maintenance of vasomotor tone by angiotonin as well as by the sympathetic hormones epinephrine and sympathin. It should be recognized that the sympathetic hormones may produce vasoconstriction in part by virtue of the fact that they inhibit the activity of the gut, and as a consequence there is a reduction in the production of metabolic substances. On the other hand, hormones such as secretin or gastrin which cause an increase in the activity of the digestive glands in all probability cause a local vasodilatation which is due to the accumulation of metabolites.

BLOOD FLOW THROUGH THE LIVER

The blood for the liver is supplied by two irrigation systems, one containing arterial, the other venous blood. The arterial blood arrives via the hepatic artery to be distributed first to the walls of the biliary channels, the portal blood vessels, Glisson's capsule and the investing connective tissue (see Fig. 393); the venous blood is drained from the splanchnic region by tributaries of the portal vein through which it is distributed to the liver parenchyma. Some of the capsular branches of the hepatic artery unite with small veins, tributaries of the portal; others end directly in capillaries within the liver lobule. The hepatic veins which empty into the vena cava furnish the only efferent channel.

The blood flow through the liver is probably greater than that through the kidney, i.e., about 1.5 liters per minute. The two together make up more than two-thirds the output as measured by the Grollman method (see Chap. 36). The absurdity of this notion is resolved only by realizing that the 4 liters per minute allowed by the Grollman method is only 60 per cent of the true cardiac output as shown by the application of the direct Fick procedure and cardiac catheterization.

The size of the portal stream is controlled entirely by the systemic blood pressure and the peripheral resistance in the gut. With the former held

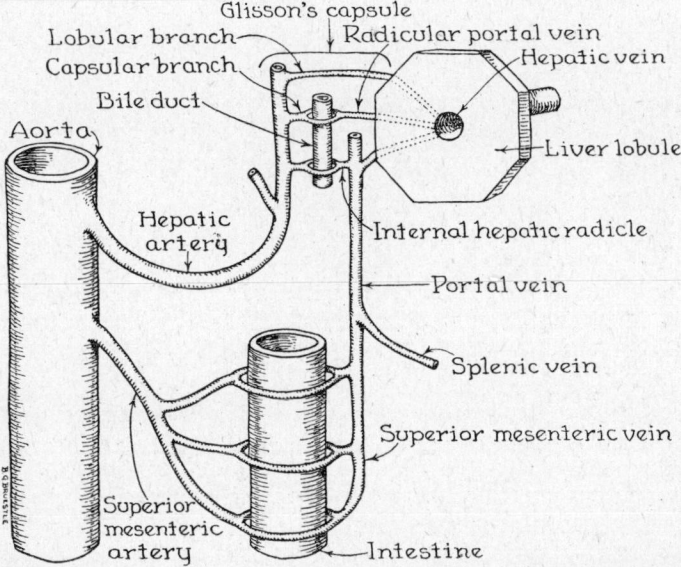

Fig. 393.—Diagram illustrating the anastomoses between the systemic and portal vessels in the liver.

physiologically constant by the blood pressure, regulation of the portal stream is more or less a reflection of the degree of visceral constriction, the control of which is discussed elsewhere. The size of the arterial stream is regulated by the tone of the terminal arterioles of the hepatic artery. Evidence as to how this is brought about is meager. Apparently there are vasomotor nerves accompanying the artery in its distribution. Accumulated metabolites in the liver may cause an increase in arterial blood flow, though this has not been clearly proved. The liver may get oxygen from either stream because the oxygen content of hepatic vein blood is sometimes below that of the portal vein blood.

Congestion of blood in the liver and a rise in portal pressure (minimally from 9 to 14 mm. Hg) comes about as a result of increased venous pressure from congestive failure of the circulation, from obstruction of the portal or hepatic vein (neoplasms), or as a result of scarring or contraction of the liver. The result of this is an increase in capillary pressure in the viscera and the accumulation of peritoneal fluid (ascites). If the obstruction is beyond the liver or if there is an increase in venous pressure, the liver is engorged and very large quantities of blood may become impacted in the venous sinuses. Normally, no appreciable part of the peripheral resistance to the portal stream resides in the liver, and changes in the tone of liver blood vessels plays no role in controlling the size of this stream. There may be an exception to this in the case of the dog, which possesses strong muscular sphincters in its hepatic veins, but such mechanisms play no role in human physiology.

The storage of blood in the liver is due to the passive engorgement of blood in its sinuses. There is always a rapid flow through the liver, and the blood in the liver is always a part of the actively circulating stream.

BLOOD SUPPLY TO THE SKELETAL MUSCLES

The blood flow to resting skeletal muscles is very small. If fibers of a muscle are separated by blunt dissection between them, little or no blood loss occurs. This is because such dissection breaks the capillaries which lie peripheral to the tonically constricted arterioles. If the muscle is cut across, however, bleeding is copious because this maneuver transects the large arterial trunks.

When the artery to a resting muscle is injected with India ink, it is found that very few capillaries are open to receive the injection. If, on the other hand, the muscle is actively contracting at the time of the injection, many more capillaries are open, indicating that blood supply to active muscles is very rich (44, 52).

The vasodilatation which accompanies activity may be due to (i) the action of metabolites produced by the muscle, (ii) cessation of a stream of vasoconstrictor impulses, (iii) production of a stream of vasodilator impulses.

Of the three possibilities we can be perfectly certain only of the first. Increased blood flow accompanies increased muscle metabolism, whether it accompany nerve stimulation or be a part of the recovery process that long outlasts the known effects of nerve stimulation. Moreover, reactive hyperemia and increased flow in response to direct stimulation occur in normal and denervated muscle alike.

The idea that the dilatation of the blood vessels in the skeletal muscles may be produced by the cessation of a stream of vasoconstrictor muscles presupposes the existence of such a stream in the normal resting individual. This is very doubtful, because spinal anesthesia that is sufficient to eliminate postural or other blood pressure regulation fails to produce the reduction in general peripheral resistance which would follow a release from vasoconstrictor control of the massive vascular bed in the muscles. Complete sympathectomy likewise has little effect on the blood pressure, and blood flow through it eliminates many of the vasoconstrictor paths to the muscles.

It has been held that, since severing the nerve to a muscle causes an increase in blood flow through the muscle, there must be vasoconstrictor influences acting through the nerve to reduce blood flow through the resting muscle. Many of these experiments were performed upon anesthetized animals or upon animals in advanced stages of circulatory deterioration. Anesthesia and shock both increase vasoconstrictor tone, and render the results of the experiments irrelevant to the question as to whether such tone exists in the normal animal. The fact that the metabolism of and blood flow through a muscle increases during the process of degeneration after denervation is a factor the relevancy of which to the problem under discussion is not always recognized.

Whether the muscle blood vessels respond to vasodilator impulses is a moot question (6). There is an immediate increase in blood flow when the muscle is stimulated through its nerve. In some experiments this immediate change is aborted by blocking the neuromuscular junction with curare, and in others it is not. The thought has been generally held, therefore, that vasodilator nerves are necessary to explain the dilatation. It is now known that acetylcholine, a strong vasodilator substance, is released on stimulating skeletal neuromuscular junctions. Since neither its release nor action is interfered with by curare, the argument for dilator nerves in muscle needs re-evaluation.

The blood vessels of skeletal muscle, like those of other tissues, are subject to the vasotonic action of renal pressor hormones. It is undecided whether epinephrine increases or decreases the tone of these blood vessels. Probably the effect is reversed with a large dose producing constriction and a small dose producing dilatation.

Reflex control of blood flow through the skeletal muscles is similar to that elsewhere. It is directed toward the maintenance of the general level of blood pressure. There may be anticipatory vasodilatations on the part of resting muscles paired or closely associated with active muscles, and there may be vasodilatation of blood vessels in resting muscles as a result of stimulating the cerebral cortex.

The peripheral resistance to blood flow through skeletal muscle depends not only on the state of the arterioles and capillaries but upon extra vascular pressure as well. When a muscle contracts, the pressure within the muscle increases so that the blood flow through its vessels is markedly reduced. This pressure may be sufficient to squeeze blood back from the small arteries to the vessel of major supply. The muscle is, however, equipped to meet such an emergency through its possession of myohemoglobin and its ability to remain active in the absence of oxygen. This arrest of blood flow which accompanies contraction explains the fatiguing effect of long-continued muscular tension as well as the marked relief one gets from shifting a load momentarily (1).

BLOOD FLOW THROUGH THE UTERUS

The role of the uterus in the female reproductive cycle largely determines its blood flow. In the barren uterus the flow waxes and wanes during the estrus cycle; in the gravid uterus the blood flow increases to provide for the growing fetus and its membranes. Finally, at parturition the flow is modified by the contractions of the uterine musculature, and after the expulsion of the fetus it returns to the level characteristic of the barren uterus. The factors which regulate the blood flow through the uterine vascular bed in each one of these three stages have not been finally determined.

The vasomotor fibers with which the uterine and vaginal vessels are supplied appear to belong entirely to the sympathetic system. Their activation is followed by vasoconstriction which is not abolished by atropine; when their tonic control is removed (for example, by transection of the spinal cord), the uterine vascular bed becomes dilated and congested for a time. Despite these indications, the nervous control of the uterine vessels must be accessory rather than essential, for sympathectomized females can conceive and give birth to normal young.

The dominant control over the vessels of the uterus appears to be exercised by hormones. For example, the uterus becomes hyperemic under the influence of estrin before its metabolic activity is increased; hence, estrin appears to have a direct effect upon the vessels themselves. The blood leaving the uterus under these circumstances is arterial in color, for the increase in the volume of the circulation appears to exceed the oxygen requirements of the tissues. However, fluid is lost and the perfused tissue becomes swollen and edematous as a result of an increased capillary filtration.

In the early stages of gestation the same relationships continue. The blood flow through the uterus is quite in excess of the oxygen requirements of the

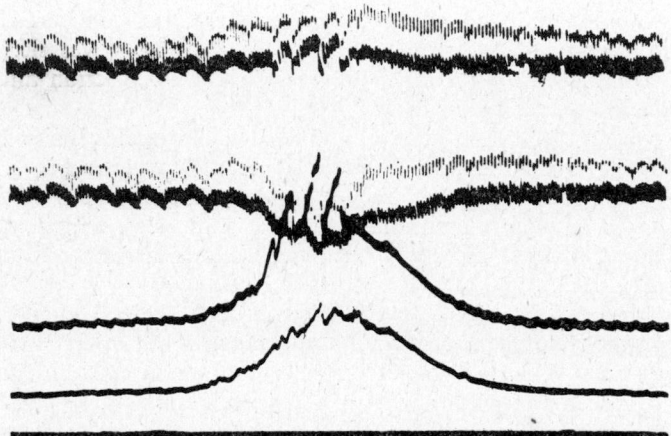

Fig. 394.—Pressure relations during labor. From above downward: arterial pressure, arterial pressure minus uterine pressure, uterine pressure, uterine pressure minus gastric pressure.

tissues it nourishes, as is indicated by the high oxygen content of the blood in the uterine veins. In the period that follows, the minute volume of blood appears to increase in parallel with the growth of placenta to reach a maximum near the end of the first two-thirds of the gestation period. Thereafter, the blood flow remains relatively constant though the metabolic requirements of the uterine contents continue to increase, with the result that the blood leaving the uterus contains progressively less oxygen. Since the blood flow appears to be correlated with the size of the placenta and not with the oxygen requirements of the tissues supplied, the evidence favors the view that the placental hormones are prominent in the control of the uterine circulation. This possibility receives some support from recent studies on the hypertension which often disturbs the later months of pregnancy. Hypertension with eclamptic-like convulsions has been produced by restricting the blood flow through the uterine arteries (54) as well as by mechanically preventing the normal increase (which is associated with pregnancy) in renal blood flow (17). The hypertension is relieved either with the termination of pregnancy or with the removal of the restriction on the renal or uterine blood flow. The evidence at present points vaguely to the possibility that the general circulation is governed during pregnancy by a hormonal mechanism which serves to protect the uterine blood flow in a fashion similar to that in which the blood flow through the kidney is protected by the renin-angiotonin mechanism.

During parturition the circulation through the uterus and the placenta is modified by the high intra-uterine pressure which develops during labor pains (65); the arterial pressure rises and the pulse pressure increases (Fig. 394), since the uterine contraction forces the venous blood from the placenta and thereby increases the venous return. In spite of this rise in blood pressure, there is a fall in the head of pressure irrigating the placenta, since the intra-uterine pressure rises more than the blood pressure.

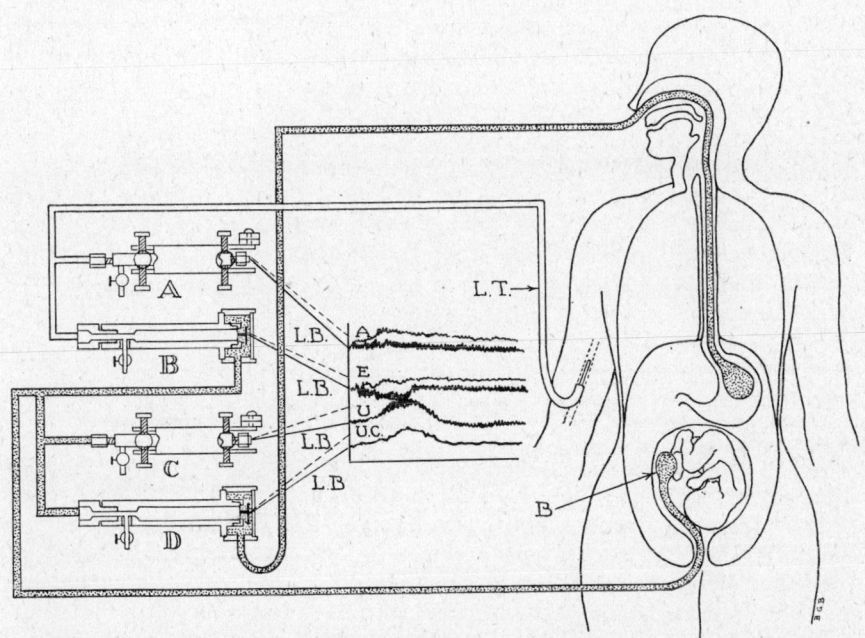

Fig. 395.—Simultaneous recording of the arterial pressure (A), of the head of pressure irrigating the placenta (E), of the intra-uterine pressure (U), and of the force which the uterine wall contributes to the intra-uterine pressure. E is obtained by leading the arterial pressure to an optical manometer, the membrane of which is enclosed in a chamber to which the intra-uterine pressure is led. The contribution of the uterine wall to intra-uterine pressure is measured by a similar differential manometer which subtracts the intragastric pressure from the uterine pressure.

The pressure within the uterus can be measured by leading an air column from a balloon in the uterus to a manometer. By comparison with a record of the blood pressure taken simultaneously, the amount by which the latter exceeds the former can be estimated. This excess pressure, or effective head of pressure, can also be recorded by means of the differential manometer (Fig. 395).

Increases in intra-uterine pressure are produced not only by the contraction of the uterine musculature but by the contraction of the abdominal walls as well, which raises the pressure within the abdomen and uterus equally. An increase in intra-uterine pressure brought about in this manner does not impair the uterine circulation, for it is transmitted directly to the abdominal and thoracic blood vessels and hence is balanced by a simultaneous increase in arterial pressure (see below). There is, therefore, no net change in pressure which irrigates the uterus unless straining is prolonged for 10 or 15 seconds to interfere with the venous return to the heart. The reflex bearing down efforts last such a short time that this factor plays no role. Voluntary bearing down is often prolonged at the urgency of the midwife (obstetrician) so that the circulation may fail for want of venous return. Bearing down before the cervix is fully dilated does not further parturition; its only effect is to exhaust the mother and to subject the fetus to anoxia. Reflex bearing down occurs when the time comes.

Careful measurements indicate that during the course of normal labor the blood flow through the placenta is insured by the natural relationship between intra-uterine and arterial pressure. Unfortunately this is not true when drugs (ergot and pituitrin) are administered to hasten the course of labor (Fig. 396). Administration of these drugs results in an abnormally high

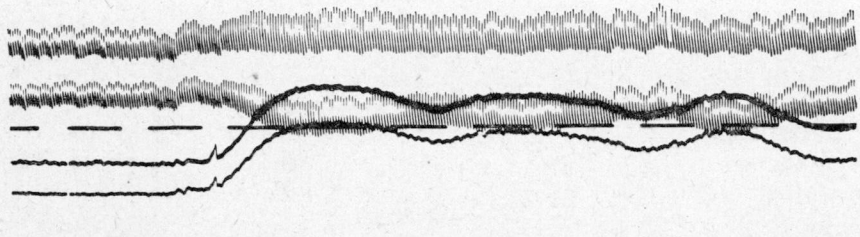

Fig 396.—The effect of pituitary extract upon the uterine and blood pressures. From above downward: arterial pressure, arterial pressure minus uterine pressure, uterine pressure, uterine pressure minus gastric pressure.

intra-uterine pressure which is maintained for a long time. This high intra-uterine pressure prevents blood from reaching the placenta for a length of time sufficient to give rise to serious signs of fetal asphyxia (cardiac slowing, weak fetal heart sounds, or even cessation of heart beat). A great deal of neonatal brain damage may be attributed to anoxia produced by the injudicious use of oxytocic drugs.

BLOOD FLOW THROUGH THE LUNGS

The pulmonary circulation serves two functions: (i) to transfer the blood from the right heart to the left, and (ii) to expose it to the pulmonary epithelium so that the exchange of gases may take place between the plasma and the alveolar air. The second function is achieved with great rapidity, for within two or three seconds blood previously in the right heart is exposed in a layer of about 10 μ in thickness and over 100 square feet in area (63). A few seconds later it is collected in the left ventricle. During the second or two in which the blood is in the lung capillaries, complete equilibrium is established between the CO_2 in the alveolar air and the plasma; at the same time it becomes almost completely oxygenated. The pulmonary circulation is in no way regulated so as to maintain constant the CO_2 pressure or hydrogen ion concentration of the blood. This regulation is a function of the manner in which the alveolar ventilation is controlled.

The right ventricle contracts synchronously with the left and ejects a volume of blood which, over a period of time, is the equivalent. The ejected blood distends the elastic reservoir of the pulmonary arterial tree and raises the pressure therein from 7 to 12 (average 10) mm. Hg above atmospheric (diastolic) to 25 to 28 (average 27) mm. Hg (systolic) (39). This limited rise in pressure produced by the systolic discharge of the right heart is an indication that the pulmonary arterial tree is more distensible than the aorta and its branches; if the equivalent volume of blood is forced into the latter by the systole of the left ventricle, the rise in pressure is nearly twice as great (40 mm. Hg). A further indication that the distensibility of the pulmonary artery is greater in proportion to its capacity than that of the systemic arteries is provided by the fact that the pulse wave velocity is much less in the former than in the latter.

The low mean pressure (20 mm. Hg) in the pulmonary artery is a function of the fact that the arterioles offer a very limited resistance to blood flow. The relatively few arterioles of the lungs permit the same amount of blood to flow as do the more numerous ones of the systemic circuit and yet support a pressure which is on the average about one-fifth as great. Hence, the peripheral resistance of the pulmonary bed now appears to be roughly one-fifth of that of the systemic bed.

The high peripheral resistance of the systemic bed serves to maintain a high pressure head in the arteries and, as we have seen, it is regulated in such fashion as to distribute blood from the arterial reservoir to different organs of the body in accordance with their needs. No such requirement exists in the case of the lungs because all parts of the lungs are similar in function and it would appear to make no difference whether blood is sent to one or another lobe. It might be expected, therefore, on a priori grounds that there are no mechanisms to regulate peripheral resistance within the lung. Against this notion is the fact that the anatomists find a rich supply of vasomotor nerves to the pulmonary arteries and arterioles (45); and the older experimental evidence indicates that influences which increase peripheral resistance in the systemic circuit have a similar effect upon the peripheral resistance in the pulmonary circuit. This older evidence is not beyond criticism. It is derived for the most part from experiments in which the lungs were artificially perfused or in which they were a part of a heart-lung preparation. Lungs under these conditions are abnormal in that their blood vessels are quite forcibly constricted (15, 23, 34, 62). Normal perfusion pressures produced a blood flow which was but one-tenth to one-twentieth of the figures obtained in life. Under these circumstances nerve stimulation and the injection of drugs might well cause an increase in the peripheral resistance of the pulmonary bed and a decrease in the blood flow through the lungs, even though such changes do not occur normally. With the development of modern methods, it is now possible to measure blood pressure in the normal unanesthetized animal and to show that the pressure in the pulmonary artery changes only to the smallest degree in response to experimental procedures. Thus, when the pulmonary blood flow is increased as a result of exercise (20) or as a result of the administration of drugs which produce systemic vasodilatation, there is an increased venous return and so an increased blood flow through the lungs, but only a very small increase in the pulmonary arterial pressure. If the peripheral resistance had remained the same, doubling the blood flow would double the difference between pressure in the arteries and veins. Actually the pressure difference between the arteries and veins increases very little, indicating that the increased blood flow is accompanied by a decrease in peripheral resistance through the lungs. This apparent decrease in peripheral resistance can be easily explained if one assumes that the blood normally flows through partially collapsed vessels which open up passively, offering little or no resistance to flow as the stream increases (34, 39, 42).

Large changes of pressure do occur in the pulmonary artery. Aside from passive changes which result from variations in intrathoracic pressure and do not distend the lung vessels, there are those which result from the backing up of blood into the lungs as a result of the inadequate functioning of the left ventricle. These changes occur clinically in congestive failure of the circulation (36) and can be produced experimentally by the injection of overwhelming doses of epinephrine that bring about a constriction in the systemic arterioles and a rise in blood pressure against which the left heart cannot pump blood (33). The rise in pulmonary arterial pressure is then equalled by a rise in pulmonary venous pressure, and the gradient of pressure between the artery and vein is either unchanged or lessened. A rise in the gradient of pressure from the pulmonary artery to the pulmonary vein can be regarded as a clear indication of an increase in the peripheral resistance of the pulmonary bed only when there is no increase in pulmonary blood flow. Clear indication of such an increase in pulmonary resistance cannot be seen as a result of the action of normal stimuli such as exercise (20), acetylcholine, epinephrine (34, 39, 42), angiotonin, renin (43), but only as a result of substances in toxic doses (64).

A vasomotor mechanism might be thought of as functioning usefully by shunting blood away from the unventilated lung, when a part of the lung is collapsed or occluded by pneumonia. It is well recognized that under these conditions the decline in the percentage saturation of the arterial blood is much less than would be expected on the basis of proportion of lung tissue which is not ventilated (58, 59). If the collapsed and normal lung each receives blood at equal rates and in equal quantities, the mixture of aerated and unaerated bloods should reduce the saturation of the arterial blood to a figure in proportion to the amount of lung tissue which is not being ventilated. However, the arterial blood of an animal with one lung collapsed is saturated with oxygen to a degree very near normal. Hence, blood must, under these circumstances, be shunted away from the collapsed part of the lung. Here, then, is a situation in which the vasomotor fibers might be expected to be active, but the redistribution appears to be achieved by other means.

The peripheral resistance of the collapsed lung is 5 to 7 mm. Hg higher than that of the normal lung because the collapsed lung is under atmospheric pressure and the normal lung is under intrathoracic pressure which is 5 to 7 mm. lower. This rise of 5 to 7 mm. Hg in the peripheral resistance is sufficient to divert blood from the collapsed lung into the normal, since blood flow through the lungs may easily increase twofold with a much smaller change in the gradient of pressure between the pulmonary artery and the left auricle. A similar increase in resistance to blood flow probably occurs when the alveoli are filled with exudate (pneumonia) and when single lobes and lobules are collapsed (atelectasis). However, this mechanism for diverting blood from the collapsed lung cannot be effective when the pulmonary vascular pressures are high and the lungs are congested as a result of left ventricular failure, for it is well known that pneumonia leads much more readily to anoxia in patients with congestive failure than it does in those with a normal circulation.

The vasomotor apparatus which is possessed by the pulmonary vascular tree does not appear, therefore, to regulate the peripheral resistance in the lungs. This conclusion seems reasonable because no useful purpose can be served by such regulation. The function of the vasomotor apparatus of the lung is to change the capacity of the pulmonary blood vessels and to vary its size as a blood reservoir.

It is well recognized (23) that changes in the pulmonary venous pressure will give rise to changes in the amount of blood contained in the lungs. As is the case with the systemic venous reservoir, pulmonary venous pressure is naturally lowered by cardio-acceleration and is increased by left ventricular failure. These changes in the pulmonary venous pressure produce passive changes in the filling of the pulmonary blood reservoir.

When the amount of blood in the lungs increases, it encroaches upon the space which is available in the chest for air (19). This decrease is most conveniently measured by determining the vital capacity. Vital capacity is markedly decreased in congestive heart failure because the pulmonary spaces which are normally filled with air are encroached upon by the congested alveolar capillaries.

A marked decrease in vital capacity occurs in the normal individual when he lies down (18, 36, 41). This decrease is related to changes in the circulation because the diminution in vital capacity is much less when the venous return is hindered by tourniquets placed about the bases of the arms and legs before the subject reclines. These tourniquets trap blood in the vascular bed of the extremities and diminish any increase in return for storage in the lungs. As a consequence, the normal postural pulmonary congestion is reduced with the result that the vital capacity of the recumbent individual is nearer that which he had possessed when standing.

Changes in intrathoracic pressure affect blood flow and blood pressure directly and indirectly. Pressure rises simultaneously and equally in the thorax, abdomen and cerebrospinal canal as a result of expiratory efforts such as coughing and straining (37). During inspiratory efforts such as gasping, the abdominal pressure may increase while the thoracic pressure decreases, and cerebrospinal pressure maintains an intermediate level.

During an expiratory effort there is no change in the pressure gradient which transfers either venous or arterial blood from one part of the three great cavities to another, but the rise in pressure in the thorax, cerebrospinal canal and abdomen is transmitted directly to the heart and blood vessels, producing a rise in the pressure of the incompressible blood contained in these vessels. This pressure rise, which may, in a vigorous cough, amount to 100 to 150 mm. Hg, puts no strain on the walls of the vessels within the three great cavities. It is transmitted along the arterial tree to the head and extremities where it produces a rise in the effective arterial pressure. During a coughing spell the peripheral arterial pressure may fluctuate over a range two or three times the normal (37, 38).

If the high intrathoracic pressure is maintained for more than a few seconds (as in straining at stool), it interferes with the venous return (Fig. 397). This reduces the width of the pulse pressure and the mean height of the arterial pressure so that the intrathoracic blood vessels are less distended than normal, though those outside the three great cavities may contain blood at a pressure that is above normal.

When the straining suddenly ceases, the high intrathoracic pressure no longer supports the arterial pressure and the pressure in the extrathoracic vessels suddenly falls by the same amount as the decrease in straining pressure. The pressure distending the intrathoracic vessels, however, does not change. This phase of the response to strain (Valsalva's experiment) is short-lived because the blood which had been dammed back in the great veins by the high intrathoracic pressure surges back to the heart and there results a great increase in the mean arterial pressure and in the pulse pressure, and often a reflex cardiac slowing. During the strain the thoracic pressure is transmitted to the great arteries in the chest and out over the arterial tree. The arterial pressure is therefore the sum of the intrathoracic pressure and pressure which is actually produced by the heart beat. Only pressure of cardiac origin distends the vessels of the thorax, abdomen and brain, but the

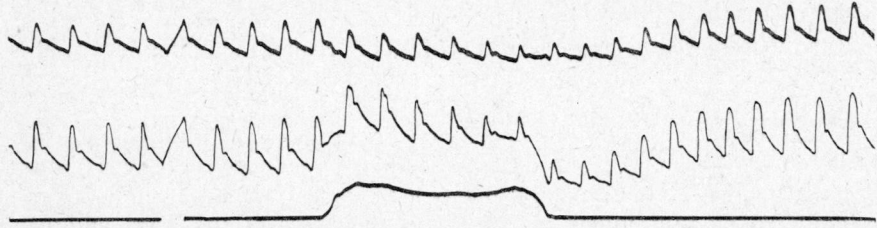

Fig. 397.—The effect of increased intrathoracic pressure upon the blood pressure in man. From below upward: intrathoracic pressure, arterial pressure, arterial pressure minus intrathoracic pressure as recorded by a differential manometer.

pressure produced by contraction of the thoracic and abdominal walls also distends the peripheral vessels.

Arterial pressure changes which result from changes in intrathoracic pressure are, therefore, of two kinds: those which result from simple propagation of thoracic pressure and those which result from changes in cardiac output produced by changes which the variations in intrathoracic pressure make in cardiac filling. In normal life the venous pressure is such that the heart is equally well filled in all phases of the respiratory cycle, but if for any reason the venous pressure is low or the intrathoracic pressure changes large, fluctuations in blood flow produce pressure changes which are added to those produced by simple propagation of intrathoracic pressure. Changes in blood pressure, due to changes in blood flow, are delayed, in relation to the phases of the respiratory cycle, by the length of time it takes to flush blood through the heart and lungs.

BLOOD STORES: CIRCULATION THROUGH THE SPLEEN

As the blood flow through an active organ is increased as compared with the inactive state, so also is the volume of blood which is present in its vascular bed. Thus in exercise, when a large number of muscles are simultaneously active and the minute volume rises to four or five times the resting value, the volume of circulating blood is increased and the pressure rises slightly. A similar increase in blood volume occurs during regulation against heat when the blood flow through the skin is increased and the minute volume may be doubled or more. Under these and like circumstances, the volume of circulating blood is increased by the withdrawals of blood from stores or depots into the active circulation. These depots include the aorta, the great veins, the portal system, the venous plexus of the skin, the liver sinusoids, the spleen, and the lungs.

Although the volume of the aorta and its larger branches does change under certain circumstances (27), these vessels cannot give up appreciable quantities of blood during activity because the arterial pressure is as great or greater than it is in the resting state, and the aorta, as a consequence, is almost as widely distended during exercise as it is at rest. The reservoirs or blood depots are, therefore, to be thought of as appendages to the venous system, providing a means, by emptying and filling, for the regulation of the venous return and so the work of the heart. From these depots sufficient blood may be withdrawn in severe exercise to increase the circulating blood volume between 25 and 30 per cent. Of this quantity an estimated 200 to 250 cc. can be contributed by the spleen; the remainder is probably provided by the portal circulation, the skin, the liver, and the lungs. Blood may be withdrawn from these depots—as pointed out above in the discussion of the circulation through the liver, the lungs and the skin—by the reduction in venous pressure which results from cardio-acceleration; also it may be forced out by the active contraction of the walls of these reservoirs evoked through the action of the sympathetic nervous system. The spleen empties actively, the other depots empty both passively and actively (22).

The smooth muscle of the capsule and trabeculae of the spleen are provided with efferent fibers by the sympathetic outflow via the splanchnics and along the splenic artery. Upon activation of these efferent nerves the spleen contracts with the production of pressure which in some animals (if the vein be occluded) may reach 100 mm. Hg, and expels its store of blood into the splenic vein. The variety of circumstances in which these fibers are active and the splenic blood is returned to the active circulation has been admirably demonstrated by Barcroft (5) on dogs with exteriorized spleens, the volume changes of which could be measured or followed visually. Among the acute circumstances—in addition to exercise and exposure to raised external temperature—in which the volume of the spleen decreases are hemorrhage, emotional conditions, anoxia, the administration of certain anesthetics such as chloroform and ether; the subacute circumstances include estrus, pregnancy and lactation. Acute or subacute, they are circumstances in which there is either an increase in blood flow or in metabolism to be balanced by an increase in blood volume or a rise in oxygen-carrying power of the blood. The balance is achieved through two mechanisms, i.e., a fall in blood pressure in the carotid sinus which is followed by reflex contraction of the spleen and anoxia via the carotid body, and an increase in the activity of the sympathetic nervous system due to the vasomotor center.

The evidence that the blood which is forced from the spleen in these conditions of stress was stored there and out of the general circulation was also provided by Barcroft. Where rats were made to breathe mixtures containing 0.6 to 0.1 per cent carbon monoxide in air, there was a lag of about 30 minutes before the concentration of CO hemoglobin in the red blood cells of the spleen became equal to that of the red cells in the circulating blood. Conversely, CO hemoglobin was lost from the hemoglobin in the spleen pulp less readily than from the general circulation when animals were given air to breathe in place of the gas mixture. These observations have been confirmed by a number of investigators and extend to other animal species.

Dilator fibers to the spleen have not been demonstrated, though a rise in pressure in the carotid sinus or stimulation of the depressor nerve in the rabbit leads to reflex dilatation of the spleen. Dilatation is, therefore, a passive process and appears to be wrought by the exposure of the spleen to arterial pressure by the relaxation of the arterioles and/or by constriction of the splenic vein by the action of the venomotor fibers which end in its musculature. Destruction of these fibers, which in the dog reach the splenic vein via the left phrenic nerve, abolishes reflex dilatation of the spleen.

The nervous control of the flow through the splenic vein appears to be important in another connection, i.e., the concentration of the blood in the spleen. In the spleens of those animals which have a well-developed muscular capsule, the rhythmic splenic contractions, increasing the internal pressure and the splenic vein by preventing the escape of splenic blood, serve to filter and to squeeze out the fluid which is returned to the general circulation via the lymph. The blood coming from the spleen in these animals—the horse, the dog and the cat—is rich in corpuscles. Cruikshank found, for example, that the blood expelled from the cat's spleen by splanchnic stimulation was equal to between 2.6 and 5.6 per cent of the total circulating blood volume and possessed an average hemoglobin percentage of 115 per cent, though some samples reached 140 per cent.

VASCULAR REACTION TO INJURY

The manner in which the vascular system reacts to injury depends upon the nature of the injury. Cutaneous injury results in a local dilatation as a result of the direct effect of chemicals released by the injured tissue and arteriolar dilatation through the axon reflex and through local segmental reflexes of the Lovén type (see above). The generalized response to cutaneous injury usually involves increased sympathetic activity with vasoconstriction and a rise in heart rate and blood pressure. This is a part of the emergency mechanism and fits the organism for flight or combat.

The effects of deep injury are often exactly the reverse. There is a local vasospasm and a general response which involves vasodilatation and slowing of the heart. The results are low blood pressure, a nauseating debilitating pain and a tendency to faint (8). This reaction often becomes a complicating factor in the genesis of hypotension in the operating room (61). The hypotension may be an adaptive response in that internal injury unfits the individual for combat and he is best able to survive if hemorrhage is prevented by a lowering of the blood pressure and a localized vasoconstriction. Often, however, the ischemia which results from internal injury carries in its wake effects which are unpleasant or even dangerous. For example, when the lining of a large vein is irritated (phlebitis), the blood flow to the extremity concerned is very much reduced. If the nerves from this vein are blocked with novocain, the ischemia of the limb is lessened and healing is promoted (2). A great deal of the pain from fractures, contracting scars, sprains and strains is due to ischemia, and it is widely recognized that blocking the vasomotor nerves to the injured part or blocking the afferents from the injured part will relieve the ischemia and promote healing (21, 47). Damage to the brain produces reflex vasospasms which cause greater and more persistent symptoms than does the damage itself. A patient with persistent hemiplegia who has not been able to use his hand for months may be restored to normal strength and dexterity by blocking the vasoconstrictor pathway to the brain at the stellate ganglion (60). Similar results are had in allied afflictions. The coronary blood vessels also respond to reflexes which originate within the body. Thus any painful experience, particularly the results of abdominal distension and indigestion, may produce coronary constriction and result in anginal pain (28).

VENOUS RETURN

During the early development of animal forms the return of blood to the heart through the veins offered no very difficult problem because primitive animals were aquatic, and, being entirely immersed, the pressure which existed in the capillaries was sufficient to move blood on through the veins and back to the heart. The fact that the body was always immersed meant that there was no hydrostatic gradient against which the venous pressure must work. When animals moved from the sea to land, the hydrostatic support of the surrounding water was left behind and the animal had to supply a mechanism that would compensate for this and insure return of blood against gravity.

It is interesting to note that most animals have in part evaded this problem. The great masses of muscle in the haunches and shoulders of ordinary quadrupeds is placed at a level definitely above that of the heart so that the blood may flow back to the heart through the force of gravity. The feet and lower legs of these animals are mostly a mass of skin, bone and tendon, the vascular supply of which is very small. Nevertheless, they have developed valves in their veins, the action of which is to direct the current of blood toward the heart. The force which moves the blood through the veins is, of course, the movement of the limb, the alternate contraction of muscles and pulling of tendons serving to press upon these veins and alternately empty them toward the heart and allow them to fill from below (31). With the development of arboreal animals and particularly with the development of the human upright position, the usefulness of venous valves became even greater. These animals and man have great masses of muscle tissue with large capillary beds which are situated well below the level of the heart and which must be protected by an active venous pump and competent venous valves from the hydrostatic pressure which resides in a column of blood reaching from the lower limbs to the heart.

The need for this mechanism is evident from the fact that when the natural movement of the leg is prevented either voluntarily or through the presence of a cast or other splint, passive congestion of the leg develops. This results in swelling of the leg and in intense discomfort which can only be alleviated by maintaining the leg at a height equal to or above that of the heart.

The valves of the superficial veins of the leg often become incompetent (varicose veins). This results in a certain degree of swelling of the feet, but, more important, results in a reflex vasoconstriction that gives rise to hypoxia of the skin of the leg and to gangrenous ulcers. The deep channels from the leg are almost always adequate to carry the venous stream because when the superficial varicose veins are obliterated surgically the gangrenous ulcers disappear promptly. Reflex vasoconstriction originating in the abnormal veins has evidently been eliminated.

The valves of the veins are a response to the need of overcoming a hydrostatic load. They are entirely absent in those parts of the body where hydrostatic loads are absent, such as the abdomen and cerebrospinal canal.

CIRCULATION THROUGH THE BRAIN

BY ROBERT G. GRENELL AND EBBE C. HOFF

The brain ranks as one of the more actively metabolizing organs of the body. Its oxygen consumption is high, and it is relatively unable to contract an oxygen debt. These facts limit the functional capacity of the brain, a capacity which itself is the limiting factor in the response of the organism as a whole to any stress which may be placed upon it. It is therefore essential that the brain receive a large and continuous stream of oxygenated blood, thus subjecting the brain cells to innumerable changes such as those in blood temperature, pH, electrolyte balance, and vitamin, hormone and other concentrations. It is further true that the physicochemical requirements vary in different regions of the brain and within the same region under various states of activity. As a consequence of its division of labor, the brain as an organ does not function in a homogeneous manner, and therefore its blood flow cannot be controlled merely by an external mechanism based on systemic conditions. The control of cerebral circulation has therefore been divided into extrinsic or extracerebral, and intrinsic or intracerebra factors.

The brain, moreover, is contained within a rigid, bony structure, the calvarium, so that its free expansion or contraction with variations in the amount of blood cannot take place to an extent possible in other organs. This conception was expressed in the so-called Monro-Kellie "doctrine" which recognizes that the brain lies in a closed box and that therefore the quantity of blood in it is at all times constant, except in those cases in which water or other matter is effused or secreted from the blood vessels. Even if the bone were removed, the heavy dura mater forms a relatively inelastic boundary. However, shifts can develop in the distribution of fluid or blood from one part of the brain to another. Volume occupied at one time by extracellular cerebrospinal fluid may at a later time be occupied by blood from arteries or veins. A sizable dilatation in any one area is compensated for by a reduction in volume occupied by extracellular fluid or blood in another area or by the cerebrospinal fluid. A factor ancillary to this convenient shifting mechanism is that of induction of change in the resistance to flow. For example, arteriolar dilatation can occur with an accompanying reduction in the lumen of large veins. No general dilatation of all the vessels is possible at any one time. It is apparent, then, that although the systemic arterial blood pressure is a principal factor in regulating the volume of blood flow through the brain it is not the sole regulator. Fluid shifts resulting from and accompanying intrinsic vascular reflexes must be looked upon as of primary importance.

Angioarchitecture. Many erroneous conclusions have arisen from failure to appreciate the anatomy of the cranial circulation.* At the base of the hemi-spheres the internal carotid and vertebral arteries are united by the circle of Willis and its six large branches. From these trunks branches project into the cortical and subcortical tissues, where they anastomose with one another through their capillaries. The cerebral veins which have been divided into two groups, external and internal, with incomplete anastomoses between them, open into the venous sinuses. These larger spaces are contained be-tween folds of the dura mater or between the dura mater and the bone. The openings of the larger cerebral veins into these sinuses have no valves, but

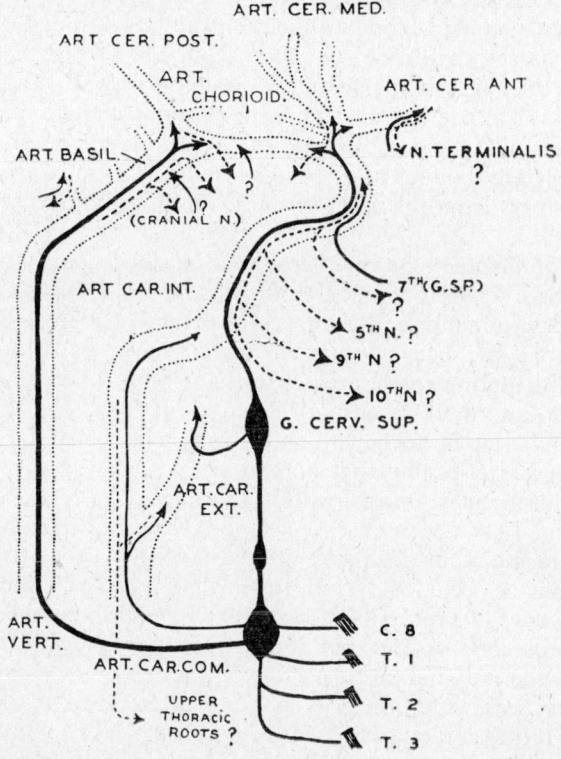

Fig. 398.—Innervation of the cerebral blood vessels—the possible anatomical pathways. Efferent nerves are drawn in solid lines and afferent nerves in broken lines. (From McNaughton, *Res. Publ. nerv. ment. Dis.*, 1938, *18*:190.)

are kept patent and protected from closure by the structure of the dura mater around the orifice. Blood may leave the brain by the internal jugular veins, by anastomoses with the orbit and the pterygoid plexus of veins, by way of emissary vessels through the cranium, and by way of channels which join the vertebral plexus of veins. This last channel operates normally in some individuals, and is capable of taking over venous drainage after occlusion of the jugular veins.

The histological appearance of the blood vessels of the brain is essentially that of vessels elsewhere in the body, except for minor differences. In the arteries the elastic fibers are possibly more numerous and have a different

* Complete descriptions of the cerebral circulation will be found in the monograph of the Association for Research in Nervous and Mental Disease (71).

29

arrangement than in other parts of the body. The veins have extremely thin walls composed primarily of connective tissue. The tributaries of the veins are received at a much more obtuse angle than that at which the arterial branches are given off. Both arteries and veins are accompanied by myelinated and unmyelinated nerve fibers in the usual way. Few ganglion cells are observed along the cerebral vessels although peripheral nerve fibers may be traced along vessels of the medulla, pons, mesencephalon, diencephalon, cortex and the vessels of the pia and choroid plexus. Studies indicate that these fibers are both afferent and efferent. Vasoconstrictor fibers pass to the vessels via the cervical sympathetic nerves. Vasodilator nerves pass to the vessels from the medulla oblongata through the facial and the great superficial petrosal nerves. Evidence of afferent impulses from pial vessels has brought about the suggestion that many common sites of headache may be due to cerebral vasodilatation. During both migraine and common headache, vascular changes and the sensitiveness of the dural sinuses and the middle meningeal artery are thought to be of importance. The meningeal vessels are supplied with fibers from the fifth, seventh, ninth, tenth and twelfth cranial nerves (Fig. 398).

End-arteries of the brain. On the theory that infarcts occur only where there is no anastomosis between arteries, Cohnheim, in 1872, inferred that vessels of the brain are terminal or end-arteries. However, it has since been observed that free anastomosis, such as occurs in the circle of Willis, does not imply equal blood distribution to all areas. Consequently, following the observations of Pfeiffer, and more recently of Scharrer in 1944, it is agreed that the vast majority of arteries in the brains of opossums, cats, rats, rabbits and monkeys are end-arteries, but that no end-arteries are present in the human brain. Precapillary anastomosis within the brains of rats, cats, rabbits, monkeys and man have been observed. However, such capillary anastomosis is insufficient to maintain adequate circulation if an artery to a given area of the cerebrum is occluded. Wolff states that it is probable that minute vessels of the order of precapillaries anastomose with precapillaries but that only rarely do cerebral arteries per se anastomose with each other.

Everywhere, the gray matter has a far richer, denser vascular supply than the white matter, and within the gray matter the vascularity varies in different cellular layers of the cortex and in different subcortical ganglia. This relative vascularity of various parts of the brain has been studied in great detail (71), and has been considered a major factor in the occurrence of disease in various parts of the nervous system. Localization of neuronal injury may be due to peculiarities of both capillary structure and arrangement, or to the volume of blood brought to a particular region. Recent investigations suggest a definite relationship between relative vascularity and relative intensity of metabolism in different regions.

The relationship of vascularity to metabolism in localized areas is still only tentative. A perfect correlation entails assumptions of constant blood flow and constant metabolism, as well as disregard of the occurrence of arteriovenous anastomoses. Furthermore, anatomical observations may be used only as suggestions of metabolic differences. It has been found that the anatomical vascularity of the cortex is just over twice that of peripheral nerve, although the established ratio of oxygen consumption is about 30 to 1.

The hemato-encephalic barrier. Clinical observations have shown that various substances introduced into the blood stream do not appear in the cerebrospinal fluid, and this has given origin to the hypothesis that a barrier exists between the two. Experiments with toxins, viruses, and aniline dyes have demonstrated, in addition, the existence of a barrier between the blood and the cerebrospinal fluid as distinct from the barrier between the blood and the central nervous system. The blood-brain barrier is a term designating those structures which separate the blood from extracellular fluid of the brain, that is, the endothelium of the capillaries. That the endothelium is the important component of the barrier is shown by the fact that supravital dyes, brilliant vital red and trypan red, do not gain entrance into the central nervous system in significant amounts and stain only the endothelium. It is also suggested that the cell membranes of the cortical tissues form a second important barrier termed the cortical barrier (67). Studies on the blood-brain barrier and the blood-cerebrospinal fluid barrier have been interpreted as demon-

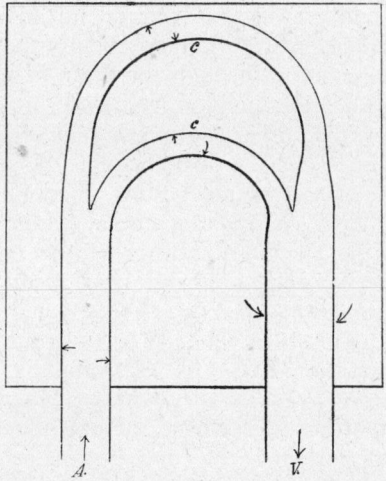

. Fig. 399.—Schema to represent the transmission of arterial pressure through the brain substance to the veins: A, the artery; V, the vein, represented as entering into and emerging from a box with rigid walls and filled with incompressible liquid; c, c, the intervening area of small arteries, etc. An expansion of the walls of the arterial system by the pulse wave or by a rise of arterial pressure increases the pressure on the surrounding liquid and this is transmitted through the liquid to the walls of the veins and compresses them, since at this point of the circuit the intravascular pressure is low.

strating that they differ widely in their permeabilities, depending on the electrical charge of the permeating substance (70). Exceptions to this permeability difference between the two have been noted in relation to cocaine, which presumably possesses the same electric charge in relation to both barriers and nonetheless permeates them both. It has also been suggested that the permeabilities of these two barriers are not necessarily different, but that the apparent difference may be explained in terms of an affinity of the brain in the case of the blood-brain barrier and its corresponding absence in the case of the blood-cerebrospinal fluid barrier. Recent studies of Aird and Strait (67) state, "Changes in the permeability of the blood-brain and the cortical barrier, or factors associated with such changes, are of fundamental neurophysiologic importance in determining susceptibility to convulsions. . . . It is suggested that any biochemical, neurophysiologic or neuropathologic change which modifies, either directly or indirectly, the permeability of the blood-brain barrier or the cortical tissue will have a corresponding effect on the susceptibility to convulsions."

REGULATION OF CEREBRAL CIRCULATION

Extrinsic control. The extracerebral regulators of the cephalic circulation consist first of intracranial pressure and second of the reflex arcs from special receptors that work through the hindbrain nuclei. By intracranial pressure is meant the pressure in the space between the skull and the brain, and therefore the pressure in the subarachnoidal liquid and presumably also in the ventricles of the brain, since the two spaces are in communication. Recent studies indicate that the intracranial pressure is usually higher than venous pressure, and is independent of arterial and venous pressures although modified by both, especially the latter. A rise of venous pressure tends to increase intracranial pressure, and vice versa. Experimental investigations show that so long as the intracranial pressure remains below that of the arteries supplying the brain, the circulation through the brain is not markedly affected, and little or no change in systemic blood pressure, pulse rate or respiration takes place. If, however, the intracranial pressure is raised abruptly to a level above general arterial pressure, the flow through the substance of the brain is prevented and a condition of anemia results, in which respiration may stop and unconsciousness supervene. Under these conditions a compensation takes place in which the anemic condition of the medulla stimulates the cardio-inhibitory center, causing a slower heart beat; at the same time it also stimulates the vasomotor center, causing a general vasoconstriction in the rest of the body, the result of which is to raise the arterial pressure and re-establish cranial circulation. Reduced to its simplest form, the normal condition may be represented by a schema such as is given in Figure 398.

Of the reflex arcs that act as extrinsic factors in regulating the cerebral circulation, the most important is the carotid sinus reflex. From the carotid zone, chemical and pressure stimuli are transmitted over the glossopharyngeal nerve. Other receptors of a similar nature can be found in the aortic arch, the heart, the pulmonary artery, the vena cava, and splenic artery; from these centers impulses to the medulla oblongata travel via the vagus nerve, or spinal cord and spinal nerves. A regulator of importance is the effect of the carbon dioxide and oxygen content of the blood upon the vasodilator and vasoconstrictor centers. Other factors that may be mentioned are arteriolar resistance throughout the body, the amount of venous blood returned to the heart, the condition of the heart muscle, and, most important of all, the systemic arterial pressure.

Active changes in the caliber of the cerebral arteries may occur, the diameter of the vessels altering inversely with systemic arterial pressure. The salient feature of this inverse relationship is the sudden marked cerebral arterial dilatation that occurs when the systemic blood pressure falls to a low level— around 70 to 80 mm. Hg. These changes thus have a steadying effect on the cerebral circulation, tending to protect the brain from extreme fluctuations in blood supply which would otherwise accompany sudden rises and falls of general arterial tension.

Intrinsic control. It has been stated that changes in the size of the cerebral vessels do occur. These changes may be either passive or active. Passive changes are often caused by changes in systemic blood pressure, and such moderate fluctuations may be overcome by changes in muscular tension of the arterial walls. Active changes in caliber may result from direct trauma to the walls of the vessels, changes in the chemical composition of arterial blood, changes in velocity of blood flow attending marked alterations in blood pressure, and from activity of vasomotor nerves (Fig. 400).

Changes in the chemical composition of arterial blood cause important alterations of blood flow. In animals, observations have been made by means of windows placed in the skull, flow recorders placed in the brain, and perfusion experiments. In man, evidence has been gathered from inspection of retinal vessels, measurement of spinal fluid pressure, including the plethysmo-

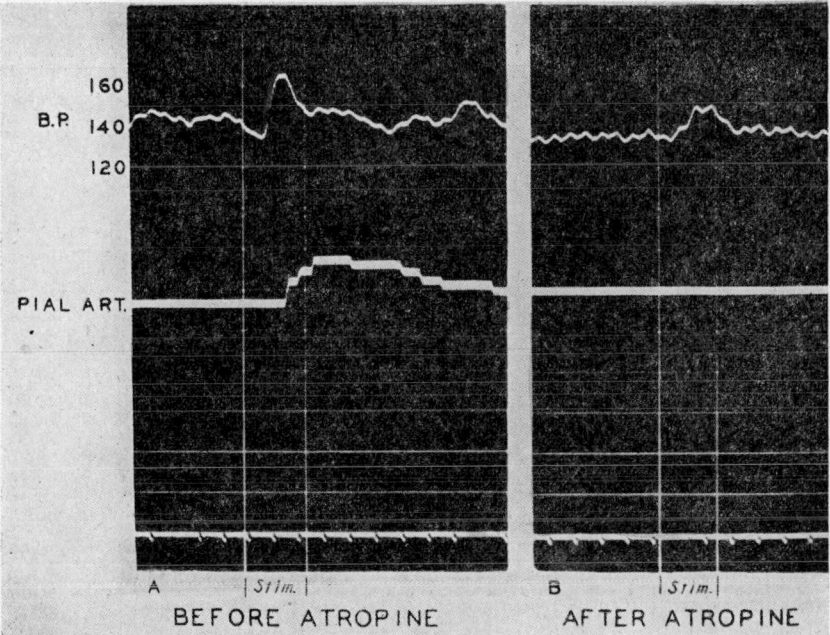

Fig. 400.—Stimulation of the geniculate ganglion before and after local atropine. A: the pial artery, 182 μ in diameter, dilated 14 per cent. B, 1 cc. of a 0.5 per cent solution of atropine sulphate was applied locally beneath a cranial window 18 minutes before this stimulation. The pial artery, 188 μ in diameter, did not change. The blood pressure rose promptly during each stimulation. (From Forbes and Cobb, *Res. Publ. Ass. nerv. ment. Dis.*, 1938, *18*:212.)

graph method, a thermo-electric flow recorder placed in an internal jugular vein, and measurements of arteriovenous oxygen differences. Increase in arterial carbon dioxide causes marked dilatation of cerebral arterioles with increase in the speed and volume of cerebral blood flow. Reduction of arterial carbon dioxide has the opposite effect. Alterations of pH produce effects that parallel those of change in CO_2 tension. The effect of changes in arterial oxygen is relatively mild, and in the reverse direction from changes induced by carbon dioxide. Anoxemia causes some dilatation of cerebral vessels and increase of blood flow. Breathing of oxygen causes mild vasoconstriction. In severe anoxemia the addition of carbon dioxide to the inhaled mixture improves cerebral blood flow and postpones loss of consciousness. In a condition of stagnant anoxia where the asphyxia of the tissues of the vessel walls is due to slowing of the blood flow, dilatation appears. This dilatation is said to be due to an asphyxial effect on the arterial wall, not to a nerve reflex, for it is unaffected by cocaine or by atropine applied locally to the vessels (74).

Increased metabolic activity within local areas of the brain itself also results in localized vasodilatation and increased blood flow. For example, stimulation of the retina by light results in localized temperature responses indicative of increased blood flow in the lateral geniculate body and the visual cortex. Cobb (68) states that the most probable explanation of this phenomenon is that the active nerve cells produce locally increased concentration of carbon dioxide which acts as a vasodilator.

In man, according to Forbes (69), no positive evidence of vasomotor nerves in the brain has been obtained, although both myelinated and unmyelinated nerves may be histologically demonstrated on intracranial blood vessels. The presence of these nerves in animals has been definitely proved, since consistent constriction of pial arteries resulted in more than 300 animals following stimulation of the cervical sympathetic nerves.

Sympathetic fibers responsible for the reaction pass through the middle ear in close association with the caroticotympanic plexus. Sympathetic nerve fibers via the stellate ganglion and vertebral nerves exercise no influence on pial arteries in the parietal region.

Cerebral vasoconstrictor nerves are stated to be only about one-tenth as effective in the pia as they are in the skin, and these vasoconstrictor effects are not distributed equally to all parts of the brain. Cervical sympathetic stimulation has little constrictor effect on the vessels of the medulla oblongata. This vasoconstrictor activity may limit undesirable fluctuations in vessel caliber, but there is no evidence from experimental work to show that it can cause the arteries to shut down sufficiently to bring about ischemia.

Evidence of a vasodilator innervation was first obtained in the sympathectomized monkey, in which it was shown that stimulation of the facial nerve near the medulla oblongata caused dilatation of pial arteries in the parietal cortex. This reaction occurred only on the same side of the head as the nerve stimulated. Cobb states (68), "Vasodilatation is significant only if it occurs when the blood pressure is normal at the beginning and remains nearly constant throughout the period of stimulation. This is important because it has been found that if the systemic arterial pressure falls below a certain critical level the pial arteries always dilate as a consequence of retarded blood flow. Local applications of cocaine and of atropine abolish the neurogenic dilatation, though they have no effect on the dilatation due to low blood pressure."

Summary. In brief, it may be concluded that the blood flow through the brain is steadier and better safeguarded than is the circulation in other organs of the body. It is regulated by extracerebral factors, the most important of which is the systemic arterial pressure, and by cerebral factors which include direct trauma, chemical changes in arterial blood, asphyxia of tissues from slow blood flow, local neuron activity with increase in flow, and vasoconstrictor and vasodilator activity. Although there are many drugs by which cerebral vessels can be dilated, there are none by which they can be strongly constricted.

REFERENCES

1. ANREP, G., BLALOCK, A. and SAMAAN, A. Effect of muscular contraction upon blood flow in skeletal muscle. *Proc. roy Soc.*, 1934, *B114*:223–245.

2. DEBAKEY, M., BURCH, G. E. and OCHSNER, A. Effect of chemical irritation of a venous segment on peripheral pulse volume. *Proc. Soc. exp. Biol.*, *N. Y.*, 1939, *41*:585–590.

3. BARCROFT, J. *The respiratory function of the blood*. Cambridge, Cambridge University Press, 1914. 320 pp.

4. BARCROFT, J., MEAKINS, J. C., DAVIES, H. W., SCOTT, J. M. D. and FETTER, W. J. On the relation of external temperature to blood volume. *Philos. Trans.*, 1923, *B211*:351–464.

5. BARCROFT, J. and STEPHENS, J. G. Observations upon the size of the spleen. *J. Physiol.*, 1927, *64*:1–22.

6. BAYLISS, W. M. *The vaso-motor system.* (*Monographs on physiology*.) New York, Longmans, Green and Co., 1923. 163 pp.

7. BAZETT, H. C. Physiological responses to heat. *Physiol. Rev.*, 1927, *7*:531–599.

8. BAZETT, H. C. and McGLONE, B. Note on the pain sensations which accompany deep punctures. *Brain*, 1928, *51*:18–23.

9. BAZETT, H. C., SUNDERMAN, F. W., DOUPE, J. and SCOTT, J. C. Climatic effects on the volume and composition of blood in man. *Amer. J. Physiol.*, 1940, *129*:69–83.

10. BROTMAN, I., BREWER, G. and HAMILTON, W. F. Circulatory responses to acetylcholine in normal dogs and in dogs with experimental aortic regurgitation. *J. Pharmacol.*, 1934, *50*:354–358.

11. CANNON, W. B., NEWTON, H. F., BRIGHT, E. M., MENKIN, V. and MOORE, R. M. Some aspects of the physiology of animals surviving complete exclusion of sympathetic nerve impulses. *Amer. J. Physiol.*, 1929, *89*:84–107.

12. CANNON, W. B. and ROSENBLUETH, A. *Autonomic neuro-effector systems*. New York, Macmillan Co., 1937, xiv, 229 pp.

13. CHASIS, H., RANGES, H. A., GOLDRING, W. and SMITH, H. W. The control of renal blood flow and glomerular filtration in normal man. *J. clin. Invest.* 1938, *17*:683–697.

14. CONNOLLY, C. J. Vasodilatation in fundulus due to color stimulation. *Biol. Bull. Wood's Hole*, 1926, *50*:207–209.

15. DALY, I. DeB. Reactions of the pulmonary and bronchial blood vessels. *Physiol. Rev.*, 1933, *13*:149–184.

16. DILL, D. B. *Life, heat and altitude*. Cambridge, Harvard University Press, 1938, xiv, 211 pp.

17. DILL, L. V. and ERICKSON, C. C. Eclampsia-like syndrome occurring in pregnant dogs and rabbits following renal artery constriction. *Proc. Soc. exp. Biol.*, *N. Y.*, 1938, *39*: 362–367.

18. DOW, P. The venous return as a factor affecting the vital capacity. *Amer. J. Physiol.*, 1939, *127*:793–795.

19. DRINKER, C. K., CHURCHILL, E. D. and FERRY, R. M. The volume of blood in the heart and lungs. *Amer. J. Physiol.*, 1926, *77*:590–624.

20. DUNN, J. S. Measurement of pressure in the right ventricle. *J. Physiol.*, 1919, *53*:iii–iv.

21. FRANKEL, E. L. Treatment of sprains by injection of procaine. *Lancet*, 1939, *2*:597.

22. FRANKLIN, K. J. *A monograph on veins*. Springfield, Ill., Charles C Thomas, 1937. 410 pp.

23. FUHNER, H. and STARLING, E. H. Experiments on the pulmonary circulation. *J. Physiol.*, 1913, *47*:286–304.

24. FREEMAN, N. E. Decrease in blood volume after prolonged hyperactivity of the sympathetic nervous system. *Amer. J. Physiol.*, 1933, *103*:185–202.

25. FREEMAN, N. E., FREEDMAN, H. and MILLER, C. C. The production of shock by the prolonged continuous injection of adrenalin in unanesthetized dogs. *Amer. J. Physiol.*, 1941, *131*:545–553.

26. FREEMAN, N. E. and ZELLER, J. W. The effect of temperature on the volume flow of blood through the sympathectomized paw of the dog with observations on the oxygen content and capacity, carbon-dioxide content and pH of the arterial and venous blood. *Amer. J. Physiol.*, 1937, *120*:475–485.

27. GIANTURCO, C. and STEGGERDA, F. R. A roentgenologic study of the shifting of blood in the circulatory system of experimental animals under the influence of various stimuli. *Amer. J. Roentgenol.*, 1937, *37*:175–179.

28. GILBERT, N. C., LEROY, G. V. and FENN, G. K. Effect of distension of abdominal viscera on blood flow in the circumflex branch of the left coronary artery of the dog. *Amer. Heart J.*, 1940, *20*:519–524.

29. GOLDBLATT, H., LYNCH, J., HANZAL, R. F. and SUMMERVILLE, W. W. The production of persistent hypertension in dogs. *Amer. J. Path.*, 1933, *9*:942–946.

30. GOLDSCHMIDT, S. and McGLONE, B. Effect of oxygen absorbed through the skin upon the vascular reaction to stasis and to histamine. *Amer. J. Physiol.*, 1934, *109*:42.

31. HALES, S. *Statical essays: containing haemastaticks; or, an account of some hydraulick and hydrostatical experiments made on the blood and blood-vessels of animals*. London, W. Innys and R. Manby, 1733. Vol. 2.

32. HAMILTON, A. S. and COLLINS, D. A. The homeostatic rôle of a renal humoral mechanism in hemorrhage and shock. *Amer. J. Physiol.*, 1942, *136*:275–284.

33. HAMILTON, W. F. Some mechanisms involved in the regulation of the circulation. *Amer. J. Physiol.*, 1932, *102*:551–558.

34. HAMILTON, W. F. Pressure relations in the pulmonary circuit, pp. 324–331 in: Publ. no. 13, *Amer. Ass. Advancement of Science*, 1940.

35. HAMILTON, W. F. and MORGAN, A. B. Mechanism of the postural reduction in vital capacity in relation to orthopnea and storage of blood in the lungs. *Amer. J. Physiol.*, 1932, *99*:526–533.

36. HAMILTON, W. F., MOORE, J. W., KINSMAN, J. M. and SPURLING, R. G. Studies on the

circulation. IV. Further analysis of the injection method, and of changes in hemodynamics under physiological and pathological conditions. *Amer. J. Physiol.*, 1932, *99*:534–551.

37. HAMILTON, W. F., WOODBURY, R. A. and HARPER, H. T., JR. Physiologic relationships between intrathoracic, intraspinal and arterial pressures. *J. Amer. med. Ass.*, 1936, *107*:853–856.

38. HAMILTON, W. F., WOODBURY, R. A. and HARPER, H. T., JR. Arterial, cerebrospinal and venous pressures in man during cough and strain. *Amer. J. Physiol.*, 1944, *141*:42–50.

39. HAMILTON, W. F., WOODBURY, R. A. and VOGT, E. Differential pressures in the lesser circulation of the unanesthetized dog. *Amer. J. Physiol.*, 1939, *125*:130–141.

40. HERRICK, J. F., GRINDLAY, J. H., BALDES, E. J. and MANN, F. C. Effect of exercise on the blood flow in the superior mesenteric, renal and common iliac arteries. *Amer. J. Physiol.*, 1940, *128*:338–344.

41. HUTCHINSON, J. *Encyclopedia of anatomy and physiology.* London, 1849–1852.

42. JOHNSON, V., HAMILTON, W. F., KATZ, L. N. and WEINSTEIN, W. Studies on the dynamics of the pulmonary circulation. *Amer. J. Physiol.*, 1937, *120*:624–634.

43. KATZ, L. N. and STEINITZ, F. S. Pulmonary arterial pressure in experimental renal hypertension. *Amer. J. Physiol.*, 1940, *128*:433–439.

44. KROGH, A. *The anatomy and physiology of capillaries,* 2nd ed. New Haven, Yale University Press, 1929. xiii, 422 pp.

45. LARSELL, O. Nerve terminations in the lung of the rabbit. *J. comp. Neurol.*, 1921, *33*:105–131.

46. LAWSON, H. and CHUMLEY, J. The effect of distension on blood flow through the intestine. *Amer. J. Physiol.*, 1940, *131*:368–377.

47. LERICHE, R. *The surgery of pain.* YOUNG, A., trans. and ed. London, Bailliere, Tindall and Cox, 1939. 512 pp.

48. LEWIS, T. *The blood vessels of the human skin and their responses.* London, Shaw and Sons, 1927. 332 pp.

49. LOVÉN, C. Über die Erweiterung von Arterien infolge einer Nervenerregung. *Ber. Sächs. Ges. (Akad.) Wiss.*, 1866, *18*:85–110.

50. LUCIANI, L. *Human physiology. III. Muscular and nervous systems.* London, Macmillan Co., 1915.

51. MARSHALL, E. K., JR. Studies on the cardiac output of the dog. II. The influence of atropine and carbon dioxide on the circulation of the unanesthetized dog. *J. Pharmacol.*, 1926, *29*:167–175.

52. MARTIN, E. G., WOOLLEY, E. C. and

MILLER, M. Capillary counts in resting and active muscles. *Amer. J. Physiol.*, 1932, *100*:407–416.

53. MEEK, W. J. and EYSTER, J. A. E. The effect of plethora and variations in venous pressure on diastolic size and output of the heart. *Amer. J. Physiol.*, 1922, *61*:186–202.

54. PAGE, E. W. The relation between hydatid moles, relative ischemia of the gravid uterus, and the placental origin of eclampsia. *Amer. J. Obstet. Gynaec.*, 1939, *37*:291–293.

55. PARKER, G. H. *The elementary nervous system. (Monographs on experimental biology.)* Philadelphia, J. B. Lippincott Co., 1919. 229 pp.

56. SCHROEDER, H. A. and STEELE, J. M. The behavior of renal blood flow after partial constriction of the renal artery. *J. exp. Med.*, 1940, *72*:707–716.

57. SMITH, H. W., ROVENSTINE, E. A., GOLDRING, W., CHASIS, H. and RANGES, H. A. The effects of spinal anesthesia on the circulation in normal, unoperated man with reference to the autonomy of the arterioles, and especially those of the renal circulation. *J. clin. Invest.*, 1939, *18*:319–341.

58. STADIE, W. C. The oxygen of the arterial and venous blood in pneumonia and its relation to cyanosis. *J. exp. Med.*, 1919, *30*:215–240.

59. TORNING, K. Experimental pneumothorax. *Acta tuberc. scand.*, 1933, *7*:233–284; *8*:1–77.

60. VOLPITTO, P. P. and RISTEEN, W. A. The use of stellate ganglion block in cerebral vascular occlusions. *Anesthesiol.*, 1943, *4*:403–408.

61. VOLPITTO, P. P., WOODBURY, R. A. and HAMILTON, W. F. Direct arterial and venous pressure measurements in man as affected by anesthesia, operation and shock. *Amer. J. Physiol.*, 1940, *128*:238–245.

62. WIGGERS, C. J. The regulation of the pulmonary circulation. *Physiol. Rev.*, 1921, *1*:239–268.

63. WILSON, H. G. The terminals of the human bronchiole. *Amer. J. Anat.*, 1922, *30*:267–295.

64. WOODBURY, R. A. and HAMILTON, W. F. The effect of histamine on the pulmonary blood pressure of various animals with and without anesthesia. *J. Pharmacol.*, 1941, *71*:293–300.

65. WOODBURY, R. A., HAMILTON, W. F. and TORPIN, R. The relationship between abdominal, uterine and arterial pressures during labor. *Amer. J. Physiol.*, 1938, *121*:640–649.

66. WOOLLARD, H. H. The innervation of blood vessels. *Heart*, 1926, *13*:319–336.

Circulation through the brain

67. AIRD, R. B. and STRAIT, L. Protective barriers of the central nervous system. *Arch. Neurol. Psychiat.*, Chicago, 1944, *51*:54–66.

68. COBB, S. and LENNOX, W. G. Cerebral circulation in intrinsic control and clinical phenomena. *Fed. Proc. Amer. Soc. exp. Biol.*, 1944, *3*:151–158.

69. FORBES, H. S. Physiologic regulation of the cerebral circulation. *Arch. Neurol. Psychiat.* Chicago, 1940, *43*:804–814.

70. FRIEDMANN, U. Blood-brain barrier. *Physiol. Rev.*, 1942, *22*:125–145.

71. RESEARCH PUBLICATIONS, ASSOCIATION FOR RESEARCH IN NERVOUS AND MENTAL DISEASES. Vol. XVIII. *Circulation of the brain and spinal cord.* The Williams and Wilkins Co., Baltimore, 1938, 790 pp.

72. ROSSEN, R., KABAT, H. and ANDERSON, J. P. Acute arrest of cerebral circulation in man. *Arch. Neurol. Psychiat.*, *Chicago*, 1943, *50*:510–528.

73. SCHARRER, E. The blood vessels of the nervous system. *Quart. Rev. Biol.*, 1944, *19*: 308–318.

74. SCHMIDT, C. F. The present status of knowledge concerning the intrinsic control of the cerebral circulation and the effects of functional derangements in it. *Fed. Proc. Amer. Soc. exp. Biol.*, 1944, *3*:131–139.

SECTION VI

RESPIRATION

BY LESLIE F. NIMS

CHAPTER 39

ANATOMY AND PHYSICS OF RESPIRATION

The term respiration, as originally used in physiology, had reference to the inspiration and expiration of air. The discovery of CO_2 in expired air by Joseph Black (1757), the discovery and investigation of the properties of O_2 by Joseph Priestley (1774), and the appreciation of the true object of the act of respiration by Antoine Lavoisier (1777), all greatly broadened the meaning of the term. Respiration now includes not only the process involved in the ventilation of the lungs and aeration of the blood, *external respiration*, but also the mechanisms of gaseous exchange between the blood and tissue elements and the chemical reactions by which the cells fix molecular O_2, *internal respiration*. Living systems are dependent for their integrity and activity upon an unceasing expenditure of energy. In all save possibly the anaerobic organisms, the availability of energy rests ultimately upon the ability of the cell to oxidize organic substrates to CO_2 and other products with molecular O_2. The CO_2 thus produced must be removed. Its accumulation would eventually block the essential energy-yielding reactions and the organisms would die. Hence respiration, in the general sense of gas exchange, is an essential and characteristic feature of most living systems.

The necessary gas exchange is accomplished simply at the cellular level. The individual cell is in immediate contact with its external environment, and adequate amounts of O_2 and CO_2 are exchanged between the cell and its surroundings by the process of diffusion. As the number of cells in the organism increases, the mechanisms of respiration become more complex. Unaided diffusion is no longer able to meet the demands for O_2. Several means have been evolved in nature to subserve the function of gas exchange. The air tubes of insects, the gills of fish, and the lungs of mammals are examples of specialized structures providing extensive surfaces through which the respiratory gases are readily exchanged. The various respiratory pigments carried in a circulatory system are examples of specialized chemical compounds providing a transportation mechanism for the respiratory gases to all parts of an organism. In man the respiratory apparatus consists of (i) an air pump, the lungs, thoracic cage and respiratory muscles; (ii) a breathing surface, the lung alveoli, where the respiratory gases of the blood are exchanged with those of the alveolar air; (iii) a transport and distribution system, the blood, heart and circulation; and (iv) a coordinating and control system, comprising a large part of the central nervous system. The complexity of the respiratory process in man makes it essential to consider individually the many mechanisms involved in gas exchange. The following four chapters will discuss separately the anatomy and physics of respiration, the transport and exchange of the respiratory gases, the neural mechanisms responsible for rhythmic breathing, and the regulation of respiration. The most important aspect of internal respiration, the cellular reactions by which energy is made available, has already been presented in Chapter 3. Although the subject is broken up into many parts, the student should remember that respiration is an integrated activity with but a single object—an adequate gas exchange between the ultimate tissue elements and the external air.

MECHANICS OF EXTERNAL RESPIRATION

The thorax in man is a closed cavity, the volume of which can be altered by the contraction of voluntary muscles (22). It contains the lungs, two large membranous elastic sacs, and the viscera of the mediastinal space. The lungs normally communicate freely with the outside air through the bronchi, trachea, and upper respiratory passages. Any change in the volume of the thorax is immediately transmitted to the lungs, and causes either a slight

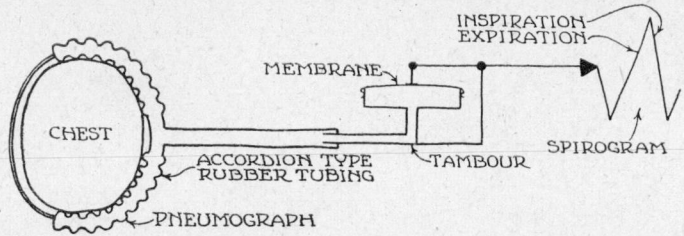

Fig. 401.—A simple apparatus for the qualitative recording of the breathing movements. On inspiration the chest expands, stretching the accordion pleated rubber tubing. The pressure in the tambour-tubing system falls and the recording stylus on the lever system rises so that the upstroke indicates inspiration.

rarefaction or a compression of the pulmonary gases. Air then flows in or out of the lungs through the open air passages until the pressure everywhere within the lungs becomes equal to the external atmospheric pressure. The position of the chest at the end of a normal expiration may be regarded as the normal or rest position of the thorax. It is the position assumed when all the muscles of respiration are at rest, and substantially, therefore, the position of the thorax in the cadaver. Starting from this position, any enlargement of the thorax constitutes an *active inspiration*, the result of which will be a flow of air into the lungs; any diminution in the thorax constitutes an *active expiration*, the result of which is that some air is expelled from the lungs. It is evident, however, that after either an active inspiration or an active expiration the thorax can passively return to its rest position; the elasticity of the lungs and the chest wall is able to accomplish this end without muscular intervention. At rest, our normal breathing movements consist of an active inspiration followed by a passive expiration.

Breathing movements. The frequency and amplitude of the respiratory movements vary greatly. Rates of inspiration as low as 4 times a minute have been reported in healthy human beings. However, the normal rate in a resting individual is considered to be 16 times a minute. During forced or labored breathing the rate may greatly exceed this value. The volume of air inhaled in a single breath, the *tidal air*, also varies greatly, the average value in the resting man being some 500 cc.

The registration of the rate and amplitude of the breathing movements can be accomplished by a variety of methods. An elastic tube placed around the chest and connected to a tambour affords a convenient method of obtaining qualitative records (Fig. 401). As the diameter of the chest changes, the volume of the elastic tube is altered, and the consequent pressure changes of the contained air are reflected by the membrane of the tambour. Records obtained with such an apparatus are given in Figure 402. These records demonstrate that inspiration (ascending limb) is followed at once by expiration. As soon as the inspiratory muscles cease to act, the elastic recoil of the chest tends to bring the thorax immediately back to its normal position. Expiration (descending limb) is at first rapid but towards the end becomes quite slow, so that a condition of rest, an expiratory pause, may intervene before inspiration commences again. Excellent quantitative records of the

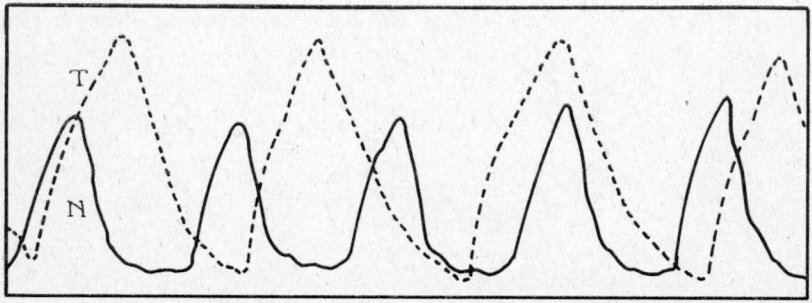

Fig. 402.—Curve of normal respiratory movements (Marey). Curve N, full line, represents the movements when the respiration is entirely normal. Upstroke, inspiration; down stroke, expiration. Curve T, dotted line, represents the increased amplitude of the movements (slight dyspnea) caused by breathing through a narrow tube which imposes a slight resistance to the flow of air. Note the respiratory pause at the end of the normal expiration.

breathing movements can be obtained with a clinical basal metabolism machine and the record obtained, a graph of volume as a function of time, is called a *spirogram*.

Ordinarily, we are unaware of the respiratory act, and such breathing made without obvious effort is called *eupnea*. In contrast, difficult or labored breathing is known as *dyspnea* (33). It is impossible to draw a sharp line of distinction between the two types of respiratory movements. There are many degrees of dyspnea, and doubtless in quiet breathing the frequency and amplitude of the movement may increase considerably before respiration becomes distinctly dyspneic. Dyspnea occurring while at rest or after mild exercise is an abnormal condition and is often indicative of a diseased state (5, 24). Patients with heart disease, untreated diabetes, nephritis, or anemia, for example, are easily rendered dyspneic. Other common terms referring to modifications of the breathing pattern are *apnea*, cessation of breathing; *hyperpnea*, increased depth of breathing; and *polypnea*, increased rate of breathing.

Inspiration. An increase in the volume of the thorax—inspiration—can be accomplished in two ways. The diaphragm can contract and effectively increase the cephalocaudal dimensions of the thorax, a method of breathing called *abdominal* because of the necessary concomitant movements of the abdominal walls; or the ribs can be elevated and increase the cross-sectional area of the chest, a method of breathing appropriately called *costal*. Either method is adequate to meet the respiratory demands of eupnea and mild exercise. However, in normal man both methods are operative at all times (Fig. 403) and are effectively coordinated to meet the increased respiratory demands of strenuous exercise. Throughout life the diaphragm is probably the main muscle of inspiration, and movements of the diaphragm account for the greater part of the total volume of air inspired during eupnea.

Contraction of the diaphragm. The diaphragm is a dome-shaped muscular structure with posterior attachments to the lumbar vertebrae and ribs on a

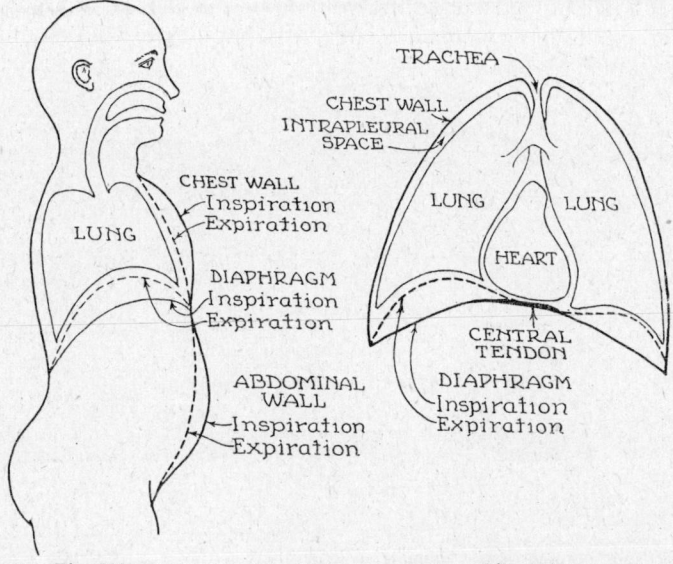

Fig. 403.   Fig. 404.

Fig. 403.—The relative positions of the chest wall, the diaphragm, and the abdominal wall at the end of a maximal inspiration and expiration. In normal breathing the diaphragm is the principal muscle of inspiration.

Fig. 404.—The relative position of the diaphragm at the end of normal inspiration and expiration. During quiet breathing the position of the central tendon changes but slightly; in forced inspiration it may descend, pulling the heart and other viscera of the mediastinal space downwards.

much lower plane than the anterior insertions in the ensiform cartilage. From these insertions the muscular sheet extends laterally along the walls of the thorax and bends over to form an arch which ends in the central tendon. This latter structure is not entirely free, since it is attached to the pericardium. In the relaxed state the right and left sides of the diaphragm are elevated above the central tendon by the pressure of the abdominal contents; in the contracted state these arches are flattened out (Fig. 404) and the displaced abdominal viscera are accommodated by a simultaneous relaxation of the abdominal musculature and protrusion of the abdominal walls. In eupnea there is little movement of the central tendon, but in forced respiration the heart may be pulled downward and the lower ribs may be pulled inward to some extent. The movement of the lower ribs is counteracted in part by the rise in abdominal pressure, and in part by contraction of the *quadratus lumborum* and the *serratus posterior inferior* muscles. The motion of the diaphragm as a whole, because of the plane of its attachments, is almost as much forward as downward and is most effective in ventilation of the lower lobes of the lungs. The diaphragm is innervated on each side by the corresponding phrenic nerve, and transection of a phrenic nerve paralyzes that half of the diaphragm on the same side.

Elevation of the ribs. Each rib is attached to the spinal column at two points, the head to the body of the vertebrae and the tubercle to the transverse process of the vertebrae. Movements of a rib may be regarded as a rotation around an axis joining these two points (Fig. 405). In the infant the ribs are nearly at right angles to the spine, and a movement of the ribs in either direction would decrease the volume of the thorax. For this reason, infantile breathing movements are largely diaphragmatic. On assumption of

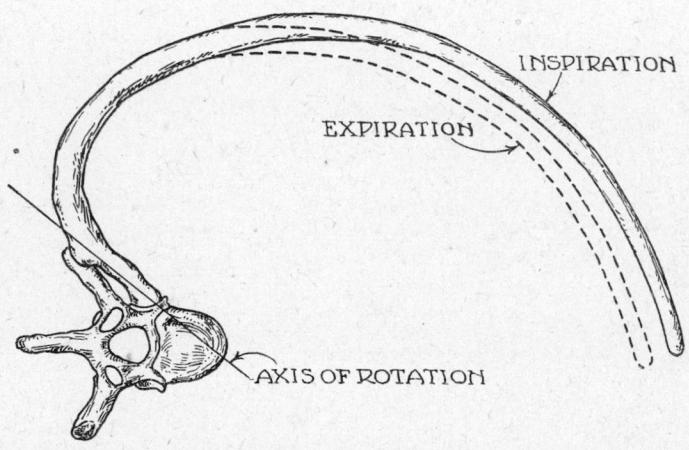

Fig. 405.—The sixth dorsal vertebra and rib. The axis differs slightly for every rib. The first 5 ribs increase the anterior-posterior diameters of the chest as they rise. The 6th to 10th effect a considerable increase in lateral diameter as well.

an upright posture, the force of gravity and the rhythmic excursions of the diaphragm assist in giving the ribs the downward slant they attain in adult life. Elevation of the ribs will then increase the diameters of the chest. The circumference of the costal arches increases in the first to sixth pair of ribs, and a considerable part of the enlargement of the thorax as the ribs rise is due to a replacement at the same level of a smaller by a larger costal arch (Fig. 406). The attachments and configurations of the first five ribs are such that when these ribs are elevated the anterior-posterior diameters of the chest are increased; the sixth to tenth ribs, however, effect a considerable increase in transverse diameters as well. Another mechanism contributing in part to the increase in transverse diameter is the eversion of the ribs on elevation, brought about by the cartilaginous attachments of the ribs to the sternum.

In eupnea the first rib and the manubrium sterni are fixed, and in dyspnea they are elevated by the contraction of the *sternocleidomastoid, scaleni,* and *pectoralis minor* muscles. The other ribs are moved toward the first rib during inspiration by the contraction of the *external intercostal* muscles. These muscles extend from the lower edge of one rib to the upper edge of the rib below. When they contract, the ribs are elevated and become more nearly at right angles to the spine (Fig. 406). Bronk and Ferguson (2) established the inspiratory function of the external intercostal and intercartilaginous portion of the internal intercostal muscles by observing the electrical activity of the motor nerves going to these muscles. They found action currents in the respective nerves occurring synchronously with the contraction of the diaphragm, thus removing any doubt as to the inspiratory function of these divisions of the intercostal muscles. Other muscles also act to elevate the ribs and are thus classed as inspiratory (15, 16). These are the *levatores costarum* and *serratus posterior superior* muscles which run downwards from the vertebral column to the ribs.

Expiration. A decrease in the volume of the thorax—expiration—can occur in various ways. The chest may return passively from its expanded state during inspiration by virtue of the elastic forces of the lungs and thorax; the *triangulus sterni* and the *interosseous* portion of the *internal intercostals*

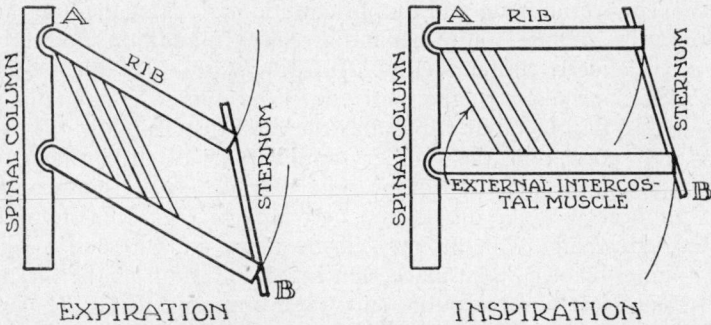

EXPIRATION   INSPIRATION

Fig. 406.—Schema to indicate the manner in which the first five ribs function to increase the anterior-posterior diameter of the chest during inspiration. The successive costal arches increase in length, and as the ribs arise, the anterior-posterior diameter of the chest is effectively extended. Note that points A and B are closer together when the ribs are elevated. The attachments of the external intercostal muscles are such that they tend to shorten the distance A–B when they contract.

may contract and depress the ribs (1); or the muscles of the abdominal wall may contract and force the diaphragm up into the thorax. During eupnea, expiration is largely passive and it is only during vigorous breathing that the expiratory muscles are called into action. The main muscles of expiration are the *internal and external oblique*, the *rectus*, and the *transversus* muscles of the abdominal wall. When these contract the pressure in the abdominal cavity is raised. If the glottis is kept open the pressure on the under surface of the diaphragm forces it into the thorax and air is effectively expelled from the lungs. If the glottis is kept firmly closed no air can escape and the increased abdominal pressure is felt mainly upon the pelvic organs, an effect which is obtained during micturition, defecation and parturition. The participation of the expiratory muscles during vigorous breathing enables both the amplitude and frequency of the respiratory movements to be increased. Forced expiration not only speeds up the expiratory phase, but also enables the thorax to be reduced below its normal capacity so that a greater quantity of air per breath is expelled from the lungs.

Accessory respiratory movements. In addition to the muscles whose action directly enlarges or diminishes the capacity of the thorax, certain other muscles connected with the air passages contract rhythmically with inspiration, and may be properly designated as accessory muscles of respiration. The muscles especially concerned are those controlling the size of the glottis and the opening of the external nares. At each inspiration the elevators of the wings of the nares come into play. The glottis is also dilated at each inspiration by the contraction of the *posterior crico-arytenoid* muscles. These movements occur in normal breathing in many animals, such as the rabbit and horse, and in some men, while in dyspneic breathing they are invariably present. The useful results of these movements is a reduction of the resistance to an inflow of air.

Breathing movements of the lungs. It is evident from a consideration of the movements of the chest wall that the lungs cannot inflate by simple expansion from a central point. The apical, posterior and mediastinal surfaces of the lung are in contact with regions of the thorax which do little moving and the portion of lungs adjacent to these surfaces can be said to expand indirectly. The sternocostal and diaphragmatic regions of the lung have the greatest motion and are said to expand directly. In addition, not all parts of the lungs are equally elastic. Keith (22) distinguishes three zones of varying degrees of expansibility: (i) the root zone containing the bronchi, arteries and veins, and fibrous tissue which has the least distensibility; (ii) the intermediate zone containing the smaller ramifications of the bronchi, arteries and veins which radiate toward the outer surface of the lungs and which contain pulmonary tissue distributed between the rays; (iii) the outer zone composed principally of pulmonary elastic tissue and air sacs in which the largest volume changes take place. During inspiration all the air passages appear to elongate and the pulmonary tissues expand to fill the new space created by the lengthening of the radiating bronchioles. The root of the lung moves forward and downward, creating the space which the indirectly expanded regions of the lung occupy at full inspiration. It is probable that during normal quiet breathing not all of the lung alveoli share equally in effecting gas exchange with the blood. The relatively smaller ventilation of the apex of the lung and other indirectly expanded regions has been offered to explain the fact that these regions are more often the site of primary pathology such as tuberculosis.

PRESSURE CHANGES

In considering the pressure changes in respiration, the distinction between the pressure in the thorax outside the lungs and the pressure within the lungs and air passages must be kept clearly in mind. The pressure in the thoracic cavity outside the lungs may be designated as the intrathoracic (intrapleural) pressure. It is the pressure exerted upon the heart, great blood vessels, thoracic duct, esophagus, and intrapleural lymph (25). The pressure within the lungs and air passages may be designated as intrapulmonic pressure, and is always greater than the intrathoracic pressure by an amount equal to the elastic force of the lungs.

Intrapulmonic pressure. The air passages and the alveoli of the lungs are in free communication with the external air; consequently in every position of rest, whether at the end of inspiration or expiration, the pressure in these cavities is equal to that of the atmospheric pressure outside. During the act of inspiration, however, the intrapulmonic pressure temporarily falls below that of the atmosphere—that is, during the inflow of air. The extent to which the pressure falls depends naturally upon the rapidity and amplitude of the inspiratory movement and upon the size of the opening to the exterior. The air is somewhat restricted in its motion by the glottis; therefore the variations in pressure below this point are probably greater than in the pharynx or nasal cavities. If the air passages are abnormally constricted at any other point, the fall of pressure during inspiration will be correspondingly magnified in the parts below the constriction, as happens, for instance, in bronchial asthma, edema of the glottis, cold in the head, etc. Under normal conditions the fall in intrapulmonic pressure during a quiet inspiration is not large, being only 2 to 3 mm. Hg. At the end of inspiration, the pressure rises again to atmospheric. During expiration the elastic recoil of the chest wall takes place with sufficient rapidity to compress the air somewhat during its escape, causing a slight, but temporary, rise in pressure: 3 mm. Hg greater than atmospheric pressure. Intrapulmonic pressure changes much greater than these may be obtained if the glottis is firmly closed during the attempted inspiration and expiration. Vigorous inspiratory movements under such conditions may lower the pressure 30 to 80 mm. Hg below atmospheric, while strong expiratory movements similarly may raise the pressure to 60 to 100 mm. Hg above atmospheric.

The smaller bronchi possess a distinct muscular layer, and contraction of these muscles can greatly modify the resistances of the air passages to the movement of air. The exact function of these muscles in the respiratory cycle is unknown (23). They are under control of the autonomic nervous system and may relax rhythmically with inspiration, affording easier entrance of air to the ultimate air sacs. In asthma they are thought to be strongly contracted and the pressure changes in the alveolar air must then be much greater than normal. Adrenaline is useful in attacks of asthma since it may cause the bronchiole musculature to relax and the alveoli to be more easily ventilated.

Intrathoracic pressure. In the fetus the lungs are solid, and completely fill the thoracic cavity, except for the part occupied by other organs. Inspiratory movements of the diaphragm at birth succeed in increasing the volume of the thorax slightly, air enters the lungs, and the careful measurements of Hermann (19) show that at this time only slight subatmospheric pressures exist in the thorax. The subatmospheric pressure of 4 mm. Hg or so found in the adult (7) is evidently developed gradually, and must be due to the fact that the thorax increases in size more rapidly and to a greater extent than the lungs, so that in order to fill the cavity the lungs become more and more stretched. The lungs are continually pulling away from the thoracic cage with a force which varies with inspiratory movements (6). The intrapleural lymph is under tension, and, like all liquids, has considerable tensile strength (intramolecular attractive forces) and is fully capable of holding the lungs expanded even during the greatest possible stresses exerted physiologically. The expanded lung is seemingly protected in normal circumstances from any danger of returning to a fetal state of consolidation. At the end of a forced expiration, the lungs are still somewhat extended and a considerable though reduced tension still exists in the intrapleural space.

Intrathoracic pressure changes throughout the respiratory cycle can be accurately measured in an anesthetized animal. A water manometer is connected by rubber tubing to a needle inserted into a small pocket of air in the intrapleural space and the pressure of the intrapleural air is measured. In man a record of the intrathoracic pressures can be obtained from a small inflated rubber balloon which is passed down the esophagus so that it lies in the thoracic region of the esophagus. The balloon will then respond to the variations in intrathoracic pressure, and a record of the pressure changes can be obtained with a suitable recording manometer. The relations between the atmospheric, the intrapulmonic and the intrathoracic pressures during a normal respiratory cycle are illustrated by Figure 407. The difference between the intrapulmonic pressure and the intrathoracic pressure is a measure not only of the elastic force of the lungs but also of the tension exerted by the intrapleural lymph. Large variations in intrathoracic pressure can markedly affect the heart and circulation (see pp. 669 and 679). The great veins and the

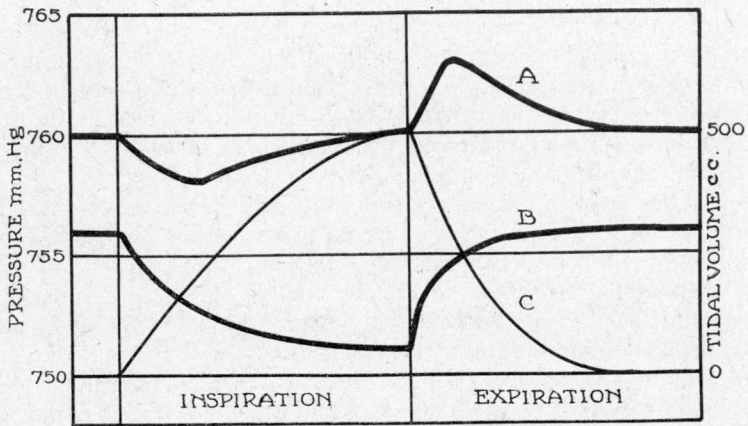

Fig. 407.—A diagram to illustrate the relationships between the intrapulmonic pressure, A, the intrathoracic pressure, B, and the tidal air volume, C. At the end of inspiration and expiration the intrapulmonic pressure is equal to the external atmospheric pressure (760 mm. Hg in this instance). The difference between the intrapulmonic and the intrathoracic pressure is a measure of the elastic force of the lungs and also the tension to which the intrapleural lymph is subjected.

right side of the heart are thin walled structures, and since they lie in the mediastinal space they are subjected to all of the variations of the intrathoracic pressure. The venous return cannot remain constant during the respiratory cycle and the heart rate and blood pressure must change accordingly. The extent of the fluctuation in rate and pressure is largely determined by the sensitivity of an individual's cardiovascular reflex control mechanisms. A simple procedure, designated as the Flack test (14), has been used as a fitness test. The subject holds his breath as long as possible while blowing into a mercury manometer with a force equal to 40 mm. Hg. The test determines both the breath holding capacity and the ability of the vascular system to maintain an adequate venous return under conditions of high intrathoracic pressure. Considerable knowledge of the subject's physical and psychological state can be obtained by taking careful notes of the pulse rate, the pressure fluctuations and the behaviour of respiration after the pressure is released.

Pneumothorax. When the pleural cavity is opened by any means, air enters and causes a greater or lesser shrinkage of the corresponding lung. This condition is called *pneumothorax* (17). Air may enter the pleural space in various ways. External communication may be established by gunshot or stab wound of the chest. Internal communication may be established by rupture of the visceral pleura, for example, rupture of a tubercle in pulmonary tuberculosis, the air in this case entering from the alveoli in the lungs. From the considerations of the mechanics of lung inflation given above, it is evident that an expandable volume of air in the pleura can greatly interfere with normal ventilation of the lungs. If a large external opening to the pleural space is kept patent the lungs may collapse completely. With a closed type of pneumothorax the interference with ventilation is dependent upon the actual volume of the air pocket (8). With any degree of pneumothorax the intrathoracic pressure rises, and since the mediastinum is not rigid, it is displaced away from the region of the trapped air. In the vicinity of the pneumothorax a more or less extensive region of the lung may collapse, and the small amount of air remaining in affected alveoli is rapidly absorbed by the circulating blood, the final result being a condition of local consolidation or incomplete expansion known as *atelectasis*. The same condition of local consolidation may also arise, of course, if for any reason the alveolar ducts or the respiratory bronchioles are blocked for any length of time. In human beings pneumothorax occurs most frequently in conditions of disease, when the visceral pleura becomes so eroded that openings appear.

Pneumothorax is often used as a therapeutic measure to reduce the extent of the respiratory movements of a diseased lung. Measured quantities of air are introduced into the pleura and give a partial collapse of the infected lung. Healing is generally promoted by placing the lung at rest. The injected air is slowly absorbed by the circulating blood from the closed pneumothorax and the lung aga n expands as the absorption takes place. To maintain the pneumothorax for any length of time, air must be injected every few days.

LUNG VOLUME

At the end of a passive expiration, the lungs contain about two and one half liters of air (21). This volume of air, the *normal capacity*, is further fractionated into a portion which can be expelled by a maximal expiration, the *reserve air*, and the liter and one half of air left, the *residual air*. The volume of air inhaled and exhaled in a single breath, the *tidal air*, amounts to about one half liter in an individual at rest. The additional volume that can be inhaled during a maximal inspiration, the *complemental air*, approximates three liters. The sum of the complemental, tidal, and reserve air volumes is called the *vital capacity*, and is equal to four and one half liters in the average adult male. The vital capacity and the various subdivisions of the expirable lung volume are easily measured with a simple spirometer. To determine the normal capacity and the residual air, it is necessary to breathe in and out of a bag containing H_2 or some other inert gas until the gas is evenly distributed throughout the lung and gas bag volumes. Chemical analysis will then give the dilution the H_2 has undergone and the total volume within which the H_2 is now distributed. This quantity is the sum of the gas bag air volume and normal capacity lung volumes. The relation between the various fractions of lung air is illustrated by Figure 408.

Complete collapse of the lungs does not occur upon removal from the thorax if they have once been inflated. Some air always remains in the alveoli and the respiratory passages. This quantity of air, the *minimal air*, is of some importance in legal medicine, for if breathing has been initiated in the infant, the lungs will float, and a simple test suffices to determine whether or not the infant was stillborn.

Vital capacity. The vital capacity is proportional to the size and physical development of a given individual (32). The average male has a vital capacity in liters about two-and-a-half times his surface area in square meters. Women have a proportionately smaller vital capacity, only twice their surface area. Athletes, particularly those engaging in sports which demand maximum muscular effort over any period of time may greatly exceed these figures. Posture itself by redistribution of body mass can affect the vital capacity; the volume is from 200 to 500 cc. greater in the erect than in the supine position (4). The difference in volume is probably due to the fact that gravity aids the inspiratory effort of the diaphragm in the erect position, but opposes it in the recumbent position. A second factor is that the volume of blood in

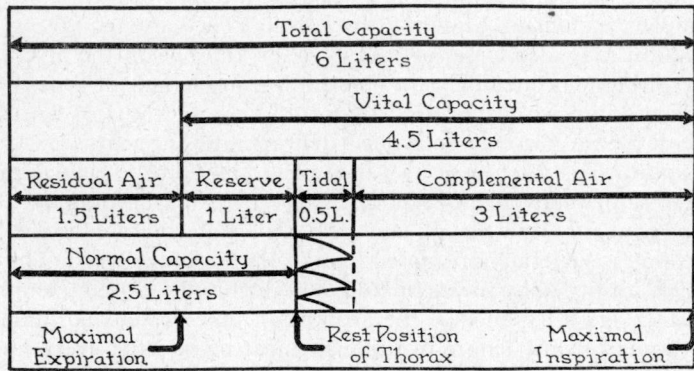

Fig. 408.—The relationship between the various measurable volumes of the lung.air. Note that the tidal air is only a small fraction of the normal capacity air.

the lungs is considerably greater when in the supine position, leaving less space to accommodate air. While a reduction of vital capacity in the supine position is of little importance to the healthy individual, it is a matter of some concern to those whose vital capacity is greatly reduced by disease. Such individuals often find it much easier to breathe in a sitting position than when flat on their backs, a condition of abnormal breathing designated as *orthopnea*. The extent of decrease of vital capacity is a sensitive indicator of the clinical condition and prognosis of several diseases, particularly heart disease and tuberculosis. A reduction in a man's vital capacity means that he cannot have a normal response to a demand for increased ventilation.* Individuals with

* It has long been recognized that orthopnea is associated with a reduction in the vital capacity, an increase in the diastolic pressure of the lesser circulation, and pulmonary edema. The rise in diastolic pressure increases the work-load of the right heart, which can be relieved, along with the labored respiration, by shifting the patient to the upright position. As a result of this shift, the vital capacity is increased, the venous pressure rises, hemoconcentration occurs slowly (hand in hand with increased peripheral edema), and the venous return is reduced as a consequence. The diminished venous return permits the left ventricle to reduce the volume of blood in the lungs and to decrease the load on the right heart. The importance of this reduction of the load on the failing heart in the upright position has been emphasized in an important paper by Levine, entitled "Some

a reduced vital capacity (60 per cent of normal) become dyspneic with only mild exercise. In heart disease, as the instructive data of Peabody and Wentworth (28) demonstrate, vital capacity closely parallels the progress of the disease. The close correlation between the vital capacity and the ability of the patient to do useful work is illustrated by Table 35.

Table 35.—*The Effect of a Reduced Vital Capacity upon the Working Ability of Patients with Heart Disease. Data of Peabody and Wentworth (28).*

Vital Capacity Per cent Normal	Number of Cases	Mortality Per cent	Symptoms of Decom-pensation	Working Per cent	Remarks
90+	25	0	0	92	Few symptoms referable to heart.
70–90	41	5	2	54	Dyspnea with exertion yet able to do moderate work.
40–70	67	17	89	7	Dyspnea with moderate exercise. Few able to work.
–40	23	61	10	0	Bedridden, with marked signs of cardiac insufficiency.

PULMONARY VENTILATION

Due to the anatomical arrangements in the lungs, not all of the inspired air is effective in the aeration of the blood. Some of it goes to refresh the important fraction of air in proximate gaseous equilibrium with arterial blood, the *alveolar air*, while the rest merely fills the air passages and can be recovered with little change in composition, the *dead space air*. To understand the meaning of these terms and the way in which air finally reaches those membranes where gaseous exchange is affected, it is necessary to review briefly some of the anatomical arrangements in the lungs which are of immediate physiological interest.

Physiological anatomy. The trachea, bronchi, and bronchioles function admirably as air passageways. Their walls possess both longitudinal elasticity and cross-sectional rigidity. The lining of ciliated epithelium is of importance in removing mucous and foreign materials from the air passageways. The smaller bronchioles possess a distinct muscular layer, and are under control of the autonomic nervous system, through the reflex activity of which the capacity and resistance of the bronchiolar system may be modified. The smallest bronchioles are expanded into a system of membranous air cells, and in the walls of these thin sacs the capillaries of the pulmonary artery are distributed.

According to Miller (26), the bronchioles give off smaller branches, the walls of which show saccular dilations similar to the *alveoli* or air sacs in which respiratory exchange takes place (see Fig. 409). These bronchioles are designated therefore as the *bronchioli respiratorii* (respiratory bronchioles). They contain muscular tissue but no cartilage and their epithelium loses its ciliated character, taking on a low cuboidal form. The respiratory bronchioles

harmful effects of recumbency in the treatment of heart disease" (*J. Amer. med. Ass.*, 1944, *126:* 80–84). He points out that since horizontal posture imposes a greater work-load on the heart in cases of gradual cardiac failure, bed rest and the horizontal position are contra-indicated. It is preferable to have edema of the ankles than edema of the lungs, and for this reason Levine insists that patients with cardiac failure be permitted to sit in a chair during the day, to walk about from time to time, and that at night they should sleep on a bed with the head elevated 9 inches above the foot.

divide, giving off the alveolar ducts which form the last subdivision of the bronchial tree. The alveolar ducts have air cells or alveoli in their walls and still possess some muscular tissue. The distal end of each duct opens out into a variable number of irregularly spherical cavities, the *atria*, and each atrium in turn opens into a number of irregular chambers, the alveolar air sacs (*sacculi alveolares*). The walls of these sacs are pouched to form a number of alveoli. Each alveolar duct with its dependent atria and air sacs constitutes a primary lobule which forms the unit of structure of the lungs, as well as the physiological unit. The respiratory exchange between the blood and the alveolar air takes place in the alveoli found in the walls of the respiratory bronchioles, the alveolar ducts, the atria, and the ultimate sacculi. The pulmonary capillaries are distributed in the walls of these alveoli. Miller calls attention to the fact that the smooth muscle in the alveolar duct shows a sphincter arrangement round the openings into the sacculi, having a position, therefore, in which it may exert an important control over the entrance of air into the ultimate air sacs. Several observers report that the bronchial musculature (23) is capable of effecting slow peristaltic movements which

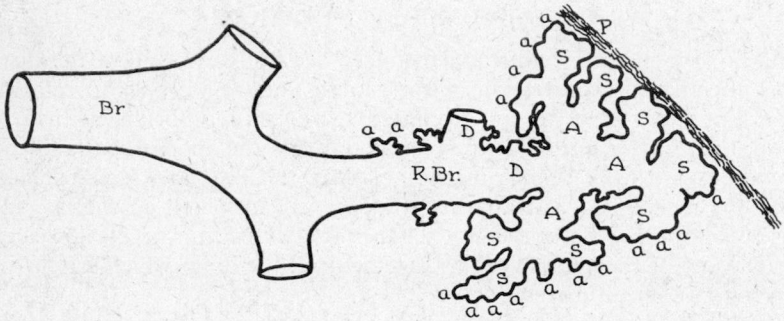

Fig. 409.—The structure of the primary lung lobule as described by Miller. Br., Bronchiole; R. Br., respiratory bronchiole; D, alveolar duct; A, atrium; S, alveolar air sacs; a, the alveoli or ultimate air sacs; P, the pleura.

pass from the periphery toward the center, and it is suggested that such movements may be valuable in contributing to the expulsion of exudates from the bronchial tubes.

Alveolar ventilation. The complex process of mixing and diffusion of gases that takes place in the lungs during inspiration can now be visualized. The air on the way to the depths of the lungs is warmed, moistened and cleansed in the nose and pharynx, and is conducted through the trachea, bronchi, and bronchioles with but little change in composition. The volume of the respiratory passages is 150 cc. and this volume is designated as the *anatomical dead space*, since the air contained in this space does not exchange gases with the blood. It is possible to calculate the size of the dead space from a knowledge of the CO_2 composition of the exhaled air and the alveolar air, together with the volume of exhaled air. When such determinations are carried out during periods of increased degrees of pulmonary ventilation, a "dead space" greater than the anatomical volume of the air passages is obtained (3). This is called the *physiological dead space* and it measures the efficiency with which the diffusion of gases has brought about complete mixing in the ultimate air sacs. A more effective alveolar ventilation for a given pulmonary ventilation is obtained if the tidal air is large and the frequency of inspiration is low. Relatively less of the total minute volume of air is then used to fill the dead space and more time is allowed for mixing of the newly inspired air with the normal capacity air of the lungs. Under normal rest conditions—a minute volume of respiration of 8 liters per minute and a tidal air of 500 cc.—5.6 liters of air $(350/500 \times 8 = 5.6)$ are available to ventilate the alveoli. For the same minute volume, but twice the normal respiratory frequency, 3.2 liters $(100/250 \times 8 = 3.2)$ are available.

At the end of expiration the air passages are filled with alveolar air; during inspiration this air is driven back into the depths of lungs by the incoming air. The increase in volume of lungs takes place principally in the atria of the primary lung lobule and the air passages increase in volume in proportion to their lengthening. The incoming air, which represents about 15 per cent of the air already present, mixes with the normal capacity air and ultimately reaches the alveoli by gaseous diffusion. This may seem to be an inefficient way to accomplish aeration of the blood, but it has the advantage that the composition of alveolar air is maintained nearly constant during the respiratory cycle. The arterial blood leaving the lungs at the beginning of inspiration does not differ markedly from that leaving the lungs at the beginning of expiration.

Pulmonary ventilation. Lung ventilation is equal to the volume of air— measured at body temperature, ambient pressure, and saturated with water vapor—taken into the lungs per minute. The respiratory minute volume amounts to 8 liters or so while at rest and may increase to 70 liters or more during very strenuous exercise. The maximum voluntary ventilatory rate is a useful index of the capabilities of an individual for doing work. If the rate is much below normal the individual is greatly handicapped and cannot do those tasks which require much exertion over any period of time. The maximum ventilatory rate, though slightly more difficult to measure than vital capacity, is probably a much better indicator of loss of respiratory reserve (9), since in some clinical conditions the maximum voluntary ventilatory rate is markedly lowered, without much reduction in vital capacity.

Artificial respiration. In laboratory experiments on animals artificial respiration is frequently employed after the use of curare, when it is necessary to open the chest, after cessation of respiration from overdoses of anesthetics, etc. The method adopted in almost all cases is the reverse of the normal procedure; the lungs are expanded by pressure. A bellows or blast worked by hand or machinery is connected with the trachea, and the lungs are dilated rhythmically. Provision is made for the escape of expired air by the use of valves, or by a small hole in the tracheal cannula. Numerous forms of respiration pumps have been devised for this purpose.

In cases of suspended respiration (human beings) from drowning, electrical shock, pressure upon the medulla, or other conditions, it is necessary to use artificial respiration (30) in order to restore normal breathing. Bellows ordinarily cannot be used in such cases. Some method must be employed to expand and contract the chest alternately, and many different procedures have been suggested. The results of observations and experiments made by several commissions who investigated the efficiency of the so-called manual methods of artificial respiration indicate that the Schafer (29), or prone pressure, method is the simplest and most reliable (13). Schafer describes

the procedure as follows: "It consists in laying the subject in the prone posture, preferably on the ground, with a thick folded garment underneath the
chest and epigastrium. The operator puts himself athwart or at the side of
the subject, facing his head, and places his hands on each side, over the
lower part of the back (lowest ribs). He then slowly throws the weight of his
body forward, to bear upon his own arms, and thus presses upon the thorax
of the subject, and forces air out of the lungs (see Fig. 410). This being effected, he gradually relaxes the pressure by bringing his own body up again
to a more erect position, but without moving the hands." These movements
are repeated regularly at the rate of 12 to 15 times per minute, until normal
respiration begins, or the possibility of its restoration is abandoned. A half
hour or more may be required before normal breathing movements start.
One distinct advantage that the Schafer method has over many others is
that the massage action of the procedure aids venous return and helps support
the circulation.

Special instruments (pulmotors, lungmotors, resuscitators), have been
devised for use, but they offer the difficulty that some training is required to
operate them properly, and they are not as a rule available for instant use.
In resuscitation, the important matter is to apply artificial respiration

Inspiration   Expiration

Fig. 410.—The posture to be adopted for effecting artificial respiration in cases of suspended
respiration (Schafer). The hands must be placed well down on the back and the pressure directed
diagonally through the body so that the body slides forward slightly under pressure.

promptly. Individuals who have ceased to breathe from accident or other
cause are in need of artificial respiration, and should be given manual treatment by the prone pressure method immediately. The delay incident to the
removal to a hospital may be fatal, and is justifiable only when there is no
one at hand to give artificial respiration. If complications exist or arise which
require hospital treatment, artificial respiration should be maintained in
transit and after the arrival at the hospital until spontaneous respiration
begins. Henderson and Haggard (18) have shown that in cases of feeble or
suspended respiration, the activity of the center may be stimulated by adding
a small amount (5 per cent) of CO_2 to the respired air. It is often advisable
to use a mixture of oxygen and 5 per cent CO_2 for resuscitation if the mixture
is available, irrespective of the method of artificial respiration employed. For
resuscitation of subjects exposed to CO gas, the CO_2 mixture is particularly
valuable (18). When long continued artificial respiration is required, the
manual method may be replaced advantageously by the Drinker (12) respirator, which makes use of a subatmospheric pressure applied to the outside
of the chest to obtain an expansion of the lungs. The body, with the exception
of the head, is placed in a chamber in which the pressure is reduced rhythmically by a pump. The thorax and the lungs are expanded by the pressure

differential created between the lungs and the exterior of the chest, and in this way respiration may be kept up indefinitely with no danger of injury to the lungs.

PROPERTIES OF GASES AND LIQUIDS

The behavior of the respiratory gases in the body cannot be understood unless the student is thoroughly familiar with the simple properties of gases and liquids. The following paragraphs present an elementary view of the kinetic concept of fluids. Fluids are thought to be composed of discrete particles (molecules) in incessant motion (20). The molecules are continually colliding with each other and with the containing vessel, and the pressure exerted by a fluid is simply the summated impacts of the molecules with a confining wall. Diffusion in a mixture of substances is also a consequence of this motion, for the continual movement of the individual particles will more or less rapidly equalize local differences in concentration produced when the mixture is made. In the gas state the individual particles are so far apart that the attraction of the particles for each other is negligibly small, and a gas, because of the incessant motion of its individual particles, will completely fill all of the available volume. Gases therefore can exert only pressure. In the liquid state the molecules still have freedom of motion, but they are so close together that they are subject to strong intramolecular attractive forces. Liquids have a volume independent of the container, and can exert both pressure and tension effects in a closed space, as the intrapleural fluid does in the thorax.

The behaviour of gases can be summarized by simple laws and principles. *Boyle's* law states that the pressure of a gas is inversely proportional to its volume, temperature remaining constant. This law is simply explained by the kinetic theory, for decreasing the volume of a gas increases the number of particles per unit volume and increases the number of impacts upon the walls of the container. *Charles'* law states that the pressure of a gas is directly proportional to its absolute temperature, volume remaining constant. This law is also simply explained by the kinetic theory, for increasing the temperature of a gas increases the velocity of the molecular motions and the force of the summated impacts. *Avogadro's* principle states that different gases which have the same volume at the same temperature and pressure contain an equal number of molecules, and is the basis of the volumetric method of determining the composition of gaseous mixtures. This principle, together with the laws of Boyle and Charles, can be combined in a simple mathematical expression, the ideal gas law.

$$PV = nRT$$

In this expression, P is the pressure exerted by the gas, V is the volume of the gas, n is the number of mols of the gas, T is the absolute temperature ($0°A = 273°C$.) and R is a constant whose value depends upon the units in which the variables are expressed. When the pressure is expressed in atmospheres, the volume in liters, and the temperature in centigrade degrees absolute, R has the value of 0.082 liter atmospheres per mol per degree. Real gases deviate slightly from this ideal expression, but the deviations are so small at ordinary temperatures that the gas law in the form given can be used with confidence to calculate the compositions or the pressures of the respiratory gases.

Partial pressures. Each gas in a mixture of gases behaves as if it alone occupied the total volume and exerts a pressure, its partial pressure, independently of the other gases present (*Dalton's* law of partial pressure). The sum of the partial pressures of the individual gases is equal to the total pressure. The partial pressures of a gas in a mixture is easily calculated from the composition of the mixture. Dalton's law in conjunction with the perfect gas law allows one to state that the partial pressure of a gas in a mixture is equal to the product of the mol fraction and the total pressure. The partial pressures of O_2, N_2 and CO_2 in dry air in mm. Hg when the total pressure is one atmosphere (760 mm. Hg) are therefore: $O_2 = 0.21 \times 760 = 160$ mm. Hg, $N_2 = 0.79 \times 760 = 600$ mm. Hg, $CO_2 = 0.004 \times 760 = 0.30$ mm. Hg. In physiology it is customary to speak of the compositions of gases in terms of volumes per cent. Avogadro's principle makes it evident that volumes per cent and mols per cent are numerically equal for gas mixtures.

Vapor pressures. The air of the lungs contains water vapor in addition to the other gases present. The water vapor obeys Dalton's law and exerts a p essure independently of the other gases present. Gases in contact with water receive water molecules by evaporation until the number of molecules leaving the liquid phase are equal to the number of molecules returning from the gas phase. Since the number leaving the liquid phase is proportional to the temperature of the liquid, the partial pressure of water in the gas phase is also proportional to the temperature. The temperature of the air in the lungs is 37° C. and the air of the lungs is thought to be in equilibrium with respect to water so that the partial pressure of water in the alveolar air is 47 mm. Hg. The composition of the respired airs is usually expressed dry, and to calculate the partial pressures from the composition it is necessary to subtract the partial pressure of water vapor from the total pressure before determining the partial pressures of other gases. For example, a sample of dry alveolar air contained 5.6 per cent of CO_2. The partial pressure of CO_2 in the alveolar air at atmospheric pressure was $0.56 \times (760-47) = 40$ mm. Hg.

Solubility and partial pressures of gases in liquids. The quantity of gas physically dissolved in a liquid at constant temperature is directly proportional to the partial pressure of the gas in the gas phase (Henry's law of solubility of gases). At equilibrium the number of gas molecules leaving the liquid per unit time is equal to the number entering the liquid and any change in the partial pressure of the gas produces a corresponding change in the equilibrium. The gas in the liquid phase also has a partial pressure and under equilibrium conditions the partial pressures of the gas in the gas phase and the liquid phase are said to be equal. To determine the partial pressure of a gas in a liquid it is necessary to determine the composition and pressures of the gas in an equilibrated gas phase.

The amount of gas dissolved in physical solution must be carefully distinguished from the pressure of the gas in solution. One cc. of blood at body temperature will dissolve and hold in physical solution 0.026 cc. of O_2, 0.013 cc. of N_2 and 0.526 cc. of CO_2 if the respective partial pressures of the gases are 760 mm. Hg. The quantity of CO_2 dissolved is therefore some 20 times that of O_2 even though the partial pressures of two gases in the blood would be equal. At the partial pressures equivalent to those found in the alveoli, blood contains 0.39 cc. of O_2, 2.64 cc. of CO_2 and 1.04 cc. of N_2 in physical solution per 100 cc. of blood. The amount of O_2 and CO_2 present in circulating blood is of course much greater than that physically dissolved. This is due to the fact that O_2 and CO_2 are carried to a large extent by the blood in chemical combination, and the chemically combined gas no longer contributes to partial pressure of the physically dissolved gas.

Determination of the amounts of O_2 and CO_2 in a particular blood sample is a procedure involving a high degree of chemical skill and has been well described in laboratory textbooks (27). The gases are extracted completely and in a condition for quantitative analysis from a sample of blood by some form of a vacuum pump and then reabsorbed one by one in suitable chemical reagents. The volume, temperature and pressure are noted at each stage of the analysis and the number of mols of each gas can then be calculated by substitution of the known quantities into the perfect gas equation. To determine the partial pressures of the gases in the blood, the blood is equilibrated with a volume of gas so small that no essential change takes place in the blood as equilibrium is approached. Chemical analysis of the gas phase will then allow a calculation of the partial pressures of the fluid phase. A similar procedure can be used to find the partial pressure of the gases in the tissues. A small volume of gas is injected beneath the skin and after being allowed to remain a suitable length of time for equilibrium, it can be recovered and analyzed (31).

A new method of measuring the O_2 partial pressures in the tissues and in blood of living animals has been developed (10). An application is made of the fact that dissolved oxygen will react electrochemically at the cathode of an electrolysis cell and give rise under standardized conditions to a current which is proportional to the amount of O_2 present. With this device it has been found that O_2 pressures below 10 mm. Hg exist in the vicinity of the nerve cells of the brain and that when these cells are stimulated to intense activity as during a convulsion the O_2 pressure falls almost to nothing (11).

REFERENCES

1. ANDERSON, F. M. and LINDSLEY, D. B. Action potentials from intercostal muscles before and after unilateral pneumonectomy. *J. Lab. clin. Med.*, 1935, *20*:623–628.

2. BRONK, D. W. and FERGUSON, L. K. The nervous control of intercostal respiration. *Amer. J. Physiol.*, 1935, *110*:700–714.

3. CARPENTER, T. M. and LEE, R. C. The influence of glucose and of fructose on the effective dead space in human respiration. *Amer. J. Physiol.*, 1933, *104*:10–17.

4. CHRISTIE, C. D. and BEAMS, A. J. The estimation of normal vital capacity with especial reference to the effect of posture. *Arch. intern. Med.*, 1922, *30*:34–39.

5. CHRISTIE, R. V. Dyspnoea: A review. *Quart. J. Med.*, 1938, *7*:421–454.

6. CHRISTIE, R. V. Elastic properties of emphysematous lung and their clinical significance. *J. clin. Invest.*, 1934, *13*:295–321.

7. CHRISTIE, R. V. and McINTOSH, C. A. Measurement of intrapleural pressure in man and its significance. *J. clin. Invest.*, 1934, *13*:279–294.

8. CHRISTIE, R. V. and McINTOSH, C. A. The lung volume and respiratory exchange after pneumothorax. *Quart. J. Med.*, 1936, *5*:445–454.

9. COURNAND, A. and RICHARDS, D. W., JR. Pulmonary insufficiency. I. Discussion of the physiological classification and presentation of clinical tests. *Amer. Rev. Tuberc.*, 1941, *44*:26–41.

10. DAVIES, P. W. and BRINK, F., JR. Microelectrodes for measuring local oxygen tension in animal tissues. *Rev. sci. Instrum.*, 1942, *13*:524–533.

11. DAVIS, E. W., McCULLOCH, W. S. and ROSEMAN, E. Rapid changes in the O_2 tension of cerebral cortex during induced convulsions. *Amer. J. Psychiat.*, 1944, *100*:825–829.

12. DRINKER, P. and McKHANN, C. F. The use of new apparatus for the prolonged administration of artificial respiration. *J. Amer. med. Soc.*, 1929, *92*:1658–1660.

13. ENGINEERING COMMITTEE OF CONFERENCE ON ELECTRIC SHOCK. Recent experience of public utilities of U. S. and Canada on use of Schäfer prone-pressure method of resuscitation. *J. indust. Hyg.*, 1928, *10*:117–127.

14. FLACK, M. Some simple tests of physical efficiency. *Lancet*, 1919 (1), *96*:210–212.

15. GESELL, R. Individuality of breathing. *Amer. J. Physiol.*, 1936, *115:*168–180.

16. GESELL, R. Fusillade patterns of inspiratory and expiratory muscles and their effects on the respiratory act. *Amer. J. Physiol.*, 1936, *116:*228–238.

17. GRAHAM, E. A. and BELL, R. D. Open pneumothorax: its relation to the treatment of empyema. *Amer. J. med. Sci.*, 1918, *156:*839–871.

18. HENDERSON, Y. and HAGGARD, H. W. The treatment of carbon monoxide asphyxia by means of oxygen + CO_2 inhalation. *J. Amer. med. Ass.*, 1922, *79:*1137–1145.

19. HERMANN, L. Das Verhalten des kindlichen Brustkastens bei der Geburt. *Pflüg. Arch. ges. Physiol.*, 1883, *30:*276–287.

20. HITCHCOCK, D. I. *Physical chemistry for students of biology and medicine*, 3rd ed. Springfield, Ill., Charles C Thomas, 1940. 266 pp.

21. HURTADO, A. and BOLLER, C. Studies of total pulmonary capacity and its subdivisions. I. Normal, absolute and relative values. *J. clin. Invest.*, 1933, *12:*793–806.

22. KEITH, A. *The mechanism of respiration in man: Further advances in physiology*. L. Hill, ed. London, E. Arnold & Co., 1909. 448 pp.

23. MACKLIN, C. C. The musculature of the bronchi and lungs. *Physiol. Rev.*, 1929, *9:*1–60.

24. MEAKINS, J. C. Dyspnea. *J. Amer. med. Ass.*, 1934, *103:*1442–1445.

25. MELTZER, S. J. On the respiratory changes of intrathoracic pressure, measured in the mediastinum posterior. *J. Physiol.*, 1892, *13:*218–238.

26. MILLER, W. S. *The lung.* Springfield, Ill., Charles C Thomas, 1937. xiv, 209 pp.

27. PETERS, J. P. and VAN SLYKE, D. D. *Quantitative clinical chemistry. Vol. II. Methods.* Baltimore, Williams & Wilkins Co., 1931. 1264 pp.

28. PEABODY, F. W. and WENTWORTH, J. D. Clinical studies of the respiration. IV. The vital capacity of the lungs and its relation to dyspnea. *Arch. intern. Med.*, 1917, *20:*443–467.

29. SCHAFER, E. A. Description of a simple and efficient method of performing artificial respiration in the human subject, especially in cases of drowning. *Med.-chir. Trans., Lond.*, 1903–04, *87:*609–623.

30. SCHAFER, E. A. Artificial respiration in its physiological aspects. *J. Amer. med. Ass.*, 1908, *51:*801–803.

31. SEEVERS, M. H. O_2 and CO_2 tensions in subcutaneous tissues of normal subjects. *Amer. J. Physiol.*, 1936, *115:*38–42.

32. WEST, H. F. Clinical studies on respiration. VI. Comparison of various standards for normal vital capacity of the lungs. *Arch. intern. Med.*, 1920, *25:*306–316.

33. WIGGERS, C. J. Physiological meaning of common clinical signs and symptoms in cardiovascular disease. *J. Amer. med. Ass.*, 1931, *96:*603–610.

CHAPTER 40

GAS EXCHANGE AND TRANSPORTATION

The essential constituents of atmospheric air important to the subject of respiration are O_2, N_2, and H_2O. The rare gases, argon, krypton, etc., have not been shown to have biological significance and in physiological gas analyses are determined and included with the values reported for N_2. The air we breathe, with respect to N_2, O_2 and CO_2, has a remarkably uniform composition. Samples of dry air taken from many sites, from sea level to the highest attainable altitudes, on analysis have given practically identical results. Man and other air breathing animals have not developed a method of O_2 storage, but are dependent upon a continuous gas exchange with the ocean of air surrounding them. Interruption of this exchange for more than a few minutes may result in a quick death.

The essential facts of external respiration are to be found in a knowledge of the compositions of inspired, expired and alveolar air. Respired air loses O_2 and gains CO_2; the blood in consequence absorbs O_2 and loses CO_2. At rest we absorb some 250 cc. of O_2 per minute and eliminate 200 cc. of CO_2. During exercise the amounts of gas exchanged may increase tenfold or more. The composition of expired air varies, of course, with the depth and frequency of the breathing movements, but the respiratory mechanisms are so controlled (Chap. 41) that the alveolar air is maintained with but slight change in composition despite wide fluctuations in the demand for O_2. Table 36 contains representative values for the composition of dry inspired, expired and alveolar air in the resting state.

Table 36.—*Composition of Dry Inspired, Expired and Alveolar Air in Man at Rest, in Mols per Cent or Volumes per Cent*

	N_2 Mols %	O_2 Mols %	CO_2 Mols %
Inspired air	79.02	20.94	0.04
Expired air	79.07	16.3	4.4
Alveolar air	80.4	14.0	5.6

The amount of O_2 absorbed is somewhat greater than the amount of CO_2 given off. This apparent discrepancy is explained by the general fact that O_2 is used to oxidize not only the C but also the H_2 of the ingested food; consequently, while most of the O_2 is eliminated in the expired air as CO_2, some of it is excreted as H_2O. The ratio of the amount of CO_2 expired to the amount of O_2 absorbed is called the respiratory quotient (R.Q.). Man on an ordinary mixed diet has an R.Q. of about 0.85 (43). If he were deriving his energy solely from carbohydrate sources his R.Q. theoretically would be unity.

Sugars may be considered as hydrated carbon compounds and no additional O_2 is needed for removal of H_2, as the following chemical reaction demonstrates:

$$C_6H_{12}O_6 + 6O_2 = 6CO_2 + 6H_2O$$

Knowledge of the R.Q. is helpful in interpreting data on O_2 consumption (15), and is necessary if the caloric value of a given amount of consumed O_2 is to be estimated (Chap. 50).

Physiological significance of N_2. The difference in concentration of the N_2 in the inspired and expired air recorded in Table 36 is not brought about by production of N_2 gas in the body; it is simply a reflection of the inequality in the amounts of O_2 and CO_2 exchanged. There is no known metabolic reaction of the human body in which molecular N_2 participates. In ordinary circumstances, N_2 acts merely as a dilutant of the O_2 in the air breathed. The N_2 in the body is in simple physical solution and exists in all the tissues and the blood at a pressure equal to its average partial pressure in the alveolar air. Caisson workers and deep sea divers of necessity breathe air under greatly increased pressure, and the amount of N_2 dissolved in their tissues at equilibrium increases in direct proportion to the enhanced partial pressures of this gas in their alveolar air. When the men return to normal pressures the tissues are supersaturated with respect to N_2, and if they are too rapidly decompressed, this gas is released from solution in the form of small bubbles distributed in many tissues and in the blood stream (24, 25). These gas bubbles, by mechanical distension of the tissues and by formation of aero-emboli, can produce a variety of clinical symptoms (29), characterized chiefly by pain, and collectively designated as *decompression sickness*. The aviator who flies above 25,000 feet may also experience decompression sickness, for his tissues are supersaturated with N_2 at the prevailing pressure. Decompression sickness can be avoided if decompression is accomplished slowly, or as is possible with the aviator, by eliminating a large part of the N_2 from the body before ascent. Under atmospheric pressures, the average man has about 1.5 liters of N_2 dissolved in his body tissues (6, 8).

Respiration and temperature control. The expired air is warmed nearly to or to the body temperature and is saturated with water vapor. Since the air we inspire is usually much cooler than the body and is far from being saturated with water vapor, it is evident that the act of breathing entails a considerable loss of body heat. Breathing is, in fact, one of the means by which the body temperature is regulated, although in man it is a subsidiary means. In other animals (the dog, for example), panting is a very important aid in controlling body temperature. Heat is lost in respiration not simply by warming the air in the air passages, but also by evaporation of water in the alveoli. The conversion of water from the liquid to the gaseous form is attended by the absorption of heat, and the lungs account for about 10 per cent of the heat exchange of the body.

Partial pressure and gas exchange. Exact measurements of the partial pressure of O_2 in the air, in the alveoli, in the arterial blood, and in the tissues demonstrate that the pressure of O_2 decreases as the cells are approached. O_2 flows from a region where its partial pressure is higher to one where its partial pressure is lower, down a pressure gradient, and at no place in the respiratory system is it necessary to assume secretion, a movement of O_2

against the partial pressure gradient, to explain the exchange. CO_2 is produced in the cells and exists there at the highest partial pressure, while in the external air the partial pressure of CO_2 is very low. CO_2, like O_2, diffuses down a pressure gradient. The partial pressures of O_2 and CO_2 in the alveolar air, the blood and the tissues determine the quantity of O_2 and CO_2 held in physical solution, the rapidity with which O_2 and CO_2 are transferred across limiting membranes and the extent to which there are completed certain of the reversible chemical reactions important for the carriage of the respiratory gases by the blood. In Table 37 are listed representative values for the partial pressures of the various respiratory gases at selected sites in the respiratory circuit.

Table 37.—*The Partial Pressures of the Respiratory Gases at Various Sites in the Respiratory Circuit of a Man at Rest.*

SAMPLE	GAS PARTIAL PRESSURE				
	O_2	CO_2	N_2	H_2O	TOTAL
	mm. Hg	mm. Hg	mm. Hg	mm. Hg	mm. Hg
Inspired air	158	0.3	596	5.7	760
Expired air	116	29	568	47	760
Alveolar air	100	40	573	47	760
Arterial blood	100	40	573	47	760
Venous blood	40	46	573	47	706
Tissues	30 or less	50 or more	573	47	700

GAS EXCHANGE IN THE LUNGS

The exchange of respiratory gases across the capillary and alveolar endothelium takes place with great rapidity. Venous blood enters the lung capillaries with a partial pressure of O_2 below and a partial pressure of CO_2 above that of the alveolar air (Table 37), and in the 0.7 of a second or so that the blood remains in the alveolar capillaries (45) it comes to practical equilibrium with the alveolar air (14). The rates at which the gases are exchanged across the alveolar surface are governed by several factors. These are: (i) the true partial pressures of the respiratory gases in the alveolar air and the capillary blood, (ii) the permeability of the limiting membranes to O_2 and CO_2, (iii) the rates of reaction of the respective gases with the blood constituent, (iv) the area of the absorbing surface, (v) the time the blood is in contact with the breathing surface, and (vi) the volume of blood exposed to the alveolar air at any one time. That the mechanisms of external respiration are extremely efficient is indicated by the fact that even under the conditions of greatest O_2 uptake, strenuous exercise, the arterial blood leaves the lungs with a full complement of O_2.

Alveolar function. The alveoli form an effective mechanism for gas exchange. They consist of an extensive network of capillaries (Fig. 411), held together by alveolar endothelium, probably the richest capillary network in the entire body (39). The capillaries are almost entirely surrounded by alveolar air and O_2 has only to diffuse through two thin layers of cells, the pulmonary and the capillary endothelium, a distance of 1 to 2 μ (34) in order to reach the blood. Some observers believe that the alveolar lining is discontinuous, and that only the capillary endothelium separates the blood from the pulmonary air (33). The total respiratory surface of the lungs has been variously estimated at from 50 to 100 square meters, 25 to 50 times the surface area of the body (18, 54).

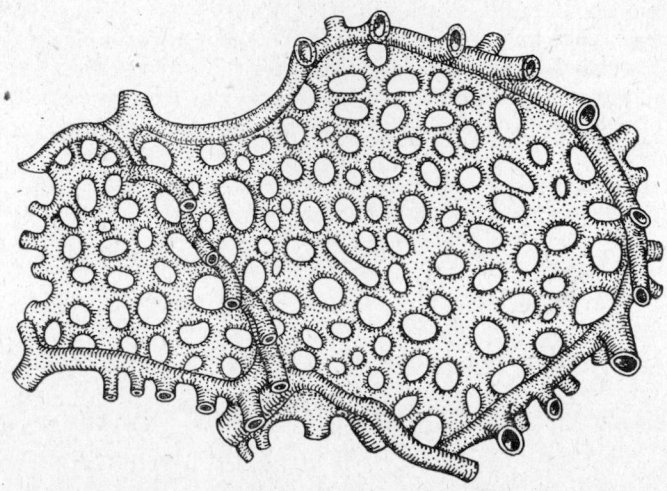

Fig. 411.—The capillary network in the lungs. Note the extensive absorption surface presented by the capillaries. (Redrawn from Miller, *The Lung*, 1937.)

In exercise, when the demands for O_2 are increased, the ventilation is also increased. More O_2 is taken into the lungs and is carried away by the arterial blood. Two factors are largely responsible for bringing about the augmented removal of O_2 from the lungs. The cardiac output is raised and more blood flows through the lungs, an adjustment that can account for a seven- or eight-fold increase in the amount of O_2 absorbed. The venous blood contains less

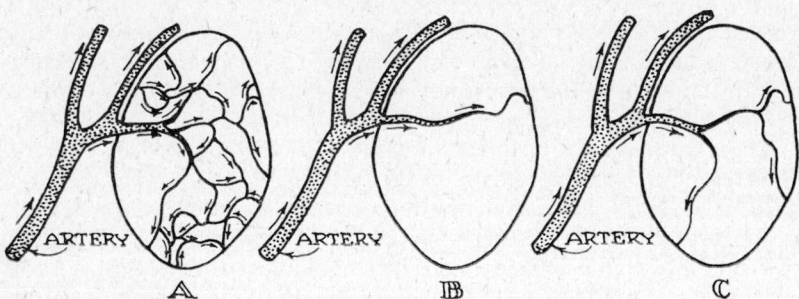

Fig. 412.—Spontaneous changes in the blood flow through a pulmonary air sac. The changes indicated would have the physiological effect of adjusting the area of the breathing surface to the O_2 needs of the animal. (From Wearn *et al.*, *Amer. J. Physiol.*, 1934, *109*:236–256.)

O_2, having lost more to the tissues, and consequently can pick up a larger amount of O_2 per unit volume while in the lungs. This arrangement can greatly increase the amount of O_2 absorbed. The lungs themselves are not entirely passive in meeting the requirements of exercise. Wearn *et al.* (53) have observed spontaneous variations in the blood supply to the air sacs (Fig. 412). Such a mechanism would serve the useful function of adjusting the area of the breathing surface to the needs of the moment. The investigations of Roughton (45) indicate that the changes in alveolar capillary circulation are probably not as great as might be inferred from Figure 412. Roughton found that the amount of blood (95 cc.) in the alveolar capillaries while the subject was at hard work was somewhat less than double the amount present (60 cc.) during resting conditions.

Alveolar air. The air in the lungs that is important physiologically is that portion in gaseous equilibrium with the arterial blood, the *alveolar air*. Strictly speaking, this is the air in direct contact with the alveolar surface. It is difficult to obtain samples of this air for chemical examination, but for most physiological work it is assumed that the air obtained at the end of a maximal expiration is representative of the composition of alveolar air. A modification of the procedure originally employed by Haldane and Priestley (22, 23) is generally used. A maximal expiration is made through a long rubber tube of about an inch in diameter, and the last fraction of air issuing from the depths of the lungs is trapped and analyzed. The exact composition of this air is a function, among other things, of the phase of the respiratory cycle and the time required to exhale the air. At present the end expiratory sample is considered to be most representative of the average condition of the alveolar air. Comroe and Dripps (12) found that end expiratory alveolar air samples of normal men contained O_2 at a partial pressure of 97.4 mm. Hg. The average partial pressure of O_2 in the arterial blood of these same subjects was 97.1 mm. Hg. The close agreement between the two sets of data demonstrate that arterial blood is nearly in perfect gaseous equilibrium with the alveolar air.

The manner in which new air reaches the alveolar surface is still somewhat unsettled. Macklin (37) believes that the alveolar sacs are not simply passively dilated but that the alveolar ducts lengthen, enlarge their lumen and increase the size of the openings into the alveolar sacs. With the increase in volume and the drop in pressure in these regions, air rushes in. The currents set up by the incoming air and the process of gaseous diffusion serve to mix the air in the alveolar sacs (13) and rapidly bring this gas to a uniform composition. It is probable that not all of the alveolar air sacs reach the same composition, particularly if disease or congestion is present. In these instances the more poorly ventilated alveoli would tend to approach gaseous equilibrium with the venous blood, and the blood passing through these alveoli would not be arterialized. Meltzer (38) showed that air currents in the trachea without respiratory movements were adequate to keep an animal alive for long periods of time. He inserted a tube down the trachea to the region of the bifurcation and supplied air or O_2 under gentle pressure. In such circumstances the major portion of O_2 that reaches the alveolar surface must do so by gaseous diffusion through the gas phase, demonstrating that gaseous diffusion is adequate to meet the O_2 requirements of a resting animal. The large variation shown by different individuals in the efficiency with which they abstract O_2 from the inhaled air is due in large part to the efficiency with which they renew their alveolar air. The asthmatic, for example, despite an ample tidal volume, may be anoxic. His finer respiratory passages are probably so constricted that inspired air traverses the alveolar ducts with difficulty, and in consequence the partial pressure of O_2 in his alveolar air may drop to abnormally low values.

30

Diffusion of gases through body tissues. The volume of gas in cc. that is transferred per minute across the pulmonary membranes when the difference in the partial pressure of the gas in the alveolar air and the capillary blood is 1 mm. Hg has been designated by Krogh (35) as the *diffusion constant* of the lungs. Krogh found the diffusion constant of O_2 to vary from a minimum of 20, resting conditions, to a maximum of 60 during exercise. The average pressure gradient across the alveolar membrane is difficult to determine. Venous blood may have a partial pressure of 40 mm. Hg or less. Since the alveolar air contains O_2 at 100 mm. Hg, the pressure gradient as the blood enters the alveolar capillaries is 60 mm. Hg. As the blood picks up its O_2, the gradient in partial pressure falls. Assuming the average pressure gradient is only one-third of the maximal, $20 \times 20 = 400$ cc. O_2 would be delivered to the blood per minute, a value well above the resting requirements of 250 cc. per minute. The maximal gas exchange (3500 cc. of O_2 or more) during exercise can also be accounted for by diffusion. The product of the diffusion constant by the average pressure gradient exceeds the amount of O_2 transferred. The blood may not remain long enough in the lungs during exercise to approach as close to gaseous equilibrium with alveolar air as it does in the resting state.

The intrinsic rate of diffusion of any substance is a function of its solubility, its molecular weight and the permeability of the medium. CO_2 is a larger molecule than O_2, but its solubility is so high in the body fluids that it diffuses through the tissues 20 to 30 times as rapidly as O_2. There is no difficulty, therefore, in accounting for the exchange of CO_2 in the lungs in spite of the much smaller pressure difference driving the CO_2 out of the blood. In a carefully controlled study, Jones *et al.* (32) have demonstrated that for substances of small molecular weight, diffusion does not seem to be a limiting factor in the exchange between the blood and the tissues anywhere in the body. They found the rate at which a variety of substances were exchanged between the blood and the tissues to be proportional to two factors: (i) the volume of blood flowing through a unit volume of tissue per minute, and (ii) the solubility of the substance in the tissue fluids.

TRANSPORT OF O_2 AND CO_2

Blood (26) can absorb a much greater quantity of O_2 and CO_2 than can be carried in simple solution. Hemoglobin (HHb)* has the chemical property of combining reversibly with both O_2 and CO_2. If the blood contained no HHb, a circulating blood volume 75 times as great as the normal would be needed to satisfy the requirements for O_2. The affinity of HHb for O_2 is so nicely adjusted that the blood leaves the lungs fully oxygenated, yet all of the O_2 can be released in the tissues. The combination of HHb with O_2, HHb $+$ $O_2 \rightleftharpoons HHbO_2$, is regulated by the partial pressure of O_2. In the lungs, at a partial pressure of 100 mm. Hg the reaction is 97 per cent complete. In the tissues, 60 per cent of the O_2 in the blood is released at a pressure greater than 20 mm. Hg.

Blood contains somewhat less than 15 grams of HHb per 100 cc. Each gram of HHb can combine with 1.34 cc. of O_2 so that blood fully oxygenated contains 20 cc. of O_2 per 100 cc. of blood (the O_2 capacity of the blood).

* HHb is used to denote un-ionized hemoglobin, and also the fact that hemoglobin acts as an acid.

Since HHb does not become 100 per cent saturated with O_2 until the pressure of O_2 is 150 mm. Hg, arterial blood leaving the lungs is only 98 per cent saturated (14). The amount of O_2 per 100 cc. of blood in a particular sample is designated as the O_2 content of the blood.

O_2 dissociation curve. If samples of blood are equilibrated with air containing O_2 at various partial pressures and the O_2 content of the samples determined, it is found that the amount of O_2 in the blood is not directly proportional to the partial pressures. A plot of the observed O_2 contents against the partial pressures of O_2 at equilibrium is distinctly S-shaped (Fig. 413). Although the chemical properties of HHb have been intensively studied (5), a simple explanation of the S-shaped dissociation curve of $HHbO_2$ in whole blood has not been given (41). The dissociation curve of purified $HHbO_2$ is hyperbolic in character. This is the expected result if the combination of O_2

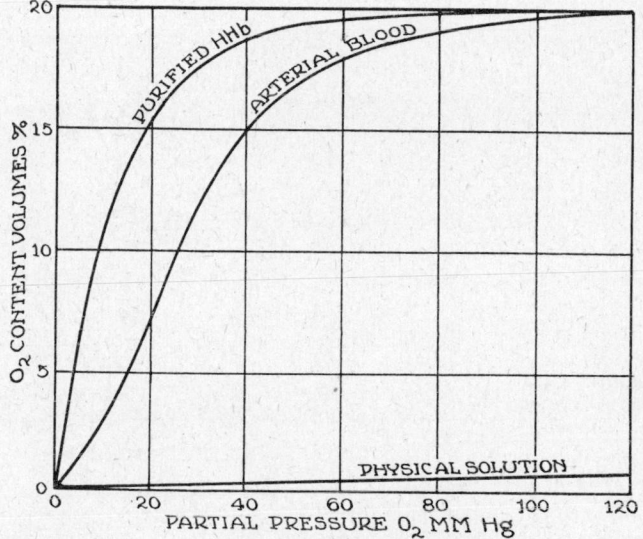

Fig. 413.—The O_2 contents of arterial blood and plasma (physical solution) and a solution of purified HHb at various partial pressures of O_2. Note the difference in shape of the absorption curves of purified HHb and arterial blood and the small amount of O_2 carried in physical solution.

with HHb is according to the reaction $HHb + O_2 = HHbO_2$. Studies of purified HHb solutions (4) have shown that the oxygenation reaction of HHb is markedly affected by the CO_2 content, the acidity, the ionic concentration, and the temperature of the medium in which the HHb is dissolved. The concentration of HHb itself is not without effect. Concentrated solutions of purified $HHbO_2$ give a distinctly S-shaped curve. The S-shaped dissociation of whole blood is most likely due to a summation of the various factors enumerated, the more important being the salt composition of blood and the fact that the HHb of blood is contained in highly concentrated form on the interior of the erythrocyte.

The actual shape of the O_2 dissociation curve of blood is of definite physiological significance. The flat portion at O_2 pressures above 80 mm. Hg insures a practically constant composition of arterial blood in the face of quite wide variations of the alveolar O_2 pressure. The steep portion between 20 and 60 mm. Hg O_2 pressure insures delivery of a large amount of the blood O_2 to the tissues with a reasonable head of pressure. An increase in salt concentration or an increase in temperature will shift the O_2 dissociation curve to the right. Less O_2 is held by the HHb at a given partial pressure of O_2. The temperature effect is of some aid in releasing O_2 to the tissues, for in the vicinity of actively metabolizing cells the temperature is somewhat higher than in resting tissues, and the rise in temperature results in a more ready release of the O_2.

Effect of CO_2 and pH on the O_2 dissociation curve. Likewise an increase in either the CO_2 pressure or the acidity of blood (10) will favor the dissociation of $HHbO_2$ (Fig. 414). The effect of CO_2 is particularly important physiologically, for the production of CO_2 by the tissues automatically favors the transfer of O_2. In fact, the amount of O_2 (or CO_2) the blood will hold is in-

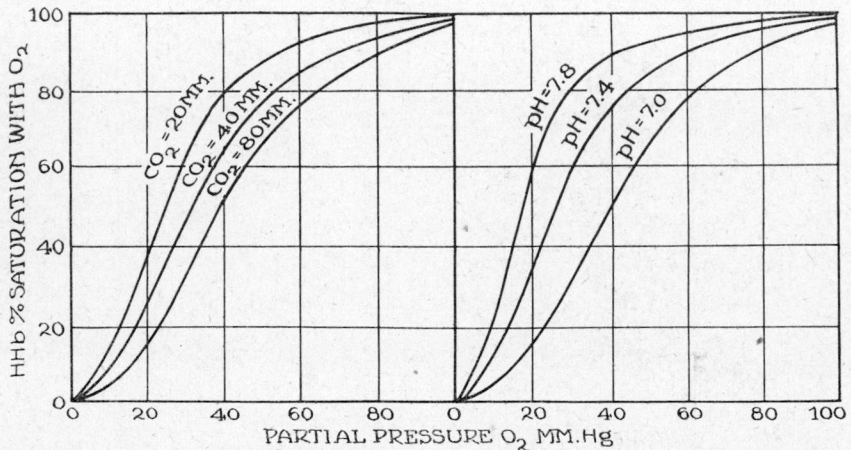

Fig. 414.—The effect of increased CO_2 pressure and increased acidity (decreased *p*H) upon the oxygen dissociation curve of whole blood. An increase of temperature also shifts the curves to the right and enhances the ease with which O_2 is unloaded in the tissues.

versely proportional to the partial pressure of CO_2 (or O_2) in the blood. The action of CO_2 in releasing O_2 from the blood is twofold. CO_2 increases the acidity of blood (lowers the *p*H) and forms carbamino compounds ($HHbCO_2$) with the hemoglobin. $HHbCO_2$ has much less affinity for O_2 than HHb (44). Both factors result in lowering the amount of O_2 blood will hold at a given O_2 pressure and greatly increase the ease with which O_2 reaches the tissues.

Condition of CO_2 in the blood. The blood contains a small amount of CO_2 in simple physical solution, but the major portion is carried in chemical combination. The forms of combined CO_2 recognized now are carbonic acid (H_2CO_3) and bicarbonate ion (HCO_3^-) present in both cells and plasma, and carbamino hemoglobin (CO_2HHb). All the forms of CO_2 are in chemical equilibrium with one another. A further complication is that the red cell is relatively impermeable to cations and at equilibrium the concentration of HCO_3^- in the cell is different from that in the plasma. A dissociation curve of CO_2 in blood can be obtained in the same way as one is obtained for O_2. Blood is equilibrated with gases containing CO_2 at various partial pressures, and the

CO_2 content of the equilibrated blood is determined by blood gas analysis. The form of the CO_2 absorption curve for both oxidized and reduced blood is given in Figure 415. The curves demonstrate that the dissociation of CO_2 is affected by partial pressure of O_2 in a fashion similar to the way the O_2 dissociation curve was affected by CO_2 pressure. Increase of either the CO_2 content or the O_2 content of the whole blood means that the O_2 pressure or the CO_2 pressure respectively is increased. The absorption of O_2 aids in the unloading of CO_2 in the lungs and the absorption of CO_2 aids in the unloading of O_2 in the tissues.

In a vacuum a $NaHCO_3$ solution gives off only half its contained CO_2. $2NaHCO_3 \rightleftharpoons Na_2CO_2 + CO_2 + H_2O$. Plasma behaves like a simple bicarbonate solution. More of its bicarbonate is extracted in a vacuum, however, because of the presence of phosphoric and other weak acids which aid in driving off its CO_2. Whole blood, on the other hand, will release all of its CO_2 to a vacuum. The difference in behavior between whole blood and plasma

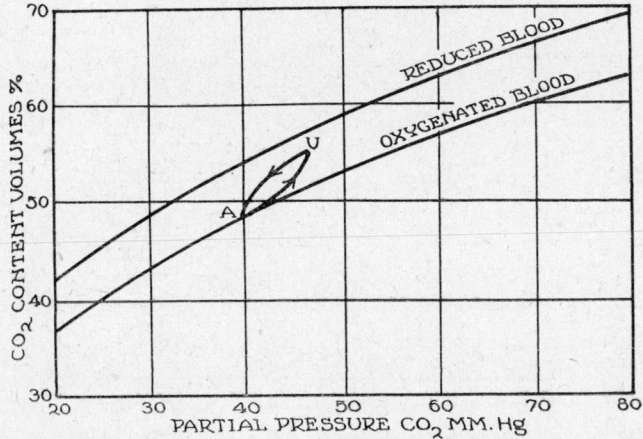

Fig. 415.—The CO_2 titration curve of whole blood. Note that oxygenated blood contains less CO_2 at a given partial pressure of CO_2 than reduced blood. Blood goes through a cycle, as indicated by A (arterial blood) and V (venous blood), in the capillaries of the tissues and the lungs.

or bicarbonate solutions is due to the acid properties of Hb. Both Hb and HbO_2 can furnish sufficient H^+ to carry the reaction $H^+ + HCO_3^- \rightleftharpoons H_2CO_3 \rightleftharpoons H_2O + CO_2$ to completion. $HHbO_2$ is a stronger acid than HHb. In the lungs, as O_2 enters the blood, the following series of reversible chemical reactions take place:

$$O_2 + HHb \rightleftharpoons HHbO_2 \rightleftharpoons HbO_2^- + H^+$$
$$H^+ + HCO_3^- \rightleftharpoons H_2CO_3 \rightleftharpoons H_2O + CO_2$$

The $HHbO_2$ releases H^+ to combine with HCO_3^-. Since the reactions are reversible, an increase of either O_2 or CO_2 in the blood will, in accordance with the law of mass action, drive the reaction in the appropriate direction. The actual titration curves of $HHbO_2$ and HHb with NaOH are given in Figure 416. From this figure it is apparent that the oxygenation of HHb can furnish 0.7 mol of H^+ to combine with HCO_3^- per mol of O_2 absorbed.

HHbCO_2. Recent investigations (49) of the state of CO_2 in the blood have indicated that approximately one-fifth of the total CO_2 is carried by the blood as $HHbCO_2$ in which, as first suggested by Henriques (28), the CO_2 is combined directly with the amino groups of the HHb molecules.

$$HHbNH_2 + CO_2 \rightleftharpoons HHbNHCOOH$$

Other protein molecules in the blood besides the HHb molecules can probably carry CO_2 in the same manner. The product formed by the combination of CO_2 with HHb is physiologically the more important of the carbamino compounds because it enters into a reversible reaction with O_2.

$$O_2 + HHbCO_2 \rightleftharpoons HHbO_2 + CO_2$$

This is an important reaction in the respiratory exchange, since it provides a rapid method (44) by which CO_2 can be taken up or released without marked changes in pH.

Velocity of the reactions. The complex series of chemical reactions that takes place in the blood as it gains or loses O_2 and CO_2 is apparently com-

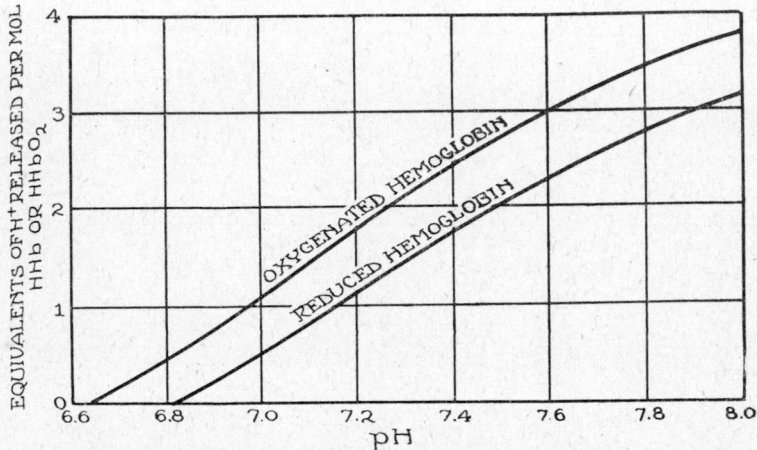

Fig. 416.—The acid-base titration curves of oxygenated and reduced HHb. As O_2 is released from HbO_2^-, the weaker base Hb^- can combine with H^+ to form HHb. For each mol of O_2 given up to the tissues, 0.7 of a mol of H^+ from the ionization of H_2CO_3 can be neutralized by the Hb without a change in pH (isohydric cycle).

pleted within the time the blood is passing through the capillaries (0.7 sec.). Roughton and others (44) have investigated the velocities of the various reactions and found that they are all rapid enough to accomplish this end with the single exception of the reaction which comprises the hydration of CO_2 $H_2O + CO_2 \xrightarrow{slow} H_2CO_3$). In a search for an explanation of the apparent speed with which this reaction is accomplished in the body, an enzyme, carbonic anhydrase, was discovered. This enzyme is not present in the plasma, but is found, like hemoglobin, in the red cells. Carbonic anhydrase speeds up the hydration of CO_2 and the dehydration of H_2CO_3 so that these reactions are also completed by the time the blood has left the capillaries.

GAS EXCHANGE IN THE TISSUES

A summary can now be given of the chemical reactions that take place in the blood, as O_2 is delivered to the tissues. Figure 417 contains in outline form the important steps in the sequence of events. The series of reactions is reversed in the lungs. CO_2 being continually produced in the tissue cells, exists there at the highest partial pressures. Diffusion of CO_2 from the cells, through the interstitial fluid, the capillary walls, and into the plasma takes place. Some of the CO_2 reacts slowly with H_2O in the plasma to form H_2CO_3 which in turn ionizes and liberates H+. A considerable part of the H+ immediately combines with the plasma proteins which tend to buffer the plasma (see Chap. 27). The major portion of the CO_2 diffuses into the red corpuscles where it can carry out two reactions. The CO_2 can combine with water exactly as it did in the plasma; however, the reaction is rapid since it is cata-lyzed by carbonic anhydrase. The H+ that is eventually released is taken up by HbO_2^- to form HHb and O_2, and the resultant O_2 diffuses out of the cell to supply the largest fraction of the O_2 gained by the tissues from the blood.

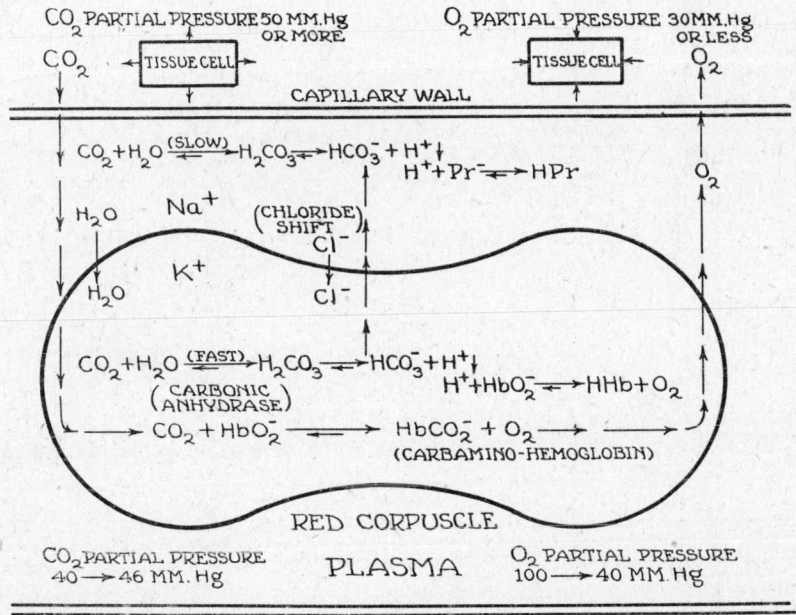

Fig. 417.—Schema to summarize the more important chemical reactions by which O_2 is made available to the tissues. The forces initiating and controlling the exchange of gases are the gra-dients in partial pressure of CO_2 and of O_2 between the capillary blood and the tissue cells.

This series of chemical reactions in the erythrocyte has been designated as the *isohydric* cycle because the uptake of CO_2 and the release of O_2 is ac-complished without the production of an excess of H+. The buffering power of HbO_2^- allows a large amount of CO_2 to be absorbed and O_2 to be given off without marked change in acidity. The excess HCO_3^- diffuses out of the cell into the plasma. Since more HCO^- diffuses out than H+ is taken by HbO_2^-, some slight excess of H+ is left in the red cell and Cl- moves in to restore the ionic balance. This exchange has been called the chloride shift and serves the useful purpose of allowing a great deal of HCO_3^- to be carried in the plasma. Some of the CO_2 combines with the various forms of HHb, the most important such reaction being with HbO_2^-, for this releases O_2 without involving a change in *p*H. The interrelations of O_2 and CO_2 in the red cell are only an example of the general mutual dependence of O_2 and CO_2 during the whole process of O_2 utilization.

Supply of O_2 to the tissues. The tissues absorb what O_2 they need from the blood and leave the rest. The amount absorbed per unit time is a function of the blood flow through the tissue and the pressure of O_2 in the tissue. Table 38 contains a quantitative statement of the exchange of O_2 and CO_2 in the brain (19).

The brain abstracts 6.7 volumes per cent of O_2 and delivers 6.6 volumes per cent of CO_2 to the blood. Brain differs somewhat from other tissues in having an R.Q. at all times close to unity. The coefficient of O_2 utilization is defined as the arterial-venous difference in O_2 concentration divided by the concentration of O_2 in the arterial blood. The brain has a coefficient of $6.7/19.6 = 34$ per cent. Active muscle can take all of the O_2 from the blood and thus have a coefficient of O_2 utilization approaching 100 per cent. When the activity of tissues increases and the need for O_2 is greater, the increased O_2 is supplied not from an increase in the O_2 content of the arterial blood, but by a greater flow of blood through the tissue. The capillaries dilate and

Table 38.—*Level of Certain Constituents of Arterial and Internal Jugular Blood in Healthy Young Men Lying Quietly at Rest. Averages for 50 Subjects.* (From Gibbs, *et al., J. biol. Chem.*, 1942, 144:325–332.)

CONSTITUENT	ARTERIAL BLOOD			INTERNAL JUGULAR BLOOD			ARTERIAL-VENOUS DIFF.		
	HIGH	LOW	AVERAGE	HIGH	LOW	AVERAGE	HIGH	LOW	AVERAGE
O_2 Content Vol. %	22.3	17.3	19.6	16.1	11.0	12.9	8.5	4.5	6.7
CO_2 Content Vol. %	50.4	44.6	48.2	57.7	51.0	54.8	8.3	4.4	6.6
CO_2 Pressure mm. Hg	44.9	36.2	39.9	54.3	46.9	49.9	12.8	6.6	10.0
pH at 38° C.	7.46	7.37	7.42	7.40	7.32	7.37	0.7	0.03	0.05

inactive capillaries open up. The increased blood flow brings more O_2 to the tissues. The pressure gradient between the capillaries and the active cells increases both because of the increased blood supply and because the cells are using O_2 at a faster rate. The venous blood returns from the cells with less O_2 than normal, and the coefficient of O_2 utilization is increased. The threefold or more increase in blood perfusion rate plus the threefold or more increase in the coefficient of O_2 utilization can mean a ninefold or more increase in the rate at which O_2 is supplied to tissues in vigorous activity.

Respiration and acid-base balance. The body has many defenses against an alteration of its acid-base balance (see Chap. 27). We have seen how O_2 and CO_2 are carried and exchanged in the blood at nearly constant pH. The blood becomes slightly more acid as it passes through the tissues. Blood flowing through the brain, for example, changes 0.05 of a pH unit (Table 38). In blood the buffer capacity is due largely to the proteins present, particularly the HHb. The body as a whole is buffered by a physiological mechanism (27). Respiration is so controlled (Chap. 42) that the partial pressure of CO_2 in the arterial blood does not deviate greatly in normal circumstances from 40 mm. Hg. If the CO_2 production in the body goes up slightly, ventilation increases and the elimination of CO_2 is rapidly adjusted so as to preserve the optimal acid-base conditions of the body. In a sense, respiration represents the first line of defense of the body against acid-base changes.

Combination of CO with HHb. HHb combines reversibly with CO in the same manner that O_2 does. The affinity of HHb for CO is 200 to 300 times greater than its affinity for O_2 so that HHb can be saturated at very low pressures of CO (46). The rate of reaction of HHb with CO is much slower than with O_2 (17). If a person is exposed to CO, an appreciable length of time is required for the CO level of the blood to reach equilibrium with the alveolar air. Like the dissociation of $HHbO_2$, the dissociation of HHbCO is markedly affected by pH, temperature, and CO_2 concentration. In addition, the reaction $HHbCO + O_2 \rightleftharpoons HHbO_2 + CO$ is displaced to the right by an increase in the O_2 pressure (law of mass action) and an increase in CO_2 pressure. For this reason, 5 or 7 per cent CO_2 in O_2 is a very effective gas mixture to use in treatment of patients who have been exposed to CO. The augmented ventilation brought about by the CO_2 also aids in the elimination of CO. The pressure gradient of CO across the alveoli is increased and CO diffuses more rapidly out of the blood.

ANOXIA

Whenever the cells of the body do not have or cannot use sufficient O_2 to carry on normal function, they are said to be suffering from anoxia. Oxygen lack represents a condition of extreme hazard to the integrity of the body. In the words of Haldane (2), anoxemia not only causes "stoppage of a machine, it is also the total ruin of the supposed machinery." Under ordinary circumstances the body has effective means of preventing anoxia, but in unusual conditions even mild degrees of anoxia lead to a vicious circle, which if not broken results in rapid deterioration and death. It is possible to distinguish between four general types of anoxia. The first three, designated by Barcroft (2) as (i) *stagnant*, (ii) *anoxic*, and (iii) *anemic* anoxia, arise respectively when (i) the flow of blood through a tissue is reduced, (ii) the exchange of O_2 across the lungs is interfered with, and (iii) the O_2 carrying capacity of blood is reduced. The fourth form, designated by Peters and Van Slyke (42) as histotoxic anoxia, occurs when the tissue cells cannot make efficient use of the O_2 available to them. Figure 418 illustrates how a knowledge of the O_2 content and the per cent saturation of arterial and venous blood enables one to distinguish between the various types of anoxia. The arterial blood has normal O_2 content in stagnant and histotoxic anoxia and a reduced O_2 content in anoxic and anemic anoxia. The venous blood contains less O_2 than normal in stagnant, anoxic and anemic anoxia, while in histotoxic anoxia the O_2 content of the venous blood is above normal. In anemic anoxia the O_2 carrying capacity of the blood is reduced below normal.

Stagnant anoxia. When the blood flow is reduced, stagnant anoxia develops. The reduction in flow may appear locally as a result of interference with the peripheral circulation as is the circumstance in arterial spasm, Raynaud's disease, embolism, or in diseases of the blood vessels. It may occur generally as it does in shock, cardiac weakness or vasomotor collapse. The military aviator in executing certain maneuvers of the airplane may suffer for short periods from stagnant anoxia of the retinas and the brain, resulting in a loss of vision followed by unconsciousness. The heart cannot pump blood against the high centrifugal forces developed during rapid turns and the brain is deprived of blood. Occlusion of the blood supply to the brain leads to unconsciousness within 6 seconds. The O_2 content of arterial blood is normal in stagnant anoxia, but the venous blood is characterized by a low per cent saturation in O_2. The blood flows through the tissues more slowly than usual and more O_2 per unit volume of blood is taken up by the tissues.

Anoxic anoxia. A reduction of the partial pressure of O_2 in the arterial blood produces anoxic anoxia. The effects are general and the conditions may be produced in a variety of ways. Anoxic anoxia is encountered in pneumonia, in drowning, in paralysis of the respiratory muscles, or from breathing gases deficient in O_2. Anoxic anoxia limits the altitudes men can attain either by

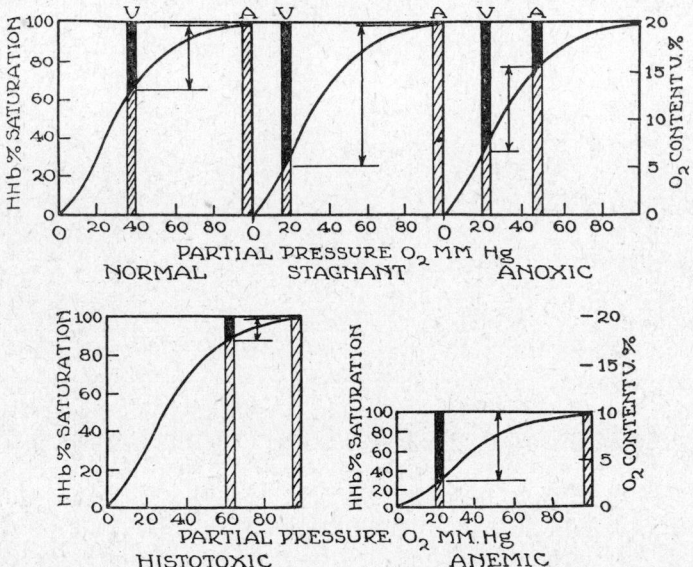

Fig. 418.—The composition of arterial (A) and venous (B) blood found in various types of anoxia and their relation to the O_2 absorption curve of hemoglobin. The cross-hatched areas indicate the amount of $HHbO_2$ present in the blood. The amount of O_2 removed from the blood as it passes through the tissues is expressed as the difference in O_2 content of the arterial and venous blood.

climbing or in an airplane. Paul Bert (9) demonstrated in 1870 that the deleterious effects of reduced barometric pressures were due not to the lowered barometric pressure, but to the lowered partial pressure of O_2. Modern high altitude flights in airplanes would have been impossible if equipment had not been developed to supply the aviator with O_2 at partial pressures approximating 150 mm. Hg. Anoxic anoxia is characterized by a low percentage saturation of the arterial and venous blood with O_2.

Histotoxic anoxia. When the utilization of O_2 by the cells is interfered with, histotoxic anoxia ensues. Alcohol, narcotics, and certain poisons such as cyanide interfere with the ability of the cells to make use of the O_2 available to them even though the supply is normal in all respects. Histotoxic anoxia is characterized by a venous O_2 saturation higher than normal. The blood in passing through the tissues does not unload its O_2 since the cells are unable to metabolize the delivered O_2. The anoxia produced may be either general or local, depending upon the distribution of the disturbing substances.

Anemic anoxia. When a reduction in the O_2 carrying capacity of the blood occurs, the result is anemic anoxia. This may occur either because there is insufficient HHb in the blood or because some of the HHb has been modified so that it can no longer transport O_2. The effects produced are general. A primary loss of HHb occurs in anemia, or after hemorrhage. Nitrites, chlorates and many other substances can change HHb into methemoglobin, a modification of HHb which has lost the ability to combine reversibly with O_2. CO produces anemic anoxia by blocking the reactive groups of HHb with which O_2 combines. Anemic anoxia is characterized by the reduced O_2 capacity values of arterial and venous blood.

Effects of O_2 Lack. In general, the symptoms associated with anoxia are more dependent upon the rapidity with which the anoxic state develops and the degree of anoxia reached than upon the type of anoxia present. This is understandable since the symptoms are the external expression of the malfunction of the anoxic cells, and it is of little moment at what stage in the respiratory process the interference with the delivery of O_2 occurs. The small differences that do exist between the various types of anoxia, with the exception of histotoxic anoxia, are to be explained by the differences in the partial pressures at which a given amount of O_2 can be delivered. In histotoxic anoxia the consequences of selectively blocking a particular chemical reaction in the oxidative chain can differ markedly from the effects of failing to provide adequate O_2 for carrying out the final steps. The symptoms of acute rapidly developing anoxia are like alcoholic intoxication, a form of histotoxic anoxia, while the symptoms of chronic anoxia are like fatigue (2). All of the cells and tissues in the body are affected in some degree by anoxia (52).

Fulminating anoxia. A rapid fall in the O_2 content of blood occurs when atmospheres deficient in O_2 are breathed, when cardiac arrest occurs, or when the breathing movements cease. Aviators at high altitudes who suddenly lose their O_2 supply, miners who walk into pockets of CH_4, or of N_2 and CO_2, and patients who are breathing N_2O undiluted with O_2 can collapse and become unconscious in a minute or less. Death may follow in a very short time unless proper treatment is immediately given. Recovery is equally rapid if the O_2 supply of the tissues is restored promptly, and is quite complete if the anoxic state has been of short duration. While the anoxic state is developing, the individual can become unconscious without ever being aware that he is in any danger, and he may, on being restored to a conscious state, deny the lapse of consciousness. During the induction of the anoxic state both the respiratory and the cardiovascular systems can be greatly stimulated. Hyperpnea, tachycardia and an elevated blood pressure may occur. As the anoxic state becomes profound the respiration slows, becomes gasping in character and finally ceases. The blood pressure falls and eventually the heart fails, usually a short time after the last breath has been taken.

Acute anoxia. If the anoxia develops more slowly, a variety of symptoms are produced. The symptoms of a mild anoxia, whether produced by alcohol, CO, or ascent in a plane to high altitudes, are indicative of malfunction of the central nervous system. At first there is a feeling of well-being, a feeling of increased satisfaction and power. As the anoxia becomes progressively greater, a period characterized by unstable emotions and loss of judgment supervenes. The individual loses critical capacity and is unaware of or cannot properly evaluate his deficiencies. Muscular incoordination, deterioration of vision and a memory loss may be pronounced. Fixity of ideas may be predominant and the individual will persist in doing foolish things even at extreme hazard to his own welfare. He may be unable to accomplish the simple procedure that will insure his safety. Hyperpnea may be pronounced or a feeling of lassitude and extreme weakness may set in. Nausea and vomiting frequently occur and the individual may suddenly collapse. Unconsciousness is often preceded by profound convulsions or may set in with cardiac syncope. The changes produced in respiration, in the heart rate and in the blood pressure are extremely variable (47), but a not uncommon finding is an increased ventilation and heart rate and an elevated blood pressure.

Chronic anoxia. If the anoxia develops so slowly that the compensating mechanisms of the body keep pace, the anoxia may be symptomless. The main effect is a loss of physiological reserve and the individual concerned suffers more or less limitation of his physical activities. Such an individual is easily fatigued, and as the chronic anoxia becomes more profound, he may become listless and constantly suffer from a feeling of extreme tiredness. Slight exertion will produce air hunger and dyspnea. Dwellers at high altitudes, even though acclimatized, may suffer at times from mountain sickness. The symptoms are headache, weakness, nausea, loss of appetite and occasionally stupor and coma (31). Rapid deterioration may set in without warning, and unless the chronic anoxia is relieved the individual may die in a cardiac crisis.

Acclimatization. The compensatory mechanisms of the body are stimulated by anoxia, and in mild degrees of anoxia the adjustment is complete and the individual becomes so perfectly adapted to his new internal and external environment that he can be ostensibly in perfect health under conditions that would be extremely hazardous if suddenly achieved. A person acclimatized to an elevation of 15,000 feet has an increased vital capacity and an increased minute volume of breathing (51). The amount of hemoglobin in the blood may almost double, an adaptation that takes several weeks to achieve (48). In fact, the O_2 capacity of the blood may be greater than normal although the partial pressure of O_2 in the alveoli and the arterial blood are much reduced (65 mm. Hg). The blood is distinctly more alkaline and contains less CO_2 at a slightly lower pressure. The acclimatization is not achieved without loss of physiological reserve. The amount of exercise required to increase the pulse rate at 14,000 feet is about 60 per cent of that at sea-level (3).

Cyanosis. Cyanosis has reference to a blue color of the skin. It may be a prominent feature of the various types of anoxia with the exception of histotoxic and some forms of anemic anoxia. In anoxia if the absolute amount of HHb (unsaturated hemoglobin) in the superficial capillaries of the skin is above 5 grams per 100 cc. of capillary blood, the skin develops a diffuse bluish color (36). Reduced HHb is purplish in hue, whereas oxygenated $HHbO_2$ is bright red in hue. It is obvious that cyanosis due to unsaturation of HHb is indicative of anoxia, but its absence does not mean anoxia is not present. In anemia there may not be enough reduced HHb at 50 per cent saturation to change the tint of the skin. The appearance of cyanosis is dependent upon the state of the capillaries, the pigmentation and the thickness of the skin. The variation in these factors from individual to individual makes cyanosis a poor indicator of the degree of anoxia. In the presence of polycythemia cyanosis is much enhanced and appears under conditions in which the normal subject shows no change at all. In anoxia produced by CO, cyanosis does not occur, since the HHbCO compound is a bright cherry red in color. Methemoglobin is dark in color, and when present in the blood in large amounts leads to appreciable cyanosis. Cyanosis occurs in normal individuals with the development of anoxic anoxia or stagnant anoxia. In the first instance arterial blood does not become fully saturated in the lung; in the second instance the blood is abnormally deoxygenated in the tissues.

Hyperpnea. A predominant feature of acute anoxia of the anoxic type is the hyperpnea produced and the attendant loss of CO_2. An animal on exposure to lowered barometric pressure increases its ventilation, CO_2 is washed out of the arterial blood and the blood becomes rapidly alkaline (11). If the degree of anoxia is not too great (arterial blood above 60 per cent saturation with O_2), the change in acid-base balance is characteristic of a respiratory alkalosis, the uncompensated loss of CO_2 (see p. 579). Mosso (40) was one of the first to recognize that a loss of CO_2 occurred and to insist upon the importance of *acapnia* in the production of the symptoms of acute anoxic anoxia. In many individuals the time sequence of symptoms during the development of anoxic anoxia are similar to the sequence of systems, subjective and objective, brought on by voluntary hyperventilation of normal air (30). Addition of CO_2 to a breathing mixture deficient in O_2 can lessen or prevent some of the changes thought to be characteristic of anoxic anoxia (20). The explanation of the mutual interaction of O_2 and CO_2 is not at hand, but evidence is increasing that CO_2 does more than play a physicochemical role in the adjustment of acid-base balance. CO_2 is utilized by animal tissues (16) and may in some manner, as yet dimly understood, regulate the rate at which the physiological oxidations are carried on in the body.

Therapeutic Use of Oxygen. In those conditions in which O_2 transfer across the lungs is impeded, as in pneumonia and pulmonary edema, dramatic relief can be obtained by allowing the patient to breathe an atmosphere enriched with O_2. The increased partial pressure of O_2 in the alveolar air increases the rate at which O_2 diffuses through the air spaces and the alveolar membranes of the lungs, and the blood leaves the lungs with a greater load of O_2. By supplying the aviator with O_2 at a constant partial pressure, his ceiling can be raised from 15,000 feet breathing air to 40,000 feet breathing O_2. The greatest benefit obtained from the use of O_2 is in those conditions in which increasing the partial pressure of O_2 in the alveolar air increases the saturation of the arterial blood leaving the lungs. If the arterial blood leaving the lungs is fully saturated, little benefit would be expected, since the amount of O_2 contained in the blood under an enhanced partial pressure of O_2 is the small additional amount that can be carried by the increased physical solubility. Some observers believe that relief of other types of anoxia can be obtained by an increase in partial pressure of O_2 in arterial blood even when the blood is fully saturated (1). The principal therapeutic usefulness of O_2, however, is still in those pathological conditions in which the diffusion constant of O_2 through the lungs is reduced. Some care must be taken in the method of O_2 administration. Comfortable masks and O_2 tents have been developed in which the atmosphere the patient breathes is easily controlled. It is common practice to maintain the O_2 concentration in the tent above 50 per cent or more, a partial pressure of 300 to 400 mm. Hg.

The extensive use of O_2 in treatment of CO anoxia is predicated upon a different principle. Increasing the partial pressure of O_2 in the arterial blood aids in the dissociation of HHbCO (see p. 000) and the CO is more easily eliminated. The objective in the treatment of CO anoxia is to restore the O_2 carrying capacity of the blood as quickly as possible.

O_2 toxicity. Paul Bert (9) first observed, and his observations have been amply confirmed (7), that O_2 at high partial pressures is not well tolerated by warm-blooded animals. Animals exposed to partial pressures of O_2 of 3 atmospheres or more give symptoms indicating that the central nervous system is profoundly affected. They may collapse and die in violent convulsions. Edema of the lungs may be produced if O_2 at partial pressures of 1 atmosphere is breathed for long periods of time, with the paradoxical result that the animal dies of anoxia. These effects limit the therapeutic use of O_2, for, in spite of the fact that it is theoretically possible to increase the partial pressure of O_2 to such an extent that the metabolic demands of the tissues could be met by the physically dissolved O_2, the tissues would die. High partial pressures of O_2 apparently can block the oxidative chain of reactions by actual destruction of some of the important enzymes (50). The reason for the inflammatory changes in the lungs with partial pressures of oxygen above 0.8 atmosphere are not clearly understood, but if O_2 is to be administered for long periods of time, it is best to keep the partial pressure of O_2 somewhat below 0.8 atmosphere.

REFERENCES

1. BARACH, A. L. *Principles and practices of inhalational therapy.* Philadelphia, J. B. Lippincott, 1944. 315 pp.

2. BARCROFT, J. Anoxemia. *Lancet,* 1920 (2), *99:*485–489.

3. BARCROFT, J. *The respiratory function of the blood. Part 1. Lessons from high altitude.* Cambridge, Cambridge Univ. Press, 1925. 207 pp.

4. BARCROFT, J. *The respiratory function of the blood. Part 2. Haemoglobin.* Cambridge, Cambridge Univ. Press, 1928. 200 pp.

5. BARCROFT, J. The significance of hemoglobin. *Physiol. Rev.,* 1924, *4:*329–351.

6. BEHNKE, A. R. Physiologic studies pertaining to deep sea diving and aviation, especially in relation to the fat content and composition of the body. *Harvey Lect.,* 1942, *37:*198–226.

7. BEHNKE, A. R., FORBES, H. S. and MOTLEY, E. P. Circulatory and visual effects of oxygen at 3 atmospheres pressure. *Amer. J. Physiol.,* 1936, *114:*436–442.

8. BEHNKE, A. R., THOMSON, R. M. and SHAW, L. A. The rate of elimination of dissolved nitrogen in man in relation to the fat and water content of the body. *Amer. J. Physiol.,* 1936, *114:* 137–146.

9. BERT, P. Barometric pressure. *Researches in experimental physiology.* HITCHCOCK, M. A. and HITCHCOCK, F. A., trans. Columbus, Ohio, College Book Co., 1943. 1055 pp.

10. BOHR, C., HASSELBALCH, K. and KROGH, A. Ueber einen in biologischer Beziehung wichtigen Einfluss, den die Kohlensäurespannung des Blutes auf dessen Saurstoffbindung übt. *Skand. Arch. Physiol.,* 1904, *16:*402–412.

11. CLARKE, R. W., MARSHALL, C. and NIMS, L. F. Blood pH during decompression. *Amer. J. Physiol.,* 1944, *142:*483–486.

12. COMROE, J. H., JR. and DRIPPS, R. D., JR. The O_2 tension of arterial blood and alveolar air in normal human subjects. *Amer. J. Physiol.,* 1944, *142:*700–707.

13. DARLING, R. C., COURNAND, A. and RICHARDS, D. W., JR. Studies on intrapulmonary mixture of gases. V. Forms of inadequate ventilation in normal and emphysematous lungs analyzed by means of breathing pure oxygen. *J. clin. Invest.,* 1944, *23:*55–67.

14. DRABKIN, D. L. and SCHMIDT, C. F. Spectrophotometric studies. XII. Observations of circulating blood in vivo and the direct determination of the saturation of hemoglobin in circulating blood. *J. biol. Chem.,* 1945, *157:* 69–83.

15. DU BOIS, E. F. *Basal metabolism in health and disease.* Philadelphia, Lea & Febiger, 1936. 494 pp.

16. EVANS, E. A., JR. Carbon dioxide utilization in animal tissue. *Science,* 1942, *96:*25–29.

17. FORBES, W. H., SARGENT, F. and ROUGHTON, F. J. W. The rate of carbon monoxide uptake by normal man. *Amer. J. Physiol* 1945, *143:*594–608.

18. GERTZ, H. Ueber die Grösse der Atmungsfläche der Lungen. *Z. Biol.*, 1928, *88:* 172–182.

19. GIBBS, E. L., LENNOX, W. G., NIMS, L. F. and GIBBS, F. A. Arterial and cerebral venous blood. Arterial-venous differences in man. *J. biol. Chem.*, 1942, *144:*325–332.

20. GIBBS, F. A., GIBBS, E. L., LENNOX, W. G. and NIMS, L. F. The value of carbon dioxide in counteracting the effects of low oxygen. *J. Aviat. Med.*, 1943, *14:*1–12.

21. HALDANE, J. S. The symptoms, causes and prevention of anoxemia. *Brit. med. J.*, 1919, *2:*65–71.

22. HALDANE, J. S. and PRIESTLEY, J. G. *Respiration*, new ed. New Haven, Yale Univ. Press, 1935. 493 pp.

23. HALDANE, J. S. and PRIESTLEY, J. G. The regulation of the lung ventilation. *J. Physiol.*, 1905, *32:*225–266.

24. HARVEY, E. N., BARNES, D. K., McELROY, W. D., WHITELEY, A. H., PEASE, D. C. and COOPER, K. W. Bubble formation in animals. I. Physical factors. *J. cell. comp. Physiol.*, 1944, *24:*1–22.

25. HARVEY, E. N., WHITELEY, A. H., McELROY, W. D., PEASE, D. C. and BARNES, D. K. Bubble formation in animals. II. Gas nuclei and their distribution in blood and tissues. *J. cell. comp. Physiol.*, 1944, *24:*23–34.

26. HENDERSON, L. J., *Blood, a study in general physiology.* New Haven, Yale Univ. Press, 1928. 397 pp.

27. HENDERSON, Y. Physiological regulation of the acid-base balance of blood and some related functions. *Physiol. Rev.*, 1925, *5:*131–160.

28. HENRIQUES, O. M. Die Bindungsweise des Kohlendioxyds in Blut. III. Der experimentelle Nachweis eines CO_2—Hämoglobin-komplexes in Lösungen von Co_2 und Hämoglobin. *Biochem. Z.*, 1928, *200:*10–17.

29. HILL, L. *Caisson sickness and the physiology of work in compressed air.* London, Edward Arnold, 1912. 255 pp.

30. HINSHAW, H. C., RUSHMER, R. F. and BOOTHBY, W. M. Hyperventilation syndrome and its importance in aviation. *J. Aviat. Med.*, 1943, *14:*100–104.

31. HURTADO, A. Chronic mountain sickness. *J. Amer. med. Ass.*, 1942, *120:*1278–1282.

32. JONES, H. B., MYERS, E. and BERG, W. E. Gas exchange, circulation and diffusion. 1945. Univ. of California [unpublished observations].

33. JOSSELYN, L. E. The nature of the pulmonary alveolar lining. *Anat. Rec.*, 1935, *62:* 147–171.

34. KROGH, A. *The anatomy and physiology of the capillaries.* New Haven, Yale Univ. Press, 1929. 422 pp.

35. KROGH, M. The diffusion of gases through the lungs of man. *J. Physiol.*, 1915, *49:*271–300.

36. LUNDSGAARD, C. and VAN SLYKE, D. D. Cyanosis. *Medicine, Baltimore*, 1923, *2:*1–76.

37. MACKLIN, C. C. The musculature of the bronchi and the lungs. *Physiol. Rev.*, 1929, *9:*1–60.

38. MELTZER, S. J. and AUER, J. Continuous respiration without respiratory movements. *J. exp. Med.*, 1909, *11:*622–625.

39. MILLER, W. S. *The lung.* Springfield, Ill., Charles C Thomas, 1937. 209 pp.

40. MOSSO, A. and MARRO, G. L'acapnie produite chez l'homme par la diminution de la pression barométrique. *Arch. ital. Biol.*, 1903, *39:*387–394.

41. PAULING, L. The oxygen equilibrium of hemoglobin and its structural interpretation. *Proc. nat. Acad. Sci.*, 1935, *21:*186–191.

42. PETERS, J. P. and VAN SLYKE, D. D. Hemoglobin and oxygen. Chap. 12 in their: *Quantitative clinical chemistry. I. Interpretations.* Baltimore, Williams and Wilkins Co., 1931. 1264 pp.

43. RICHARDSON, H. B. The respiratory quotient. *Physiol. Rev.*, 1929, *9:*61–125.

44. ROUGHTON, F. J. W. Recent work on carbon dioxide transport by the blood. *Physiol. Rev.*, 1935, *15:*241–296.

45. ROUGHTON, F. J. W. The average time spent by the blood in the human capillary and its relation to the rates of CO-uptake and elimination in man. *Amer. J. Physiol.*, 1945, *143:*621–633.

46. ROUGHTON, F. J. W. The kinetics of the reaction $CO + O_2Hb \rightarrow O_2 + COHb$ in human blood at body temperatures. *Amer. J. Physiol.*, 1945, *143:*609–620.

47. SCHNEIDER, E. C. Physiological effects of altitude. *Physiol. Rev.*, 1921, *1:*631–659.

48. SCHNEIDER, E. C. and HAVENS, L. C. The changes in content of haemoglobin and red corpuscles in the blood of man at high altitudes. *Amer. J. Physiol.*, 1915, *36:*380–397.

49. STADIE, W. C. and O'BRIEN, H. The carbamate equilibria. II. The equilibrium of oxyhemoglobin and reduced hemoglobin. *J. biol. Chem.*, 1937, *117:*439–470.

50. STADIE, W. C., RIGGS, B. C. and HAUGAARD, N. Oxygen poisoning. *Amer. J. med. Sci.*, 1944, *207:*84–114.

51. TALBOTT, J. H. and DILL, D. B. Clinical observations at high altitudes. Observations on six healthy persons living at 17,500 feet and a report of one case of chronic mountain sickness. *Amer. J. med. Sci.*, 1936, *192:*626–639.

52. VAN LIERE, E. J. *Anoxia, its effects on the body.* Chicago, Univ. of Chicago Press, 1942. xiv, 269 pp.

53. WEARN, J. T., ERNSTENE, A. C., BROMER, A. W., BARR, J. S., GERMAN, W. J. and ZSCHIESCHE, L. J. The normal behavior of the pulmonary blood vessels with observations on the intermittence of the flow of blood in the arterioles and capillaries. *Amer. J. Physiol.*, 1934, *109:*236–256.

54. WILLSON, H. G. The terminals of the human bronchiole. *Amer. J. Anat.*, 1922, *30:* 267–287.

CHAPTER 41

ORGANIZATION OF THE NEURAL MECHANISMS RESPONSIBLE FOR RHYTHMIC RESPIRATION

BY ROBERT F. PITTS

Rhythmic breathing depends upon the integrated activities of three closely related nervous mechanisms: the *medullary respiratory center*, the *Hering-Breuer reflex mechanism*, and the *pneumotaxic center*. The medullary respiratory center distributes nerve impulses to the various spinal and cranial motor nuclei which innervate the respiratory muscles, and so initiates and coordinates their contractions. The Hering-Breuer reflex mechanism and the pneumotaxic center rhythmically interrupt the discharge of impulses by the respiratory center, and so provide for the alternation of inspiration and expiration. The properties and the organization of these nervous mechanisms are subjects to be considered in this chapter. The several mechanisms which regulate the rate and depth of breathing will be considered in the succeeding chapter.

MEDULLARY RESPIRATORY CENTER

Localization. Galen recognized the fact that the brain controls breathing, for he observed that death from respiratory failure results from cutting the spinal cord just below the foramen magnum. Longet, Brown-Séquard, Bechterew and others during the past century (7) determined the approximate location of the respiratory center in the medulla oblongata by comparing the effects on respiration of gross lesions in different parts of the brain. Recently, however, the limits of the respiratory center have been defined precisely by the application of exacting physiological and histological techniques. Gesell, Bricker and Magee (11) recorded the spontaneous nerve action potentials, which are associated with breathing, through fine needle electrodes thrust into the interior of the brain. Pitts, Magoun and Ranson (29), using similar electrodes, stimulated the interior of the brain with repetitive condenser shocks, and recorded the respiratory responses which were obtained. The sites at which potentials were recorded, or the sites of stimulation, were identified in stained serial sections of the brain, and maps were made defining the precise limits of the center. Such a map of the respiratory center of the cat obtained by the method of stimulation* is shown in Figure 419. The center lies within the reticular formation of the medulla oblongata, caudal to the level of entrance of the eighth cranial nerves, and dorsal to the upper four-fifths of the inferior olivary nuclei. It is separated into two functional subdivisions, a dorsal *expiratory center* and a ventral *inspiratory center*, which are moderately discrete morphologically. The inspiratory center corresponds closely with the diffuse ventral part of the inferior retic-

---

* Maps obtained by the stimulation method not only reveal the extent of the center, but also make possible the identification of its two major subdivisions. Maps obtained by the method of recording nerve action potentials have so far defined only the overall limits of the center.

896

ular nucleus. The expiratory center, on the other hand, occupies a region of the dorsal reticular formation sparsely populated with scattered neurons which show no evidence of any nuclear grouping. The general confines of the respiratory center in the monkey (4) and in the dog (11) are similar to

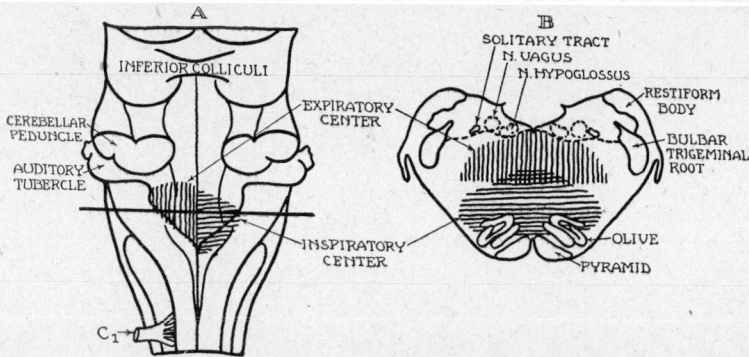

Fig. 419.—The location of the respiratory centers in the cat. A, dorsal view of the lower brain stem after removal of the cerebellum which shows the expiratory center on the left and the inspiratory center on the right, projected onto the floor of the fourth ventricle. Both centers are bilateral, but for clarity each has been projected only on one side. B, transverse section of the medulla oblongata at the level indicated by the heavy horizontal line in A, which shows the dorsal position of the expiratory center and the ventral position of the inspiratory center within the reticular formation. (Modified from Pitts, Magoun, and Ranson, *Amer. J. Physiol.*, 1939, *126:* 673.)

those described for the cat, although the differentiation into inspiratory and expiratory centers is less evident in the dog. The main features of this localization are probably applicable to man also, for Finley (9) has described clinical cases in which a destructive disease process, affecting the neurons of

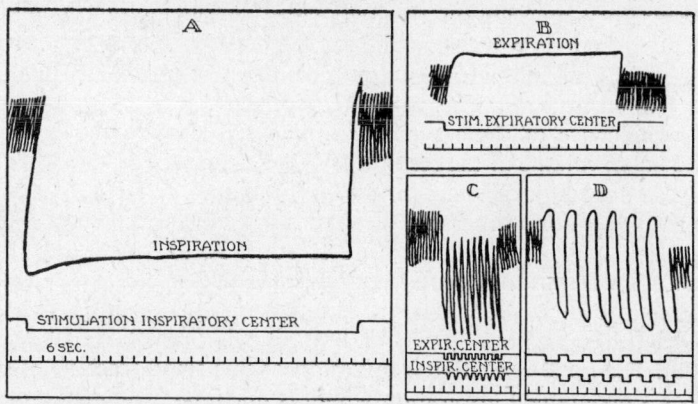

Fig. 420.—The respiratory responses produced by stimulation of the respiratory centers of the cat with repetitive shocks of an intensity of 8 V. and a frequency of 240/sec. A, stimulation of the inspiratory center; B, stimulation of the expiratory center; C and D, alternate stimulation of the two centers. (From Pitts, Magoun and Ranson, *Amer. J. Physiol.*, 1939, *126:*673.)

the reticular formation overlying the olivary nuclei, has resulted in death from primary respiratory failure.

The respiratory responses which are obtained on stimulating these two divisions of the respiratory center of the cat are illustrated in Figure 420.

Repetitive stimulation of the inspiratory center produces deep maximal inspiration which is tonically maintained as long as stimulation is continued (Fig. 420, A). The inspiration results from contraction of the diaphragm, the inspiratory muscles of the thorax, and the accessory inspiratory muscles around the neck and shoulder girdle. Often the mouth is widely opened, the nares dilated, and the tongue retracted. Thus all of the muscles which participate in spontaneous deep inspiration are caused to contract maximally. The volume of air inspired may amount to as much as ten times the normal tidal air, and inspiration can be maintained until the animal dies of asphyxia. On the other hand, repetitive stimulation of the expiratory center produces maintained expiration (Fig. 420, B), which results in part from active contraction of expiratory muscles of the thorax and abdomen, and in part from inhibition of contraction of inspiratory muscles. Alternate stimulation of these two centers produces coordinate respiratory movements which can be readily controlled in rate and depth (Fig. 420, C, D). Since stimulation of the two centers simultaneously leads to inspiration, the inspiratory center is obviously the dominant one.

Organization of the Respiratory Center. The neurons of the respiratory center are scattered through a complex meshwork of ascending, descending and crossing nerve fibers from which they receive numerous collateral terminations. They are excited by nerve impulses derived from a variety of sources, and according to Kappers this fact accounts for their diffuse distribution within the reticular formation. But despite this diffuseness of distribution, they are united into a functional whole by virtue of their rich synaptic interconnections. These linkages are of two functionally distinct types. The synaptic connections which link the constituent neurons of a given center are excitatory. They coordinate the activities of the many neurons of that center and provide for the simultaneous contraction of widely distributed respiratory muscles on the two sides of the body. In contrast, the synaptic connections which link the two centers are inhibitory, and provide for the reciprocal inhibition of one group of respiratory muscles as the group of opposite function is caused to contract.

The significance of these synaptic linkages is emphasized by comparing the total cubic volume of the respiratory center, and the fraction of the center which one must stimulate to produce a maximal respiratory response. In the cat the inspiratory center and the expiratory center each occupies a volume of the reticular formation amounting to some 30 to 50 cu. mm. When one stimulates the inspiratory center through fine needle electrodes with shocks of an intensity of 8 volts, the stimulating current spreads out around the electrode tips to excite a sphere of tissue having a volume of about 1 cu. mm. (25). The rapid repetitive stimulation of this small fraction of the center produces a maintained inspiration which is maximal. The inspiration cannot be increased by the simultaneous stimulation of another small fraction of the center on the opposite side of the midline. This indicates not only that all of the neurons of the inspiratory center can be excited by impulses transmitted synaptically from a small stimulated focus, less than one-thirtieth of the whole; but also that all of the neurons of the expiratory center can be simultaneously inhibited.

Eupneic respiration is largely an inspiratory act, i.e., expiration is passive. However, when the depth of breathing is increased, both inspiratory and expiratory muscles participate. Under these conditions the inspiratory muscles relax during contraction of the expiratory muscles and vice versa. This alternation of contraction of the two muscle groups is the obvious consequence of the inhibitory connections between the two divisions of the respiratory center. Often, however, inhibition of the inspiratory center is incomplete during expiration, and a weak tonic contraction of certain inspiratory muscles persists throughout expiration. When this persistent discharge of the inspiratory center becomes significant, the midrespiratory volume of the chest is increased, and the complemental volume is correspondingly reduced.

Respiratory motor pathways. The neurons of the respiratory center send their axons to the nuclei of the 5th, 7th, 9th, 10th, 11th, and 12th cranial nerves which supply the striated muscles of the jaws, mouth, nares, pharynx, larynx and tongue and the smooth muscles of the bronchial tree. Of these, only the pharyngeal, laryngeal and bronchial muscles are normally active in eupnea, but all may participate in the forced respiratory efforts of hyperpnea and dyspnea, and in the rhythmic movements of panting. Axons of these respiratory neurons also enter the anterior and anterolateral columns of the spinal cord to form the descending respiratory motor tracts (24). They connect with the spinal motor nuclei controlling the diaphragm, the muscles of the thorax and abdomen, and the accessory respiratory muscles around the shoulder girdle. Most of the fibers which descend through the spinal cord do so without crossing and innervate the respiratory muscles on the same side. Accordingly, when the anterior part of the upper cervical spinal cord is damaged on one side, the respiratory muscles of that side are paralyzed. However, some descending fibers must make crossed connections within the cord, for the paralysis is only temporary and nearly complete recovery occurs within a few weeks. Extensive damage to the anterior quadrants of both sides of the spinal cord in the upper cervical region leads to immediate death from respiratory failure.

Properties of the Respiratory Center. The neurons of the respiratory center are sensitive to their chemical environment. Like the taste receptors which are specialized to respond to such chemical stimuli as salt, sugar or acid, these neurons are specialized to respond to an increase in the carbon dioxide pressure of the arterial blood which perfuses the medulla oblongata. Moreover, like other nerve cells they are excited by nerve impulses which are delivered to them by afferents entering the medulla in the cranial nerves, and by collaterals of the major ascending and descending tracts. These chemical and synaptic stimuli excite the neurons of the respiratory center and cause them to discharge impulses repetitively. The impulses are conducted to the cranial nerve nuclei and to the phrenic and intercostal nuclei where they stimulate the final respiratory motoneurons. These motoneurons likewise discharge repetitive impulses which pass out over the peripheral motor nerve fibers to stimulate the respiratory muscles.

The neurons of the respiratory center vary considerably in threshold. Only a small proportion of them are active in eupnea, and these discharge impulses at a low frequency. When the carbon dioxide pressure of the arterial blood rises, or when the inflow of excitatory nerve messages from peripheral receptors increases, less excitable neurons begin to discharge impulses. Moreover, the frequency of discharge of all the active neurons rises. Thus, the total outflow of impulses from the respiratory center is greatly increased. On the whole, the thresholds of neurons of the expiratory center are higher than those of the neurons of the inspiratory center. As a consequence, expiration in eupnea is largely passive. However, when breathing is stimulated, the expiratory center becomes active, and the contraction of expiratory muscles assists in the expulsion of air from the lungs.

Nature of respiratory motor nerve discharge. The nature of the nervous activity controlling the contraction of respiratory muscles was first clearly outlined by Adrian and Bronk (2) and by Bronk and Ferguson (5) in their studies on the impulses carried by individual respiratory motor nerve fibers. They dissected from the phrenic and intercostal nerve trunks tiny twigs composed of only a few functional motor fibers, and recorded from these twigs normal respiratory action potentials. The impulses carried by each of the fibers could be identified by their characteristic spike potentials. Such a record of the impulses in three phrenic nerve fibers is shown in Figure 421, D.

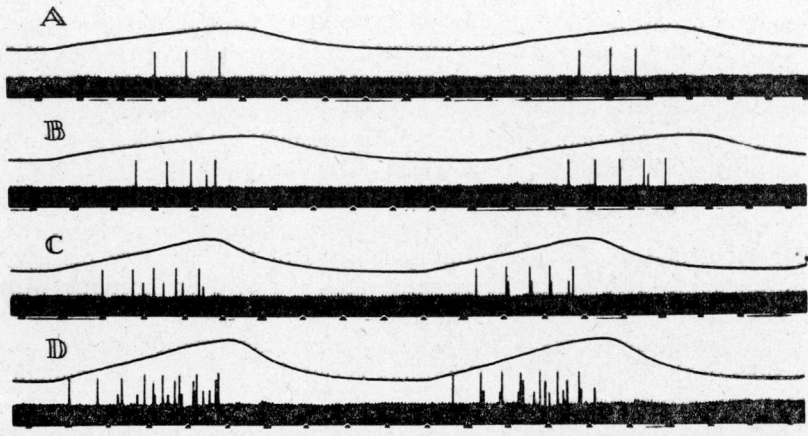

Fig. 421.—An increase in the frequency of discharge and recruitment of additional phrenic motoneurons in the cat resulting from the inhalation of carbon dioxide. A limited volume of oxygen was rebreathed and carbon dioxide was allowed to accumulate progressively in the inspired gas, records A to D. Upper trace, respiration, upstroke indicates inspiration; middle record, impulses in three phrenic motoneurons distinguishable by differences in spike height; lower trace, time in 1/5 sec.

It was found that the frequency of impulses carried by respiratory fibers is rather low, e.g., from 5 to 30 impulses per sec., a frequency which is much too low to produce a smooth tetanic contraction of the individual muscle fascicles. Since the nerve impulses normally carried by the many fibers composing the motor nerves are out of step, and since the individual muscle fascicles which are stimulated by these impulses twitch asynchronously, the respiratory contraction as a whole is normally smooth.

Pattern of respiratory motor impulses. Gesell, Magee and Bricker (12) have pointed out that the pattern of inspiratory motor impulses is such as to produce a muscular contraction of gradually increasing strength to overcome the increasing resistance of the expanding thorax. As is evident from Figure 421, D, the frequency of impulses is low at the start of inspiration and gradually rises as inspiration proceeds. Some fibers transmit impulses throughout the inspiratory cycle, whereas others begin only after inspiration is well under way. These two factors, progressive increase in the frequency of impulses and progressive recruitment of more and more active elements, provide for the increments of contractile energy which are necessary to expand the thorax. The discharge ceases suddenly at the end of inspiration, freeing the potential energy stored in the thorax in the form of elastic tension, and air is expelled from the lungs. When respiration is stimulated so that expiration becomes active, the pattern of the expiratory motor impulses is found to differ from that of the inspiratory. The frequency of discharge is greatest at the start of expiration, and either remains nearly constant or declines gradually as expiration proceeds. The discharge ceases abruptly with the onset of the succeeding inspiration. The expiratory motor discharge not only increases the extent of lung deflation over that attained in passive eupneic expiration, but also accelerates the rate of expulsion of air. This latter factor allows one to take another breath earlier than would be possible if the deflation of the lungs remained wholly a passive process.

Mechanism of grading the depth of breathing. When breathing is stimulated, three changes occur in the discharge of respiratory motor nerves which account for the greater amplitude and force of contraction of the respiratory muscles (2, 5). The frequency of the impulses carried by the individual nerve fibers increases, the duration of the trains of impulses increases, and the number of nerve fibers which carry impulses increases. The operation of these three mechanisms in phrenic motor fibers is evident from the records shown in Figure 421. In this experiment respiration was progressively stimulated by causing the animal to rebreathe a limited volume of oxygen and allowing carbon dioxide to accumulate. It is apparent that the frequency of impulses in the fiber of spike potential rose progressively through records A to D, that the trains of impulses lengthened, and that additional motor fibers were recruited. An increase in depth of active expiration is brought about by the operation of these same mechanisms in motoneurons which control the expiratory muscles.

Mechanism of repetitive discharge of impulses. Neurons of the respiratory center exhibit two types of rhythmic activity: the rhythmic discharge of repetitive impulses, and the rhythmic alternation of phases of activity and quiescence. The first of these rhythmic processes concerns us here. The second, i.e., the rhythm of breathing, will be dealt with in the succeeding sections of this chapter. The rhythmic repetitive discharge of impulses depends upon properties inherent in the neurons of the respiratory center. However, this rhythmicity is not peculiar to them for it characterizes the normal activities of all nerve cells and of slowly adapting receptor organs as well. Adrian and Zotterman (3) have proposed a schematic explanation for rhythmic activity of this type based upon their studies of sensory receptors. Their explanation accounts not only for the repetitive discharge of impulses when a constant stimulus is applied to a receptor, but also for the observed increase in frequency of discharge when the stimulus intensity is increased. With appropriate modifications this explanation can be applied to the discharge of impulses by neurons of the respiratory center, as described below (28). It is known that a nerve cell is absolutely refractory for 1 to 2 msecs. after it has discharged an impulse, and no matter how great the strength of the stimulus, it cannot be re-excited. It recovers its excitability gradually during a relative refractory interval, and returns to its resting state only after many milliseconds (20). A hypothetical curve of recovery of excitability lasting 100

msecs. is plotted in Figure 422. For any short interval of time one may consider the sum of all the stimuli acting on a given neuron of the respiratory
center as being essentially constant, and represent this sum on the chart as a
horizontal line, such as line A in Figure 422. These stimuli include the carbon dioxide pressure of the fluid environment and the many nerve impulses
which impinge upon the neuron. An increase in the sum of these stimuli is
represented on the chart as line B, and a further increase as line C. Let us
assume that such stimuli acting on a neuron do not prevent it from recovering
its excitability after it has discharged an impulse. Furthermore, let us assume
that it will again discharge an impulse when it recovers sufficiently so that
its threshold is exceeded by the sum of all the stimuli acting upon it. If an
impulse is discharged at the time designated by point *1* on line B of Figure
422, it is evident that another will be discharged at point *2*, and repeating the
recovery process, that a third will be discharged at point *3*. An increase in the
sum of the stimuli, represented by line C, obviously will increase the frequency of discharge of impulses because the neuron will be re-excited earlier
in its recovery cycle. A decrease in the sum of the stimuli, represented by line

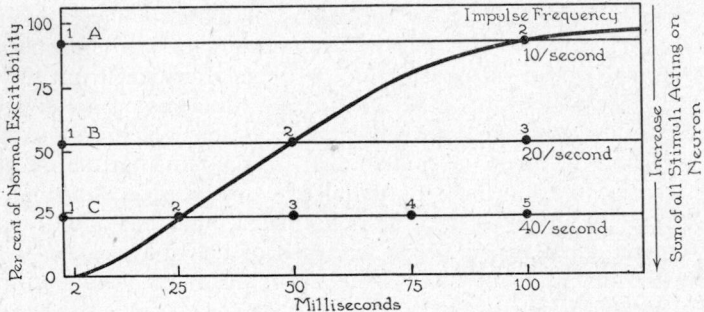

Fig. 422.—A diagrammatic representation of the mechanism of repetitive activity of a respiratory motoneuron based upon the time course of its recovery of excitability following the
discharge of an impulse.

A, will decrease the frequency of discharge of impulses, because the neuron
must recover its excitability more completely before it will again be re-excited.

Gesell (10) has speculated further on the nature of repetitive phenomena.
He maintains that a potential difference between the dendrites and the axon
hillock of the respiratory neuron causes a constant electrotonic current to
flow between these points. If such a current exists, it might constitute the
constant stimulus which we have represented in Figure 422 by the horizontal
lines. Gesell believes that this electrotonic current is increased by nerve
impulses impinging on the neuron, and by an increase in carbon dioxide
pressure in the surrounding medium. Each nerve impulse arriving at a synaptic bouton is presumed to liberate a small quantity of acetylcholine which
increases the potential difference between the dendrites and the axon hillock
and hence the flow of electrotonic current. Carbon dioxide is thought to
stimulate the neuron by decreasing the rate of destruction of this acetylcholine
by cholinesterase, and thus indirectly to increase the electrotonic current.
The experimental evidence in support of this hypothesis of Gesell is indirect,
and the assumptions on which it is based are controversial. It remains at
present, therefore, an interesting speculation.

HERING-BREUER VAGAL REFLEXES

Respiratory movements stimulate receptors within the lungs, and the impulses which are conducted to the respiratory center over afferent fibers in the vagus nerves modify breathing in three important ways. They accelerate the respiratory rhythm, reduce the respiratory amplitude, and in conjunction with inhibitory impulses from the pneumotaxic center convert the repetitive activity of the respiratory center into rhythmic respiration.

Elftmann (8) has recently described in detail some six histologically distinct varieties of branched nerve endings, which lie in the walls of the respiratory bronchioles, alveolar ducts, air sacs and alveoli. These endings are stimulated mechanically by the stretching and collapse of the thin elastic pulmonary membranes. They are insensitive to changes in chemical composition of the alveolar air and are therefore proprioceptive in function. They are analogous to the muscle tension receptors which reflexly modify somatic motor activity.

Hering and Breuer in 1868 (16) were the first to study the changes in breathing which are produced when these receptors are stimulated by inflating and deflating the lungs. As is shown in Figure 423, A, sharp overinflation of the lungs inhibits inspiration and produces apnea in expiration. In contrast, sharp

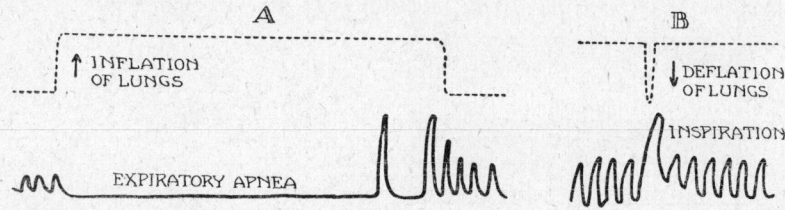

Fig. 423.—Apnea produced by maintained inflation of the lungs, record A, and deep inspiration produced by brief deflation of the lungs, record B, in the rabbit. The upper dotted trace indicates inflation and deflation of the lungs. The lower trace records the inspiratory contractions of a slip of the diaphragm. (From Head, *J. Physiol.*, 1889, *10*:1.)

overdeflation of the lungs stimulates a brief powerful inspiratory effort (Fig. 423, B). Both effects are abolished by cutting the vagus nerves. Hering and Breuer maintained that in normal breathing the expansion of the lungs during inspiration reflexly inhibits that inspiration and excites the succeeding expiration, whereas the collapse of the lungs during expiration reflexly inhibits that expiration and excites the succeeding inspiration. This concept of *Selbsteuerung* or *autoregulation of respiration by the vagi* has been amplified and modified in some important respects, as described below.

Respiratory reflexes stimulated by inflation of the lungs. Inflation of the lungs stimulates two functionally distinct types of receptors. Receptors of the first type are stimulated by moderate inflation of the lungs in eupnea, and are stimulated more intensely by marked inflation of the lungs in hyperpnea. Impulses from these receptors reflexly inhibit the inspiratory center,* and play a major role in determining the respiratory rhythm. Receptors of the second type are stimulated only by marked inflation of the lungs in hyperpnea. Impulses from these receptors reflexly excite the inspi-

* According to Gesell and Moyer (13) and Pitts, Magoun and Ranson (30), impulses from these receptors excite the expiratory center and thus reciprocally inhibit the inspiratory center. The reflex, however, may logically be considered as an inspiratory inhibitory one, because the major effect of excitation of the expiratory center in eupnea is inhibition of the inspiratory center.

ratory center and provide a brief additional respiratory drive which helps to attain deep inspiration. This latter reflex is of less general significance than the former.

The properties of the receptors responsible for the *inspiratory-inhibitory reflex* were first studied by Adrian (1) who recorded the action potentials of single vagal afferent fibers whose pulmonary terminations were stimulated by distension of the lungs. The majority of these receptors respond repetitively with little adaptation to constant lung inflation (Fig. 424, left). The frequency of discharge of impulses increases linearly with increasing volumes of inflation. The various receptors differ considerably in threshold, some responding at low, others only at high, volumes of inflation. Accordingly, as the lungs expand progressively during inspiration, both the number of receptors which discharge impulses and the frequency of impulses discharged by the individual receptors increase progressively. At a critical volume of lung inflation, the magnitude of this inflow of impulses is sufficient to inhibit inspiration. As the lungs deflate, the inhibitory discharge diminishes, the inspiratory center again becomes active, and a new respiratory cycle is initiated.

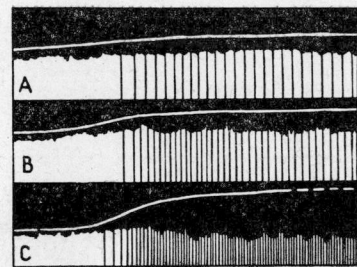 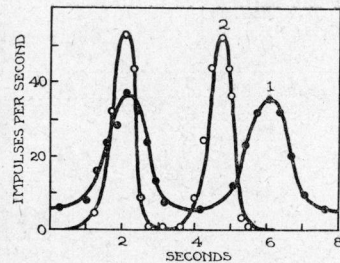

Fig. 424.—The response of pulmonary receptors to inflation of the lungs in the cat. Left, records A, B, and C, impulses discharged by a single stretch receptor when the lungs were inflated with 65 cc., 115 cc., and 230 cc. of air. The white trace indicates inflation of the lungs. Right, frequency of stretch impulses discharged by a single stretch receptor during two spontaneous respiratory cycles, under eupneic conditions in curve 1, and under conditions of hyperpnea produced by carbon dioxide inhalation in curve 2. (From Adrian, *J. Physiol.*, 1933, *79*:332.)

In Figure 424, right, is plotted the frequency of impulses discharged by a single receptor during two eupneic and two hyperpneic respiratory cycles. In eupneic respiration an inflow of impulses sufficient to inhibit inspiration is attained with moderate expansion of the lungs (curve 1). When the respiratory center is stimulated by causing the animal to inhale carbon dioxide, a greater inflow of impulses, attained by greater expansion of the lungs, is necessary to inhibit inspiration (curve 2).

The properties of the receptors responsible for the *inspiratory-excitatory reflex* were studied by Knowlton and Larrabee (18) and by Worzniak and Gesell (37). These receptors are stimulated only by volumes of lung inflation greater than are attained in eupnea, and since they adapt rapidly, their discharge is brief. They serve to re-enforce the discharge of the inspiratory center reflexly during the peak inspiratory efforts of hyperpnea, and probably play no role in eupneic breathing (18).

Respiratory reflexes stimulated by deflation of the lungs. In the deep breathing of hyperpnea active contraction of the expiratory muscles collapses the lungs sufficiently to stimulate the pulmonary *deflation receptors*. The activation of these receptors in deep expiration reflexly stimulates the succeeding

inspiration earlier and more forcibly than would occur otherwise. In pneumothorax the lungs are partially collapsed at all times, and the powerful gasping
inspiratory efforts which characterize this condition undoubtedly result
from the stimulation of the receptors sensitive to lung deflation. But contrary
to the original Hering-Breuer hypothesis, it has been found that the extent of
the lung deflation attained in quiet expiration is not sufficient to stimulate
these receptors (1, 19). Expiration in eupnea is largely passive and the succeeding inspiration often follows after an appreciable pause. Under these
conditions there is no evidence of active reflex excitation of inspiration.
Rather, the inspiratory center gradually begins to discharge impulses spontaneously when the inhibitory impulses from the *inflation receptors* diminish
toward the end of expiration.

Sensitization of the Hering-Breuer reflexes in diseases affecting the lungs.
Breathing is commonly rapid and shallow in those clinical conditions in
which the lungs are engorged, or consolidated, or in some other way rendered
less elastic. In animal experiments it has been found that the intravenous in-

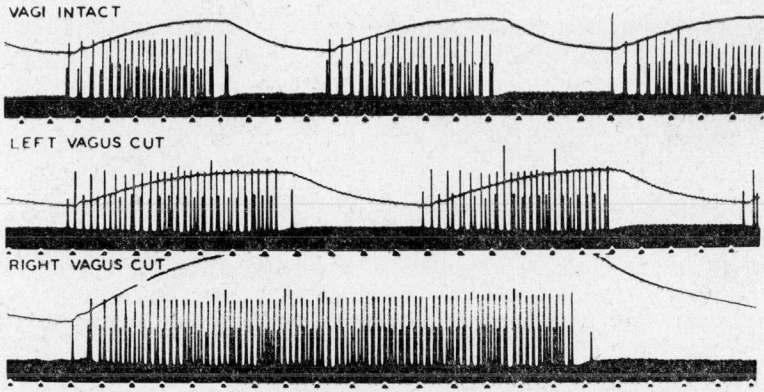

Fig. 425.—Slowing and deepening of respiration produced by cutting the vagus nerves in a
decerebrate cat. Upper trace, respiration, upstroke indicates inspiration; middle record, impulses
in two phrenic motoneurons; lower trace, time in 1/5 sec. (From Pitts, *J. Neurophysiol.*, 1942, *5*:
403.)

jection of fine particulate matter, which produces vascular engorgement and
edema of the lungs, likewise causes rapid and shallow breathing. Partridge
(23) has shown under these conditions that the pulmonary receptors which
are stimulated by lung inflation discharge impulses at frequencies much
higher than normal. Accordingly, Christie (6) claims that the reduced elasticity of the lungs in heart failure, pneumonia, and pulmonary fibrosis so
sensitizes the receptors responsible for the Hering-Breuer reflexes that their
discharge is much increased for any given degree of expansion or collapse of
the lungs. Inspiration and expiration are therefore reduced in amplitude and
the rhythm of breathing is accelerated. Christie believes that much of the
shortness of breath which characterizes these clinical conditions has its
origin in overactive Hering-Breuer reflexes.

Effects of vagotomy on breathing. When the vagus nerves of an animal are
cut and the Hering-Breuer reflexes eliminated, breathing slows and deepens.
The alterations in nervous activity which underlie these changes in breathing
are illustrated in Figure 425 by records of the impulses discharged by two

phrenic motoneurons. It is obvious that the slowing of respiration results mainly from prolongation of the discharge of the inspiratory center. Normally this discharge is shortened reflexly by inhibitory impulses from the lungs. The deepening of inspiration results from prolongation of the inspiratory discharge and from the attainment of a higher frequency of discharge as well. In addition, neurons which were previously quiescent may begin to discharge impulses after vagotomy. The loss of inhibitory impulses from the lungs therefore adequately accounts for the increase in depth of inspiration, as well as for the decrease in rate of breathing. As will be more evident later from a discussion of the pneumotaxic center, the vagal inspiratory-inhibitory reflex also plays an important role in conferring rhythmicity on the respiratory center.

Effects of stimulation of the vagus nerves on breathing. A common laboratory experiment is the observation of the respiratory responses which result from stimulation of the central end of the cut vagus nerve. Although it might be supposed that this would serve as a simple demonstration of the Hering-Breuer reflexes, it must be remembered that the vagus carries many types of afferents which affect the respiratory center in diverse ways. The various pulmonary afferents which we have just described both stimulate and inhibit inspiration. Afferents from the larynx, trachea, and bronchi either inhibit inspiration or stimulate the powerful inspiratory and expiratory efforts of the cough. Afferents from chemoreceptors in the aortic glomi stimulate both inspiration and expiration. Afferents from pressure receptors in the aorta inhibit inspiration. The thresholds of these afferents to electrical stimulation differ. The effect on breathing which one observes on stimulating the vagus depends, therefore, upon the intensity of the stimulus, but it also depends upon the relative dominance of the specific reflex response which is elicited. In general there is a tendency for low intensity and low frequency stimulation to increase the rate and depth of breathing, while high frequency and high intensity stimulation produce apnea in expiration.

PNEUMOTAXIC CENTER AND THE RHYTHM OF BREATHING

The periodic inhibition of inspiration by vagal afferents whose endings are stimulated by lung inflation largely determines the rhythm of breathing. Since respiration remains rhythmic, although slower and deeper, after section of the vagus nerves, some other inhibitory mechanism must be capable of substituting for the reflex one. Two divergent views as to the nature of this mechanism have arisen. The first of these views holds that the periodicity of breathing depends upon properties inherent in the neurons of the respiratory center; i.e., the individual respiratory neurons when freed of all regulatory control, still discharge impulses in rhythmically repeated trains (1, 10, 32, 36). The second of these views maintains that the periodicity of breathing is impressed upon the neurons of the respiratory center by an inhibitory mechanism which lies within the brain stem, and which functions in a manner analogous to the vagal inhibitory mechanism (21, 22, 31, 33). This latter view is the one which is supported by the bulk of the positive experimental evidence, and the one which we shall develop in this section.

Location and function of the pneumotaxic center. The brain stem inhibitory mechanism mentioned above was named the *pneumotaxic center* by Lumsden. It is a bilateral mechanism which lies within the tegmentum rostral to the medullary respiratory center. According to Stella, it lies within the upper few millimeters of the pons, but its exact limits have not been accurately defined. The pneumotaxic center is connected with the inspiratory and expiratory divisions of the respiratory center by ascending and descending pathways which lie in the lateral part of the brain stem ventral to the spinal trigeminal tracts (see Fig. 427). These pathways transmit impulses rostrally from the inspiratory center to the pneumotaxic center, and caudally from the pneumotaxic center to the expiratory center. The functioning of this circuit (inspiratory center to pneumotaxic center to expiratory center) accounts for rhythmicity of breathing after the vagus nerves are cut. The evidence upon which this view is based and the probable mode of action of this mechanism are described immediately below.

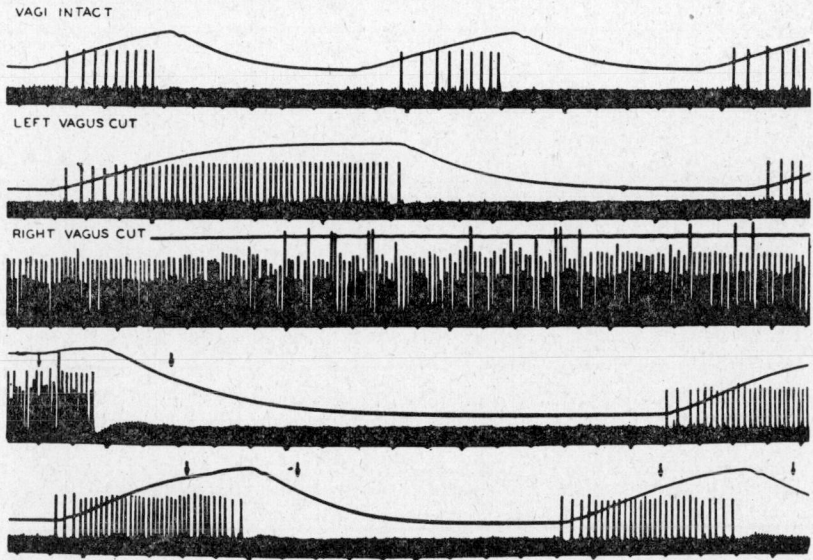

Fig. 426.—The production of apneusis by cutting the vagus nerves, and the restoration o rhythmic respiration by the central stimulation of one vagus nerve in a cat in which the pneumotaxic center had been removed by transecting the brain through the pons. Upper trace, respiration, upstroke indicates inspiration; middle record, impulses in two phrenic motoneurons; lower trace, time in 1/5 sec. In the two lowest records the central end of one vagus nerve was stimulated with rapid repetitive shocks during the intervals between each pair of arrows. (From Pitts, *J. Neurophysiol.*, 1942, *5:*403.)

If the brain of an animal is transected at the level of junction of the pons and medulla oblongata, the pneumotaxic circuit is broken (cf. upper dashed line of Fig. 427). Respiration in such a preparation is essentially normal so long as the vagus nerves are intact, as is illustrated in the top record of Figure 426. When one vagus nerve is cut, inspiration is prolonged and the rhythm of breathing slows. When the second vagus nerve is cut, rhythmic respiration is abolished. The animal inspires deeply and the inspiration is maintained until death from asphyxia supervenes. The maintained inspiration or apneusis, as it has been termed by Lumsden, is the result of the continuous repetitive discharge of impulses by the inspiratory center. This repetitive discharge is evident in the third record of Figure 426, in which impulses of two phrenic motoneurons may be identified. It is apparent that removal of the pneumotaxic mechanism and section of the vagus nerves release the respiratory center from all significant inhibitory influences, and that the neurons of the inspiratory center, under such conditions of isolation, discharge a continuous series of impulses. Thus the rhythm of breathing must depend upon inhibitory influences exerted by the vagal and pneumotaxic mechanisms, not upon properties inherent within the neurons of the respiratory center. As is shown in the lower two records of Figure 426, the continuous discharge of the inspiratory center may be reconverted into an intermittent respiratory discharge by stimulating the central end of one of the cut vagus nerves for a few tenths of a second at the peak of each inspiration. Such stimulation mimics the bursts of impulses which normally originate in the pulmonary inflation receptors each time the lungs expand. Thus replacement of this periodic inflow of inhibitory afferent impulses with appropriately timed stimuli reestablishes rhythmic respiration.

Figure 425 illustrates in a more positive way the activities of the pneumotaxic center. In this experiment the pneumotaxic mechanism was intact, for the animal had been decerebrated by transecting the brain between the superior and inferior colliculi, i.e., well rostral to the pons. The slow rhythm of breathing which resulted from cutting both vagus nerves is dependent upon the periodic inhibition of the inspiratory center by the pneumotaxic center. Subsequent transection of the brain below the pons, i.e., elimination of the pneumotaxic center, abolishes this rhythmicity and brings about maintained inspiration or apneusis.

The probable mechanism of action of the pneumotaxic center can now be appreciated by referring to Figure 427. When the neurons of the inspiratory center begin to discharge, impulses are transmitted over descending spinal pathways to the spinal motor nuclei, and over ascending tegmental pathways to the pneumotaxic center. As this ascending barrage of impulses reaches a critical magnitude, the pneumotaxic center is caused to discharge. Descending impulses stimulate the expiratory center, which in turn inhibits the inspiratory center. When the inspiratory center is inhibited, the pneumotaxic circuit ceases to conduct. Inhibition of the inspiratory center dies away and the cycle is repeated.

Properties of the isolated respiratory center. Isolation of the respiratory center from the vagal and pneumotaxic inhibitory mechanisms causes maintained inspiration, not maintained expiration. This result undoubtedly depends upon the lower threshold and general dominance of activity of the neurons of the inspiratory center. These neurons discharge impulses continuously under combined stimulation by their chemical environment and by afferent impulses, and maintain the neurons of the expiratory center in a state of continuous reciprocal inhibition. Stella has shown that the discharge of the isolated inspiratory center, as indicated by the depth of the apneusis, may be increased by causing the animal to inhale carbon dioxide, and may be reduced by artificial overventilation (34). Thus the center in isolation responds normally to chemical stimulation. It likewise responds normally to reflex stimulation, for excitation of the carotid chemoreceptors (35) and peripheral pain receptors likewise increases the depth of the apneusis. Indeed, the depth of apneusis is determined by exactly the same mechanisms that determine the depth of normal rhythmic inspiration, namely, by the frequency of discharge of the individual motoneurons, and by the number of motoneurons which discharge impulses (27).

Relative contribution of the two inhibitory mechanisms to the rhythm of breathing. Under most conditions the vagal inhibitory mechanism plays a more prominent role than the pneumotaxic mechanism in determining the rhythm of respiration. This view is derived from the observation that section of the vagus nerves usually slows and deepens respiration markedly. However, when body temperature rises, panting occurs and the rate of breathing may reach 200 per minute or more. In contrast to the normal, this rapid rhythm of breathing is but little affected by cutting the vagus nerves (15). It seems, rather, to be determined predominantly by the pneumotaxic mechanism, for lesions within the pons which damage the pneumotaxic center or its connections with the respiratory center cause an immediate slowing and deepening of respiration (17, 31). It is probable that impulses from the thermoregulatory centers in the hypothalamus facilitate the pneumotaxic center and render it more responsive to impulses from the inspiratory center. It is therefore excited earlier in the inspiratory cycle, stimulates the expiratory center sooner, and thereby inhibits inspiration before the vagal inhibitory discharge reaches an effective magnitude. Under these conditions, the pneumotaxic center becomes the dominant mechanism regulating the rate of breathing.

FUNCTIONAL ORGANIZATION OF THE RESPIRATORY COMPLEX

It is apparent from the above discussion that the control of respiration must be considered not only in terms of the properties of the individual respiratory neurons, but also in terms of the functional organization of the entire respiratory complex. The elements of this organization are presented in a much reduced and diagrammatic form in Figure 427. It must be kept in mind that a diagram of such a mechanism to be intelligible must be oversimplified. Thus numbers of elements are reduced to a minimum, the histologf ical complexity of their endings is ignored, and all afferents except those o- the vagus which mediate the Hering-Breuer inhibitory reflex have been omitted. The purpose of this diagram is to direct the imagination, not to replace it. As illustrated in Figure 427, the initiation of the respiratory movements and the control of their depth and frequency may be considered in terms of the properties and the mode of integration of three basic neural mechanisms: (i) the respiratory center-motoneuron mechanism, (ii) the vagal inhibitory mechanism, and (iii) the pneumotaxic mechanism.

Respiratory center-motoneuron mechanism. The neurons of the respiratory center are sensitive to the carbon dioxide pressure of their fluid environment. Since the large volume of the reserve and residual airs effectively buffers the alveolar and arterial gas pressures against any but slight tidal variations, this chemical stimulus is essentially a constant one. Nerve impulses from a variety of peripheral receptors and from more rostral portions of the brain also stimulate these neurons. They respond to these various stimuli by the repetitive discharge of impulses at frequencies proportional to the sum of all the stimuli acting upon them. Since they vary in threshold, less responsive neurons are recruited as these stimuli increase. In general the neurons of the inspiratory center are more excitable than are those of the expiratory center; and under conditions of eupneic respiration, breathing is largely dependent on the intermittent activity of the dominant inspiratory center. However, under conditions which lead to hyperpneic respiration, the expiratory center is stimulated and expiration likewise becomes active. Connections between the two centers provide for the reciprocal inhibition of one center during the phase of activity of the other (Fig. 427).

Impulses from the two centers are conducted over descending spinal pathways and stimulate the final motoneurons which innervate the respiratory muscles (Fig. 427). These motoneurons discharge impulses at frequencies proportional to the numbers of impulses impinging upon them. They too differ in threshold, and when the discharge of the respiratory center increases, additional motoneurons are recruited. Regulation of the depth of respiration depends, therefore, upon the properties and the organization of the respiratory center-motoneuron mechanism.

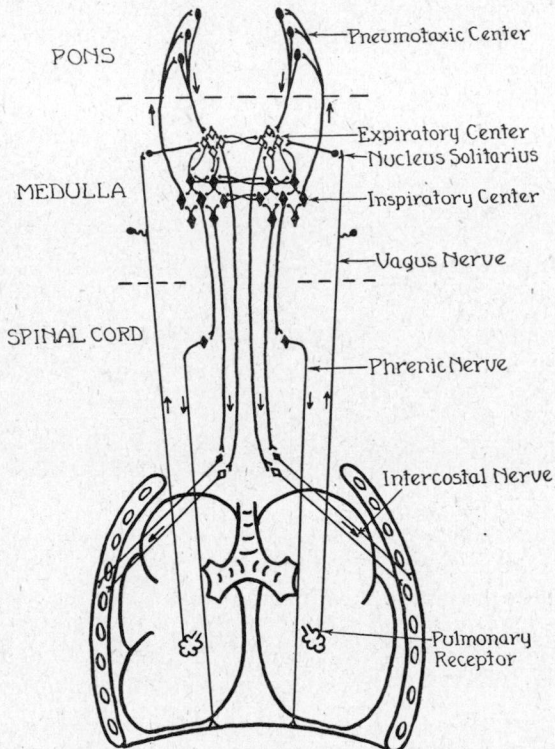

Fig. 427.—A diagrammatic representation of the basic neural mechanisms responsible for rhythmic respiration.

When the respiratory center-motoneuron mechanism is isolated from the vagal and pneumotaxic mechanisms which normally modulate its activity (see dashed lines in Fig. 427), maintained inspiration or apneusis results. Since the inspiratory center is the dominant division of the respiratory center and has the lowest threshold to chemical and neural stimuli, the discharge of impulses by inspiratory neurons is continuous, and the expiratory center is maintained in a state of continuous inhibition.

Vagal inhibitory mechanism. Inflation of the lungs in inspiration stimulates receptors within the pulmonary parenchyma, and causes them to discharge impulses which are conducted centrally over the vagus nerves to the expiratory center (Fig. 427). When this barrage of impulses becomes sufficiently intense, the expiratory center is stimulated. In eupnea, stimulation of the expiratory center results mainly in inhibition of the inspiratory center, and therefore leads to passive expiration. As the lungs deflate, impulses from the pulmonary inflation receptors diminish, activity of the expiratory center ceases, and the inspiratory center again begins to discharge. When respiration is stimulated, either by an increase in the carbon dioxide pressure of the arterial blood or by an increase in the inflow of excitatory nerve messages, inspiration proceeds more rapidly and to a greater depth before inhibition occurs. The expiratory center becomes active, and contraction of the expiratory muscles speeds the collapse of the chest. The greater depth of expiration stimulates deflation receptors which reflexly excite the succeeding inspiration. The increase in velocity of both inspiration and expiration shortens the duration of the respiratory cycle and increases the rate of respiration. The addition of the vagal inhibitory mechanism to the respiratory center-motoneuron mechanism imparts rhythmicity to respiration and provides the basis for an increase in rate of respiration.

Pneumotaxic inhibitory mechanism. The pneumotaxic inhibitory mechanism functions in a manner analogous to the vagal inhibitory mechanism, but differs in that it lies wholly within the brain stem (Fig. 427). Impulses which originate in the inspiratory center are transmitted rostrally to the pneumotaxic center, and then are relayed caudally to the expiratory center. When this barrage of impulses becomes sufficiently intense, the expiratory center is stimulated and the inspiratory center is reciprocally inhibited. The outflow of impulses to the pneumotaxic center ceases, the activity of the expiratory center declines, and the inspiratory center escapes from inhibition. In eupneic respiration this mechanism is subsidiary to the vagal reflex mechanism. However, when the vagus nerves are cut, rhythmicity of respiration depends solely on the pneumotaxic mechanism. Moreover, in the intact animal under conditions which cause panting, the pneumotaxic center is so facilitated by impulses which descend from the thermoregulatory centers in the hypothalamus that it becomes the dominant factor in determining the respiratory rhythm.

REFERENCES

1. ADRIAN, E. D. Afferent impulses in the vagus and their effect on respiration. *J. Physiol.*, 1933, *79*:332–358.

2. ADRIAN, E. D. and BRONK, D. W. The discharge of impulses in motor nerve fibers. Part I. Impulses in single fibers of the phrenic nerves. *J. Physiol.*,1928, *66*:81–101.

3. ADRIAN, E. D. and ZOTTERMAN, Y. The impulses produced by sensory nerve endings. Part II. The response of a single end organ. *J. Physiol.*, 1926, *61*:151–171.

4. BEATON, L. E. and MAGOUN, H. W. Localization of the medullary respiratory centers in the monkey. *Amer. J. Physiol.*, 1941, *134*:177–185.

5. BRONK, D. W. and FERGUSON, L. K. The nervous control of intercostal respiration. *Amer. J. Physiol.*, 1935, *110*:700–707.

6. CHRISTIE, R. V. Dyspnoea: a review. *Quart. J. Med.*, 1938, *31*:421–454.

7. CORDIER, D. and HEYMANS, C. Le centre respiratoire. *Ann. Physiol. Physicochim. biol.*, 1935, *11*:535–757.

8. ELFTMANN, A. G. The afferent and parasympathetic innervation of the lung and trachea of the dog. *Amer. J. Anat.*, 1943, *72*:1–27.

9. FINLEY, L. H. The neuro-anatomy in respiratory failure; report of 2 cases. *Arch. Neurol. Psychiat., Chicago*, 1931, *26*:754–783.

10. GESELL, R., BRASSFIELD, C. R. and HAMILTON, M. A. An acid-humoral mechanism of nerve cell activation. *Amer. J. Physiol.*, 1942, *136*:604–608.

11. GESELL, R., BRICKER, J. and MAGEE, C. Structural and functional organization of the central mechanism controlling breathing. *Amer. J. Physiol.*, 1936, *117*:423–452.

12. GESELL, R., MAGEE, C. and BRICKER, J. Activity patterns of the respiratory neurons and muscles. *Amer. J. Physiol.*, 1940, *128*:615–628.

13. GESELL, R. and MOYER, C. The dual excitatory action of the vagal stretch reflex. *Amer. J. Physiol.*, 1941, *131*:674–680.

14. HEAD, H. On the regulation of respiration. *J. Physiol.*, 1889, *10*:1–70.

15. HIESTAND, W. A. and RANDALL, W. C. Influence of proprioceptive vagal afferents on panting and accessory panting movements in the mammals and birds. *Amer. J. Physiol.*, 1942, *138*:12–15.

16. HERING, E. Die Selbsteuerung der Athmung durch den Nervus vagus. *S. B. Akad. Wiss. Wien*, 1868, *57* (2): 672–677; see also: BREUER, J., *Ibid*, 1868, *58* (2): 909.

17. KELLER, A. D. Nervous control of respiration. I. Observations on the localization of the respiratory mechanism in the isthmus, pons and upper medulla of the cat. *Amer. J. Physiol.*, 1929, *89*:289–309.

18. KNOWLTON, G. C. and LARRABEE, M. G. A unitary analysis of afferent vagal fibers stimulated by changes in lung volume. *Amer. J. Physiol.*, 1941, *133*:P351.

19. LARRABEE, M. G. and KNOWLTON, G. C. Excitation and inhibition of the inspiratory center by afferent impulses from the lungs. *Amer. J. Physiol.*, 1941, *133*:P360.

20. LORENTE DE NÓ, R. and GRAHAM, H. T. Recovery cycle of motoneurons. *Amer. J. Physiol.*, 1938, *123*:388–399.

21. LUMSDEN, T. Observations on the respiratory centres in the cat. *J. Physiol.*, 1923, *57*: 153–160.

22. MARCKWALD, M. Die Athembewegungen und deren Innervation beim Kaninchen. *Z. Biol.*, 1887, *23*:149–283.

23. PARTRIDGE, R. C. Vagal and phrenic impulses and respiration. *Canad. med. Ass. J.*, 1935, *33*:11–22.

24. PITTS, R. F. The respiratory center and its descending pathways. *J. comp. Neurol.*, 1940, *72*:605–625.

25. PITTS, R. F. The differentiation of respiratory centers. *Amer. J. Physiol.*, 1941, *134*: 192–201.

26. PITTS, R. F. Excitation and inhibition of phrenic motor neurons. *J. Neurophysiol.*, 1942, *5*:75–88.

27. PITTS, R. F. The function of components of the respiratory complex. *J. Neurophysiol.*, 1942, *5*:403–413.

28. PITTS, R. F. The basis for repetitive activity in phrenic motoneurons. *J. Neurophysiol.*, 1943, *6*:439–454.

29. PITTS, R. F., MAGOUN, H. W. and RANSON, S. W. Localization of the medullary respiratory centers in the cat. *Amer. J. Physiol.*, 1939, *126*:673–688.

30. PITTS, R. F., MAGOUN, H. W. and RANSON, S. W. Interrelations of the respiratory centers in the cat. *Amer. J. Physiol.*, 1939, *126*:689–701.

31. PITTS, R. F., MAGOUN, H. W. and RANSON, S. W. The origin of respiratory rhythmicity. *Amer. J. Physiol.*, 1939, *127*:654–670.

32. ROSENTHAL, J. Die Physiologie der Athembewegungen und der Innervation derselben. *Hermanns Handb. Physiol.*, 1882, *4* (Part 2): 262–286.

33. STELLA, G. On the mechanism of production and the physiological significance of "apneusis." *J. Physiol.*, 1938, *93*:10–23.

34. STELLA, G. The dependence of the activity of the "apneustic centre" on the carbon dioxide of the arterial blood. *J. Physiol.*, 1938, *93*:263–275.

35. STELLA, G. The reflex response of the "apneustic" centre to stimulation of the chemoreceptors of the carotid sinus. *J. Physiol.*, 1939, *95*:365–372.

36. WINTERSTEIN, H. Die automatische Tätigkeit der Atemzentren. *Pflüg. Arch. ges. Physiol.*, 1911, *138*:159–166.

37. WORZNIAK, J. J. and GESELL, R. The proprioceptive drive of the respiratory act *Amer. J. Physiol.*, 1939, *126*:P658.

CHAPTER 42

REGULATION OF RESPIRATION

BY ROBERT F. PITTS

Pulmonary ventilation is fundamentally regulated to satisfy the varying metabolic demands of the body. At times, however, the respiratory system participates in certain specialized activities which are not concerned with gas exchange, such as speaking, blowing, straining, coughing and sneezing. To accomplish these varied ends, respiration is regulated both by *chemical mechanisms* which are responsive to the metabolic needs of the body, and by *nervous mechanisms* which modify the basic pattern of breathing to fit the needs of the moment. Although specific circumstances may be cited in which one or the other of these mechanisms plays the dominant role in regulating respiration, the rate, depth, and rhythm of breathing are finally determined by the summated contributions of both. The nature of these regulatory mechanisms and their mode of integration are subjects to be considered in this chapter.

CHEMICAL CONTROL OF RESPIRATION

The activity of the respiratory center is regulated in two ways by changes in the chemical composition of the arterial blood. (i) The neurons of the respiratory center are directly responsive to changes in CO_2 pressure, acidity, rate of flow, temperature, and O_2 pressure of the arterial blood which perfuses the medulla oblongata. The CO_2 pressure is by far the most significant of these factors in the regulation of breathing. (ii) Chemoreceptors located in the carotid and aortic glomi are stimulated by a decrease in O_2 pressure, and by an increase in acidity and CO_2 pressure of the arterial blood which richly supplies them. Nerve impulses from the chemoreceptors are conducted to the medulla oblongata over afferent fibers of the 9th and 10th cranial nerves. These impulses reflexly regulate the activity of the respiratory center. A decrease in the O_2 pressure of the arterial blood is the most significant of these chemoreceptor stimuli.

Chemical control of the respiratory center by CO_2

The partial pressure of CO_2 in the arterial blood and alveolar air is maintained relatively constant at approximately 40 mm. Hg. This constancy depends upon the sensitivity of the neurons of the respiratory center to very small changes in the carbon dioxide pressure of their fluid environment. An increase in the rate of production of CO_2 tends to raise its arterial partial pressure and thus to stimulate the respiratory center. The increased ventilation which results lowers the pressure toward normal. Conversely, when less CO_2 is produced, the decrease in arterial partial pressure depresses the respiratory center. The decreased ventilation which results allows the pressure to rise toward normal. Within limits, therefore, pulmonary ventilation varies in direct proportion to the rate of production of CO_2.

31   913

Relation between pulmonary ventilation and alveolar pressure of CO_2. The quantitative relation between pulmonary ventilation and alveolar CO_2 pressure was first systematically studied by Haldane and Priestley (24). One of their experiments is summarized in Table 39. Since atmospheric air contains essentially no CO_2 (0.03 per cent), the addition of even small amounts of this gas to the inspired air tends to raise its alveolar pressure, and thus to stimulate breathing. During the control observations listed in the first line of Table 39, the subject breathed normal atmospheric air, and his pulmonary ventilation amounted to 9.4 liters per minute. CO_2 constituted 5.6 per cent of the dry alveolar air and therefore exerted a partial pressure within the lungs of 41 mm. Hg. The addition of 0.79, 2.02, and 3.07 per cent CO_2 to the inspired air progressively increased pulmonary ventilation to 10.4, 12.9 and 18.2 liters per minute. The increments of alveolar pressure which produced these changes in ventilation were very small; in fact, they were less than the experimental error of the determination, which amounted to $\pm$ 1.0 mm. Hg. Campbell, Douglas, Haldane and Hobson (7) have found in the average individual that a rise in pressure of 1.5 mm. Hg doubles pulmonary ventilation,

Table 39.—*Stimulation of Respiration in Man by an Increase in the Carbon Dioxide Content of the Inspired Air.* (From Haldane and Priestley, *J. Physiol.*, 1905, *32*:225.)

CO_2 INSPIRED	CO_2 ALVEOLAR	pCO_2 ALVEOLAR	TIDAL AIR	RESPIRATORY RATE	PULMONARY VENTILATION
PER CENT	PER CENT	MM.HG	CC.	/MIN.	L./MIN.
0.03	5.6	41	673	14	9.4
0.79	5.5	40	739	14	10.4
2.02	5.6	41	864	15	12.9
3.07	5.5	40	1216	15	18.2
5.14	6.2	45	1771	19	33.7
6.02	6.6	48	2104	27	56.8

and that a change of one-twentieth of this amount perceptibly increases breathing. Had no increase in ventilation occurred when 3.07 per cent CO_2 was inhaled, the partial pressure of this gas in the alveolar air would have increased by more than 20 mm. Hg. It is apparent, therefore, that the increase in ventilation compensated almost perfectly for the increase in CO_2 inhaled. When the inspired air contained 5.14 per cent CO_2, i.e., nearly as much as the alveolar air contained normally, compensation was less perfect, and the alveolar pressure rose to 45 mm. Hg. This increase of 4.0 mm. Hg in CO_2 pressure increased pulmonary ventilation to 33.7 liters per minute. When the inspired air contained 6.14 per cent CO_2, the alveolar pressure rose still further to 48 mm. Hg, and pulmonary ventilation increased to 56.8 liters per minute. In most subjects ventilation is increased progressively by increasing the concentration of CO_2 in the inspired air to 9.0 per cent. However, when the concentration rises above 9.0 per cent, respiration is depressed, for the gas has anesthetic properties. The maximum ventilation which can be produced in this manner amounts to 60 to 70 liters per minute (2, 36), yet the same individual during violent exercise may breathe as much as 120 liters per minute. Obviously the hyperpnea of severe muscular exercise must depend to a considerable extent on other excitatory mechanisms. The nature of these mechanisms and the extent of their contribution will be considered later.

A reduction in alveolar CO_2 pressure depresses the respiratory center, and if excitatory stimuli are reduced to a negligible minimum, apnea results. Under optimum conditions apnea of brief duration may be produced by a fall in CO_2 pressure of 1.5 mm. Hg (7). If one voluntarily breathes as deeply and as rapidly as possible, the alveolar CO_2 pressure may be reduced far more than this—in fact, by 20 to 30 mm. Hg. The spirometer tracing in Figure 428,

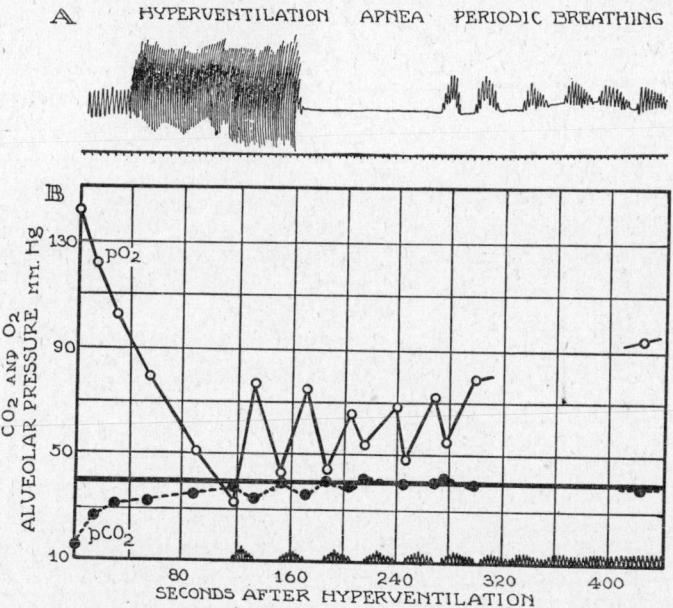

Fig. 428.—The effects of voluntary hyperventilation on the respiration of man. A, illustrates apnea of 2 min. duration following a 2 min. period of voluntary hyperventilation. The apnea was succeeded by periodic breathing. B, variations in alveolar oxygen and carbon dioxide pressures following hyperventilation, which account for the apnea and periodic breathing. Note that alveolar oxygen pressure was high and carbon dioxide pressure low immediately following the overbreathing. The carbon dioxide pressure rose, but before it returned to normal (heavy horizontal line), the oxygen pressure fell sufficiently to stimulate respiration reflexly. The first series of respirations then occurred (see bottom of chart), elevating oxygen pressure and lowering carbon dioxide pressure. The cyclic repetition of these changes account for periodic breathing. (From Douglas and Haldane; *J. Physiol.*, 1909, *38*:401.)

A, shows that the apnea which results when this voluntary effort is stopped may persist for as long as two minutes. Furthermore, when spontaneous breathing returns, it is frequently periodic in character. The factors which determine the duration of the apnea and the periodicity of the succeeding respiration were first elucidated by Douglas and Haldane (14). Their results are illustrated graphically in Figure 428, B. By voluntary hyperventilation, the alveolar pressure of CO_2 was reduced from a normal value of 40 mm. Hg to 15 mm. Hg, and the alveolar pressure of O_2 was elevated from a normal value of 100 mm. Hg to 140 mm. Hg. During the succeeding apnea the CO_2 pressure rose gradually, whereas the O_2 pressure fell precipitously. The subject became cyanotic and began to breathe again before the CO_2

pressure had returned to its normal value. The reduction of the O_2 pressure in the arterial blood to a value near 30 mm. Hg stimulated the respiratory center reflexly by activating the carotid and aortic chemoreceptors. A few breaths restored the pressure of O_2 to normal, and thus diminished the reflex respiratory drive. However, the short period of breathing depressed the respiratory center even more by further lowering the CO_2 pressure, and apnea again supervened. Gradually after repeated alternate periods of apnea and rhythmic breathing, the alveolar and arterial pressures of both O_2 and CO_2 were restored to normal, and respiration again became regular.

Periodic breathing in disease. Two types of periodic breathing are seen clinically and are termed respectively *Cheyne-Stokes' breathing* and *Biot's breathing*. The former is characterized by a periodic waxing and waning of the amplitude of respiration much like that illustrated in the latter part of Figure 428, A. Periods of apnea or merely of reduced respiratory amplitude alternate with periods of hyperpnea. The transition from one to the other is typically gradual. In contrast, Biot's breathing is characterized by the abrupt alternation of periods of apnea and of hyperpnea. The Cheyne-Stokes type of rhythm is the more common and is seen in cases of decompensated heart disease, uremia, elevated intracranial pressure, and narcotic poisoning. It is occasionally observed in normal individuals at high altitude, and as pointed out above may be induced in some by voluntary overbreathing. The cause of the periodicity may not be the same in all instances, but in the majority there seems to be a common factor, namely, depression of the neurons of the respiratory center and diminution of their sensitivity to CO_2. Pulmonary ventilation is reduced as a result of this diminished sensitivity, and the O_2 pressure of the arterial blood falls below normal. Chemoreceptor reflexes then drive the respiratory center until the O_2 pressure rises to normal and the reflex stimulus is abolished. However, hyperventilation lowers the arterial CO_2 pressure to such a level that it no longer stimulates the depressed respiratory center, and apnea results. The depression and reduction of sensitivity of the respiratory center in the conditions mentioned above may be produced by sluggishness of the brain circulation, by anoxemia, or by narcotic depression of the respiratory center. The relief of these causative factors by the administration of cerebral vasodilator drugs, by the inhalation of mixtures of O_2 and CO_2, or by the administration of central nervous stimulants, often abolishes the periodicity of breathing. In some instances, according to Christie, a very different mechanism is involved, namely, a periodic fluctuation in the distensibility of the lungs caused by variations in pulmonary venous pressure. Rhythmic decreases in distensibility periodically sensitize the Hering-Breuer reflexes and lead to alternation of phases of apnea and hyperpnea (cf. p. 903).

Variations in the sensitivity of the respiratory center to CO_2. Anesthetics in general reduce the sensitivity of the respiratory center to carbon dioxide (16). Accordingly, pulmonary ventilation is reduced and the arterial and alveolar carbon dioxide pressures are elevated. These effects are especially great under deep barbiturate and morphine anesthesia, and because of the severe reduction in pulmonary ventilation which occurs, the arterial oxygen pressure falls to very low levels. If anesthesia is profound and if the degree of cyanosis is great, breathing may depend solely on the reflex stimulation of the respiratory center by impulses from the carotid and aortic chemoreceptors, i.e., the center is unresponsive to CO_2. If pure O_2 is administered to relieve the anoxemia, breathing may stop as a consequence of the withdrawal of the reflex respiratory drive (34). While the exact reason is not very clear, death has resulted from the administration of O_2 to deeply anesthetized patients who were markedly cyanotic. Perhaps the apnea which O_2 produces under these conditions permits the arterial pressure of CO_2 to rise to such an extent that the gas exerts an anesthetic effect upon the brain. This increase in depth of anesthesia might well be the cause of death.

Of more general interest are those physiological variations in sensitivity of the respiratory center to CO_2* which are produced by alterations in acid-base balance. When the alkali reserve of the body is depleted either by the ingestion of acid or by the metabolic production of acid, the respiratory center becomes more sensitive to CO_2. Pulmonary ventilation increases, and

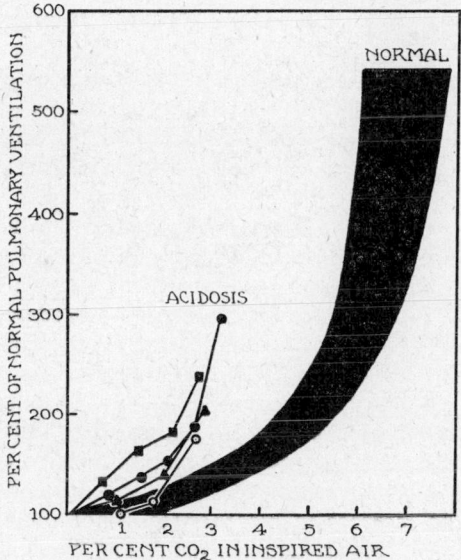

Fig. 429.—A comparison of the increase in pulmonary ventilation produced by the inhalation of increasing percentages of carbon dioxide in normal individuals and in patients in acidosis. (From Peabody, *Arch. intern. Med.*, 1915, *16*:846.)

the arterial CO_2 pressure is maintained at a level below normal. As illustrated in Figure 429, the inhalation of gas mixtures containing CO_2 in low concentrations produces a greater increase in ventilation in patients in acidosis than in normal subjects. In the normal individuals studied by Peabody (39), ventilation was doubled by increasing CO_2 in the inspired air to 4.3 to 5.3 per cent.† In the patients in mild acidosis ventilation was doubled by increasing the CO_2 in the inspired air to 2 to 3 per cent.

This increased sensitivity of the respiratory center to CO_2 plays a major compensatory role in maintaining the neutrality of the body fluids when the

* The term "sensitivity of the respiratory center to CO_2" is used here in a generic sense. At present there is no universally accepted explanation for the observed changes in sensitivity, although two possible explanations are considered under the section headed *Mode of action of CO_2 on the respiratory center* (p. 918).

† From Table 39 it is apparent that ventilation was doubled in Haldane's subject by the inhalation of 3.07 per cent CO_2.

alkali reserve of the body is reduced. The nature of this compensation will be apparent from the following considerations. Normal arterial plasma contains approximately 24 mM of $NaHCO_3$ and 1.2 mM of CO_2 per liter (40). The quantity of CO_2 dissolved in plasma is determined by the arterial pressure of the gas and by its solubility. The hydrogen ion concentration of the plasma, on the other hand, is inversely related to the ratio of $NaHCO_3/CO_2$, which at pH 7.4 amounts to 20 (24/1.2). If the concentration of bicarbonate in the plasma were reduced, and if the concentration of CO_2 were to remain the same, their ratio would decrease and the plasma would become more acid. Actually pulmonary ventilation increases so that the concentration of CO_2 is reduced nearly in proportion to the reduction in concentration of bicarbonate. Therefore the ratio of $NaHCO_3/CO_2$ is maintained near 20, although the absolute quantities of both are reduced. According to Banus, Corman, Perlo and Popkin (1), the compensatory mechanism is so efficient that arterial pH is held constant within 0.01 pH units despite wide variations in bicarbonate concentration.

There is a limit to the capacity of the compensatory mechanism to prevent changes in acidity of the blood. In the terminal stages of diabetic acidosis and chronic nephritis plasma bicarbonate may be reduced to 5 mM per liter (3). Respiration becomes very deep and full and the dyspnea so extreme that it is aptly described as *air hunger*. *Kussmaul breathing* is a clinical term applied to the same condition. As a consequence of the hyperventilation the alveolar CO_2 pressure may be reduced to 10 mm. Hg (4). However, compensation is incomplete and arterial pH may fall to 7.1. An increase in acidity of the blood of this order of magnitude not only increases the sensitivity of the respiratory center to CO_2, but reflexly excites the center as well by stimulating the carotid and aortic chemoreceptors.

When the alkali reserve of the body is elevated by the ingestion of $NaHCO_3$, the respiratory center becomes less sensitive to CO_2. Pulmonary ventilation is reduced and the arterial CO_2 pressure is maintained at a level above normal. Within limits, the concentration of CO_2 dissolved in the plasma is increased in proportion to the increase in bicarbonate. Since the ratio of the two is unchanged, the arterial pH is kept constant. The capacity of this compensatory mechanism to prevent alkalosis is definitely limited. A reduction in pulmonary ventilation reduces the arterial O_2 pressure at the same time that it increases the CO_2 pressure. When the O_2 pressure falls appreciably, the respiratory center is driven reflexly by impulses from the carotid and aortic chemoreceptors.

Mode of action of CO_2 on the respiratory center. Three hypotheses have been advanced to explain the mode of action of CO_2 as a respiratory stimulant. (i) Haldane (23) and recently Banus and his associates (1) have claimed that it acts by virtue of its properties as an acid when dissolved in blood; i.e., CO_2 is hydrated in part to form H_2CO_3, which dissociates to a certain extent to yield hydrogen ions. An increase in CO_2 pressure increases the acidity of the arterial blood and the interstitial fluid surrounding the reticular neurons. This increase in acidity is considered to be the effective respiratory stimulus. As pointed out by Gesell (22), ventilation does not always vary in accordance with the acidity of the blood. For example, the blood may be rendered more alkaline by the intravenous injection of both Na_2CO_3 and $NaHCO_3$. The former produces the expected depression of breathing, whereas the latter, at least temporarily, stimulates breathing. The explanation of this anomaly is as follows. Na_2CO_3 is transformed in the blood to bicarbonate, and the CO_2 pressure is thereby diminished. In contrast, $NaHCO_3$ is in part transformed to CO_2, and the pressure of this gas is thereby increased. Therefore the CO_2 pressure rather than the concentration of hydrogen ions in the blood appears to be the significant stimulating factor. (ii) Gesell has retained in his hypothesis the fundamental concept of the stimulating properties of hydrogen ions, but has resolved the discrepancies noted above by assuming that the acidity of the interior of the respiratory neurons is the factor which determines their discharge. Jacobs (31) has shown that CO_2 readily penetrates most cells, whereas hydrogen ions do not. Presumably CO_2 penetrates the respiratory neurons and is hydrated within the neurons to form H_2CO_3. The intracellular acidity is therefore directly related to the extracellular pressure of CO_2. Evidence in support of this hypothesis has been critically reviewed by Bernthal (5). Either of these first two hypotheses provides a readily apparent reason for the increased sensitivity of the respiratory center to CO_2 in acidosis. The bicarbonate concentration of both plasma and cells is reduced. Accordingly, a given increment in CO_2 pressure produces a greater change in hydrogen ion concentration than is produced normally. (iii) Recently Nielsen (36) and Schmidt and Comroe (45) have advanced the hypothesis that CO_2 has a specific stimulating action on the respiratory neurons independent of its properties as an acid. Nielsen has shown in man that the administration of NH_4Cl may increase the acidity of the blood by $0.08\,pH$ units, yet increase ventilation by only 0.7 liters per minute. In contrast, the inhalation of CO_2 may increase the acidity of the blood by only $0.04\,pH$ units, yet increase ventilation by 10.0 liters per minute. Obviously the acidity of the blood cannot be the factor which determines ventilation. The assumption was made that in both instances intracellular acidity increased to the same extent as extracellular acidity. If this is true, intracellular acidity likewise cannot be the factor which determines ventilation. Nielsen believes, therefore, that CO_2 as a molecular species should be considered the effective respiratory stimulus. While the above line of evidence is by no means conclusive, it is becoming increasingly apparent that CO_2 can be metabolized by cells (17), and that in low concentrations it increases the rate of O_2 consumption of certain tissues (50). If it also affects the oxidative metabolism of the respiratory neurons, it might well govern their activity in this way.* At present it is impossible to choose between the hypothesis of Gesell and that of Nielsen, and it is best for the student to retain an open mind on the question.

Control of the Respiratory Center by Changes in Rate of Flow, Temperature, and O_2 Pressure of the Arterial Blood. The neurons of the respiratory center produce CO_2 as a result of their own metabolic activity. As a consequence, a reduction in the flow of blood through the medulla oblongata leads to a local increase in pressure of CO_2 within the center, and breathing is stimulated. Conversely, an increase in the flow of blood leads to a local reduction in pressure of CO_2 in the center, and breathing is depressed. However, changes in flow produce relatively minor changes in ventilation (42). To demonstrate these changes in ventilation one must first denervate the carotid and aortic

---

* According to F. N. Craig (*J. gen. Physiol.*, 1944, 27:325–338), CO_2 increases glycolysis but not O_2 consumption of tissue slices of the medulla oblongata. Perhaps the rate of glycolysis of neurons of the respiratory center is a factor determining their rate of discharge of impulses.

receptors, for the reflexes produced by changing either the blood pressure or the blood flow in these receptor areas cause much greater changes in ventilation. It is improbable, therefore, that alterations in blood flow through the center play any significant role in respiratory regulation in the normal individual. Even in congestive heart failure, in which condition a reduction in flow has been suggested as the possible cause of dyspnea and orthopnea, cerebral blood flow has been shown to be within normal limits (26).

The rate of respiration increases when the body temperature rises in fever. Depth of respiration also increases, although to a lesser extent than rate. The production of CO_2 is greater in fever, but this fact does not adequately explain the hyperpnea, for the alveolar pressure of CO_2 is reduced and the blood becomes more alkaline (40). It is reasonable to assume that the frequency of discharge of impulses by respiratory neurons increases as the temperature rises, thereby increasing the depth of respiration. In addition, impulses descending from the thermoregulatory center in the hypothalamus probably facilitate the pneumotaxic center (cf. p. 906), thereby increasing the rate of respiration.

Reduction in the O_2 pressure of the arterial blood below its normal level of 95 to 100 mm. Hg primarily depresses the neurons of the respiratory center and reduces ventilation (20, 48). If the O_2 pressure is lowered moderately, a transient phase of stimulation may follow the initial depression (19, 35, 51). These changes can be demonstrated only after the carotid and aortic chemoreceptors have been denervated, for reflex excitation of the respiratory center occurs when these receptors are intact. In man, breathing is usually stimulated slightly by the inhalation of pure O_2, a procedure which markedly elevates the arterial pressure of this gas. It is claimed on this basis that the normal pressure of O_2 in the arterial blood is below the optimum for the proper functioning of the respiratory neurons, and that they are slightly depressed at all times (5). However, it may be that increasing oxygen pressure to such abnormally high levels produces a pathological increase in the oxidative processes of the neurons, and that this is the cause of respiratory stimulation. It is noteworthy that the dog does not show this increase in ventilation. Whatever may be the answer, it is doubtful whether the effects on the respiratory neurons of variations in O_2 pressure play any role in respiratory regulation under normal conditions. In severe anoxemia the depression of the center may limit the reflex stimulation which can be effected by the chemoreceptors.

Significance of the several factors which affect the activity of the respiratory neurons. The sensitivity of the respiratory center to the arterial pressure of CO_2 is the most significant single factor in determining the rate and depth of respiration of the resting individual. It is not the sole regulatory factor under these conditions, for, as will be pointed out below, the inflow of impulses from the carotid and aortic glomi constitute a continuous though slight reflex respiratory drive. Under the stresses of acidosis and fever, the increase in sensitivity of the neurons to CO_2 and the increase in their activity as a function of temperature play a role in regulating ventilation. Changes in blood flow through the brain have little significance in controlling respiration, and the effects of O_2 pressure on the center are of importance only because a reduction in pressure depresses the respiratory neurons. As will be apparent from the discussion to follow, reflex regulation of respiration plays a much more prominent role than central regulation in determining ventilation at high altitudes and in severe muscular exercise.

Reflex chemical control of the respiratory center

Two distinct types of receptors, *chemoreceptors* and *pressoreceptors*, are located at the bifurcations of the carotid arteries and at the arch of the aorta. Because of their sensitivity to changes in composition of the arterial blood and to changes in intravascular pressure, they play important roles in the reflex regulation of respiration and circulation.* Chemoreceptor reflexes are more significant in the regulation of respiration than are pressoreceptor reflexes. The latter are more significant in the regulation of circulation. The

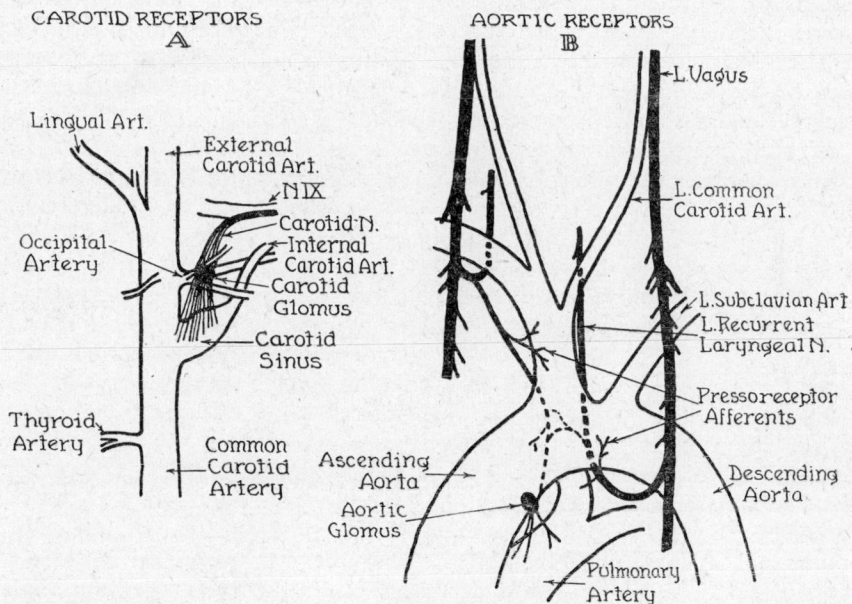

Fig. 430.—Diagrammatic representation of the location and neural connections of the carotid and aortic chemoreceptors and pressoreceptors in the dog. (From Comroe, *Amer. J. Physiol.*, 1939, *127*:176; and Comroe and Schmidt, *Amer. J. Physiol.*, 1938, *121*:75.)

chemoreceptors are stimulated by a decrease in O_2 pressure, by a rise in CO_2 pressure, and by an increase in acidity of the arterial blood. The pressoreceptors are stimulated by an increase in arterial blood pressure. The chemoreceptor respiratory reflexes, which concern us here, serve three important purposes: (i) they exert a slight tonic regulatory influence on eupneic respiration; (ii) they are the predominant if not the sole cause of stimulation of respiration under conditions in which the O_2 pressure of the arterial blood is reduced; (iii) they drive the respiratory center under adverse conditions such as deep anesthesia and severe anoxia which markedly depress the respiratory neurons.

* A systematic study of the aortic reflexes was begun in 1927 by J. F. and C. Heymans (30) and was extended to the carotid reflexes in 1930 by C. Heymans, Bouckaert, Dautrebande (29) and others. Their contributions revolutionized concepts of respiratory and circulatory control, and in 1938 C. Heymans was awarded the Nobel Prize in Physiology.

Morphology of the carotid and aortic receptors. The *carotid* and *aortic glomi* are the chemoreceptor organs. The carotid glomi are small epithelioid bodies attached to the occipital arteries close to their points of origin from the external carotid arteries. The aortic glomus is single and lies within the concavity of the arch of the aorta. The relations of the glomi in the dog are shown diagrammatically in Figure 430, taken from the work of Comroe (8) and Comroe and Schmidt (11). According to DeCastro (13) and Nonidez (38), the glomi are formed of cords of rounded epithelioid receptor cells separated from the blood stream only by the thin walls of sinusoidal capillaries. Afferent nerve fibers end on and between the receptor cells. These afferents emerge from the carotid glomi to form the *carotid nerves* (nerves of Hering) which join the glossopharyngeal nerves and enter the medulla oblongata. The afferents from the single aortic glomus enter both the right and left *depressor nerves* (nerves of Cyon) which run centrally in the vagus trunks.

The pressoreceptors lie within the adventitia and media of the *carotid sinuses*, the *aortic arch*, and the *innominate artery* adjacent to the arch. The sensitive endings are represented by terminal or subterminal dilations of the afferent fibers which ramify within the outer coats of the vessel wall. Distension of the vessel wall by a rise in blood pressure mechanically stimulates these

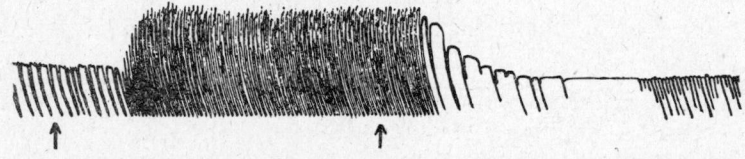

Fig. 431.—Hyperpnea produced in the dog by increasing the carbon dioxide pressure and hydrogen ion concentration of the fluid perfusing the isolated carotid glomi. During the time interval marked off by the arrows a perfusion fluid containing 61.6 vol. per cent carbon dioxide (*p*H 7.33) was substituted for one containing 19.8 vol. per cent (*p*H 7.40). The latency in the response was due to dead space in the perfusion system. (From Heymans, Bouckaert and Dautrebande, *Arch. int. Pharmacodyn.*, 1930, *39*:400.)

endings. The afferent fibers from the carotid sinuses pass through and around the glomi and enter the carotid nerves. The afferent fibers from the aortic arch and innominate artery join the depressor nerves.

Chemoreceptor Reflexes from the Carotid and Aortic Glomi. Heymans and his associates (29) studied the respiratory reflexes produced by perfusing the carotid glomi with Ringer's solution which had been altered in composition in various ways. Their method of perfusion was to insert an inflow cannula directed toward the head into each common carotid artery. All vascular connections of the region of the bifurcation were carefully ligated to prevent any of the perfusion solution from reaching the brain. An outflow cannula was inserted into each external carotid artery directed toward the bifurcation (cf. Fig. 430, A). In effect the carotid receptor area on each side was isolated except for its nerve connections and could readily be perfused with solutions of known composition. The perfusion pressure was kept constant so that pressoreceptor reflexes would not confuse the results. The brain of the animal was adequately supplied with blood through the intact vertebral arteries. It was found that a decrease in oxygen pressure, an increase in CO_2 pressure, and an increase in acidity of the perfusion fluid caused marked reflex stimulation of breathing. Figure 431 illustrates the hyperpnea which was produced by substituting a perfusion fluid containing 61.6 vol. per cent CO_2 (pH 7.33) for one containing 19.8 vol. per cent CO_2 (pH 7.40) during the time interval marked off by the arrows. The latency in the response was due to dead space in the perfusion system. It is evident that the combined stimulus of increased CO_2 pressure and increased acidity markedly increased both depth and rate of respiration. The hyperventilation reduced the CO_2 pressure of the arterial blood supplying the respiratory center, and when the reflex drive was withdrawn, apnea resulted.

To study the aortic chemoreceptor reflexes an ingenious cross perfusion technique was devised. The head of an animal was completely isolated from its body except for the vagus nerves, which carry afferent impulses from the aortic glomus to the respiratory center, and for the spinal cord, which carries the efferent impulses from the respiratory center to the thoracic muscles. The head was kept alive by perfusing it with blood from another animal. A change in composition of the arterial blood of the body obviously could affect the respiratory center in the isolated head only through the intact reflex connections. Utilizing this preparation it was found that reflexes identical to those described above could be obtained by chemical stimulation of the aortic glomus.

Subsequent workers have fully confirmed the results just described, but the changes in the perfusion fluids which were employed in these original experiments to demonstrate the reflexes were far beyond the range of variation encountered in normal life. More recent work has been directed to an analysis of the role played by these reflexes under physiological conditions. Excellent reviews of this still controversial subject by Schmidt and Comroe (44), Gesell (21), and Bernthal (5) are available.

Role of chemoreceptor reflexes in respiratory regulation. It is generally agreed that the chemoreceptor reflexes are responsible for the stimulation of breathing which occurs when the O_2 pressure of the arterial blood is reduced. An experiment of Gemmill and Reeves (20), shown in Figure 432, A, illustrates this point clearly. The ventilation of a normal dog was immediately doubled when nitrogen was inhaled for only 30 seconds. After the chemoreceptors were denervated* no increase in ventilation was produced when nitrogen was inhaled for 60 seconds. Instead, ventilation was reduced, for as has been pointed out previously, anoxia depresses the respiratory center. In contrast, the chemoreceptor reflexes contribute little if anything to the stimulation of breathing which occurs when the CO_2 pressure of the arterial blood is increased. It is evident from Figure 432, B, that ventilation was increased just as much by the inhalation of 5 per cent CO_2 when the chemoreceptors were denervated as when they were intact. The reason for this has been previously emphasized, namely, the sensitivity of the respiratory center to changes in CO_2 pressure of the arterial blood.

The major controversy over function of the chemoreceptors is concerned with the role which they play in the regulation of eupneic respiration. Schmidt and his associates (44) feel that their contribution is negligible under normal conditions, and that they may be considered as an emergency mechanism

---

* Since the carotid but not the aortic chemoreceptors were denervated, the elimination of chemoreceptor afferents was incomplete in these experiments. However, the general results of this investigation have been amply confirmed by subsequent work in which a complete denervation was effected (4, 21, 45).

which functions only when the organism is subjected to the stresses of anoxia and severe acidosis. This view is based upon the following lines of evidence. The sensitivity of the isolated carotid glomi of the anesthetized dog to changes in O_2 pressure, CO_2 pressure and acidity of the perfusion fluid was rather low in their studies. For example, the O_2 pressure had to be lowered 20 mm. Hg or more, the CO_2 pressure raised by 10 mm. Hg or more, and the acidity of the blood increased by 0.1 pH units or more (46) in order to produce a perceptible increase in ventilation. Such changes are obviously beyond the range of physiological variations in eupnea. In addition, the partial pressures of the blood gases and the pH of the blood are maintained within normal limits in animals in which all known chemoreceptors have been removed, and in which ventilation is controlled chemically by the respiratory center alone (51).

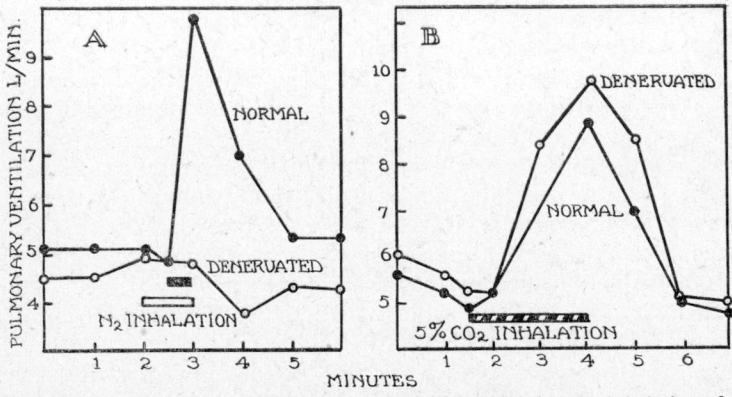

Fig. 432.—A comparison of the respiratory response of an animal to the inhalation of nitrogen and to the inhalation of 5 per cent carbon dioxide in air before and after denervation of the carotid glomi. A, the response to inhalation of nitrogen. In the normal animal, a 30 sec. test period of nitrogen inhalation, indicated by the black bar, approximately doubled ventilation. In the denervated animal a 60 sec. test period, open bar, depressed respiration. B, the response to inhalation of 5.0 per cent carbon dioxide. In the normal and the denervated animal pulmonary ventilation increased to approximately the same extent. (From Gemmill and Reeves, *Amer. J. Physiol.*, 1933, *105*:487.)

Others, however, have found rather greater sensitivity of the chemoreceptors to their chemical environment than that indicated above, and accordingly believe that the chemoreceptor reflexes play a more significant role in eupnea. Evidence to this effect has recently been reviewed in detail by Bernthal (5). The most extreme view is that of Heymans and Bouckaert (28), who believe that the chemoreceptor reflexes play a more important role than central regulatory mechanisms under all conditions. A moderate view is more in line with experimental fact, namely, the chemoreceptor reflexes exert a real though small regulatory influence on the respiratory center in eupnea. The loss of this small factor of reflex excitation leads to no serious disturbance of respiratory control since other excitatory factors tend to compensate. Two rather direct lines of experimental evidence support this view. The inhalation of pure O_2 decreases the ventilation of a normal dog by about 15 per cent (51). The increase in arterial O_2 pressure produced in this manner presumably relieves a normally existing anoxic stimulus to the chemoreceptors. This indicates that the chemoreceptor reflexes account for at least 15 per cent of normal ventilation.* Studies of nerve impulses originating in carotid chemo-receptors of the cat indicate that these endings discharge impulses under conditions of normal arterial O_2 pressure, and therefore must contribute reflexly to the normal control of respiration. An illustrative experiment of von Euler, Liljestrand, and Zotterman (18) is presented in Figure 433. Impulses were recorded from a small slip of the carotid nerve after the caro-tid sinus pressoreceptor fibers had all been cut. The animal was overventilated at a constant rate with gas mixtures containing O_2 and nitrogen in varying proportions. A few impulses were discharged when the gas contained 29.0 per cent O_2, more when it contained 20.9 per cent O_2 (atmospheric air), and still more when the O_2 content was reduced below normal. However, the impulses were markedly increased only when the inspired gas contained 12.0 per cent or less O_2. This correlates well with the known fact that respiration in man is significantly stimulated only when the inspired gas contains 12 to 14 per cent or less O_2. Experiments of a similar nature have shown that the sensitivity of the receptors to CO_2 is such that the normal pressure of this

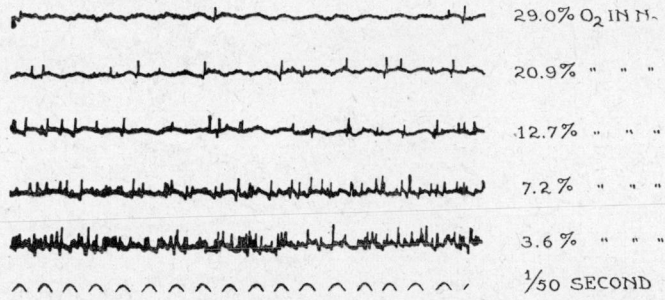

Fig. 433.—Impulses from chemoreceptors of the carotid glomus of a cat during artificial over-ventilation with gas mixtures in which the oxygen content was progressively reduced. Note that some impulses were discharged even when the gas contained 29.0 per cent oxygen, and that the discharge progressively increased as the oxygen content was lowered. (From von Euler, Liljes-trand and Zotterman, *Skand. Arch. Physiol.*, 1940, *83*:132.)

gas in the arterial blood likewise serves as a slight reflex stimulus to res-piration (41). Whether the hydrogen ion concentration of the normal arterial blood is sufficient to stimulate these receptors is unknown, but their sensi-tivity is such that they respond in severe acidosis and thus contribute reflexly to the hyperpnea which characterizes this condition (cf. p. 917).

Effects of a Reduction in Oxygen Pressure on the Respiration of Man. A re-duction in the pressure of O_2 in the arterial blood is a much less effective stimulus to respiration than is an increase in the pressure of CO_2, and can rarely maintain ventilation for any appreciable time by as much as 100 per cent above normal. However, the respiratory response to reduced O_2 pressure in the inspired air is of much more practical importance than is the response to increased CO_2 pressure. Military aircraft of today have been so perfected as to ceiling and rate of ascent that the limitations of flight operation are almost entirely physiological and not mechanical. One of the major factors which limits high altitude flying is anoxia.

* It was pointed out above (cf. p. 920) that the inhalation of O_2 by man commonly increases rather than decreases ventilation. It may well be that the chemoreceptors play a less significant role in the control of eupnea in man than in the dog.

Haldane and others have shown that the alveolar pressure of O_2 during quiet breathing of atmospheric air at sea level averages around 100 mm. Hg. According to Comroe and Dripps (10), the arterial pressure of O_2 is nearly the same as the alveolar pressure, the former averaging 97.1 mm. Hg, the latter averaging 97.4 mm. Hg. Lutz and Schneider (33), who studied the respiratory response of man in a low pressure chamber, found evidence of slight respiratory stimulation at a simulated altitude of 4000 feet. As is shown in Table 40, at this altitude alveolar oxygen pressure had decreased from a normal value of 103 mm. Hg to 84 mm. Hg, and ventilation had increased from 7.61 to 7.98 liters per minute. Because of this increased ventilation, the alveolar CO_2 pressure fell from a normal value of 39.7 mm. Hg to 37.0 mm. Hg. With ascent to progressively higher altitudes, alveolar O_2 pressure decreased and ventilation increased. CO_2 pressure was reduced in proportion to the increase in ventilation. Even at an altitude of 20,000 feet, with a decrease in alveolar oxygen pressure to about one-third of normal, respiration was stimulated only moderately. The reduction in CO_2 pressure to 30.0 mm. Hg obviously limited the respiratory response, for in the absence of the stimulus

Table 40.—*Stimulation of Respiration in Man at High Altitudes. Altitudes Simulated by a Reduction in Barometric Pressure within a Steel Chamber.* (From Lutz and Schneider, *Amer. J. Physiol.*, 1919, 50:280.)

Barometric Pressure (mm. Hg)	760	656	560	480	410	352
Altitude (feet)	0	4000	8000	12,000	16,000	20,000
Alveolar Pressure (mm. Hg)						
pO_2	103.0	84.0	66.0	53.3	42.6	34.8
pCO_2	39.7	37.0	36.2	33.6	31.3	30.0
Ventilation (L./min.)	7.61	7.98	8.59	9.7	10.5	11.6

of anoxia, apnea might reasonably have been expected to occur. Furthermore, the neurons of the respiratory center are depressed by anoxia, and this factor must have limited the respiratory response still more. The increase in ventilation which resulted, although only moderate, represents the reflex stimulation of a depressed respiratory center by nerve impulses from the carotid and aortic chemoreceptors. General symptoms of anoxia at such an altitude are usually severe, for other nervous functions are also depressed. Recent studies have emphasized the fact that normal healthy adults vary considerably in their respiratory response to lowered O_2 pressure. In fact, some lose consciousness at moderate altitudes without showing any significant respiratory stimulation.

Effects of O_2 administration at high altitudes. The inhalation of pure O_2 in place of atmospheric air increases the altitude which can be tolerated by an aviator. At sea level the partial pressure of O_2 in dry atmospheric air is 159 mm. Hg, i.e., 20.93 per cent of 760 mm. Hg. At 20,000 feet it is only 73.7 mm. Hg. If O_2 is the only gas present in the inspired air, it exerts the full barometric pressure, which at 20,000 feet amounts to 352 mm. Hg. For obvious reasons, at this altitude anoxia is prevented by breathing O_2. The greatest altitude which can be tolerated during the inhalation of O_2 is subject to predictable limitations, as will be evident from the following considerations. At all times water vapor exerts a pressure of 47 mm. Hg within the alveoli. If oxygenation of the blood is to be adequate, the alveolar pressure of O_2 must be at least 80 mm. Hg. If the depressing effects of low CO_2 pressure are to be avoided, the alveolar pressure of this gas must be maintained near 40 mm. Hg. The sum of these pressures, 167 mm. Hg, is equivalent to an altitude of between 36,000 and 37,000 feet. This altitude is somewhat lower than the actual ceiling attainable in operational flights, during which some anoxemia and some reduction in CO_2 pressure are tolerated. Flights much above 40,000 to 42,000 feet must either be made in a plane with a pressurized cabin, or some positive pressure breathing appliance must be employed. At 63,000 feet the barometric pressure is 46.9 mm. Hg. If an individual were exposed to this barometric pressure, the alveoli would be completely filled with water vapor to the exclusion of CO_2 and O_2, and theoretically the blood would boil at body temperature.

Anoxemia is a cause of respiratory stimulation and contributes to respiratory distress in patients who suffer from diseases which interfere with the diffusion of oxygen across the pulmonary membranes. The inhalation of O_2 relieves the anoxemia and reduces the respiratory distress. However, other factors such as increased rigidity of the lungs may prevent the complete relief of the dyspnea.

NERVOUS CONTROL OF RESPIRATION

The chemical mechanisms described above subserve a general regulatory function; i.e., they adjust the average rate of gas exchange to satisfy the average metabolic needs of the body. Certain nervous mechanisms, e.g., the reflex mechanism which is stimulated by movements of muscles and joints, play a similar role in increasing the general level of ventilation in severe muscular exercise. Other nervous mechanisms, both voluntary and reflex in character, subserve a more specific regulatory function, i.e., they modify the force and rhythm of the individual respiratory movements to adapt them to the immediate needs of the body. These modifications are ordinarily woven into the general pattern of breathing without disturbing the alveolar and arterial gas pressures to any appreciable extent. The nature and integration of these several nervous regulatory mechanisms are described below.

Voluntary control of respiration. It is commonly known that the rate and depth of breathing are subject to voluntary control. Figure 428 illustrates how very powerful this control can be. In this experiment, voluntary hyperventilation reduced the alveolar CO_2 pressure to 15 mm. Hg, and was succeeded by apnea of two minutes' duration when the involuntary chemical regulatory mechanisms were permitted to resume control. In hysterical states hyperventilation of this order of magnitude may persist for hours, and because of the alkalosis which it induces, may cause tetany. Voluntary apnea may also be maintained for sufficient periods of time to disturb seriously the composition of the internal fluid environment. If one stops breathing at the end of a normal expiration, the breath may be held for 30 to 45 seconds. At the breaking point, the alveolar pressure of carbon dioxide may rise to 50 mm. Hg, and the alveolar pressure of oxygen may fall to 60 mm. Hg. If one first inhales oxygen, the breath may be held for 90 seconds or more, and the alveolar pressure of carbon dioxide may rise above 60 mm. Hg. It is obvious that the length of time that the breath can be held is limited by the intensity of both the direct (CO_2 excess) and reflex (O_2 lack) chemical stimuli acting on the respiratory center. If the alveolar pressure of CO_2 is lowered and that of O_2 is raised by voluntary hyperventilation and by the inhalation of O_2, the breath may be held for as long as 5 to 8 minutes.

In ordinary life voluntary regulation of breathing is important in such activities as speaking, singing, whistling, playing of wind instruments, straining, etc. Also, during the performance of delicate manual operations, breathing is held in abeyance. These various activities are usually carried out with minimal disturbances in alveolar gas pressures. In fact, as everyone knows, it is very difficult to talk during the period of hyperpnea which follows a bout of exercise, when chemical stimuli are still overactive and drive the respiratory center.

Voluntary regulation of breathing depends upon the control of the respiratory center by nerve impulses which descend from the cerebral cortex. Spencer (49), Bucy and Case (6) and Smith (47) have described a number of cortical areas which on electrical stimulation modify respiratory movements. Krogh and Lindhard (32) believe that the cortical areas which control somatic motor activity likewise control the respiratory center, for ventilation increases promptly with the first movement in exercise. The motor control of speech in man is known to be centered in Broca's area in the inferior frontal gyrus of the left cerebral cortex. Impulses from the hypothalamus as well as from the cerebral cortex probably drive the respiratory center in states of emotional stress.

Reflex control of respiration

Two very important respiratory reflexes have already been described in other connections, namely, the Hering-Breuer reflexes and the chemoreceptor reflexes. One might well include the discussion of these reflexes in the present section. However, the Hering-Breuer reflexes are such an intimate part of the complex which is responsible for rhythmic breathing that it was felt best to present them in that connection. Likewise, the chemoreceptor reflexes are ordinarily considered under the heading of respiratory reflexes, but functionally they are more allied to the chemical mechanisms which control breathing. There remain, therefore, for present consideration the pressoreceptor reflexes, initiated by changes in blood pressure; the protective reflexes, initiated by harmful stimuli; and the muscle and joint reflexes, initiated by movements in exercise.

Pressoreceptor respiratory reflexes. A sharp rise in arterial blood pressure produces apnea, whereas a sudden fall in arterial blood pressure produces hyperpnea (27). The apnea accompanying a rise in pressure results mainly from stimulation of the pressoreceptors of the carotid sinus and aortic arch. Impulses from these receptors reflexly inhibit the inspiratory center. The hyperpnea accompanying a fall in pressure results mainly from the withdrawal of these inhibitory impulses which are normally discharged at low frequency when the blood pressure is at the usual levels. Although the pressoreceptor impulses may normally exert a tonic restraining influence on the respiratory center, the pressoreceptor reflexes are of much less general significance than the chemoreceptor reflexes in the regulation of respiration. Denervation of the pressoreceptors has no permanent effect on breathing after the initial brief phase of respiratory stimulation. Schmidt (43) believes that the presso-receptor reflexes in terrestrial forms are vestigial remnants of reflexes which play an important regulatory role in deep sea animals which are subjected to wide variations in hydrostatic pressure.

Protective reflexes. Stimulation of cutaneous afferent nerves produces hyperpnea in lightly anesthetized animals, increasing both rate and depth of respiration. Presumably the afferent fibers which mediate the sensation of pain are responsible for this stimulation of breathing. The reflex hyperpnea is of sufficient intensity to lower arterial CO_2 pressure, and to be succeeded by apnea on cessation of stimulation. In unanesthetized animals, of course, such stimulation would call forth appropriate defensive measures, and the increased production of CO_2 which results from the increased activity would prevent a fall in the alveolar pressure of this gas. One may presume that this respiratory reflex, like the vasopressor reflex which accompanies it, fits the organism for flight or combat. Pleural pain, on the other hand, tends to reduce the amplitude of the respiratory movements and to increase their rate. Shallow breathing in pneumonia reduces the frictional contact between the sensitive parietal pleura and the roughened visceral pleura of the affected lobe, and protects these surfaces from excessive mechanical trauma. The production of a slight pneumothorax to separate the pleural surfaces gives dramatic relief of pain and increases the depth of breathing.

Reflexes arising from stimulation of receptors within the respiratory tract are concerned with protection of the tract itself. Students are all familiar with the reflex apnea produced in animals by the first breath of an irritant vapor such as ether. The cough and the sneeze are other expressions of protective reflexes concerned with the expulsion of foreign materials from the tract. Each of these latter reflexes begins as a deep inspiration, succeeded by a forced expiration. In the cough, following the inspiration the glottis is briefly closed to build up pressure, and when opened, a violent blast of air escapes through the mouth. In the sneeze, the glottis remains open but the communications between pharynx and mouth and between pharynx and nasopharynx are briefly closed by contraction of the fauces and elevation of the palate. With the opening of the nasopharyngeal passage, air is forcibly expelled through the nose. The cough reflex is stimulated by irritation of endings of the 10th cranial nerve in the larynx, trachea, and bronchi. The sneeze reflex is stimulated by irritation of endings of the 5th cranial nerve in the mucosa of the nose and nasopharynx.

Reflexes from muscle and joint receptors and from receptors in the right heart. Harrison and his associates (25) made the interesting observation in man that movements of the hand are accompanied by an increase in ventilation, even when the circulation is completely cut off by a pressure cuff so that metabolic products from the active muscles cannot reach the respiratory center. They suggested that peripheral receptors are stimulated by movement, and that impulses from these receptors reflexly stimulate breathing. To exclude all possibility of a chemical substance being liberated into the general circulation, they repeated their observations on anesthetized animals in which they had sectioned the muscles, bone, and blood vessels of the leg and had left intact only the sciatic nerve. Passive movement of this isolated limb still increased breathing. Comroe and Schmidt (12) have recently confirmed and extended these observations in both animals and man. In the human, passive movement of one leg at the knee 100 times per minute with the circulation occluded increased ventilation by 40 per cent. While this change was rather small, the movements which brought it about were passive, and involved small muscle masses and few joints. Furthermore, the increase in ventilation must have caused a fall in alveolar CO_2 pressure sufficient to limit the respiratory response. Presumably in muscular exercise the more intense stimulation of a greater number of receptors, plus the increased production of CO_2, would increase ventilation to a much greater extent. Comroe and Schmidt lay special stress on joint receptors as the major site of origin of these reflexes.

Table 41.—*Stimulation of Respiration in Man by Exercise of Increasing Severity.* (From Douglas and Haldane, *J. Physiol.*, 1912, *45*:235.)

CONDITION	O_2 CONSUMPTION	CO_2 PRODUCTION	RESPIRATORY RATE	PULMONARY VENTILATION	pCO_2 ALVEOLAR
	CC./MIN.	CC./MIN.	/MIN.	L./MIN.	MM.HG
Rest	237	197	16.8	7.67	42.6
Walking 2M./hr.	780	662	14.7	18.6	43.0
Walking 3M./hr.	1065	922	16.2	24.8	43.5
Walking 4M./hr.	1595	1398	18.2	37.3	45.7
Walking 5M./hr.	2543	2386	19.5	60.9	43.5

Harrison (26) has presented evidence of another reflex which may contribute to respiratory stimulation in exercise. He has shown that a rise in venous pressure in the great veins and atrium of the right heart reflexly increases ventilation. In exercise an increase in systemic venous pressure is routinely observed. Moreover, Harrison believes that this reflex contributes to dyspnea and orthopnea in congestive heart failure, in which condition venous pressure may rise to high levels.

Stimulation of respiration in exercise

Ventilation is increased in severe muscular exercise to as much as 120 liters per minute. No known single respiratory stimulant, either chemical or nervous, can effect an increase in ventilation of this order of magnitude. Comroe (9) in a recent review on respiration in exercise points out that many types of stimuli must summate at the respiratory center to increase ventilation to such an extent. While a number of the possible stimuli have been identified, their relative contributions to the hyperpnea of exercise have not been quantitated. Furthermore, the absolute and relative contributions of each stimulus undoubtedly vary with the severity of the exertion. These stimuli include an increase in arterial CO_2 pressure (at least in the initial stages of mild exercise), a rise in body temperature, the production of lactic acid, the secretion of adrenaline and an increase in the number of nerve impulses from the cerebral motor cortex, from muscles and joints, from chemoreceptors, from the lungs, and from the right atrium.

In relatively mild muscular exercise an increase in arterial CO_2 pressure may play some role in increasing ventilation. An experiment of Douglas and Haldane (15) illustrating this point is presented in Table 41. Walking at speeds up to 4 miles per hour was accompanied by a progressive rise in alveolar CO_2 pressure from 42.6 mm. Hg at rest to 45.7 mm. Hg at 4 miles per hour. If one compares Table 39 (p. 914) with Table 41, it is apparent that an increase in CO_2 pressure of this order of magnitude is roughly sufficient to produce the observed increase in ventilation, namely, an increase from 7.67 liters per minute to 37.3 liters per minute. However, walking at a speed of 5 miles per hour was accompanied by an actual fall in alveolar CO_2 pressure, although ventilation increased to 60.9 liters per minute. In exercise of still greater severity, the alveolar CO_2 pressure may fall to levels considerably below the resting level, yet ventilation may increase to 100 to 120 liters per minute. It is evident that other factors play a more prominent role than CO_2 pressure in increasing ventilation in severe exercise. But it is equally evident that CO_2 must play some role, for the increased rate of production of this gas prevents a fall in its alveolar pressure of such magnitude as would limit the respiratory response.

In severe exercise lactic acid is produced by the contraction of muscles insufficiently supplied with O_2, and blood bicarbonate is transformed in part to lactate. Under these conditions the sensitivity of the respiratory center to CO_2 is increased. Furthermore, the increased acidity of the blood stimulates the chemoreceptor reflexes. Body temperature rises by several degrees and adrenaline is liberated into the blood stream. Nerve impulses from the active muscles and joints, from the lungs and right heart, and from the cerebral motor cortex impinge on the respiratory center in increased numbers. All of these stimuli summate at the respiratory center, and the activity of the center is increased in proportion to the sum of all the stimuli acting upon it. Accordingly, exercise is by far the most potent cause of respiratory stimulation.

REFERENCES

1. BANUS, M. G., CORMAN, H. H., PERLO, V. P. and POPKIN, G. L. The sensitivity of the respiratory center to hydrogen ion concentration. Amer. J. Physiol., 1944, 142:121–130.

2. BARCROFT, J and MARGARIA, R. Some effects of carbonic acid on the character of human respiration. J. Physiol., 1931, 72:175–185.

3. BEDDARD, A. P., PEMBRY, M. S. and SPRIGGS, E. I. The quantity and pressure of carbon dioxide in venous blood and in alveolar air in cases of diabetes and diabetic coma. J. Physiol., 1904, 31:xliv–xlvi.

4. BEDDARD, A. P., PEMBRY, M. S. and SPRIGGS, E. I. Further observations of the quantity and pressure of carbon dioxide in venous blood and in alveolar air in cases of diabetes and diabetic coma. J. Physiol., 1908, 37:xxxix–xli.

5. BERNTHAL, T. Respiration. Ann. Rev. Physiol., 1944, 6:155–194.

6. BUCY, P. C. and CASE, T. J. Cortical innervation of respiratory movements. J. nerv. ment. Dis., 1936, 84:156–168.

7. CAMPBELL, J. M. H., DOUGLAS, C. G., HALDANE, J. S. and HOBSON, F. G. The response of the respiratory centre to carbonic acid, oxygen, and hydrogen ion concentration. J. Physiol., 1913, 46:301–318.

8. COMROE, J. H. The location and function of the chemoreceptors of the aorta. Amer. J. Physiol., 1939, 127:176–191.

9. COMROE, J. H. The hyperpnea of muscular exercise. Physiol. Rev., 1944, 24:319–339.

10. COMROE, J. H. and DRIPPS, R. D. The oxygen tension of arterial blood and alveolar air in normal human subjects. Amer. J. Physiol., 1944, 142:700–707.

11. COMROE, J. H. and SCHMIDT, C. F. The part played by reflexes from the carotid body in the chemical regulation of respiration in the dog. Amer. J. Physiol., 1938, 121:75–97.

12. COMROE, J. H. and SCHMIDT, C. F. Reflexes from the limbs as a factor in the hyperpnea of muscular exertion. Amer. J. Physiol., 1943, 138:536–547.

13. DeCASTRO, F. Sur la structure et l'innervation de la glande intercarotidienne (glomus caroticum) de l'homme et des mammifères, et sur un nouveau système d'innervation autonome du nerf glossopharyngien. Trab. Lab. Invest. biol. Univ. Madr., 1926, 24:365–432.

14. DOUGLAS, C. G. and HALDANE, J. S. The causes of periodic or Cheyne-Stokes breathing. J. Physiol., 1909, 38:401–419.

15. DOUGLAS, C. G. and HALDANE, J. S. The capacity of the air passages under varying

physiological conditions. *J. Physiol.*, 1912, *45*:235–238.

16. DRIPPS, R. D. and DUMKE, P. R. The effect of narcotics on the balance between central and chemoreceptor control of respiration. *J. Pharmacol.*, 1943, *77*:290–300.

17. EVANS, E. A., JR., VENNESLAND, B. and SLOTIN, L. The mechanism of carbon dioxide fixation in cell-free extracts of pigeon liver. *J. biol. Chem.*, 1943, *147*:771–784.

18. EULER, U. S. VON, LILJESTRAND, G. and ZOTTERMAN, Y. The excitation mechanism of the chemoreceptors of the carotid body. *Skand. Arch. Physiol.*, 1940, *83*:132–152.

19. GEMMILL, C. L., GEILING, E. M. K. and REEVES, D. L. The respiratory effect of prolonged anoxemia in the normal dog before and after denervation of the carotid sinuses. *Amer. J. Physiol.*, 1934, *109*:709–713.

20. GEMMILL, C. L. and REEVES, D. L. The effect of anoxemia in normal dogs before and after denervation of the carotid sinuses. *Amer. J. Physiol.*, 1933, *105*:487–495.

21. GESELL, R. Respiration and its adjustments. *Ann. Rev. Physiol.*, 1939, *1*:185–216.

22. GESELL, R. The chemical regulation of respiration. *Physiol. Rev.*, 1925, *5*:551–595.

23. HALDANE, J. S. *Respiration*. New Haven, Yale Univ. Press, 1922. xviii, 427 pp.

24. HALDANE, J. S. and PRIESTLEY, J. G. The regulation of lung ventilation. *J. Physiol.*, 1905, *32*:225–266.

25. HARRISON, W. G., JR., CALHOUN, J. A. and HARRISON, T. R. Afferent impulses as a cause of increased ventilation during muscular exercise. *Amer. J. Physiol.*, 1932, *100*:68–73.

26. HARRISON, T. R., HARRISON, W. G., CALHOUN, J. A. and MARSH, J. P. Congestive heart failure. XVII. The mechanism of dyspnea on exertion. *Arch. intern. Med.*, 1932, *50*:690–720.

27. HEYMANS, C. and BOUCKAERT, J. J. Sinus caroticus and respiratory reflexes. I. Cerebral blood flow and respiration. Adrenaaline apnoea. *J. Physiol.*, 1930, *69*:254–266.

28. HEYMANS, C. and BOUCKAERT, J. J. Les chémo-récepteurs du sinus carotidien. *Ergebn. Physiol.*, 1939, *41*:28–55.

29. HEYMANS, C., BOUCKAERT, J. J. and DAUTREBANDE, L. Sinus carotidien et réflexes respiratoires. II. Influences respiratoires réflexes de l'acidose, de l'alcalose, de l'anhydride carbonique, de l'ion hydrogène, et de l'anoxémie. Sinus carotidiens et échanges respiratoires dans les poumons et au dela poumons. *Arch. int. Pharmacodyn.*, 1930, *39*:400–445.

30. HEYMANS, J. F. and HEYMANS, C. Sur les modifications directes et sur la regulation réflexe de l'activité du centre respiratoire de la tête isolée du chien. *Arch. int. Pharmacodyn.*, 1927, *33*:273–371.

31. JACOBS, M. H. To what extent are the physiological effects of carbon dioxide due to hydrogen ions? *Amer. J. Physiol.*, 1920, *51*:321–331.

32. KROGH, A. and LINDHARD, J. The regulation of respiration and circulation during the initial stages of muscular work. *J. Physiol.*, 1913, *47*:112–136.

33. LUTZ, B. R. and SCHNEIDER, E. C. Alveolar air and respiratory volume at low oxygen tensions. *Amer. J. Physiol.*, 1919, *50*:280–301.

34. MARSHALL, E. K. and ROSENFELD, M. Depression of respiration by oxygen. *J. Pharmacol.*, 1936, *57*:437–457.

35. MOYER, C. A. and BEECHER, H. K. Central stimulation of respiration during hypoxia. *Amer. J. Physiol.*, 1942, *136*:13–21.

36. NIELSEN, M. Untersuchungen über die Atemregulation beim Menschen, besonders mit Hinblick auf die Art des chemischen Reizes. *Skand. Arch. Physiol.*, 1936, *74*:87–208.

37. NIELSEN, M. Die Respirationsarbeit bei Körperruhe und bei Muskelarbeit. *Skand. Arch. Physiol.*, 1936, *74*:299–316.

38. NONIDEZ, J. F. The aortic (depressor) nerve and its associated epithelioid body, the glomus aorticum. *Amer. J. Anat.*, 1935, *57*:259–301.

39. PEABODY, F. W. Clinical studies on the respiration. I. The effect of carbon dioxide in the inspired air on patients with cardiac disease. *Arch. intern. Med.*, 1915, *16*:846–864.

40. PETERS, J. P. and VAN SLYKE, D. D. *Quantitative clinical chemistry. Interpretations.* Baltimore, Williams and Wilkins Co., 1931. (See Chap. 18: Carbonic acid and acid-base balance.)

41. SAMAAN, A. and STELLA, G. The response of the chemical receptors of the carotid sinus to tension of CO_2 in the arterial blood in the cat. *J. Physiol.*, 1935, *85*:309–319.

42. SCHMIDT, C. F. Carotid sinus reflexes to the respiratory center. II. Attempt at evaluation. *Amer. J. Physiol.*, 1932, *102*:119–137.

43. SCHMIDT, C. F. The respiration. Chaps. 38–47 in: BARD, P., ed., *MacLeod's Physiology in modern medicine*, 9th ed. St. Louis, C. V. Mosby Co., 1941.

44. SCHMIDT, C. F. and COMROE, J. H. Functions of the carotid and aortic bodies. *Physiol. Rev.*, 1940, *20*:115–157.

45. SCHMIDT, C. F. and COMROE, J. H. Respiration. *Ann. Rev. Physiol.*, 1941, *3*:151–184.

46. SCHMIDT, C. F., COMROE, J. H. and DRIPPS, R. D. Carotid body reflexes in the dog. *Proc. Soc. exp. Biol., N. Y.*, 1939, *42*:31–32.

47. SMITH, W. K. The representation of respiratory movements in the cerebral cortex. *J. Neurophysiol.*, 1938, *1*:55–68.

48. SMYTH, D. H. The study of the carotid sinus respiratory reflexes by means of chronic experiments. *J. Physiol.*, 1937: *88*:425–435.

49. SPENCER, W. G. The effect produced upon respiration by faradic excitation of the cerebrum in the monkey, dog, cat, and rabbit. *Philos. Trans.*, 1894, *B185*:609–757.

50. WARREN, C. O. The rôle of bicarbonate in the action of the serum in supporting tissue respiration. *J. biol. Chem.*, 1944, *156*:559–569.

51. WATT, J. G., DUMKE, R. R. and COMROE, J. H. Effects of inhalation of 100 per cent and 14 per cent oxygen upon respiration of unanesthetized dogs before and after chemoreceptor denervation. *Amer. J. Physiol.*, 1943, *138*:610–617.

SECTION VII

BODY FLUIDS AND KIDNEY

BY ROBERT W. CLARKE

INTRODUCTION

The middle of the nineteenth century marks the beginning of the rapid, modern development of renal physiology. In 1842 Bowman (2), who first described clearly the structure of the Malpighian corpuscle and its anatomical relations to the uriniferous tubule, advanced the general theory that water and salts "pass from the blood into the capsule at the glomerulus, and that the characteristic nitrogenous elements of the urine are secreted through the epithelium of the tubules. Ludwig (6) at about the same time proposed what was designated as a mechanical theory of secretion, according to which the urine is produced in the glomeruli by filtration from the plasma, that is, by an excess of pressure which forces the water and dissolved substances, with the exception of the proteins, through the epithelium into the cavity of the capsule. As this liquid, containing all the constituents of urine in diluted form, passes down the tubule it becomes converted to urine of normal concentration by processes of diffusion with the blood (or lymph) in the surrounding capillaries. It will be noted that a major difference between the two theories lies in the function attributed to the tubular epithelium. In Bowman's theory the cells are secretory while in Ludwig's theory they constitute a passive membrane through which absorption takes place by diffusion. Later Heidenhain (5) proposed a modification and extension of Bowman's theory which he supported by numerous well conceived experiments. According to this author, both the glomerular and the tubular epithelium are secreting structures. At the glomerulus water and salts are secreted, and in the tubules the characteristic elements of the urine are eliminated. His theory stood in direct opposition to that of Ludwig in attributing the formation of urine not to physical causes (filtration, diffusion) but to processes of cellular activity.

"The ideas expressed in these three theories have furnished the basis for most of the subsequent discussions of the problem. A vast amount of experimental work has been done upon the subject, and theories of numerous kinds have been proposed. The view most commonly adopted at present may be considered as a modification of Ludwig's theory. Expressed in general terms, it assumes that in the glomeruli there is a filtration of water and solutes from the blood plasma, with the exception of colloidal substances like protein, and that in passing down the tubules water and dissolved substances are reabsorbed until the normal concentration and composition of the urine is reached. The reabsorption is not considered as a simple matter of diffusion, but as a selective process controlled by the activity of the cells.

933

The tubular epithelial cells are believed to possess also an excretory activity for certain constituents of the urine or for foreign substances."*

The appearance in 1917 of Cushny's monograph and its revised edition (4) a few years later marks the close of one era of the physiology of the kidney.

The work of Claude Bernard (7) touched many fields of physiology, among them the one from which comes his often quoted statement, *la fixité du milieu intérieur est la condition de la vie libre, indépendante* (*l.c.* p. 254). This theme has been elaborated by many, among them Barcroft (1) and Cannon (3). The constancy of the internal environment is not a mold into which physiology must be fitted, but a pattern from which deviations have proved to be fully as instructive as conformance. In the following chapters both constancy and variability of the matrix of cellular environment will be found to be of equal importance in the physiology of body water. The reader will find throughout this Section the dependence of current thinking on the rise of quantitative methods of investigation, applied first to experimental animals, and, in most of the cases cited, also applied to man.

REFERENCES

1. BARCROFT, J. *Features in the architecture of physiological function.* New York, Macmillan Co., 1934. x, 368 pp.

2. BOWMAN, W. On the structure and use of the Malpighian bodies of the kidney, with observations on the circulation through that gland. *Philos. Trans.*, 1842, part I, pp. 57–80.

3. CANNON, W. B. *The wisdom of the body.* New York, W. W. Norton, [1932]. [xv], 312 pp.

4. CUSHNY, A. R. *The secretion of the urine*, 2nd ed. London, Longmans, Green and Co., 1926, xii, 288 pp.

5. HEIDENHAIN, R. Die Harnabsonderung. *Hermanns Handb. Physiol.*, 1883, *V*. part 1: 279–373.

6. LUDWIG, C. Nieren und Harnbereitung. *Wagners Handw. Physiol.*, 1844, *2*:628–640.

7. OLMSTED, J. M. D. *Claude Bernard physiologist.* New York, Harper and Brothers, 1938. xvi, 272 pp.

* From Howell's *Textbook of Physiology*, 14th ed., 1940.

CHAPTER 43

PHYSIOLOGY OF BODY FLUIDS

BY J. RUSSELL ELKINTON

Water is the largest single constituent of living organisms and constitutes the universal medium in which all the complex processes of life take place. In this sense the metabolism of body water is inseparable from any of the metabolic and physiological processes of the organism elucidated in the various sections of this book. The distribution and regulation of body water and the various types of fluid of which it is the solvent, however, are of such importance to the understanding of the functioning of the organism as to warrant separate consideration.

The physiology of body water can only be considered in conjunction with certain of its main solutes (17, 18, 22, 43, 48, 49, 50). While water is the medium for the exchanges and metabolism of many organic solutes, its movements are primarily tied up with those of its major solutes, the electrolytes, which consist of inorganic ions and ionized proteins. These solutes in body water constitute the *body fluids* under discussion.

FUNCTIONAL DIVISIONS

Modern views of water metabolism conceive the mammalian organism as one continuous aqueous phase. This is enclosed by a specialized envelope, the integument, through which are certain paths of exchange with the environment. Within this envelope all water is freely diffusible and available as a solvent for the main constituent solutes, the electrolytes. As a consequence, the *total concentration* of electrolytes is the same throughout all parts of the body. In contrast, the *composition* varies extensively. These differentiated patterns of solutes are the result of restraints to their free exchange between certain parts of the body. Upon these restraints depend the functional divisions of the body fluids. The term *functional* is applied to these divisions in order to emphasize their functional roles in the organism. The names applied to them, however, are anatomical and are descriptive of their anatomical sites. In point of fact, the anatomical divisions and the functional divisions may not strictly coincide (see below, p. 939), but their identity is sufficiently close to warrant the application of the anatomical name to the functional division in general usage.

Extracellular and Intracellular Phases. Total body fluids are separated into two main divisions, the *extracellular fluid* and the *intracellular fluid* (Fig. 434). This division is the result of the differential restraint of electrolytes at the cell boundary, i.e., the pattern of electrolytes inside body cells differs greatly from that of the fluid outside the cells. Intracellular fluid contains potassium as the predominant cation and phosphate and protein as the main anions, while the chief ions of extracellular fluid are sodium, chloride

935

and bicarbonate.* The function of these two fluid compartments differs as well as their electrolyte composition. Cell fluid is the medium in which the processes of cell metabolism take place. Extracellular fluid lies between the cells and the external environment and constitutes for the cells what Claude Bernard termed "the internal environment." It serves both as a buffer to preserve a constant environment to the cells, and as a path of exchange for many substances between the cells and the outside world.

Blood Plasma and Interstitial Fluid. Extracellular fluid in turn is divided into that portion which lies within the vascular system, the *plasma*, and that which lies between the capillaries and the cells, the *interstitial fluid*. These subdivisions depend upon a different type of restraint of solutes: the relative impermeability of the capillary endothelium to the plasma proteins. Plasma contains protein in much greater concentration than interstitial fluid. Functionally the plasma portion of extracellular fluid provides rapid mixing of extracellular fluid throughout the body as well as immediate access to the

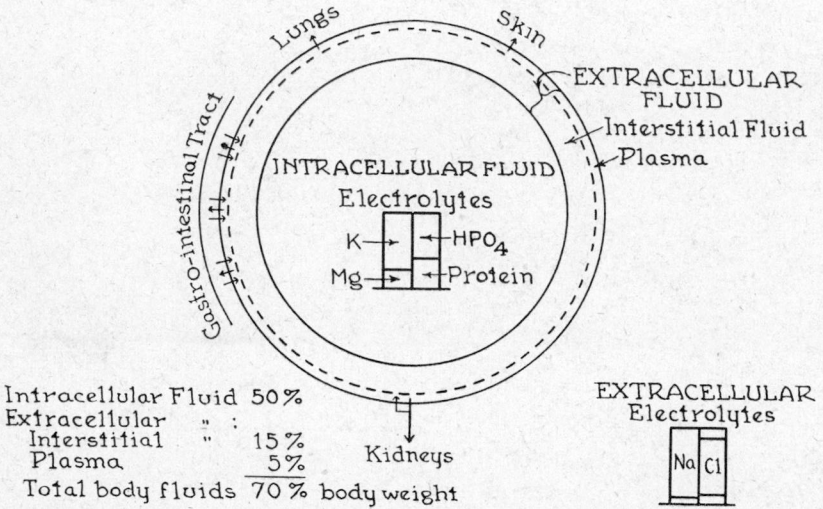

Fig. 434.—Schematic diagram of the divisions of the body fluids, and their principal ionic contents.

paths of exchange with the external world, the skin, lungs, gastro-intestinal tract, and kidneys. Blood plasma also provides the one sample of extracellular fluid readily available for analysis.†

Individual Tissue Fluids. So far we have spoken of the body fluids as a homogeneous system. This system is composed of many different types of tissue which vary in the relative distribution of fluid between the cellular and extracellular phases, and in electrolyte pattern. Usually skeletal muscle provides the main working model for our concept of body fluid physiology as it is the preponderant tissue of the body. There are also certain highly

---

* The ionic composition of extracellular fluid suggests that sea water was its phylogenetic precursor, the principal ionic constituents of sea water being sodium and chloride (38).

† Blood *serum* is plasma minus its fibrinogen which is separated in the process of clotting. Serum is more commonly used for chemical analysis than plasma because the use of anticoagulants is avoided. As there is no significant change in volume, the concentrations of solutes are identical.

specialized or differentiated fluids which are set apart from the rest of the body fluids by special tissue barriers: the cerebrospinal fluid, the aqueous humor of the eye, and the synovial fluid of joints. In respect to their main cation and anion content these fluids resemble interstitial fluid, but quantitatively they do not bulk large compared to the total body fluids, and will not be discussed here.

INTERNAL EXCHANGES

Fluid Exchanges Between Blood Plasma and Interstitial Fluid. The capillary membrane is permeable to inorganic ions but not to colloid solutes and the plasma proteins. According to the Starling theory (60), transfers of fluid between these two compartments of extracellular fluid are controlled by the relative hydrostatic and protein osmotic pressure of the two phases. Fluid is driven from the capillary by the hydrostatic pressure in the capillary and the osmotic pressure of such proteins as are present in the interstitial fluid; fluid is returned from the interstitial spaces to the capillary by the colloid osmotic pressure of the plasma proteins and the hydrostatic pressure of the tissues due to their elasticity (Fig. 435). Because the effective hydrostatic

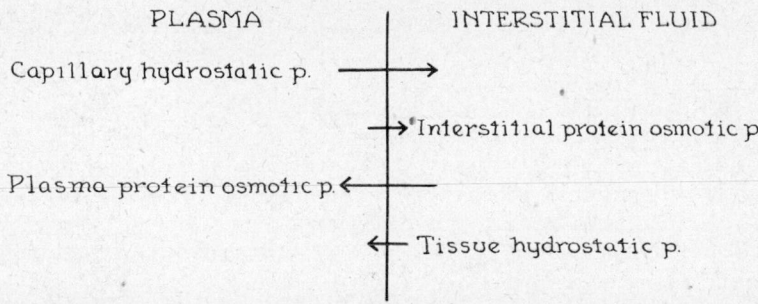

Fig. 435.—Forces which determine the distribution of fluid between plasma and interstitial spaces.

pressure is higher and the effective osmotic pressure is lower at the arterial end than they are at the venous end of the capillary, fluid passes from the capillary at the arterial end and returns to it at the venous, constituting a continuous circulation between the two fluid compartments. Landis (34) has demonstrated that in the human extremities these pressures are of the right magnitude to produce such transfers of fluid. It should be recognized, however, that the Starling theory has certain inherent difficulties in that it is a static model of a dynamic situation. Effective hydrostatic and osmotic pressures are self-limiting variables; others must be involved to explain the maintenance of an abnormal distribution of fluid between the two phases, as in chronic edema. The precise mechanisms of such variables which must include changes in lymph flow, in tissue tension, and in vasomotor activity are not known.

The major portion of the osmotic pressure of the plasma proteins is exerted by the plasma albumin because it is present in much higher molar concentration than the globulin. To the colloid osmotic pressure of the plasma proteins is added a small increment of pressure due to the Gibbs-Donnan effect of the nondiffusible proteins (see Chap. 27, p. 571). While albumin and globulin are largely restrained by the capillary endothelium, this impermeability is only relative, and its degree may vary in certain tissues.

The protein content of edema fluids usually does not exceed 0.5 per cent, while the concentration in hepatic lymph and that in the thoracic duct is approximately as great as in plasma.

Volume of blood and plasma. The volume of the circulating plasma is at all times the net resultant of accretions from, and losses of fluid to, the interstitial spaces. Several methods have been employed to measure the plasma volume in the intact organism. Assumption that the volume through which certain intravenously injected dyes, such as brilliant vital red or the blue dye, T-1824, are distributed is identical with the volume of plasma, is based on the fact that these dyes are combined with plasma proteins and the theory that plasma proteins are restrained by the capillary endothelium. The use of such dyes, however, must give a volume larger than the true plasma volume, as the dyes, along with plasma protein, escape into the lymphatics. Inasmuch as this loss of dye from the vascular system is irregular, it is difficult to make an adequate correction for it. If the ratio of cells to plasma in blood is known, the blood volume may be computed from the plasma volume. Average values obtained by the blue dye, T-1824, have given values of 4.6 liters for a normal adult or 72 cc. per kilogram (23). Carbon monoxide may be used to measure blood volume because of its affinity for the hemoglobin in red blood cells. Values so obtained in normal subjects are usually slightly smaller than those computed from the blue dye and from hematocrit data (29). In pathological states the latter may greatly exceed the former (30). As red cells are less likely than plasma proteins to escape from the vascular system, the carbon monoxide method of measuring blood volume is probably the more reliable.

Changes in plasma volume may also be estimated from changes in the ratio of red cells to plasma in whole blood as measured by the hematocrit, and from the concentration of hemoglobin. The basic assumption is that the total circulating red cell mass has not changed in respect to number of red cells or total hemoglobin content. The inclusion of the hemoglobin concentration as well as the hematocrit values corrects for any changes in volume of the red cells that may occur in response to changes in serum electrolyte concentration. The further assumption is involved that the red cells are evenly distributed through the blood stream and in the samples of blood taken for analysis. Given the initial plasma volume, V_1, the final plasma volume, V_2, is calculated as follows:

$$V_2 = \frac{V_1 (1 - Hkt_2) Hb_1,}{(1 - Hkt_1) Hb_2}$$

where Hkt_1 and Hkt_2 and Hb_1 and Hb_2 are the initial and final hematocrit values and hemoglobin concentration respectively. As the underlying assumptions are probably never completely valid, this method of calculation of changes in plasma volume is rough at best, even under acute circumstances. For routine clinical use, however, it is usually the only method available. Changes in the concentration of plasma protein may also be used to calculate changes in plasma volume. But as protein is continually being added to and removed from the total circulating plasma protein, this calculation is even less accurate than that based on contents of red cells and hemoglobin.

Although a normal blood volume is only one of the variables which determine the adequacy of the circulation, reduction in blood volume or plasma volume almost always results in impairment of the circulatory dynamics. For this reason, changes in the volume of blood and plasma associated with various types of dehydration and traumatic and hemorrhagic shock are of intense practical interest (see p. 958).

Blood and lymph. Lymph is a specialized portion of interstitial fluid. It, too, is an ultrafiltrate of serum and differs only from interstitial fluid in that it contains a higher concentration of protein and flows through certain established channels in the tissues. It appears to be a special mechanism for the transfer of colloidal and particulate matter from the interstitial spaces to the venous blood. The flow of lymph is maintained by its colloid osmotic pressure in relation to the rest of the interstitial fluid, by tissue pressure, and by muscular contraction and a system of valves.

Fluid Exchanges between Cells and Extracellular Fluid. *Identity and volume of extracellular fluid.* As has been indicated above (p. 935), two main divisions of body fluid exist which differ in anatomical site, ionic composition, and function. One of these divisions is predominantly extracellular, is composed principally of sodium, chloride, and bicarbonate, and functions as an environment for body cells. Its precise volume and composition depend somewhat on the technique employed in its measurement.

In the intact living organism it is possible to demonstrate that various substances, when injected intravenously, are apparently distributed through a volume approximating 20 to 30 per cent of the body weight. The limitations of distribution of the substances suggest that they are, in the main, excluded from cells. These substances include sulfocyanate, bromide, magnesium, sucrose, mannitol, sulfate, radioactive sodium, and radioactive chloride. The apparent volume of distribution is calculated as follows:

$$\text{Apparent volume of distribution} = \frac{\text{Amount injected} - \text{amount excreted}}{\text{Rise in concentration in serum water}}.$$

This calculation depends upon the assumptions that the substance is neither formed nor destroyed in the body, that it is uniformly distributed through some portion of the body water, and that its concentration in water of serum is a fair sample of its concentration throughout this portion. Use of this technique yields values which vary considerably among substances used, as well as among species of experimental subjects. In man, the apparent volumes of distribution of sucrose, sulfocyanate and radioactive sodium have been found to range from 13 to 29, 16 to 28, and 21 to 29 per cent of the body weight respectively (32, 36), while in the dog, average values for radioactive chloride, radioactive sodium and sulfocyanate have been found to be respectively 25, 28 and 36 per cent of the body weight (64).

The wide divergence among the apparent volumes of distribution of these various substances indicates that they can hardly occupy the same anatomical space—that is, a fraction of these substances penetrates beyond the extracellular space. This interpretation is supported by another kind of evidence: analysis of tissue electrolytes. Analyses of whole bodies of animals yield amounts of chloride and sodium which, at the concentration in which they were present in serum, would be distributed through a volume of fluid equivalent to 20 to 30 per cent of the body weight (25). In relation to their respective concentrations, however, the amount of sodium was in excess of that of chloride, i.e., its volume of distribution was larger. Analyses of skeletal muscle also indicate sodium and chloride to be present in about the same fraction of muscle water, but sodium to be in excess of chloride (6, 15, 26).

Muscle analysis. Water content is determined by weighing the muscle specimen before and after desiccation in a drying oven. The fat content is removed from the dried residue and its magnitude determined by weight measurements before and after this process. The fat-free dried residue is then analyzed for electrolytes.

Given the content of water, solids, chloride, sodium, and potassium of a fat-free aliquot of muscle and the content of the same substances in the blood serum of the same organism, the distribution of water and electrolytes may be calculated (15, 26). On the basic assumption that all the chloride is extracellular and that its concentration is that of an ultrafiltrate of serum, the volume of the extracellular phase (F) is determined (Hastings and Eichelberger system of calculation):

$$(F) = \frac{(Cl)_M}{\{Cl\}_F} \times 1000$$

where:

$(Cl)_M$ = mEq. chloride per kg. muscle
$\{Cl\}_F$ = "   "   " " extracellular phase
$= \dfrac{0.99}{0.95} \times [Cl]_S$

where:

$[Cl]_S$ = mEq. chloride per kg. serum water

The figure 0.99 is assumed to be the concentration of water in the extracellular phase in gm. of water per gm. of fluid. The figure 0.95 is the Donnan factor, or ratio $[Cl]_S/[Cl]_F$, where $[Cl]_F$ is the mEq. Cl per kg. of extracellular water.

The concentration of water in the intracellular phase $\{H_2O\}_C$ is then calculated:

$$\{H_2O\}_C = \frac{(H_2O)_C}{(C)} = \frac{(H_2O)_M - (H_2O)_F}{(C)}$$

where:

$(H_2O)_C$ = gm. intracellular water per kg. muscle
$(H_2O)_M$ = gm. water per kg. muscle
$(H_2O)_F$ = gm. extracellular water per kg. muscle
$= 0.99 \times (F)$
(C) = gm. intracellular phase per kg. muscle
$= 1000 - (F)$.

From the concentration of sodium and potassium in serum, the amounts of these electrolytes in the intracellular phase may be calculated: mEq. intracellular sodium per kg. muscle $(Na)_C$, is determined:

$$(Na)_C = (Na)_M - [(H_2O)_F \times [Na]_F]$$

where:

$(Na)_M$ = mEq. sodium per kg. muscle
$[Na]_F$ = "   "   " " extracellular water
$= 0.95 \times [Na]_S$

where:

$[Na]_S$ = mEq. sodium per kg. serum water.

mEq. intracellular potassium per kg. muscle, $(K)_C$, is similarly calculated:

$$(K)_C = (K)_M - [(H_2O)_F \times [K]_F]$$

where:

$(K)_M$ = mEq. potassium per kg. muscle
$[K]_F$ = "   "   " " extracellular water
$= 0.95 \times [K]_S$

where:

$[K]_S$ = mEq. potassium per kg. serum water.

Manery, Danielson and Hastings (40) have suggested that this method of calculation would more nearly represent the morphological truth if the extracellular phase is identified with connective tissue diluted with serum ultrafiltrate. This correction increases slightly the magnitude of the extracellular phase by the amount of connective tissue protein present. Darrow, Harrison and Taffel (6) have pointed out that, as the volumes of the extracellular and intracellular phases may vary independently of each other, it is more desirable to express the concentration of cellular electrolytes in terms of some relatively fixed cellular constituent. For this reason Darrow and coworkers express the water and electrolyte contents of muscle in units per 100 grams of fat-free solids. Table 42 presents the average values for the water and electrolyte content of skeletal muscle in two series of normal dogs, one series from Hastings and Eichelberger and one from Darrow, Harrison and Taffel. It is evident that both methods of calculation assign a significant portion of the sodium in skeletal muscle to the intracellular phase.

Table 42.—Water and Electrolyte Content of Skeletal Muscle of Normal Dogs.

	A	B
PER KG. FAT-FREE WET MUSCLE		
Total muscle chloride $(Cl)_M$, mEq.	21.5	20.7
" " sodium $(Na)_M$, "	32.4	29.2
" " potassium $(K)_M$, "	82.1	93.7
water $(H_2O)_M$, gm.	765	772
Extracellular phase (F), "	174	169
Intracellular " (C), "	826	831
" water $(H_2O)_C$, "	593	605
" sodium $(Na)_C$, mEq.	7.2	3.9
" potassium $(K)_C$, "	81.4	92.9
PER 100 GM. FAT-FREE SOLIDS		
Total muscle chloride, mEq.	9.2	9.1
" " sodium, "	13.8	12.8
" " potassium, "	35.0	41.1
" " water, gm.	326	339
" " solids, "	100	100
Extracellular water, "	73	73
Intracellular " "	252	266
" sodium, mEq.	3.1	1.7
" potassium, mEq.	34.6	40.8

Column A presents the data from 20 normal dogs of Hastings and Eichelberger (26), column B represents the data from 4 normal dogs of Darrow, Harrison, and Taffel (6). The data from each series is calculated both per kg. fat-free wet muscle and per 100 gm. of fat-free solids. Differences between the two series of data are probably due to actual variations between the two groups of animals.

The application of this type of analysis to various kinds of tissue has amply demonstrated that, although sodium and chloride in the main are restrained to the extracellular phase, in certain tissues small portions of these ions are intracellular. This is true for sodium in skeletal and cardiac muscle, and for chloride in gastric mucosa, erythrocytes, tendon, and testes (42). The intracellular portions of these ions are not freely diffusible with those of the extracellular phase, for they cannot be easily washed out of cells (1), nor do they readily exchange with injected radioactive ions (39, 41). Nevertheless, these intracellular fractions of the predominantly extracellular electrolytes are significant because alterations in their magnitude do occur under certain pathological conditions (low potassium diets, administration of desoxycorticosterone, and water depletion), and because their presence ex-, plains the discrepancies between the apparent volumes of distribution of radioactive chloride and radioactive sodium.

The experimental facts presented in the preceding paragraphs should make it abundantly clear why it is impossible to identify the anatomical extracellular fluid with the apparent volume of distribution of any one of these substances. For this reason the terms *chloride space, sodium space,* or *sulfocyanate space* are frequently employed to identify more accurately the fluid phase under discussion. Although chloride ion is the most nearly excluded from cells, the *chloride space* must still be somewhat larger than the true extracellular fluid. It has been suggested that the predominantly intracellular ion, potassium, might be used to define the extracellular fluid, i.e., extracellular fluid is that portion of body fluids from which potassium is excluded in high concentrations. This definition is probably fairly accurate but is of little practical use in its measurement. It may yet prove that the apparent volume of distribution of disaccharides such as sucrose, and mannitol, most closely correspond to the true extracellular fluid space.

Although the determinations of the apparent volumes of distribution of the substances under discussion are doubtful measures of the *absolute* volume of extracellular fluid, differences between two serially determined volumes may more accurately measure *change* in volume of extracellular fluid. Such a change may also be calculated from the balance (difference between intake and output) of chloride or sodium if the initial and final concentrations of these ions in serum and the initial extracellular volume are known:

$$\text{Change in volume} = \frac{(\text{Change in serum conc.} \times \text{initial volume}) + \text{balance}}{\text{Final concentration in serum}}.$$

Results of the experimental use of the apparent volumes of distribution of radioactive chloride, radioactive sodium, and sulfocyanate are similar (Fig. 436) to those obtained by chloride and sodium balances (64).

Volume of the total and intracellular fluid. The volume of the intracellular fluid can be determined by subtracting the volume of the extracellular fluid from that of the total body water. Values for the latter have been obtained in animals by direct desiccation, averaging 65 per cent of the body weight for dogs, 70 per cent for *Macacus rhesus* monkeys, and 75 per cent for rabbits (25). Determinations of the total volume of body water by the volume of distribution of an injected substance have been successful only by the use of heavy water, D_2O. With this, volumes of 65 to 73 per cent of the body weight have been found in guinea pigs and rabbits (16, 27). No other substance has been found which distributes itself evenly through the total body fluid and is neither formed nor destroyed in the body. Attempts have been made to use urea and thio-urea, but they do not meet the above criteria. *Change* in total water volume can be calculated from the change in body weight and the metabolic food mixture, as described below (p. 954). Given the change in volume of extracellular fluid determined as above, change in intracellular fluid volume may be estimated by difference (12).

Changes in volume of intracellular fluid may also be estimated from the balance of cell base, potassium. Any such calculation rests on the assumption that no changes occur in the amount of osmotically inactive base in cells.

The validity of this assumption has been questioned (14). The use of potassium balances in the measurement of changes in cell fluid volume should therefore be restricted to long-term experiments. In such experiments the accuracy of the method of difference described above is diminished by the increasing uncertainty in quantitation of water of oxidation.

Transfers of water. As water is freely diffusible across the cell membrane, movements of water are determined by the concentrations of osmotically active electrolytes which are restrained to either side (8) (see p. 935).* This is illustrated in Fig. 437 in which are indicated the shifts of water between cells and extracellular fluid which occur in response to changes in concentration of electrolyte in the latter fluid. Water is transferred until the two fluid phases are again in equilibrium. Such osmotic shifts of water occur more commonly in response to abnormal alteration in concentration of ex-

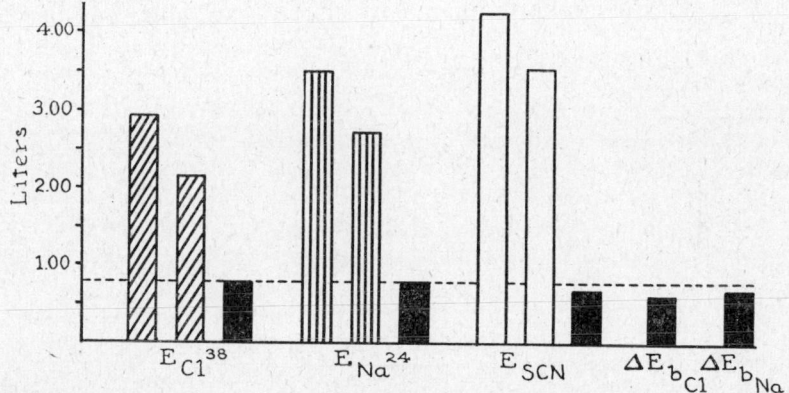

Fig. 436.—Relation of the absolute volumes of distribution of radioactive chloride, radioactive sodium, and sulfocyanate, to change in volume of the extracellular fluid. Data indicate changes induced in a dog by water deprivation for 12 days (64). Cross hatched columns represent the apparent volumes of distribution of radioactive chloride, $E_{Cl^{38}}$, before and after; vertically lined columns those of radioactive sodium, $E_{Na^{24}}$; open columns those of sulfocyanate. Solid columns represent the *change* in volume as measured by the difference between the two volumes of distribution of each substance, as well as by chloride balance, $\Delta E_{b_{Cl}}$, and by sodium balance, $\Delta E_{b_{Na}}$. Although the absolute volumes of distribution of Cl^{38}, Na^{24}, and SCN are of quite different magnitude, changes in the three volumes of distribution agree well with one another and with the changes calculated from chloride and sodium balances (dotted line).

tracellular electrolyte, but changes in the concentration of osmotically active intracellular electrolyte may also lead to shifts of water.

Electrolytes may be transferred across the cell membrane or change in *p*H of cell fluid may ionize or render osmotically inactive (by binding with cell protein) electrolytes which are already present within the cell. Thus the

* The total *osmolar concentration* of a fluid consists of the concentration of osmotically active solutes in the fluid. This concentration may be given in units of *milliosmols per liter*, which is obtained by dividing milligrams per liter by the molecular weight. Valency is not taken into account as in the chemically equivalent unit *milliequivalent per liter* (see footnote on p. 945). The milliosmolar value of a single ion is therefore equal to its millimolar value, but for ionized salt the ions are additive. For example, 1 millimol of NaCl equals 1 milliequivalent and 2 milliosmols because it dissociates into two univalent ions. For extracellular fluid the *total osmolar concentration* is composed almost entirely of electrolytes; organic solutes, principally glucose and urea, contribute but little. Furthermore, these organic solutes diffuse freely throughout all the divisions of body fluids, and hence do not influence the distribution of water among the several divisions. For this reason the term *total ionic* or *electrolyte concentration* of the body fluids is used in this chapter instead of the *total osmolar concentration*.

distribution of water is directly dependent upon the distribution of osmotically active electrolytes between the two phases.

Transfers of electrolytes. Electrolytes do not pass freely across the cell boundary by diffusion. The fact that cellular electrolytes must accumulate in the cell during growth and are released under certain abnormal conditions, as well as the presence of small amounts of "extracellular" ions within the cells of certain tissues, indicates that transfers of electrolytes across the cell membranes do occur. Such transfers which occur irrespective of concentration gradients as well as the maintenance of those gradients must require the expenditure of large amounts of energy. Presumably this energy is derived from associated metabolic activities. This has been experimentally demonstrated (4). The passage of potassium or inorganic phosphate into red cells from serum, which occurs when blood is placed in the incubator, is

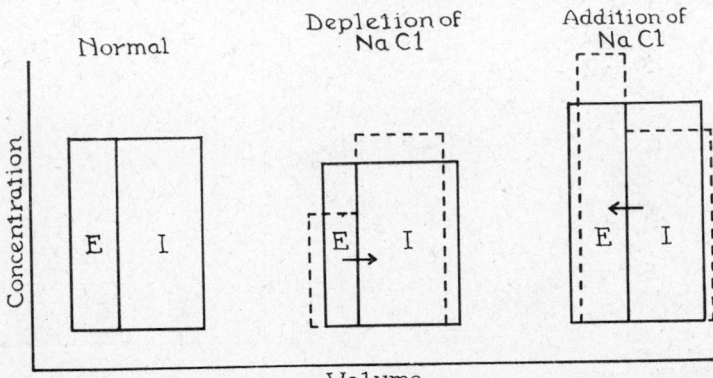

Fig. 437.—The Darrow-Yannet diagram: the re-establishment of osmotic equilibrium following changes in total concentration of extracellular electrolyte, by transfers of water between cells and extracellular fluid. Total ionic concentration is plotted along the ordinates, volume along the abscissae; areas, therefore, represent total amount of electrolyte in each phase. The vertical line dividing the extracellular fluid (E) from the intracellular fluid (I) represents the cell boundary. The dotted outline in the middle and right-hand figures represents the initial state, differing only from the normal in the left-hand figure by the subtraction from, or the addition to, the extracellular phase of a certain amount of salt. Diminution of extracellular electrolyte concentration by depletion of salt (or addition of water) lowers the osmotic pressure of this compartment and results in a shift of water into cells. Elevation of this concentration by addition of salt (or depletion of water) raises the osmotic pressure and results in a shift of water from cells to extracellular fluid.

prevented by the partial arrest of metabolic activities through chilling. When the blood is again placed in the incubator, increments of potassium and inorganic phosphate again move into the cells against their respective concentration gradients.

EXTERNAL EXCHANGES

Regulation of Acid-Base Equilibrium. The ionic composition of the body fluids, as well as their volume and total electrolyte concentration, are regulated to a large extent in the various exchanges with the external environment. For this reason the acid-base equilibrium is first considered before describing the external exchanges. For a more comprehensive discussion of acid-base equilibrium, the reader is referred to Section IV, Chapter 27.

The reaction of the body fluids is slightly alkaline, i.e., hydroxyl ions somewhat exceed the hydrogen ions. But the quantity of these ions present is exceedingly small in relation to the other cations and anions. As the body fluids are electrically neutral, the sum of the cations or bases equals that of the anions or acids. The pattern for normal human serum is shown in Fig. 438,* in which it is seen that the chief basic cation is sodium and the main acid anions are chloride and bicarbonate. In this slightly alkaline medium, the proteins function as anions. The pattern for interstitial fluid differs only in the replacement of protein by chloride in the anion column. The ionic composition of cell fluid cannot be described so quantitatively but is much different qualitatively in that potassium and phosphate are the principal cation and anion respectively.

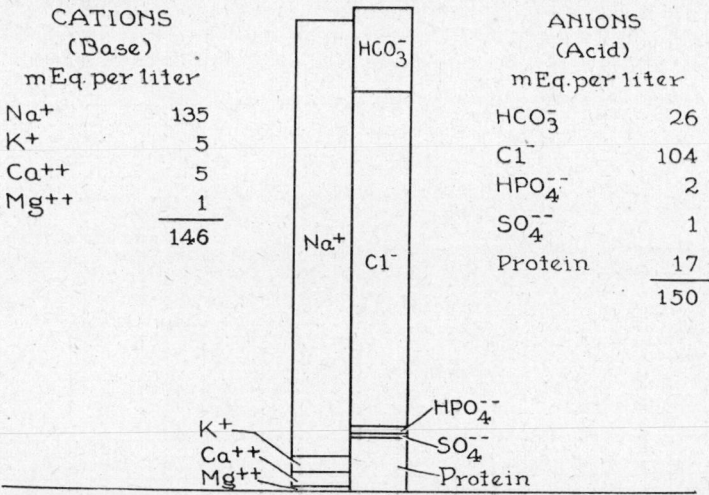

CATIONS (Base) mEq. per liter

Na^+	135
K^+	5
Ca^{++}	5
Mg^{++}	1
	146

ANIONS (Acid) mEq. per liter

HCO_3^-	26
Cl^-	104
HPO_4^{--}	2
SO_4^{--}	1
Protein	17
	150

Fig. 438.—Electrolyte pattern of normal human serum. Although serum is an electrically neutral solution, a small excess of anions over cations is represented in the figure. This is due to uncertainty as to how much protein is ionized and how much chloride is bound to lipids. Evidence exists that this latter fraction of chloride equals approximately 5 mEq. per liter, which would leave 99 mEq. of chloride ion.

The mechanisms for regulation of the balance of cations and anions and the concentration of hydrogen ions (or pH) are several. Dilution through the whole volume of body fluids by rapid mixing through the circulation mitigates changes in reaction. A series of buffers is present which also protects the pH against changes of any serious magnitude. These are salts of weak acids which combine with strong acid to form a neutral salt and a slightly dissociated weak acid, and consist primarily of the proteins, bicarbonates and phosphates.

Strong acid + buffer salt $\rightleftharpoons$ neutral salt + weak acid
$HCl + Na_n$ Protein $\rightleftharpoons NaCl + Na_{(n-1)}$ H Protein
$HCl + NaHCO_3$ $\rightleftharpoons NaCl + H_2CO_3$
$HCl + Na_2HPO_4$ $\rightleftharpoons NaCl + NaH_2PO_4$

* The relative magnitude of concentrations of electrolytes can be compared only in terms of chemical equivalence. For this reason the unit *milliequivalent per liter* is used. This unit is derived from the unit of *milligrams per liter* by dividing by atomic weight and multiplying by valency. In the case of univalent ions 1 millimol is equal to 1 milliequivalent; in the case of divalent ions 1 millimol is equal to 2 milliequivalents. The concentration of chloride in serum expressed as *mg.*

of NaCl per 100 cc. may be converted to *mEq. per liter* by multiplying by $\frac{10}{58.46}$ or 0.171. The concentration in serum of bicarbonate may be calculated in *mEq. per liter* by multiplying the total CO_2 content expressed in *volumes per cent* by the factor 0.423. This factor combines the conversion of total CO_2 from volumes per cent to mEq. per liter and the subtraction of the CO_2 present as H_2CO_3, according to its solubility coefficient.

32

Of these three buffers, bicarbonate is the most important. Carbonic acid is being continually formed in the normal metabolism of the body and is also volatile and readily eliminated through the lungs. It competes with the salts of the weaker buffer acids to form bicarbonates. The hydrogen ion concentration of a solution containing a buffer acid and its salt varies directly with the ratio of the acid to the salt. This was expressed by Henderson for carbonic acid in the equation:

$$[H^+] = K \frac{[H_2CO_3]}{[BHCO_3]}$$

in which K is the dissociation constant and B is the base of the bicarbonate.* The ratio of H_2CO_3 to $BHCO_3$ of 3 volumes per cent to 60 volumes per cent of CO_2 is normally maintained within narrow limits in the body. This is done primarily by the very sensitive regulation of respiration which controls the rate of excretion of CO_2 through the lungs. Compensatory changes in bicarbonate can also be effected by the kidney.

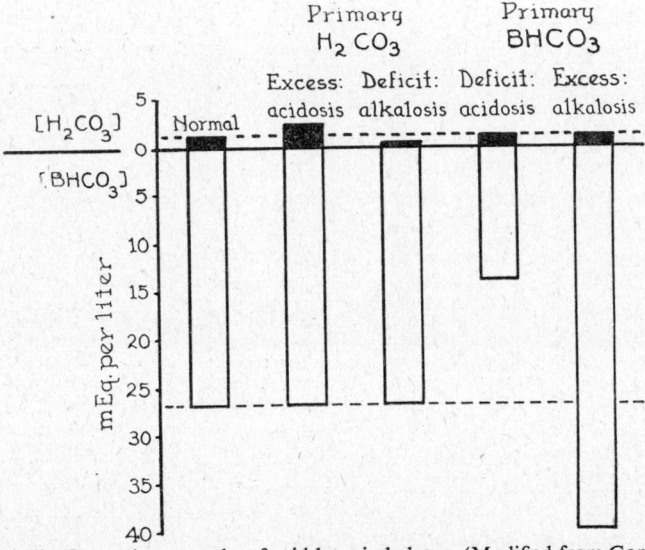

Fig. 439.—The four primary paths of acid-base imbalance. (Modified from Gamble, *Chemical anatomy, physiology, and pathology of extracellular fluid*, Boston, 1942.) See also Figure 293, p. 580.

Thus changes in the hydrogen ion concentration can be the result of changes in either the numerator (H_2CO_3) or the denominator ($BHCO_3$) of the Henderson equation (Fig. 439). Changes in the concentration of H_2CO_3 are produced by alterations in respiration which vary the CO_2 tension in the pulmonary alveoli. An acidosis results from a *primary H_2CO_3 excess* due to various types of pulmonary disease, such as emphysema, in which the excretion of CO_2 is impeded and the concentration of H_2CO_3 elevated. Conversely an alkalosis is the result of *primary H_2CO_3 deficit* due to pulmonary overventilation produced by central stimulation.

Changes in *pH* may also result from changes in the denominator ($BHCO_3$). Because HCO_3^- is always available to combine with any basic cations not

* The logarithmic form of this equation has been used in the description of acid-base equilibrium and buffer action in Chapter 27, beginning on page 574.

in combination with other anions, the concentration of bicarbonate may be changed by either a change in concentration of total base or (inversely) a change in the sum of the concentrations of the other anions. Acidosis is the result of a *primary deficit of BHCO₃* which may stem from either a decrease in concentration of total base or an increase in concentration of the other acid ions. Alkalosis occurs with a *primary excess of BHCO₃* which may be caused by either an increase in total base or, more commonly, a decrease in other acid ions.

Change in concentration of one of the factors, H_2CO_3 or $BHCO_3$, is almost always accompanied by compensatory change in the other. Such compensation is usually partial, but occasionally may be so complete that the normal ratio of the two, 1:20, is maintained and the *p*H unaltered. Because of the rapid response of respiratory rate and volume to alterations in *p*H, the concentration of H_2CO_3 may be quickly altered by hypo- or hyperventilation to compensate for primary changes in concentration of $BHCO_3$. The compensatory renal response to primary changes in H_2CO_3 is a slower process. In conditions of chronic pulmonary disease in which alveolar exchanges of CO_2 are impeded over long periods of time, the tubular reabsorption of chloride is diminished, the concentration of chloride in serum falls, and a compensatory increase in the concentration of $BHCO_3$ is achieved. For discussion of the renal regulation of acid-base equilibrium see below (p. 979).

Fluid Exchanges through Lungs and Skin. Losses of water and solutes through the lungs and skin are obligatory exchanges related primarily to the regulation of body temperature rather than to regulation of volume or composition of the body fluids themselves. The one exception to this statement is the control of hydrogen ion concentration achieved by variation in the rate of CO_2 excretion through the lungs. Otherwise, water and solutes are lost entirely according to the requirements for loss of body heat.

Insensible perspiration. Under normal resting conditions of heat production (in an environment of comfortable temperature and moderate humidity) approximately 25 per cent of the heat produced is continuously lost by vaporization of water through the lungs and skin. This ratio is so constant under these conditions that the total caloric expenditure may be calculated from the insensible water loss (see p. 955). The loss of this vaporized water is divided about equally between these two routes. In the lungs the alveolar air becomes highly saturated with water vapor which is lost to the lower vapor tension of environmental air. In the skin, water escapes as vapor rather than passing through the skin in the liquid form. No solutes are lost with this insensible loss of water. As production of heat and respiration are continuous processes, water is thus being continuously lost to the body. This is reflected in the body weight as the *insensible loss of weight.* Insensible perspiration is not increased in patients with chronic edema but may be elevated in overhydration produced by the simultaneous administration of water and pituitrin. It is decreased in dehydration and in myxedema.

Sensible perspiration (sweating). Direct radiation and vaporization of water through lungs and skin may be unable to meet the demands for dissipation of heat because of either an increased heat production or a rise in environmental temperature or humidity. Under these conditions the mechanism of heat loss by evaporation of sweat is called into action. Sweat is produced by the active secretion of sweat glands, and contains solutes as well as water.

As sweat is modified extracellular fluid, sodium and chloride are the main constituent solutes. These electrolytes are present in approximately equal proportion and in concentrations considerably less than those of extracellular fluid, ranging from 10 to 90 mm. per liter. Excessive loss of this hypotonic fluid may lead to serious salt depletion and even greater water depletion.

Both volume and salt content of sweat may be modified by various factors (31). Acclimatization to environmental high temperature and humidity includes both increased volume of sweat under given conditions, and diminution of salt content of the sweat produced. It is not entirely clear whether this decline in chloride concentration of sweat observed in acclimatization is due to the decrease in volume of extracellular fluid or to the diminution in skin and rectal temperatures which occur in acclimatization. Individuals vary greatly in their sweating response to environmental conditions. Women, who are able to reduce their heat production in high temperatures, sweat less, and lose less chloride per volume of sweat than do men. Species differences exist in sweating. Dogs have no sweat glands and respond to high temperatures by panting, a mechanism for increasing vaporization of water and heat loss

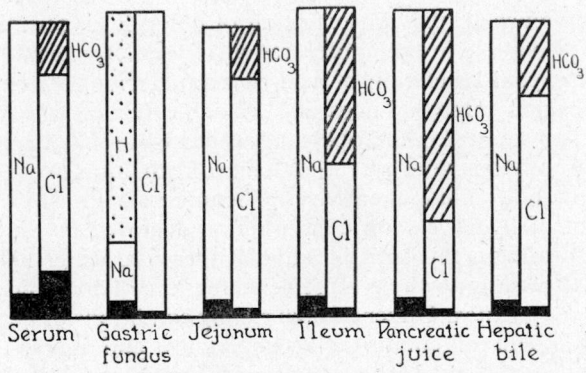

Fig. 440.—Comparison of the electrolyte pattern of serum with those of various gastro-intestinal fluids.

through the lungs. As this is less efficient than sweating, the dog tolerates high temperatures poorly. Man can more readily lose heat by sweating but is handicapped by the hazard of salt depletion. The desert burro is able to lose heat through the secretion of a sweat which is practically pure water (10). This mechanism prevents depletion of salt and insofar as water is more available than salt, it is an adaptation to an environment of great heat.

Fluid Exchanges in the Gastro-intestinal Tract. The exchanges which occur between the body fluids and the alimentary canal are primarily concerned with the addition to the body of water and various organic and inorganic solutes. These exchanges play no part in the normal regulation of body fluids as a constant internal environment.

The sensation of *thirst* which controls the ingestion of water has been ascribed to the sensory stimuli from a dry mouth. This has been disproved, as thirst persists in the presence of interrupted nerve supply to the mouth, and as thirst can be abolished by taking water through a stomach tube. Thirst appears to be more directly related to the volume and composition of the body fluids. Water deficits are fairly accurately replaced. Dogs with hypertonic body fluids and body cells depleted of water will drink copiously. Dogs with hypotonic body fluids and swollen body cells are not thirsty (9). These facts suggest that thirst is related to the concentratións of solutes and the state of hydration of tissue cells (10).

The role of alimentary exchanges in the body fluid economy has been precisely elucidated by Gamble (17, 18). Large volumes of fluid are continuously being secreted into the gastro-intestinal tract and reabsorbed into the body fluids, volumes that approximate 3 to 4 liters per day. These fluids are differentiated in their electrolyte patterns in various parts of the gastro-intestinal canal, but their total osmolar concentration is the same as that of the body fluids from which they are derived (Fig. 440). These fluids are modified portions of the extracellular fluid, as is indicated by the predominance of sodium as the cation and chloride and bicarbonate as the anions. In the gastric juice secreted from the prepyloric mucosa, sodium is replaced by hydrogen ion; elsewhere sodium is the chief cation. In the stomach and upper small intestine, the main anion is chloride. In the fluids from the lower segments of the gut bicarbonate tends to replace chloride as the chief anion.

Solutions introduced into the gut undergo alterations which depend upon their composition. Plain water or solutions hypotonic to the body fluids result in the absorption of water from, and the excretion of salt into, the fluid in the intestinal canal until the latter becomes isotonic with the body fluids. Conversely, hypertonic salt solutions lose salt to, and gain water from, the body; hypertonic solutions of organic materials, such as glucose, withdraw both salt and water until isotonicity is reached. Thus, by processes of diffusion in response to osmotic dictates, the normal ionic pattern and osmolar concentration tends to be restored in each segment of the intestinal tract. Cells of the intestinal mucosa, unlike renal tubular cells, cannot produce hypertonic fluids. The addition of unabsorbable ions, like sulfate, causes an increase in fluid volume in the intestinal canal.

Simple diffusion, however, will not explain the mass movements of isotonic fluid which take place across the intestinal wall. Wells (62) has presented evidence that such fluid movements are the resultant of the forces of the colloid osmotic pressure of proteins in the intestinal villi and the intra-intestinal pressure tending to move fluid into the lacteals and the hydrostatic pressure in the lacteal fluid tending to move fluid into the intestinal canal.

$$\text{Rate of movements of fluid into intestine} = \left(\text{hydrostatic p. in lacteals} - \text{colloid osmotic p. in lacteals} \right) - \text{hydrostatic p. in intestine.}$$

During the ingestion of food and fluids, congestion of the circulation in the intestinal wall raises the hydrostatic pressure in the lacteals, favoring the movement of fluid into the gut. When absorption begins, the circulatory congestion disappears, the intra-intestinal pressure is elevated, and the fluid moves in the opposite direction.

The secretion of such large volumes of salt-containing fluids into the gastro-intestinal tract renders the organism especially vulnerable to severe salt and water depletion in any abnormal condition which interferes with the normal reabsorption of these fluids. These abnormal conditions and the various types of fluid depletion which they produce, are discussed below (p. 960).

Fluid Exchanges in the Kidney. As the kidney is the only organ that can facultatively separate water and salt and so elaborate a fluid hypertonic or hypotonic to the rest of the body fluids, the major regulation of these fluids devolves upon it. In this capacity the kidney is an organ of *conservation* as well as of excretion, for upon its fluid exchanges rests the maintenance of a constant internal environment, the prerequisite of vertebrate life. Body water and its ionic solutes are kept within various limits in optimum absolute amounts and in optimum proportion to each other. Any disturbance of one of the dimensions of total volume or total osmolar concentration leads to modification of the other dimensions by the kidney. Not only are these two dimensions of the body fluids zealously guarded, but also the relative concentrations of individual solutes; the kidney plays a major role in the preservation of acid-base equilibrium.

The mechanisms of glomerular filtration, tubular reabsorption and tubular secretion, by which the kidney performs the functions mentioned above are described in detail in the next chapter. For purposes of this discussion of the relation of these processes to the state of the body fluids, it must suffice to state them as follows. Water and solutes of the glomerular filtrate enter the renal tubules in concentrations of a protein-free filtrate of plasma. In the tubules most of the water and solutes are differentially reabsorbed according to the needs for conservation of the body fluids. Some substances which are absent in the glomerular filtrate are secreted in the tubules. The final volume and composition of urine are the net result of these three processes of filtration, reabsorption and secretion (54, 59).

In the formation of urine the volume of water and the amounts and kinds of solutes passing through the kidney are closely interdependent. The mammalian kidney is able to produce a hypertonic urine by reabsorption of water against a concentration gradient. Normally, 99 per cent of the water in the glomerular filtrate is reabsorbed in the tubules. This concentrating power of the kidney is limited by the types and amounts of solutes present in the tubules, i.e., solutes may limit the reabsorption of water and so determine urine volume. Conversely, the volume of water which escapes reabsorption may affect the reabsorption of solutes.

The limitation of the reabsorption of water by solutes present in the tubules does not depend simply upon their total osmotic pressure. Solutes fall into two groups which can be concentrated independently of each other. In one class is urea, in the other are the electrolytes, sodium, chloride, potassium, inorganic phosphate, and glucose and creatinine. These two groups do not compete for water, i.e., the addition of one to urine does not modify the concentration of the other. The individual solutes of the second group, however, do so compete; consequently, the limiting concentration of the group is the sum of the osmolar concentrations of its individual constituents. Maximum economy of water therefore depends upon the optimum proportion rather than the total amount of solutes present.

Water and urea. As the tubular reabsorption of urea is more limited than that of water, the concentration of urea is always greater in urine than in serum. The quantity of water required for the excretion of urea thus depends on the amount of urea in the glomerular filtrate which in turn is determined by the rate of protein catabolism. Furthermore, the effect of urea excretion on water excretion is not limited to a maximal concentration as the two are proportional at all rates of excretion of urea (19, 20). As water becomes more and more limited, less and less is available for each increment of urea excreted until the maximal concentration is reached. Under such circumstances, which are usually found in water deprivation or dehydration, urea clearances fall and the concentration of nonprotein nitrogen in body fluids rises. The rate of protein catabolism becomes the determinant of the volume of urine until the renal circulation fails and glomerular filtration ceases entirely (63). On the other hand, if the amount of urea presenting for excretion is minimal in relation to the water available, the reabsorption of water and the fall of urine volume is not proportional because of the other solutes present.

Water and electrolytes. Although the tubular reabsorption of urea is always less than that of water, the reabsorption of electrolytes, principally sodium and chloride, under certain circumstances may exceed that of water. Moderate excesses of water in the body result in a diuresis of essentially chloride-free urine, the lowered serum chloride concentration being associated with an increased reabsorption of chloride in the renal tubule. Large excesses of water, however, lead to such an increase in rate of glomerular filtration that not all the sodium and chloride in the filtrate is reabsorbed (57). Under these conditions salt depletion of the body may ensue.

In depletion of water and salt the urinary excretion of water is greatly diminished and that of sodium chloride may cease entirely. Reduction of volume and ionic concentration of the extracellular fluid results in a greatly increased tubular reabsorption of water and sodium chloride, the latter of which may be complete. Diminished plasma volume and peripheral circulatory collapse are commonly present in this condition and lead to reduction of glomerular filtration as well (44).

When depletion of water in excess of salt occurs, the concentrations of sodium and chloride are elevated in serum. Nevertheless, the reabsorption of sodium and chloride is increased and the elevations of the serum concentration are maintained (11). This retention of salt permits the excretion of other solutes in its place in the limited urinary water. It also results in an osmotic shift of water from body cells and thus mitigates the fall in extracellular fluid volume. A similar reaction occurs when salt is given in excess of water. A diuresis is produced which leads to dehydration, but the reabsorption of sodium and chloride is increased so that the serum concentrations remain elevated. If sodium sulfate or phosphate is given instead of or with sodium chloride, the reabsorption of sulfate or phosphate is diminished while that of chloride is accelerated (56). In the competition for water between electrolytes, foreign anions are thus selectively excreted in preference to chloride. If potassium salts are administered, the potassium is excreted more rapidly than sodium but does not replace sodium in urine, for the excretion of the latter is also accelerated. Under conditions of severe dehydration without sodium chloride loss, potassium continues to be excreted in the presence of complete reabsorption of sodium (11). This appears to be a further mechanism by which cell water is made available.

Water and glucose. Glucose is usually completely reabsorbed in the tubule. When reabsorption of glucose is incomplete, it competes with the electrolytes for water. The result is not increased reabsorption of sodium and chloride but decreased reabsorption of water. Glycosuria, therefore, leads to depletion of both water and salt.

Renal regulation of acid-base balance. The relative concentrations in the body fluids of the individual electrolytes are regulated by their relative rates of reabsorption in the renal tubules (18, 48). The reabsorption rates of cations and anions are not independent of each other, for the excretion of one involves the excretion of the other. Excess base or cation is excreted with HCO_3^- which is ever available from the constant metabolic processes of oxidation. Excess acids or anions would deplete the body fluids of base were it not for the renal mechanism which conserves base to protect the constancy of total ionic content and concentration. This mechanism consists of the formation in the kidney of ammonia which replaces the cation, sodium. In addition, some anions are excreted in excess of cations as free, un-ionized acids. Resultant excessive changes of pH of urine are prevented by the buffer effects of urinary phosphates and bicarbonates. As the formation of ammonia requires time, a sudden excess of acid may be associated with a diminished reabsorption and moderate depletion of sodium. In diseased kidneys these mechanisms for base conservation may be so damaged that large amounts of base are wasted from the body (see p. 960).

Endocrine control of renal fluid exchanges. The tubular reabsorption of water is controlled to a large extent by the hormone of the *posterior lobe* of the *pituitary*. Destruction of this gland, or of the hypothalamic centers which control it, results in the condition, diabetes insipidus, which is characterized by profuse polyuria of very dilute urine and by severe thirst. The primary defect appears to be an inhibition of the tubular reabsorption of water. As pituitrin has no effect in nonmammalian species whose kidneys lack both the loop of Henle and the capacity to produce a hypertonic urine, the hormone probably acts on this portion of the tubule.

Patients or animals with diabetes insipidus are always dehydrated to a lesser or greater degree. At the onset of the condition as experimentally produced, some salt is lost in the diuresis before equilibrium is established, and ingestion of water never quite catches up with its renal excretion. Deprivation of water leads to a much more rapid dehydration and elevation of the serum concentrations of sodium and chloride than occurs in the normal organism (58). This is due partly to increased reabsorption of salt but chiefly to excretion of water in excess of salt. Solutes do have some influence on the volume of urine in this condition. Administration of salt increases and restriction of salt decreases the diuresis. Starvation also diminishes the polyuria as the reduced catabolism of protein presents less urea for excretion.

Administration of *pituitrin* alone to a normal subject has no effect on the volume of urine. However, if it is given with water, the diuresis which the water would normally produce is inhibited. As the excretion of salt continues unaffected, hypotonicity of body fluids and water intoxication are readily produced. This effect of the hormone varies directly with the amount of water given.

The hormone of the *adrenal cortex* has a direct effect on the tubular reabsorption of sodium and potassium. In adrenal cortical insufficiency, as seen in patients with Addison's disease or in adrenalectomized animals, decreased tubular reabsorption of sodium leads to a severe sodium deficit (37). Secondary to the loss of sodium a diuresis occurs which leads to depletion of water as well. But as sodium is usually lost in excess of water, the concentration of sodium in extracellular fluid is lowered. This results in an osmotic shift of water into cells. Such subjects are peculiarly susceptible to water intoxication. The effect of adrenal cortical insufficiency on potassium is opposite to that on sodium. Increased tubular reabsorption of potassium leads to elevation of its concentration in extracellular fluids and its retention in body cells (24). As water does not seem to be taken up with it into the intracellular compartment, this increment of cell potassium is probably in an osmotically inactive form.

Administration of cortical extract to a patient with Addison's disease leads to retention of sodium and excretion of potassium by the kidney. Desoxycorticosterone acts in a similar way on the electrolyte balance. In large doses it may even lead to excessive retention of sodium and water, or edema, and to a potassium depletion which may be reflected in lowered concentration of serum potassium. Such potassium depletion has been shown to be associated with degeneration of cardiac muscle and cardiac failure (7). For this reason, it is important to give a diet containing adequate amounts of potassium, as well as sodium and water, to any patient receiving either cortical extract or desoxycorticosterone. In the normal subject, in contrast to the cortical insufficient subject, administration of desoxycorticosterone leads to a profuse diuresis or "diabetes insipidus."

It should be emphasized that the abnormal reaction of the kidney to electrolytes is only one aspect of adrenal cortical insufficiency. Severe alterations in the circulation and in carbohydrate metabolism are also present. Diminution of plasma volume with hemoconcentration and circulatory failure regularly occurs. Fluid is lost from plasma to the interstitial spaces as well as to urine. Such changes are not merely the result of sodium and water depletion. The cortical hormone must have some direct effect on the circulation well in advance of restoration of the electrolyte balance.

The circulation and renal exchanges. The ability of the kidney to regulate the volume and composition of the body fluids is completely dependent on an adequate circulation of blood. Fluids from other tissues can only enter into renal exchanges as plasma passing through the renal circulation. Any abnormal condition of the cardiovascular system, such as a lowered concentration of plasma albumin, cardiac failure, or peripheral vascular collapse, which interferes with its function as a mixing agent of the body fluids, interferes with their regulation by the kidney. Furthermore, glomerular filtration is directly dependent upon the renal blood flow. The commonest cause of anuria or oliguria is peripheral circulatory collapse with inadequate renal blood flow. Thus a diminished plasma and blood volume with its attendant circulatory failure, such as occurs in secondary traumatic or hemorrhagic shock and in depletion of salt and water (see p. 958), is usually associated with a collapse of renal function. The elevation of the concentration of nonprotein nitrogen in body fluids, which is seen in these conditions, is usually explicable on this basis.

WATER BALANCE

Water Requirements. Water is lost by vaporization through the lungs and skin, in stool, in urine, and under certain conditions in sweat. Water is made available to the body by ingestion in food and drink and from the oxidation of foodstuffs. These fractions of intake and output of water, with their approximate magnitude in a normal adult, may be tabulated:

Intake		Output	
Drink:	1200 cc.	Urine:	1400 cc.
Water in food:	1000 cc.	Stool:	200 cc.
Water of oxidation:	300 cc.	Insensible water:	900 cc.
Total	2500 cc.		2500 cc.

Losses of water by vaporization, sweat, and in stool are obligatory, that is, they are maintained for the most part without regard to the intake. Adjustments of output to intake are made mainly by alterations in the volume of urine. Under conditions of diminished intake of water and salt this renal adjustment is limited by the power of the kidneys to concentrate urea. As the excretion of urea requires a certain minimum volume of urine, the rate of water loss through the kidneys under these conditions is dependent upon the rate of protein catabolism (63).

The largest fraction of water intake is usually that drunk as plain water or as other aqueous solutions. It is not always appreciated that a sizeable portion of the daily water intake is found in food. The water content of lean meat is approximately 75 per cent of its total weight. Vegetables also have a large water content. Besides the water ingested, water is also made available from the oxidation of the foodstuffs in the metabolic mixture. Table 43 shows the amount of water formed from each foodstuff, as well as the CO_2 eliminated and the O_2 consumed in the oxidation.

Table 43

	O_2	CO_2	WATER OF OXIDATION
	GRAMS	GRAMS	GRAMS
1 gram carbohydrate	1.14	1.55	0.60
1 gram fat	2.89	2.81	1.07
1 gram protein	1.40	1.48	0.41

Measurement of Water Balance. *Change in volume of distribution* of an injected substance as a measure of water balance has been successful only in the case of heavy water, D_2O (see p. 942), and hence is not a very practical method for this measurement.

Change in body weight corrected for solids lost and food burned can be readily used to measure change in body water if the metabolic mixture is known (46, 52, 53). This relationship is expressed in the following equation:

$$\Delta W = (Wt_2 - Wt_1) + (S_e - S_i) + (C + F + 0.49P).$$

where ΔW is the change in water (water balance), Wt_1 and Wt_2 are the initial and final body weights, S_e and S_i are the solids excreted and ingested, and C, F and P are the respective weights of carbohydrate, fat and protein oxidized.

The derivation of this equation is as follows:

$$\text{Insensible weight loss (IL)} = (Wt_1 - Wt_2) + (wt_i - wt_e), \qquad 1.$$

where Wt_1 and Wt_2 are the initial and final body weights, and wt_i and wt_e are the weights of ingesta and excreta respectively.

$$\text{Insensible water loss (IP)} = \text{IL} + O_2 - CO_2, \qquad 2.$$

since the processes of metabolism whereby insensible weight becomes insensible water loss involves the absorption of oxygen and the elimination of CO_2. Substituting Equation 1 in Equation 2:

$$IP = Wt_1 - Wt_2 + wt_i - wt_e + O_2 - CO_2. \qquad 3.$$

The change in total water, or water balance, ΔW, may be expressed thus:

$$\Delta W = w_i - w_e + w_{ox} - IP \qquad 4.$$

where w_i and w_e are the water contents of ingesta and excreta, and w_{ox} is the water of oxidation. Substituting Equation 3:

$$\Delta W = w_i - w_e + w_{ox} - Wt_1 + Wt_2 - wt_i + wt_e - O_2 + CO_2 \qquad 5.$$

As $wt_i - w_i$ and $wt_e - w_e$ are the solids of the ingesta and excreta, Equation 5 may be written:

$$\Delta W = Wt_2 - Wt_1 + S_e - S_i + w_{ox} - O_2 + CO_2 \qquad 6.$$

From the data in Table 43 it follows that $(w_{ox} - O_2 + CO_2) = (C + F + 0.49P)$ for

1 gram carbohydrate (C) = 0.60 − 1.14 + 1.55 = 1 gram
1 gram fat (F)   = 1.07 − 2.89 + 2.81 = 1 gram
1 gram protein (P)   = 0.41 − 1.40 + 1.48 = 0.49 gram

Equation 6 may therefore be written:

$$\Delta W = (Wt_2 - Wt_1) + (S_e - S_i) + (C + F + 0.49P) \qquad 7.$$

Water balance = weight balance + solids lost + food burned.

Body weights and the solid content of ingesta and excreta are easily measured. Accurate determination of the metabolic mixture requires the use of indirect calorimetry. Where such is not available, the metabolic mixture may be estimated in the following manner, with results which are less accurate but usually sufficiently adequate for the calculation of the water balance. Carbohydrate burned is assumed to equal the carbohydrate eaten. Protein burned is calculated from the nonprotein nitrogen excreted in the urine with a small correction for changes in nonprotein nitrogen concentration in the body fluids. Fat burned is estimated from the total caloric expenditure after deductions have been made for the calories contributed by carbohydrate and protein. The total caloric expenditure may be estimated from the insensible weight loss (see p. 947). This calculation of fat burned, F, may be made by the equation:

$$F = (IL - 2.12 C - 1.69 P)/3.78,$$

where IL is the insensible weight loss, and C and P the carbohydrate and protein burned respectively (35). This calculation of total caloric expenditure from the insensible weight loss is, of course, erroneous in any condition in which the normal relationship of the two is not maintained, e.g., dehydration, and under conditions of sweating where sensible perspiration is not measured separately from insensible weight loss.

Clinical estimation of water balance usually can be made only roughly and by indirect means. Where initial and final body weights are available, the problem is somewhat simplified. Knowledge of intake and output is but an approximate guide as the loss of sensible water and the addition of water of oxidation are not known. In a normal sized afebrile adult the insensible water loss usually lies between 800 and 1200 cc. per day. This makes an approximate computation of output possible, and intake may be adjusted accordingly. If water is lost by abnormal routes, such as in vomitus or in drainage from an intestinal fistula, the volume must be added to the output of urine and insensible water, and the intake increased by a like amount. Sweating may introduce a large error.

More commonly the necessity arises of judging de novo the degree of dehydration already present. As the absolute volume cannot be measured, indirect clues must be resorted to. These include the clinical state of the patient and evidences of peripheral vascular collapse: hypotension, hemo-concentration, and oliguria or anuria with an elevation of the concentration in blood of nonprotein nitrogen. Such circulatory impairment is the result of a diminished plasma volume which is associated with certain types of depletion of water and salt (see p. 959). Chemical determination of serum

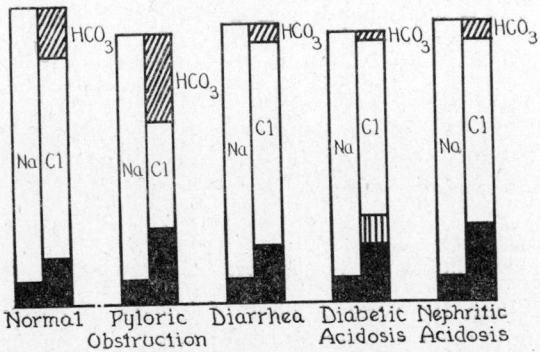

Fig. 441.—Comparison of the normal serum electrolyte pattern with the abnormal serum patterns found in certain diseases.

carbon dioxide content and chloride concentrations gives an approximate measure of changes in the total electrolyte concentration in body fluids,* but this is only one of the two dimensions of concentration and volume. A low value for $CO_2 + Cl$ indicates only a relative deficiency of salt in relation to water and so gives no absolute information. Such a measure is of great value, however, if considered in conjunction with the type of salt and water depletion suspected (Fig. 441).

PATHOLOGICAL PHYSIOLOGY OF BODY FLUIDS

Disease states and abnormal environmental conditions may produce many alterations in the external and internal fluid exchanges. As a result, the total body fluid as well as its several functional divisions may be changed inde-pendently in the two dimensions of volume and composition. Alterations in one dimension of a fluid phase usually produce changes in the other di-mension of that phase, as well as in the dimensions of the other fluid divisions. The main types of these pathological patterns are illustrated in Figure 442 in which increases and decreases in volume of the two phases, extracellular and intracellular, are shown in combination with hyper-, hypo-, and isotonic concentrations of electrolytes. Clinical states in which these patterns are found and experimental procedures by which they may be produced are

* This is only true where there is no large change in the other anions, such as there is in the ketosis of diabetic acidosis (Fig. 441).

indicated under the diagrams. In these conditions extracellular electrolyte (in particular the basic ion sodium, since it controls the total amount of electrolyte present in the phase) is more readily increased and depleted than that of intracellular fluid. For this reason, in discussion of clinical disorders movements of *salt* in relation to water generally refer to *sodium salts*. Cell

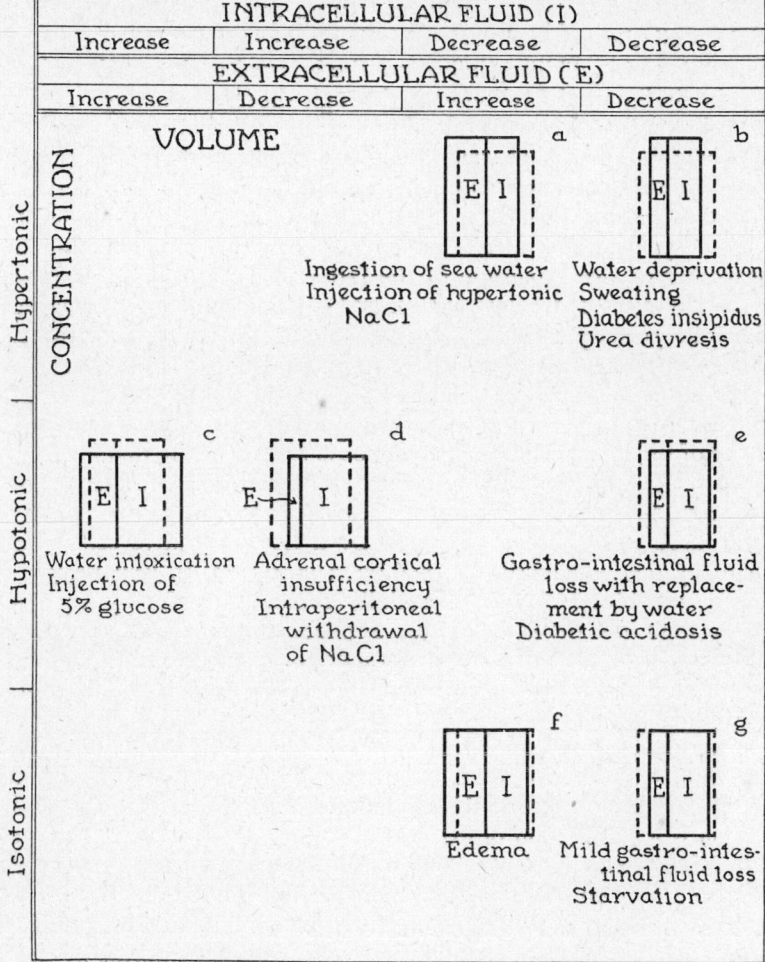

Fig. 442.—Variations in total ionic concentration and in volume of the two phases of body fluids found in various clinical and experimental conditions. Total ionic concentration is plotted along the ordinate, volume along the abscissa, as in Figure 437. The dotted outline represents the normal pattern, the solid lines the pattern of the conditions listed thereunder. The possible directions of change in concentration are listed along the ordinate, the possible combinations of change in volume of the two phases are indicated along the abscissa. "E" refers to extracellular fluid, "I" to intracellular fluid.

base (potassium) is lost in some conditions but is almost never augmented; because of this, certain combinations of changes in volume and total concentration are not found, and are omitted from Figure 442.

The diagrams in Figure 442 relate only to volume and total ionic concentration of the two main fluid phases. Other types of changes in the body fluids also occur; this must be considered in any adequate description of a pathological state. Distortions of the relative proportions of extracellular ions disturb the acid-base equilibrium, and lead to compensatory reactions for its adjustment as well as for adjustments of total volume and total osmolar concentration. Alterations in distribution of fluid between the two divisions of the extracellular phase, plasma and interstitial fluid, are intimately associated with these other types of changes. An adequate circulation of blood is essential to all the external exchanges between extracellular fluid and the environment, and in addition influences the internal exchanges by mitigating changes in the ˙internal environment through thorough mixing. Changes in plasma volume, therefore, which lead to serious disturbances in the dynamics of the circulation, may have such disastrous effects on the whole body economy that abnormalities in this fluid division will be considered first.

Diminished Plasma Volume. Clinical abnormalities in distribution of fluid between the plasma and interstitial spaces consist principally of diminution of the former or overexpansion of the latter. This last condition is termed *edema* and is discussed below (see p. 961). Diminution of plasma volume may have its primary causation in abnormalities of the vascular system. In *traumatic and burn shock** peripheral vascular collapse is associated with a diminished blood and plasma volume. Much of the fluid lost from the plasma is extravasated with plasma protein through damaged capillary endothelium at the site of the injury. Although evidence is unconvincing that a generalized increase in capillary permeability occurs in other tissues, localized losses of plasma may take place elsewhere. As plasma is lost in excess of red blood cells, the drop in volume is indicated by a rise in relative cell volume as measured by the hematocrit, i.e., hemoconcentration. In *hemorrhagic shock* the decrease in blood volume is partially compensated for by a passage of interstitial fluid into the vascular system producing a hemodilution in which the relative cell volume and concentration of plasma protein fall. The evidence that extracellular fluid lost by hemorrhage is replaced by fluid from body cells is conflicting.

In certain types of *salt and water depletion*, described below, diminution in plasma volume and peripheral circulatory collapse are secondary results but are of primary importance as the immediate cause of death to the organism. As plasma is a subdivision of extracellular fluid, this is true in those conditions in which extracellular volume and base are depleted. Fall in plasma volume occurs much more readily when the loss of sodium is primary and in excess of water (28, 33, 45), as in gastro-intestinal fluid loss plus replacement by water, in the experimental removal of sodium chloride by the intraperitoneal route, and in adrenal cortical insufficiency.

The fall in plasma volume and hemoconcentration is so marked in *adrenal cortical insufficiency* that the cortical hormone has been thought to have a direct effect on the permeability of the capillary membrane. Although there is no good evidence that the hormone has such a direct generalized effect on the capillaries of the body, it must have some indirect effect not mediated through depletion of sodium and extracellular fluid volume. It has been shown that after adrenalectomy, recovery from crises under the influence of

---

* The types of *shock* discussed in this section are those in which a significant loss of fluid from the vascular system is a major factor. There are other types of shock (such as primary or neurogenic shock, insulin shock) in which such loss of fluid is not a primary factor.

cortical extract alone precedes readjustment of electrolytes and water. Thus factors other than depletion of sodium and water are involved in this condition.

Depletion of Water in Excess of Salt (Fig. 442, b). *Water deprivation.* Complete withdrawal of water from the mammalian organism results in depletion of water in excess of salt because of the continued insensible loss of water of vaporization for the obligatory dissipation of heat. This water loss is distributed over both phases of body fluids and the total concentration of base is elevated, as is evidenced by the rise in serum sodium concentration (11). When starvation is an added condition, the withdrawal of intracellular fluid is accomplished by three processes. As a result of the insensible loss of water from the extracellular fluid, the concentration of extracellular base rises and water shifts from the cells to re-establish osmotic equilibrium. Because of the starvation, tissue protein is burned and its accompanying cell water is released. An additional decrement of cell water is lost, with potassium in excess of nitrogen. This transfer of potassium across the cell membrane and its renal excretion occurs in various types of water depletion, and results in further mitigating extracellular water loss at the expense of intracellular water (12). In prolonged food and water deprivation this is accomplished by replacement of sodium by potassium in the urine, the former of which almost entirely disappears despite its elevated concentration in blood.

The rate of water loss is determined not only by the insensible water loss (which diminishes in dehydration) but also by the volume of urine. The latter in turn depends upon the rate of protein catabolism (see p. 951) and is usually sufficiently great, at maximal concentration, to eliminate the urea formed from the catabolism of protein, thus preventing the accumulation of urea in the fluids of the body. This is true as long as the renal circulation is adequate. Ultimately the plasma volume diminishes, along with the rest of the body fluids, to the point where circulatory collapse ensues.

Sweating in the subject deprived of water accelerates the rise in total ionic concentration of the body fluids and accentuates the diminution of extracellular fluid volume. This is because sweat is a hypotonic solution of sodium chloride and its excessive secretion produces both a loss of extracellular base and an even greater loss of water. As a result, circulatory collapse is more rapidly induced than in simple water deprivation.

In *diabetes insipidus* insufficiency of the posterior pituitary hormone produces a copious diuresis because of failure of reabsorption of water in the renal tubule (see p. 952). In consequence water is lost greatly in excess of salt, and unless replaced by water ingested, dehydration of both fluid phases and hypertonicity of the body fluids usually ensue. Extreme thirst and the availability of water usually prevent such an occurrence in this disease. Similar results may be produced by the administration of *urea* to the experimental subject.

Depletion of Salt in Excess of Water. One effect of *adrenal cortical insufficiency* is the wasting of sodium and the retention of potassium by the kidney (24, 37). This results in the type of distortion of body fluids shown in Figure 442, d, i.e., hypotonicity of body fluids with shift of water from the extracellular fluid into the cells. Associated with this is a diminution in plasma volume and great susceptibility to circulatory failure. Very similar effects on the body fluids may be produced experimentally by the *intraperitoneal injection of 5* *per cent glucose solution*, and its withdrawal 3 to 4 hours later (9). At this time sodium chloride has diffused into the glucose solution and very little of the water has been absorbed. The net result of withdrawal is the removal of extracellular base with no change in volume of total body water. Depletion of sodium also occurs in *chronic renal insufficiency* because of failure of the usual renal mechanism to conserve base.

Prolonged *gastro-intestinal fluid loss* with replacement by water alone is probably the most common clinical example of this type of disturbance of body fluid physiology (21). The loss of such fluid by vomiting, diarrhea, fistula, or intubation is a removal of isotonic extracellular fluid. If such a subject is deprived of all water intake, his body fluids would tend to become hypertonic, for the insensible loss of water without salt is occurring simultaneously. However, these patients frequently are given salt-free fluids. As dehydration and salt depletion progresses, the total ionic concentration falls as the kidney attempts to preserve volume at the expense of concentration by not excreting all of the salt-free fluid taken. Under such conditions patients are usually in a fasting state in which the loss of cell water due to oxidation of protein exceeds the gain due to re-establishment of osmotic equilibrium. The net results of these processes are a large diminution in extracellular fluid volume, a somewhat smaller decrease in intracellular fluid volume, and a drop in total ionic concentration of both fluids (Fig. 442, e).

The effect of depletion of gastro-intestinal fluids on the acid-base balance as well as on the total ionic concentration and volume of body fluids must be considered. In gastric juice hydrogen replaces sodium as the principal cation (Fig. 440, p. 948); loss of gastric juice therefore entails a loss of chloride in excess of sodium. As a result, although an absolute deficit of sodium has been incurred, there is a relative increase in bicarbonate with a metabolic alkalosis (Fig. 441). In the presence of an associated ketosis due to fasting, the relative increase in bicarbonate may be partially or completely offset by the increase in ketone acids. Compensatory responses to such a gastric alkalosis include not only respiratory retention of CO_2 but also renal excretion of sodium bicarbonate. This further depletes the body of sodium until the kidney will no longer sacrifice extracellular base to preserve the acid-base balance. At this point sodium bicarbonate disappears from the urine which becomes acid despite the prevailing alkalosis. Loss of more alkaline fluids from lower levels of the intestinal tract may produce little change in the acid-base equilibrium or may even result in a metabolic acidosis (Fig. 441).

In *diabetic acidosis* disturbances of the body fluid pattern occur which are similar in many ways to those due to losses of gastro-intestinal fluids (2, 51). The production of excessive amounts of ketone acids leads to depletion of sodium and chloride through the kidney. Vomiting is also frequently present. The result is a severe dehydration and sodium depletion with hypotonic body fluids and a marked diminution in extracellular fluid volume (Fig. 442, e). The relative fall in base concentration plus the extra anions, the ketones, produce a severe metabolic acidosis (Fig. 441).

Depletion of Salt in Proportion to Water (Fig. 442, g). In *starvation* without water deprivation there is an initial renal excretion of extracellular base and water during the first few days; thereafter base and water are lost proportionately from both phases of body fluids as tissues are wasted and nitrogen presents for renal excretion (3, 5). The body fluids remain isotonic.

Mild gastro-intestinal fluid loss in which the intake of water without salt does not exceed the insensible water loss results in much the same isotonic fluid pattern as starvation except that the depletion of extracellular base and water may be somewhat larger.

Retention of Water in Excess of Salt (Fig. 442, c). *Water intoxication* may be produced experimentally by the forced ingestion of water, plus the administration of pituitrin, or by the parenteral administration of isotonic glucose solutions in amounts in excess of the kidney's ability to excrete water (55). Clinically, it is found where large amounts of water have been taken by sodium depleted subjects, usually as a result of excessive sweating (61). The extreme manifestations are muscle cramps ("heat cramps") and eventually convulsions, and are presumably due to the marked drop in ionic concentration of the body fluids and overexpansion of the intracellular fluid.

Retention of Salt in Excess of Water (Fig. 442, a). The addition to body fluids of a solution of sodium salts in concentration greater than that attainable in urine results inevitably in marked hypertonicity of body fluids and an expansion of extracellular fluid at the expense of intracellular fluid volume (65). Presumably such is the result of continued *ingestion of undiluted sea water*, which is approximately a 3.5 per cent solution of NaCl and Na_2SO_4 (13). Although this has never been directly demonstrated in a human subject, the analogous situation has been reproduced in dogs by the repeated injection of 5 per cent NaCl solution. When the intracellular dehydration progressed to 40 to 50 per cent of the initial volume, central nervous system impairment was observed and respiratory failure occurred. As would be expected with the expanded extracellular volume, the circulation was well maintained until the end.

Retention of Salt in Proportion to Water (Fig. 442, f). *Edema* is the clinical name for the accumulation of excess extracellular fluid at isotonic concentration. Such extra fluid may be evenly distributed throughout all tissues; more commonly it is pooled in certain tissues. This uneven distribution is usually the result of some disturbance of the factors which control the exchanges of fluids between the plasma and the interstitial divisions of the extracellular fluid (see p. 937). Increased capillary hydrostatic pressure, increased colloid osmotic pressure in the interstitial fluid, decreased colloid osmotic pressure in plasma, and decreased tissue pressure, all tend to increase the volume of interstitial fluid. The extra sodium and water present in such interstitial pools cannot be excreted by the kidney because of their inaccessibility to the circulating plasma. Edema is most commonly found in those conditions in which the hydrostatic pressure in the capillary is elevated, as in *congestive heart failure* and mechanical *obstruction to the venous return*, and in those conditions in which the colloid osmotic pressure is lowered because of a low concentration of serum albumin, as in *cirrhosis of the liver, malnutrition,* and the *nephrotic stage of chronic glomerulonephritis*.

The body fluid abnormalities associated with *nephritis* have not been considered separately or included in Figure 442 because of the wide variety of alterations which may be present and which depend upon the stage of the disease and the coincidental treatment (47, 49). Edema, as stated above, is common in the nephrotic stage because the excessive albuminuria leads to a low concentration of serum albumin. The edema of acute glomerulonephritis is usually the result of both a generalized increase in permeability of the vascular endothelium to serum albumin and an associated congestive heart failure. On the other hand, in the terminal stages of chronic glomerulonephritis, sodium is wasted by the kidney with the result that the body fluids become hypotonic, extracellular volume is diminished, and a metabolic acidosis ensues.

REFERENCES

1. AMBERSON, W. R., NASH, T. P., MULDER, A. G. and BINNS, D. The relationship between tissue chloride and plasma chloride. *Amer. J. Physiol.*, 1938, *122*:224–235.

2. ATCHLEY, D. W., LOEB, R. F., RICHARDS, D. W., JR., BENEDICT, E. M. and DRISCOLL, M. E. On diabetic acidosis. A detailed study of electrolyte balances following the withdrawal and reestablishment of insulin therapy. *J. clin. Invest.*, 1933, *12*:297–326.

3. BENEDICT, F. G. *A study of prolonged fasting.* Washington, D. C. Carnegie Institution of Washington, 1915. 416 pp.

4. DANOWSKI, T. S. The transfer of potassium across the human blood cell membrane. *J. biol. Chem.*, 1941, *139*:693–705.

5. DANOWSKI, T. S., ELKINTON, J. R. and WINKLER, A. W. The deleterious effect in dogs of a dry protein ration. *J. clin. Invest.*, 1944, *23*:816–823.

6. DARROW, D. C., HARRISON, H. E. and TAFFEL, M. Tissue electrolytes in adrenal insufficiency, *J. biol. Chem.*, 1939, *130*:487–502.

7. DARROW, D. C. and MILLER, H. C. The production of cardiac lesions by repeated injections of desoxycorticosterone acetate. *J. clin. Invest.*, 1942, *21*:601–611.

8. DARROW, D. C. and YANNET, H. The changes in the distribution of body water accompanying increase and decrease in extracellular electrolyte. *J. clin. Invest.*, 1935, *14*: 266–275.

9. DARROW, D. C. and YANNET, H. Metabolic studies of the changes in body electrolyte and distribution of body water induced experimentally by deficit of extracellular electrolyte. *J. clin. Invest.*, 1936, *15*:419–427.

10. DILL, D. B. *Life, heat, and altitude. Physiological effects of hot climates and great heights.* Cambridge, Harvard University Press, 1938. xiv, 211 pp.

11. ELKINTON, J. R. and TAFFEL, M. Prolonged water deprivation in the dog. *J. clin. Invest.*, 1942, *21*:787–794.

12. ELKINTON, J. R. and WINKLER, A. W. Transfers of intracellular potassium in experimental dehydration. *J. clin. Invest.*, 1944, *23*: 93–101.

13. ELKINTON, J. R. and WINKLER, A. W. Physiologic effects of drinking undiluted sea water. *War Medicine*, 1944, *6*:241–246.

14. ELKINTON, J. R., WINKLER, A. W. and DANOWSKI, T. S. Inactive cell base and the measurement of changes in cell water. *Yale J. Biol. Med.*, 1944, *17*:383–393.

15. FENN, W. O. Electrolytes in muscle. *Physiol. Rev.*, 1936, *16*:450–487.

16. FLEXNER, L. B., GELLHORN, A. and MERRELL, M. Studies on rates of exchange of

substances between the blood and extravascular fluid. I. The exchange of water in the guinea pig. *J. biol. Chem.*, 1942, *144*:35–40.

17. GAMBLE, J. L. Extracellular fluid. *Johns Hopk. Hosp. Bull.*, 1937, *61*:151–197.

18. GAMBLE, J. L. *Chemical anatomy, physiology, and pathology of extracellular fluid.* A lecture syllabus. Boston, Department of Pediatrics, Harvard Medical School, 1942.

19. GAMBLE, J. L., MCKHANN, C. F., BUTLER, A. M. and TUTHILL, E. An economy of water in renal function referable to urea. *Amer. J. Physiol.*, 1934, *109*:139–154.

20. GAMBLE, J. L., PUTNAM, M. C. amd MCKHANN, C. F. The optimal water requirement in renal function. I. Measurements of water drinking by rats according to increments of urea and of several salts in the food. *Amer. J. Physiol.*, 1929, *88*:571–580.

21. GAMBLE, J. L. and Ross, S. G. The factors in the dehydration following pyloric obstruction. *J. clin. Invest.*, 1924–25, *1*:403–423.

22. GAMBLE, J. F., Ross, G. S. and TISDALL, F. F. The metabolism of fixed base during fasting. *J. biol. Chem.*, 1923, *57*:633–695.

23. GIBSON, J. G., 2ND and EVANS, W. A., JR. Clinical studies of the blood volume. I. Clinical application of a method employing the azo dye "Evans blue" and the spectrophotometer. *J. clin. Invest.*, 1937, *16*:301–316.

24. HARRISON, H. E. and DARROW, D. C. The distribution of body water and electrolytes in adrenal insufficiency. *J. clin. Invest.*, 1938, *17*:77–86.

25. HARRISON, H. E., DARROW, D. C. and YANNET, H. The total electrolyte content of animals and its probable relation to the distribution of body water. *J. biol. Chem.*, 1936, *113*:515–529.

26. HASTINGS, A. B. and EICHELBERGER, L. The exchange of salt and water between muscle and blood. I. The effect of an increase in total body water produced by the intravenous injection of isotonic salt solutions. *J. biol. Chem.*, 1937, *117*:73–93.

27. HEVESY, G. and JACOBSEN, C. F. Rate of passage of water through capillary and cell walls. *Acta physiol. scand.*, 1940, *1*:11–18.

28. HOPPER, J., JR., ELKINTON, J. R. and WINKLER, A. W. Plasma volume of dogs in dehydration, with and without salt loss. *J. clin. Invest.*, 1944, *23*:111–117.

29. HOPPER, J., JR., TABOR, H. and WINKLER, A. W. Simultaneous measurements of the blood volume in man and dog by means of Evans blue dye, T-1824, and by means of carbon monoxide. I. Normal subjects. *J. clin. Invest.*, 1944, *23*:628–635.

30. HOPPER, J., JR., WINKLER, A. W. and ELKINTON, J. R. Simultaneous measurements of the blood volume in man and dog by means of Evans blue dye, T-1824, and by means of carbon monoxide. II. Under abnormal conditions, including secondary shock. *J. clin. Invest.*, 1944, *23:*636–648.

31. JOHNSON, R. E., PITTS, G. C., and CONSOLAZIO, F. C. Factors influencing chloride concentration in human sweat. *Amer. J. Physiol.*, 1944, *141:*575–589.

32. KALTREIDER, N. L., MENEELY, G. R., ALLEN, J. R. and BALE, W. F. Determination of the volume of the extracellular fluid of the body with radioactive sodium. *J. exp. Med.*, 1941, *74:*569–590.

33. KERPEL-FRONIUS, E. Über die Beziehungenzwischen Salz- und Wasserhaushalt bei experi mentellen Wasserverlusten. *Z. Kinderheilk.* 1936, *57:*489–504.

34. LANDIS, E. M. Capillary pressure and capillary permeability. *Physiol. Rev.*, 1934, *14:*404–481.

35. LAVIETES, P. H. The metabolic measurement of water exchange. *J. clin. Invest.*, 1935, *14:*57–69.

36. LAVIETES, P. H., BOURDILLON, J. and KLINGHOFFER, K. A. The volume of the extracellular fluids of the body. *J. clin. Invest.*, 1936, *15:*261–268.

37. LOEB, R. F., ATCHLEY, D. W., BENEDICT, E. M. and LELAND, J. Electrolyte balance studies in adrenalectomized dogs with particular reference to the excretion of sodium. *J. exp. Med.*, 1933, *57:*775–792.

38. MACALLUM, A. B. The paleochemistry of the body fluids and tissues. *Physiol. Rev.*, 1926, *6:*316–357.

39. MANERY, J. F. and BALE, W. F. The penetration of radioactive sodium and phosphorus into the extra- and intracellular phases of tissues. *Amer. J. Physiol.*, 1941, *132:*215–231.

40. MANERY, J. F., DANIELSON, I. S. and HASTINGS, A. B. Connective tissue electrolytes. *J. biol. Chem.*, 1938, *124:*359–375.

41. MANERY, J. F. and HAEGE, L. F. The extent to which radioactive chloride penetrates tissues, and its significance. *Amer. J. Physiol.*, 1941, *134:*83–93.

42. MANERY, J. F. and HASTINGS, A. B. The distribution of electrolytes in mammalian tissues. *J. biol. Chem.*, 1939, *127:*657–676.

43. McCANCE, R. A. Medical problems in mineral metabolism. I. Legacies of evolution. II. Sodium deficiencies in clinical medicine. III. Experimental human salt deficiency. *Lancet*, 1936, *1:*643–650, 704–710, 765–768, 823–830.

44. McCANCE, R. A. and WIDDOWSON, E. M. The excretion of urine in man during experimental salt deficiency. *J. Physiol.*, 1937, *91:*222–231.

45. NADAL, J. W., PEDERSEN, S. and MADDOCK, W. G. A comparison between dehydration from salt loss and from water deprivation. *J. clin. Invest.*, 1941, *20:*691–703.

46. NEWBURGH, L. H., JOHNSTON, M. W. and FALCON-LESSES, M. Measurement of total water exchange. *J. clin. Invest.*, 1929–30, *8:*161–196.

47. PETERS, J. P. Salt and water metabolism in nephritis. *Medicine*, 1932, *11:*435–535.

48. PETERS, J. P. *Body water: the exchange of fluids in man.* Springfield, Ill., Charles C Thomas, 1935. 405 pp.

49. PETERS, J. P. Water balance in health and in disease. Chap. 6 in: DUNCAN, G. *Diseases of metabolism.* Philadelphia, W. B. Saunders Co., 1942.

50. PETERS, J. P. Water exchange. *Physiol. Rev.*, 1944, *24:*491–531.

51. PETERS, J. P., KYDD, D. M., EISENMAN, A. J. and HALD, P. M. The nature of diabetic acidosis. *J. clin. Invest.*, 1933, *12:*377–391.

52. PETERS, J. P., KYDD, D. M. and LAVIETES, P. H. A note on the calculation of water exchange. *J. clin. Invest.*, 1933, *12:*689–693.

53. PETERS, J. P. and LAVIETES, P. H. The nature of "preformed water." *J. clin. Invest.*, 1933, *12:*695–712.

54. RICHARDS, A. N. The Croonian Lecture. Processes of urine formation. *Proc. roy. Soc.*, 1938, *B126:*398–432.

55. ROWNTREE, L. G. The effects on mammals of the administration of excessive quantities of water. *J. Pharmacol.*, 1926, *29:*135–159.

56. SCHWARTZ, B. M., SMITH, P. K. and WINKLER, A. W. Renal excretion of sulfate. *Amer. J. Physiol.*, 1942, *137:*658–670.

57. SHANNON, J. A. Glomerular filtration and urea excretion in relation to urine flow in the dog. *Amer. J. Physiol.*, 1936, *117:*206–225.

58. SHANNON, J. A. The control of the renal excretion of water. I. The effect of variations in the state of hydration on water excretion in dogs with diabetes insipidus. *J. exp. Med.*, 1942, *76:*371–386.

59. SMITH, H. W. *Lectures on the kidney.* Lawrence, Kansas, University of Kansas, 1943. 134 pp.

60. STARLING, E. H. On the absorption of fluids from the connective tissue spaces. *J. Physiol.*, 1895–96, *19:*312–326.

61. TALBOTT, J. H. Heat cramps. *Medicine, Baltimore*, 1935, *14:*323–376.

62. WELLS, H. S. The balance of physical forces which determine the rate and direction of flow of fluid through the intestinal mucosa. *Amer. J. Physiol.*, 1940, *130:*410–419.

63. WINKLER, A. W., DANOWSKI, T. S., ELKINTON, J. R. and PETERS, J. P. Electrolyte and fluid studies during water deprivation and starvation in human subjects, and the effect of ingestion of fish, of carbohydrate, and of salt solutions. *J. clin. Invest.*, 1944, *23:*807–815.

64. WINKLER, A. W., ELKINTON, J. R. and EISENMAN, A. J. Comparison of sulfocyanate with radioactive chloride and sodium in the measurement of extracellular fluid. *Amer. J. Physiol.*, 1943, *139:*239–246.

65. WINKLER, A. W., ELKINTON, J. R., HOPPER, J., JR., and HOFF, H. E. Experimental hypertonicity: alterations in the distribution of body water, and the cause of death. *J. clin. Invest.*, 1944, *23:*103–109.

CHAPTER 44

THE KIDNEY

STRUCTURE OF THE KIDNEY

Form and structure of the nephron. The human kidney is a compound tubular gland, each organ being composed of about one million complete functional units called nephrons. Each nephron consists of a glomerular capsule and a renal tubule, the latter consisting of proximal and distal convoluted portions with a characteristic thin portion, the loop of Henle, interposed between them. The collecting duct, into which the distal tubule delivers

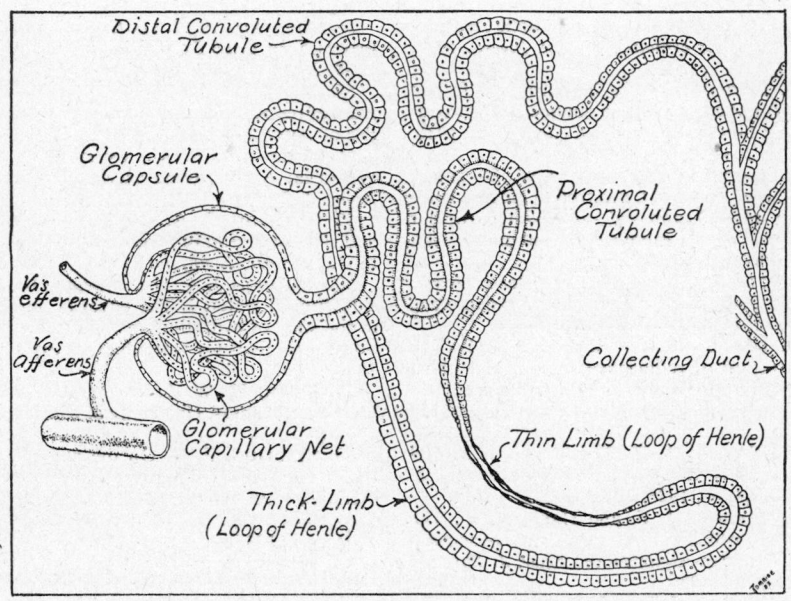

Fig. 443.—Diagram of a nephron. (After Homer Smith.)

the urine, has no known function except that of a conduit. The renal pelvis, the ureters, the bladder and the urethra likewise have no part in the formation of urine, and their actions in storing it and conducting it to the exterior are treated elsewhere. In the diagram of a nephron (Fig. 443) the functionally important aspects of renal anatomy have been emphasized and other features have been distorted. The cells which compose the nephron have several characteristic forms. In the glomerular capsule and in portions of the loop of Henle they are thin squamous epithelial cells, while in both convoluted portions they are large truncated pyramidal cells. Many characteristic differences in microscopic structure and staining reactions are known, which will be referred to briefly here so far as they seem to have a physiological bearing, although for a complete description reference must be made to works on histology.

Blood vascular system. Blood from the primary divisions of the renal artery is delivered into the arciform arteries which lie at the boundary between the renal cortex and the medulla. From these vessels the interlobular arteries course towards the outer surface of the organ, giving off many branches to near-by Malpighian corpuscles, the afferent glomerular arterioles.

The wall of the afferent arteriole, *vas afferens*, just before it enters the glomerulus, is characterized by specialized smooth muscle cells which form a cuff just before the capillary branching occurs. These cells do not have an exceptionally dense nerve supply, but are nevertheless important in the regulation of renal blood flow. The glomerular capillary tuft itself is closely invested with the extremely thin visceral layer of the cells which make up Bowman's capsule, and there is no interstitial space interposed at this region between the blood stream and the lumen of the nephron. Nearly all of the blood entering the kidney passes through the glomerular capillaries; and since these capillaries are fed through an exceptionally large and direct arterial system, the hydrostatic pressure within them is great enough to suggest that the formation of a plasma filtrate, in conformity with the Starling hypothesis (p. 613), is the primary function of the Malpighian corpuscle. The efferent glomerular arteriole, *vas efferens*, has the smooth muscle fibers characteristic of an arteriole rather than a vein, and it also is an important mechanism in the regulation of renal blood flow.

The efferent glomerular arteriole breaks up at once into a network of capillaries which closely surround the convoluted tubules and the straight portions directed radially to the loop of Henle in the renal medulla. The venules formed by the reunion of these peritubular capillaries feed into the arciform veins and thence into the renal vein.

The characteristic feature of the circulation in the kidney is the provision of two capillary beds connected in series so that the blood, after passing through the glomerular system, proceeds through the second, the peritubular system. In addition to all of the factors which control the flow of blood through a peripheral capillary bed in other parts of the body, the kidney possesses a variable resistance in the efferent glomerular arteriole by which changes can be made in the capillary pressure, especially in the glomerular tuft. When it is recalled that outward filtration from capillaries (Table 18, p. 615) takes place at the arteriolar end where the effective filtration pressure is high, while osmotic reabsorption occurs at the venous end, it becomes at once apparent that the efferent arteriole may be a device by which the filtration and reabsorption are isolated in separate parts of the renal vascular structure. That this is actually the case will be abundantly demonstrated in the following discussion.

Juxtaglomerular apparatus. As the tubule returns toward the cortex of the kidney, after forming Henle's loop, it passes many glomeruli in the vicinity where it originated. Microscopic examination shows that where the distal tubule passes very close to the afferent arteriole there is a modification of the tubular cells which become closely packed, forming *macula densa*. In direct contact with this lies the portion of the afferent arteriole referred to above as having a concentration of smooth muscle fibers. It has been postulated that each tubule returns to its own glomerulus and that the juxtaglomerular apparatus is a device by which the blood flow through the afferent arteriole is modified according to the amount or composition of the fluid in the distal convoluted tubule.

Renal lymphatic system. Lymph vessels are found throughout the kidney and leave it by two routes. The superficial lymphatics, largely in the capsule, pass through the perirenal fat to lumbar lymph nodes, while the deeper vessels exit at the hilus along with the blood vessels. Nothing is known concerning any special features of their normal function.

AMOUNT AND COMPOSITION OF THE URINE

In the preceding chapter it has been shown that the kidney is the variable site of water output by which the body conserves or expends water as the balance between input and the other routes of water excretion demands. Large variations are encountered in the day to day and even in the minute to minute rates of urine formation. It is a general finding that a normal adult produces from one to two liters a day, or roughly one milliliter a minute. The rate of flow is low at night while sleeping, and is promptly diminished by exercise even though sweating be not significant. On the other hand, most fluids taken by mouth result in a temporary elevation of urine flow, sometimes above ten milliliters a minute for a short time.

Table 44.—Principal Constituents of Urine

DAILY OUTPUT—GRAMS			
Water	1500	Chloride	6
Urea	30	Potassium	2
Creatinine	1	Sulfur	1
Sodium	4	Phosphorus	1

It appears to be certain that if the kidney did not have to excrete dissolved substances it could, when necessary, reduce the water excretion to zero. There are, however, many solutes which the kidney cannot retain in the body; and whenever anuria is observed it is a very serious, though sometimes temporary, disorder. Persistent anuria soon leads to death, by the rise of plasma potassium concentration to levels which induce heart failure, or by other means. Some persons show persistently large daily urine volumes which are traceable to an unusually large water intake as the result of habit. The principal solutes present in urine are the nitrogen-containing residues of protein metabolism and the electrolytes ingested as such or produced in the body from various precursors. There are many constituents of urine whose presence or amount have special significance. Those which are of metabolic importance are discussed elsewhere, while those which illustrate particular aspects of renal function will be considered in this chapter.

QUANTITATIVE METHODS IN RENAL PHYSIOLOGY

The development of the modern quantitative methods for studying kidney function makes it desirable to consider first the various capabilities of the organ and to follow this analysis with a study of the extent to which various renal functions are stimulated or inhibited in response to the needs of the organism as a whole. In an effort to eliminate unknown factors which might interfere, most experimenters with human renal function keep their subjects under observation in bed in as nearly as possible the basal condition. The storage function of the bladder is circumvented by the use of a urethral catheter; and if necessary, the individual ureters are catheterized and the urine is collected separately from the two kidneys. A steady state of the circulatory system is verified as far as possible by measurements of blood pressure and heart rate; and constancy of blood composition is achieved, when the excretion of an unusual blood component is being studied, by continuous intravenous infusion.

Students of renal physiology usually assume that all the cells which make up Bowman's capsule, being identical in form and apparent structure, have the same function. The cells which make up the remainder of the nephron, the renal tubule, showing marked differences in form and staining reactions, have a correspondingly broad range of physiological activities. There are several processes by which materials move from one place to another, and it is essential to the further analysis of kidney function to keep them clearly in mind. The simplest is convection, in which a fluid with its solutes moves en masse, due to the presence of a physical force manifested as a pressure gradient. The second type of movement is diffusion, in which a substance leaves a region where its concentration is high, i.e., where its pressure is great, and proceeds to places where its concentration is low. Between two different solutions there can be quite independent movements of the solvents and the solutes at the same time. The third type of translocation is termed "secretion," and is characterized by the fact that metabolic energy is expended to cause the moving material to go as fast as it goes or in the particular direction which it actually takes. Each of these three processes has been the subject of studies both in the mammalian kidney and in simpler tissues and nonliving models, and the laws which describe their quantitative behavior are fairly well known. The application of these laws to the intact human kidney has been investigated in many ways, but the study of simultaneous renal clearances has been most fruitful.

Renal clearance. A renal clearance is a quantitative measure of renal activity in respect to any solute which the kidney transfers from the blood to the urine. The significance of the term is made obvious by a formal definition: a renal clearance is the volume of blood which would be completely cleared of any constituent by the removal of the amount of that constituent which the kidney excretes in one minute. To calculate a clearance it is necessary to know only the rate of excretion of some substance and its simultaneous concentration in the blood. Greatest experimental accuracy is obtained by using the same analytical method for both blood and urine. The urine concentration obtained by analysis is multipled by the rate of urine formation to give the rate of solute excretion. The conventional symbols and the method of calculation are as follows:

V = rate of urine production, in milliliters per minute

U = concentration of a named urinary constituent, in milligrams per milliliter.

B, P or S = concentration of the same substance in blood, plasma or serum, in milligrams per milliliter.

C = blood, plasma or serum clearance of the named substance, in milliliters per minute.

$$C = \frac{UV}{B}.$$

The choice of B, P or S, and hence the calculation of a blood, plasma or serum clearance, is usually dictated by the significance to be attached to the clearance. In the case of a substance equally distributed between plasma and cells, B and P will have practically the same value, and the blood and plasma clearances will be the same. This is the case with urea, the substance to which clearance methods were first applied (1). On the other hand, the clearance of potassium is always a plasma or serum clearance since the potassium within the erythrocytes is not immediately available to the kidney for excretion. The choice between the use of plasma or serum depends on whether the disturbances set up by an anticoagulant interfere with the analytical procedures or the purpose of the observations. In every case it must be remembered that a clearance statement must always name the space which is cleared, the volume of that space, and the substance removed.

GLOMERULAR FUNCTION

The structure of the glomerulus suggests the possibility that it may function as a filtration apparatus. The wide capillary bed with its narrow outlet must slow down the stream and bring the blood under a relatively high lateral pressure. The filtration pressure is the difference in pressure between the blood in the capillaries and the liquid in the capsule, but the effect of this pressure upon the outflow of water is partially antagonized by the tissue pressure and by the osmotic pressure of the plasma proteins unless these capillaries, in contrast to most others in the body, are permeable to plasma proteins (Fig. 435, p. 937).

The most direct evidence that urine formation does, in fact, commence at the glomerulus with the formation of a protein-free filtrate of plasma is furnished in a series of papers by A. N. Richards and his coworkers, and summarized in 1929 in his Beaumont Foundation Lecture (12). Methods were perfected by which a fine quartz pipette held in a micromanipulator was inserted into one of the glomerular spaces in an illuminated kidney of a frog under microscopic observation. Minute amounts of fluid (*ca.* 0.001 ml. per hour) were collected and subjected to chemical analysis. The analyses demonstrated that in total concentration of solutes as given by vapor pressure, in the total concentration of electrolytes as shown by conductivity measurements, in its *p*H, chlorides, phosphates, glucose, urea, uric acid and creatinine, the glomerular urine has the composition of an ultrafiltrate of the blood plasma. It was possible, moreover, to arrive at an estimate of the degree or porosity of the glomerular membrane. The polysaccharide, inulin, with a molecular weight of 5100, when injected into the blood passes the membrane freely. Purified egg albumin, molecular weight 40,000, also gets through, while serum albumin, 68,000, does not. Measurements were made of the glomerular capillary pressure, which was found to be high enough to provide for ultrafiltration. There is no doubt, therefore, that in all animals which can be studied by these direct methods the function of the glomerulus is ultrafiltration.

Glomerular function in man. The similarities in structure between the amphibian and mammalian glomeruli are sufficiently striking to warrant the assumption of a filtration process as a working hypothesis for the mammals including man. In order to test this hypothesis in man, it is necessary to use indirect methods, and these have been developed by many workers and brought finally to their present state principally by H. W. Smith (16, 17), and his collaborators (6).

The volume of filtrate formed at the glomeruli can be computed if two facts about it are known: (i) the concentration of some solute in it, and (ii) the absolute amount of that solute involved. The work of Richards, referred to above, has given strong assurance that the concentrations of some substances in plasma and glomerular filtrate are identical, and the former may therefore be used as an exact measure of the latter. To evaluate the second factor, evidence must be presented that in its passage through the renal tubule there has been no change by reabsorptive removal, secretory addition or chemical alteration in the amount of the substance under investigation. It is now agreed that several substances can be so used to establish and measure glomerular filtration; among them inulin has had the widest application.

The following specifications, laid down by Smith (17), will be met by every substance which is applicable to the measurement of glomerular filtration in man.

"1. Any substance, X, to be completely filterable through the glomeruli, must be completely filterable from plasma through artificial membranes impermeable to plasma proteins but permeable to smaller molecules.

"2. As presumptive evidence against tubular excretion, X should not be excreted by the aglomerular fish kidney.

"3. a. The rate of excretion of X (UV) should increase over wide limits in simple, direct proportion to the plasma concentration (P); i.e., the clearance, UV/P, should be independent of the plasma concentration. This condition in large measure excludes the possibility of tubular excretion and tubular reabsorption.

"b. Where 3. a. cannot be demonstrated, because of inconstancy in the rate of filtration itself, it is of equal force to show that the clearance of X is constant, relative to the clearance of some other substance, at various plasma levels of X.

"4. Assuming that adequate doses of phlorizin completely block the tubular reabsorption of glucose, then in the phlorizinized animal the clearance of X should be equal to the glucose clearance. (This, of course, is not evidence that phlorizin does not block the tubular excretion or reabsorption of X itself.)

"5. Where the simultaneous clearances of two or more substances are identical under a wide variety of conditions (plasma level, urine flow, etc.), this may be taken as evidence that both substances are excreted by the glomeruli, without interference from the variable factors of tubular reabsorption or tubular excretion.

"6. Where a completely filterable substance is excreted in part by tubular activity, the clearance of that substance when depressed by elevating the plasma level should approach the clearance of X as the limiting asymptote."

For complete details of the tests which demonstrate the fitness of inulin in each of the six postulates, Smith's book (17) or the original papers cited therein should be consulted. In summary it may be stated that inulin is satisfactory, and we proceed therefore to the use of the method and the results found in man. To carry out this test of renal function, inulin is maintained at an approximately constant concentration in the blood by continuous intravenous infusion; urine samples are obtained at accurately timed intervals, by catheter, and the minute rate of urine flow is calculated. A blood sample, usually at the middle of each urine period, furnishes the basis for the datum, plasma inulin concentration, and a portion of the urine is analyzed by the same method for its inulin content. Using the same notation that was introduced earlier, the argument proceeds as follows: the inulin concentration of the glomerular filtrate is the same as plasma, P, while in the urine inulin is found at a different (and always higher) concentration, U. This increase in concentration was effected solely by the removal of water from the filtrate (no inulin being reabsorbed), and the extent of the water reabsorption is given by the ratio, $\dfrac{U}{P}$. Since the urine volume (per minute), V, is what was left after the concentrating process was completed, when it is multiplied by the extent of concentration, $\dfrac{U}{P}$, one obtains the volume at the start, that is, the volume (per minute) of the glomerular filtrate. This has obviously the dimensions of a clearance, $C = \dfrac{UV}{P}$; and, in brief, the inulin clearance and rate of glomerular filtration are identical.

The rate of glomerular filtration in man has been determined with considerable accuracy, and has been found to be quite predictable for normal subjects in the basal condition. Smith (16, p. 97) summarizes his data on 67 normal men: the average inulin clearance is 131 ml. per minute, and on 21 normal women 117 ml. per minute. Uniformity in the data was improved by making proportionate adjustments of the observed values according to the deviation of the surface area of the subject from 1.73 sq. meters, the average value for adults.

The rate of glomerular filtration may be modified by a large number of physiological and pathological factors, the latter being outside the scope of this book. Since the filtration process derives its driving energy from the circulatory system, which is also the source of the materials involved, it is necessary to consider glomerular blood flow and pressure as primary determinants of filtration. Experiments made several years ago by Richards and Plant (14) showed that when an excised rabbit's kidney is perfused at a constant rate of flow by a pump, the addition of a small amount of adrenaline to the perfusate caused the pressure to rise, indicating vasoconstriction, and the kidney to swell, indicating an expansible vascular bed upstream from the constriction. These facts point to the efferent glomerular arteriole as the site of adrenaline action in these experiments. It is not possible to keep the blood pressure constant in man, but a method is available, and will be discussed at length later on, for the measurement of human renal blood flow. When adrenaline is given to a human subject, there is a renal vasoconstriction as shown by a sharply reduced renal blood flow in spite of an elevated mean arterial pressure, but only a moderate reduction in filtration rate. The fraction of the perfusing plasma which is filtered off at the glomeruli is greatly increased, and one must conclude from the data that although the blood flow is reduced, its effective filtration pressure is increased in almost the same proportion. The efferent glomerular arteriole is therefore at least an important but possibly not the sole site of the renal action of adrenaline. The converse experiment has been carried out, showing that a marked renal hyperemia, induced by the injection of typhoid vaccine, was accompanied by a slight rise in filtration rate and a large decrease in filtration fraction, again pointing to the efferent arteriole as an important factor in glomerular control.

TUBULAR FUNCTIONS

That the cells of the renal tubules have secretory powers is suggested by observations too numerous even to list. Among the more striking ones are those on the aglomerular fish, whose kidneys, in spite of a complete lack of glomeruli, produce urine of the usual amount and complexity. Cultures in vitro of fragments of embryonic tubules of the chicken show the power of transferring phenol red against a steep concentration gradient, a power which they lose, reversibly, if oxygen is withdrawn, and which is obviously secretory in nature (4). The absence of glucose from normal urine is another evidence of secretory power of renal cells, for glucose is certainly present in glomerular filtrate and also in renal venous blood. It must be kept in mind that secretion as defined on page 967 is a process which may be directed outward for the removal of wastes or inward for the absorption or reclamation of materials useful to the body. Many substances in the latter category are present in the glomerular filtrate, but thus far there is no known normal constituent of blood which is excreted into the urine by secretory activity of the tubules.* In the following paragraphs certain illustrative examples of both types will be considered in detail.

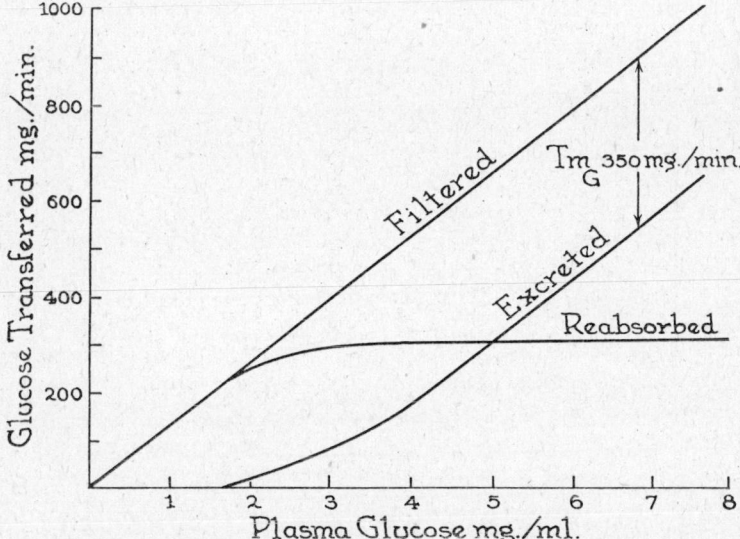

Fig. 444.—Renal tubular reabsorption or rejection of glucose in man.

Renal excretion of typical solutes. Glucose is normally not excreted by the kidney, but the urine contains large amounts when the blood concentration is abnormally high. The blood concentration of glucose at which glycosuria is ust present is termed the threshold, and it is important to understand the renal mechanisms which establish and regulate the threshold for sugar. It is quite possible by the intravenous infusion technique to maintain in a normal, unanesthetized human subject constant levels of plasma inulin and glucose, and to readjust the value of the latter at will. Analyses of plasma and urine permit the calculation of glomerular filtration (the inulin clearance), and this value, multiplied by the plasma (and hence filtrate) concentration of glucose, gives the rate at which glucose is delivered to the tubules. The difference between this value and the amount which is found in the urine is the quantity restored to the blood stream by the secretory activity of the tubules. The

* In man and the primates creatinine is secreted by the tubules into the urine at a moderate rate when the plasma concentration is artificially raised, and the true normal creatinine is doubtless excreted in the same manner. In most other animals there is no tubular transfer of creatinine.

results of such an experiment are shown graphically in Figure 444, in which the amounts of glucose filtered and excreted are plotted against the plasma glucose concentration. It will be noticed that at all levels of plasma glucose at which a good glycuresis is evident the rate of glucose excretion falls 350 mg. per minute below the rate of glucose filtration. No matter how the supply of glucose to the tubules may vary, as long as enough is presented to them to saturate the secretory mechanism, it works at maximum capacity. The limit to this capacity is set by at present unknown limitations of intermediary metabolites or of energy-producing processes within the cells. The fact that the excretion line is curved at its lower end is a consequence of the fact that all of the nephrons do not become saturated at the same glucose levels. This is probably due to differences from one nephron to another in the amount of glucose reabsorbing tissue compared to filtering capacity. The

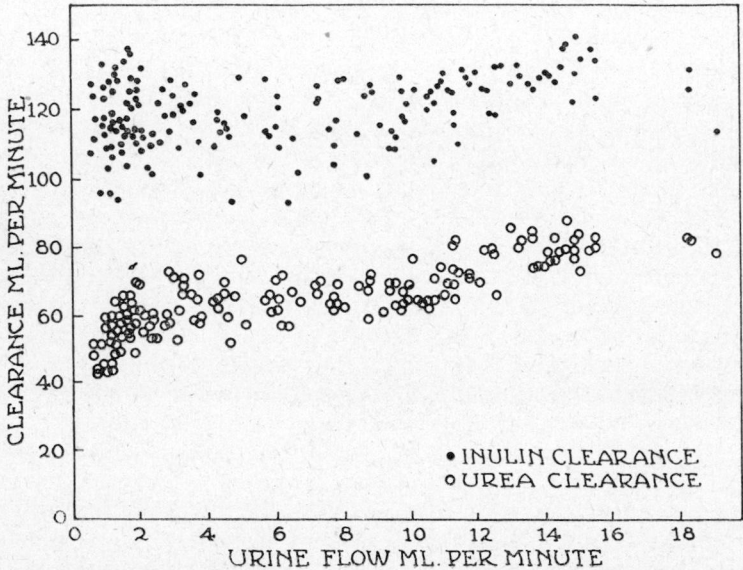

Fig. 445.—Inulin and urea clearances in the normal human subject. All individual data have been corrected to the ideal body size, 1.73 sq. meters surface area. (From Goldring and Chasis, *Hypertension and hypertensive disease*, 1944.)

notion of a glucose threshold now becomes attached to a dynamic process in the kidney rather than a plasma glucose level high enough to exceed a fixed excretory barrier.

Urea is excreted by a filtration and reabsorption process, but the latter is carried out by a means different from that described for glucose. It was the apparently complex behavior of the kidney toward urea that led to the development of the clearance formula and the introduction of the clearance concept (10, pp. 345–354). Studies on man, supplemented by many careful experiments on dogs (15), point to the conclusion that urea is reabsorbed by the tubules by a process not characterizable as urea secretion. The reabsorption of urea is linked to the reabsorption of water, a fact which is shown in Figure 445. When plotted against urine flow, urea clearance rises steeply at first but much more slowly as polyuria becomes more pronounced, and when $V > 2$ ml./min., it becomes practically constant. Simultaneous measurements of glomerular filtration rate and calculations of the rate of delivery of urea to the tubules show that as water is reabsorbed and the urea concentration rises, the rate of reabsorption also rises. This would mark urea reabsorption as a diffusion process, but until sufficient data are available to show quantitatively that diffusion alone can account for it, the question of mechanism must be left open. Urea clearance is quite independent of blood urea levels, a condition inherent for all substances which are excreted largely or entirely by filtration alone, and a depression of the clearance below the expected value is a sign of disordered kidney function. Other tests are necessary to show accurately where and how much renal deficit exists.

Amino acids are present in the glomerular filtrate but are normally absent from the urine and therefore are subject to tubular reabsorption and are returned to the blood, although small amounts doubtless enter into renal tissue metabolism. The excretion of these compounds can be used as an example of the secretory transfer of different substances by a common cellular mechanism. Pitts (11) has studied the simultaneous excretion of creatine, glycin, alanine and glutamic acid in unanesthetized dogs, and has found that when the plasma concentration of each of these amino acids is raised by intravenous infusion the rate of reabsorption appears to approach a constant maximum limiting value, or Tm. If, on the other hand, the plasma level of creatine is held constant while alanine is gradually added to the circulating blood, the reabsorption of alanine progressively rises but that of creatine suffers a depression to one-quarter of its initial value. It is postulated, on the basis of experiments of this sort, that at some point these secretory mechanisms make use of a common limiting factor, which, when it is used to full capacity, prevents any further gain in rate of secretory transfer. This limiting rate of reabsorption was seen in the study of glucose excretion, and it might also have been pointed out that there are several other sugars (e.g., xylose) which, when present, compete with glucose for secretory reabsorption. The blood levels of amino acids in the above experiments were far higher than normal, and the physiological limit to their reabsorption is probably never even remotely approached in normal human subjects.

Electrolytes, the inorganic ions in particular, are excreted by the filtration-reabsorption mechanism, except ammonium which exists in only negligible quantities in the plasma. It is probable that the reabsorptive processes act on specific ions, but due to the strict necessity for electrical neutrality within a solution, the transfer of an ion of one sign will carry along another of the opposite sign. If one ingests sodium chloride, the kidney has no difficulty in excreting the two ions together. This indicates that the reabsorptive processes for sodium and chloride can work at the same rate under the right set of conditions. Potassium is much less readily reabsorbed than either sodium or chloride; and if potassium chloride is injected, the potassium will be excreted at a relatively faster rate than the chloride, and the kidney uses the next most available anion, namely, bicarbonate, to keep the required electrical neutrality. Ammonium appears in the urine in the situation where the reabsorption of anions is minimal and that of cations is being stimulated. In this case the total cation excretion is being controlled by the anion excretion. The renal tubules have the power to synthesize ammonium salts from a neutral precursor, possibly glutamine, and exchange ammonium ions for ions of fixed base, the latter being returned to the blood while the former are excreted in the urine. The excretion of electrolytes, especially bicarbonate and phosphate, will be discussed further in connection with the part taken by the kidney in acid-base regulation.

Limits of tubular activity. The ability of the tubules to absorb or reject water is now apparent as the principal means by which the rate of urine production is modified. Variations in the measured rate of glomerular filtration have already been discussed, and little correlation of that function with urine flow can be found, although filtration does diminish with pronounced oliguria. It is known that a posterior pituitary hormone exerts a vigorous stimulating effect on the water reabsorbing action of the renal tubules, for in its absence the intense polyuria of diabetes insipidus occurs. When it is artificially administered during polyuria, the urine flow is depressed to a very low rate. Even with large amounts of postpituitary hormone, naturally liberated in response to dehydration or injected into the body, tubular water reabsorption is not complete. The solutes remaining in the renal tubule become more and more concentrated as water is withdrawn, thus making further dehydration more and more difficult, until a limit is finally reached. But the total solute concentration, i.e., the osmotic pressure of the tubular contents, is not a simple factor and the sole limit. This is shown by the fact that the maximum osmotic pressure of urine containing little urea is raised much further if urea is also being excreted in large quantities (see also Chap. 43, p. 950). There is no adequate explanation for this demonstrated ability of the kidney to produce a more concentrated solution of salts and urea than of either alone. There is much evidence that water reabsorption takes place in two steps. Richards' experiments (13) show that in the frog water is reabsorbed at all regions in the tubule where solutes are being taken up, and presumably the same thing occurs in the proximal segment of the mammalian tubule. The loop of Henle is absent in the frog, and is found only in animals which can produce a urine hypertonic to their blood. It has also been shown by Burgess, Harvey and Marshall (3) that the antidiuretic effect of postpituitary extract is significant only in kidneys where there is a loop of Henle, and it is an attractive hypothesis, therefore, that in man the loop of Henle, under pituitary control, is the site of the final water reabsorption and hence is the primary determinant of urine flow.

It is being found useful to study the function of the kidney by means of test substances never present in the blood except as the result of artificial administration. Two of them, phenol red and diodrast, will be discussed in some detail, and a third, para-amino-hippuric acid, will receive briefer comment. Phenol red (phenolsulfonphthalein) was one of a large series of synthetic compounds which were tested as intravenous cathartics. It had no cathartic effect, but its prompt excretion was observed at once, due to the color which it gives to the urine. Its excretion was so rapid that a purely empirical test of renal function was devised and is still in widespread use. Following the subcutaneous injection of a small amount of phenol red (abbreviated to PSP by clinicians), the average normal person will excrete at least 40 per cent within the first hour and a total of at least 60 per cent in the first two hours. Renal failure was found to be accompanied by a more or less marked retention or delay in excretion of the dye. Further physiological investigation showed that aglomerular kidneys rapidly excrete it, and that in the dog glomerular filtration is inadequate by far to account for its rate of appearance in the urine. The amount of phenol red in glomerular filtrate cannot be judged from its concentration in the plasma due to the fact that a considerable portion of it becomes associated or "bound" to plasma albumin and is therefore restrained from passing through the glomerular capillary walls (19). The fraction of the total which is bound varies somewhat with the total concentration (being about 80 per cent at low plasma levels) and with the usual concentration of plasma albumin. The bound portion, while un-filterable, can be removed from the blood by tubular secretion due to the fact that it is in constant equilibrium with the free portion. The secretory cells establish a diffusion gradient from the blood to their interior, and as fast as the free and diffusible dye leaves the plasma the bound portion dissociates to replenish it.

When the excretion of phenol red was studied in man by the clearance method (7), it was found that phenol red clearances exceeded about threefold the simultaneous inulin clearances, there being 350 to 400 ml. of blood cleared of the dye each minute. This indicates, when allowance is made for plasma binding, that over 90 per cent of the excreted dye is handled by a tubular secretory process. A search for other compounds which might be excreted in a similar manner led to the study of a group of iodine-containing materials which had been introduced for the purpose of obtaining x-ray pictures of the urinary tract. Of these, diodrast has proved most useful. Diodrast is a synthetic organic molecule containing two atoms of iodine which are quite inert in the body but which can be quantitatively split off by suitable reagents and thus form the basis of an accurate method of assay. Diodrast clearances in man are about twice as great as phenol red clearances, a fact of considerable interest to be discussed subsequently. By raising the plasma concentration of diodrast, it has been shown that the amount excreted by secretion rises to a maximum, marking the limit of tubular activity in this particular respect. The tubules become thus saturated when the plasma level is about 50 mg. per cent diodrast iodine. In a series of normal men Smith (16, p. 97) reports an average maximal secretory capacity of 52 mg. of iodine per minute. Smith has introduced the term "tubular maximum," symbolized Tm, for the highest rate, expressed in milligrams per minute, at which the secretory activity of the tubules can transfer their appropriate substrate. The secretory reabsorption of glucose, taking place independently in other cells, has likewise a Tm, as was described above. We may summarize the data on tubular maxima as follows:

Normal men	Tm_D	=	52	mg./min.
	Tm_G	=	375	" "
Normal women	Tm_D	=	43	" "
	Tm_G	=	303	" "
Normal adults (6)	Tm_{PAH}	=	76.1	" "

Para-amino-hippuric acid has recently been found to be secreted as vigorously as diodrast, and will supplement if not replace the latter as a substance for the evaluation of renal function.

The tubular maxima of glucose and diodrast deserve consideration not only for the light which is thrown while establishing them on certain fundamental renal processes, but also for the information that can be obtained through them as to the state of the kidney as a whole. One might expect to find that the maximal ability to reabsorb glucose would be related to the maximal capacity for glomerular filtration, that is, that Tm_G would be proportional to C_{In}, but sufficient data are not yet available on this point. The inulin clearance shows a good correlation with the diodrast Tm in normal subjects, thus enabling one to feel fairly certain that a subject whose inulin clearance is suspiciously low is not abnormal if his diodrast Tm is proportionately reduced; he merely has small kidneys. The application of these methods to renal and cardiovascular disease is proceeding rapidly, but is beyond the scope of this book.

The clearances of several organic compounds are plotted in Figure 446 against varying plasma concentrations. When proper allowance is made for

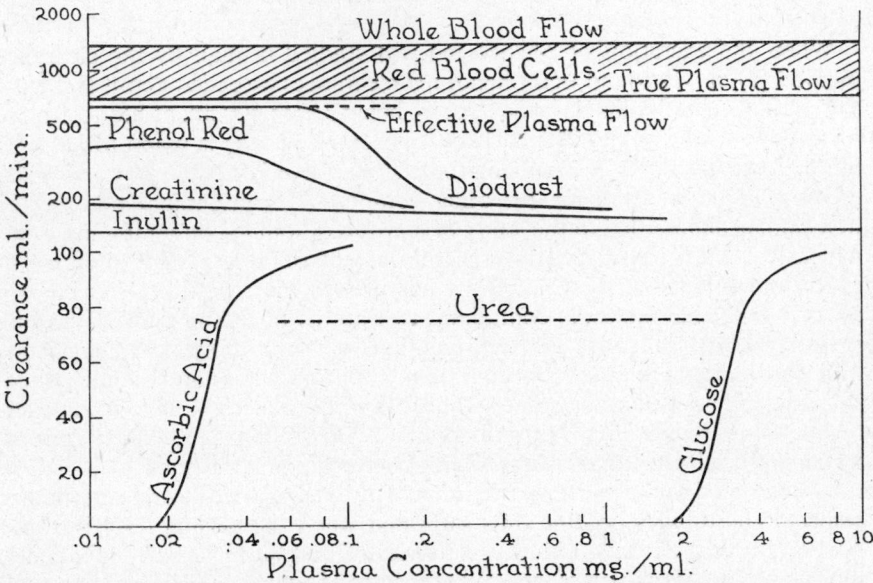

Fig. 446.—Diagrammatic summary of excretion of various compounds by the human kidney. (Modified from Smith, *Lectures on the kidney*, 1943.)

binding by plasma proteins, any substance whose clearance is below that of inulin is subject to tubular reabsorption; if above that of inulin, to tubular secretion. The significance of the plotted blood and plasma flow data is developed in the following paragraph.

RENAL CIRCULATION

Measurements of blood flow. The renal circulation has been studied in man and in animals by direct and indirect methods. In animals mechanical or thermal Stromuhrs have been applied to the renal blood vessels, but the operative interference required and the uncertainties of calibration have resulted in general distrust of the results except for the conclusions that renal blood flow is large and variable. The application of the Fick principle has been successfully carried out in dogs by explanting the kidney to a subcutaneous site, leaving its pedicle intact. It is then easy to draw simultaneous samples of arterial and renal venous blood. A series of analyses of these samples and urine produced at the same time, for some constituent which is neither made nor destroyed by the kidney, provides the data for the calculation of blood flow. Van Slyke (21) reported blood flows of 2 to 10 ml. per gram of kidney per minute, using urea as the basis of calculation.

The chief difficulty with the application of Fick methods to the kidney is the difficulty in getting samples of renal venous blood without disturbing the whole animal or causing reflex vasomotor effects from needling the renal vein. The great vigor with which certain substances are removed from the blood by the secretory cells of the tubules has led to an examination of the possibility that they may be completely absent from venous blood. If that were the case, V in the Fick equation being zero, an arterial analysis and the rate of excretion would permit calculation of the blood flow. The Fick equation and the clearance equation are then identical. It has already been stated that the clearance of phenol red in man is about 350 ml. per minute, and that of diodrast double that amount, $C_D = 700$ ml. per minute. Since these clearance measurements were made with renal activity in a steady state, the plasma which was cleared of diodrast must have passed through the kidneys at the same time that the analyzed urine was being formed. This plasma entering the renal vein was of course accompanied by an unknown volume of plasma from which no diodrast was extracted, since it did not pass near secretory tissue, and the true plasma flow must have exceeded the "effective plasma flow" by an unknown amount (Fig. 446). The analysis of renal venous blood in similar experiments on animals leads one to estimate that about 90 per cent of the plasma passing through the kidney is cleared of diodrast, and therefore the true plasma flow is about 10 per cent higher than the diodrast plasma clearance. In a recent report (22) of the renal extraction of para-amino-hippurate by the human kidney, 88 per cent removal was found in eight normal subjects. This method of measuring renal plasma flow is being applied to human cases of cardiovascular disorders such as hypertension and shock, as well as to cases of renal disease. Para-amino-hippurate is excreted by the same mechanism as diodrast, and because of its lower cost and more satisfactory analytical methods it may replace the latter as a measure of both effective renal blood flow and excretory Tm.

Dynamics of glomerular function. In the previous discussion of glomerular activity (p. 968), no attention was paid to the portion of the blood which did not permeate the capillary walls. With moderately accurate estimates now available of the magnitude of the plasma flow, it is possible to compute the "filtration fraction," that is, the fraction of the perfusing plasma which is filtered. This is, of course, $C_{In} \div C_D$ and normally is about 0.20. Nothing is known about the fall in hydrostatic pressure along the glomerular capillaries, and therefore it is impossible to state whether or not there is some reabsorption of filtrate near the downstream end of the vessels as is the case in other capillary beds. The fact that the glomerular capillaries are kept high on the arteriovenous pressure gradient by the obstructive action of the efferent arteriole leads most workers to assume that filtration proceeds until filtration equilibrium is reached and stops at that point. When the filtration fraction is 0.2, the plasma proteins become concentrated in 80 per cent of their former volume, and the colloidal osmotic pressure is significantly raised. This blood loses much of its hydrostatic pressure in passing the narrow efferent arteriole, and it then rapidly reabsorbs water and solutes from the interstitial spaces around the tubules. The hydrostatic pressure within Bow-

33

man's capsule must be sufficient to account for the flow of fluid on into the pelvis of the kidney, and is certainly great enough to be one of the conditioning factors in glomerular filtration. No measurement has been made of its size in man, but the work of Winton (23) has demonstrated that the intracapsular pressure is probably from 10 to 20 mm. Hg in the dog.

Both the efferent and afferent arterioles are supplied with sympathetic nerves, and many attempts have been made to explain the correlation between the vasomotor and excretory functions of the organ. Smith has shown that in artificially produced renal hyperemia in man the filtration fraction falls as the blood flow rises, and vice versa in experimental ischemia (18). These observations definitely point to the efferent arteriole as the principal, if not the sole, site of vasomotor regulation in the experiments cited.

REGULATION OF RENAL ACTIVITY

Hormonal control. Brief mention has been made previously (p. 977) of the functions of the nerves of the kidney. The sensory nerves certainly mediate pain, and possibly bring about vasomotor reflexes at an entirely subconscious level of activity. No specific influence of the autonomic innervation of the organ except that on the blood vessels has yet been demonstrated. Various hormones, on the other hand, are highly important in the regulation of renal function. The role of the posterior lobe of the pituitary has been alluded to elsewhere in connection with the control of urine volume. In animals or man in whom the posterior lobe is deficient or is no longer functionally controlled by the supra-optic nuclei, a chronic polyuria, termed diabetes insipidus, is found. A degree of dehydration is produced which the body counteracts in part by an increased thirst which is satisfied by water alone, since the urine is very hypotonic and little salt is lost. The latter phenomenon is a manifestation of the ability of the hormone to suppress the reabsorption of sodium chloride by the renal tubules. The renal action is probably on the sodium ion and is in direct opposition to that of the adrenal cortical hormone which promotes the reabsorption of sodium. The pituitary hormone is certainly not a primary factor in the control of sodium balance by the kidney, for its action is best shown under conditions of oliguria, where the rate of glomerular filtration is considerably reduced, and there is therefore much less filtered sodium to be reabsorbed.

The influence of the adrenal cortex on the kidney is referred to elsewhere (pp. 958, 959). In the absence of natural supplies of the hormone, as in Addison's disease, there are two outstanding renal defects. The first is the excretion of large amounts of sodium together with chloride, due to diminished tubular reabsorption. All evidence points to the sodium as the solute on the reabsorption of which the action of the hormone takes place; the chloride may be replaced by bicarbonate or any other available anion. The second defect is an increased reabsorption of potassium, and it is quite unknown how or whether the tubular transfers of these two cations are linked together. The study of adrenal cortical control of the kidney is made difficult by the fact that the exact chemical structure of the natural hormone or hormones is not certainly known, and that several substances extractable from the adrenal cortex and similar ones produced elsewhere in the body or synthesized outside of it have, to varying degrees, the renal effects shown by cortical extracts and produced by cortical implants. Desoxycorticosterone is of the greatest practical importance on account of its powerful action and ready availability at low cost.

Acid-base balance of the urine. The acid-base balance of normal human urine is varied by the kidney over a range of hydrogen ion concentrations of pH 5 to pH 8. The urine is a buffered solution of electrolytes, which means that moderate amounts of water can be added to or removed from a given sample with little change in the pH, if care be taken not to disturb the volatile acid, H_2CO_3. The pH of the urine may be discussed without much reference to the prevailing rate of water excretion, the emphasis being placed on the amounts of the various ions being excreted, and the ratios of free acid to salt in the various buffer systems represented. This does not mean that water excretion is independent of acid-base balance, for some of the most potent diuretic agents appear to act by virtue of their acidifying or alkalinizing powers.

In recently reported experiments on unanesthetized dogs, Pitts and Alexander (11a) show that the urine formed during HCl acidosis possesses a buffer pattern and titratable acidity which cannot be explained on the basis of selective tubular reabsorption of $NaHCO_3$ and Na_2HPO_4 and the excretion of all of the filtered H_2CO_3 and NaH_2PO_4. They show that the tubules must acidify the urine by the exchange H^+, which is obtained from plasma H_2CO_3, for Na^+ of the tubular contents and the return of the latter to the blood.

Carbonic acid is the only volatile substance to be considered in the study of body electrolytes. Ammonia may be present in large quantities but in 0.1 M concentration at pH 8 it exerts a pressure of only 0.04 mm. Hg. The ketone acids are not volatile, although they may furnish by decomposition within the body considerable amounts of the nonelectrolyte, acetone, to the exhaled air. The pressure of CO_2 in urine as it leaves the kidney has not been thoroughly studied. Many observations have been made on man and on animals, but most of the experimenters failed to collect ureteral urine or to have the subject in a steady state during the time that urine was accumulating in the bladder. The mixing of acid urine with previously excreted alkaline and bicarbonate-rich urine in the bladder would produce values of pCO_2 higher than those for which the kidney can be held accountable. The renal tubule is certainly permeable to HCO_3^- because the urine usually contains far less than the filtered amount. The permeability of the tubule to CO_2 may be subject to as yet unknown regulatory influences, for several workers have found urine pCO_2 in excess of 150 mm. Hg when the body has excess fixed base to be excreted, as, for example, after exercise. The ability of the kidney to excrete this base with bicarbonate permits the conservation of chloride, and the simultaneous presence of high urinary pCO_2 prevents the occurrence of a degree of alkalinity which would render urinary phosphates insoluble.

The ions appearing in urine may be those derived from strong electrolytes having no buffering power in the physiological range of acidity, and those from weak electrolytes which contribute to the physiological variations in urinary acidity. In the former category are Na^+, K^+, Ca^{++}, Mg^{++}, NH_4^+, Cl^-, $SO_4^=$; in the latter, HCO_3^-, $HPO_4^=$ and anions of several organic acids. Maintenance of bodily equilibrium with respect to the volatile acid, carbonic acid, has been discussed as one of the functions of the respiratory system. Equilibria with respect to the other electrolytes have been considered as problems of conservation or excretion of fixed acids or fixed bases.

RENAL HYPERTENSION

It has long been known that associated with human hypertensive disease there is often renal damage and defective renal function. Having these facts in mind and recalling the demonstration by Tigerstedt and Bergman in 1898 (20) of the pressor effects of kidney extracts, Goldblatt and his collaborators in 1934 (5) announced a new experimental attack upon the problem. They succeeded in producing renal ischemia through a clamp applied to the renal artery, and their findings have stimulated a widespread interest in the analysis of hypertension, the physiological processes which may produce it, and possible remedial measures applicable to hypertensive disease in man.

Soon after an adjustable clamp is applied to one renal artery and the blood flow to that kidney is considerably reduced, the animal will show an elevated arterial blood pressure, which, after persisting for a number of weeks, will gradually return to normal. If both kidneys are rendered ischemic, or if one is so treated and the other removed, the ensuing hypertension is more severe and long lasting. Hypertension from unilateral ischemia is promptly relieved by removal of the clamp or by extirpation of the ischemic kidney. All of the above results have been duplicated when the kidney to be clamped is first transplanted to a distant region (neck or groin), a procedure which completely and permanently denervates it. It is necessary to conclude, therefore, that a kidney made experimentally ischemic produces some pressor agent and that the normal organ can in some way neutralize its effects or destroy it.

Experimental renal hypertension has been shown to be due to the liberation from the kidney of a substance, renin, which indirectly causes a rise of blood pressure. The analysis of the renin mechanism was initiated largely by two groups of workers in Argentina and in the United States (2, 9), and the following facts are now clear, although the terminology is still confused. As stated above, the substance liberated by the offended kidney is called renin. It has the properties of a proteolytic enzyme but is not itself a pressor substance. Its substrate is one of the normal plasma globulins, and the product of their reaction is a substance which causes constriction of peripheral arterioles. Lamport (8) summarizes the terminology as follows, the first suggested Argentine terms in italics and the North American in capitals:

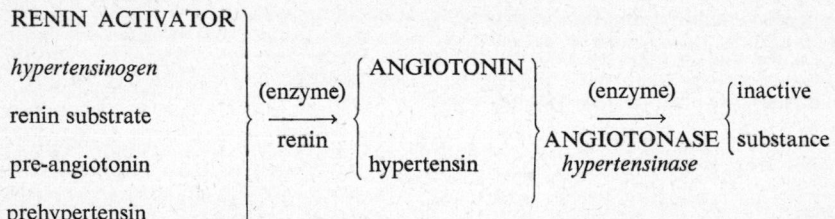

Angiotonase (hypertensinase) is also formed by the kidney, and its increased production is believed to account for the generally transient effects of one ischemic organ when the other is still present.

The site of formation of renin in the kidney is still unknown, and the necessary conditions for its liberation have not been worked out. Anoxemia seems not to promote its formation, nor does moderate histotoxic anoxia from cyanide poisoning. There is no good experimental support for the theory that reduced pulse pressure or diminished movement of renal interstitial fluid or lymph is responsible.

The counterpart of renal hypertension as described above is sometimes seen in man, but only in those relatively rare human cases where bilateral renal circulatory disturbance is the primary event can the analogy be accepted as valid. One cannot deny the very frequent appearance of renal damage in hypertension, but this can in the great majority of cases be a secondary manifestation of the primary disorder, or an actual result of the hypertensive state.

REFERENCES

1. AUSTIN, J. H., STILLMAN, E. and VAN SLYKE, D. D. Factors governing the excretion rate of urea. J. biol. Chem., 1921, 46:91–112.

2. BRAUN-MENENDEZ, E. Kidney. Ann. Rev. Physiol., 1944, 6:265–294.

3. BURGESS, W. W., HARVEY, A. M. and MARSHALL, E. K., JR. The site of the antidiuretic action of pituitary extract. J. Pharmacol., 1933, 49:237–249.

4. CHAMBERS, R., BECK, L. V. and BELKIN, M. Secretion in tissue cultures. I. Inhibition of phenol red accumulation in the chick kidney. J. cell. comp. Physiol., 1935, 6:425–439.

5. GOLDBLATT, H. Studies on experimental hypertension. XII. The experimental production and pathogenesis of hypertension due to renal ischemia. Amer. J. clin. Path., 1940, 10:40–72.

6. GOLDRING, W. and CHASIS, H. Hypertension and hypertensive disease. New York, The Commonwealth Fund, 1944. xv, 253 pp.

7. GOLDRING, W., CLARKE, R. W. and SMITH, H. W. The phenol red clearance in normal man. J. clin. Invest., 1936, 15:221–228.

8. LAMPORT, H. Kidney. Ann. Rev. Physiol., 1945, 7:331–364.

9. PAGE, I. H. Special aspects of the problem of the renal origin of hypertension. Bull. N. Y. Acad. Med., 1943, 19:461–477.

10. PETERS, J. P. and VAN SLYKE, D. D. Quantitative clinical chemistry. I. Interpretations. Baltimore, Williams and Wilkins, 1935. xviii, 1264 pp.

11. PITTS, R. F. A comparison of the renal reabsorptive processes for several amino acids. Amer. J. Physiol., 1944, 140:535–547.

11a. PITTS, R. F. and ALEXANDER, R. S. The nature of the renal tubular mechanism for acidifying the urine. Amer. J. Physiol., 1945, 144:239–254.

12. RICHARDS, A. N. Methods and results of direct investigations of the function of the kidney. (The Beaumont Foundation Lectures,

Series no. 8). Baltimore, Williams and Wilkins, 1929. vii, 64 pp.

13. RICHARDS, A. N. Processes of urine formation. (The Croonian Lecture). Proc. roy. Soc., 1938, B126:398–432.

14. RICHARDS, A. N. and PLANT, O. H. Urine formation in the perfused kidney. The influence of adrenalin on the volume of the perfused kidney. Amer. J. Physiol., 1922, 59:184–190.

15. SHANNON, J. A. Glomerular filtration and urea excretion in relation to urine flow in the dog. Amer. J. Physiol., 1936, 117:206–225.

16. SMITH, H. W. Lectures on the kidney. Lawrence, University of Kansas [1943]. 134 pp.*

17. SMITH, H. W. The physiology of the kidney. New York, Oxford University Press, [1937]. 310 pp.

18. SMITH, H. W. Studies in the physiology of the kidney. Lawrence, University of Kansas, 1939. 106 pp.*

19. SMITH, W. W. and SMITH, H. W. Protein binding of phenol red, diodrast, and other substances in plasma. J. biol. Chem., 1938, 124:107–113.

20. TIGERSTEDT, R. and BERGMAN, P. G. Niere und Kreislauf. Skand. Arch. Physiol., 1898, 8:223–271.

21. VAN SLYKE, D. D., HILLER, A. and MILLER, B. F. The clearance, extraction percentage and estimated filtration of sodium ferrocyanide in the mammalian kidney. Comparison with inulin, creatinine and urea. Amer. J. Physiol., 1935, 113:611–628.

22. WARREN, J. V., MERRILL, A. J. and BRANNON, E. S. Observations on renal venous blood in normal unanesthetized subjects and patients with severe congestive heart failure. J. clin. Invest., 1944, 23:928.

23. WINTON, F. R. Physical factors involved in the activities of the mammalian kidney. Physiol. Rev., 1937, 17:408–435.

* The three Porter Lectures (18) are included in revised form with the two Welch Lectures (16).

SECTION VIII

PHYSIOLOGY OF DIGESTION AND SECRETION OF THE ALIMENTARY TRACT

BY GEORGE R. COWGILL

CHAPTER 45

GENERAL FUNCTIONS OF THE ALIMENTARY TRACT

The living body is characterized by the property of being able to take in various kinds of matter and make them over to become a part of the organism itself. This involves: (i) the mechanical disintegration of food masses; (ii) thorough mixing of the small particles thus obtained with digestive juices to render them soluble; (iii) chemical breakdown by hydrolytic enzymes of the large molecules of proteins, poly- and disaccharides, and lipids to yield smaller molecules that can be absorbed and utilized by the body; (iv) the solution of these products of digestion, and of the inorganic salts and organic extractives of the foods in the digestive fluids; (v) the absorption of these many substances in solution by the intestinal epithelium; and finally, (vi) the excretion of waste materials which accumulate in the large intestine. These many processes take place in the alimentary tract which is essentially a tube provided with a muscular wall, lined with glandular epithelium and here and there provided with openings through which the secretions of accessory glands are discharged to perform their respective digestive functions in the lumen of the tube. Study of the physiology of the alimentary tract requires, therefore, that consideration be given to each of these particular processes. The first of these may properly be discussed under the general heading of movements of the alimentary canal which includes not only the mechanical disintegration of the ingested food masses but the mechanical processes by which food masses are moved through the canal and related phenomena.

MOVEMENTS OF THE ALIMENTARY CANAL

Mastication. Mastication is an entirely voluntary act occurring in the mouth through the cooperation of the muscles of the jaw and the teeth. The articulation of the mandibles with the skull permits a variety of movements; the jaw may be raised and lowered, may be projected and retracted, or may be moved from side to side, or various combinations of these different directions of movement may be effected. The muscles concerned in these movements and their innervation are described as follows: The masseter, temporal, and internal pterygoids raise the jaw; these muscles are innervated through the inferior maxillary division of the trigeminal. The jaw is depressed mainly by the action of the digastric muscle, assisted in some cases by the mylohyoid and the geniohyoid. The two former receive motor fibers from the inferior maxillary division of the fifth cranial, the last from a branch of the hypoglossal. The lateral movements of the jaws are produced by the external pterygoids, when acting separately. Simultaneous contraction of these muscles on both sides causes projection of the lower jaw. In this latter case forcible retraction of the jaw is produced by the contraction of a part of the temporal muscle. The external pterygoids also receive their motor fibers from the fifth cranial nerve, through its inferior maxillary division. The grinding movements commonly used in masticating the food between the molar teeth are produced by a combination of the action of the external pterygoids, the elevators, and perhaps the depressors. At the same time the movements of the tongue and of the muscles of the cheeks and lips serve to keep the food properly placed for the action of the teeth, and to gather it into position for the act of swallowing.

In certain studies the average size of the mouthful proved to be about 5 ml. The weight of the mass after mastication was from 3.2 to 6.5 grams; about one-fourth of this weight was due to the saliva secreted during the masticatory act. Examination revealed that the mass was full of particles most of which were less than 2 mm. in diameter, with some, however, measuring as much as 7 to 12 mm. It is obvious that data of this sort can be only roughly approximate because people vary so much in the degree to which they chew their food before swallowing it. Some animals, notably certain carnivores, swallow relatively large pieces of food without much mastication; on the other hand, the ruminant not only chews and swallows the raw food but is provided with a mechanism for regurgitating such a swallowed mass and rechewing it. These extremes can obviously cover a wide range of size of individual particles to be found in the chewed mass. Appropriate sensory nerve endings in the tongue, gums, and cheek play a role in determining when the proper degree of fineness of the food has been reached, and this is related to ease of swallowing. It is very difficult to swallow a dry bolus. From this it is evident that mixing of the food mass with saliva is important. An additional fact of interest concerns the presence of taste organs in the mouth and olfactory nerve endings in the nasal passages. These sensory endings are stimulated by the food mass as it is moved about in the mouth and its various odoriferous substances are thereby released. It is now known that the sensation of "taste" involves not only stimulation of the so-called taste buds in the mouth but has an olfactory component as well.

Some faddists have assumed that prolonged chewing of food has great value because of the larger amount of saliva secreted and therefore more complete digestion of the food mass. Two considerations may be cited against this view. Salivary digestion continues in the stomach for about a half hour after the first bolus enters the stomach. This is because each succeeding bolus as it enters the stomach tends to lie in the center of the preceding one, and requires about half an hour to become the outside layer in contact with the gastric mucosa, at which time it is mixed with the acid gastric juice, and the salivary enzyme which it contains is inactivated. The second fact of interest is that fluids leave the stomach sooner than semifluid and relatively solid material. Too prolonged chewing means that only highly fluid material reaches the stomach; since it leaves the viscus sooner, it is possible that there would be some failure of desired gastric digestion. This is well illustrated by the observations of Childrey, Alvarez and Mann (22) on dogs and those of Gianturco (32) on cats. Dogs have been observed to digest meat more completely when swallowed in large pieces than when ingested in a finely ground form (22). In cats fed lumps of meat mixed with barium Gianturco (32) noticed by an x-ray technique that such lumps were held in the stomach for a considerable period and slowly dissolved away. When ground meat was given, however, it passed quickly from the stomach into the intestine with presumably only slight digestion by the gastric juice.

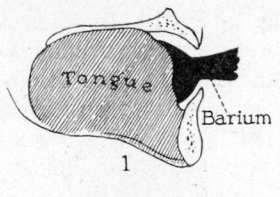

A series of retouched tracings of x-ray films showing the movements of the tongue in swallowing.

1. The tip of the tongue is depressed and the barium accumulates above and in front of the tip and behind the teeth

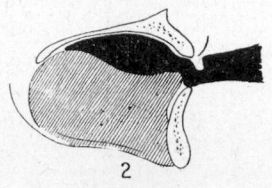

2. The tip of the tongue comes up and the dorsum of the tongue sinks.

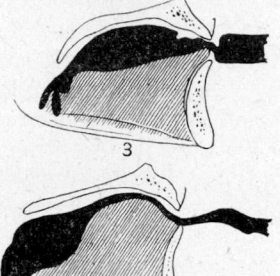

3. The tip of the tongue remains up. The dorsum and the base sink. The dorsum of the tongue becomes an inclined plane which slants downward from before backward.

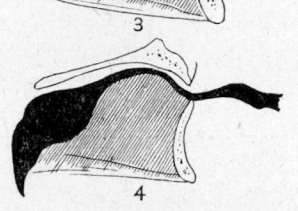

4. The anterior half of the tongue rises as a globular mass to the roof of the mouth. The base of the tongue is depressed further. The patient now has the maximum mouthful.

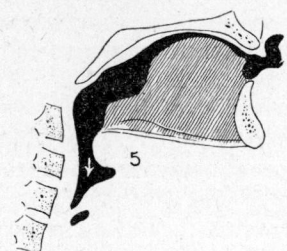

5. The anterior half of the tongue remains at the roof of the mouth. The posterior half and the base of the tongue rise and are seen under the fluoroscope to shoot suddenly backward, driving the barium quickly down the pharynx.

Fig. 447.—The movements of the tongue at the beginning of the swallowing act. (From Mosher, *Laryngoscope*, St. Louis, 1927, *37*:237.)

Some measurements have been made of the force exerted during crushing and chewing. By means of an instrument invented for the purpose, Black (8) determined that the molars come together usually with a force of from 100 to 160 pounds; in the case of the incisors the force was from 30 to 80 pounds. In order to crack hazelnuts a force of from 115 to 173 pounds is required. According to Triska (78), dogs, when chewing bones, exert a pressure as high as 165 kg. (366 pounds) on each 10 sq. mm. of surface.

Deglutition. The act of swallowing is a complicated reflex movement which may be initiated voluntarily but is, for the most part completed quite independently of the will. The classical description of the act given by Magendie divides it into three stages, corresponding to the three anatomical regions— mouth, pharynx, and esophagus—through which the swallowed morsel passes on its way to the stomach. The *first stage*, which is voluntary in nature, consists in the passage of the bolus of food through the isthmus of the fauces —that is, the opening lying between the ridges formed by the palatoglossi muscles, the so-called anterior pillars of the fauces. The masticated food is formed into a bolus by the action of the tongue against the palate and at the same time lubricated by mixing with saliva, then moved toward the back of the mouth by elevation of the front of the tongue (Fig. 447). Moistening of the food morsel by the saliva is very important: it is exceedingly difficult or impossible to swallow dry material. Mosher (62) has published interesting details of the movements of the tongue, epiglottis and hyoid bone in swallowing, revealed in a roentgenologic study. An important result of the elevation of the front of the tongue is to prevent escape of the bolus through the oral opening. The sudden contraction and backward movement of the posterior half of the tongue also serves to force the bolus through the pharynx into the upper end of the esophagus. Barclay (5) believes that an additional factor assisting the movement of the bolus through the pharynx is suction, the negative pressure resulting from an elevation of the larynx and the backward movement of the tongue. It is evident that any factor which interferes with these movements of the tongue or the moistening of the bolus by appropriate secretion of saliva can operate to produce *dysphagia in the first stage* of swallowing.

The *second stage of swallowing*, a purely involuntary process, is fundamentally a complicated coordinated reflex act by which the bolus is passed through the pharynx into the esophagus. The whole act is very rapid as well as complex, so that not more than about one-fifth of a second elapses between the beginning of the contraction of the mylohyoids and the entrance of food into the upper end of the esophagus. The nervous mechanisms involved in this reflex are sensitive receptors located in various parts of the pharynx and back of the mouth, particularly the anterior pillars which are most sensitive, and after them the posterior pillars (Fig. 448), a swallowing center located in the medulla oblongata close to the respiratory center, and effectors located in various muscles of the pharynx and larynx. When food is passed through the pharynx into the upper esophagus, it is important that certain openings into other passages be closed. The mouth cavity is shut off by the position of the tongue against the palate and by the contraction of the muscles of the anterior pillars of the fauces. The opening into the nasal cavity is closed by the elevation of the soft palate (action of the levator palati and tensor palati muscles) and the contraction of the posterior pillars of the fauces (palatopharyngeal muscles) and the elevation of the uvula (azygos uvulae muscle). The soft palate, uvula, and posterior pillars thus form a sloping surface shutting off the nasal chamber and facilitating the passage of the food backward through the pharynx. The respiratory opening into the larynx is closed by the adduction of the vocal cords (lateral crico-arytenoids and constrictors of the glottis) and by the strong elevation of the entire larynx. If the elevation of the larynx is prevented, by fixation of the thyroid for example, the act of swallowing becomes impossible. There is also at this time, apparently as a regular part of the swallowing reflex, a slight inspiratory movement of the diaphragm, the so-called respiration of swallowing. The movements of the epiglottis during this stage of swallowing have been much discussed; authorities do not agree on the details concerning this matter. Formerly it was believed that the epiglottis is pressed down upon the laryngeal orifice like the lid of a box, thus effectually protecting the respiratory passage. Most recent observers incline to the view that it is not necessary for the protection of the larynx that the epiglottis be actually folded down over it by the contraction of its own muscles; x-ray examinations indicate, on the contrary, that it retains its upright position. The forcible lifting of the larynx, together with the descent of the base of the tongue, effects the same results

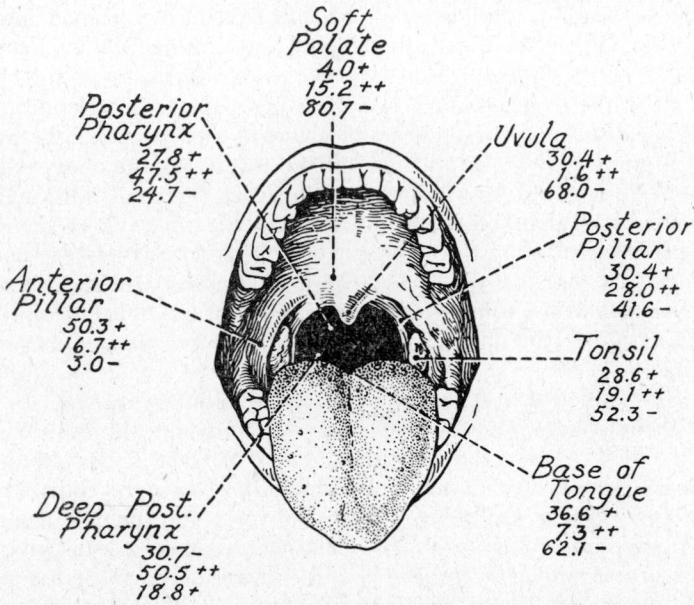

Fig. 448.—A study of the sensory areas eliciting the swallowing reflex. (After Pommerenke, from Bard's *Macleod's Physiology in modern medicine*, 9th ed. St. Louis, C. V. Mosby Co., 1941.)

by mechanically crowding the parts together, and the larynx is still further guarded by the approximation of the false and true vocal cords, thus closing the glottis. Any factor that interferes in the operation of this reflex can obviously cause *dysphagia in the second stage*. Injuries to the nervous and muscular elements involved in the reflex are common causes. Such dysphagia can also be the result of the application of anesthetics to the areas in the back of the mouth and pharynx provided with the receptors, and mechanical failure of various passages to close because of loss of tissue through operation, gunshot wounds and the like.

The *third stage of swallowing* deals with the passage of the food bolus along the esophagus and through the cardiac sphincter into the stomach. The mechanism by which food passes along the esophagus depends to some extent on the physical consistency of the swallowed material. Long ago (1883) Kronecker and Meltzer (48, 58) showed that when the food is liquid or very soft, it is shot through the whole length of the esophagus by the force of the initial act of swallowing, arriving at the lower end of the esophagus in about 0.1 second, and may then pass immediately into the stomach or lie some moments in the esophagus according to the conditions controlling the opening of the cardiac orifice. On the basis of his more recent observations, Greving (35) reached essentially the same conclusions. When, however, food is solid or semisolid, as was shown by Cannon and Moser (15), it is forced down the esophagus by a peristaltic movement of the musculature. The upper portion of the esophagus contains cross-striated fibers indicating rapid contractions; the lower end consists of smooth muscle only, while the intermediate portion is a mixture of the two varieties. The circular muscles are constricted from above downward by an advancing muscular wave. The peristaltic wave takes about five or six seconds to reach the stomach, and on its arrival the cardiac sphincter, which ordinarily is contracted, relaxes and permits the bolus to pass into the stomach. There are some species differences in this respect. For example, in the dog cross-striated muscle fibers are found throughout the entire length of the esophagus, and therefore the peristaltic wave moves much more rapidly and at a uniform rate all the way. In those species that drink with the head down it is evident that both the squirting action in swallowing and the peristaltic mechanism play important roles even against the force of gravity. In man gravity plays a role because Schreiber (75) showed that when the persons being studied tried to swallow while standing on their heads, the barium mixture could not be passed into the stomach; it merely lodged in the esophagus and the upper edge of the column approached the cardia but it did not pass through. Palugyay (66, 67) showed that when patients are put in the Trendelenburg position material passes through the esophagus seven times more slowly than normal.

The peristaltic wave is not a simple conduction of contractions from one portion of the muscular wall to another but involves an extrinsic nervous mechanism. It begins as part of the response to sensory stimulation of receptors in the back of the mouth and pharynx (Fig. 448). Existence of the extrinsic nervous mechanism is proved by experiments of Mosso (63) where, after removal of an entire segment from the esophagus, the peristaltic wave passed in due time to the portion of the esophagus left on the stomach side, in spite of the anatomical break. A striking proof of this fact is seen in the case cited by von Mikulicz of a man in whom a portion of the esophagus had been resected on account of a carcinoma. The lower end of the esophagus was given a fistulous opening in the neck and it was found that food introduced into this opening was not moved toward the stomach until the patient made a swallowing movement (60). The afferent nerves concerned in this reflex are the sensory fibers to the mucous membrane of the pharynx and esophagus, including branches of the glossopharyngeal, trigeminal, vagus, and superior laryngeal division of the vagus. Artificial stimulation of this last nerve in the lower animals is known to produce swallowing movements. If the esophageal branches of the vagus nerve are sectioned but the muscular coats left intact, the esophagus becomes dilated above the level of the cut and contracted below, and no peristaltic wave can pass along. If the muscular wall is crushed or otherwise injured, the peristaltic wave will start, reach the site of the injury, and after an appropriate interval reappear in the intact muscle beyond the injury, provided the nerves remain intact. In the lower part of the esophagus where the muscle fibers are of the smooth muscle variety, the wave of peristalsis moves along independently of extrinsic nerve as is the case in the intestines. The difference between the upper and lower parts is thus related to the difference in the type of muscular fibers and their innervation.

Reference has already been made to a swallowing center located in the medulla just above that of respiration. These centers are doubtless connected because during swallowing the respiratory center is inhibited for a moment. The glossopharyngeal nerve carries afferent fibers which can exercise a profound inhibitory influence on the swallowing center. If swallowing movements are begun by stimulating the central end of the cut superior laryngeal nerve, they can be instantly inhibited by simultaneous stimulation of the glossopharyngeal, and this inhibition extends to the respiratory center as well—the respiratory movements stopping in whatever stage they may be at the time. If the glossopharyngeal nerves are cut, a tonic contraction of the esophagus ensues which may last several days. From this it is evident that the inhibiting impulses are acting continuously over these nerves. The swallowing center receives impulses from the afferent nerves already mentioned. The motor fibers concerned in the reflex comprise the hypoglossal, the trigeminal, the glossopharyngeal, the vagus, and the spinal accessory nerves.

In addition to the main reflex already discussed, certain secondary reflexes exist, called forth by stimulation of sensory fibers in the esophageal wall. These stimuli lead to reflex contraction of the musculature above the bolus, and thus the liberation of a series of reflexes which are sufficient to move the bolus downward. If the primary reflex initiated at the beginning of the swallow proves inefficient, and only succeeds in forcing the bolus into the upper portion of the esophagus, then this secondary or accessory mechanism comes into play and insures the transportation of the bolus to the stomach. In this series of secondary reflexes, as in the more complicated primary reflex, the vagus nerve forms a part of the path and the reflex center lies, therefore, in the medulla.

Any factor that can interfere in the passage of the bolus through the esophagus can cause *dysphagia in the third stage*. These may be injuries to the nerve paths involved, or purely mechanical in nature such as an enlarged thyroid gland, neoplasms, an aneurysm, the traction exerted by scar tissue pulling the esophagus to one side thus making passage of the bolus difficult, and the stenosis following ulceration due to the swallowing of corrosive poisons.

Cardiac Sphincter. At the cardia or cardiac orifice the circular layer of muscle acts as a sphincter. When the stomach is empty this sphincter is thrown into tone, and thus shuts off the gastric cavity from the esophagus. This tone is controlled by the vagus nerve, stimulation of which causes relaxation followed by strong contraction. The vagus carries inhibitory adrenergic fibers to the sphincter whereas the splanchnics supply excitatory cholinergic fibers, stimulation of which can bring about cardiospasm (9). In addition, the sphincter is supplied from the intrinsic plexus (plexus of Auerbach), which, as elsewhere in the alimentary canal, seems to be capable of regulating the movements of the musculature independently of the extrinsic nerves. Cannon (14) believed that the tonic contraction of the sphincter which occurs when the stomach contains food is maintained by a reflex through the intrinsic plexus, the stimulus initiating the reflex being due to the free hydrochloric acid present in the gastric secretion. Regurgitation of food into the esophagus occurs only when the intragastric pressure is fairly high. The material thus escaping into the esophagus stimulates a peristaltic wave which pushes it back into the stomach. Since this wave starts in the absence of other phases of the swallowing process, it is doubtless due, or at least related, to the secondary reflexes in the lower esophagus already described.

Anatomy of the Stomach. The stomach in man belongs to the simple type as distinguished from the compound stomachs of some of the other mam-

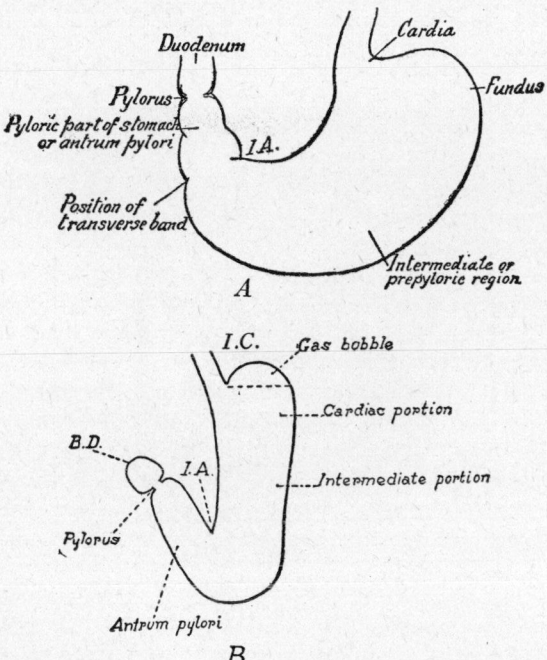

Fig. 449.—*A*, the shape and parts of the stomach as usually represented: *I.A.*, the incisura angularis. *B*, the shape and position of the stomach in the upright position as shown by the x-ray: *I.A.*, the incisura angularis; *I.C.*, the incisura cardiaca; *B.D.*, the duodenal bulb.

malia—the ruminating animals, for example. Physiological and histological investigations have shown, however, that the so-called simple stomachs are divided into parts that have different properties and functions. The shape and relations of the stomach in man vary somewhat with the posture and the amount of food. According to the conventional description which is derived from dissection of the cadaver, the organ occupies an obliquely transverse position in the abdomen (Fig. 449). It may be divided into two main portions, the fundus and the antrum pylori or pyloric part, the line of division being indicated on the smaller curvature by a fissure, the incisura angularis. The fundus forms the dilated rounded portion extending from the esophagus to the incisura, and it may be subdivided further into the cardiac part, lying around the opening of the esophagus, and the intermediate part, between the cardiac region and the incisura. The fundic and pyloric parts differ in the structure of the mucous membrane, in the character of the muscular coat (that of the pylorus being stronger), and in the character of their physiological activity during digestion.

In the upright position and filled with food the stomach, according to the description of the roentgenologists (21, 44), occupies a more vertical position and has a tubular shape, as represented in Figures 449 and 450, the lower pole lying in the region of the umbilicus. The esophagus enters the stomach at an angle, and the pyloric part makes quite a sharp angle with the fundus at the incisura, giving what is called the fish-hook shape. At the cardiac pole of the stomach there is usually a collection of gas, said to be mainly swallowed air. The portion of the duodenum just beyond the pylorus seems to be a specialized part to receive and retain for a time the food as it is discharged from the stomach. It is given the name of duodenal bulb or pyloric cap (Fig. 450).

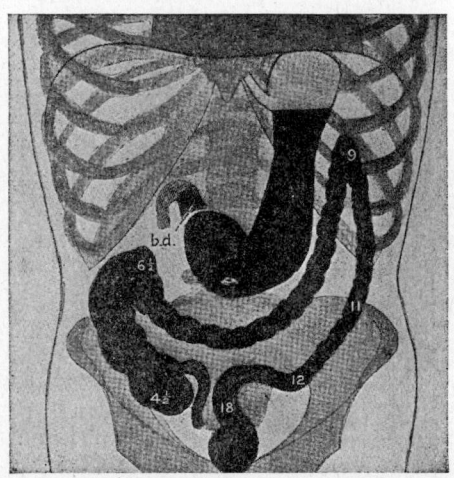

Fig. 450.—The stomach, duodenal bulb (*b.d.*), and the large intestine. The figures along the large intestine indicate the time after the ingestion of a meal when the food reaches the different parts of the colon. (From Hurst.)

Musculature of the Stomach. The musculature of the stomach is usually divided into three layers—a longitudinal, an oblique, and a circular coat. The longitudinal coat is external and is continuous at the cardia with the longitudinal fibers of the esophagus; it spreads out from this point along the length of the stomach, forming a layer of varying thickness; along the curvatures the layer is stronger than on the front and posterior surfaces, while at the pyloric end it increases considerably in thickness, and passes over the pylorus to be continued directly into the longitudinal coat of the duodenum. The layer of oblique fibers is quite incomplete; it seems to be continuous with the circular fibers of the esophagus and spreads out from the cardia for a certain distance over the front and posterior surfaces of the fundus of the stomach, but toward the pyloric end disappears, seeming to pass into the circular fibers. The circular coat, which is placed between the two preceding layers, is the thickest and most important part of the musculature of the stomach. At the fundus the circular bands are thin and somewhat loosely placed, but toward the pyloric end they increase much in thickness, forming a strong, muscular mass, which, as we shall see, plays the most important part in the movements of the stomach. At the pylorus itself a special development of this layer functions as a sphincter pylori, which with the aid of a circular fold of the mucous membrane makes it possible to shut off the duodenum completely from the cavity of the stomach. The line of separation between the antrum pylori and the body of the stomach is made by a special thickening of the circular fibers which forms a structure known as the "transverse band" by the older writers (7). Under certain conditions, such as vomiting, stimulation of the vagus, etc., this band may be contracted with such force as to separate the antrum entirely from the fundic end of the stomach.

Movements of the Stomach. The solid food remains in the stomach for several hours, and during this time the musculature contracts in such a way that the thinner portions as they are formed by digestion are ejected from time to time through the pylorus into the intestine. Except at the definite intervals when the pyloric sphincter relaxes, the food is entirely shut off from the rest of the alimentary canal by the tonic closure of the sphincters at the cardia and the pylorus. There is a certain orderliness in the movements of the stomach, and especially in the separation and ejection of the more liquid from the solid parts, which shows the existence of a specially adapted mechanism. These movements have been studied by many investigators, making use of various experimental methods. The first noteworthy contributions to this subject were those made in this country by Beaumont in his famous observations upon Alexis St. Martin, the Canadian voyageur, who had a permanent fistulous opening in his stomach as the result of a gunshot wound (65). In recent years the subject has been studied with great success by means of the x-rays (11, 74), on the excised stomach, and by means of tambours or sounds introduced into the stomach to measure the pressure changes (61). These researches all unite in emphasizing one fundamental point—namely, that the fundic end of the stomach is less actively concerned in these movements but serves rather as a reservoir for retaining the bulk of the food, while the muscular pyloric region is the apparatus which mainly triturates the food and forces it out from time to time into the duodenum. According to the observations made with the x-ray apparatus, movements begin a few minutes after the entrance of food into the stomach. Small contractions start in the middle region of the stomach and run toward the pylorus. These moving waves of contraction appear at regular intervals. The pyloric portion becomes lengthened and it may be noticed that in this region the peristaltic waves become more and more forcible as digestion progresses. These running waves or rings of contraction serve to press the stomach contents against the pylorus. According to Cannon, they occur in the cat at intervals of 10 seconds and each wave requires about 20 seconds to reach the pylorus. In man, the human stomach undergoes a succession of rapid changes in shape (Fig. 451), due to the peristaltic waves which pass over it toward the pylorus. Cole (23, 24, 25) calls the period of gastric activity intervening between a phase of complete relaxation and the reappearance of this phase a gastric cycle. Several cycles may occur during the passage of a wave. Cole believed four cycles to be the most common type, but Alvarez reports the three-cycle as being most frequent in his experience. Individuals who show the rapid one-cycle type of wave are very rare. The passage of an individual cycle takes from 2 to 3 seconds. Therefore the time required for the passage of a four-cycle type of wave from its origin to the pyloric sphincter will be from 8 to 12 seconds; it rarely exceeds 10 seconds. The obvious result of these movements is to mix the food thoroughly, in the intermediate and pyloric portions of the stomach, with the acid gastric juice and to reduce it to a thin liquid mass—the chyme. At certain intervals the pyloric sphincter relaxes and the contraction wave squeezes some of the fluid contents into the duodenum.

The stomach thus serves as a reservoir into which a large amount of food can be placed at once, or within a short period, there to be reduced to a liquid or semiliquid condition, partly by digestion, partly mechanically, and then periodically discharged into the intestine in small amounts. Dogs in which the entire stomach has been removed, the esophagus being sutured to the duodenum, when eating for the first time after the operation show signs

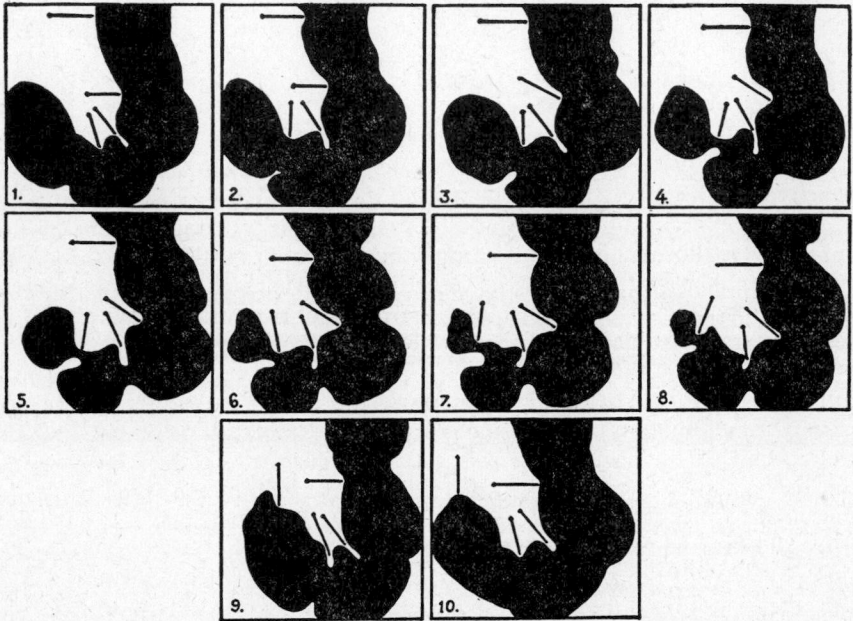

Fig. 451.—Illustration of a gastric cycle. Drawings made from skiagrams of the human stomach taken at intervals after food. (After Cole, from Bard's *Macleod's Physiology in modern medicine*, 9th ed. St. Louis, C. V. Mosby Co., 1941.)

of distress and immediately change their eating habits. Instead of bolting their food they learn to consume it very slowly over a period of many hours (45). Evidently one important function of the stomach is to protect the intestine from receiving too large quantities of material at any one time. The ability of the stomach to adapt itself to large amounts of food has been shown to be quite remarkable. What really happens is that the stomach expands sufficiently to accommodate the mass without at the same time appreciably increasing the pressure exerted on it. Grey (36) made measurements of the intragastric pressure when the stomach of the living animal is distended by fluid and observed that even when the organ was distended to the point of rupture, the intragastric pressure showed very little change. The excised stomach was found to lose this adaptive power in considerable degree.

Innervation and Movements of the Stomach. The stomach receives nerve fibers from two sources—the vagi and the splanchnics—but its orderly movements are merely regulated through these extrinsic fibers and the details of this regulation are only imperfectly understood. McSwiney (55) and Alvarez (2) have reviewed the extensive literature dealing with this question. The essentially automatic character of the organ is well illustrated by the fact that the excised stomach, when kept warm, continues to execute regular movements which, if not identical with those observed under normal conditions, have at least an orderly sequence. Also, many investigators—older workers like Heidenhain (40) and Cannon (13), and more recently McCrea, McSwiney and Stopford (53, 54)—have observed that gastric digestion may proceed normally both as regards secretion and movements after section of the extrinsic nerves. We may regard the stomach, considered as a motor mechanism, as an automatic organ like the heart. Its stimuli to movement arise within itself, probably within its intrinsic nerve plexus, but these movements are regulated by the action of the extrinsic nerve fibers so as to adapt them to varying conditions. The extrinsic nerves not only supply the stomach with afferent fibers, motor and secretory, but also carry afferent fibers from the stomach to the central nervous system. Regarding the purely efferent action of the extrinsic nerves, the results of numerous experiments seem to show that in general the fibers received along the vagus path are motor, artificial stimulation of them causing more or less well-marked contractions of part or all of the musculature of the stomach. It has been shown that the sphincter pylori as well as the rest of the musculature is supplied by motor fibers from these nerves. The fibers coming through the splanchnics, on the contrary, are mainly inhibitory. When stimulated they cause a dilatation of the contracted stomach and a relaxation of the sphincter pylori. This division of function between the two nerves does not seem, however, to be complete (55). According to present information, inhibitory effects may be obtained from stimulation of the vagi and motor effects from the sympathetic nerves. Whether one effect or the other is obtained from either nerve appears to be influenced by the condition of tonus in the stomach. Through the reflex activity of these nerves the movements of the stomach may be influenced, favorably or unfavorably, by conditions directly or indirectly affecting the central nervous system. Cannon, in his observations upon cats, found that all movements of the stomach ceased as soon as the animal showed signs of anxiety, rage or distress.

Effects of Stomach Movements on Food. When food enters the stomach, the organ expands sufficiently to accommodate the mass and maintains fairly steady tonic contractions on which are soon superimposed the peristaltic waves already described. Grützner (37) successively fed to rats morsels of food of different colors. After a short period the animals were sacrificed, and the stomach frozen and sectioned. The colored materials were found to be in layers for which a simple explanation is at hand. Each swallowed bolus, when entering the stomach, tends to lodge in the center of the material already there. This is illustrated in Figure 452. It is evident that the material at the fundic end may remain undisturbed for a long time and thus escape mixture with the acid gastric juice, so far at least as the interior of the mass is concerned. This explains the observation that salivary digestion of starchy foods can proceed in the stomach for approximately half an hour after the food has been swallowed. As the outer layers of food are digested, the food is slowly forced into the more active pyloric antrum from which it soon is moved on to the pylorus and then into the small intestine. These phenomena seen in experimental animals have also been observed in man. Studies have been made of the time required for colored material, given after the swallow-

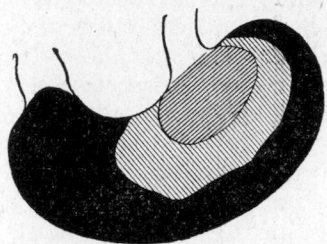

Fig. 452.—Section of frozen stomach of rat during digestion to show the stratification of food given at different times. The food was given in three portions and colored differently: first, black; second, white (indicated by vertical marking); third, red (indicated by transverse marking). (From Grützner, *Pflüg. Arch. ges. Physiol.,* 1905, *106:*463.)

ing of a test meal, to appear in the pyloric region as revealed by removal through a stomach tube. Approximately twenty minutes were required. Furthermore, material removed from the cardiac end was lumpy whereas that from the pyloric end was semifluid and homogeneous in nature.

Hunger Contractions. After the stomach has been empty for a certain time we experience sensations of hunger that are more or less of a subpainful

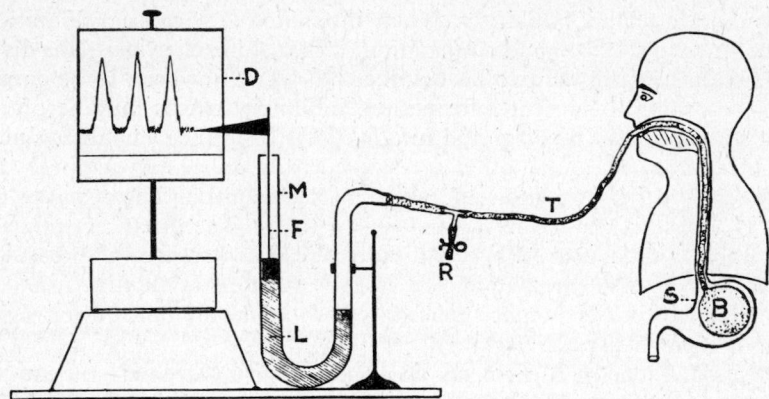

Fig. 453.—Diagram showing method of recording gastric hunger contractions of the empty stomach of normal persons. *B,* rubber balloon in stomach. *D,* kymograph. *F,* cork float with recording flag. *M,* manometer. *L,* manometer fluid (bromoform, chloroform or water). *R,* rubber tube connecting balloon with manometer. *S,* stomach. *T,* side tube for inflation of stomach balloon. (From Carlson, *The control of hunger in health and disease.* Chicago, University of Chicago Press, 1916.)

character. Cannon and Washburn (16) were the first to show that these sensations appear simultaneously with contractions of the stomach, and they suggested that these contractions cause the pangs of hunger. Washburn swallowed a thin-walled rubber balloon fastened on the end of a tube. The balloon was then moderately distended with air and connected with a suitable manometer and recording device. By this technique contractions of the fundus of the stomach could be permanently recorded (Fig. 453). In addition, a timing record was obtained as well as a record of a hunger pang experienced by the subject who pressed a key at the appropriate moment. "In order to avoid any error that might arise from artificial pressure on the balloon, a pneumograph fastened below the ribs, was made to record the movements of the abdominal wall. Uniformity of these movements would show that no special contractions of the abdominal muscles were made" (see Fig. 203 in Chap. 19). Examination of the records revealed that what the subject called a "hunger pang" occurred simultaneously with such contractions, hence the term "hunger contractions." These particular movements were further investigated by Carlson (19) who had the good fortune to be able to make numerous observations on a man with a permanent gastric fistula (known in the literature as Mr. V). Carlson and Luckhardt (19) also subjected themselves to complete starvation for four days. It has long been known that during prolonged starvation normal persons at first experience intense sensations of hunger which last, however, for only a few days, then become less

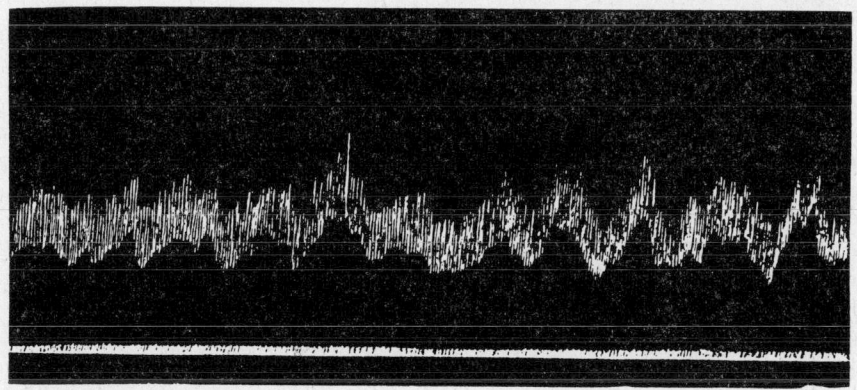

Fig. 454.—Tracing showing the tonus rhythm of the stomach (man) after a meal. (From Carlson, *The control of hunger in health and disease*. Chicago, University of Chicago Press, 1916.)

pronounced and finally disappear almost entirely. The observations which Carlson and Luckhardt made in their four-day fast confirmed this: the tonus and also the frequency and intensity of the contractions of the empty stomach became progressively more pronounced in the course of the starvation. The appetite for food paralleled very well the sensation of hunger, and both of these sensations were perceptibly diminished on the fourth or last day of the fast. On this last day a distinct repugnance or indifference toward food was experienced. On eating food the sensations of hunger disappeared rapidly. Complete recovery from a sense of general weakness did not occur, however, until the second or third day after breaking the fast. The results of this study support the view that these contractions of the stomach can truly be called hunger contractions (see also Chap. 19, p. 386).

When the balloon is placed in the empty stomach of a normal person, the record shows four types of waves. One is due to the arterial pulse and another to respiratory movements. The fact that the apparatus responds to the pressure changes due to these causes constitutes good proof of its sensitivity. The third type of wave has been called the *tonus rhythm* (Fig. 454) and is caused by contractions of the fundus; these are not usually interpreted subjectively as hunger pangs. The fourth type of contraction is most significant and consists of periods of relatively powerful rhythmic contractions which alternate with periods of quiescence. Each individual contraction of this type lasts for about thirty seconds and may be superimposed upon the tonus rhythm; it is subjectively interpreted as "hunger." These contractions occur usually in series, the number in a period varying from about 20 to as many as 70. The series begins with comparatively feeble contractions with long intervening pauses. Finally the pauses disappear and the contractions become more pronounced. In some instances, more often in young individuals, they may finally become so pronounced as to result in a virtual tetanus lasting several minutes. The duration of the entire hunger period—series of hunger contractions—can vary from about half an hour to as long as one and a half hours; the average is from 30 to 45 or 50 minutes.

Carlson and Ginsburg (20) found that the "empty stomach of the newborn infant shows the periods of gastric hunger contractions before the infant has had any experience with food. The hunger periods are more frequent in the infant than in the adult . . . in the newborn and very young infant the quiescence of the empty stomach lasts from ten to sixty minutes; in the adult usually from one to three hours." During sleep the contractions could be so vigorous as to produce signs of restlessness followed in some instances by an awakening and crying. Observations made on 30 normal breast-fed infants from 24 hours to four weeks old, suggest, according to Carlson, that the stomach of a normal infant is ready to receive food from two to three hours after the previous nursing, these being the minimum and maximum times of onset of the hunger contractions. It is reasonable to suggest that these observations have some bearing on the pediatric question as to how often the infant should be fed. It is important to note in this connection that the infants studied by Carlson were found to show considerable variation in this respect. These hunger contractions are of wide occurrence, having been recorded by Carlson and his students in many animals including the cat, dog, rabbit, guinea pig, bird, frog and turtle; however, certain differences in type are noted in these different animals.

It should not be supposed that these tonus and hunger contractions appear only when the stomach is practically empty of food. The only period when the fundus does not exhibit them is immediately after a large meal. When a moderate meal has been eaten the tonus rhythm reappears in about 30 minutes. It gradually increases in intensity until the stomach has nearly emptied itself, at which time the tonus is quite conspicuous; the hunger contractions now begin to appear. From this it is evident that man can experience hunger pangs even when the stomach still contains some food. As the stomach empties itself after a meal the peristaltic waves of contraction arise nearer and nearer to the cardiac end and pass over gradually into the hunger contractions characteristic of the empty stomach (73). In experimental animals Carlson was able to show that the hunger contractions of the empty stomach occur after complete isolation from the brain and spinal cord but at longer intervals and with less vigor. The possible role of chemical changes in the blood is suggested by the observation that lowering of the blood sugar level by about 25 per cent through the injection of insulin is associated with the appearance of vigorous hunger contractions which are abolished promptly by the injection of glucose. It is well known that individuals who have received too much insulin experience pronounced hunger contractions. Various stimuli acting on sensory nerves can affect the hunger contractions. The tasting and chewing of palatable food always produces inhibition of the tonus and a diminution or disappearance of the hunger contractions. Even the chewing of an indifferent substance like paraffin can produce a distinct inhibition unless the contraction has become tetanic in nature. Swallowing movements, even in the absence of food in the mouth, can bring about a transitory inhibition of the gastric tonus; this has been described as a "receptive relaxation" of the stomach. Associated with such diminution in tonus and hunger contractions is a perceptible decrease in the hunger pains. Such observations constitute further support of the idea that hunger pains are due to these "hunger contractions." Stimulation of the gastric mucosa itself can also affect the hunger contractions. This was demonstrated when Carlson introduced various substances into the stomach of Mr. V., his patient. Ice-cold water was more effective in causing this inhibition than water at body temperature. Weak acids of varying strengths such as could be present in the stomach through the gastric hydrochloric acid caused a marked inhibition of the contractions but this inhibition was only temporary, which explains the fact that the hunger movements can occur when the acid juice but no food is present, as in starvation. Weak solutions of alkali have about the effect of an equal volume of water; weak solutions of local anesthetics are without effect. Beer, wine, brandy, and diluted pure alcohol inhibit both the tonus and the contractions, the period of the inhibition varying with the volume of the beverage introduced into the stomach and its content of alcohol. These observations may seem to disagree with the rather common experience that the taking of alcoholic beverages increases the appetite. It should be remembered, however, that what is called "appetite" is undoubtedly a complex which includes many psychic elements (see Chap. 19, p. 387) in contrast to the sensation of hunger which depends upon a local mechanism in the stomach wall. Inhibition of the hunger contractions can also be brought about by the presence of various substances in the small intestine, but studies on dogs provided with a completely denervated stomach or a completely denervated autotransplanted gastric pouch show that a depressant humoral factor, a chalone, plays a role here (69). Other inhibitory factors that have been discovered are smoking, tightening of the belt, vigorous muscular exercise, and application of cold to the surface of the body. The elements of the nervous system involved in these phenomena are shown in Figure 455. According to Carlson, "The vagi nerves are the main, if not the only, afferent pathway for the gastric hunger impulses. . . . The primary hunger center is therefore the sensory nuclei of the vagi nerves in the medulla (fasciculus solitarius)." Rogers (72) showed that the hunger behavior of the decerebrated pigeon is completely abolished on removal of the optic thalami. The cortical factors in hunger are unknown.

Emptying of the Stomach. The mechanism involved in the emptying of the stomach has been studied by several techniques. Observations have been made of the behavior of the stomach of anesthetized animals the abdominal cavities of which had been opened to expose the organ. Serial radiographs have been obtained and studied. Duodenal fistulae have been produced in experimental animals and observations made of various conditions associated with the discharge of material through the pylorus. In some studies this has been combined with the use of balloons to record pressures and waves of contraction progressing through the pyloric antrum, pyloric valve and first part of the duodenum. An early view proposed by Pavlov and studied in some detail by Cannon was that the acidity of the chyme is the chief controlling factor. According to this theory, an appropriate concentration of acid on the stomach side of the pylorus causes it to open; the presence of acid on the duodenal side operates to keep it closed. Attractive as this view was, too many facts failed to harmonize with it. Water and egg white rapidly leave the stomach; individuals whose stomachs fail to

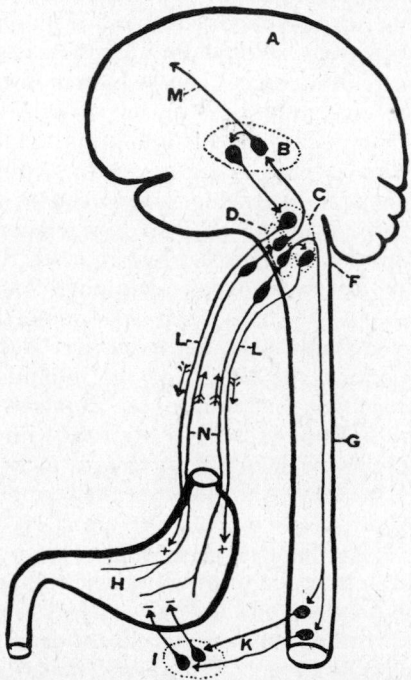

Fig. 455.—Diagram of the nervous mechanism of the hunger sense. *A*, cerebrum. *B*, optic thalami. *C*, motor nuclei of the vagi nerves. *D*, sensory nuclei of the vagi nerves. *F*, medulla oblongata. *G*, spinal cord. *H*, stomach. *I*, visceral sympathetic ganglia. *K*, splanchnic nerves. *L*, motor fibers to the stomach. *M*, sensory paths (hunger) to cerebrum (hypothetical). *N*, sensory fibers from stomach in the vagi. + indicates motor, − indicates inhibitory effects, → indicates direction of nervous conduction. (From Carlson, *The control of hunger in health and disease.* Chicago, University of Chicago Press, 1916.)

secrete acid nevertheless do achieve a suitable emptying of the organ. Acid in the stomach does not apparently cause relaxation of the sphincter. Acid in the duodenum does bring about a temporary contraction of the sphincter together with an inhibition of peristalsis, but the concentration required is greater than that usually occurring during digestion. The evidence at hand indicates that so far as the duodenal contents regulate the emptying of the stomach their effect is to be attributed to the food material of the chyme, or their digestive products, acting reflexly or through hormone production on gastric peristalsis rather than on the tonicity of the sphincter (76). It has been shown that fat in the duodenum causes inhibition of gastric movements.

Proteins or proteoses have a similar although smaller effect, and carbohydrates are still less active. These observations fall in with the fact that fats in the diet tend to prolong the emptying of the stomach.

Much evidence can be cited in support of the view that the mechanism of emptying is in some way related to the nervous one involved in gastric peristalsis. Studies of serial radiograms.(23, 24, 25) show the activities of the pyloric sphincter to be directly related to contractions of the antrum. Graphic records of pressures in the stomach combined with fluoroscopic observations (52, 81, 82) likewise have shown the discharge to be associated with the passage of a peristaltic wave over the stomach and on into the duodenum. According to Thomas, Crider and Mogan (77), the effect of duodenal stimulation on the emptying mechanism is exerted, not through reflex changes in the tonus of the sphincter, but principally through a reflex mechanism that governs the force of gastric peristalsis. Two reflexes with receptors in the duodenum are suggested by the results of their study: a local excitatory reflex identified with the myenteric reflex, and a central inhibitory reflex over the vagus designated the *enterogastric reflex*. Meschan and Quigley (59, 68) showed by means of three tandem balloons located in the pyloric antrum, pyloric sphincter and the duodenal bulb in trained unanesthetized dogs that these three regions function together as a unit and that vagotomy does not alter this relationship in any fundamental way. The inhibitory effects on emptying of various substances placed in the intestine were greatly decreased or abolished by vagotomy but these observations were interpreted to mean that such substances exert their influence through the enterogastric reflex. Another reflex of interest here is the *ileogastric reflex*. It operates when there is food in both the lower ileum and the stomach. In this situation the emptying of the stomach is slight until the ileum has passed its material on to the cecum.

The temperature of swallowed food does not appear to have any pronounced influence on either the gastric contractions or the rate of discharge through the pylorus. The presence of much gas in the stomach, however, can significantly retard the emptying by reducing the efficiency of the peristaltic waves in moving the food. X-ray observations have been made of animals in which the feeding of a standard amount of food was followed by the introduction of air. The presence of the air did not diminish the frequency or strength of the peristaltic waves but did interfere with their efficient action on the food. Some gas is usually present in the stomach and readily revealed by a bright area in the x-ray film. It is evident, then, that the presence of unusually large amounts of gas can be a factor in causing delayed emptying of the stomach.

Movements of the Small Intestine. The muscles of the small and large intestine are arranged in two layers—an outer longitudinal and an inner circular coat—and between these coats and in the submucous coat there are present the nerve plexuses of Auerbach and Meissner. The general arrangement of muscles and nerves is similar, therefore, to that prevailing in the stomach, and in accordance with this we find that the physiological activities are of much the same character, only, perhaps, not quite so complex.

Two main forms of intestinal movement have been distinguished—the pendular or rhythmic and the peristaltic.

Rhythmical movements. This consists essentially in a series of local constrictions of the intestinal wall, the constrictions occurring rhythmically at those points at which the masses of food lie.

Cannon (12) studied these movements most successfully by the x-ray technique. He observed that as a result of these contractions the masses or strings of food lying in the intestine are suddenly segmented, repeatedly and in a definite manner, into a number of small pieces, which move to and fro as the pieces combine and are again separated (see Fig. 456). These segmentations may proceed at the rate of 30 per minute for a certain time, and the apparent result is that the material is well mixed with the digestive secretions and is brought thoroughly into contact with the absorptive walls. During these rhythmical contractions there is no steady progression of the food; it remains in the same region, although subjected to repeated divisions. From time to time the separated pieces are caught by an advancing peristaltic wave, moved forward a certain distance, and gathered again into a new mass. In this new location the rhythmical contractions again segment and churn the mass before a new peristaltic wave moves it on. According to this description, the rhythmical movements are local contractions (mainly of the circular muscles) which seem to be due to the local distension caused

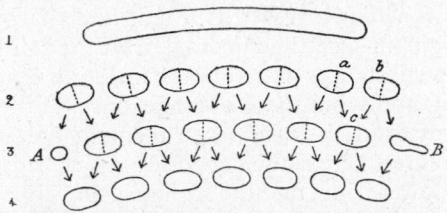

Fig. 456.—Diagram to show the effect of the rhythmical constricting movements of the small intestine upon the contained food. A string of food, 1, is divided suddenly into a series of segments, 2; each of the latter is again divided and the process is repeated a number of times, 3 and 4. Eventually a peristaltic wave sweeps these segments forward a certain distance and gathers them again into a long string, as in 1. The process of segmentation is then repeated as described above. (From Cannon, *Amer. J. Physiol.*, 1901–02, *6*:256.)

by the food. These occur rhythmically for a certain period and then cease until a new series is started, and it is obvious that they must play a very important part in promoting both the digestion and absorption of the food. The immediate cause of the alternation from one type of movement to the other is not known. Babkin has suggested that it may be connected with changes in the chemical composition of the chyme. Acid, alkali and some of the products of digestion have an effect on the contractions of the muscles as well as the mechanical stimulus of the bolus. Mall (56) has suggested that these rhythmical contractions of the circular coats may also act as a pumping mechanism upon the venous plexuses in the walls and thus aid in driving the blood into the portal system. Similar movements have been observed in the human being. These rhythmical contractions do not occur at a uniform rate throughout the small intestine but diminish in frequency with distance from the pylorus (1, 3). Whereas the rate may be from 17 to 21 per minute in a segment of the duodenum, the rate in a segment of the ileum is about 10 to 12 per minute. Associated with these differences in frequency are also inverse variations in the amplitude of the contractions of the intestinal muscle; as the contractions become less frequent their amplitude increases.

Tone and irritability of the intestine also decrease progressively from the duodenum to the ileum, together with a lowered respiratory metabolism. These observations support the view that the intestinal contractions are myogenic in origin; additional support for this view is obtained from studies showing that these rhythmic contractions are not abolished by the application of cocaine or nicotine. Alvarez summarizes these phenomena in the term *metabolic gradient* and believes that this gradient is an important factor also for peristalsis, in both its intensity and the direction it can take.

Peristalsis. The peristaltic movement consists in a constriction of the walls of the intestine, which, beginning at a certain point, passes downward away from the stomach. The wave of constriction may be recorded by the use of suitable apparatus. When thus recorded it is found that the advancing area of constriction is preceded by an area of inhibition or relaxation so that the peristaltic movement consists of two parts, following in a definite sequence, which seem to combine to facilitate the movement onward of the intestinal contents; for it is obvious that the wave of constriction will be

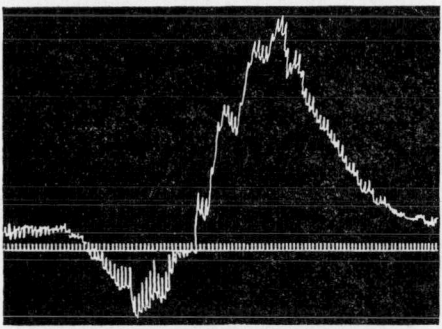

Fig. 457.—Peristaltic contractions of the small intestine (dog). The horizontal line gives the time in seconds. The curve was obtained by recording the diameter of the intestine at a given point during the passage of a peristaltic wave. It will be seen that there was first a dilatation (wave of inhibition), followed by a strong contraction. The smaller waves on the intestinal curve are due to the effect of the respiratory movements on the recording mechanism.

more effective in forcing the contents forward if just in front of it the intestine is relaxed by inhibition of the tonicity of the muscular coat (Fig. 457). Bayliss and Starling (6), to whom we owe the discovery of this twofold character of the movement, regarded it as a reflex which is controlled within the intestinal wall itself through its intrinsic ganglia and their afferent and efferent connections. When a bolus is inserted into the intestine at any point, its effect upon the nerve fibers is such as to cause a reflex contraction of the muscle above the bolus (i.e., toward the stomach) and a reflex inhibition or dilatation below. They speak of this definite relationship as the *law of the intestine;* it is described also under the name *myenteric reflex.* It is obvious that the circular layer of muscles is chiefly involved in peristalsis, since constriction can only be produced by contraction of this layer. In this analysis of the mechanism of peristalsis the part taken by the longitudinal muscles is not specified. Raiford and Mulinos (70), who studied the myenteric reflex in an exteriorized portion of the intestine of the dog, disagree with the Bayliss and Starling claim that the dilatation in front of the bolus is caused by inhibition, and instead attribute it to a contraction of the longitudinal muscles below the point of stimulation causing dilatation of the lumen, followed by a contraction of the circular muscle above this point. The latter act follows the former after an interval of three to five seconds. According to this interpretation of the reflex, then, the facilitating effect of a dilatation in front of the bolus is obtained not by an inhibition of the circular muscles but by a contraction of the longitudinal muscles. On the basis of their particular observations Alvarez and Zimmerman (4) have argued from observations in rabbits recorded by cinema film that this dilatation does not represent any specific inhibition of contractions of the circular muscles, or contraction of longitudinal muscle, but is merely an expansive effect of the mass of the bolus. The term "antiperistalsis" is used to describe the same form of movement running in the opposite direction—that is, toward the stomach. Antiperistalsis is said not to occur under normal conditions; it has been observed in isolated pieces of intestine or in the exposed intestine of living animals when stimulated artificially or after complete intestinal obstruction (Cannon). Alvarez claims that it does occur at times in the upper part of the small intestine because the metabolic gradient of this portion is higher. The peristaltic wave normally passes downward and this direction of movement is dependent upon some definite arrangement in the intestinal walls as shown by the experiments of Mall (57) upon reversal of the intestine. In these experiments a portion of the small intestine was resected, turned around, and sutured in place again, so that in this piece what was the lower end became the upper end. In those animals that made a good recovery the nutritive condition gradually became very serious, and when the animals were killed and examined it was found that there was an accumulation of food at the stomach end of the reversed piece of intestine, and that this region showed marked dilatation.

According to the observations made upon man by means of the x-ray, the normal peristaltic waves run only a few inches from the point at which they start (44), and their course is quite rapid. After the cessation of the peristaltic wave there is a period of rest during which the column of food undergoes segmentation by the action of the localized rhythmic contractions already described. At times there occurs a swift movement called the *peristaltic rush* which sweeps without pause for much greater distances. The general story of the movement of food is, therefore, as follows: the stomach discharges food at intervals into the intestine, and each such charge makes its passage along the intestine in a series of short runs (due to the peristaltic contractions), each run moving the column on for a few inches. Occasionally a greater distance is traversed by a peristaltic rush. The first column or charge of food reaches the ileocecal sphincter in four to four and a half hours on the average—about the time that the last portions of food are leaving the stomach. Hurst states that in the last few inches of the ileum the food accumulates and is passed only slowly into the colon through the ileocecal sphincter.

An interesting feature of the forward movement of food in the small intestine is that described by Carey (17, 18) and confirmed by Reid, Ivy and Quigley (71) under a variety of physiological conditions. Carey studied the fibers of the longitudinal and circular muscles in the wall of the intestine and noticed that they were arranged in spiral fashion. When a bolus was placed in an excised loop, it moved forward in a counterclockwise spiral path when viewed from the cephalic end. When an x-ray technique was employed, the same conclusion was reached. There was no difference between jejunum and ileum in this respect, and this rotational propulsion was not altered by alimentation or by various drugs.

Movements of the Intestinal Villi. Hambleton (38) first called attention to the fact that if the intestine of a living animal is opened and spread out under suitable conditions so that the villi may be examined under a binocular microscope, it can be shown that they exhibit active movements of two kinds: (i) lashing movements from side to side in various directions; (ii) what might be called pumping movements, in which the villi are alternately extended and contracted. Doubtless these movements are due to the contractions of the muscular slips, which run into the stroma of the villi from the muscularis mucosae. These observations have been confirmed by other observers (46) who give reasons for believing that the movements occur only when digestion is in progress and are connected probably with the act of absorption. The shape of the villi and their mode of motion vary in different animals. In the dog and cat they are finger-shaped and the contractions take place in the long diameter. In the rodents they are flattened or tongue-shaped, and the contractions are in the cross diameter. Either movement would tend to empty the central lacteal. The normal frequency of the rhythmic pumping movements is about six per minute. It seems necessary for the villi to swell with fluid before they can begin the pumping movement. These contractions have been observed in isolated villi floating in oxygenated Ringer's solution (80). Motion pictures of these villi movements have been made by Kokas and Ludany (47). Verzar (79), in whose laboratory much interesting work on this subject has been done, has reported that the villi respond to such chemical stimuli as yeast extract, condiments, histamine, physostigmine and a special hormone to which was given the name "villikinine." In all probability these movements of the villi assist in the absorption of substances such as fat which fill the central lacteal in the form of emulsified droplets; the pumping would serve to move such material on into the larger collecting lacteals.

Nervous Control of the Intestinal Movements. There is some evidence to show that the rhythmical contractions of the intestines are muscular in origin (myogenic), while the more coordinated peristaltic movements depend upon the intrinsic nervous mechanism. The intestine is, however, not dependent for either movement upon its connections with the central nervous system. Like the stomach, it is an automatic organ whose activity is simply regulated through its extrinsic nerves.

The small intestine obtains its supply of extrinsic nerve fibers from two sources, a bulbar autonomic (parasympathetic) supply by way of the vagi and a thoracic autonomic (sympathetic) supply by way of the splanchnic nerves and the superior mesenteric ganglia. Stimulation of the vagi causes contraction or increased tonus in the intestinal musculature, while stimulation of the splanchnics, on the contrary, causes relaxation or inhibition of tonus (except in the ileocecal sphincter). The paths of these fibers through the central nervous system are not known, but there are evidently connections extending to the higher brain centers, since psychical states are known to influence the movements of the intestines; and according to some observers, stimulation of portions of the cerebral cortex may produce contraction or relaxation of the walls of the small and large intestines.

There is a definite parallelism between the effects of splanchnic stimulation and those of epinephrine, shown by observations of the rhythmic contractions of an isolated strip of the small intestine suspended in a bath of oxygenated saline solution. The addition of only a trace of epinephrine results in complete inhibition of the movement. Since it is known that there is an increased secretion of this hormone during fright, anger and other emotional states, this may serve to explain the marked inhibition of intestinal movement that occurs during these states. These observations are readily explained by the assumption that the small intestine is provided with parasympathetic nerves which are cholinergic (see p. 1033). This is supported by the work of Bunting and associates (10) who prepared denervated intestinal loops to be used as indicators of the presence of acetylcholine or similar substances, and found that stimulation of the vagus was followed by contraction of the test loop.

The *ileocecal sphincter* responds to stimulation of the vagus and the splanchnics differently from the rest of the intestine. It opens when the bolus presses on it from the ileum and remains closed in response to pressure from the cecum and to this extent may be said to obey the so-called law of the intestine. On the other hand, when stimulation of the splanchnics is producing inhibition of movement throughout the intestine there is a strong contraction of this sphincter; stimulation of the vagus has no effect on it. This unique response to splanchnic stimulation has an obvious physiological advantage. When all intestinal movements are being inhibited, contraction of the ileocecal sphincter serves to prevent material in the small intestine from draining into the large intestine.

Factors Affecting Intestinal Movements. Experiments have shown that the movements of the intestines may be evoked in many ways in addition to direct stimulation of the extrinsic nerves. Chemical stimuli may be applied directly to the intestinal wall. Mechanical stimulation—pinching, for example, or the introduction of a bolus into the intestinal lumen—may start peristaltic movements. In this connection one may cite the interesting observation by Alvarez (1) who was able to insert a balloon into an intestinal fistula in man; when the inflated balloon attached to a string was not allowed to move with the peristaltic wave because the string was held taut, the patient soon complained of distress. It seems evident that more vigorous contractions were produced under these conditions in an attempt to force the balloon forward, and these were associated with the symptoms of colic. Violent movements may be produced also by shutting off the blood supply, and again temporarily when the supply is re-established. A condition of dyspnea may also start movements in the intestines or in some cases inhibit movements which are already in progress, the stimulus in this case seeming to act upon the central nervous system and to stimulate both the motor and the inhibitory fibers. Oxygen gas within the bowels tends to suspend the movements of the intestine, while CO_2, CH_4, and H_2S act as stimuli, increasing the movements. Organic acids, such as acetic, propionic, formic and caprylic, which may be formed normally within the intestine as the result of bacterial action, act also as strong stimulants. The presence of bile favors peristaltic movements. Animals who have their bile diverted from the intestine become constipated and such stools as are evacuated are highly putrefactive. It has been shown that the presence of bile promotes peristaltic movements. Chemical substances of the types just mentioned occur normally in the intestines and may have an important directive influence upon the intestinal movements. Some evidence has also been obtained supporting the view that stimulation of intestinal contractions can be one feature of an allergic reaction to certain foods.

Movements of the Large Intestine. The opening from the small intestine into the large is controlled both by the ileocecal valve and by a sphincter, the ileocecal or ileocolic sphincter. This sphincter is normally in tonus and its condition of tonus is regulated through the thoracic autonomic fibers received by way of the splanchnic nerve and superior mesenteric ganglion (30). The musculature in the large intestine has the same general arrangement as in the small, and the usual view has been that the movements are similar, although more infrequent, so that the material received from the small intestine is slowly moved along while becoming more and more solid from the loss of water. The contents of the ascending colon are soft and semiliquid, but in the distal end of the transverse colon they attain the consistency of the feces. In the cat (12), as seen by the x-ray, the most frequent movement in the ascending colon and cecum is that which Cannon described as antiperistalsis but which Garry (31) felt should not be so named. Garry wrote: "There seem to be two definite types of movement. It is not justifiable to call one peristalsis and the other antiperistalsis, and the difference between them is not yet elucidated." This questionable antiperistalsis consists of running waves of constriction passing toward the ileocecal valve, and set up by the presence of the more or less liquid food material present in the canal. These waves occur in groups separated by periods of rest. They seem to originate from a constricted ring which pulsates, each contraction starting an anastaltic wave. The presence of the ileocecal valve prevents the material from being forced back into the small intestine. The value of this peculiar reversal of the normal movement of the bowels at this particular point would seem to lie in the fact that it delays the passage of the material toward the rectum, and by thoroughly mixing it gives increased opportunities for the completion of the processes of digestion and absorption; but from the reports received from x-ray examinations in man it is doubtful whether this kind of movement is usual in the human being. These observers lay stress upon a different kind of movement which they designate as *mass peristalsis*, that is, strong peristaltic movements which last only a few seconds but move the contents from one division to another, from ascending to transverse colon, etc. These movements occur only rarely, three or four times a day. Hurst connects them with the act of eating, assuming the existence of a gastrocolic reflex which is set into play by the entrance of food into the stomach. According to this view, the food is moved along the colon at long intervals by the sudden displacements caused by the mass peristalsis. In between, the contents are not moved except for the local agitation caused by the rhythmic contractions of the haustra (haustral churning) which have some resemblance to the rhythmic segmentation phenomena seen in the small intestine. In the pelvic colon two types of peristaltic waves have been observed, (i) a slow movement, and (ii) Holzknecht's "large colonic movements" by which intestinal contents are carried along through a considerable part of the large intestine, movements similar to the peristaltic rush that occurs in the small intestine. The large colonic movement has been seen in man particularly after a meal and is believed to be part of the *gastrocolic reflex* most often observed after the first meal of the day. There are good grounds for believing that when a "large movement" occurs as part of the act of defecation, it is largely responsible for the subjective impression that emptying has been fairly complete.

The large intestine receives its nerve supply from two sources (Fig. 458): (i) Fibers which leave the spinal cord in the lumbar nerves (second to fifth in the cat), pass to the sympathetic chain and thence to the inferior mesenteric ganglia, which probably form the termination of the preganglionic fibers. From this point the path is continued by fibers running in the hypogastric

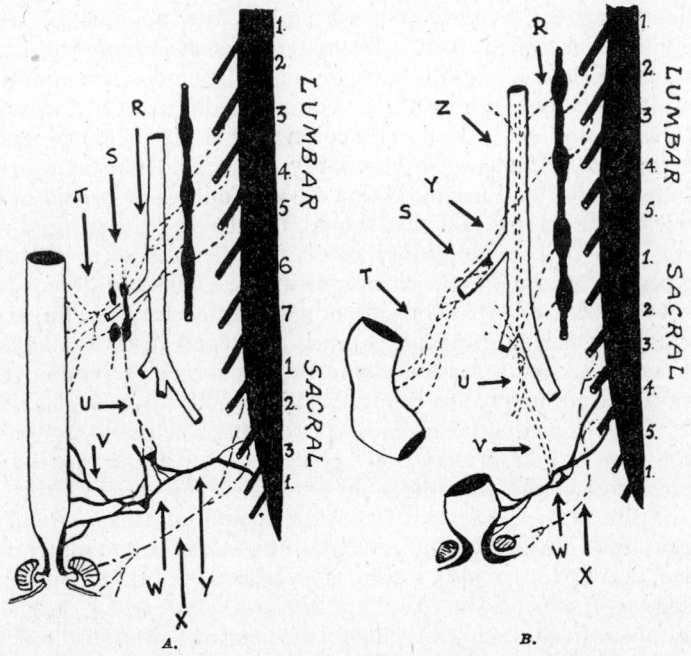

Fig. 458.—Nervous outflow to the distal colon (*A*) in the cat, and (*B*) in man.

A: *R*, spinal rami to inferior mesenteric ganglia; *S*, inferior mesenteric ganglia; *T*, lumbar colonic nerves; *U*, hypogastric nerve; *V*, sacral colonic nerves; *W*, pelvic plexus; *X*, pudendal nerve; *Y*, pelvic nerve.

B: *R*, pelvic splanchnic nerves; *S*, inferior mesenteric plexus; *T*, inferior mesenteric nerves; *U*, presacral nerve; *V*, hypogastric nerve; W, hypogastric plexus; *X*, pudendal nerve; *Y*, inter-mesenteric nerve; *Z*, intermesenteric plexus. (After Garry, from Bard's *Macleod's Physiology in modern medicine*, 9th ed. St. Louis, C. V. Mosby Co., 1941.)

nerves and plexus. Stimulation of these fibers has given different results in the hands of various observers but the general view (49, 50, 51) is that they are inhibitory. (ii) Fibers that leave the cord in the sacral nerves (second to fourth) form part of the nervi erigentes or pelvic nerves and enter into the hypogastric plexus. When stimulated, these fibers cause contractions of the muscular coats; they may be regarded, therefore, as motor fibers. As in the case of the small intestine and stomach, we may assume that these motor and inhibitory fibers serve for the reflex regulation and adaptation of the movements. In this connection attention may be called to the difference in innervation between the stomach and small intestine on the one hand, and the colon and rectum on the other. In all cases the motor fibers are mainly of parasympathetic origin, but the stomach and small intestine receive their supply by way of the bulbar autonomics (vagi), while the colon and rectum are innervated through the sacral autonomics (pelvic nerve). On the other hand, the inhibitory fibers are mainly sympathetic, emerging from the cord in the thoracic outflow (thoracic autonomics). The fibers for the small intestine and stomach pass by way of the splanchnic and superior mesenteric ganglion, while those for the colon and rectum run via the inferior mesenteric ganglion.

A knowledge of the functions of these various nerves is of value in surgery because good results have been obtained by cutting them in Hirschsprung's disease (inhibition of the colon and contraction of the internal anal sphincter in infants). The value of similar surgical treatment of intractable constipation remains to be determined.

Defecation—the Laxation Problem. The undigested and indigestible parts of the food, together with some of the *debris* and secretions from the alimentary tract, eventually reach the pelvic colon and rectum. Authorities differ as to whether the rectum normally contains fecal material or not. According to observations made upon man by means of x-rays, fecal material is normally absent from the rectum except just before defecation. It seems probable that a distinct desire to defecate is felt only when the feces have actually entered the rectum and produced some distension. The fecal material is retained within the rectum by the action of the two sphincter muscles which close the anal opening. One of these muscles, the internal sphincter, is a strong band of the circular layer of involuntary muscle which forms one of the coats of the rectum. When the rectum contains fecal material, this muscle is thrown into a condition of tonic contraction until the act of defecation begins, when it is relaxed. The external sphincter ani is composed of striated muscle tissue and is under the control of the will to a certain extent. It is supplied by a motor nerve, the Nn. hemorrhoidales inferiores, arising from the N. pudendus and eventually from the sacral spinal nerves. This muscle, therefore, like striated muscle in general, is innervated directly from the spinal cord, but it possesses properties which are to some extent intermediate between those of plain and of striated muscle. Both the internal and the external sphincter are normally in tonus and unite in protecting the anal opening. The force of the tonic contraction of the internal is somewhat less (30 to 60 per cent) than that of the external sphincter. The internal sphincter, like the rest of the musculature of the rectum, receives a double nerve supply, one set of fibers coming to it through the pelvic nerve (sacral autonomics) and one set through the hypogastric nerve by way of the inferior mesenteric ganglion (thoracic autonomics). The action of the efferent fibers in these nerves has been a matter of dispute, and possibly the results may differ in different animals. According to one account the sphincter responds in the same way as the rest of the circular muscle of the rectum, that is to say, it is thrown into contraction by stimulation of the pelvic nerve, and is inhibited by stimulation of the hypogastric nerve, but other workers state that the sphincter receives part, at least, of its motor fibers from the hypogastric nerve. The act of defecation as it occurs normally is partly a voluntary and partly an involuntary act, the part taken by each varying with circumstances. The involuntary act consists in peristaltic contractions of the rectum or, indeed, of the whole colon, together with an inhibition of the sphincters, and in a strong call to defecation this act is effective in emptying the bowel without voluntary aid other than the relaxation of the external sphincter. Under ordinary conditions the desire to defecate is aroused by the passage of feces from the pelvic colon into the rectum. A voluntary act then follows, consisting in a contraction of the abdominal muscles, or, according to Hurst (44), a contraction of both the diaphragm and the abdominal muscles, the effect of which is to increase greatly the pressure in the abdomen, since the glottis is kept closed, and thus force more of the feces into the rectum. Through the stimulus thus produced in the rectum the involuntary peristalsis is liberated, the movement starting well back in the colon and including as part of the reflex an inhibition of the internal sphincter.

Goltz (33, 34) observed that in dogs in which the spinal cord had been severed in the lower thoracic region defecation was performed normally. In later experiments, in which the entire spinal cord was removed except in the cervical and upper part of the thoracic region, it was found that the animal, after it had recovered from the operation, had a normal movement once or twice a day, indicating that the rectum and lower bowels acted by virtue of their intrinsic mechanism. An interesting result of these experiments was the fact that the external sphincter suffered no atrophy, although its motor nerve was destroyed, and that it eventually regained its tonic activity.

The lower bowel is to some extent able to expand and thus accommodate varying amounts of material. Balloon experiments have demonstrated this. The studies of Hines, Lueth and Ivy (42) showed that there is a certain threshold value of the pressure in the rectum, at least in normal people capable of stimulating the mechanism for defecation. The observations of Cowgill and associates (26, 27, 28) suggest that it is this varying degree of expansion that accounts in part for the varying size of the stool. In animals like the rat, in which semidiarrhea is not so easily produced as in man by varying the food, laxation rate—stools formed and passed in unit time—is a good measure of the laxative effect of foods. If the amount of material to be eliminated is greater than can be taken care of by the capacity for expansion, more stools will have to be formed and passed in unit time.

Food can affect the mechanism of laxation in two ways, (i) by its bulk or mass upon which the colonic wall may contract, and (ii) by the presence of substances which have a druglike action on the intestine. The first is well illustrated by the shorter time required for passage through the intestinal tract and elimination of a food that contains a significantly larger amount of indigestible material—a diet with greater "bulkage" or "roughage." The second type of influence is seen when the ingestion of a small amount of certain foods is associated with an increase in laxation far beyond what might be expected from consideration of its roughage content. In their studies with wheat bran, Cowgill and collaborators (26, 28) obtained data suggesting that in healthy men an intake of not less than 90 to 100 mg. of "crude fiber" per kilogram of body weight per day should be associated with satisfactory laxation as determined by amount of material eliminated and the subjective impressions of the individual. Observations made with patients suffering from chronic constipation showed that these individuals, as compared with the normal subjects, had greater capacity to break down in the alimentary tract, possibly by bacterial action, the "crude fiber" present in certain fruits and vegetables with resultant failure to secure satisfactory laxation. It has since been shown (29, 41, 83) that what has been called crude fiber consists chiefly of lignin, cellulose and hemicellulose, these carbohydrates being present in varying amounts, and that these substances undergo bacterial decomposition in the intestine, lignin being the most resistant and hemicellulose the least. Sometimes a prolonged constipation is desired. In operations in the anal region it is obviously an advantage to avoid infecting the wound through defecation until healing is well established. It has been found clinically that lean meat is the best food to feed such a patient. In their study of the low-residue diet Hosoi, Alvarez and Mann (43) tested numerous foods and found lean meat to have, in fact, a low-residue value, thus confirming the clinical impressions.

Vomiting. The act of vomiting causes an ejection of the contents of the stomach through the esophagus and mouth to the exterior. It was long debated whether the force producing this ejection comes from a strong contraction of the walls of the stomach itself or whether it is due mainly to the action of the walls of the abdomen. A forcible spasmodic contraction of the abdominal muscles takes place, as may easily be observed by anyone upon himself, and it is now believed that the contraction of these muscles is the principal factor in vomiting. Magendie found that if the stomach was extirpated and a bladder containing water was substituted in its place and connected with the esophagus, injection of an emetic caused a typical vomiting movement with ejection of the contents of the bladder. Gianuzzi showed, on the other hand, that upon a curarized animal vomiting could not be produced by an emetic—because, apparently, the muscles of the abdomen were paralyzed by the curare. There are on record a number of observations which tend to show that the stomach is not passive during the act. On the contrary, it may exhibit contractions, more or less violent in character. According to Openchowski (64), the pylorus is closed and the pyloric end of the stomach firmly contracted so as to drive the contents toward the dilated cardiac portion. Cannon states that in cats the normal peristaltic waves pass over the pyloric portion in the period preceding the vomiting and that finally a strong contraction at the "transverse band" completely shuts off the pyloric portion from the body of the stomach, which at this time is quite relaxed. The act of vomiting is, in fact, a complex reflex movement into which many muscles enter. The following events are described: the vomiting is usually preceded by a sensation of nausea and a reflex flow of saliva into the mouth. These phenomena are succeeded or accompanied by retching movements, which consist essentially in deep, spasmodic inspirations with a closed glottis. The effect of these movements is to compress the stomach by the descent of the diaphragm, and at the same time to increase decidedly the negative pressure in the thorax, and therefore in the thoracic portion of the esophagus. During one of these retching movements the act of vomiting is effected by a convulsive contraction of the abdominal wall that exerts a sudden additional strong pressure upon the stomach. At the same time the cardiac orifice of the stomach is dilated, probably by an inhibition of the sphincter, and according to the above description the fundic end of the stomach is also dilated, while the pyloric end is in strong contraction. The stomach contents are, therefore, forced

34

violently out of the stomach through the esophagus, the negative pressure in the latter probably assisting in the act. The passage through the esophagus is effected mainly by the force of the contraction of the abdominal muscles; there is no evidence of antiperistaltic movements on the part of the esophagus itself. During the ejection of the contents of the stomach the glottis is kept closed by the adductor muscles, and usually the nasal chamber is likewise shut off from the pharynx by the contraction of the posterior pillars of the fauces on the palate and uvula. In violent vomiting, however, the vomited material may break through this latter barrier and be ejected partially through the nose.

Nervous mechanism of vomiting. That vomiting is a reflex act is abundantly shown by the frequency with which it is produced in consequence of the stimulation of sensory nerves or as the result of injuries to various parts of the central nervous system. After lesions or injuries of the brain vomiting often results. Disagreeable emotions and disturbances of the sense of equilibrium may produce the same result. Irritation of the mucous membrane of various parts of the alimentary canal (as, for example, tickling the back of the pharynx with the finger); disturbances of the urogenital apparatus, the liver, and other visceral organs; artificial stimulation of the trunk of the vagus and of other sensory nerves, all may cause vomiting. Under ordinary conditions, however, irritation of the sensory nerves of the gastric mucous membrane is the most common cause of vomiting. This effect may result from the products of fermentation in the stomach in cases of indigestion, or may be produced intentionally by local emetics, such as mustard, taken into the stomach. The afferent path in this case is through the sensory fibers of the vagus. The efferent paths of the reflex are found in the motor nerves innervating the muscles concerned in the vomiting—namely, the vagus, the phrenics, and the spinal nerves supplying the abdominal muscles. Whether or not there is a definite vomiting center in which the afferent impulses are received and through which a coordinated series of efferent impulses is sent out to the various muscles has not been satisfactorily determined. It has been shown that the portion of the nervous system through which the reflex is effected lies in the medulla, and it may be observed that the muscles concerned in the act, outside those of the stomach, are respiratory muscles. Vomiting, in fact, consists essentially in a simultaneous spasmodic contraction of expiratory (abdominal) muscles and inspiratory muscles (diaphragm). It has therefore been suggested that the reflex involves the stimulation of the respiratory center or some part of it. Thomas claims to have located a vomiting center in the medulla in the immediate neighborhood of the calamus scriptorius. The act of vomiting may be produced not only as a reflex from various sensory nerves, but may also be caused by direct action upon the medullary centers. The action of apomorphine is most easily explained by supposing that it acts directly on the nerve centers (39).

REFERENCES

1. ALVAREZ, W. C. Physiologic studies on the motor activities of the stomach and bowel of man. *Amer. J. Physiol.*, 1929, *88*:65–0662.

2. ALVAREZ, W. C. *An introduction to gastro-enterology, being the third edition of The mechanics of the digestive tract.* New York, Paul B. Hoeber, Inc., 1940. xxii, 778 pp. (See particularly p. 241 ff.)

3. ALVAREZ, W. C. and STARKWEATHER, E. The metabolic gradient underlying intestinal peristalsis. *Amer. J. Physiol.*, 1918, *46*:186–208.

4. ALVAREZ, W. C. and ZIMMERMAN, A.

The absence of inhibition ahead of peristaltic rushes. *Amer. J. Physiol.*, 1927, *83*:52–59.

5. BARCLAY, A. E. Normal mechanism of swallowing. *Proc. Mayo Clin.*, 1930, *5*:251–257.

6. BAYLISS, W. M. and STARLING, E. H. The movements and innervation of the small intestine. *J. Physiol.*, 1899, *24*:99–143.

7. BEAUMONT, W. *Physiology of digestion*, 2nd ed., corrected by S. Beaumont. Burlington [Vt.], Chauncey Goodrich, 1847. 303 pp.

8. BLACK, G. V. An investigation of the physical characters of the human teeth in relation to their diseases, and to practical dental operations, together with the physical characters of filling materials. *Dent. Cosmos*, 1895, *37*:469–484.

9. VON BRUCKE, F. T. and STERN, P. Pharmakologische Untersuchungen über die Innervation des Mageneinganges. *Arch. exp. Path. Pharmak.*, 1938, *189*:311–326.

10. BUNTING, H., MEEK, W. J. and MAASKE, C. A. The chemical transmission of vagal effects to the small intestine. *Amer. J. Physiol.*, 1935, *114*:100–105.

11. CANNON, W. B. The movements of the stomach studied by means of Röntgen rays. *Amer. J. Physiol.*, 1898, *1*:359–382.

12. CANNON, W. B. The movements of the intestines studied by means of the Röntgen rays. *Amer. J. Physiol.*, 1901–02, *6*:251–277.

13. CANNON, W. B. Further observations on the mechanism of the pylorus. *Amer. J. Physiol.*, 1905–06, *15*:xxv.

14. CANNON, W. B. *The mechanical factors of digestion*. (International Medical Monographs.) London, Edward Arnold and Co., 1911. xii, 228 pp.

15. CANNON, W. B. and MOSER, A. The movements of the food in the oesophagus. *Amer. J. Physiol.*, 1898, *1*:435–444.

16. CANNON, W. B. and WASHBURN, A. L. An explanation of hunger. *Amer. J. Physiol.*, 1911–12, *29*:441–454.

17. CAREY, E. J. Studies in the dynamics of histogenesis. I. Tension of differential growth as a stimulus to myogenesis. *J. gen. Physiol.*, 1919–20, *2*:357–372; II. *ibid.*, 1920–21, *3*:61–83; [III]. Growth motive force as a dynamic stimulus to the genesis of muscular and skeletal tissues. *Anat. Rec.*, 1920, *19*:199–326.

18. CAREY, E. J. Studies on the structure and function of the small intestine. *Anat. Rec.*, 1921, *21*:189–214.

19. CARLSON, A. J. *The control of hunger in health and disease*. Chicago, University of Chicago Press, 1919, 2nd imp. vii, 319 pp.

20. CARLSON, A. J. and GINSBURG, H. Contributions to the physiology of the stomach. XXIV. The tonus and hunger contractions of the stomach of the new-born. *Amer. J. Physiol.*, 1915, *38*:29–32.

21. CARMAN, R. D. and MILLER, A. *The Roentgen diagnosis of diseases of the alimentary canal*, 2nd ed. Philadelphia, W. B. Saunders Co., 1920.

22. CHILDREY, J. H., ALVAREZ, W. C. and MANN, F. C. Digestion. Efficiency with various foods and under different conditions. *Arch intern. Med.*, 1930, *46*:361–374.

23. COLE, L. G. The value of serial radiography in gastro-intestinal diagnosis. *J. Amer. med. Ass.*, 1912, *59*:1947–1951.

24. COLE, L. G. Physiology of the pylorus, pileus ventriculi and duodenum as observed roentgenographically. *J. Amer. med. Ass.*, 1913, *61*:762–767.

25. COLE, L. G. Motor phenomenon of the stomach, pylorus and cap observed roentgenographically. *Amer. J. Physiol.*, 1916–17, *42*:618–619.

26. COWGILL, G. R. and ANDERSON, W. E. Laxative effects of wheat bran and "washed bran" in healthy men. *J. Amer. med. Ass.*, 1932, *98*:1866–1875.

27. COWGILL, G. R., ANDERSON, W. E. and SULLIVAN, A. J. The form of the stool as a criterion of laxation. *J. Amer. med. Ass.*, 1933, *101*:273–275.

28. COWGILL, G. R. and SULLIVAN, A. J. Further studies on the use of wheat bran as a laxative. Observations on patients. *J. Amer. med. Ass.*, 1933, *100*:795–802.

29. CRAMPTON, E. W. and MAYNARD, L. A. The relation of cellulose and lignin content to the nutritive value of animal foods. *J. Nutrit.*, 1938, *15*:383–395.

30. ELLIOTT, T. R. On the innervation of the ileocolic sphincter. *J. Physiol.*, 1904, *31*:157–168.

31. GARRY, R. C. The movements of the large intestine. *Physiol. Rev.*, 1934, *14*:103–132.

32. GIANTURCO, C. Some mechanical factors of gastric physiology. I. The empty stomach and its various ways of filling. The pressure exerted by the gastric walls on the gastric content. The physical changes occurring to the foodstuff during digestion. *Amer. J. Roentgenol.*, 1934, *31*:735–744.

33. GOLTZ, F. Ueber die Funktionen des Lendenmarks des Hundes. *Pflüg. Arch. ges. Physiol.*, 1874, *8*:460–498.

34. GOLTZ, F. and EWALD, J. R. Der Hund mit verkürztem Rückenmark. (Nach gemeinschaftlich angestellten Beobachtungen.) *Pflüg. Arch. ges. Physiol.*, 1896, *63*:362–400.

35. GREVING, R. Die Innervation der Speiseröhre. *Z. angew. Anat.*, 1920, *5*:327–357.

36. GREY, E. G. Observations on the postural activity of the stomach. *Amer. J. Physiol.*, 1917–18, *45*:272–285.

37. GRÜTZNER, P. Ein Beitrag zum Mechanismus der Magenverdauung. *Pflüg. Arch. ges. Physiol.*, 1905, *106*:463–522.

38. HAMBLETON, B. F. Note upon the movements of the intestinal villi. *Amer. J. Physiol.*, 1914, *34*:446–447.

39. HATCHER, R. A. The mechanism of vomiting. *Physiol. Rev.*, 1924, *4*:479–504.

40. HEIDENHAIN, R. Algemeine Bedingungen der Absonderung. *Hermanns Handb. Physiol.*, 1881, *5* (1): 106–121.

41. HELLER, V. G. and WALL, R. The indigestible carbohydrates of foods. *J. Nutrit.*, 1940, *19*:141–149.

42. HINES, L. E., LUETH, H. C. and IVY, A. C. Motility of the rectum in normal and constipated subjects. *Arch intern. Med.*, 1929, *44*:147–152.

43. HOSOI, K., ALVAREZ, W. C. and MANN, F. C. Intestinal absorption—a search for a low residue diet. *Arch. intern. Med.*, 1928, *41*:112–126.

44. HURST, A. F. Physiology of the intestinal movements. In his: *Constipation and allied intestinal disorders*, 2nd ed. (Oxford Medical Publications.) London, H. Frowde, 1919. 460 pp.

45. IVY, A. C., MORGAN, J. E. and FARRELL, J. I. Effects of total gastrectomy; experimental achylia gastrica in dogs with occurrence of spontaneous anaemia and anaemia of pregnancy. *Surg. Gynec. Obstet.*, 1931, *53*:611–620.

46. VON KOKAS, E. Vergleichend-physiologische Untersuchungen über die Bewegung der Darmzotten. *Pflüg. Arch. ges. Physiol.*, 1930, *225*:416–420.

47. VON KOKAS, E. and VON LUDANY, G. Weitere Untersuchungen über die Bewegung der Darmzotten. *Pflüg. Arch. ges. Physiol.*, 1930, *225*:421–428.

48. KRONECKER, H. and MELTZER, S. Der Schluckmechanismus, seine Erregung und seine Hemmung. *Arch. Anat. Physiol., Lpz.*, 1883, *7* (Suppl.): 328–360.

49. LANGLEY, J. N. and ANDERSON, H. K. On reflex action from sympathetic ganglia. *J. Physiol.*, 1894, *16*:410–440.

50. LANGLEY, J. N. and ANDERSON, H. K. The constituents of the hypogastric nerves. *J. Physiol.*, 1894–95, *17*:177–191.

51. LANGLEY, J. N. and ANDERSON, H. K. On the innervation of the pelvic and adjoining viscera. I. The lower part of the intestine. *J. Physiol.*, 1895, *18*:67–105; VI. Histological and physiological observations upon the effects of section of the sacral nerves. *Ibid.*, 1896, *19*:372–384; VII. Anatomical observations. *Ibid.*, 1896, *20*:372–406.

52. LUCKHARDT, A. B., PHILLIPS, H. T. and CARLSON, A. J. Contributions to the physiology of the stomach. LI. The control of the pylorus. *Amer. J. Physiol.*, 1919–20, *50*:57–66.

53. MCCREA, E. D., MCSWINEY, B. A. and STOPFORD, J. S. B. Effect of section of the vagi nerves on the motor activity of the stomach. *J. Physiol.*, 1925, *60*:xxix-xxx.

54. MCCREA, E. D., MCSWINEY, B. A. and STOPFORD, J. S. B. Effect on the stomach of section of the vagi nerves. *Quart. J. exp. Physiol.*, 1926, *16*:195–206.

55. MCSWINEY, B. A. Innervation of the stomach. *Physiol. Rev.*, 1931, *11*:478–514.

56. MALL, F. P. A study of the intestinal contractions. *Johns Hopk. Hosp. Rep.*, 1896, *1*:37–75.

57. MALL, F. P. Reversal of the intestine. *Johns Hopk. Hosp. Rep.*, 1896, *1*:93–110.

58. MELTZER, S. J. A further experimental contribution to the knowledge of the mechanism of deglutition. *J. exp. Med.*, 1897, *2*:453–464.

59. MESCHAN, I. and QUIGLEY, J. P. Spontaneous motility of the pyloric sphincter and adjacent regions of the gut in the anesthetized dog. *Amer. J. Physiol.*, 1938, *121*:350–357.

60. VON MIKULICZ, J. Beiträge zur Physiologie der Speiseröhre und der Cardia. *Mitt. Grenzegeb. Med. Chir.*, 1903, *12*:569–601.

61. MORITZ, F. Studien über die motorische Thatigkeit des Magens. *Z. Biol.*, 1895, *32*:313–369.

62. MOSHER, H. P. X-ray study of movements of the tongue, epiglottis and hyoid bone in swallowing, followed by a discussion of difficulty caused by retropharyngeal diverticulum, postcricoid webs and exostoses of cervical vertebrae. *Laryngoscope, St Louis*, 1927, *37*:235–262.

63. MOSSO, A. Ueber die Bewegungen der Speiseröhre. *Untersuch. Naturl. Mensch. Tiere.*, 1876, *11*:327–349.

64. OPENCHOWSKI, T. Ueber Centren und Leitungsbahnen für die Musculatur des Magens. *Arch. Anat. Physiol., Lpz.*, 1889, *13*:549–556.

65. OSLER, W. William Beaumont. A pioneer American physiologist. *J. Amer. med. Ass.*, 1902, *39*:1223–1231.

66. PALUGYAY, J. Die Diagnose des beginnenden Kardia-Karzinoms mittels Durchleuchtung in Beckenhochlagerung und über die Röntgenologie der Kardia überhaupt. *Fortschr. Röntgenstr.*, 1922, *13*:35–38.

67. PALUGYAY, J. Röntgenstudien über den oesophagealen Schluckakt. Ein Beitrag zur Speiseröhrenphysiologie. *Pflüg. Arch. ges. Physiol.*, 1923, *200*:620–641.

68. QUIGLEY, J. P. and MESCHAN, I. The role of the vagus in the regulation of the pyloric sphincter and adjacent portions of the gut, with special reference to the process of gastric evacuation. *Amer. J. Physiol.*, 1938, *123*:166.

69. QUIGLEY, J. P. and PHELPS, K. R. The mechanism of gastric inhibition following ingestion of carbohydrate. *Amer. J. Physiol.*, 1934, *109*:85.

70. RAIFORD, T. and MULINOS, M. G. The myenteric reflex as exhibited by the exteriorized colon of the dog. *Amer. J. Physiol.*, 1934, *110*:129–136.

71. REID, P. E., IVY, A. C. and QUIGLEY, J. P. Spiral propulsion of a bolus in the intestine. *Amer. J. Physiol.*, 1934, *109*:483–487.

72. ROGERS, F. T. The hunger mechanism in birds. *Proc. Soc. exp. Biol., N. Y.*, 1916, *13*:119–121.

73. ROGERS, F. T. and HARDT, L. L. J. Contributions to the physiology of the stomach. XXVI. The relation between the digestion contractions of the filled, and the hunger contractions of the "empty" stomach. *Amer. J. Physiol.*, 1915, *38*:274–284.

74. ROUX, J.-C. and BALTHAZARD, V. Étude du fonctionnement moteur de l'estomac. *Arch. Physiol. norm. path.*, 1898, *10* (5.s): 85–94.

75. SCHREIBER, J. Ueber den bewegenden Einfluss der Schwerkraft beim Trinken in aufrechter- und Kopfstellung. *Arch. VerdauKr.*, 1915, *21*:1–15.

76. THOMAS, J. E. Mechanism of gastric evacuation. *J. Amer. med. Ass.*, 1931, *97*:1663–1668.

77. THOMAS, J. E., CRIDER, J. O. and MOGAN, C. J. A study of reflexes involving the pyloric sphincter and antrum and their rôle in gastri evacuation. *Amer. J. Physiol.*, 1934, *108*:683–700.

78. TRISKA, W. Experimentelle Studien über Beisskraft. *Pflüg. Arch. ges. Physiol.*, 1924, *204*:660–667.

79. VERZAR, F. and McDOUGALL, E. J. *Absorption from the intestine.* New York, Longmans, Green and Co., 1936. 294 pp.

80. WELLS, H. S. and JOHNSON, R. G. Observations on the intestinal villi and their circulation. *Amer. J. Physiol.*, 1934, *109*:108–109.

81. WHEELON, H. and THOMAS, J. E. Observations on the motility of the antrum and the relation of rhythmic activity of the pyloric sphincter to that of the antrum. *J. lab. clin. Med.*, 1920, *6*:124.

82. WHEELON, H. and THOMAS, J. E. Observations on the motility of the duodenum and the relation of duodenal activity to that of the pars pylorica. *Amer. J. Physiol.*, 1922, *59*:72–96.

83. WILLIAMS, R. D. and OLMSTED, W. H. The effect of cellulose, hemicellulose and lignin on the weight of the stool: a contribution to the study of laxation in man. *J. Nutrit.*, 1936 *11*:433–449.

CHAPTER 46

GENERAL CONSIDERATIONS UPON THE COMPOSITION OF FOOD AND THE ACTION OF ENZYMES

Food and Foodstuffs. The term food when used in a popular sense includes everything that we eat for the purpose of nourishing the body. From this point of view the food of mankind is of a most varied character, comprising a great variety of products of the animal and vegetable kingdoms. Chemical analysis of the animal and vegetable foods shows, however, that they all contain one or more of six different classes of substances which are designated as the foodstuffs (older names, alimentary or proximate principles) on the belief that they form the useful constituents of our foods. The classification of foodstuffs usually given is as follows:

$$
\text{Foodstuffs} \begin{cases} \text{Water} \\ \text{Inorganic salts} \\ \text{Proteins} \\ \text{Carbohydrates} \\ \text{Fats} \\ \text{Vitamins} \end{cases}
$$

From the scientific point of view, a foodstuff or food may be defined as a substance necessary to the normal composition of the body, as in the case of water and salts, or as a substance which can be acted upon by the tissues of the body in such a way as to yield energy (heat, for example) or to furnish material for the production, repair, or normal activity of living tissue. Moreover, to be a food in the physiological sense, the substance must not directly or indirectly affect injuriously the normal nutritive processes of the tissues. The six substances named above are all foods in this sense. It has been demonstrated by feeding experiments that animals can be maintained and can grow normally when supplied with purified proteins, fats, and carbohydrates, together with water, the necessary inorganic salts, and the vitamins. The water and certain salts of sodium, potassium, chlorine, calcium, phosphorus, magnesium, iron, iodine, copper, manganese, zinc, and perhaps other elements are necessary to maintain the normal composition of the tissue and certain of its functions. Complete withdrawal of any of these constituents would eventually adversely affect the growth of the young, or maintenance of the adult, or reproduction—in some cases produce all of these effects, in others only some of them—or even result in death if the period of deprivation is sufficiently extended. The vitamins form a group of organic substances found in varying amounts in the ordinary foods which are not useful as sources of energy in the sense that energy is derived by their own combustion, but are essential in various ways to normal metabolism. Their chemical composition is known, in part at least, but their mode of action is not fully understood. Proteins, fats and carbohydrates are complex organic substances the chemical structure of which is known in whole or in part. When eaten and digested, the products of digestion enter the body liquids and are employed either in the synthesis of the more complex living matter or undergo various chemical changes, spoken of in general as metabolism, which result finally in the breaking up of their complex molecules with a liberation of some of their internal energy. The complex changes of metabolism or nutrition are, in the long run, mainly exothermic—that is, they are attended by the production of heat. Some of the chemical or internal energy that held the complex molecules together assumes the form of heat when these molecules are broken down by oxidative changes to simpler, more stable structures such as water, carbon dioxide and urea. Thus, in practical dietetics, proteins, carbohydrates and fats are considered in their combustion in metabolism to yield to the body four, four and nine large calories per gram, respectively. After they have undergone certain changes during digestion, proteins, carbohydrates and fats form materials upon which the tissue cells are adjusted to act. The foods that we eat are mixtures with a very varied composition, but when this material is digested and offered to the tissues for nutrition the substances that are usable as sources of energy are found to be fairly limited in number, consisting of three simple sugars (glucose, levulose and galactose), a few neutral fats (chiefly the glycerol esters of palmitic, stearic, oleic and butyric acids) and the 21 or 22 amino acids composing the various proteins. Other complex organic compounds containing chemical energy are either useless or injurious to the tissues, or they have a structure such that the tissues cannot act upon them. Such substances cannot be considered as foods in the scientific sense. When, therefore, we desire to know the food value of any animal or vegetable product, we analyze it to determine its composition as regards water, various essential elements (the essential mineral nutrients), proteins, carbohydrates, fats and vitamins. The table on pages 1016–1017 may be taken as an indication of the average composition of some representative commonly used foods. An examination of this table shows that the animal foods, particularly the meats, are characterized by their small percentage in carbohydrate and by a relatively large amount of protein or of protein and fat. With respect to the last two foodstuffs, meats can also differ appreciably among themselves.

The vegetable foods are distinguished, as a rule, by their large content of carbohydrates and the relatively small amounts of proteins and fats, as seen, for example, in the composition of rice, corn, wheat and potatoes. Nevertheless, it will be noticed that the proportion of protein in some of the vegetables is not at all insignificant. They are characterized by their richness in carbohydrates rather than by a deficiency in proteins. The composition of peas and other leguminous foods is remarkable for the large percentage of protein, which exceeds that found in meats. Other facts of interest are revealed by examination of this table. *Calcium:* milk, milk products (cheese) and soybeans are excellent sources; on the basis of amount present in relation to calories yielded, certain leafy vegetables (cabbage) are good sources in contrast to other leaves (spinach), the calcium of which is less available to the body because of the presence of oxalic acid which forms insoluble calcium oxalate in the alimentary tract. *Phosphorus:* this element is quite widespread; diets rich in plant foods will contain more than other types of dietaries. *Iron:* liver and dried brewery yeast are outstanding in their value; certain other meats and the soybean constitute good sources. *Vitamin A:* liver, and

Table 45.—Composition and Nutritive

	FOOD ENERGY	PROTEIN	FAT	CARBO-HYDRATE	CALCIUM
	CAL.	GM.	GM.	GM.	MG.
Meats, Fish, Poultry, Eggs					
Bacon, medium fat	626	9.1	65	1.1	13
Beef heart, fresh	126	(16.5)	(6.3)	(0.7)	10
Beef, round steak	194	19.3	13.0	0	11
Chicken, boned, canned	185	22.5	10.6	(0)	32
Fish, miscellaneous, medium fat	98	19.0	2.5	0	21
Liver, beef, fresh	131	(19.8)	(4.2)	(3.6)	8
Eggs, hen's, fresh	158	12.8	11.5	0.7	54
Milk and Cheese					
Fresh, whole, cow's	69	3.5	3.9	4.9	118
Cheese, American Cheddar type	393	23.9	32.3	1.7	873
Cereal and Grain Products					
Flour, wheat, white patent	355	10.8	0.9	75.9	19
Flour, wheat, white patent, enriched	355	10.8	0.9	75.9	19
Flour, whole wheat	360	13.0	2.0	72.4	38
Bread, white, enriched	261	8.5	2.0	52.3	(56)
Bread, whole wheat	262	9.5	3.5	48.0	(60)
Cornmeal, yellow, degerminated	356	8.3	1.2	78.0	10
Oatmeal, dry, uncooked	396	14.2	7.4	68.2	54
Rice, white, uncooked	351	7.6	0.3	79.4	9
Dry Beans and Peas, Nuts					
Beans, common or kidney, dry seed	350	22.0	1.5	62.1	148
Peanuts, roasted	600	26.9	44.2	23.6	74
Peas, split	354	24.5	1.0	61.7	73
Soybeans, dry, whole, mature	351	34.9	18.1	(12.0)	227
Vegetables					
Cabbage, fresh	29	1.4	0.2	5.3	46
Carrots, fresh	45	1.2	0.3	9.3	39
Peppers, green	29	1.2	0.2	5.7	11
Potatoes	85	2.0	0.1	19.1	11
Spinach	25	2.3	0.3	3.2	(0)
Sweetpotatoes	125	1.8	0.7	27.9	30
Tomatoes	23	1.0	0.3	4.0	11
Fruits					
Apples, fresh	64	0.3	0.4	14.9	6
Bananas, fresh	99	1.2	0.2	23.0	8
Blueberries	68	0.6	0.6	15.1	16
Cantaloups	23	0.6	0.2	4.6	17
Oranges	50	0.9	0.2	11.2	33
Orange juice, canned	55	0.6	0.1	12.9	(33)
Peaches, fresh	51	0.5	0.1	12.0	8
Miscellaneous					
Wheat germ	389	25.2	10.0	49.5	84
Yeast, dried brewery	348	46.1	1.6	37.4	106
Yeast, compressed (bakery)	109	13.3	0.4	13.0	25

* Committee on Food Composition of the Food and Nutrition Board, National Research
portion, and are averages or representative values of numerous analyses. When the data are
† International units.

Value of Some Representative Foods*

PHOSPHORUS	IRON	VITAMIN A VALUE	THIAMINE	RIBOFLAVIN	NIACIN	ASCORBIC ACID
MG.	MG.	I.U.†	MG.	MG.	MG.	M.G.
108	0.8	(0)	(0.42)	(0.10)	(2.1)	0
236	6.2	(0)	0.54	0.90	6.8	13.8
208	2.9	(0)	0.12	0.15	5.2	0
(218)	(1.9)	trace	0.01	0.15	3.7	2
218	1.0		0.07	0.07	4.2	(2)
373	12.1	19,200	0.27	2.80	16.1	30.9
210	2.7	1,140	0.11	0.34	0.1	0
93	0.07	(160)	0.04	0.17	0.1	1
610	(0.57)	1,740	0.04	0.50	(0.2)	(0)
93	0.7	(0)	0.07	0.03	0.9	0
93	(2.9)	(0)	(0.44)	(0.26)	(3.5)	0
385	3.8	(0)	0.56	0.12	5.6	0
(100)	(1.8)	(0)	(0.24)	(0.15)	(2.2)	0
370	2.6	(0)	0.28	0.15	3.5	0
140	1.0	300	0.15	0.06	0.9	0
365	5.2	(0)	0.55	0.14	1.1	0
92	0.7	(0)	0.05	0.03	1.4	0
463	10.3	0	0.57	0.37	1.8	2
393	1.9	0	0.30	0.16	16.2	(0)
397	6.0	370	0.93	0.37	2.9	2
586	8.0	110	1.14	0.31	2.1	trace
31	0.5	80	0.07	0.06	0.3	52
37	0.8	12,000	0.07	0.06	0.5	6
25	0.4	630	0.07	0.04	0.4	120
56	0.7	20	0.11	0.04	1.2	15
55	3.0	9,400	0.12	0.24	0.7	59
49	0.7	7,700	0.10	0.06	0.7	22
27	0.6	1,100	0.06	0.04	0.6	23
10	0.3	90	0.04	0.02	0.2	4
28	0.6	430	0.09	0.06	0.6	10
13	0.8	280	(0.03)	(0.07)	(0.3)	16
16	0.4	3,420	0.06	0.04	0.8	33
23	0.4	(190)	0.08	0.03	0.2	50
(23)	(0.4)	(100)	0.07	0.02	0.2	42
22	0.6	880	0.02	0.05	0.9	8
1,096	8.1	(0)	2.05	0.80	4.6	(0)
1,893	18.2	(0)	9.69	5.45	36.2	(0)
605	4.9	(0)	0.45	2.07	28.2	(0)

Council, Washington, D. C., 1945. All values are on a 100-gram basis, pertain to the edible
scanty, the figures are enclosed in parentheses.

the colored vegetables and fruits which contain appreciable amounts of provitamin A, the pigment carotene, are our best sources. *Thiamine:* among animal foods liver is the best source. It is an interesting fact that the muscle of the pig is many times richer in vitamin B_1 than beef muscle. In the plant kingdom this vitamin is concentrated in the seed which accounts for the high values for the whole grains and legumes. *Riboflavin:* liver, milk, milk products and yeast are excellent; eggs are good. *Niacin (nicotinic acid):* important foods furnishing this dietary essential are liver, heart muscle and other meats, yeast, the peanut and the soybean. *Ascorbic acid (vitamin C):* peppers constitute the richest known natural source of this factor. Among our commonly used foods the citrus fruits and their juices contain the largest amounts, and the tomato and its juice rank next. Broadly speaking, all of the fresh vegetables and fruits that are usually eaten in the raw state (in the salad dish for example) contribute significant amounts of this vitamin.

Analyses such as are given here are indispensable in determining the true nutritive value of foods. Nevertheless, it must be borne in mind that the chemical composition of a food is not alone sufficient to determine its precise value in nutrition. It is obviously true that it is not what we eat, but what we digest and absorb, that is nutritious to the body, so that, in addition to determining the proportions of foodstuffs in any given food, it is necessary to determine to what extent the several constituents are digested and absorbed. This factor can be obtained only by actual experiments. It may be said here, however, that in general the proteins of animal foods are more completely digested than are those of vegetables. Moreover, the animal proteins are better fitted by their composition to serve as replacement material for animal tissues. In the animal foods, chemical analysis comes nearer to expressing directly the nutritive value, but we shall find that the proteins are not all of equal value in metabolism, and the same fact is true probably to some extent for the different fats and carbohydrates. There is much to be learned regarding the specific action of the many varieties of foodstuffs which, at present, cannot be stated in a table of analyses of the foods. For example, the nitrogen contained in the foodstuffs is usually assumed to be present in the form of protein, this substance actually being determined conventionally by analyzing for nitrogen and multiplying the result by a factor. As a matter of fact, some of the nitrogen may be present in the form of amino acids, nitrogenous bases like betaine (true particularly of plant leaves) and other nonprotein substances, and the use of a factor in such cases really gives quite erroneous results.

With regard to the distribution of the vitamins in foods, the data already at hand are the results in some cases of feeding experiments on animals like the rat, in other instances of chemical analyses, and in still other cases of assays involving the growth of micro-organisms—microbio-assays. For some of the vitamins no really satisfactory chemical method of analysis has as yet been found and therefore some form of bio-assay is required. The history of investigation in this field shows that when the exact chemical structure of a vitamin molecule has been discovered, sooner or later a chemical method for its determination has been worked out. It is reasonable, therefore, to expect that eventually even those vitamins that must still be assayed by a biological method will be determined by a more expeditious chemical procedure.

Accessory Articles of Diet. In addition to the foodstuffs proper, our foods contain numerous other substances which in one way or another are useful in nutrition, although not absolutely necessary. These substances, differing in nature and importance, may be classified under the three heads of:

Flavors: The various oils or esters that give odor and taste to foods.
Condiments: Pepper, salt, mustard, etc.
Stimulants: Alcohol, tea, coffee, cocoa, etc.

Chemical Changes of the Foodstuffs During Digestion. The physiology of digestion consists chiefly in the study of the chemical changes that the food undergoes during its passage through the alimentary canal. These changes are effected through the agency of a group of bodies known as enzymes, the exact chemical action of which is more obscure than that of the ordinary agents with which we have to deal. It will save repetition to give here certain general facts that are known with reference to these bodies, reserving for later treatment the details of the action of the specific enzymes found in the different digestive secretions.

ENZYMES AND THEIR ACTION

Historical note. To the older physicians the process of the digestion of food was a great mystery. Some of them conceived it as a chemical or vital process described under such general terms as concoction, fermentation or putrefaction, while others stressed the mechanical or triturating action of the stomach. As late as the beginning of the nineteenth century little positive knowledge had been obtained in regard to the nature of the changes affecting the food. The usual description in textbooks of that period was limited to the statement that the food is dissolved in the stomach to make a liquid known as chyme, which later in the intestine is converted to the milky chyle by a process of chylification, and is absorbed by the lacteals. At that time the lacteals were considered to be the chief if not the sole absorbents of the digested food. The profitable line of work in the early nineteenth century began with a study of fermentations. The significance and use of the term "fermentation" have varied greatly during the course of years. The word at first was applied to certain obvious and apparently spontaneous changes in organic materials which are accompanied by the liberation of bubbles of gas: such, for instance, as the alcoholic fermentations, in which alcohol is formed from sugar, with the liberation of carbon dioxide; the acid fermentations, as in the souring of milk; and the putrefactive fermentations, by means of which animal substances are disintegrated, with the production of offensive odors. These mysterious phenomena excited naturally the interest of investigators, and with the development of chemical knowledge numerous other processes were discovered which resemble the typical fermentations in that they seem to be due to specific agents whose mode of action differs from the usual chemical reactions, especially in the fact that the causative agent itself (or the ferment, as it is called) is not destroyed or used up in the reaction. Thus it was discovered that germinating barley grains contain a component which can be extracted by water and which can convert starch into sugar (Kirchhoff, 1814). Later this substance was separated by precipitation with alcohol and was given the name of diastase (Payen and Persoz, 1833). About the same time (1831) Leuchs found that saliva has the property of changing starch to sugar, and Miahle suggested that this reaction is due to a ferment, similar to the diastase of barley grains, for which he proposed the name "animal diastase." Schwann in 1836 demonstrated the existence of a ferment (pepsin) in gastric juice capable of acting upon albuminous substances, and a number of similar bodies were soon discovered: trypsin in the pancreatic juice, amygdalin, invertin, etc. These substances were all designated as ferments, and their action was compared to that of the alcoholic fermentation with yeast, the process of putrefaction, etc. Naturally very many theories have been proposed regarding the cause of the processes of fermentation. For the historical development and interrelation of these theories references must be made to special works (6, 10).* It is

* See also various review articles on enzymes in the volumes of *Annual Review of Biochemistry*, the first of which appeared in 1932.

sufficient here to say that the brilliant work of Pasteur established the fact that the fermentations in the old sense—alcoholic, acid, and putrefactive—are due to the presence and activity of living organisms. He showed, moreover, that many diseases are likewise due to the activity of minute living organisms, and thus justified the view held by some of the older physicians that there is a similarity in the processes of fermentation and disease. The clear demonstration of the importance of living organisms in some fermentations and the equally clear proof of the existence of another group of ferment actions in which living material is not directly concerned led to a classification which divided ferments into two great groups: the living or organized ferments, such as the yeast cell, bacteria, etc.; and the nonliving or unorganized ferments, such as pepsin, trypsin, etc., which later were generally designated as enzymes (Kühne). The separation appeared to be satisfactory until Buchner (1897) showed that an unorganized ferment, an enzyme (zymase) capable of producing alcohol from sugar, may be extracted from yeast cells. Later the same observer (1903) succeeded in extracting enzymes from the lactic acid-producing bacteria and the acetic acid-producing bacteria which are capable of giving the same reactions as the living bacteria. These discoveries indicate clearly that there is no essential difference between the activity of living and nonliving ferments. The so-called organized ferments probably produce their effects not by virtue of their specific life metabolism, but by the manufacture within their substance of specific enzymes. If we accept this conclusion, then the general explanation of fermentation is to be sought in the nature of the enzymatic processes.

Within recent years the study of the enzymes has attracted especial attention. The general point of view regarding their mode of action is that advocated especially by Ostwald (7). He assumed, reviving an older view (Berzelius), that the ferment actions are similar to those of catalysis. By catalysis we mean a chemical reaction which is brought about or facilitated by the mere contact or presence of certain substances, the catalyzers, which are not themselves altered by the reaction. Thus, hydrogen and oxygen at ordinary temperatures do not combine to form water, but if spongy platinum is present the two gases unite readily. The platinum does not enter into the reaction, at least it undergoes no permanent change, and it is said, therefore, to act by catalysis. Many similar catalytic reactions are known, and the chemists have reached the important generalization that in such reactions the catalyzer, platinum in the above instance, simply hastens a process which would occur without it, but much more slowly. A catalyzer is a substance, therefore, that alters the velocity of a reaction, but does not initiate it. This idea is illustrated very clearly by the catalysis of hydrogen peroxide. This substance decomposes spontaneously into water and oxygen according to the reaction $H_2O_2 = H_2O + O$, but the decomposition is greatly hastened by the presence of a catalyzer. Thus, Bredig has shown that platinum in very fine suspension, so-called colloidal solution, exerts a marked accelerating influence upon this reaction; one part of the colloidal platinum to 350 million parts of water may still exercise a perceptible effect. The blood and aqueous extracts of various tissues also catalyze the hydrogen peroxide readily, and this effect has been attributed to the action of an enzyme (catalase). The view has been proposed, therefore, that the enzymes of the body act like the catalyzers of inorganic origin: they influence the velocity and direction of certain special reactions and may be designated in general as organic catalysts. In some respects these organic catalysts differ from the ideal inorganic catalyst referred to above. For example, they appear in some cases to initiate as well as to accelerate the reaction and to some extent they may be destroyed or removed in the reaction.

Reversible Reactions. It has been shown that under proper conditions many chemical reactions are reversible—that is, may take place in opposite directions. For instance, acetic acid and ethyl alcohol brought together react with the production of ethyl acetate and water:

$$CH_3COOH + C_2H_5OH = CH_3COOC_2H_5 + H_2O$$
Acetic acid   Alcohol   Ethyl acetate   Water

On the other hand, ethyl acetate and water react with the formation of some acetic acid and ethyl alcohol, so that the reaction indicated in the above equation takes place in opposite directions, figuratively speaking—a fact which may be indicated by a symbol of this kind:

$$CH_3COOH + C_2H_5OH \rightleftharpoons CH_3COOC_2H_5 + H_2O$$

It is evident that in a reversible reaction of this sort the opposite changes will eventually strike an equilibrium, the solution or mixture will contain some of all four substances, and this equilibrium will remain constant as long as the conditions are unchanged. If the conditions are altered, however— if, for example, some of the substances formed are removed or the mixture is altered as to its concentration—then the reaction will proceed unequally in the two directions until a new equilibrium is established. The importance, in the present connection, of this conception of reversibility of reactions is found in the fact that a number of the catalytic reactions are also reversible. The catalyzer may not only accelerate a reaction between two substances but may also accelerate the recomposition of the products into the original substances. An excellent instance of this double effect has been obtained by Kastle and Loevenhart in experiments upon one of the enzymes of the animal body, lipase. Lipase is the enzyme which in the body acts upon the neutral fats, converting them into fatty acids and glycerin—a process that takes place in the digestion and absorption of fats. The authors just named (3, 4) made use of a simple ester analogous to the fats, ethyl butyrate, and showed that lipase causes not only a hydrolysis of this substance into ethyl alcohol and butyric acid, but also a synthesis of the two last-named substances into ethyl butyrate and water. The reaction effected by the lipase is therefore reversible and may be expressed as:

$$C_3H_7COOC_2H_5 + H_2O \rightleftharpoons C_3H_7COOH + C_2H_5OH$$
Ethyl butyrate   Water   Butyric acid   Ethyl alcohol

Lipase is capable of exerting probably a similar reversible reaction on the fats in the body. Assuming the existence of such an action in the body, it is possible to explain not only the digestion of fats but also their formation in the tissues and their absorption from the tissues during starvation. That is, according to the conditions of concentration, etc., one and the same enzyme may cause a splitting up of the neutral fat into fatty acids and glycerol or a storing up of neutral fat by the synthesis of fatty acid and glycerol. In the subcutaneous tissues, therefore, fat may be stored, to a certain point, or, if the conditions are altered, the fat that is there may be changed over to the fatty acids and glycerol and be oxidized in the body as food.

Specificity of Enzymes. A most interesting feature of the activity of an enzyme is that it is specific. The enzymes that act upon the carbohydrates are not capable of affecting the proteins or fats, and vice versa. So in the fermentation of closely related bodies such as the disaccharids, the enzyme that acts upon the maltose is not capable of affecting the lactose; each requires seemingly its own specific enzyme. In fact, there is no clear proof that any single enzyme can produce more than one kind of ferment action. If in any extract or secretion two or more kinds of ferment action can be demonstrated, the tendency at present is to attribute these different activities to the existence of separate enzymes. The pancreatic juice, for example, splits proteins, starches and fats and curdles milk, and there are assumed to be four different enzymes present—namely, trypsin, diastase, lipase and rennin. So if an extract containing diastase is also capable of decomposing hydrogen peroxide it is believed that this latter effect is due to the existence of a special enzyme, catalase. Each ferment is adapted to act upon or become attached to a molecule with a certain definite structure—fitted to it, in fact, as a key to its lock. According to Willstätter (11), each enzyme contains a special reactive group which combines with a definite atomic grouping in the substance acted upon. In this respect the action of the so-called hydrolytic enzymes differs markedly from that of the dilute acids or alkalies which hydrolyze many different substances without indication of any specificity. It has become customary to speak of the substance upon which an enzyme acts as its *substrate*, and it has been assumed that the action of the enzyme takes place in two stages: first, the combination of the enzyme and the substrate; second, the breaking down of this compound to give the final product of the reaction. There is reason for believing that these two stages may be separated, and that enzymes, which on account of certain conditions (such as heating) have lost their power of decomposing the substrate, may still have the power of combining with it. There are toxins (diphtheria toxin, for example) that can be treated so as to lose their toxicity yet retain their power to enter into the chemical combinations essential for antibody formation. Such derivatives of toxins are designated "toxoids." Bayliss has suggested "zymoid" as the name for the analogous derivative of an enzyme.

Definition and Classification of Enzymes. On the basis of the considerations presented in the preceding paragraphs Oppenheimer (6) suggests the following definition: An enzyme is a substance, produced by living cells, which acts by catalysis. The enzyme itself remains unchanged in this process, and it acts specifically—that is, each enzyme exerts its activity only upon substances the molecules of which have a certain definite structural and stereo-chemical arrangement. The enzymes of the body are organic substances of a colloid structure with a detailed chemical composition which is still a matter of discussion, although in a number of cases, as will be described later, it has been shown that they belong to the group of proteins. A distinction is made frequently between *endo-enzymes* and *exo-enzymes*. In the latter group are included those enzymes which are eliminated from the cells in which they are formed, and which are found, therefore, in solution in the secretions—for example, the ptyalin of the saliva or the pepsin of the gastric juice. By endo-enzymes is meant a group of intracellular enzymes which are not secreted, but are held within the cells. To obtain them in solution or suspension it is necessary to destroy the cells, usually by mechanical means, such as grinding or freezing, with subsequent extraction, and, in some cases, by submitting the ground mass to a great pressure in a hydraulic press. The liquid obtained by this latter method is known as the "press juice" of the tissue. In life the endo-enzymes play their part within the bounds of the cells in which they are contained, and probably constitute the chief means through which are effected the metabolic processes that characterize living matter.

With regard to the names and classification of the different enzymes, there is some lack of uniformity. Duclaux (2) has suggested that an enzyme be designated by the name of the body on which its action is exerted, and that all of them be given the termination -*ase*. The enzyme acting on fat on this system would be named lipase; that on starch, amylase; that on maltose, maltase, etc. The suggestion has been followed in part only, the older enzymes which were first discovered being referred to most frequently under their original names. The advances in biochemistry in recent years have tended to multiply greatly the number of specific enzymes called upon to explain different stages in functional metabolism. These will be referred to in the proper places. At this point attention need be called only to the terminology used for certain of the more general types of enzymatic activity occurring in the body.

1. The proteolytic or protein-splitting enzymes. Examples: pepsin of gastric juice, trypsin of pancreatic juice. They cause a hydrolytic cleavage of the protein molecule.
2. The amylolytic or starch-splitting enzymes. Examples: ptyalin or salivary diastase, amylase or pancreatic diastase. Their action is closely similar to that of the classical enzyme of this group—diastase—found in germinating barley grains. They cause a hydrolytic cleavage of the starch molecule.
3. The lipolytic or fat-splitting enzymes. Example: the lipase found in the pancreatic secretion, in the liver, connective tissues, blood, etc. They cause a hydrolytic cleavage of the fat molecule.
4. The sugar-splitting enzymes. These again fall into two subgroups: (i) The inverting enzymes, which convert the double sugars or disaccharides into the monosaccharides. Examples: maltase, which splits maltose to glucose; invertase, which splits cane sugar to glucose and levulose; and lactase, which splits milk sugar (lactose) to glucose and galactose. (ii) The enzymes which split the monosaccharides. There is evidence of the presence in the tissues of an enzyme or an enzyme system capable of splitting the sugar of the blood and tissues (glucose) into lactic acid.
5. The coagulating enzymes, which convert soluble to insoluble proteins. Example: the coagulation of the casein of milk by rennin.
6. The oxidizing enzymes or oxidases. A group of enzymes which set up oxidation processes. Some of the details of the activity of these enzymes are considered in the discussion of physiological oxidations.
7. The dehydrogenating enzymes or dehydrogenases. In the process of physiological oxidation the first step in many cases is the removal of hydrogen from the substrate. This is effected through the activity of specific dehydrogenating enzymes.
8. The deaminizing enzymes, which split off an NH_2 group from the amino acids. Thus alanine (aminopropionic acid) by hydrolysis or oxidation loses its NH_2 group as ammonia and passes into lactic acid.

$$CH_3CHNH_2COOH + H_2O = NH_3 + CH_3CHOHCOOH$$

9. The phosphatases. Enzymes widely present in animal tissues, particularly in calcifying cartilage, kidney cortex and intestinal mucosa. They cause hydrolysis of monophosphoric esters with the production of phosphoric acid. Their action is reversible.

The enzymes contained in the first, second, third and fourth of these groups are the ones that play the chief roles in the digestive processes, and it will be noticed that they all act by *hydrolysis*—that is, they cause the molecules of the substance to undergo decomposition or cleavage by a reaction with water. Thus, in the conversion of maltose to glucose by the action of maltase the reaction may be expressed by the equation:

$$C_{12}H_{22}O_{11} + H_2O = C_6H_{12}O_6 = C_6H_{12}O_6$$
$$\text{Maltose} \qquad\qquad \text{Glucose} \quad\; \text{Glucose}$$

And the hydrolysis of the neutral fats by lipase may be expressed so:

$$C_3H_5(C_{18}H_{35}O_2)_3 + 3H_2O = C_3H_5(OH)_3 = 3(C_{18}H_{36}O_2)$$

Tristearin · · · · · · · · · · · · · Glycerol   Stearic acid

The proteolytic enzymes or proteases likewise act through hydrolysis and at least one point of attack is at the linkage, —CO—NH—, of one amino acid grouping with another.

General Properties of Enzymes. The specific reactions of the various enzymes of the body are referred to under separate heads. The following general characteristics may be noted:

Solubility. Most of the enzymes are soluble in water or salt solutions, or in glycerol. By these means they may be extracted conveniently from the various tissues.

Temperature. The body enzymes are characterized by the fact that they are destroyed by high temperatures (60°C. to 80°C.) and that their effect is retarded in part or entirely by low temperatures. Most of them show an optimum activity at temperatures approximating that of the body.

Precipitation, adsorption. The enzymes are precipitated from their solutions in part at least by excess of alcohol. The enzymes, moreover, show an interesting tendency to be carried down mechanically by flocculent precipitates produced in their solutions or by suspensions of alumina earths or gels. The mode of union of the enzyme with the precipitate in these cases comes under the general head of adsorption. It consists in a concentration of the enzyme at the limiting surface between the particles of the precipitate and the solution.

Incompleteness of their action. In any given mixture of a substrate and its enzyme the action of the latter is usually not complete—that is, all of the substrate does not disappear. One explanation for this fact has been found in the reversibility of the action of the enzyme when this is known to occur. If the reaction proceeds in both directions, then evidently under fixed conditions a final equilibrium will be reached in which no further apparent change takes place, although in reality the condition is not one of rest but of balance between opposing processes proceeding at a definite rate. In addition to this factor it may be shown in some cases that the products of the reaction serve to retard further action, possibly by forming a compound of some kind with the enzyme. Within the body itself the action of an enzyme may be complete, since the products are removed by absorption.

Active and inactive form. In many cases it can be shown that the enzyme exists within the cell in an inactive form, and even when secreted it may still be inactive. This antecedent or inactive stage is usually designated as *zymogen* or *proferment*. The zymogen may be stored in the cell in the form of granules which are converted into active enzyme at the moment of secretion, or it may be secreted in inactive form and require the cooperation of some other substance before it is capable of effecting its normal reaction. In such cases the second substance is said to activate the enzyme. In connection with the process of activation, various terms have been employed to designate the substance responsible for the activation. According to one classification inorganic substances causing activation are designated simply as *activators*, while organic substances playing a similar role are named *kinases*. An example of the latter is found in the case of the enterokinase which activates the trypsin of the pancreatic secretion. Activation is an indefinite term. It implies that some change has been effected in the chemical structure of the substance acted upon, such as a loss of electrons, which increases its reactivity.

Co-enzymes or coferments. In addition to the process of activation, it would seem that in some cases the action of an enzyme is facilitated by, or perhaps is even dependent upon, the presence of an accessory substance. A co-enzyme may be an inorganic substance, such as salts of calcium or mag-

Partial List of the Enzymes Concerned in the Processes of Digestion and Nutrition

	ENZYME	WHERE CHIEFLY FOUND	ACTION
Act on carbohydrates	Ptyalin (salivary Diastase)	Salivary secretion	Converts starch to sugar (maltose)
	Amylase (pancreatic diastase)	Pancreatic secretion	Converts starch to sugar (maltose)
	Liver glycogenase	Liver	Converts glycogen to glucose
	Muscle glycogenase	Muscles	Converts glycogen to glucose
	Sucrase	Small intestine	Converts cane sugar to glucose and levulose
	Maltase	Small intestine, salivary and pancreatic secretion	Converts maltose to glucose
	Lactase	Small intestine	Converts lactose to glucose and galactose
	Glycolytic?	Muscles?	Splits sugar to lactic acid
Acts on fats	Lipase (steapsin)	Pancreatic secretion, fat, tissues, blood, etc.	Splits neutral fats to fatty acids and glycerol
Act on proteins	Pepsin	Gastric juice	Converts proteins to proteoses and peptones
	Trypsin	Pancreatic juice	Splits proteins into smaller polypeptid groupings
	Erepsin	Small intestine	Splits peptids into their constituent amino acids: is undoubtedly a mixture of peptidases
	Rennin	Stomach	Acts on casein of milk, converting it into paracasein, which, in the presence of calcium ions, forms a milk clot
	Aminopeptidase	Small intestine	Acts on polypeptides containing a free amino group; probably a group of enzymes
	Carboxypeptidase	Pancreas	Acts on polypeptides containing a free carboxyl group
	Group of autolytic enzymes	Tissues generally	Splits proteins into nitrogenous bases and amino bodies
	Nucleases	Pancreas, spleen, thymus, etc.	Split nucleic acid with formation of purine bases, etc.

Partial List of the Enzymes Concerned in the Processes of Digestion and Nutrition—(Continued)

	ENZYME	WHERE CHIEFLY FOUND	ACTION
Deaminizing enzymes	Guanase	Thymus, adrenals, pancreas	Converts guanine to xanthine by splitting off an NH_2 group as ammonia (NH_3)
	Adenase	Spleen, pancreas, liver	Converts adenine to hypoxanthine by splitting off an NH_2 group as ammonia (NH_3)
	Deaminase?	Tissues generally	Splits off the NH_2 group from the amino acids with the formation of non-nitrogenous organic acids
	Oxidases	Lungs, liver, muscle, etc.	Cause oxidation of organic substances, as in the conversion of hypoxanthine to xanthine and of xanthine to uric acid
	Reductases	Tissues generally	Cause reduction or hydrogenation
	Catalase	Many tissues	Decomposes hydrogen peroxide
	Arginase	Liver, spleen	Splits arginine with production of urea and ornithine (diaminovaleric acid)
	Carboxylase ?	Tissues generally	Splits off CO_2 from the carboxyl group

nesium, or a complex organic compound. Its mode of action is difficult to explain in complete detail and probably differs in character in the several instances observed. In some cases it may be supposed that after the enzyme combines with its substrate, further effect upon the substrate depends on the activity of the co-enzyme. Examples of this combined activity are furnished by the influence of bile salts upon lipase and the effect of adenosine-triphosphoric acid upon the enzymatic conversion of hexosephosphate to lactic acid.

Chemical Composition of Enzymes. Many efforts have been made to determine the chemical nature of enzymes and their mode of action, but the problem has not yet been completely solved. The difficulty has been to isolate them in pure condition. Willstätter (10) and his coworkers have purified and differentiated some of them by adsorption on kaolin and various preparations of aluminum hydroxide. From the results of their work the general theory was developed that the enzymes are composed of one or more chemically active groups combined with a colloid carrier. The character of the colloid influences the properties of the enzyme, conferring upon it stability and catalytic activity, but the specificity and power of combination with the substrate depend upon the chemically active group.

In the older methods of purification the products usually gave protein reactions and some workers believed, therefore, that enzymes are essentially protein bodies, but there was always the possibility that the protein present was an impurity and not the active substance. This objection has been practically removed through the use of newer methods of preparation which have made it possible to obtain the enzymes, or some of them, in the form of crystals. The first result of this kind was reported by Sumner (8, 9). He prepared a crystalline protein from the meal of the jack-bean which had the properties of a urease, that is, it was capable of hydrolyzing urea to ammonium carbonate. The crystals had a high degree of ferment activity and on chemical examination showed the reactions and composition of a protein. Later the brilliant work of Northrop (5) and his colleagues demonstrated that pepsin and trypsin, as well as their inactive forms, pepsinogen and trypsinogen, can be obtained as crystals which are pure proteins and have powerful proteolytic activity. Other enzymes that have been crystallized are chymotrypsin, one of the proteolytic enzymes of the pancreatic secretion, amylase, a carboxypeptidase, a protease from papain, catalase and a respiratory enzyme, flavin enzyme, present in the tissues generally. With regard to the last two it seems to be agreed that they consist of protein combined with a chemically active group which is not protein, but the others are proteins alone, and their specific activity as enzymes must be referred to some peculiarity in the arrangement of the amino acids in the molecule.

So far as work has gone at present, the results indicate that some of the enzymes, especially those concerned with the hydrolysis of the foods in digestion, are protein bodies of specific structure, while others consist, in terms of Willstätter's hypothesis, of a protein combined with a reactive or so-called prosthetic group, both parts being necessary for enzymatic activity.

REFERENCES

1. BAYLISS, W. M. *The nature of enzyme action.* 5th ed. London, Longmans, Green and Co., 1925. 200 pp.

2. DUCLAUX, E. *Traite de microbiologie.* Paris, Masson et Cie., 1898–1899. 2 vols.

3. KASTLE, J. H. and LOEVENHART, A. S. Concerning lipase, the fat-splitting enzyme, and the reversibility of its action. *Amer. chem. J.,* 1900, *24*:491–525.

4. LOEVENHART, A. S. On the relation of lipase to fat metabolism—lipogenesis. *Amer. J. Physiol.,* 1901–02, *6*:331–350.

5. NORTHROP, J. H. Isolation and properties of pepsin and trypsin. *Harvey Lect.,* 1934–35, *30*:229–270.

6. OPPENHEIMER, K. *Fermente und ihre Wirkungen.* Leipzig, Georg Thieme, 1924–1929. 4 vols.

7. OSTWALD, W. *Lehrbuch der allgemeinen Chemie,* 2nd ed. Leipzig, 1903.

8. SUMNER, J. B. The isolation and crystallization of the enzyme urease. *J. biol. Chem.,* 1926, *69*:435–441.

9. SUMNER, J. B. and HAND, D. B. Crystalline urease, II. *J. biol. Chem.,* 1928, *76*:149–162.

10. WALDSCHMIDT-LEITZ, E. The mode of action and differentiation of proteolytic enzymes. *Physiol. Rev.,* 1931, *11*:358–370.

11. WILLSTÄTTER, R. Problems of modern enzyme chemistry. *Chem. Rev.,* 1933, *13*:501–512.

CHAPTER 47

THE SALIVARY GLANDS AND THEIR DIGESTIVE ACTION

The first of the secretions with which the food comes into contact is the saliva. This is a mixed secretion from the large salivary glands and the small unnamed mucous and serous glands that open into the mouth cavity.

Salivary Glands. The salivary glands in man are three in number on each side—the parotid, the submaxillary, and the sublingual. The parotid gland communicates with the mouth by a large duct (Stensen's duct) which opens upon the inner surface of the cheek opposite the second molar tooth of the upper jaw. The submaxillary gland lies below the lower jaw, and its duct (Wharton's duct) opens into the mouth cavity at the side of the frenum of the tongue. The sublingual gland lies in the floor of the mouth to the side of the frenum and opens into the mouth cavity by a number (8 to 20) of small

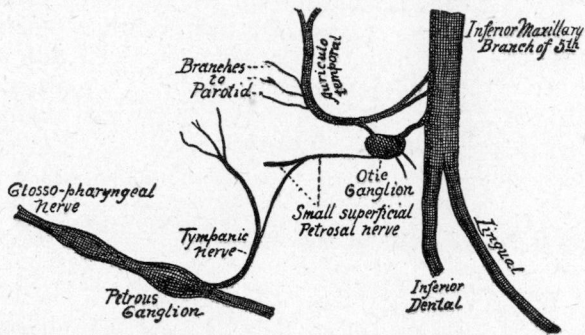

Fig. 459.—Schematic representation of the course of the cerebral fibers to the parotid gland.

ducts known as the ducts of Rivinus. One larger duct that runs parallel with the duct of Wharton and opens separately into the mouth cavity is sometimes present in man. It is known as the duct of Bartholin and occurs normally in the dog.

The course of the nerve fibers supplying the large salivary glands is interesting in view of the physiological results of their stimulation. The description here given applies especially to their arrangement in the dog. These glands receive their nerve supply from two general sources—namely, the bulbar autonomics or parasympathetic fibers and the thoracic autonomics or sympathetic fibers. The parotid gland receives its parasympathetic fibers from the glossopharyngeal or ninth cranial nerve; they pass into a branch of this nerve, known as the tympanic branch or nerve of Jacobson, and thence to the small superficial petrosal nerve, through which they reach the otic ganglion. From this ganglion they pass (postganglionic fibers) by way of the auriculotemporal branch of the inferior maxillary division of the fifth cranial nerve to the parotid gland (Fig. 459). The sympathetic fibers pass to the superior cervical ganglion by way of the cervical sympathetic, and thence as

postganglionic fibers in branches which accompany the arteries distributed
to the gland. The parasympathetic supply for the submaxillary and sublingual glands arises from the brain in the facial nerve and passes out in the
chorda tympani branch (Fig. 460). This latter nerve, after emerging from the
tympanic cavity through the Gasserian fissure, joins the lingual nerve. After
running with this nerve for a short distance, the secretory (and vasodilator)
nerve fibers destined for the submaxillary and sublingual glands branch off
and pass to the glands, following the course of the ducts. Where the chorda
tympani fibers leave the lingual there is a small ganglion which has received
the name of submaxillary ganglion. The nerve fibers to the glands pass close
to this ganglion, but Langley showed that only those destined for the sublingual gland really connect with the nerve cells of the ganglion, and he
suggests, therefore, that it should be called the sublingual instead of the
submaxillary ganglion. The nerve fibers for the submaxillary gland make

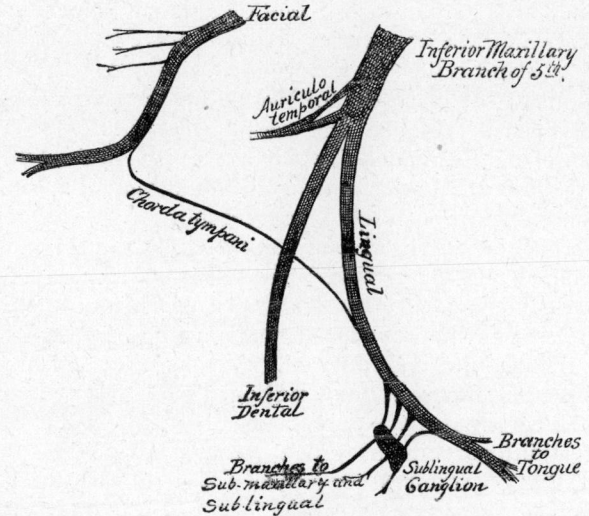

Fig. 460.—Schematic representation of the course of the chorda tympani nerve to the submaxillary gland.

connections with nerve cells lying mainly within the hilus of the gland itself.
The supply of sympathetic fibers has the same general course as those for
the parotid—namely, through the cervical sympathetic to the superior
cervical ganglion and thence to the glands.

Histological Structure. The salivary glands belong to the type of compound tubular glands, that is, the secreting portions are tubular in shape,
although in cross-sections these tubes may present various outlines according
as the plane of the section passes through them. The parotid is described
usually as a typical serous or albuminous gland. Its secreting epithelium is
composed of cells which in the fresh condition as well as in preserved specimens contain numerous fine granules and its secretion contains some albumin. The submaxillary gland differs in histology in different animals. In
some, as the dog or cat, the secretory tubes are composed chiefly or exclusively
of gland cells of the mucous type. In man the gland is of a mixed type, the
secretory tubes containing both mucous and albuminous cells. The sublingual

gland in man also contains both varieties of cells, although the mucous cells predominate. In accordance with these histological characteristics it is found that the secretion from the submaxillary and sublingual glands is thick and mucilaginous as compared with that from the parotid.

The salivary glands possess definite secretory nerves which when stimulated cause the formation of a secretion. This fact indicates that there must be a direct contact of some kind between the gland cells and the terminations of the secretory fibers. The ending of the nerve fibers in the submaxillary and sublingual glands has been described by a number of observers (6). The accounts differ somewhat as to details of the finer anatomy, but it seems to be clearly established that the secretory fibers from the chorda tympani end around the intrinsic nerve ganglion cells of the glands (preganglionic fibers), and from these latter cells axons (postganglionic fibers) are distributed to the secreting cells, passing to these cells along the duct. The nerve fibers terminate in a plexus upon the membrana propria of the alveoli, and from this plexus fine fibrils pass inward to end on and between the secreting cells. It would seem from these observations that the nerve fibrils do not penetrate or fuse with the gland cells, as was formerly supposed, but form a terminal network in contact with the cells, following thus the general schema for the connection between nerve fibers and peripheral tissues.

Composition of the Secretion. The saliva as it is found in the mouth is a colorless or opalescent, turbid, and viscid liquid with a specific gravity of about 1.003 and a neutral or slightly acid reaction ($pH = 6.6$ to 7.1). It may contain numerous flat cells derived from the epithelium of the mouth, and from the peculiar spherical cells known as salivary corpuscles, which seem to be altered leukocytes. The important constituents of the secretion are mucin, a diastatic enzyme known as ptyalin, maltase, traces of protein and of potassium thiocyanide, and inorganic salts such as potassium and sodium chloride, potassium sulfate, sodium carbonate, and calcium carbonate and phosphate. The carbonates are particularly abundant in the saliva, and the secretion, in addition, contains much carbon dioxide in solution. Thus, Pflüger found that 65 volumes per cent of CO_2 might be obtained from the saliva, of which 42.5 per cent was in the form of carbonates. The amount of CO_2 in solution and combined is an indication of the active chemical changes occurring in the gland.

Of the organic constituents of the saliva, the protein exists in small and variable quantities, and its exact nature is not determined. The mucin gives to the saliva its ropy, mucilaginous character. This substance belongs to the group of combined proteins, glycoproteins, consisting of a protein combined with a carbohydrate group. The most interesting constituent of the mixed saliva is the ptyalin or salivary diastase. This body belongs to the group of enzymes or organic ferments, the general properties of which have been described. In some animals (dog) ptyalin seems to be normally absent from the fresh saliva.

The secretions of the parotid and the submaxillary glands can be obtained separately by inserting a cannula into the openings of the ducts in the mouth, or, according to the method of Pavlov, by transferring the end of the duct so that it opens upon the skin instead of in the mouth, thus making a salivary fistula. The secretion of the sublingual can only be obtained in sufficient quantities for analysis from the lower animals. Examination of the separate secretions shows that the main difference lies in the fact that the parotid saliva contains no mucin, while that of the submaxillary and especially of the sublingual gland is rich in mucin. The parotid saliva of man seems to be particularly rich in ptyalin as compared with that of the submaxillary.

The Secretory Nerves. The existence of secretory nerves to the salivary glands was discovered by Ludwig in 1851. The discovery is particularly interesting in that it marks the beginning of our knowledge of this kind of nerve fiber. Ludwig found that stimulation of the chorda tympani nerve causes a flow of saliva from the submaxillary gland. He also established several important facts with regard to the pressure and composition of the secretion which will be referred to presently. It was afterward shown that the salivary glands receive a double nerve supply—in part by way of the cervical sympathetic and in part through cerebral nerves. It was discovered also that not only are secretory fibers carried to the glands by these paths but that vasomotor fibers are contained in the same nerves, and the arrangement of these latter fibers is such that the cerebral nerves (parasympathetic supply) contain vasodilator fibers that cause a dilatation of the small arteries in the glands and an accelerated blood flow, while the sympathetic carries vaso-constrictor fibers whose stimulation causes a constriction of the small arteries and a diminished blood flow. The effect of stimulating these two sets of fibers is found to vary somewhat in different animals. For purposes of description we may confine ourselves to the effects observed on dogs, since much of our fundamental knowledge upon the subject is derived from Heidenhain's (4, 5) experiments upon this animal. If the chorda tympani nerve is stimulated by weak induction shocks, the gland begins to secrete promptly and the secretion, by proper regulation of the stimulation, may be kept up for hours. The secretion thus obtained is thin and watery, flows freely, is abundant in amount, and contains not more than 1 or 2 per cent of total solids. At the same time there is an increased flow of blood through the gland. The whole gland takes on a redder color than in the resting gland, and may show a distinct pulse—all of which points to a dilatation of the small arteries. If now the sympathetic fibers are stimulated, quite different results are obtained. The secretion is relatively small in amount, flows slowly, is thick and turbid, and may contain as much as 6 per cent of total solids. At the same time the gland becomes pale, and if the veins are cut the flow from them is slower than in the resting gland, thus indicating that a vaso-constriction has occurred.

The increased vascular supply to the gland accompanying the abundant flow of "chorda saliva" and the diminished flow of blood during the scanty secretion of "sympathetic saliva" suggest naturally the idea that the whole process of secretion may be, at bottom, a vasomotor phenomenon, the amount of secretion depending only on the quantity and pressure of the blood flowing through the gland. It has been shown conclusively that this idea is erroneous and that definite secretory fibers exist. The following facts may be quoted in support of this statement: (i) Ludwig showed that if a mercury manometer is connected with the duct of the submaxillary gland and the chorda is then stimulated for a certain time, the pressure in the duct may become greater than the blood pressure in the gland. This fact shows that the secretion is not derived entirely by processes of filtration from the blood. (ii) If the blood flow be shut off completely from the gland, stimulation of the chorda still gives a secretion for a short time. (iii) If atropine is injected into the gland, stimulation of the chorda causes vascular dilatation but no secretion. This may be explained by supposing that the atropine paralyzes the secretory but not the dilator fibers. (iv) Quinine hydrochloride injected into the gland causes vascular dilatation but no secretion. In this case the secretory fibers are still irritable, since stimulation of the chorda gives the usual secretion.

A still more marked difference between the effect of stimulation of the parasympathetic and the sympathetic fibers may be observed in the case of the parotid gland in the dog. Stimulation of the parasympathetic fibers in any part of their course gives an abundant, thin and watery saliva, poor in solid constituents. Stimulation of the sympathetic fibers alone (provided the parasympathetic fibers have not been stimulated shortly before and the tympanic nerve has been cut to prevent a reflex effect) usually gives no perceptible secretion at all. But in this last stimulation a marked effect is produced upon the gland, in spite of the absence of a visible secretion. This is shown by the fact that subsequent or simultaneous stimulation of the parasympathetic fibers causes a secretion very unlike that given by the parasympathetic fibers alone in that it is rich in organic constituents. The amount of organic matter in the secretion may be tenfold that of the saliva obtained by stimulation of the parasympathetic fibers alone.

Relation of the composition of the secretion to the strength of stimulation. If the stimulus to the chorda is gradually increased in strength, care being taken not to fatigue the gland, the chemical composition of the secretion is found to change with regard to the relative amounts of the water, the salts and the organic material. The water and the salts increase in amount with the increased strength of stimulus up to a certain maximal limit, which for the salts is about 0.77 per cent. It is important to observe that this effect may be obtained from a perfectly fresh gland as well as from a gland which had previously been secreting actively. With regard to the organic constituents the precise result obtained depends on the condition of the gland. If previous to the stimulation the gland was in a resting condition and unfatigued, then increased strength of stimulation is followed at first by a rise in the percentage of organic constituents, and this rise in the beginning is more marked than in the case of the salts. But with continued stimulation the increase in organic material soon ceases, and finally the amount begins actually to diminish and may fall to a low point in spite of the stronger stimulation. On the other hand, if the gland at the beginning of the experiment had been previously worked to a considerable extent, then an increase in the stimulating current, while it augments the amount of water and salts, either may have no effect at all upon the organic constituents or may cause only a temporary increase, quickly followed by a fall. Similar results may be obtained from stimulation of the parotid gland. The above facts led Heidenhain to believe that the conditions determining the secretion of the organic material are different from those controlling the water and salts, and in his theory of trophic and secretory fibers he gave a rational explanation of the differences observed.

Theory of Trophic and Secretory Nerve Fibers. This theory supposes that two physiological varieties of nerve fibers are distributed to the salivary glands. One of these varieties controls the secretion of the water and inorganic salts and its fibers may be called secretory fibers proper; while the other, to which the name trophic is given, causes the formation of the organic constituents of the secretion, probably by a direct influence on the metabolism of the cells. Were the trophic fibers to act alone, the organic products would be formed within the cell but there would be no visible secretion, and this is the hypothesis which Heidenhain used to explain the results of the experiments described above upon stimulation of the sympathetic fibers to the parotid of the dog. In this animal, according to his experiments, the sympathetic branches to the parotid contain exclusively or almost exclusively trophic fibers, while in the parasympathetic branches both trophic and secretory fibers proper are present; but this conclusion has not been entirely confirmed by more recent observers who find that while the parasympathetic nerves contain both secretory and trophic fibers, the sympathetic supplies mainly secretory fibers. The existence of two physiological varieties of fibers appears, however, to be established. Whether these fibers supply the same cells in the gland, each calling forth its own response, or whether they innervate structurally different cells, remains to be determined.

The effect of stimulation of the sympathetic and parasympathetic fibers was formerly explained as being the result of the direct action of the nerve impulses upon the metabolism of the cell cytoplasm. A different view now widely accepted assumes that the influence of the nerve fibers in this as in other organs with such a double nerve supply is exerted indirectly through humoral substances formed at the nerve terminals. With respect to the sympathetic fibers, an adrenaline-like substance is formed; something of the nature of acetylcholine is produced in the parasympathetic fibers. In view of these facts Dale has proposed the terms "adrenergic" and "cholinergic" as appropriate names for these respective nerve fibers or impulses.

The way in which the trophic ("adrenergic") fibers act has been briefly indicated. They may be supposed to set up metabolic changes in the protoplasm of the cells, leading to the formation of certain definite products such as mucin or ptyalin. That such changes do occur is abundantly shown by microscopical examination of the resting and the active gland (see Fig. 461). That these changes involve processes of oxidation is shown by the fact that during activity the gland takes up more oxygen and gives off more carbon dioxide. There is evidence to show that these gland cells during activity form fresh material from the nourishment supplied by the blood, that is, that anabolic or synthetic processes occur along with the catabolic changes. The latter are the more obvious, and are the changes which are usually associated with the action of the so-called trophic nerve fibers.

The method of action of the secretory fibers proper is difficult to understand. Experiments have shown that the amount of water given off from the blood during secretion is somewhat greater than the amount contained in the saliva (83) and there is reason to believe that the difference between the two is accounted for by an increase in the flow of lymph from the gland during activity. A satisfactory explanation of the causes leading to and controlling the flow of water cannot yet be given. In a general way it has been assumed that the effect of the nerve impulses is to cause the splitting up of some complex substance in the cells with the production of an increased number of smaller molecules, whereby the osmotic pressure is increased and a flow of water is set up from the lymph into the cells. If we assume further that the limiting layer of the cells, toward the lumen, is made more permeable, then we can understand how the water drawn into the cells from the lymph is in turn discharged into the ducts. In support of this view can be cited the observation that in those cells with *zymogen granules* the granules near the lumen border become converted into spheres containing dissolved salts in smaller relative amounts than occur in the lymph surrounding the cells. These swollen particles are then ruptured at the periphery of the cell and discharged into the lumen of the gland. This theory receives support from the work of Langstroth and collaborators (10, 11) who studied the secretion of protein material both by the pancreas and by the submaxillary gland after stimulation of the parasympathetic nerve supply. Their own interpretation of their data was stated as follows: "(a) The mechanisms responsible for the secretion of protein material, that responsible for the secretion of water, and that controlling membrane permeability, operate at rates dependent on the rate at which some activating substance is liberated within the gland by

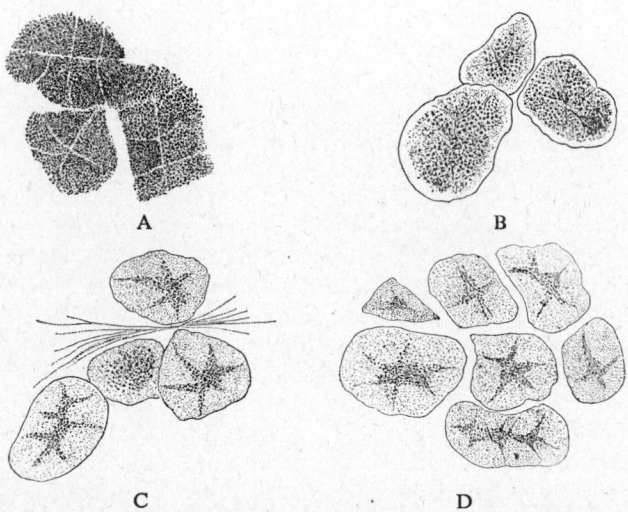

A   B

C   D

Fig. 461.—Parotid gland of the rabbit in a fresh state, showing portions of the secreting tubules: *A*, in a resting condition; *B*, after secretion caused by pilocarpine; *C*, after stronger secretion, pilocarpine and stimulation of sympathetic; *D*, after long-continued stimulation of sympathetic. (After Langley.)

the stimulation, and (b) the mechanism responsible for the secretion of protein material consists of a chemical reaction which transforms granule material to a form readily carried out of the cells by the flow of water."

Histological Changes during Activity. The cells of both the albuminous and mucous glands undergo distinct histological changes in consequence of prolonged activity, and these changes may be recognized both in preparations from the fresh gland and in preserved specimens. In the parotid gland Heidenhain studied the changes in stained sections after hardening in alcohol. In the resting gland the cells are compactly filled with granules that stain readily and are imbedded in a clear ground substance that does not stain. The nucleus is small and more or less irregular in outline. After stimulation of the tympanic nerve the cells show but little alteration, but stimulation of the sympathetic produces a marked change. The cells become smaller, the nuclei more rounded, and the granules more closely packed. This last appearance seems, however, to be due to the hardening reagents used. A truer picture of what occurs may be obtained from a study of sections of the fresh gland. Langley (7), who first used this method, described his results in the following manner: When the animal is in a fasting condition the cells have a granular appearance throughout their substance, the outlines of the different cells being faintly marked by light lines (Fig. 461, A). When the gland is made to secrete by giving the animal food, by injecting pilocarpine, or by stimulating the sympathetic nerves, the granules begin to disappear from the outer borders of the cells (Fig. 461, B), so that each cell now shows an outer, clear border and an inner granular one. If the stimulation is continued the granules become fewer in number and are collected near the lumen and the margins of the cells, the clear zone increases in extent, and the cells become smaller (Fig. 461, C, D). Evidently the granular material is used in some way to make the organic material of the secretion. Since the ptyalin is a conspicuous organic constituent of the secretion, it is assumed that the granules in the resting gland contain the ptyalin, or rather the preliminary material from

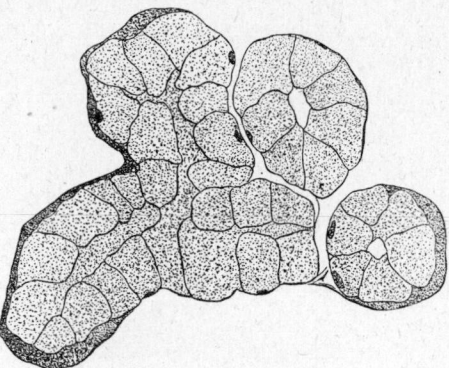

Fig. 462.—Mucous gland: submaxillary of dog; resting stage.

which the ptyalin is constructed during the act of secretion. On this latter assumption the granules are frequently spoken of as zymogen granules. During the act of secretion two distinct processes seem to be going on in the cell, leaving out of consideration, for the moment, the secretion of the water and the salts. In the first place, the zymogen granules undergo a change such that they are forced or dissolved out of the cell, and second, a constructive metabolism or anabolism is set up, leading to the formation of new protoplasmic material from the substances contained in the blood and lymph. The new material thus formed is a clear, nongranular substance, which appears first toward the basal sides of the cells. We may suppose that the clear substance during the resting periods undergoes metabolic changes, whether of a catabolic or anabolic character cannot be safely asserted, leading to the formation of new granules, and the cells are again ready to form a secretion of normal composition. It should be borne in mind that in these experiments the glands were stimulated beyond normal limits. Under ordinary conditions the cells are probably never depleted of their granular material to the extent represented in the figures.

In the cells of the mucous glands, equally marked changes may be observed after prolonged activity. In stained sections of the resting gland the cells are large and clear (Fig. 462), with flattened nuclei placed well toward the base of the cell. When the gland is made to secrete, the nuclei become more spherical and lie more toward the middle of the cell, and the cells themselves become distinctly smaller. After prolonged secretion the changes become more marked (Fig. 463) and, according to Heidenhain, some of the mucous cells may break down completely. According to most of the later observers, however, the mucous cells do not actually disintegrate, but form again new material during the period of rest, as in the case of the goblet cells of the intestine. In the mucous as in the albuminous cells, observations upon pieces of the fresh gland seem to give more reliable results than those upon preserved specimens. Langley (8) showed that in the fresh mucous cells of the submaxillary gland numerous large granules may be discovered, about 125 to 250 to a cell. These granules are comparable to those found in the goblet cells, and may be interpreted as consisting of mucin or some preparatory material from which mucin is formed. The granules are sensitive to reagents; addition of water causes them to swell up and disappear. It may be assumed that this happens during secretion, the granules becoming converted to a mucin mass which is extruded from the cell.

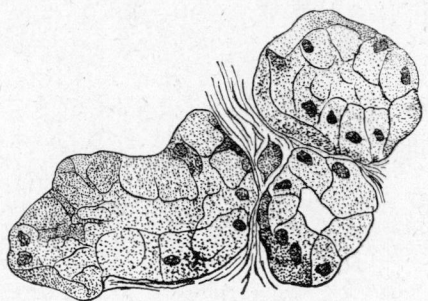

Fig. 463.—Mucous gland: submaxillary of dog after eight hours' stimulation of the chorda tympani.

Action of Atropine, Pilocarpine, and Nicotine upon the Secretory Nerves. The action of drugs upon the salivary glands and their secretions belongs properly to pharmacology, but the effects of the three drugs mentioned are so decided that they have a peculiar physiological interest. Atropine in small doses injected either into the blood or into the gland duct prevents the action of the parasympathetic fibers (tympanic nerve or chorda tympani) upon the glands. This effect was formerly explained by assuming that the atropine paralyzes the endings of the secretory fibers, but this view seems not to be correct since there is evidence that the humoral agent, the acetylcholine, is still formed, implying a normal activity of the nerve terminals. The atropine reacts with the secreting cell or some part of it in such a way that it is not affected by the acetylcholine. That the gland cell as a whole is not paralyzed is indicated by the fact that, with doses sufficient to throw out entirely the secreting action of the parasympathetic fibers, the sympathetic fibers are still effective when stimulated. Pilocarpine has directly the opposite effect to atropine. In minimal doses it sets up a continuous secretion of saliva, which may be explained upon the supposition that it stimulates the endings of the secretory fibers in the gland. Within certain limits these drugs antagonize each other—that is, the effect of pilocarpine may be removed by the subsequent application of atropine, and vice versa. Nicotine, according to the experiments of Langley (9), prevents the action of the secretory nerves, not by affecting the gland cells or the endings of the nerve fibers around them, but by paralyzing the connections between the preganglionic and postganglionic fibers. If, for example, the superior cervical ganglion is painted with a solution of nicotine, stimulation of the cervical sympathetic gives no secretion; stimulation, however, of the ganglion or between the ganglion and gland gives the usual effect.

Paralytic Secretion. A remarkable phenomenon in connection with the salivary glands is the so-called paralytic secretion. It has been known for a long time that if the chorda tympani is cut the submaxillary gland after a certain time, one to three days, begins to secrete slowly, and the secretion continues uninterruptedly for a long period—as long, perhaps, as several weeks—and eventually the gland itself undergoes atrophy. Langley states that section of the chorda on one side is followed by a continuous secretion from the glands on both sides; the secretion from the gland of the opposite side he designates as the antiparalytic or antilytic secretion. After section of the chorda the nerve fibers peripheral to the section degenerate, the process being completed within a few days. These fibers, however, do not run directly to the gland cell; they terminate in synapses around sympathetic nerve cells placed somewhere along their course—in the sublingual ganglion, for instance, or within the gland substance itself. It is the axons from these second nerve units that end around the secreting cells. Langley has accumulated some facts to show that within the period of continuance of the paralytic secretion (five to six weeks) the fibers of the sympathetic cells are still irritable to stimulation. He is inclined to believe, therefore, that the continuous secretion is due to a continuous excitation, from some cause, of the local nervous mechanism in the gland. A natural extension of this view which has been suggested (Pavlov) is that normally the activity of the sympathetic cells or of the secreting cells is kept in check by inhibitory fibers. After section of the chorda the action of these fibers falls out and the secretion continues until the glandular tissue undergoes atrophy.

Normal Mechanism of Salivary Secretion. Under normal conditions the flow of saliva from the salivary glands is the result of a reflex stimulation of the secretory nerves. The sensory fibers concerned in this reflex must be chiefly fibers of the glossopharyngeal and lingual nerves supplying the mouth and tongue. Sapid bodies and various other chemical or mechanical stimuli applied to the tongue or mucous membrane of the mouth produce a flow of saliva. The normal flow during mastication must be effected by a reflex of this kind, the sensory impulse being carried to a center and thence transmitted through the efferent nerves to the glands. It is found that section of the chorda prevents the reflex, in spite of the fact that the sympathetic fibers are still intact. No satisfactory explanation of the normal functions of the secretory fibers in the sympathetic has yet been given. Various authors have suggested that possibly the three large salivary glands respond normally to different stimuli. This view has been supported by Pavlov, who reports that in the dog, at least, the parotid and the submaxillary may react quite differently. When fistulas were made of the ducts of these glands it was found that the submaxillary responded readily to a great number of stimuli, such as the sight of food, chewing of meats, acids, etc. The parotid, on the contrary, seemed to react only when dry food, dry powdered meat, or bread was placed in the mouth. Dryness in this case appeared to be the efficient stimulus.

Pavlov lays stress upon the adaptability of the secretion of saliva to the character of the material chewed. Dry, solid food stimulates a large flow of saliva, such as is necessary in order to chew it properly and to form it into a bolus for swallowing. Foods containing much water, on the contrary, excite but little flow of saliva. If one places a handful of clean stones in the mouth of a dog he will move them around with his tongue for a while and then drop them from his mouth, but little or no saliva is secreted. If the same material is given in the form of fine sand a rich flow of saliva is produced, and the necessity for the reflex is evident in this case, since otherwise the material could not be conveniently removed from the mouth. Such adaptations must be regarded from the physiological point of view as special reflexes depending upon some difference in the nervous mechanism set into play (13, 14, 15).

Since the flow of saliva is normally a definite reflex, we should expect a distinct salivary secretion center. This center has been located by physiological experiments in the medulla oblongata, in the formatio reticularis lateral to the facial nucleus. The experiments (16) consisted in dividing the chorda and the nervus tympanicus and, after a suitable interval, examining sections of the medulla for the appearance of degenerative changes (chromatolysis, Chap. 9). Owing to the wide connections of nerve cells in the central nervous system, we should expect this center to be affected by stimuli from various sources. As a matter of fact, it is known that the center and through it the glands may be called into activity by stimulation of the sensory fibers of the sciatic, splanchnic, and particularly the vagus nerves. So, too, various psychical acts, such as the thought of savory food and the feeling of nausea preceding vomiting, may be accompanied by a flow of saliva, the effect in this case being due probably to stimulation of the secretion center by nervous impulses descending from the higher nerve centers. It will be remembered that there is some evidence (Chap. 11) for the existence in the hypothalamic region of the diencephalon of a general integrating center for the sympathetic and possibly also for the parasympathetic system as a whole. Lastly, the medullary center may be inhibited as well as stimulated. The well-known effect of fear, embarrassment, or anxiety in producing a parched throat may be explained in this way as due to the inhibitory action of nerve impulses arising in the cerebral centers.

Electrical Changes in the Gland during Activity. It has been shown that the salivary as well as other glands suffer certain changes in electrical potential during activity which are comparable in a general way to the "action potential" observed in muscles and nerves (2).

Digestive Action of Saliva—Ptyalin. The digestive action proper of the saliva is limited to the starchy food. In human beings and most mammals the saliva contains an active enzyme belonging to the group of diastases or amylases and designated usually as ptyalin or salivary diastase. It may be prepared in purified form from saliva by precipitation with alcohol, but its chemical nature is not definitely known, although the closely related diastatic enzyme of the pancreatic juice, the amylase, has been obtained in crystals which seem to be protein in nature (3). In some animals (horse) it has been claimed that the ptyalin as secreted from the gland is in an inactive or zymogen form, which, on coming into contact with the mucous membrane of the mouth, is converted to active ptyalin by an organic kinase, *oro-kinase* (12), said to be produced in the small buccal glands found in the oral mucous membrane. The saliva of the dog has no ptyalin and therefore this animal must rely on the amylase in its pancreatic juice for all digestion of ingested starch. Saliva or preparations of ptyalin act readily upon boiled starch, converting it into sugar. This action may be demonstrated very readily by holding a little starch paste or starchy food, such as boiled pota-toes, in the mouth for a few minutes. If the solution is then examined the presence of sugar is readily shown by its reducing action on solutions of copper sulfate (Fehling's solution). Under the influence of the enzyme the starch molecules take up water and undergo cleavage into simpler molecules. The steps in the process and the final products have been investigated, but much yet remains in doubt. The end-result of the reaction is the formation of maltose, a disaccharide, having the general formula $C_{12}H_{22}O_{11}$, and some form [of dextrin, a noncrystallizable polysaccharide. So far as the ptyalin itself is concerned, its specific action is to convert starch to maltose. It seems very certain, however, that a number of intermediate products are formed so that the hydrolysis probably takes place in successive stages. There is little agreement as to the exact nature of the intermediate substances. The following fact, however, may be easily demonstrated in a salivary digestion carried on in a vessel and examined from time to time. The starch at first gives its deep blue reaction with iodine; later, instead of a blue, a red reac-tion is obtained with iodine, and this has been attributed to a special form of dextrin, erythrodextrin, so named on account of its red reaction. Still later this reaction fails and chemical examination shows the presence of maltose and a form of dextrin which gives no color reaction with iodine and is there-fore named achroödextrin. The products formed in this reaction are probably not absorbed as such. The absorption takes place mainly, no doubt, after the food reaches the small intestine, and there is evidence that before absorp-tion the maltose is acted upon by maltase and converted into the simple sugar, glucose. The ptyalin digestion seems, therefore, to be preparatory, and the combined action of ptyalin and maltase is necessary to get the starch into a condition ready for true use by the body. Under the influence of these two enzymes, the complex starch molecule, consisting of a number of $C_6H_{10}O_5$ groups, is broken down into its constituent elements or building stones—that is to say, to the simple sugars of the formula $C_6H_{12}O_6$. The simple sugars or monosaccharides ($C_6H_{12}O_6$), the double sugars or disaccharides ($C_{12}H_{22}O_{11}$), and the dextrins, starches, and cellulose or polysaccharides, with the general formula $(C_6H_{10}O_5)_n$, constitute a series of increasing complexity as regards the size of the molecule. By hydrolysis, with enzymes or with acids, the polysaccharides are hydrated and split to form the simpler members of the series, while, on the other hand, in the living organism the simple sugars may be synthesized by combining two or more of the groups with dehydra-tion to form the higher polysaccharides, the animal and vegetable starches.

It is a question of practical importance how far salivary digestion affects the starchy foods under usual circumstances. The chewing process in the mouth thoroughly mixes the food and saliva, or should do so, but the bolus is swallowed much too quickly to enable the enzyme to complete its action. In the stomach the gastric juice is sufficiently acid to destroy the ptyalin, and it was therefore supposed formerly that salivary digestion is promptly arrested on the entrance of the food into the stomach, and is normally of but little value as a digestive process. Later knowledge regarding the conditions in the stomach (p. 993) shows, on the contrary, that some of the food in an ordinary meal may remain in the fundic end of the stomach for an hour or more untouched by the acid secretion. There is every reason to believe, therefore, that salivary digestion may be carried on in the stomach to an important extent.

Conditions Influencing the Action of Ptyalin. *Temperature.* As in the case of the other enzymes, ptyalin is very susceptible to changes of temperature. At 0° C. its activity is said to be suspended entirely. The intensity of its action increases with increase of temperature from this point, and reaches its maximum at about 40° C. If the temperature is raised much beyond this point, the action decreases, and at from 65° to 70° C. the enzyme is destroyed. In these latter points ptyalin differs from diastase, the enzyme of malt. Diastase shows a maximum action at 50° C. and is destroyed at 80° C.

Effect of reaction. The normal reaction of saliva is neutral or slightly acid (pH 6.6. to 7.1). Chittenden has shown that ptyalin acts well in a perfectly neutral medium. A strong alkaline reaction retards or prevents its action. The most marked influence is exerted by acids. Free hydrochloric acid to the extent of only 0.003 per cent (Chittenden) is sufficient practically to stop the amylolytic action of the enzyme, and a slight further increase in acidity not only stops the action but also destroys the enzyme.

Condition of the starch. It is a well-known fact that the conversion of starch to sugar by enzymes takes place much more rapidly with cooked starch— for example, starch paste. In the latter material sugar begins to appear in a few minutes, provided a good enzyme solution is used. With starch in a raw condition, on the contrary, it may be many minutes, or even several hours, before sugar can be detected. The longer time required for raw starch is partly explained by the fact that the starch grains are surrounded by a layer of cellulose or cellulose-like material that resists the action of ptyalin. When boiled, this layer breaks and the starch in the interior becomes exposed. In addition, the starch itself is changed during the boiling; it takes up water, and in this hydrated condition is acted upon more rapidly by the ptyalin. The practical value of cooking vegetable foods is evident from these statements.

Functions of the Saliva. In addition to the digestive action of the saliva on starchy foods it fulfills other important functions. By moistening the food it enables us to reduce the material to a consistency suitable for swallowing and for manipulation by the tongue and other muscles. Moreover, the presence of mucin serves doubtless as a kind of lubricator that insures a smooth passage along the esophageal canal. Finally by dissolving dry and solid food it provides a necessary step in the process of stimulating the taste nerves, and, as described in Chapter 48, the activity of the taste sensations may play an important part in the secretion of the gastric juice.

REFERENCES

1. BARCROFT, J. The gaseous metabolism of the submaxillary gland. II. On the absorption of water from the blood during its passage through the active gland. *J. Physiol.*, 1900, 25:479–486.

2. BIEDERMANN, W. *Electro-physiology.*

Translated by F. A. Welby. London, The Macmillan Co., 1896. 2 vols.

3. CALDWELL, M. L., BOOHER, L. E. and SHERMAN, H. C. Crystalline amylase. *Science*, 1931, 74:37.

4. HEIDENHAIN, R. Ueber secretorische und

trophische Drüsennerven. *Pflüg. Arch ges. Physiol.*, 1878, *17*:1–67.

5. HEIDENHAIN, R. Kurze Darstellung die Entwicklungsganges der Absonderungslehre. *Hermanns Handb. Physiol.*, 1881, *5* (1):1–420.

6. HUBER, G. C. Observations on the innervation of the sublingual and submaxillary glands. *J. exp. Med.*, 1896, *1*:281–295.

7. LANGLEY, J. N. On the changes in serous glands during secretion. *J. Physiol.*, 1879, *2*:261–280.

8. LANGLEY, J. N. On the histology of the mucous salivary glands, and on the behaviour of their mucous constituents. *J. Physiol.*, 1889, *10*:433–457.

9. LANGLEY, J. N. and DICKINSON, W. L. On the local paralysis of peripheral ganglia, and on the connexion of different classes of nerve fibres with them. *Proc. roy. Soc.*, 1889, *46*:423–431.

10. LANGSTROTH, G. O., McRAE, D. R. and KOMAROV, S. A. The synthesis and secretion of protein material by the pancreas. *Canad. J. Res.*, 1939, *D17*:137–149.

11. LANGSTROTH, G. O., McRAE, D. R. and STAVRAKY, G. W. The secretion of protein material in the parasympathetic submaxillary saliva. *Proc. roy. Soc.*, 1938, *B125*:335–347.

12. PALMER, C. C., ANDERSON, A. L., PETERSON, W. E. and MALCOMSON, A. W. Orokinase and salivary digestion studies in the horse. *Amer. J. Physiol.*, 1917, *43*:457–474.

13. PAVLOV, I. P. Psychische Erregung der Speicheldrüsen. *Ergebn. Physiol.*, 1904, *3* (1): 176–193.

14. PAVLOV, I. P. Sur la sécrétion psychique des glandes salivaires. *Arch. int. Physiol.*, 1904, *1*:119–135.

15. PAVLOV, I. P. *The work of the digestive glands*, 2nd English ed. Translated by W. H. Thompson. London, C. Griffin and Co., Ltd., 1910. xiv, 266 pp.

16. YAGITA, K. Ueber das Speichelskretionscentrum. *Neurol. Zbl.*, 1909, *287*:38–753.

35

CHAPTER 48

DIGESTION AND ABSORPTION IN THE STOMACH

The muscular mechanisms by means of which the stomach is charged with food and this, in turn, discharged, small portions at a time into the duodenum, have been described. The present chapter deals only with the chemical and mechanical changes in the food during its stay in the stomach and the extent to which the products of digestion are absorbed.

Gastric Glands. The mucous membrane of the stomach has a surface epithelium composed of columnar cells whose chief function, so far as we know, is the secretion of mucus. Throughout its whole extent the membrane is penetrated by short tubular glands, simple or slightly branched, which fall into two varieties, the fundic and the pyloric glands. Two or three types of cells are found in the fundic glands. Heidenhain distinguished two types, the *chief* or central cells which form a continuous lining to the tubules and are present in all the glands, and the *parietal* or border cells which are chiefly in the central (prepyloric) region (Fig. 464). These latter cells do not form a continuous lining to the tubule but occur somewhat irregularly. They are supposed to secrete the hydrochloric acid of the gastric juice, and for that reason Langley suggested for them the name *oxyntic* cells. (They have also been called *Belegzellen, acid,* and *delomorphous* cells.) The chief cells, according to Bensley (3), fall into two groups, those in the neck of the gland, which seem to have as their main function the secretion of mucus and might therefore be designated, according to Lim, as the mucoid cells (called *neck chief* cells), and the deeper lying cells which are responsible for the secretion of pepsin and are spoken of as the *peptic* cells (also called *body chief, central,* and *adelomorphous* cells). In the glands of the pyloric region (antrum pylori) the parietal or oxyntic cells are lacking; the cells lining the tubules all belong to the group of chief cells and, according to Bensley, are of the mucoid (neck chief?) rather than the peptic type. The pyloric glands secrete an alkaline liquid, which, according to Heidenhain, contains pepsin, but later observers state that the secretion from the pyloric end of the stomach is entirely free from pepsin. In summary, then, there are four types of cells that contribute material to what is commonly called gastric juice.

Histological Changes in the Gastric Glands During Secretion. The cells of the gastric glands, especially the chief cells, show distinct changes as the result of prolonged activity. In preserved specimens taken from dogs fed at intervals of 24 hours Heidenhain found that in the fasting condition the chief cells were large and clear; that during the first six hours of digestion the chief cells as well as the border cells increased in size; but that in a second period, extending from the sixth to the fifteenth hour, the chief cells became gradually smaller, while the parietal cells remained large or even increased in size. After the fifteenth hour the chief cells increased in size, gradually passing back to the fasting condition (see Fig. 464).

1042

Langley (29) succeeded in following the changes in a more satisfactory way by observations made directly upon the living gland. He found that the chief cells in the fasting stage are charged with granules and that during digestion the granules are dissolved, disappearing first from the base of the cell, which then becomes filled with a nongranular material. Observations similar to those made upon other glands demonstrate that these granules represent in all probability a preliminary material from which the gastric enzymes are made during the act of secretion. The granules, therefore, are sometimes described as zymogen granules.

Means of Obtaining the Gastric Secretion and Its Normal Composition. The secretion of the gastric membrane is formed in the minute tubular glands

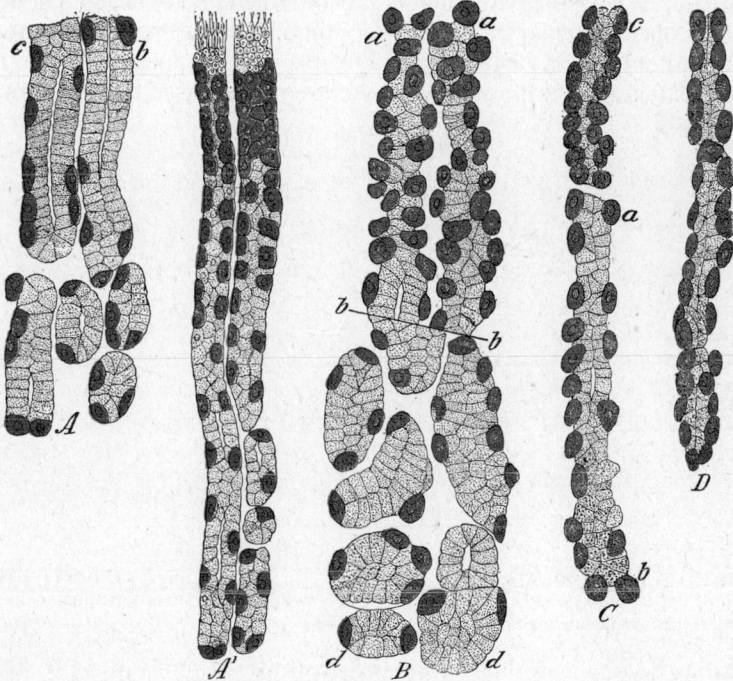

Fig. 464.—Glands of the fundus (dog): *A* and *A*¹, during hunger, resting condition; *B*, during the first stage of digestion; *C* and *D*, the second stage of digestion, showing the diminution in the size of the "chief" or central cells. (After Heidenhain.)

scattered over its surface. As there is no common duct, the difficulty of obtaining the secretion for analysis or experiment is considerable. This difficulty has been overcome at different times by the invention of special methods. The older methods used to obtain normal gastric juice were very unsatisfactory. An animal was made to swallow a clean sponge to which a string was attached so that the sponge could afterward be removed and its contents be squeezed out; or it was made to eat some indigestible material, to start the secretion of juice; the animal was then killed at the proper time and the contents of its stomach were collected.

The experiments of the older observers on gastric digestion, especially those of the Abbé Spallanzani (1729–1799), furnish most interesting reading. Spallanzani, not content with making experiments on numerous animals (frogs, birds, mammals, etc.) had the courage to carry out a great many upon himself. He swallowed foods of various kinds and in various conditions sewed in linen bags or inclosed in perforated wooden tubes which in turn were covered with linen. The bags and tubes were subsequently passed in the stools and were examined as to the amount and nature of their contents. He seems to have experienced no injury from his experiments, although normally his powers of digestion were quite feeble. As proof that the triturating power of the stomach is not very great he calls attention to the fact that some of the wooden tubes were made very thin, so that the slightest pressure would crush them, and yet they were voided uninjured. So also he found that cherries and grapes when swallowed whole, even if entirely ripe, were usually passed unbroken.

A better method of obtaining normal juice was suggested by the famous observations of Beaumont (2) upon Alexis St. Martin who, by the premature discharge of his gun, was wounded in the abdomen and stomach. On healing, a fistulous opening remained in the abdominal wall, leading into the stomach, so that the contents of the latter could be inspected. Beaumont made numerous interesting and most valuable observations upon his patient. Since that

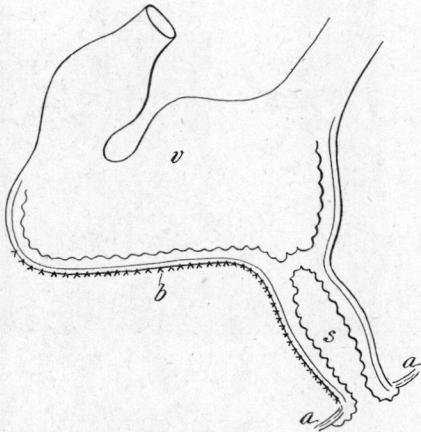

Fig. 465.—To show Pavlov's operation for making an isolated fundic sac from the stomach: *v*, cavity of the stomach; *s*, the fundic sac, shut off from the stomach and opening at the abdominal wall, *a*, *a*; *b* indicates the line of sutures. (Pavlov.)

time it has become customary to make fistulous openings into the stomachs of dogs whenever it is necessary to have the normal juice for examination. A similar surgical procedure is followed in human cases in which the esophagus has been occluded by an accident of one kind or another, usually as a result of drinking strong lye. In these cases a fistulous opening is established through the abdominal wall into the stomach. Through this opening the individual can be fed successfully, and, when desired, specimens of gastric juice can be obtained. The study of these exceptional cases has added greatly to our knowledge of the functions of the stomach. Gastric juice may be obtained from human beings also in cases of vomiting or by means of the stomach tube, but in such cases it is necessarily more or less diluted or mixed with food and cannot be used for exact analyses, although specimens of gastric juice obtained by these methods are employed in the diagnosis and treatment of gastric disorders.

From the standpoint of experimental investigation, a very important addition to our methods was made by Heidenhain. This observer showed that a portion of the stomach—the fundic end, for instance, or the pyloric end—might be cut away from the rest of the organ and be given an artificial opening to the exterior. By this means the secretion of an isolated fundic or pyloric sac may be obtained and examined as to its quantity and properties. The method was subsequently improved by Pavlov, whose important contributions are referred to below. Figure 465 gives an idea of the operations as made by Pavlov to isolate a fundic sac with its blood and nerve supply uninjured.

The normal gastric secretion is a thin, colorless or nearly colorless liquid with a strong acid reaction and a characteristic odor. Its specific gravity varies, but it is never great, the average being about 1.002 to 1.003. Upon analysis the gastric juice is found to contain some protein, some mucin, and inorganic salts, but the essential constituents are an acid (HCl) and two or possibly three enzymes: pepsin, rennin, and lipase. According to Rosemann (37, 38), the secretion in dogs has a specific gravity of 1.002 to 1.004 and contains 0.4277 per cent of dry material, of which 0.1325 per cent is ash. Analysis of the ash shows that it contains 24 per cent of potassium, 19 per cent of sodium, and 0.18 per cent of calcium. The HCl amounts to 0.55 per cent. This author states that in one animal during a period of secretion lasting three and a quarter hours about 5 gm. of chlorine were given off in the secretion in the form of chlorides, an amount about equal to that contained in the entire blood. Carlson (7), from his studies upon a human case with a permanent gastric fistula, gives the following figures for the normal secretion:

Acidity	Free HCl	= 0.40 to 0.50 per cent
	Total acidity	= 0.45 to 0.60 per cent
Solids	Organic	= 0.42 to 0.46 per cent
	Inorganic	= 0.13 to 0.14 per cent
Specific gravity		= 1.006 to 1.009
Osmotic concentration		= −0.55° to −0.52° C.
Total nitrogen		= 0.051 to 0.075 per cent
Amino acid nitrogen		= 3 to 10 mg. per 100 cc.
Ammonia		= 2 to 8 mg. per 100 cc.
Chlorides		= 0.50 to 0.58 per cent

In addition to the constituents that are revealed by chemical analysis, there is some evidence (34) that the gastric secretion contains a substance which has some essential connection with the process of production of blood corpuscles. When concentrated preparations of the juice are injected intramuscularly in patients suffering from pernicious anemia they cause an increased formation of blood corpuscles. Later work has shown that this factor (intrinsic factor) in the gastric juice reacts with some constituent of the food, extrinsic factor, to produce the principle that stimulates the formation of red corpuscles.

The total quantity of gastric juice secreted in a day must be quite large. In the dog, experiments indicate that the amount varies between 1000 and 2600 cc. In 24 hours the gastric glands secrete from two to three times as much chlorine as is found in blood. Under normal conditions this material is reabsorbed from the intestinal tract and there is no loss of chlorides from the blood, but if experimentally the gastric juice is drained off to the exterior, the animal dies in a few days "with symptoms of anorexia, weakness, loss of weight, decreased urinary secretion, and profound depression" (11). These symptoms may be alleviated and the animal be kept alive by adequate intravenous injections of isotonic solutions of sodium chloride.

Gastric juice does not give a coagulum upon boiling, but the digestive enzymes are thereby destroyed. One of the interesting facts about this secretion is the way in which it withstands putrefaction. It may be kept for a long time, for months even, without becoming putrid and with very little change, if any, in its digestive action or in its total acidity. This fact shows that the juice possesses antiseptic properties, and it is usually supposed that the presence of the free acid accounts for this quality.

Acid of Gastric Juice. The nature of the free acid in gastric juice was formerly the subject of dispute, some claiming that the acidity is due to HCl since this acid can be distilled off from the gastric juice, others contending that an organic acid, lactic acid, is present in the secretion. All recent experiments tend to prove that the acidity is due to HCl. This fact was first demonstrated satisfactorily by the analyses of Schmidt who showed that if, in a given specimen of gastric juice, the chlorides were all precipitated by silver nitrate and the total amount of chlorine was determined, more was found than could be held in combination by the bases present in the secretion. Evidently some of the chlorine must have been present in combination with hydrogen as hydrochloric acid and confirmatory evidence of one kind or another has since been obtained. The percentage of HCl in the secretion as it is obtained from an isolated fundic sac of the stomach varies from 0.4 to 0.5 per cent, and we may suppose that this figure represents the approximate concentration of acid in the juice as secreted. The most exact measurements reported for dog's gastric juice collected from a Pavlov pouch in such a way as to reduce to a minimum any neutralization of the acid with secreted mucus, thus giving the best estimate of acidity of the juice as secreted by the parietal cells, are those of Hollander and Cowgill (18). The value of this maximum acidity in pH units was 0.91 $\pm$ 0.02. These authors consider their data to support the view that "the unaltered secretion of the parietal cell is isotonic with the blood . . . and that the true acidity of this secretion is determined by the osmotic equilibria of the animal." When the contents of a normal stomach are examined during digestion the acidity is much lower, varying around 0.2 per cent as a maximum. This low acidity may be accounted for in part by dilution, by neutralization from the alkaline salts of the saliva or the gastric mucosa, or by combination with the protein of the food, but Boldyreff (5) states that the activity is reduced mainly by a regurgitation of the alkaline duodenal contents which occurs at periods during digestion. He considers that this regurgitation is a self-regulating mechanism for maintaining the low acidity of the gastric contents. The normal occurrence of regurgitation during gastric digestion is confirmed by several observers. Different workers have agreed that there is an inverse relation between the neutral chloride content of the juice and the acidity: as the acidity rises in any one experiment the neutral chloride content falls, and as the acidity falls the other rises. Some investigators have explained this as due to the secretion, by certain cells of the stomach, of a specific buffer-containing nonacid fluid—an adaptive type of secretion. The formation of a nonacid fluid by both the fundus and pyloric mucosa is well substantiated (31, 33). Hollander (16), in discussing this theory, points out that in the secretory epithelium of the stomach there are the four types of cells already described, and only one type, the parietal cell, forms HCl. This author offers good reasons for believing that the postulated adaptive buffer secretion may be simply an isotonic mixture of neutral chloride and several buffer salts similar to blood plasma in its acid-base composition. This view receives good support from the data obtained by Wilhelmj and associates (44, 45) on the chloride concentration of the nonacid secretion from dogs' pyloric and whole stomach pouches, as well as similar data of Bolton and Goodhart (6) pertaining to the nonacid component from the fundus juice of cats. Clinicians make a distinction between free and combined acid in the gastric secretion. By the first term is meant that the acid exists in solution as in so much water, and is, therefore, largely dissociated with the production of a corresponding amount of hydrogen ions. Under the second term is included the acid that is combined in some way with the protein material. In this form the acid is less dissociated and the acidity—that is to say, the concentration of hydrogen ions—is much less. Methods have been devised for estimating the total acidity and the free and combined acid. For physiological purposes it is preferable to abandon the use of the terms free and combined acid, and instead to express the degree of acidity in terms of the actual hydrogen ion concentration, since the activity of the pepsin is controlled by this factor. Reference has already been made to the pH value of 0.91 for the juice as secreted. This is a bit stronger than a tenth normal solution (18). Experiments show that an acidity as high as this is not favorable to the digestive action of pepsin, and, as a matter of fact, it is found (as was stated above) that in ordinary digestion the contents of the stomach always exhibit a lower acidity. According to Michaelis and Davidsohn (32), the acidity of the gastric contents after a test meal is equal to a concentration in H-ions of 0.017 n or pH 1.67. The optimum acidity for peptic digestion is placed at about pH 1.6. Concentrations of acid above or below this point would, therefore, present less favorable conditions for digestion. When there is no free HCl in the gastric contents (the acid all being combined with protein) the acidity is low, the H-ion concentration not rising above pH 3, i.e., a thousandth-normal solution. At this concentration the digestive action of the pepsin is relatively feeble (40).

Origin of the HCl. That the acid of the gastric juice is a mineral acid and is present in considerable strength is a remarkable fact that has excited much interest. Attempts have been made to ascertain the histological elements concerned in its secretion and the nature of the chemical reaction or reactions by which it is produced. With regard to the first point, it is generally believed that the parietal cells of the gastric tubules constitute the acid-secreting cells. This belief is founded upon the general fact that in the region in which these cells are chiefly present—that is, the middle region of the stomach—the secretion is distinctly acid, and where they are absent or scanty in number the secretion is alkaline or less acid. In the pyloric region, for instance, these cells are lacking entirely and the secretion is alkaline. Moreover, microchemical reactions seem to show clearly that the parietal cells are particularly rich in chlorides, and this fact serves to connect them with the production of the acid. It seems perfectly evident that the HCl must be formed in the long run from the chlorides of the blood. The chief chloride is NaCl, and by some means this compound is broken up; the chlorine is combined with hydrogen, and is then secreted upon the free surface of the stomach as HCl.

Maly long ago suggested that acid phosphates may be produced in the first instance, and then by reacting with the sodium chloride may give hydrochloric acid, according to the formula $NaH_2PO_4 + NaCl = Na_2HPO_4 + HCl$, the HCl being secreted, while the base is retained in the tissues and blood as an alkaline salt, presumably as sodium bicarbonate, thus accounting for the "alkaline tide," or decrease in the acid output in the urine after gastric digestion. Many observers have attempted by microchemical methods to determine the exact points in the gastric glands at which the acid is formed, but most of these attempts have given results which have been difficult to interpret. Harvey and Bensley (15), by making use of dyes (cyanimin and neutral red) which give different colors in neutral, alkaline, and acid media, state that the free acid is found only on the internal surface of the stomach or in the necks of the glands. Dawson and Ivy (10) believe that the methods used by other observers have been faulty in that the procedure was such as to arrest normal secretion in the glands. Their own experiments, in which they used dogs with a Pavlov pouch from which specimens of the mucosa could be taken and examined with a minimum loss of time, gave inconclusive results, except to indicate that the parietal cells show an acid reaction and that therefore the acid is probably formed within the cell itself.

Table 46.—*Formation of Hydrochloric Acid in the Stomach.* (From Davenport and Fisher, *Amer. J. Physiol.*, 1940, *131*:165.)

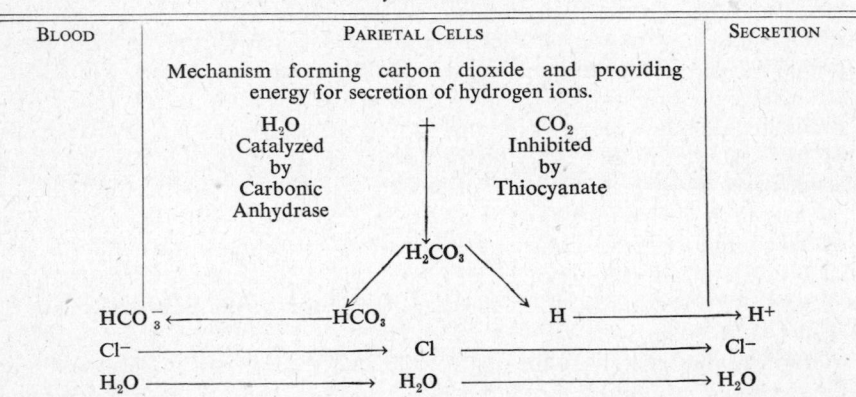

One of the newer theories of formation of the HCl is that proposed by Davenport and Fisher (9) called the carbonic anhydrase theory. Carbonic anhydrase is an enzyme that accelerates the hydration of CO_2 and the dehydration of carbonic acid. It has been found to be concentrated in the red blood cell and absent from the plasma. Davenport and Fisher discovered that this enzyme is present in the gastric mucosa of a variety of animal species, and that nearly all of it is located within the parietal cell and in concentrations just as great or even greater than in the red blood cell. The carbonic anhydrase theory assumes that the carbon dioxide formed within the parietal cell by its own metabolic activity is converted immediately into carbonic acid by virtue of the presence of carbonic anhydrase. The acid then ionizes and the resulting hydrogen ions are diverted into the parietal secretion. At the same time the bicarbonate ions are passed into the blood for an equivalent amount of chloride ions which are then diverted into the secretion to complete the formation of hydrochloric acid. The theory is set forth in Table 46.

For a good discussion of the evidence available for and against this theory the reader should consult the review by Gray (14). Against this view it has been argued by Hollander (17) that "a considerable amount of evidence based on the study of inhibitors of this enzyme has so far failed to yield confirmatory evidence." After his own consideration of the available experimental evidence, Hollander reached the conclusion that a *"membrane hydrolysis* of the ordinary, inorganic chlorides of the cytoplasm satisfies the morphological requirements of this problem." The HCl from the inorganic chlorides is separated from the reactants by postulating that the wall of the intracellular canaliculus is a membrane which is irreciprocally permeable only to water (and therefore H-ion) and Cl-ion (and the other halides). When any secretory stimulus acts on the parietal cell it sets up a process by which water is driven out of the cell in two directions. The fluid passing forward into the intracellular canaliculus carries H-ion and Cl-ion with it, thus effecting the membrane hydrolysis of the neutral chlorides with simultaneous separation of the HCl so formed. At the same time, the fluid going in the opposite direction transports the alkalinized buffers of the cytoplasm, which represent the neutralized alkali involved, across the cell wall proper, back into the tissue fluid and on into the general circulation. The chemical reactions at the wall of the intracellular canaliculus might be formulated as follows:

$$NaCl + H_2O \longrightarrow HCl + NaOH; NaOH + NaH_2PO_4 \longrightarrow H_2O + Na_2HPO_4$$

(and similarly for other buffer salts in the cytoplasm and lymph). This theory gains support from physical chemistry because some comparable purely physicochemical systems have been described (4, 8) in which there occur the simultaneous formation and separation of HCl from NaCl in the presence of a weak acid to buffer the base liberated by the reaction. Also Rassers (36) has obtained from the gastric mucosa of the pig a water-insoluble "lecithalbumin" having the interesting property of binding base and simultaneously liberating HCl from aqueous NaCl.

From the foregoing very brief review it must be evident that no theory advanced to date is entirely satisfactory, but further researches suggested by current hypotheses may yield fruitful results.

Secretory Nerves of the Gastric Glands. Although several facts indicated to the older observers that the secretion of gastric juice is under the control of nerve fibers, we owe the actual experimental demonstration of this fact to Pavlov who proved the existence of secretory fibers in the vagus nerve. Direct stimulation of the peripheral end of the cut vagus causes a secretion of gastric juice after a long latent period of several minutes. This long latency may be due possibly to the presence in the vagus of inhibitory fibers to the gland, which, being stimulated simultaneously with the secretory fibers, delay the action of the latter. Very striking proof of the general fact that the secretion is due to the action of vagus fibers is furnished by such experiments as these: Pavlov divided the esophagus in the neck and brought the two ends to the skin so as to make separate fistulous openings to the exterior. Under these conditions when the animal ate and swallowed food it was discharged to the exterior instead of entering the stomach. The animal thus had the enjoyment of eating without food actually entering the stomach. Eating in this style forms what the author calls a fictitious or sham meal (*Scheinfütterung*). It was found that it causes an abundant flow of gastric juice as long as the vagi are intact, but has no effect on the secretion when these nerves are cut. Evidently, therefore, the sensations of taste, odor, etc., developed during the mastication and swallowing of food, set up reflexly a stimulation of secretory fibers in the vagus. Pavlov designated a secretion produced in this way as a psychic secretion—a term which implies that the reflex must be attended by conscious sensations. Other observers, such as Carlson, give to it the name of appetite secretion. Under normal conditions the term psychic or appetite secretion may be the correct one to use, but it is possible that the fundamental reflex nerve paths need not necessarily involve stimulation of cortical cells, in view of Zeliony's (46) observations on a decorticate dog. In favorable cases the fictitious feeding has been continued for five to six hours and a large amount of gastric juice (700 cc.) has been collected from a fistula although no food actually entered the stomach. It is important to note, also, that a psychical secretion, once started, may continue for a long time after the stimulus (the eating) has ceased. Experiments have been made upon human beings under similar conditions. Thus, Hornberg (20) reports the case of a boy with a stricture of the esophagus and a fistula in the stomach. Food when chewed and swallowed did not reach the stomach, but was regurgitated; it caused, nevertheless, an active psychical secretion in the empty stomach.

Normal Mechanism of the Secretion of the Gastric Juice. It has usually been assumed that the gastric glands are quiescent when the stomach is empty and are stimulated to activity during the eating and digestion of food. According to the results published by Carlson (7a), this view is not wholly correct. Even in the period of fasting there is a small continuous secretion varying from 10 to 60 cc. per hour, but during the act of eating and throughout the period of gastric digestion the rate of secretion is increased greatly, reaching a flow of as much as 3.5 cc. per minute. The present explanation of the origin, maintenance, and regulation of this flow of secretion is due chiefly to the work of Pavlov and pupils, and Ivy and associates (23). The process may be pictured briefly as follows: In an ordinary meal the secretion first started is due to the sensations of eating—that is, it is a psychical secretion according to Pavlov. The afferent stimuli originate in the mouth and nostrils; the efferent path, the secretory fibers, is through the vagus nerve. This reflex insures the beginning at least of gastric digestion, but its effect is supplemented by a further action arising in the stomach itself.

Some foods contain substances designated as secretagogues that are able to cause a secretion of gastric juice when taken into the stomach. Thus, meat extracts, meat juices, soups, etc., are particularly effective in this respect; milk and water cause less secretion. Certain common articles of food, such as bread and white of eggs, have no effect of this kind. If introduced into the stomach of a dog through a fistula so as not to arouse a psychical secretion—for instance, while the dog's attention is diverted or while he is sleeping—they cause no flow of gastric juice and are not digested. If such articles of food are eaten, however, they cause a psychical secretion, and when this has acted upon the foods some products of their digestion, in turn, become capable of arousing a further flow of gastric juice. The steps in the mechanism of secretion are, therefore, three: (i) the psychical secretion or appetite secretion; (ii) the secretion from secretagogues contained in the food; (iii) the secretion from secretagogues contained in the products of digestion. The manner in which these secretagogues act cannot be stated positively. Since the gastric glands possess secretory nerve fibers, the first explanation to suggest itself is that the secretagogues by acting on sensory fibers in the gastric mucosa reflexly stimulate the secretory fibers. This explanation, however, is rendered untenable by the fact that the effect of these substances is obtained after complete severance of the nervous connections of the stomach. If, therefore, this so-called chemical secretion is produced by a nervous reflex, the reflex must take place through the intrinsic ganglion cells (Popielski). Edkins (12) suggested a hormone mechanism based upon the observation that extracts of the pyloric mucous membrane, made by boiling in water, acid or peptone solutions, when injected into the blood cause a marked secretion of gastric juice. Edkins theorized that the secretagogues, whether preformed in the food or formed during digestion, act upon the pyloric mucous membrane and form a substance which he designated as *gastrin* or *gastric secretin*, and this substance after absorption into the blood is carried to the gastric glands and stimulates them to secretion. Two important facts can be cited against this theory: (i) a gastric secretin has been obtained by extraction with 0.4 per cent HCl from the mucous membrane of all parts of the stomach and, indeed, from a variety of plant and animal tissues; and (ii) attempts to demonstrate this particular hormone in the blood have met with failure or unsatisfactory results. But there is no question that an effective excitant of gastric secretion may be obtained from the pyloric mucous membrane by extraction with dilute acid. Some observers (39) identify this active substance with histamine. It is well known that histamine provokes a secretion of gastric juice, and it is used frequently in experimental work for this purpose. But other workers (28) state that a protein-like substance, soluble in 80 per cent alcohol and entirely free from histamine, may extracted from the pyloric mucous membrane and shown to have a strong stimulating action upon the secretion of gastric juice. In accordance with this description of the process it may be noted that in the normal secretion of the gastric glands two kinds of stimulation are brought into action. There is a *nervous secretion* due to the action of the secretory fibers in the vagus, and a *chemical secretion* due to the chemical stimulation of the secretagogues or of the hormones produced by them.

Work done upon this subject by Carlson (7a) and his associates has supplemented and in some points corrected the results obtained by Pavlov. They have shown that mechanical stimulation of the mucous membrane excites the secretion of the glands. This had been an old belief from the time of Beaumont, but had been denied by Pavlov. Ivy and Farrell (24) have given a striking demonstration that the glands can be stimulated by substances brought to them through the circulation, i.e., that a so-called humoral mechanism is or may be concerned in the production of the gastric juice. They cut out a pouch from the fundus of the stomach of a dog and transplanted it into the mammary gland. In successful cases they found that this isolated pouch secreted gastric juice when the dog was fed or when gastrin or histamine was injected. It has been shown also that the digestive products of proteins, fats, and carbohydrates while in the upper portion of the intestine are capable of provoking a gastric secretion (25). On the basis of such results these workers conclude that there are three phases in the normal response of the gastric glands: (i) the *cephalic phase*, i.e., the secretion aroused reflexly through the brain from the taste, odor and sight of food—the phase usually designated as the psychical secretion or the appetite secretion; (ii) the *gastric phase*, in which the glands are stimulated mechanically by the food and chemically by the secretagogues contained in them or formed from them; (iii) the *intestinal phase* due to the action of the products of digestion and the acid of the gastric juice on the intestinal mucosa. It is evident from these statements that the control of the secretory process in the stomach during a meal is more complex than was supposed formerly. The relative significance of the different stimuli is not clearly understood at present.

The researches of Pavlov and his coworkers seem to indicate that the quantity and properties of the secretion vary with the character of the food.

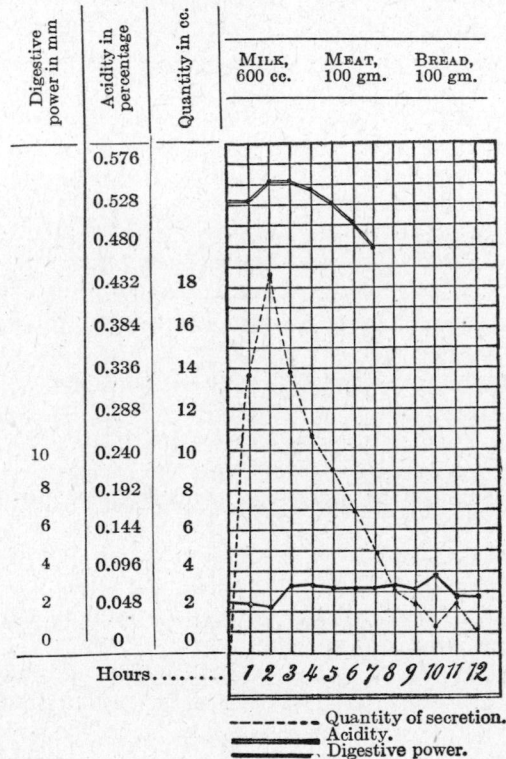

Fig. 466.—Diagram showing the variation in quantity of gastric secretion in the dog after a mixed meal; also the variations in acidity and in digestive power. (After Khigine.)

The quantity of the secretion varies also—other conditions being the same—with the amount of food to be digested, and, so far as the psychical or appetite secretion is concerned, with the palatableness of the food. The apparatus is adjusted in this respect to work economically. Different kinds of food produce secretions varying not only as regards quantity but also in their acidity and digestive action. The secretion produced by bread, though less in quantity than that caused by meat, possesses a greater digestive action. On a given diet the secretion assumes certain characteristics, and Pavlov is convinced that further work will disclose the fact that the secretion of the stomach is not caused normally by general stimuli, all affecting it alike, but by specific stimuli contained in the food or produced during digestion, their action being of such a kind as to arouse reflexly the secretion best adapted to the food ingested.

One of the curves, showing the effect of a mixed diet (milk, 600 cc.; meat, 100 gm.; bread, 100 gm.) upon the gastric secretion, as determined by Pavlov's method, is reproduced in Figure 466. It will be noticed that the secretion began shortly after the ingestion of the food (7 minutes), and increased rapidly to a maximum that was reached in two hours. After the second hour the flow decreased rapidly and nearly uniformly to about the tenth hour. The acidity rose slightly between the first and second hours, and then fell gradually. The digestive power showed an increase between the second and third hours.

Reference has already been made to Ivy's description of the cephalic, gastric and intestinal phases of gastric secretion. This serves to explain in part these Pavlov observations described as adaptation of the secretion to the character of the food being digested. Another physiological basis of explanation of this is seen in the fact that there are at least two separate secretory mechanisms important in this connection, the one involved in the secretion of pepsin (and perhaps other organic factors) and that by which hydrochloric acid is formed and poured out into the lumen of the stomach. Gilman and Cowgill (13), using a method for determining pepsin that is more delicate than the old Metts-tube technique, were able to show that repeated subcutaneous injections of histamine evoke repeated detectable responses in flow of HCl and water (volume of flow) but no such responses with respect to pepsin content of the secretion. Vineberg and Babkin (43) compared histamine and pilocarpine for their effects on the gastric secretory mechanism and concluded that the latter drug influences particularly the flow of pepsin; their attempts to use these findings in the development of a new gastric function test met with failure because the effective dose of pilocarpine proved to be too toxic. Their claim that pilocarpine stimulates only the pepsin secreting mechanism—not the acid formation—was not supported, however, by the work of Hollander and Stein (19). The discovery of a physiologically useful agent that is highly specific in its action on the pepsin secreting cells remains to be made.

Nature and Properties of Pepsin. Pepsin (Schwann, 1836) is a typical proteolytic enzyme that exhibits the striking peculiarity of acting only in acid media; hence peptic digestion in the stomach is the result of the combined action of pepsin and hydrochloric acid. Pepsin is influenced in its action by temperature, as is the case with the other enzymes; low temperatures retard and may even suspend its activity, while high temperatures increase it. The optimum temperature is stated to be from 37° to 40° C., while exposure for some time to 80° C. results, when the pepsin is in a moist condition, in the total destruction of the enzyme. Pepsin may be extracted from the gastric mucous membrane by a variety of methods and in different degrees of purity and strength. The commercial preparations of pepsin consist usually of some form of extract of the gastric mucous membrane to which starch or sugar of milk has been added. Laboratory preparations are made conveniently by mincing thoroughly the mucous membrane and then extracting for a long time with glycerol. Glycerol extracts, if not too much diluted with water or blood, keep for an indefinite time. Purer preparations of pepsin have been made by various workers using progressively better methods. Such preparations always gave tests for protein, but inasmuch as impurities were always present there was uncertainty as to whether or not pepsin itself is protein in character. This uncertainty was removed by the work of Northrop (see Chap. 46) who succeeded in obtaining pepsin in crystalline form. The crystals on analysis showed 14.5 per cent of nitrogen and gave the reactions of a protein. In the secreting cells pepsin itself is not found, but a preliminary material, zymogen or pepsinogen, is present and may be extracted readily. Northrop has obtained this pepsinogen also in purified form as crystals and shown that it is a protein. Pepsinogen, the inactive form, passes over into pepsin, the active enzyme, in the presence of acid, by a process of auto-catalysis, so that although excreted from the cells as pepsinogen it is quickly changed to the active enzyme in the acid juice. Human gastric juice is said to contain about 1 mg. of pepsin to each cubic centimeter.

Artificial Gastric Juice. In studying peptic digestion it is not necessary for all purposes to establish a gastric fistula. The active agents of the normal juice are pepsin and an acid of a proper strength; and, as the pepsin can be extracted and preserved in various ways and the hydrochloric acid can easily be made of the proper strength, an artificial juice can be obtained at any time and may be used in place of the normal secretion for many purposes. The artificial juice thus made, when kept at a temperature of from 37° to 40° C., will digest proteins rapidly.

Pepsin Hydrochloric Acid Digestion of Proteins. It has long been known that solid proteins, when exposed to the action of a normal or an artificial gastric juice, swell up and eventually pass into solution. The soluble protein thus formed is not coagulated by heat, and is characterized also by being more diffusible than other forms of soluble proteins. This end-product of digestion was formerly conceived as a soluble protein with properties fitting it for rapid absorption, and the name of *peptone* was given it. It was quickly found, however, that the process is complicated—that in the conversion to so-called "peptone" the protein under digestion passes through a number of inter-mediate stages. The accepted view for many years was that the protein molecules undergo hydrolysis in successive stages with the formation of smaller and more soluble molecules. Four intermediate stages were described: (i) The formation of a soluble acid albumin (syntonin) under the combined influence of the acid and the pepsin. Neutralization of the digestive mixture at this stage results in a precipitation of this product. (ii) A hydrolysis of the albumin with the formation of simpler proteins designated as primary proteoses or albumoses. (iii) A further splitting with the production of still simpler and more soluble molecules, the secondary proteoses (deutero-albumoses), and finally the peptones. None of these stages was defined in a chemical sense, but they were isolated more or less successfully by various methods of precipitation. The last product, the peptone, which marks the end of the action of the pepsin, is characterized by certain reactions. It is readily soluble in water, gives a characteristic biuret reaction, and is not precipitated by heat or by complete saturation of its solutions with ammonium sulfate. While there is no doubt that the end-result of peptic digestion is the production of soluble proteins of smaller molecular weight than the original proteins, to which the general name peptone may be given, the interpretation of the process is different from that formerly held. Proteins when completely hydrolyzed break up into a number of amino acids which represent the ultimate constituents or building stones of the protein molecule. Fischer showed that these amino acids may be linked together by a union of the COOH group in one acid with the NH_2 group in another, with loss of H_2O, to form what he called peptids. These peptids contain two or more amino acids and it has been accepted that this mode of linkage is an essential feature in the building up of the protein molecule (42). When pepsin acts upon protein it is known that no amino acids are produced—hence pepsin is not able to break all the peptid linkages and resolve the molecule into its building stones, as may be done by acids and by some enzymes. Waldschmidt-Leitz suggests that the pepsin splits the molecule of protein into a number of large fragments, each of which has the composition of a polypeptid. From this point of view peptone would be designated as a polypeptid of unknown composition.

The end-result of the action of the pepsin in the stomach is the conversion of more or less of the protein of the food into a simpler and more soluble form. The action of the enzyme is preparatory to the more complete hydrolysis that takes place in the intestine under the influence of the trypsin and erepsin, for, as we shall see, the protein of the food is not absorbed into the blood as peptones, but suffers first a further hydrolysis to amino acids and simple peptids. While the pepsin is, therefore, a relatively weak proteolytic enzyme, it plays an important role in initiating the splitting up of the protein molecule, and its value in this respect is increased by the fact that it is adapted to act upon many kinds of proteins and bring them to a stage suitable for the more complete action of the proteolytic enzymes of the intestinal secretion.

The Rennin Enzyme (Rennet, Chymosin, or Chymase). The property possessed by the mucous membrane of the calf's stomach of curdling milk has been known from remote times, and has been utilized in the manufacture of cheese and curds. This action takes place with remarkable rapidity under favorable conditions, a large mass of milk setting to a firm coagulum within a very brief time. It has been shown that this effect is due to an enzyme. Crystallized pepsin itself will cause coagulation of milk but it is generally believed that the mucous membrane of the stomach contains another enzyme, designated as *rennin*, which is especially characterized by this property. It has not as yet been isolated in such pure form as the pepsin, but Tauber and Kleiner (41) have obtained it from the calf's stomach in a form which has powerful rennetic but no peptic action. It differs from pepsin in this lack of proteolytic power and also in its iso-electric point. It contains sulfur and these authors believe that chemically it is a thioproteose. The rennin, like the pepsin, is supposed to be formed in the chief cells of the gastric tubules and to be present in the glands in a zymogen form, prorennin or prochymosin which after secretion is converted to the active enzyme. This conversion takes place very readily under the influence of acid. Rennin (or its zymogen) may be obtained easily from the mucous membrane of the stomach (with the exception of the pyloric end) by extracting with glycerol or water or by digesting with dilute acid. Good extracts of rennin cause the milk to clot with great rapidity at a temperature of 40° C.; the milk (cow's milk) if undisturbed sets at first into a solid clot, which afterwards shrinks and presses out a clear, yellowish liquid—the whey. With human milk the curd is much less firm and takes the form of loose flocculi. The whole process resembles much the coltting of blood. The time of clotting is said to vary inversely as the amount of rennin, or, in other words, the product of the amount of rennin and the time necessary for clotting is a constant. The curdling of the milk involves two apparently independent processes: (i) the rennin acts upon the casein of the milk and converts it into a substance known as paracasein. The paracasein then reacts with the calcium salts of the milk, forming an insoluble protein, which constitutes the curd or coagulum. According to this view the enzyme does not cause clotting directly (1). What takes place when the casein is changed to paracasein is not entirely understood. Hammarsten originally regarded the change as a cleavage process, and this view is still supported by some authors. According to Bosworth, the molecule of casein is split into two molecules with the same composition as the casein but half the molecular weight. A more recent view is that the rennin belongs to the group of proteolytic enzymes or proteases and causes initial changes in the casein, probably through a process of hydrolysis, which are similar in general to those induced by other enzymes of the same group, namely, a breaking up of a protein aggregate into a simpler, more dispersible form without any deep-seated chemical alteration. It should be added that casein is also precipitated from milk by the addition of an excess of acid. The curdling of sour milk in the formation of bonnyclabber is a well-known illustration of this fact. When milk stands for some time the action of bacteria upon the milk-sugar leads to the formation of lactic acid, and when this acid reaches a certain concentration it causes the precipitation of the casein.

So far as our positive knowledge goes, the action of rennin is confined to milk. Casein is the chief protein constituent of milk, and has, therefore, an important nutritive value. The value of the curdling action is not at once apparent, but we may suppose that casein is more easily digested under the conditions that exist in the body after it has been brought into a solid form, or, perhaps, the coagulation of the casein ensures that it will be retained in the stomach and be submitted to gastric digestion instead of being ejected promptly into the duodenum, as happens with liquid material. The action of rennin, so far as is known, goes no further than the curdling; the digestion of the curd is carried on by the pepsin, and later, in the intestines, by the trypsin, as in the case of other proteins.

Digestive Changes Undergone by the Food in the Stomach. In addition to the pepsin and rennin various observers have described other enzymes in the gastric juice or gastric membrane, but the evidence at hand is uncertain regarding these latter. As was said above, it is probable that the ptyalin swallowed with the food continues to exert its action upon the starchy material in the fundus for a long time, so that in this way the starch digestion in the stomach may be important. Regarding the fats, it is usually believed that they undergo no truly digestive change in the stomach. They are set free from their intimate mixture with other foodstuffs by the dissolving action of the gastric juice upon proteins, they are liquefied by the heat of the body, and they are disseminated through the chyme in a coarse emulsion by the movements of the stomach. In this way they are mechanically prepared so that the subsequent action of the pancreatic juice is much favored. Some observers (21) state that the gastric juice does normally contain a lipase capable of causing hydrolytic cleavage of the neutral fat into fatty acid and glycerol. It would appear, however, that this lipase is readily destroyed by an acidity of 0.2 per cent HCl, so that if it is of functional importance in gastric digestion its action, like that of the ptyalin, must be confined to the early period of digestion before the contents of the stomach have reached their normal acidity. Regarding the proteins, the practical point of interest is as to how far they are digested during their stay in the stomach. It seems probable that this question does not admit of a categorical answer, that is, the extent of the digestion varies under different circumstances—with the consistency of the food, the duration of its stay in the stomach, etc. In the liquid material (chyme) forced through the pylorus into the duodenum one may find unchanged proteins or the final or intermediate products of pepsin digestion, the so-called proteoses and peptone. It is stated, however, that most of the material is in the intermediate stage of proteoses (London). The true value of peptic digestion is not so much in its own action as in its combined action with the trypsin, or the trypsin and erepsin found in the intestine. The preliminary digestion in the stomach is important as regards the protein foods from several standpoints: (i) in the matter of mechanical preparation of the food and its discharge in convenient quantities easily handled by the duodenum; (ii) in the more or less complete hydrolysis to proteoses and peptones, whereby the subsequent action of the proteolytic enzymes of the intestine must be greatly accelerated. These and other facts seem to indicate that the peptic digestion is not so much an end in itself as a preparation for subsequent intestinal digestion. The stomach, therefore, may be removed without a fatal result. Many cases are on record in which the stomach was removed by surgical operation, the esophagus being stitched to the duodenum (27). The animals did well and seemed perfectly normal, although later observations indicate that after a period of some months loss of weight may occur as well as an anemic condition which may be fatal, probably on account of loss of the "intrinsic factor" concerned in the formation of red blood corpuscles.

Absorption in the Stomach. In the stomach it is possible that there may be absorption of the following substances: Water; salts; sugars and dextrins that may have been formed in salivary digestion from starch or that may have been eaten as such; the proteoses and peptones formed in the peptic digestion of proteins. In addition, absorption of soluble or liquid substances—drugs, alcohol, etc., that have been swallowed—may occur. It was formerly assumed, without definite proof, that the stomach absorbs easily such things as water, salts, sugars and peptones. Actual experiments, however, made under conditions as nearly normal as possible show, upon the whole, that absorption does not take place readily in the stomach. The methods made use of in these experiments have varied, but the most interesting results have been obtained by establishing a fistula of the duodenum just beyond the pylorus (30). After producing this fistula food may be given to the animal, and the contents of the stomach as they pass out through the pyloric opening may be caught and examined.

Water. Experiments of the character just described show that water when taken alone is practically not absorbed at all in the stomach. Von Mering's experiments especially show that as soon as water is introduced into the stomach it begins to pass into the intestine, being forced out in a series of spurts by the contractions of the stomach. Within a comparatively short time practically all the water can be recovered in this way, none or very little having been absorbed in the stomach. For example, in a large dog with a fistula in the duodenum 500 cc. of water were given through the mouth. Within 25 minutes 495 cc. had been forced out of the stomach through the duodenal fistula. This result is not true for all liquids; alcohol, for example, is absorbed readily.

Salts. The absorption of salts from the stomach has not been investigated thoroughly. According to Brandl, sodium iodide is absorbed very slowly or not at all in dilute solutions. Not until its solutions reach a concentration of 3 per cent or more does its absorption become important. This result, if applicable to all the soluble inorganic salts, would indicate that under ordinary conditions they are practically not absorbed in the stomach, since it cannot be supposed that they are normally swallowed in solutions so concentrated as 3 per cent. In the same direction Meltzer reports that solutions of strychnine are absorbed with difficulty from the stomach as compared with the intestines, rectum, or even the pharynx. It is said that the absorption of sodium iodide is very much facilitated by the use of condiments such as mustard and pepper, or alcohol, which act either by causing a greater congestion of the mucous membrane or perhaps by directly stimulating the epithelial cells.

Sugars and peptones. In regard to the sugars the experiments of von Mering and Brandl indicate that while absorption takes place it is not rapid nor marked unless the solutions are quite concentrated (5 per cent), and we may infer, therefore, that in an ordinary meal the sugar formed from the starchy foods by the action of the ptyalin is passed on to the intestine for further digestion and absorption. Whether or not any of the digested proteins are absorbed from the stomach has been and still is a matter of controversy. Some of the older experimenters stated that as much as 20 to 30 per cent of the protein of a meal might be absorbed in the stomach, but the results of later work, on the contrary, indicate that little or no absorption takes place under normal conditions (30). When a definite amount of protein was introduced into the stomach of an experimental animal it could all be recovered, as estimated by nitrogen determinations, from a duodenal fistula.

Fats. As we have seen, fats probably undergo no digestive changes in the stomach. The processes of saponification and emulsification are supposed to be preliminary steps to absorption, and these processes take place usually after the fats have reached the small intestine. Actual absorption of fat from the stomach probably does not occur under normal conditions. It is true that in the experiments of Inouye (22), where the cardiac and pyloric ends of the stomach were ligated and fat thus held within the viscus for many hours, some histological evidence of the absorption of fat was obtained. It is obvious, however, that the conditions of such experiments were most unphysiological, and therefore their significance may well be questioned.

REFERENCES

1. BANG, I. Über den chemischen Vorgang bei der Milchgerinnung durch Lab. *Skand. Arch. Physiol.*, 1911, *25*:105–144.

2. BEAUMONT, W. *The Physiology of digestion,* 2nd ed. Corrected by S. Beaumont. Burlington [Vt.], Chauncey Goodrich, 1847. 303 pp.

3. BENSLEY, R. R. The structure of the mammalian gastric glands. *Quart. J. micr. Sci.*, 1898, *41*:361–389.

4. BEUTNER, R. and CAPLAN, M. Electromotive effect of concentration of tissue membranes as the result of HCl formation. *Proc. Soc. exp. Biol., N. Y.*, 1931–32, *29*:596–598.

5. BOLDYREFF, W. The self-regulation of the acidity of the gastric contents and the real acidity of the gastric juice. *Quart. J. exp. Physiol.*, 1914, *7*:1–12.

6. BOLTON, C. and GOODHART, G. W. The variations in the acidity of the gastric juice

during secretion. *J. Physiol.*, 1931, *73*:115–135.

7. CARLSON, A. J. *The control of hunger in health and disease.* Chicago, University of Chicago Press, 1919. vii, 319 pp.

7a. CARLSON, A. J. The secretion of gastric juice in health and disease. *Physiol. Rev.*, 1923, *3*:1–40.

8. CLOWES, G. H. A. Protoplasmic equilibrium. *J. phys. Chem.*, 1916, *20*:407–450.

9. DAVENPORT, H. W. and FISHER, R. B. The mechanism of the secretion of acid by the gastric mucosa. *Amer. J. Physiol.*, 1940–41, *131*:165–175.

10. DAWSON, A. B. and IVY, A. C. Contribution to the physiology of the gastric secretion. X. Formation of hydrochloric acid by the gastric mucosa. *Amer. J. Physiol.*, 1926, *76*:158–169.

11. DRAGSTEDT, L. R. and ELLIS, J. C. Fatal effect of total loss of gastric juice. *Proc. Chicago Inst. Med.*, 1930, *8*:30–32.

12. EDKINS, J. S. The chemical mechanism of gastric secretion. *J. Physiol.*, 1906, *34*:133–144.

13. GILMAN, A. and COWGILL, G. R. The effect of histamine upon the secretion of gastric pepsin. *Amer. J. Physiol.*, 1931, *97*:124–130.

14. GRAY, J. S. The formation of acid by the gastric glands. *Fed. Proc. Amer. Soc. exp. Biol.*, 1942, *1*:255–260.

15. HARVEY, C. H. and BENSLEY, R. R. Upon the formation of hydrochloric acid in the foveolae and on the surface of the gastric mucous membrane and the non-acid character of the contents of gland cells and lumina. *Biol. Bull. Wood's Hole*, 1912, *23*:225–249.

16. HOLLANDER, F. The components of the gastric secretion. *Amer. J. Digestive Dis.*, 1936–37, *3*:651–655.

17. HOLLANDER, F. The chemistry and mechanics of hydrochloric acid formation in the stomach. *Gastro-enterol.*, 1943, *1*:401–430.

18. HOLLANDER, F. and COWGILL, G. R. Studies in gastric secretion. I. Gastric juice of constant acidity. *J. biol. Chem.*, 1931, *91*:151–182.

19. HOLLANDER, F. and STEIN, J. Mucus, acid and water secretion in the stomach following the injection of pilocarpine. *Amer. J. Physiol.*, 1943, *140*:136–147.

20. HORNBERG, A. F. Beiträge zur Kenntniss der Absonderungsbedingungen des Magensaftes beim Menschen. *Skand. Arch. Physiol.*, 1904, *15*:209–258.

21. HULL, M. and Keeton, R. W. The existence of a gastric lipase. *J. biol. Chem.*, 1917, *32*:127–140.

22. INOUYE, T. The question of fat absorption from the mammalian stomach. *Amer. J. Physiol.*, 1924, *69*:116–124.

23. IVY, A. C. Contributions to the physiology of the stomach. IX. The causes of gastric secretion: their practical significance and the mechanisms concerned. *J. Amer. med. Ass.*, 1925, *85*:877–880.

24. IVY, A. C. and FARRELL, J. I. Contribu-tions to the physiology of gastric secretion. VIII. The proof of a humoral mechanism. A new procedure for the study of gastric physiology. *Amer. J. Physiol.*, 1925, *74*:639–649.

25. IVY, A. C. and McILVAIN, G. B. The excitation of gastric secretion by application of substances to the duodenal and jejunal mucosa. *Amer. J. Physiol.*, 1923–24, *67*:124–140.

26. IVY, A. C. and McILVAIN, G. B. Contributions to the physiology of gastric secretion. IV. The stimulation of gastric secretion by hydrolyzed proteins. *Amer. J. Physiol.*, 1924–25, *71*:583–620.

27. IVY, A. C., MORGAN, J. E. and FARRELL, J. I. Effects of total gastrectomy; experimental achylia gastrica in dogs with occurrence of spontaneous anaemia and anaemia of pregnancy. *Surg. Gynec. Obstet.*, 1931, *53*:611–620.

28. KOMAROV, S. A. Gastrin. *Proc. Soc. exp. Biol., N. Y.*, 1938, *38*:514–516.

29. LANGLEY, J. N. On the histology of the mammalian gastric glands, and the relation of pepsin to the granules of the chief-cells. *J. Physiol.*, 1880–82, *3*:269–291.

30. LONDON, E. S. and POWLOWZOWA, W. W. Zur Frage der Verdauung und Resorption im Magen des Hundes. *Hoppe-Seyl. Z.*, 1909, *62*:446–450.

31. MARTIN, L. Gastric secretion—the electrolytes before and their changes at various periods after histamine stimulation. *Ann. intern. Med.*, 1932, *6*:91–128.

32. MICHAELIS, L. and DAVIDSOHN, H. Die Bedeutung und die Messung der Magensaftacidität. *Z. exp. Path. Ther.*, 1910–11, *8*:398–413.

33. MITCHELL, T. C. The buffer substances of the gastric juice, and their relation to gastric mucus. *J. Physiol.*, 1931, *73*:427–443.

34. MORRIS, R. S., SCHIFF, L., BURGER, G. and SHERMAN, J. E. Specific hematopoietic hormone in normal gastric juice; preliminary note. *J. Amer. med. Ass.*, 1932, *98*:1080–1081.

35. OSLER, W. William Beaumont. A pioneer American physiologist. *J. Amer. med. Ass.*, 1902, *39*:1223–1231.

36. RASSERS, J. R. F. Sur le problème de la sécrétion d'acide chlorhydrique dans l'estomac. *Arch. néerl. Physiol.*, 1928, *13*:514–520.

37. ROSEMANN, R. Beiträge zur Physiologie der Verdauung. I. Die Ergenschaften und die Zusammensetzung des durch Scheinfütterung gewonnenen Hundemagensaftes. *Pflüg. Arch. ges. Physiol.*, 1907, *118*:467–524.

38. ROSEMANN, R. Zur Physiologie und Pathologie der Säurabsonderung der Magenschleimhaut. *Virchows Arch.*, 1920, *229*:67–89.

39. SACKS, J., IVY, A. C., BURGESS, J. P. and VANDOLAH, J. E. Histamine as the hormone for gastric secretion. *Amer. J. Physiol.*, 1932, *101*:331–338.

40. SHOHL, A. T. Determination of the acidity of gastric contents. I. Determination and significance of acidity. *Johns Hopk. Hosp. Bull.*, 1920, *31*:152–158.

41. TAUBER, H. and KLEINER, I. S. Studies

on rennin. I. The purification of rennin and its separation from pepsin. *J. biol. Chem.*, 1932, *96*:745–753.

42. VICKERY, H. B. and OSBORNE, T. B. A review of hypotheses of the structure of proteins. *Physiol. Rev.*, 1928, *8*:393–446.

43. VINEBERG, A. M. and BABKIN, B. P. Histamine and pilocarpin in relation to the gastric secretion. *Amer. J. Physiol.*, 1931, *97*:69–73.

44. WILHELMJ, C. M., HENRICH, L. C. and HILL, F. C. A study of the intragastric factors in the regulation of gastric acidity. *Amer. J. Physiol.*, 1934–35, *110*:251–260.

45. WILHELMJ, C. M., HENRICH, L. C., NEIGUS, I. and HILL, F. C. The origin and significance of neutral chloride in the secretions of the stomach and duodenum. *Amer. J. Physiol.*, 1935, *112*:15–20.

46. ZELIONY, G. P. Observations on dogs with cerebral hemispheres removed. *XIth Int. Physiol. Congr.*, 1923.

CHAPTER 49

DIGESTION AND ABSORPTION IN THE INTESTINES

The food undergoes its most profound digestive changes in the intestines, and here also the products of digestion are mainly absorbed. The intestinal digestion begins in the duodenum, and is largely completed by the time the food arrives at the ileocecal valve. It is effected through the combined action of three secretions—the pancreatic juice, the secretion from the intestinal glands (succus entericus), and the bile. These secretions are mixed with the food from the duodenum on, so that their action proceeds simultaneously. For purposes of description it is necessary to speak of each more or less separately.

PANCREAS

The pancreas forms a long, narrow gland reaching from the spleen to the curvature of the duodenum. Its main duct in man (duct of Wirsung) opens into the duodenum, together with the common bile duct, about 8 to 10 cm. beyond the pylorus. The points at which the duct or ducts of the pancreas enters the intestine vary somewhat in different mammals. In the dog there are two chief ducts, one opening, together with the bile duct, about 3 to 5 cm. below the pylorus, while a second enters the duodenum some 3 to 5 cm. farther down. In rabbits the principal pancreatic duct opens separately into the duodenum about 35 cm. below the opening of the bile duct. The pancreas is a compound tubular gland like the salivary glands. The cells lining the secreting portion of the tubules, the alveoli, belong to the serous or albuminous type. They are characterized by the fact that the outer portion of each cell is composed of a clear, nongranular material which stains readily, while the inner portion, the portion facing the lumen, contains numerous granules. Histological study of the gland after active secretion, as compared with the resting state, has shown that these granules represent a preparatory material for secretion. As the secretion proceeds the granules are dissolved and discharged into the lumen, while during the periods of rest new granules are formed by metabolic processes at the expense, apparently, of the nongranular material in the basal portion of the cell (Heidenhain, Kühne, Lea). The histological picture of secretion is in general the same in this as in the salivary and gastric glands, only somewhat more distinctly shown. On the supposition that the granules constitute an antecedent material from which the enzymes of the secretion are formed they are frequently designated as zymogen granules. The pancreas contains also certain peculiar groups of cells, the islands (or bodies) of Langerhans. These cells probably have nothing to do with the digestive activity of the pancreas. Their function is referred to in Section IX.

Composition of the Secretion. The pancreatic secretion is an alkaline liquid which in some animals is thin and limpid, in others thick and glairy. The secretion in man belongs to the former type; it is described as water-clear and as having a specific gravity of 1.0075. The secretion may be collected by opening the abdomen and inserting a cannula directly into the duct, or a permanent fistula may be made by the method of Pavlov. This method, applicable to the dog, consists in cutting out a small portion of the duodenum where the pancreatic duct opens and then suturing this piece, the mucous membrane outward, into the abdominal wall. The secretion of the human pancreas has been collected in several cases in which it was necessary to drain off the pancreatic juice to the exterior. From the observations made in one case (12) it appears that the secretion in man is quite abundant, amounting to 500 to 800 cc. per day. In the dog observations made upon animals with a permanent fistula indicate a flow of from 200 to 750 cc. a day. The secretion possesses a strong alkaline reaction, due to the presence of sodium carbonate; it also contains a small amount of coagulable protein and a number of organic substances in traces. The important constituents, however, are a number of digestive enzymes, proteolytic, lipolytic and amylolytic, capable of hydrolyzing the three main classes of foodstuffs, the proteins, the fats and the starches. The proteolytic action is effected through a group of enzymes of which the chief members have been called trypsin, chymotrypsin and erepsin. Trypsin was regarded as attacking native proteins and capable of hydrolyzing them to the amino acid stage. Erepsin was considered to be an enzyme which acted primarily on proteoses and peptones, breaking them down to yield mixtures of amino acids. Thus erepsin was regarded as an agent that completes the work of pepsin. The present view is somewhat different. What was formerly called erepsin and found to be present in both the pancreas and the small intestine is now believed to be a mixture of enzymes one of which, carboxypeptidase, is normally present in pancreatic juice. Furthermore, pure trypsin has been found not to hydrolyze proteins beyond the proteose and polypeptide stage. Northrop has also pointed out the existence in pancreatic juice of another proteolytic agent, chymotrypsin. It differs from trypsin in two ways; first, chymotrypsin has a greater rennin-like action than trypsin; second, whereas trypsinogen is activated by entero-kinase to form the active trypsin, chymotrypsinogen is activated by trypsin to form active chymotrypsin. The first difference helps to settle the controversy that has existed over the question whether there is a rennin in pancreatic juice.

Secretory Nerve Fibers to the Pancreas. The pancreas receives its nerve supply immediately from the celiac plexus, but stimulation of the nerves going to this plexus—namely, the splanchnics and the vagi—have given negative results in the hands of most observers so far as the pancreatic secretion is concerned. Pavlov (27) and his coworkers claim to have been more successful. Mechanical stimulation or electrical stimulation of the vagus or splanchnic gave them a marked flow of pancreatic juice, but when the latter form of stimulus was used upon the splanchnic, it was necessary to cut the nerve some days previously in order that the vasoconstrictor fibers might degenerate. The secretion provoked by stimulation of the vagus is more easily obtained when the stimulus is applied to the nerve in the thorax below the origin of the branches to the heart. The secretion obtained upon stimulation of the nerves is characterized, as in the case of the gastric glands, by a long latent period of some minutes—a fact that is explained, although not satisfactorily, on the assumption that the nerve trunks stimulated contain both secretory and inhibitory fibers and that the antagonistic action of the latter delays the appearance of the secretion. These observations have been taken as proof of the existence of secretory nerve fibers to the pancreas, the fibers running chiefly in the vagus nerve.

Recently Crider and Thomas (7) have reported numerous observations of the secretion of pancreatic juice obtained after cutting the extrinsic nerves. These observations have been interpreted as favoring the view that "the vagus nerves influence the external secretory function of the pancreas through the augmentation or inhibition of local reflexes." In other experiments these same authors studied the pancreatic secretagogue action of products of protein digestion (35). Many earlier workers had shown that the injection of peptone is followed by a flow of pancreatic juice. Since it is known that such an injection likewise stimulates the flow of gastric juice, the effect on the pancreas has generally been assumed to be an indirect one due to the discharge

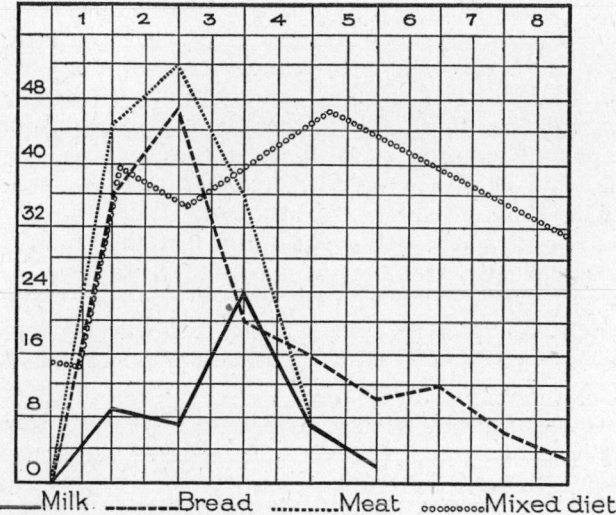

Fig. 467.—Four curves of the secretion of the pancreatic juice. Three (from Walter) show the secretion in dogs on different diets: solid line, on 600 cc. of milk; dashed line, on 250 gm. of bread; dotted line, on 100 gm. of meat. The curve composed of circles (from Glaessner) shows the secretion in man on a mixed diet—soup, meat and bread. The figures 1, 2, 3, etc., along the abscissa, indicate hours after the beginning of the meal. The figures along the ordinate indicate the quantity of the secretion in cubic centimeters.

of gastric acid into the duodenum with resultant stimulation of the pancreatic secretin mechanism (see below). Thomas and Crider (35) compared the injection of peptone with other stimuli in dogs provided with a cannulated duodenal fistula placed opposite the opening of the main pancreatic duct. The secretion produced by peptone stimulation had a higher specific gravity and contained many times more nitrogen per cubic centimeter than that produced by water, acid or the hormone secretin (discussed below). Curiously enough, this secretion resembled that caused by the drug pilocarpine and other stimuli that act through or on the secretory nerves. It was concluded, therefore, that peptones act through a nervous mechanism, a view that received further support from the histological examination of the changes in the acinar cells of the pancreas which proved to be similar to those resulting from stimulation of the vagus nerves (29).

Curves of Secretion. The rate of flow of the pancreatic juice with reference to the period of digestion has been determined by a number of observers. In the careful experiments reported by Walter it is shown that the quantity of secretion is dependent to a considerable extent upon the character of the food. Thus, the flow is more abundant and reaches its maximum sooner after a meal of bread alone than after a meal of meat alone. It seems possible that the latter point, the time at which the maximum flow is reached, may depend upon the difference in rate at which these foods are ejected from the stomach. Cannon (6) has shown that the carbohydrate foods leave the stomach sooner than the proteins or fats. It is stated, however, that the composition of the secretion varies also with the character of the food, and indeed shows an adaptation to the character of the food. The secretion caused by protein food is especially rich in trypsin, that caused by fatty food in lipase, etc. The mechanism by which this adaptation is secured is not understood. Glaessner (12) has measured the rate of flow in man, and his curve for a mixed diet is represented also (in red) in Figure 467. These curves indicate in general that the secretion of pancreatic juice begins very soon after food enters the stomach, and increases rapidly to a maximum, which is reached somewhere between the second and fourth hour. According to Glaessner's case, there is a continuous small secretion of the juice during fasting. In dogs with a permanent fistula most observers have stated that there is an entire cessation of the flow when the stomach is empty, but some later work with improved technique appears to show, on the contrary, that there is a considerable continuous secretion which is augmented by meals and by the action of secretin (42).

Normal Mechanism of the Pancreatic Secretion—Secretin. Much light was thrown upon the mechanism of pancreatic secretion by the discovery of Dolinsky in 1895 that acids brought into contact with the mucous membrane of the duodenum set up promptly a secretion of pancreatic juice. As soon as any of the acid contents of the stomach pass through the pylorus this action begins. Assuming that the pancreatic gland possesses secretory fibers, it was thought at first that the acid acts reflexly through these fibers—that is, the acid in the duodenum acting upon sensory endings causes a reflex stimulation of the efferent secretory fibers. Popielski showed, however, that the same effect takes place after section of the vagus and splanchnic nerves and Bayliss and Starling (2) have called attention to another more probable explanation. These authors found that if the mucous membrane of the duodenum (or jejunum) is scraped off and treated with acid (0.4 per cent HCl), the extract thus made when injected into the blood sets up an active secretion of pancreatic juice. They have shown that this effect is due to a special substance, *secretin*, which is formed by the action of the acid upon some substance (prosecretin) present in the mucous membrane. Secretin is not an enzyme, since its activity is not destroyed by boiling or by the action of alcohol. It belongs to the group of hormones. According to these authors the normal sequence of events is as follows: the acid of the gastric juice upon reaching the duodenum produces secretin; this, in turn, is absorbed by the blood, carried to the pancreas, and stimulates this organ to activity. For many years the specific nature of this substance was debated, because it was found that crude extracts of intestinal mucosa containing this secretin also contained a depressor substance—vasodilatin—and it could be argued that the stimulatory effect of the secretin was really due to vasodilatin; furthermore, numerous extracts of both plant and animal tissues were discovered to contain vaso-dilatin. Mellanby (23) has suggested that the effective agent in liberating it is not the acid of the gastric juice but the bile that is emptied into the intestine during gastric digestion; the bile salts as they are absorbed carry the secretin into the blood and in this way it is transported to the pancreas. The observa-tions of Dragstedt and Woodbury (8, 9) and Thomas and Crider (36), how-ever, do not confirm these ideas. The fact that pancreatic juice is secreted in individuals suffering from gastric achlorhydria suggests that, although acid in the intestine may serve as an effective stimulus, it cannot be the only stimulus. Luckhardt, Barlow and Weaver (21) were able to make potent extracts that were devoid of depressor substances, thus confirming the view that there is a hormonal agent of the type postulated by Bayliss and Starling. It remained for Agren (1) to isolate secretin in crystalline form. His product proved to be a protein which was found to contain the amino acid lysine but no tyrosine, tryptophane or cystine. It behaved as a basic substance that gave some but not all the common tests for protein, and was digested by proteinases. It could be inactivated by treatment with 0.1 N sodium hydroxide, and this loss of activity was associated with the development of a positive ninhydrin reaction which pointed to the inactivation being due to a splitting of a peptide linkage without further disruption of the molecule. The activity could not be due to free amino groups. The intravenous injection of pure secretin resulted in secretion by the pancreas, the liver and the intestinal glands, an action that has been called a "generalized intestinal diuretic" effect; such injections produced no lowering of the blood pressure and no effect on the gallbladder or on isolated segments of intestinal muscle of the rabbit.

It could of course be argued that Agren has merely isolated a chemical agent having the property of stimulating the pancreas to secrete; whether such an agent is produced in the organism under normal conditions can only be determined by appropriate physiological experiments. Such experiments have been performed and the results confirm the view that there is indeed a hormone mechanism of the type postulated by the secretin theory. Farrell and Ivy (11) succeeded in transplanting the tail of the pancreas under the skin with its duct opening to the exterior, thus establishing a fistula. When the transplant had become supplied with new blood vessels, the original blood and nerve supply was severed. It was observed that the ingestion of food or hydrochloric acid resulted in the flow of juice from the transplanted tissue. Against these experiments it could be argued that food products absorbed from the intestine might have been responsible for the effect. Therefore dogs were operated upon and provided with transplants of both pancreatic and jejunal tissue (16). When hydrochloric acid was placed in the transplanted jejunum, juice was secreted by the transplanted pancreas. In appropriate control experiments other substances had no such effect. Still (32) has reviewed the literature concerning secretin which the interested reader may consult with profit.

According to the evidence at present in our possession we must believe that the pancreatic secretion, like the gastric secretion, consists of two parts: (i) a *nervous secretion* caused by the secretory fibers in the vagus and splanch-nic, the action of which is mediated through a peripheral or local reflex mechanism; (ii) a *chemical secretion* due to the action of a hormone (secretin) produced in the intestinal mucosa. These two secretions are said to present quite different characters (30). The former is thick, opalescent, rich in ferments and proteins but poor in alkalies; its flow is suspended by the action of atropine. Administration of pilocarpine, on the contrary, excites this secretion, as well as the presence of certain products of protein digestion in the intestine. The chemical secretion is thin and watery, contains relatively little ferment or proteins, and is rich in alkali. The trypsin in it is secreted in inactive form and the secretion is not affected by the administration of atropine. Mellanby has suggested that the secretin mechanism, calling forth as it does a secretion richer in alkali, has as its chief function not so much the provision of a juice rich in enzymes as one that is important for neutralizing the acid of the gastric chyme. Thomas and Crider (34) have determined in dogs the threshold pH at which acid in the intestine begins to act as a stimulus for pancreatic secretion and reported it to vary between 3.0 and 5.0 depending on the acid used; "the practical threshold for bringing about pancreatic digestion at a rate comparable to that normally present during digestion would probably be in the neighborhood of pH 4.0." Since in dogs fed raw meat the contents of the first part of the duodenum were found (33) to vary in acidity between pH 2.4 and 7.0 but were generally nearer pH 4.0, the acidity of the intestinal contents during digestion is adequate to stimulate the pancreas.

Activation of the Trypsin—Enterokinase. It was discovered in Pavlov's laboratory by Chepowalnikow that the pancreatic juice obtained from a fistula may have little or no digestive action on proteins, but if brought into contact with the duodenal membrane or an extract of this membrane it shows at once powerful proteolytic properties. This discovery has been confirmed repeatedly. Apparently the proteolytic enzyme of the juice is secreted in a zymogen or pro-enzyme form (trypsinogen), which is activated or converted to trypsin by something contained in the mucous membrane of the small intestine (duodenum, jejunum). This something Pavlov supposed to be an enzyme, because it can be inactivated by heat, and since its action is on another enzyme, "a ferment of ferments," he designated it as a kinase or enterokinase which by hydrolytic action upon the trypsinogen converts it to active trypsin. This view has been adopted generally, but one cannot say that it has been definitely established. Some later workers believe that the enterokinase acts rather as a coferment. Others hold the view that trypsin is secreted in active form but in combination with an inhibitory substance. According to this view the enterokinase serves to neutralize the inhibitory factor and thus free the trypsin.

Digestive Action of Pancreatic Juice. The most significant digestive action of the secretion depends upon its three groups of proteolytic, amylolytic, and lipolytic enzymes, the specific effects of which may be considered separately. In addition, as reference to the list of enzymes tabulated on page 1025 will show, there are present nucleases that split nucleic acid to form purine bases, and the deaminizing enzymes guanase and adenase.

Action of the proteolytic enzymes. The proteolytic action of the pancreatic juice differs from that of the gastric juice in that it takes place in an alkaline or neutral or feebly acid medium and its effect is to break down the protein molecule more completely. Under favorable conditions the protein is split to its constituent amino acids. In the pancreatic juice as secreted normally it was formerly supposed that only one proteolytic enzyme is present to which Kühne, in 1897, gave the name "trypsin." When we speak of the secretion in general terms this usage is still followed. The digestive action of the pancreatic juice upon proteins is spoken of as its tryptic effect. As a matter of fact, investigation has shown that the juice contains several proteolytic enzymes which act upon the protein molecule or its split products, each of which probably has its own field of action, although the complete story of their interaction is not known. Northrop and Kunitz (19, 25) have been able to obtain from commercial preparations of trypsin an active enzyme in crystalline form which they designate as trypsin or crystalline trypsin. It is a protein substance containing 15 per cent nitrogen and has a molecular weight of about 34,000. It shows constant physical and chemical properties and is a true proteinase causing hydrolysis of such proteins as casein and gelatin, although the hydrolysis is not carried to the stage of amino acids. This trypsin is secreted in an inactive form, trypsinogen, which these authors have also obtained in crystals. As thus obtained the trypsinogen is activated, that is, converted to trypsin by an autocatalytic process. But in the normal secretion this activation takes place rapidly in the intestine under the influence of the enterokinase, as described above. In addition to the trypsin these authors have isolated a second proteinase in crystalline form which they call chymotrypsin, since in addition to its proteolytic activity it has the property of clotting milk. Chymotrypsin exists also in an active and an inactive form, chymotrypsin and chymotrypsinogen. The change from the inactive to the active form is effected rapidly by trypsin. The significance of the presence of two active proteinases is not clear but Northrop suggests that they may act on different linkages in the protein molecule. Other proteolytic enzymes in the secretion have been detected, such as erepsin, aminopeptidase, and carboxypeptidase, the action of which is exerted upon the hydrolytic products, the peptids, formed by the trypsin and the chymotrypsin. The best known of this group is the erepsin, which was discovered first in the intestinal secretion (p. 1072). It belongs to the class of peptidases, that is, the enzymes which act upon the peptids or polypeptids, hydrolyzing them to amino acids. The erepsin of the pancreatic juice seems to be identical with that found in the intestinal secretion. It does not act upon the complex proteins and, therefore, in both pancreatic and intestinal digestion it may be assumed that it supplements the effect of the proteinases, the pepsin, trypsin and chymotrypsin, which carry the hydrolysis only to a polypeptid stage.

In the normal digestion of proteins it is believed that they are broken down completely to the amino acids and are absorbed in that form, but it is possible that some absorption of the simple peptid or polypeptid compounds may take place. In any given digestive mixture the actual products formed depend on the length of time the enzymes are allowed to act and the conditions, favorable or unfavorable, under which they act. The end-products usually obtained most easily are tyrosine, leucine, aspartic acid, glutaminic acid, tryptophane, lysine, arginine, histidine. The first two of these substances have been known for a long time and may be obtained easily in crystalline form from pancreatic digestions. If the enzymes are allowed to exert their complete action upon the protein the end-products are closely similar to those obtained by boiling protein with acids. The hydrolysis caused by the acids and by the enzymes seems to be nearly identical, although that caused by the acids is probably more complete and perhaps is attended by secondary reactions. The numerous products obtained by this complete hydrolysis consist chiefly of amino acids—that is, organic acids containing one or more amino groups (NH_2) in direct union with carbon. Most of them are mono-amino acids, that is, contain one NH_2 group, and this group is united with the carbon occupying the *alpha* position.

A list of the known amino acids obtained from proteolytic cleavage of the protein molecule is appended. Twenty-seven or twenty-eight such substances have been obtained by cleavage of proteins. Not all of them are contained in any one protein, but some proteins—casein for example—yield as many as seventeen to nineteen different amino acids. For a more complete description of their properties and chemical relationships reference must be made to textbooks on physiological chemistry. With regard to the nomenclature used, it will be borne in mind that the various carbon atoms in the straight chain of the fatty acids are designated by Greek letters that indicate their position in relation to the carboxyl (COOH) group, as may be illustrated by the formula for caproic acid:

$$CH_3 \quad CH_2 \quad CH_2 \quad CH_2 \quad CH_2 \quad COOH$$
$$\epsilon \qquad \delta \qquad \gamma \qquad \beta \qquad \alpha$$

I. Aliphatic, mono-amino, monocarboxylic acids

    1. Glycine or glycocoll, amino-acetic acid
       $CH_2(NH_2)COOH$

    2. Alanine, α-aminopropionic acid
       $CH_3CH(NH_2)COOH$

    3. Valine, or α-amino-isovaleric acid

       CH_3
           $\searrow CHCH(NH_2)COOH$
       CH_3

    4. Norleucine, or α-aminocaproic acid
       $CH_3CH_2CH_2CH_2CHNH_2COOH$

    5. Leucine, or α-amino-isocaproic acid

       CH_3
           $\searrow CHCH_2CH(NH_2)COOH$
       CH_3

    6. Isoleucine, or α-amino β-methyl β-ethyl propionic acid

       CH_3
           $\searrow CHCHNH_2COOH$
       C_2H_5

II. Aliphatic, mono-amino, monocarboxylic, hydroxy acids

    7. Serine, or β-hydroxy-α-aminopropionic acid
       $CH_2OHCH(NH_2)COOH$

    8. Threonine, or β-hydroxy-α-aminobutyric acid
       $CH_3CHOHCH(NH_2)COOH$

III. Aliphatic, mono-amino, dicarboxylic acids

    9. Aspartic acid, or α-aminosuccinic acid
       $HOOCCH_2CH(NH_2)COOH$

    10. Glutamic acid, or α-aminoglutaric acid
       $HOOCCH_2CH_2CH(NH_2)COOH$

    11. Hydroxyglutamic acid, or β-hydroxy-α-aminoglutaric acid
       $HOOCCH_2CHOHCH(NH_2)COOH$

IV. Aliphatic, amino acids containing sulphur

12. Cystine (di-cysteine) or di-(β-thio-α-aminopropionic acid)
    HOOCCH(NH$_2$)CH$_2$S—SCH$_2$CH(NH$_2$)COOH

13. Methionine, or γ-methylthio-α-aminobutyric acid
    CH$_3$SCH$_2$CH$_2$CH(NH$_2$)COOH

V. Amino acids with aromatic nucleus

14. Phenylalanine, or β-phenyl-α-aminopropionic acid
    C$_6$H$_5$CH$_2$CH(NH$_2$)COOH

15. Tyrosine, or β-p-hydroxyphenyl-α-aminopropionic acid
    HOC$_6$H$_4$CH$_2$CH(NH$_2$)COOH

16. Di-iodotyrosine
    HOC$_6$H$_2$I$_2$CH$_2$CH(NH$_2$)COOH

17. Thyroxine
    HOC$_6$H$_2$I$_2$OC$_6$H$_2$I$_2$CH$_2$CH(NH$_2$)COOH

VI. Basic aliphatic amino acids

18. Lysine, or α-ϵ-diaminocaproic acid
    (NH$_2$)CH$_2$CH$_2$CH$_2$CH$_2$CH(NH$_2$)COOH

19. Arginine, or δ-guanidine-α-aminovaleric acid
    CN$_3$H$_4$CH$_2$CH$_2$CH$_2$CH(NH$_2$)COOH

20. Ornithine, or α-δ-diaminovaleric acid
    (NH$_2$)CH$_2$CH$_2$CH$_2$CH(NH$_2$)COOH

21. Citrulline, or δ-urea-α-aminovaleric acid
    NH$_2$CONHCH$_2$CH$_2$CH$_2$CH(NH$_2$)COOH

VII. Amino acids with heterocyclic nucleus

22. Tryptophane, or β-indole-α-aminopropionic acid
    C$_8$H$_6$NCH$_2$CH(NH$_2$)COOH

23. Histidine, or β-imidazole-α-aminopropionic acid

24. Proline, or α-pyrrolidine carboxylic acid

25. Hydroxyproline, or hydroxypyrrolidine carboxylic acid

Significance of protein digestion. It was formerly supposed that the object of peptic and tryptic digestion is to convert the insoluble and nondialyzable proteins into the simpler, more soluble, and more diffusible peptones and proteoses. In this way absorption of protein material was explained. This view, however, did not prove to be satisfactory. On the one hand, it has not been possible to show that peptones or proteoses are present in the blood; on the other hand, a better knowledge of the processes of tryptic or of tryptic-ereptic digestion demonstrated that the process does not stop at the peptone stage. The usual belief as stated above is that the protein molecule is entirely broken down into the various amino acids. The value of this complete splitting of the protein of the food lies in the possibility that thereby the body is able to construct its own peculiar type of protein. Many different kinds of proteins are taken as food, and many of them, if absorbed directly into the blood, would not only be unfitted to supply the protein needs of the tissues but would act as a foreign material capable of causing pathological reactions, such as the condition of hypersensitivity which we know ensues when a foreign protein is injected into the blood. But if the proteins are broken down more or less completely during digestion, the tissue cells may reconstruct from the pieces or building stones a form of protein adaptable to their needs, and more or less characteristic for that particular organism. Just as the letters of the alphabet may be combined in different ways to make different words, so the various amino acids may be combined to make proteins of many kinds.

Action of the diastatic enzyme (*amylase*) *of the pancreatic secretion.* This enzyme is found in the secretion of the pancreas or it may be extracted from the gland. Its action upon starchy foods is similar to or identical with that of ptyalin. It causes a hydrolysis of the starch, with the production finally of maltose and achroödextrin. Before absorption these substances are further acted upon by the maltase of the intestinal secretion and converted to glucose. The starchy food that escapes digestion in the mouth and stomach becomes mixed with this enzyme in the duodenum, and from that time until it reaches the end of the large intestine conditions are favorable for its conversion to maltose. Most of this digestion is probably completed, under normal conditions, before the contents of the intestinal canal reach the ileocecal valve. Caldwell, Booher and Sherman (5) state that they have obtained this enzyme in the form of minute, elongated isotropic crystals of a protein nature.

Action of the lipolytic enzyme (*lipase*). The importance of the pancreatic secretion in the digestion of fats was first clearly stated by Bernard in 1849. We know now that this secretion contains an active enzyme capable of hydrolyzing or saponifying the neutral fats. These latter bodies are chemically esters of the trihydric alcohol glycerol. When hydrolyzed they break up into glycerol and the constituent fatty acid. The action of lipase may be represented, therefore, by the following reaction in the case of palmitin:

$$C_3H_5(C_{15}H_{31}COO)_3 + 3H_2O = C_3H_5(OH)_3 + 3(C_{15}H_{31}COOH)$$
$$\text{Palmitin} \qquad\qquad \text{Glycerol} \qquad \text{Palmitic acid}$$

When lipae from any source is added to neutral oils its splitting action is readily recognized by the development of an acid reaction due to the formation of the fatty acid. If a bit of freh pancreas is added to butter, for example, and the mixture is kept at body temperature, the hydrolysis of the fats is soon made evident by the rancid odor due to the butyric acid produced. When pancreatic juice is mixed with oils or liquid fats two phenomena may be noticed: (i) the splitting of the fat already referred to, and (ii) the emulsification of the fat. The latter process is very striking. An oil is emulsified when it is broken up into minute globules that do not coalesce. Artificial emulsions may be made by vigorous and prolonged shaking of the oil in a viscous solution of soap, mucilage, etc. Milk may be regarded as a natural emulsion that separates slowly on standing, as the fat rises to the top to form the cream. When a little pancreatic juice is added to oil at the body temperature the mixture, after standing for some time, will emulsify readily with very little shaking or even spontaneously. The emulsification is due to the formation of soaps. The lipase splits some of the fats, and the fatty acid liberated combines with the alkaline salts present to form soaps. The presence of the small amount of soap formed in this way at the beginning of the reaction is then instrumental in causing the emulsification of the remainder of the neutral fat. The emulsification produced under these conditions is very fine and quite permanent, and it was formerly believed that the formation of this emulsion is the main function of the pancreatic juice so far as fats are concerned. It was thought that in the form of fine droplets the fat may be taken up directly by the epithelial cells of the villi, and this view was supported by the histological fact that during the digestion of fats the epithelial cells may be shown to contain fine oil drops in their interior. The tendency of recent work, however, has been to indicate that most, if not all, fat is split into fatty acids and glycerol before absorption, and that the emulsification may be regarded, from a physiological standpoint, as a mechanical preparation for the further action of the lipase rather than as a direct preparation for the act of absorption. The two products of the action of the lipase, the glycerol and the fatty acid, are absorbed by the epithelium. The fatty acids themselves are insoluble in water and it has been supposed that they form soaps with the sodium salts present and are absorbed in this form. Verzar (40), however, calls attention to the fact that the alkali soaps are not stable in solutions with a pH below 9, and that the intestinal contents during digestion have a neutral or even faintly acid reaction. He finds that the fatty acids form soluble and diffusible compounds with the bile salts, sodium glycocholate and taurocholate, which are stable at pH 6.2, and suggests that the fatty acids are absorbed in this form. After absorption the two constituents are resynthesized, with loss of water, to form a neutral fat. Droplets of fat are found in the epithelial cells during the period of absorption. It is probable, moreover, that during the synthesis the fatty acids are combined with the glycerol in such proportions as to make for the most part the fat characteristic of the animal; for instance, fat has a high melting point in the sheep and a lower melting point in the dog. The entire story of the changes undergone by fat during absorption is not completely known. There is evidence, for example, that during the processes of absorption and transportation some, at least, is converted to a phospholipid compound, lecithin (3).

The lipase as formed in the pancreas is easily destroyed, especially by acids. For this reason probably it is not usually found in simple extracts of the gland made by laboratory methods. It should be added, also, that the action of this enzyme is aided very materially by the presence of bile. This latter secretion contains no lipase itself, but mixtures of bile and pancreatic juice split the neutral fats much more rapidly than the pancreatic juice alone. This effect is now explained on the hypothesis that the bile acids or the bile acids and the lecithin either activate a portion of the lipase which is in the state of a proferment or play the part of a coferment (p. 1025). In addition, as was stated in the preceding paragraph, the bile acids may play a direct part in promoting the absorption of the fatty acids after they are formed by combining with these acids to make a soluble and diffusible compound.

INTESTINAL SECRETION (SUCCUS ENTERICUS)

The small intestine is lined with tubular glands, the crypts of Lieberkühn, which in parts of the intestine at least give rise to a liquid secretion, the so-called intestinal juice. To obtain this secretion recourse has been had to the operation known as the Thiry-Vella fistula. In this operation a small portion of the intestine is isolated by cutting through the intestinal wall at two points a certain distance apart. The continuity of the canal is re-established by appropriate suture, while the piece cut out, with its blood and nerve supply intact, is given an opening to the exterior by suturing to the abdominal wall. If one end of this isolated segment is closed and the other end made to open to the exterior, one has what is called a Thiry loop; if both ends open to the outside, one has a Thiry-Vella loop. In this way a small pouch or loop of the intestine is separated from the rest of the alimentary canal and is so arranged that its secretion can be obtained through the fistulous openings, or material of any kind can be introduced into the loop and be removed after a given time to determine what absorption has taken place. The secretion from these loops is usually said to be small in quantity, especially in the jejunum. Pregl has estimated that as much as three liters may be formed in the whole of the small intestine in the course of a day, but this estimate does not rest upon very satisfactory data. The liquid gives an alkaline reaction owing to the presence of sodium carbonate. According to the older observations this liquid has little digestive action when obtained without mixture with the pancreatic secretion, but extracts of the walls of the small intestine or the juice squeezed from these walls have been found, on the contrary, to contain four or five different enzymes and to exert a most important influence upon intestinal digestion. It has been a question whether these enzymes are discharged into the external secretion or whether they play their important role as endo-enzymes within the lining cells of the intestine. Formerly the latter view was held, but more recent work indicates that the enzymes are given off to the secretion and exert their action within the lumen of the intestine as the final stage in the preparation of the food for absorption. These enzymes and their actions are as follows:

(i) Enterokinase (see p. 1066), an enzyme or coferment which activates the trypsin of the pancreatic juice. According to one view, the precursor of this substance is secreted with the pancreatic juice and is in some way made effective by a reaction with the cells of the intestine.

(ii) Erepsin. This enzyme, discovered by Cohnheim, acts especially upon the simpler polypeptids. It belongs to the general group of peptidases, that is, enzymes which cause hydrolysis of peptids. Its splitting action upon these compounds is supposed to be complete, and the natural suggestion regarding this enzyme is that it supplements the work begun by the trypsin and pepsin. Erepsin occurs not only in the intestinal mucosa but also, it will be remembered, in the pancreatic secretion. It has been extracted, in fact, from various tissues, and according to Willstätter and Bamann is a characteristic endo-enzyme of the leukocytes. This source of erepsin may explain its general occurrence in the tissues. On the theory that proteins during digestion are broken down completely to their constituent amino acids, the importance of this enzyme in the normal digestion of proteins has gained increased recognition in recent years. The digestion of the protein begun by the pepsin or by the trypsin is carried to completion by the action of the erepsin.

(iii) Three enzymes capable of hydrolyzing the disaccharides into the monosaccharides. These enzymes are the following: maltase, which acts upon maltose (and dextrin); invertase or sucrase or invertin, which acts upon cane sugar; and lactase, which acts upon lactose. The maltase acts upon the products formed in the digestion of starches, the maltose and dextrin, converting them to glucose according to the general formula:

$$C_{12}H_{22}O_{11} + H_2O = C_6H_{12}O_6 = C_6H_{12}O_6$$
$$\text{Maltose} \qquad\qquad \text{Glucose} \qquad \text{Glucose}$$

In the same way invertase converts cane sugar to glucose and levulose, and lactase changes milk sugar to glucose and galactose. This hydrolytic action is necessary to prepare the carbohydrate food for nutritive purposes. The disaccharides cannot be used by the tissues and would escape in the urine, but in the form of glucose or glucose and levulose they are readily used by the tissues in their normal metabolic processes.

(iv) Nuclease. An enzyme to which this name may be given is said to occur in the small intestine. It acts upon the nucleic acid component of nucleoproteins, splitting it with the formation of the corresponding purine and pyrimidine nucleotides (see p. 1025).

(v) Secretin. As explained above, this hormone plays an important role in the control of the secretion of the pancreatic juice and the bile. It is not an enzyme, but a hormone which is secreted or formed in the intestinal mucosa, and under the influence of acids or of acids and bile is absorbed, carried to the pancreas, and causes a flow of pancreatic secretion (see p. 1064).

SMALL INTESTINE

Absorption. Absorption takes place very readily in the small intestine. The general correctness of this statement may be shown by the use of isolated loops of the intestine. Salt solutions of varying strengths or even blood serum nearly identical in composition with the animal's own blood may be absorbed completely from these loops. Examination of the contents of the intestine in the duodenum and at the ileocecal valve shows that the products formed in digestion have largely disappeared in traversing this distance. All the information that we possess indicates, in fact, that the mucous membrane of the small intestine absorbs readily, and it is one of the problems of this part of physiology to explain the means by which this absorption is effected. Anatomically two paths are open to the products absorbed. They may enter the blood directly by passing into the capillaries of the villi, or they may enter the lacteals of the villi, pass into the lymph circulation, and through the thoracic duct of the lymphatic system eventually reach the blood vascular system. The older physiologists assumed that absorption takes place exclusively through the central lacteals of the villi and hence these vessels were described as the absorbents. We now know that the digested and resynthesized fats are absorbed by way of the lacteals, but that the other products of digestion are absorbed mainly through the blood vessels, and therefore enter the portal system and pass through the liver before reaching the general circulation. According to observations made upon a patient with a fistula at the end of the small intestine (22), food begins to pass into the large intestine in from two to five and a quarter hours after eating, and it requires nine or more hours before the last of a meal has passed the ileocecal valve; this estimate includes, of course, the time in the stomach. During this passage absorption of the digested products takes place nearly completely. In the fistula case referred to above, it was found that 85 per cent of the protein had disappeared, and similar facts are known regarding the other foodstuffs. The problems that have excited the greatest interest have been, first, the exact form in which the digested products are absorbed, and second, the means by which this absorption is effected. With regard to the last question, much work has been done to ascertain whether the known physical laws of diffusion, osmosis, and inhibition are sufficient to account for the movements of the absorbed substances or whether it is necessary to refer them in part to some unknown activities of the living epithelial cells. It would seem that diffusion and osmosis readily occur in the intestines. Concentrated solutions of neutral salts—sodium chloride, for instance—if introduced into a Thiry-Vella loop, cause a flow of water into the lumen in accordance with their high osmotic pressure and, on the other hand, some of the sodium chloride diffuses into the blood in accordance with the laws of diffusion. It seems equally clear, however, that absorption as it actually takes place is not governed simply by the differences in concentration between the contents of the intestine and the blood or lymph but depends largely upon the properties of the separating wall of living epithelial cells. Thus, the animal's own serum (14), possessing presumably the same concentration and osmotic pressure as the animal's blood, is absorbed completely from an isolated intestinal loop. So also it has been shown that in the absorption of salts from the intestine (41) the rapidity of absorption stands in no direct relation to the diffusion velocity. The energy that effects the absorption is furnished, therefore, by the wall of the intestine, presumably by the epithelial cells. That this source of energy is connected with the living structure is indicated by the fact that when the walls are injured by the action of sodium fluoride, potassium arsenate, etc., their absorptive power is diminished and absorption then follows the laws of diffusion and osmosis. Reviews of the literature on this topic should be consulted for further details (13, 39).

Absorption of the carbohydrates. Our carbohydrate food is absorbed, for the most part, as simple sugars—monosaccharides. As has been said, there is reason to believe that but little sugar is absorbed in the stomach. Cane sugar and milk sugar are hydrolyzed in the small intestine by invertase and lactase, the first being converted to glucose and levulose, the second to glucose and galactose. If, however, these substances are fed in excess they are absorbed in part without conversion to simple sugar and in that case may be eliminated in the urine. As the bulk of our carbohydrate food is taken in the form of starch, the conditions for absorption in this case are more favorable. The time required for the digestion of the starch to maltose and dextrin, and the subsequent hydrolysis of these substances to glucose insures a slower and more complete absorption. Five hundred grams or more of starch may be digested and absorbed in the course of the day and it all reaches the blood in the form of glucose. This glucose enters the portal vein and is distributed first to the liver. In this organ the excess of sugar is withdrawn from the blood and stored as glycogen, so that the amount of sugar in the general circulation is thereby kept quite constant—about 0.1 per cent. When a large amount of carbohydrate food is eaten, however, it is possible that the liver may not be able to remove the excess completely. In that case the amount of sugar in the general circulation may be increased above normal, giving a condition of *hyperglycemia*, and the excess may be excreted in the urine, thus bringing about the condition known as *alimentary glycosuria*. The amount of any carbohydrate that can be eaten without producing alimentary glycosuria is designated by Hofmeister (15) as the assimilation limit of that carbohydrate or, to use another terminology, it establishes the degree of *tolerance* of the animal for the particular carbohydrate employed. If taken beyond this limit there is a physiological excess, and some sugar is lost in the urine. The assimilation limit varies with a great many conditions; but, so far as the different forms of carbohydrates are concerned, it is lowest for the milk sugar and highest for starch. That starch may be eaten in larger amounts than sugar without raising the percentage of sugar in the systemic blood above the normal level is in accord with what we know of the digestion of the two forms of carbohydrates. Glucose requires no digestion; it is absorbed as such, while cane sugar needs only to be inverted. Starch, on the contrary, requires the action of ptyalin or amylase and subsequent hydrolysis by maltase. Its absorption will therefore be much slower than that of the sugars. In fact, it probably goes on for the period of four or five hours, during which an ordinary meal is making its progress from pylorus to ileocecal valve. During this period the entire quantity of blood in the body is passed through the mesenteric arteries over and over again, and it is probable that even in the portal vein the quantity of sugar at any one moment rises but little above the normal level, and this small excess is largely held back by the liver cells so that the systemic circulation is protected from becoming hyperglycemic.

So far as the carbohydrates escape absorption as sugar, they are liable to undergo acid fermentation from the bacteria always present in the intestine. As the result of this fermentation there may be produced acetic acid, lactic acid, butyric acid, succinic acid, carbon dioxide, alcohol, hydrogen, etc. This fermentation probably occurs to some extent in the small intestines under normal conditions. MacFadyen and associates (22), in the case already referred to, found that the contents of the intestine at the ileocecal valve contained acid equivalent to that of a 0.1 per cent solution of acetic acid. Under less normal conditions, such as excess of sugars in the diet or deficient absorption, the large production of acid may lead to irritation of the intestine—diarrhea, etc.

Absorption of fats. Numerous theories have been held in regard to the mode of absorption of fats. It has been supposed that the emulsified (neutral) fat is ingested directly by the epithelial cells, that the fat droplets enter between the epithelial cells in the so-called cement substance, that the fat droplets are ingested by leukocytes that lie between the epithelial cells, or lastly that the fat is first split into fatty acid and glycerol and is absorbed by the epithelial cells in these forms. The tendency of recent work is altogether in favor of this last view, and we may adopt it as expressing the theory generally accepted at present. During digestion the epithelial cells contain fat droplets without doubt, but it seems probable that these droplets are formed in situ by a synthesis of the absorbed glycerol and fatty acids. The border of the cell is said to be free from fat globules—a fact which would indicate that the neutral fat is not mechanically digested as oil drops. But, granting that the fat is absorbed in solution as fatty acids and glycerol, the mechanism of absorption is not wholly clear. It is known that the bile as well as the pancreatic juice plays an important part in the process. The pancreatic juice furnishes the lipase, the bile furnishes the bile salts (sodium glycocholate and taurocholate) which aid the lipase in splitting the neutral fat, and, moreover, aid greatly the absorption of the split fats. This latter function is due probably to the fact that the bile (bile salts) combines with the fatty acids and thus brings them into contact, in soluble form, with the epithelial cells. When the bile is drained off from the intestine by a fistula of the gallbladder or duct, a large proportion of the fatty foods escapes absorption and appears in the feces. Direct observation shows that the fat after passing the epithelial lining and entering the stroma of the villus is taken up by the lymphatic vessels, the so-called lacteals. This fact is beautifully demonstrated by the mere appearance of the lymphatics of the mesentery after a meal containing fats. These vessels are filled with milky chyle during the period of absorption so that their entire course is revealed. The chyle on microscopical examination is found to contain fat in the form of an extremely fine emulsion. In this form it is carried to the thoracic duct and thence to the venous circulation. For hours after a meal the blood contains this chyle fat. If a specimen of blood is taken during this time and centrifugalized in the usual way, the chyle fat may be collected at the top in the form of a cream. It is an easy matter to insert a cannula into the thoracic duct at the point at which it opens into the subclavian and jugular veins and thus collect the entire amount of fat absorbed from the intestines by way of the lacteals. Experiments of this kind show that, after deducting the amount of fat that escapes absorption and is lost in the feces, the amount that may be recovered from the thoracic duct is less than that taken in the food. It seems probable, therefore, that some of the fat is absorbed directly by the blood vessels of the villi. The portion thus absorbed enters the portal vein and passes through the liver before reaching the general circulation. The liver holds back more or less of the fat taking this route, as it is found that during absorption the liver cells show an accumulation of fat droplets in their interior. The amount of fat that may be absorbed from the intestines varies with the nature of the fat. Experiments show that the more fluid fats, such as olive oil, are absorbed more completely, i.e., less is lost in the feces than in the case of the more solid fats. Comparative experiments have given such results as the following: olive oil—absorption, 97.7 per cent; goose and pork fat, 97.5 per cent; mutton fat, 90 to 92.5 per cent; spermaceti, 15 per cent. The amount of fat that may be lost in the feces varies also with other conditions. If, for instance, an excess is taken with the food or if the bile flow is diminished or suppressed the percentage in the feces is increased.

Absorption of proteins. Most of the experimental work on record shows that the digested proteins are absorbed by the blood vessels of the villi, although after excessive feeding of protein a portion may be taken up also in the lymphatics (24). This accepted belief rests upon two facts: (i) (Schmidt-

Mülhemi) if the thoracic duct (and right lymphatic duct) is ligated so as to shut off the lymphatic circulation, an animal will absorb and metabolize the usual amount of protein as is indicated by the urea excreted during the period; (ii) (Munk) if a fistula of the thoracic duct is established and the total lymph flow from the intestine is collected during the period of absorption after a diet of protein, it is found that there is no increase in the quantity of lymph or in its protein contents. The form in which the digested protein enters the blood has long been a matter of controversy. On the view given above—that the protein of the food is split into its constituent amino acids by the successive action of the pepsin, trypsin, and erepsin—we should expect to find these amino acids in the blood, unless (according to an early assumption) they are again synthesized to protein while passing through the intestinal wall. In recent years methods have been devised for the recognition of amino acids in such a liquid as blood. The application of these methods tends to support the view that the amino acids enter the blood as such without undergoing synthesis. Various amino acids have been obtained from the blood in crystalline form. Van Slyke and Meyer (38) have shown that in the blood of dogs amino acids are constantly present in small amounts (3 to 5 mg. of amino acid nitrogen to 100 cc. of blood), and that after a meal of meat this concentration is definitely increased. In the light of this and subsequent work of numerous investigators, we may suppose that the normal course of events is as follows: the digested proteins are absorbed almost entirely in the form of amino acids and distributed to the tissues by the blood. In view of the phenomena of food allergy which suggest that at least some fairly large molecules of protein may be absorbed, it may be questioned whether the digestion to the amino acid stage is always complete. The tissues select and store certain of the amino acids, and probably in each organ subsequent use is made of them to build up new tissue or to repair the wastes of metabolism, or, in the glands, to construct the protein of the secretion. In the mammary gland of the lactating animal it has been shown that the amino acids in the mammary venous blood are distinctly less in amount than in the arterial blood. Hence it is a fair inference that the milk proteins are synthesized in the mammary gland from the amino acids brought to it in the arterial blood. There is probably no special form of circulating protein which serves as a pabulum for tissue repair and growth, but the amino acids themselves constitute the form in which nitrogen food is presented to the different tissues, just as glucose constitutes the circulatory form of carbohydrate food. Each tissue builds up its own form of protein from the amino acids offered to it, and the amino acids not used for this synthesis may be deaminized and then employed for energy purposes. There is evidence that in the liver especially many of the amino acids arising from the digested food undergo deaminization, the nitrogen being eliminated as urea. During starvation the amino acid content of the blood is maintained, probably because the tissues themselves or some of them undergo self-digestion or autolysis and thus furnish food material for the active tissues.

Examination of the contents of the small intestine at its junction with the large shows that under normal conditions most of the protein has been absorbed before reaching this point. The process is continued in the large intestine, modified somewhat by bacterial action, and the amount that finally escapes absorption and appears in the feces varies, in perfectly normal individuals, with the character of the protein eaten. The easily digestible animal foods—such as milk, eggs and meat—are absorbed to the extent of 97 to 99 per cent, while with vegetable foods the utilization is less complete. The difference is not due, however, to any peculiarity of the vegetable proteins; it is probably an incidental result of the presence of the indigestible cellulose found in our vegetable foods. From 17 to 30 per cent of the protein may be lost in the feces if the vegetable food is in such form as not to be attacked readily by the digestive secretions.

Reaction of the Intestinal Contents. The secretions emptying into the small intestine—the succus entericus, the bile, and the pancreatic juice—all have a slightly alkaline reaction and we should expect, therefore, to find the reaction of the intestinal contents on the alkaline side. Most observers have reported, however, that during digestion the reaction of the contents is acid. Bollman and Mann (4) have been able to study this point under normal conditions by establishing fistulae in a dog at different points along the intestine. They find that in this animal the contents from the duodenum down are alkaline in the fasting condition, pH 7 to pH 7.6, but during digestion the acid chyme discharged from the stomach occasions rapid fluctuations in reaction. On a diet of milk or meat the reaction in the duodenum may vary between pH 3.8 and pH 6.6, with a mean reading around pH 5.5 and it may be as long as five to eight hours before it returns to the resting figure. In the jejunum the reaction during such meals is on the acid side, but the fluctuations are not so great. In the ileum it was found that even during digestion the reaction did not drop below the neutral point, pH 7.

When carbohydrates and fats form a conspicuous feature of the diet we would expect a greater tendency toward an acid reaction. In the human case referred to on page 1075 in whom there was a fistula at the end of the ileum, it will be remembered that the contents at this point were distinctly acid.

LARGE INTESTINE

Digestion and Absorption. Observations upon the secretions of the large intestine have been made upon human beings in cases of anus preternaturalis in whom the lower portion of the intestine was practically isolated, and also upon lower animals in which an artificial anus was established at the end of the small intestine. These observations all indicate that the secretion of the large intestine, while it contains much mucus and shows an alkaline reaction, is not characterized by the presence of distinctive enzymes. When the contents of the small intestine pass the valve they still contain a certain amount of unabsorbed food material. As was stated in Chapter 48, these contents remain a long time in the large intestine, and since they contain the digestive enzymes received in the duodenum the digestive and absorptive processes no doubt continue as in the small intestine. This general fact is well illustrated in experiments made upon dogs in which most of the small intestine (70 to 83 per cent) had been removed (10). These animals could digest and absorb well and formed normal feces, provided care was taken with the diet. An excess of fat or indigestible material caused diarrhea and serious loss of food material in the feces. An interesting feature in the large intestine is the marked absorption of water. In the small intestine water is absorbed no doubt in large quantities, but its loss is evidently made good by diffusion or secretion of water into the intestine, since the contents at the ileocecal valve are still quite fluid. In the large intestine the absorption of water is not compensated by a secretion; the material loses water rapidly while in the ascending colon, and before it reaches the descending colon it has acquired the consistency of the feces. The alkaline reaction of the contents of the large intestine makes a favorable environment for the growth of bacteria, particularly the putrefactive bacteria that attack protein material. Putrefaction is a normal occurrence in the large intestine, and much interest has been shown in its extent and its possible physiological significance.

BACTERIAL ACTION

Small Intestine. In the intestines are found numerous bacteria which are able to hydrolyze the food material, particularly the carbohydrates and proteins. Fermentation of the carbohydrates undoubtedly occurs to a variable extent, depending on conditions, but none of the products of fermentation can be regarded as distinctly toxic. Putrefaction of the protein molecule, on the other hand, gives rise to a number of nitrogenous split products, some of which are supposed to have a toxic action. Under normal conditions, on a mixed diet, it appears that in the small intestine carbohydrate fermentation is the characteristic action of the bacteria, while in the large intestine protein putrefaction undoubtedly occurs. There has been considerable discussion as to the conditions that restrain the protein putrefaction in the small intestine. It has been pointed out that some of the bacteria of the small intestine, *Bacillus coli*, for example, do not cause protein hydrolysis as long as carbohydrate material (sugar) is present (17, 18), so that the mere presence of carbohydrate material serves to protect the protein from the action of the bacteria. In addition, as long as carbohydrates are present and are undergoing fermentation, the organic acids produced tend to neutralize the alkalinity of the intestinal secretion, and may even give an acid reaction to the intestinal contents. An acid reaction is unfavorable to the activity of the bacteria that attack the proteins, and in this way, under conditions of a normal diet, the process of putrefaction in the small intestine is warded off. From this standpoint it would seem to follow that the nature of the bacterial activity in the small intestine will vary with the character of the diet and, moreover, that the diet may be chosen intentionally so as to favor one or the other kind of bacterial action.

Large Intestine. In the large intestine protein putrefaction is a constant and normal occurrence. The reaction here is stated to be alkaline, and whatever protein may have escaped digestion and absorption is in turn acted upon by the bacteria and undergoes so-called putrefactive fermentation. The splitting up of the protein molecule by this process is very complete; not only are the proteins broken down to their amino acids but these latter are also destroyed with a liberation of the contained groups. The list of end-products of putrefaction is a long one. Besides peptones, proteoses, ammonia and the various amino acids, there may be produced such substances as indol, skatol, phenol, phenylpropionic and phenylacetic acid, fatty acids, carbon dioxide, hydrogen, marsh gas, hydrogen sulfide, etc. Many of these products are given off in the feces, while others are absorbed in part and excreted subsequently in the urine. In this latter connection special interest attaches to the phenol, indol and skatol. Phenol or carbolic acid, C_6H_5OH, after absorption is combined, in part, with sulfuric acid to form an ethereal sulfate (conjugated sulfate) or phenolsulfonic acid, $C_6H_5OSO_2OH$, and in this form is found in the urine. So also with cresol. The indol and skatol (methylindol), are also absorbed, undergo oxidation to indoxyl and skatoxyl, and are then combined or conjugated with sulfuric acid, like the phenol, and in this form are found in the urine. These bodies have long been known to occur in the urine, and the proof that the indol and skatol arise from the tryptophane group in the large intestine is so conclusive as not to admit of any doubt. The amount to which they occur in the urine is, therefore, an indication of the extent of the putrefaction in the large intestine. We may assume that the indol and skatol arise from the tryptophane group in the protein molecule, and the phenol and cresol from the tyrosine and phenylalanine. There is evidence that other more or less toxic substances belonging to the group of *amines* are produced by the further action of the bacteria on the amino acids in the protein molecule.

The amines are formed from the amino acids by a process of decarboxylation, as expressed in the formula—

$$RCH_2CHNH_2COOH - CO_2 = RCH_2CH_2NH_2$$

As a group they have a druglike action on the body resembling that of epinephrine—that is, they may cause a rise or fall of blood pressure, acceleration of heart, etc. Some of the amines that have been described are putrescine or tetramethylendiamine from arginine, cadaverine or pentamethylendiamine from lysine, iminazolethylamine (histamine) from histidine, indolethylamine from tryptophane, oxyphenylethylamine (tyramine) from tyrosine.

Is the Putrefactive Process of Physiological Importance? Recognizing that fermentation by means of bacteria is a normal occurrence in the gastro-intestinal canal, the question has arisen whether this process is in any way necessary to normal digestion and nutrition. It is well known that excessive bacterial action may lead to intestinal troubles, such as diarrhea, or possibly to more serious interference with general nutrition owing to the formation of toxic products, such as the amines. It is, however, possible that some amount of bacterial action may be necessary for completely normal digestion. As a special case it has been pointed out that the gastro-intestinal tract is not provided with enzymes capable of acting upon cellulose, a material that forms such an important constituent of vegetable foods. Bacteria, on the other hand, may hydrolyze the cellulose and render it useful in nutrition. Leaving aside this special case, the question as to the necessity of bacterial action has been investigated directly by attempting to rear young animals under perfectly sterile conditions. Nuttall and Thierfelder (26) report some interesting experiments upon guinea-pigs in which the young animals from birth were kept sterile and fed with perfectly sterile food. They found that the animals lived and increased in weight, and concluded, therefore, that the intestinal bacteria are not necessary to normal nutrition. This conclusion is supported by the observations of Levin (20), who finds that animals in the Arctic regions in many cases have no bacteria in their intestines. Schottelius (31) reports contrary results upon chickens. When kept sterile they lost steadily in weight and showed normal growth only when supplied with food containing bacteria. The idea that the relations between the bacteria and the animal that harbors them constitute a kind of symbiosis in which each derives a benefit from the other has not as yet been fully explored through physiological experiments. Something of the kind is suggested by the discovery that vitamin K, essential in the formation of the prothrombin of the blood, is produced in the intestines as a result of putrefactive processes, and that at least two members of the vitamin B complex—pantothenic acid and biotin—are produced by intestinal bacteria and absorbed by the host organism. The contrary view, that bacterial putrefaction is the occasion for constant danger to the human organism, has been stated in extreme form, perhaps, by Metchnikoff. This author has advanced the view that the constant production and absorption of bacterial toxins from the intestine is one of the important causes of a loss of resistance on the part of the body to the changes which bring on senescence and death.

Composition of the Feces. The feces differ widely in amount and in composition with the character of the food. Upon a diet composed exclusively of meats, they are small in amount and dark in color; with an ordinary mixed diet the amount is increased; and it is largest with an exclusively vegetable diet, especially with vegetables containing a large amount of cellulose. When the processes of digestion and absorption are entirely normal the feces should be well formed and devoid of offensive odors. If they are soft or liquid with a disagreeable odor, as may happen from mere indiscretions in diet as well as from distinctly pathological causes, it is an indication of some abnormality in the digestive mechanism, and, as far as the odor is concerned, of an excessive putrefaction. The average weight of the feces in 24 hours upon a mixed diet is given as 170 gm., while with a vegetable diet it may amount to as much as 400 or 500 gm. The quantitative composition, therefore, varies greatly with the diet. Qualitatively, we find in the feces the following things: (i) Indigestible material, such as ligaments of meat or cellulose from vegetables. (ii) Undigested material, such as fragments of meat, starch or fats which have in some way escaped digestion. Naturally, the quantity of this material present is slight under normal conditions. Some fats, however, are almost always found in feces, either as neutral fats in the food or by a deficient secretion of bile. (iii) Products of the intestinal secretions. Study of the contents of intestinal loops (28, 37) shows that the feces in man on an average diet are composed in part of the unabsorbed material of the intestinal secretion. The nitrogen of the feces, formerly supposed to represent only undigested food, seems rather to have its origin largely in these secretions, together with the cellular debris thrown off from the walls of the intestines. (iv) Products of bacterial decomposition. The most characteristic of these products are indol and skatol. They are crystalline bodies possessing a disagreeable, fecal odor; this is especially true of skatol, to which the odor of the feces is mainly due. (v) Cholesterol, or a derivative, which is found always in small amounts, and is probably derived from the bile. (vi) Some of the purine bases, especially guanine and adenine. (vii) Mucus and epithelial cells thrown off from the intestinal wall. (viii) Pigment. In addition to the color due to the undigested food or to the metallic compounds contained in it, there is normally present in the feces a pigment, urobilin or stercobilin, derived from the pigments (bilirubin) of the bile. Urobilin is formed from the bilirubin by reduction in the large intestine. (ix) Inorganic salts—salts of sodium, potassium, calcium, magnesium, and iron, but chiefly the last three together with phosphoric acid. The significance of the calcium and iron salts will be referred to in Chapter 52, when speaking of their nutritive importance. (x) Micro-organisms. Great quantities of bacteria of different kinds are found in the feces.

In addition to the feces, a quantity of gas is often found in the large intestine that may also be eliminated through the rectum. This gas varies in composition. The following substances have been found at one time or another: CH_4, CO_2, H_2, N_2, H_2S. They arise mainly from the bacterial fermentation of the proteins, although some of the N_2 may be derived from air swallowed with the food.

REFERENCES

1. AGREN, G. Über die pharmacodynamischen Wirkungen und chemischen Eigenschaften des Secretins. *Skand. Arch. Physiol.*, 1934, 70:10–87.

2. BAYLISS, W. M. and STARLING, E. H. The mechanism of pancreatic secretion. *J. Physiol.*, 1902, 28:323–353.

3. BLOOR, W. R. Fat transport in the animal body. *Physiol. Rev.*, 1939, 19:557–577.

4. BOLLMAN, J. L. and MANN, F. C. Acidity of the contents of the intestine. *Proc. Mayo Clin.*, 1930, 5:68.

5. CALDWELL, M. L., BOOHER, L. E. and SHERMAN, H. C. Crystalline amylase. *Science*, 1931, 74:37.

6. CANNON, W. B. The passage of different food-stuffs from the stomach and through the small intestine. *Amer. J. Physiol.*, 1904–05, 12:387–418.

7. CRIDER, J. O. and THOMAS, J. E. Secretion of pancreatic juice after cutting the extrinsic nerves. *Amer. J. Physiol.*, 1944, 141:730–737.

8. DRAGSTEDT, L. R. and WOODBURY, R. A. Mechanism of pancreatic secretion. *Proc. Soc. exp. Biol., N. Y.*, 1933, 31:178–179.

9. DRAGSTEDT, L. R. and WOODBURY, R. A. The relation of bile to the secretion of pancreatic juice. *Amer. J. Physiol.*, 1934, 107:584–588.

10. ERLANGER, J. and HEWLETT, A. W. A study of the metabolism in dogs with shortened small intestines. *Amer. J. Physiol.*, 1901–02, 6:1–30.

11. FARRELL, J. I. and IVY, A. C. Contributions to the physiology of the pancreas. II. The proof of a humoral mechanism for external pancreatic secretion. *Amer. J. Physiol.*, 1926, 78:325–338.

12. GLAESSNER, K. Ueber menschliches Pankreassekret. *Hoppe-Seyl. Z.*, 1903–04, 40:465–479.

13. GOLDSCHMIDT, S. On the mechanism of absorption from the intestine. *Physiol. Rev.*, 1921, 1:421–453.

14. HEIDENHAIN, R. Neue Versuche über die Aufsangung in Dünndarm. *Pflüg. Arch. ges. Physiol.*, 1894, 56:579–631.

15. HOFMEISTER, F. 18. Ueber Resorption und Assimilation der Nährstoffe. *Arch. exp. Path. Pharmak.*, 1889, 25:240–256; 22. *Idem.*, 1890, 26:355–370.

16. IVY, A. C., FARRELL, J. I. and LUETH, H. C. Contributions to the physiology of the pancreas. III. A hormone for external pancreatic secretion. *Amer. J. Physiol.*, 1927, 82:27–33.

17. KENDALL, A. I. Lactic acid bacteria; what are they supposed to do? *Boston med. surg. J.*, 1910, 163:322–325.

18. KENDALL, A. I. Certain aspects of intestinal bacteriology in health and disease. *Wis. med. J.*, 1913–14, 12:1–8.

19. KUNITZ, K. and NORTHROP, J. H. Crystalline chymo-trypsin and chymo-tripsinogen. I. Isolation, crystallization, and general properties of a new proteolytic enzyme and its precursor. *J. gen. Physiol.*, 1934–35, 18:433–458.

20. LEVIN, E. Bakteriologische Darmuntersuchungen. *Skand. Arch. Physiol.*, 1904, 16:249–262.

21. LUCKHARDT, A. B., BARLOW, O. W. and WEAVER, M. M. Note on a rapid and simple method of preparing a highly active pancreatic secretin solution. *Amer. J. Physiol.*, 1926, 76:182.

22. MacFADYEN, A., NENCKI, M. and SIEBER, N. Untersuchungen über die chemischen Vorgänge im menschlichen Dünndarm. *Arch. exp. Path. Pharmak.*, 1891, 28:311–350.

23. MELLANBY, J. The secretion of pancreatic juice. *J. Physiol.*, 1926, 61:419–435.

24. MENDEL, L. B. On the paths of absorption for proteids. *Amer. J. Physiol.*, 1898–99, 2:137–141.

25. NORTHROP, J. H. and KUNITZ, M. Crystalline trypsin. I-V. *J. gen. Physiol.*, 1932–33, 16:267–348.

26. NUTTALL, G. H. F. and THIERFELDER, J. Thierisches Leben ohne Bakterien im Verdauungskanal. *Hoppe-Seyl. Z.*, 1895, 21:109–121; 1896, 22:62–73; 1897, 23:231–235.

27. PAVLOV, I. P. *The work of the digestive glands*, 2nd English ed. Translated by W. H. Thompson. London, C. Griffin and Co., Ltd., 1910. xiv, 266 pp.

28. PRAUSNITZ, W. Die chemische Zusammensetzung des Kothes bei verschiedenartiger Ernährung. *Z. Biol.*, 1897, 35:335–347.

29. RAMSAY, A. J., THOMAS, J. E. and CRIDER, J. O. Changes in the acinar cells of the pancreas in response to the presence of peptone in the small intestine. *Anat. Rec.*, 1943, 86:87–98.

30. SAWITSCH, W. W. Beiträge zur Physiologie der Pankreassaftsekretion. *Zbl. ges. Physiol. Path. Stoffw.*, 1909, 10:1–18.

31. SCHOTTELIUS, M. Die Bedeutung der Darmbakterien für die Ernährung. II. *Arch. Hyg., Berl.*, 1902, 42:48–70.

32. STILL, E. V. Secretin. *Physiol. Rev.*, 1931, 11:328–357.

33. THOMAS, J. E. The maximal acidity of

the intestinal contents during digestion. *Amer. J. Digestive Dis.*, 1940, *7*:195–197.

34. THOMAS, J. E. and CRIDER, J. O. A quantitative study of acid in the intestine as a stimulus for the pancreas. *Amer. J. Physiol.*, 1940, *131*:349–356.

35. THOMAS, J. E. and CRIDER, J. O. The pancreatic secretagogue action of products of protein digestion. *Amer. J. Physiol.*, 1941, *134*:656–663.

36. THOMAS, J. E. and CRIDER, J. O. The effect of bile in the intestine on the secretion of pancreatic juice. *Amer. J. Physiol.*, 1943, *138*:548–552.

37. TSUBOI, J. Ueber die Stickstoffausscheidung aus dem Darm. *Z. Biol.*, 1897, *35*:68–93.

38. VAN SLYKE, D. D. and MEYER, G. M. The fate of protein digestion products in the body. III. The absorption of amino-acids from the blood by the tissues. *J. biol. Chem.*, 1913, *16*:197–212; IV. The locus of chemical transformation of absorbed amino-acids. *Ibid.*, 213–229; V. The effects of feeding and fasting on the amino-acid content of the tissues. *Ibid.*, 231–233.

39. VERZAR, F. Die Resorption aus dem Darm. *Handb. norm. path. Physiol.*, 1929, *4*:3–81.

40. VERZAR, F. and KUTHY, A. Die Bedeutung der Gallensäuren für die Fettresorption. *Biochem. Z.*, 1929, *205*:369–379.

41. WALLACE, G. B. and CUSHNY, A. R. Ueber Darmresorption und die salinischen Abführmittel. *Pflüg. Arch. ges. Physiol.*, 1899, *77*:202–209.

42. ZUCKER, T. F., NEWBURGER, P. G. and BERG, B. N. Continuous pancreatic secretion. *Amer. J. Physiol.*, 1932, *102*:193–221.

SECTION IX

METABOLISM AND NUTRITION

BY JOHN R. BROBECK

CHAPTER 50

INTRODUCTION TO QUANTITATIVE METABOLISM

Metabolism is the name given to the energy transformations which occur in biological systems. The ability to effect such transformations distinguishes living cells from inanimate substance, gives to the former their peculiar properties of irritability, growth and reproduction, and makes possible the processes of conduction, contraction and secretion which characterize various specialized types of cells. Every physiological phenomenon is energized by metabolic reactions, and, consequently, the study of metabolism underlies all physiology.

Food. All of the energy which brings about physiological processes in mammals is derived from a single source, namely, oxidative chemical reactions in which carbon dioxide and water are produced with the liberation of free energy and heat. The continuity of the reactions demands a continuous replacement of carbon and hydrogen, while the nature of the reactions imposes narrow limits upon the possible chemical combinations in which the two elements may be supplied. In general, a mammal is able to use only carbon and hydrogen previously synthesized into compounds which resemble the constituents of mammalian protoplasm, or, in other words, only carbohydrate, protein or fat. Such compounds may be obtained temporarily from reserves within the body of the individual; ultimately, however, they must come from plant or animal tissue present in the diet. Unlike the animals which are thus entirely dependent upon their foodstuffs, the plants are able directly to utilize radiant energy from the sun and so to synthesize complex organic molecules. Man, who cannot do this, lives by taking as food compounds which have been synthesized by other organisms.

Heat. Foodstuff energy may be disposed of by man in three ways, one of which is conversion to heat. To a limited extent the liberation of heat within living cells resembles the combustion of a foodstuff in an open flame; but where the flame liberates heat abruptly and completely with the almost instantaneous oxidation of carbon and hydrogen, the cell achieves the same results in a stepwise fashion which involves the transfer of hydrogen ions and electrons through a series of enzymatic reactions, accompanied by a gradual evolution of the heat of combustion. Mammals depend upon these exothermic reactions for the maintenance of their relatively constant body temperature, although not infrequently the body has more heat than it needs for temperature regulation and must dissipate extra heat in order to avoid hyperthermia. In metabolic study, heat is measured by its effect upon the temperature of water. The unit employed is the calorie—that is, the amount of heat necessary to raise the temperature of one gram of water one degree centigrade, or more accurately, the amount of heat required to raise one gram of water from 14.5° to 15.5° C. This unit is sometimes designated as a small calorie to distinguish it from the large Calorie (kcal.)—that is, the quantity of heat necessary to raise the temperature of one kilogram of water one degree centigrade. The large Calorie is equal to 1000 small calories. The amount of heat that can be derived from a given foodstuff may be measured in the bomb calorimeter of Bertholet. A weighed amount of a sample is placed on a platinum wire in an atmosphere of oxygen within a metal chamber or "bomb." The chamber is then tightly closed and suspended in a water bath. An electric current through the platinum wire ignites the specimen, allowing complete combustion with the formation of water, carbon dioxide, and, in the case of protein, oxides of nitrogen, sulfur and phosphorus. From the weight of the water in the bath and its temperature change, the heat of combustion may be calculated after a correction has been made for heat storage within the calorimeter. Because the amount of liberated heat depends upon the chemical nature of the sample, every compound has its own characteristic heat of combustion. Thus, glucose liberates 3.74 kcal. while glycogen yields 4.3 kcal. per gm.; and animal fats average 9.5 kcal. per gm., although 1 gm. of butter or lard liberates only 9.2 kcal. Animal proteins yield about 5.6 kcal. per gm. in the bomb calorimeter, but in the body they liberate only about 4.3 kcal. per gm. because they are incompletely oxidized by the cells. The end-products of biological protein oxidation, chiefly urea and ammonia, are capable of further oxidation; consequently, a certain amount of energy is lost when they are excreted unoxidized. Carbohydrate and fat, however, are oxidized to carbon dioxide and water in the body as well as in the calorimeter.*

Work. A second form into which energy may be changed is *work* which is physically measured as the product of mass and distance. Most of the energy responsible for mechanical work is liberated in skeletal muscle (pp. 78–94), but only a fraction of the liberated energy can be accounted for as work because the muscle loses as heat about four times as much energy as it transforms into work. Moreover, work is not always accomplished by muscular activity; for example, a man may carry a heavy load in a circuit at the completion of which the potential energy of the load is no greater than it was at the beginning of the excursion. Yet the man spent a significant amount of energy in the muscular exercise he performed. It must be concluded that energy so expended was entirely changed into heat—heat of friction plus heat which accompanied the oxidative reactions that made the exercise possible.

Other types of work are performed by other types of cells. One of the more common is "secretory" work, accomplished whenever a cell concentrates a substance outside one of its borders or whenever a cell maintains a diffusion gradient across its membrane. An example is the formation of a hydrochloric acid solution by the parietal cells of the gastric mucosa. In concentrating hydrogen ions from the 0.00004 milliequivalents per liter of blood plasma to the 100 to 150 mEq. per liter of gastric hydrochloric acid, the parietal cells do work and give the HCl solution a potential energy that

---

* In dietetics, somewhat lower calorific values are ordinarily used in order to make allowance for the presence of plant as well as animal fats and proteins, and for the possibility of incomplete intestinal absorption. The values generally used are: carbohydrate, 4.1; fat, 9.3; and protein, 4.1 kcal. per gm.

will be liberated as heat if the ions are permitted to mix again with the other elements of plasma. This type of work is carried on by many different cells of the body—those of the digestive glands and liver, the renal tubules and many others. In most instances the work they accomplish in an adult individual does not permanently increase the potential or kinetic energy of the body as a whole because some other organ or cell dissipates their work as heat. Thus, gastric hydrochloric acid is finally neutralized and returned to the circulating blood by the intestine, and its potential energy disappears as heat in the process.

Storage. A third possible method of disposition of foodstuff energy is *storage*, which is sometimes said to represent "chemical work" because it involves the expenditure of energy in the synthesis of compounds the degradation of which may ultimately accomplish work. Like its mechanical counterpart, chemical work is a somewhat inefficient process that is always accompanied by the liberation of heat. In all probability the amount of heat varies from one type of synthesis to another, but data are not available for comparison of the efficiencies of the various reactions in question. Animals normally set aside reserves of fat, protein and, to a lesser extent, carbohydrate in certain specialized tissues; and during fasting and other emergencies, these reserves are mobilized and transported via the circulation to the cells expending energy. Since the reserves are chemically similar to digested and absorbed foodstuffs, the body apparently does not discriminate between the two, but oxidizes its own stores through the pathways where foodstuffs are ordinarily utilized.

In addition to the depots which serve the whole body, there is another, less stable, type of storage where a single cell may set aside its own temporary reserve. The latter process involves the synthesis of unstable compounds typified by the carbohydrate-phosphoric acid esters described in detail in Chapter 3. In order to accomplish a phosphorylation reaction, energy must be added to the system. This energy is usually obtained from oxidative reactions, and much of it is later recovered and used for work when the "energy-rich" bond is broken down with the liberation of inorganic phosphate. Muscular contraction is dependent upon such transitory storage, and there is reason to believe that a number of other familiar phenomena may eventually be shown to involve the formation and breakdown of "energy-rich" chemical bonds (8).

For convenience in description, metabolism is often subdivided into *anabolism* and *catabolism* which literally mean "to build up" and "to throw down," respectively. Anabolism includes digestion and storage of food and is said to be synthetic in nature; it leaves the organism better prepared for emergency situations and makes growth possible. Assimilation is used as a synonym for anabolism. On the other hand, catabolism or the utilization of stored substance is said to be analytic, and it tends to leave the animal impoverished. Individual reactions are sometimes difficult to classify under these two headings. For example, in the conversion of carbohydrate to fat, the end-result is anabolic because energy is stored through a synthetic reaction, but the process is catabolic since carbohydrate is burned to carbon dioxide and water in order to provide energy for fat synthesis. Perhaps a higher degree of precision may be attained by defining anabolism as net energy storage and catabolism as the dissipation of energy as work or heat. Conversion of carbohydrate to fat, therefore, is catabolic; but the overall process of carbohydrate absorption and fat formation is unquestionably one of anabolism.

BASAL METABOLISM

To study the overall energy exchange or metabolism of a human subject is to attempt to discover the relationships among the four variable factors already identified, viz., food, work, heat and storage. Upon casual examination such study appears to present several difficult if not almost insoluble problems because of the number of variable factors to be considered. Their number may be reduced, however, by the careful selection of experimental conditions. If an experiment is begun only after the subject's most recent meal has been digested and absorbed, the number of variables is reduced by one-fourth since food energy no longer needs to be taken into account. And if the subject avoids voluntary muscular exercise during the experiment he thereby removes from consideration another factor—work output—since, although the respiratory muscles and the heart continue their activity, they accomplish no permanent increase in the potential or kinetic energy of the blood, lungs, respiratory air, etc., all of which have the same position at the end as at the beginning of the experiment. There then remain to be measured only two factors, heat and stored energy, of which the former is now the sole method of energy dissipation while the latter is the only energy source. The laws of thermodynamics at once suggest that these two are equal in amount; attention is therefore to be directed to the principles which underlie the proof of this hypothesis.

Direct Calorimetry. Estimation of the total heat production of a human subject by recording the temperature change of a known weight of water is theoretically a simple procedure, but its performance requires elaborate and expensive apparatus. One must be able to measure or to control every avenue of heat loss—to the environmental air, to other physical objects and into vaporized water—as well as to detect positive or negative heat storage, i.e., temperature change, in the subject or in the apparatus. For the period of the test the subject is placed at rest within a thermically insulated chamber or box, a calorimeter (Fig. 468). Within the chamber are tubes through which water can be circulated from the outside; a meter measures the rate of circulation, while thermometers or thermocouples indicate the temperature of the water entering and leaving the chamber. Provision is made also for the circulation of air and for measuring its rate of circulation, temperature change, and the amount of water vapor it takes up from the skin and respiratory membranes of the subject; this last measurement is important because water absorbs 0.58 Calories per gram when it passes from the liquid to the vapor state at 33° C. Heat produced by the subject may be transmitted into the circulating water or into the current of air including its water vapor, or the heat may be stored by the contents of the chamber including the subject; no heat storage will occur, however, if the rate of flow and temperature of the circulating water are properly adjusted to the rate of heat production. The subject's total heat production will then equal his heat loss which can be calculated from the measurements made upon the currents of water and air. By this method, the method of direct calorimetry, Harris and Benedict (6) found that the total heat production of a fasting, resting male subject is about 1,600 kcal. per day. Application of the method is not limited to the

fasting, resting state, however, and the total heat production may be estimated under any given set of conditions of feeding, activity and environmental temperature.

Indirect Calorimetry. One cannot directly measure the energy value of the
stored material converted to heat by the subject's body during the period of
direct calorimetry, but an indirect estimation is possible, based upon the
calorific values of the various types of foodstuffs as they have been measured
in the bomb calorimeter. In order to make use of these calorific values, one
must know the relative and absolute amounts of protein, carbohydrate and
fat in the "metabolic mixture" (the catabolized tissue). Protein catabolism,
fortunately, may be estimated by measuring the amount of nitrogen excreted
in the urine; this is possible because protein contains nitrogen in the rather
constant proportion of one part in 6.25, and because nitrogen is eliminated
only through the kidneys, largely in the form of urea. In a fasting, resting

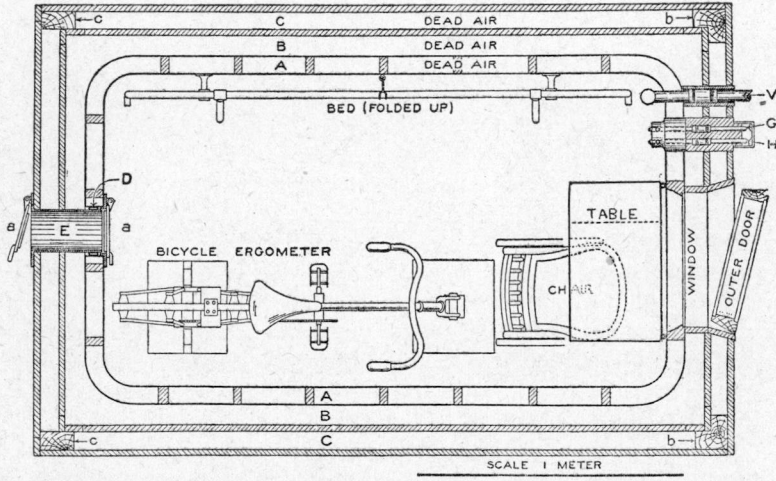

Fig. 468.—Horizontal section of respiration calorimeter. Portions shaded are of wood: A, dead
air space between Cu and Zn walls; B, dead air space between Zn wall and inside wooden wall;
C, dead air space between inside and outside wooden walls; D, pneumatic-packing air and heat
insulated; E, food aperture tube; a, a, airtight ports (glass); G, ingoing water for absorbing heat;
H, outcoming water; V, ventilating air current. (From Atwater and Benedict.)

subject all of the urinary nitrogen is derived from protein, the energy of
which has been dissipated as heat. Multiplying urinary nitrogen in grams by
6.25 gives the weight of the protein utilized during the time of formation of
the urine, and multiplying the weight of protein by 4.3 yields the number of
Calories of heat liberated in its combustion.

There remains to be determined the heat derived from carbohydrate and
fat, which may be calculated from the oxygen consumption and carbon dioxide production just as protein utilization may be estimated from the urinary
nitrogen excretion. If the oxygen uptake and carbon dioxide production are
measured during a period when the nitrogen excretion is known, the composition of the metabolic mixture may be determined with a reasonable degree of accuracy. To do this requires the measurement of the so-called
"respiratory metabolism," or, in other words, the magnitude of the exchange
of oxygen and carbon dioxide across the respiratory epithelium.

Carbon dioxide production. Oxygen utilization and carbon dioxide production may be studied by several different techniques, with apparatus usually identified by the name of its designer (see ref. 4, pp. 93–124). Carbon dioxide production is measured by one of three possible methods. (i) It may be measured gravimetrically after the gas has chemically combined with a substance like "soda-lime." In the Atwater-Rosa-Benedict respiration calorimeter this method is used for the estimation of carbon dioxide production while the subject's heat loss is being measured by direct calorimetry (Fig. 468); air from the calorimeter is continuously circulated through a series of vessels which absorb, first, water vapor from the subject's lungs and skin; second, carbon dioxide; and third, water liberated by the union of carbon dioxide and soda-lime in the preceding vessel of the series (Fig. 469). When the sum of the initial weights of the second and third vessels is subtracted from the sum of their final weights, the difference is the weight of the carbon dioxide

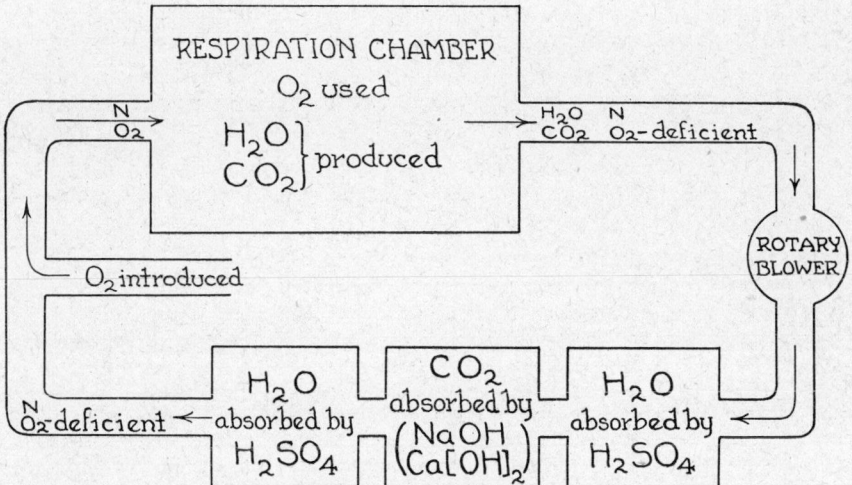

Fig. 469.—Diagram of circulation of air for combined direct and indirect calorimetry. (From Atwater and Benedict.)

produced by the subject. This method of estimating carbon dioxide has been widely used in clinical as well as in experimental work. (ii) Carbon dioxide may be measured volumetrically if the gas is first absorbed in an alkaline solution from which it is later displaced by adding a dilute solution of sulfuric acid. In the Knipping apparatus this procedure is followed and the volume of the evolved gas is measured. (iii) An indirectly volumetric measurement may be obtained by determining the volume of the exhaled "air" and its carbon dioxide concentration after the exhaled gases have been collected in a Douglas bag or in the spirometer of the Tissot apparatus. The total carbon dioxide production is equal to the volume of the exhaled gas multiplied by the carbon dioxide concentration. This is a popular method for experiments where the portable character of the Douglas bag is advantageous.

Oxygen consumption. Oxygen consumption may be estimated by three techniques, two of which are suitable for use with human subjects while the third is reserved for studies on small animals. (i) In the Benedict-Roth apparatus, or the Krogh apparatus, the subject breathes from and into an oxygen-containing system which includes a spirometer (Fig. 470). The amount of oxygen used may be calculated either from the changing volume of the spirometer or by measuring the amount of oxygen which must be added to restore the initial volume of the system. As the apparatus is now used clinically, the former measurement is employed; in the Atwater-Rosa-Benedict respiration calorimeter, however, a cylinder of oxygen is weighed before and after the original volume of the system has been restored. (ii) With a spirometer or a Douglas bag the oxygen consumption may be estimated simultaneously with the third method of carbon dioxide analysis described above. All exhaled gas is collected for a given period, and later analyzed in order to determine its concentration of oxygen, nitrogen (and carbon dioxide). Since nitrogen is a passive gas in respiration, the total amount of nitrogen

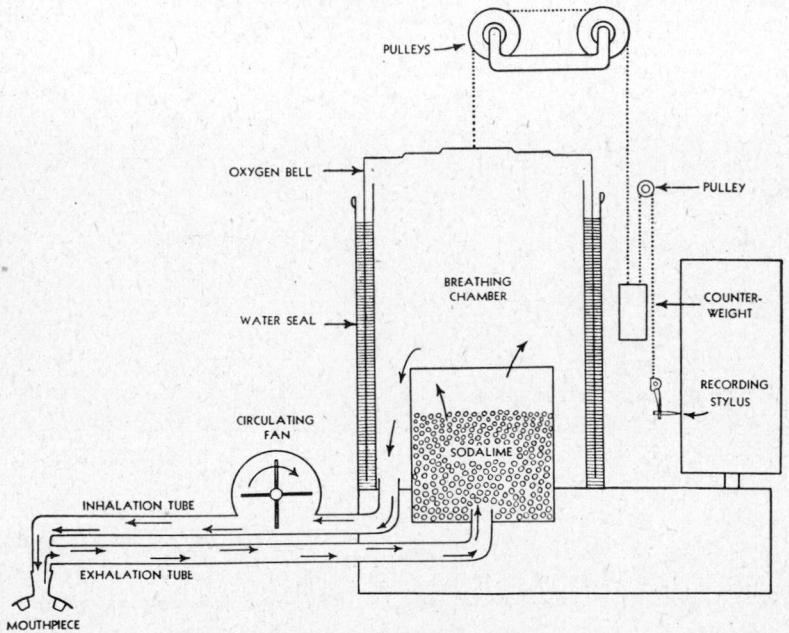

Fig. 470.—Sanborn apparatus (modified Benedict apparatus) for direct estimation of human oxygen consumption.

in the bag must equal the nitrogen of the inspired air. Knowing the volume of the exhaled air and its nitrogen content, therefore, the volume of inspired air may be calculated arithmetically. The amount of oxygen in the inspired air may then be calculated by multiplying volume by concentration; subtracting the amount of oxygen in the exhaled air gives the oxygen uptake of the subject. (iii) The oxygen consumption of small animals may be estimated gravimetrically in an apparatus originally designed by Haldane (Fig. 471). The animal is placed in a chamber through which a current of dry, carbon dioxide-free air is drawn. As the air leaves the chamber it is passed over chemicals which remove the carbon dioxide and water added to it by the animal. The chamber (containing the animal) and the carbon dioxide and water absorption tubes are weighed at the beginning and again at the end of the experiment. It is evident that the system as a whole can gain weight only by the process of oxygen uptake in the lungs—oxygen which is eventually combined with carbon and hydrogen to form the carbon dioxide and water absorbed from the outgoing air. The oxygen consumption is equal, therefore, to the final weight of the animal plus CO_2 plus H_2O, minus the initial weight of the animal. In this way the oxygen uptake is determined without knowledge of the volume of either the incoming or outgoing air, provided that no CO_2 or H_2O enters or leaves the system as a whole.

Calorific value of oxygen. Respiratory quotient. Oxygen reacts with carbohydrate, protein or fat in certain definite proportions with the formation of a definite quantity of carbon dioxide and water. In the oxidation of glucose, the relationships among the four substances are expressed by this equation:

$$C_6H_{12}O_6 + 6O_2 \longrightarrow 6CO_2 + 6H_2O$$

One gram-molecular weight of glucose (180 gm.) combines with six times the gram-molecular weight of oxygen (192 gm.) to form 264 gm. of carbon dioxide and 108 gm. of water. The oxygen and carbon dioxide each have a volume of $22.4 \times 6 = 134.4$ liters. It follows, then, that 1 gm. of glucose reacts with $134.4 \div 180 = 0.75$ liters of oxygen to form an equal volume of carbon dioxide with the liberation of 3.74 kcal. of heat; and further, that

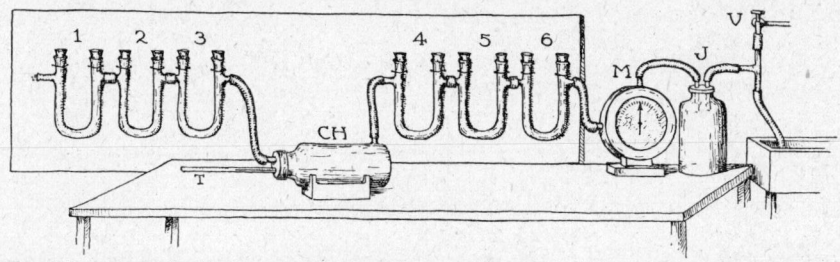

Fig. 471.—Open circuit system (modified from Haldane) for performing indirect calorimetry upon small laboratory animals. H_2O and CO_2 are removed from ingoing air in tubes 1, 2 and 3. The CO_2 and H_2O given off by the animal are absorbed in tubes 4, 5 and 6. M is a gas meter; V connects with a vacuum pump.

1 liter of oxygen is the equivalent of $3.74 \div 0.75 = 5$ kcal. of heat when glucose is oxidized. One gm. of starch or glycogen liberates slightly more heat than 1 gm. of glucose, but the former require also proportionately more oxygen; consequently, the calorific value of oxygen remains approximately 5 kcal. per liter for the oxidation of any carbohydrate.

A similar calculation may be made for the reaction in which a typical fat, the glyceride of oleic, palmitic and stearic acids, is oxidized, thus:

$$\begin{matrix} C_{15}H_{31}COO \searrow \\ C_{17}H_{35}COO - C_3H_5 + 78O_2 \longrightarrow 55CO_2 + 52H_2O \\ C_{17}H_{33}COO \nearrow \end{matrix}$$

Here, a gram-molecular weight of the fat (860 gm.) combines with $22.4 \times 78 = 1747.2$ liters of oxygen to form $22.4 \times 55 = 1232.0$ liters of carbon dioxide; therefore, 1 gm. combines with $1747.2 \div 860 = 2.03$ liters of oxygen to form 1.43 liters of carbon dioxide, liberating 9.5 kcal. of heat; or 1 liter of oxygen is the equivalent of $9.5 \div 2.03 = 4.7$ kcal. when this particular fat is oxidized.

Although a similar calculation for the oxidation of protein is more difficult because of its more complex chemical structure, approximately 0.97 liters of oxygen are believed to be required per gram of protein, with the formation of 0.78 liters of carbon dioxide and the liberation of 4.3 kcal. of heat; or, 1 liter of oxygen is the equivalent of 4.5 kcal. when protein is oxidized. If one compares the results of the calculations included in the last three paragraphs, one notices that the ratio of carbon dioxide to oxygen differs for the three classes of foodstuffs. This ratio is called the *respiratory quotient* and may be written thus:

$$\frac{\text{Vol. of } CO_2}{\text{Vol. of } O_2} = \text{R.Q.}$$

For carbohydrate the respiratory quotient is always 1.0, for fat about 0.70, and for protein about 0.80. Table 47 summarizes these data.

Table 47

	CARBOHYDRATE	ANIMAL FAT	ANIMAL PROTEIN
Calories per gm.*	3.7 –4.3	9.5	4.3
Liters of CO_2 per gm.	0.75–0.83	1.43	0.78
Liters of O_2 per gm.	0.75–0.83	2.03	0.97
Respiratory quotient	1.00	0.70–0.71	0.80–0.82
Calorific value of 1 liter of O_2	5.0 kcal.	4.7 kcal.	4.5 kcal.

 * See footnote, page 1085.

Because the respiratory quotient is based solely upon the rate of exchange of the respiratory gases, the R.Q. may be affected by factors other than those already considered here (Fig. 472). Thus, an interference with CO_2 transport such as occurs in acidosis or during hyperventilation very quickly obscures the metabolic significance of the R.Q. because the amount of CO_2 given off in the lungs is then determined largely by the severity of the respiratory irregularity rather than by the composition of the metabolic mixture. Interconversions of foodstuffs similarly affect the R.Q., while certain other reactions of the intermediary metabolism, notably ketogenesis, also alter the $\frac{CO_2}{O_2}$ ratio. This subject is more fully discussed later (p. 1129). In spite of the possibility of its being influenced by any or all of these factors, however, the respiratory quotient is a reliable guide to the composition of the metabolic mixture if the measurements upon which it is based are made under well controlled experimental conditions.

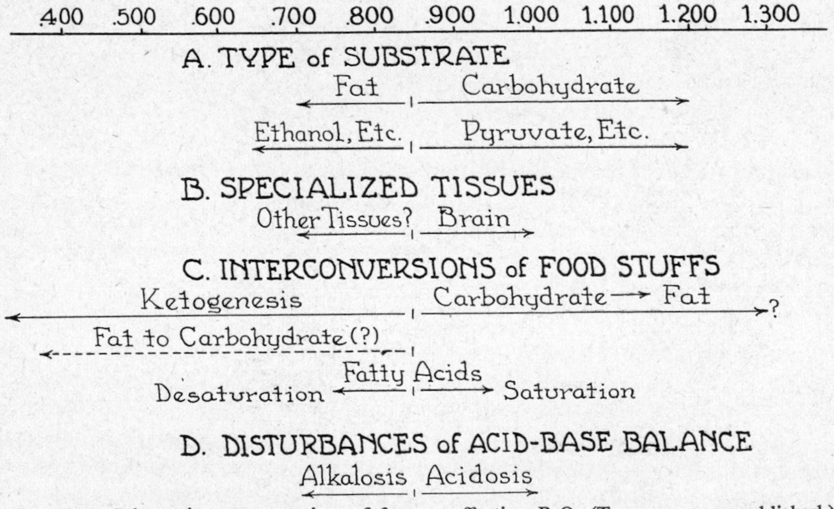

.400   .500   .600   .700   .800   .900   1.000   1.100   1.200   1.300

A. TYPE of SUBSTRATE
Fat ←——→ Carbohydrate
Ethanol, Etc. ←——→ Pyruvate, Etc.

B. SPECIALIZED TISSUES
Other Tissues? ←——→ Brain

C. INTERCONVERSIONS of FOOD STUFFS
←—— Ketogenesis —— | Carbohydrate —→ Fat —→?
←----- Fat to Carbohydrate(?) ----- |
Desaturation ←—— Fatty Acids ——→ Saturation

D. DISTURBANCES of ACID-BASE BALANCE
Alkalosis ←——→ Acidosis

Fig. 472.—Schematic representation of factors affecting R.Q. (Tepperman, unpublished.)

When the oxygen consumption, carbon dioxide production and nitrogen excretion of the individual are known, the composition of his metabolic mixture can be determined as follows: the nitrogen excretion is multiplied by 6.25 to give the number of grams of protein oxidized which, in turn, is multiplied by 0.97 to give the volume of oxygen, or by 0.78 to give the volume of carbon dioxide involved in protein catabolism. From the total respiratory exchange the oxygen and carbon dioxide of protein metabolism are next subtracted, leaving the amounts of oxygen and carbon dioxide associated with the utilization of carbohydrate and fat, together. In other words, the total oxygen consumption minus the oxygen utilized in protein oxidation equals the nonprotein oxygen consumption; and the nonprotein carbon dioxide production may be calculated by a similar procedure. From these two there may be obtained the *nonprotein respiratory quotient* which expresses the relationship between the carbon dioxide and oxygen produced and used, respectively, in the oxidation of fat and carbohydrate. Mathematical analysis

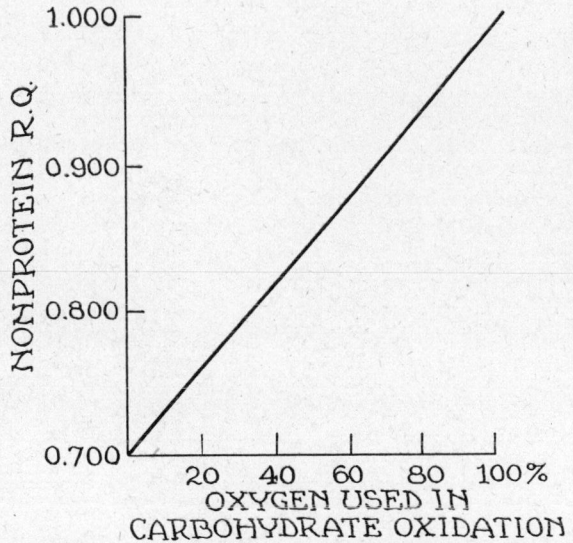

Fig. 473.—Linear relationship between nonprotein R.Q. and percentage of total nonprotein oxygen consumption used in oxidation of carbohydrate.

of the nonprotein R.Q. will then reveal the amount of fat and of carbohydrate utilized. For example, if the nonprotein R.Q. is near 0.70, it means that only fat has been burned, whereas if the value approaches 1.00, the oxidation of only carbohydrate is suggested. These relationships have been expressed graphically in Figure 473 in such a way that the percentage of oxygen used in carbohydrate catabolism may be read along the abscissa. From this percentage and the total nonprotein oxygen consumption the volume of oxygen used either in carbohydrate or in fat catabolism may be calculated, and the heat derived from each may be determined by multiplying the volume of oxygen by the calorific value of oxygen for that type of compound. The sum of the two quantities of heat so arrived at, plus the heat derived from the oxidation of protein (see above), is the total heat production as estimated indirectly from the measurement of the respiratory metabolism. The procedure in its entirety is known as *indirect calorimetry*.

Physiological Conservation of Energy. The calculations just outlined complete the experiment in which the total heat production of a fasting, resting human subject was to be compared with the energy value of the catabolized tissues. In summary, the total energy expenditure has been measured by the technique of direct calorimetry, under circumstances where all of the energy was converted to heat because the subject performed no work and accomplished no energy storage. The amount of energy dissipated as heat has also been estimated by the method of indirect calorimetry, in which the amount and the composition of the metabolic mixture have been determined from the oxygen consumption, carbon dioxide production and urinary nitrogen excretion. The results of indirect calorimetry may be expressed in Calories because the calorific values of carbohydrate, fat and protein have been determined experimentally. Interpretation of these results is based upon the chemical theory of combining weights. Rubner in 1894 was the first to show that the energy value of the metabolic mixture is equal to the total heat production of the fasting, resting individual. The physicist naturally says that the two quantities could not be unequal in the face of the first law of thermodynamics; but the physiologist is proud of his ability to prove the point.

The total energy exchange of the fasting, resting subject has been given a special name, the *basal metabolism* (sometimes referred to as the basal metabolic rate or B.M.R.). As a clinical test the determination is usually made in the morning, after a good night's sleep, 12 to 14 hours after the most recent meal and after the subject has been physically, mentally and emotionally at rest for 30 minutes. In order to perform an independent determination of the basal metabolism, the oxygen consumption, carbon dioxide production and nitrogen excretion must be measured; but one may avoid the necessity of measuring all three by taking advantage of previously published results. Thus, in a large series of determinations DuBois (4, p. 93) found that under "basal" conditions the R.Q. is normally about 0.82 and the calorific value of oxygen about 4.8 Calories per liter. Consequently, by using his figures the basal metabolism may be estimated from the oxygen consumption alone, with a desirable saving of time and effort. The principles underlying the procedure are not changed by the use of the DuBois data; on the contrary, in using these data one assumes that Dr. DuBois has shared the labor of the experiment in question by carrying out the more difficult parts of the analysis.

Factors Which Affect Basal Metabolism. *Body size.* To be able to measure the energy exchange of a given subject leads naturally to the investigation of the metabolism of different individuals of the same or even of different animal species, and to an attempt to find some basis upon which a valid comparison of metabolic rates may be made. As one might expect, large animals carry on a greater energy exchange than smaller animals, but the increase with size is not directly proportional to body mass or weight. A straight line relationship between the two may be obtained, however, by plotting the logarithms of the two factors or by plotting metabolism against a power function of the weight (Figs. 474 and 475). Of the great number of functions which have been proposed, the two-thirds or three-fourths power seems best to reconcile the data now at hand, and this mode of expression is frequently used in studies of the metabolism of laboratory or domestic animals. In clinical laboratories, on the other hand, metabolism has long been referred to

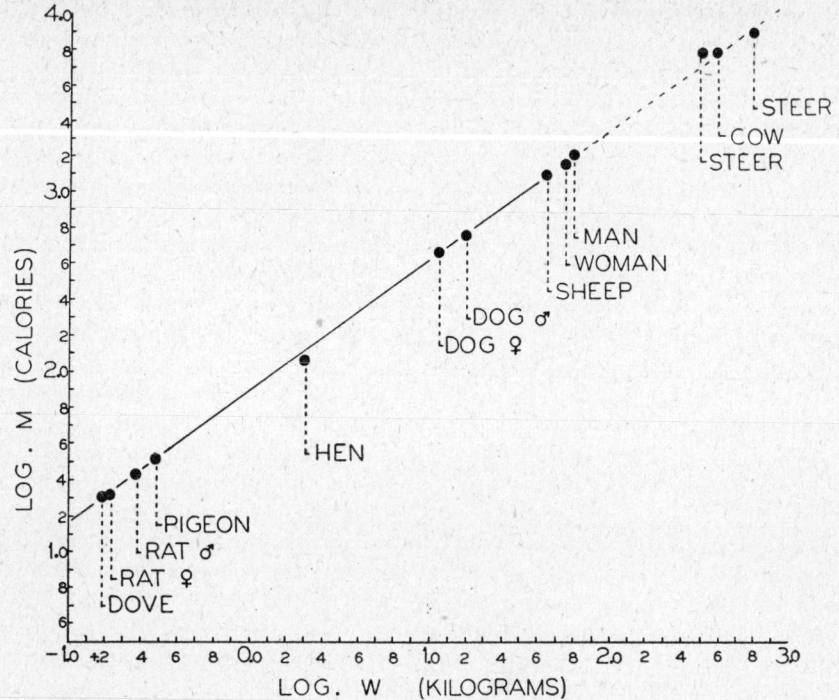

Fig. 474.—Log. of metabolism/log. of body weight. (After Kleiber, *Hilgardia*, 1932, *6*:315–353.

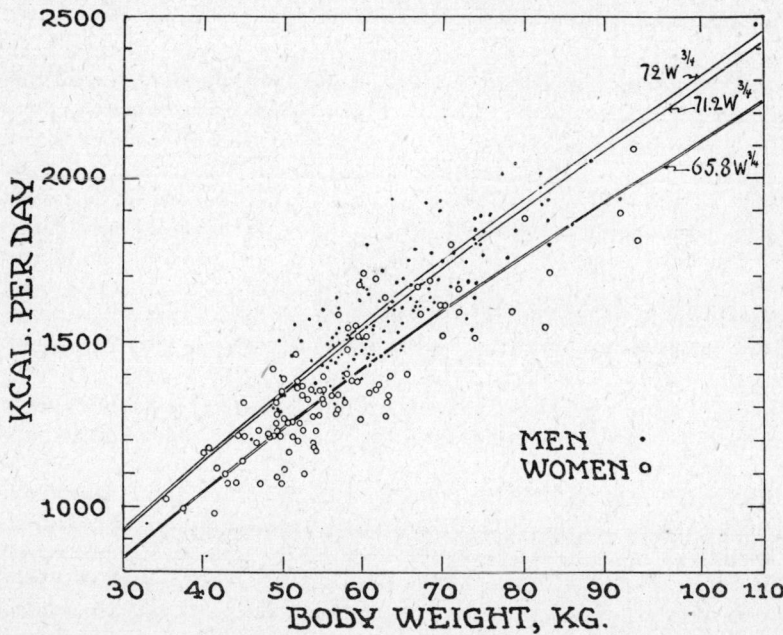

Fig. 475.—Basal metabolism of men and women. Data have been calculated to a standard age of 30 years and a standard specific stature of 4.34 dm. kg.$^{-\frac{1}{3}}$ (men) or 4.21 dm. kg.$^{-\frac{1}{3}}$ (women). (From Kleiber, unpublished.)

the surface area of the subject because, in the opinion of many investigators, the shape of the body and its area are of equal or even greater importance than its mass. But unlike the body weight which can be determined easily, surface area is difficult to measure. Even in a laboratory well equipped for the task, the procedure is tedious and time consuming because the skin is geometrically so highly irregular. A method more convenient than direct measurement is needed, therefore, to facilitate the study of large groups of patients where time does not permit the determination of the surface area of every subject. In response to this need, many attempts have been made to express the results of direct measurements by some sort of formula based upon quantities such as weight and height which are easily measured. Of the proposed formulae, the one most widely used for human subjects was presented by DuBois and DuBois (3) as follows: $A = W^{0.425} \times H^{0.725} \times 0.007184$ where A is the surface area in square meters, W is weight in kilograms and H is height in centimeters. The formula makes allowance for the possibility that the surface area of a tall individual may be no greater or even less than that of a shorter, stout subject, and for the fact that of two subjects of equal height, the heavier will have the greater skin surface. Only two measurements are required and they may be made with ease and accuracy. In fact, the facility with which surface area is now calculated tends to overshadow the long and difficult history of the problem.

Although the basal metabolism per unit of surface area may be estimated either in liters of oxygen per hour or in Calories per hour, physicians have adopted yet another method of expressing their results. They usually express the basal metabolic rate as a percentage above or below certain standard levels which were established by Harris and Benedict (6) or by Boothby, Berkson and Dunn (2) in their large series of determinations made on normal individuals (Table 48). Expressed in this form, a basal metabolic rate of $+7$ signifies a total heat production 7 per cent above the standard average for individuals of that sex and age group. Plus 10 and minus 10 are usually taken as the normal limits since, in a large series, 80 to 90 per cent of the results fall within ± 10 per cent of the mean for the group. Expression in percentage is a simple and convenient procedure, but it occasionally leads to careless thinking because the actual heat production is disregarded once the calculation has been made. In the case of an obese subject, for example, to say that the basal metabolic rate is normal is only to say that heat production has increased in proportion to the increase in surface area. This tends to obscure the magnitude of the real increase in total heat production—the conversion into heat of perhaps twice as much energy as the normal subject dissipates in this way. Only by referring to the heat production per se, in Calories per hour, does one appreciate the enormously enhanced rate of energy exchange of the obese patient (5, pp. 534 ff.).

Growth. Age is a second factor to be considered in evaluating the energy exchange of different individuals, since the magnitude of the fasting, resting metabolism changes as the individual grows, matures and then approaches senility. For his size, the growing youth has a higher metabolic rate than the adult because growth is an energy expending process. It is normally accompanied by a hearty "appetite," an increased food consumption or energy intake and, consequently, an elevation of the total metabolism or energy exchange. This elevation is comprised of these three factors: (i) In the form of protoplasm, energy is retained during growth, since every increase in the size and weight of the body represents the laying aside or storage of chemical energy. (ii) Storage takes place through the synthesis of protein, fat and carbohydrates, all of which require for their synthesis the addition of free energy to the system. Such energy is ordinarily obtained from oxidative reactions simultaneously carried on in the growing cells. (iii) But free energy liberation and utilization is always accompanied by the loss of a considerable fraction of the energy as heat. It is small wonder that growing children may need almost as much or even more food than their parents. Moreover, the energy exchange of a growing youth is maintained at a high level even during a short period of fasting like the one required for the measurement of the basal metabolic rate, when the growing body continues its customary synthetic reactions at the expense of previously stored materials, just as an adult under similar conditions uses stored energy in place of his temporarily unavailable foodstuffs. The elevated basal metabolic rate of growth is an expression of the fact that even during fasting the synthesis of protoplasm or anabolism is

Table 48.—*The DuBois Normal Standards as Modified by Boothby and Sandiford*
Calories per square meter per hour

AGE	MALES	FEMALES	AGE	MALES	FEMALES
5	(53.0)	(51.6)	20–24	41.0	36.9
6	52.7	50.7	25–29	40.3	36.6
7	52.0	49.3	30–34	39.8	36.2
8	51.2	48.1	35–39	39.2	35.8
9	50.4	46.9	40–44	38.3	35.3
10	49.5	45.8	45–49	37.8	35.0
11	48.6	44.6	50–54	37.2	34.5
12	47.8	43.4	55–59	36.6	34.1
13	47.1	42.0			
14	46.2	41.0	60–64	36.0	33.8
15	45.3	39.6	65–69	35.3	33.4
16	44.7	38.5			
17	43.7	37.4	70–74	(34.8)	(32.8)
18	42.9	37.3			
19	42.1	37.2	75–79	(34.2)	(32.3)

going on at an appreciably higher rate than in the adult. It follows that the rate of catabolism is proportionately elevated and the situation is well described as one in which the rate of "turnover" of tissue constituents is increased.

Miscellaneous factors. Data published from several different laboratories (4, p. 180) have shown that basal metabolism is to a certain extent determined by the sex of the individual. The fasting, resting energy exchange of women tends to be 6 to 10 per cent lower than that of a male subject of comparable size, but the reason for this difference is not known. The circumstances under which the individual, either male or female, has been living are also important. Basal heat production is lower in subjects who have been maintained on calorically restricted diets than it is in well-fed individuals, and acclimatization to either a remarkably cold or a hot environment significantly changes the basal metabolic rate (see below).

Basal metabolism is not to be thought of as the lowest possible energy exchange because during sleep the heat production falls below the "basal" level. The difference, amounting to approximately 10 per cent, is at least partially attributable to a more complete muscular relaxation in sleep. The expression, "basal metabolism," may be applied only to measurements performed when the subject is awake.

TOTAL METABOLISM

Effect of Food. Attempts to measure and to compare the energy exchange of fasting, resting individuals have led, then, to the concept of the basal metabolism; upon this concept as a foundation an outline of more complicated energy exchanges may now be attempted. To introduce one of the factors hitherto almost disregarded in this discussion, what effect does food have upon metabolism? First and most important, food serves as a source of energy and allows the body to conserve or even to add to its own reserves. Dietary carbohydrate, fat and protein, after they have been digested and absorbed, tend to be oxidized in place of compounds derived from tissues of the body. Food energy, however, cannot be substituted calorie for calorie for stored chemical energy because food causes an elevation of the total energy exchange which is manifested as an increase in the heat production of the individual. Rubner in 1885 showed that for each class of foodstuffs a characteristic amount of extra heat is produced; protein food elevates the heat production for a period of some hours by an amount which equals 25 to 30 per cent of the energy value of the protein that was fed, while fat and carbohydrate evoke less marked, but nevertheless appreciable, rises. Unfortunately, there is no general agreement regarding the method of expressing this effect, whether the extra heat in calories shall be referred to the caloric value of the food or to some other quantity such as the resulting extra nitrogen excretion. For this reason there remains some controversy as to whether or not the magnitude of the effect varies with age, nutritional state, environmental temperature, or the conditions of activity of the endocrine glands.

The effect of food upon total energy exchange was designated by Rubner as *specific dynamic action* or the S.D.A. Its conciseness recommends the term for general use, especially in the abbreviated form; but the nature of the effect is probably not accurately denoted by these words. In reality, the extra heat is an expression of the body's ability to use its own reserves more efficiently than it can use foodstuffs. Suppose that the heat production of a fasting, resting subject is measured, and the subject is then given an amount of protein calorically equal to his total heat production (estimated) for the next four or five hours. If his heat production is followed while the protein is being catabolized, it will become evident that the protein failed to satisfy his energy requirement because the total energy expenditure rose by about 25 to 30 per cent of the calorific value of the protein. While it is true that the food tended to spare the body's reserves, it is also true that the extra energy spent in the utilization of the food was obtained from those same reserves. And in order completely to prevent the simultaneous oxidation of tissue reserves, the caloric value of protein food must be one-fourth to one-third greater than the basal energy exchange during the time the food will be oxidized. In the case of food made up of carbohydrate or fat, however, a smaller excess will be sufficient.

At the present time the site of liberation of all of the extra heat cannot be identified, although it has been shown that only an insignificant portion is contributed by the digestive glands and the muscle of the gastro-intestinal tract, inasmuch as the specific dynamic action is only slightly diminished when amino acids, for example, are given intravenously rather than orally. Various suggestions have been offered, but experimental results seem to bear out the general theory proposed by Rubner, namely, that the excess heat production is the result of intermediary processes of metabolism of the absorbed food. Wilhelmj, Bollman and Mann have shown by experiments on hepatectomized dogs that a large fraction of the heat liberated in the utilization of amino acids is normally produced in the liver, probably in the course of the deamination of the acids and the formation of urea (12). The heat is so-called free heat, which is not available for the work of the tissues although it contributes to the heat of the body and is of value during exposure to low environmental temperatures.

Muscular Exercise. Another variable of great importance is muscular exercise which is accompanied by the liberation of energy and heat in striated muscle cells (Chap. 3). Under favorable circumstances the ratio between the heat and the calorific value of the work accomplished may be 4 to 1; or, the efficiency of muscle is about 20 per cent. This compares favorably with the efficiency of a steam engine (10–25 per cent) or a gasoline motor (25 per cent). If muscular contractions neither raise an object nor change a momentum,

Table 49.—*Average Normal Output of Carbon Dioxide and Heat from the Body*

| | AVERAGE QUANTITIES PER HOUR | |
CONDITIONS OF MUSCULAR ACTIVITY	CARBON DIOXIDE, GM.	HEAT, KCAL.
Man at rest, sleeping	25	65
Man at rest, awake, sitting up	35	100
Man at light muscular exercise	55	170
Man at moderately active muscular exercise	100	290
Man at severe muscular exercise	150	450
Man at very severe muscular exercise	210	600

however, their net efficiency may be much less than 20 per cent, and under certain conditions all of the energy may be ultimately dissipated as heat. The energy may then be measured directly in a respiration calorimeter; in this way Benedict (1) showed that the overall heat production may be increased as much as tenfold during severe muscular exertion (Table 49). In the liberation of this heat or in doing work, an equivalent amount of either foodstuff or reserve chemical energy is utilized by the muscles, and the oxygen consumption and carbon dioxide production rise proportionately. One result of this elevated energy exchange is that a subject who increases his activity requires more food if his energy balance is to be maintained (Chap. 53).

Environmental Temperature. Heat produced by muscular activity may or may not be advantageous to the body, depending largely on the environmental temperature at that time. In a warm environment where the body already has all of the heat it needs, muscular exertion presents a serious problem in heat dissipation; but in the cold, the heat of muscular contraction materially aids the maintenance of a normal body temperature, and mammals possess a physiological mechanism—shivering—which operates in cold environments to provide heat by this means. Shivering brings about an abrupt rise in oxygen consumption, heat production and overall energy exchange, but it is not the only reaction through which the metabolic rate is affected by temperature, since exposure to cold increases the *basal* oxygen consumption entirely apart from the shivering reaction. This elevation of the basal metabolic rate develops gradually during cold exposure, and is associated with histologic changes in the thyroid gland which indicate that the thyroid is hyperactive, liberating into the blood stream an unusually large amount of its hormone. The hormone, in turn, acts upon the cells of the body to enhance their rate of heat production.

Thyroid gland. The thyroid, a bi-lobed organ at each side of the trachea, has long been known to be an endocrine gland necessary for normal function of most of the other organs and tissues of the body. When the thyroid fails to secrete the proper amount of its hormone, the individual acquires peculiarities of appearance and behavior known as *cretinism* (in children) or *myxedema* (in adults). The two conditions are essentially the same except that in the child there occurs a failure of growth and development which naturally is not apparent in the adult. In severe cases a diagnosis of either of these conditions can be made from the appearance of the patient, but such cases are now rare in this country because most patients receive early treatment which prevents the development of classic cretinism or myxedema. The progress of either the juvenile or the adult disease can be arrested, and in most instances the individual can be restored to normal appearance and activity by the administration of preparations obtained from the thyroid glands of domestic animals.* Since iodine is required by the thyroid gland for the synthesis of thyroxin, a certain type of hypothyroidism known as *colloid goiter* occurs when the diet is deficient in iodine. This type of hypothyroidism naturally improves upon the administration of thyroid preparations, but it also responds simply to the addition of iodine to the diet, because here the thyroid is able to synthesize thyroxin when its precursors are made available.

Conditions in which the thyroid gland becomes overactive also occur in man; they are known collectively as *hyperthyroidism*, while the term *exophthalmic goiter* is commonly applied to one type of this disorder. Although the cause of pathological hyperthyroidism is obscure, in at least some cases the disease may have its origin in the anterior pituitary gland. The latter organ normally controls the rate of synthesis of the thyroid hormone by way of the thyrotropic hormone, a compound secreted into the blood stream by cells of the pars anterior, and carried to the thyroid where it activates the glandular cells of that organ. The elevation of heat production noted during prolonged cold exposure is initiated by the anterior hypophysis through a series of reactions involving the thyrotropic hormone, the thyroid gland and its hormone, thyroglobulin, which has as its principal action the enhancement of the rate of overall energy exchange. Virtually all tissues of the body respond

---

* These preparations owe their potency to their content of one or both of two iodine-containing amino acids, thyroxin and di-iodotyrosine (a precursor of thyroxin). Upon absorption from the agastro-intestinal tract, this thyroxin becomes associated with plasma globulin to form thyroglobulin, the form in which the hormone produced by the thyroid normally exists in the body fluids. The thyroxin which the patient with myxedema must secure from an external source is in a normal individual manufactured within the thyroid gland from iodine and protien present in his food (p. 1152). The chemical reactions of the normal synthesis are yet unknown, although something of their nature has been learned from the study of animals fed radioactive iodine, or given drugs such as thiouracil which apparently interfere with the discharge of the hormone from the gland.

to the hormone by an increase in their rate of oxidation. That the abnormalities typical of hypothyroidism and of hyperthyroidism are the result of a slowing down or a speeding up, respectively, of metabolic reactions was first shown by Magnus Levy (9), who discovered that patients with thyroid disease exhibit characteristic alterations in their fasting, resting oxygen consumption. Consequently the basal metabolic rate is now widely used as an aid in making diagnoses of thyroid dysfunction, since in hyperthyroidism the basal oxygen consumption may be increased by as much as 75 per cent, while hypothyroidism may be accompanied by rates of minus 20 to minus 40. Correction of the thyroid abnormality by appropriate medical or surgical treatment allows the basal metabolic rate to return to a normal level. As one might expect, both types of thyroid abnormality tend to be accompanied by deficits of temperature regulation; hyperthyroidism with its high level of heat production makes the patient uncomfortable in the summer, while hypothyroidism causes discomfort in cold winter weather.

Fever. Many of the pathological alterations of total energy exchange encountered clinically are related in one way or another to the normal variations already described. Fever, or elevation of body temperature, however, brings into play a factor as yet unmentioned here. In the inorganic chemistry laboratory it can easily be shown that the speed of a reaction varies with its temperature in such a way that the rate is approximately doubled for each elevation of 10° C. When the body temperature rises above the normal level, an increase in the rate of its basic reactions is therefore to be expected. It is not definitely known, however, whether an increased heat production is initially partially responsible for the fever or whether the fever brings about the increased heat production. It seems probable that the initial temperature change depends upon other factors such as cutaneous vasoconstriction, shivering and suppression of sweating and that these are followed by an augmentation of basal heat production when the rate of oxidative reactions has been increased by the temperature change.

REFERENCES

1. BENEDICT, F. G. Investigations at the nutrition laboratory of the Carnegie Institution of Washington, Boston, Massachusetts. *Science*, 1915, *42*:75–84.

2. BOOTHBY, W. M., BERKSON, J. and DUNN, H. L. Studies of the energy metabolism of normal individuals: a standard for basal metabolism with a nomogram for clinical application. *Amer. J. Physiol.*, 1936, *116*:468–484.

3. DuBois, D. and DuBois, E. F. Clinical calorimetry. Tenth paper. A formula to estimate the approximate surface area if height and weight be known. *Arch. intern. Med.*, 1916, *17*:863–871.

4. DuBois, E. F. *Basal metabolism in health and disease*, 3rd ed. Philadelphia, Lea and Febiger, 1936. 494 pp.

5. EVANS, F. A. Obesity. Pp. 513–591 in: DUNCAN, G. C. *Diseases of metabolism*. Philadelphia and London, W. B. Saunders Co., 1942.

6. HARRIS, J. A. and BENEDICT, F. G. *A biometric study of basal metabolism in man*. Washington, Carnegie Institution of Washington, Publ. 279, 1919. vi, 266 pp.

7. KLEIBER, M. Body size and metabolism. *Hilgardia*, 1932, *6*:315–353.

8. LIPMANN, F. Metabolic generation and utilization of phosphate bond energy. *Adv. Enzymology*, 1941, *1*:99–162.

9. MAGNUS-LEVY, A. Untersuchungen zur Schilddrüsenfrage. *Z. klin. Med.*, 1897, *33*:269–314.

10. RUBNER, M. Beiträge zur Lehre vom Kraftwechsel. *S. B. bayer. Akad. Wiss.*, 1885, *15*:452–461.

11. RUBNER, M. Die Quelle der thierischen Wärme. *Z. Biol.*, 1894, *30*:73–142.

12. WILHELMJ, C. M. The specific dynamic action of food. *Physiol. Rev.*, 1935, *15*:202–220.

CHAPTER 51

INTERMEDIARY METABOLISM

Of even greater physiological significance than the energy exchange of the body as a whole (described in the preceding chapter) are the metabolic reactions of the individual organs and tissues which go to make up the overall metabolism. These individual reactions may be studied by experimental procedures based upon the principles of direct and indirect calorimetry. Thus, the heat production of a tissue, like that of the whole body, may be measured in a calorimeter of appropriate size, or may be inferred from its oxygen consumption and carbon dioxide production, which, in turn, may be obtained in many instances by measuring the oxygen and carbon dioxide concentrations of blood entering and leaving the organ, together with the rate of blood flow. Moreover, in experimental animals it is sometimes possible to determine the metabolic rate of an organ such as the liver by measuring the total respiratory exchange of the animal before and again after the organ is removed by a surgical operation. Or better, the respiratory metabolism of a representative sample from the organ may be measured directly in a system like the Warburg apparatus, where a thin slice of tissue or a suspension of cells is allowed for a few hours to carry on its usual metabolic reactions at a constant temperature in a buffered solution supplied with an adequate amount of oxygen (7). Each of these procedures has its own limitations, and some of them are technically quite difficult to perform; but through them much has been learned about the rate of energy exchange within the individual tissues. Nevertheless, the data so obtained give an account of only the overall reactions within the cells, and fail to reveal in chemical terms the nature of the reactions through which energy exchanges occur. In order to investigate the so-called "intermediary" metabolism, i.e., the chemical reactions in which carbohydrates, lipids and proteins and their derivatives participate with oxygen and water, more highly specialized chemical techniques must be used. Fortunately, many of the compounds which take part in the intermediary metabolism can be isolated and identified, changes in their concentrations in body fluids can be followed, and reactions in which they participate can be brought about outside the body in the test tube or beaker of a chemical laboratory. Hence, from this type of in vitro investigation the significance of many of the body's chemical constituents has been discovered and the mechanisms of energy metabolism are beginning to become known.

Enzymatic Catalysis. Chemical reactions occur in biological systems according to the principles and laws of general chemical theory, and they are unique only in that their speed is hastened by organic catalysts known as enzymes. Without this catalysis the reactions would not occur rapidly enough to provide energy for normal physiological responses. An enzyme is a protein elaborated by a living cell, active as a catalyst even after it has been removed from the cell which formed it (Chap. 46). The catalytic activity of an enzyme depends upon its protein constitution, but certain enzymes contain an additional nonprotein center of activity which is designated by the term "prosthetic group." A typical prosthetic group takes part in the reaction catalyzed by the enzyme, not as a catalyst (the protein has this function), but as a kind of cosubstrate; that is, the prosthetic group actually undergoes a reversible chemical change. Oxidative enzymes have been classified according to the nature of their prosthetic groups. Green (11), for example, divides them into the iron porphyrin proteins, pyridinoproteins, flavoproteins, copper proteins, thiaminoproteins, and a group the structure of which is not yet known. The connection between the protein and the prosthetic group varies in its stability from one enzyme to another, and by prolonged dialysis some enzymes can be separated into their two component parts. One part, the protein, is readily destroyed by heat (as is the complete enzyme), and is often rather loosely referred to as an "enzyme" although by itself it is inactive. The other part, also in itself impotent to effect the original reaction, is relatively heat-stable and of low molecular weight, and is usually called a "co-enzyme" when it is found separate from the protein (although it is identical with the original prosthetic group). When the co-enzyme is added to the inactive protein (the "enzyme") one obtains an active compound which is able to function as a complete enzyme. It is fair to note, however, that some of the prosthetic groups of known enzymes have not yet been isolated as co-enzymes, and there is still some controversy as to whether or not every co-enzyme really represents a dissociated prosthetic group. The problem is one of terminology, complicated by a lack of knowledge of the intricacies of enzyme action.

Like the more familiar reactions of the inorganic chemistry laboratory, some metabolic reactions are easily reversible and some are not. If the reaction involves only an insignificant change in potential chemical energy, it is usually reversible; but if that change is large, the reaction appears to run only "downhill," i.e., in the direction of a decrease in potential energy and an increase in entropy. Both types of reaction are catalyzed by enzymes, and reference has already been made to the fact that an enzyme, like any other catalyst, does not in itself determine the direction of any given reaction (Chap. 46). Thus, the enzyme phosphorylase, which catalyzes the synthesis of glycogen *from* glucose-1-phosphate, also catalyzes the breakdown of glycogen *to* glucose-1-phosphate. Whether glycogen is built up or broken down is determined by other considerations of which perhaps the most obvious are the relative concentrations of the reacting substances. Therefore, this and many other similarly *reversible* reactions may be driven almost to completion in one direction if the end-products of the reaction are in some way removed in order to maintain their concentrations at levels low enough to prevent a reversal of the original reaction and the attainment of an equilibrium state. On the other hand, if its free energy change is large, a reaction spontaneously goes so far in the "downhill" direction that it becomes, in effect, *irreversible*. For example, the interaction of glucose and adenosine triphosphate (catalyzed by hexokinase) to yield glucose-6-phosphate and adenosine diphosphate always moves in this one direction because of the high energy level of the ATO. Fortunately, living cells possess mechanisms for "detouring" around such an irreversible reaction and for bringing about the "uphill" or synthetic reactions which will not occur spontaneously alone. This the cells do by coupling their syntheses with supplementary oxidative or energy yielding reactions which serve as a source of chemical power. Thus, ADP is reconverted to ATP by an oxidative phosphorylation (Chap. 3), while glucose-6-phosphate may be split to glucose and phosphate by another enzyme, phosphatase. It follows, therefore, that whenever an important change in free energy is in question, the breakdown and the synthesis of a given compound may occur by quite different pathways, since the former may take place relatively directly, while the latter must proceed through one or more of these coupled reactions.

CARBOHYDRATE METABOLISM*

Carbohydrates of Biological Importance. Carbohydrate metabolism includes all of the reactions undergone in the body by the carbohydrates of the diet and by those formed in the body from noncarbohydrate sources. In these two categories are included the following: (i) the polysaccharides—starch and glycogen; (ii) the disaccharides—maltose, sucrose and lactose; (iii) the monosaccharides—the hexose sugars (glucose, fructose and galactose) and certain pentoses (ribose and others). The metabolism of the disaccharides and polysaccharides as such (with the exception of glycogen and lactose), however, is completed before they leave the gastro-intestinal tract where they are hydrolyzed to the monosaccharides, glucose, fructose or galactose.

The processes of intermediary metabolism, therefore, are concerned primarily with the monosaccharides, with the compounds into which they may be converted and the compounds from which they may be formed. Among these compounds are: (i) glycogen, composed of a still undetermined number of glucose units; (ii) pyruvic acid (CH_3—CO—COOH), lactic acid (CH_3—CHOH—COOH) and acetic acid (CH_3—COOH) which are the three most familar of the series of compounds intermediate between glucose and CO_2 and H_2O; (iii) certain less easily isolated intermediary compounds such as the phosphoric acid esters of hexose and triose sugars, the four-carbon dicarboxylic acids (succinic, fumaric, malic and oxalo-acetic), as well as the five- and six-carbon compounds thought to participate in the so-called tricarboxylic (citric) acid cycle (Chap. 3); (iv) neutral fats which may be synthesized from carbohydrate; and (v) glycerol and the amino acids from which glucose may be produced. Of primary importance is the understanding of the overall pattern of carbohydrate metabolism and the roles played by glucose, glycogen, lactic and pyruvic acids ("lactate" and "pyruvate"). Once their relationships are thoroughly understood by the student, the positions of the less familiar intermediate compounds are more easily grasped.

Carbohydrate Supply of the Body. *Blood glucose as a dynamic equilibrium.* The blood glucose (blood sugar) is a well-known form of carbohydrate, present in whole blood of mammals in the fasting state in a concentration of about 60 to 80 mg. per 100 ml., although after a meal rich in carbohydrate the concentration may temporarily rise as high as 130 to 140 mg. per 100 ml. Glucose is a reducing sugar, and the ordinary methods for determining its concentration are based upon this property; but there are other reducing sub-

* The three subjects included in this chapter, namely, carbohydrate, protein and lipid metabolism, have been more fully discussed by Dr. C. N. H. Long (19) and Dr. Abraham White (32, 33) in their interesting and valuable chapters in Duncan's *Diseases of metabolism*, 1942.

stances of noncarbohydrate nature present in blood, and in testing for glucose care must be taken to exclude, as far as possible, the effects of these other compounds. The generally accepted normal blood sugar levels of a few years ago were appreciably higher than those now accepted for this reason, namely, that newer techniques more adequately exclude the nonsugar reducing substances such as glutathione, ascorbic acid, and others.

The blood glucose must be regarded as a form in which carbohydrate is transported via the circulation from one part of the body to another. Certain of the organs (the gut and the liver) may increase the glucose content of the blood perfusing them but other organs (the brain, active muscle, as well as the liver under appropriate circumstances) withdraw glucose from the blood. In view of these diverse influences to which it is subjected, the relative constancy of the blood glucose level is a truly remarkable phenomenon which can be explained only by the fact that when glucose is being added to the blood, some other part of the body is able almost immediately to take up the excess; and similarly, when the level tends to fall because glucose is being rapidly used, there are reserves which may be drawn upon for replacement. In either of these situations the organ primarily responsible for taking up the surplus or restoring the deficiency is the liver. Mann and his collaborators (see 23) found that when the liver has been removed from a dog, the blood glucose progressively falls over a period of hours and the animal dies; but if glucose solution is given by infusion or hypodermoclysis, the animal will live until the injected glucose has been utilized, when hypoglycemia will again become evident. Conversely, since a hepatectomized dog is unable normally to dispose of excess glucose, an extremely high blood sugar level (hyperglycemia) occurs immediately following glucose administration. The liver owes its commanding position in the control of the blood sugar level to its ability either to synthesize glucose into glycogen and fat, or to convert glycogen and certain amino acids into glucose, as circumstances may require.

If for some reason (usually either experimental or pathological in origin) the blood sugar does fall below a level of approximately 40 mg. per 100 ml., the subject undergoes a characteristic series of reactions which are attributable to the effects of the hypoglycemia upon neurons of the central nervous system. A sense of weakness and hunger may be noted, followed by sweating, cutaneous vasomotor reactions (either vasoconstriction or vasodilatation), salivation, lacrimation, shivering and involuntary urination and defecation; convulsions, coma and death may ensue if the sequence is not interrupted by the administration of glucose. Hyperglycemia, on the other hand, when it occurs following the ingestion of food or as an experimentally or pathologically evoked phenomenon, in itself causes no symptoms. If the hyperglycemia is severe enough (above 250 mg. per 100 ml.), glucose is lost from the blood through the kidneys, and glycosuria may be demonstrated by testing the urine for reducing sugar. Although the renal tubules normally reabsorb all of the glucose filtered through the glomerular membrane (p. 971), there is a limit to the rate at which it can be reabsorbed. When this limit is surpassed and glucose appears in the urine, the blood sugar level is said to exceed the renal threshold for glucose. Diabetes mellitus is the most commonly encountered condition in which this situation exists.

Both the rate at which glucose is added to the plasma and the rate of its removal are regulated in a large part by hormones secreted by the endocrine glands. In this regulation the following glands appear to participate rather directly: the anterior lobe of the hypophysis, the pancreatic islets, and the cortices and medullae of the adrenals. (All of these except the islets are discussed on pp. 1175–1181, below.) The function of the islets of Langerhans is well known, and consists in the manufacture and liberation of insulin, a hormone which lowers the blood glucose. When insulin is given *intravenously* to a normal animal or human subject, the blood sugar begins to fall within a period of a few minutes, the magnitude of the fall depending to a certain extent upon how much insulin was injected. If the dose is not large, the insulin will be inactivated in the body within 30 to 60 minutes, and the blood sugar will then begin to be restored, unless the mechanisms of restoration are inadequate as, for example, in the hypophysectomized animal (Fig. 476).

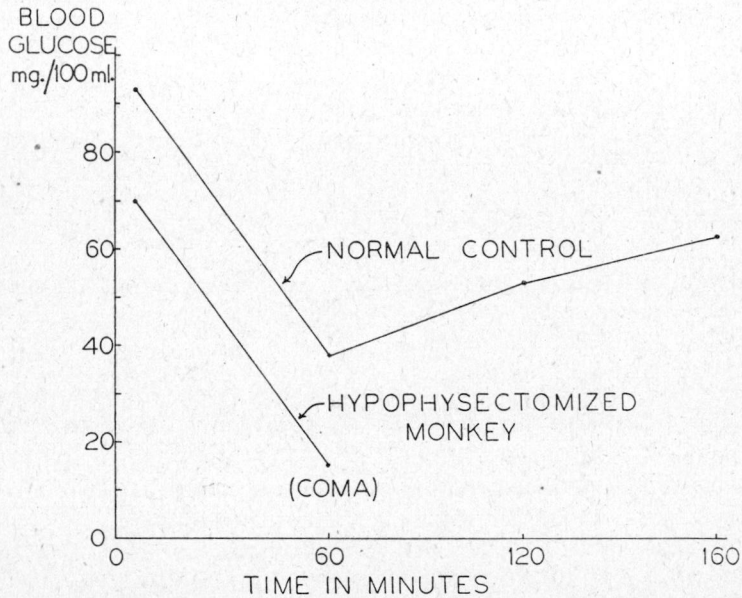

Fig. 476.—Insulin hypoglycemia in a normal monkey given 8.6 units of insulin intravenously, and in a hypophysectomized monkey given 2.0 units. (After Hartman, Firor and Geiling, *Amer. J. Physiol.*, 1930, *95*:662–669.)

Given subcutaneously as it is in clinical practice, the effect of insulin is more prolonged and more variable both in duration and magnitude of the response because the rate of absorption from the subcutaneous tissue is slow but not constant. Insulin apparently exerts its effect primarily upon the rate of removal of glucose from the plasma, but the chemistry of its action has not been discovered. In the absence of insulin (i.e., in the depancreatized animal), the concentration of blood sugar increases to 5 to 6 times its normal value, presumably because the rate at which it is formed exceeds by that much its rate of removal. Banting and Best's (1, 2) discovery of a successful technique for the isolation and purification of insulin provided a means for counteracting the effects of extirpation of the islets and, more important, for treating human cases of diabetes mellitus, a disease similar in most respects to the diabetes of the depancreatized experimental animal.

The normal, physiological state of the blood sugar, then, represents what may be designated as a "dynamic equilibrium." This phrase implies that the blood glucose is relatively constant, but it also implies that this constancy is the result not of inactivity, but rather of a resilient type of adjustment between the rates at which glucose is added to the blood and withdrawn from it. The body's ability to maintain this equilibrium is often tested both experimentally and clinically by temporarily upsetting the equilibrium and measuring the length of time necessary for restoration to occur. Two different types of procedures are used. One is called a test of insulin "sensitivity" and consists in measuring the severity and duration of the hypoglycemia evoked by a known quantity of insulin (Fig. 476). In this way the adequacy of mechanisms responsible for the addition of glucose to the circulating blood may be tested. The other procedure is known as a test of glucose "tolerance,"

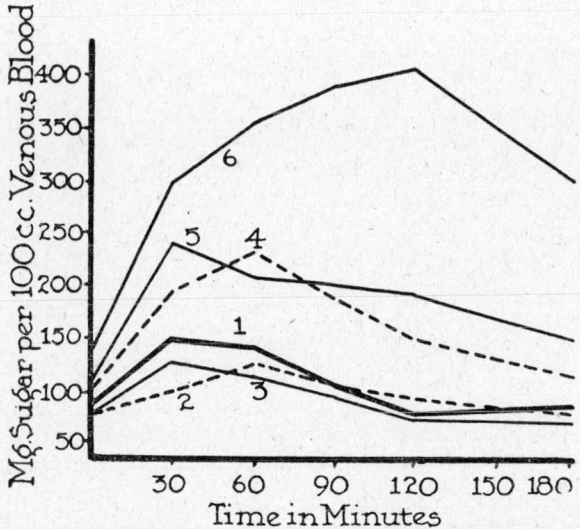

Fig. 477.—Glucose tolerance curves. 1, normal; 2, a case of hypothyroidism; 3, a case of renal diabetes; 4, a case of hyperthyroidism; 5, a case of mild diabetes; 6, a case of severe diabetes. (Data collected in the Hospital Laboratories of the Research and Educational Hospitals, Chicago, Ill. From Levinson and MacFate, *Clinical laboratory diagnosis*, 2nd ed. Philadelphia, Lea and Febiger, 1943.)

which consists in measuring the height and the duration of the hyperglycemia produced by the administration (either orally or by injection) of a known quantity of glucose or glucose solution. (The intravenous gives somewhat more uniform results that the oral route of administration because the latter is influenced by the rate of intestinal absorption. In hypothyroidism, absorption is delayed.) By this means the integrity of the mechanisms through which glucose is utilized and stored may be determined (Fig. 477).

Liver glycogen and carbohydrate storage. The possibility that liver glycogen represents a stored form of glucose was first proposed by the great French physiologist, Claude Bernard (25), who suggested that the liver is able either to remove excess glucose from the blood of the hepatic circulation or to add glucose to that blood. Either response depends upon the liver's ability to effect a series of reversible reactions in which the complex polysaccharide, glycogen, is synthesized from hexose units with the removal of water. This relationship is expressed empirically in the following equation:

$$n\,[C_6H_{12}O_6] \rightleftharpoons (C_6H_{10}O_5)_n H_2O + n-1\ H_2O$$

The liver of a well-fed dog may contain as much as 3 to 5 per cent glycogen —a reservoir from which glucose may be supplied to the tissues using it. If the human liver stores an equivalent amount, in the fed state there are available possibly 75 grams or slightly more than 300 Calories. But if an animal is fasted before the liver is removed for analysis, the glycogen content is found to be quite low—a few tenths of 1 per cent—which signifies that the once generous store has been converted to glucose and used by the body.

Although Claude Bernard performed his classic experiments upon liver glycogen almost ninety years ago, little was added by way of further elucidation of these important relationships until the last two decades when physiological chemists began to identify the intermediary stages of the reaction and to isolate the enzymes responsible for each step (see 6). The first step in the synthesis of glycogen from glucose is catalyzed by hexokinase and yields glucose-6-phosphate, with adenosine triphosphate (ATP) serving as a phosphate donor. Under the influence of another enzyme, phosphoglucomutase, an intramolecular rearrangement then occurs which yields glucose-1-phosphate (the so-called Cori ester); this compound is, in turn, acted upon by a third enzyme, phosphorylase, which removes the phosphate and synthesizes glycogen. The entire series of reactions can be carried out in a test tube in the presence of appropriate amounts of each of these substances and certain metallic ions. It should be noted, however, that no glycogen will be formed unless there is already present in the reacting mixture a small amount of preformed glycogen. This is said to "prime" the reaction, possibly by furnishing a skeleton to which glucose units may be added. In test tube experiments, as glycogen is formed inorganic phosphate accumulates and soon inhibits the reaction unless some provision is made for chemically disposing of the phosphate. But this effect is apparently of negligible importance in the liver cell because other enzyme systems take up the phosphate and ultimately return it to the adenine phosphates to resynthesize ATP. These reactions have been summarized in the following equation:

$$\text{Glucose} \xrightarrow{\ \text{Hexokinase and ATP}\ } \text{Glucose-6-phosphate} \underset{}{\overset{\text{Phosphoglucomutase}}{\rightleftharpoons}}$$

$$\text{Glucose-1-phosphate} \underset{}{\overset{\text{Phosphorylase}}{\rightleftharpoons}} \text{Glycogen} + PO_4$$

Fructose may also serve as a source of glycogen by way of this same series of reactions since there is present in the liver an enzyme identified as isomerase because it is able to convert fructose-6-phosphate into glucose-6-phosphate.

Glycogen breakdown (glycogenolysis or glucogenesis) occurs through the reversal of this same series of reactions, with the exception that the hexokinase reaction which would form ATP is not reversible (see above). Instead, free glucose is formed by the action of another widely distributed enzyme—phosphatase—which splits glucose-6-phosphate to glucose and inorganic phosphate. The glucose thus liberated diffuses out of the hepatic cell into the blood in the liver sinusoids, provided that the glucose concentration of that blood is below that of the intracellular fluid.

Gluconeogenesis. The liver also supplies the blood with glucose derived from other sources, namely, from certain amino acids and from the glycerol portion of fat molecules. Reactions by which this is accomplished are designated by the term "gluconeogenesis," which suggests the noncarbohydrate origin of the material from which the glucose is produced. Further details of the reactions will be found in the discussion of protein metabolism, later. The glucose formed from these sources is indistinguishable by ordinary tests from that derived from starch, glycogen or the disaccharides, and its fate in the body does not need to be separately considered.

Peripheral Utilization of Carbohydrate. *In skeletal muscle.* The gastro-intestinal tract and the liver, then, act as purveyors of carbohydrate to the organism, while the circulatory system functions as a distributor of glucose to the cells of every tissue and organ. In the cells the chemical energy of the glucose is liberated as heat or work, or storage takes place, depending upon the nature of the individual cell. Not all of the reactions involved in glucose utilization have been discovered, but enough has been learned about the metabolism of one particular tissue—skeletal muscle—to yield a valuable insight into the nature of intracellular processes in general. One of the interesting characteristics of skeletal muscle is its ability to synthesize and retain glycogen. By setting aside a carbohydrate reserve (from 0.5 to 1.0 per cent of the weight of the muscle) the cell insures itself against the possibility that it may be called upon to work at a time when the supply of blood glucose is not immediately adequate. The reactions through which muscle glycogen is synthesized from glucose appear to be identical with those which occur in the liver. Moreover, the breakdown or hydrolysis of muscle glycogen evidently begins by way of reactions similar to those described above for liver glycogen, but in the muscle the phosphate radical is not split off at the hexose stage as it may be in the liver but is retained until there has been accomplished a series of reactions which ultimately yield the three-carbon compounds, pyruvic or lactic acids. Details of these reactions have been presented in Chapter 3 of this text where they should now be reviewed. Two general pathways of utilization are known to exist, designated as aerobic and anaerobic to indicate their dependence and independence, respectively, of molecular oxygen. Of the two, anaerobic glycolysis has been the more widely studied, but lack of knowledge of the other should not obscure its position as the quantitatively more important under normal conditions. *Aerobic* metabolism derives from a carbohydrate molecule all of its energy, since the carbon and hydrogen are thereby completely oxidized. *Anaerobic* glycolysis of a molecule of glucose, on the other hand, yields two molecules of lactic acid, the energy content of which is approximately nine-tenths that of the original glucose. It is obvious that unless lactate can be utilized in some way, the body will lose an important source of energy whenever the muscle cell is obliged to carry on anaerobic metabolism. There appear to be two pathways by which lactate may be reclaimed. In the presence of oxygen, lactate may be oxidized back to pyruvic acid in the muscle cell where it may then re-enter the usual catabolic channels or may be resynthesized to glycogen; or, because of its high diffusibility the lactate may actually leave the muscle, diffuse into the blood and lymph and thus be carried to the liver where its utilization or synthesis into glycogen and a subsequent conversion to blood glucose may be accomplished. The latter method of disposal is sometimes

37

referred to as the "Cori cycle" because Cori first outlined the scheme— muscle glycogen→ lactic acid→ liver glycogen→ blood glucose→ (muscle glycogen). .

Significance of blood lactic and pyruvic acids. Lactic acid is one of the four products of carbohydrate catabolism which leave the muscle in what are now thought to be significant concentrations; the others are carbon dioxide, water and pyruvic acid. All other intermediary products are either present in a very low concentration at any given time or else they are relatively indiffusible and their presence in muscle is not easily detected by analysis of the blood going to or coming from the muscle. But lactate and pyruvate are

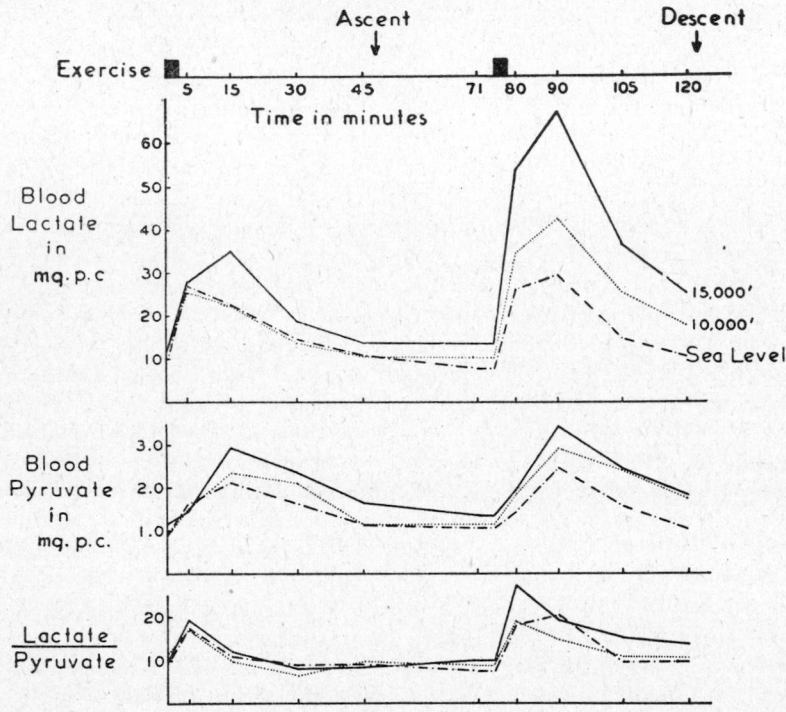

Fig. 478.—Elevation of blood lactic and pyruvic acid levels following exercise on a bicycle ergometer. The graphs include three different control periods of exercise at sea level, each of which is followed by another exercise period either at sea level or at a simulated altitude of 10,000 or 15,000 feet. (Tepperman, personal communication.)

diffusible ions and their concentrations in the blood vary with alterations in muscle metabolism. Whenever muscular exercise is performed under circumstances where the supply of oxygen to the muscles is limited (either by the unaccustomed severity of the exercise or by a low partial pressure of oxygen in the respiratory mixture), the blood lactate and pyruvate rise as illustrated in Figure 478. The magnitude of the rises reveals the extent to which anaerobic glycolysis is taking place. But when lactate and pyruvate cease to be formed in large quantities and when the liver has removed the acids already produced, the blood levels again return to their resting values.

Utilization in other organs. Skeletal muscle is only one of the many sites in which carbohydrate is broken down to yield energy and heat, but it happens to be the one site in which the intermediary reactions have been intensively, and on the whole successfully, studied. For the present it must serve, therefore, as a model of the lines along which a description of metabolic reactions in their entirety will be ultimately completed. Eventually one must distinguish the processes through which energy is made available for mechanical work from the processes associated with organic syntheses and from those responsible for other phenomena such as secretion, conduction, etc. Although such distinctions are not possible at the present time, further study will undoubtedly clarify these relationships.

Diversion of Carbohydrate into Pathways of Protein or Lipid Metabolism. Because the animal organism freely converts carbohydrate into fat and, with certain limitations, into amino acids, this discussion of carbohydrate utilization cannot be concluded without mention of the possibility of these interconversions. Pyruvic acid ($CH_3COCOOH$) appears to represent an important crossroad in the metabolism of the various foodstuffs since it participates in both aerobic and anaerobic metabolism, since it may be formed by the deamination of amino acids, and since it theoretically represents a way-station in the synthesis of fat from carbohydrate. This last reaction, in particular, is of great theoretical and practical interest, and will be further discussed later in this chapter.

PROTEIN METABOLISM

Amino Acids as Protein Constituents. Protein utilization also proceeds in two stages, one of which is accomplished in the gastro-intestinal tract where the proteolytic enzymes secreted by digestive glands reduce the large, complex molecules of protein foodstuffs to their constituent parts, the amino acids, or to relatively simple chains of amino acids, the peptides. In molecular weight the proteins range from 13,000 to several millions, but the amino acids vary only from 75 (glycine) to 240 (cystine), which is well within the dimensions of the simple carbohydrates. (The molecular weight of glucose is 180.) Because of their smaller size, relative simplicity and limited number, the amino acids can be studied with relative ease both inside and outside the body, where the physiology of the proteins, on the contrary, can now be investigated only to a limited extent.

Sources of Amino Acids. *Products of digestion.* From the intestine the products of protein digestion are absorbed into the portal blood stream and into the lymph which soon joins the venous blood in the left innominate vein. The addition of these peptides and amino acids to the plasma naturally tends to raise the level of plasma amino nitrogen. Van Slyke (29) found, however, that the rise is much greater in the blood of the portal vein than in that of the systemic circulation, and this observation suggested to him that the liver removes from the blood perfusing it many of the excess amino acids and simple peptides. When their concentration in the portal blood rises, the liver removes them rapidly enough to minimize their effect upon the composition of the blood of the systemic circulation, but the peripheral tissues also take up and temporarily store a significant quantity. The relative constancy of the blood amino acid level, therefore, is the result of a well-regulated balance between the rates at which these compounds are added to the blood by organs like the intestine and liver and removed therefrom by organs such as the liver or skeletal muscle. The expression, "dynamic equilibrium," applies as well to the state of the blood amino acids as it does to that of the blood sugar.

From tissue proteins. Although the gastro-intestinal tract contributes a large quantity of amino acids to the portal blood during the digestion of protein food, the gut is by no means the only source of these compounds. Schoenheimer (27) has shown that a continual interchange of amino acids occurs between the plasma and the protein constituents of organs like the liver, the kidney, spleen and skeletal muscle, as well as the plasma proteins. During fasting or starvation the tissue proteins yield to the blood more amino acids than they withdraw, and thus certain organs, principally the liver and skeletal muscle, clearly become sources of blood amino acid nitrogen. This accounts in a large part for the weight loss of starvation, and explains why certain organs lose more weight than others (Table 50).

Parenteral administration. Since all of the protein used by the body is reduced to or almost to amino acids in the course of its digestion and absorption, the organism should be able to substitute for its dietary protein requirement an equivalent amount of a proper mixture of amino acids. The first

Table 50.—*Weight Loss During Starvation in the Cat.* (*From Voit.*)

	Supposed Weight of Organs Before Starvation	Actual Loss of Organs in Gm.	Loss to Each 100 Gm. of Fresh Organ (Percentage Loss)
Bone	393.4	54.7	13.9
Muscle	1408.4	429.4	30.5
Liver	91.9	49.4	53.7
Kidney	25.1	6.5	25.9
Spleen	8.7	5.8	66.7
Pancreas	6.5	1.1	17.0
Testes	2.5	1.0	40.0
Lungs	15.8	2.8	17.7
Heart	11.5	0.3	2.6
Intestines	118.0	20.9	18.0
Brain and cord	40.7	1.3	3.2
Skin and hair	432.8	89.3	20.6
Fat	275.4	267.2	97.0
Blood	138.5	37.3	27.0
Remainder	136.0	50.0	36.8

experiments of this kind were made by Loewi who fed dogs a diet consisting of a certain amount of carbohydrate and fat, and protein which had been previously submitted to a prolonged pancreatic digestion until it was completely hydrolyzed. On this diet the animals were able to synthesize protein. As a matter of fact, animals will live and thrive on a similar diet without the addition of fats or carbohydrates. Moreover, the amino acid mixture need not be administered via the gastro-intestinal tract but may be injected intravenously (9). Administration intravenously is an invaluable procedure in the treatment of patients unable to take or to retain proteins given orally, and this discovery has made possible the nutrition of patients who would otherwise suffer from protein starvation. Naturally enough, when given intravenously the so-called "indispensable" amino acids are just as important as when they are given orally, and the "dispensable" acids retain their dispensable character by either route of administration (p. 1137).

Amino Acid Utilization. *Protein synthesis.* The fate of the amino acids taken up by the liver is highly variable, but it may be predicted from a knowledge of the physiological state of the individual including his age, nutritional status, activity and the environmental temperature. For a short time, at least, the liver stores a small amount of amino acid nitrogen (30) but the greater part of the amino acids are not directly stored but are either (i) synthesized into protein, (ii) oxidized to carbon dioxide, water and urea, (iii) converted to carbohydrate or to fat, or (iv) used in the formation of certain amino acid derivatives such as glutathione, epinephrine, creatine, etc.

Little is known of the chemical reactions responsible for protein synthesis because the structure of protein molecules has not been clearly revealed. But there is no doubt that the amino acids present in the blood and interstitial fluids are precursors of tissue protein nor that synthesis of the latter is, in its end-result, the antithesis of the hydrolytic reactions through which proteins are degraded by the organic chemist to yield amino acids. According to the now universally accepted theory of protein structure based upon the classic studies of Emil Fischer (10), proteins consist of amino acids united by what is known as the "peptide linkage" in which the amino group of one acid unites with the carboxyl group of another, thus:

$$\underset{H}{\overset{R}{\underset{|}{\overset{|}{H_2N-C-COOH}}}} + \underset{H}{\overset{R}{\underset{|}{\overset{|}{H_2N-C-COOH}}}} \rightleftharpoons \underset{H}{\overset{R}{\underset{|}{\overset{|}{H_2N-C-CO-NH}}}}-\underset{H}{\overset{R}{\underset{|}{\overset{|}{C-COOH}}}} + H_2O$$

By reactions of this type simple peptides and even polypeptides have been prepared from amino acids in the laboratory, and Bergmann and Fruton (3) have shown that compounds so prepared will serve as substrates for the familiar proteolytic enzymes, trypsin, chymotrypsin, pepsin, cathepsin and others. Since enzymes are highly specific toward their substrates, the obvious conclusion is that the synthetic compounds closely resemble the naturally occurring substrates of the individual enzymes. The peptide bonds prepared in vitro, therefore, are probably quite like the bonds formed when protein synthesis takes place within living cells. The various proteins synthesized by the body evidently differ from one another in both the relative and the absolute amounts of the several amino acids present in the protein molecule, and also in the order or pattern into which the amino acids become organized. The number of possible patterns into which 22 or more amino acids might be arranged to yield compounds with molecular weights up to several millions is beyond comprehension. How the cells of the body are able properly to arrange such complex patterns and how a given cell is able consistently to produce its own characteristic proteins are fascinating problems still awaiting solution.

That protein synthesis enhances the individual's total energy exchange has been noted in connection with the high basal metabolic rate of growing subjects (p. 1097). When the opposite reaction occurs, viz., protein breakdown or the hydrolysis of a peptide linkage, energy is liberated as heat, and the amount of energy so liberated is large enough to be a limiting factor in determining the direction of the reaction. That is, in the presence of the appropriate enzyme (or a strong acid or alkali) peptides are spontaneously hydrolyzed with the evolution of heat; but a peptide cannot be synthesized from a mixture of amino acids even in the presence of the appropriate enzyme unless energy is supplied to the mixture from some other reaction. The source of this extra energy within a living cell is unknown;* ultimately, however, the energy must come from the oxidation of a foodstuff and hence, the high basal metabolism associated with active growth.

Table 51.—*Fate of Amino Nitrogen in Normal Adult Rats.*

(Isotopic amino acids—corresponding to 25 mg. N per day for 3 days—were added to normal stock diet.)

MATERIAL ANALYZED	PER CENT OF ADMINISTERED N15 RECOVERED	
	AFTER FEEDING *l*(—)-LEUCINE	AFTER FEEDING GLYCINE
	PER CENT	PER CENT
Excreta		
Feces	2.2	2.6
Urine	27.4	40.8
Animal Body		
Nonprotein N	8.2	11.1
Protein N	56.5	44.3
Total	94.3	98.8

(Reprinted from Rudolf Schoenhiemer, *The dynamic state of body constituents*, Cambridge, Mass., Harvard University Press, 1942.)

Although only meager data are available concerning rates of reaction and the quantities of compounds involved in intermediary protein metabolism, the well conceived experiments of Schoenheimer have sketched a clear outline of the overall picture of these reactions. Schoenheimer and his colleagues (27) labeled or "tagged" amino acid molecules or portions of molecules by

Table 52.—*N15 Content of Protein Nitrogen Obtained from Different Organs After Feeding l*(—)-*Leucine and Glycine (25 mg. N per Day).*

(Calculated for 100 atom per cent N15 in compound administered.)

ORGAN	AFTER FEEDING *l*(—)-LEUCINE	AFTER FEEDING GLYCINE
Serum	1.67	1.78
Hemoglobin	0.29	0.46
Liver	0.94	1.40
Intestinal wall	1.49	0.98
Kidney	1.38	....
Heart	0.89	....
Spleen	1.10	....
Testes	0.77	....
Skin	0.18	....
Muscle	0.31	0.29

(Reprinted from Rudolf Schoenheimer, *The dynamic state of body constituents.* Cambridge, Mass., Harvard University Press, 1942.)

incorporating into them known amounts of the isotopic atoms, heavy nitrogen (N15) and deuterium (heavy hydrogen). Weighed amounts of the labeled amino acids were then fed to mature animals in nitrogen equilibrium (p. 1119). When the carcasses of the rats were analyzed three days later, it was found

* Several interesting theories have been proposed by Bergmann and Fruton (3).

that the animals had retained each amino acid in the form of protein to the extent of about half of the total amount which had been fed three days previously (Table 51). The various parts of the body retained different amounts: plasma proteins retained the largest relative quantity while the skeletal muscles retained the largest absolute amount (Table 52). Further study showed that much of the isotopic nitrogen had been transferred from the amino acid fed in the diet into certain other amino acids of the tissue proteins. Thus, not only was there an exchange of whole amino acids between the diet and the tissue proteins, but there was also an exchange of amino nitrogen between the amino acids of the diet and those of the tissues. The mechanisms of these exchanges are unknown, but, to a certain extent at least, they must involve an exchange of amino groups as such, since when Schoenheimer fed the animals isotopic nitrogen in the form of ammonium citrate the nitrogen (N^{15}) of the NH_4^+ quickly became incorporated into tissue proteins. The exchange is probably enzymatic in nature, and the name, "transaminase," has been given to the type of enzyme believed to be responsible for the reaction. The only transaminases thus far isolated from tissues, however, are capable of effecting an exchange of amino groups among only a very few of the relatively large number of compounds which must participate in these reactions under normal conditions.

Schoenheimer and his colleagues noted interesting and provocative differences between various amino acids in their rates of reaction and in the types of reactions in which they participate, and he thereby helped clarify present knowledge of their metabolic pathways. With regard to protein synthesis in general, his study may be summarized as follows: Even in the adult animal, protein synthesis occurs at a surprisingly rapid rate (which presumably equals the rate of protein breakdown, since nitrogen balance is maintained—see later); this synthesis involves portions of the molecules of tissue proteins and represents a rapid splitting and resynthesis of peptide bonds whereby amino acids present in body fluids are introduced into the proteins; and in this synthesis the cells use even fractions of amino acid molecules with the result that an amino group may be utilized separately from the carbon chain with which it was originally associated. In a younger individual who is actively retaining nitrogen, the rate of protein synthesis exceeds the rate of its breakdown, and this disproportion between the two opposing reactions brings about an absolute increase in tissue proteins which is one of the essential features of the growth process.

Proteins into which amino acids are synthesized render to the organism a multitude of different services. Most important of all are the enzymes which carry on the energy exchanges that make possible all physiological and biological phenomena. Moreover, the transmission of hereditary characters is determined largely by nucleoproteins—the genes—present in the ovum and spermatazoon from which the individual develops. Fibrous proteins of connective tissue, bone, the skin, etc., support and protect the organism, while other proteins maintain the characteristic organization of each cell and every tissue. Plasma proteins have already been discussed (Chap. 27); through their inability easily to penetrate capillary membranes they play a decisive role in the regulation of body water distribution, and they are believed to represent one form in which protein is transported throughout the body (22). They include, also, the fibrinogen which takes part in blood clotting, and the antibodies which confer resistance or immunity to disease. Some of the hormones, i.e., those of the anterior lobe of the hypophysis, the thyroid, parathyroid and pancreatic islets, evidently circulate with the plasma proteins. All of these compounds and many others related to them must be acquired by the individual through synthetic reactions which commence with amino acids or with simple peptides. Beginning with the relatively minute quantity present in the fertilized ovum, the individual finally attains adulthood by manufacturing and retaining the proteins necessary for his own characteristic structure and his particular types of energy exchange.

Deamination. Amino acids which are not withdrawn from body fluids in the course of protein synthesis may be oxidized directly or may be converted to carbohydrate or fat. In either case the characteristic amino group is removed, leaving a carbon-hydrogen-oxygen-containing chain closely related to the three- and four-carbon compounds which serve as intermediaries in the oxidation of carbohydrate and fat and which are indistinguishable by ordinary chemical tests from similar compounds derived from other sources. At this stage of utilization an arbitrary division into protein, carbohydrate and fat metabolism is scarcely possible since the past history of the molecule is of little significance to the cell using the intermediary compound. Recognizing this fact, physiological chemists have applied the term "metabolic pool" to the whole collection of intermediary metabolic products among which the body's chemical reactions and interchanges occur. Deaminated amino acid residues enter this "pool" where they may become involved in enzymatic reactions which oxidize them to carbon dioxide and water, with the liberation of energy and heat. But, on the other hand, the deaminated residues from certain amino acids may be withdrawn from the "pool" and used in the synthesis of protein again, or glucose, glycogen, fatty acids or neutral fat. Thus they may again become capable of identification and classification as one or another of the three basic foodstuffs.

Conversion to glucose or glycogen. That protein can be converted to carbohydrate was first suggested by the experiments of Claude Bernard (25) who found that after an animal's liver glycogen had been depleted by fasting it could be replenished by feeding protein but not by feeding fat. His observations have been confirmed by more recent investigations which show that whenever carbohydrate reserves are depleted in a normal animal, a large fraction of any protein or of amino acid mixtures fed to the animal can be quantitatively accounted for as glycogen, glucose, or their derivatives. Lusk (20) and his colleagues were able to study the carbohydrate forming potentialities of individual amino acids in dogs given phlorhizin, a drug which selectively inhibits glucose reabsorption in the cells of the renal tubules. Since under the influence of phlorhizin glucose cannot be reabsorbed, it is quantitatively excreted in the urine, the blood sugar falls to low levels and the animal suffers from a generalized carbohydrate deficiency which is only temporarily relieved by glucose administration. When protein is fed to such an animal, the glucose and the urea nitrogen in the urine rise proportionately (Fig. 479), suggesting that some of the protein has been deaminated and converted to glucose. How much of the protein has been so utilized may be calculated by multiplying the weight of the extra urinary nitrogen by 6.25, since nitrogen is present in protein to the extent of 1 part in 6.25. Lusk found that the ratio of urinary glucose to nitrogen, the D:N ratio, amounted to as much as 3.65

grams of glucose to every gram of nitrogen; or, in other words, 6.25 grams
of protein yielded 3.65 grams of glucose in the phlorhizinized dog, or 58 per
cent of the protein was converted to glucose. Drury (8) has more recently
suggested that if account is also taken of glucose which is not excreted because
it is catabolized before it reaches the kidneys, the true D:N ratio may be as
high as 5 or 6, which suggests that protein may be converted to carbohydrate
in a ratio of 1:1. To interpret these results properly one must remember that
the experiments were carried out on adult dogs under conditions where the
formation of glucose from every possible source proceeds at a maximal rate
because of the extreme glucose deficiency occasioned by the enormous glucose loss in the urine.

Although the glycogenic property of certain amino acids is most easily
measured in animals under the influence of phlorhizin, this same conversion

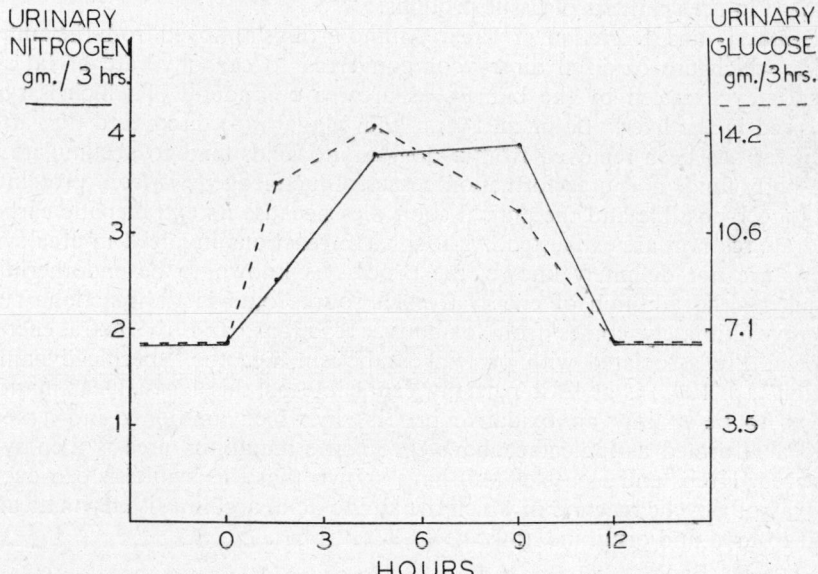

Fig. 479.—Curve showing the urinary excretion of glucose and nitrogen by a phlorhizinized
dog fed 500 gm. of meat. (From Lusk, *The elements of the science of nutrition*, 4th ed. Philadelphia, W. B. Saunders Co., 1928.)

also proceeds under more nearly normal conditions. Some protein is always
being changed to carbohydrate just as some carbohydrate is always being
used in amino acid synthesis. The ability to effect gluconeogenesis is of particular importance if dietary supplies of carbohydrate are limited as they are
when an animal is living on a meat diet, or during fasting or starvation. There
are a few cells in the body, including those of the central nervous system,
which can use as a source of energy nothing but carbohydrate, and these
cells cannot survive even a brief fast if the liver is not able to supply them
with glucose derived from tissue protein. More than half of the 22 accepted
amino acids have been shown to form glucose in the rat or in the dog. The
chemical reactions responsible for the conversion have not been discovered,
but there is reason to believe that the amino group is removed by an oxidative reaction which yields a keto acid. Thus, deamination of alanine yields
pyruvic acid which is readily converted to glucose or glycogen by the liver.

$$CH_3CH(NH_2)COOH \longrightarrow CH_3COCOOH \longrightarrow glucose$$
$$\text{alanine} \qquad\qquad \text{pyruvic acid}$$

Conversion to fat. Because deamination of the glycogenic amino acids yields compounds identical with certain of the intermediaries of carbohydrate metabolism, the formation of fat from protein and from carbohydrate may occur via the same series of reactions or, specifically, by way of pyruvic acid. In addition, certain amino acids are directly diverted into the pathways of fat metabolism through oxidative deaminations which yield ketone bodies, but since only a limited number of amino acids have been shown to undergo this type of conversion, the significance of this ketogenesis is not clear. Whatever may be the intermediate chemical reactions, it is evident that by converting protein to fat the individual accumulates an energy reserve and conserves most of the potential energy of whatever surplus dietary protein is not utilized in the synthesis of tissue proteins.

Synthesis and Excretion of Urea. Amino groups removed from the amino acids which are oxidized directly or converted to carbohydrate or fat are eventually excreted by the kidneys as urea, a compound of which is synthesized in the liver.* Bollman, Mann and Magath (5) discovered that after the liver has been removed from a dog, amino acids tend to accumulate in the body fluids and urea formation ceases. Gluconeogenesis from protein is no longer possible and the animal soon dies because its extrahepatic carbohydrate reserves are exhausted. Although the reactions involved in urea synthesis are not definitely known, the process is known to be endothermic, requiring the addition of energy from a source outside the reaction. This energy ultimately comes from oxidative reactions, and the extra energy expenditure associated with protein catabolism, i.e., the "specific dynamic action" (p. 1098) is at least partially explicable on this basis. Deamination seems to be mainly an oxidative process in which ammonia and a keto acid are formed as indicated above. From the ammonia, urea is then synthesized. Krebs and Henseleit (16) have shown that this synthesis can occur by way of a cyclic reaction in which the amino acid, arginine, is enzymatically split to urea and ornithine, thus:

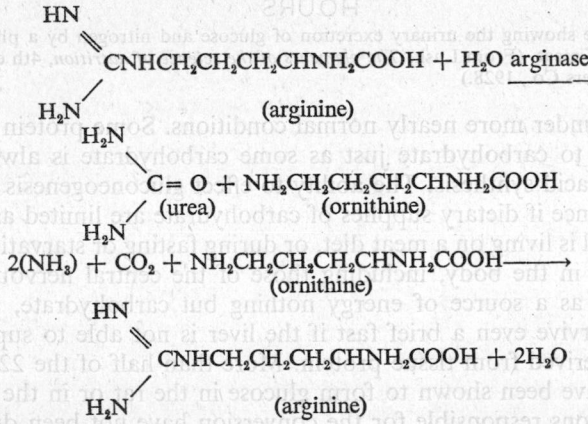

* Deamination occurs also in the kidney where the amino groups thus split off are subsequently excreted as ammonium ions. This reaction is an important mechanism of acid-base regulation, but has not been established as a notable process in the elimination of the end-products of protein catabolism in general.

Ornithine, in turn, combines with carbon dioxide and with two molecules of the ammonia liberated by the deamination of additional molecules of amino acids; the product of the combination is arginine, and the cycle is thereby completed. In his work with isotopic nitrogen Schoenheimer (27) learned that amino groups are indeed rapidly exchanged among the various amino acids, the amidine group of arginine, and urea. This suggests that perhaps a major portion of the urea formed by the liver of an intact animal is produced through the "ornithine cycle." Presumably, tissue protein may be broken down or hydrolyzed to amino acids or simple peptides in any organ of the body. These amino acids and peptides then diffuse into the interstitial fluid of that organ and reach the blood by which they are carried to the liver. Here deamination

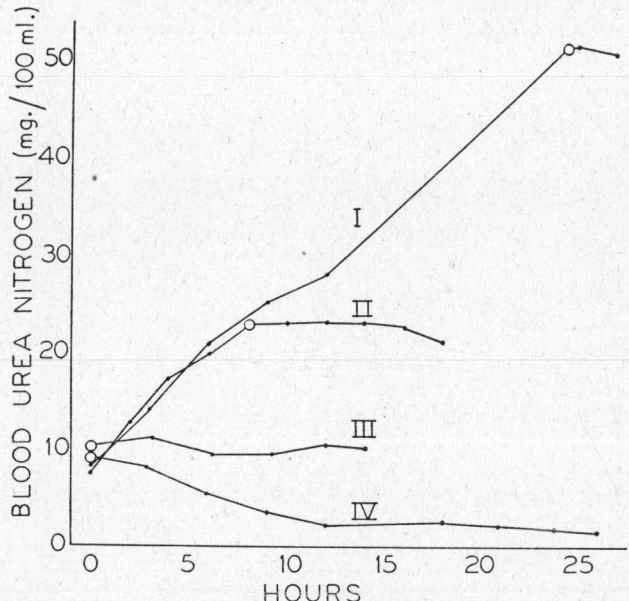

Fig. 480.—Curves showing the effect of removal of the liver at *O*, on the blood urea nitrogen at different levels. Curve I shows the effect of removal of the liver at *O*, 24 hours after removal of both kidneys; curve II, the effect of removal of the liver 8 hours after removal of both kidneys; curve III, the effect of simultaneous removal of the liver and both kidneys; and curve IV, the effect of removal of the liver, urinary secretion being maintained. (From Bollman, Mann and Magath, *Amer. J. Physiol.*, 1924, *69*:382.)

occurs, ammonia is formed, arginine is synthesized from CO_2, ammonia and ornithine, and in a reaction catalyzed by the enzyme, arginase, urea and ornithine are then produced. The urea diffuses back into the blood of the hepatic sinusoids and after traversing the heart and lungs, it reaches the kidney where a certain amount is excreted in the urine (Fig. 480).

Nitrogen equilibrium. This urea contains most of the nitrogen which is taken as a measure of protein catabolism when energy exchange is investigated by the method of indirect calorimetry (p. 1088). About 16 per cent of the protein molecule is composed of nitrogen which is excreted as urea when protein is oxidized or converted to fat or carbohydrate, so that if the weight of nitrogen is multiplied by 6.25, the weight of protein from which it is derived is obtained. If an estimation is made of the nitrogen content of the food eaten during the period of urine collection, a balance may be struck which will determine whether the body is gaining or losing nitrogen. If the balance is even, the body is in nitrogen equilibrium—that is, it is receiving in the food as much protein nitrogen as it is metabolizing and eliminating in the excreta. If there is a plus balance in favor of the food, the body must be storing protein; while if the balance is minus, the body must be losing protein. During the period of growth, in convalescence, etc., the body does store protein, and under these conditions the balance is in favor of food nitrogen. But throughout adult life under normal conditions the diet is so regulated unconsciously

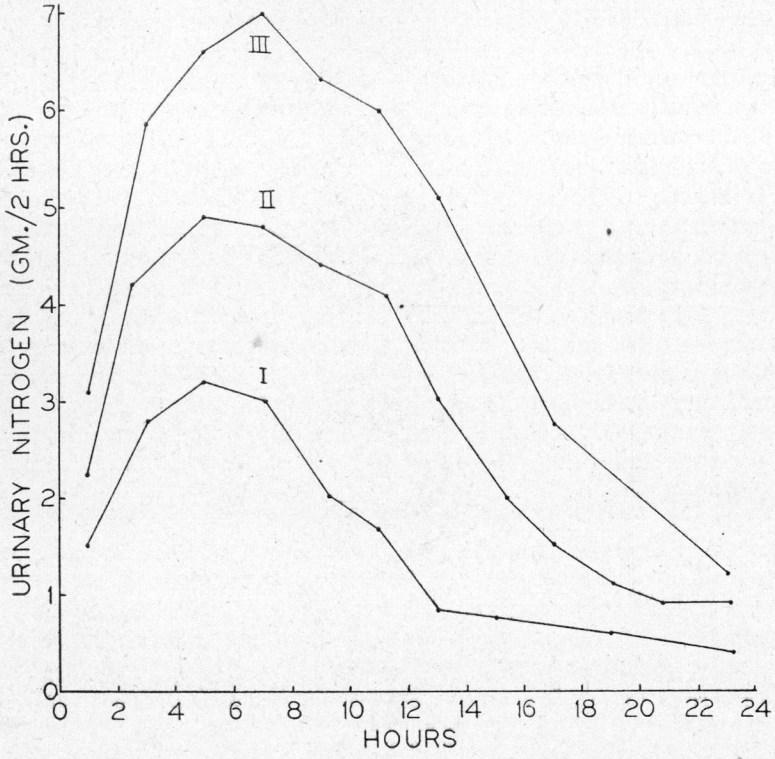

Fig. 481.—Excretion of urinary nitrogen by a dog—I, after 500 gm. meat + 50 gm. fat + 350 cc. water; II, after 1000 gm. meat + 200 cc. water; III, after 1500 gm. meat + 500 cc. water. On each of these days the animal was in nitrogen equilibrium. (From Lusk, *The elements of the science of nutrition*, 4th ed. W. B. Saunders Co., 1928.)

that a nitrogen equilibrium is maintained through long periods. It is important also to bear in mind that nitrogen or protein equilibrium may be established at different levels (Fig. 481). If, for instance, a man in nitrogen equilibrium on a diet containing 10 gm. of nitrogen per day is given 20 gm., the extra protein is metabolized and nitrogen equilibrium becomes established at a higher level. Whereas under the first condition 10 gm. of nitrogen entered the body in the form of protein and 10 gm. left in the nitrogenous excreta, under the second condition 20 gm. are furnished per day in the food and 20 gm. are lost by excretion. Experimentally there has been found to be a certain low limit of protein which just suffices to maintain nitrogen equilibrium (Chap.

52), and between this level and the capacity of the body to digest and absorb protein food, nitrogen equilibrium may be maintained upon any given amount of protein.

An animal may be brought into nitrogen equilibrium on protein food alone, the amount of protein required being relatively large. If nonprotein foodstuffs are now added to the diet, the amount of protein necessary to maintain nitrogen equilibrium may be reduced correspondingly. With reference to the consumption of protein in the body the nonprotein foods are all *protein-sparers;* that is, when only protein food is available the body uses it for processes which can be carried on with carbohydrate or fat if they are subsequently added to the diet. As has been indicated above, the reactions in which the three classes of foodstuffs may be used interchangeably are those which yield energy and heat.

Other Protein Derivatives. Within the past fifty years much has been learned about the metabolism of the amino acids, especially with reference to the body's handling of the characteristic chemical groupings of the different acids and to specific reactions in which they participate. There is also beginning to be built up an important body of knowledge about the metabolism of certain protein derivatives such as choline, creatine and creatinine, glutathione, taurine and others, as well as what are called "substituted" proteins, i.e., nucleoproteins, glycoproteins, lipoproteins and phosphoproteins. Study of the metabolism of these compounds promises to yield data of inestimable value regarding protein metabolism in particular and the mechanisms of physiological energy exchange in general. For the present, however, these subjects remain more directly the concern of the biochemist than of the physiologist, and for their study one must refer to biochemical textbooks, monographs and periodicals.

LIPID METABOLISM

Nutritive Value of Lipids. The lipids of food are absorbed into the lacteals chiefly as neutral fats which enter the blood either directly or by way of the chyle of the great thoracic duct. This fat remains in the circulation for an appreciable time, being slowly taken up by tissues which participate in lipid metabolism. Speaking generally, the essential nutritive value of foodstuff fats is that they furnish energy to the body; for this they are well suited because they contain more energy, weight for weight, than the proteins or the carbohydrates. In a well-nourished animal a large amount of fat is found normally in the adipose tissues, particularly in the so-called "panniculus adiposus" beneath the skin, in the folds of the peritoneum and in the perirenal tissues. Physiologically, this body fat is a reserve supply of nourishment. When food is eaten in excess of the actual metabolic activity of the body, the excess is stored mainly in the adipose tissue as fat, to be drawn upon in case of need, as, for instance, during partial or complete starvation. A starving animal, after its relatively small supply of pre-formed glycogen is exhausted, lives entirely upon body proteins and fats; the larger the supply of fat, the more effectively will the protein tissues be conserved and the longer can the individual survive complete food deprivation. Lipids are oxidized for energy and heat, however, not only during complete abstention from food, but continually in the course of normal everyday metabolism.

Plasma lipids. Like glucose and the amino acids, lipids are transported throughout the body by the blood, especially by the plasma. The nature of the combinations in which lipids exist in plasma is not definitely known, but for convenience in classification the following types of compounds are usually considered separately:

1. Fatty acids esterified with glycerol to form neutral fat;
2. Free cholesterol (not esterified);
3. Cholesterol esters of the fatty acids;
4. Phospholipids of three types, as follows:

    a. Lecithins, composed of glycerol esterified with two molecules of fatty acid and combined with a molecule of phosphoric acid which, in turn, is united with a molecule of the nitrogenous base, choline;

    b. Cephalins, made up of glycerol and two fatty acid molecules, plus phosphoric acid and the nitrogenous base, amino-ethyl alcohol (colamine);

    c. Sphingomyelins, containing no glycerol but composed of a fatty acid, phosphoric acid, choline and another nitrogenous base, sphingosine;

5. Compounds as yet unidentified, present in relatively small amounts.

From this summary it is evident that the total fatty acid content of plasma is normally distributed among three types of compounds, viz., neutral fat, cholesterol esters and the phospholipids. Glycerol is likewise present both in neutral fat and in the phospholipids, lecithin and cephalin, while the total cholesterol is divided into free (28 per cent) and esterified cholesterol (72 per cent). With the exception of phosphoric acid and the nitrogenous bases, therefore, each of the elementary constituents of the plasma lipids exists in more than one combination, and this fact is of considerable importance in the interpretation of changes in the concentration of the individual lipid fractions.

Many attempts have been made to establish normal values and to discover the factors which determine the plasma lipid concentrations. Beyond the fact that hyperlipemia occurs during absorption of fat from the gut, however, and that prolonged starvation evokes a significant rise in cholesterol and phospholipid (14), little is known of the mechanisms of their regulation under normal conditions. The values vary somewhat from one individual to another and even from day to day in any one individual, but in spite of this variability, normal levels have been determined. By the methods of Peters and Man (26) the total fatty acid content of human serum ranges from 5.6 to 19.0 mEq. per liter; cholesterol varies from 123 to 274 mg. per 100 ml.; lipid phosphorus, from 6.4 to 12.0 mg. per 100 ml.; and neutral fat (expressed as fatty acid), 0.1 to 6.1 mEq. per liter.

Two interesting problems concerning lipid transport remain to be solved. The first is how lipids which are naturally immiscible with water are so readily distributed throughout the watery fluids of the body. And the second is to explain the ability of lipid molecules freely to penetrate certain cellular membranes as well as their apparent inability to penetrate others. Provocative hypotheses have been proposed to account for each of these phenomena, one of the more attractive of which is the suggestion that the phospholipids lecithin and cephalin are important intermediaries in fatty acid transport. These phospholipids are thought to be capable of serving this function because they are miscible with water and because they are able to diffuse through membranes similar to those of blood capillaries (4). But conclusive experimental data have not yet been presented to establish either this hypothesis or others proposed to account for the same phenomena.

Lipid Utilization. *Fat storage.* Lipids absorbed from the intestine are carried by the plasma to three possible fates, one of which is storage in the adipose tissue of the body. By far the largest part of this storage occurs in the subcutaneous tissue, the omentum, pericardium and retroperitoneal tissue and between the fibers of skeletal muscles. In these locations lipids are deposited mainly in the form of neutral fat—that is, glycerol esters of the fatty acids. Views upon the origin of body fat have undergone a number of changes in the last hundred years, illustrating in an interesting way how development of experimental methods leads often at first to half-truths which are corrected later by more extensive work. Dumas and others held to the natural view that the fat of the body originates directly from the fat of the food. Liebig (18), applying his more exact methods, demonstrated that in some cases this source is insufficient to account for all the fat. The fat yielded by the milk of a cow, for instance, may be greater in quantity than the fat contained in the food. He also pointed out that the fat of each species of animal is more or less peculiar, the fat of the sheep having a higher melting point than pork fat, and both differing in composition from the fat taken as food. He was led to attribute the source of body fat chiefly to the carbohydrate food, and this belief agreed well with the experience of agriculturists as to the use of such foods in fattening animals for market. The modern point of view is that the fat of the body originates partly from the lipids of the food, and partly from carbohydrate and protein through interconversions discussed below.

The first proof that food fats may be deposited as such in the adipose tissues of the body was obtained in dogs by feeding foreign fats (linseed oil, grapeseed oil and mutton fat) and demonstrating that those fats can afterward be recognized in the tissues of the animals. Other feeding experiments suggest that the normal fat of the food undergoes a similar fate. Thus, Hofmann used a dog weighing 26 kg. and allowed it to starve until its weight was reduced to 16 kg. It was then fed for five days on a little meat and large quantities of fat. At the end of that time it was killed and analyzed. The body contained 1353 gm. of fat, of which only 131 gm. could have come from the protein used, assuming that this material can serve as a fat former. Much of the fat found, therefore, was probably derived from the fat of the food. More recently, Schoenheimer (27) has labeled individual fatty acid molecules with isotopic hydrogen (deuterium) and has proved that of the total number of labeled molecules fed to the animal, a large proportion was deposited in the adipose tissues unchanged. Moreover, he found that a continual interchange of fatty acids occurs between lipids of the diet and those of the animal's depots, and he clearly demonstrated that even when the individual's caloric intake equals or exceeds his expenditure, a significant amount of depot fat is continuously being replaced by dietary fatty acids. Two separate processes may be presumed to be involved in this reaction—one, a process of deposition, the other a process of removal from the depots. If the animal is in energy balance, the rates at which the two proceed must be equal; but when balance is disturbed, the rate of one may exceed the other and the depots may either increase or decrease in size. The regulation of the rates of these reactions has been discussed in Chapter 53, page 1179.

Pathways of oxidation. Lipids not stored in depots of the adipose tissue and lipids withdrawn from those depots may be oxidized within the cells of the body with the liberation of heat and energy; and although the reactions through which their oxidation occurs have not been discovered, there appear to be two general pathways involved. When oxidation occurs via one of them, so-called "direct utilization," intermediary compounds do not accumulate in body fluids in sufficient concentration thus far to have attracted the attention of biochemists. During utilization via the other pathway, on the contrary, intermediary compounds known as ketone bodies—beta-hydroxy-butyric acid, aceto-acetic acid and acetone—do tend to accumulate, and their concentrations may rise to levels high enough seriously to disturb the normal acid-base equilibrium of body fluids.

Knowledge of the pathways of oxidation of the fatty acids is still in a highly speculative state, capable of being discussed only in terms of theories proposed to account for the few established facts. Of the theories thus far advanced, the best known is designated as successive beta-oxidation and was proposed originally by Knoop (15), who arrived at the theory from a study of the oxidation products of the phenyl compounds of fatty acids. He found that phenyl proprionic acid, $C_6H_5CH_2CH_2COOH$, on oxidation yields benzoic acid, C_6H_5COOH, without the intermediate formation of phenyl acetic acid, $C_6H_5CH_2COOH$, as might have been expected if the oxidation had taken place at the alpha carbon. By oxidation at the beta carbon the two end carbons were oxidized off with the production of benzoic acid. When the longer fatty acid chains—butyric, valerianic, caproic, etc.—were combined with the phenyl radicle and oxidized it was found that the acids with an even number of carbon atoms gave phenyl acetic acid as an end-product, while those with an odd number gave benzoic acid. On this and other evidence he founded his theory of beta-oxidation. According to this theory, the long carbon chain of the fatty acid is oxidized at the beta carbon atom (the second carbon from the carboxyl group), the two end carbons are split off as acetic acid, and a fatty acid containing two less carbon atoms remains. All of the naturally occurring fatty acids, including stearic, oleic and palmitic, contain an even number of carbon atoms and according to the theory would be broken down through simpler acids to the butyric acid state. This, in turn, would be oxidized to CO_2 and H_2O. The oxidation of one molecule of palmitic acid (C_{16}), for example, should result in the successive formation of one molecule of acetic acid and one of myristic (C_{14}), another of acetic and one of lauric (C_{12}), then capric (C_{10}), caprylic (octanoic C_8), caproic (hexanoic, C_6) and butyric acids. The last of these contains the same number of carbon atoms as the ketone bodies, beta-hydroxy-butyric and aceto-acetic acids.

Three serious objections have been raised to the theory of successive beta-oxidations as it was originally conceived. In the first place, in tissues performing lipid oxidation the intermediary acids of the sequence just named (including acetic acid) are not found in anything like the concentrations to be expected if the oxidation were proceeding via this type of reaction. In fact, some of the hypothetical intermediaries are evidently not present at all. Second, many investigators have found that oxidation may occur also at the alpha and at the gamma carbon atoms, as well as at the beta carbon as described by Knoop (15). And finally, from both in vivo and in vitro experiments it is now clear that the ratio between the number of molecules of fatty acid oxidized and ketone bodies formed is not 1:1 as the beta-oxidation theory suggests, but rather that as many as 4 ketone molecules may be produced from one molecule of a fatty acid such as palmitic acid. In order to account for these observations, a theory originally proposed by Hurtley (13) has been revived. Hurtley suggested that within the fatty acid molecule multiple oxidations occur, affecting every other carbon atom; and furthermore, that at every fourth carbon atom the oxidation goes to completion so that the molecule is split into a number of four-carbon compounds—in the case of palmitic acid, into four molecules of aceto-acetic acid. Attractive as it is, however, the theory of multiple alternate oxidations fails to account for several other well-known facts regarding ketone formation. For instance, caproic (hexanoic, C_6) acid yields more ketones than butyric acid (C_4), while certain branched chain acids yield ketones in amounts not accounted for by Hurtley's theory. MacKay (21) has therefore proposed still another theory which has now gained wide acceptance as the "beta-oxidation-condensation" theory; here a complete oxidation is assumed to occur at alternate carbon atoms of the fatty acid molecule with the production (perhaps simultaneously) of a number of two carbon molecules, probably acetic acid or a derivative of it. But condensations then occur among the acetic acid molecules to yield aceto-acetic acid and hence the other ketones. By a process such as this a molecule of a six-carbon acid (caproic) would yield one and one-half molecules of aceto-acetic acid where butyric acid would yield only one ketone, and the branched chain acids would yield ketones in proportion to their potential yield of two-carbon residues. That such condensations do occur when ketones are produced in liver slices has been demonstrated by Weinhouse, Medes and Floyd (31), who incorporated isotopic carbon into the carboxyl group of octanoic (caprylic) acid. The isotopic carbon was eventually found in aceto-acetic acid in equal concentrations in the carbonyl (-CO-) and carboxyl (-COOH) groups, suggesting that a significant amount of the ketone must have been formed by condensation of two of the terminal carboxyl groups from the original octanoic acid.

Ketones are now believed to be compounds normally produced in the course of the oxidation of fatty acids. Both in the intact animal and in tissue slices, ketones are readily formed in the liver; and in the intact animal their concentration there may rise high enough to cause them to diffuse into the blood of the hepatic sinusoids and thus to evoke a generalized ketonemia. Carried throughout the body by the plasma, they are then taken up by cells where their oxidation to carbon dioxide and water is completed. Ketonemia is most intense when the body is deriving the greater part of its energy and heat from lipid catabolism, as, for example, during starvation (Fig. 482) or in diabetes mellitus. And ketonemia can be reduced during starvation by administering carbohydrate which provides another type of substrate and reduces the need for lipid oxidation. Similarly, in diabetes mellitus where available carbohydrate is not utilized because of the absence of adequate amounts of insulin, administration of insulin promotes glucose utilization, relieves the individual's dependence upon fat catabolism and causes diminution of the ketosis. The ability to achieve this response is of great importance in the management of clinical diabetes mellitus because, although the keto acids are valuable sources of energy, they are also fairly strong organic acids, and as such they disturb the mechanisms of acid-base regulation in body fluids and may even bring about fatal acidosis if severe, uncontrolled ketonemia is allowed to persist.

Whether the "direct" utilization of fatty acids also involves ketone production is not known, but there is reason to believe that even if ketones are produced extrahepatically, the liver is the only organ capable of adding them to the blood with which it is perfused. If formed in other tissues they must be present either in low concentrations or in nondiffusible combinations which restrict any tendency toward ketonemia. The liver supplies ketones to the periphery as it supplies blood glucose, and the amount supplied depends upon the extent of the animal's utilization of lipids for heat and energy. Various attempts have been made to determine in quantitative terms the importance of hepatic ketogenesis as a pathway of fat utilization. Thus, Stadie (28) and others have suggested that whereas the peripheral utilization of ketones theoretically could occur rapidly enough to account for four to six times the animal's basal heat production, experimental data indicate rather that even

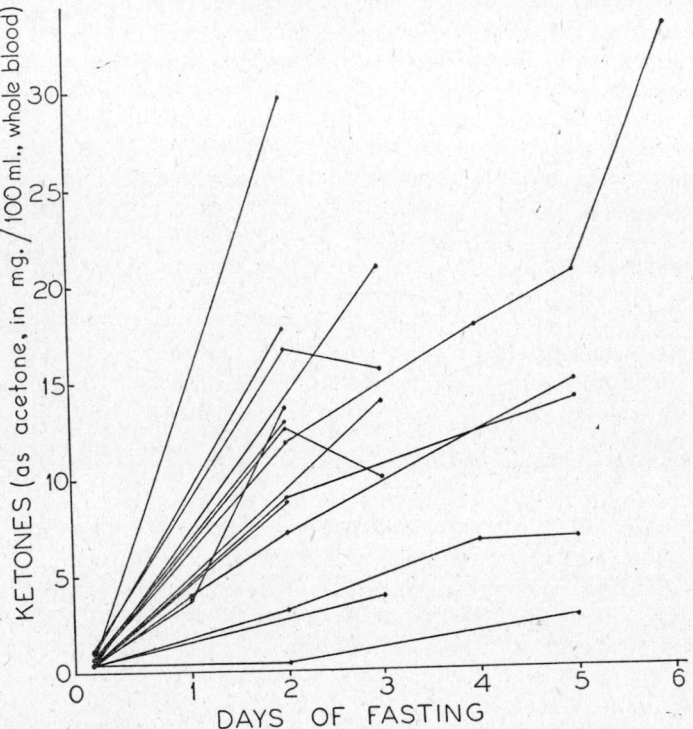

Fig. 482.—Blood ketone changes in human subjects during starvation. (From Kartin, Man, Winkler and Peters, *J. Clin. Invest.*, 1944, *23*:824–835.)

in uncontrolled pancreatic diabetes with its severe ketosis only about 30 per cent of the total amount of fat catabolized is first converted to ketones in the liver and subsequently oxidized in other organs of the body. Although more is known about ketogenesis, therefore, than about other pathways of utilization, the still undiscovered reactions appear to be quantitatively more important than those reactions heretofore described.

Role of the liver in lipid metabolism. By virtue of its ability to provide the rest of the body with the easily oxidizable ketones, the liver plays a dominating role in lipid utilization as well as in carbohydrate and protein metabolism. Through the use of isotopic elements some of the reactions carried on by hepatic cells can be identified in a general way and the rates at which they go on can be measured. Even more attention has been given, however, to a more generalized phenomenon, namely, the fat content of the liver. Pathologists, physicians and surgeons have long known that certain disease entities are characterized by the accumulation of fat in liver cells. This accumulation has sometimes been regarded as an evidence of "degeneration" within the cells, sometimes as the result of what is called "fatty infiltration," but study of patients with these diseases has failed to reveal the cause of the hepatic lipoidosis. Experimental study has been more profitable, and it is now evident that this condition is not a disease in itself but is, rather, a sign of any of several different types of disturbance. Fatty liver is to lipid metabolism what hyperglycemia is to carbohydrate metabolism—a rather commonly encountered phenomenon which is abnormal only when it reaches levels higher than the normal range. Most of the experimental work has been done on rats or depancreatized dogs (Table 53). In the former, a diet relatively high in cholesterol leads to the deposition of cholesterol esters in the liver; diets high in

Table 53.—*Comparison of the Effects of Lipotropic Factors*

REGIMEN USED FOR PRODUCTION OF FATTY LIVERS	CHOLINE	LIPOCAIC	INOSITOL
Depancreatized dogs	++*	++*	− ?
Rats:			
High fat diet, thiamine	++*	0	−
High fat diet, all B vitamins	++*	−	−
High fat diet, cholesterol	+*	0	+
Fat-free diet, thiamine	++*	−	0
Fat-free diet, thiamine and riboflavin	++*	−	−
Fat-free diet, thiamine, riboflavin, pyridoxine and			
pantothenic acid	+*	−	+*
Fat-free diet, above 4 vitamins and biotin	0	++	++
Fat-free diet, B vitamins and cholesterol	+	+	+

Note: ++ Strong lipotropic action.
    + Moderate lipotropic action.
    0 No lipotropic action.
    − Lack of data.
*Verified in two or more laboratories. (From McHenry and Patterson, *Phys. Rev.*, 1944, *24:*160.)

neutral fat or low in choline bring about a deposition of glycerol esters of the fatty acids, as does starvation of the animal; and certain members of the vitamin B complex—especially thiamine—and biotin promote the accumulation of fat in the liver when they are added to the diet of the rat. Depancreatized dogs whose diabetes is controlled with insulin also exhibit remarkably fatty livers. Since the concentration of fats within the organ depends upon the rate at which fat enters and the rate at which it leaves the hepatic cells, an alteration in either of these factors may evoke fatty infiltration. Thus, on a high-fat diet or during starvation where the animal is catabolizing large quantities of fatty acids, the rate of their transport into the liver cells is probably increased, and the lipoidosis is a manifestation of the increased turnover of liver lipids under these conditions. In pancreatectomized dogs and in rats fed biotin, on the other hand, the fats are thought to accumulate because the hepatic cells are unable to dispose of an amount of fat which they usually handle without difficulty. This deficiency may be the result of an inability to synthesize phospholipids, since the accumulation of fat can be prevented by adding to the diet compounds known to be components of phospholipid molecules.

Substances which prevent hepatic lipoidosis are said to have a "lipotropic" action. Three types of lipotropic factors have now been distinguished, of which the most generally effective is choline, one of the constituents of the lecithins and sphingomyelins. Inositol, also present in phospholipids, is particularly effective against biotin fatty livers. And finally, "lipocaic," a substance of as yet unknown chemical composition which can be extracted from the pancreas, prevents the development of fatty infiltration in depan-creatized dogs (Table 53). In spite of the relatively extensive experimental study of these various factors, however, the relationships between the experimentally produced and the clinically observed conditions are not at all obvious.

Conversion of Carbohydrate to Fat. That body fat may originate from carbohydrate was first demonstrated by feeding experiments. Thus, Rubner fed a dog (5.85 kg.) for two days on a diet of sugar, starch and fat with a total carbon content equal to 176.6 gm. During this period the animal excreted 87.1 gm. of carbon. There were retained in the body, therefore, 89.5 gm. of carbon. The fat fed, 4.7 gm., contained (4.7 × 0.77) 3.6 gm. of carbon. The total nitrogen excreted during this period was 2.55 gm., which indicated a metabolism, therefore, of 16 gm. (2.55 × 6.25) of body protein. Making the improbable assumption that all of the carbon of this protein was retained in the body, this would account for 8.32 gm. of carbon (16 × 0.52); so that 3.6 plus 8.32 or 12 gm. of carbon might have originated from sources other than the carbohydrate of the food, leaving, therefore, 89.5 minus 12 or 77.5 gm. of carbon, which could have arisen only from the carbohydrate. This quantity of carbon could have been retained only as glycogen or fat. Allowing for the greatest possible storage of glycogen, 78 gm. or 34.6 gm. of carbon, there would still remain 42.9 gm. of carbon, which could have been retained only as fat. Numerous other fattening experiments of different kinds have been made in which it has been shown that the fat laid on by the animal could not be accounted for by the fat of the food, nor by assuming that it originated from protein.

The chemistry of the change from carbohydrate to fat is not understood and the reactions have not been brought about in the absence of living cells; but it is evident that in the long run an important series of reductions must be accomplished. The oxygen content of fatty acids is only about 11 per cent, while oxygen constitutes about 53 per cent of the glucose molecule. This difference is attributable to the fact that fatty acids are relatively less oxidized than glucose; or, conversely, that compared with the hydrogen and carbon atoms of fatty acids, the hydrogen and carbon of glucose are partially oxidized. To transfer carbon and hydrogen from the glucose to the fatty acid level of less nearly complete oxidation requires the addition of energy to the system—an amount of energy equal to the difference between the potential chemical energies of the two types of compounds, plus the energy lost as heat in the reaction as a whole. The transformation is catabolic, therefore, since it is accompanied by an expenditure of energy—an expenditure which may contribute to the "specific dynamic action" of carbohydrate food. Under appropriate conditions, the conversion of any significant amount of glucose to fat can be detected by its effect upon the overall respiratory quotient of the animal (Chap. 50). The quantity of CO_2 produced in the conversion is greater than the O_2 uptake, and the elimination of the extra carbon dioxide by the lungs naturally alters the respiratory $\dfrac{CO_2}{O_2}$ ratio. Since the numerator is thereby increased, the R.Q. rises proportionately. This change can be observed in isolated tissues such as liver slices as well as in the intact animal. Under conditions where large quantities of fat are being synthesized from carbohydrate, the overall R.Q. may rise well above unity (at least as high as 1.22).

REFERENCES

1. BANTING, F. G. and BEST, C. H. The internal secretion of the pancreas. *J. lab. clin. Med.*, 1922, *7*:251–266.

2. BANTING, F. G. and BEST, C. H. Pancreatic extracts. *J. lab. clin. Med.*, 1922, *7*:464–472.

3. BERGMANN, M. and FRUTON, J. S. The significance of coupled reactions for the enzymatic hydrolysis and synthesis of proteins. *Ann. N. Y. Acad. Sci.*, 1944, *45*:409–423.

4. BLOOR, W. R. *Biochemistry of the fatty acids.* (American Chemical Society monograph series.) New York, Reinhold Publishing Corp., 1943. 387 pp.

5. BOLLMAN, J. L., MANN, F. C. and MAGATH, T. B. Studies on the physiology of the liver. VIII. Effect of total removal of the liver on the formation of urea. *Amer. J. Physiol.*, 1924, *69*:371–392.

6. CORI, C. F. Phosphorylation of glycogen and glucose. *Biol. Symposia*, 1941, *5*:131–140.

7. DIXON, M. *Manometric methods as applied to the measurement of cell respiration and other processes*, 2nd ed. Cambridge, University Press, 1943. 155 pp.

8. DRURY, D. R. The significance of the D:N ratio and its bearing on the mechanism of diabetes mellitus. *J. clin. Invest.*, 1942, *21*:153–159.

9. ELMAN, R. Maintenance of nitrogen balance by the intravenous administration of plasma proteins and protein hydrolysates. *Physiol. Rev.*, 1944, *24*:372–389.

10. FISCHER, E. *Untersuchungen über Aminosäuren, Polypeptide und Proteine.* Berlin, J. Springer, 1906.

11. GREEN, D. E. *Mechanisms of biological oxidations.* Cambridge, University Press, 1940. 181 pp.

12. HARTMAN, C. G., FIROR, W. M. and GEILING, E. M. K. The anterior lobe and menstruation. *Amer. J. Physiol.*, 1930, *95*:662–669.

13. HURTLEY, W. H. The four carbon atom acids of diabetic urine. *Quart. J. Med.*, 1916, *9*:301–408.

14. KARTIN, B. L., MAN, E. B., WINKLER, A. W. and PETERS, J. P. Blood ketones and serum lipids in starvation and water deprivation. *J. clin. Invest.*, 1944, *23*:824–835.

15. KNOOP, F. Der Abbau aromatischer Fettsäuren im Tierkörper. *Beitr. chem. Physiol. Path.*, 1905, *6*:150–162.

16. KREBS, H. A. and HENSELEIT, K. Untersuchungen über die Harnstoffbildung im Tierkörper. *Hoppe-Seyl. Z.*, 1932, *210*:33–66.

17. LEVINSON, S. A. and MACFATE, R. P. *Clinical laboratory diagnosis.* Philadelphia, Lea and Febiger, 1943. 980 pp.

18. VON LIEBIG, J. *Die organische Chemie in ihrer Anwendung auf Physiologie und Pathologie.* Braunschweig, F. Vieweg und Sohn, 1842.

19. LONG, C. N. H. Carbohydrate metabolism. Chap. 2 in: DUNCAN, G. G. *Diseases of metabolism.* Philadelphia, W. B. Saunders Co., 1942.

20. LUSK, G. *The elements of the science of nutrition*, 4th ed. Philadelphia, W. B. Saunders Co., 1928. 844 pp.

21. MACKAY, E. M. The significance of ketosis. *J. clin. Endocrinol.*, 1943, *3*:101–110.

22. MADDEN, S. C. and WHIPPLE, G. H. Plasma proteins: their source, production and utilization. *Physiol. Rev.*, 1940, *20*:194–217.

23. MANN, F. C. The effects of complete and of partial removal of the liver. *Medicine, Baltimore*, 1927, *6*:419–511.

24. MCHENRY, E. W. and PATTERSON, J. M. Lipotropic factors. *Physiol. Rev.*, 1944, *24*:128–167.

25. OLMSTED, J. M. D. *Claude Bernard, physiologist.* New York, Harper and Bros., 1938. xvi, 272 pp.

26. PETERS, J. P. and MAN, E. B. The interrelations of serum lipids in normal persons. *J. clin. Invest.*, 1943, *22*:707–714.

27. SCHOENHEIMER, R. *The dynamic state of body constituents.* Cambridge, Harvard University Press, 1942. 78 pp.

28. STADIE, W. C. Fat metabolism in diabetes mellitus. *J. clin. Invest.*, 1940, *19*:843–861.

29. VAN SLYKE, D. D. The present significance of the amino acids in physiology and pathology. *Arch. intern. Med.*, 1917, *19*:56–78.

30. VAN SLYKE, D. D. Physiology of the amino acids. *Science*, 1942, *95*:259–263.

31. WEINHOUSE, S., MEDES, G. and FLOYD, N. F. Fatty acid metabolism. The mechanism of ketone body synthesis from fatty acids, with isotopic carbon as tracer. *J. biol. Chem.*, 1944, *155*:143–151.

32. WHITE, A. Protein metabolism. Chap. 3 in: DUNCAN, G. G. *Diseases of metabolism.* Philadelphia, W. B. Saunders Co., 1942.

33. WHITE, A. Lipid metabolism. Chap. 4 in: DUNCAN, G. G. *Diseases of metabolism.* Philadelphia, W. B. Saunders Co., 1942.

CHAPTER 52

NUTRITION*

In the two preceding chapters, the categories and classifications into which the reactions of energy exchange naturally fall have been outlined; there remain for discussion in this and in the following chapter the limiting factors and the mechanisms of control to which the individual's metabolism is subjected. One of the more important types of limitation is suggested by the word "nutrition," which is the science of the relationships between food intake and metabolism. Its study deals with dietary requirements, with the effects to be produced by altering the composition of the diet, or, more specifically, with the fate of each component of the food and with the amount of each component needed for optimal growth, development and performance. Generally speaking, the animal relies upon its food for two types of material: (i) compounds which provide energy, and (ii) compounds which in themselves are not sources of energy but which participate in the reactions where energy exchanges occur. An *adequate* diet includes sufficient amounts of both types of compounds, while a *deficient* diet leads to characteristic abnormalities in the appearance or behavior of the subject—changes which can be prevented or cured by adding to the diet as a *supplement* the substance or substances in which it is deficient.

FOOD AS A SOURCE OF ENERGY

Caloric Requirements. As a source of energy the first and perhaps the most important qualification of an adequate diet is quantity, which in nutrition is measured in Calories (kcal.). Whether a diet is ample depends upon the relationship between its potential chemical energy and the total metabolism of the individual. If intake exceeds expenditure, food is converted into depot fat for storage, while if the food intake is smaller than the energy output, a loss of body weight will occur as the reserves are used up. Under conditions of equilibrium the two are approximately equal so that over a period of weeks or months the size of storage depots changes very little. Total energy expenditure includes the number of calories of heat lost during the subject's usual sleeping period, plus the fasting basal heat production while he is awake. It further includes the heat expended in assimilating food, the heat produced during muscular exercise and the thermal equivalent of the physical work he accomplishes (Table 54). If growth is occurring, extra food must be provided for storage of protein, and since growth is accompanied by an elevated basal heat production, this also must be taken into account. Heat production likewise varies with the environmental temperature, especially when a comparison is made in subjects well acclimatized to different temperatures; allowance may have to be made, therefore, for extra heat lost in the course of temperature regulation. If the individual is a pregnant or lactating woman, she will require extra dietary calories to compensate for these avenues of expenditure.

---

* *Handbook of nutrition* (2), recently published by the American Medical Association, contains a comprehensive series of articles by outstanding American investigators in this field.

And finally, in the light of studies which have shown that anxiety or apprehension will elevate the total heat production, the food requirement will be increased in proportion to the degree that the subject, although neither working nor assimilating food, habitually fails to achieve the relaxed, comfortable state which is, by definition, "basal."

Human caloric needs, however, have not been measured with enough precision to require the consideration of all these factors in every case. This is partly because data upon which to base nutritional opinions are inadequate, but primarily because metabolic experiments usually give somewhat variable results. Neither the estimation of the caloric value of a diet nor the measurement of total energy expenditure can be made with any great accuracy. For this reason, diets recommended for adults usually take into account only the sex and occupation of the individual (Table 54), pregnancy and lactation in women, and in the case of children, sex and age. Table 55 summarizes the daily food allowances recommended by the Food and Nutrition Board of the National Research Council for each sex and for children of every age group.

Table 54.—*Total Energy Requirement Every Twenty-four Hours, Including Eight Hours of Labor, as Estimated by Becker and Hämäläinen*

MEN	CALORIES
Tailors	2600–2800
Bookbinders	3000
Shoemakers	3100
Metal workers	3400–3500
Painters	3500–3600
Cabinet makers	3500–3600
Stone masons	4700–5200
Wood sawers	5500–6000
WOMEN	
Seamstresses (with hand needle)	2000
Seamstresses (with machine)	2100–2300
Bookbinders	2100–2300
Household servants	2500–3200
Washerwomen	2900–3700

(From DuBois and Chambers in *Handbook of nutrition*, Chicago, American Medical Association, 1943.)

These allowances are liberal enough to take care of normal variations in energy exchange. There remains the problem of converting these allowances in Calories into more familiar quantities of food. One gram of carbohydrate yields about 4.1 kcal., 1 gm. of fat provides 9.3 kcal., and protein yields about 4.1 kcal. per gm.; but the use of these values is complicated by three difficulties, namely: (i) many foodstuffs are not pure carbohydrate, fat nor protein; (ii) in most foods the nutriment is diluted with a variable amount of water which may be nine-tenths or more of the weight of the food; and (iii) most kitchens do not have facilities for weighing food, nor are most cooks eager to undertake such weighing even if balances were available. To overcome these difficulties, scientists interested in nutrition have analyzed portions of food ready for serving and have published tables which may be used to estimate the calorific value of almost any meal (Tables 56 and 57). Students of dietetics and of home economics have brought this procedure to a high level of usefulness in planning diets for normal persons, but the procedure is even more important in clinical practice where the treatment of both obesity and leanness is based upon the physician's ability to estimate the patient's total energy requirements and the calorific value of his foodstuffs.

Table 55.—Recommended Dietary Allowances Revised, 1945*

(REPRINT AND CIRCULAR SERIES, NUMBER 122, AUGUST, 1945, NATIONAL RESEARCH COUNCIL, 2101 CONSTITUTION AVENUE, WASHINGTON 25, D. C.)

	CALORIES	PROTEIN, GRAMS	CALCIUM GRAMS	IRON MG.	VITAMIN A† I.U.	THIAMINE MG.‡	RIBO-FLAVIN MG.‡	NIACIN (NICO-TINIC ACID) MG.‡	ASCORBIC ACID MG.	VITAMIN D I.U.
Man (156 lb., 70 kg.)										
Sedentary	2500	70	0.8	12§	5000	1.2	1.6	12	75	=
Moderately active	3000	70	0.8	12§	5000	1.5	2.0	15	75	=
Very active	4500	70	0.8	12§	5000	2.0	2.6	20	75	=
Woman (125 lb., 56 kg.)										
Sedentary	2100	60	0.8	12	5000	1.1	1.5	11	70	=
Moderately active	2500	60	0.8	12	5000	1.2	1.6	12	70	=
Very active	3000	60	0.8	12	5000	1.5	2.0	15	70	=
Pregnancy (latter half)	2500¶	85	1.5	15	6000	1.8	2.5	18	100	400 to 800
Lactation	3000	100	2.0	15	8000	2.0	3.0	20	150	400 to 800
Children up to 12 yrs.**:										
Under 1 yr.††	100/2.2 lb. (1 kg.)	3.5/2.2 lb. (1 kg.)		6	1500	0.4	0.6	4	30	400 to 800
1– 3 yrs. (29 lb., 13 kg.)	1200	40	1.0	7	2000	0.6	0.9	6	35	400
4– 6 yrs. (43 lb., 19 kg.)	1600	50	1.0	8	2500	0.8	1.2	8	50	400
7– 9 yrs. (56 lb., 25 kg.)	2000	60	1.0	10	3500	1.0	1.5	10	60	400
10–12 yrs. (76 lb., 34 kg.)	2500	70	1.2	12	4500	1.2	1.8	12	75	400
Children over 12 yrs.**:										
Girls, 13–15 yrs. (110 lb., 49 kg.)	2600	80	1.3	15	5000	1.3	2.0	13	80	400
16–20 yrs. (121 lb., 54 kg.)	2400	75	1.0	15	5000	1.2	1.8	12	80	400
Boys, 13–15 yrs. (105 lb., 47 kg.)	3200	85	1.4	15	5000	1.5	2.0	15	90	400
16–20 yrs. (143 lb., 64 kg.)	3800	100	1.4	15	6000	1.8	2.5	18	100	400

* Tentative goal toward which to aim in planning practical dietaries; can be met by a good diet with a variety of natural foods. Such a diet will also provide other minerals and vitamins, the requirements for which are less well known. This revision at press, August 1945, to be published as National Research Council Reprint and Circular Series No. 122 "Recommended Dietary Allowances, Revised, 1945."

† The allowance depends on the relative amounts of vitamin A and carotene. The allowances of the table are based on the premise that approximately two thirds of the vitamin A value of the average diet in this country is contributed by carotene and that carotene has half or less than half the value of vitamin A.

‡ For adults (except pregnant and lactating women) on diets supplying 2,000 calories or less, such as reducing diets, the allowances of thiamine, riboflavin, and niacin may be 1 mg., 1.5 mg. and 10 mg. respectively. The fact that figures are given for different calorie levels for thiamine, riboflavin, and niacin, does not imply that we can estimate the requirement of these factors within 500 calories, but they are added merely for simplicity of calculation. Other members of the B complex also are required, though no values can be given. Foods supplying adequate thiamine, riboflavin, and niacin will tend to supply sufficient of the remaining B vitamins.

§ There is evidence that the male adult needs little or no iron. The requirement will be provided if the diet is satisfactory in other respects.

‖ For persons who have no opportunity for exposure to clear sunshine and for elderly persons, the ingestion of small amounts of vitamin D may be desirable. Other adults probably have little need for vitamin D.

¶ During the latter part of pregnancy the allowance should increase approximately 20 per cent over the preceding level. The value of 2500 calories represents the allowance for pregnant, sedentary women.

** Allowances for children are based on the needs for the middle year in each group (as 2, 5, 8, etc.) and are for moderate activity and for average weight at the middle year of the age group.

†† Needs of infants increase from month to month with size and activity. The amounts given are for approximately 6 to 8 months. The dietary requirements for some of the nutrients such as protein and calcium are less if derived largely from human milk.

Table 56.—Gross Planning of Diets

TABULATION OF THE AVERAGE SERVING OF SOME FOODS

CEREAL—100 CAL.

Cornflakes, 1¼ cup
Cream of Wheat, ⅔ cup
Grapenuts, 3 tbs.
Muffets or shredded wheat, 1
Oatmeal, ¾ cup cooked
Puffed wheat or rice, 1 cup

FRUITS—100 CAL.

Apples, 1 large
Apricots (dried), 8 halves
Banana, 1 small
Canned cherries, ⅔ cup
Grapefruit, ½, 1 cup juice
Grapes, 1 med. bunch
Orange, 1 large, 1 cup juice
Pear, 3 halves
Peaches, 3 halves
Pineapple, 1 slice
Prunes, 3–4
Watermelon, large serving

BREADS, ETC.—100 CAL.

White or brown, 1 thick slice
Parker house roll, 1
Saltines, 6
Oyster crackers, 36
Melba toast, 2 slices
Zwieback, 3 slices

POTATOES (OR SUBSTITUTE)—100 CAL.

White potato, 1 med.
Potato chips, ⅔ cup
Sweet potato, ½ med.
Macaroni, 1 cup cooked
Noodles, ¾ cup cooked

VEGETABLES—100 CAL.

Baked beans, ⅓ cup
Lima beans, ½ cup
Kidney beans, ½ cup
Peas, ¾ cup
Corn, ⅓ cup

DESSERTS—100 CAL.

Ginger snaps, vanilla wafers, choc. wafers, 5
Macaroons, 2 or 3
Fruits (see above)
Sugar cookies, 1

DESSERTS—200 CAL.

Pie, small piece
Puddings, average serving
Fried cakes, 1
Cake, average piece
Ice cream, average serving

VEGETABLES—25 CAL.

Asparagus, 6 stalks
Cabbage, ⅔ cup cooked
Beets, 1

Cauliflower, large serving
Greens, ½ cup
Mushrooms, 6
Sauerkraut, ½ cup
Spinach, ½ cup
Tomato fresh, 1 med.
Tomato canned, ½ cup
Tomato juice, ½ cup
Turnips, ½ cup

MEATS—150 CAL.

Porterhouse, sirloin, rump, average serving
Pork loin, 1 med. chop
Veal cutlet, large serving
Ham, small serving
Leg of lamb, small serving
Broiler, large serving
Fowl, small serving

MEATS (OR SUBSTITUTE)—100 CAL.

Liver, average serving
Sausage, Frankfort, 1
Cottage cheese, 5–6 tbs.
Cheese, 1¼ in. cube
Oysters, ⅔ cup
Scallops, ¼ cup
Bacon, 2–3 slices
Sausage, pork, 1 small
Fish, average serving (except salmon, mackerel whitefish, roe, small serving)
Egg, 1 to 1⅓

BEVERAGES—100 CAL.

Milk, ⅔ cup
Skim milk, 1⅓ cup
Buttermilk, 1⅓ cup
Carbonated drinks, 1¼ cup
Fruit juice, 1 cup

MISCELLANEOUS—50 CAL.

Butter, ½ tbs.—1 pat
Sugar, 2½ tsp.
Cream (coffee), 2 tbs.

MISCELLANEOUS—100 CAL.

Mayonnaise, 1 tbs.
Jelly, 1½ tbs.
Cream (whipping), 2 tbs.

*CANDIES—100 CAL.

Caramels, 1
Nougats, 1½
Chocolate peppermints, 1½
Gum drops, 3
Marshmallows, 4
Fudge, 1 in. cube
Milk chocolate, ⅓ of 5¢ bar.

* These prepared foods are not included in the table; the measures are given merely as suggestions of the approximate values.

Household measures are given as approximate amounts and when accurate diets are to be calculated, they serve only as a guide.

(From Hawley and Maurer-Mast, *The fundamentals of nutrition.* Springfield, Ill., Charles C Thomas, 1940.)

Distribution of Calories. *Carbohydrate and fat used almost interchangeably.* Although a given number of calories may be supplied by any one or by many different combinations of the three basic foodstuffs (carbohydrate, protein and fat), certain combinations of these three are more desirable than others because the total calorific value is only one of the qualifications of an adequate diet. In general, fat and carbohydrate seem to be almost interchangeable since both can furnish either energy or heat, and neither can make growth possible unless protein or amino acid nitrogen is also available. Since fat and carbohydrate are composed of the same elements, the ability of the body to use either one is not surprising. But there is at least one way in which the body discriminates between the two, inasmuch as certain cells—those of the central nervous system, for example—can evidently burn only carbohydrate.

Table 57.—General Outline for Menu Planning.

BREAKFAST		LUNCH	
Choice of fruits	100	Soup with crackers	150
Choice of cereals	100	Salad	200
Milk for cereals ($\frac{1}{3}$ c.)	50	Bread and butter	150
Bread, 1 slice	50	Glass milk	150
Butter, 1 pat	50	Dessert	200
Coffee			—
Cream, 2 tbs.	50		850
Sugar, 5 tsp.	100		
Egg (if desired)	75		
	—		
	575		

DINNER	
Small glass tomato juice	25
Choice of meats	300
Potato, with seasoning	200
Choice of vegetables	50
Leafy salad, salad dressing	200
Bread and butter	150
Dessert	200–300
	————
	1225
1 glass of milk before retiring	150

Such a diet would yield approximately 2800 Calories, which is sufficient for the average business man. (70 kilo man × 40 kcal./kilo)

The foods in Table 56 may be so grouped because of their similarity in percentage composition.

(From Hawley and Maurer-Mast, *The fundamentals of nutrition.* Springfield, Ill., Charles C Thomas, 1940.)

When none of this foodstuff is present in the diet, the body draws upon its own stores and eventually begins to carry on a significant gluconeogenesis or conversion of protein to carbohydrate. This conversion can be detected chemically because the total nitrogen excretion rises as soon as any significant amount of gluconeogenesis is undertaken, since the nitrogen of the protein is excreted in the urine. Carbohydrate and fat are not completely interchangeable, therefore, even though a normal animal or human subject may do very well on a carbohydrate-free diet if the diet also contains adequate amounts of the glycogenic amino acids (Chap. 51).

Irreplaceability of amino nitrogen. The inability of carbohydrate and fat to replace protein in the growth process has been noted above; only protein contains nitrogen in a form available for protoplasmic construction. The human body, like those of all other mammals, is unable to utilize for protein synthesis the gaseous nitrogen dissolved in body fluids at the partial pressure of atmospheric nitrogen, and consequently, when growth is to occur, the diet must contain an appropriate amount of protein or protein derivatives. But even when growth is not taking place (in an adult whose tissues have come as close to chemical equilibrium as they will during life), a certain small amount of protein nitrogen must be supplied. Even though the body uses nitrogen with great economy especially when the dietary supply is limited, a small, definite amount is lost in the urine daily; to replace this "wear and tear" loss of nitrogen, an adult male needs daily about 0.3 gm. of protein per kg. of body weight. The total amount of protein needed, then, varies with the nutritional state of the individual, and more protein is required during growth or when the carbohydrate content of the diet is low. Since it is impossible precisely to measure metabolic requirements, the dietary supply should be liberal enough to allow for normal variations in the rate of protein utilization and for emergency situations. This is sometimes called "the factor of safety," an allowance which is made to compensate for possible errors in calculation in any given case. The Food and Nutrition Board of the National Research Council (Table 55) recommends 1 gm. of protein per kg. of body weight per day for adult male subjects, an amount large enough to replace the "wear and tear" nitrogen loss and to prevent protein deficiency if the individual's requirements should be above the normal average. Babies and children should receive relatively larger quantities, ranging from 4 gm. per kg. per day at the age of 1 to 3 years, down to 2 gm. per kg. per day at the age of 17 to 18 years. It is interesting to notice that no allowance is made in this table for variations with activity; whether or not work increases protein utilization is still undecided. Extra quantities of dietary protein are recommended, however, during pregnancy and lactation.

Since protein can be converted by the body either to carbohydrate or to fat, one is led to the conclusion that protein by itself may be the only foodstuff necessary for life. The conclusion is justified insofar as two requirements are concerned: (i) protein may furnish all of the needed energy, and (ii) it also provides the amino nitrogen necessary for growth. But the body has requirements other than these two, and protein will not meet all of them (see later). There is, moreover, no general agreement among the authorities regarding the desirability of a high protein intake. In laboratory rats, high protein diets are said to cause kidney lesions and urinary abnormalities which lead to the early death of the animals. Results of human experiments, however, have not been conclusive, although in the relatively small group of men who have voluntarily subsisted on high protein intakes for months at a time, no remarkable ill effects have been reported. Further study is necessary, particularly in the matter of the experimentally produced renal lesions.

Again in order to provide a margin of safety, recommendations are usually made for the distribution of calories in the diet. DuBois and Chambers (7) have suggested that 15 per cent of the calories should be taken as protein, 45 per cent as fat and 40 per cent as carbohydrate. The reasons for the relatively high fat content will become evident in the discussion of essential fatty acids and vitamins, below. In normal individuals, appetite is a reasonably good guide in making this distribution, and even the proper amount of protein will be voluntarily ingested if a free choice of food is made possible.

"Essential" Amino Acids. Although a remarkable diversity of synthetic chemical reactions can be accomplished by living mammalian cells, there are a few important, relatively simple organic compounds which the body either cannot synthesize at all or cannot synthesize rapidly enough to enable the animal to be independent of a dietary supply. In other words, there are needed in the diet not only carbon, hydrogen, oxygen and nitrogen atoms as such, but also certain combinations of these atoms if the animal is to continue in health. It is convenient to classify these necessary compounds under three headings, "essential" amino acids, "essential" fatty acids, and vitamins; of these the last are perhaps the most numerous and diversified both in chemical nature and physiological function. Dividing the caloric intake among the three different types of foodstuffs as described in the paragraph above tends to promote the intake of adequate amounts of the "essential" chemical groupings because a varied diet is more likely to be a complete one.

In the process of protein synthesis, living cells form complex molecules composed of amino acids in certain characteristic combinations and groupings. The combinations that can be effected by any given cell are limited in

Table 58.—Classification of the Amino Acids with Respect to Their Growth Effects

ESSENTIAL	NONESSENTIAL
Lysine	Glycine
Tryptophane	Alanine
Histidine	Serine
Phenylalanine	Norleucine
Leucine	Aspartic acid
Isoleucine	Glutamic acid
Threonine	Hydroxyglutamic acid
Methionine	Proline
Valine	Hydroxyproline
*Arginine	Citrulline
	Tyrosine
	Cystine
	Hydroxylysine

* Arginine can be synthesized by the animal organism, but not at a sufficiently rapid rate to meet the demands of *normal* growth.

number and when a cell is unable to carry out its characteristic type of synthesis, it can accomplish none at all. One of the ways in which protein synthesis can be experimentally inhibited is by withholding from the diet the amino acids which the cell can use. To a certain extent interconversions do occur among the various amino acids within the body (Chap. 51), but Osborne and Mendel (14) and, more recently, Rose (16) have shown that there are ten of the amino acids which must be present in the diet if normal growth is to occur in the rat (Table 58). These are either wholly incapable of synthesis by the animal or cannot be synthesized rapidly enough for the animal's needs; but when adequate amounts of these ten are fed to the animal, synthesis of the other amino acids and protein is possible and normal growth follows. They have been called "essential" amino acids. Human experiments suggest that man's requirements are much like those of the rat, although the evidence is not yet complete. Proteins are sometimes classified as to their *nutritive* or *biological* value according to their "essential" amino acid content and their ability to make possible optimal growth. Milk protein is high in this ability as are other proteins of animal origin; vegetable proteins, on the contrary, generally contain smaller amounts of the essential amino acids. Under ordinary conditions of food distribution and food choice, the question may not be important, yet when food is scarce or when compounds are being selected for parenteral administration, attention should be given to the amino acid composition of the material provided.

"Essential" Fatty Acids. At the present time, knowledge of human requirements for essential fatty acids is still quite unsatisfactory, but the importance of these substances in the nutrition of laboratory rats has been demonstrated by Burr and Burr (see 4) and others. When rats are given a fat-free diet, they develop the classic signs of dietary deficiency—failure of growth, deterioration in the appearance of their fur, drying and scaling of the skin and tail, and reproductive irregularities. This deficiency cannot be cured by adding to the diet the fat soluble vitamins but it can be either prevented or cured by supplying any one of three unsaturated fatty acids—linoleic $[CH_3(CH_2)_4CH = CHCH_2CH = CH(CH_2)_7COOH]$, linolenic $[CH_3CH_2CH = CHCH_2 CH = CHCH_2CH = CH(CH_2)_7COOH]$, or arachidonic $[CH_3(CH_2)_4CH = CHCH_2CH = CHCH_2CH = CHCH_2CH = CH (CH_2)_3COOH]$ acid. The specific use to which these saturated acids are put is not known, but they may become constituents of the phospholipid molecules, the function of which, again, is not clear. Because the essential fatty acids are so widely distributed in plant as well as in animal fats, symptoms of their deficiency are not likely to appear when even small amounts of fat are present in the diet although quantitative requirements remain to be determined.

VITAMINS (1, 18)

Study of the vitamins and their metabolic activity has become at once so intensive and so comprehensive that it threatens to overshadow other phases of nutrition. Within the past 35 years a formidable collection of data has been compiled upon this subject. The pathologist has described grossly and microscopically the tissue and cellular changes produced by specific deficiencies. By repeated fractionation of active preparations the physiological chemist has obtained preparations approaching chemical purity, and with the collaboration of his colleague, the organic chemist, has isolated most of the vitamins in pure form. He has then attempted to learn their position in the intermediary metabolism of the animal. In the meantime, the organic chemist has determined the vitamin's structural formula and has possibly synthesized an active compound that can be given orally, subcutaneously or intravenously. The pharmacologist has studied the effects of administration by these various routes; the absorption, fate in the body and excretion of the vitamin; the extent to which storage takes place; and the question of toxicity from overdosage. With this information he is able to recommend to the clinician the dose to be used in treating deficiency in every possible stage of severity. In clinical laboratories, attempts have been made to diagnose vitamin deficiencies by specific chemical tests upon blood samples or the urine or feces of the patient. The bacteriologist has investigated the vitamin requirements of bacteria as a means of facilitating the biological assay of foodstuffs and vitamin preparations, and has studied the ability of various bacteria to synthesize individual vitamins. And all of this has been accompanied by intensive effort on the part of dietitians and public health authorities to provide everyone with an adequate dietary intake of the vitamin in question.

In the following pages no attempt will be made to give in great detail the results of all of this study. That is not only impossible, but probably inadvisable since excellent monographs are readily available. By way of introduction to the subject there will be discussed, however, those vitamins for which dietary allowances have been recommended by the Food and Nutrition Board of the National Research Council, and also certain other vitamins that are of clinical interest.

Thiamine. Thiamine is now the accepted name for the vitamin originally designated as water-soluble B, later called vitamin B_1, or aneurin because of its physiological action. It occurs naturally as a water-soluble, relatively heat-labile, factor which was first discovered through research carried out in the Dutch East Indies on beriberi, a human deficiency disease. Early experiments were conducted with water extracts of foods such as rice polishings and protein-free milk, known to be rich in the active principle. As the experiments progressed, these rather crude extracts were found to contain not one but several active principles which were successively isolated. (They have been called B_2, B_3, B_4, B_5 and B_6, but they are chemically and physiologically different from thiamine.) In 1936 the structural formula of thiamine was determined and its synthesis was accomplished a year later (5). The molecule is composed of a pyrimidine nucleus and a thiazole nucleus which readily split apart in a neutral or alkaline solution, especially when heat is applied. In acid solutions thiamine is quite stable. The name "thiamine" was chosen to suggest the structural formula of the molecule.*

The role of thiamine in intermediary metabolism is not definitely established, but there is abundant evidence that it somehow participates in carbohydrate metabolism. In the metabolic economy of yeast cells, a pyrophosphoric acid ester of thiamine acts as a co-enzyme with carboxylase to make possible the following reaction:

$$CH_3COCOOH \xrightarrow[\text{thiamine pyrophosphate}]{\text{carboxylase and}} CH_3CHO + CO_2$$

This is an *anaerobic* reaction in which pyruvic acid is oxidized to acetaldehyde and carbon dioxide. When the diet is deficient in thiamine, pyruvic acid accumulates in the body fluids, evidently because the tissues are unable to dispose of it; administration of thiamine is said to return the blood pyruvic acid level, for example, to a normal value either by effecting pyruvic acid oxidation or possibly by way of some other reaction as yet unknown. This theory offers a reasonable explanation for two clinical phenomena. (i) Thiamine requirements are known to be higher on a high carbohydrate than on an isocaloric, low carbohydrate diet. (ii) The central nervous system which depends mainly on carbohydrate as a source of energy is usually the first to suffer when the thiamine intake is low.

Symptoms of deficiency. Human subjects with thiamine deficiency present symptoms and signs usually referable either to the nervous system or to the cardiovascular system or to both. In the first of these, "dry beriberi," there occurs a neuritis which usually involves many different peripheral nerves, producing anatomical changes easily seen upon microscopical examination of the affected tissue. Histological changes in the central nervous system have also been described, especially in the posterior columns of the spinal cord. All of these lesions are at first reversible by thiamine administration; if untreated, however, they become permanent, irreparable damage. The patient notices weakness, a sense of heaviness, tenderness to pressure, and finally a loss of sensation in the regions of distribution of the affected nerves. Cardiovascular involvement produces what is called "wet beriberi" because it is characterized by accumulations of fluid in the interstitial spaces (edema). In the heart, the fluid increases the size of the organ, but this change, for some unknown reason, affects primarily the right side. Swelling of the feet and ankles is typical of the disease, and cardiovascular deficiency may develop rapidly, producing difficult respiration (dyspnea) and other signs of heart failure which may be terminated by the sudden death of the patient.

Exact description of the results of thiamine deficiency is complicated by the fact that a loss of appetite occurs early in the disease, and many of the observed changes are in all probability the effect of a reduced food intake rather than a sign of specific deficiency. Anorexia is usually ascribed to an inability of the gastro-intestinal tract to function normally in the absence of thiamine, but whether or not this is caused by involvement of the nerves supplying the gut is not clear.

Human requirements. In spite of the large amount of data regarding thiamine requirements in man, there is no general agreement about the minimal adequate intake. The requirement evidently varies with the total energy exchange of the subject, especially with the fraction of the caloric output contributed by the catabolism of carbohydrate. As little as 0.24 mg. per 1000 kcal. in the diet may possibly provide protection against thiamine deficiency, but the National Research Council recommends an intake of from 1.2 to 2.0 mg. per day for subjects ingesting from 2500 to 4500 Calories per day, respectively (Table 55).

Dietary sources. Naturally occurring thiamine is supplied by a great variety of foods, although there are few which supply large amounts. Peas and beans, whole grains and nuts, are relatively rich in thiamine, while meats, especially the lean portion, eggs, milk, vegetables and fruits add significant quantities to the average diet. Refined foods like white flour contain little. In preventing thiamine deficiency, diversity of diet is to be encouraged with emphasis upon whole grain flour and cereals, or upon products such as bread which are now generally *enriched* by the addition of synthetic vitamin B_1.

In conclusion, an interesting observation suggests that the body is not entirely dependent upon dietary sources of thiamine since bacteria in the large bowel are able to synthesize this compound. That this synthesis is not always adequate in amount is evident. Nevertheless, reference should be made to Chapter 49 in which the general problem of bacterial action in the intestine is more fully described.

Riboflavin.[*] Unlike thiamine which was studied as a vitamin for several years before it was isolated chemically, riboflavin was identified and isolated in another connection before its importance as a vitamin was known. In 1932 Warburg and Christian (21) described a reaction in which a hexose-monophosphoric acid ester, a glucose derivative, is oxidized through the action of a "yellow enzyme"; upon isolation, this enzyme was found to be composed of a specific protein combined with a phosphoric acid ester of a pigment which was then called "lactoflavin" because it had been previously found to be a constituent of milk. When ribose was found to be a part of this pigment complex, "lactoflavin" was replaced by the name "riboflavin." In the meantime, the heat-stable fraction of the original vitamin B extract had been shown to be composed of several factors, one of which, essential for the growth and maintenance of experimental animals, was present in preparations that had an intense yellow color and a characteristic green fluorescence under ultraviolet light; in this country this was designated as vitamin G, but abroad it was usually spoken of as B_2. Further research proved that the vitamin is identical with the riboflavin portion of the yellow enzyme.

The "yellow enzyme" and other enzymes containing riboflavin appear to be present in all cells of the body where they evidently participate in oxidation-reduction reactions. Inability of the cells to effect these reactions at a normal rate is assumed to be responsible for the appearance of the riboflavin deficiency syndrome, the characteristics of which vary somewhat from one animal to another. In man, lesions of the skin at the angles of the mouth (*cheilosis*) and of the epithelium of the lips and tongue have been described, as have ocular changes including alteration in the structure of the cornea (interstitial keratitis) and the conjunctivae. Nonspecific drying and scaling of the skin have also been observed. All of these lesions are said to respond to riboflavin therapy.

Sources and requirements. Riboflavin is present in some degree in most natural foods, especially in liver, egg white, leafy vegetables, yeast, fruits and milk. In spite of its wide distribution, many clinicians believe that riboflavin deficiency is a fairly common syndrome appearing in patients whose dietary habits are grossly abnormal or in subjects whose rate of absorption, utilization or excretion of the vitamin may be disturbed. Human requirements are not definitely known, but the National Research Council recommends from 1.6 to 2.6 mg. per day for subjects with a total daily energy exchange of 2500 to 4500 Calories. Recently reported experiments suggest that riboflavin deficiency would be much more common than it is were there not present in the gastro-intestinal tract of man bacteria able to synthesize this vitamin.

[*]

$$CH_2(CHOH)_3CH_2OH$$

Niacin (Nicotinic Acid).* First prepared in 1867 as a derivative of nicotine, the importance of nicotinic acid as a vitamin was established only a few years ago when the original crude extracts of the water-soluble vitamin B principles began to be fractionated and chemically identified. Goldberger and Tanner (10) had already demonstrated that pellagra is a disease caused by dietary deficiency of what was called the pellagra preventative (or P-P) factor. Efforts to identify this factor were unsuccessful, however, until Elvehjem and his associates (8) found that nicotinic acid will cure a canine disease known as "blacktongue," which is the counterpart of human pellagra. Nicotinic acid was then used in treating the human deficiency, with strikingly successful results.

Nicotinic acid is a constituent of two compounds, diphosphopyridine-nucleotide (cozymase or co-enzyme I) and triphosphopyridinenucleotide (phosphocozymase or co-enzyme II), which participate as co-enzymes in reactions associated with carbohydrate metabolism (Chap. 3). Each of these co-enzymes is formed of nicotinic acid amide, adenylic acid, two molecules of ribose, and two or three phosphate radicals, respectively. The "enzymes" with which they act are proteins, each possessing a specific affinity for a particular substrate; and although each of the pyridinenucleotides is thus able to participate in a variety of reactions (because of the variety of "enzymes" with which they may be associated), in all of them the co-enzyme has the function of a hydrogen acceptor—that is, in the reaction it gains two hydrogen atoms. In some reactions this accomplishes the oxidation of the substrate, in other cases, its fermentation. Symptoms of nicotinic acid deficiency are thought to be attributable to the animal's inability to carry on these reactions in the absence of an adequate supply of the vitamin for the synthesis of the co-enzyme molecules.

Symptoms of deficiency. Among the experimental animals, uncomplicated nicotinic acid deficiency can be produced only in the dog, pig and monkey. All of these exhibit signs related to those of pellagra which in man is typically characterized by bilaterally symmetrical lesions of the skin, especially of the extremities; by gastro-intestinal disturbances including nausea, vomiting, diarrhea and a deficient secretion of gastric hydrochloric acid; and by central nervous system changes associated with anxiety, loss of memory, mental confusion, delirium, mania and "dementia." The classic triad of pellagra symptoms is dermatitis, diarrhea and dementia, but any one patient may show only one or two of these three symptoms. A more complete description of the disease as it appears among the population of southeastern United States may be found in the chapter by Spies and Butt (18).

Sources and requirements. Nicotinic acid administration quickly cures outspoken symptoms of pellagra, but it is almost certain that the disease usually seen clinically represents a multiple deficiency. For this reason therapy is undertaken with nicotinic acid plus other components of the vitamin B complex such as thiamine and riboflavin. Diets containing cornmeal or refined

*

$$
\begin{array}{c}
\text{H} \\
\text{C} \\
\text{H—C} \quad \text{C—COOH} \\
\text{H—C} \quad \text{C—H} \\
\text{N}
\end{array}
$$

white flour as the principal sources of calories not infrequently produce symptoms of nicotinic acid deficiency, but it is not yet clear whether this is due solely to their relatively low content of the vitamin or whether with these foods there is for some reason an elevated nicotinic acid requirement. Whole wheat is fairly rich in the vitamin; deficiency can be prevented by substituting whole wheat bread for white bread or by enriching the latter with nicotinic acid. Brewer's yeast is widely used clinically as a source of nicotinic acid as well as of the other components of the vitamin B complex. Liver and lean meats, peanuts and vegetables are valuable dietary sources. The vitamin is relatively stable and is not destroyed by cooking, but, like other water-soluble factors, it may be discarded along with the cooking water from vegetables.

Human requirements are not definitely known because the vague and non-specific character of early signs of deficiency make difficult the determination of adequate dosage. Vitamin tolerance tests have not yielded conclusive data because of technical difficulty in measuring the amount of the various excretory products formed from nicotinic acid. Recommendations are usually made, therefore, by extrapolation from animal experiments on the not unreasonable assumption that the need is proportional to total energy exchange. The 12 to 20 mg. per day specified in Table 55 are believed by some investigators to be an unnecessarily generous allowance.

Pyridoxine—B_6. Pyridoxine is one of the more recently isolated and synthesized components of the vitamin B complex. In experimental animals—the rat, chick, dog and pig—deficiency of this substance produces what is called *acrodynia* (painful extremities) with swelling, ulceration and necrosis of the skin of the paws, nose, tips of the ears and circumoral region. Growth retardation has also been observed and may be evident before the skin lesions develop; in the dog, a microcytic hypochromic anemia occurs. Pyridoxine therapy cures all of these abnormalities.

The physiological action of vitamin B_6 is still unknown and specific deficiency in man has not been clearly demonstrated. Human requirements have not been determined but estimates have been made upon the basis of animal experiments. In spite of the lack of satisfactory information regarding human needs, the compound has been tried clinically for the therapy of a variety of conditions of obscure or unknown etiology. Whether it is effective is highly questionable.

Choline. In the course of early studies on experimental pancreatic diabetes, fatty infiltration of the liver was often encountered in depancreatized animals, but this infiltration was found not to be an evidence of insulin deficiency since it could be prevented by the addition of certain substances to the diet of the animal. Choline was found to be one of the compounds responsible for the effectiveness of the different supplements (13). Choline has been identified as a part of the molecule of the phospholipids, lecithin and sphingomyelin, which also contain fatty acids, and the suggestion has been made that in the absence of choline the liver is unable to synthesize the lecithin and sphingomyelin molecules from fatty acids (Chap. 51). Accumulation of fat in the liver cells therefore follows this inability of the cells to dispose of it in their normal way. Although choline itself can be synthesized in the body, the rate of synthesis is evidently not always adequate, yet the extent to which man is dependent upon dietary supplies is not known. Since the deposition of excessive quantities of fat in the liver is a commonly encountered clinical problem, however, human application of these experimental data may eventually be attained.

Ascorbic Acid. The now accepted name of vitamin C, "ascorbic acid," suggests both the pharmacological action and chemical properties of the vitamin. Two different laboratories almost simultaneously reported their discovery of the antiscorbutic (antiscurvy) action of the compound. In one case (12) the compound was isolated by the successive fractionation of biologically active extracts; in the other laboratory, the compound had been previously isolated as a constituent of the adrenal cortex and other tissues in the course of studies upon oxidation-reduction systems, but its antiscorbutic effect was not discovered until 1932 (19). Chemically, the vitamin is l-ascorbic acid, a 6-carbon lactone with the following structural formula:

$$HO-\underset{\underset{\displaystyle H}{\overset{\displaystyle |}{\underset{|}{C}}}}{\overset{\overset{\displaystyle H}{|}}{C}}-\underset{\underset{\displaystyle H}{\overset{\displaystyle |}{O}}}{\overset{\overset{\displaystyle H}{|}}{C}}-\underset{\underset{\displaystyle H}{\overset{\displaystyle |}{O}}}{\overset{\overset{\displaystyle O}{|}}{C}}=\underset{\underset{\displaystyle H}{\overset{\displaystyle |}{C}}}{\overset{\overset{\displaystyle O}{|}}{C}}-\overset{O}{C}=O$$

The compound is readily oxidized to form a dehydro-ascorbic acid which, in turn, can be easily reduced to the original structure. Chemical study has clearly shown that the hydrogen transfers associated with these oxidation-reduction reactions can be brought about outside the body through the action of various enzyme systems. For this reason the vitamin is assumed to play some important role in the hydrogen transport of cellular oxidation processes, but this assumption has never been verified in animal tissue although there is good evidence for its applicability to plant metabolism.

In human subjects, one of the first evidences of ascorbic acid deficiency is the rather abrupt appearance of hemorrhages in the skin, mucous membranes, subperiosteal regions, serous cavities including the joint spaces, or elsewhere in the body. The bleeding is the result of an increased capillary fragility, and the swellings produced by the hemorrhage may be excruciatingly painful. Another evidence of deficiency is to be found in the abnormal development of tissues embryologically derived from mesenchyme; collagenous connective tissue, bone, teeth, tendons and even skeletal muscles fail to attain their normal structure and therefore fail to develop their characteristic rigidity, density or elasticity, as the case may be. Although the biochemical nature of the abnormality is not known, the deficiency is assumed to concern specifically the formation of various intercellular substances by cells of the connective tissue derivatives. This failure of formation is naturally more common and more obvious in rapidly growing infants and children than in the adult, and infantile scurvy was for a time confused with rickets because both diseases produce skeletal abnormalities.

Requirements and sources. Human ascorbic acid requirements have been studied by a great many different techniques ranging from measurement of the amount necessary to maintain normal capillary fragility to the determination of ascorbic acid tolerance or saturation. Unfortunately, there is no unanimous agreement among the results of all of these tests. The allowances of Table 55 are thought to provide generous amounts, at least twice the amount which some studies show to be needed daily. Since fresh orange juice contains about 0.5 mg. per cc. (15 mg. per ounce), the infant's requirement of

30 mg. can be supplied by two ounces. The appearance of scurvy has long been associated with diets deficient in fresh meats and vegetables, while citrus fruits have traditionally been used for the prevention or cure of the disease. Tomatoes, leafy vegetables, growing seeds such as green peas, and other actively growing plant tissues are all relatively rich in ascorbic acid. Cooking any of these foods in air, however, destroys the potency of the vitamin by complete and irreversible oxidation of the molecule. When such a food is to be used primarily for its vitamin C potency, it should be eaten uncooked or after a type of cooking (such as commercial canning) where there is no exposure to air.

Vitamin A. There is no generally accepted chemical name for vitamin A even though the structural formula of the vitamin is known and its synthesis has been accomplished (9). Chemically the vitamin is a derivative of naturally occurring plant pigments called *carotenoids,* four of which—alpha, beta and gamma carotene and cryptoxanthin—serve as source of vitamin A. Of these, beta carotene is the best source since upon hydrolysis it yields two molecules of the vitamin where the other carotenes yield only one molecule. The mechanism by which animals form the vitamin from beta carotene has not been discovered, but the transformation evidently occurs in the liver. Natural foods may contain either vitamin A or carotene or both. Plants ordinarily supply beta carotene in proportion to their green, yellow or orange color since carotene concentration is, in general, proportional to the total concentration of plant pigments. In foods of animal origin such as eggs and milk, however, color is not a reliable index of the potential vitamin A activity since the pigments may be carotenoids other than the four active compounds named above. Moreover, eggs and milk may contain colorless vitamin A, formed by the animal from its own dietary precursors. One of the more remarkable facts about vitamin A metabolism is the extent to which this substance is stored in the liver; in the mammal, the concentration may be as high as 10 to 20 mg. per gm., and this reserve can be used by the animal when dietary sources are inadequate. In the liver of certain fish—the cod, halibut, percomorph and others—the concentration is many times greater, but the metabolic significance of this reserve is not known. Two types of vitamin A have been discovered in fish livers; the name "vitamin A_1" is given to the type obtained from salt water species while "A_2" designates that present in fresh water fish.

Because the vitamin and the carotenes are fat-soluble and can be esterified with fatty acids, their metabolism is closely related to the handling of fat by the body. In the intestine they are emulsified by bile salts and absorbed from the gut along with fatty acids and other lipids. From the gastro-intestinal tract the carotenes are apparently conveyed to the liver where they are taken up by the phagocytic Kupffer cells; by some as yet unknown process the carotenes are then hydrolyzed to form vitamin A which may be stored in the liver. Deficiency states may follow interference with this sequence at any stage—specifically, when absorption is incomplete or when the liver is unable to perform its normal function.

Evidences of deficiency. Symptoms of vitamin A deficiency, similar in experimental animals and in man, appear to represent two types of abnormality. One of these is a disturbance of function of the receptive mechanism in the retinal rods of the eye. Vitamin A is present in the rod cells as one portion of a compound called "visual purple" (*rhodopsin*) which undergoes a reversible reaction to form visual yellow (*xanthopsin*) when light strikes the cell; as the result of this reaction, nerve impulses are initiated in the retinal neurons. Although the reaction is evidently a reversible one, like other reactions in the body the efficiency of the reversal is less than 100 per cent. Consequently, the retina must be almost continuously supplied with a minute but highly critical amount of the vitamin for replenishment of the visual purple stores of the rods. Vitamin A deficiency brings about an inability to achieve normal adaptation to conditions of low light intensity—"night blindness" or *nyctalopia*—because the process of dark adaptation is achieved through the function of the rod cells. There is evidence, however, that vitamin A may participate also in the formation of visual violet (*iodopsin*), the light-sensitive pigment of the cones (20).

Attempts to measure quantitatively the effectiveness of dark adaptation as an index of vitamin A deficiency were at first enthusiastically undertaken; but more recently the procedure has fallen somewhat into disrepute, not only because of technical difficulties but also because interpretation of already published results is almost impossible since so many different techniques and criteria have been used by different investigators.

The second type of abnormality in vitamin A deficiency concerns the integrity of the epithelial tissues of the body. Changes are commonly noted in the cornea and conjunctiva of the eye and in the skin, but they may be found also in the respiratory system, kidney, ureter and bladder, the uterus, and elsewhere. In the skin of man, the deficiency causes drying, scaling, atrophy of sweat and sebaceous glands, and a papular eruption produced by hyperkeratosis of the hair follicles. Experimental animals have been found to develop lesions of peripheral nerves and the central nervous system, and numerous other symptoms and lesions have also been described but they are too diversified in nature to be considered in greater detail here.

Sources and requirements. Dietary sources of vitamin A or its precursors include the leafy vegetables, green seeds (peas and beans), and green stalks (asparagus, broccoli and celery); carrots and sweet potatoes; tomatoes and peppers; eggs, cream and whole milk. Fish liver oils are widely used as dietary supplements, especially for infants and young children. Recommendations are made in Table 55 in terms of International Units rather than by the weight of the vitamin because naturally occurring preparations are used and they must be individually assayed biologically. The standard test in the United States measures the ability of the unknown preparation to restore growth of vitamin A deficient rats, in comparison with the potency of crystalline beta carotene. One International Unit is the equivalent of 0.0006 mg. (six-tenths microgram) of the crystalline compound. A few drops of some of the richer fish liver oil preparations will supply the 5000 Units per day recommended by the National Research Council, but a normal adult does not need supplementary amounts if his diet is reasonably diversified.

Vitamin D. This name identifies a group of some ten compounds, although only two of the ten have been shown to have any importance in human nutrition. The two are alike in that they represent "ultraviolet light-activated" forms of naturally occurring sterols. *Ergosterol*, a sterol of plant origin, upon activation becomes vitamin D_2 or *calciferol* by an internal rearrangement of molecular structure; and 7-dehydrocholesterol, a constituent of animal lipids, is called vitamin D_3 when it undergoes a similar change. Any wave length of light absorbed by the provitamin or parent sterol will effect the activation; in the course of the reaction there is formed a series of compounds, one of which is the vitamin. If the irradiation is of sufficient intensity and duration, there is ultimately formed a toxic sterol the production of which must be avoided in preparations to be used clinically. Activation of the provitamins occurs naturally through the action of ultraviolet light upon the sterols of the skin and its appendages.

Vitamin D deficiency. Vitamin D avitaminosis in children is called "rickets," a disease which involves the teeth and growing bones; it causes swelling of the ends of the long bones and ribs, a change in the shape and density of the calvarium (*craniotabes*) and other evidence of a failure of calcification of regions where calcium salts are normally deposited during the growth process. Normal calcification fails to occur in the developing bone; irregular growth of cartilage follows, and deformations such as bowed legs may be produced by stresses to which the abnormally pliable bones are subjected. Roentgenological examination (x-ray) is used both clinically and experimentally for the diagnosis of vitamin D deficiency because by this method the presence of faulty calcification can be discovered without operative procedure. Deposition of calcium phosphate in the bones appears to be the result of a reversible chemical reaction which depends for its completeness upon a relatively high concentration and a continual supply of the reactant substances, calcium and phosphate. The skeletal lesions of rickets are the result of an inadequate intestinal absorption of calcium and phosphorus present in the diet, because when bodily stores of vitamin D are low, the calcium and phosphorus of the foodstuffs are not absorbed but are lost in the feces. In the adult, vitamin D deficiency causes *osteomalacia* or a decrease in bone density which appears to be attributable to the fact that the rate of removal of calcium and phosphate overtakes and surpasses the rate of deposition of the salts in the bone.

Because of its similarity to other lipids, vitamin D requires the presence of bile salts for its absorption from the intestine. The vitamin is stored in fairly large quantities in the body, especially in the liver which supplies adequate amounts for the absorption of calcium and phosphorus when the dietary intake of vitamin D is temporarily inadequate.

The rate of deposition of calcium and phosphate in bone is also affected by the hormone of the parathyroid glands. When an excessive amount of the hormone is present in body fluids, calcium is withdrawn from bone, the blood calcium rises to high levels, and large amounts of calcium and phosphate are lost in the urine. Parathyroid deficiency, on the other hand, is characterized by a diminished urinary excretion of calcium and by a low blood calcium level. One rather striking consequence of this hypocalcemia is "parathyroid tetany," consisting of involuntary twitching and spasm of skeletal muscles which arise from an increased excitability of peripheral neuromuscular mechanisms. Although the mode of action of the hormone is not known, two actions appear to be concerned, viz., an effect upon the kidney which determines the extent of tubular reabsorption of calcium and phosphate, and an effect directly upon bone which alters the rate of deposition of mineral salts there.

Sources and requirements. Average American diets contain very little vitamin D, although fresh and canned salmon, tuna, sardines and herring contain significant amounts. Milk and eggs also provide small but appreciable quantities. Experimental evidence has shown that by the action of ultraviolet light on the human skin, the activated sterols can be formed in quantities sufficient to prevent deficiency; but since exposure to sunlight is limited in the northern United States, especially during the winter months, and since growing bones readily suffer from vitamin D deficiency, fish liver oils are now widely used here as supplements for the diet of infants and young children. In Table 55, the National Research Council recommends 400 to 800 International Units per day as a minimal intake for children less than a year in age. This amount is conveniently provided by relatively small amounts of the same fish liver oils which contain vitamin A. Preparations are assayed for vitamin D activity by a biological test that compares with a standard solution of irradiated ergosterol their potency in reversing the development of rickets in vitamin D deficient rats.

Vitamin K. The liver plays an essential role in the utilization of a third fat-soluble vitamin, vitamin K. In the course of experimental studies upon chicks fed synthetic diets, Dam (6) observed the development of a disease characterized by retardation of blood clotting. Since the blood was unable to seal off with clots even minor discontinuities in the vascular system, severe hemorrhage often followed the slightest trauma. It was later found that the abnormality was the result of a prothrombin deficiency in the circulating plasma, a deficiency which could be remedied by adding to the diet foods containing a fat-soluble vitamin which was appropriately termed "Koagulationsvitamin." Attempts to isolate the vitamin have been only partially successful since at least two naturally occurring forms are known, only one of which has been chemically identified and synthesized. This one is known as vitamin K_1, or 2-methyl-3-phytyl-1,4-naphthoquinone.

Study of the biological activity of chemically related substances has shown that a synthetic compound, 2-methyl-1,4-naphthoquinone (*menadione*), is about three times as active as either of the naturally occurring vitamins in preventing hemorrhagic disease in the chick.

Vitamin K is required for the synthesis of prothrombin in other species, including man, as well as in the chick. Like vitamin D, vitamin K requires the presence of bile salts for its proper absorption from the intestine; and like carotene, vitamin K is effective only when the liver is able to utilize the vitamin. The mechanism of action of vitamin K is not known, but evidently it cannot be replaced in the process of prothrombin synthesis. Vitamin K therapy will cure hypoprothrombinemia (low blood prothrombin level) within a few hours if the liver itself is not damaged; and, on the other hand, hypoprothrombinemia may occur even in the presence of adequate amounts of vitamin K if the liver is damaged in some way which hinders prothrombin synthesis.

Deficiency in infants. Vitamin K deficiency apparently does not occur in normal human adults, but when intestinal absorption of the vitamin or hepatic synthesis of prothrombin is disturbed, prolonged bleeding may follow. For this reason menadione is widely used by surgeons and physicians caring for patients with prolonged gastro-intestinal disturbance, with liver damage, or with involvement of the gallbladder and bile duct system with obstruction to the flow of bile from the liver to the intestine. In the normal human infant, moreover, Brinkhous and his collaborators (3) have shown that low levels of circulating prothrombin do occur and that vitamin K administration either to the infant or to the mother before the birth of the baby will effectively raise the blood prothrombin concentration. Why the newborn baby shows this deficiency is unknown, but these observations have made possible the treatment of an often fatal disease called "hemorrhagic disease of the newborn" for which no successful treatment previously existed. The condition can now be entirely prevented.

Distribution of vitamin K in the various foodstuffs is not a problem of nutritional importance, but it may be noted that the vitamin is usually present in proportion to the chlorophyl concentration of the plant. Daily requirements are not known; the question, "How much?" is entirely a clinical problem, which the physician solves by prescribing a milligram or two of one of the synthetic preparations, to be given orally or by injection as the case may require.

INORGANIC COMPONENTS OF THE DIET

From the diet, then, the body obtains (i) a supply of carbon and hydrogen which, upon oxidation, provide energy for work; (ii) carbon, hydrogen and nitrogen (and sulfur, see below) for growth; and (iii) certain "essential" combinations of atoms which the body cannot otherwise synthesize rapidly enough to prevent deficiency states when dietary supplies of these compounds are limited. Finally, the diet also must contain atoms other than carbon, hydrogen and nitrogen if growth and maintenance are to proceed normally. Tissues and body fluids naturally contain large quantities of water, and significant amounts of other inorganic materials including the elements sodium, potassium, calcium and magnesium; chlorine, phosphorus and sulfur; as well as smaller but appreciable quantities of iron, copper, iodine, manganese, cobalt, zinc and nickel. The fact that the total quantity of each of these elements increases as growth occurs (Table 59) suggests that they may become a part of organic molecules. Osborne and Mendel discovered that animals fed synthetic diets failed to grow normally unless adequate amounts of inorganic salts were present in the diet, and they were led to compose a salt mixture which has been widely used in the feeding of laboratory animals (15).

One of these elements, *sulfur*, is a constituent of the amino acids methionine and cystine; the former is one of the "essential" amino acids referred to above. As a constituent of these two amino acids, sulfur becomes an integral part of the protein molecule. Two other elements, *potassium* and *phosphorus*, also occur in relatively large intracellular concentrations which are evidently related in some way to the protein content of the cell. Skeletal muscles, for example, contain 109 gm. of the 150 gm. of potassium in the adult body, as well as 58.5 gm. of the 670 gm. of phosphorus (Table 60). Although the physiological significance of the intracellular concentration of potassium and phosphorus is not entirely clear, in the form of phosphate the phosphorus is

Table 59.—*Mineral Content of the Whole Body at Different Ages**

WHOLE BODY	TOTAL WEIGHT (GM.)	FAT (GM.)	WATER (GM.)	DRY WEIGHT (GM.)	ASH (GM.)	N (GM.)	NA (GM.)	K (GM.)	CA (GM.)	MG (GM.)	CL (GM.)	P (GM.)	S (GM.)
Fetus, 3–4 mo.	126	0.6	116	10	1.5	1.0	1.29	1.0	0.42	0.022	0.34	0.27	0.74
Fetus, 5 mo.	500	5	455	45	8.5	6.0	1.85	1.4	2.9	0.10	1.25	1.8	
Fetus, 6 mo.	880	19	755	125	19.0	12	2.4	2.1	5.3	0.17	1.60	3.25	1.55
Fetus, 7 mo.	1155	32	975	180	30	20	2.8	2.1	6.9	0.23	2.95	4.3	1.7
Premature, 7 mo.	1190	36	970	220	32	20			8.6	0.25	3.05	4.4	
New-born	(KG.) 2.9	(KG.) 0.35	(KG.) 2.08	(KG.) 0.8	(KG.) 0.1	55	4.7	5.1	23.6	0.7	5.0	13.8	6.3
Adult	70.0	12.6	41.4	29.0	3.0	2100	63.0	150.0	1160.0	21.0	85.0	670.0	112.0
Adult/5 months fetus	140	252	90	650	430	420	49	150	400	210	67	410	150
Adult/new-born	23	36	20	36	33	38	13	29	50	30	17	48	18

* Calculated from the literature.
(From Shohl, *Mineral metabolism*, New York, Reinhold Publishing Corp., 1939.)

Table 60.—Weights of the Organs of the New-born and Adult, and Mineral Content of Adult Organs*

ORGAN	NEW-BORN WEIGHT (KG.)	NEW-BORN (%)	ADULT WEIGHT (KG.)	ADULT (%)	FAT (KG.)	H_2O (KG.)	NA (GM.)	K (GM.)	CA (GM.)	MG (GM.)	CL (GM.)	P (GM.)	S (GM.)
Whole body	3.1		66.2										
Muscles	.78	25.1	28.7	43.0	2.1	21.0	19.1	109.0	1.85	6.10	13.5	58.5	60.
Skeleton	.43	13.7	11.6	17.5	1.1	5.1	18.7	6.4	1150.00	11.0	20.	530.	16.
Blood serum	.13	} 6.5	2.7	} 7.0		2.5	9.1	0.5	0.27	0.09	10.	0.4	
Blood cells	.06		1.8		0.03	1.2	?	7.6	?	0.11	5.2	1.8	
Skin	.61	19.7	4.8	7.3	0.7	3.1	6.5	4.4	0.8	0.5	12.2	2.4	18.
Subcutaneous tissue			12.6	19.0	8.2	4.2					16.		
Brain	.38	12.3	1.4	2.2	0.17	1.1	2.1	4.1	0.15	0.2	1.8	4.6	
Liver	.14	4.6	1.8	2.7	0.38	1.1	2.7	3.1	0.17	0.31	2.3	3.2	2.9
Intestines	.07	2.1	1.4	2.2	0.13	1.1	3.0	4.5	0.21	0.12	1.0	1.5	0.5
Lungs	.05	1.8	1.0	1.5	0.02	0.8	2.4	1.5	0.17	0.07	2.6	1.2	
Kidney	.02	0.8	0.3	0.5	0.015	0.2	0.5	0.5	0.07	0.07	0.7	0.4	
Heart	.02	0.8	0.3	0.5	0.025	0.2	0.4	0.3	0.03	0.05	0.4		
Spleen	.01	0.3	0.16	0.2	0.005	0.1			0.02	0.02	0.3	0.6	
Pancreas	.004	0.1	0.1	0.1	0.010	0.1	0.8	0.2	0.02	0.02	0.2	0.3	

* Calculated from the literature.
(From Shohl, Mineral metabolism, New York, Reinhold Publishing Corp., 1939.)

known to play a highly important role in enzymatic reactions involving transfers of electrons and hydrogen ions. In the muscle cells, these reactions make possible the contraction process. Potassium, on the other hand, is stored in the cell during protein synthesis, is released when protein is broken down, and appears to be largely responsible for the maintenance of normal water distribution as discussed below.

Inorganic compounds participate in another growth reaction—the formation of bone. Most of the *calcium* of the adult body is present in the bone as phosphate and carbonate salts which give the skeleton its characteristic rigidity. *Magnesium*, too, is present mainly in the osseous tissue. For normal bone to develop, calcium and *phosphorus* must be present in the diet in approximately the concentration in which they are deposited in bone, a calcium/phosphorus ratio of 2.15. Vitamin D makes possible the effective absorption of the two elements from the gastro-intestinal tract.

A third type of tissue which requires a particular element for normal function is the thyroid gland. *Iodine* is present in the thyroxin molecule, the hormone of this gland, and when dietary iodine deficiency exists for more than a few weeks, the gland begins to undergo a peculiar enlargement which produces a swelling in the neck called *goiter*. Diets of the population of the inland regions of the United States are naturally low in iodine content; goiter was therefore commonly observed in those regions until iodized salt began to be marketed and generally used. By adding potassium iodide to table salt in the proportion of 0.01 of 1 per cent, iodine deficiency can be completely prevented in the individuals who use this preparation.

Growth of other organs naturally requires the presence of certain inorganic substances for the synthesis of typical compounds, i.e., the central nervous system with its phospholipids, but the subject will not be further considered here; textbooks of biochemistry may be consulted for further details. Attention should be directed, however, to the occurrence in cells throughout the body of a class of compounds, the enzymes and co-enzymes, the activity and probably also the synthesis of which require the presence of the "trace" elements. Phosphate ions have already been mentioned in this connection; iron, copper, manganese, zinc and possibly cobalt and nickel have also been shown to be required for certain enzymatic reactions. In some instances—for example, the iron of hemoglobin—the metallic atom is a part of the prosthetic group, the chemically highly active configuration which, with a specific protein, composes the enzyme molecule. In other cases, such as certain copper-containing enzymes, the copper atom itself appears to be the prosthetic group. And in still other reactions the inorganic substance functions as a co-enzyme which may not be an integral part of the enzyme molecule. Since the adult has larger amounts of all of the enzymes in question than does the infant, a dietary supply of the appropriate metals is a necessity for normal growth.

In addition to their function in the foregoing chemical reactions, mineral elements have important physical actions, one of which is the maintenance of the normal composition of body fluids. *Sodium* and *chloride* effectively regulate the pattern of water distribution by means of their osmotic pressure effects in the extracellular fluid and their apparent inability to move freely across cellular membranes. They contribute also to the regulation of the hydrogen ion concentration, as do the bicarbonate, phosphate and protein ions. Irritability, conductivity and contractility of living tissue are profoundly affected by changes in the concentration of sodium, potassium and calcium in fluids bathing the cells. Since growth includes an overall increase in the total water content of the body, the total amount of its dissolved substances and ions must likewise increase from dietary sources.

The needs of the adult organism for inorganic salts are next to be considered. Although the total amount of any one element in the body may not increase appreciably from one year to the next, dietary provision must be made for small, constant losses of each element in the course of a constant turnover of atoms within compounds already synthesized. For example, when an atom of calcium is precipitated in bone as part of a molecule of calcium phosphate, the calcium is not fixed there permanently; as in any other saturated solution of a slightly soluble salt, re-solution and precipitation are continually in process. There is also a constant interchange between intracellular and extracellular, between intravascular and extravascular compartments all over the body. The single calcium atom may be deposited in bone for a time, only to be taken up again by the interstitial fluid, returned to the blood stream, and finally released into the gut along with the secretion of one of the intestinal glands. In the course of this continual exchange some of the atoms are lost along the way—through the kidneys, the skin and the gastro-intestinal tract. The adult organism needs dietary provision for these losses even though the loss of any one element may be quantitatively minute.

In Table 55 the National Research Council has made recommendations for only two of the elements referred to in the preceding discussion, calcium and iron, because reasonably diversified diets supply all of the other elements in adequate amounts (when iodized salt is used when indicated). Iron deficiency probably does not occur in normal individuals on average diets because the body efficiently conserves its iron reserve; but when iron is lost from the body in significant quantities, as in the case of persistent blood loss, or when hemoglobin is being synthesized rapidly following hemorrhage, extra quantities of iron are needed. Growing children and pregnant and lactating women similarly need extra calcium to compensate for their enhanced calcium requirements.

NUTRITION IN PUBLIC HEALTH

Although its basic laboratory study is not by any means complete, the science of nutrition has outgrown the research laboratory and the clinic, and now requires the services of public health officials, public school teachers, economists, and specialists trained in many different techniques related to the production, processing, distribution and preparation of food. Knowledge of the means of treating deficiency diseases led naturally to an interest in preventing these diseases in the first place. Applied nutrition became, therefore, a problem in public health and as such it is being successfully attacked in individual communities, among certain social and economic groups, and even on a national and international scale. Through the vision, endeavor and generosity of the more prosperous peoples, a broad field of human interest and achievement here awaits exploitation not only in wartime but also in peacetime.

In the United States, one of the most successful phases of this program has been carried out through the public schools, where scientific discoveries have been made a part of everyday knowledge through dietary education. The program deserves continual and enthusiastic support. Women's organizations and popular periodicals (with the schools) have also undertaken the training of housewives in the preparation of attractive and economical yet adequate diets. Laboratory research has shown that even inexpensive food products may provide all of the known dietary essentials, while, on the other hand, an expensive diet is not necessarily a complete one. That is, the price of food is not a reliable index of its nutritional quality. With the cooperation of many different agencies including representatives of food producers and distributors, reliable criteria for the selection of foods have been made available to almost everyone; and housewives have been instructed in cooking techniques to the end that the nutritional quality of food may not be lost through overcooking, exposure, or other mishandling. Such education is a vital part of public health nutrition since it translates scientific discovery into public benefit.

As a public health program, nutrition has raised several perplexing questions of public policy and has become an economic problem of first importance. In spite of general recognition of the need for providing an adequate diet within the financial range of every income group, the question of who is to pay for such provision is still a debated one. To a certain extent this is a problem of food production; the marketing of foods possessing nutritional quality above the average is to be encouraged while the sale of less desirable varieties should be made difficult. The problem is also one of food processing and of distribution; nutritionally, a food distribution system is palpably defective if it permits human need to exist side by side with food surplus.

Another highly controversial question concerns the use of food supplements, especially the vitamins. Most of the vitamins can be prepared in pure form, and even the most deficient diet can therefore be made entirely adequate by adding the necessary food supplements. Is it desirable so to fortify foodstuffs artificially? At the present time, the cost of such fortification exceeds the cost of buying an acceptable diet in the first place. Moreover, most physicians agree that concentrated vitamins should not be so used but should be reserved for the treatment of specific deficiencies. They believe that the average individual should be encouraged to acquire natural vitamins from common food sources. This medical point of view is in keeping with the traditional and commendable practice of avoiding unnecessary medication of the patient. On the other hand, millions of dollars are spent for vitamin preparations in the United States each year, which suggests that the foregoing medical opinion is a minority one; the weight of popular advertising, at least, supports the opposition. One fact is clear: most of the money paid for popularly advertised vitamin preparations is wasted because the body can neither use nor store excess vitamins and is therefore obliged to excrete them. Both medical and governmental authorities, however, have approved of the addition of *selected* food supplements to a certain few inexpensive staple foods in order to correct specific deficiencies which cannot be remedied by public education. The question as a whole is far from solved, but this particular practice at least typifies the public service possibilities that exist in the field of nutrition.

REFERENCES

1. AMERICAN MEDICAL ASSOCIATION. *The vitamins. A symposium arranged under the auspices of the Council on Pharmacy and Chemistry and the Council on Foods.* Chicago, American Medical Association, 1939. 637 pp.

2. AMERICAN MEDICAL ASSOCIATION. *Handbook of nutrition. A symposium prepared under the auspices of the Council on Foods and Nutrition.* Chicago, American Medical Association, 1943. 586 pp.

3. BRINKHOUS, K. M., SMITH, H. P. and WARNER, E. D. Plasma prothrombin level in normal infancy and in hemorrhagic disease of the newborn. *Amer. J. med. Sci.*, 1937, *193:* 475–480.

4. BURR, G. O. Significance of the essential fatty acids. *Fed. Proc. Amer. Soc. exp. Biol.*, 1942, *1:*224–233.

5. CLINE, J. K., WILLIAMS, R. R. and FINKELSTEIN, J. Studies of crystalline vitamin B_1: XVII. Synthesis of vitamin B_1. *J. Amer. chem. Soc.*, 1937, *59:*1052–1054.

6. DAM, H. The antihaemorrhagic vitamin of the chick. *Nature, Lond.*, 1935, *135:*652–653.

7. DuBois, E. F. and CHAMBERS, W. H. Calories in medical practice. Chap. 4 in: American Medical Association. *Handbook of nutrition.* Chicago, American Medical Association, 1943.

8. ELVEHJEM, C. A. Relation of nicotinic acid to pellagra. *Physiol. Rev.*, 1940, *20:*249–271.

9. FUSON, R. C. and CHRIST, R. E. The condensation of β-cyclocitral with dimethylacrolein. *Science*, 1936, *84:*294–295.

10. GOLDBERGER, J. and TANNER, W. F. A study of the treatment and prevention of pellagra. *Publ. Hlth Rep., Wash.*, 1924, *39:*87–107.

11. HAWLEY, E. E. and MAURER-MAST E. E. *The fundamentals of nutrition.* Springfield, Ill., Charles C Thomas, 1940. 477 pp.

12. KING, C. G. and WAUGH, W. A. The chemical nature of vitamin C. *Science*, 1932, *75:*357–358.

13. MacLEAN, D. L. and BEST, C. H. Choline and liver fat. *Brit. J. exp. Path.*, 1934, *15:*193–199.

14. OSBORNE, T. B. and MENDEL, L. B. Amino-acids in nutrition and growth. *J. biol. Chem.*, 1914, *17:*325–349.

15. OSBORNE, T. B. and MENDEL, L. B. The inorganic elements in nutrition. *J. biol. Chem.*, 1918, *34:*131–140.

16. ROSE, W. C. The nutritive significance of the amino acids. *Physiol. Rev.*, 1938, *18:*109–136.

17. SHOHL, A. T. *Mineral metabolism.* (American Chemical Society monograph series). New York, Reinhold Publishing Corp., 1939. 384 pp.

18. SPIES, T. D. and BUTT, H. R. Vitamins and avitaminoses. Chap. 8 in: DUNCAN, G. G. *Diseases of metabolism.* Philadelphia, W. B. Saunders Co., 1942. 985 pp.

19. SVIRBELY, J. L. and SZENT-GYÖRGYI, A. Hexuronic acid as the antiscorbutic factor. *Nature, Lond.*, 1932, *129:*576.

20. WALD, G. and STEVEN, D. An experiment in human vitamin A-deficiency. *Proc. nat. Acad. Sci., Wash.*, 1939, *25:*344–349.

21. WARBURG, O. and CHRISTIAN, W. Über ein neues Oxydationsferment und sein Absorptionsspektrum. *Biochem. Z.*, 1932, *254* 438–458.

CHAPTER 53

REGULATION OF ENERGY EXCHANGE

REGULATION OF FOOD INTAKE

The fact that a man is able to maintain a balance between his energy intake and expenditure suggests that he possesses some means of adjusting his food intake to his work and heat loss. Theoretically, at least, this adjustment might be achieved in either of two ways: (i) Energy output might be limited by the food intake. If this were true, work and heat loss would rise when large supplies of food were available, while expenditure would be restricted when food was limited. This type of adjustment is not exhibited by man, however, since even heavy work can be performed and often is performed by fasting individuals. Moreover, like other mammals, man normally maintains a fairly constant body temperature which can be attained only by adapting the rate of heat production and heat loss to the environmental temperature rather than to the available energy supply. (ii) On the other hand, energy expenditure might determine the food intake. That this type of adjustment actually occurs in a human subject is easily demonstrated, since a change in occupation which alters the total energy output is normally associated with a proportional change in food intake, while a change in the prevailing environmental temperature is accompanied by a similar adaptation. Food intake appears to be conditioned, therefore, by the heat loss and work output of the body. One naturally asks, "By what mechanisms is this relationship maintained?" That is to say, "How is the food intake regulated so as to achieve energy balance?"

Desire for Food. Sensations of "hunger" and "satiety" at once suggest themselves as important factors in the answer to these questions. Everyone knows that the sensation of hunger impels a man to eat and that his eating is usually terminated by a feeling of satiety. What is hunger, then, and what is satiety? Cannon and Washburn (7) discovered that the epigastric sensation known as a "hunger pain" occurs simultaneously with the transmission of a wave of contraction through the musculature of the empty stomach (Chaps. 19 and 45). These waves of gastric contraction recur periodically, and Cannon and Washburn found that during the intervening quiescent intervals their subject was no longer conscious of the sensation of hunger. Their observations were confirmed and extended by Carlson (8) who attempted to determine the cause of the gastric activity. Since hunger contractions are presumably related to the tissue's "need" of food, it was logical to search for some underlying change in the chemical composition of body fluids and Carlson suggested that this change may be in some way associated with a "lessened amount of sugar available for the use of the tissues."

This hypothesis implied that hypoglycemia might be expected to induce the contractions which give rise to the sensation of hunger. Consequently, insulin, the blood sugar depressing hormone of the pancreatic islets, began to be used clinically as a means of stimulating the appetite of underweight patients. Insulin was given just before mealtime to produce a mild hypo-glycemia for the purpose of intensifying or prolonging the normal gastric hunger contractions. This procedure is apparently a successful one, but con-siderable doubt has arisen regarding the validity of the hypothesis upon which it is based. Scott and his collaborators (27) were unable to correlate spon-taneous fluctuations of the blood sugar level with the desire for food, and at the present time the whole problem appears to be as far from solution as it ever was.

Objective Study of Food Intake. Sensations of hunger and satiety cannot be studied in laboratory animals because both terms imply a subjective experience or "feeling" which can be verified only in the human species. In the laboratory, however, an animal's food intake can be measured directly, experimental conditions can be controlled and altered individually, and by measuring the amount of food ingested per unit time, conclusions may be drawn regarding the function of mechanisms which normally impel the animal to eat more or less, as circumstances may require. From this type of study, the following relationships have been established: (i) Within certain limits, the common laboratory animals are able to compensate for periods of food deprivation by increasing their intake when food is again made avail-able. (ii) Normal immature animals increase their food intake as growth occurs. (iii) Hypophysectomy depresses food intake and growth. (iv) The injection of anterior lobe extracts which cause nitrogen retention increases the food intake of intact as well as of hypophysectomized animals. (v) Insulin, when properly administered before feeding time, increases food intake (20). (vi) Depancreatized animals with the hyperglycemia and glycosuria of "pan-creatic" diabetes eat large amounts of food. (vii) Administration of thyroid preparations enhances food intake, while (viii) thyroidectomy depresses the level of food intake by about 20 per cent at ordinary room temperatures. (ix) In cold environments food consumption rises and (x) in hot environments it falls below the normal, control levels. (xi) Animals allowed to exercise by running eat more than inactive controls. (xii) Food intake reaches high levels during lactation. (xiii) During fever the food intake is spontaneously depressed (in human subjects as well as in experimental animals). (xiv) Animals and patients with the stomach denervated or even completely removed eat the same amount of food as normal controls although the feeding habits of the former may be changed in such a way that they eat smaller amounts of food more often.

Most of these observations apply to human subjects as truly as to experi-mental animals, but data obtained in the laboratory are more impressive than clinical results because human "appetite" is influenced by a multitude of factors, including mental or psychic attitudes, which either do not exist or can be fairly well controlled in the lower animals.

With the exception of fever and, possibly, insulin hypoglycemia, all of the experimental conditions enumerated above are alike in that each of them represents a change in the rate of energy expenditure to which the animal responds with an alteration of food intake. During recovery from fasting, during growth or nitrogen retention, lactation, cold exposure, exercise, pan-creatic diabetes, experimental hyperthyroidism and, possibly, hyperinsulinism the energy requirement of the animal is enhanced; the *hyperphagia* or in-creased food intake, therefore, appears to be a compensatory process. And

the decreased food intake of exposure to warm environments, of hypophysectomy or thyroidectomy similarly reflects the diminished energy requirements of the animal in question. The significance of these adjustments in
maintaining energy balance does not need further comment. Only during fever
is the food intake *decreased* while the total energy expenditure is *increased*
above normal levels.

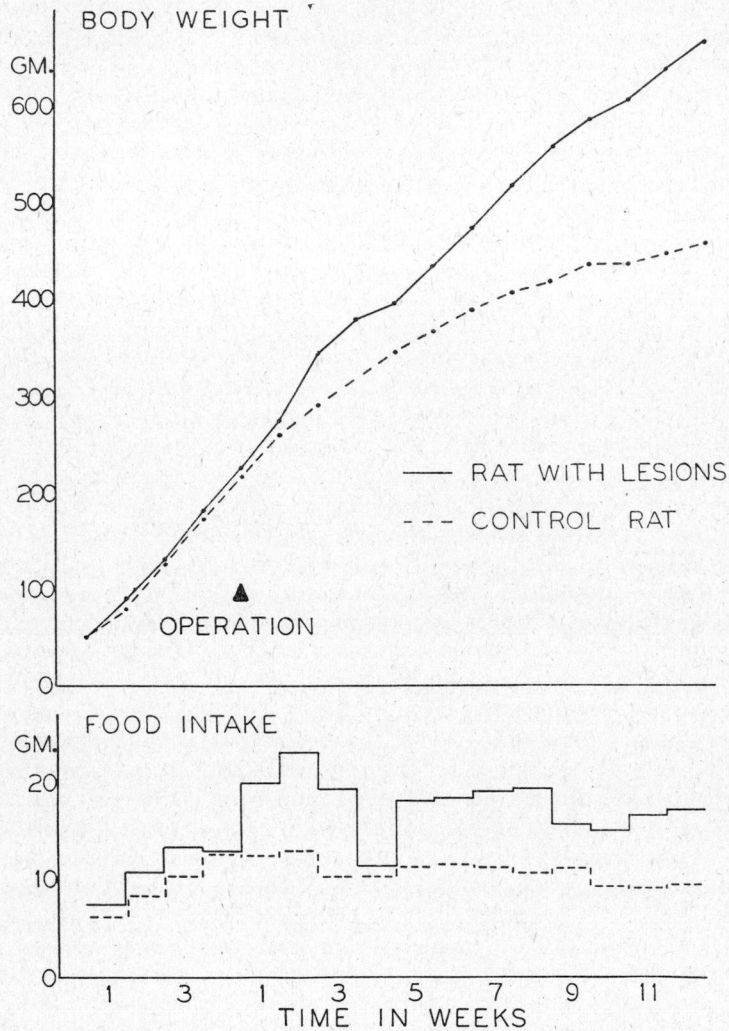

Fig. 483.—Effect of appropriate hypothalamic lesions upon food intake and weight gain in the
albino rat. (From Brobeck, Tepperman and Long, *Yale J. Biol. Med.*, 1943, *15*:831–853.)

There is one other experimentally produced condition which is characterized by an increased food intake. Animals with relatively small, bilaterally
symmetrical lesions of the hypothalamus eat large quantities of food, as
much as two or three times the normal daily intake (5). Since their rate of
energy expenditure does not appear to be directly altered by the lesions, their
hyperphagia upsets the normal equilibrium between intake and output, and

the animals are faced with the problem of getting rid of a huge food surplus. They dispose of this by burning some of it and by storing the remainder (the larger portion) as fat, with the result that they eventually become remarkably obese (Fig. 483). This condition is known as "hypothalamic obesity" and is said to be caused by "hypothalamic hyperphagia." It has been observed in rats, cats, dogs and monkeys, and there is no reason to question its identity with the obesity of human subjects who suffer from tumors, infections or other pathological processes involving the base of the brain including the hypothalamus.

The hyperphagia of animals with hypothalamic lesions must be distinguished from all of the other types of hyperphagia enumerated above. In growth, hyperthyroidism and cold exposure, the enhanced food intake is a compensatory response to a condition of altered energy expenditure. Energy equilibrium is not disturbed by the extra food but, rather, maintained, and the animal's ability to increase its food intake proves that the mechanisms which regulate the energy supply are functioning normally. However, in the animal with hypothalamic lesions, the enhanced food consumption appears to be the result of a basic disturbance in the regulatory mechanisms themselves. The nature of the regulatory defect is not known—indeed, since the normal regulatory mechanisms have not even been identified, one of the oldest problems known to the physiologist remains unsolved, i.e., the discovery of the neurological basis of hunger, appetite and satiety, or the mechanism of regulation of food intake.

REGULATION OF MOTOR OUTPUT

In beginning a study of the regulation of motor output a differentiation must be attempted between subjective experience and objective performance as a similar distinction was made above in the study of food intake. Like hunger, a "drive" or "urge" to activity is a subjective phenomenon, not easily measured. Human "drives," for example, appear to be so complex and interrelated that quantitative study is difficult if not almost impossible, and the strength of "drive" in an experimental animal cannot be measured at all. It is possible, however, to estimate a man's total work accomplishment with a fair degree of precision by techniques outlined in Chapter 50. In laboratory animals, certain types of motor performance can also be measured. The data obtained in this way are like the food intake records described above; they are objective in nature, can be expressed in physical terms, and may serve as an index of the animal's motivation when compared with suitable control data. One *measures* the total motor output, therefore, and *infers* from the data so obtained the strength of the "urge" or "drive" responsible for the performance.

Measurement of Locomotor Activity. The measurement of motor output requires the use of apparatus specifically adapted to the type of activity in question. Experimental animals ordinarily do not accomplish "work" as man does, but they do use food energy for muscular contractions, especially those contractions by means of which they move from one place to another. With appropriate apparatus this locomotor activity can be measured and may be taken, in the words of Slonaker (28, p. 21), "as an indicator of all of the activities of an individual. Numerous observations of the activities of the rat readily convinces one of the fact that though running is only one phase of activity, it goes hand in hand with and is proportional to the other activities."

Normal activity rhythms. A convenient and widely used device for measuring locomotion is called the "activity cage"; it consists either of a table or a wide wheel which rotates freely on a bearing-suspended shaft. A counter records each revolution as the animal's walking or running turns the cage on its axis. Beside the "activity" cage there is usually placed a small "living" cage in which food and water are provided. With this type of apparatus some of the factors which influence motor output have been discovered. Wang (32) and Slonaker (29) have shown that the sex cycle of the female definitely affects spontaneous activity, since on the day of estrus, rats run eight or ten times as much as they run on the intervening days of their cycle (Fig. 484). Ovariectomy abolishes this estral hyperactivity, and the implantation of ovaries subsequently restores the response. Male rats fail to show a similar rhythm although castrate males with implanted ovaries are said to undergo

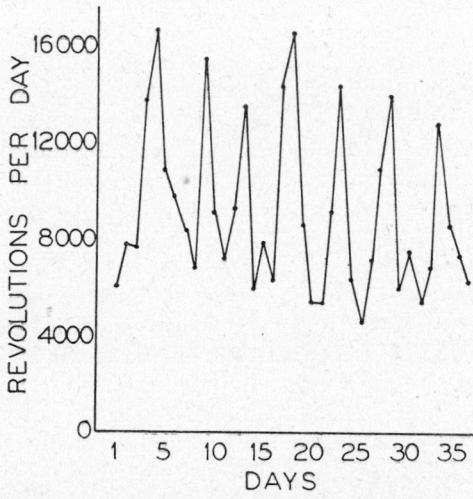

Fig. 484.—Activity rhythm in a female rat. Peaks of activity coincide with estrus.

cyclic changes in activity which suggest the female type of behavior. Richter (23) discovered that both male and female rats accomplish most of their running just before they begin to eat and that the ingestion of food is followed by a period of quiescence.

Browman (6) found that still another rhythm of activity is associated with the diurnal cycle of light and dark. Rats are more active in the dark, and by artificially controlling the lighting conditions, the rats can be made to run more during the dark daytime periods than during the lighted nighttime hours. He found also that temperature variations tend to influence the activity when the effect of light and dark has been abolished by blinding the animals. His blinded rats ran more in cooler than in warmer environments.

The results of all these experiments can be summarized at once with the statement that the activity of rats is increased by the dark, in cold environments, just before feeding time and, in the female, during estrus; activity is depressed in the light, in warm environments, after feeding and during diestrus. The cause of activity rhythms is not known and at the present time one cannot say whether each rhythm is unique in its origin or whether they all depend upon some common basic mechanism. From a metabolic point of view their regulation has one distinctive character. Slonaker (28), though he did not measure the food intake of his animals, noticed that active rats gained less weight than inactive controls. More recent experiments (4) in which the food intake was controlled have shown that active rats in cages free to turn gain significantly less weight than rats which cannot run because their cages have been locked (Fig. 485). The active rats use as a source of muscular energy the foodstuffs which inactive animals are able to store as fat and protein. In other words, locomotor activity definitely enhances total energy utilization since extra food must be supplied to active rats if energy equilibrium is to be attained. Rather surprising, therefore, is the observation that at least two of the conditions in which hyperactivity normally occurs are characterized by either an actual or an incipient energy deficit. Both in cold exposure and just before a feeding period, the rat is undergoing a progressive

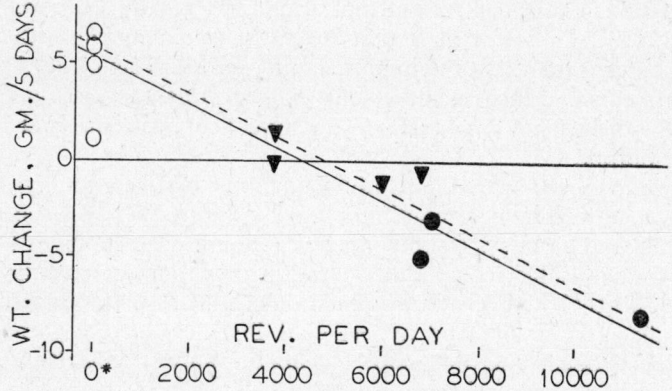

Fig. 485.—Negative correlation between locomotor activity and weight gain in female rats maintained on a constant food intake in a constant temperature room. (From Brobeck, *Amer. J. Physiol.*, 1945, *143*:1–5.)

depletion of energy reserves because of increased heat production in the former and limitation of supply in the latter instance. But in the face of this real or threatened energy deficit, the animal further increases the rate of energy utilization by indulging in the luxury of locomotor hyperactivity. A related phenomenon appears when the food intake is arbitrarily restricted in quantity; on an amount of food which allows a regular gain of body weight by inactive rats, animals free to run in activity cages will exercise enough to bring about a continual weight loss (Fig. 485). Whatever the nature of the mechanisms regulating motor output, it is clear that their function is not directed solely toward the goal of energy balance.

An appropriate analogy can be drawn between the regulation of food intake and the regulation of motor output. Variations in the amount of food eaten by experimental animals fall into two categories (see above): (i) There are variations which are effected through the normal regulatory mechanisms in response to some environmental or physiological change of state; and (ii) there are variations which are brought about by the failure of function of those same mechanisms, or following disturbances caused by operative procedures. These same two categories apply as well to motor output. The activity rhythms and alterations already described evidently belong to the former class of variation since they are achieved through the normal function of the animal's regulatory mechanisms, even though the identity of those mechanisms is not known. There remain to be discussed several conditions which belong in the second category because, in the regulation of activity, they represent abnormalities similar to the hyperphagia of animals with hypothalamic lesions, i.e., a failure of function of normal physiological controls.

Regulatory deficits. There are a certain few clinical conditions, one of which is an infectious disease called *encephalitis lethargica,* in which muscular activity may be reduced even to the point of complete flaccidity of all the voluntary muscles. At autopsy, neurons of the posterior hypothalamus have been found to be damaged or destroyed as the result of the infection, and this observation has led to the opinion that normal activity is maintained in some way by this part of the brain stem. This opinion is supported by studies on monkeys, cats and rats (15, 21). Animals with experimentally produced discrete lesions of the central and posterior hypothalamus become lethargic and tend to be somnolent; in activity cages the rats may run little or not at all. Ranson suggested that the hypothalamus is a "waking center," and from his experiments and those of other investigators, one may conclude that this part of the diencephalon participates in some way in the normal regulation of motor output.

Opposed to the lethargy and inactivity of animals with certain hypothalamic lesions is a state of almost continuous locomotion that has been produced in rats, cats and monkeys by the bilateral ablation of portions of the frontal cortex. Animals subjected to this operation move almost constantly about the cage. As Ruch and Shenkin pointed out (24), the disturbance is not one of generalized irritability and hyperexcitability, because the animals are in other respects docile and quiescent. The abnormality specifically changes the amount of the animal's locomotion. In the literature there is no general agreement concerning the exact location within the frontal lobe of effective lesions; that is, whether the removal of one and only one area of the frontal cortex invariably evokes the abnormality is not settled. Of all the conflicting reports, the data of Ruch and Shenkin are perhaps the most impressive because their ablations were small and discrete where other investigators removed larger portions of the brain. Ruch and Shenkin were able to produce hyperactivity in monkeys by bilateral lesions restricted to a small area which lies on the orbital surface of the frontal lobes. They suggested that the varying results of previous studies might be accounted for on the supposition that the excised portion of the brain included or did not include that particular area, as the case might be. Ruch and Shenkin further observed that although the regulation of motor output was abnormal in their monkeys, regulation of food intake was normally maintained. In spite of the high level of energy expenditure occasioned by their hyperactivity, the animals lost only a small amount of weight because they ate more food than they had eaten before the operation.

Experimental study suggests, therefore, that at least two levels of the central nervous system participate in the normal regulation of motor output, namely, the hypothalamus and the frontal cortex, especially a specific area on the orbital surface of the frontal lobe. At the present time it is impossible to say whether or not these two levels function together to bring about the normal rhythms of locomotor activity. It is fairly clear, however, that the energy utilization of normal animals may undergo large quantitative changes because their motor output varies from time to time, and that under certain circumstances these variations may tend to upset rather than to preserve energy equilibrium.

REGULATION OF HEAT LOSS

Nature of Thermal Equilibrium. In the body, as in a test tube, a chemical reaction is speeded up by an elevation and slowed down by a depression of the temperature at which the reaction is accomplished. The rate of reaction is approximately doubled by a rise of 10° C. The metabolism of reptiles, amphibia and fish responds to every alteration of environmental temperature because they are *poikilothermic*, i.e., their body temperature changes with their surroundings. On winter days they are "cold blooded" because their temperature approximates that of the surrounding air or water, and in the summer their body temperature rises to equal or even to exceed the temperature of the surrounding medium because the production of heat is more rapid than its loss. With every environmental change they undergo a corresponding change in the rate of their metabolic processes, and their every activity, therefore, is conditioned by the weather. Birds and mammals, on the other hand, are said to be "warm blooded" or *homothermic* because their body temperature is, within wide limits, independent of the outside temperature; it remains practically constant during winter and summer, whether the surrounding air is warmer or cooler than the body. The importance of their ability to regulate body temperature cannot be over-estimated because it underlies the control of every metabolic reaction. Of all the factors responsible for the normal pattern of biochemical reactions in man or any other mammal, a relatively constant body temperature is one of the most important. Without this, most of the other mechanisms of regulation would be impotent because the changes with which they would have to contend would be of a greater magnitude than they are able to handle. Through the regulation of the temperature of the body as a whole, the finer, more subtle adjustments of metabolism are made possible.

Mammals achieve their relatively constant temperature through the activity of specialized cells which are sensitive to temperature changes, and through the ability of the body as a whole to alter its rate of heat production and heat loss. In any one individual, body temperature is really a measure of heat content or storage; a fall in temperature indicates a decrease while a rise denotes an increase in the total heat content of the body. Under every circumstance, heat content and body temperature depend upon the interaction of two factors, the rate of heat production and the rate of heat dissipation or loss. When heat production is constant, an increase in the rate of heat loss (which may be caused by exposure to a cold environment) will bring about a fall in body temperature or hypothermia; and a decreased rate of heat loss (which may be the result of exposure to a hot environment) will cause fever or hyperthermia. If the rate of loss is constant, however, hypothermia or hyperthermia will follow depression or elevation, respectively, of the rate of heat production.

The temperature of the human body is usually measured by placing a thermometer in the mouth, rectum or vagina, but the temperature of any other part of the body can be recorded under appropriate conditions. Thermocouples are widely used for this purpose because they may be arranged to give continuous records of the temperature of many different regions. They are particularly useful in following skin temperatures in the course of experimental studies on the physiology of temperature regulation. Since the total heat content of the body depends upon the interaction of heat production and loss, the temperature is seldom constant but continually varies as first the rate of production and then the rate of loss is altered either by environmental or physiological changes. These spontaneous variations are naturally greatest in the more exposed parts of the body, the skin and the extremities,

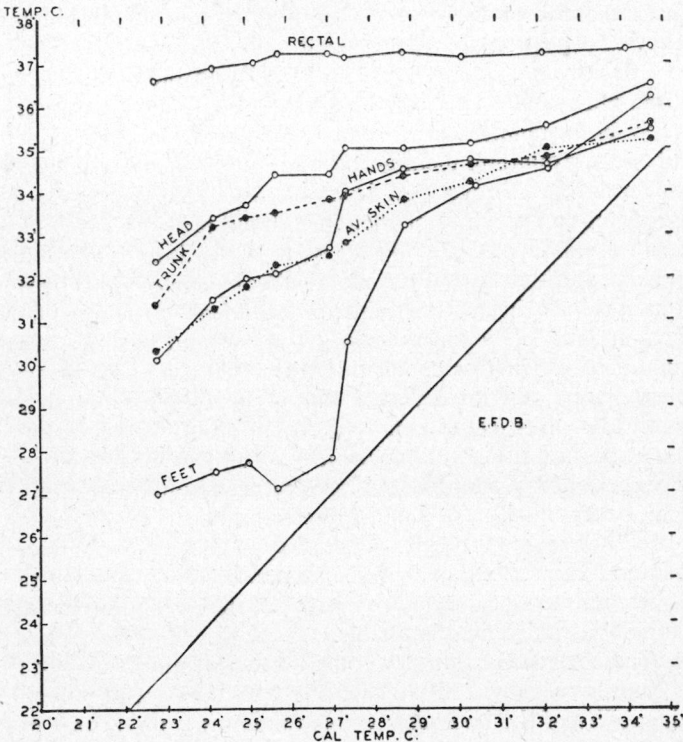

Fig. 486.—Skin and rectal temperatures of subject D, during basal experiments at different environmental temperatures. (From DuBois, *Bull. N. Y. Acad. Med.*, 1939, *15*:143–173.)

and least in the interior; rectal temperature, therefore, is more nearly constant than oral temperature because the latter is often affected by local changes in the rate of heat loss. (Hot or cold food or fluids, mouth breathing, the temperature of the air, smoking, and other factors alter the oral temperature.) Although 98.6° and 99.6° F. are sometimes considered to be the normal oral and rectal temperatures, respectively, any single determination will yield one of these values only by chance because of the continuous fluctuations referred to above. It is better to speak of a normal "range" of temperature; orally, this range is from 98° to 99° F., while the rectal temperature range is from 99° to 100° F.

The temperature of the skin is naturally somewhat lower than that of the interior. At indoor temperatures, 70° F. (21° C.), the skin of the forehead is about 91.5° F., but it varies with the temperature of the surrounding air, the amount of movement of the air, the character of the clothing, etc. Observations show that under ordinary conditions the temperatures of different parts of the skin are by no means the same since the skin of the extremities tends to be cooler than that of the trunk (Fig. 486). The temperature of the body as a whole undergoes also a distinct variation during the day, a diurnal rhythm. This daily variation has been measured by many observers, and shows individual peculiarities that depend largely upon the manner of living, time of meals, etc. In general it may be said that the lowest temperature is shown early in the morning—6 to 7 A.M.; that it rises slowly during the day to reach its maximum in the evening, 5 to 7 P.M., and falls again during the night. The difference between early morning and late afternoon or evening may amount to a degree or more centigrade, and this fact must be borne in mind by physicians when observing the temperature of patients. Age also has a slight influence. Newborn infants and young children have a somewhat higher temperature than adults. The difference may amount to half a degree or a degree centigrade. It is known, also, that the heat-regulating mechanism in infants and young children is not so efficient as in adults, and that febrile disturbances are, therefore, more easily excited in the former than in the latter.

The biochemical reactions responsible for metabolism are of a nature which imposes two different requirements upon the mechanisms regulating body temperature. In the first place, most biochemical reactions are effected through the action of enzymes ("organic catalysts") which are especially sensitive to temperature change. A fall of only a few degrees may almost completely inhibit the activity of the enzyme, and unless the body temperature is maintained above a certain minimal level (within a few degrees of 99° F., rectal temperature), the continuity of energy exchange will be so retarded that normal behavior is impossible and death of the animal may result. Secondly, heat is liberated in the course of biological oxidations and unless provision is made for heat dissipation, there are situations in which over-heating of the body may occur. This would increase the rate of metabolism and elevate still further the amount of heat formed, thereby laying a heavy work load upon the cells of the cardiovascular and respiratory systems which must distribute foodstuffs and oxygen and remove the products of metabolism. Moreover, at high temperatures (above 106° F.) the normal function of cells of the central nervous system is impossible, and prostration, coma and even death will ensue as the neurons succumb to the effect of the heat. Tissue proteins in general are heat-sensitive compounds and the enzymes, in particular, become irreversibly inactivated when subjected to heat. For the continuation of metabolic processes, therefore, the body temperature must be high enough for a certain rate of enzymatic activity and yet not so high as to inactivate the enzymes, including those of the central nervous system.

In view of the fact that temperature regulation is sometimes a problem of warming and sometimes a question of cooling the body, one is not surprised to find that there is an environmental temperature at which both of those problems are least difficult to solve. When an unclothed man or a laboratory animal is at rest in the postabsorptive state, a normal body temperature is most easily maintained at a room temperature of about 86° F. (30° C.). The individual is then able to lose to the environment all of the heat formed by his basal metabolic processes, retaining only the amount which comprises normal storage, without calling upon any of the reserve mechanisms of heat loss. At this temperature, however, it is not possible to dispose of the extra heat produced during muscular exercise or during the assimilation of food unless some accessory method of heat dissipation is utilized. For everyday living, man is more comfortable in environments somewhat cooler than 86° F. where he can more easily dissipate in his clothed condition the heat he produces in excess of his basal output.

Heat Production. The circumstances under which heat production normally varies have already been discussed in Chapter 50; briefly, the heat production is lowest during sleep, is somewhat higher when the subject is awake but fasting and resting, and shows characteristic elevations after the ingestion of food and during and after muscular exercise. Muscular contractions are attended by the liberation of relatively large amounts of heat, and it is a part of everyone's experience that by work or other muscular activity the effect of outside cold may be counteracted. Stamping the feet, swinging the arms and slapping the hands are familiar means of warming the extremities on cold days; these procedures increase the blood flow and therefore the temperature of the part in question, but they also elevate the total heat production. Shivering is another reaction which accomplishes the same result, since the basal heat production may be more than doubled by this involuntary activity of skeletal muscles. In normal animals, shivering always tends to maintain temperature equilibrium since the animal shivers only when hypothermia threatens to occur. Voluntary exercise, on the contrary, may either preserve or disturb the equilibrium, depending upon the environmental conditions at the time the exercise is carried out. On a cold day the heat so produced contributes to the maintenance of body temperature, but on a hot day exercise multiplies the problems of adequate heat dissipation.

For many years physiologists have been attempting to prove or disprove the hypothesis that the rate of heat production can be changed by mechanisms which do not involve the contraction of skeletal muscles. Small experimental animals like the rat are evidently able to vary their rate of heat production in the space of a few hours by some mechanism in which the hormones of the thyroid gland, the adrenal cortex and, possibly, the adrenal medulla participate without any obvious change in either voluntary or involuntary muscular activity. When normal rats are exposed to a cold environment, their oxygen consumption and carbon dioxide production rise, nitrogen excretion is enhanced, and they eat more food than animals kept at the usual laboratory temperature. Both the adrenal cortex and the thyroid undergo changes that can be detected by chemical analysis of the gland or by histological examination; these changes are caused by the adrenotropic and thyrotropic hormones of the anterior lobe, and they evidently accompany an increased rate of production of adrenal cortical and thyroid hormone, respectively. When either the adrenal glands or the thyroid is removed from a rat, the animal loses its normal resistance to cold and may die if exposed to 0° C. for more than a few hours. The hormones secreted by the adrenal and the thyroid apparently take part either directly or indirectly in the catabolic processes which bring about the extra heat production of normal rats exposed to cold. Whether or not a similar reaction takes place in man is still undecided because man protects himself against cold by clothing and artificial heat with the result that alterations in the rate of his physiological heat production are less important than they are in the lower animals. Such alterations are known to occur, however, upon prolonged exposure to unusual environmental temperatures; they then are considered to be a part of the reaction pattern known as "acclimatization."

Heat Loss. *Physical processes.* Heat is normally lost from the body by three physical processes, radiation, conduction and the vaporization of water, the relative importance of which varies with environmental conditions. Du-

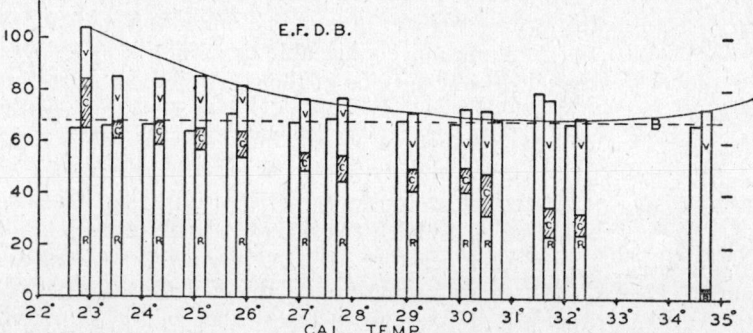

Fig. 487.—Changes in heat production and heat loss in nude male subject, in basal condition, at varying external temperatures. Blank columns to left indicate heat production; columns to right, heat elimination; V, vaporization; C, convection; R, radiation. The figures along the ordinate indicate Calories per hour, those along the abscissa the temperature, centigrade. (From DuBois.)

Bois and Hardy (13) estimated that under experimental conditions in the laboratory, with external temperatures of 70° to 80° F., loss by radiation constitutes 60 to 65 per cent of the total, and the loss by evaporation about 20 to 30 per cent. These figures change greatly, of course, with variations in external temperature, as indicated in Figure 487 which represents results obtained by DuBois (13) and his coworkers upon a nude subject, in "basal" condition, exposed to varying temperatures while in a respiration calorimeter.

Table 61.—Heat Loss in Fasting Dog

Temperature	Calories Lost by Radiation and Conduction	Calories Lost by Evaporation	Total Calories of Metabolism
7° C.	78.5	7.9	86.4
15	55.3	7.7	63.0
20	45.3	10.6	55.9
25	41.0	13.2	54.2
30	33.2	23.0	56.2

It will be noted that at low temperatures radiation is the main factor in heat dissipation, whereas at temperatures of 34° to 35° C. (93° to 95° F.) radiation and conduction drop out and heat loss is effected only through vaporization. The data of Table 61 compiled by Rubner* from experiments made upon a fasting dog, illustrate the same general phenomena in another species.

* For the most easily available account of Rubner's many contributions to the study of metabolism, see Lusk (18).

Radiation is the transfer of heat from the surface of one object to that of another without physical contact between the two. It can be accomplished only when a temperature gradient exists between the two objects, but when the transfer is in progress the temperature gradient tends to disappear as the warmer object loses and the cooler object gains heat. The body radiates heat to every relatively cool object which is near the individual—the furnishings of a room and its floor, walls and ceiling, the ground, pavement, buildings, bodies of water, or any other natural or artificial surface. Not infrequently the process of radiation is a hindrance in physiological temperature regulation because it usually effects a transfer of heat in a direction disadvantageous to the body. When surrounding objects are able to radiate heat to the body because they are warmer than the surface of the skin, the heat usually is not needed because the basal heat production equals or exceeds the need of the moment; and in a cool environment when the body needs to conserve heat, this heat may be lost to cooler objects in the vicinity. In the experiment of DuBois and his coworkers, for example, at an environmental temperature of 23° C. a large amount of heat which the body could ill afford to lose was lost by radiation, while at a temperature of 34° C. there was no loss by radiation at all (Fig. 487). There are exceptions to this generalization, it is true. Radiant heat from the sun reflected from the surface of the snow enables one to ski in clothing of light weight even when the temperature of the air is fairly low; and the temperature of radiating surfaces can be artificially controlled by means of a heating or cooling system in order to facilitate rather than to hinder the process of temperature regulation.

Conduction is a less important means of heat loss; it includes the transfer of heat to any substance in contact with the body—the air which covers the skin, the clothing, the tidal air which is warmed in the respiratory passages and the lungs, and the foodstuffs and water taken into the gastro-intestinal tract, in addition to other physical objects with which contact is made from time to time. Here again the direction of heat transfer usually tends to oppose the body's need, for cool air further cools the body while hot air intensifies the problem of heat dissipation. By artificially regulating the temperature of the ambient air, the situation can be improved; air conditioning units operate on this principle, providing warm air in the winter and cool air in the summer in order to minimize and to promote heat loss, respectively. Still a third physical process, vaporization of water, removes heat from the surface of the skin and the respiratory tract because one gram of water takes up 0.58 Calories from its surroundings when it passes from the liquid to the vapor state at a temperature of about 33° C. Since the skin and respiratory membranes are always moist, heat is continually lost by this route except when the air around the body is saturated with water so that evaporation cannot occur. When the air is dry as in a desert region, water evaporates almost instantaneously from the skin; prevention of overheating is much easier, therefore, in a hot, dry climate than in a hot, humid one.

Physiological mechanisms. Loss of heat from the body, then, takes place principally at two surfaces, the skin and the epithelium of the respiratory system, and under constant environmental conditions the amount of heat lost depends upon surface area, temperature and humidity and the rate of air flow over the surface. For any given temperature gradient between the body and its environment, the total heat transfer varies directly with the surface area. This accounts for the fact that a large individual normally loses more heat than a smaller one and also for the observation already mentioned in Chapter 50 that obese patients dissipate more heat than normal subjects. (In order to maintain a normal body temperature, an obese patient must produce more heat and use more oxygen and more food than a normal individual under the same environmental conditions.) On first thought one is tempted to conclude that variations in surface area play no important role in the physiological reactions associated with temperature regulation, but this opinion is not justified because the area of exposed skin is affected by the posture of the body. The position of the arms, for example, determines whether or not heat exchange can occur at the surface of the axillae. In experimental animals exposed to cold, a marked reduction in the area of exposed skin is brought about when the animal assumes a spheroid form by adducting the legs and flexing the spinal column, while a corresponding increase accompanies warm exposure as the result of abduction of the extremities and extension of the spine. In the case of the respiratory epithelium, similar alterations of the exposed area may likewise occur, especially in those animals which pant in warm environments (see later).

In view of the fact that the loss of heat both by radiation and conduction is proportional to the temperature gradient between the surface of the body and its environment, the ability of the animal to change each of the temperatures in question is of considerable interest. Man creates environmental temperatures of his own choosing by constructing buildings equipped with artificial heating and cooling systems; in this way he is able to secure a favorable temperature gradient whatever the natural weather conditions. The lower animals attain the same general result by moving from one environment to another, but their range of choice is obviously more limited than man's. Changes in the temperature of the body surfaces, on the other hand, are brought about in man and the lower animals through the activity of three different physiological mechanisms. In the first place, surface temperature is largely determined by the ease with which heat is transported from the depths to the surface of the body. This transport is partially accomplished by conduction through tissues and tissue fluids, a process which is not easily altered in a quantitative sense; but more important than this, heat is brought to the surface by the circulating blood. Water, present in blood to the extent of about 80 per cent by volume, has a high heat capacity and is able, therefore, to take up relatively large quantities of heat in warmer parts of the body and to give up this heat in the cooler regions. In the cutaneous circulation, for example, heat is ordinarily given up by the blood, the temperature of which is thereby lowered while the temperature of the skin rises. The total amount of heat brought to a given area is conditioned by the rate of blood flow through the area. If the arterioles are constricted, the rate of flow is retarded, the total heat transfer from blood to skin tends to be small and the skin remains cool; but with arteriolar dilatation the rate of flow is brisk, a large quantity of heat may be exchanged and the skin becomes warm. Eventually the temperature of the skin might equal that of the circulating blood were it not for the intervention of the other mechanisms shortly to be described.

Secondly, surface temperature depends upon the ease with which heat is transferred from the body to the environment and vice versa; if conduction or radiation is retarded by the interposition of some heat-insulating material, surface temperature will undergo a corresponding change. With effective insulation, although the temperature of the skin may remain at a high level under the clothing, the rate of heat loss may be greatly reduced because, as far as heat loss is concerned, the body has replaced its natural surface with an artificial one (the clothing) having a temperature only a few degrees removed from that of the environment. Insulative clothing may be designed to give protection against heat as well as cold, but man ordinarily needs that protection only when he is exposed to unusually high temperatures, i.e., those encountered by firefighters where asbestos clothing may enable a man to survive a short exposure to the extreme heat. The skin of the lower animals carries its own insulating material in the form of hair or fur. Through the phenomenon of *horripilation*, erection of the hair, the thickness of the layer of nonconducting air entrapped between the individual hairs can be increased and the temperature gradient between the surface of the hairy coat and a cool environment is thereby reduced. In a warm environment the hair lies flat, providing only a thin layer of insulation which more easily transfers heat from the skin to the animal's surroundings. Insulating material, either clothing or fur, limits cutaneous heat exchange, therefore, by replacing the temperature gradient between the body of a nude subject and his environment with three such gradients. One of these three exists between the skin and the inner surface of the insulation, another exists between the outer surface of the insulation and the environment, and the third gradient is found between the inner and outer surfaces of the insulation. The effectiveness of clothing in decreasing heat loss is proportional to the magnitude of this third gradient, which in turn depends upon the nature and thickness of the nonconducting substance.

Finally, the temperature of body surfaces is modified by the humidity of the surface since 0.580 Calories of heat are removed by the vaporization of each gram of water from the respiratory membranes or the skin. There is a certain rather small amount of water, amounting in man to about 50 ml. per hour, which is always lost from these two surfaces because they are moist; this is known as the "insensible water loss" to distinguish it from the "sensible" loss which is the sweat. Because the humidity of the respiratory passages is not subject to wide variation, quantitative changes in the rate of heat loss can be brought about there only by changing the area of the exposed surface. In the process of panting, a large increase in the total quantity of heat lost from the mouth and respiratory tract is effected by exposing to the air a larger surface of the oral and lingual epithelium. The rate of air flow across these surfaces is also a physiological variable, and as an integral part of the panting response, the movement of air is tremendously enhanced by the rapid, shallow breathing. In spite of the increased rate of evaporation which is thereby made possible, the epithelium is kept moist by a more generous flow from the salivary glands. Man's rate of heat loss is similarly altered by the vaporization of water, but the excess water is not vaporized from the respiratory membranes but from the surface of the skin. Dill (11) reported a maximal rate of evaporation of water of over 1.6 liters per hour during work in a hot, dry atmosphere. This is the equivalent of 870 Calories per hour or almost 7000 Calories during an eight-hour day. Most of the water which made this evaporation possible was secreted by the sweat glands.

Before taking up the role of the central nervous system in temperature regulation, a final word must be added concerning the physiological importance of the mechanisms which determine heat loss. In general, each mechanism becomes active when by its activity the thermal equilibrium tends to be preserved. Thus cutaneous vasomotor changes, erection of the hair, panting and sweating are well integrated in the prevailing pattern of either heat loss or conservation. There are a few circumstances, it is true, in which one or another type of inappropriate response may be evoked, but in a normal subject under any ordinary set of environmental conditions, the regulation of these reactions is both typical and highly predictable. The presence or absence of any one of them may be used as a fairly reliable indicator of the direction of heat flow at the moment. When generalized sweating begins, for example, one can safely conclude that heat production temporarily exceeds heat loss, while the cessation of sweating denotes the opposite situation, namely, a loss temporarily in excess of production. Horripilation and panting are almost equally predictable. Cutaneous vasomotor changes, however, are a somewhat less reliable indicator because they serve other functions as well as temperature regulation.

Role of the Central Nervous System in Temperature Regulation. All of the reactions which have been identified with the maintenance of thermal equilibrium are under the control of the central nervous system. (The only reaction to which this statement may not apply is the increased rate of heat production upon cold exposure, in the absence of any detectable change in the activity of skeletal muscles.) This control is exerted through both the somatic and the visceral motor nerves. The somatic motor fibers activate the respiratory muscles which produce panting, as well as the muscles of the trunk and extremities responsible for posture, for "voluntary" activity and for shivering. The visceral motor neurons of the autonomic nervous system activate the cutaneous blood vessels, the sweat glands and the pilo-erector muscles of the hair follicles. Preservation of a relatively constant body temperature may require, therefore, the participation of several different levels of the central nervous system and integration of the activity of those levels. Where this integration is achieved is a problem of some importance.

Effects of hypothalamic lesions. Integration of the reactions which maintain temperature equilibrium is accomplished in the hypothalamus, the ventral portion of the diencephalon lying behind the optic chiasma, above the hypophysis and rostral to the cerebral peduncles of the midbrain. The hypothalamus evidently functions as a physiological thermostat which is able to change the rate of heat production and heat dissipation through its influence upon the somatic and visceral motor neurons of the brain stem and spinal cord (22). Physiologically the hypothalamus has been divided into two regions because two different types of deficit follow hypothalamic damage. When bilateral lesions are made in the anterior hypothalamus (specifically, in the anterior portion of the lateral hypothalamic area), the animal becomes unable to prevent overheating when exposed to a warm environment. Panting and sweating no longer occur, and fatal hyperthermia may ensue because of the animal's inability to increase the rate of heat loss. Lesions of the posterior hypothalamus bring about this same type of abnormality by interrupting descending fibers from the anterior region, but in addition the animal also becomes unable to maintain a normal body temperature when exposed to cold. Where the animal with anteriorly placed lesions reacts normally in the cold but experiences hyperthermia in the heat, the animal with posterior lesions exhibits hypothermia in the cold as well as hyperthermia in a warm environment. The anterior hypothalamus is therefore said to be normally responsible for protection against hot environments while the posterior hypothalamus confers resistance to cold.

Temperature-sensitive receptors. Through the somatic and visceral motor neurons of the brain and spinal cord, the hypothalamus normally modulates the rate of heat formation and dissipation in such a way that the total heat content of the body is only minimally altered even in the face of fairly wide variations in the temperature of the environment and in the physiological state of the body (in sleep, exercise, the ingestion of food, etc.). In the paragraph above, the nature of the hypothalamic regulation has been outlined; there remains for discussion the question of how this part of the diencephalon is called into action and what factors determine whether the mechanisms of heat loss or those of heat conservation are brought into play at any given moment.

Unfortunately, a categorical answer cannot be given to either of these questions because, although convincing data have been obtained in several laboratories, those data are generally indirect in nature. The hypothalamus has been found to be inherently sensitive to local temperature changes, and Magoun and his collaborators (19) were able selectively to activate mechanisms of heat loss (polypnea, panting and sweating) by heating the anterior hypothalamus of the cat by means of a high frequency current (Figs. 488 and 489). The most responsive region was shown to lie in the suprachiasmatic and preoptic regions, but a zone of lesser sensitivity extended caudally into the dorsal part of the hypothalamus. Later experiments on the monkey (3) revealed the presence of a similar heat-sensitive region in this species, although its location is somewhat more rostral than in the cat. These experiments suggest that the anterior hypothalamus is normally activated by any local rise of temperature or, more specifically, by the existence of a temperature gradient between the fluid outside and that inside the neurons. Such a gradient might be brought about in the intact animal whenever one organ of the body, for example a skeletal muscle, produces enough extra heat to warm the blood through the muscle and thus to elevate the temperature of the blood perfusing the hypothalamus. When the temperature gradient disappears or becomes reversed because the body surface has dissipated the extra heat, the anterior hypothalamus evidently becomes inactive again as it did in the experiments of Magoun, *et al.*, when the heating current was turned off.

The experiments of Barbour (1) suggested also that the brain stem contains neurons which are sensitive to locally applied "cold," but the location of these cells has not been determined because of the difficulty in selectively cooling isolated regions without injuring other parts of the brain. Heat can be *applied* by electrical means as noted above, but no method is yet available for *withdrawing* heat (that is, applying "cold") by any comparable procedure. Assuming that the somewhat fragmentary data now available are correct, however, an attractive hypothesis can be formulated, as follows: The body's reaction to either a hot or a cold environment is determined by the effect of that environment upon the temperature of the circulating blood and, ultimately, upon the nature of the temperature gradient which is thereby established between the fluid outside and inside the membrane at the surface of the hypothalamic neurons. This hypothesis would probably be adopted

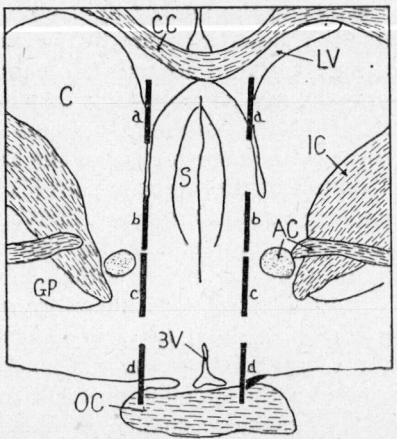

Fig. 488.—Transverse section through the brain of cat. The positions of the two electrodes during heating are shown at *a*, *b*, *c* and *d*. AC is the anterior commissure; C, caudate nucleus; CC, corpus callosum; GP, globus pallidus; IC, internal capsule; LV, lateral ventricle; OC, optic chiasma; S, septum; 3V, third ventricle. (From Magoun, Harrison, Brobeck and Ranson, *J. Neurophysiol.*, 1938, *1*:101–114.)

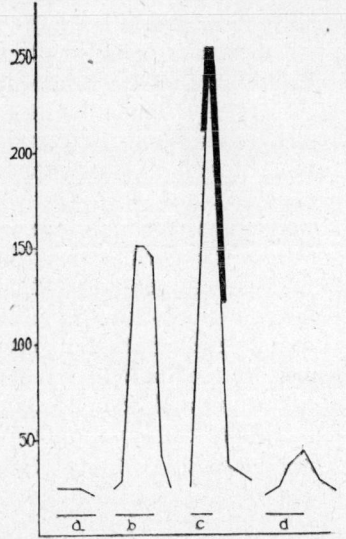

Fig. 489.—Chart showing the respective respiratory responses obtained from heating at positions *a*, *b*, *c* and *d* in Fig. 488. Respiratory rate is shown on the ordinate; panting is shown by a heavy line. Period *a* represents 5 min., other times all in proportion. (From Magoun, Harrison, Brobeck and Ranson, *J. Neurophysiol.*, 1938, *1*:101–114.)

without reservation were it not for the fact that certain investigators have found that panting and sweating, for example, are sometimes brought about before there has occurred any demonstrable rise in the temperature of the blood. This latter type of response seems to have either one of two explana-

39

tions. Ranson (22) has suggested that when panting occurs in the dog in the absence of a rise in the total heat content of the body, the panting may be a conditioned reflex evoked by some stimulus which is not thermal in nature. Sunlight is such a stimulus, and other stimuli are probably equally effective. The animal comes to associate the intense light with the problem of heat dissipation which normally follows exposure to the sun, and eventually the processes of heat loss may be set in action even before a problem of temperature control arises. Another possible explanation is suggested by the observation that sweating and vasomotor reactions may be initiated or inhibited by local changes in the temperature of the skin, mediated by way of the cutaneous, temperature-sensitive end-organs (2). One may tentatively conclude that these end-organs constitute the body's first line of defense against temperature change and, furthermore, that this line is effective because it is in communication with the hypothalamus. Adjustment of the direction and level of hypothalamic activity, therefore, appears to be brought about by one or both of two different types of temperature sensitive cells. One type, located in the anterior hypothalamus and preoptic region, is affected by the temperature of the circulating blood; the other, a peripheral mechanism, responds to temperature changes in the neighborhood of the end-organs of certain cutaneous nerve fibers.

Fever. Before concluding the discussion or temperature regulation, a word must be said about fever, hyperthermia, or pyrexia. By definition, the word *fever* refers to any condition in which the temperature of the body is above the normal range of 98° to 99° F. orally, or 99° to 100° F. in the rectum. Every such elevation means that the body contains more heat than it did before the fever began; with the onset of fever either the rate of heat dissipation must have decreased or the rate of heat production increased or both changes occurred at once. In reality, the onset is usually marked by the reactions normally observed when a subject is exposed to cold—shivering (shaking chill), pilo-erection ("gooseflesh"), cutaneous vasoconstriction and the absence of sweat. All of these conspire to augment the total amount of heat contained within the body. The termination of a bout of fever, on the other hand, is characterized by the normal reactions of heat exposure— muscular relaxation, sweating and cutaneous vasodilatation. In this way the extra heat previously stored is rather quickly disposed of and the body temperature returns to the normal level. Both the onset and termination of fever are effected, therefore, through the activity of mechanisms normally responsible for thermal equilibrium, and fever is abnormal only in that the mechanisms of heat production and conservation are called into action at a time when their function is apparently not needed because there exists no threat to thermal equilibrium.

If the hypothalamus is considered to be a "physiological thermostat," fever is a condition in which the thermostat has been set at a higher than normal level. How this is brought about is not known, but it is evidently the result of some direct action upon hypothalamic neurons. By some as yet undiscovered means the neurons of the anterior hypothalamic and preoptic regions are inhibited while those of the posterior hypothalamus are stimulated to attempt to set up a new equilibrium at a higher level. The response is not an all-or-nothing change, for fever may be established almost anywhere within the range between the normal and the lethal temperature;

moreover, fluctuations of temperature are commonly observed. In spite of the frequent occurrence of hyperthermia and its wide clinical use as an index of the course of disease, however, the physiological significance of this condition is not known and whether or not it hastens recovery from infection, for instance, is undecided.

One specific type of fever should be mentioned because it represents an interesting physiological state that is often seen clinically, especially in pediatric practice. Known as "dehydration fever," it occurs in ill-fed infants, but it may also develop in adults whose water intake is limited or whose water loss is greatly increased by profuse and prolonged sweating. In any case, when an adequate amount of water (and NaCl) is made available within the body, sweat is liberally excreted and the fever disappears. Suppression of sweating as the result of dehydration is assumed to be responsible for the hyperthermia in the first place, but whether the dehydration directly inhibits the activity of the sweat glands or whether that inhibition arises from hypothalamic dehydration has not been determined.

Finally, to return to the general problem of energy exchange and the normal equilibrium between intake and expenditure, the significance of physiological heat loss may be summarized as follows: The rate at which foodstuffs are converted into heat is made to vary in response to the stresses imposed upon the body by the environmental temperature. Heat is produced seemingly without regard for the overall energy balance which must be maintained, if at all, through the activity of the mechanisms controlling food intake (see above). In other words, energy balance may be freely sacrificed by the mechanisms which preserve thermal equilibrium. For temperature regulation, however, the body is not dependent solely upon alterations in the rate of heat production, since mechanisms are also available for increasing or decreasing the rate of heat loss per se.

REGULATION OF ENERGY STORAGE

Nature of Energy Reserves. Between the processes of food intake and energy expenditure there is interposed a kind of physiological "shock absorber," able to cushion the interaction of supply and demand. This "shock absorber" is composed of the reserve chemical energy stored within the cells. It is "elastic" and can expand to conserve surplus food which is present in the diet, or contract to give up its substance in times of emergency or when the diet is insufficient. Its response, therefore, is biphasic in character, and the process of storage may be said to be mathematically either positive or negative—*positive* when reserves are being accumulated and *negative* when they are being used up. For many years there was a tendency to believe that once a molecule had been stored in a cell it remained there indefinitely or until called upon when other sources of energy were inadequate. This idea naturally grew out of the discovery that the chemical composition of the tissues of the adult individual remains approximately constant for long periods of time—for months and even years. Since the isotopic elements have become available for biological study, however, and since it has become possible to label or "tag" individual atoms so that their presence in a tissue may be detected and the compound of which they are a part may be identified, the idea that energy reserves are chemically inactive has had to be discarded. Schoenheimer and his colleagues (26) were able to show that a continual interchange takes place between the dietary and cellular proteins, and that similar interchange is always in progress between dietary and depot fat. A molecule stored in a cell is not permanently fixed there but may be taken up again by the blood or lymph while its former place in the cell is assumed by a molecule that may have been only recently absorbed from the animal's food. Schoenheimer has called this the "dynamic state of body constituents." It is evident that the terms "positive" or "negative" storage have only a relative significance, because if a continual interchange is in progress, positive storage can only mean that the rate of deposition for the moment exceeds the rate of reabsorption of the compound in question. That is, the net result is positive in sign. Negative storage is understood to mean that the reserves are being withdrawn more rapidly than they are being replaced.

Carbohydrate reserves. The glycogen of the skeletal muscles, heart and liver constitutes the main carbohydrate reserve of the mammal. In the post-absorptive state the human body is believed to contain 100 to 150 grams of glycogen which is the equivalent of 400 to 600 Calories of heat; of this amount only about one-tenth is found in the liver while the remainder is stored within muscle cells. The ingestion of carbohydrate food leads (i) to a marked increase in liver glycogen which may then amount to as much as 75 grams or 5 per cent of the weight of the organ, and (ii) to a less dramatic but nevertheless significant increase in muscle glycogen. Muscular exercise, on the other hand, produces a fall in muscle glycogen; in the normal animal this depletion is only temporary because the resting level is later restored from glucose of the circulating plasma which is in turn replenished by the liver, either from its own glycogen or by gluconeogenesis, i.e., the conversion of protein to carbohydrate. Even under the most favorable conditions, therefore, the total amount of reserve carbohydrate available to the individual is not large, and the metabolic significance of glycogen is derived not so much from its total quantity as from the possibility of both a rapid turn-over and a transitory storage, both of which tend to adapt the energy supply to the energy expenditure at any given moment. Consequently, a small but adequate amount of carbohydrate is always available for the supply of those cells which can use no other foodstuff and which are not able to lay aside their own reserves. Because the liver is able to convert certain amino acids to glucose, however, the tissue proteins represent a large potential supply of carbohydrate, far overshadowing the carbohydrate present as such in the body at any one time.

Like many other reversible biological reactions, carbohydrate storage may be either positive or negative in sign, and the direction of the reaction appears to be determined by carbohydrate levels in body fluids. If liver glycogen is low and blood glucose is relatively high (because sugar is being absorbed from the intestine), the reaction in the liver moves in the direction of glycogen synthesis. But if liver glycogen is relatively abundant and blood glucose is being used rapidly by the tissues, the reaction moves in the direction of glycogen breakdown or glycolysis. A similar relationship exists between blood sugar and muscle glycogen. The direction of the reaction apparently conforms to the law of mass action, and although many intermediary chemical changes are known to be involved in the transformation of glucose to glycogen or vice versa, it is possible, nevertheless, to predict the direction of the whole series of reactions if the relative levels of glucose and glycogen inside and outside the cell are known. Or, more correctly, it is possible to make this prediction from the law of mass action provided that the glycogen content of the cell has not already attained a certain maximal level, for there is a limit to the amount of glycogen which can be stored in either liver or muscle. When this limit is reached, glucose is no longer stored as carbohydrate but is converted to fat in which form an almost unlimited energy reserve can be accumulated as described below.

Experiments upon animals from which the individual endocrine glands have been surgically removed and upon those same animals and also normal animals injected with various hormones have shown that the processes of glycogen synthesis and breakdown are profoundly affected by the activity of the organs of internal secretion. In the absence of insulin (the hormone of the pancreatic islets) liver glycogen falls to low levels, and even though large amounts of carbohydrate are present in the diet, normal hepatic storage will not occur unless insulin is made available at the same time. Muscle glycogen, on the other hand, is fairly well maintained in depancreatized animals, although insulin is said to promote the storage of muscle glycogen in well-fed, intact animals. The hormone of the adrenal medulla, epinephrine, affects both liver and muscle reserves by causing the breakdown of glycogen to glucose phosphates which in muscle are further split to form lactic acid and in the liver are hydrolyzed to glucose. Epinephrine is sometimes used to produce hyperglycemia because the glucose so formed in the liver diffuses into the blood circulating through that organ and thereby elevates the blood sugar level.

In the regulation of carbohydrate storage the anterior lobe of the hypophysis and the cortex of the adrenal likewise participate. Hypophysectomized animals subjected to a fast of only a few hours have low reserves of both liver and muscle glycogen at a time when depletion of the stores of normal animals is scarcely perceptible; the injection of anterior lobe extracts containing what has been called the "glycostatic" factor restores the normal glycogen levels. Moreover, fasted adrenalectomized rats undergo a rapid depletion of liver glycogen alone, which can be returned to the normal level by the administration of cortical extract. Here is a complicated situation, first, because the hypophysis is normally responsible for the activity of the adrenal cortex through the influence of the corticotropic hormone, and second, because it is not easy to decide whether the storage of glycogen is the result of an increased rate of synthesis or a decreased rate of breakdown and utilization. Russell (25) has reported the results of experiments which suggest that the anterior lobe, apart from its corticotropic action, is responsible primarily for the maintenance of the normal rate of carbohydrate utilization, while the adrenal cortex regulates the rate of formation of carbohydrate from protein, i.e., gluconeogenesis. When the anterior lobe is removed, Russell's data show that the rate of peripheral utilization of glucose is enhanced with the result that first the liver and then the muscle glycogen stores are depleted; conversely, under the influence of the "glycostatic" principle the rate of utilization is inhibited, the rate of glycogen breakdown is thereby retarded and accumulation of glycogen up to the normal limit again takes place. When the adrenals are removed, however, positive glycogen storage no longer occurs in the liver of fasted animals because the glucose from which glycogen is normally formed during fasting is no longer available. Glycogen already formed is used up without the possibility of its replacement. As Long (17) has shown, the injection of cortical extract re-establishes the process of gluconeogenesis in the liver, glucose is formed and glycogen synthesis can then be effected. If this conception of these mechanisms is correct, it is evident that neither the anterior lobe nor the adrenal cortex participates directly in the mechanisms of glycogen storage, but that both glands appear to exert their effects by way of their ability either to increase or to decrease the amount of carbohydrate available for glycogen storage. Epinephrine, by contrast, evidently takes part in the process of glycogenolysis in some more direct, specific manner, since this hormone will bring about the breakdown of glycogen to form glucose even when a hyperglycemia is already present. Further study of the mechanisms of hormonal action will undoubtedly clarify what is now a rather confusing picture.

Protein reserves. The total protein content of the body of a male subject weighing 70 kilograms is about 14 kilograms, or 20 per cent of the body weight. If the subject of the experiment is a well-fed adult, adding protein to his diet fails to induce any significant positive storage of protein, but rather increases the urinary excretion of nitrogen and possibly also the storage of fat which is formed from deaminated amino acid residues. But if protein is removed from the diet or if the subject is fasted, a negative storage will occur as tissue protein is broken down to amino acids which are then deaminated and catabolized to furnish energy and heat to the body. When protein or amino acid nitrogen is again made available in the diet in large enough quantities, a positive storage will be observed until a reconstitution of tissue protein has taken place. The body of the normal, well-fed adult, therefore, contains reserve protein to the extent of two or three kilograms or about 16 per cent of the total protein content, and although further positive storage does not normally occur, negative storage may take place as the reserve is utilized during protein starvation. Once the protein reserves have been depleted, positive storage can then be achieved.

In a growing animal, on the other hand, either positive or negative protein storage may occur. The growth hormone of the anterior lobe of the hypophysis selectively facilitates nitrogen retention and protein synthesis; consequently, a growing youth will retain as protein a larger fraction of a given amount of dietary nitrogen than is normally retained by the adult. Surgical removal of the hypophysis of a young animal inhibits growth and produces the familiar picture of pituitary dwarfism. By the injection of anterior lobe extracts, nitrogen retention can be brought about in hypophysectomized animals; and if the total amount of food given to the animal is restricted to the pre-injection intake, the rate of formation of fat will be found to be decreased by the anterior lobe hormone because tissue protein is now being formed at the expense of food which was previously being converted into fat. If the food intake is not restricted, however, the rate of fat formation may be unchanged by the injected hormone since the animal spontaneously increases its food intake and thus gains both the energy and the amino acid nitrogen needed for the growth process. The growth principle, recently isolated by Li and Evans (16), is appropriately regarded, therefore, as probably the most important factor in the regulation of growth, and of the rate of positive protein storage in the adult as well. Nevertheless, the mechanisms which regulate the rate of liberation of the hormone by the anterior lobe of the hypophysis in the young as well as in the adult animal are completely unknown.

Immature as well as mature individuals may undergo negative protein storage under the influence of the hormone of the adrenal cortex. Extracts of this gland increase the amount of nitrogen and potassium excreted in the urine, evidence that intracellular protein is being catabolized by the animals treated with the hormone. Most of this protein is apparently converted to carbohydrate and then utilized by the body for energy or heat (17). Under a great many different conditions of environmental stress—cold exposure, anoxia, severe exercise, infection, trauma, burns, starvation, etc.—the rate of liberation of the adrenal cortical hormone is enhanced, protein catabolism is thereby increased and the urinary excretion of nitrogen rises to high levels. Dougherty and White (12) have shown that the protein of lymphoid tissue, the thymus and lymph nodes, is particularly sensitive to the action of cortical hormone, the injection of which effects a remarkable loss of weight of lymphoid tissue. The same result can be brought about in animals with intact adrenal glands by injecting the corticotropic principle of the anterior lobe, which activates the adrenal cortices and thereby increases the breakdown of protein. Ultimately, then, the rate of protein catabolism is controlled by the anterior lobe of the hypophysis by way of the adrenal cortex, but again, the factors responsible for the control of the anterior lobe have not been identified.

Lipid reserves. Like the storage of carbohydrate and protein, lipid storage may be either positive or negative in sign, it is accomplished through chemical reactions which appear to be easily reversible, and a continual interchange normally occurs between substances circulating in the blood and compounds already deposited in the tissues. In one remarkable particular, however, the storage of fat differs from the storage of carbohydrate and protein: positive storage of carbohydrate and protein occurs only in immature, growing animals or in adults whose reserves have been temporarily depleted, and in every case there is a normal limit above which the body's content of these two types of compounds cannot be elevated. When the depots are full, no more can be added. But in the storage of fat there appears to be almost no limit to the amount which can be deposited and retained by either the growing youth or the adult. Net positive storage can evidently continue for an indefinite period of time, since the available depots of the subcutaneous tissue, omentum, subperitoneal tissue, epicardium, the skeletal muscles and other parts of the body never appear to become full and may contain altogether more than 100 kilograms of fat.

Regulation of lipid storage by the central nervous system or by the endocrine glands has never been proved to be of any importance in either the normal or the obese subject. It is true that in the liver an excessive fatty infiltration may occur as the result of a dietary choline deficiency, or following carbon tetrachloride or phosphorus poisoning, or in various other types of metabolic disorder; but the lipid accumulation in each of these conditions appears to be the result of a failure of normal metabolism rather than a typical mechanism for the creation of reserve supplies of fat (Chap. 51). It is like the hyperglycemia of diabetes mellitus—an interesting abnormality from which a great deal has been learned regarding normal metabolic processes, but not in itself a means of energy storage. Most of the available evidence suggests that under normal circumstances the formation of depot fat is conditioned entirely by the existing relationship between energy supply and demand. When supply exceeds demand, fat is stored; when demand exceeds supply, negative storage takes place. In view of the fact that the calorific value of fat is twice that of carbohydrate or protein, a certain economy of bulk is achieved by storing energy in the adipose tissue, especially since fat, unlike the other foodstuffs, is stored almost anhydrously.

The nature of these relationships suggests that the excessive deposition of fat in obese individuals may have any one or any combination of three primary causes. (i) Food intake may be larger than normal. In clinical medicine obesity of this type is often encountered, but because the mechanisms which influence food intake are so complicated in human subjects, the cause of the abnormal "appetite" is not often discovered. In the laboratory this obesity has been observed in two types of experimental animals, viz., (a) hereditary obesity of yellow female mice, originally described by Danforth (10) and later shown by Conn (9) to be caused by an excessive food intake; (b) the hypothalamic obesity referred to earlier in this chapter. The problem here does not concern the regulation of fat storage, but rather the regulation of food intake. (ii) Food intake may be normal but work output may be diminished. Whether this condition occurs clinically has not been established, although the suggestion has been made by Greene (14) that otherwise normal subjects may gain weight rapidly when they suffer some traumatic injury which confines them to bed for a period of weeks or months. Hetherington and Ranson (15) described this type of obesity in rats with hypothalamic lesions; some of their animals ate approximately the same amount of food as the controls, but the operated rats exhibited a striking reduction in motor output as measured in "activity" cages. (iii) If the food intake and work accomplishment are within normal limits, the deposition of an excessive amount of fat should follow any reduction in the total amount of heat lost by the body. Attempts to test this possibility have repeatedly shown that the basal heat production, at least, is not depressed in obese subjects as measured by the basal metabolic rate. On the contrary, the total basal heat production of obese subjects is greater than the normal average (30). Moreover, the amount of heat produced following the ingestion of food, the so-called "specific dynamic action" of food, has also been measured and shown to be quantitatively insignificant as an etiological factor in obesity (31). Furthermore, measurements of the heat production associated with muscular exercise in normal and obese patients suggest that muscular efficiency is depressed in obesity and not enhanced as it would have to be if this were an important etiological factor.

Although obesity theoretically might occur upon the reduction of either work output or heat loss if the food intake is maintained at the normal level, it is well to notice that in the normal individual the food intake is fairly well adjusted to energy expenditure. When expenditure increases because of exposure to cold or work, food consumption spontaneously becomes larger; and, within limits, warm environments and rest tend to depress the food intake. It follows, then, that even if obesity should be proved to be the result of a diminished work or heat output in the presence of a normal intake, the propriety of regarding this food consumption as "normal" might be questioned on good grounds, since if a normal energy balance were maintained, food intake would be proportionately diminished. In the last analysis, all three types of mechanism by which obesity has been theoretically explained must be tentatively regarded as fundamentally alike because each of them requires the presence of either an absolute or a relative hyperphagia.

REFERENCES

1. BARBOUR, H. G. Die Wirkung unmittelbarer Erwärmung und Abkühlung der Wärmezentra auf die Körpertemperatur. *Arch. exp. Path. Pharmak.*, 1912, *70:*1–26.

2. BAZETT, H. C. Physiological responses to heat. *Physiol. Rev.*, 1927, *7:*531–599.

3. BEATON, L. F., McKINLEY, W. A., BERRY, C. M. and RANSON, S. W. Localization of cerebral center activating heat-loss mechanisms in monkeys. *J. Neurophysiol.*, 1941, *4:*478–485.

4. BROBECK, J. R. Effects of variations in activity, food intake and environmental temperature on weight gain in the albino rat. *Amer. J. Physiol.*, 1945, *143:*1–5.

5. BROBECK, J. R., TEPPERMAN, J. and LONG, C. N. H. Experimental hypothalamic hyperphagia in the albino rat. *Yale J. Biol. Med.*, 1943, *15:*831–853.

6. BROWMAN, L. G. The effect of controlled temperatures upon the spontaneous activity rhythms of the albino rat. *J. exp. Zool.*, 1943, *94:*477–489.

7. CANNON, W. B. and WASHBURN, A. L. An explanation of hunger. *Amer. J. Physiol.*, 1912, *29:*441–454.

8. CARLSON, A. J. *The control of hunger in health and disease.* Chicago, University of Chicago Press, 1919. vii, 319 pp.

9. CONN, J. W. Obesity. II. Etiological aspects. *Physiol. Rev.*, 1944, *24:*31–45.

10. DANFORTH, C. H. Hereditary adiposity in mice. *J. Hered.*, 1927, *18:*153–162.

11. DILL, D. B. *Life, heat and altitude.* Cambridge, Harvard University Press, 1938. 211 pp.

12. DOUGHERTY, T. F. and WHITE, A. Influence of hormones on lymphoid tissue structure and function. The role of the pituitary adrenotropic hormone in the regulation of the lymphocytes and other cellular elements of the blood *Endocrinology*, 1944, *35:*1–14.

13. DUBOIS, E. F. Heat loss from the human body. *Bull. N. Y. Acad. Med.*, Ser. 2, 1939, *15:*143–173.

14. GREENE, J. A. Clinical study of the etiology of obesity. *Ann. intern. Med.*, 1939, *12:*1797–1803.

15. HETHERINGTON, A. W. and RANSON, S. W. The spontaneous activity and food intake of rats with hypothalamic lesions. *Amer. J. Physiol.*, 1942, *136:*609–617.

16. LI, C. H. and EVANS, H. M. The isolation of pituitary growth hormone. *Science*, 1944, *99:*183–184.

17. LONG, C. N. H. A discussion of the mechanism of action of adrenal cortical hormones on carbohydrate and protein metabolism. *Endocrinology*, 1942, *30:*870–883.

18. LUSK, G. *The elements of the science of nutrition*, 4th ed. Philadelphia, W. B. Saunders Co., 1928. 844 pp.

19. MAGOUN, H. W., HARRISON, F., BROBECK, J. R. and RANSON, S. W. Activation of heat loss mechanisms by local heating of the brain. *J. Neurophysiol.*, 1938, *1:*101–114.

20. MORGAN, C. T. and MORGAN, J. D. Studies in hunger. I. The effects of insulin upon the rat's rate of eating. *J. genet. Psychol.*, 1940, *56:*137–147.

21. RANSON, S. W. Some functions of the hypothalamus. *Harvey Lect.*, 1936–37, *32:*92–121.

22. RANSON, S. W. Regulation of body temperature. *Res. Publ. Ass. nerv. ment. Dis.*, 1940, *20:*342–399.

23. RICHTER, C. P. Animal behavior and internal drives. *Quart. Rev. Biol.*, 1927, *2:*307–343.

24. RUCH, T. C. and SHENKIN, H. A. The relation of area 13 on orbital surface of frontal lobes to hyperactivity and hyperphagia in monkeys. *J. Neurophysiol.*, 1943, *6:*349–360.

25. RUSSELL, J. A. The adrenals and hypophysis in the carbohydrate metabolism of the eviscerated rat. *Amer. J. Physiol.*, 1943, *140:*98–106.

26. SCHOENHEIMER, R. *The dynamic state of body constituents.* Cambridge, Harvard University Press, 1942. 78 pp.

27. SCOTT, W. W., SCOTT, C. C. and LUCKHARDT, A. B. Observations on the blood sugar level before, during and after hunger periods in humans. *Amer. J. Physiol.*, 1938, *123:*243–247.

28. SLONAKER, J. R. The normal activity of the albino rat from birth to natural death, its rate of growth and the duration of life. *J. Anim. Behav.*, 1912, *2:*20–42.

29. SLONAKER, J. R. Analysis of daily activity of the albino rat. *Amer. J. Physiol.*, 1925, *73:*485–503.

30. STRANG, J. M. and EVANS, F. A. The energy exchange in obesity. *J. clin. Invest.*, 1928, *6:*277–289.

31. STRANG, J. M. and McCLUGAGE, H. B. The specific dynamic action of food in abnormal states of nutrition. *Amer. J. med. Sci.*, 1931, *182:*49–81.

32. WANG, G. H. A sexual activity rhythm in the female rat. *Amer. Nat.*, 1924, *58:*36–42.

SECTION X

PHYSIOLOGY OF REPRODUCTION

By William U. Gardner

The most characteristic feature differentiating the animate from the inanimate is the capacity of the former to reproduce itself. It might be considered that all life is directed toward the maintenance of the species and therefore that all vital processes constitute essential phases in the physiology of reproduction. Such a broad aspect of reproduction will not be considered here. However, since reproduction is such a fundamental phenomenon it is not surprising that, at times, it is difficult to distinguish sharply between those physiological processes concerned directly with reproduction and those indirectly concerned.

Most physiological processes form complete units within one living body; integrating or coordinating mechanisms do not have to span the space between two organisms. Reproduction in higher animals, however, requires a physiological adjustment between at least two separate living units. The maintenance of the species is a responsibility not entrusted to one individual; the contributions of two individuals are essential. The immature organism of mammalian complexity cannot instantaneously adapt itself to an independent existence. After a period of intra-uterine residence of the developing organism provision must be made also for its extra-uterine life, again a process demanding a physiological coordination between two organisms.

With reproduction sex must also be considered, and yet "there is no such biological entity as sex." By sex reference is made to the total morphological and functional difference within the species which can be associated with the production of either sperm or ova. It is impossible to define sex without allusion to sexes, without comparing or contrasting morphological differences in the gametes, the somatic proportions or modifications of the body, or even in temperament or psychological qualities.

The early studies on reproduction were concerned mainly with the elucidation of the morphological differences or homologies of the male and female. After the discovery of and application of the microscope to biological material, attention was directed to studies of sperm and finally, but little over one hundred years ago, the first mammalian ova were described. Later studies were concerned with the cytological aspect of the marriage of the sperm and the ova to produce a single cell capable of multiplication and differentiation and finally of becoming another individual of the species. At the same time the somatic differentiation of the developing organism was being studied and, in the maturing body, a sequence of morphological alterations was associated with the production of new generations of gametes and with the protection and nourishment of the fertilized ovum, embryo, fetus and newborn.

A young Dutch physician, Regnier de Graaf, in 1672 first described the ovarian follicles (Graafian follicle). He, however, mistook the follicles for eggs, undoubtedly influenced by the observations on the ovaries of birds. He considered that "all men and animals take their origin from an egg—existing before coitus in the female testicles." The ova were not discovered until Karl Ernst von Baer in 1827 first observed the small barely macroscopic globules in the ovarian follicles of a dog. Although sperm are much smaller than ova, their discovery followed that of the large Graafian follicles by but a few years. This was probably due to the independent existence of sperm in a fluid medium which facilitated their microscopic observation. Antony van Leeuwenhoek first illustrated mammalian sperm in 1678.

Inquiry into the mechanisms regulating the production of germ cells and the attainment of their destiny contribute to our knowledge of physiology of reproduction. The nervous system was first studied in great detail as a system facilitating internal coordination of body function. Early studies indicated, however, that some other mechanisms existed to regulate at least certain aspects of reproductive phenomena. The relation of the gonads to certain phases of sexual manifestations was known from early times. After the postulation of internal secretions or hormones as regulators of body functions it was assumed that the gonads might function also as endocrine glands. Experiments involving gonadal ablation and transplantation affirmed these assumptions, and subsequently extracts of the gonads and finally chemical substances isolated from the gonads were found active in substituting for some gonadal functions. Almost simultaneously the pituitary gland was shown to regulate the functions of the gonads, and more recently the function of the mammary glands. A multiplicity of specific hormones, several of which have been isolated as chemical entities, enter into the physiological aspects of reproduction. Even so, the mechanisms regulating several aspects of the phenomena are not yet known and the probable interrelations of the known hormones are understood incompletely.

CHAPTER 54

REPRODUCTION IN THE FEMALE

THE OVARY AND ITS HORMONES

During the period of active sexual life, the ovaries undergo profound rhythmic structural and functional changes which are associated with modifications in the structure and function of other tissues, glands or organs and even the behavioral characteristics of the mammalian organism. The maturation of the ova in mammals is not a continuous process but an interrupted one; one follicle or group of follicles grows, matures and ovulates in the adult ovary at one time and others at more or less regular successive intervals. The intervals determined by the cyclic ovarian changes are designated estrous cycles in the many subprimate mammalian species and menstrual cycles in man and other primates. These two types of cycles are similar in that they both reflect the activity of the ovaries, but they are quite different in details to be mentioned later.

The term estrus (oestrus is preferred by the British) was first used by Walter Heape in 1901 to denote the periods of sexual excitement or "heat" occurring in many animals. The adjectival form is estrous. Animals of many species have periods of sexual activity restricted to but a few weeks or months during one or two seasons of the year, and are known as seasonal breeders. In some of these species the females are continually receptive to the male (in estrus) for a period of weeks or months providing copulation does not occur. Other species show a series of estrous cycles, and in the absence of copulation eventually become anestrous at the beginning of the nonbreeding season.

The ovaries exhibit three different types of cycles. One type corresponds to the life cycle of the individual during which they develop, attain functional maturity and ultimate senescence. A second type of cycle, the estrous or menstrual cycles, occurs during the span of sexually active life. The reproductive or third type of cycle also occurs during the period of sexually active life, is repeated with each gestation, and in man is about ten times as long as a menstrual cycle. Reference will be made to details of the different ovarian cycles later.

Evidence of ovarian endocrine function was first determined by observations on animals subsequent to ovariectomy. The genital tissues retained their infantile characteristics if the animals were young when gonadectomized, or the uteri, mammary glands and vaginal mucosae atrophied if sexually mature animals were ovariectomized. Successful transplants or grafts of ovaries made at different sites largely restored the atrophic genital tissues.*

* Successful transplantations of gonads in mammals have been made from one individual to a second site in the same individual (autotransplantation), or from one individual to a closely related individual within the same species (homotransplantation). Grafts of ovaries of one species into another (heterotransplantation) or even of unrelated animals of the same species are but questionably or never successful. Grafts of gonads can be most successfully made in gonadectomized hosts, an observation that at one time led investigators to assume a gonadal antagonism or a competition of the intact and transplanted gonads for some vital substance, designated X-substance by Heape.

The early experiments did not adequately reveal whether the follicles or the corpora lutea that formed after ovulation were the source of the endocrine secretion. Histological examination of the ovarian tissues indicated that the corpora lutea were more obviously glandular than the granulosa cells and surrounding theca of the follicles. In rabbits the corpora lutea were first noted to be essential for the growth of the endometria to a state at which they would permit implantation of fertilized ova. Pregnancy terminated in rabbits and in animals of several other species when the corpora lutea were removed (8).

The ovary is surrounded, except at the hilus, by a layer of cuboidal epithelial cells which constitute the germinal epithelium (Fig. 490). In some species new ova may arise from this layer and migrate into the ovary even during adult life but it is doubtful if new ova arise after birth in man. The ovaries at birth contain several hundred thousand ova—a number which progressively diminishes throughout life. The ova develop within follicles which have an inner layer or layers of granulosal cells and outer layers of cells contributed by

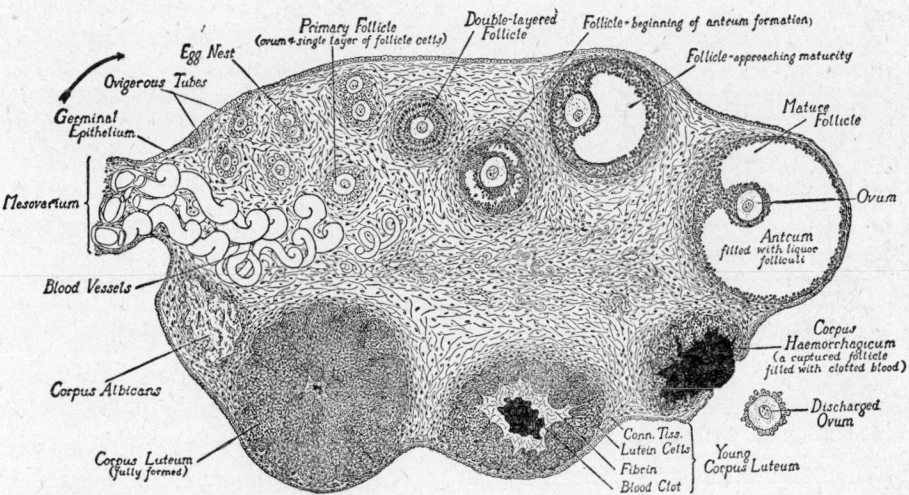

Fig. 490.—Schematic diagram of a mammalian ovary showing the sequence of events in the origin, growth and rupture of the ovarian follicle and the formation and retrogression of a corpus luteum. (From Patten, *Embryology of the pig*, Philadelphia, P. Blakiston & Son, 1927.)

the ovarian stroma, the theca. A mature follicle contains a cavity filled with liquor folliculi surrounded by a syncytial mass of granulosal cells. In one clump of these cells, the cumulus oophorus, the ovum is embedded. Surrounding the basement membrane upon which the outermost granulosal cells rest are two layers of ovarian stroma which form a vascular theca interna, which may contain cells with cytoplasmic secretory granules, and a more fibrous theca externa. After ovulation the mature ovum (in man about 120μ in diameter) escapes and the granulosal cells transform into the luteal cells of a corpus luteum. The vascular ovarian stroma consists of fibroblast-like cells in animals of most species. The stromal cells, however, change in appearance under some conditions to be mentioned later.

Most of the ova do not attain maturity. During an average life span only 400 to 450 may ovulate. The remainder and by far the greater number of the ova and their follicles regress at different stages in their development.

The endocrine function of the testis was demonstrated first by Arnold Berthold in 1849. He was so impressed by the secondary sexual characters of cockerels that he used them in his experiments. Castrated cockerels (capons) acquired a normal cock's appearance and attitude when testes were transplanted into their abdominal cavities. Although Leydig (1857) described the glandular interstitial cells, now called Leydig cells, in the intertubular areas of the testis, they have only recently been shown to be the source of male hormones.

The endocrine activity of the ovaries was first shown convincingly when Emil Knauer (1896) noted that autotransplantation of ovaries prevented the atrophy of the uterus subsequent to ovariectomy, and demonstrated that neural connections between the uteri and ovaries, if they did exist, were not essential.

In 1917 Stockard and Papanicolaou discovered that the type of cells obtained in the smears of the vaginal epithelia of guinea pigs could be correlated with the development of follicles in the ovary. When large follicles formed and ovulated the epithelial cells were cornified. Similarly in rats and mice the vaginal mucosae cast off cornified epithelial cells which could be detected on smears at those times during the cycle when large or ovulating follicles were present. The morphological changes in the vaginal smear indicative of estrus appeared in some animals in which ovulation and the formation of corpora

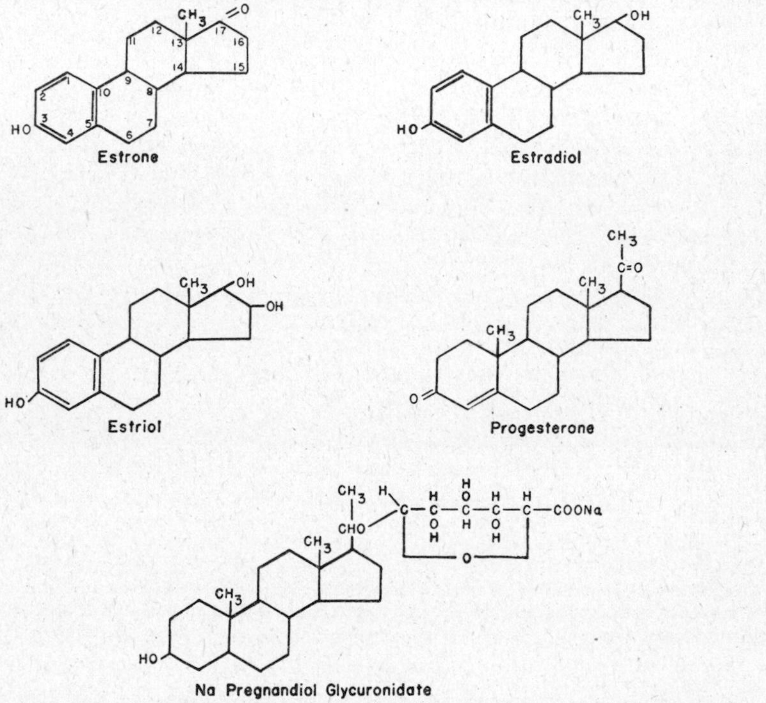

Fig. 491.—The structural formulae of three normally occurring estrogens, of progesterone, and of sodium pregnandiol glucuronidate.

lutea did not occur, indicating that the follicles alone could elicit cyclic activity. Liquor folliculi from large follicles or lipoid soluble extracts of this liquor contained a substance which would induce vaginal cornification in castrated mice; in other words, would replace the endocrine function of the ovaries with their large follicles. Allen and Doisy (3), who in 1923 first demonstrated the active substance in cell free preparations, called it the ovarian follicular hormone or the primary ovarian hormone. Although the granulosal cells were first thought to secrete follicular hormone, recent histological and histochemical studies indicate that the theca interna is its source (11).

The primary ovarian hormone was detected also in corpora lutea, blood, other body tissues and in urine; in fact, during pregnancy the urine of women contains very large amounts of the hormone. Two active chemical substances were identified in pregnancy urines, one called *theelin* or *estrone* (3-hydroxy-17-keto-1:3:5-estratriene) and one called *theelol* or *estriol* (3-16-17-trihydroxy-1:3:5-estratriene). Later a third and very active chemical was extracted from pigs' ovaries and identified as a partially reduced derivative of estrone called *estradiol* (3-17-dihydroxy-1:3:5-estratriene). All of these compounds are biologically active in producing vaginal cornification and other changes in the genital tissues (12). Collectively they are called *estrogens*. The adjective designating their action is *estrogenic*. It has been stated that the estrogen is the hormone of the woman or female because it is essential for the development of the accessory genital organs and secondary sexual characters.

The corpora lutea which develop from the ruptured follicles were first associated with uterine growth to facilitate implantation of the ovum, with mammary development and the maintenance of pregnancy. Early attempts to obtain active extracts of ovarian hormones were made with ovaries containing corpora lutea. It was not until 1929, however, that extracts of corpora lutea were obtained by Corner and Allen which would maintain pregnancy in ovariectomized rabbits and induce an endometrium capable of implanting a fertilized ovum. The active chemical isolated from these extracts is called progesterone (3,20-diketoΔ4-pregnene). Progesterone has been found in extracts of the adrenal cortex and "progestin" in extracts of the placenta but in no other body tissues or fluids. The most probable excretory product of progesterone in man is sodium pregnandiol glucuronidate (Fig. 491).

A number of synthetic chemicals which do not possess a cyclopentenophenanthrene nucleus also possess estrogenic activity. The most active of these compounds of 4:4'-dihydroxy-$\alpha\beta$-diethylstilbene, or, as it is commonly called, *stilbestrol*, is almost five times as active as estrone (13). Many combinations of alkyl groups have been substituted for the ethyl groups. Unlike the normally occurring estrogens, stilbestrol is relatively less readily destroyed during absorption by the gastro-intestinal tract and hence more suitable for oral administration.

Estrogen is assayed biologically by determining the minimal amount required to produce vaginal cornification in castrated rats or mice from 48 to 56 hours after the first, a series of injections. The International Unit (I.U.) is 0.1 μg. of estrone, or approximately one Mouse Unit (M.U.). Other biological tests are now available for detecting much smaller amounts of hormone in which the response to local application of the hormone in the rat's vagina or the early response of the immature rat's uterus is determined. Colorimetric methods are also available for the estimation of the estrogens.

Progesterone is determined biologically by its capacity to induce formation of a progestational endometrium in young adult rabbits. One mg. of the pure chemical equals 1 International Unit (I.U.), the amount of hormone which when injected during a period of 5 days will elicit a progestational reaction by the sixth day (a Corner-Allen unit). Much smaller amounts are effective when applied directly to the endometrium.

In addition to the ovary estrogens are produced at other sites such as the testes of stallions, the adrenal glands and adrenal tumors, and the placentas of pregnant animals (12).

THE MENSTRUAL CYCLE

A menstrual cycle usually is defined as the period which in the normal nonpregnant primate extends from the onset of one period of uterine bleeding to the onset of the following period. Being rhythmic, the menstrual cycle might be dated from any other obvious point but in man the onset of menstruation is the one most constantly apparent phenomenon. The most frequent length of the cycle in man is 28 days although it may range from 20 days to about 35 days in apparently normal individuals (24). Cycles ranging from 25 to 30 days in length are very common, even in the same individual. It has been well stated that the one regularity of the menstrual cycle is its irregularity. This is not unexpected in view of the numerous factors which must act in the regulation of the cycle.

The menstrual cycle is divided into several phases determined largely by the histology of the endometrium (Fig. 492). The first part of the cycle, the period of *menstruation*, most frequently lasts five days although again the length of the period may vary. During menstruation hemorrhage occurs in the endometrial stroma which loses its vitality and, together with the unclotted interstitial blood, is sloughed into the uterine lumen to attain exit through the vagina as the menstrual discharge. Menstruation is a period characterized by endometrial degeneration. The second period of the cycle is called the *preovulatory stage* (proliferative stage) and lasts for approximately seven to

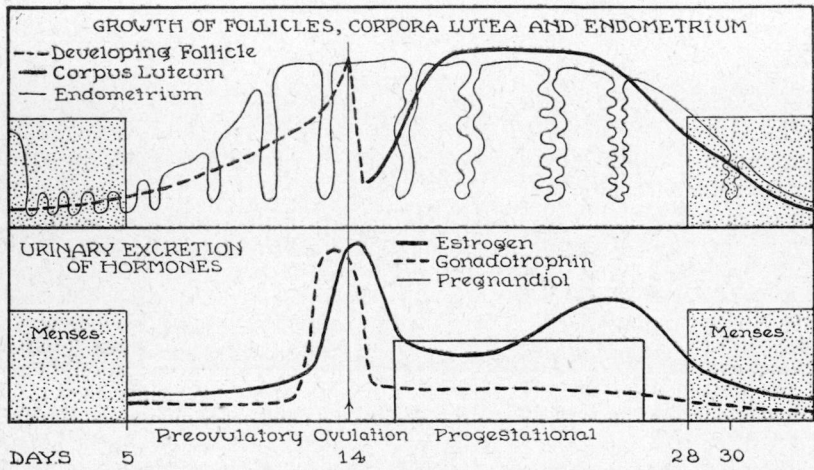

Fig. 492.—Diagrammatic presentation of the increased thickness of the endometrium and changes in shape of the endometrial glands in relation to the size of the ovarian follicles and corpora lutea and the urinary excretion of sex hormones and gonadotrophins during a menstrual cycle.

ten days (4). The epithelium of the uterine mucosa grows out from the remnants of glands in the basalis to repair the surface of the lumen and the entire endometrium increases in thickness. The straight uterine glands which develop at this time are lined by columnar epithelium. The third period of the cycle is called the *progestational stage* (secretory stage). This period extends over approximately the last 12 to 14 days of the cycle. The endometria during this period are modified progressively until the stroma becomes loose and edematous and the actively secreting glands become extremely folded and tortuous. Endometria of this type are ready to receive and implant a fertilized ovum. If a fertile ovum is not available, however, the uterine mucosa again degenerates. The changes in the developing endometrial structure are not rapid; they blend into one another. Actually different areas of the uterine lining of the same individual may be at different stages at any one time (6).

The absence of menses subsequent to menarche is designated as a condition of amenorrhea. Certain premonitory symptoms frequently precede the onset of menstruation, such as pains in the back or head or a general feeling of discomfort. When these symptoms are unusually painful and protracted the condition is designated dysmenorrhea. Approximately 35 cc. of blood are usually lost during menses although the amount may range from 10 to 200 cc. The blood characteristically does not clot during normal menses.

Some authors include two other stages: a stage of repair, following menstruation, and an "interval" stage during the middle of the cycle. These stages are not included in the preceding classification because the period of repair occurs during menstruation as well as subsequent to it. The "interval" implies a period of rest or absence of change which does not necessarily exist. It should be remembered that, although the existence of definite stages is implied, the endometrial changes are progressive rather than stepwise. A progestational or secretory stage does not appear in those cycles in which ovulation does not take place. In such cycles the term "premenstrual" would be more satisfactory. The morphological condition of the endometrium at different stages of ovarian development was first associated and described by Hitschmann and Adler (32).

Relation between the ovaries and the menstrual cycle. Just before the onset of menstruation the corpus luteum begins to regress. Progesterone which is formed by the corpora lutea is no longer elaborated. The endometrium which developed under the influence of this hormone cannot be maintained without it. The rapid degeneration is accompanied by endometrial sloughing and hemorrhage. During and after menstruation one or more follicles of moderate size begin to grow more rapidly than other similar follicles. As they attain large sizes the endometrium increases in thickness. By approximately the midpoint of the menstrual cycle one follicle attains maturity and ovulates. The other larger follicles usually regress—become *atretic*. After ovulation the follicle collapses, the granulosa cells are transformed into luteal cells and become well vascularized to form a corpus luteum. During this period the progestational endometrium develops under the influence of the hormones produced by the corpus luteum (32).

The endometria of the preovulatory type are attained during the period of follicular growth and of the progestational type during the period of the dominance of the corpus luteum. The rhythmicity of the uterus is maintained by the rhythmic changes in the ovaries. During some cycles ovulation may not occur and corpora lutea fail to form (42). This would be a sterile cycle and might be considered abnormal. Such *anovulatory* cycles are superficially indistinguishable from the *ovulatory* cycles. If corpora lutea do not form, progestational endometria do not develop. The large follicle or follicles persist about two weeks beyond the usual time of ovulation and, as they undergo atresia, uterine hemorrhage and slough occur. In such circumstances menstruation occurs from a preovulatory type of endometrium.

Endocrine factors in the menstrual cycle

Women, when ovariectomized at any time during the latter two or three weeks of the menstrual cycle, usually show uterine bleeding within two to six days after the operation. Also menstruation usually follows section or damage to the spinal cord when these lesions occur during the latter part of the cycle. The entire cycle may be shortened to twelve days or more in such cases. Monkeys also menstruate subsequent to ovariectomy even if the operation is performed as early as the seventh day of the cycle (2, 53). Also (i) experimental section of the ventral roots of the lower thoracic or upper lumbar spinal nerves, (ii) hemisection of the cord or (iii) section of the splanchnics was followed by precocious uterine bleeding. Subsequent cycles in these animals occurred at intervals similar to those observed preoperatively, an indication that the neural lesions probably produced transitory trophic deficiencies in the ovaries which were reflected by uterine regression and bleeding.

Estrogens when administered to ovariectomized primates in adequate amounts for ten days or more induce endometrial hypertrophy; if the stimulus is adequate, a preovulatory or proliferative type of endometrium develops (4). Uterine bleeding occurs within six to ten days subsequent to the discontinuance of the injections, the so-called *estrogen-withdrawal bleeding* or menstruation from a proliferative endometrium (Fig. 493). If estrogens are given daily in large amounts, menstruation may be prevented for very long periods; if

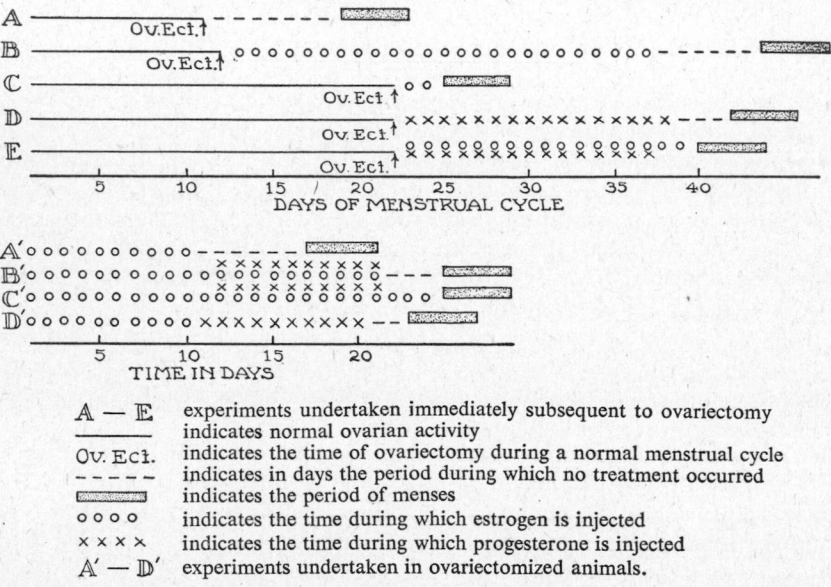

Fig. 493.—Diagram of experimental procedures undertaken on women or female monkeys to elucidate the problem of menstruation.

in smaller amounts, periodic bleeding may occur in spite of continuous treatment, the uterus periodically becoming refractory to the levels of hormone administered.

When estrogens are given to intact monkeys or women menstruation is inhibited if the administration starts during the first part of the cycle but not if started during the latter part of the cycle. Approximately two days after the removal of a functional corpus luteum menstruation occurs and cannot be prevented even if estrogens are injected (58). The simultaneous administration of estrogen and progesterone induces a progestational (secretory or premenstrual) endometrium which bleeds within about two or three days if injections of both hormones are discontinued or if progesterone alone is withheld, demonstrating again that estrogens will not prevent bleeding from a progestational endometrium that develops either in the normal cycle or is induced experimentally (see Fig. 493).

Menstruation cannot be considered an actively induced process (9). It occurs upon cessation of stimulation of the endometrium, and from either a preovulatory or a progestational endometrium, it accompanies uterine involution or regression. Although the uteri of all mammals regress cyclically, marked hemorrhage or menstruation is limited to the noncornuate uteri of primates.

The factors associated with menstruation have been studied in great detail in monkeys by directly observing the uterine mucosa subsequent to transplantation into the anterior chamber of the eye (35). The endometrial transplants undergo cyclic changes similar to those of the intact uteri. One to five days preceding the onset of bleeding, the endometrial circulation is impaired, apparently by an unusual resistance to flow through the coiled arteries in the deeper layers of the endometrium. During this period the endometrium regresses and becomes thinner. Four to twenty-four hours before menstruation the coiled arteries constrict for periods of several hours, further reducing the blood supply to the peripheral tissues. At intervals first one and then another artery dilates and hemorrhage occurs from the distal arterioles or capillaries into the superficial parts of the endometrium, forming small hematomas. After a short period (30 seconds to a few minutes) of hemorrhage the arteries again contract and bleeding ceases. Other coiled endometrial arteries likewise dilate, bleed and constrict although not simultaneously. Each artery bleeds only once during each cycle; successive series of arteries bleed at different intervals throughout the menstrual period, so one small area of endometrium may hemorrhage, slough and be repaired before another area has sloughed.

Attempts to induce menstrual bleeding by drugs or means which will effect ischemia, hyperemia or alter vascular permeation by fluids have been made frequently but the results have not contributed significantly to the explanation of the periodic hemorrhage.

Evidence of hormone production during the menstrual cycle

Hormones may be consumed in eliciting responses in the end-organs upon which they act, may be destroyed within the body at sites remote from the end-organ, or be excreted in the urine. The amounts of estrogen, progesterone or gonadotrophin produced may be estimated by determining the requirements of exogenous hormone necessary to restore the function of genital tissues subsequent to ovariectomy. The rates at which some of these hormones are excreted may give an indication of the time and rate of their production. Estrogen is excreted in the urine in detectable amounts throughout the menstrual cycle but in the greatest quantity at the middle of the cycle (38, 57). Some women may again show a second period of increased elimination of estrogens during the latter third of the cycle; the amount excreted during the progestational stage is always greater than during the preovulatory phase.

Approximately 0.40 mg. is the minimal amount of estrone required daily in ovariectomized women to produce an endometrium which will show a menstrual hemorrhage subsequent to discontinuance of the injections (56). About 10 mg. of estrone would be required per cycle. Because only about 1 mg. of estrone in terms of estrogenic activity is excreted per cycle, it might be concluded that only about one-tenth of the total amount that is produced is eliminated, a quantity comparable to that excreted subsequent to injection of known doses. The sodium pregnandiol glucuronidate content of the urine can be determined gravimetrically during 6 to 12 days of the latter part of the cycle (54). This excretory product of progesterone usually first appears in the urine in detectable amounts about two days after ovulation and is not excreted in appreciable amounts during the two days before menstruation. Pregnandiol is excreted during the periods when active corpora lutea are present in the ovaries and therefore is not found during anovulatory cycles. Estimates of the amount of progesterone produced in man during the menstrual cycle range from 5 to 20 mg. per day, or 50 to 200 mg. during one cycle. From 20 to 60 mg. of pregnandiol glucuronidate are usually excreted per cycle, an amount equivalent to approximately one half of the progesterone which is considered to be produced (55).

The urinary excretion of the estrogenic hormones and of the metabolite of progesterone correlate rather closely with the sequence of ovarian changes on the one hand, and the functional changes in the endometrium on the other. Estrogens apparently are produced also by the corpora lutea; estrogenic activity has been demonstrated in extracts of these glands. The increased elimination of estrogens during the latter part of the cycle adds further evidence for the duality of the endocrine activity of the corpora lutea.

Comparison of the menstrual and estrous cycles

Among most subhuman or subprimate species the most obvious manifestation of sexual activity in the females occurs during the period of receptivity to the male or the period of estrus. The cycles are dated from the onset of

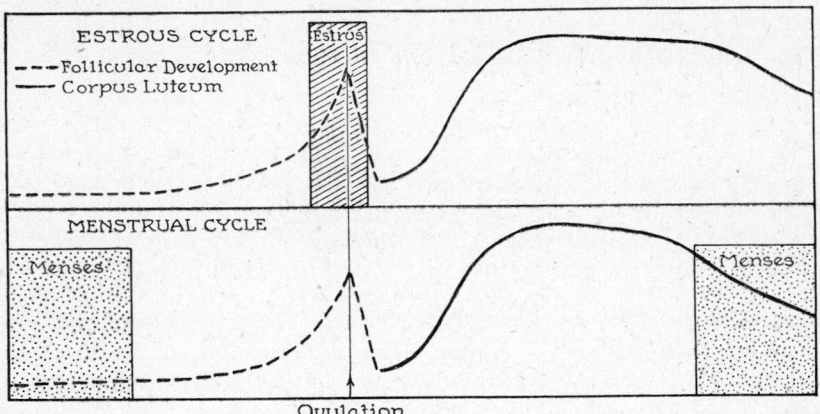

Fig. 494.—A diagrammatic presentation of the homology of ovarian changes in the estrous and menstrual cycles. The cycles are dated from their most obvious events, namely, estrus and menstruation.

one period of estrus to another and are called estrous cycles. Some species, such as the rat and mouse, have cycles of four to five days; the guinea pigs' cycles last about sixteen days. Many modifications of the estrous cycles occur in animals of different species. In rabbits prolonged periods of estrus terminate only with copulation which results in pregnancy, or if the matings are sterile, in pseudopregnancy. In the absence of mating a prolonged anestrum follows the protracted estrus (Fig. 494).

Ovulation occurs during estrus so that sperm may be available to fertilize the ovum. During the menstrual cycles ovulation occurs at the intermenstrum. If ovulation, however, were taken as the point of reference to start the cycles they would be comparable in so far as the sequences of ovarian changes are concerned.

Estrous behavior or sexual receptivity of laboratory animals may be induced subsequent to ovariectomy by the injection of large amounts of estrogens. The administration of small amounts of estrogens when followed by small doses of progesterone will also induce estrous behavior in ovariectomized rats and guinea pigs, probably reproducing the conditions eliciting estrus during the normal cycle and indicating that progesterone is produced by the large preovulatory follicles. Sexual receptivity in subhuman primates is greatest during the intermenstrual period. In man the periods of greatest sexual receptivity have been less definitely determined.

Time of ovulation

Many attempts have been made to estimate the time of ovulation in man. Direct methods, such as recovery of ova from the uterine tubes, identification of recent corpora lutea, recovery of young embryos, and observations on pregnancies subsequent to restricted intercourse have been used. Attempts to associate ovulation with basal body temperatures, types of cells in the vaginal smears, endometrial structure, excretion of pregnandiol, intermenstrual hemorrhage and pain, and fluctuation in electrical potentials have been used as indirect methods of estimating the time of ovulation (10, 25, 42, 44). In rhesus monkeys, Hartman has been able to determine the time of ovulation by digital palpation of the ovaries through the rectal walls and has checked his observations further by controlled matings. In a large series of animals ovulation occurred between the eighth and twenty-third days of the 28 day cycles with the greater number occurring between the tenth and thirteenth days. In man, ovulation apparently usually takes place at comparable times of the cycle, essentially in the middle of the cycle (25, 34). In abnormally long or short cycles the preovulatory portions show the greatest variation and the postovulatory period tends to be the most uniform, usually 14 to 16 days (54). It is very difficult to ignore some reports that ovulation and fertilization may occur at unusual times of the cycle, even during menstruation.

Regulation of ovarian function during the menstrual cycle

The rhythmic estrous or menstrual cycles are the result of humoral interreactions between the ovaries and the pituitary. The relation between the ovaries and the pituitary gland was first indicated when disturbances in genital development and function were noted in patients with hypophyseal tumors of certain types. When techniques were devised whereby the pituitaries could be removed from experimental animals the interpretations made from the earlier observations became established facts. The pituitary became known as the director of ovarian function (49, 50). The ovarian-stimulating activity of the pituitary—it also stimulates the testes—is referred to as gonadotrophic activity or gonadotropic activity; the two terms are currently used synonymously. The gonad-stimulating substances are called gonadotrophins or gonadotropins. The rhythmic nature of ovarian activity could not be explained on the basis of hypophyseal dominance alone. A reciprocal relationship between the pituitary and the ovaries was demonstrated; the pituitary in turn was influenced by the ovaries, the interreaction between the two endocrine glands providing a basis upon which the female sexual cycles may be explained.

Almost simultaneously Aschheim and Zondek (5) and Smith and Engle (50) observed that urine of pregnant women and pituitary glands contained substances which would incite precocious sexual maturity by direct stimulation of the gonads of immature animals. The ovaries of animals from which the pituitaries were removed remained small and the follicles failed to grow to a large size. The gonadal deficiencies following pituitary ablation and their restoration by replacement therapy definitely established the pituitary as a gland concerned in reproduction.

Among at least some species of animals it is known that the pituitaries of adult males and females differ and that this difference is determined by the gonads. Ovaries transplanted into adult intact or castrated male rats fail to show cyclic changes of the usual type. The ovarian follicles grow but fail to ovulate and corpora lutea do not form. It is known that male rats' hypophyses contain more gonadotrophin than those of the females but that they will not establish a rhythmic relationship with the transplanted ovaries, while ovaries transplanted into ovariectomized adult female rats show the usual cyclic changes.

If, within one day after birth, testes are transplanted into litter-mate female rats, the pituitaries of the hosts will be physiologically similar to those of males (37). Even if the graft is removed after sexual maturity the former host remains in constant estrus and fails to show estrous cycles. The testes transplanted into the immature animal induce an irreversible change in the female host's pituitary. More recently it has been shown that the ovarian cycles may be similarly modified in rats treated with certain androgens during their early postnatal life. The sex difference in the hypophysis is apparently determined by the gonad.

Extracts or implants of pituitary glands induce the precocious growth of the ovarian follicles in immature experimental animals. In rats and mice these stimulated follicles may ovulate and form corpora lutea. The injection of some relatively purified pituitary extracts produced growth mainly of the ovarian follicles, while others induced ovulation and the formation of corpora lutea as well. These observations led to the impression that at least two pituitary gonadotrophic hormones exist, an assumption that has since been demonstrated to be a fact (16). One hormone, called follicle-stimulating hormone (FSH), induces ovarian follicular growth in immature or in hypophysectomized female rats. A second pituitary hormone when given by itself has little or no effect on the size of the ovaries but when administered with a small dose of FSH will induce follicular maturation, ovulation and the formation of corpora lutea. It is called luteinizing hormone (LH) or interstitial cell stimulating hormone (ICSH) because it also acts on the interstitial cells of both ovaries and testes (17). A small amount of LH will greatly augment the response of a small dose of FSH (synergistic effect). Before extensive follicular growth and maturation will occur in hypophysectomized rodents, both gonadotrophic hormones must be injected. Recent experiments indicate that a third pituitary hormone, the lactogenic hormone, may be essential for the functional development of the corpora lutea (Fig. 495).

The manner in which the two ovarian hormones and the two or three gonadotrophic hormones reciprocally and jointly act to establish the estrous or menstrual cycles is not definitely known. The estrous cycles in rats have been explained as follows: The pituitary hormone FSH, especially when a little LH is present (synergistic effect), stimulates follicular growth and the production of estrogen. The estrogen acts upon the pituitary to stimulate the formation of increased amounts of LH (this has been demonstrated) and a decrease in the amount of FSH. Under such conditions ovulation and the formation of corpora lutea occur. When the corpora lutea begin to regress the amounts of ovarian hormones are reduced, with the result that the pituitary again produces FSH to repeat the cycle, a very probable sequence since FSH increases subsequent to castration or ovarian insufficiency. Cyclic changes in the amount of LH have been demonstrated in the pituitaries of rats, the greatest amount being found at estrus.

Similar reciprocal gonad-hypophyseal relationships probably exist during the menstrual cycle in man but they have not been so thoroughly demonstrated. Cyclic variations occur in the levels of excretion of urinary gonadotrophin, the greatest amount appearing during the midcycle, usually just before or about the time of the peak of estrogen excretion. Very small amounts of hormone appear in the early part of the cycle.

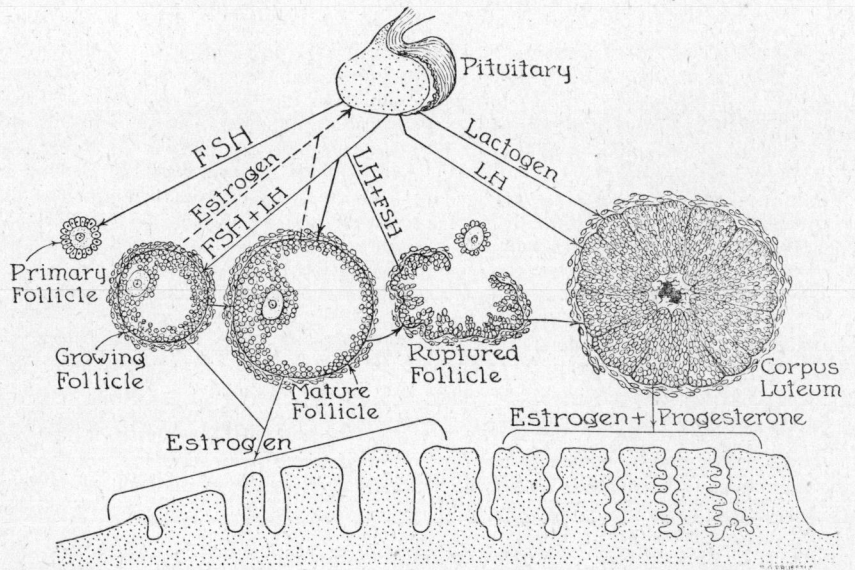

Fig. 495.—Ovarian and pituitary interrelationships in the mammalian cycle. FSH (follicle stimulating hormone) is responsible for follicular growth. FSH and a small amount of LH (luteinizing hormone) stimulate further follicular growth and estrogen production which in turn increases the amount of LH produced. Large amounts of LH and probably small amounts of FSH induce ovulation. The corpora lutea develop under the influence of LH and become functionally active in the presence of lactogen.

The corpora lutea formed during the normal four- to five-day estrous cycles of rats are not functional. They do not produce appreciable amounts of progesterone unless mating, even sterile mating, occurs and results in pregnancy or pseudopregnancy. During pregnancy estrous cycles are prevented during the 21 day gestation period, but during pseudopregnancy, for only 12 days. In this way the estrous cycles of the rat and mouse differ from those of some other species; they normally have no progestational stage. Sterile mating or even the stimulation of the cervix of estrous rats electrically or with a glass rod will evoke the formation of functional corpora lutea and a progestational stage. During this time further estrous cycles are prevented for about 12 days and the uterus under the influence of the corpora lutea will form deciduomata (the maternal part of the placenta) upon stimulation. The injection of gonadotrophin will also produce pseudopregnancy in normal rats. Hypophysectomized rats do not form functional corpora lutea when FSH and LH are injected; uterine deciduomata do not develop in the adequately traumatized uteri. If lactogenic hormone is administered, however, the corpora lutea produce progesterone which will facilitate the formation of deciduomata (15). These experiments demonstrate that at least in this species the final development and functional activity of the corpora lutea depend upon a distinct hormone, the lactogenic hormone, which is also called lactogen, mammotrophin, prolactin or galactin.

Ovulation has not been induced consistently in man or primates under experimental conditions. Apparently a delicate balance between the amount of FSH and LH must be maintained for follicular growth, and this balance must be readjusted at a proper time to induce ovulation. Follicles may be stimulated to a point beyond which they can be induced to ovulate and thus may become cystic. After much research on the most desirable balances between FSH and LH and on the duration and total doses of the gonadotrophic treatment it has been possible to induce ovulation rather consistently in monkeys (27). The experiments in which gonadotrophins have been used to induce ovulation in women have not been too convincing.

The amount of gonadotrophic hormone in the pituitary gland may be estimated by implanting hypophyseal tissue or by injecting extracts of the tissue into immature female rats or mice. The ovaries of the immature rodents are stimulated and incite uterine growth. By determining the minimal weight of fresh or desiccated tissue which will produce a given increase in ovarian or uterine weight, the relative amounts of hormone in different glands can be estimated. This bio-assay technique has been used to determine the amount of gonadotrophic hormone in the pituitaries of experimental animals throughout their life span. Little hormone is found in the pituitaries of immature rats, more at sexual maturity, and large amounts subsequent to ovariectomy. The injection of estrogen lowers the gonadotrophic content of the pituitaries of both ovariectomized rats and postmenopausal women (43).

Gonadotrophins are obtained from hypophyseal tissue, from the urine of pregnant women (PU) and blood serum of pregnant mares (PMS). The pituitary gonadotrophins are glycoproteins containing mannose. The LH (ICSH) obtained from the pituitaries of pigs and sheep differ greatly in their physiochemical qualities, the molecular weight of the former is 90,000 in contrast to 40,000 and the iso-electric points, amino acid and sugar contents differ. The physiochemical properties of FSH are not so well known (17).

Approximately 5 to 10 mg. of LH are required to repair the ovarian interstitial tissue of young hypophysectomized rats. The hormone is also assayed using the increase in weight of the ventral prostates of young hypophysectomized rats. FSH is biologically determined by the effect on increasing the size of the ovaries through follicular growth in hypophysectomized animals. Although it will incite follicular growth it will not result in estrogen production.

LIFE CYCLE OF THE OVARY

At birth the ovaries exhibit little evidence of endocrine function; they consist largely of groups of ova and primary follicles in a vascular stroma, and are surrounded by a germinal epithelium except at the hilus. Interstitial cells of a secretory nature have been observed in the ovaries of the newborn in some species but they disappear shortly after birth. In man extensive follicular growth does not occur until the onset of puberty at the age of ten to fourteen years. At this time the *secondary sexual characters* begin to develop; pubic and axillary hair begin to grow and the adult types of body contour appear. Also the *accessory reproductive organs*, the uterus, vagina and mammary glands start to develop at this time. Hypogonadal individuals or individuals ovariectomized before sexual maturity do not show the usual changes of the secondary sexual characters or of the accessory reproductive organs.

Puberty

Puberty is that period of life during which the accessory reproductive organs and secondary sexual characters develop and which terminates at menarche, the first menstrual period. The age at which the first indication of pubertal development occurs and the rate of progression of the development of the accessory reproductive organs preceding menarche differ from individual to individual. The menstrual periods usually begin in individuals between 13 and 15 years of age, although the ages at menarche may range from 10 to 18 years. The early cycles are usually irregular, several months of amenorrhea (absence of menses) may separate the menses. Many of the early cycles may occur in the absence of ovulation—be anovulatory. After irregular cycles extending over periods of different lengths, more or less regular and normal ovulatory menstrual cycles occur.

During the prepubertal stage gonadotrophic hormone is produced in barely detectable amounts; very little of it can be detected in the urine. At puberty the amount of gonadotrophic hormone in the urine increases to approach that excreted in the adult. That puberty must be initiated by the pituitary is indicated by the fact that the ovaries of immature animals are stimulated with gonadotrophic hormones. What regulates the assumption of the gonad stimulation by the pituitary is unknown. It is interesting that at the time of puberty one of the most common concomitant factors is an accentuation of the rate of body growth. If accentuated growth occurs at an early age the menstrual cycles start at a correspondingly early date, and a delayed accentuation of somatic growth is usually associated with a late menarche (47). The year of the greatest increment of growth is usually the year of menarche. This relation between the growth-stimulating and gonadotrophic functions of the pituitary affords material for interesting conjecture.

Albright, *et al.*, (1) have recently described the association of hypo-ovarian states in patients of less than normal stature. The individuals produce gonadotrophic hormone but little sex hormone and presumably are also deficient in growth hormones. On the other hand, precocious sexual maturity due to gonadal tumors, to adrenal cortical tumors of some types, or to some intracranial neoplasia with resulting hypergonadism may be associated with small stature; growth of these individuals is usually augmented during the early stages of the disease but stops precociously after the brief abnormally early accentuated phase. As a result such individuals are usually dwarfed as well as sexually precocious.

Menopause

After 30 to 40 years of repeated reproductive and menstrual cycles the number of follicles in the ovaries is almost depleted. The menses may become profuse (menorrhagia) and painful (dysmenorrhea) or may become short and the cycles irregular, eventually ceasing entirely. The cyclic production of ovarian hormones ceases, the mammary glands atrophy and the uterus and vagina show variable amounts of regression. This period of gradual subsidence of ovarian function is called the *climacteric* and culminates in the complete cessation of cyclic ovarian activity, the *menopause* (47). Urinary excretion of estrogen declines and of pregnandiol ceases, but the excretion of gonadotrophic hormone (APL—anterior pituitary-like hormone) is augmented. The gonadotrophic hormone in the urine of postmenopausal women is characterized by a high content of a substance that stimulates ovarian follicles and by little of the hormone inciting the formation of corpora lutea;

in this manner it resembles the follicle-stimulating hormone (FSH) of the pituitary gland. An augmented excretion of gonadotrophic hormone also occurs in artificial menopause induced by surgical removal of the ovaries or x-ray sterilization during the period of sexual maturity. The hormone in the urines of menopausal women is apparently of hypophyseal origin and may decrease when estrogens are injected (43). The conclusion must be that the menopause results from the senile changes in the ovary. In the absence of the inhibiting or regulatory effect of ovarian hormones upon the hypophysis, the latter gland produces an excessive amount of gonadotrophic hormone. The changes in the pituitary gland at puberty which result in the onset of gonadotrophic activity are not reversed at the menopause; the pituitary, once it starts to stimulate ovarian function, attempts to continue even after the ovary no longer responds.

In addition to the morphological regression in the accessory genital organs, vasomotor and personality changes frequently accompany the menopause. Vasomotor changes (hot flashes) result from a vascular dilatation in the skin of the head, neck and upper trunk with flushing, increased sweating and a sensation of suffocation. The hot flashes may be stopped by injecting estrogens, even in amounts inadequate to decrease the amount of urinary gonadotrophin (prolan A). The treatment of menopausal *symptoms* is one of the most common clinical uses of estrogens. The ovarian deficiency after the menopause may not be sufficient to permit complete atrophy of the vaginal mucosa or to result in the disappearance of ovarian hormones from the blood or urine; subthreshold cycles may even occur.

PREGNANCY—THE REPRODUCTIVE CYCLE

An ovum must be fertilized within a few hours after it leaves the follicle at ovulation; at least such conclusions have been drawn from extensive observations upon laboratory animals (7). If guinea pigs are inseminated artificially from 12 to 18 hours after ovulation a high incidence of pregnancies terminates in abortions or no pregnancy occurs. Artificial insemination during estrus, and therefore within three or four hours either before or after ovulation, instituted normal pregnancies. The period of fertilizability of the ovum must be brief. During its migration to the uterus through the uterine tubes the fertilized ovum divides to form a mass of cells still surrounded by the zona pellucida. Unfertilized ova usually reach the uterus before dissolution.

The developing ovum reaches the uterus within a few days after ovulation and at a time when the endometrium shows early progestational development. The ovum remains free in the uterus for a few days before implantation, during which time the zona pellucida is dissolved. In some mammalian species the blastocysts may remain in this stage for weeks or months before implanting and continuing their growth. The earliest intra-uterine human and monkeys' blastocysts that have been observed have been about eight days old and may still be free in the uterus. The process of attachment (implantation) is instigated by the blastocyst from which the extra-embryonic trophoblast grows and invades the endometrium which in its turn contributes to the maternal part of the placenta. Both cells from the developing blastocyst and uterine decidua contribute to the placenta. In some animals the mechanical stimulus of a foreign body other than an ovum or irritation of the lining of the uterus may elicit a response of the progestational endometrium with the result that deciduomata (the maternal components of the placenta) form. Similar observations have not been made in man in which the maternal part of the placenta has formed only in contact with the developing trophoblast.

The uterus with its implanted embryo has a definite effect upon the maternal organism; within a few days after the physical union of ovum and mother the uterus is prevented from undergoing the usual menstrual regression. The corpora lutea persist in an active stage for longer periods than usual, at least for 25 days. Estrogen and progestin are produced in larger amounts subsequent to implantation and gonadotrophin is excreted in such large amounts that, by the time the expected menstrual period is missed, enough gonadotrophin is excreted to give a positive test for pregnancy (14, 23).

Aschheim and Zondek (5) discovered large amounts of gonadotrophic hormone in the urines of pregnant women (anterior pituitary-like hormone, APL; pregnancy urine hormone, PU; or prolan) and suggested that its detection might be used in the diagnosis of pregnancy. In this test 2 cc. of urine or an alcoholic precipitate of urine are injected into

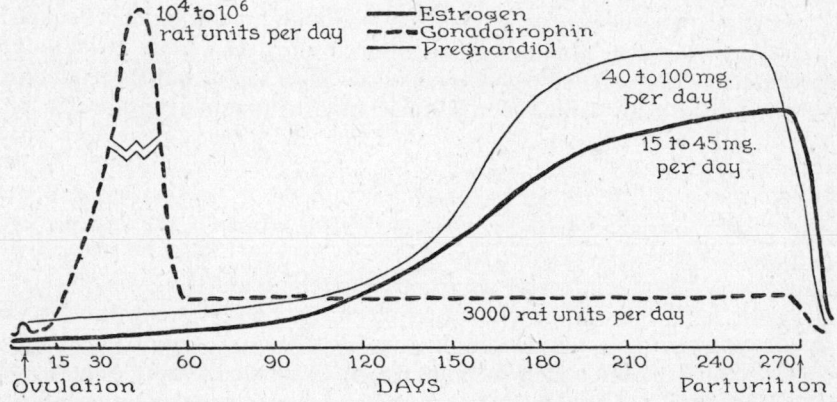

Fig. 496.—Diagrammatic presentation of the excretion of ovarian hormones and gonadotrophins during pregnancy. At the peak of gonadotrophin excretion over 100,000 Rat Units are eliminated daily. 60 to 100 mg. of pregnandiol and 15 to 45 mg. of estrogens are also excreted daily at the period of maximal output. The greatest part of the estrogen is estriol which is much less active biologically then estrone or estradiol so that the bioassay technique will not reveal such large amounts. Of the total as much as 1 to 3 mg. may be estrone.

immature mice (or rats). The animals are sacrificed four days (100 hours) after the first of the six injections, which are given during the first two days, and their ovaries are examined. An increase in weight of the ovaries with the formation of large follicles and corpora lutea, some of which may show hemorrhagic spots (blood points) constitute a positive response. Later Friedman discovered that a single intravenous injection of pregnancy urine induces ovulation in young or isolated female rabbits (19). Ruptured follicles can be detected within 24 hours after the injection. It is necessary that the rabbits be isolated as they ovulate upon copulation or even upon copulatory movements in the presence of other females. Ovulation occurs within about 12 hours after copulation or after the injection of gonadotrophin or PU in this species. The Aschheim-Zondek and Friedman tests have become routine diagnostic procedures. False positive responses are given with urines of patients with certain genital tumors, among them chorio-epitheliomas which contain tissue similar to that which produces gonadotrophin in the normal placenta. False negative tests rarely or never occur.

After the first month of pregnancy the ovaries may be removed and the pregnancy continues to a successful termination in man and in monkeys (26). The placenta after this time compensates for the endocrine function of the ovaries. The pituitaries also have been removed from animals of some species during the latter part of the first half of gestation and pregnancy continued in a normal manner.

Large amounts of estrogen, pregnandiol and gonadotrophin are excreted during pregnancy (Fig. 496). The peak of gonadotrophin excretion occurs at about the forty-fifth to fiftieth day or about one month after the first missed menses; over 100,000 Rat Units may be excreted daily (14). Pregnandiol and estrogens are excreted in progressively larger amounts as pregnancy progresses, tending to be maximal a few days before parturition. The functions of the large amounts of hormones elaborated at this time are not known (48). The large amounts of gonadotrophin apparently have little stimulating effect upon the ovary although some evidence exists that it may assist in maintaining function of the corpora lutea during early pregnancy. Considerable fluctuations in the rate of excretion occur among different individuals, fluctuations which cannot be definitely associated with any unusual concomitants.

During pregnancy follicular growth and ovulation are inhibited. The uterus increases in size to accommodate the embryo and fetus; both the number and size of the smooth muscle cells increase. Distension and the endocrine environment both contribute to the stimulation of myometrial growth.

Physiology of the placenta

The placenta serves essentially two primary functions: in the first place, it is an organ of exchange between the mother and embryo or fetus; and in the second place, it is an endocrine gland producing internal secretions to maintain a compatible environment for the two closely related organisms. At the time of fertilization the ovum contains a small amount of nutriment in its cytoplasm, an amount which in mammalian ova will support only a very limited growth. The uterine secretions may maintain embryonic growth for a brief period—certainly this must occur in the opossum in which the ova never become implanted—but the greater amount of nutriment is received in man by the direct contact of the fetal portion of the placenta with the maternal blood. The exchanges of gases through the placenta is not considered here.

As an endocrine gland the placenta must produce estrogens, progesterone and gonadotrophin; it must be the source for the high titers of these substances in the blood and urine during pregnancy. These hormones have all been obtained by extraction of placental tissue; they are most abundant in the fetal part, the chorionic trophoblast, rather than in the decidua. Recent studies have indicated that the syncytial layers of the trophoblast are concerned with the production of the steroid hormones and that the cytotrophoblast produces the gonadotrophins (59). Histochemical studies indicate the presence of steroids in the protoplasm of the syncytium. Human placental tissues grown in cultures will produce gonadotrophin that can be bio-assayed in immature mice, although the cultures contain largely the Langhans cells of the cytotrophoblast (33). Also the amount of gonadotrophin produced by the intact placenta tends to parallel the amount of cytotrophoblast, which is maximal early in pregnancy and decreases later in pregnancy. During the latter part of pregnancy the number, size and amount of cytoplasmic vacuolation of the cytotrophoblast are reduced. Some experiments have indicated that the placenta also produces lactogenic hormone and growth hormone.

The placenta seems to have a definite life span. If a monkey's or mouse's fetuses are destroyed in utero without detaching the placentas the latter will persist to be delivered at the same time that normal parturition would have occurred. Under such conditions the placentas continue to produce hormones in much the same manner as during normal pregnancy in so far as revealed by the weight of the host, the development of the mammary glands and the structure of the vaginal epithelium. As has been stated, the life of the placenta may be prolonged for several days by the injection of progesterone during the latter part of gestation, a unique biological condition in which a hormone appears to act directly upon the gland in which it is produced.

Influence of maternal hormones upon the embryo and fetus

The large amounts of circulating gonadotrophic and steroid hormones are not without effect on the intra-uterine young of some species. The ovaries may be somewhat stimulated; in man the uterus, vagina, prostate and sometimes the breasts of the newborn are hypertrophied or stimulated, presumably by the high levels of estrogen. Rapid involution follows birth (18). Menstruation is sometimes observed within a few days after birth and is attributed to cessation of exposure to maternal hormones. Large amounts of estrogen, when injected into pregnant rodents, have produced anomalous development of the accessory genital organs although androgens have provoked more striking genital changes when similarly administered (22), not only to pregnant rodents, but to monkeys. It is possible that the high levels of estrogens during pregnancy may produce male intersexes which are not rare in the human population.

Mechanism of parturition

Pregnancy lasts approximately nine months or ten lunar months in man. Each species has a characteristic period of gestation although slight variations in duration are not uncommon. It has been suggested that the period of gestation is a multiple of the estrous or menstrual cycle—for example, in man equal to ten menstrual cycles. The cause of the termination of a normal pregnancy is unknown although many experiments have been undertaken to clarify the problem. In many species the removal of the corpora lutea terminates pregnancy; however, such is not true in man. The administration of progesterone or the experimental production of a new group of functional corpora lutea by the injection of gonadotrophins during the latter part of gestation may prevent or delay parturition in laboratory animals (29). Under such conditions the young continue to grow and may attain sufficient size to rupture the uterus or may die in utero several days after the expected parturition. It seems possible that parturition might be attributed to a decrease in the amount of available progesterone, either that produced by the corpora lutea or, in man, by the placenta. Pregnandiol excretion may decline during the last few days of a normal gestation period, indicating a decrease in the production of progesterone (23). It will be recalled that a similar endocrine change precedes menstruation in an ovulatory cycle; however, what determines when the production of progesterone will cease or decrease is not known. Estimations of the production of progesterone as determined by pregnandiol excretion in man do not distinguish between individuals who have normal gestation periods and those showing threatened abortions. Threatened abortions are thought to be prevented when the patients receive exogenous progesterone, one of the most common clinical uses of this hormone.

Estrogen as well as pregnandiol excretion tends to be maximal during a period eight to ten days before parturition and decreases thereafter, but the wide day to day fluctuations and variations in different individuals prevent any evaluation of the proximity of delivery from such data. Some investigators have observed an increase in the urinary excretion of free estrogens, in contrast to conjugated estrogens, just preceding parturition, and assumed that the presence of the more active free estrogen might account for the increase of spontaneous irritability of the pregnant uterus and hence terminate gestation. More recent experiments have shown, however, that enormous doses of estrogen may be administered without altering the course of pregnancy in monkeys and man (41).

The effect of the oxytocic substance of the posterior lobe of the hypophysis upon the contractions of the uterus has suggested that an increased secretion of this hormone might cause parturition, and observations indicate that there may be an unusual liberation of oxytocic material toward the end of pregnancy. Several investigators, however, have shown that normal delivery may occur after removal of the entire pituitary or of its posterior lobe, hence indicating its nonessential nature in normal deliveries.

Delivery occurs in consequence of more or less periodic contraction of the uterine muscles. The independence of uterine muscular activity from extrinsic innervation has been shown by observations of parturition in animals with bisected spinal cords or complete removal of the sympathetic chains (39). Extrinsic innervation may act upon the uterus in man, however, since emotional disturbances may provoke premature parturition. The stimulus of suckling is presumed to increase the contraction of the postpartum uterus.

MECHANISM OF SPERM TRANSPORT

The sperm are deposited in the vagina at copulation and must be transported through the uterine cervix, fundus and tubes to approach and fertilize an ovum. The orgasm may result in muscular contractions which suck the sperm through the cervix; in some species they appear in the uterus immediately after copulation. The quality of the mucus secreted by the cervical glands changes during the menstrual cycle, the mucus being much thinner during the intermenstrual period. The less viscous and alkaline cervical secretions probably permit the transmission of sperm through the cervical canal although the mechanism of sperm transport into the uterus is not well understood. The transport of sperm through the uterus is facilitated by uterine contractions. Transport through the uterine tubes may be provided by upward beating paths of cilia (the greater number of cilia beat toward the uterus to assist in the downward transport of the ovum, however), by antiperistaltic tubal contractions, or by a tendency of sperm to swim against a current created by the downward beating cilia, and hence to orient themselves up the tubes and be largely or entirely self-propelled. When two kinds of sperm from two species or sperm and some nonmotile substance are placed simultaneously in the vagina, uterine cervix or uterus they do not attain the same levels of the genital tract at the same time, indicating that both the intrinsic motility of the sperm and uterine factors are involved in sperm transport. In addition to permitting the passage of sperm, the cervical mucus must prevent the passage of the vaginal bacterial flora into the usually aseptic uterus.

Some additional actions of female sex hormones

Carcinogenesis. Many experiments have been undertaken to determine whether the estrogens which provoke normal growth and development of the genital tissues might also instigate unrestricted or malignant growth (20). Mice given estrogens may acquire mammary, uterine cervical, hypophyseal, testicular or lymphoid tumors. Special inherited susceptibilities or influences transmitted from mother to offspring are required in addition to the endocrine influences before tumors of some organs will develop; estrogens will not incite mammary tumors in mice of all strains. Some nonmalignant overgrowths such as uterine fibroids or cystic endometrial hyperplasias are associated with evidence of hormonal disturbances in man and may be induced in some experimental animals by estrogens. The carcinogenic or tumorigenic action of the different estrogens is proportional to their estrogenic activity, the more active estrogens being more effective than those requiring larger threshold doses for minimal responses.

Calcium and Lipid Metabolism. Serum calcium and lipid levels increase in birds when eggs are being formed. Similar changes occur in birds when estrogens are injected; very high levels of serum calcium and lipids may result. In addition, trabecular bone grows into the bone marrow, increasing the amount of bone. Extreme endosteal ossification occurs in the bones of estrogen-treated mice and their breaking strengths are increased. The negative calcium balances in some women with postmenopausal osteoporosis become positive when estrogens are administered, and the symptoms are alleviated.

Pelvis. Estrogens cause a dissolution of the pubes at the symphyses in animals of some species, in this way increasing the size of the birth canal. In guinea pigs a relaxation of the pubes occurs preceding parturition and can be reproduced in nonparous animals by estrogen and a distinct hormone, *relaxin*. The loosening of the sacro-iliac joints and pubic symphyses during pregnancy in some women probably results from the action of ovarian hormones (4).

OVULATION

In man ovulation normally occurs spontaneously, that is, without the superimposition of extrinsic stimuli. The limited and not too well controlled endocrine studies on the induction of ovulation in women have contributed little information. A rapid growth of the follicles must occur during a few hours preceding rupture, or at least such is true for all experimental animals. The actual rupture of the follicle has been said to result (i) from increased intrafollicular pressure accompanying an augmented secretion of liquor folliculi, (ii) from ischemia and loss of tissue viability secondary to the increased follicular pressure, and (iii) from enzymes which digest the follicular wall. If any one of these theories is correct (none will account for the formation of cystic follicles), the increased follicular pressures or enzymes or other factors antedating ovulation nevertheless must result from gonadotrophic stimulation.

Ovulation normally occurs subsequent to copulation in rabbits, ferrets, cats, and in animals of some other species. The inciting stimulus in these animals must be in part neural; the semen does not contain an ovulation-provoking factor. The neural stimulation attending mating does not involve the ovaries directly because transplanted ovaries deprived of their normal innervation or ovaries of sympathectomized animals will ovulate; also direct stimulation of the ovarian innervation will not provoke ovulation. It will be recalled that the intravenous injections of gonadotrophins induce ovulation. The stimulus of copulation must therefore act upon the hypophysis to release an ovulation-stimulating hormone. If a rabbit's pituitary is removed more than one hour subsequent to mating, ovulation will occur; whereas if hypophysectomy is performed immediately after copulation, follicular maturation and·rupture do not result. The release of·gonadotrophin following copulation has been shown also by changes in the cellular structure and by decrease of hormone content of the pituitary gland.

The pathways of the transmission of the ovulatory stimuli have been investigated extensively. Section of the sacral cord and abdominal sympathectomy, removal of the superior cervical ganglia and thoracolumbar sympathectomy did not prevent postcoital ovulation in rabbits. Faradic stimulation of the brain, pituitary or tuber cinereum resulted in ovulation. Rabbits with sectioned hypophyseal stalks did not ovulate after mating. These observations indicate that the excretion of gonadotrophin to produce follicular rupture, in some species at least, requires an intact hypothalamicohypophyseal connection which may be stimulated through afferents from several sources other than from the genitalia. On the other hand, rats in which the pituitary has been removed and retransplanted into the sella turcica may show complete cycles, and section of the stalk does not prevent ovulation, demonstrating a species difference. It should be recalled that in rats, as in primates, follicular rupture occurs spontaneously, that is, without the added stimulus of copulation. In these species another mechanism intrinsic to the animal must be active in periodically inciting the excretion of gonadotrophin (28, 31).

Neural lesions also may modify sexual behavior as well as reproductive functions. Hypothalamic lesions in guinea pigs may prevent either estrous behavior or ovarian development; in fact, it has been indicated that the hypothalamus may regulate gonadotrophic function in this species. More work must be done before much can be said about the neural factors in the physiology of reproduction in other than a few species of animals. Lesions of the central nervous system undoubtedly disturb reproduction in man. Hypothalamic lesions may lead to menstrual irregularities or hypofunction. On the other hand, hypothalamic injury may cause precocious sexual maturity. The genital abnormalities in these cases are usually associated with other evidences of pituitary dysfunction.

PHYSIOLOGY OF THE MYOMETRIUM

The uterine musculature (myometrium) of adult sexually active mammals undergoes spontaneous rhythmic contractions. Many observations have been made upon the intact uteri or isolated uterine muscle preparations of experimental animals, especially of rabbits. In most species the spontaneous contractions are strongest and most frequent when the uteri are under the influence of estrogens, and during the progestational stage the myometria are relatively quiescent. Pituitrin, an active principle obtained from the posterior pituitary, increases the tonus and height of contractions of the uterine muscle of rabbits subjected to estrogens, but not when progesterone is acting upon the uterus; whereas in animals of most other species pituitrin will incite contractions at all stages of the cycle. The extrinsic innervation of the uterus does not alter the humoral modifications of spontaneous irritability; transplanted denervated uteri respond as do intact uteri (39).

Variations in the spontaneous contractility of the human myometrium also occur at different phases of the menstrual cycle or in uteri under the influence of any one or more of the estrogenic, progestational or androgenic hormones. Some difference of opinion exists among the numerous investigators who have studied this problem. During the preovulatory stage the uterus undergoes rhythmic small contractions at a relatively rapid rate; in the progestational stage the contractions are more irregular, of greater amplitude, and usually occur at a much slower frequency. Unmistakable changes of the pattern of contractibility have been described within 48 hours after ovulation. At all stages of the cycle pituitrin usually increases uterine tone and the amplitude of contractions, although the changes may be slight. Uteri of individuals in the late premenstrual stage were most receptive to pituitrin. During anovulatory

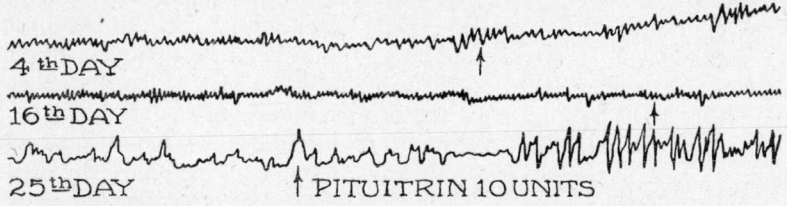

Fig. 497.—Recordings of uterine contractions of a 25 year old woman obtained by use of an intra-uterine balloon. At the points designated by the arrows 10 units of pituitrin were injected. Pregnandiol did not appear in the urine of this patient until about the 18th day of the cycle so the first two recordings were taken during preovulatory stages. Biopsies taken on the 28th day of the cycle showed a progestational endometrium. (After Henry and Browne, 1943.)

cycles the myometrial contractions are of the preovulatory type throughout as would be expected in the absence of a functional corpus luteum (30). The uteri of castrated females show little or no spontaneous motility (Fig. 497).

Premenstrual pains or dysmenorrhea may be due to uterine ischemia associated with marked myometrial contractions. Progesterone, when administered to patients with painful postpartum uterine contractions, alleviated the pain although without inhibiting the contractions. Emotional stress may increase myometrial activity during the premenstrual phase.

Uterine contractions in man are usually determined by inserting a small thin-walled balloon through the cervix into the uterine lumen, then filling the balloon and tube connecting it to an adequate recording apparatus with water at a pressure of 10 to 40 mm. Hg. The volume of the uterine lumen varies with the stage of the cycle, tending to be greatest during the progestational stage. If the amount of fluid in the balloon is large, as it might well be, in the isotonically distended uteri during the progestational stage in contrast to the preovulatory stage, a small contraction might displace a larger amount of fluid and be recorded as a stronger contraction. Technical irregularities have been used to explain some of the differences in observation in the hands of different investigators.

The uterine contractions of experimental animals may be obtained by a similar technique, by the direct observation of the uteri at laparotomy or through "abdominal windows" or by in vitro studies on uteri or uterine muscle strips.

PHYSIOLOGY OF THE VAGINA

The profound and rapid transformation of the vaginal epithelium in rats and mice was mentioned with reference to the bio-assay of estrogens. In these species the rapid proliferation of the deeper cells may result in a complete replacement of the entire vaginal epithelium within three days. A vaginal epithelium but two or three cell layers thick in a castrated mouse or rat may be transformed into a thick stratified squamous structure, the outer layers of which consist of cornified cells. At the same time the large numbers of polymorphonuclear leukocytes characteristic of the diestrous vaginal wall and contents disappear (4).

In man marked changes also occur in the vaginal structure. At birth the vaginal epithelium is thick, a response to the high estrogen content of the intra-uterine environment (18). Within a few days the vaginal epithelium is again thin and remains so until puberty. Periodic changes in the vaginal epithelium occur during the menstrual cycles and may be detected by the examination of smears of the vaginal contents. The changes are not as easily discerned or in many cases so definite as in rodents. During the mid-intermenstrum the smears contain few leukocytes and many isolated cornified or partially cornified cells with very small pyknotic nuclei, the vaginal pH is low and the glycogen content of the cells high. During the progestational stage the partially cornified cells appear in clumps, noncornified epithelial cells increase in number, and leukocytes and bacteria are abundant. Some investigators consider the human vaginal smears sufficiently definite to permit an estimation of adequate therapy; in other words, as a means of bio-assay within the patient. Estrogen administered to the postmenopausal patient will induce a type of vaginal mucosa characteristic of the mid-inter-menstrual period. The addition of progesterone will transform the cornified epithelium into one similar to that seen during the normal premenstrual stage (36).

The presence of glycogen in the vaginal epithelial cells is apparently attributable to the action of both estrogen and progesterone. The function of the intracellular glycogen is unknown although the suggestion has been made that it is responsible for the high acidity of the vaginal secretions. The glycogen content is highest in the premenstrual period while the pH is lowest during the midcycle; the alkaline cervical secretions may reduce the acidity during the latter part of the cycle.

INACTIVATION OF HORMONES

When estrogens are injected into man only a small amount of the original hormone may be recovered in the urine. The greater part of the hormone is destroyed or inactivated within the body. The liver is the most active site in destroying the hormones. In experimental animals estrogens injected in the peritoneal cavity or the spleen are much less effective than when injected subcutaneously where the hormone is not absorbed and circulated directly into the portal venous system. The incubation of estrogens with minced or finely sliced liver in vitro results in the rapid destruction of the hormone. Men or women with severe liver disease may show hyperestrogenic responses, apparently elicited by the endogenous hormones which are not destroyed rapidly enough to prevent their accumulation above threshold levels. It has been assumed that an "estrinase" may be present in hepatic and other estrogen-destroying tissues. Tyrosinase will also inactivate estrogens in vitro. The end-products of these reactions are not known. The activity of the more potent estrogens, estradiol and estrone, is reduced under some conditions by transformation into the less active estriol which is excreted as a water soluble conjugated estrogen. In some species the active α-estradiol may be converted in part to the inactive isomer, β-estradiol. Three methods of the inactivation of estrogen have been mentioned: (i) transformation to inactive products, at present of undetermined nature, (ii) transformation to less active or conjugated estrogens, or (iii) transformation to inactive isomers (12, 38).

Progesterone is changed in part into the inactive pregnandiol glucuronidate in man although probably not in other species. Where this change occurs is not known, although a greater amount of pregnandiol is excreted when estrogen is administered simultaneously or in women with well developed endometria than when the hormone is injected into males or hysterectomized females. The equivalent of somewhat less than one half of the hormone injected is usually recovered under the best conditions. The method of inactivation of the rest of the progesterone is not known. In most species pregnandiol glucuronidate is not excreted and the metabolic derivative of progesterone has not been detected.

Whether hormones are utilized in the reactions they incite or whether they act as catalysts has been considered. With the methods available there is no evidence that they are utilized in the responses they elicit. The estrogens might well be considered as stimulators of growth of the genital tissues in vivo at all stages from at least late fetal life until death. They have not been effective in stimulating the growth of tissues in vitro under cultural conditions. Progesterone, although it will also stimulate the growth of some genital tissues when given in large amounts, is more intimately concerned with the differentiation of tissues, their stimulation to secretory activity as revealed in the progestational endometrium, and the accumulation of glycogen in the vaginal mucosa. These generalizations are not true in all instances, however; for example, the growth of the maternal placenta depends upon progesterone.

DEVELOPMENT AND FUNCTION OF THE MAMMARY GLANDS

Milk is necessary for the postpartum nutrition of the young of most species during the period of adaptation to extra-uterine life. The mechanisms regulating and synchronizing mammary development and function with sexual and reproductive functions are distinctly mammalian and might be considered a comparatively recent phylogenetic acquisition. It is not unexpected, therefore, that the physiological regulatory mechanisms of mammary growth and function differ from those of the other female accessory organs.

Normal development

The breasts are modified skin glands first formed during embryonic life and frequently undergoing considerable development during the late fetal stage, presumably under the influence of circulating hormones produced in the placenta. The intra-uterine influences removed at birth may be responsible for the cystic distension of the breast with a serous fluid called witch's milk. Subsequent to birth, or to the early postnatal hypertrophy, the breasts become very small and persist in this stage until the onset of puberty. With the assumption of ovarian activity the breasts hypertrophy, and both the stroma and parenchyma increase in amount. After menarche further mammary growth occurs, probably in cycles paralleling the menstrual cycles. Cyclic mammary growth occurs during the estrous cycles of young mammals of some species (52).

The prepubertal glands consist of rudimentary ducts extending but a short distance below the flattened nipple areas. During puberty the ducts grow by apical proliferation and the number of branching ducts increases until a complex compound tubular gland is formed during adolescence. It is probable that some alveoli also develop during the menstrual cycles. The greater number of mammary alveoli, however, develop during pregnancy, probably during the first part of pregnancy, transforming the breast to a compound tubulo-alveolar gland. Although the gland may be morphologically complete for some time during the latter part of gestation, lactation usually does not begin until after parturition. If the breasts are suckled and the accumulated colostrum and milk are removed the gland may function for some time—in some instances for periods of several years. Eventually the glands regress, the alveoli are largely reabsorbed, leaving again essentially a compound tubular mammary structure. After the menopause only the larger ducts may persist in an abundant fibrofatty stroma.

Lactation rarely occurs except following pregnancy in man. Acidophilic cell tumors of the pituitary are associated with acromegaly and during the early stages of the disease spontaneous lactation frequently occurs.

Experimental studies on mammary development

Comparatively few observations have been made on the influence of hormones on the human breast. Hypogonadal or postmenopausal women show some breast hypertrophy following the topical or systemic applications of estrogens. A feeling of fullness and tenderness of the breasts may occur at the same time. It is assumed that a growth of the parenchymal tissues occurs under such conditions.

The humoral factors in the development of the mammary glands of experimental animals have been studied extensively. In some species, including the monkey, *Macacus rhesus*, the mammary glands of males or ovariectomized immature females develop into complete compound tubulo-alveolar glands during prolonged periods of treatment with estrogen (21). The duration of the period of treatment required for complete mammary growth differs in the different species. In monkeys a period of about six months, approximately the duration of normal pregnancy, was needed to attain mammary growth comparable to that observed at normal parturition. Animals of those species in which normal mammary development occurs during a shorter period responded more rapidly to injected hormones.

Progesterone is also required in addition to estrogen for complete mammary growth in animals of some species, e.g., the rabbit. It is probable that progesterone may also facilitate mammary growth in other species as well. The problem of mammary growth is not as simple as presented above, however, for in hypophysectomized animals, of some species at least, the breasts do not develop when estrogens or estrogens and progesterone are injected. Estrogen and progesterone will incite some mammary growth in hypophysectomized animals of some species. If, however, a pituitary hormone, called mammogen by one group of investigators, or lactogenic hormone is injected with ovarian hormones, mammary growth does occur. Some pituitary factor seems to be necessary for mammary growth; in this respect the breasts differ from other accessory genital tissues such as the vagina and uterus which respond to the ovarian steroids in the absence of the hypophysis. The mechanism of mammary development is further complicated when an explanation is sought for unilateral proliferation of the subjacent breast tissue following cutaneous application of estrogens in amounts too small to elicit systemic effects. If estrogens act indirectly through the pituitary upon the breasts, such reactions would not be expected; all the breasts should be stimulated. Estrogen can act directly upon the subjacent mammary tissue in intact but not in hypophysectomized animals, however. Further work must be done on more species before the endocrine stimulation of mammary growth is understood. A specific hypophyseal hormone may be required or, possibly, the general debility of hypophysectomized animals may be responsible for the restriction of mammary growth.

Lactation. Although the breasts grow when estrogens are administered to intact animals, a pituitary hormone is necessary to stimulate mammary secretion. The lactogenic hormone (prolactin, galactin or mammotrophin), when injected into animals with completely developed mammary glands, induces lactation. The cuboidal or low columnar cells of the alveoli and the smallest ducts increase in height, elaborate and excrete milk which distends the glands. Normal lactation ceases immediately when the hypophysis is removed, but is maintained if lactogen and adrenotrophic hormone or lactogen and adrenal cortical extracts are given. The maintenance of normal adrenal function or a substitution for adrenal deficiency is necessary before lactation can be maintained in hypophysectomized animals. Both the onset and maintenance of lactation require lactogen. The amount of milk secreted during the peak of lactation cannot be increased by lactogen; but during the declining phase of milk secretion, milk production may be increased in goats and cows. Lactogen has been used clinically in attempts to increase the milk yield in nursing women but the results have not been convincing. It is probable that deficiencies in milk production are due usually to factors other than inadequate lactogen.

The lactogenic activity of pituitary extracts was first shown by Stricker and Grüter in 1928 and was confirmed by many other investigators. Riddle (40) noted that the pituitary hormone which induced growth of the pigeon's crop gland (pigeon's milk) was the same as the one stimulating lactation. The stimulation of the growth of the pigeon's crop gland is used in the bio-assay of lactogen; a short test that is used for the detection of the hormone and that facilitated the chemical isolation of lactogen by White, et al., who prepared the first pituitary hormone to be obtained in a pure state. One International Unit equals 1 mg. of a standard preparation and contains about 35 Pigeon Units of the purified hormone (60).

Mechanisms Regulating the Onset of Lactation. Normally lactation begins about the time of or shortly after parturition. The synchronization of the onset of lactation with parturition has been explained by assuming that estrogen produced during pregnancy inhibits the liberation of lactogen by the pituitary. Withdrawal of estrogen, as occurs at parturition, permits lactogen production and the onset of lactation. If this is true, estrogen should inhibit lactation, and it does in experimental animals. Clinically, also, estrogen is used to prevent painful engorgement of the breast after parturition when nursing does not occur (51). Estrogen does not prevent the action of lactogen when it is given with the latter hormone, indicating that the steroid hormone acts upon the pituitary and not the mammary glands directly. The physiological regulation of the onset of lactation seemed to be controlled by a reciprocal gonad-hypophyseal relationship in a manner comparable to that regulating the estrous or menstrual cycles; however, some recent experiments argue against this theory.

Monkeys given estrogens for long periods begin to lactate (21). Similarly young virgin goats or heifers subjected to prolonged treatment with the synthetic estrogen, stilbestrol, begin to lactate and may produce large quantities of milk. Estrogen increases the lactogen content of the pituitary glands of nonparous or male rats. The injection of estrogen over long periods might be assumed to increase the production of lactogen by the pituitary until a point is reached at which lactation starts. Why estrogens inhibit an established lactation cannot be accounted for by this explanation. The enigmatic situation whereby estrogens inhibit established lactation and induce lactation requires further investigation.

The stimulus of suckling in lactating rats stimulates the production of milk in nonsuckled glands for a longer period than if suckling were not permitted, indicating some neural mechanism in the regulation of lactation. Denervated breasts lactated if suckling was permitted on some innervated nipples but lactation failed when only the denervated nipples were suckled. The hypophyses of rats which are actively suckling contain less lactogen than those of rats from which the young have been removed for 24 hours—an observation interpreted as showing a release of lactogen under the stimulus of suckling. How much of a role the stimulus of nursing plays in lactation in animals of other species is not known (45).

Attempts to increase the production of milk by injection of additional lactogen have not been encouraging. Other means have been found to increase milk production; in cows the amount of milk produced is increased up to 30 per cent and the amount of solids in the milk may be increased by administering thyroxin or thyroglobulin. During lactation the amount of thyrotrophic hormone produced is increased. Lactation may occur in thyroidectomized animals but the amount of milk is below normal.

Extracts of the posterior hypophysis (pituitrin) incites the removal of milk from the breast by causing a contraction of the muscle or contractile elements of the alveoli and ducts. The active material is probably the oxytocic factor. Glands from which as much milk has been removed as can be obtained by usual means yield additional quantities when pituitrin is given. The increased intramammary pressure subsequent to pituitrin administration can be readily demonstrated by cannulating the primary ducts.

REFERENCES

1. ALBRIGHT, F., SMITH, P. H. and FRASER, R. A syndrome characterized by primary ovarian insufficiency and decreased stature. Report of 11 cases with a digression on hormonal control of axillary and pubic hair. *Amer. J. med. Sci.*, 1942, *204*:625–648.

2. ALLEN, E. The menstrual cycle of the monkey, Macacus rhesus: Observations on normal animals, the effects of removal of the ovaries and the effects of injections of ovarian and placental extracts into the spayed animals. *Contrib. to Embryol. Carneg. Instn*, 1927, *19*:1–44.

3. ALLEN, E. and DOISY, E. A. An ovarian hormone: A preliminary report on its location, extraction, and partial purification, and action in test animals. *J. Amer. med. Ass.*, 1923, *81*: 819–821.

4. ALLEN, E., HISAW, F. L. and GARDNER, W. U. The endocrine functions of the ovaries.

pp. 452–629 in: *Sex and internal secretions*, 2d ed. Baltimore, Williams & Wilkins Company, 1939.

5. ASCHHEIM, S. Die Schwangerschafts-diagnose aus dem Harn durch Nachweis des Hypophysenvorderlappen Hormons; Grundlagen und Technik der Methode. *Klin. Wschr.*, 1928, *7*:1404–1411.

6. BARTELMEZ, G. W. The human uterine mucous membrane during menstruation. *Amer. J. Obstet. Gynec.*, 1931, *21*:623–643.

7. BLANDAU, R. J. and YOUNG, W. C. The effects of delayed fertilization on the development of the guinea pig ovum. *Anat. Rec.*, 1939, *64*:303–329.

8. CORNER, G. W. Physiology of the corpus luteum. I. The effect of very early ablation of the corpus luteum upon embryos and uterus. *Amer. J. Physiol.*, 1928, *86*:74–81.

9. CORNER, G. W. The nature of the menstrual cycle. *Harvey Lect.*, 1932–1933, *28*:67–89.

10. D'AMOUR, F. E. A comparison of the methods used in determining the time of ovulation. *J. clin. Endocrinol.*, 1943, *3*:41–48.

11. DEMPSEY, E. W. and BASSETT, D. L. Observations on the fluorescence, birefrigence and histochemistry of the rat ovary during the reproductive cycle. *Endocrinology*, 1943, *33*:384–401.

12. DOISY, E. A. The metabolism of estrogens. *Biological Symposia*, 1942, *9*:21–40.

13. DODDS, E. C., GOLDBERG, L., LAWSON, W. and ROBINSON, R. Oestrogenic activity of alkylated stilboestrols. *Nature, Lond.*, 1938, *142*:34.

14. EVANS, H. M., KOHLS, C. L. and WONDER, D. H. Gonadotropic hormone in the blood and urine during early pregnancy. *J. Amer. med. Ass.*, 1937, *108*:287–289.

15. EVANS, H. M., SIMPSON, M. E., LYONS, W. and TURPEINEN, K. Anterior pituitary hormones which favor the production of traumatic uterine placentoma. *Endocrinology*, 1941, *28*:933–945.

16. FEVOLD, H. L. The follicle stimulating and luteinizing hormones of the anterior pituitary. pp. 966–1002 in: *Sex and internal secretions*, 2d ed. Baltimore, Williams & Wilkins Company, 1939.

17. FRANKEL-CONRAT, H., LI, C. H., SIMPSON, M. E. and EVANS, H. M. Interstitial cell stimulating hormone. I. Biological properties. II. Method of preparation and some physiochemical studies. III. Methods of estimating the hormonal content of pituitaries. *Endocrinology*, 1940, *27*:793–817.

18. FRANKEL, L. and PAPANICOLAOU, G. N. Growth, desquamation and involution of the vaginal epithelium of fetuses and children with a consideration of the related hormonal factors. *Amer. J. Anat.*, 1938, *62*:427–451.

19. FRIEDMAN, M. H. Mechanism of ovulation in the rabbit; ovulation produced by injection of urine from pregnant women. *Amer. J. Physiol.*, 1929, *90*:617–622.

20. GARDNER, W. U. Tumors in experimental animals receiving steroid hormones. *Surgery*, 1944, *16*:8–32.

21. GARDNER, W. U. and VAN WAGENEN, G. Experimental development of the mammary gland of the monkey. *Endocrinology*, 1938, *22*:164–172.

22. GREENE, R. R. Hormonal factors in sex inversion: the effects of sex hormones on embryonic sexual structures of the rat. *Biological Symposia*, 1942, *9*:105–123.

23. HAIN, A. M. The excretion of oestrogen and pregnandiol by pregnant and parturient women. *J. Endocrinology*, 1940–41, *2*:104–140.

24. HAMAN, J. O. The length of the menstrual cycle. *Amer. J. Obstet. Gynec.*, 1942, *43*:870–873.

25. HARTMAN, C. G. *Time of ovulation in women*. Baltimore, Williams & Wilkins Company, 1936, 228 pp.

26. HARTMAN, C. G. Non-effect of ovariectomy on the twenty-fifth day of pregnancy in the rhesus monkey. *Proc. Soc. exp. Biol., N. Y.*, 1941, *48*:221–223.

27. HARTMAN, C. G. Further attempts to cause ovulation by means of gonadotropes in the adult rhesus monkey. *Contrib. to Embryol. Carneg. Instn*, 1942, *30*:111–126.

28. HATERIUS, H. C. Studies on a neurohypophyseal mechanism influencing gonadotropic activity. *Cold Spr. Harb. Symposia*, 1937, *5*:280–288.

29. HECKEL, C. P. and ALLEN, W. M. Prolongation of pregnancy in the rabbit by injection of progesterone. *Amer. J. Obstet. Gynec.*, 1938, *35*:131–137.

30. HENRY, J. S. and BROWNE, J. S. L. The contractions of the human uterus during the menstrual cycle. The effect of progesterone and posterior pituitary extract upon the motility of the human uterus. *Amer. J. Obstet. Gynec.*, 1943, *45*:927–949.

31. HINSEY, J. C. The relation of the nervous system to ovulation and other phenomena in the female reproductive tract. *Cold Spr. Harb. Symposia*, 1937, *5*:269–276.

32. HITSCHMANN, F. and ADLER, L. Der Bau de Uterusschleimhaut des geschlechtsreifen Weibes mit besonderer Berücksichtigung der Menstruation. *Mschr. Geburtsh. Gynäk.*, 1908, *27*:1–82.

33. JONES, G. E. S., GEY, G. O. and GEY, M. K. Hormone production by placental cells maintained in continuous culture. *Johns Hopk. Hosp. Bull.*, 1943, *72*:26–38.

34. KNAUS, H. H. *Periodic fertility and sterility in women*, trans. by Kitchin and Kitchin, Vienna, Maudrich, 1934, 147 pp.

35. MARKEE, J. E. Menstruation in intraovular endometrial transplants in the rhesus monkey. *Contrib. to Embryol. Carneg. Instn*, 1940, *28*:221–308.

36. PAPANICOLAOU, G. N. and SHORR, E. The action of ovarian follicular hormone in the menopause as indicated by vaginal smears. *Amer. J. Obstet. Gynec.*, 1936, *31*:3–28.

37. PFEIFFER, C. A. Sexual differences of hypophyses and their determination by gonads. *Amer. J. Anat.*, 1936, *58*:195–225.

38. PINCUS, G. and PEARLMAN, W. H. The intermediate metabolism of the sex hormone. *Vitamins and hormones*, 1943, *1*:293–344.

39. REYNOLDS S. R. M. *Physiology of the uterus.* New York, Paul B. Hoeber, Inc., 1939, 447 pp.

40. RIDDLE, O. and BATES, R. W. The preparation assay and action of lactogenic hormone. pp. 1088–1117 in: *Sex and internal secretions*, 2d ed. Baltimore, Williams & Wilkins Company, 1939.

41. ROBINSON, A. L., DANTNOW, M. M. and JEFFCOATE, T. N. A. Induction of abortion and labour by means of oestrin. *Brit. med. J.*, 1935, *1*:749–753.

42. ROCK, J. and BARTLETT, M. K. Biopsy studies of human endometrium; criteria of dating and information about amenorrhea, menorrhagia and time of ovulation. *J. Amer. med. Ass.*, 1937, *108*:2022–2028.

43. ROWLANDS, I. W. and SHARPEY-SCHAFER, E. P. Effect of oestradiol benzoate on the amount of gonadotrophin found in the pituitary gland and urine in post-menopausal women. *Brit. med. J.*, 1940, *1*:205–207.

44. RUBENSTEIN, B. B. The relation of cyclic changes in the human vaginal smears to body temperatures and basal metabolic rates. *Amer. J. Physiol.*, 1937, *119*:635–641.

45. SELYE, H., COLLIP, J. B. and THOMPSON, D. L. Nervous and hormonal factors in lactation. *Endocrinology*, 1934, *18*:237–247.

46. SHORR, E. The menopause. *Bull. N. Y. Acad. Med.*, 1940, *16*:453–474.

47. SIMMONS, K. and GREULICH, W. W. Menarchal age and the height, weight, and skeletal age of girls 7–17 years. *J. Pediat.*, 1943, *22*:518–548.

48. SMITH, G. S., SMITH, O. W. and PINCUS, G. Total urinary estrogen, estrone, estriol, during a menstrual cycle and during a pregnancy. *Amer. J. Physiol.*, 1938, *121*:98–106.

49. SMITH, P. E. Hypophysectomy and replacement therapy in the rat. *Amer. J. Anat.*, 1930, *45*:205–273.

50. SMITH, P. E. and ENGLE, E. T. Experimental evidence regarding the rôle of the anterior pituitary in the development and regulation of the genital system. *Amer. J. Anat.*, 1927, *40*:159–217.

51. STEWART, H. L. and PRATT, J. P. Inhibition of lactation. *Amer. J. Obstet. Gynec.*, 1941, *41*:555–566.

52. TURNER, C. W. The mammary glands. pp. 740–803 in: *Sex and internal secretions*, 2d ed. Baltimore, Williams & Wilkins Company, 1939.

53. VAN WAGENEN, G. and ZUCKERMAN, S. Uterine bleeding of monkeys in relation to neural and vascular processes. II. Spinal cord transection and the oestrin level. *Amer. J. Physiol.*, 1933, *106*:416–422.

54. VENNING, E. H. and BROWNE, J. S. L. Studies on corpus luteum function. I. The urinary excretion of sodium pregnandiol glucuronidate in the human menstrual cycle. *Endocrinology*, 1937, *21*:711–721.

55. VENNING, E. H. and BROWNE, J. S. L. A study of the metabolism of crystalline progesterone. *Endocrinology*, 1940, *27*:707–720.

56. WERNER, A. A. and COLLIER, W. D. Production of endometrial growth in castrated women; minimum dosage of theelin that is required. *J. Amer. med. Ass.*, 1933, *101*:1466–1472.

57. WERNER, S. C. Quantitative study of the urinary excretion of hypophyseal gonadotropin, estrogen and androgen of normal women. *J. clin. Invest.*, 1941, *20*:21–30.

58. WIESBADER, H., ENGLE, E. T. and SMITH, P. E. Menstrual bleeding after corpus luteum excision followed by estrin or progestin therapy. *Amer. J. Obstet. Gynec.*, 1936, *32*:1039–1043.

59. WISLOCKI, G. B. and BENNET, H. S. The histology and cytology of the human and monkey placenta, with special reference to the trophoblast. *Amer. J. Anat.*, 1943, *73*:335–450.

60. WHITE, A. The lactogenic hormone and mammogen. *Ann. N. Y. Acad. Sci.*, 1943, 341–382.

CHAPTER 55

REPRODUCTION IN THE MALE

By Charles W. Hooker

The function of the male reproductive system, as such, is the production of spermatozoa and their delivery in suitable condition for fertilization of the ovum produced and housed in the female. The elaboration of spermatozoa occurs in the testes; the remainder of the genital system (Fig. 498) consists of excurrent ducts that store and transport the spermatozoa to the exterior and of a series of glands whose secretions add body to the fluid containing the outgoing spermatozoa. In addition to producing spermatozoa, the testes are responsible for the functional maintenance of the rest of the genital

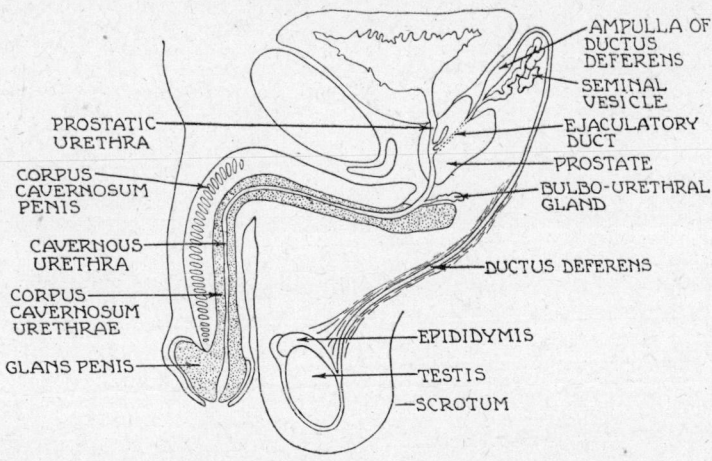

Fig. 498.—Diagram of the male reproductive system. (Modified from Eberth.)

system and for the development and maintenance of the somatic characters that are peculiarly masculine. The latter, an endocrine function of the testes, was recognized by the ancients who practiced castration of domestic animals. Aristotle was familiar with many of the consequences of castration in man.

Effects of Castration—Transplantation of Testes. Excision of the testes produces permanent sterility by removing the site of production of spermatozoa. This operation in adults of all higher animals and man also results in atrophy of the genital tract and in the loss of many masculine characters. If the castration is done prior to the attainment of sexual maturity, the genital organs remain infantile and many masculine traits fail to manifest themselves. The effects of castration are dramatic in many animals, as is obvious in comparing the physique and temperament of the bull and the ox or of the stallion and the gelding. In the fowl, castration results in a regression of the

1213

prominent head furnishings (comb, wattles, ear lobes) of the cockerel to the pallid, modest structures of the capon (Fig. 499). The striking growth of the antlers in some male deer or of the horns in certain male goats and sheep is prevented by castration. Other structures normally developed only in the male, such as the spurs of the cockerel, are not so influenced by castration.

The effects of castration in man are perhaps less conspicuous than in the animals mentioned, but they are no less profound (11, 35). If a child is castrated, the pubertal changes do not occur. The high pitch of the voice is retained; the beard and body hair develop poorly; the body proportions do not become masculine; the genital organs, both internal and external, remain infantile in size and structure; masculine aggressiveness is deficient or absent. If the operation is performed after puberty, the effects are similar but often less marked, and some of them may require a long period to become apparent.

As with other endocrine glands, the first attempts at replacement therapy after castration consisted of the transplantation of testes. Testicular transplants have been made with various degrees of success in many species of

Fig. 499.—The head of a White Leghorn cockerel (left) and capon (right) showing the effects of castration upon the comb, wattles, and ear lobes.

animals (23). If the graft takes, it is usually capable of substituting for the somatic actions of the host's testes. In the nineteen-twenties testicular transplants ("goat glands" or "monkey glands") to man received wide popular attention and had many therapeutic claims made for them. Of course, in the establishment of a testicular graft many of the factors operate that influence any other transplantation. Of these, one of the most significant is the taxonomic or chemical kinship of host and donor species or individuals. Suffice it to say, the practice with respect to human hosts has apparently been largely abandoned.

Androgens—Chemistry and Metabolism. Although Brown-Séquard's report in 1898 of rejuvenation after injections of aqueous extracts of testicular tissue into himself created much interest, it is generally agreed that the first active testicular extract was prepared in 1927 by McGee, who used fat solvents. Similar extracts were soon found capable of correcting the recognized changes produced in a variety of animals by castration. Masculinizing activity was also found in extracts of urine, blood, cerebrospinal fluid, and bile; the epididymis is apparently the only organ besides the testes, however, whose extracts contain significant levels of male sex hormone.

Several pure male hormone compounds (androgens) have been obtained from natural sources or synthesized (20). Androsterone was prepared from human urine by Butenandt in 1931 and synthesized in 1934 by Ruzicka. Testosterone was obtained from testicular tissue of bulls in 1935 by David, and synthesized in the same year by Ruzicka and by Butenandt. These are the most active of the androgens, one international unit of biological activity being present in 100 μg of androsterone and in 13 to 16 μg of testosterone. Several compounds related to androsterone and known collectively as 17-ketosteroids have been isolated from human urine. Some of these substances are active biologically as androgens; others are not.

TESTOSTERONE   ANDROSTERONE

It is generally presumed that testosterone is the male sex hormone secreted by the testes and that androsterone and certain of the other androgenic compounds found in urine are its excreted metabolites. Testosterone has been identified thus far, however, only in testicular tissue of bulls, although extracts of the testes of several species of mammals possess androgenic activity. Human urine is apparently unique in exhibiting a high content of androgenic activity; in comparison the activity of urine from the stallion, bull, ram, dog, and rat is quite low (20). The conversion of testosterone into androsterone in the body is, however, supported by the observation that injection of large amounts of testosterone into men is followed by the excretion of increased amounts of androsterone in the urine (4). The same transformation occurs in the monkey and chimpanzee.

The liver is apparently a chief site of modification and inactivation of androgens. Although vitamin B-complex deficiency seriously impairs the ability of the liver to inactivate estrogens, the same deficiency does not significantly disturb the capacity to inactivate testosterone (1). Normal men excrete an average of approximately 14 mg. of 17-ketosteroids daily. It has been suggested that 5 mg. represent testicular androgen and that the remaining 9 mg. are of adrenal origin (6). The evidence for this is the decrease from 14 to 9 mg. after castration and from 14 to 5 mg. with severe adrenal insufficiency. In panhypopituitarism the level falls to zero.

Estrogenic as well as androgenic substances have been extracted from testicular tissue. The urine of normal men contains estrogenic material, and the urine of the stallion is the richest known natural source of estrogens. After castration in both man and the stallion, the urinary excretion of estrogen is greatly decreased. The function of testicular estrogen has not been determined, but the excretion of estrogens by man is increased by the administration of testosterone.

Assay of androgens. The original extraction and later purification and synthesis of androgenic compounds depended upon having at hand means of recognizing the active substance. Since the chemical nature of these substances was unknown, biological responses to them were necessarily employed. These biological tests are still valuable in the assay of the androgen content of various tissues and fluids in the clinical study of a variety of disorders. The basis of the tests is the prevention or correction of changes produced by castration in certain animals. Probably the most widely employed reaction is growth of the comb of the capon (Fig. 499), and it is upon this reaction that the International Unit (I.U.) of androgenic activity is based. The International Unit is activity equal to that of 100 μg. of pure androsterone. The standard test involves the daily intramuscular or subcutaneous injection of the unknown material into a group of Leghorn capons over a period of five days. At the end of this period the change in the size of the comb in response to 1 I.U. of androgen daily is an increase of 5 mm. in the length plus the height. Another widely used test involves maintenance or restoration of the weight and microscopic structure of the seminal vesicles (Fig. 500) and prostate glands of castrated rats.

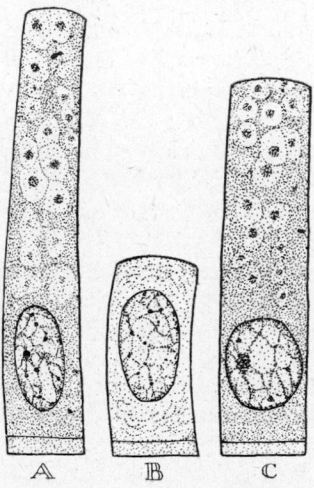

Fig. 500.—Cells from the epithelium of the seminal vesicle of the rat to show the effect of castration and restitution by injected androgen. A, from normal animal; B, twenty days after castration; C, from a 20-day castrate treated with androgen. (Redrawn from Moore, Hughes, and Gallagher.)

The usual procedure in bio-assaying androgens has been to administer them systemically, that is, subcutaneously or intramuscularly. It is becoming more common to apply the androgen directly to the structure whose growth is to be induced, for example the comb of the capon. With this method of administration a response is induced by much smaller amounts of androgen; distinct growth of the comb has been caused by a *total* of 1.2 μg. of androsterone, while the *daily* dose of this substance is 100 μg. when given systemically. It is interesting that testosterone and androsterone exhibit identical activity when applied directly, although testosterone is roughly seven times as active as androsterone when they are administered systemically. The significance of this observation is only beginning to receive consideration.

Chemical methods are also available for the determination of androgens, and have been used chiefly upon urinary material. Perhaps the most widely used of these reactions is the colorimetric method originated by Zimmerman. This test depends upon the development of a color when m-dinitrobenzene reacts with ketones in alkaline solution. Another colorimetric method involves the development of a blue color by the application of $SbCl_3$ to the neutral ketonic extracts of urine. A polarographic method requiring the application of a ketone reaction has also been introduced. These methods are in effect tests for certain chemical groups and may give positive tests when no biologically active androgens or even 17-ketosteroids are present.

Actions and Functions of Androgen. The actions of the androgenic hormones involve many parts of the body and many physiological functions not obviously related to reproduction (11, 35). The list of functions or actions of androgenic hormones is impressive, but probably is still incomplete. Their identification has been based upon study of the effects of castration or of testicular insufficiency, the repair of these changes by administration of androgens, the effects of excessive amounts of administered androgens, and the correlation of levels of excreted androgen with different bodily states.

Genital system. Each of the several portions of the genital tract (Fig. 498) is under the controlling influence of the testicular hormone. In the absence of adequate androgen, in the boy or in the eunuch for example, the scrotum is small and its proximal end tends to be wider than the distal end. After puberty the scrotum is much larger, with the distal portion expanded and the proximal portion relatively narrower (9). To some extent, the size and conformation of the scrotum depend upon the weight and degree of distension exerted by the testes; but in the absence of testes the scrotum may approach normal size and configuration when adequate androgen is supplied artificially. The full development of the penis likewise is contingent upon stimulation by androgen; it remains infantile when insufficient androgen is available and grows when androgen is administered (11, 35). The several excurrent ducts are also dependent upon androgen for the establishment and maintenance of mature size and structure. The attainment and maintenance of adult size and secretory function in the accessory glands of reproduction—seminal vesicles, prostate, bulbo-urethral glands—also require adequate stimulation by androgen. The effects of androgen are shown most conspicuously by the epithelium of these glands (Fig. 500); indeed, the height of the epithelium is often, within limits, proportional to the level of stimulating androgen (23).

The control of the structure and function of the normal prostate gland by androgen suggests that benign hypertrophy of the prostate may perhaps be related to some aberration in the action or production of androgens. This prostatic change is common in men in the later decades of life and consists of a nonmalignant enlargement of one or more portions of the prostate and a consequent difficulty in voiding. On the basis of prostatic control at earlier ages, hypertrophy would appear to demand a greatly increased level of stimulation by androgen; yet it occurs at ages when the production of androgen has presumably declined. Some authors have reported the condition developing many years after castration, while other authors have observed regression of the enlarged prostate and a relief of the urinary distress upon castration. Still other investigators have reported relief of the urinary difficulties after administration of androgen without any effect upon the prostate itself; the symptomatic relief is attributed to a strengthening of the bladder musculature sufficiently to overcome the urethral obstruction. Finally, the level of excretion of 17-ketosteroids by patients with prostatic hypertrophy is reported to be not significantly different from that by men of the same age without prostatic disease. The observations are too inconsistent and conflicting to permit a decision as to whether androgens are an important factor in this disease. Estrogens have also received consideration as possible etiological agents, largely because they modify the prostate glands in mice and rats, the most striking effect being a squamous metaplasia. No convincing evidence for the involvement of estrogens has been advanced, and the possibility is apparently losing favor.

In contrast, carcinoma of the prostate is strikingly affected by the testes, and castration has become a widely employed therapeutic measure (16). The operation apparently does not always influence the primary tumor nor does it prolong the life of the patient, but it causes a dramatic regression of the metastatic growths and an almost immediate diminution in the pain that characteristically accompanies this tumor. The administration of estrogens has the same effect, presumably by producing a physiological castration through inhibition of the hypophysis.

Hair. Hair is a conspicuous secondary sex character, with the type, pattern, and degree of growth differing in the two sexes and influenced by androgen. The extent of the influence of the androgen evidently depends upon the genetic constitution of the individual, and every generalization apparently has its exceptions in virile men. Growth of hair over the trunk and the extremities is heavier in the presence of androgens. Hair in the axillary and pubic regions depends upon androgen for its full development; it does not appear until

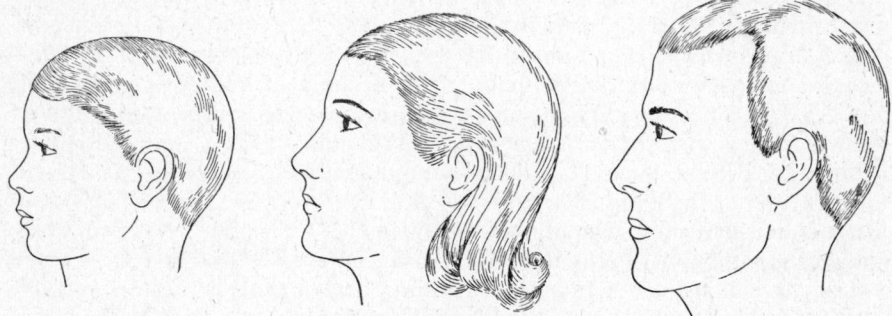

Fig. 501.—Patterns of distribution of head hair. The hair-lines of the child and adult woman are alike, while that of the adult man usually shows an indentation in the lateral frontal region. (From Greulich *et al.*, *Monogr. Soc. Res. Child Development*, 1942, 7:1–85.)

puberty, and is sparse in castrates and in eunuchoid men (11, 35). In the female the upper border of the hair-covered pubic areas is usually horizontal, whereas in the male the pubic hair usually extends upward along the linea alba to, or beyond, the umbilicus. After castration pubic hair is less luxuriant, and the upward extension of the superior border often disappears. The pattern of head hair is different in the two sexes and apparently determined by androgen (9). In immature boys and in girls and women the hair-line on the forehead is in the form of a continuous bowlike curve (Fig. 501). In mature men the hair-line is usually marked by a recession (calvity) over the lateral frontal region on each side. Calvities are poorly developed or absent in some unquestionably virile men, but apparently they are always absent in hypogonadal or prepubertally castrated men and can usually be induced in the latter by administration of androgen. This sexual difference in growth of head hair is probably related to common baldness, which is traditionally found only in the male, begins only after puberty, is absent in prepubertally castrated men, and frequently appears after masculinization of women. Moreover, the condition may be induced in many castrated men by administration of therapeutic levels of androgen. Baldness appears to be a hereditary trait that requires a physiological level of androgen for its development; that is, no amount of androgen can induce baldness in an individual not carrying the hereditary factors for the condition (12).

Sebaceous glands. The sebaceous glands of the skin are also influenced by androgens. Acne vulgaris, an inflammation of the sebaceous glands, does not appear until puberty, but during adolescence is present in the majority of both males and females. Inasmuch as the disorder does not develop in castrates but may be induced by administered androgens, the androgens appear to be prerequisites and incitants of acne, although a variety of other factors may also be involved (10). The high incidence of acne in females does not argue against the primacy of androgen in the disorder since androgens are normally present in fairly high levels in the female. A basis for the acnegenic action of the androgens may lie in their enhancing secretory activity of the sebaceous glands as revealed by oiliness of the skin beginning normally at puberty and in hypogonadal patients upon treatment with androgens (10).

Color of skin. The color of the skin is also influenced by androgens. In castrates and eunuchoids the skin is furrowed or finely wrinkled, soft, and sallow. After administration of androgens and in normal men the skin is firmer, ruddier, and has a darker color (11, 35). Castrates have little or no ability to tan, whereas upon administration of androgens the skin may tan many months after exposure to sunlight (11). In a spectrophotometric study (5) it was found that, as compared with normal men, castrates have a lower quantity of hemoglobin in the skin and that a higher proportion is reduced hemoglobin; carotene is present in greater amounts in the skin; melanin levels are slightly subnormal. Administration of androgen brought the levels of all of these substances within the normal range.

Subcutaneous fat. In many instances the pattern of distribution of subcutaneous fat appears to be influenced by androgens (11, 35). In normal adults abdominal fat usually accumulates above the umbilicus in the male and below the umbilicus in the female. In castrates fat frequently accumulates in the mammary region, over the trochanters, and in the mons pubis, although these fatty depots may be absent in other castrates of long standing. The ability of administered androgens to modify fat distribution has not been forcibly demonstrated.

Voice. One of the most readily recognized actions of androgens is upon the depth of the voice (11, 35). The eunuchoid and prepubertal castrate retain the voice of the immature boy. The administration of androgens results in a lowering of the voice which may, however, take the form merely of hoarseness. These vocal changes may not be accompanied by any especial enlargement of the laryngeal cartilages. Androgens affect the voice of women in much the same way, causing hoarseness and deepening. Castration after puberty frequently has no effect upon the depth of the voice.

Skeleton. There are many indications that the androgens affect skeletal growth, but the relationship appears beset with inconsistencies. The pubertal spurt in somatic growth suggests androgen as a possible causative agent. On the other hand, the prepubertal castrate and the eunuchoid are frequently quite tall and characterized by the disproportionately great length of the bones of the extremities. The administration of androgens is reported to accelerate the closure of the epiphyses and to lead to the termination of growth in tall eunuchoid boys (17). Contrariwise, the same dose levels of androgens are reported to provoke growth in stunted, eunuchoid boys (28). The effects in animals are equally confusing. Administration of large amounts of androgens retards growth in rats; but when large amounts of androgens are given along with large amounts of estrogens somatic growth is less inhibited than when estrogens are given alone.

Muscle. The usually greater muscularity of the male as compared with the female appears to be at least partially attributable to androgens. Muscular growth and increased strength are pubertal traits, and a relative muscular weakness usually characterizes castrated and eunuchoid men (35). A striking generalized muscular hypertrophy may be induced in guinea pigs by administration of androgens (26). Increased muscular strength and endurance have also been induced in castrated and hypogonadal men by administration of androgens (32). To what extent these effects are the result of increased well-being and metabolic improvement has not been entirely established.

Vascular system. A testicular deficiency arising before puberty is characteristically accompanied by paleness. Occasionally postpubertal deficiency precipitates hot flashes and flushing of the skin similar to those of the menopausal female (11, 35). In analyzing the apparent relationship of the cardiovascular system and androgens it has been found that the cutaneous vascular bed of castrates is smaller than in normal men and has less blood flowing through it, and that cutaneous areas with large venous beds contain more reduced hemoglobin, suggesting a venous dilatation in these areas. These changes were reversed by administration of testosterone propionate, and in more "arterial" regions of the skin the volume of blood was increased and it contained more oxyhemoglobin (5). The small blood vessels of the skin are characterized by fluctuations in excitability in castrated men, and their excitability is reduced by administration of testosterone (29). The effects of androgens upon blood vessels have led to their successful use as therapeutic agents in vascular disease.

Metabolism. Androgens cause retention of nitrogen, sodium, potassium, inorganic phosphorus, and chlorides, with the effect being less in intact than in castrated or eunuchoid men (18). Creatine is excreted in quite small amounts in normal men, although prepubertal boys, castrates, and eunuchoids ordinarily exhibit a creatinuria. This difference in creatine metabolism and excretion is partially to be attributed to androgens inasmuch as these substances usually reduce creatinuria and increase creatine tolerance. The basal metabolism may increase 5 to 15 per cent during treatment with androgen without any change in respiratory quotient, this despite a gain in body weight that may, however, be partially the result of retention of electrolyte and water. As might be expected in the light of their effects upon metabolism, treatment with androgens is also reported to produce significant increases in red cell count, hemoglobin, and hematocrit values (22). These blood changes are considered comparable to those during normal adolescence.

In addition to the numerous actions of androgens in the male, these substances have important effects in the female that have prompted their clinical employment in a variety of gynecological disorders.

Androgen in Different Periods of Life. A plausible interpretation of *embryonic sexual differentiation* is the genetic determination of the differentiation of the morphologically indifferent gonad into a testis or ovary. The newly differentiated testis could conceivably secrete an androgen which would provoke growth and differentiation in the male components of the morphologically bipotential genital tract, and either induce or allow regression of the female components. Observations made in experiments involving administration of sex hormones to embryos of many species have apparently lent support to the concept of a directional influence of these hormones. In general, androgens have stimulated the male homologues and estrogens the female homologues (7). These effects, however, have not been entirely uniform, and more and more doubt is being entertained that the hormones of the embryonic gonad regulate differentiation (24); but once embryonic sexual differentiation is completed, the sex hormones may cause abnormal development of the

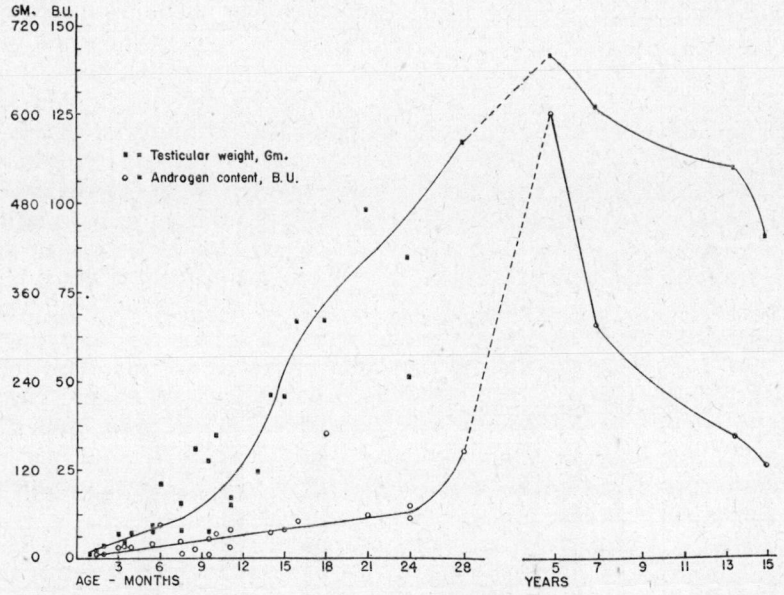

Fig. 502.—The androgen content and weight of the testes of bulls of different ages. Sexual maturity, as indicated by motile spermatozoa in the epididymis, is attained around the age of nine months. The rapid growth of the testes at this time is almost exclusively tubular, and is not accompanied by a change in the rate of increase in androgen. (From Hooker, *Amer. J. Anat.*, 1944, *74*:1–37.)

genital system in the fetus and be important factors in such malformations as pseudohermaphroditism (7).

Puberty. During childhood there is normally little evidence of the activity or presence of the testicular hormone (9). Small amounts of androgens are present in the urine, but these substances may have an adrenal origin. At puberty, however, a dramatic change occurs. In the short span of a few years the child is transformed into a man. The genital system undergoes rapid growth and maturation, and secondary sex characters such as the beard, body hair, and deeper voice make their appearance (9). These changes are clearly dependent upon androgens as shown by their absence in the castrate and by their evocation by administered androgens. This fact, plus the observation that the changes are preceded and accompanied by accelerated growth of the testes, support the almost universal belief that pubertal changes are the result of an abrupt and conspicuous increase in the production of androgen by the testes. This entirely plausible explanation, however, is not supported by the few studies the problem has received. Most investigators have reported a steady increase in the excretion of androgen with increased age during puberty and adolescence, with no conspicuous increase to coincide with the onset of puberty (9). It has been pointed out, however, that variation among individuals of the same age is great with respect to degree of sexual maturation and that comparisons should be made not with age but with development. The testicular level of androgen has been examined only in the bull (15). Here the rise in androgen with increased age was uniform in the young animal, and no conspicuous alteration in level accompanied pubertal changes (Fig. 502). The little evidence available accordingly suggests that pubertal changes are not the result of a greatly increased production of androgen.

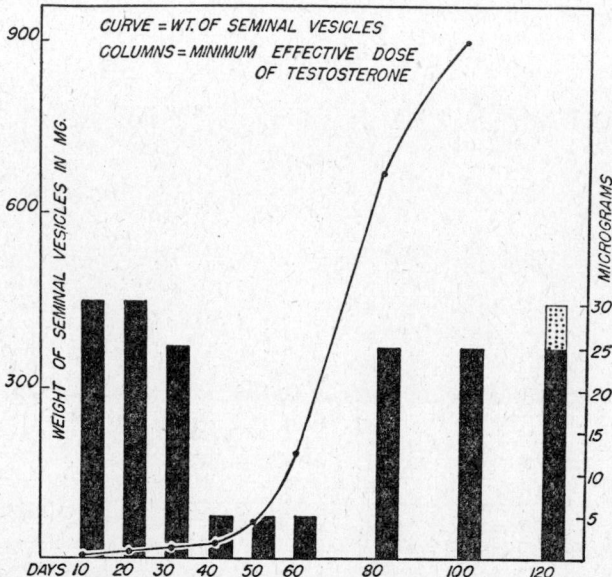

Fig. 503.—Chart showing dose level of testosterone required at different ages to elicit a response in the seminal vesicles of rats castrated at birth. The curve shows the growth of the seminal vesicles of normal rats. (From Hooker, *Endocrinology*, 1942, *30*:77–84.)

Recent work in laboratory animals (14) indicates that a major factor responsible for pubertal changes is a tremendous increase at this age in the responsiveness of the tissues to androgen (Fig. 503).

Sexual maturity. During sexual maturity androgens are responsible for the maintenance of most sex characters, as shown by the effects of castration. The absence of evident fluctuations in masculinity indicates a steady state of production and action of androgen. Some tendency toward cyclic patterns has been suggested, but has not been established.

Old age. It is popularly supposed that the decline in vigor in advanced age is the result of decline in testicular activity. The level of urinary androgen in man is somewhat lower (6) and in the bull the level of testicular androgen is diminished (15), but whether these levels are sufficiently decreased to account for senile changes is not established. Many clinical endocrinologists recognize a male climacteric occurring at about the same age as the menopause in women. It is characterized by decline in vigor and by vascular instability and other phenomena not unlike those of the menopause, and can frequently be alleviated by the administration of androgens (11, 35).

Site of Production of Testicular Androgen. The testis (Fig. 504) is composed of many tortuously coiled seminiferous tubules and an intertubular stroma of connective tissue. Located in the stroma are numbers of epithelioid cells resembling gland cells, the interstitial cells of Leydig. The androgen secreted by the testis obviously must be elaborated in either or both the tubules and the intertubular tissue. That the tubules are not the primary source of the androgen is shown by the usual absence of castration phenomena after atrophy or damage of the tubules, provided the intertubular tissue remains essentially normal. Moreover, tubular growth (Fig. 502) is accompanied by no increase

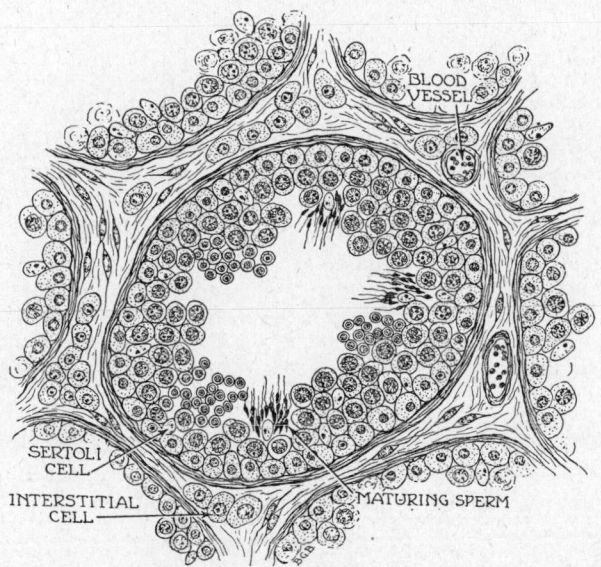

Fig. 504.—A small area of a human testis, showing one tubule and portions of several others in cross section and the intertubular tissue.

in the androgen content of the testes (15). If the tubules are not the source of the androgen, obviously the intertubular tissue must perform this function, and histochemical studies have revealed the presence of sterones resembling the active androgens in the intertubular spaces but not in the tubules (27). Stimulation of the testis by gonadotrophins results in evident production of androgen only if the Leydig cells are stimulated (8). Large quantities of androgen are apparently secreted by experimental tumors of the Leydig cells in mice and by spontaneous interstitial cell tumors in boys. Finally, the changes in level of testicular androgen in the bull are paralleled by appropriate cytological changes in the Leydig cells (15). It is almost certain that the Leydig cells are the site of production of testicular androgen.

Regulation of Production of Androgen. The testis is under the control of the hypophysis, as shown by atrophy of the testes and the appearance of castration changes after hypophysectomy and by the restoration of full testicular function upon the administration of suitable gonadotrophic substances. Of the two hypophyseal gonadotrophins, follicle stimulating hormone (FSH) and luteinizing hormone (LH) or interstitial cell stimulating hormone (ICSH), FSH apparently has no influence upon the production of androgen when given alone. Purified ICSH when given alone, however, is capable of provoking the production of sufficient androgen to restore the reproductive system to an essentially normal condition. When the two purified gonadotrophins are given simultaneously the effect upon production of androgen is greater than when ICSH is given alone (8). These studies have been carried out chiefly upon the rat, and it is unknown whether the general principles apply also to man. Other gonadotrophic preparations, such as that from pregnancy urine, and other hypophyseal fractions, such as extracts of lactogenic hormone, have been reported to incite the production of androgen in the testes; but the analysis here is incomplete.

The testes in turn affect the production of gonadotrophins by the hypophysis. Castration produces cytological changes in the hypophysis, and results in an increase in the gonadotrophin content of the hypophysis, blood, and urine. The administration of androgen to the castrate restores the normal cytology of the hypophysis and returns the several gonadotrophin levels to normal. In the intact individual the administration of androgen depresses the gonadotrophin level. Thus there exists a mutual regulation of gonadotrophin and androgen production.

Extratesticular Androgen. In addition to being produced by the testes, androgenic substances are also elaborated in other sites, notably the adrenal glands and the ovaries, and especially by tumors of these organs. Certain tumors of the adrenal cortex in boys may induce precocious puberty, and in women these tumors may be masculinizing to the extent of provoking growth of a beard, a generalized hypertrichosis, lowering of the voice, and even baldness. After removal of the tumor the masculine traits regress, showing the tumor to be the source of the androgen. An increase in urinary 17-ketosteroids usually accompanies these tumors (33); indeed, such a rise may be pathognomonic for certain adrenal tumors.

A number of experiments in animals have shown that androgen may be produced by the normal adrenal gland. In the prepubertal rat the presence of androgen is indicated by the cytology of the prostate upon which castration has no effect at this age, although adrenalectomy promptly results in typical castration atrophy of this organ. The administration of adrenotrophic preparations has been reported to evoke the production of androgen in castrated but not adrenalectomized rats. The identity of the androgenic substance of the adrenal is unknown.

Certain ovarian tumors in women are also virilizing, inducing masculinization comparable to that in the presence of virilizing tumors of the adrenals. In several species of laboratory animals the ovaries may exert masculinizing actions under various experimental conditions, many of which involve an alteration of gonadotrophic stimulation of the ovaries. In some animals the androgen is apparently secreted by the interstitial cells of the ovary, while in other species the cells of the theca interna are thought to have this function.

Spermatogenesis and Spermatozoa. The testes arise in the abdominal region of the embryo and typically undergo a descent into the scrotum late in fetal life. The cause and mechanism of the descent are not understood, but it not infrequently happens that one and occasionally both testes fail to descend, the condition being known as cryptorchidism. In the undescended testis spermatogenesis is inhibited and the testis is usually sterile. Androgen production is by no means abolished, but there is evidence that it is decreased in level (23, 25). Perhaps the most serious aspect of the undescended testis is its liability to becoming cancerous, which vastly exceeds that of the scrotal testis (2).

The adverse effect of cryptorchidism upon spermatogenesis appears to be the result of the higher temperatures to which the testes are subjected when they fail to descend (23). Experimental procedures that raise the temperature of the testes and many febrile diseases also suppress spermatogenesis and consequently cause sterility, which may be transitory or permanent. Whether the action of heat upon the seminiferous tubules is direct or involves intermediary mechanisms is not yet known.

Like the production of androgen, the production of spermatozoa is under the control of the hypophysis. Hypofunction of the hypophysis results in defective spermatogenesis, and extirpation of the hypophysis is promptly followed by cessation of spermatogenesis. Certain gonadotrophic preparations are capable of inducing spermatogenesis precociously in immature animals and of restoring spermatogenesis in hypophysectomized animals. The hypophyseal gonadotrophin specifically affecting spermatogenesis is follicle stimulating hormone (FSH); the other gonadotrophin, ICSH (or LH), is without direct effect upon this process (8). These generalizations appear well established for the rat; but the situation in man has not been fully analyzed, perhaps largely because it does not lend itself to controlled experiments of this nature. Indeed, failure of spermatogenesis in man is not consistently corrected by administration of gonadotrophins (3). It will be apparent, however, that the defect may not always be solely the result of deficient gonadotrophin; other influences of an unknown nature may need to be corrected before the gonadotrophin can exert such action as it may possess. The control of spermatogenesis in man and a rational means of correcting deficiencies are important problems that demand much further study.

Although seemingly paradoxical, injections of testosterone sustain spermatogenesis in hypophysectomized animals (25); even more striking is the fact that testosterone will restore spermatogenesis after atrophy of the tubules has become pronounced as a result of hypophysectomy. These observations have been made in a number of laboratory animals including the monkey. The mechanism of this action of androgen is at present largely conjectural, the confusing consideration being that sex hormones characteristically suppress the gonadotrophic function of the hypophysis. Accordingly, androgen would be expected to inhibit spermatogenesis after the manner of estrogens. Inasmuch as the production of spermatozoa occurs only in scrotal testes (of scrotal animals, that is), maintenance or growth of the scrotum may be the mode of action of the androgen. This being the case, the control of spermatogenesis by the hypophysis might be considered to be indirect—that the hypophysis stimulates androgen production by the testis, and androgen stimulates the scrotum and keeps the testis deep in the scrotum where spermatogenesis itself needs no stimulus. Clearly the action of androgen is hardly consistent with apparently well-founded principles of the hypophyseal control of spermatogenesis. The unifying concept has thus far proved elusive.

Morphologically mature spermatozoa within the testis are in most mammals nonmotile and incapable of fertilizing the ovum. The acquisition of motility and of fertilizing capacity occurs in the epididymis, and appears to be part of the developmental process within the spermatozoa rather than a response to epididymal secretions. The attainment of fertilizing capacity is in part the acquisition of tolerance to temperatures higher than that of the testis; otherwise, the high temperatures of the female genital tract would kill or inactivate the spermatozoa.

The number of spermatozoa in one ejaculation is estimated to be in the neighborhood of 300,000,000 to 500,000,000 (36). Fewer than 60,000,000 spermatozoa in a cubic centimeter of semen is usually associated with sterility. Abnormal spermatozoa, for example with two heads or double tails, are common, and sterility is usually present when they amount to 20 per cent of the total spermatozoa. Sterility may, however, be present when the number of morphologically defective spermatozoa is low and the total sperm count within the normal range. In certain of these cases the only recognizable defect may be abnormal movements of the spermatozoa, such as swimming in a circle rather than in a more or less straight line.

The necessity that millions of spermatozoa be introduced into the female genital tract to insure fertilization of the ovum by a single spermatozoon may find explanation in an enzyme present in sperm suspensions. This enzyme, hyaluronidase, is capable of liquefying the gel in which the cells surrounding the tubal egg of the rat are embedded; and it increased the fertilizing capacity of sperm suspensions upon artificial insemination of the rabbit to the extent that one-sixth as many spermatozoa were required to effect fertilization (30).

The cervical canal is usually filled by mucus that acts as a barrier against the entry of spermatozoa into the uterus. To overcome this obstacle, spermatozoa are said to be endowed with a similar, or perhaps identical, mucolytic enzyme that enables them to burrow through the cervical mucus (21).

One significant outcome of studies of spermatozoa and of male sterility has been the recognition of the high incidence of sterility of the male. Contrary to the belief for centuries that in a barren marriage the woman is usually the sterile individual, it is now known that equally often it is the male who is sterile (36).

Functions of Genital Organs. The function of the scrotum as a relatively cool repository for the testes has already been mentioned. The ductuli efferentia, ductus epididymis, ductus deferens, ejaculatory duct, and urethra in the order named (Fig. 498) convey spermatozoa from the testis to the outside of the body. The epididymis and the ampulla of the ductus deferens also serve as depots for the storage of spermatozoa; it is now generally agreed that in man and various other mammals the seminal vesicles do not function as reservoirs for spermatozoa. The seminal vesicles, prostate, and bulbourethral glands contribute the bulk of the semen.

Spermatozoa in the testis are nonmotile and suspended in a small quantity of fluid. Possibly the pressure of accumulating fluid forces them into the efferent ductules. Spermatozoan motility is acquired in the epididymis, where the spermatozoa may survive for many weeks. Although spermatozoa taken from the epididymis are highly motile, it is probable that their movements are slight within this organ. It is presumed that their activity is accompanied by the production of CO_2 which renders the fluid acid and inhibits further movement; in any event, acid immobilizes spermatozoa in vitro. Accordingly, if ejaculated spermatozoa are to exhibit the motility necessary for their fertilizing the ovum, the acid of the epididymal fluid must be neutralized. The urethra, acid because of residual droplets of urine, and the vaginal fluid must also be neutralized for the same reason. By virtue of its alkalinity the fluid of the prostate presumably has this function. It is usually thought that in ejaculation the several components of the genital tract discharge their contents in an orderly sequence. The para-urethral glands of Littré and the bulbo-urethral glands discharge first, their secretions serving to lubricate the urethra. The prostatic secretion is added next and exerts its neutralizing function. Next the hordes of spermatozoa in the ampulla of the ductus deferens are discharged. Finally, according to this presumption, the seminal vesicles project their bulky secretion.

In many rodents ejaculated semen coagulates in the vagina and cervix, forming a so-called copulation or vaginal plug. The plug consists of the fluid of the seminal vesicles coagulated by an enzyme elaborated in one of the pairs of lobes of the prostatic complex. The function of the copulation plug is not definitely known; it has been suggested that it prevents escape of semen from the genital tract of the female, but it may also be the stimulus that induces pseudopregnancy in these species. The semen in some primates also coagulates, and in the monkey a specific area of the prostate elaborates the coagulating enzyme (34). Whether a similar functional localization obtains in the human prostate apparently has not been determined. The function served by coagulation of the ejaculum in primates has not been ascertained. It is interesting that the coagulation of semen is in some respects like the coagulation of blood: calcium is necessary, and after standing the coagulum liquefies.

A group of modified sebaceous glands, the preputial glands, are situated in the prepuce in the region of the corona and pour their secretion onto the glans penis. Smegma is largely the accumulated secretion of these glands.

Erection. Erection is primarily a vascular phenomenon and is dependent upon the morphological pattern of the penis. This organ consists of three cylindrical masses of erectile tissue, two corpora cavernosa penis which lie side by side and above a third cord of erectile tissue, the corpus cavernosum urethrae, which transmits the urethra. The expanded distal end of the corpus cavernosum urethrae forms the glans. Each corpus cavernosum is surrounded by a dense fibrous coat, the tunica albuginea, and all three are enclosed by a layer of fairly dense fascia. At the root of the penis the corpora cavernosa penis diverge laterally as the crura to attach to the pubic arch, and each is covered by a sheet of skeletal muscle, the ischiocavernosus muscle. The expanded corpus cavernosum urethrae extends in the midline to the point of entry of the prostatic urethra and is also covered by a sheet of skeletal muscle, the bulbocavernosus.

The erectile tissue receives arterial blood by way of terminal branches of the internal pudendal arteries. These are (Fig. 505) a pair of dorsal arteries that lie on the dorsal surface of the tunica albuginea, a cavernous artery running longitudinally in each corpus cavernosum penis, and a pair of bulbo-urethral arteries that enter the corpus cavernosum urethrae at the bulb and course longitudinally forward. Branches of these arteries open into the cavernous spaces. Venous blood leaves the penis by way of two veins, the superficial dorsal vein which drains the glans and the corpus cavernosum urethrae and the deep dorsal vein which lies between the dorsal arteries and receives tributaries from the corpora cavernosa penis.

The erectile tissue of the corpora cavernosa is a spongelike system of irregular vascular spaces that are interspersed between the arteries and veins. In the flaccid state these spaces are more or less collapsed and contain little blood; but during erection they are quite large cavities distended with blood. This is the immediate mechanism of erection.

The intima of the arteries of the penis has longitudinal ridges which serve to occlude the arteries partially and to restrict the quantity of blood entering the cavernous sinuses (19). Upon dilatation of these arteries the flow of blood into the penis is tremendously increased and the sinuses are filled. The larger veins of the penis are said to possess funnel-like valves that impede the return of blood from the penis (19). Moreover, distension of the vascular spaces is thought to press the veins of the cavernous bodies against the tunica albuginea and to restrict escape of blood from the spaces through these veins. Thus the principal event appears to be arterial dilatation; restriction of venous return appears to be largely passive. The pressure in the cavernous spaces

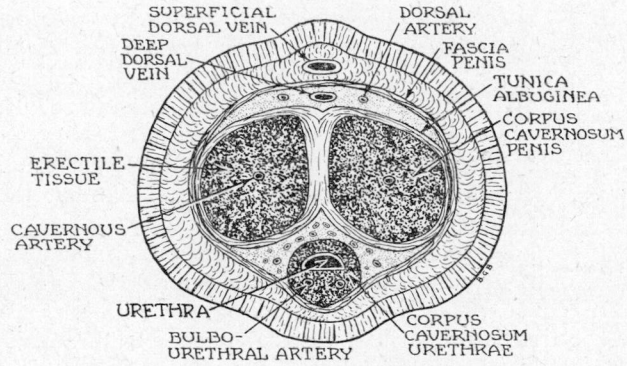

Fig. 505.—Cross section of the shaft of the penis. (Redrawn from Callander.)

during erection approximates that in the carotid artery (13). It has frequently been suggested that contractions of the ischiocavernosus muscles assist in erection by constricting the veins. Such action is now considered to be of a minor nature (13, 19). Return of the penis to the flaccid state is initiated by constriction of the arteries. A gradual escape of blood from the cavernous spaces would lower the pressure in the vascular spaces and presumably would result in a reduction of the passive constriction of the veins, and hence a progressively more rapid return of flaccidity.

Dilatation of the penile arteries and erection are induced by stimulation of the pelvic splanchnic nerves, whence their name *nervi erigentes* (Fig. 506). Stimulation of the sympathetic nerve supply results in constriction of the arteries of the penis and subsidence of erection. A center for reflex erection apparently exists in the sacral spinal cord, as shown by stimulation of the glans eliciting erection only when the pudendal nerve is intact. Psychic stimulation will produce erection after destruction of the sacral cord but not after destruction of the lumbar cord.

Androgens influence erectile ability (11), but whether this capacity depends upon the presence of androgens seems to be to some extent an individual idiosyncrasy. The administration of therapeutic levels of androgen may cause frequent erections in animals and in children as young as 18 months of age. In adult eunuchoids and castrates erections are often infrequent, especially if the castration was done before puberty. In these individuals administration of androgens greatly increases erectile ability. In some men, however, castration seems to have little or no effect upon erectile ability.

Ejaculation. As used commonly, this term denotes two distinct actions (31). The first, or emission, is the sudden contraction of the smooth muscle of the internal genital organs which delivers semen into the urethra. The second, or

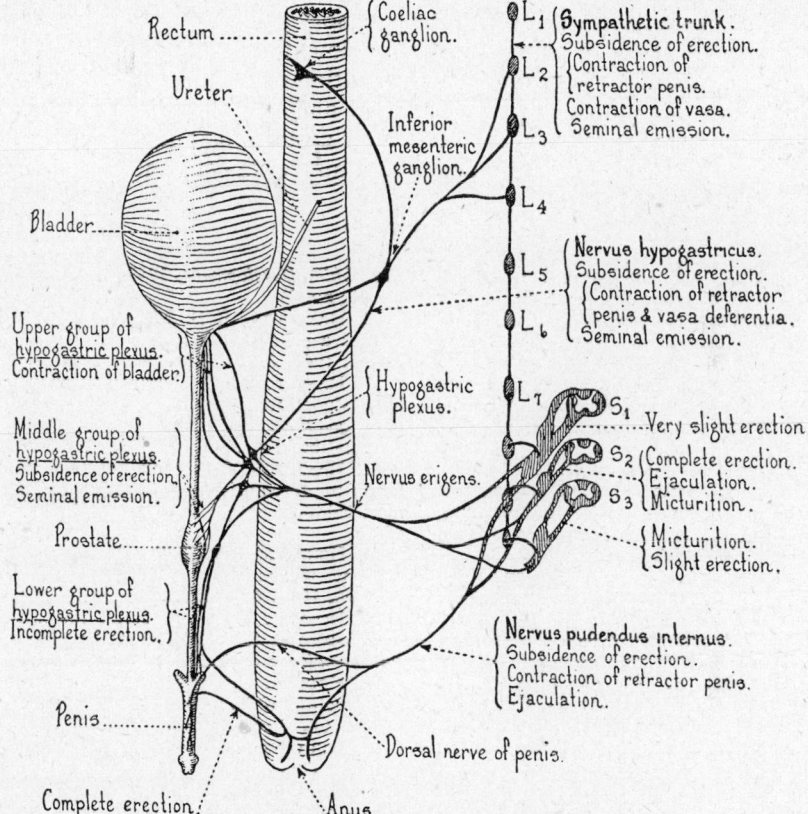

Fig. 506.—Diagram summarizing the functional innervation of the genital organs of the male cat. (From Semans and Langworthy, *J. Urol.*, 1938, *40*:836-846.)

ejaculation in the restricted sense, is the expulsion of seminal fluid from the urethra by contraction of the bulbocavernosus (skeletal) muscle. The process is basically a reflex phenomenon. The afferent impulses arise chiefly in the sense organs of the glans and are transmitted by the internal pudendal nerves to the spinal cord. Efferent impulses leave the upper lumbar segments of the spinal cord and travel over the lumbar rami communicantes and hypogastric nerves through the hypogastric plexus and evoke emission. The impulses that elicit ejaculation are parasympathetic and travel over the internal pudendal nerves. It is generally considered that an ejaculatory center in the lumbosacral spinal cord integrates the reflexes. The neural control of emission and ejaculation has been studied chiefly in the cat (Fig. 506), but the same pattern of control appears to obtain in man.

The several sensations associated with ejaculation constitute the orgasm. The origin, with respect to both mechanism and location, of these sensations is not fully known. Afferent impulses presumably reach the cerebral cortex, much like impulses giving rise to other visceral sensations. Since sexual sensations are of a primitive nature, it is usually assumed that many of the afferent impulses do not ascend higher than the thalamus. The causative impulses apparently spread through much of the entire autonomic nervous system and elicit reactions in other viscera.

Inasmuch as secretory activity of the accessory genital glands is dependent upon adequate levels of androgen, it is obvious that emission is dependent to an extent upon this hormone. After castration ejaculation may not occur, although in some individuals an ejaculatory ability, but with a small quantity of fluid, may be retained for years after castration. The administration of androgen restores ejaculatory ability and may even cause nocturnal emissions in castrates (11, 35).

REFERENCES

1. BISKIND, M. S. and BISKIND, G. R. Inactivation of testosterone propionate in the liver during vitamin B complex deficiency. Alteration of the estrogen-androgen equilibrium. *Endocrinology*, 1943, *32*:97–102.

2. CAMPBELL, H. E. Incidence of malignant growth of the undescended testicle. A critical and statistical study. *Arch. Surg., Chicago*, 1942, *44*:353–369.

3. DAVIS, C. D., PULLEN, R. L., MADDEN, J. H. M. and HAMBLEN, E. C. Therapy of seminal inadequacy. I. Use of pituitary, chorionic and equine gonadotropins. *J. clin. Endocrinol.*, 1943, *3*:268–273.

4. DORFMAN, R. I., COOK, J. W. and HAMILTON, J. B. Conversion by the human of the testis hormone, testosterone, into the urinary androgen, androsterone. *J. biol. Chem.*, 1939, *130*:285–295.

5. EDWARDS, E. A., HAMILTON, J. B., DUNTLEY, S. Q. and HUBERT, G. Cutaneous vascular and pigmentary changes in castrate and eunuchoid men. *Endocrinology*, 1941, *28*:119–128.

6. FRASER, R. W., FORBES, A. P., ALBRIGHT, F., SULKOWITCH, H. and REIFENSTEIN, E. C. Jr. Colorimetric assay of 17-ketosteroids in urine. A survey of the use of this test in endocrine investigation, diagnosis, and therapy. *J. clin. Endocrinol.*, 1941, *1*:234–256.

7. GREENE, R. R. Embryology of sexual structure and hermaphroditism. *J. clin. Endocrinol.*, 1944, *4*:335–348.

8. GREEP, R. O., VAN DYKE, H. B. and CHOW, B. F. Gonadotropins of the swine pituitary. I. Various biological effects of purified thylakentrin (FSH) and pure metakentrin (ICSH). *Endocrinology*, 1942, *30*:635–649.

9. GREULICH, W. W., DORFMAN, R. I., CATCHPOLE, H. R., SOLOMON, C. I. and CULOTTA, C. S. Somatic and endocrine studies of puberal and adolescent boys. *Monogr. Soc.* *Res. Child Development*, 1942, *7*:1–85 (Serial no. 33, no. 3).

10. HAMILTON, J. B. Male hormone substance: a prime factor in acne. *J. clin. Endocrinol.*, 1941, *1*:570–592.

11. HAMILTON, J. B. Therapeutics of testicular dysfunction. Chap. 17 in: *Glandular physiology and therapy*. Chicago, American Medical Association, 1942.

12. HAMILTON, J. B. Male hormone stimulation is prerequisite and an incitant in common baldness. *Amer. J. Anat.*, 1942, *71*:451–480.

13. HENDERSON, V. E. and ROEPKE, M. H. On the mechanism of erection. *Amer. J. Physiol.*, 1933, *106*:441–448.

14. HOOKER, C. W. Pubertal increase in responsiveness to androgen in the male rat. *Endocrinology*, 1942, *30*:77–84.

15. HOOKER, C. W. The postnatal history and function of the interstitial cells of the testis of the bull. *Amer. J. Anat.*, 1944, *74*:1–37.

16. HUGGINS, C., STEVENS, R. E., JR. and HODGES, C. V. Studies on prostatic cancer. II. The effects of castration on advanced carcinoma of the prostate gland. *Arch. Surg., Chicago*, 1941, *43*:209–223.

17. HURXTHAL, L. M. Treatment of gigantism: Observations on a pituitary giant for six years. *J. clin. Endocrinol.*, 1943, *3*:12–19.

18. KENYON, A. T., KNOWLTON, K., SANDIFORD, I., KOCH, F. C. and LOTWIN, G. A comparative study of the metabolic effects of testosterone propionate in normal men and women and in eunuchoidism. *Endocrinology*, 1940, *26*:26–45.

19. KISS, F. Anatomisch–histologische Untersuchungen über die Erektion. *Z. ges. Anat.*, 1921, *61*:455–521.

20. KOCH, F. C. The male sex hormones. *Physiol. Rev.*, 1937, *17*:153–238.

21. KURZROK, R. and MILLER, E. G., JR. Biochemical studies of human semen and its

relation to mucus of the cervix uteri. *Amer. J. Obstet. Gynaec.*, 1928, *15*:56–72.

22. McCULLAGH, E. P. and JONES, R. Effect of androgens on the blood count of men. *J. clin. Endocrinol.*, 1942, *2*:243–251.

23. MOORE, C. R. Biology of the testes. Pp. 353–451: *Sex and internal secretions*, 2d ed. Baltimore, Williams & Wilkins, 1939.

24. MOORE, C. R. Gonad hormones and sex differentiation. *Amer. Nat.*, 1944, *78*:97–130.

25. NELSON, W. O. Some factors involved in the control of the gametogenic and endocrine functions of the testis. *Cold Spr. Harb. Symp. quant. Biol.*, 1937, *5*:123–135.

26. PAPANICOLAOU, G. N. and FALK, E. A. General muscular hypertrophy induced by androgenic hormone. *Science*, 1938, *87*:238–239.

27. POLLOCK, W. F. Histochemical studies of the interstitial cells of the testis. *Anat. Rec.*, 1942, *84*:23–29.

28. RAPFOGEL, I. The effect of testosterone propionate upon skeletal development of a eunuch. *Endocrinology*, 1940, *27*:179–184.

29. REYNOLDS, S. R. M., HAMILTON, J. B., DiPALMA, J. R., HUBERT, G. R. and FOSTER, F. I. Dermovascular actions of certain steroid hormones in castrate, eunuchoid and normal men. *J. clin. Endocrinol.*, 1942, *2*:228–236.

30. ROWLANDS, I. W. Capacity of hyaluronidase to increase the fertilizing power. of sperm. *Nature, Lond.*, 1944, *154*:332.

31. SEMANS, J. H. and LANGWORTHY, O. R. Observations on the neurophysiology of sexual function in the male cat. *J. Urol.*, 1938, *40*:836–846.

32. SIMONSON, E., KEARNS, W. M. and EN-ZER, N. Effect of oral administration of methyltestosterone on fatigue in eunuchoids and castrates. *Endocrinology*, 1941, *28*:506–512.

33. TALBOT, N. B., BUTLER, A. M. and BER-MAN, R. A. Adrenal cortical hyperplasia with virilism: Diagnosis, course and treatment. *J. clin. Invest.*, 1942, *21*:559–570.

34. VAN WAGENEN, G. The coagulating function of the cranial lobe of the prostate gland in the monkey. *Anat. Rec.*, 1936, *66*:411–421.

35. VEST, S. A., and BARELARE, B., JR. Androgens and the treatment of testicular hypofunction. *Clinics*, 1943, *1*:1216–1265.

36. WEISMAN, A. I. *Spermatozoa and sterility*. New York, Paul B. Hoeber, Inc., 1941. 314 pp.

CHAPTER 56

GENETIC ASPECTS OF PHYSIOLOGY

By Walter Landauer

The present chapter will deal in a brief and necessarily fragmentary fashion with the role which heredity plays in the origin, support and regulation of physiological functions. It will be assumed that the reader is familiar with the basic concepts of genetics. A more than passing acquaintance with the phenomena of cell division and of structure and behavior of the chromosomes during mitosis and meiosis belongs to the foundations of all biological knowledge. A thorough understanding of the principles of Mendelian genetics is requisite to a proper perspective of the evolution and maintenance of all phenomena of life from the lowest plants to man.

The fundamental laws of genetics were discovered in studies on plants and lower animals. Their validity is universal. Many basic investigations were and continue to be made on superficial traits, such as hair color or pigmentation of the eyes, but experience has shown that generalizations thus obtained apply as well to more complex physiological processes. There is nothing strange in the fact that the mode of inheritance of physiological functions is generally intricate. All bodily activities are links in a chain which must not be broken if the flow of life is to continue smoothly. Hence, forces of selection, in the process of evolution, appear to have forged each link out of multiple strands. Functional stability is thus maintained through genetical complexity.

We know next to nothing, as yet, about the chemical means by which the genes produce their effects. There is considerable reason to believe, however, that the developmental functions of genes occur at definite rates and at specific times and that the intersection of the gene-determined rates of chemical processes at given stages results in a pattern of increasing complexity. The activity of genes may well be comparable to pharmacodynamic effects, the resulting pattern producing an increasing variety of pharmacodynamic responses. Systemic or general effects presumably are followed by local or specific ones, as morphological differentiation provides the machinery for added physiological functions.

The following pages are designed to illustrate the genetic aspects of physiology by reference to a few specific examples.

Determination of sex

The mechanisms which result in sex determination are instructive in many respects, for they reveal the basic simplicity of genetic phenomena as well as their many complexities.

The somatic cells of the human body contain in their nuclei 24 pairs of chromosomes. Each of these chromosomes, with all its genes, is reduplicated during mitosis and, by a process of equal distribution to the daughter cells, the number of chromosomes is kept constant throughout the body. An important exception occurs, however, at the time when the reproductive cells are formed. In order that the cells of the progeny may contain the same number of chromosomes as were present in the parents, it is necessary that the chromosome number be reduced to half, prior to the union of egg and sperm. This reduction occurs during the meiotic divisions which take place in the process of gamete formation. The meiotic events lead to the distribution of equal sets of whole chromosomes, resulting in reproductive cells with 24 chromosomes each. The ever-recurring cycle of mitosis and meiosis insures the constancy of chromosome number from generation to generation, just as mitosis itself safeguards the equal distribution of genes from cell to cell.

The meiotic divisions, however, have another important function, viz., that of providing a mechanism for the determination of sex. A careful examination of the chromosomes of our body has shown that in the female the partners of all 24 pairs are alike in size and shape (but the pairs differ from one to another). In the male, on the other hand, the somatic cells contain one pair of unequal chromosomes, one of them being much smaller than the other. The large chromosome of the pair is referred to as the X chromosome, its partner as the Y chromosome. All somatic cells of the male, therefore, contain the 23 pairs of nonsexual chromosomes or autosomes plus one pair made up of one X and one Y chromosome. The female somatic cells have the 23 pairs of autosomes, together with a pair of X chromosomes.

What happens when the reproductive cells are formed can be easily foreseen. In the ovary the evenly balanced sets of chromosomes are distributed equally to all ova, each receiving 23 autosomes and one X chromosome. All ova are alike in this respect. In the testis, on the other hand, the meiotic divisions lead to the formation of unequal cells, one half containing 23 autosomes and an X chromosome, the other half 23 autosomes and a Y chromosome. Thus, there are formed equal numbers of two different kinds of sperm. Eggs which are fertilized by sperm with an X chromosome produce females, those fertilized by sperm with a Y chromosome result in males.

If both kinds of sperm had equal chances to contribute to propagation, equal numbers of the two sexes would be born. This is not so. It is a well-known fact that the population sex ratio is approximately 105 or 106 males to 100 females. Moreover, it has been found that among stillborn and aborted fetuses the proportion of males is higher still. It follows that more male than female-determining sperm cells succeed in fertilizing eggs. This may be due to a difference in the speed with which the two kinds of sperm travel up the uterus and oviducts or to other, as yet unsuspected, causes.

There is one important difference between the genetic mechanism of sex determination and that of the transmission of autosomal traits. The process of sex determination is not based on the segregation of genetically heterogeneous pairs of genes, but on the meiotic separation of the XX and XY chromosomes. It has been learned from animal experimentation that the X chromosome pairs contain genes which (in the case of male heterogamety) produce female development in homozygous condition. Yet, there is also convincing proof that the sex-determining genes are not confined to the X chromosomes but are present in the autosomes as well, and that the sex genes of the X chromosomes act merely as the differential which pulls the balance of sex-determining factors in one direction or the other.

We know now that this dependence on a multiplicity of genes is the rule, rather than an exception, in the genetic determination of all kinds of hereditary traits. The delicate balance which exists between the sex-determining genes of the autosomes and those in the X chromosomes can be disturbed, either experimentally or by natural accidents, and, thereby, lead to intersexuality.

This can be illustrated by evidence from experiments with the fruit fly, *Drosophila melanogaster*. The normal processes of reproduction are, with regard to the chromosome mechanism, very similar in *Drosophila* and in man, the female having two sets of autosomes and two X chromosomes, the male two sets of autosomes but only one X chromosome (plus a Y chromosome which need not be considered in this discussion). A variety of intersexes were discovered in the progenies of triploid *Drosophila* females, that is, animals which had three sets of autosomes as well as three X chromosomes instead of the usual two sets. The descendants of these cytologically abnormal females contained various combinations of autosomes and sex chromosomes, and this led, as far as sex determination is concerned, to the results shown in Table 62.

Table 62.—Sexual Types in Drosophila

SETS OF AUTOSOMES (A)	X CHROMOSOMES	SEX INDEX (RATIO X/A)	RESULTING SEX
2	2	1.0	normal female
3	3	1.0	" "
4	4	1.0	" "
3	2	0.67	intersex
2	1	0.50	male

It is evident that intersexuality is the product of a disturbance in the balance of autosomes and X chromosomes.

In reality the processes of sex determination and the origin of intersexuality are much more complex phenomena than appears from the foregoing simplified presentation. It is known, for instance, that intersexuality, and even hermaphroditism, can also be produced by autosomal genes (e.g., in *Drosophila virilis*).

The manner in which such intersexuality is impressed upon the embryo has considerable general interest since similar processes are likely to be of frequent occurrence in the genic control of development. On the basis of studies concerning intersexuality in the gypsy moth, *Lymantria dispar*, Goldschmidt first enunciated the concept of developmental rates for an explanation of the actual events. "It was shown that a definite event in the development of intersexes, the turning point at which sex changes, could occur at different times, depending in an orderly way upon the genetic constitution of the individual. It was argued that such a perfectly orderly dependence of the time of such a change from a similarly orderly set of conditions of the sex genes could be understood only if two competing sets of reactions of orderly but varying velocities were involved. Sex genes, then, were conceived as controlling the rate of production of sex-determining stuffs" (5). This interesting hypothesis is not yet universally accepted and awaits further experimental scrutiny.

GENETIC FACTORS AND PHYSIOLOGICAL FUNCTIONS

Scientific investigation is all too frequently impeded by verbal misconceptions. In posing possible approaches toward the solution of a problem the student should beware of nothing more than of simplified or ill-considered alternatives. Two such propositions are of interest here, the one relating to "form or function," the other to "heredity or environment."

Form and function

Does the form of an organism determine its habits of living, and does the form of an organ decide its manner of functioning? Or, conversely, is it the physiological activity which shapes morphological structure? It is obvious now that an affirmative answer to either of these questions would obscure the most important point, viz., the fact that form and function are interrelated.

This inextricable interdependence of form and function and the role which hereditary factors and environmental forces play in their mutual relations are well illustrated by the results of observations on so-called Frizzle fowl (16). Frizzle chickens owe their name to a peculiar curliness of their feathers which presumably is caused by defective or abnormal keratinization. This abnormality of feather formation is inherited in an incompletely dominant manner, the homozygous birds showing a more extreme degree of frizzling than the heterozygous ones. In fact, in homozygous Frizzle fowl the feathers are so poorly formed that they wear off quickly, leaving the birds more or less completely bare.

The hereditary error of feather development brings about a complex chain of events which includes the following signs and symptoms. The heart rate is accelerated and both ventricles of the heart are hypertrophied. The blood volume is greater than normal and the spleen is enlarged. Weight (relative to the body) of crop, gizzard, pancreas and kidneys, length of the coeca, capacity of the intestinal tract (from duodenum to large intestine) are in excess of what is normal. The adrenals are hypertrophied. The white cells of the blood may show a relative agranulocytosis and relative granulopenia. The metabolic rate is above normal, food consumption increased, water vaporization reduced. The thyroids may be reduced in size or much enlarged; their histological structure may vary from exhaustion atrophy to hypertrophy and hyperplasia. The ovaries mature late and may remain atrophic; the testes frequently show interstitial edema and tubular damage. These conditions of the gonads may result in low fecundity or sterility. General body growth falls below normal. Body temperature may be subnormal. Viability is reduced.

This formidable array of symptoms takes its inception in a single event: increased loss of body heat on account of the lack of protection due to the abnormal plumage. Immediate consequences are subnormal body temperature, stimulation of cellular oxidation and increased metabolic rate. From here, one chain of adaptations leads to acceleration of heart rate, ventricular hypertrophy, enlarged blood volume, and excessive size of spleen. In order to sustain the acceleration of these vital processes more food is consumed and this, in turn, produces enlargement of the intestinal parts, hypertrophy of the pancreas and of the kidneys. A heavy burden falls on the adrenals and thyroid and they show corresponding changes. Reduced water vaporization is another adjustment useful to the body economy.

Compensation in the various organs and their functions may be complete or it may be deficient and end in a breakdown. In any event, structure and form of the organs are molded by the demands of functional requirements. Conversely, the extent to which physiological functions can satisfy the demands of the body is limited by the latitude of adaptation which form and structure of individual organs can undergo.

It might be said that the story of Frizzle fowl is a typical illustration of the forcefulness of the environment. It is; but it is just as much a demonstration of the effectiveness of hereditary adaptability. Form and function are fashioned at the crossroads of physiological demand and supply, fashioned by the dialectical relations between hereditary potentialities and the environment.

There is much evidence for the conclusion that normal organisms of all kinds have in the course of evolution accumulated a large store of defense mechanisms which are of no use under ordinary circumstances, but come into play promptly when exceptional demands are to be satisfied. In the experimental work with Frizzle chickens two instances of this kind were observed. One of these is a recessive mutation which suppresses to a large extent the effect of the Frizzle gene, thereby protecting the organism against excessive heat loss. This mutation occurs widely among normal stocks of fowl. The other genetic safeguard affects size and activity of the thyroid gland. It is clear from all observations with Frizzle fowl that the thyroids are one of the weakest links resisting the physiological strain which the abnormal plumage condition produces. It is of particular interest, therefore, that in the course of breeding Frizzle chickens genetic factors were accumulated, presumably by natural selection, which strengthened this link by making the thyroids respond more readily with increase in size and in activity.

Heredity and environment

A great many books and pamphlets have been filled with the partisan views of those who have wished to make either "nature" or "nurture" all-responsible for the fates of man, beast or plant. The insanities of racial bigotry no less than the inanities of many a eugenical program have long stood in the way of an understanding of the fact that in the great majority of cases the issue of developmental processes or of reactions of mature organisms is sealed by a complex interaction of forces from within and without.*

There are cases, to be sure, in which environmental agencies play no role at all or at best a negligible one; such are, for instance, albinism or the blood groups. As a rule, however, the gene-determined events depend in their end result to a variable degree on interaction between forces of the external and internal environment.

The problems of natural *resistance to disease* have brought to light a wealth of information relating to the relative contributions of definite genetic factors, of various physiological conditions of the organism, and of the external environment to the pathological events which occur in particular instances (24). It is known that hereditary factors may play an important role in making an organism immune against a specific infection. This is well illustrated by

* For an intelligent discussion of the race problem see Montagu (21).

experiments which Schott made on the resistance of mice to a typhoid-like disease produced by *Bacterium aertrycke*. In his initial population, mortality on exposure to a constant dose of the infective agent amounted to 82 per cent. Selective matings from the survivors produced a first generation in which, under the same conditions, mortality was only 64 per cent. Continued, breeding experiments gave mortalities of 46 per cent in the second generation, 40 per cent in the third, 36 per cent in the fourth, 33 per cent in the fifth, and 24 per cent in the sixth generation. From control tests it appears that the virulence of the organism had remained constant throughout the experimental period (30). In many other instances the inheritance of resistance to specific agents of disease has been demonstrated, if not always with as spectacular success. In these cases we are dealing with individual resistance. In addition, it is known that racial or strain differences of resistance exist for many infectious diseases and there is widespread species specificity of susceptibility to particular pathogens. All these differences undoubtedly have a genetic foundation. From present evidence it appears that, as a rule, genetic factors for individual resistance are specific with regard to each particular type of bacterium or virus. More than one pair of genes is generally involved in producing resistance to a specific infectious agent and, generally, resistance is the dominant, susceptibility the recessive, trait.

These genetic factors are but a part of the mechanism of disease resistance, though an important one. About their physiological mode of expression we know little as yet. In one instance, it was shown that a hereditary deficiency of blood complement in guinea pigs was associated with increased susceptibility to infection with *Salmonella choleraesuis* (26). In another instance, the number of erythrocytes was greater in a family of chickens which was relatively resistant to infection with *Salmonella pullorum* than it was in the control stock (28).

Sex and endocrine function play an important role in natural resistance. For humans, it is known that the rates of incidence and mortality are greater among males than females for pneumonia, amebic dysentery, poliomyelitis, osteomyelitis, measles, encephalitis and meningitis. The reverse, viz., greater female morbidity and mortality, have been found for diphtheria, whooping cough, rheumatic fever and influenza. During pregnancy and lactation an increase occurs in natural protective antibodies. The sera of gravid women contain natural agglutinins to *Shigella dysenteriae* in the absence of an antecedent history of dysentery; bactericidal antibodies to *Bacillus anthracis*, generally lacking in nongravid women and in men, appear during pregnancy; the virucidal titer to the poliomyelitis virus rises considerably during pregnancy; resistance to many other infectious diseases is increased.

Adrenal insufficiency produces a lowering in natural resistance, probably via a disturbance of antibody formation. Reduced resistance to various infections has been found in diabetes mellitus and also after experimental pancreatectomy. The same was observed after hypophysectomy.

The lymphoid tissues, the reticulo-endothelial system and the spleen have important functions in the chain of disease-resisting agencies. The same is true for the liver which is known to play a role in complement formation. Nutrition in general, various vitamins in particular, and such oxidative catalysts as copper and manganese, all have vital functions in providing disease resistance.

Genetic factors presumably play an important role in providing the foundations for many of the functions which have been enumerated. In addition there are, of course, factors of the external environment, such as temperature or barometric pressure, which influence disease resistance. Yet these external forces will also be mediated by gene-controlled internal processes.

Cancer research has brought to light a large amount of interesting information which illustrates the intimate integration of hereditary constitution and susceptibility (23). Age (presumably as it is reflected in the functional condition of various organs) and external irritants, in addition to the genetic constitution and virus infections, are particularly important factors in striking the balance between resistance and susceptibility to malignant tumors.

A similar interplay of external agencies, of particular physiological conditions within the organism, and of constitutional factors which are determined by specific genes has been reported for many noninfectious diseases and may safely be assumed to exist in all of them. Even against the noxious effects of poisons, organisms may devise hereditary safeguards. A dramatic instance of this kind has been reported for certain scale insects which are found in California citrus groves. Observations on the results of spraying disclosed that these insects developed, by natural selection, a marked resistance to hydrocyanic acid and at least one species developed also a tolerance to methyl bromide and ethylene oxide (25). In extensive experiments with mice it was shown that the sexual functions (mating, pregnancy, castration) exert a definite influence on the degree of resistance to poisoning with arsenic and other substances (1).

These examples should suffice to demonstrate that the effects of hereditary factors are as ever-present in the life of an organism as are the varying influences of its surroundings.

The attainment of mature *body size* is the end result of all the events which contribute to or interfere with embryonic and postnatal growth. An additional factor is, of course, the size of the zygote with which development begins. Even very slight size differences of early embryos are bound to result in appreciable divergencies of size if the rate of cell multiplication is the same in the two cases. Instances of this type have been demonstrated in plants, but not in higher animals.

A study of two breeds of rabbits, differing in adult body size by a factor of more than three, revealed that no difference in size existed in very young embryos (3, 7). On the other hand, it was shown that differential growth rates appeared in early embryonic stages and these led soon to differences of body size. The same mechanism, i.e. differential growth rates, is probably the most important agency controlling intraspecific size differences among mammals generally. In man, it is known that cell size is the same for dwarfs, people of average size and giants. In addition to initial size differences of the egg cell and to dissimilarities of growth rate, duration of the period of growth may be a factor in determining ultimate size. Secondary sexual differences in mature body size are probably, in part at least, of this nature.

Mammalian embryos and fetuses are well protected by their uterine shelter against many environmental factors. This protection is, however, by no means complete. It is well known that litter size has an influence on weight at birth and even on weight at maturity. This is simply due to competition for food. Factors of a similar kind, if less directly mediated, are presumably responsible for weight differences among the progenies of reciprocal crosses between large and small breeds, the cross in which the mothers are from the larger breed generally producing somewhat heavier young.

After birth, nutrition plays, of course, an essential role in the attainment of final body size, but this is not the place to discuss the many nutritional factors which influence growth. Even when the amount and composition of food and other external factors are kept constant, size and weight of the body are variable. This fact points to the conclusion that many intrinsic agencies are involved in the process of producing mature size and weight, and this conclusion, in turn, is born out by genetic analysis.

In crosses of large and small races of one and the same species it is common to find that the progenies are intermediate in weight. In F_2 generations from such crosses the variability in size and weight is greatly increased as compared with the F_1, the extremes approaching the original large and small race. The "blending" phenotype of the F_1 generation and the heightened variability of the F_2 indicate the presence of multiple genetic factors. The correctness of this conclusion and the actual occurrence of segregation of multiple genes for body size can be demonstrated in F_3 generations. For, if F_2 animals from either end of the range of distribution are mated inter se, i.e., large to large and small to small, the resulting progenies will differ significantly, showing that the respective parents had a dissimilar genetic constitution.*

We do not know the nature of the most fundamental genetic growth factors although it may be surmised that they are concerned with those biochemical processes which are at the basis of all life. One such factor may have been uncovered in observations concerning the relation of glutathione to hereditary size differences. In studies with rabbits and chickens, it was found that at birth, or even earlier, the glutathione concentration of the body serves as a reliable index of genetic differences in adult body size (6, 8, 9).

It is necessary to distinguish between factors, presumably hereditary, which (i) are essential for growth but do not contribute to racial or even species-specific size differences; (ii) account for intraspecific size differences; (iii) are selective adaptations to particular environments; and finally (iv) are factors of pathological growth. Although there are no sharp delimitations between any two of these four categories, they provide useful points of departure for discussion.

To the group of factors which are essential for growth, but which do not contribute to intraspecific (racial) differences in size, belong, strictly speaking, all those processes which are involved in vital functions. The pituitary gland may serve as an example. Hypophysectomy in young animals brings body growth to a complete stop, demonstrating that the functions of this gland are essential for increase in size. Yet there is evidence that hereditary intraspecific size differences, as far as normal growth is concerned, are quite independent of the pituitary (27).

There are, however, hereditary variations of body size which are caused by abnormalities of endocrine glands. In mice, for instance, dwarfism is inherited as a simple recessive trait. The eosinophile cells are lacking in the anterior pituitary of such animals. Under the influence of pituitary transplants these dwarfs may grow to normal size, may become sexually mature, and do,

* For a good example of this type of analysis see Waters (38).

in fact, show no abnormalities except for the anterior pituitary (31, 32). Dwarfism due to abnormal functioning of the thyroid glands was found in fowl and constitutes also an hereditary trait (15, 35).

Evolutionary forces affecting body size can be seen at work in the many observations which fit into the generalization known as Bergmann's rule. The essence of this rule is that among homoiothermic animals representatives of the same species grow to a larger size when inhabiting a cold climate than when they are living in a warmer region. Similar orderly differences of body size according to the environmental temperature are found for nearly related species. Since there is a relative decrease of body surface with increasing body size, we are dealing with an adaptation which is of great value in the body's heat economy. There is little doubt that all such adjustments of body size have a complex hereditary basis which has been established very gradually by natural selection.

The fact that such adjustments of body size take place readily in particular environments, as attested by their common occurrence, is proof for the conclusion that animal species must generally possess a greater fund of genetic potentialities than are usually utilized. We have seen that this is confirmed by genetic analysis. The majority of "size" genes seems to exert their effect on the body as a whole, but, in addition, there are genetic factors which have a selective influence on parts (42).

Sensory reactions, temperament, mentality

The genetic analysis of physiological processes which have a bearing on sensory reactions, on temperament, mentality and behavior is in its earliest beginnings.

Among human hereditary variants of sensory reactions the sex-linked transmission of red-green color blindness has been studied most extensively. Of greater interest from the viewpoint of "normal" physiological reactions is the fact that genetic differences appear to be widespread with regard to the sense of taste and of smell. Phenyl-thio-carbamide dissolved in water has, even in high dilution, an intensely bitter taste to a great many people. Yet others find it entirely tasteless unless it is used in saturated solution. There are, in other words, great differences in the threshold of taste response to this particular organic substance. These differences of sensory threshold are hereditary, the ability to taste phenyl-thio-carbamide being dominant over the relative lack of ability to discern it (2). A similar demonstration has been made for di-phenyl-guanidine. As in the case of phenyl-thio-carbamide, the faculty to taste di-phenyl-guanidine is dominant, but the taste reactions to the two substances are quite independent of each other (33). Similar disparities of taste response exist for other substances, but their hereditary basis has not yet been studied. Again, the reactions to certain odors vary greatly from person to person, and there is little reason to doubt that these differences are also hereditary. These observations certainly furnish a sound basis for Blakeslee's conclusion, "Our world is what our senses tell us. Each lives in a different world."

What is true for the sense reactions presumably holds also for temperament and intellect. The main difficulties of analysis in these fields stem from our lack of knowledge of what are the fundamental units, for only after these units are recognized can we hope to make successful genetic analyses.

With regard to problems of temperament an interesting study has been made of the "individual tempo" (4). The experimental subjects were asked (i) to strike with the finger against a table or to tap with the foot on the floor in the tempo most agreeable to them; (ii) to select the most agreeable speed of a metronome. It was found that each person has a very definite preference for one particular tempo and that this preference is little, if at all, influenced by age, sex or stimulants (such as alcohol or coffee). The following mean percentage deviations between individuals were found in one series of such tests; identical twins 7.8 (this does not differ from intra-individual variability), fraternal twins 15.0, siblings 14.5, unrelated persons 19.5. Between identical twins the deviation was significantly lower than between fraternal twins; there was no significant difference between fraternal twins and siblings; within these last two groups the deviations were significantly less than between unrelated persons. The results of these studies are a strong indication for the presence of genetical determiners of the individual tempo. This conclusion was further strengthened by observations on families. The data in Table 63 show the results for those cases in which the parents were alike in their individual tempo. The exact mode of inheritance is still uncertain. In fact, there is the distinct possibility that we are not really dealing with a simple and elementary character. What is important, however, is that the genetic nature of "individual tempo" has been established and that it is a reasonably con-

Table 63.—The Transmission of "Individual Tempo" from Parents to Children

PAIRS OF PARENTS	NUMBER OF CHILDREN	INDIVIDUAL TEMPO OF PARENTS	CHILDREN IN PER CENT		
			RAPID	MEDIUM	SLOW
8	25	rapid	56.0	40.0	4.0
25	90	medium	17.2	65.7	17.2
8	28	slow	0	28.6	71.4

stant trait for each individual, at least as long as he continues in good health. It remains to be seen whether or not the variations in individual tempo are founded on differences in physiological functions.

The foregoing examples have shown that particular reactions of the sense organs and specific expressions of temperament are typical for each individual. It may be surmised that a very large number of such traits combine in each personality. The same is true, a fortiori, for intelligence, special talents and social behavior. In many instances of this kind we have evidence suggesting the presence of genetic determiners and much information in these fields springs from comparisons between identical and fraternal twins. Before we can hope, however, to obtain an exact genetic analysis, it will be necessary to recognize what are the physiological unit-traits. A beginning in this direction has been made in breeding dogs for special purposes (13). In man, we have convincing evidence that such traits as musical talents are hereditary (29). A prerequisite for the possibility of musical talent to find expression is the presence of musical aptitude. The latter quality has been broken down into a number of elements, such as sense of pitch, time, intensity, harmony and rhythm. Training apparently has no effect whatever on the senses of pitch, time and intensity; the senses of harmony and rhythm can be developed only to the extent made possible by the individual's inherent capacities. Given these basic qualifications, "talent" must be present to produce an outstanding artist. There is definite evidence for the genetic nature of talent, but the mode of transmission of this unquestionably complex trait remains to be determined.

Much information of general value has been obtained from inquiries concerning the role of hereditary factors in criminality (18, 34). The first important study in this field was that of Lange who made a comparison of the lives of 13 identical and 17 fraternal unisexual twins. At least one of each of these twins had a criminal record. Among the fraternal twins there were only two cases in which the second twin had also come into conflict with the penal code, but among the identical twins this was true for 10 out of 13. Similar findings have been recorded by other observers. In fact, even more convincing evidence for the role of hereditary factors can be seen in the details of the case histories. In many instances the time of first and subsequent delinquencies, the type of offense, the behavior of the accused in court and in jail, showed the most patent similarity among the identical twins, but no comparable likeness was observable among the fraternal twins. It is quite clear also from these studies that the environment in which such persons grow up and live, especially their social relations, may influence their behavior greatly. After all, what a man inherits, whether it be in regard to social relations, special talents or bodily physiological processes, is merely the capacity to react to specific situations within a definite latitude. To many infectious diseases there are all degrees of hereditary resistance; yet without exposure to infection these protective forces do not come into play. Even so, an individual's possibilities of response to social, artistic or intellectual environments reveal themselves only as the actual contacts are made.*

DEVELOPMENTAL CORRELATIONS

There are a good many traits whose presence or absence is governed by a single pair of genes; there are probably many more which are conditioned by multiple genetic factors. It may well be, of course, that the complexity of genetic transmission, which is found in most physiological traits, is more apparent than real and is due to an imperfect understanding of what are the basic processes with which the genes are concerned. In other instances a seemingly simple hereditary mechanism produces a variety of effects on different organs and systems. Whenever such cases have been analyzed sufficiently, it was found that complex syndromes of this kind are brought about by developmental correlations of one sort or another.

In discussing the peculiarities of Frizzle fowl (p. 1235), we have already encountered a complex chain of morphological, physiological and pathological events, all of which are indirect consequences of a single gene effect on the plumage. In Frizzle fowl most of the secondary changes occur during postnatal growth and in adult life. We shall here present some instances in which complex aberrations, due to a simple mutation effect, take place entirely or for the most part during embryonic development.

Grüneberg has described a lethal mutation of rats which has the following principal features (10). The thorax is deformed, the cartilaginous part of the ribs much thickened; there is thoracic kyphosis with compensating cervical and lumbar lordosis; the tracheal and bronchial cartilage is hyperplastic;

---

* For much valuable material on these problems the reader is referred to the book by Newman, Freeman and Holzinger (22). For a critical review of this book see McNemar (20).

growth after birth is retarded; the snout is abnormally short; there is faulty occlusion of the incisors; both lungs show emphysema with collapse of some parts; the right auricle of the heart is always, and the right ventricle some-

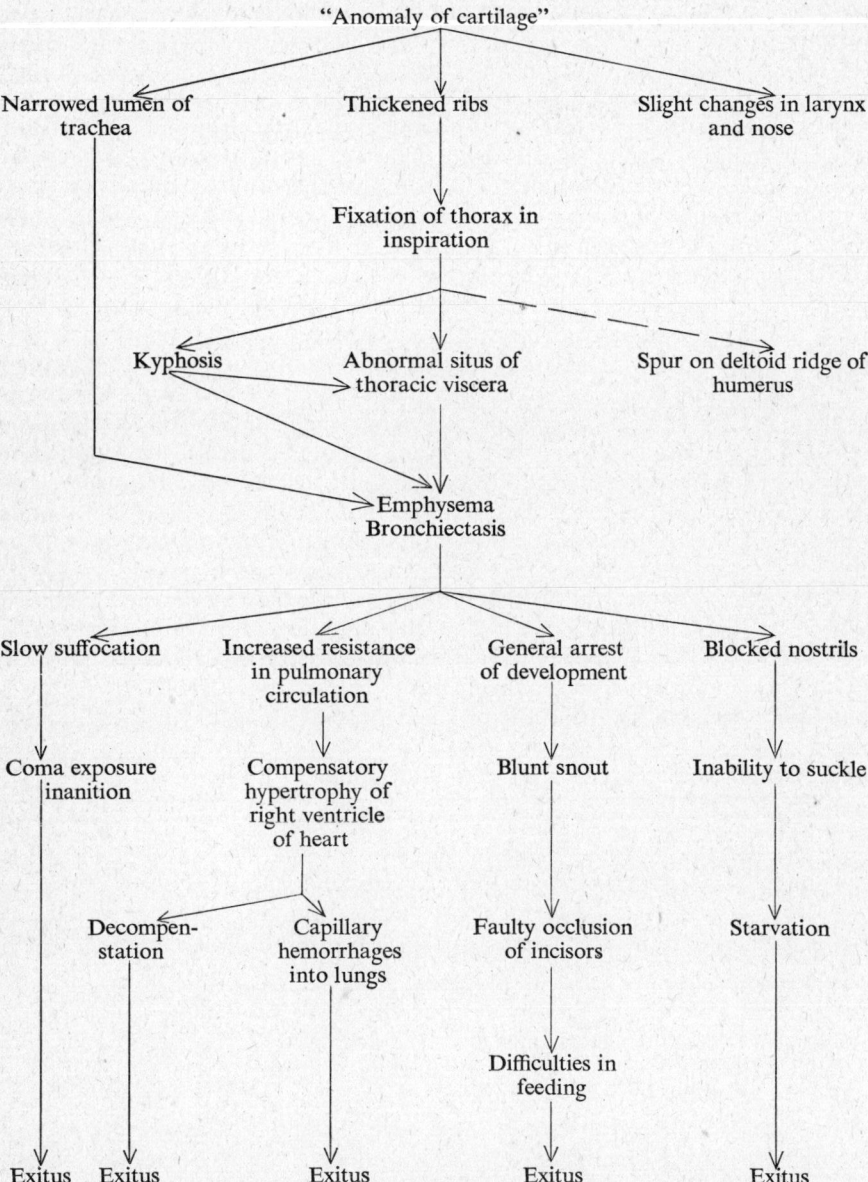

Fig. 507.—Diagram of probable causal relationships in Grüneberg's rat lethal mutation, described in text.

times, dilated. Death occurs generally within the first month after birth. Grüneberg gives the above diagram (Fig. 507) in demonstration of the probable causal relationships of the syndrome.

An abnormality of cartilage presumably is the only disturbance of development which is an immediate result of the mutation. The effects which are more directly due to the basic disturbance are completely constant and regularly found in all the lethal embryos; effects further removed from the original gene action tend to become more and more variable and may occasionally be missing altogether. The original cartilage abnormality may, in turn, trace to still earlier and yet undiscovered events.

A recessive lethal mutation of mice is another case in point (11). The affected individuals die within a few minutes after parturition. They have a steep, bulging forehead, consisting of bilateral protuberances which correspond to the cerebral hemispheres. The top of the skull is covered by skin, but the flat cranial bones are lacking. The snout is shortened; the eyes (unlike those of normal newborn mice) are open; there are variable abnormalities of the facial sinus hairs. The primary effect of the mutation is again an abnormality of cartilage. This was present, to a variable extent, in all skeletal parts which were examined (basis of skull, Meckel's cartilage, sternum, vertebrae, metacarpals, metatarsals). Serious damage occurs in the basicranial cartilage, leading to a shortening and deformation of the skull. The telencephalon is forced upwards owing to the shortened skull basis. This leads to telescoping of the lower parts of the brain, interference with the foramen of Magendie, and hydrocephalus. Pressure against the cranial parts of the head prevents formation of flat bones over the hydrocephalic bulge. Skin strains presumably are responsible for the open eyelids and the anomalies of sinus hair. Death is caused by intracerebral hemorrhages.

A mechanism of an entirely different type is revealed by hereditary abnormalities of eyes and feet in mice (12). The mutation in question is recessive and has a rather irregular mode of transmission, probably on account of the existence of numerous modifying factors. The morphological expression is also quite variable and, presumably, for the same reasons. The eye abnormalities range from slight defects of the eyelids to their complete absence and from slight atrophy of the eye to anophthalmia. Either one or both eyes may be affected. In the extremities one may find clubfoot with dorsal or palmar flexion and syndactylism, syndactylism alone, hypodactylism, congenital amputation of the feet, or polydactylism. To a certain extent it was possible to separate the various abnormalities and their location by continued selection, thus demonstrating the existence of specific genetic modifiers. Embryological studies by Bagg revealed that subcutaneous extravasations of blood occurred during embryonic development near the sites of the later defects. Blebs filled with serous fluid were thus shown to produce mechanical obstacles to normal development. Size and location of the blebs determine extent and position of the defects. According to studies by Bonnevie the appearance of the blebs is preceded by an overproduction of cerebrospinal fluid in early stages of development of these mice. The fluid escapes (as it does to a limited extent normally) through a foramen of the myelencephalon and thence travels along routes determined by least resistance. In normal development the small amounts of cerebrospinal fluid are resorbed promptly, but the much larger quantities produced in this stock cannot be disposed of in this fashion and hence lead to the varied pressure effects found later.

It must not be concluded from the preceding discussion that all syndromes of developmental abnormalities are of a hereditary nature. To give but one example to the contrary, it has been shown that a diet deficient in riboflavin, if fed to pregnant rats, will produce in a considerable proportion of their young a shortening or even absence of the tibia, fibula, radius, ulna and of bones of the fore and hind feet, shortening of the mandible, fusion of the ribs, and various deformities of the sternum, maxilla, clavicle and scapula (36, 37).

SOME PRACTICAL APPLICATIONS

The facts presented in this chapter convey a sense of the general interest and importance which genetic studies have for a fuller understanding and appreciation of physiology. There remains to be pointed out that a proper evaluation of the facts of genetics can guide us in many decisions of practical importance. Primary prerequisites for rendering genetics increasingly useful are the accumulation of facts, their proper interpretation, and their critical evaluation by statistical methods. The physician who is a good observer has an unusual opportunity to add to our knowledge of human genetics. He must always be aware of the fact that little is gained by the statement that a certain trait is hereditary. We want to know the mode of transmission of this trait and the physiological repercussions of the gene's presence.

Such terms as "hereditary syphilis" or "hereditary tuberculosis" still have wide currency in medical literature. There is nothing to justify them. We have seen that a trait can be congenital without being hereditary. Clear distinctions in this respect are the more necessary as facts come to light in current research which demonstrate that the mother's genetic constitution may, in utero or post partum, influence the fate of her progeny. It has been shown, for instance, that in mice the incidence of mammary tumors or of leukemia may vary greatly according to whether the young have been nursed by mothers with a genetic constitution for high or low frequency of these neoplasms (12).

That an appreciation of genetic facts may be of immediate importance is illustrated by the following examples. A case is on record of the sudden death from allergic shock of a nurse who participated in an experiment in which minute amounts of guinea pig hemoglobin were injected intradermally. The family history, taken after the accident, revealed not only that the patient herself had suffered from asthma and had shown cutaneous reactions to various foreign proteins, but that her mother had asthma and hay fever, that a brother was subject to hay fever and a sister to acne, and that a first cousin had died in convulsions ten minutes after a subcutaneous injection of diphtheria antitoxin (14). With these facts at hand in advance and a knowledge of the hereditary nature of allergic reactions (incomplete dominance [39]), the person in question would scarcely have been admitted to the experiment.

In 1940 Landsteiner and Wiener announced the discovery of an agglutinable factor (Rh) in human blood which is recognizable by immune sera for the blood of rhesus monkeys. It was found subsequently that five different kinds of Rh agglutinogens exist and that the presence or absence of these factors is determined by a series of six major allelic genes, presence of any one type of the Rh factors being dominant over its absence (17, 41). In addition, there are a number of rarer, intermediate alleles (40). About 85 per cent of the American white population are Rh positive, the remaining 15 per cent are Rh negative. In matings of Rh— women and Rh+ men a high percentage of the pregnancies end in abortions, stillbirths, or the delivery of children who will, shortly after birth, die of erythroblastosis. The events which lead to such situations are as follows (19). The presence of an Rh-rh fetus in the rh-rh mother results in iso-immunization of the Rh— mother by the Rh+ fetal blood. The passage of maternal immune agglutinins through the placenta then causes fatal disturbances in red cell formation of the fetus. The first one or two pregnancies may result in normal infants because a sufficient degree of iso-immunization of the mother has not yet occurred. In fact, a small percentage of Rh negative women are incapable of forming anti-Rh antibodies and their progeny escapes unharmed. The chances that such mother-fetus conflicts will arise are naturally dependent on the genetic constitution of the father. In matings involving Rh negative women and men who are homozygous Rh positive, every pregnancy is in danger, whereas this holds true for only half of the pregnancies in the case of heterozygous fathers. Thanks to the complexity of the Rh factor, the genetic constitution of an individual can in many cases be determined by immunological methods. This in turn makes it possible to predict the chances of obtaining viable offspring in marriage of Rh+ men and Rh— women. In matings of Rh positive females the question of iso-immunization, of course, never arises.

Beyond such facts of immediate practical importance, the results of genetics can provide useful guidance in human contacts and social relations. Protagonists of racial prejudice will find neither comfort nor support in the lessons of genetics, and those who are striving toward an improvement of human existence will have to conclude that betterment of man's surroundings must take precedence over such necessarily slow and uncertain steps as eugenic sterilization.

REFERENCES

1. AGDUHR, E. Contributions to the knowledge of the mechanism behind the heightened resistance brought about by the normal sexual functions. *Uppsala LäkFören. Förh.*, 1941, *47*: 1–54.

2. BLAKESLEE, A. F. Genetics of sensory thresholds: taste for phenyl thio carbamide. *Proc. nat. Acad. Sci., Wash.*, 1932, *18*:120–130.

3. CASTLE, W. E. and GREGORY, P. W. The embryological basis of size inheritance in the rabbit. *J. Morph.*, 1929, *48*:81–93.

4. FRISCHEISEN-KÖHLER, I. *Das persönliche Tempo. Eine erbbiologische Untersuchung.* Leipzig, G. Thieme, 1933. 63 pp.

5. GOLDSCHMIDT, R. *Physiological genetics.* New York, McGraw-Hill, 1938. ix, 375 pp.

6. GREGORY, P. W., ASMUNDSON, V. S. and Goss, H. Glutathione concentration and hereditary size. V. Comparative studies with Barred Plymouth Rock and White Leghorn embryos. *J. exp. Zool.*, 1936, *73*:263–284.

7. GREGORY, P. W. and CASTLE, W. E. Further studies on the embryological basis of size inheritance in the rabbit. *J. exp. Zool.*, 1931, *59*:199–211.

8. GREGORY, P. W. and Goss, H. Glutathione concentration and hereditary body size. II. Glutathione concentration in non-nursed young of six populations of rabbits differing in genetic constitution for adult size. *J. exp. Zool.*, 1933, *66*:155–173.

9. GREGORY, P. W., Goss, H. and ASMUND-SON, V. S. Glutathione concentration and hereditary size. VI. Comparative post-hatching studies with Barred Plymouth Rocks and White Leghorns. *Growth*, 1937, *1*:89–102.

10. GRÜNEBERG, H. An analysis of the "pleiotropic" effects of a new lethal mutation in the rat (*Mus norvegicus*). *Proc. roy. Soc.*, 1938, *B125*:123–144.

11. GRÜNEBERG, H. Congenital hydrocephalus in the mouse, a case of spurious pleiotropism. *J. Genet.*, 1943, *45*:1–21.

12. GRÜNEBERG, H. *The genetics of the mouse.* Cambridge, University Press, 1943. xii, 412 pp.

13. HUMPHREY, E. and WARNER, L. *Working dogs.* Baltimore, Johns Hopkins University Press, 1934. xiv, 253 pp.

14. HUNT, E. L. Death from allergic shock. *New Engl. J. Med.*, 1943, *228*:502–507.

15. LANDAUER, W Thyrogenous dwarfism (myxoedema infantilis) in the domestic fowl. *Amer. J. Anat.*, 1929, *43*:1–20.

16. LANDAUER, W. Form and function in Frizzle fowl: the interaction of hereditary potentialities and environmental temperature. *Biol. Symposia*, 1942, *6*:127–166.

17. LANDSTEINER, K. and WIENER, A. S. An agglutinable factor in human blood recognized by immune sera for rhesus blood. *Proc. Soc. exp. Biol., N. Y.*, 1940, *43*:223.

18. LANGE, J. *Crime and destiny.* New York, A. and C. Boni, 1931. 96 pp.

19. LEVINE, P. Serological factors as pos-

sible causes in spontaneous abortions. *J. Hered.*, 1943, *34:*71–80.

20. McNEMAR, Q. Newman, Freeman and Holzinger's twins: a study of heredity and environment. *Psychol. Bull.*, 1938, *35:*237–249.

21. MONTAGU, M. F. A. *Man's most dangerous myth: the fallacy of race.* New York, Columbia University Press, 1942. xii, 216 pp.

22. NEWMAN, H. H., FREEMAN, F. N. and HOLZINGER, K. J. *Twins. A study of heredity and environment.* Chicago, University of Chicago Press, 1937. xvi, 369 pp.

23. OBERLING, C. *The riddle of cancer.* New Haven, Yale University Press, 1944. ix, 196 pp.

24. PERLA, D. and MARMORSTON, J. *Natural resistance and clinical medicine.* Boston, Little, Brown and Co., 1941. xx, 1344 pp.

25. QUAYLE, H. J. The development of resistance to hydrocyanic acid in certain scale insects. *Hilgardia*, 1938, *11:*183–210.

26. RICH, F. A. Concerning blood complement. *Bull. Vt. agric. Exp. Sta.*, 1923, *230.*

27. ROBB, R. C. On the nature of hereditary size limitation. I. Body growth in giant and pigmy rabbits. *J. exp. Biol.*, 1929, *6:*293–310.

28. ROBERTS, E. and CARD, L. E. Inheritance of resistance to bacterial infection in animals. A genetic study of pullorum disease. *Bull. Ill. agric. Exp. Sta.*, 1935, *419.*

29. SCHEINFELD, A. *You and heredity.* New York, F. A. Stokes Co., 1939. 434 pp.

30. SCHOTT, R. G. The inheritance of resistance to Salmonella aertrycke in various strains of mice. *Genetics*, 1932, *17:*203–229.

31. SMITH, P. E. and MACDOWELL, E. C. An hereditary anterior-pituitary deficiency in the mouse. *Anat. Rec.*, 1930, *46:*249–257.

32. SNELL, G. D. Dwarf, a new Mendelian recessive character of the house mouse. *Proc. nat. Acad. Sci., Wash.*, 1929, *15:*733–734.

33. SNYDER, L. H. and DAVIDSON, D. F. Studies in human inheritance. XVIII. The inheritance of taste deficiency to diphenylguanidine. *Eugen. News*, 1937, *22:*1–2.

34. STUMPFL, F. *Studien über Vererbung und Entstehung geistiger Störungen. V. Erbanlage und Verbrechen.* Berlin, J. Springer, 1935. vi, 302 pp.

35. UPP, C. W. Further data on the inheritance of dwarfism in fowls. *Poult. Sci.*, 1934, *13:*157–165.

36. WARKANY, J. and NELSON, R. C. Skeleton abnormalities in the offspring of rats reared on deficient diets. *Anat. Rec.*, 1941, *79:*83–94.

37. WARKANY, J. and SCHRAFFENBERGER, E. Congenital malformations induced in rats by maternal nutritional deficiency. VI. The preventive factor. *J. Nutrit.*, 1944, *27:*477–484.

38. WATERS, N. F. Inheritance of body-weight in domestic fowl. *Bull. R. I. agric. Exp. Sta.*, 1931, *228.*

39. WIENER, A. S. The inheritance of all rgic disease. *Ohio J. Sci.*, 1936, *36:*147–148.

40. WIENER, A. S. The Rh series of allelic genes. *Science*, 1944, *100:*595–597.

41. WIENER, A. S., SONN, E. B. and BELKIN, R. B. Heredity of the Rh blood types. *J. exp. Med.*, 1944, *79:*235–253.

42. WRIGHT, S. General, group, and special size factors. *Genetics*, 1932, *17:*603–619.

INDEX

ABDOMINAL viscera, innervation of, autonomic, 227
Ablation, of cerebellum. See *Cerebellum*.
  of cerebral cortex areas, effects of, 281
  regional, of cortical areas, 281
Absorption, in colon, 1078
  in intestines, 1061–1082
  in stomach, 1042–1058
  substances involved, 1057
Acapnia, in anoxia, 893
  hysterical, 927
  periodic breathing and, 915
  respiratory center by depression, 915
  voluntary hyperventilation and, 915, 927
Acceleration, 205
  angular, semicircular canals and, 206
  linear, semicircular canals and, 205
Acclimatization, anoxia and, 892
  body fluids and, 948
Accommodation, of eye, 446, *446*
  age changes in, 448, *449*
  amplitude of, 450
  autonomic action in, 231
  in hyperopia, 453
  limits of, 448
  near and far point, 448
  of nerve, 21–22
Acetyl-beta-methylcholine, and cardiac output, 828
Acetylcholine, autonomic nerve section and, 228
  autonomic stimulation by, 234
  in blood flow, 829, 831
  effect on coronary vessels, 808
    on nervous tissue, 133
  electronic theory of nerve impulse initiation and, 902
  liberation of, at nerve termination, 125
    in nervous tissue, 132
  in location of vasoconstrictor center, 699
  in mammalian heart, *233*
  in nerve, 119, 132, 134
  at neuromuscular junction, 125
  potassium and, interrelations, 821
  responses to, pre- and postganglionic, *132*
  in salivary glands, 1036
  sensitization to, 236
  of iris, *237*
  in spinal shock, 181
  sweat gland sensitivity to, 228
  in sympathetic ganglia, 131
  in vagus inhibition, 786

Acetylene method, 796
Achlorhydria, in pernicious anemia, 557
Achromatic series in color vision, 489
Achromatopsia, 497
Acid. See specific names of, as *Amino, Arachidonic, Fatty, Linoleic*. etc.
  -base balance. See *Acid-base equilibrium*.
  dissociation curves, 575, *575*
  equilibrium, 573
    carbon dioxide in, 576
    charts of experimental, *580*
    control of, by respiration, 888
    effect on electrocardiogram, 824
    effect of respiration on, 576, 579
    experimental shifts in, 579
    graphs of, *575, 580*
    heart and, 824
    Henderson equation for, 946
    kidney effect on, 578. See also *Kidney*.
    regulation of, 944
      renal, 952
      respiratory, 917
    T wave and, 815
    of urine, 979
  imbalance, primary paths of, *946*
  titration curves. See *Titration*.
  reaction, of intestinal contents, 1078
Acidosis, chemoreceptor stimulation in, 922
  diabetic, body fluids in, 960
  in respiration, 918
  respiratory and metabolic, 579
  sensitivity of respiratory center to carbon dioxide in, 917, *917*
Acne, androgens and, 1219
Acrodynia, in pyridoxine deficiency, 1143
Action potential(s), 8, *103*
  complete, of superior cervical ganglion, *128*
  of heart, 748
  of nerve, auditory, 426, *427*, 431
  of optic nerve, 477
  in pacemaker localization, 719
Activators, of enzymes, 1024
Activity, locomotor, 1159. See also *Locomotor activity*.
  effect of, on weight gain, 1161, *1161*
  normal, records of, *537*
  rhythms, 1160, *1160*
Adaptation. See *Sense organs*.
Addison's disease, renal defects in, 978
Adenase, 1026
Adenosine triphosphate, of muscle, 60

Adenylic acid, action of, on arterioles, 709
  system, 69, *69*
  of muscle, 60, *69*
Adrenal(s), in blood glucose regulation, 1106
  cortex, effect of, on kidney function, 952, 958, 978
  and protein breakdown, 1179
  cortical insufficiency, plasma volume decrease in, 958
  and glycogen breakdown, 1177
  and heat production, 1166
  in lactation, 1209
  and resistance to disease, 1237
Adrenaline, in asthma, 865
  in autonomic stimulation, 234
  in cardiac impulse, conduction of, auriculo-ventricular, 789
  output and, 801
  effect of, on autonomic nervous system, 220, 228, 233
    on cardiac impulse, 789
    on coronary circulation, 806
      vessels, 808
      heart rate, 789
  extrasystoles and, 790
  responses of isotonic nictitating membrane to, *236*
  sensitization to, 236–237
  in spinal shock, 181
  in vasoconstriction, 655
Aero-otitis media, 413
Affect, definition of, 306
  thalamic localization of, 367
Afferent fibers, in muscle nerve, *159*
Afibrinogenemia, bleeding tendency in, 587
After-discharge, 130
  in sympathetic ganglion, 130
  -images, in color vision, 491
  -potential(s), 11, *103*, *104*, 116
    in ganglia, 128–129
    lability of, 104
    of muscle, 33
    negative, 104
    of nerve, 104, 106–107
    positive, 104
    relation to recovery cycle, 105
Age, advanced, androgens during, 1222
  effect of, on aorta, 646
    on blood pressure, 674
    on electroencephalogram, 526
    on volume of aorta, *647*, *648*
Ageusia, 307
Agglutination, serological, 560
Agglutinins, of blood, 560
Agnosia, 542
Air. See specific types, as *Alveolar air.*
  conduction of sound waves, 431
  hunger, 918
  in lung, relationship between measurable volumes of, *868*

Albumin(s), of plasma, in hemorrhage, 602
  serum, 583
Alcohol, effect of, on appetite, 997
Alcoholism, anoxia in, 891
Alimentary canal, movements of, 982
  glycosuria, 1075
  tract, functions of, general, 982–1010
    secretion of, 982–1082
Alkaline reaction, of intestinal contents, 1078
  tide, 1048
Alkalosis, in respiration, 918
  respiratory and metabolic, 579
  sensitivity of respiratory center to CO_2 in, 918
Allergy, inheritance of, 1245
All-or-nothing relation, 52–54
  contraction and, 53, *54*
Alpha waves, of electroencephalogram, 525
Altitude, high, anoxia and, 925
  effects of oxygen administration at, 926
  respiration at, 925
Alveolar air, 869
  composition of, 877
  gaseous equilibrium with arterial blood and, 881
  partial pressures of, 879
  sampling of, 881
  ducts, blocking of, 867
  ventilation, 870
Alveolus(i), 870
  anatomy of, 879
  function of, 879
  mixing of gases in, 881
  partial pressure of carbon dioxide in, 879
  respiratory surface of, 880
  ventilation of, 865
Amenorrhea, 1188
American physiology, historical backgrounds of, 1–5
Ametropia, 451
Amines, *from* intestinal putrefaction, 1080
Amino acids, 1055, 1062
  administration of, parenteral, 1112
  in blood, 1077
  classification of, 1137
  conversion to carbohydrate of, 1116
    to fat, 1118
  deamination of, 1116
  as digestive products, 1111
  essential, 1137
  formulae and list of, 1068
  in glomerular filtrate, 973
  glycogenic, 1117
  in muscle, 58
  in plasma, 1111
  as protein constituents, 1111
  in protein synthesis, 1112
  from proteins of tissue, 1112
  from proteolytic cleavage of protein molecule, 1068
  sources of, 1111

Amino nitrogen, fate of, 1114
Aminopeptidase, 1025, 1067
Ammonia production, of nerves, 119
Ammonium salts, synthesis of, glutamine in, 973
Ampulla, angular acceleration and, *208*
  of living fish, *207*
Amylase, 1023, 1025, 1075
  action of, 1070
Amylolytic enzymes, 1023
Amytal, in hyperthermia, 248
Anabolism, in metabolism, 1086
Anastomoses, between arteries in brain, 849
  intercoronary, 804
  in liver, of systemic and portal vessels, 835
Androgens, action of, physiologic, 1217
  assay of, 1216
  chemistry of, 1214
  in different periods of life, 1220
  effect of, on ejaculation, 1230
    on erection, 1228
    on hypophysis of, 1224
    on seminal vesicle following castration, *1216*
    on spermatogenesis of, 1225
  extratesticular, 1224
  functions of, 1217
  as male hormones, 1214
  metabolism of, 1214
  production of, regulation of, 1223
    site of, in testes, 1223
  sources of, 1215
  synthesis of, 1215
  in testes, *1221*
Androsterone, 1215, *1215*
Anelectrotonus, 26
Anemia, cardiac output in, 801
  cerebral, 852
  erythrocytes and, 556
  gastric juice in treatment of, 1045
  heart murmurs in, 644
    rate in, 784
  types of, 556
Anesthesia, respiratory center depression by, 916
  thermal, 352
Angioarchitecture, of brain blood vessels, 848
Angioscotometry, 506
Angiotonase, in renal hypertension, 980
Angiotonin, action of, on arterioles, 709
  in blood flow, 829, 830
  effect of, on arteriole tone, 694
  hypertension and, 676
  -inhibitor, 676
  and kidney blood flow, 833
  in renal hypertension, 980
Angular acceleration, in ampulla and semicircular canal, *208*
Anisotropy, in contractile tissues, 57
Anomalies, of development, heredity in, 1242

Anorexia, in thiamine deficiency, 1140
Anosmia, 307
Anoxemia, afferent nerve impulses from chemoreceptors in, 925
  alveolar carbon dioxide pressure in, 926
  aortic and carotid chemoreceptor stimulation by, 922
  Biot's breathing and, 916
  Cheyne-Stokes' breathing and, 916
  deep anesthesia and, 916
  effect of, on cerebral circulation, 853
  formation of blood cells in, 557
  general, effect of, on heart 814
  in heart, conduction disturbances and, 816
  as limiting factor in flying, 927
    in response to alkaloids, 918
  localized, effects of, of heart, 816
  periodic breathing and, 915
  receptors sensitive to, 921
  relation of, to dyspnea, 927
  relief of, by oxygen at high altitudes, 926
  respiratory center depression by, 916, 920
    stimulation by, transient, 920
    response in man to, 925
  R wave in, 815
  T wave in, 815
Anoxia, 889
  acclimatization and, 892
  acute, 891
  anemic, 889, 891
  anoxic, 889, 890
  in blood flow, 829
  chronic, 892
  composition of arterial and venous blood in, *890*
  cyanosis in, 892
  in dark adaptation, 471
  effect of carbon dioxide on, 893
    on electrocardiogram, 814
  fulminating, 891
  and high altitude flying, 925
  histotoxic, 889, 890
  respiration in, 893
  stagnant, 889
  of tissue, in shock, 603
Anterior medullary velum. See *Valve of Vieussens.*
Antibodies, of blood, 560
Anticoagulants, 589, 592, 599
Antigens, blood, 560
Antiperistalsis, 1002
Antrum pylori, 989
Aorta, abdominal, flow in, pressure and velocity of, *649*
  effect of age on, 646
  hemodynamics of, 646
  insufficiency of, hemodynamics in, 649
  pressure in, in coronary circulation control, 810
  volume of, effect of age on, *647, 648*

Aortic arch, effects of denervation of, 714
  nerve supply of, *701*
  receptor organs in, 852
  glomus, function of, 923
    morphology of, *921*
  insufficiency, cardiac output in, 801
Aphasia, 543
Apnea, 860
  hyperventilation and. 915
  irritant vapors and, 929
  lung inflation and, 903, *903*
  voluntary, 927
Apneusis, control of depth of, 908
  definition of, 907
  production of, 907, *907*
Appetite, 387
  effect of alcohol on, 997
  as hunger component, 386
  taste sensation in relation to, 383
Apraxia, 543
Arachidonic acid, 1138
Areas, of cerebral cortex. See *Cerebral cortex, areas of.*
  of cerebrum. See *Cerebrum, areas of.*
Arginase, 1026
  in urea synthesis, 1118
Arginine, in urea synthesis, 1118
Arterial blood pressure. See *Blood pressure.*
Artery(ies). See also *Blood Vessels.*
  of brain, anastomosis of, 849
    anatomy of, 849
    regulation of, 851
  coronary, 803
    anastomoses of, 804
  "end" of heart, 804
Arterioles, 607, *608*
  in arterial pressure regulation, 710
  constriction of, 692
  control of peripheral resistance by, 710
  dilatation of, 692
  hemodynamics of, 650
  hormone effect on, 708
  in lungs, blocking of, 867
  metabolite effects on, 708
  regulation of nervous, *829*, 694
    chemical, 705, 715
  tone of, angiotonin effect on, 694
    epinephrine effect on, 694
Arteriovenous anastomosis, cardiac output in, 801
Artificial respiration. See *Respiration, artificial.*
Aschheim-Zondek test for pregnancy, 1199
Ascites, factors in, 836
  in heart failure, 679
Ascorbic acid, 1144
  deficiency of, symptoms of, 1144
  dietary, recommended allowance of, 1132
  in food, 1017
  requirements of, 1144

Ascorbic acid, sources of, 1144
Aspiration, mechanics of, 859
  pressure cycle of, 866
  volume, of lung, 867
Association areas, 525–546
  functions of, 525
  projection nature of, 535
Astereognosis, 332
Asthma, adrenaline in, 865
Astigmia (astigmatism), 453, *454*
Ataxia, 299
  relation of posterior columns to, 351
Atelectasis, 867
  effect, on blood flow, 843
Athetosis, basal ganglia and cerebral cortex in, 292
ATP (adenosine triphosphate), 60
Atrium(a), of alveolar ducts, 870
  respiratory reflexes from distension of, 930
Atropine, in autonomic stimulation, 234
  cardiac putput and, 801, 828
  effect on hypothalamus. 247
    on salivary glands, 1036
  in stimulation of geniculate ganglion, *853*
  vagus and, 788
Attitudinal reflexes, 192
Audibility curve, 418, *418, 419*
Audiogram, 418, *418, 419*
Audiometry, 419
Audition. See *Hearing.*
Auditory pathway, 434
  bilaterality of, 437, *437*
  radiations, thalamocortical, 436
  system, *435*
Auricle(s), arrest of, in potassium poisoning, 821
  cardiac impulse conduction in, 725
  contraction of, 729
  electrocardiogram and, 747
  extrasystoles in, 769
  fibrillation of, 774
  flutter, 774
  systole of. See *Systole, auricular.*
Auriculopressor reflex, 704
Auriculoventricular bundle, 727
  conduction, sympathetic, 789
    vagus, 787
  node, 726
    in conduction of cardiac impulse, 726
    vagus, effect on, 786
  valves, in systole, auricular, 729
    ventricular, 731
Auscultatory method, in measurement of blood pressure, 673
Austin Flint murmur, 740
Autonomic epilepsy, 247
  disturbances, due to cerebral cortex area injury, 283
  function, cerebral regulation of. See *Cerebrum, autonomic function of.*
  hypothalamic level of, 242

Autonomic function of medulla oblongata. See *Medulla oblongata*.
medullary level of, 241
pontine level of, 242
in spinal animal, 241
of spinal cord. See *Spinal cord*.
spinal level of, 241
motor area, 252
nerve section, acetylcholine in, 228
nervous system, 241–253. See also *Parasympathetic nervous system, Sympathetic nervous system*.
afferents, 227
visceral, 227–228
definition of, 218, 220, 229
drug, effects on, 220
efferents, 222–225
visceral, *219*
embryology of, 221
functional levels of, 220, 225, 241
general action of, 230
history of, 218, 220
homeostasis and, 229
neurohormones of, 236
parasympathetic division, 225
peripheral division, 218–239
reflexes of, 228
in psinal shock, 179
regulation of, functional, 228
principles of, 228
sex and, 225
and temperature regulation, 1171
thoracolumbar division, 220, 222
representation, relation of, to somatic motor, *252*
stimulation, pharmacological agents for, 233, 234
A-V block. See *Block, auriculoventricular*.
Avogadro's principle, 873
Axon, definition, 96
reflex. See *reflex(es)*.

BABINSKI sign, in cerebral cortex injury, 282, 284
in spinal shock, 179
Bachman's bundle, 719
Bacterial action, in colon, 1079
in intestine, 1079
Bainbridge reflex, 704, 790
Bain's modification of Loewi's technique, *232*
Baldness, 1218
Ballistocardiograph, *798*, 799, 800
Bárány test, 209
Barbiturates, in hyperthermia, 248. See also names of specific barbiturates.
hypothalamus and, 248
in mental disorders, rationale of, 250
BARRON, Donald H.: Vasomotor regulation, 692–709

Basal condition, cardiac output in, 800
heart rate in, 781
ganglia, activation of, by cerebral cortex, 290
anatomical considerations of, 288
and cerebral cortex, interconnections between, *289*
and cerebrum, 288
clinical physiology of, 292
excitability of, 289
experimental lesions of, 291
inhibitory effects of, 289
metabolic rate, 1094
and hypothalamic lesions, 249, See also *Hypothalamus, lesions of*.
rise of, in response to cold, 248
standards for, normal, 1096
metabolism. See *Metbolism, basal*.
Basophils. See *Leukocytes*.
Bathesthesia, 307
Batschinski's law, 637
Beaumont, gastric studies, 991, 1044
Behavior, continuity of, 541
disturbances in cerebral cortex injury, 283
after removal of motor areas, 283
feeding, taste as guide in, 383
Bell-Magendie law, exception to, 697
Benedict apparatus, for metabolism, basal, *1090*
Benzedrine, in hyperactivity, 536
in spinal shock, 181
Berger rhythm. See *Electroencephalogram*.
Bergmann's rule, of body size in relation to environment, 1240
Beriberi, in thiamine deficiency, 1139
Bernoulli's principle, 650
Beta-oxidation of fatty acids, 1125
-condensation of fatty acids, 1124
Beta waves, of encephalogram, 525
Bicarbonate, deficit and excess of, 947
Bigeminus rhythm, in electrocardiogram, 773
Bile, in intestinal digestion, 1061
salts, 1076
as capillary poison, 619
Bingham's formula for plastic flow, 640, 657
Binocular rivalry, 510
Biot's breathing, 916
Biotin, synthesis of, in intestines, 1081
Birefringence, in contractile tissues, 57
Bjerrum screen, 506
Blacktongue, in dog, 1142
Bladder, innervation of, autonomic, 231
reflexes, in spinal shock, 180
Bleeding tendency, clinical tests for, 587
Blind spot, 511
Block auriculoventricular, electrocardiogram in, 766, *766*
bundle-branch, electrocardiogram in, 766, *767, 768*
heart, cardiac impulse and, 766

Block, intra-auricular, electrocardiogram in, 765
  intraventricular, electrocardiogram in, *768*
  partial, electrocardiogram in, 766
  sino-auricular, electrocardiogram in. 765
  vagus in, 766
Blood, agglutinins, 560
  altitude effects on, 557
  amino acids in, 1077
  anions and cations of, 549
  antibodies, 560
  anticoagulants of, 550, 558, 589, 598, 599
  antigens, 560
    factors, in forensic medicine, 561
  arterial, composition of, 888
    gaseous equilibrium with alveolar air and, 881
  bicarbonate, 885
  bleeding time, 587, 588
  -brain barrier, 851
  buffers in, 575
  carbon dioxide condition in, 884
    pressure of, in apnea, voluntary, 927
      and bicarbonate concentration, relationship between, 918
      and chemoreceptor respiratory reflexes, 922
      effects on respiratory center, 899. 909, 913, 923, 930
      in eupnea, 913
      in exercise, 930
      at high altitudes, 926
      in hyperventilation, 914
      partial, 879
    titration curve of, 885, *885*
  cells, 549, 553, *554*. See also *Erythrocytes, Leukocytes.*
    counting of, 553
    formation of. See *Hematopoiesis.*
    morphology of, 553. See also *Erythrocytes, Leukocytes.*
    and plasma, relative volumes of, 551
    red. See *Erythrocytes.*
    sedimentation of, 550
    white. See *Leukocytes.*
  -cerebrospinal fluid barrier, 851
  chemical composition of, 566
  chylomicrons in, 549
  circulation of, forces maintaining, 645
  clotting. See *Blood, coagulation of.*
  coagulation of, 549, 586
    bleeding tendencies in defects of, 587
    blood platelets in relation to, 595
    calcium in, 592
    clot retraction in, 595, 596
    factors in, 589
    heparin in, 598
    interpretations of data on, 599
    lytic actions in, 595
    modifying mechanisms in, 597
    physiological function of, 587

Blood coagulation, proteolytic enzymes in, 594
  salmine in, 598
  scope of problem of, 588
  stages in, 588, 597
  theories of, 599
  thromboplastic substances in, 593
  time of, 588, 597
  composition of, gaseous, 888
  donors, types of, 560
  "dust," 549
  equilibria in, 568
  fibrin in, 549, 586, *587*
  fibrinogen in, 549, 586
  flow of, 640, 657. See also *Flow.*
    accessory factors in, 679
    through brain, 848
      in factors regulating, 852
    cerebral, angioarchitecture of, 848
      effect on respiration, 919
    control of, chemical, 828
      hormonal, 828
      nervous, 828
    cutaneous, and temperature regulation, 1169
    in exercise, 645
    hindrance in, 658
    in hyperemia, 829
    in ischemia, 830
    in kidney, 658, 833
    in liver, 834
    in lungs, 840, 879
    measurement of, 660
      in capillaries of human retina, 664, *665*
    microscopy of, 660
    through organs, 667
      effect of vasodilatation on, 667
    pressure and velocity of, *649*
    in pulmonary air sac, *880*
    renal, Fick principle in measurement of, 976
      measurement of, 976
      regulation of, 978
    resistance to, peripheral, 657
    through skeletal muscles, 836
    to skin, 829
      regulation and body temperature, 832
      control of, chemical, 829
        hormonal, 831
        nervous, 830
      eserine in, 832
    in special regions, 828–854
    through spleen, 844
    and sympathectomy, 830
    through uterus, 837
    velocity of, 648
      differences in, 665
      mean, in arteries, veins, and capillaries, 664

Blood, flow of, velocity of, relative, in different parts of vascular system, *664*
   and pressure of, 660.680
   and volume of, 660
   through viscera, 834
  fluidity, 639
  formed elements in, 549, 553. See also *Erythrocytes, Leukocytes.*
  fucntions of, 548
  gas exchange in, 886
  gases in, chemical analysis of, 875
  glucose, 1104
   liver maintenance of, 1105
  groups, 560
   classifications of, 560
  hemoconia in, 549
  hydrostatic pressure of, 667
  hypocalcemia, parathyroid hormone in, 1147
  ions in, 549
  lactic acid of, 1110, *1110*
   content, in heart, 825
  mobility of, 656
  osmotic pressure of, 568
  oxygen capacity of, 585
   content of, 882, *883*
   pressure of, in apnea, voluntary, 927
    and chemoreceptor respiratory reflexes, 921
    effects of, on respiration in man, 925
    in eupnea, 926
    at high altitudes, 926
    in hyperventilation, 915
    on respiratory center, 919
   saturation in, 883
   transport of, 882
  perfusion, pressure-flow curves, 655, *656*
  *p*H of, 573
   effect on oxygen dissociation curve, 884, *884*
   as respiratory center stimulus, 918
   as stimulus to chemoreceptor respiratory reflexes, 922
  physiology of, chemical aspects of, 566. 585
  plasma, 549. See also *Plasma.*
  plasticity of, 652
  platelets, *554*, 564
   deficiencies, bleeding tendencies in, 587
   as elements of blood, 549
   function of, 565
   in hemophilia, 565
   heparin in, preservation of, 565
   in relation to coagulation of blood, 595
  preservation of, 558
  pressure, 649
   in anoxemia, general, 814
   aortic, coronary blood flow and, 810, *811*
   arterial, 667. See also *Blood pressure; Blood pressure, venous.*
   in brain, *852*

Blood pressure, carotid sinus effect on, 702
  cerebral regulation of, 251
  diastolic, 670
  in different parts of vascular system, *671*
  effect of increased intrathoracic pressure on, *844*
  elevated, in anoxia, 891
  factors affecting, 674
  -flow relationship, 654
  hypertension and, 675
  in large arteries, 672
  in lesser circulation, 841
  mean, in arteries, veins and capillaries, 671
   of systolic and diastolic pressures, 670
  measurement of, methods in, 673
   by Stephen Hales, 667
  normal, 674
   in parturition, *838*
  periodic variations in, 700
  plasma calcium in, *822*
   magnesium and, *823*
   potassium and, *820*
  pulse, contour of, *688*
  recording of, mercury manometer in, *669*
   methods of, 668
   in parturition, *839*
  regulation of, 710–715
  respiratory reflexes from rise in, 928
  systemic, fall in, following section of vagi, *704*
   in hyperventilation, *707*
  systolic, 670
  Traube-Hering waves in, *700*, 701
  in vascular system, *650*
  venous, 677
   cardiac regulation of, 714
   effective, 680
   gravity, effect on, 677
   in heart failure, 679
   in lesser circulation, 842
   measurement of, 678
  -volume relationship, in vena cava, *651*
  properties and constituents of, 548–604
  proteins in, 567, 581, 589, 590
  pyruvic acid of, 1110, *1110*
  reactions in, velocity of, 886
   Rh factor of, 561
  as rehological fluid, 644, 652
  rheology of, properties of, in vitro, 652, 653
   in vivo, 653
  sedimentation rate of, 550
  serum, 549. See also *Serum.*
   definition of, 936
   electrolyte pattern of, *945*
    blood, comparison of, with gastrointestinal fluids, 948
    normal and abnormal, *956*
  solutes in, distribution of, 567, 572
  specific gravity of, 550, 585

Blood, splenomegaly in, 562
  storage in liver, 836
    in lungs, 843
    in spleen, 844
  substitutes, 602, 604
  temperature of, 549
  thrombus formation in, 586
  transfusion of. See *Transfusions.*
  transport of oxygen and carbon dioxide by, 882
  turbulence of, 644
  urea nitrogen, effect of hepatectomy on, *1119*
  vascular system, of kidney, 965
  venous, composition of, 888
  vessels. See also *Arteries, Arterioles, Capillaries, Veins, Venules.*
    anastomoses of, intercoronary, 804
    of brain, 848
      anatomy of, 849
      angioarchitecture of, 848
      arterial anastomosis of, 849
      blood flow of, 852
      caliber changes in, 852
      control of, carotid sinus in, 852
        nervous, 854
      cerebral factors regulating, 852
      dilatation of, 852
      drug action on, 854
      innervation of, *849*, 854
      regulation of, 852
      relative vascularity of parts, 850
      vasoconstriction in, 854
      vasodilatation in, 854
      vasomotor control of, 854
    coronary, 803
    dimensions of, 649
    effect of ascorbic acid deficiency on, 1144
    elasticity of, 652
    flow, in diseased, 653
    magnesium dilatation of, 824
    response of, to chemical stimulation, 715
    role in circulation, 645
    Thebesian, 805
  viscosity of, 550, 639
    apparent, 656
  volume, 552
    cells and plasma in, 551
    clinical importance of, 939
    determination of, 552
    measurement of, 938
    venous pressure and, 714
  water content of, 566
  wetting by, 644
  yield pressure of, 656
    definition of, 655, *655*
B.M.R. See *Basal metabolic rate.*
Body fluids, 933–962. See also *Fluid.*
  abnormalities, in nephritis, 961
  acclimatization and 948

Body fluids in acidosis, diabetic, 960
  alkalinity of, 944
  circulation and renal exchanges of, 953
  distribution of, clinical abnormalities in, 958
  exchange of external, 944
    internal, 937
  functional divisions of, 935
  ionic composition of, 936 *936*
    concentration of, *957*
  pathological physiology of, 956
  physiology of, 935–962
  shock due to loss of, 958
  transfer of, Starling theory of, 937
  types of, 935. See also *Fluids, types of.*
  volume of, *957*
  size, factors in, 1238
    heart rate and, relation between, 782
    and metabolism, basal, 1094, *1095*
  temperature, 1163
    and cutaneous vasodilatation, 832
    regulation of, and blood flow through skin, 832
    respiration in, rate and depth of, 909, 920
    variations in, 1164
  water, measurement of, with D_2O, 942
    with heavy water, 942, 954
    with potassium, 942
    with thio-urea, 942
    with urea, 942
    transfers of, 943
Bone conduction, 433
  of sound waves, 433
  parathyroid effects on, 1147
  sex hormone action on, 1203
Bowditch, Henry, in history of physiology, 2
Boyle's law, 873
Bradycardia, in hypercalcemia, 821
Brain, anastomoses between vessels of, 849
  arterial pressure in, *851*
  blood flow through, 848
    and hemato-encephalic barrier, 850
    vessels of, 848
      circulation in, control of, extrinsic, 852
        intrinsic, 852
      innervation of, *849*
  calcarine fissure in, 515
    cytoarchitecture of transition zone in, *515*
  circulation in, alterations in, 853
    effect of anoxemia on, 853
    of blood composition on, 853
    of carbon dioxide on, 853
  cytoarchitecture of, *257*
  end-arteries of, 850
  floor of fourth ventricle of, *700*
  frontal areas, hyperactivity following ablation of, 1162
  nuclei of, and lateral geniculate bodies, 513

Brain stem, bulbar nucleus and pathways for taste, 376
  sensory systems of, 352
  transverse section of, during heating, *1173*
  vascular nerves, sources of, 850, 854
  waves. See *Electroencephagram.*
Breast. See *Mammary glands.*
Breathing. See *Respiration.*
BROBECK, JOHN R.: Intermediary metabolism 1102—1129
  Introduction to quantitative metabolism, 1084—1101
  Nutrition, 1130—1155
  Regulation of energy exchange, 1156—1181
Broca's area, as motor speech area, 544
Bromide, distribution of, in body, 939
Bronchi, 859
  muscles of, 865
Bronchial musculature, function of, 870
Bronchioles, respiratory, 869
Brown-Séquard's syndrome, 183, *184*
Buffer(s), action of, acid-base, 573
  carbon dioxide in, 576
  in blood, 574. See also *Blood, buffers in.*
  in body fluids, 945
Bulbospinal correlation system, 173—176
Bundle, Bachman's 719
Bundle-branch block. See *Block.*
  of His, 726
Burns, closed plaster treatment of, 628

CALCIFEROL, as source of vitamin D, 1146
Calcium. See also *Plasma calcium.*
  dietary, 1149
    recommended allowance of, 1132
  in electrical discharge, of heart, 724
  in food, 1016
  ions in blood coagulation, 592
  metabolism, sex hormones in, 1203
  parathyroid glands and, 1147
  and vitamin D, 1147
Caloric reactions, 209
  requirements, of diet, 1130
    and occupation, 1131
  values, of various foods, 1134
Calorie(s), defined, 1085
  dietary, recommended allowance of, 1132
  distribution of, 1135
  in food, 1016
Calorimeter, bomb, 1085
  respiration, of Atwater-Rosa-Benedict, 1087, *1088, 1089*
Calorimetry, direct, 1087, 1088–1090
  indirect, 1088, *1089, 1091*
Canal, auditory. See *Eustachian tube.*
Cannon, Walter, in history of physiology, 3
Capillary(ies), 607–620
  42

Capillary(ies), *and* adjacent lymph vessel, *621*
  anatomical arrangement of, 607
  atypical, 620
  a-v, 607, *608*
  blood pressure in, 614
  of brain, 850
  of choroid plexus, 620
  of ciliary body, 620
  contraction of, 609
  dilatation, and tissue activity, 617
  direct observation of, 607, 660
  effect of histamine on, 611
    *p*H variations on, 609
  fluid transfer across, 569
  fragility of, 588
    ascorbic acid and, 1144
  of glomerulus of kidney, 620
  hemodynamics of, 651
  inter-endothelial cement of, 609
  of liver, 620
  network, in lungs, *880*
  permeability, 610, 613
    effects of chemical agents on, 616
      ionic composition of environment on, 618
      poisons on, 619
      temperature on, 618
    gradient of, 616
    retardation of, by chemical substances, 618
    variation in, 616
  pituitary control of dilatation of, 611
  poisons, 619
    lymphagogues as, 625
  porosity of, *617*
  pulmonary, distribution of, 870
  reactions, 610
    effects of, chemical agents and, 610
  relation to arterioles, *608*
  Rouget cells of, 608
  of skin, 611
  of spleen, 620
  structure of, 608, *608*
    walls of, 608
  tone, 618
  triple response of, 611
  variations in number of open, 609
  wall, vitamin C and, 618
Carbamino hemoglobin, 884
Carbohydrate(s). See also *Enzymes, amylolytic.*
  absorption of, in intestine, 1074
  of biological importance, 1104
  conversion of amino acids to, 1116
    to fat, 1128
  enzymes acting on, 1025
  fermentation of, in intestines, 1075
  in food, 1016
  as foodstuff, 1014
  lactic acid resynthesized to, 77
  in lipid metabolism, 1111

Carbohydrate(s), metabolism, of heart, 825
    and hypothalamic lesions, 249. See also
        Hypothalamus, lesions of.
    intermediary, 1104
    muscle energy source, 73
    in protein metabolism, 1111
    reserve, glycogen in, 1176
    tolerance, 1075
    utilization of, non-muscle, 1110
        in skeletal muscle, 1109
Carbon, dietary, 1149
    dioxide in acid-base equilibrium, 576
        action of, on respiratory center, 899,
            908, 913, 923, 930
            on respiratory chemoreceptors, 922
        alveolar pressure and pulmonary ven-
            tilation, relation between. 914
        buffer action of, 576. See also *Buffer.*
        combination of, with hemoglobin, 885
        condition of, in blood, 884
        in dark adaptation, rate of, 471
        effect on cerebral circulation, 853
            on coronary vessels, 809, *810*
            on electroencephalogram, 527
            on oxygen dissociation curve, 884,
                884
            on respiratory motor nerve discharge,
                900
            on respiratory response, *924*
        measure of respiratory exchange, 1089
        partial pressure, in alveoli, 879
            in blood, 879
        pressure, and apnea, 915
            and diabetes, 918
            and nephritis, 918
        production of, 877
        in respiration, 858
        respiratory center depression by excess,
            914, 916
            stimulus, mechanism of action, 901,
                918
        in resuscitation, 872
        in saliva, 1030
        sensitivity of respiratory center to, 916
        stimulation of neuron by, 902
        titration curve, of blood, *885*
        transport of, by blood, 882, 884
    monoxide, combination with hemoglobin,
        889
        hemoglobin, 562
        method, for blood volume, 552
        poisoning, 582
            treatment of, 984
Carbonates, in saliva, 1030
Carbonic acid, excess and deficit of, 946
    anhydrase, 886
        theory, of formation of gastric hydro-
            chloric acid, 1048
Carboxylase ?, 1026
Carboxypeptidase, 1025, 1062, 1067
Carcinogenesis, sex hormone action in, 1203

Carcinoma, of prostate gland, androgens
    and, 1218
Cardia, of stomach, 988
Cardiac cycle, events of, 717–780
        mechanical, 729, *730*. See also *Sys-
            tole, Diastasis, Diastole.*
    impulse. See also *Heart beat, Heart con-
        traction.*
        adrenaline effect on, 789
        conduction of, 725
            auricular-ventricular, 726
            disturbances of, 765
            intra-auricular, 725
            intraventricular, 727
                potassium effect on, 821
                Purkinje fibers in, 727
            heart block and, 766
            origin of, myogenic, 720, 725
                neurogenic, 720, 725
            potassium effect on, 821
            Purkinje fibers and, 727
    muscle, conduction rate in, 51
        electrical and mechanical events, 51–52
        length-tension relations, 51, *51*
        spike potential in, 51
    output, 781–802, 829
        in anoxemia, general, 814
        in arterial pressure regulation, 710
        in basal condition, 800
        blood flow in, peripheral, 828
        estimation of, 795
            acetylene method, 796
            ballistocardiograph, 799
            CO_2 technique, 796
            dilution method, 798
            Fick method, 796
                indirect, 796
            pulse pressure method, 799
        heart rate influence on, 790
        influence of acetyl-beta-methylcholine
            on, 828
            of atropine on, 828
        peripheral vasomotor control of, 828
        reserve of heart in, 794
        Starling's law in, 792
        variations in, factors involved, 799
    sphincter, of stomach, 988
    and vasomotor centers, comparison of,
        with other tissues, 715
Cardio-aortic reflexes, 852
Cardiometer, 693
Cardiovascular collapse, sodium depletion
    and, 820
    inefficiency, sodium depletion and, 820
    regulation, by cerebrum, 251
    -respiratory crisis, in anoxemia, general,
        815
Carotene, dietary, recommended allowance
    of, 1133
    vitamin A and, 1145
Carotid body, 702

Carotid glomus, function of, 922
  morphology of, *921*
  sinus, afferent nerve endings in, *702*
    cerebral vasomotor control by, 852
    control of brain circulation by, 852
    effect on blood pressure, 702
      of denervation, 714
    heart rate and, 787
    hypersensitivity of, 787
    nerve supply of, *701*
    pressure, coronary blood flow and, 808
    reflex, 787, *788*
    reflexes of, and cerebral circulation, 852
    spleen contraction and, 845
Casein, rennin action on, 1056
Castration, effects of, 1213, *1214*, 1215
  on seminal vesicle, *1216*
Catabolism, in metabolism, 1086
Catalase, 1022, 1026
Catalytic action of enzymes, 1020, 1102
Catelectrotonus, 26
  compared with end-plate potential of
    muscle, 122–123
Cathepsin, 1113
Cell(s), in blood. See *Blood cells.*
  of gastric glands, 1042
  Kupffer, 563
  membrane, permeability of, factors in-
    fluencing, 560
  pus, 564
  reticulo-endothelial, 563
Center, respiratory. See *Respiratory center.*
Centipoise, definition of, 637
Central excitatory state, 144
  latency, 144
  nervous system. See also *Excitation, Para-
    sympathetic nervous system, Sympa-
    thetic nervous system.*
    diseases, heart rate in, 784
    motor functions, 178–304
    respiration and, 858
    synaptic transmission in, 134
    and temperature regulation, 1171
    vascularity of various parts of, 850
  reflex time, 144
Cephalin, 1122
  in blood coagulation, 593
Cerebellum, ablation of, 299
  anatomy of, 294
  cerebrum and, 294–303
    interrelations between, 302
  connections of, afferent and efferent, *298,*
    298
  cortex of, *295*
  dorsal surface of, *301*
  flocculonodular lobe of, 294
  functional analysis of, 299
  histology of, *296*
  lobes of, ablation, 300
  pontocerebellar receiving area of, *302*
  schema of, *296*

Cerebral blood vessels. See also *Blood vessels, Brain, blood vessels of.*
  cortex, 255–271, 354, 525–546. See also
    Cerebrum.
    ablation of, regional, clinical use of, 185
    activation of basal ganglia by, 290
    areas of, *257*
      ablation of, regional, 281
      association of, 535
      auditory, 436
      cytoarchitecture, *280*
      homolateral, interrelations of, 280
      interaction between, 279
      motor, 277, 279, 284
        location of, *275*
        precentral, *266, 267*
      projection, 265
      striate, 515
        visual function of, 521
    autonomic disturbances of, 283
    and basal ganglia, interconnections be-
      tween, *289*
    Broca's area of, 544
    cells of, 258, 262
    control of respiration by, 928
    corticostriate connections in, 290
    cytoarchitectural maps of, 263
    electrical activity of, 525
    excitable, extent of, 277
    function of, 365
      localization of, 281
      motor, 273–287
      psychic, 255
    gyri of, and olfaction, 406
    histology of, physiological deductions
      from, 260
    laminar organization of, 256, 261
    language area in, *544*
    parietal lobe, ablation of, 362
      activity of, electrical, 360
      sensory function of, in man, *327,*
        365
      stimulation of, electrical, 360
      strychnine in, 360
    placing reactions, 198
      effect on, *199*
    prefrontal areas of, effects of damage to,
      540
      on hyperactivity, 535
    lobe, cytoarchitecture of, *285*
    projections from, motor, 269. See also
      *Corticospinal projections, Extra-
      pyramidal projections.*
      thalamic, 357
      parietal lobe, 356
    relation to learned responses, 532
    righting reflexes, 195
    sections through, *261*
    sensory functions, localization of, 359
    subdivisions of, *264*
    suppressor strips of, 279

Cerebral cortex, temporal lobe of, ablation of, 542
  and thalamus, as functional unit, 354. See also *Thalamus.*
  topographical organization of, significance of in vision, 517
  tracts of, 271
  visual area. See also *Visual fields.*
    ablation of, 521
    cytoarchitecture and subdivisions of, 515
    interconnections of, 522
    levels of function in, 523
    macular sparing lesions of, 518
    topographical organization of, 515
  dominance, 286
  hemispheres. See *Cerebrum.*
  nerve(s). See *Nerve(s).*
Cerebrum. See also *Cerebral cortex.*
  ablation of, regional, 264, 281
  areas of, 265, *266, 267, 268, 269*
    primordial, *265*
    projection, *265*
  autonomic functions of, 250
  basal ganglia and, 288–292
  cardiovascular regulation and, 251
  cerebellum and, interrelations between, 302
  cytoarchitecture of, 255, 256, *257.* See also *Cerebral cortex.*
  excitability of, 274
  gastro-intestinal functions and, 251
  hemispheres of, interaction between, 286
  medulla of, 258
    association system of, 258, *259*
    commissural system of, 260
    projection system of, 258, *259*
  organization of, structural, 266
  projection areas in, development of, 265
  stimulation of, 264
  surfaces of, *265*
Cervical sympathetic. See *Sympathetic nervous system.*
Chalone, inhibition of hunger contractions by, 997
Charles' law, 873
Chauveau's hemodromograph, 662, *663*
Cheilosis, in riboflavin deficiency, 1141
Chemoreceptors, 307, *921*
  functions of, 923
  impulses from, during artificial overventilation, *925*
  reflexes, 922. See also *Reflex(es).*
Chemotaxis, 562
  of leukocytes, 562
Chest, elasticity of, 865
Cheyne-Stokes' breathing, 916
Chloride, dietary, 1152
  intracellular, 941
  radioactive, distribution of, in body, 939
  space, 942

Chlorine, dietary, 1149
Cholesterol, plasma, 1122
Choline, 1122
  deficiency of, effect on liver, 1143
  lipotropic action of, 1128
Cholinesterase, 125, 133
  in autonomic stimulation, 234
  electrotonic current increase in nerve impulse by, 902
  function of, 125, 133
  in neuromuscular transmission, 125
Chorda saliva, 1031
  tympani nerve, to salivary glands, 1029
Chordotomy, clinical use of, 185
  effects of, 184–185
  in pain control, 349
  relief of visceral pain by, 400
  and sensibility, vibratory, 326, 349
  in torsion spasm, involuntary, 185
Choreo-athetosis, ablation of, regional, of cerebral cortex in, 185
  chordotomy in, 185
Chromatic series, in color vision, 489
Chromosomes, number of, 1232
  sex, 1233
Chronaxie, 23, *23*
Chylomicrons, 549
Chymase, 1055. See also *Rennin.*
Chyme, 1057
Chymosin, 1055. See also *Rennin.*
Chymotrypsin, 1062, 1067, 1113
Chymotrypsinogen, 1067
Ciliary body, 447
  muscle, 447
Circulation. See also *Blood circulation, Blood flow, Pulmonary circulation, Systemic circulation.*
  of brain, anastomoses in, 849
    regulation of, 852
  capillary, 607
  coronary, exercise and, 807
  of heart, 803. See also *Coronary circulation.*
  organs of, 606–854
  respiration effects on, 646
  through special organs, 828–854
  time, definition of, 666
    methods of determining, 666
    pulmonary, 666
  tissue pressure in, 645
Circus motion, auricular fibrillation and, 775
Citrate(s), as anticoagulants, 589
  solutions, anticoagulant, 558, 589
CLARKE, Robert W.: The kidney, 964–981
Climacteric, 1197
Clonic response, *154*
Clonus, genesis of, *154*
  mechanism of, 153–514
Closed plaster treatment of burns, frostbite and flesh wounds, 628
Clot retraction, 596

Clothing, and temperature regulation, 1170
Coagulation, blood. 586–605. See also *Blood, coagulation of.*
    interpretations of data on, 599
    theories of, 599
    of semen, 1227
Cobalt, dietary, 1149
Cochlea, 414, *414, 415*
    electrical activity of, 425, *426*
    mechanism of, 423
    spiral ganglion of, 434
    tonal localization in, 429
Co-enzymes, 1025
    I. See *Cozymase.*
    II, 64
Coferments, 1025
Colamine, 1122
Cold, physiologic responses to, 248
    sensations. See *Temperature sense.*
Colloid(s), fluidity of, 639
    foreign, in hemorrhage, use of, 602
    osmotic pressure, of plasma proteins, 937
    suprafluid, 640
Colon, absorption in, 1078
    bacterial action in, 1079
    digestion in, 1078
    innervation of, 1006, *1006*
    mass peristalsis in, 1005
    movements of, 1005
    nervous outflow to, *1006*
    putrefaction in, 1079
Color(s), blindness, 496
    genetics of, 1240
    tests of, 500
    complementary, in color vision, 491
    confusions, 498
    contrasts in color vision, 492
    mixture, 490, 494
    site of, 494
    primary, in color vision, 491
    receptors, specific, 495, *494, 495*
    saturation, in vision, 490
    triangle, 498
    vision, 489
        color zones of retina, 489, 507
        laws of, 490
        response in, dominator, 496
            modulator, 496
        theories of, 492
        zones of retina, 507
Complemental air, in lung, 867
Concentration of blood, units of, 566
Condiments in food, 1019
Conditioned eyeblinks, differences between unconditioned and, *536*
    reflexes. See *Conditioned responses, Delayed reaction, Delayed response.*
    response. See also *Delayed reaction, Delayed response.*
        establishment of, *530,* 531
        extinction of, experimental, 531

Conditioned response, inhibition of, 531
    limits of, 534
    neurophysiological basis of, 532
    neurosis and, experimental, 534
Conduction, all-or-nothing, 49
    auriculoventricular, of cardiac impulse, 726
    of cardiac impulse, 725
    disturbances of, in electrocardiogram, 765
    heart. See *Auriculoventricular conduction, Heart, conduction, Intraventricular conduction, Ventricular conduction.*
    in heat dissipation, 1167
    intra-auricular, of cardiac impulse, 725
    intraventricular, of cardiac impulse, 727
    membrane, 17–19
    in nerve fibers, immature and regenerating, 112
        individual. See *Nerve(s).*
    nerve-muscle reflex sequence in, 7, *8*
    of sound waves, routes of, 431
    velocity of cutaneous sensory impulses, 342
        in muscle, 33–34
        in nerve fibers, growing, 112
            regenerating, 112
        in neuron soma, 113
Conductor. See *Linear conductor; Volume conductor.*
Cones. See *Retina.*
Consciousness, forebrain and, 255
Consistency, in fluids, 640
Constriction, pupillary, 231
Contraction, all-or-nothing relation and, 53, *54*
    of auricle, 729
    energy liberated during, 83, 85, 88, 89, 90
    graded, 54
    heart. See *Cardiac impulse, Heart beat, Heart contraction, Systole.*
    hypertrophy and, relations between, 794
    isometric, 79
    myocardium, 792
    nerve-muscle reflex sequence in, 7, *8*
    oxygen lack and, 816
    spontaneous, in smooth muscle, 48
    summary of, 92
    "tone" of smooth muscle and, 49
    twitch, 34, *35*
    of ventricles, 731
Contracture, 39
Convergence, 126, 134
    functional consequences of, 126
    inhibitory, 167
    as mechanism of referred pain, 398
    principle of, definition, 126
    -projection theory, of referred pain, 398, 399
    synaptic, in retina, 478
        transmission, 126
Convolution, precentral. See *Precentral.*

Copper, dietary, 1149
Copulation, as ovulation stimulus, 1204
Core conductor theory, 17, 28
Cori cycle, 1110
Cornea, nutrition of, 457
Corneoretinal electrical potential, 477
Coronary circulation, 803
    anastomoses of, 804
    control of, autonomic hormones in, 808
        chemical, 808
        mechanical, 810
        nervous, 806
    denervation of heart and, 807
    regulation of, 806, 808, 810, *811*
    vagus in, 775
    occlusion, acute, anoxemia in, 816
    vessels, anastomoses between, 804
        anatomy of, 803
        drug effects on, 808, 809
        ischemia of, 809
        Thebesian vessels and, 805
Corpus callosum, 286
    cerebelli, 294
    luteum, development of, 1187
Cortex, of cerebellum, *295*
    cerebral. See *Cerebral cortex.*
    somatosensory, map of, *361*
    spinal, dissociation of control, 176
Cortico-autonomic representation, *252*
Corticopontine tracts, 271
Corticospinal projections, 269
Corticostriate connections, *290*
    projections, 270
Corticothalamic tracts, 271
Cough reflex, 929
COWGILL, GEORGE R.: Digestion and absorption in the intestines, 1061–1083
    Digestion and absorption in the stomach, 1042–1060
    General considerations upon the composition of food and the action of enzymes, 1014–1027
    General functions of the alimentary tract, 982–1013
    The salivary glands and their digestive action, 1028–1041
Cozymase, 68
    muscle, 64
Cranial circulation. See *Brain.*
    nerves. See also *Nerve(s).*
        III, 220, 221
        V, nuclei of origin of. See *Nerve(s).*
        VII, 220, 221
        IX, 220, 221
        X, 220, 221
Craniosacral division, of autonomic nervous system, 225. See also *Parasympathetic nervous system.*
Craniotabes, vitamin D deficiency in, 1147
Creatine phosphate, breakdown of, in nerve activity, 119

Creatinine, renal excretion of, 971
Crenation, of erythrocytes, 559
Cretinism, 1100
Crista acustica, 202, *203*
Cryptorchidism, 1225
Cupula, 202, 203, *203*, 207
Curare, action at neuromuscular junction, 122–125
Curarization, end-plate potential after, 122, *122, 123*
    spike potential after, 122, *122, 123*
Current of injury in anoxemia localized, 817, *817, 818*
    of heart, 817
Cushing, Harvey, in history of physiology, 3
Cutaneous sensibility. See *Sensibility.*
Cyanosis, 892
    in heart failure, 679
        congestive, 645
    in polycythemia, 645
Cybulski's photohematachometer, 663, *663*
Cystine, 1149
Cytoarchitecture, of brain, *257*
    of cerebral cortex, 255–269. See also *Cerebral cortex.*

DALTON, on color blindness, 496, 499
    in history of physiology, 4
Dalton's law, 874
Dark adaptation, course of, 468
    curve of, 469, *469*
    factors influencing rate of, 469. See also *Light adaptation.*
    metabolic factors in, 471
    significance of, 463
    visual purple and, 471
    vitamin A in, 470, 1146
        effect on locomotor activity of, 1160
Darrow-Yannet diagram, of osmotic equilibrium, *944*
Dead space, air, 869
    anatomical, 870
    physiological, 870
Deafness, central, 434
    measurement of. See *Audiometry.*
    middle ear, 433
    nerve, 434
    otosclerosis causing, 432
    perception, 434
    transmission of, 433
    types of, 433
Deaminase ?, 1026
Deamination, 1116
Decerebrate animal, static reactions in, local, 193
        segmental, 194
    rigidity, 187
        abolition of, 190
        anatomy of, 188
        "autogenous inhibition" in, 190
        cat in, *187*

Decerebrate rigidity, cerebral hemorrhage and, 188
  decerebrate animal in, 193
  and decorticate rigidity, comparison, *191*
  dorsal roots in, 189
  extroceptive stimulus in, 193
  forebrain centers in, 188
  history of, 187
  labyrinth in, 194
  lengthening reaction in, 190
  in man, 191
  muscle receptors in, 189, 190
  neck reflexes in, tonic, 194
  posture in, in animals, 191
  as "proprioceptive" reflex, 189
  proprioceptive stimulus in, 193
  pyramidal tract in, 188
  red nucleus in, 188
  "release" phenomenon of, 188
  "shortening reaction" in, 191
  stimulus in, 193
  stretch reflex in, 191
  vestibular nuclei in, 188, 190
  vestibulospinal projections in, 188, 190
Decibel, definition of, 420
Decompression sickness, 878
Decorticate rigidity, 187–200
  and decerebrate rigidity, comparison of, *191*
  in man, 191
Decortication, conditioned responses after, 532
Deep sensibility, classification of, 324
Defecation, 1007
  control of, muscular, 1007
    nervous, 1007
Deflation receptors, 904
Deglutition, 985
  muscles of, 985
  nervous mechanisms of, 985
Dehydrogenases, 1023
Delayed alternation, 539
  reaction, 538
  response, 538
    apparatus for eliciting, *539*
Delta waves, of encephalogram, 525
Demarkation potential, 9, 11
Dendrite, definition of, 96
Depressor afferents, in vasomotor center control, 701
Dermatomes, 224, 338
  as basis for lamination of spinal tracts, 349, 350
  boundaries of, in man in quadrupedal position, *340*
  cervical and upper thoracic, of monkey, *337*
  chart of lower extremity, *340*
  cortical representation of, 361
  demarcation of, herpes zoster in, 339

Dermatomes, dermacation of, methods for, 339
  distribution of, 339
  of man, *338*
  order of, in cortical representation, *362*
  postaxial, 340
  pre-axial, 340
  significance of, clinical, 341
Dermographism, 612
Desoxycorticosterone, effect of, on kidney function, 953, 978
Deuteranopia and deuteranomaly, 496
Deuterium, 1114
  measurements of body water with, 942, 954
Dextrocardiogram, 758
Diabetes insipidus, 245, 246. See also *Water metabolism.*
  dehydration in, 952
  renal function in, 978
  water depletion in, 959
  mellitus, glucose tolerance in, *1107*
    heart in, carbohydrate utilization by, 825
      lactic acid utilization by, 825
    respiration in, 918
  renal, glucose tolerance in, *1107*
  respiration in, 918
Dial, in hyperthermia, 248
Diapedesis, 563. See also *Leukocytes.*
Diaphragm, 860
  action of, in inspiration, 862
  contraction of, 861
  innervation of, 862
  position of, in respiration, *861*
  in swallowing, 986
Diastase, 1022, 1023
Diastasis, in cardiac cycle, 732
Diastole, coronary blood flow during, 812
  ventricular, 732
Diastolic pressure, 670
Dicoumarin, 591
Dicumarol, in lowering of prothrombin level, 591
Diet, accessory factors in, 1019
  deficient, taste as therapeutic guide in, 383
  food allowances in, National Research Council, recommendations, 1132
  inorganic components of, 1149
  margin of safety in, 1136
  planning of, 1134
  protein in, irreplaceability of, 1135
Diffusion. See specific topics as *Gases.*
  constant, of lungs, 882
Digestion, chemical changes of foodstuffs during, 1019
  in colon, 1078
  intestinal, 1061–1082
    pancreatic juice in, 1061
    succus entericus in, 1061
  mastication in, 983
  physiology of, 982–1082

Digestion of proteins, significance of, 1069
  saliva in, 1038
  in stomach, 1042–1058
Digitalis, cardiac putput and, 801
Di-iodotyrosine, thyroxin precursor, 1100
Dilatation, pupillary, 231
Diodrast, and renal Tm, 975
  renal excretion of, 975
  in study of kidney function, 964
Diopter, definition of, 450
Diphosphopyridine nucleotide. See *Cozymase*.
Diplopia, 505, *509*
Dipole hypothesis, in heart, 748
Discharge, nerve, frequency of, in relation
    to stimulation, *310*
  nonspecific, 309
  zone, *143*
    definition of, 128
    relation to subliminal fringe, 142
Discrimination, as cortical function, 363
  in thalamic syndrome, 368
Disease, periodic breathing in, 916
  resistance, factors in, 1237
Disinhibition, 532
Dissociation. See *Sensation*.
  curves, acid-base, 575, *575*
Distractibility, 539
Diuresis, in diabetes insipidus, 959
Divergence, 126, 134
  principle of, definition of, 126
  in spatial sensory functions, 331
  in sunaptic transmission, 126
D:N ratio, in amino acid utilization, 1117
Dominator response in color vision, 495
Donder's reduced eye, 443, *444*
Donnan membrane equilibrium, 570
Dorsolateral fasciculus. See *Tract of Lissauer*.
Douglas bag, 1090
Drinker respirator, in artificial respiration, 872
Drives, psychological, 1159
Drugs effect of, on cerebral blood vessels, 854
  on cardiac output, 801
  on coronary vessels, 808
  on electroencephalogram, 527
  on intra-uterine pressure, 840
  sympathomimetic, 233, 234
Duodenal bulb, stomach, and large intestine, *990*
Duplicity theory of vision, 463
Dye method, for blood volume, 552
Dysesthesia, 344. See also *Hyperpathia*.
Dysmenorrhea, 1189
  progesterone in, 1205
Dysmetria, 299
Dysphagia, 985
Dyspnea, 860
  and acidosis, 918
  and anoxemia, 927

Dyspnea, carbon dioxide pressure of arterial
    blood and, 917
  cerebral blood flow and, 920
  in heart failure, 679
  Hering-Breuer reflexes and, 905, 916, 927
  in thiamine deficiency , 1140
  venous pressure and, 930

EAGLE theory of blood coagulation, 600
Ear, anatomy of, 414
  basilar membrane of, 413, 424
  bones of, 409, *410*, 431
  cochlea, mapping of, 430, *430*
    microphonic response of, 425, 429
    place theory of, 424
    resonance theory of Helmholtz, 424
    tonal localization in, 428
  external, 409
  inner, *410*, 413, *414*, *415*
  middle, 409, *410*
    deafness, 433
    muscles of, 411
  muscles of, 411
  physiology of, 409
  round window of, 432
  sound transmission through, 411, 431, 433
Eclampsia, magnesium in, 824
Edema, 625
  body fluids in, 958
  capillary injury causing, 612
  conditions in which appearing, 961
  due to water and salt retention, 961
  fluids, protein content of, 938
  peripheral, in heart failure, 679
  prevention of, use of plaster in, 628
  pulmonary, in heart failure, 679
  in thiamine deficiency, 1140
Edinger-Westphal nucleus, 214, *214*
Edkin's theory, of gastric juice, hormonal, 1051
EEG. See *Electroencephalogram*.
Einthoven's triangle, 755, 762
Ejaculation, 1229
  mechanism of, 1227, 1229
Ejaculatory center, 1229
Electric current, conduction of, medium for, 14
    distribution in nerve, 17
      in volume conductors, 14
    flow of, and excitability, 19
    and interaction of nerve fibers, 114
    at neuromuscular junction, 121
    during spike potential, 11, 28
    at synapses, 131
Electrical determination of skin resistance,
    in demarcation of dermatomes, 339
  potential, of nerve, 9
    of pacemaker, 722
  stimulation, in location of vasoconstrictor
    center, 699

Electrocardiogram, acid-base equilibrium effect on, 824
  in anoxemia, general, 815
    localized, 816, 817
  in anoxia, 814
  auricular fibrillation in, 774
    acetylcholine precipitating, 775, *776*
    flutter in, 774
  axis of, electrical, 762, *764*
  cardiac cycle and, relations of, 747
  chest leads in, 754
  conduction disturbances in, 765
  conventions of, 741
  dextro-, 758
  ectopic beats in, 769
    bigeminus rhythm in, 725, 773
    localization of, 760, 769
    ventricular, 770
      escape, 771
  Einthoven's triangle, 755, 762
  history of, 740
  in hypercalcemia, *822*
  injury current in, 817, *817*, *818*
  interference theory in, 749
  intervals of, 741, *742*
  leads in, 741
    chest, 757
      standards for, 741
  levo-, 758
  membrane theory in 748
  myocardial infarction in, 816
  nomenclature of, 741, 744
  *p*H changes and, 824
  plasma lactic acid effect of, 825
    magnesium and, 824
  in potassium excess, 821, *821*
  potential differences in, limited, 752
  P-R interval in, 742
  representation in, geographical, 750
  standards in, normal, 741
  T waves, coronary, 818
  ventricular complex in, 747
    fibrillation in, 776
  waves of, 742
Electroencephalogram, *526*
  factors influencing, 526
  Fourier's analysis of, 525
  in various conditions, *527*
  wave forms of, 526
Electrolyte(s), balance, in shock, 694
  clinical importance of intracellular, 941
  content, of striated muscle, 941
  differential restraint of, 935
  extracellular, osmotic equilibrium following changes *in*, *944*
  pattern, serum, comparison of, with gastro-intestinal fluids, *948*
    in normal human serum, *945*
  serum, normal and abnormal, *956*
  renal excretion of, 973
  tissue, distribution of, in body, 939
  transfers of, 944

Electrolyte(s), *of* urine, 951
  volume of, in relation to extracellular fluid, *943*
Electromotive force, electrical potential and, 10
Electrophoresis, in plasma protein analysis. See *Proteins, plasma.*
Electroretinogram (ERG), 477
Electrotonic current, increase of, in nerve impulse, by cholinesterase, 902
  theory of nerve cell discharge, 902
Electrotonus, 17
  in muscle, compared with end-plate potential, 122–123
ELKINTON, J. Russell: Physiology of body fluids, 935–963
Embryo, hormone action on, 1201
  sexual differentiation in, 1220
Emission, 1229
Emmetropia, 451, *452*
Emmetropic eye, 450
Emotional expression, 249
Emotions, effect on blood pressure, 675
  of temporal lobectomy on, 542
  in relation to prefrontal lobe, 541
Encephalitis lethargica, 1162
Encephalization, 180
End-arteries, of brain, 850
  of heart, 804
Endocrine(s), androgens and, interrelationships of, 1215
  control, of menstrual cycle, 1189
    of parturition, 1201
    of renal fluid exchanges, 952
  function, of gonads, 1185
    of placenta, 1200
  innervation of, 245. See also *Hormones;* specific endocrine organs.
  in metabolism, 1100, 1147
    and resistance to disease, 1237
Endo-enzymes, 1022
Endolymph of semicircular canals, 202, 207, 209
Endometrium, during menstrual cycle, *1188*
  histology of, in menstruation, 1188
End-organs, recruitment of, 311
  types of, 322
Endothelium, hemato-encephalic barrier and, 851
End-plate delay, 121. See also *Neuromuscular delay.*
  potential, 121
    after curarization, 122, *122*, *123*, *124*
    relation to electrotonus, 122–123
      to propagated impulse, 123–124
    summation of, 125
Energy, conservation of, physiological, 1094
  consumption, during relaxation, 81
  exchange, of organs and tissues, 1102
    regulation of, 1156–1181
    thyroid gland and, 1100
  of flowing fluid, 632

Energy of fluid, 632
  in food, 1016
  liberation of, in muscle, 78
      contraction, 83, 85
      during shortening, 88
  phosphate bond, 60
      oxidation and, 74
  relaxation and, 81
  reserves, nature of, 1175
  storage of, 1086
      regulation of, 1175
  transformations of, 1084
      in muscle, 56–95
  yielding systems, of muscle, 78
Enophthalmos, 231
Enterogastric reflex, 999
Enterokinase, 1062, 1066, 1072
Environment, and heredity, 1236
  internal, 936
Enzymes, action of, 1019–1027
      incompleteness of, 1024
      temperature for, 1024
  activators of, 1024
  active and inactive, 1024
  amylolytic, 1062
  autolytic, 1025
  as catalysts, 1020
  classification of, 1022
  coagulating, 1023
  composition of, chemical, 1026
  deaminizing, 1023
  definition of, 1022, 1102
  dehydrogenating, 1023
  digestive, 1019
      specific, 1022. See also specific names of,
          as Lipase, Pepsin.
  effect of temperature on, 1165
  fat-splitting, 1023
  gastric, 1045
  glycolytic ?, 1025
  history of, 1019
  hyaluronidase, 1226
  kinases of, 1024
  lipolytic, 1023, 1062
  list of, partial, 1025
  and metallic ions, 1152
  muscle, 72
  oxidizing, 1023
  precipitation and adsorption of, 1024
  proferment of, 1024
  properties of, general, 1024
  proteolytic, 1023
      action of, 1062, 1066
      in blood coagulation, 594
      substrates for, 1113
  reactions of, reversibility of, 1103
      reversible, 1020
  solubility of, 1024
  specificity of, 1021
  substrate of, 1022
  trace elements, in action of, 1152

Enzymes, yellow, and riboflavin, 1141
  zymogen of, 1024
Eosinophilia, 563
Eosinophils. See Leukocytes.
Ephedrine, in spinal shock, 181
Epicritic sensibility. See Sensibility.
Epilepsy, effect of, on electroencephalogram,
      527
  electroencephalographic patterns in, 528
Epileptic discharge, focal, localization of,
      529
Epinephrine, in blood flow, 829
  effect of, on arteriole tone, 694
      on intestinal movements, 1004
  and glycogen breakdown, 1177
  and kidney blood flow, 833
Epithelium, vaginal, smears of, 1186, 1206
Equilibrium. See specific types, as Acid-base
          equilibrium; Membrane equilibrium, etc.
  osmotic, Darrow-Yannet diagram of, 944
Erection, mechanism of, 1227
Erepsin, 1025, 1055, 1057, 1062, 1067, 1072,
      1077
Ergosterol, as source of vitamin D, 1146
Erythroblastosis foetalis, due to Rh factor,
      561
Erythrocytes, 554. See also Blood cells.
  antigens of, 560
  crenation of, 559
  destruction of, abnormal, 558
      normal, 557
  as elements of blood, 549
  formation of, 555
  fragility test of, 559
  iron requirement for, 556
  isohydric cycle in, 887
  life history of, 555
  maturation of, 557
  morphology, 553
  oxygen carrying function of, 555
  respiratory gases, transport by, 887
  spherocytosis of, 559
Erythroplastids, 564
Erythropoiesis. See Erythrocytes, maturation
      of.
"Escape" mechanism, vagus in, 771
Eserine, 126
  action of, on nervous tissue, 133
  in autonomic stimulation, 234
  and blood flow in skin, 832
  cholesterase inhibitant, in neuromuscular
      transmission, 126
  in vagal stimulation, 234
Esophagus, innervation of, autonomic, 227
Esophoria, 505
Esotropia, 506
Esthesiometer, 329
Estradiol, 1186, 1186
Estriol, 1186, 1186
Estrogens, 1186, 1186
  clinical uses of, 1198

Estrogens, effect of, on lactation, 1210
excretion of, 1191
inactivation of, 1206
in male, 1215
in prostatic carcinoma, 1218
Estrone, 1186, *1186*
Estrous cycles, 1184, 1197
Estrus, definition of, 1185
effect on locomotor activity of, 1160, *1160*
and menstrual cycles, comparison of, 1192, *1192*
Euglobulins. See *Globulins.*
Eupnea, 860
character of respiratory motor discharge in, 898, 909
chemoreceptors in control of, 925
expiration in, 900
expiratory center in, stimulation of, 911
reflexes in, chemoreceptor, 923
Hering-Breuer, 903
respiratory, 903
respiratory center in, regulation of, chemical, 920
Eustachian tube, 412
Ewald's laws, 209
Excitability, alpha, 24–25
of basal ganglia, 289
of cerebrum. See *Cerebrum.*
changes, at anode, 25–26
at cathode, 19–22
decrease in, 22. See also *Postcathodal depression; Accommodation; Excitation.*
extinction in, 274, *276*
facilitation in, 276, *276*
gamma, 24
of heart, 721
H-ion concentration and, 274
inhibition in, 276
of nerve cells, respiration and, 901
resting, 22
Excitable cortex, extent of. See *Cerebral cortex.*
Excitation. See also *Excitability.*
electrical, 19–26
inhibition and, 167
nerve-muscle reflex sequence in, 7, *8*
prolonged, in central nervous system, 143
time, 23, *23*
Excitatory state, "central," 143
local, 21
and synaptic stimulation, 138
synaptic connections, of respiratory center, 898
Excretion, renal, of typical solutes, 971
Exemia, 619
Exercise, carbon dioxide pressure in, 930
coronary circulation and, 807
effect on blood pressure, 675
energy requirements of, *70, 71*
Harvard step test in, 783
heart rate and, relation between, 782

Exercise, muscular, effect upon metabolism, total, 1099
respiration stimulation in, 930
velocity of blood flow in, 645
Exo-enzymes, 1022
Exophoria, 505
Exophthalmos, 231
Exotropia, 506
Experimental method, in physiology, 1
Expiration. See also *Respiration.*
inhibition of, and lung deflation, 904
muscles of, 863
respiratory pause following, 860
types of, 859
Expired air, composition of, 877
Expiratory center. See also *Respiratory center.*
reciprocal connections of, with respiratory center, 898
stimulation of, effects of, 898
in eupnea, 911
subdivision of respiratory center, 896, 897. See also *Respiratory center.*
Extension reflex, stimulus response to, 187
Extensor thrust, 160
Exteroceptive stimulus, in decerebrate rigidity, 193
Exteroceptors, 307
Extinction, in excitability, 274. See also *Excitability.*
Extrapyramidal projections, 270
Extrasystoles, auricular, 769
premature, 726
in pacemaker localization, 719
ventricular, 770
adrenaline in, 790
premature, 726
Extrinsic potential, 26–27, *27.* See also *Potential.*
Eye. See also *Retina.*
accommodation of, 446, *446*
age changes in, 448, *449*
amplitude of, 450
in hyperopia, 453
limits of, 448
near and far point, 448
anatomy of, 448
axes of rotation of, 503
emmetropic, 450
fields, frontal, 277, 284
fundus of, ophthalmoscopic examination of, 459
horizontal section of, *447*
innervation of, autonomic, smooth muscle in, 231
as instrument, optical, 440–462
intra-ocular pressure of, 457
iris of, 455
and pupil, reflex of, to light, 456, *456*
lens of, 448
movements of, 503

Eye, movements of, Listing's law of, 505
  muscles, actions of individual, *504*
  nutrition of, 457, 459
  optical defects, astigmia, 453–455
    emmetropia, 451
    hyperopia, 453
    myopia (near-sightedness), 451
    of normal eye, 450
    presbyopia, 449, 453
  pupil of, 455
  reduced eye of Listing-Donders, 443, *444*
  refraction of, abnormalities in, 451
    index of, 443
  refractive surfaces of, 443, *443*
    power of, role of cornea and lens in, 450
  retinal image, as factor in space perception, 444
    formation of, 443
  visual fields of, 506
Eyeball, rotation center of, 503
Eyeblinks, conditioned and unconditioned, *536*

FACIAL nerves. See *Nerve(s)*.
Facilitation ,126 ,*127* ,128. See also *Discharge zone; Subliminal fringe*.
  definition of, 26, 128
  detonator action in, definition of, 130
  in excitability, 276. See also *Excitability*.
  neuromuscular, end-plate potentials and, 125
  periods of, 130
  spatial summation in, definition of, 130
  supernormal period and, 130
  in sympathetic ganglia, 128, 130
  temporal summation in, definition of, 130
  Wedensky, 26, 140
Fainting, 603
  hemodynamics of, 646
Fat. See also *Enzymes, lipolytic; Lipid*.
  absorption of, in intestine, 1075
    in stomach, 1058
  conversion to, of amino acids, 1118
    of carbohydrate, 1128
  enzyme acting on, 1025
  in food, 1016
  as foodstuff, 1014
  heart utilization by, 826
  subcutaneous, effect of androgens on, 1219
Fatigue, of sense organs, 312
Fatty acids, beta-oxidation of, 1124
    -condensation of, 1125
    essential, 1138
    ketones from, 1125
    oxidation of, 1123
    multiple alternate, 1125
    plasma, 1122
Feces, composition of, 1081
Feeling tone, 306
Female reproduction, 1184–1210

FERGUSON, JOHN H.: Coagulation of blood: transfusion problems in hemorrhage and shock, 586–605
  General properties of blood: the formed elements, 548-565
Ferguson theory of blood coagulation, 600
Fermentation, in muscle, 62
Ferroheme. See *Heme*.
Ferrohemoglobin, 581
Ferry-Porter law, 465
Fertilization, spermatozoa and, 1226
Fetus, hormone action on, 1201
Fever, cardiac output in, 801
  dehydration, 1175
  and food intake, 1157
  heart rate in, 784
  hypothalamus in, 1174
  respiration in, rate and depth of, 909, 920
  and total metabolism, 1101
Fiber, muscle, 57
  "spectrum," of nerves, 341
Fibril, muscle, 57
Fibrillation, auricular, 774
    circus motion in, 775
    clinical conditions showing, 774
    in electrocardiogram, 774
    vagus stimulation in, 774
  ventricular, 776
    in electrocardiogram, 776
    in hypercalcemia, 821
    initiation of, 778
Fibrin, blood, 586. See also *Blood*.
  films, 592
  foams, 584, 592
  gel, 586
Fibrinogen, 589
  blood, 586. See also *Blood*.
  physiological significance of, 590
Fibrinolysin, in coagulation of blood, 594
Fibrinolysis, 595
Fick principle, in cardiac output estimation, 795
  in measurement of renal blood flow, 976
Figure writing, 332
Flaccid paralysis, 273
  from cerebral cortex injury, 281
Flack test, in respiration, 866
Flavoproteins, muscle, 72
Flexor reflex, 156. See also *Reflex(es), flexor*.
  motoneuron discharges of, 161
  tendon jerk, 160
Flicker fusion frequency, 465
Flocculonodular lobe, of cerebellum, 294
Flourens' law, 209
Flow of blood, 640, 657
    formulas for, 657
    fluid, heart murmurs and, 738
    liquid, principles of, 630
    measurement of, 634
    plastic, 640
    formulas for, 640, 657

Flow, resistance to, 635
 of suspensions, 640
 types of, 631
 velocity of, in tubes, 632
 viscous, velocity of fluid in, *632*
  pressure during, *635*
  resistances for, *639*
Flowmeter. See also *Stromuhr.*
 electromagnetic, 663
Fluids. See also *Flow, Turbulence, Resistance.*
 body, 933–962. See also *Body fluids.*
 colloidal, 639
 elastic, 640
 energy of, 632
 exchanges between plasma and interstitial
  fluid, 937
  in gastro-intestinal tract, 948
  in kidney, 950
   endocrine control of, 952
  through lungs and skin, 947
  Starling theory of, 569
 extracellular, 935
  clinical abnormalities in, 957
  fluid, exchanges between cells, 939
  identity of, 939
  volume of, 939
   absolute, 942
   in relation to electrolytes, *943*
 flowing, énergy of, 632
 interstitial, 936
 intracellular, clinical abnormalities in,
  957
  composition of, 935
  volume of, 942
 loss, gastro-intestinal, 960
 pressure, 873. See also *pressure.*
 properties of, 873
 types of, 631
 velocity, in viscous flow, *632*
Fluidity. See also structures having, as *Blood,
 Colloid(s), Plasma*, etc.
 apparent, 643
 coefficient of, 637
Fluorides, as anticoagulants, 589. See also
 Anticoagulants.
Flutter, auricular, 774
 in electrocardiogram, 774
Follicle stimulating hormone (FSH), 1194,
 1224, 1225
Food(s). See also *Caloric, Calorie(s).*
 caloric values of average servings, 1134
 composition of, 1014–1019
 desire for, 1156
 effect upon metabolism, total, 1098
 as energy source, 1084, 1130
 flavors in, 1019
 and foodstuffs, general considerations of,
  1014
 intake, in obesity, 1180
  objective study of, 1157
  regulation of, 1156

Food(s), representative, composition and
 nutritive value of, 1016–1017
 requirements of, 1130
 stratification of, in stomach, 993
Foodstuffs, accessory factors in, 1019
 calories of, 1085
 chemical changes in, during digestion, 1019
 classification of, 1014
 heat of combustion, 1085
 interchangeable, 1135
 storage of, in body, 1086
Forebrain centers, decerebrate rigidity and,
 188
Formula, Bingham's, for plastic flow, 640, 657
 Nutting's, for plastic flow, 640, 657
Fox's chart, in sensory examination, *327*
Fragility, capillary, ascorbic acid and, 1144
 erythrocyte, test for, 559
 test, osmotic, 559
Friedman test, for pregnancy, 1199
Frontal eye field, subdivisions of, *277*
 lobes, and motor output, 1162. See also
  Cerebral cortex.
Frostbite, closed plaster treatment of, 628
FSH, 1194
FULTON, John F.: Autonomic nervous sys-
  tem: central division, 241–254
  Cerebral cortex: cytoarchitecture and
   projections, 255–272
  Cerebral cortex: motor functions, 273–
   287
  Cerebrum and basal ganglia, 288–293
  Cerebrum and cerebellum, 294–304
  Decerebrate and decorticate rigidity: the
   postural reflexes, 187–201
  Historical backgrounds of American
   physiology, 1–6
  The human spinal cord: spinal injuries,
   178–186
  Labyrinthine acceleratory reflexes: the
   medulla oblongata and cranial nerves,
   202–217
Fundus of eye, ophthalmoscopic examination of, 459
 of stomach, 989
Fusion rate, critical. See *Muscle.*

GALACTIN, 1209
Galvani's "contraction without metals," 114
 nerve cells, interaction between, experiment on, 114
Ganglion(a), activity, potential signs of, 128
 autonomic, synaptic transmission in, neuromuscular transmission and, 126
 cardiac, 226
 celiac, 222
 cervical, inferior, 222
  middle, 222
  superior, 222
 ciliary, 213, 231

Ganglion(s), collateral, 222
　facilitation in. See *Facilitation.*
　Gasserian, 215, 352
　geniculate, 216
　　stimulation of, atropine in, *853*
　lumbar, 222
　mesenteric, superior, 222
　occlusion in. See *Occlusion.*
　peripheral, 222
　prevertebral, 222
　semilunar, 352
　sphenopalatine, 226
　spiral, 434
　　of cochlea, 434
　stellate, 222
　　effect on heart rate, 789
　superior cervical, action potential of, 128
　sympathetic, recovery curve of, *129*
　synaptic transmission in, 126
　　transmitter of, 131
　terminal, 222
　Vidian, 245
GARDNER, William U.: Reproduction in the
　female, 1184–1212
Gas(es), in blood, chemical analysis of, 875
　determination of dissolved, 875
　diffusion of, 873
　　through body, 882
　exchange of, factors governing, in lungs,
　　879
　　in lungs, 879
　　and partial pressure, 878
　　in respiration, 858
　　in tissues, 886
　　and transportation of, 877–894
　laws, 873
　partial pressure of, 874
　　in liquids, 874
　properties of, 873
　solubility of, 874
Gasserian ganglion, 352
Gastric cycle, *992*
　digestion, regurgitation into stomach dur-
　　ing, 1046
　glands, 1042, *1043*
　　cells of, 1042
　　during secretion, histological changes in,
　　　1042
　　nerves of, secretory, 1049
　　secretion of, appetite, 1051
　　　chemical, 1051
　　　nervous, 1051
　　　psychic, 1051
　hydrochloric acid, membrane hydrolysis
　　in formation of, 1049
　juice, acid of, 1046
　　in anemia, treatment of, 1045
　　artificial, 1054
　　hydrochloric acid in, origin of, 1047
　　intrinsic factor of, 1045
　　*p*H of, 1047
　　secretion of, hormonal, 1051

Gastric juice, secretion of, mechanism, 1050
　mucin, 1045
　secretagogues, 1050
　secretion, composition of, 1043
　　methods of obtaining, 1043
　　phases of, cephalic, 1051
　　　gastric, 1052
　　　intestinal, 1052
　　quantity and digestive power of, varia-
　　　tion in, *1052*
Gastrin, 834, 1051
Gastrocolic reflex, 1006
Gastro-intestinal diseases, heart rate in, 784
　tract. See also *Alimentary tract.*
　　and cerebrum, 251
　　fluid exchanges in, 948
Genes, nucleoproteins of, significance of,
　1115
Genetic. See also *Heredity.*
　factors, and physiological functions, 1235
Genetics, of intersexuality, 1234
　practical applicatoins of, 1245
　of sex determination, 1233
Geniculate body, lateral, 512
　　section through, *514*
Geniculostriate bundle, 514
Genital organs, functions of, 1226
　innervation of, *1229*
Gennari, line of, 515
Gibbs-Donnan effect, 937
　equilibrium. See *Donnan.*
Glands, adrenal, preganglionic fiber to, 222
　endocrine. See *Endocrines.*
　gastric, 1042. See also *Gastric.*
　parathyroid, effects of, 1147
　pyloric, of stomach, 1042. See also *Pyloric.*
　thyroid gland, effects of, 1100
　salivary, 1028–1040. See also *Salivary.*
Globin, 582
Globulin(s), preparations, in measles, treat-
　ment, 584
　serum, 583
Globulin-X, muscle, 59
Glomerular filtrate, amino acids in, 973
　filtration, measurement of, 970
　　specifications for, 969
　　rate of, 970
　function, 968
　　dynamics of, 977
Glomus(i), aortic and carotid, morphology
　of, 921
Glossopharyngeal nerves. See *Nerve(s).*
Glottis, in cough and sneeze, 929
Glycogenesis, 1108. See also *Glycogen, Gly-
　colysis.*
Glyconeogenesis, 1109
　in amino acid utilization, 1117
Glucose, of blood, 1104
　excretion, and phlorhizin, 1116
　heart utilization of, 826
　origin of, noncarbohydrate, 1109
　renal excretion of, 971

Glucose and renal Tm, 971
tolerance, 1107, *1107*
tubular reabsorption or rejection of, *971*
of urine, 951
of phlorhizinized dog, *1117*
Glutamine, in ammonium salts synthesis, 973
Glutathione, and body size, 1239
Glycogen breakdown, 1108, 1177
as carbohydrate reserve, 1176
enzymolysis of, 64, *66*
heart utilization of, 826
of liver, 1107
storage of, 1107
muscle, 59
storage, 1176
synthesis of, 1108
in vagina, 1206
Glycogenase, 1025
Glycogenolysis, 1108
Glycolysis, 62. See also *Glucogenesis, Glycogen.*
aerobic, 1109
anaerobic, 1109
summary of, 69
Glycosuria, alimentary, 1075
Gnosis, 337
Goiter,
colloid, 1100
exophthalmic, 1100
in iodine deficiency, 1152
Golgi-Mazzoni corpuscles, 322
silver technique, for retina, 475
tendon organ, 323
Gonadotrophins, 1194, 1224, 1225
composition of, 1196
in pregnancy urine, 1196
Grafts, ovarian, 1184
Grasp reflex, 197
Gravity, effect on blood pressure, arterial, 676
GRENELL, ROBERT GORDON: Autonomic nervous system: peripheral division, 218–240
Growth, effect of, on food intake, 1157
and metabolism, basal, 1096
and minerals of diet, 1152
as protein storage, 1178
Grüneberg's, lethal mutation of rats, 1242, *1243*
Guanase, 1026
Gustation. See *Taste.*
Gyrus(i), arterior transverse temporal (Heschl), 436
in olfaction, 406
postcentral, ablation of, threshold discrimination curves in, *363*
of temporal lobe, 542

HABITUATION, 532
Hair distribution secondary sex characteristic, *1218*

Hair, androgen action on growth of, 1218
Haldane system, for indirect calorimetry, *1091*
Hales, measurement of arterial blood pressure by, 667
HAMILTON, William F.: Circulation through special regions, 828–857
The pulse, 682–691
Regulation of arterial pressure, 710–716
Harvard step test in exercise, 783
Head's protopathic-epicritic hypothesis, tabular summary of, 336
Headache, vascular innervation and, 850
Hearing. See also *Ear, Sound, Cerebral cortex, auditory area of.*
conduction of sound waves in, 431
frequency theory of, 431
loudness or intensity, audibility curve and audiometry, 418
decibel in, 420
frequency of nerve impulses as basis of, 427
physical basis of, 417
threshold for, 418
pitch, cochlear mechanism of, 424, 428
place or resonance theory of, 424, 428
physical correlate of, 417
place theory of, 424
testing of, 419
Heart. See also *Auricle, Cardiac muscle, Myocardium, Ventricle,* etc.
beat, 812. See also *Cardiac impulse, Heart contraction.*
apex, in systole, ventricular, 732
origin of, 717
theories of, 720
vagus weakening of, 786
block, potassium poisoning in, 821
carbohydrate metabolism, 825
circulation of, 803. See also *Coronary circulation.*
conduction, in anoxemia, 816
auriculoventricular, 726
pathways of, accessory, 727
disturbances in, in anoxemia, 816
intraventricular, 727, *728*
vagus effect on, 786
contractility of, in anoxemia, localized, 816
contraction, 812. See also *Cardiac impulse, Heart beat. Systole.*
cardiac reserve and, 794
heart failure and, 794
sequence of, 717
cycle of. See *Cardiac cycle.*
denervated, coronary circulation in, 807
in diabetes, carbohydrate utilization by. 825
disease, fibrillation, auricular, in, 774
heart rate in, 784, *785*
periodic breathing in, 916
vital capacity of lung in, 868
ectopic beats in. See *Electrocardiogram.*

Heart, effects of anoxemia, general, 814
  efficiency of, factors in, 813, *813*
  electrical discharge in, rhythmic, 721
      metabolic factors in, 724
  "end-arteries" of, 804
  excitability of, 721
  failure, cardiac output in, 801
    congestive, cyanosis in, 645
      progressive, anoxemia in, 816
      vascular effects of, 679
    vital capacity in, 679
  hypertrophy of, 794
  hypoxia of, effects of, 814, *814*
  injury current of. See *Injury current.*
  innervation of, autonomic, 226
  inorganic ions and, 819
  irritability of, 720
  magnesium and, *823*
  mammalian, acetylcholine in, *233*
  metabolism. See also *Metabolism.*
    oxygen in, 812
  murmur(s), Austin Flint, 740
    clinical conditions associated with, 738
    diastolic, 738, *739*
    fluid flow and turbulence in, 738
    in stenosis, of valves, 738
  muscle. See *Myocardium.*
  nerve supply of, 51
  nutrition of, 803–827
  output of. See *Cardiac output.*
  pacemaker of. See *Pacemaker.*
  plasma calcium and, *822*
    magnesium and, *823*
    potassium and, *820*
• "prepotential" of, 724
  rate, in anoxemia, general, 814
    in basal condition, 781
    body size and, relation between, 782
    cardiac output and, 790
    carotid sinus and, 787
    in clinical affections, 784
    control of, parasympathetic, 785
      sympathetic, 789
    coronary blood flow and, 811
    effect on cardiac output, 790
    exercise and, relation between, 782
    increase in, factors in, 782
    Marey's law and, 787
    pacemaker metabolic rate and, 785, *786*
    physical fitness and, 783
    regulation of, 781
      reflex, 787
    in sleep, 782
    standards of, normal, 781
    vagus inhibition of, 785, *788*
  recovery periods in, 723, 725. See also
      Heart, refractory period.
      supernormal, 723, 724
  reflexes from receptors in, 929
  refractory period of, 721, *722.* See also
      Heart, recovery period.

Heart, reserve, cardiac output, 794
  rhythm, bigeminus, 725
  role in circulation, 645
  sinus arrhythmia, vagus and, 788
  sound(s), 732, *733*
    abnormalities of, 736, *736, 737*
    auricular, *733,* 735, *736*
    first, 732, *733*
    gallop rhythms, 738
    murmurs, 738, *739*
    opening snap, of mitral valves, *737,*
      738
    second, 732, *733,* 734, *734*
    splitting of, 736, *736, 737*
    systole and, relation of, 733
    third, 732, *733,* 735
  Starling's law of, 792
  stroke volume, regulation of, 792
  supernormal period in, 724, 773
  surface, excitation of, 727, *728*
  vagal tone of, 787
  venous damage in, 806
  volume conductor, 14
Heat conservation mechanisms, 248
  cramps, water intoxication in, 961
  loss, 1167
    mechanisms, 247
    physiological mechanisms of, 1168
    processes contributing to, 1167
    rate of, 1170
      regulation of, 1163, 1167
  metabolic, 1084
  muscle. See *Muscle, heat.*
  perception, 305
  production and heat loss, changes in, *1167*
    mechanisms, 248
    resting, in nerve. See *Nerve(s).*
  rate of production of, 1166
  regulation, 246
    hypothalamus in, 242
Heating, respiratory responses during, *1173*
  transverse section of brain during, *1173*
Heidenhain's isolated fundic sac, 1044
Helmholtz, inventor of ophthalmoscope, 459
  resonance theory of hearing, 424
  theory of color vision, 492
Hematocrit, 551
  normal values, 552, 585
  value, specific gravity and, 585
Hemato-encephalic barrier, 850
  concept of affinity and lack of affinity, 851
  endothelial barrier, 851
Hematopoiesis, 555
Heme, 582
Hemeralopia, 470
Hemianopsia, 307
  macular sparing in, 513, 518
Hemidecortication, sensory disturbances
  from, 367
Hemiparesis. See *Hemiplegia.*
Hemiplegia, 368

Hemoconcentration, in adrenal cortical insufficiency, 958
following tissue injury, 619
Hemoconia, 549
Hemocytometry, 553
Hemodromograph, Chauveau's, 662, *663*
Hemodynamics, 630–659
Bernoulli's principle in, 650–651
of blood vessels. See also specific groups, as *Aorta, Arterioles, Veins,* etc.
Hemoglobin, acid properties of, 885
acid-base titration curves of, *886*
carbon dioxide and, combination, 885
monoxide, 562, 581
combination with, 889
chemical alteration of, 561
colorimetric determination of, 582
concentration, normal, in blood, 585
specific gravity and, 585
formation, iron in relation to, 556
muscle, 71
oxygen and, combination with, 882
content of, 883
dissociation curve of, 883
*p*H of, 582
properties of, 581
types of, 581
Hemolysis, 558
osmotic, 558
serological, 560
toxic, 560
Hemophilia, bleeding tendency in, 587
blood composition in, 594
platelets in, 565
Hemorrhage, 601
events in, course of, 601
management of, 601
transfusion problems in, 601–604
Hemorrhagic diathesis. See *Bleeding tendency.*
disease, of newborn, 1148
Hemostatic preparations, thrombin in, 592
Henderson equation, for acid-base equilibrium, 946
Henderson-Hasselbach equation, of mass action, 574
Henle, loop of, 964
Heparin, as anticoagulant, 589
in blood coagulation, 598
clinical uses of, 598
platelets, preservation, 565
Heredity. See also *Genetic.*
of allergy, 1245
and body size, 1238
and cancer, 1238
and criminality, 1242
developmental correlations in, 1242
and environment, 1236
interrelated factors of, 1235
of morphological defects, 1242
nucleoproteins of genes in, 1115
and resistance to disease, 1236

Heredity, Rh factor in, 1246
of sensory reactions, 1240
and temperament, 1241
Hering experiment, on nerve cells, interaction between, 114
Hering-Breuer reflexes. See *Reflexes, Hering-Breuer.*
Hering's diagram, of eye muscle, action, 504
theory of color vision, 493
Herpes-zoster, in demarcation of dermatomes, 339
Heschl's gyrus, of temporal lobe, 542
Heterophoria, 505
Hindrance, in blood flow, 658
Hippocampal gyrus, of temporal lobe, 542
Hirschsprung's disease, denervation in, 1007
Histamine, action of, on arterioles, 709
and blood flow, 830
Histidine, in globin. See *Globin.*
Histology, of muscles, 190
HITCHCOCK, David I.: Chemical aspects of the physiology of blood, 566–585
HOFF, Hebbel E.: Cardiac output: regulation and estimation, 781–802
Events of the cardiac cycle, 717–780
The nutrition of the heart, 803–827
Holmgren test of color blindness, 500
Homeostasis, theory of, 229
Homothermic animals, 1163
HOOKER, Charles W.: Reproduction in the male, 1213–1231
Hopping reaction(s), 200
cortical localization of, 363
functional localization of, 200
as test of somatic sensation, 324
Hormonal control, of visceral bloodflow, 834
Hormone(s), autonomic, in coronary circulation control, 808
control, of myometrium contractions, 1205
of renal activity by, 978
effects of, on arterioles, 708
on blood flow, 828
excretion of, during pregnancy, 1199, *1199*
follicle stimulating (FSH), 1194
gonadotrophic, 1224, 1225
interstitial cell stimulating (ICSH), 1194
lactogenic, 1209
luteinizing (LH), 1194
maternal, action of, on embryo and fetus, 1201
ovarian, 1186
ovulation stimulating, 1205
parathyroid, 1147
production of, during menstrual cycle, 1191
sex. See also *Sex hormones.*
inactivation of, 1206
sympathetic. See *Sympathin.*
thyroid, 1100
Horner's syndrome, 231

Horripilation, in temperature regulation, 1170
Howell theory of blood coagulation, 599
HOWELL, William, in history of physiology, 1
H-substance, 611
Hunger, 1156
  center, 997
  contractions, factors affecting, 996
    of human stomach, recording of, *387*
    inhibition of, 997
    and sensations of, *388*
    of stomach, 994, *994*
  factors in, 389
  hypoglycemia in, 1156
  inhibiting agents in, 997
  pain, 1156
  as physiological state, 388
  as sensation, 386
  sense, nervous mechanism of, *998*
Hurthle's manometer, *670*
Hyaluronidase, 1226
Hydrochloric acid, gastric, 1045
    carbonic anhydrase theory of formation of, 1048
    origin of, 1047
Hydrogen, dietary, 1149
  ion concentration. See *pH*.
  isotopes of, 1114
Hydrolysis, 1023
Hydrostatic pressure in tissues, 937. See also *Pressure*.
Hydrothorax, in heart failure, 679
Hypalgesia, extramedullary tumors, as cause of, 349
Hyperactivity, 535
  benzedrine in, 536
  following ablation of frontal areas, 1162
  prefrontal lesions causing, 535, *537*
  records of, *537*
Hyperalgesia, 307. See also *Hyperpathia*.
Hypercalcemia, blood coagulation in, 593
Hypercapnea. See *Carbon dioxide*.
Hypercarpia. See *Carbon dioxide*.
Hyperemia, blood flow in, 829
  H-substance in, 611
  renal, experimental, 978
Hyperesthesia of skin surface, in demarcation of dermatomes, 339
Hyperglycemia, 1075, 1105
Hypermetria, 299
Hypermetrophia, 451, *452*, 453
Hyperopia, 451, *452*, 453
  eye accommodation in, 453
Hyperpathia, in clinical conditions, 344
  due to irritation, 345
  inhibition of, due to novocaine, 3
  of modality dissociation, 345
  nerve fiber size and, 345
  and protopathic sensibility, 336
  in tabes dorsalis and peripheral neuropathy, 344
  in thalamic syndrome, 368

Hyperphagia, compensatory, 1157
  hypothalamic, 249
  lesions causing, 1159
Hyperphoria, 505
Hyperpiesia, blood pressure in, 675
Hyperpnea, 860
  in anoxia, 891, 893
  and carbon dioxide, 914
  at high altitudes, 926
  hysterical, 927
  respiratory motor nerve discharge in, 900
    reflexes in, 903
  as result of *p*H and increased carbon dioxide pressure, *922*
  voluntary, 915, 928
Hypertensin, in hypertension, 676
  in renal hypertension, 980
Hypertensinase, in renal hypertension, 980
Hypertensinogen in renal hypertension, 980
Hypertension, 675, 833, 838
  essential, 675
  heart in, hypertrophy of, 794
  hypertrophy of myocardium and, 794
  kidney in, 833
  neurogenic, 714
  renal, 980
    experimental, 980
  uterus in, 838
Hyperthermia, 246, 248, 1163
  barbiturates in, 248. See also names of specific barbiturates.
  dial in, 248
  due to hypothalamic lesions, 248
Hyperthyroidism, cardiac output in, 801
  glucose tolerance in, *1107*
  heart murmurs in, 645
  metabolism in, 1100
Hypertropia, 506
Hyperventilation, fall in systemic pressure following, *707*
  voluntary, effect of, on respiration, *915*
Hypesthesia, 307
Hypocalcemia, in coagulation of blood, 593
  parathyroid glands in, 1147
Hypocapnia. S3e *Acapnia*.
Hypocarbia. See *Acapnia*.
Hypoglycemia, effects of, 1105
  and hunger, 1156
  from insulin, 1106, *1106*
Hypometria, 299
Hypophysectomy, effect on food intake of, 1157
  testes and, 1223, 1225
Hypophysis. See also *Pituitary*.
  anterior lobe of, and glycogen storage, 1177
    and protein storage, 1178
  innervation of, 245. See also *Pituitary*.
  thyrotropic hormone of, 1100
Hypoprothrombinemia, 591
  bleeding tendency in, 587
Hypotension, 846

Hypertension, vasodilatation in, 688
Hypothalamic area, anatomical organization of, 243
  hyperphagia, 1159
  obesity, 1159
Hypothalamus, autonomic centers in, 242
  barbiturates and, 248
  blood supply of, 243
  connections of, 243
    with pneumotaxic center, 909
  effect of atropine on, 247. See also *Atropine.*
    pituitrin on, 247. See also *Pituitrin.*
  electrical stimulation of, 250
    effects of, 243
  emotional expression and, 249
  and food intake, 1158, *1158*
  functions of, 242
  in heat regulation, 246
  hyperphagia and, 249
  lesions of, and basal metabolic rate, 249
    and carbohydrate metabolism, 249
    hyperthermia due to, 248
    poikilothermy due to, 248
  level, of autonomic function. See *Autonomic function.*
  longitudinal section of, *246*
  and mental disorders, 250
  and motor output, 1162
  nuclei of, 244. See also *Nuclei.*
  obesity and, 249, 1180
  outflow, 225
  and panting, 909, 920
  and respiration, 909
  in sex cycle, 1204
  sexual functions and, 249
  stimulation, 235
  strychninization of, 250
  and temperature regulation, 1171
  and water metabolism, 245. See also *Water metabolism.*
Hypothermesthesia, 307
Hypothermia, 1163
Hypothyroidism, glucose tolerance in, *1107*
  metabolism in, 1100
Hypoxia. See *Oxygen.*

ICSH, 1194
Ileocecal sphincter, control of, 1004
Ileogastric reflex, 999
Impulse, 17. See also *Nerve impulse.*
Incisura angularis, 989
Index of refraction of ocular media, 443
Infarct, of heart, following anoxemia, localized, 816
Infarction, myocardial, Q wave in, 819
  T wave in, 819
Inflammation, leukotaxis in, 612
  vascular reactions in, 612
-nflation receptors, 905
-nhibition, 165

Inhibition, central, 165, 167
  depressant actions in, 116
  direct, 170
  duration of, 166
  in excitability, 276
  and excitation, 167
  of flexor reflex, 167
  hypotheses of, 169
  indirect, 167
  of inspiration, lung inflation and, 903
  intensity of, 166
  of knee-jerk, 165, 167
  latency of, 165
  nature of, 167
  occlusion of, 167
  of stretch reflex, 151
  in sympathetic ganglia, 130
  of two-neuron arc reflex, *169*
  Wedensky, 26
Inhibitory mechanisms, contribution of, to respiratory rhythm, 909
  synaptic connections, of respiratory center, 898
Injury current, in anoxemia, localized, 817, *817, 818*
  vascular relation to, 846
Innervation, of endocrines, 245. See also *Endocrines.*
  of hypophysis, 245. See also *Pituitary.*
  identical, or co-contraction, 162
  of islets of Langerhans, 245. See also *Islets of Langerhans.*
  of pancreas, 245. See also *Pancreas.*
  of pituitary. 245. See also *Pituitary.*
  ratio, 40
  reciprocal, 162, *168*, 169
    double, 162
  of thyroid, 245
Inogen theory, 61
Inorganic components of diet, 1149
  salts, as foodstuff, 1014
    gastric, 1045
    in saliva, 1030
Inositol, lipotropic action of, 1128
Inspiration, 860. See also *Respiration.*
  diaphragm action in, 862
  frequency of, 859
  muscles of, 862
  rib movements in, 862
  types of, 859
Inspiratory center. See *also Respiratory center.*
  discharge of, mechanism of grading, 901
  properties of, 899, 908
  reciprocal connections of, with expiratory center, 898
  stimulation of, effects of, 898
  subdivision of respiratory center, 896, *897.* See also *Respiratory center.*
Inspired air, composition of, 877
Insulin, and appetite, 1157
  clinical use of, in production of hypoglycemia, 1157

Insulin, effect on hunger contractions, 997
  and glcogen storage, 1177
  hypoglycemia due to, 1106, *1106*
  sensitivity, 1107
Intelligence, prefrontal lobe, relation to, 541
Interneuron(s), activity of, 136
  synapses on, *139*
Internuncial barrage, neurons *vs.* interneurons, 136
Interoceptors, 307
Intersexuality, genetics of, 1234
Interstitial cell stimulating hormone (ICSH), 1194, 1224, 1225
Intestinal loop, Thiry and Thiry-Vella, 1072
Intestine(s), absorption in, 1061–1082
  of carbohydrates, 1074
  of fats, 1075
  of proteins, 1076
  bacterial action in, 1079
  content of, reaction of, 1078
  digestion in, 1061–1082
    bile in, 1061
    intestinal glands in, 1061
  duodenal bulb, and stomach, *990*
  large. See *Colon.*
  law of, 1001
  metabolic gradient in, 1001
  movements of, 999
    effect of epinephrine on, 1004
    factors affecting, 1004
    nervous control of, 1003
    rhythmical, 999, *1000*
  peristalsis in, 1001, *1001*
  putrefaction in, amines from, 1080
  putrefactive process in, physiological importance of, 1080
  secretion of, (succus entericus), 1072
  small, 1073. See also *Intestine(s).*
  villi of, movements of, 1003
Intracellular electrolytes, clinical importance of, 941
Intra-ocular pressure, 457
Intrapleural pressure, 864
Intrapulmonic and intrathoracic pressure, relation between, *866*
  pressure, 864, 866
Intrathoracic and intrapulmonic pressure, relation between, *866*
  pressure, 864, 866
  measurement of, 866
Intraventricular block. See *Block.*
  conduction, 727
  injections, effect on hypothalamus, 247
Inulin clearance, 971, *972*
  excretion of, 969
Invertase, 1023, 1025, 1073
Invertin, 1073
Iodine, dietary, 1149, 1152
  in thyroid dysfunction, 1100
  thyroxin and, 1100
Iodopsin, 468
  visual violet, action of vitamin A on, 1146

Ions, distribution of, between cells and plasma, 572
  inorganic, heart and, 819
  in membrane equilibrium, 570. See also *Membrane.*
Iris of eye, 455
Iron, dietary, 1149
  recommended allowance of, 1132
  requirement of, 556
  in food, 1017
  in relation to hemoglobin formation, 556
"Irritable focus," 400
Irritation, hyperpathia due to, 345
Ischemia, blood flow in, 830
  in coronary vessels, 809
  experimental, 978
  uterine, in dysmenorrhea, 1205
Ishihara test of color blindness, 501, *501*
Islets of Langerhans, function of, 1106
  innervation of, 245
Isohydric cycle, in erythrocytes, 887
Isotopes, heavy hydrogen (deuterium), 1114
  nitrogen (N^{15}), 1114
  in metabolic research, 1114

Jansky blood group classification, 560
Junction, neuromuscular, 7, 121
  curare action at. See *Curare, Curarization.*
  neuromyal, 121
Junctional potential. See *End-plate potential.*

Keratitis, interstitial, in riboflavin deficiency, 1141
Ketonemia, 1125
Ketone(s), in blood, 1126
  changes in, during starvation, *1126*
  from fatty acids, 1125
Ketosteroids, 1215
Kidney, 964–981. See also *Glomerular.*
  action, effect of, on acid-base balance, 578
  activity, regulation of, 978
  ammonia production by, 973
  anatomy of, 964
  blood flow in, 658
    Fick principle in measurement of, 976
    regulation of, 978
  vascular system of, 965
  circulation of, measurement of, 976
  defects, in Addison's disease, 978
  excretion, of typical solutes, 971
    of various compounds by, *976*
  fluid exchanges in, 950
  function, in diabetes insipidus, 978
    endocrine control of, 952
    study of, by test substances, 974
  in hypertension, 833

Kidney, juxtaglomerular apparatus of, 965
lymphatic system of, 966
parathyroid effects on, 1147
physiology of, 933
quantitative methods in, 966
pituitary and, 246
secretion of, definition of, 967
tubular maximum, 975
reabsorption or rejection of glucose, *971*
tubules, ammonium salts synthesis by, 973
function of, 970
limits of activity of, 974
Kinases, of enzymes, 1024
Kinesthesia. See *Muscle sense.*
Kinesthesis, 324
Knee jerk, 152
inhibition of, 165
silent period of, 153, 170
of spinal preparation, *165*
Korotkow, sounds of, 673
Krause end-bulb, 314, 315
Kussmaul breathing, 918
K vitamins. See *Vitamins.*
Kymograph, first use of, by Ludwig, 668

LABOR (childbirth). See *Parturition.*
Labyrinth, anatomy of, 202
decerebrate rigidity and, 194
grasp reflex, 197
innervation of, *205*
osseus, 413
reflexes, acceleratory. See *Reflexes.*
Labyrinthectomy, 2–0
Labyrinthine reactions, rules for interpreting, 209
reflexes, righting, 196
tonic, 194
Lacrimal glands, innervation of, autonomic, 226
Lacrimation, 226
Lactase, 1023, 1025, 1073
Lactation, 1209
dietary allowances for, recommended, 1132
effect of estrogens on, 1210
of stilbestrol on, 1210
of thyroid on, 1210
and food intake, 1157
neural mechanism in, 1210
pituitary in, 1207
regulation of, 1209
Lactic acid, of blood, 1110, *1110*
heart utilization of, 825
muscle, 61
Lactogen, 1207
in milk production, 1210
Lactogenic hormone, 1209
Lamination, of ascending tracts. See *Tract(s).*
Laminectomy, effect of, on kidney blood flow, 833
in spinal compression, 183

LAMPORT, Harold: Hemodynamics, 630–659
LANDAUER, Walter: Genetic aspects of physiology, 1232–1247
Landsteiner blood group classification, 560
Larynx, effects of androgens on, 1219
Law, acoustical, of Ohm, 423
of adequate stimulus, 308
Batschinski's, 637
Bell-Magendie, exception to, 697
Boyle's 873
Charles', 873
Dalton's, 874
Ewald's 209
Flourens', 209
Listing's, of eye movement, 505
Marey's, of heart, 787
of mass action, 574
Ohm's, 637
Poiseuille's, 631, 635, 636
of projection, 328
Starling's, of heart, 792
of thermodynamics, 1087
Weber-Fechner, in sensation, 313
Laxation, effect of food on, 1008
problem, 1007
Learning, 529
experiments of Pavlov on, 295
methods in study of, 529
trace responses in, 531
Lecat's experiment, 445
Lecithin, 1122
Lemniscus, medial, 353
Lengthening reactions, in decerebrate rigidity, 190
Lens(es), convex, formation of image by, 442, *442*
refraction of light by, *441*
of eye, 448
nutrition of, 457
formula for principal focus, 442
properties of, 440
Leukocytes, *554*, 562
ameboid motility of, 562
chemotaxis of, 562
as elements of blood, 549
fate of, 563
functions of, 563
migration of, 563
morphology of, 555
in pus cell formation, 564
reticulo-endothelial system and, 563
in septicemia, 563. See also *Septicemia.*
types of, 555
Leukotaxin, 612
Leukotaxine, 562
Leukotaxis, in inflammation, 612
Levocardiogram, 758
Leydig cells, in androgen production, 1223
LH, 1194
Light adaptation, 468, 471. See also *Dark adaptation.*

Light adaptation, curve of, 471
  effect of, on locomotor activity, 1160
  reflex, 456, *456*, 513
  refraction of, by convex lens, *1111*
Linear conductor, 14
Linoleic acid, 1138
Lipase, 1022, 1023
  action of, 1021, 1070
  gastric, 1045
Lipid(s). See also *Fat.*
  from carbohydrates, 1128
  intermediary metabolism of, 1121
  metabolism of, carbohydrates in, 1111
    liver in, 1126
    sex hormones in, 1203
  nutritive value of, 1121
  oxidation of, 1123
  plasma, 1121
  reserves, 1179
  storage of, 1122
  transport of, 1122
  utilization of, 1122
Lipocaic, lipotropic action of, 1128
Lipoprotein, in blood coagulation, 593
Lipotropic factors, 1127
Liquids, properties of, 873
Lissauer, tract of, 347
  afferent pressor impulses and, 703
Listing's law, of eye movement, 505
Liver, in androgen metabolism, 1215
  and blood glucose, 1105
  choline deficiency affecting, 1143
  fat content of, 1127
  glycogen storage in, 1107
    as carbohydrate reserve, 1176
  in lipid metabolism, 1126
  and resistance to disease, 1237
  storage of blood in, 836
  systemic and portal vessels in, *835*
LLOYD, David P. C.: Electrical properties of
    nerve and muscle, 7–31
  Functional activity of muscle, 33–35
  Functional properties of neurons, 96–
    120
  Intercellular transmission, 121–145
  Principles of spinal reflex activity, 146–
    177
Lobectomy, temporal, effects of, 542
Lobotomy, prefrontal, 540
Localization. See *Topognosis.*
  and projection, distinction between, 328
Locke's solution, 558
Locomotor activity, measurement of, 1159
Loewi's technique, Bain's modification of,
    232
Lovén reflexes, 831, 846
Ludwig's stromuhr, 660, *661*
Luminosity of spectrum. See *Visibility curve.*
Lung(s), 859
  air in, relationship between measureable
    volumes of, *868*

Lung(s), air sac, blood flow through, *880*
  arterioles in, blocking of, 867
  blood flow in, 879
  blood flow through, 840
    storage in, 843
  capillary network in, *880*
  complemental air in, 867
  deflation of, and expiration inhibition, 904
    and respiratory reflexes, 904
  diffusion constant of, 882
    of gases in, 881
  diseases, Hering-Breuer reflexes in, sensi-
    tization of, 905
  edema of, oxygen and, 894
  elasticity of, 864, 865
  factors governing exchange of gases in,
    879
  fluid exchanges through, 947
  gas exchange in, 879
  inflation of, in apnea, *903*
    and respiratory reflexes, 903
    response of pulmonary receptors to, *904*
  innervation of, autonomic, 227
  lobule, structure of, *870*
  measurement of vital capacity of, 867
  minimal air in, 868
  normal capacity of, 867
  oxygen diffusion in, 882
  receptors in, 903. See also *Receptors.*
  reserve air in, 867
  residual air in, 867
  respiratory reflexes from stretch and col-
    lapse, 903
    surface of, 880
  rigidity and dyspnea in, 905
  tidal air in, 867
  ventilation of, 867, 869, 871
  vital capacity of, 867
    effect of posture on, 868
    on working ability of, 869
    in heart disease, 868
    in tuberculosis, 868
  volume of, 867
Lungmotor, in artificial respiration, 872
Luteinizing hormone (LH), 1194, 1224
Lymph, cell content of, 626
  composition of, 622
  flow, 623
    clinical considerations of, 628
    effects of chemical agents on, 624
      of tissue activity on, 624
    exercise and, 623
    rate of, 626
  formation, Starling's theory, 622
  function of, 622
  intrapleural, 865
  protein content of, 938
  source of, 939
  vessel, and capillary, *621*
  volume of, total, 623
Lymphagogues, 620

Lymphatic(s), 620–627
  arrangement and structure of, 620
  system, of kidney, 966
Lymphocytes. See *Leukocytes.*
Lymphoid tissue, 627
  and resistance to disease, 1237

MACULA, representation of, bilateral, *519*
  sparing of, 518
Magnesium. See also *Plasma magnesium.*
  dietary, 1149
  distribution of, in body, 939
Magnet reaction, 193
Magnus and de Kleijn reflexes, 195
Male climacteric, 1222
  estrogens in 1215. See also *Estrogens.*
  reproduction in, 1213–1230
  reproductive system in, *1213*, 1217
  sterility in, 1226
Maltase, 1023, 1025, 1073, 1075
  in saliva, 1030, 1039
Maly's theory, of gastric hydrochloric acid
  formation, 1048
Mammary glands, development of, experi-
    mental studies on, 1208
  and function of, 1207
    normal, 1207
    pituitrin effect on, 1210
Mammotrophin, 1209
Manganese, dietary, 1149
Mannitol, distribution of, in body, 939
Manometer, 633
  differential, 634
  Hurthle's, *670*
  mercury, and connections, *668*
  principles of, 685, *685*, 686
Marey's law of the heart, 787
Martin, Newell, in history of physiology, 2
Mastication, 982
  in digestion, 983
  muscles of, 982
    innervation of, 982
Measles, globulin preparations in treatment
  of, 584
Mechanoreceptors, 307
Mecholyl, in autonomic stimulation, 234
Mediastinal space, 866
Medium, conducting, electric current in, 14.
    See also *Volume, conductor.*
  dielectric, electric current in, 14
Medulla, of cerebrum. See *Cerebrum.*
  hunger center and, 997
  oblongata, 212
    autonomic functions of, 241
    respiratory center and, 896
  swallowing center of, 985
  vomiting reflex, 1010
Medullary level, of autonomic function. See
  Autonomic function.
Meissner corpuscles, 319, 322

Membrane, capacity, 17, 28
  conductivity, 17
  electromotive force of, 18, 29
  equilibrium, ions in, 570
  hydrolysis, in formation of gastric hydro-
    chloric acid, 1049
  nictitating, 231, 236, *236*
    responses to, isotonic, *236*
  of Reissner, 414
  resistance of, 17–19, 29
  theory, in electrocardiogram, 748
Menadione, synthetic vitamin K, 591, 1148
Ménière's disease, 210
Menopause, 1197
  treatment of, estrogens in, 1198
Menstrual cycle, 1187
  anovulatory, 1189
  endocrine control of, 1189
  endometrium in, *1188*
  hormone production during, 1191
  ovulatory, 1189
  regulation of, 1193
  relation of ovaries to, 1189
  stages of, 1188
  and estrous cycles, comparison of, 1192, *1192*
Menstruation, experimental procedures in,
  1190
Mental disorders, barbiturates in, 250
  and hypothalamic activity, 250
Menus, planning of, 1135
Merkel's discs, 322
Metabolic gradient, in intestine, 1001
  pool, definition of, 1116
Metabolism, 116
  androgen effects on, 1220
  basal, 1087. See also *Basal metabolic rate.*
  and body size, 1094, *1095*
  and growth, 1096
  measurement of, 1087
  and nutrition, 1098
  and sex, 1097
  and sleep, 1097
  carbohydrate, of heart, 825
  changes of, exothermic, 1015
  fat, of heart, 826
  intermediary, 1102–1129
  lipid, carbohydrates in, 1111
  and nutrition, 1084–1181
  of proteins, 1111
    carbohydrates in, 1111
  quantitative, 1084–1101
  respiratory, 1088
  sex hormones in, 1203
  total, 1098
    effect of food, 1098
    in fever, 1101
    and muscular exercise, 1099
    and temperature, environmental, 1099
    and thyroid gland, 1100
  water, hypothalamus in, 242. See also *Wa-
    ter metabolism.*

Metabolites, effects of, on arterioles, 708
Metallic ions, and enzymes, 1152
Metarterioles, 607
Metathrombin, 599
Methemoglobin, 561, 581, 891, 893
Methionine, 1149
Meyer's loop or detour, 514
Micturition, nerves governing, 231
Midbrain preparation, 195
Migraine, blood vessels in, 849
Milk production, lactogen in, 1210
Milliequivalent, definition of, 945
Millilambert, definition of, 464
Minerals, body content of, 1150
Minimal air, in lung, 868
Minimum separable. See *Visual acuity.*
Mitchell, Silas, in history of physiology, 4
Mixtures, fluidity of, 639
Mobility, in fluids, 640. See also *Blood.*
Modal excitation fields, 331
Modulator response in color vision, 496
Molecular volume, free, fluidity and, 637
Monge's disease, 557
Monocytes. See *Leukocytes.*
Monro-Kellie doctrine, 848
Morawitz theory of blood coagulation, 600
Moss blood group classification, 560
Motion sickness, 195
Motoneuron(s), 7, *8*
    clonus and, 153
    mechanism, of respiratory center, 909
    pool, and discharge zone, relation between, *143*
        fractionation of, 157
    respiratory, repetitive activity of, *902*
    responses, to presynaptic volleys, 136
    silent period of, 153
    soma, spike potentials of. See *Spike potential.*
    synapses on, *139*
    synaptic delay of, *141*
Motor areas, in cerebral cortex, location of, 275
    nerve discharge mechanism of repetitive, 901
        respiratory, character of, 900
    output, regulation of, 1159
        regulatory deficits of, 1162
            clinical manifestations of, 1162
    unit, definition, 39
        discharge rates, 40
        recruitment of, 41
        response, asynchronous, 41
        size of, 40
        tension, 40
Mountain sickness, 892
Movement, due to ablation, of cerebral cortex areas, 281
Mucin, 1030, 1033, 1036, 1040
Mucous gland, submaxillary, *1035, 1036*

Müller, Johannes. See *Nerve, energies, specific doctrine of.*
Müller's orbital muscle, innervation of, autonomic, 231
Murmur(s), cardiac, 645
    heart, 738
        in anemia, 644
        functional, 644
Muscle(s). See also *Motor unit, Muscular, Myocardium.*
    abdominal, action of, in expiration, 863
    action, in body, 42
    activity of, functional, 32–55
    after-potential, 33
    all-or-nothing relation in, 52
    antagonism of pairs, 43
    antigravity, in decerebrate rigidity, 188
    of bronchi, 865
    carbohydrate oxidation, 72
    characteristics of, general, 56
    chemical composition, 59
        adenosine triphosphate, 60, 66, 69, 74, 80
        adenylic acid system, 60, 69, *69*
        cozymase, 64, 65, 67, 72
        glucose, 59, 65, 75
        glycogen, 59, 65, 66
        lactic acid, 61, 62, 67, 70, 76, 80
        muscle hemoglobin, 71
        myosin, 57, 59, 74, 93
        phosphocreatine, 60, 67, 69, 75, 78
        proteins, 59
    reaction in, fermentation, 62
        oxidation, 62
    ciliary, 447
    contraction, energy liberation during, 83
        Fenn's classification of, 32
        isometric, 32, 34
        isotonic, 32
        natural, 39
        time, definition, 34
            of mammalian, 37
        range of, 34, *35*
        voluntary, 42, *42*
    critical fusion rate, 37
    delta state of, 39
    electrical properties of, 7–31
    end-plate potential and spike potential of, comparison between, *122*
    energy liberation in, 79
        phosphate bond, 60, 61, *69*
        production, anaerobic, 62
            oxidative, 62, 70, 82
        transformations in, 56–95
        yielding systems, 78
    enzymes, adenyl prophosphatase, 58, 69, 74
        cytochrome oxidase system, 72
        flavoproteins, 72
        phosphorylase, 65, 66, 72
    of expiration, 863

Muscle(s), eye, actions of individual, 504
  facial, sensory innervation of, 352
  fiber, 57
  fibril, 57
  fusion rate, critical, 37, 41
  glycogen storage in, as carbohydrate reserve, 1176
  glycolysis, 62, 77
    essential reactions of, 65, *65*, 66
  heat production, 79, 116
    and chemical change, 80
    measurement of, 79
    phases of, 79, *81*, 82
  hemoglobin, 71
  histology of, 190
  innervation of, autonomic, 226, 227
    of dilator pupillae, 231
    of heart, 226
    Müller's orbital, 231
    of sphincter pupillae, 231
  inogen theory, 61
  of inspiration, 862
  latent period, 33
  length and tension, relation between, 38, *38*
  mechanics of, 32, 42
  of middle ear, 411
  nerve, distribution of afferent fibers in, *159*
  optical properites of, 57
  oxidation in, 77
    quotient, 76
  parathyroid effects on, 1147
  phosphate bond energy, and glycolysis, 66, 67, 69
    and oxidation, 74
  phosphorolysis, 66
  portein, 58, 93
  receptors, decerebrate rigidity in, 189, 190
  relaxation, energy in, 81
  respiratory systems of, 71
  response to stimuli, repetitive, 37
    two, 35
  retractor lentis, 448
  rigor in, 39, 56
  role in circulation, 645
  sense, 307, 322
    discovery of, 323
    receptors for, 323
    stimulus for, adequate, 323
    tests of, 324
  shortening, heat of, 87, 88
    pace and speed of, 89
  skeletal, blood supply to, 836
    carbohydrate utilization in, 1109
  smooth. See *Smooth muscle.*
  spike potential, 33. See also *Spike potential.*
  spindle, in sensation, 323
    as stretch afferent, 190
  staircase phenomenon, 36, *36*
  stapedius, 411

Muscle(s), stimulation of, threshold, 19, *20*
  striated, analysis of, 940
    electrolyte and content of water, 941
  structure, 57
  tensor tympani, 411
  tetanus, complete, 37
  tetany, parathyroid in, 1147
  tone, 153
  torque of, 43
  treppe, 36
  tricarboxylic acid cycle, 73
  two joint, advantage of, 45
  work, 32, 88, 91, 93
    negative, 43
    positive, 43
Muscle-nerve junctions, 7, 121
Muscular activity, principles of, 7–177
  strength, effects of androgen on, 1220
Myenteric reflex, 1001
Myocardial infarction, Q wave in, 819
Myocardium, action potential of, 766
  metabolism. See *Metbolism.*
  refractory period of, 721
  rhythmicity of, 723
Myogen, muscle, 59
Myometrium, contractions of, 1204
  hormone control of, 1205
  physiology of, 1204
Myopia, 451, *452*
Myosin, 93
  muscle, 57, 59
Myotatic reflex. See *Stretch reflex.*
Myxedema, cardiac output in, 801
  heart rate in, 784
  metabolism in, 1100

NASAL cavity, *403*
National Research Council, dietary allowances recommended by, 1132
Near-sightedness. See *Myopia.*
Neck reflex, righting, 197
Negative adaptation, 532
Nembutal, in hyperthermia, 248
Nephritis, body fluid abnormalities in, 961
  magnesium in, 824
  respiration in, 918
Nephron, diagram of, *964*
  form and structure of, 964
Nerve(s). See also *Innervation, Nervous, Nucleus.*
  acoustic, 434
  afferent endings, in carotid sinus, *702*
    fiber constitution, 109
  after-potentials in, 104, 118
  auditory, 434
    action potentials of, 426, *427*, 431
  cells. See also *Neurons.*
    of cerebral cortex, 258
    discharge, electrotonic theory of, 902
    excitability of, 901
    mature, phylogenetic development of, *260*

Nerve(s) cells, refractory nature of, following impulse, 901
  cerebral, nuclei of origin of, *213*
  chemical reaction of, 118
  chorda tympani, as taste pathway, 376, *377*
  conduction in, independent, 98, *98*
  control, of blood flow, 828
    of caliber of arterioles, *828, 829*
    of visceral blood flow, 834
  of coronary vessels, 806
  cranial, I, olfactory, 212
    II, optic, 212
    III, 220, 221
    III, oculomotor, 212
    IV, trochlear, 215
    V, trigeminal, 215
    VI, abducens, 215
    VII, 220, 221
    VII, facial, 216
    VIII, 434
    VIII, vestibular division, 203, 205
    IX, 220, 221
    IX, glossopharyngeal, 216
    X, 220, 221
    X, vagus, 216
    XI, accessory, 216
    XII, hypoglossal, 216
    origin and function of, 212–217
      of third and fourth, *214*
      and respiratory motor pathways, 899
  deafness, 434
  depressor, 701
  electric current distribution in, 17–19
    properties of, 7–31
  endings, free, 323
    in pain sensation, 318
  energy, specific, 308
    doctrine of, 308
      in hearing, 424
  facial, sensory connections of, 353
    as taste pathway, 376
  fibers. See also *Spinal fibers.*
    "A," "B," "C," 99, 105, *106*
    "A," sensory function of, 342
      properties of, 100, 105
    accessory fibers of sense organ, 318, 323
    adrenergic, of salivary glands, 1033
    "B" and "C" fibers, comparison of, with "A" fibers, 105–107, *106*
    "C" and "A," pain and, 342
    cholinergic, of salivary glands, 1033
    conduction in, immature, 112
      individual, 114
      regenerating, 112
      velocity of, 112
    "fiber spectrum" of, 100, 341
    interaction of, 115, *115*
    mammalian, properties of, 107, *108*
    for pain, fast and slow, 344
    phrenic, spike potentials of, following inhalation of carbon dioxide, *900*

Nerve(s) fibers, postganglionic autonomic, 218, 225
  preganglionic autonomic, 218, 225
    from spinal cord, *238*
  propriospinal, 110, *110*
  relation of conduction velocity and spike amplitude, 101, *101*
    to size, 100, *100*
    to threshold, 102, *102*
    of size to reflex function, 158
  in tabes dorsalis, 344
  types of, 98
  unmyelinated, pain and, 341
  fifth cranial, nuclei of origin of, *215*
  glossopharyngeal, sensory connections of, 353
    as taste pathway, 376
  of heart, magnesium action on, 824
  heat production of, 116
    correlation with activity of, 118
      with chemical changes in, 118
    during and after activity in, 117, *118*
    effect of oxygen deprivation on, 118
    phases of, 117, *117, 118*
    resting, 116, *117*
    spike potential and, 118
  impulses, afferent, from lung receptors, 903
    concept of, 27
    conduction in sensory fibers of, 341
    definition of, 27
    energy relations of, 30
    increase of electrotonic current in nerve impulse by, 902
    local circuit theory of, 28, *28*
    repetitive discharge of, mechanism of, 901
    respiratory motor, frequency of, 900
      pattern of, 900
    sensory frequency as function of intensity, 427
  interaction between, 114
  lesions of, effect on taste, *378*
  metabolism of, 118
  motor, fiber constitution, 107
  -muscle junctions, 7, 121
  optic, 460
    action potentials of, 478
  parasympathetic, of coronary vessels, as vasoconstrictors, 806
    effect on heart rate, 785
  pelvic splanchnic, 1228
  peripheral. See *Peripheral nerves.*
  refractory period of, 104
  regeneration and conduction, 112
  respiration of, 118
  resting heat of, 116
  saphenous, spike potential of, complete, 99–100, *99*
  secretory, of salivary glands, 1031

Nerve(s), sensory loss due to section of, 334
  plethysmographic studies of, 831
  in somatic sensation, 309
  spike potential, compound, 96, 102
  spinal, sacral, 220, 221
    sensory connections of, 353
    thoracolumbar, 220, 221
  splanchnic, 227
    stimulation of, vasomotor effect of, 695
  stimulation of, threshold, 19, 20
  supply, of aortic arch, 701
    of carotid sinus, 701
  sympathetic, of coronary vessels, as vaso-
      dilators, 806
    effect on, heart rate, 789
    in erection, 1228
    fiber constitution, 109
  trigeminal, central connections of, 352
    distribution of sensory fibers of, 214
    mesencephalic root of, 352
    neuralgia of, 353
    sensory connections of, 353
    as taste pathway, 376
  vagus. See Vagus.
  vascular, of brain, source of, 849, 854
  vasoconstrictor, course and distribution of,
      694
  vasodilator, 702
    course and distribution of, 696
Nervi erigentes, 225, 227, 1228
Nervous activity, principles of, 7–177
  system, autonomic, 218–239. See also
      Autonomic nervous system, Parasym-
      pathetic nervous system, Sympathetic
      nervous system.
    sensory functions of, 305–546
    visceral. See Visceral nervous system.
Neural mechanisms, responsible for rhyth-
    mic respiration, 896–911
Neuralgia, trigeminal, 353
Neuritis, in thiamine deficiency, 1140
Neurohormones, autonomic, 236
Neurohypophysis, 245. See also Pituitary.
Neuromuscular delay, 121
  transmission of, 121
    hypothesis of, chemical, 125
      electrical, 125
Neuron(s). See also Nerve(s) cells.
  arc reflex. See Reflex, neuron arc.
    types of, 147
  circuits, 136
    closed chain, 135
    multiple chain, 135
  cortical, 263
  definition of, 96
  function of, 8
  interaction between, 114
  intracortical chains of, 263
  parts of, 96
  properties of, functional, 96–120
  propriospinal, 171, 174

Neuron(s), propriospinal, distribution of, 171
  respiratory motor, organization of, 898
    properties of, 899, 908
    significance of factors affecting activity
        of, 920
  of reticular formation, clinical importance
      of, 897
  sensory, primitive, 371
  soma, conduction in. See Conduction.
  stimulation of, antidromic, 113
    by carbon dioxide, 902
  threshold of. See Threshold.
  types of, 7, 8
Neuropathy, peripheral, hyperpathia in,
    344
Neurosis(es), effects of prefrontal lesions on,
    540
  experimental, 534
  hypothalamus and, 250
Neutrophils. See Leukocytes.
Niacin, 1142
  deficiency of, symptoms of, 1142
  dietary, recommended allowance of, 1132
  in food, 1017
  requirements of, 1142
  sources of, 1142
Nickel, dietary, 1149
Nicotinamide nucleotide. See Cozymase.
Nicotine, action of, on salivary glands, 1036
  effect of, on autonomic nervous system,
      230, 234
Nicotinic acid. See Niacin.
Night blindness, 470
  vitamin A in, 1146
Nims, Leslie F.: Anatomy and physics of
    respiration, 858–876
  Gas exchange and transportation, 877–
      895
Nitrogen, amino, fate of, 1114
  dietary, 1149
  effect of, on respiratory response, 924
  equilibrium, 1119
  excretion, measure of nitrogen metabolism
      1088
    in phlorhizinized dog, 1116
  isotopes of, 1114
  in respiration, function of, 878
  solubility of, 878
  urinary, excretion of, 1120
  in urine, of phlorhizinized dog, 1117
Nociceptive reaction, 156
Nociceptors, 307
Node. See specific nodes as Auriculoventric-
    ular, Sino-auricular node, etc.
  of Tawara, 726
Nolf theory of blood coagulation, 600
North American Medico-Chirurgical Re-
    view, establishment of, 4
Nose. See Olfaction, Olfactory.
Nuclear delay, 144
Nucleases, 1025, 1073

Nucleus(i), of anterior column, 173
  of brain, arcuate, 379, *380*
    lesions of, taste and, *380*
    cochlear, dorsal, 434
      ventral, 434
    and lateral geniculate bodies, 513
    oculomotor, 231
  of cranial nerves, 212, *213*
  dorsomedial hypothalamic, *244*
  Edinger-Westphal, 214, *214*
  hypothalamic, *244*
    lateral, *244*
    posterior, *244*
    ventromedial, *244*
  intermediate, *148*, 176
  interpeduncular, *244*
  lateral, 214
  main sensory, 352
  mammillary, lateral, *244*
    medial, *244*
  median, 214
  paraventricular, *244*
  premammillary, *244*
  preoptic, lateral, *244*
    medial, *244*
  proprius of ventral horn, 173
  reticular, inferior, inspiratory center and, 896
  spinal, 352
  suprachiasmatic, *244*
  supramammillary, *244*
  supra-optic, *244*, 245
  of thalamus, 364
Nutrition, 1130–1154. See also *Metabolism*.
  importance of digestion in, 1018
  metabolism and, 1084–1181
    total, 1098
  in public health, 1153
  and resistance to disease, 1237
Nutting's formula for plastic flow, 640, 657
Nyctalopia, vitamin A in, 1146
Nystagmus, caloric, 209
  definition of, 206
  and Ewald's laws, 209
  and Flourens' law, 209
  and linear acceleration, 207
  postcaloric, 209
  postrotatory, 206
  during rotation, 206

OBESITY, causes of, 1180
  hypothalamus and, 249, 1159
Occipital eye fields, of cerebral cortex, 286
Occlusion, 126, *127*, 128
  of inhibition, 167
Ohm, acoustical law of, 423
Ohm's law, 637
Olfacties, 403
Olfaction, end-organs of, 402
  gyri of cerebral cortex and, 406

Olfaction and olfactory pathways, 402–408
  tactile components of, 404
  tests of, 402
Olfactometer, *403*
Olfactory bulb, 405
  component of taste, 983
  mucosa, histology of, 402
  pathways, central, 405
  stimuli, 402
  system, connections of, *406*
    functions of, 407
  threshold, 402
Oligocythemia, 557
Oncometer, 693
Ophthalmometer, 459
Ophthalmoscope, *458*, 459
Opsonins, phagocytosis and, 563
Optic chiasm, 512
  disc, ophthalmoscopic appearance of, *460*
  nerve. See *Nerve(s), optic*.
  thalamus. See *Thalamus*.
  tract, 512
Optical defects and visual acuity, 450, 481
    488
Organ of Corti, 414, *415*
Orgasm, 1230
Ornithine cycle, 1118
  in urea synthesis, 1118
Orokinase, 1039
Orthopnea, 868
Oscillograph, cathode-ray, 9
Oscillographic records, relationship of discharge to stimulation, *310*
Oscillometer, 674
Oscillometric method, in measurement of blood pressure, 674
Osmolar centration, definition of, 943
Osmotic equilibrium, of blood, 568
  fragility test. See *Fragility*.
  pressure, 568
    colloid, 569, 571
Osseus labyrinth, 413
Ossicles, auditory. See *Ear*.
Osteomalacia, vitamin D deficiency in, 1147
Ovarian function, regulation of, during menstrual cycle, 1193
  and pituitary interrelationships, 1195, *1195*
Ovariectomy, effect of, on menstruation, 1187
  on sex characters, 1184
Ovary, 1184, *1185*
  activity of, 1185, *1185*
  endocrine function of, 1186
  histology of, 1185
  hormones of, 1184
  life cycle of, 1196
  relation of, to menstrual cycle, 1189
  transplantation of, 1184
Overresponse. See *Paresthesia*.
Overventilation, impulses from chemoreceptors during, *925*

Ovulation, 1203
  in animals, 1204
  hypothalamus and, 249
  induction of, 1196
  neural factors in, 1204
  time of, 1193, 1204
Ovum, spermatozoa and, 1226
Oxalates, as anticoagulants, 551, 589
Oxidases, 1023, 1026
Oxidation. See also *Muscle, respiratory systems; Muscle, hemoglobin.*
  citric acid cycle, 73, *74*
  multiple alternate, of fatty acids, 1125
  in muscle, 62
  oxidation-reduction systems, 72, *74*
  phosphate bond energy and, 73
  quotient, 76
  tricarboxylic acid cycle, 73, *74*
Oxygen administration, effects of, at high altitudes, 926
  alveolar and arterial pressures of, 926
  availability to tissues of, *887*
  in blood, deficient. See *Anoxia.*
    partial pressures of, 875
  calorific value of, 1091
  coefficient, utilization of, 888
  consumption of, 877
  content, of blood, 882
    and hemoglobin, *883*
  debt, 77
  diffusion of, in lungs, 882
  dissociation curve, 883, 884
    effect of carbon dioxide on, 884, *884*
    *of p*H on, 884, *884*
  effect on coronary flow, 809, *810*
  heart demands for, 812, *813, 814*
  hemoglobin and, reaction with, 882
  lack, chemoreceptor stimulation by, 923
    effects of, 891
    on respiration at high altitudes, 926
    respiratory center depression by, 920
  measure of respiratory exchange, 1088
  partial pressure in alveoli, 879
    in blood, 879
  pressure of, in tissues, 875
  in respiration, 858
  saturation in blood of, 883
  supply of, to tissues, 888
  therapeutic use of, in anoxia, 893
  in tissues, partial pressures of, 875
  toxicity of, 894
  transport of, by blood, 882
Oxyhemoglobin, 581
Oxytocin. See *Pituitrin.*

P WAVE, 742, 747
P-P factor, 1142. See also *Niacin.*
Pacemaker, action potential in localization of, 719
  ectopic, 790

Pacemaker, electrical potentials of, 722
  of embryo, development of, 717
  extrasystoles in localization of, 719
  localization of, experimental, 719
  metabolic rate, heart rate and, relation between, 785, *786*
  presinus wave in localization of, 720
Pacinian corpuscle, 322, 323
Pain, conduction of, by A-delta fibers, 344
  control of, visceral afferent fibers in, 228
  cutaneous, 317
  deep, 317
    segmental reference of, *398*
  nociceptive, 318
  referred, 385–400
    convergence-projection theory of, 398, *399*
  relief, chordotomy in, 185
  response, double, evidence for, 344
  sensation of, 306
  somatic, cortical localization of, 360
    deep, 307, 324, 397
    measurement of, 320
    neurohistological basis of, 318
    pain response in, double, 344
    protopathic characteristics of, 337
    as specific modality of sensation, 318
    stimulus for, adequate, 317
    thalamic localization of, 367
    unmyelinated fibers of, 341
  superficial, 317
    reference of, *395*
  theory of, and intense stimulation, 318
  visceral, 317, 390
    afferent pathway of, peripheral, 390
    chordotomy for relief of, 400
    deep pain in relation to, 397
    parietal, referred, 395
      unreferred, 393
    pathways of, from gastro-intestinal tract, *391*
      from genito-urinary tract, *392*
    referred, 393, 396
      mechanism of, 397
    stimulus for, adequate, 390
    sympathetic nervous system in, 390
    types of, 393
    unreferred (splanchnic), 396
    and warmth sensibility, apparatus for measurement of, *320*
Pallesthesia, 325, 366
Palpatory method, in measurement of blood pressure, 673
Pancreas, 1061
  innervation of, 245
  secretion of, curves of, *1063*, 1064
    mechanism of, 1064
  secretory nerves to, 1062
Pancreatic amylase, action of, 1070
  digestion, of proteins, end-products in, 1067

Pancreatic fistula, 1062
  juice, composition of, 1022
    digestive action of, 1066
    in intestinal digestion, 1061
    secretion of, 1063, *1063*, 1073
      chemical, 1066
      nervous, 1065
  lipase, action of, 1070
  secretion, composition of, 1061
Panting, in temperature regulation, 1170
Pantothenic acid, synthesis of, in intestines, 1081
Papain, in blood coagulation, 589, 594. See also *Fibrinogen.*
Para-amino-hippuric acid, measurement of renal circulation by, 977
  and renal Tm, 975
  in study of kidney function, 974
Paralysis, flaccid, 273
  spastic, 273
Parathyroid glands, metabolism and, 1147
  hormone, deficiency of, effect of, 1147
Parasympathetic nerves, to colon, 1006
  to intestine, 1003
  nervous system. See also *Vagus.*
    acetylcholine and, 233
    anatomy, 225, 231
    bulbar outflow, 225
    coronary circulation control and, 807
    craniosacral, 220, 225
    definition, 220, 225
    divisions of, 225
    general action, 230
    heat regulation and,247
    homeostasis and, 230
    hunger and, 388
    hypothalamic outflow, 225
    hypothalamus and, 242
    peripheral resistance regulation by, 712
    postganglionic fibers, 225
    preganglionic fibers, 225
    reciprocal linkage, with sympathetic nervous system, 790
    reflex afferents in, 385
    sacral outflow, 220, 225
    tectal outflow, 225, 231
    visceral pain and, 386, 390
Paresthesia, 368
Parkinsonian tremor, neural mechanism of, *291*
Parotid gland, 1028, *1034*
  innervation of, *1028*
  stimulation of, by pilocarpine, *1034*
Partial pressure, of alveolar air, 879
  of carbon dioxide in alveoli, 879
    in blood, 879
  gas exchange and, 878
  of gases, 874
    in liquids, 874
  of oxygen in alveoli, 879
    in blood, 875, 879
    in tissues, 875

Partial pressure, of respiratory gases, 879
Parturition, blood flow through uterus during, 839
  pressure relations during, *838*
  control of, endocrine, 1201
  heart rate in, 784
  mechanism of, 1201
PATTON, Harry D.: Olfaction and olfactory pathways, 402–408
  and Theodore C. Ruch: Taste, 370–384
Pavlov's isolated fundic sac, 1044
Pellagra, 1142
  -preventive factor, 1142. See also *Niacin.*
Pelvic viscera, innervation of, autonomic, 227
Pelvis, sex hormone action on, 1203
Penis, cross section of, *1228*
  structure of, 1227
Pepsin, 1023, 1025, 1077, 1113
  digestive action of, 1047
  gastric, 1045
  nature and properties of, 1053
Pepsinogen, 1054
Peptide(s), 1055
  linkage, of amino acids, 1113
Peptone(s), 1054, 1057, 1062
  absorption of, in stomach, 1058
Perception, 305. See also *Sense(s), Stereognosis, Topognosis, Sensibility, two-point, definition of.*
  disturbances of, by cortical lesions, 366. See also *Sense(s), Stereognosis, Topog sis, Two-point sensibility.*
  of size, shape, figure writing, 331. See also *Sense(s), Stereognosis, Topognosis, Sensibility, two-point.*
  visual, spatial perception, 444
  wetness, 305
Pericarditis, constrictive, cardiac output in, 801
Perikaryon, definition, 96
Perilymph, of semicircular canals, 202
Perimeter, use of, in charting visual field, 506
Perimetric chart, *507, 508*
Perimetry, 506
Periodic breathing, 915
  clinical importance of, 916
Peripheral nerves, "preganglionic fibers" of, 218
  resistance, control of, by arterioles, 710
    regulation of, mechanisms of, 712
    in shock, 603
Peristalsis, 987
  in colon, 1005
  gastric, in emptying of stomach, 998
  mechanisms in, nervous, 987
  in small intestine, 1001
Peristaltic rush, 1002
  wave. See *Peristalsis.*
Peritoneatomes, 339
Permeability, capillary. See *Capillary permeability.*

Permeability of cell membrane. See *Cell.*

Personality, in relation to prefrontal lobe, 541

perspiration, types of, 947

*p*H. See also *Acid-base equilibrium, Body fluids.*

  of blood, 573. See also *Blood.*

  in carbohydrate metabolism, of heart, 825

  definition and derivation of, 573

  in electrical discharge, of heart, 724

  increased, in hyperpnea, *922*

Phagocytosis, 563

  opsonins in, 563

Phantom limb, 328

Phenol red, in study of kidney function, 974

Phenomenon. See also specific name of, as *Schiff-Sherrington phenomenon.*

  staircase, in muscle, 36

Phlebomanometer, *677, 678*

Phlorhizin, effect of, on glucose excretion, 1116

Phonocardiogram, 733, *733*

Phosphatases, 1023

Phosphate(s), bond energy, 60

  in nerves, 119. See also *Nerve(s).*

  parathyroid effects on, 1147

Phosphocozymase, 64

Phosphocreatine, muscle, 60

Phospholipids, in blood coagulation, 593

  plasma, 1122

Phosphorus, dietary, 1149

  in food, 1017

Phosphorylation, 74

  energy storage by, 1086

Phosphorolysis, muscle, 66

Phosphotriose, 65

Photohematachometer, Cybulski's, 663, *663*

Photon, definition of, 465

Physiological functions, and genetic factors, 1235

Physiology, first chair of, 3

  laboratories of, 1

  genetic aspects of, 1232–1246

Pigments, respiratory, 858

Pilocarpine, action of, on salivary glands, 1036

  effect of, on autonomic nervous system, 230

  in parotid gland stimulation, *1034*

Piloerection, 232, 252

  in response to cold, 248

Pilomotor activity, 232

Pitressin, effect on coronary flow, 808

  in vasoconstriction, 654

Pitts, Robert F.: Organization of the neural mechanisms responsible for rhythmic respiration, 896–912

  Regulation of respiration, 913–934

Pituitary, in blood glucose regulation, 1106

  and body size, 1239

  control, of capillary dilatation, 611

  extracts, effect on food intake of, 1157

Pituitary, innervation of, 245

  secretory cells of, *244*

  and kidney, 246. See also *Kidney.*

  in lactation, 1207

  lactogenic activity of, 1209

  and ovarian interrelationships, 1195, *1195*

  posterior, action of, on kidney function, 952, 978

  in reproduction, 1194

  role of, in ovulation, 1205

  thyrotropic hormone of, 1100

Pituitrin, action of, on arterioles, 708

  effect of, on hypothalamus, 247

    on kidney function, 952

    on mammary glands, 1210

  in uterine contractions, *1205*

Placenta, endocrine function of, 1200

  physiology of, 1200

Placing reactions, 198

  cerebral cortex effect on, *199*

  chin, 199

  contact, 198

  cortical localization of, 363

  functional localization of, 200

  positional, 199

  proprioceptive, 199

  as test of somatic sensibility, 324

  visual and vestibular, 198

Plasma, 936

  anticoagulants of, 550

  and blood cells, relative volumes of, 551

  calcium, effects on heart, 821, *822*

    in ventricular fibrillation, 821

  colloid osmotic pressure of, 569

  composition of, 549

  fluidity of, 639

  lipids, 1121

  magnesium in, physiological effects of, 824, *824*

  potassium, effect on T wave, 821

    heart block and, 821

    physiological effects of, 821, *820, 821*

  preservation of, 558

  proteins in, 583, 589. See also *Proteins, plasma.*

    colloid osmotic pressure of, 937

    colloidal osmotic pressure and, 549

  rheology of, 652

  sodium in, 819

    depletion in effects of, 820

    physiological effects of, 820, *820*

  solutes in, 567

  specific gravity of, 550, 584

  types of, use in hemorrhage, 602

  ultrafiltrate of, glomerular urine as, 968

  volume, clinical importance of, 939

    diminished, 958

    fall in, in adrenal cortical insufficiency, 958

    measurement of, 938

Plaster treatment, closed, clinical applications of, 628

Plastic flow. See *Flow*.

Platelets, of blood. See *Blood*.

Plethysmograph, 667, 692, *693*

Pleural space, 867

Pleuratomes, 339

Pleurisy, and respiratory reflexes, 929

Plexus(es), peripheral, autonomic, 221
    preaortic, 227

Pluck reflex, 160

Pneumographic records, of breathing, pain
    and, 343, *343*. See *Breathing*.

Pneumonia, dyspnea in, 905, 927
    effect on blood flow, 842

Pneumotaxic center, 896
    connections of hypothalamus with, 909,
        911
    destruction of, effects on respiration of,
        907, 909
    function of, 906, 911
        in hyperthermia, 909, 920
    functional relation of, to respiratory
        center, 908
    localization of, 906
    panting and, 909
    relation of apneusis to, 907
    respiratory center connections with, 907,
        910
        rhythm and, 906, 911
        and rhythm of breathing, 906
    inhibitory mechanism, of respiratory cen-
        ter, 911

Pneumothorax, 867
    Hering-Breuer reflexes in, role of, 905

Poikilothermic animals, 1163

Poikilothermy, due to hypothalamic lesions,
    248

Poise, definition of, 637

Poiseuille, father of rheology, 630

Poiseuille's law, 631

Polarization, anodal, 26
    cathodal, 26

Polycythemia, cyanosis in, 645
    idiopathic, 557

Polypnea, 860

Polyuria, 245
    in diabetes insipidus, 952

PONDER, Eric: The capillaries and the lym-
    phatics, 607–629
    The velocity and pressure of blood flow,
        660–681

Pons, effects of lesions of, on respiration, 909

Pontine level, of autonomic function. See
    Autonomic function.

Ponto-cerebellar receiving area, subdivisions
    of, *302*

Position sense, 324. See also *Muscle sense.*
    tests for, 324

Postcathodal depression, 22

Posterior columns, of spinal cord. See *Spinal
    cord.*
    lobe. See *Pituitary.*

Postural reflexes, 192, 198

Posture(s), abnormal, relief of, chordotomy
    in, 184
    anoxia in, 891, 892
    effect of, on vital capacity, 868
    reflex, thalamic, *198*
    and temperature regulation, 1169

Potassium. See also *Plasma potassium.*
    dietary, 1149
    in electrical discharge, of heart, 724
    intoxication, syndrome of, 821, *820*
    measurements of body water with, 942
    thiocyanide, in saliva, 1030

Potential. See also specific names of, as *Ac-
    tion potential; Demarkation potential;
    Electrical potential; Extrinsic potential;
    Spike potential; End-plate potential.*
    electric, corneoretinal, 477
        in electrocardiogram, 752
        optic nerve, retinal interaction and, 478
        retinal, 477
    electrotonic, 26, *27*
    end-plate. See *End-plate potential.*
    microphonic of inner ear, 425, 429
    oxidation-reduction, *73*
    "prepotential," 724

P-Q interval, of electrocardiogram, 741

P-R interval, of electrocardiogram, 741, *742*

Pre-angiotonin, in renal hypertension, 980

Precentral convolution, 281

Prefrontal area, of cerebral cortex. See *Cere-
    bral cortex.*
    lobe, cerebral, cytoarchitecture of, 285
    lobotomy, effects of, 540

Preganglionic fibers. See *Nerve fibers.*

Pregnancy, 1198
    cardiac output in, 801
    dietary allowances for, recommended
        amounts, 113
    hormone excretion during, 1199, *1199*
    and resistance to disease, 1237
    tests of, diagnostic, 1199
    urine, gonadotrophins in, 1196, 1199

Pregnandiol, 1186, *1186*, 1207
    structural formula of, 1186

Prehypertensin, in renal hypertension, 980

Presbyopia, 449, 453

Presinus wave, in pacemaker localization,
    720

Pressor afferents, in vasomotor center con-
    trol, 701, 703

Pressoreceptors, 921, *921*
    location of, 922
    morphology of, 922

Pressure, carbon dioxide, and acidosis, 918
    and alkalosis, 918
    in apnea, voluntary, 927
    of arterial blood, and dyspnea, 917
    and bicarbonate concentration, rela-
        tionship in blood, between, 918
    in eupnea, 913

Pressure, carbon dioxide, in exercise, 930
  at high altitudes, 926
  in hyperventilation, 915
  increased, in production of hyperpnea, *922*
  colloid osmotic. See also *Colloid osmotic pressure.*
  of plasma proteins, 549
  during viscous flow, *635*
  -flow curves, *641*
  fluid, measurement of, *633*
  hydrostatic, in tissues, 937
  intracranial, elevated, periodic breathing in, 916
  intra-ocular, 457
  intrapulmonic and intrathoracic, relation between, *866*
  oxygen, in alveolar air in apnea, voluntary, 927
    at high altitudes, 926
    and periodic breathing, 915
    and voluntary hyperventilation, 915
  pulsatile, effect on fluid flow, 643
  pulsations, optical tracings of, *683*
  sense, 307, 321
  tissue, exerting, on circulation, 645
  venous, respiratory reflexes and, 930
  -volume relationship, in inferior vena cava, *651*
  wave, 644, 647, 649
Priapism, in spinal animal, 241
Principle, Bernoulli's, 650
Proferment, of enzymes, 1024
Progesterone, 1186, *1186*
  in dysmenorrhea, 1205
  inactivation of, 1207
Projection areas, cerebral, development of, 265. See also *Cerebrum.*
  law of, 328
  and localization, distinction between, 328
  of sensations, visual, 445
Projections, cerebral. See *Cerebral cortex.*
  ipsilateral pyramidal, 282
Prolactin, 1209. See also *Lactogen.*
Proprioception, 324, 365
"Proprioceptive," reflex, in decereberate rigidity, 189
  stimulus in decereberate rigidity, 193
Proprioceptors, 150, 307. See also *Muscle sense.*
Propriospinal neurons. See *Neurons.*
Prostate gland, carcinoma of, 1218
  effect of androgens on, 1217
  hypertrophy of, androgens and, 1217
Prosthetic group, in enzyme, 1103
Prostigmine, in autonomic stimulation, 234
Protanopia and protanomaly, 496
Protein(s). See also *Amino acids, Enzymes, proteolytic.*
  absorption of, in intestine, 1076
  amino acid composition of, 1111

Protein(s), amino acids obtained by proteolytic cleavage of, 1068
  biological importance of, 1115
  of blood. See *Blood.*
  breakdown, 1179
  derivatives of, 1121
  dietary, recommended allowance of, 1132
  digestion of, end-products in, 1067
    significance of, 1069
  enzymes acting on, 1025
  in fibers, muscle, 58
  in food, 1016
  as foodstuff, 1014
  gastric, 1045
  irreplaceability of, in diet, 1135
  metabolism, 1111
    carbohydrates in, 1111
    intermediary, 1111
  nitrogen, N^{15} content of, 1114
  pepsin hydrochloric acid digestion of, 1054
  plasma, 583, 589
    albumin of, 583
    concentration of, 584
    determination of, 584
    specific gravity of, 584
  reserves, 1178
  in saliva, 1030
  synthesis, in amino acid utilization, 1112
Protein-sparing foods, 1121
Protein-splitting enzymes, 1023
Proteolytic enzymes, 1023
Proteoses, 1054, 1057, 1062
Prothrombin, 590
  deficiency of. See *Hypoprothrombinemia.*
  physiological significance of, 591
  in vitamin K deficiency, 1148
Protopathic sensibility. See *Sensibility.*
Protopathic epicritic hypothesis, of Head, 335
Pseudoglobulins. See *Globulins*
Ptyalin, 1023, 1025, 1030, 1035, 1038, 1057, 1070, 1075
  action of, conditions influencing, 1040
Puberty, androgens in, 1221
  in female, 1197
Public health, nutrition in, 1153
Pulmonary artery, receptor organs in, 852
  capillaries, distribution of, 870
  circulation, hemodynamics of, 630. See also *Flow, Fluid, Turbulence, Resistance.*
  fibrosis, dyspnea in, 905, 927
  receptors, 903. See also *Receptors.*
    response of, to inflation of lungs, *904*
  reflexes, 903. See also *Reflex(es).*
  ventilation, 869, 871
    and carbon dioxide alveolar pressure, relation between, 914
    effects of increased carbon dioxide and acidosis on, 917, *917*
Pulmotor, in artificial respiration, 872
Pulsatile pressure. See *Pressure, pulsatile.*

Pulsations, pressure, optical tracings of, *683*
   surface, optical capsule for recording, *685*
Pulse. See also *Heart rate.*
   arterial, 682–691. See also *Pulse, wave.*
      pressure, contour of, *688*
      tracing records of, *690*
   central, 688
   form of, 686
   hypodynamic, record of, *689*
   peripheral, 688
   pressure, 670, 682
   propagation of, 647
   venous, 690. See also *Venous blood pressure.*
      tracing records of, *690*
   "water-hammer," 689
   wave, 686
      characteristics of, 689
      recording of, 684
      reflected, 687
      velocity of, 683
Pupil, dilatation of, 231
   of eye, 455
   reflexes, 231
Purkinje network, 727
Purpura, thrombocytopenic, bleeding tendency in, 587
Putrefaction, intestinal, 1079
   amines from, 1080
Putrefactive process in intestine, physiological importance of, 1080
Pyloric glands, of stomach, 1042
Pyramidal system, control of spinal neurons by, 176
   tract, 269
Pyridine-adenine nucleotide. See *Cozymase.*
Pyridoxine, 1143
Pyruvic acid, blood, 1110, *1110*
   in metabolism, 1111
   oxidation of, in nerves, 119

Q wave, interpretation of, 755, 761
   in myocardial infarction, 819
   standards or, normal, 743, 746
QRS complex, of electrocardiogram, 742, *742, 743, 744*
Q-T interval, of electrocardiogram, 743
Quadrant lesions, dorsal, in spinal injuries, 183
   ventral, in spinal injuries, 183

R.Q. See *Respiratory quotient.*
R wave, in anoxemia, 815
   interpretation of, 756, 760
   standards for, normal, 744, 746
Radiation(s), in heat dissipation, 1167
   thalamocortical auditory, 436
Radium, dorsal quadrant lesions due to, 184

Rami communicantes, gray, 223
   white, 222
Raynaud's disease, autonomic nervous system and, 236
Reaction. See specific names of, as *Static reaction.*
Receptor(s), aortic, morphology of, 922
   carotid, morphology of, 922
   deflation, 904
   inflation, 905
   for inspiratory-inhibitory reflex, 904
   organs for reflex control, in carotid sinus, 852
      in regulation of brain circulation, 852
   pulmonary, response of, to inflation of lungs, *904*
   swallowing, 985
   temperature-sensitive, 1172
   tension, 150
   visual, discharge of, 478
Reciprocal innervation, 162
   and subnormality, 169–170
Reciprocity, in interneurons, 134
   principle of, definition, 134
Recruitment, of end-organs, 311
Rectum, reflexes, in spinal shock, 180. See also *Colon.*
Reductases, 1026
Referred pain. See *Pain, visceral.*
Reflex(es), acceleratory, of labyrinth, 202–212
   acoustic, 412
   activity, spinal. See *Spinal.*
   afferents, in parasympathetic nervous system. See *Parasympathetic.*
      in sympathetic nervous system. See *Sympathetic.*
   Anrep and Segall, in coronary circulation control, 807
   arc, visceral, *223*
   auriculopressor, 704
   autonomic, 228
   axon, and blood flow through skin, 831
      and cardiac output, 828
   Bainbridge, 704, 790
   cardio-aortic, 852
   changes in, in cerebral cortex injury, 282, 283
   chemoreceptor, 922
   conditioned. See *Conditioned responses.*
   connections, functional significance of, 161
   contractions, *166*
   coordination, 162
   cough, 929
   of crossed extension, *156*
   "delta" flexor, 161
   discharges, *159*
      segmental, 148
   extensor, crossed, 162
      thrust, 160
   enterogastric, 999

Reflex(es), flexion, variation in pattern of, 158
flexor, 156
  inhibition of, 167
  and multineuron arcs, 160
  stimulus, response to, 187
  transmission of, 158
gastrocolic, 1006
general, in blood flow, 828
from heart receptors, 929
Hering-Breuer, sensitization of, in lung diseases, 905
ileogastric, 999
inspiratory-inhibitory, receptors responsible for, 904
interaction of, *164*
local, and cardiac output, 828
  in sympathetic system, 228
Lovén, 831, 846
mechanism, circumscribed, 147, *149*, 161
  diffuse, 147, 161
  extrinsic control of, 173
  Hering-Breuer, 896
  structure of, 146
from muscles and joints, in control of respiration, 929, 930
myenteric, 1001
myotatic or stretch, 149
neck, tonic, in decerebrate animal, 194
  in spinal animal, 192
neuron arc, multi-, 147
    flexor reflexes and, 160
    three-, 147, 158
    two-, 147, 158
      inhibition of, *169*
      stretch reflexes and. See *Reflexes, stretch.*
"pluck" or flexor tendon jerk, 160
postural, 192
pressoreceptor, and inhibition of respiration, 928
proprioceptive, 150
protective, in control of respiration, 929
of pupil to light, 456, *456*
jrom receptors in right heart, 929
in rectum, in spinal shock, 180
respiratory, anoxia and, 922
  aortic and carotid, 921, 928
  arterial pressure and, 921, 928
  and blood pH, 918, 922
  from blood pressure rise, 928
  carbon dioxide and, 922
  chemoreceptor, 913, 916
  deflation of lung and, 904
  and depressed states, 916
  from distension of atrium, 930
  dyspnea and, 905, 916, 927
  effects of vagotomy on, 905, *905*
  in eupnea, 903, 923
  and exercise, 930
  Hering-Breuer, 903, 909, 916

Reflex(es), respiratory, in hyperpnea, 903
  and inflation of lungs, 903
  lung distensibility and, 905, 916, 927
  from muscles and joints, 929
  pain and, 909
  and pleurisy, 929
  pressoreceptor, 921, 928
  protective, 929
  rhythm of breathing and, 905, 909
  from right atrium, 930
  stimulator of vagus and, 906
  venous pressure and, 930
rhythmic, 163, *163*
righting, 195
  body, 197
  in cat, *196*
  labyrinthine, 196
  neck, 197
  optical, 197
sequence, 7, *8*
sneeze, 242, 929
spinal, long, 171
stretch, 149, *150*, *151*
  in decerebrate rigidity, 187, 193
  distribution of, 154
  functional significance of, 155
  inhibition of, 151
  intensity of, 187
  maintenance of, 187
  phasic, 152
  role in stepping and running, 155
  static, 152
  transmission of, 158
  and two-neuron arc, 160
swallowing, 242
  sensory areas for, *986*
unconditioned, 529
vasomotor, and cardiac output, 828
  methods for study of, 692
visceral, 386
vomiting, 242, 1009
Refraction of eye, abnormalities in, 451
  index of, 443
  of light by convex lens, *441*
Refractive surfaces of eye, 443, *443*
  of nerve, 30, 104
  relation of, to spike potential, 105
  in sense organ discharge, 311
Rein's thermostromuhr, 662
Reissner's membrane, 414
Relaxation, energy liberated during, 81
Relaxin in guinea pig parturition, 1203
Renal. See also *Kidney.*
  clearance, definition of, 967
  hypertension, experimental, 980
  physiology, theories of, 933. See also *Kidney.*
Renin, and kidney blood flow, 833
  mechanism, terminology of, 980
  in production of experimental renal hypertension, 980

Rennet, 1055. See also *Rennin*.
Rennin, 1022, 1023, 1025, 1055
  action of, on casein, 1056
  gastric, 1045, 1055
Reproduction, in female, 1184–1210
  in male, 1213–1230
  physiology of, 1182–1246
Reproductive cycle, 1198
  system, in male, *1213*, 1217
Reserve air, in lung, 867
Residual air, in lung, 867
Resistance, electrical, 637
  to flow of suspensions, 642
  fluid, 635, 637
  formula for, 657
  membrane, 17, 29
  peripheral, 646, 657
    to blood flow, 657
  for viscous flow, 639
Respiration. See also *Aspiration, Expiration, Inspiration, Respiratory, Apnea, Dyspnea, Eupnea, Hyperpnea*, etc.
  abdominal, 861
  accessory movements in, 864
  and acid-base balance, 888
  in acidosis, 917, *917*, 922
  acidosis and alkalosis in, 918
  and air hunger, 918
  alkali reserve and, 917
  anatomy of, 858–875
  apparatus for, 858
  artificial, 871, *872*
    apparatus for, 872
  autoregulation of, by vagi, 903
  Biot's, 916
  carbon dioxide in, 858
    pressure of blood on, 899, 913, 922
  central nervous system and, 858
  cerebral blood flow and, 919, 928
  Cheyne-Stokes', 916
  control of, chemical, 913
    hypothalamic, 909, 920, 928
    nervous, 927
    reflex, protective, 929
    voluntary, 927
  costal, 861
  depression of, narcotic, 916
  depth of, mechanism for grading, 901
  in diabetes, 918
  diffusion in, 858
  effect of, on acid-base balance in blood, 576, 579
    destruction of pneumotaxic center on, 907
    lesions of pons on, 909
    oxygen pressure of blood on, 925
    voluntary hyperventilation on, *915*
  eupnea, 898
  in exercise, 930
  external, 858, 877
    mechanics of, 859

Respiration, gas exchange in, 877
  in lungs, 879
  at high altitudes, 925
  inhibition of, and irritant vapors, 929
    pressoreceptor reflexes and, 928
  internal, 858
  Kussmaul's, 918
  lung movements in, 864
    ventilation in, 869
  minute volume of, 871
  motor nerve impulses in, character of, 900
    origin of, 901
  movements in, amplitude of, 859
    frequency of, 859
  in nephritis, 918
  organization of, functional, neural mechanisms in, 909
  pattern of, modifications in, 860
  periodic, 916
    clinical importance of, 916
  *p*H of blood and, 917, 922
  physics of, 858–931
  physiological significance of, 878
  pneumographic records of, pain and, 343, *343*
  pneumotaxic center and, 906
    inhibitory mechanism of, 911
  in pneumothorax, 905
  position of respiratory organs in, *861*
  pressure changes in, 864
  in pulmonary disease, 905, 916, 927
  reflex control of, pressoreceptor, 928
  regulation of, 913–931
    chemoreceptor reflexes in, 923
  respired air in, composition of, 877
  rhythm of, inhibitory mechanisms and, 909
    origin of, 906
    and pneumotaxic center, 906
  rhythmic, neural mechanisms responsible for, 896–911
  rib action in, *863*
    and vertebra in, 862
  role in circulation, 646
  stimulation of, by carbon dioxide increase in inspired air, 914
  and temperature control, 878
  vagal inhibitory mechanism of, 910
Respirator, Drinker, in artificial respiration, 872
Respiratory bronchioles, 869
  -cardiovascular crisis, in anoxemia, general, 815
  center, breathing regulation by, 900, 905
    carbon dioxide action on, 899, 913, 923, 930
  of cerebral cortex, 285
  control of, 919
    cerebral cortical, 927
    chemical, 913
  effects of acapnia on, 915
    acidosis and alkalosis on, 917

Respiratory center, effects of anesthesia on, 916
  anoxia on, 920, 923, 926
  blood flow on, 919
  carbon dioxide excess on, 914, 916
  electrical stimulation of, *897*
  functional relation of pneumotaxic center to, 908
  inspiratory and expiratory divisions of, 896, *897*
  isolated, properties of, 908
  localization of, 896, *897*
  medullary. See *Respiratory center.*
  mode of action of carbon dioxide on, 918
  -motoneuron mechanism, 909
  neural discharge of, nature of, 899
  neurons of, properties of, 899, 908
    synaptic connections of, excitatory, 898
      inhibitory, 898
    organization of, 898
      functional, 909
    properties of, 899
    regulation of, in exercise, 930
      reflex, 903, 921
    regulatory mechanisms of, chemical, direct, 920
      reflex, 924
  respiratory rhythm and, 906
  sensitivity of, to carbon dioxide, 914
    variations in, to carbon dioxide, 916
  temperature effects on, 909, 920
  in vomiting, 1010
  complex, functional organization of, 909
  impulses, frequency of, factors controlling, 901
  mechanisms, organization of, 898, 909
  motoneuron, repetitive activity of, *902*
  motor impulses, pattern of, 900
    nerve discharge, character of, 900
      after inhalation of carbon dioxide, *900*
      pattern of, 900
    neurons, 899
    pathways, 899
    cranial nerve, connections of, 899
  movements, apparatus for recording, *859*
    normal, curve of, *860*
    registration of, methods of, 860
  muscles, nervous control of, 900
  nerve impulses, discharge of, carbon dioxide pressure and, 900
  neurons. See *Neuron(s).*
  organs, physiological anatomy of, 869
  pigments, 858
  quotient, 877
    calculation of, 1091
    in carbohydrate conversion to fat, 1128
    factors affecting, 1092
    nonprotein calculation of, 1093

Respiratory responses, due to heating, *1173*
  to nitrogen and carbon dioxide, following denervation, *924*
  structures, specialization of, 858
  tract, vagus effect on, 787
Response(s), clonic. See *Clonic.*
  extension, 187
  flexion reflex in, 187
Resuscitation, 872
Resuscitator, in artificial respiration, 872
Reticular formation, clinical importance of diseases involving, 897
  of medulla, respiratory center and, 896, 897
Reticulo-endothelial system, leukocytes and, 563
  and resistance to disease, 1237
Retina, areal interaction of, 476, 479
  blind spot of, 511
  blood flow in capillaries of, measurement of, 664, *665*
  color zones of, 507
  corresponding points of, 508
  electric potentials of, 477
  electrical activity of, 477
  functional anatomy of, 473
  grain of, 482, 518
  innervation of, 512
  macula of, 511
  maculopapillary bundle of, 511
  nerve fibers in, diagram of, *511*
  photochemical cycle of, 472, *473*
  photochemistry of, 466
  projection of, upon calcarine fissure, *516*
  regional variations of, 476, 485
  rods and cones of, 474, 477, 485
  summation in, 479. See also *Summation.*
Retinene, 472
Retinoscope, 459, 461
Reynolds number, 631, 644
Rh factor in blood, 561
  erythroblastosis foetalis due to, 561
  in heredity, 1245
Rhe, definition of, 637
Rheobase, 23
Rheology, 630. See also body fluids as *Blood, Plasma, Serum.*
Rhodopsin. See *Visual purple.*
Riboflavin, 1141
  deficiency of, 1245
  dietary, recommended allowance of, 1132
  in food, 1017
  requirements of, 1141
  sources of, 1141
Ribs, action of, in respiration, *863*
  movements of, in inspiration, 862
  and vertebra, *862*
Ricco's law, 479
Rickets, vitamin D deficiency in, 1147
Righting reflexes, 195

Rigidity, decerebrate, 187–200. See also *Decerebrate rigidity.*
decorticate, 187–200. See also *Decorticate rigidity.*
Rigor, muscle, 56
Ringer's solution, 819
modified, 558
Rods and cones, chemical mechanism of, 471. See also *Retina, functional anatomy.*
Rouget cells, of capillaries, 608, *608*
Round window of ear, 432
RUCH, Theodore C.: Association areas and the cerebral cortex in general, 525–547
Audition and the auditory pathways, 409–439
Binocular vision and central visual pathways, 503–524
Neural basis of somatic sensation, 334–369
Somatic sensation, 305–334
Visceral sensation and referred pain, 385–401
Vision, 463–502
and Harry D. Patton: Taste, 370–384

S WAVE, interpretation of, 756, 762
normal standards for, 744, 746
S.D.A., 1098
Saccharides, in nutrition, 1104
Saccule, of semicircular canals, 203, 211
Sacculi alveolares, 870
Saline, in hemorrhage, role of, 601
Saliva, adaptability of, to material chewed, 1038
composition of, 1030
digestive action of, 1038
functions of, 1040
paralytic secretion of, 1037
secretion of, center for, 1038
mechanism of, 1037
Salivary glands, 1028–1040. See also *Submaxillary, Parotid, Sublingual glands.*
acetylcholine in, 1036
action of drugs on, 1036
adrenergic nerve fibers of, 1033
digestive action of, 1028–1040
electrical changes during activity of, 1038
histological changes during activity of, 1034, *1034*
structure of, 1029, 1034
innervation of, 1028
autonomic, 226
nerve fibers of, cholinergic, 1033
secretory, 1031
trophic, 1032
secretion of, composition of, relation to strength of stimulation, 1032
Salivation, 226
Salmine, in blood coagulation, 598

Salt(s), absorption of, in stomach, 1058
depletion, in proportion to water, 960
in water excess, 959
inorganic, as foodstuff, 1014
solutions, in hemolysis, 558
in water depletion, 958
water retention in, 961
Sanborn apparatus (modified Benedict apparatus), *1090*
Saponin, as capillary poison, 619
Satiety, 1156
Scala media, 414
tympani, 414
vestibuli, 414
Schaefer prone pressure method, of artificial respiration, 871, *872*
Schiff-Sherrington phenomenon in spinal shock, 181
Scoterythrous, 498
Scrotum, effects of androgens on, 1217, 1225
Scurvy, in ascorbic acid deficiency, 1144
Sebaceous glands, effects of androgens on, 1219
Secretin, 834, 1064
Segmental reactions, static, in spinal animal, 192
Semen, coagulation of, 1227
Semicircular canal(s), anatomy of, 202
angular acceleration and, *208*
function of, 205. See also *Acceleration, Nystagmus.*
historical note on, 203
position of, *202, 204, 205*
stimulation of, 206
Semilunar ganglion, 352
valves, in systole, ventricular, 731
Seminal vesicle, effect of castration on, *1216*
Sensation(s). See also *Threshold.*
clinical terminology of, 307
cold. See *Temperature sense.*
common, 306
cutaneous, 307
deep, 307, 322, 335. See also *Muscle sense.*
pain, 307, 324, 397
pressure, 307, 324
dissociation of, due to nerve section, 334
false, 334
topographical, 334
hunger, 386. See also *Hunger.*
osseous, 325, 366
projection of, 328
as mechanism of referred pain, 398
in stimulation of cerebral cortex, 360
somatic, 305–332
A and C fibers in, 342
nerves in, 309
neural basis of, 334–368
and stimulus, Weber-Fechner law of, 313
superficial. See *Sensibility, cutaneous.*
visceral, 307. See also *Visceral.*
warmth. See *Temperature sense.*

Sense(s). See also *Sensation*.
  classification of, clinical, 307
    Sherrington's, 307
  common, 305
  modalities of, 305
  number and classification of, 305
  organic, 386
  organs. See also *Sensation*.
    adaptation in, 312, *312*
      rate of, 313
      for cold, 314
    discharge of, 309, 321, 323
      adaptation, 313
      frequency of, as function of intensity, 310
      recruitment of, end-organs and, 311
      refractory period of, 311
      and stimulus intensity, *311*
      Weber-Fechner law in, 313
    fatigue of, 312
    for heat, and cold, 314
      types of, 323
    muscle, 323
    somatic, adaptation in, *312*
    for touch, 319
  special, 305, 307
Sensibility. See also *Threshold*.
  cutaneous, nature of, 306
  deep, 322
    synonyms of, 324
  epicritic, 335
    role of cerebral cortex in, 365
  pain and warmth, apparatus for measurement of, *320*
  protopathic, 335
    quantitative theory of, 336
    thalamic basis of, 366
  punctiform, discovery and significance of, 306
  for touch-pressure, 321
  for warmth and cold, 315
  remaining, in demarcation of dermatomes, 339
  skin, figure writing test of, 332
    thermal, *316*
  touch, distribution of, 322
  two-point, 329
    cortical localization of, 366, 368
    neural basis of, 330
      factors in, *331*
  vibratory, 325, 366
Sensitivity, differential, 309
Sensitization, to acetylcholine, 236–237
  to adrenaline, 236–237
  iris, acetylcholine, in, *237*
Sensory areas for swallowing reflex, *986*
  disturbances, of cortical type, 368
  examination, Fox's chart for recording, *327*
  functions, 305–546
    cortical localization of, 325, 359

Sensory functions, of spinothalamic tract, 346, 351. See also *Tract(s)*.
  of thalamus, 366
  impulses, cutaneous, conduction velocity of, 342
  innervation, of viscera. See *Viscera*.
  root fields. See *Dermatomes*.
  stimulation, effect of, on electroencephalogram, 526
  stimuli, localization of. See *Topognosis*.
  systems, of brain stem. See *Brain stem*.
  tracts, of spinal cord. See *Spinal cord*.
  unit, definition of, 319
    two-point threshold in relation to, 330
Septicemia, leukocytes in, 563
Serum, blood. See also *Blood*.
  composition of, 549
  fluidity of, 639
  pigments in, 549
  rheology of, 652
Sex, determination of, 1232
  hormones, action of, on bone, 1203
    on myometrium, 1205
    on pelvis, 1203
    bio-assay of, 1187
    in calcium metabolism, 1203
    in carcinogenesis, 1203
    excretion of, 1188
    female, actions of, 1203
    in metabolism, 1203
    and metabolism, basal, 1097
  organs, innervation, 225, 227
  and resistance to disease, 1237
Sexual differentiation, embryonic, 1220
  functions, hypothalamus and, 249
  maturity, androgens during, 1222
Sham feeding, 1049
  rage, hypothalamus and, 250
    clinical manifestation of, 250
Sherrington's classification of senses, 307
Shivering, in temperature maintenance, 1166
Shock, anaphylactic, bleeding tendency in, 587
  body fluid loss causing, 958
  cardiac output in, 801
  "conditioning," 21
  events in, course of, 603
  nature and treatment of, 602
  secondary, heart rate in 784
  "test," 21
  transfusion problems in, 601–604
  types of, 602
"Shortening reaction," in decerebrate rigidity, 191
Sickness, motion, 195
Sign, of Babinski, in cerebral cortex injury 282, 284
  local, in reflex action, 158
Silent period, definition, 153. See also *Moto, neuron(s)*.
Single unit, auditory nerve, 427

Sino-auricular node, action potential of, 719
    Bachman's bundle and, 719
    pacemaker in, mammalian, 718
    presinus wave of, 720
    in systole, auricular, 729
    vagus effect on, 786
Sinus venosus, heart beat and, 717. See also
    Pacemaker.
Skeleton, effects of androgens on, 1219
Skiascope, 461
Skin, blood flow in, 829
    effects of androgen on, 1219
    fluid exchanges through, 947
    innervation of, *315*
    resistance, 224
        electrical, *224*
    sensibility, 332
    temperature, 1163
        regulation, 1168
Sleep, effect of, on electroencephalogram,
    526
Smegma, 1227
Smooth muscle, 46–51
    of blood vessels, 46
    classification of, 46
    mechanical properties of, 49, *50*
    multi-unit, 46
    nictitating membrane, 47, *47*
    tension release in, 50
    "tone" of, 49
    visceral, 48, *49*
Snake venom, in blood coagulation, 589. See
    also *Fibrinogen*.
Sneeze reflex, 242, 929
Snellen visual acuity chart, 488
Sodium. See also *Plasma sodium*.
    citrate, responses to, pre- and postgangli-
        onic, *132*
    depletion, effects of, on body fluids, 959
    dietary, 1149, 1152
    intracellular, 941
    radioactive, distribution of, in body, 939
    space, 942
Soma, definition, 96
Somatic motor representation, relation of, to
    autonomic, *252*
    sensation, 305–332. See also *Sensation,
        somatic.*
Somesthesia, 307
Sound, dimensions of, physical and psycho-
    logical, 409–423
    intensity of, 417
    Korotkow, 673
    loudness of, 417
    pitch of, 417
    quality of, 421
    timbre of, 421, *422*
    wave, compound, 421, *422, 423*
        dimensions of, 416, *416*
        pendular, 421
        routes of conduction of, 431

Sound wave, simple, 421
    sinusoidal, 421
Spastic paralysis, 273
Spatial summation, essential conditions for,
    138–140
Specific dynamic action, in metabolism, 1098
    and urea synthesis, 1118
    gravity, of blood, determination of, 584
    of blood and plasma, 550, 584
Sperm transport, mechanism of, 1202
Spermatogenesis, 1224
Spermatozoa, 1213, 1225
Spherocytosis, of erythrocytes, 559
Sphincter(s). See organs involved, as *Stom-
    ach.*
Sphingomyelins, 1122
Sphygmographs, 684
Sphygmomanometer, 672, *672*
Spike potential, 11, 30
    of auditory nerve, 426
    in cardiac impulse, 727
    compound, 96
        synthesis of, 102
        after curarization, 122, *122, 123, 124*
    diphasic, 11, *13*
    monophasic, 11, *12*
    of motoneuron soma, *113*
    of muscle, 33, 122
    muscle stimuli, repetitive, and, 37
    of nerve, 96–104
    nerve heat production and, 118
    of phrenic nerve fibers, following inhala-
        tion of carbon dioxide, *900*
    relation of, amplitude to conduction
        velocity, 101
        to refractory period, 105
    triphasic, 17, *16*
Spinal animal, 192, 241
    carotid sinus, and blood pressure in, 242
    neck reflexes in, tonic, 192
    priapism in, 241
    static reactions in, general, 192
        local, 192
    canal, widening of, 348
    compression, cervical dislocations and,
        183
        laminectomy in, 183
        physiology of, 182
        "spinal concussion," 182
    cord, autonomic functions of, 241
        cross section of, *148*, 269, 347, 348
            showing lamination, *349*
        functional organization of, *172, 174,
            175*
        human, injuries of, 178–186
        longitudinal section of, *147*
        pathways for visceral sensation, 400
        posterior columns of, in control of
            movement, 351
            sensory functions of, 350
        preganglionic fibers from, 238

Spinal cord section, effect of, on menstrual cycle, 1190
   sensory tracts of, 345
   transection, complete, effects of, 178
"decompression," physiology of, 182, 183
fibers, ascending, 110
   descending, 111
   propriospinal, 110, *110*
injuries, transection level of, and, 181
lesions, diagram of, *184*
level, of autonomic function. See *Autonomic function.*
nerve(s). See *Nerve(s).*
reflex activity, 146–176
root, posterior, cross section of, *342*
shock, 178–182, 241, 698
   Babinski's sign in, 179
   flexor spasm and, 179
   hyperactivity in, 180
   hyporeflexia in, 178
   nature of, 180–181
   pharmacological agents in, 181
   reflexes in, autonomic, 179
      bladder, 180, 181
      extension, 179
      flexion, 179
      mass, 179
      rectal, 180
   release, gradual, in, 181
      "phenomenon" and, 181
      reverse in, 181
   Schiff-Sherrington phenomenon in, 181
tracts, fiber of, 109, *110*, *111*
transections, incomplete, 183
   Brown-Séquard's syndrome, 183
   quadrant lesions in, 183
Spindles, muscle, 190
Spine. See *Spinal.*
Spirogram, 860
Spirometer, in measurement of vital capacity of lung, 867
Splanchnic pain. See *Pain, visceral.*
Spleen, blood flow through, 844
  as blood reservoir, 562
  blood storage in, 844
  contraction of, factors in, 845
  dilatation of, factors in, 846
  and resistance to disease, 1237
  vasomotor nerves of, 846
Splenic artery, receptor organs in, 852
Splenomegaly, in blood diseases, 562
Squint, 506
Stapedius muscle, 411
Starch-splitting enzymes, 1023
Starling's law of the heart, 52, 792
  theory of fluid exchange, 569
  of fluid transfer, 937
  of lymph formation, 622
Starvation, blood ketone changes during, *1126*
  weight loss of various organs during, 1112

Static reactions, 192
  local, in decerebrate animal, 193
  in spinal animal, 192
  segmental, in decerebrate animal, 194
Steapsin, 1025
Stenosis, aortic, heart murmurs in, 738
  mitral, heart murmurs in, 738, *739*
Stepping movements, genesis of, 163, *163*
Stereognosis, 332
Sterility in male, 1226
Stilbestrol, effect of, on lactation, 1210
  synthetic estrogen, 1187
Stimulants in food, 1019
Stimulation, antidromic, of neurons. See *Neuron(s).*
  by brief shocks, 19
  by constant currents, 21
  electric shock for, 19
  intensity of, in relation to discharge, *310*
  synaptic, and local excitatory state, 138
Stimulus(i), adequate, 308
  intensity, and sense organ discharge, *311*
  maximal, 19
  sensory, localization of. See *Topognosis.*
  stretch, in muscle spindles, *189*
  subliminal, 19
  threshold, 19
Stomach, absorption in, substances involved, 1057
  anatomy of, 989, *989*
  contractions, tonus rhythm of, 995, *995*
  digestion and absorption in, 1042–1058
     changes of food in, 1056
  duodenal bulb, and large intestine, *990*
  emptying of, 997
     gastric peristalsis in, 998
  food in, stratification of, 993, *994*
  fundic sac, isolated, 1045
     operation for, *1044*
  gastric cycle of, 992
  hunger contractions of, 994
  hydrochloric acid in, formation of, 1048
  innervation of, 993
  movements of, 991
     effects on food, 993
  musculature of, 990
  pyloric glands of, 1042
     sac, isolated, 1045
  receptive relaxation of, 997
  sphincter of, cardiac, 988
Strabismus, 505, 510
Strength-duration curve, 23–25, *24*
Stretch afferent. See *Muscle spindle.*
Stretch-movement, 151, 152
Stretch-posture, 151, 152
Stretch-reflex, 149–156. See also *Reflex(es), stretch.*
  stimulus, in muscle spindles, *189*
Striopallidum, 291
Stromaprotein, muscle, 59

Stromuhr, Ludwig's, 660, *661*
  types of, 662
Strychnine, hypothalamus and, 250
Strychninization of root entry zone, in demarcation of dermatomes, 339
Subliminal fringe, definition, 128, 138
  relation to discharge zone, 142
Sublingual gland, 1028
Submaxillary gland, 1028
  cells of, *1035, 1036*
  chorda tympani nerve to, *1029*
  innervation of, 1029
Subnormality, in ganglia, 129
  and reciprocal innervation, 169
Substantia gelatinosa Rolandi, 347
Succus entericus, 1072
  in intestinal digestion, 1061
Sucrase, 1025, 1073
Sucrose, distribution of, in body, 939
Sudomotor activity, 232
Sugar(s), absorption of, in stomach, 1058
  rise, in blood, in response to cold, 248
  -splitting enzymes, 1023
Sulfate, distribution of, in body, 939
Sulfocyanate, distribution of, in body, 939
  space, 942
Sulfur, dietary, 1149
Summation, areal, in retina, 479
  time in retina, 479
Supernormality, and facilitation, 130
  in ganglia, 129
Supporting reaction, negative, 194
  positive, 193
Suppression. See *Inhibition.*
Suppressor strips, 279
Supra-opticohypophysial system, 243
Surface(s) area, formula for, 1096
  effect on blood coagulation, 596
Suspensions, resistance to flow of, 658
Swallowing, 985
  reflex, 242
  respiration of, 986
  stages of, 985
Sweat, 947
  glands, innervation of, autonomic, 232
Sweating, role of, 947
  in temperature regulation, 1170
Symbiosis, between bacteria and intestine, 1080
Sympathectomy, and blood flow, 830
  effects of, 235
Sympathetic nerves, to colon, 1006
  of intestine, 1003
  nervous system, 222. See also *Nerve(s), sympathetic.*
    afferents, visceral, 227
    anatomy of, 220, 226
    in cardiac impulse, conduction of, auriculoventricular, 789
    cervical division, 222
    coronary circulation control and, 806

Sympathetic nervous system, definition, 220
  emotion and 230
  eye and, 231
  hypothalamus and, 242
  innervation of, heart, 226
  local reflexes, 228
  origin of term, 218
  peripheral resistance regulation by, 712
  postganglionic fibers of, 220
  preganglionic fibers of, 220
  reciprocal linkage, with parasympathetic nervous system, 790
  reflex afferents of, 386
  role in visceral pain, 390
  sweating, 232
  thoracolumbar division, 220
Sympathin, in autonomic stimulation, 235
  in blood flow, 829
  E, 831
  effect on, heart rate, 789. See also *Adrenaline.*
  I, 831
Synapse(s), on interneuron. See *Interneuron.*
  on motoneurons. See *Motoneurons.*
  summation of, 140
Synaptic connections, of respiratory center, 898
  delay, in central nervous system, 140
    interpretation of, 141
    of motoneurons, *141*
    in sympathetic ganglia, 128
  scale, 134, *135*, 138, 142
    definition of, 134
    structure of, *135*
  stimulation, degrees of, 129
    as a local process, 138
  transmission. See *Transmission.*
  transmitter, hypothesis, chemical, 131
    electrical, 131
Syncope, 603
Syndrome, Brown-Séquard's, in spinal injuries, 183
  Horner's, 231
  of potassium intoxication, 821, *820*
  of visual disorientation, 523
Synkamin, synthetic vitamin K, 591
Syntonin, 1054
Syringomyelia, 348
Systemic arterial pressure, and cerebral blood flow regulation, 848, 851, 854
  circulation, hemodynamics of, 630
Systole, in anoxemia, general, 814, *814*
  auricular, 729
    course of, 729
  coronary blood flow during, 812
  effect of, in coronary circulation control, 812
  ventricular, course of, 731
    phases of, 731

Systolic pressure, 670. See also *Blood pressure.*

Tabes dorsalis, 156
  hyperpathia in, 344
Tachycardia, in anoxia, 891
  cardiac output in, 801
  in hypercalcemia, 821
Taste, 370–384
  arcuate nucleus lesions and, *380*
  blindness, 373
  buds, 374, *374*
    innervation of, 375
    specificity of, 375
  bulbar nuclei and tracts in, 376, 381
  clinical examination of, 382
  cortical representation, 379
  differences between smell and, 370
  effect of nerve lesions on, *378*
  food intake and, 383
  genetic factors in, 1240
  modalities of, 371
  nerve pathways of. See also *Nerve(s), Brain stem.*
    neural pathways for, 374
  olfactory component of, 983
  pathways of, 376, 381, *381*
    from face, 381
    peripheral, 376
  receptors for, 371, 374
  and smell, as chemical senses, 370
  solutions for testing, 382
  tests of taste sensibility, *372*, 373, 382
  thalamic localization of, 379, 381
  threshold of, 373, 383
Tawara, node of, 726
Teleceptors, 307
Temperature of blood, 549
  body, 1163. See also *Fever.*
    control of, respiration and, 878
    factors in, 1168. See also *Heat loss.*
    variations in, 1164
  effect of, on enzymes, 1165
    on metabolism, 1163
    on testis, 1225
  environmental, effect of, on body temperature, *1164*
    on locomotor activity, 1160
    upon metabolism, total, 1100
    and food intake, 1157
  sense, 314
    cold and warm spots, 315
    for cold, paradoxical, 314
    receptor for, 314
    stimulus for, 316
  skin, 1163
Temporal lobe. See also *Cerebral cortex.*
  gyri of, 542
  lobectomy, effects of, 542
Tendon jerk, 153
Tension receptors. See *Receptors.*

Tensor tympani, 411
Test(s), Aschheim-Zondek, for pregnancy, 1199
  of cardiac output, acetylene technique, 796
    CO_2 technique, 796
    dilution method, 798
    pulse pressure method, 799
  Flack, in respiration, 866
  Friedman, for pregnancy, 1199
Testis(es), androgens from, 1215
  androgens in, *1221*
  cross section of, *1223*
  effect of heat on, 1225
  endocrine function of, 1185
  hormones of, 1185
  structure of, 1225
  transplantation of, 1213
Tetany, parathyroid, hypocalcemia in, 1147
Testosterone, 1215, *1215*
  doses of, in castrated rats, *1222*
Thalamic nuclei, connections and projections of, *364*
Thalamocortical projections, density and extent of, 358
  ipsilateral character of, 358
  organization of, functional, 357
    topographical, 357, *358*, *359*
Thalamus, anatomical study of, methods for, 354
  animal, 195
  and cerebral cortex, as functional unit, 354
  cross sections at different levels of, *355*
  nuclear mass of, *354*
  nuclei and connections of, 355
  sensory functions of, 366
  syndrome from damage to, 368
  taste localization in, 379, 381
  thalamocortical projections of, 357
Theelin, 1186
Theelol, 1186
Thermal analgesia, 352
  equilibrium, 1163
Thermodynamics, laws of, 1087
Thermostromuhr, Rein's, 662, *662*
Thiamine, 1139
  deficiency of, symptoms of, 1140
  dietary, recommended allowance of, 1132
    sources of, 1140
  in food, 1017
  human requirements of, 1140
Thio-urea, measurement of body water with 942
Thirst, 389, 948
  sensory basis of, 289
Thiry intestinal loop, 1072
Thiry-Vella intestinal loop, 1072, 1074
Thoracolumbar division, of autonomic nervous system, 220

Thorax, 859
  rest position of, 859
Threshold, 27
  difference, 465
  of ganglion cells, 129
  local changes on neuron soma, 138
  of neurons, 143
  relation to conduction velocity in nerve, 102
  two-point, 329
    variations of, regional, 329, *329*
Thrombin, 591
  absence of, in blood coagulation, 597
  fate of, in serum, 599
  hemostatic preparations of, 592
Thrombokinase, 593
Thromboplastic substances, in blood coagu-
    lation, 593
Thromboplastin, 593
Thrombus, composition of, 586
Thyroglobulin, 1100
Thyroid, and basal metabolic rate, 1101
  and dietary iodine, 1152
  diseases of, heart rate in, 784, *784*
  dysfunctions of, 1100
  effect of, on lactation, 1210
  and food intake, 1157
  and heat production, 1166
  innervation of, 245
Thyrotoxicosis, fibrillation, auricular, in, 774
Thyroxin, 1100
  effect on heart rate, 784
Tic douloureux, 353
Tidal air, 860
  in lung, 867
  volume, in relation to intrathoracic and
    intrapulmonic pressure, *866*
Tissue electrolytes, distribution of, in body,
    939
  fluids, 936. See also *Fluid(s)*.
  hydrostatic pressure of, 937
  pressure, in circulation, 645
Titration curves, acid-base, 574, *575*
Tm, renal, 975
Tonal gaps, 429
Tone, in muscle. See *Muscle*.
  vasomotor, 646, 658
Tongue, swallowing movements of, *984*
Tonic reflexes, labyrinthine in decerebrate
    animal, 194
  neck, in decerebrate animal, 194
Topognosis, 326
  cortical localization of, 366, 368
  neural basis of, 330, *331*
Torque, muscle, 43, *43*, *44*
Torsion spasm, involuntary, ablation, re-
    gional, of cerebral cortex in, 185
  chordotomy in, 185
Touch-pressure, 307, 321
  receptors for, 319, 321
  stimulus for, adequate, 321
  subqualities of, 321
  sense of, 306

Touch sensibility. See *Sensibility*.
Trace elements, dietary, 1152
Trachea, 859
Tract(s), ascending, lamination of, 349, *349*
  brain, auditory thalamocortical projec-
      tions, 436
    tractus solitarius, 376
  cerebral cortex, 271
  gastro-intestinal. See *Alimentary tract*.
  lateral lemniscus, 434, 436
  of Lissauer, 347
  optic, 512
  spinal, fiber constitution of, 109, *110*,
      111
  spinothalamic, in brain stem, 353
    functional anatomy of, 347
    sensory function of, 346, 351
    surgical section of. See *Chordotomy*.
Tractotomy, 353
Transaminase, 1115
Transamination, 1115
Transfusions, preservation of blood for, 558,
    589
  problems in, 586–605
Transmission, intercellular, 121–144
  neuromuscular, 7, *8*
  in sympathetic ganglia, 126–134
  synaptic, 7, *8*
    in central nervous system, 134–144
    in ganglia, 126. See also *Convergence,
        Divergence, Reciprocity*.
Trapezoid body, 435
Traube-Hering waves, *700*, 701
Tremor, 299
  basal ganglia and cerebral cortex in, 292
  in muscle response, 156
Treppe, in muscle, 36
Trigeminal nerve(s). See also *Nerve(s)*.
  distribution of sensory fibers of, *214*
  tractotomy, 353
Triphosphopyridine nucleotide, 64
Triple response, 611
Tritanopia, 496
Trypsin, 1022, 1023, 1025, 1055, 1062, 1067,
    1077, 1113
  activation of, 1066
  in coagulation of blood, 594
Trypsinogen, 1066
Tube, caliber, 636
  effect on fluid flow, 636, 742
  elastic, 644
  elasticity, 643
  length of, pressure and, 635, 642
  nonrigidity of, 643
  pressure in, pulsatile, 643
  rigidity, 643
Tuberculosis, vital capacity of lung in, 868
Turbulence, 631, 644. See also *Flow, Fluid,
    Resistance*.
  of blood, 644
  heart murmurs and, 738
  Reynolds' number in, 631

T wave, acid-base equilibrium and, 815
anoxemia and, 815
coronary, in electrocardiogram, 818
in infarction, myocardial, 819
interpretation of, 756, 761
plasma potassium and, 821
standards for, 744
Tyrode's solution, 558

UREA clearance, 972, *972*
excretion of, 1118
measurements of body water with, 942
nitrogen, blood, effect of hepatectomy on, *1119*
renal excretion of, 972
synthesis of, 1118
of urine, 950
Urine, acid-base balance of, 979
amount and composition of, 966
androgens from, 1215
electrolytes and water in, 951
formation of, 950
glomerular, as plasma ultrafiltrate, 968
glucose ,excretion, by phlorhizinized dog, *1117*
and water in, 951
mineral loss in, parathyroids and, 1147
nitrogen excretion, *1120*
by phlorhizinized dog, *1117*
pregnancy, gonadotrophins in, 1196, 1199
urea and water in, 950
Uterine contractions, determinations of, 1205
pressure, pituitary extract, effect on, *840*
Uterus, 1187, 1204
blood flow through, 837
contractions of, pituitrin in, *1205*
in hypertension, 838
Utilization time, 22, *22*
in synaptic delay, 141
Utricle, 202, 207, 211

VAGINA, glycogen in, 1206
physiology of, 1206
smears of, epithelial, 1186, 1206
Vagotomy, effects of, on respiratory reflexes, 905, *905*
Vagus(i), in auricular fibrillation, 775
autoregulation of respiration by, 903
in block, of heart, 766
in cardiac impulse, conduction of, auriculoventricular, 787
output, 785, *788*
in circulation, coronary, 775
in conduction, auriculoventricular, 766
division of, apneusis produced by, *907*
drug effects on, 787, 788
effect on heart nodes, 786
rate, 788
respiratory tract, 787, 788
in "escape" mechanism, 771

Vagus(i), fibers, in heart, distribution of, 786
in fibrillation, auricular, 775
hunger center and, 997
inhibition, reflex, of coronary vessels, 807
nerves. See *Vagus(i)*. See also *Nerve(s)*.
in pancreatic secretion, 1063
regulation of, reflex, 787
respiratory afferents in, 906
response to central stimulation of, 906
section of, systemic blood pressure fall following, *704*
sensory connections of, 353
stimulation, eserine in, *234*
substance, release of, in Loewi's technique, *232*
Valve(s), of heart. See *Auriculoventricular, valves, Semilunar valves.*
of Vieussens, 215
Vapor pressure, 874
Vas afferens, of kidney, 965
Vascular reaction, to injury, 846
reflexes. See *Reflexes, vasomotor.*
system, pressure in, *650*
Vasoconstriction, in brain blood vessels, 854
drug effects on, 654
reflex, 241
in response to cold, 248
result of, 693
in shock, 603
Vasoconstrictor center, See also *Vasomotor center.*
location of, methods for, 699
nerves, course and distribution of, 694
Vasodilatation, and blood flow through organ, 667
in brain blood vessels, 854
cutaneous, body temperature response to, 832
in hypotension, 688
reflex, 241
of skin vessels, in demarcation of dermatomes, 339
Vasodilatin, 1064
Vasodilator(s), center. See *Vasomotor center.*
excitation of, *703*
nerves, course and distribution of, 696
Vasomotor action, methods to determine, 692
and cardiac centers, comparison of, with other tissues, 715
center(s), 703, 715
control of, by higher centers, 704
medullary, 698
reciprocal relations of, 701
nervous control of, 701
spinal, 698
control, peripheral, of cardiac output, 828
effect, of splanchnic nerve stimulation, *695*
nerves, to pulmonary arterioles, 841

Vasomotor nerves to spleen, 846
  nervous system, 237
  regulation, 692–709
  tone, 646, 658
Veins, of brain, 849
  cardiac, damage to, 806
  heart, 804
  hemodynamics of, 651
  Thebesian vessels, 805
Vena cava, inferior, pressure-volume relationship in, *651*
  receptor organs in, 852
Venom, as capillary poison, 619
Venous blood pressure. See *Blood pressure, venous.*
  cistern, 680
  return, 847
Ventilation, alveolar, 870, 881
  in lung, 869
  pulmonary, 869, 871
Ventricle(s), contraction of, 731
  diastole, 732
  ectopic beats, 770
  electrocardiogram and, 747
  "escape," 771
  extrasystole, 732
  filling of, 732
  fourth, destruction of floor of, in location of vasoconstrictor center, 699
  floor of, *700*
  systole, 731
Ventricular complex, in electrocardiogram, 747
  conduction, 727
  fibrillation. See also *Fibrillation.*
  in electrocardiogram, 776
  initiation of, 778
Venules, 607, *608*
  hemodynamics of, 651
Veratrine, in nerve activity, 118
  heat production, 119
Vertebra and rib, *862*
Vessels, blood, dimensions of, 649
Vestibular placing reactions, 198
Vestibule, 414
Vibratory sensibility, 325, 366
Vidian ganglion, 245. See also *Ganglion.*
Vieussens, valve of, 215
Virilizing tumors, 1224
Viscera. See also specific names as *Bladder, Stomach,* etc.
  afferent fibers in control of pain, 228
  innervation of, autonomic, 227
    sensory, 385
    segmental, 394
Visceral blood flow, chemical control of, 834
    hormonal control of, 834
    nervous control of, 834
  nervous system, *219*, 385
  pain, 390. See also *Pain.*
  reflex arc, *223*

Visceral sensation, 385–400
  central pathways of, 400
Visceratomes, 339
Viscosity. See also structures having, as *Blood, Colloid(s), Plasma,* etc.
  apparent, 643
  flow and, 637
  temperature and, 635
Viscous flow. See *Flow, viscous.*
Visibility curve, 464, *464*, 467
  in color blindness, 497
  visual purple and, 468
Vision, 463–501. See also *Cerebral cortex, visual areas of, Dark and light adaptation, Retina.*
  acuity of. See *Visual acuity.*
  anoxia and, 889, 892
  binocular, 503–523
    depth perception in, 510
    diplopia in, 509
    rivalry, 510
    solidity perception in, 510
    and visual fields, 506
  color, 489
    after images in, 491
    blindness in, 496
      classification of, 496, 500
      tests of, 500
    complementary colors in, 491
    confusions in, 498
    color mixture in, site of, 494
      receptors in, specific, 495, *494, 495*
    contrast in, 492
    laws of, 490
    mixture in, 491, 494
    primary colors in, 491
    response in, dominator, 496
      modulator, 496
    retinal zones of, 507
    saturation in, 490
    specific color receptors in, 494
    theories of, 492
  contour, 463, 488
    functional grain and, 488
  detail, visual acuity and, 480
  duplicity theory of, 463
  effect of brain resections on, *520*
  of vitamin A deficiency on, 1146
  far point for, 449
  monochromatic, 497
  near point for, 448
  pattern of, 522. See also *Visual acuity.*
  photochemical basis of, 466
  stimulus to, 463
    equation for, 472
    threshold for, 465
Visual acuity, biologic significance of, 463
    chart, Snellen's, 488
    cortical mechanism of, 517
    curves of, *484, 486, 487*

Visual acuity, detail vision and, 480
    factors determining, 481
    measures of, 480
    mechanism of, *483*
    tests for, 481, 488
      clinical, 488
    angle, 444
    area(s). See also *Cerebral cortex.*
      ablation of, 521
      of cerebral cortex, topographical organization of, 515
      interconnection of, 522
      topographical organization of, 515
    disorientation, syndrome of, 523
    fields, 506
      binocular *vs.* monocular, 507
      charting of, 506
      diplopia in, 509
      hemianopic defects of, 513
      macular sparing defects of, 518
      measurement of, 506
      of retina, 507
    function, of striate area, 521
    images, suppression of, 509
    pathways, central, 511–523
      diagram of, *512*
    pattern, central mechanism of, 522
    placing reactions, 198
    purple, 466
      action of vitamin A on, 1146
      dark adaptation and, 471
      visibility curve and, 468
    sensation, higher levels of, in man, 523
    violet, 468
      action of vitamin A on, 1146
Vital capacity, effect of posture, 868
    o lung, 867
      effect on working ability of, 869
      in heart disease, 868
      in tuberculosis, 868
Vitamin A, 1145
    in dark adaptation, 470
    deficiency of, symptoms of, 1145
    dietary, recommended allowance of, 1132
    in food, 1017
    requirements of, 1146
    in retina, photochemistry of, 473
    sources of, 1146
Vitamin B₁, 1139. See also *Thiamine.*
Vitamin B₂, 1141. See also *Riboflavin.*
Vitamin B₆, 1143. See also *Pyridoxine.*
Vitamin C, 1144. See also *Ascorbic acid.*
Vitamin D, 1146
    absorption of calcium and phosphorus, 1152
    dietary, recommended allowance of, 1132
    requirements of, 1147
    sources of, 1146
Vitamin K, 591, 1148
    deficiency of, prothrombin in, 1148
    synthesis of, in intestines, 1080

Vitamins, 1138
    in fat storage, 1127
    in food, 1017
Voice, depth of, effect of androgens on, 1219
Volume conductor, electrical current distribution in, 14
Vomiting, events in, 1009
    nervous, mechanism of, 1010
    reflex, 242

WARMTH sensation. See *Temperature sense.*
Water. See also *Body water.*
    absorption of, in stomach, 1057
    balance, estimation of, clinical, 955
      kidney in, 953
      measurement of, 954
      thirst and, 389
    content, of striated muscle, 941
    depletion, in diabetes insipidus, 959
      in salt excess, 959
    deprivation, effects of, 959
    excess, salt retention in, 961
    as foodstuff, 1014
    heavy, measurements of body water with, 942, 954
    intake of, 954
    intoxication, 961
      clinical signs of, 961
    loss, insensible, 1170
      sensible, 1170
    metabolism. See also *Diabetes insipidus.*
      hypothalamus in, 242, 245
    output of, 954
    requirements, 953
    retention in salt excess, 961
      in proportion to salt, 961
    and salt depletion, 958
      proportion in, 960
    vaporization of, and body temperature, 1167
Weber-Fechner law, definition of, 314
    for photoreceptors, 478
    in sensation, 313
    for vision, 465
Wedensky facilitation, neuromuscular, 125
    phenomenon, 724
Weight gain, effect of locomotor activity on, 1161, *1161*
    loss, insensible, 955
Wetness perception, 305
Wetting by blood, 644
    effect of, on flow in tubes, 632
Wever and Bray effect, 425
WEYMOUTH, Frank W.: The eye as an optical instrument, 440–462
Wheal formation, due to injured capillaries, 612
WILHELMI, Alfred E.: Energy transformations in muscle, 56–95

Willis, circle of, 849
Witzelsucht, 542
Work, "chemical," 1086
   definition of, physical, 32
   of heart, 812, *813*
     factors in, 794
   mechanical, 1085
   of muscle, 88, 93
   "secretory," 1085
Wounds, closed plaster treatment of, 628

YELLOW enzyme, and riboflavin, 1141
Yield pressure, 640, 643
   of blood, 656
     definition of, 655, *655*
Young-Helmholtz theory of color vision, 492

ZINC, dietary, 1149
Zone(s), of depolarization, 12, 28, 30
Zymogen, of enzymes, 1024
   granules, 1034, 1035, 1043, 1061